A Century of Care

A HISTORY of THE MEDICAL and DENTAL DEFENCE UNION of SCOTLAND

A Century
of Care

A HISTORY of
THE MEDICAL and DENTAL
DEFENCE UNION of SCOTLAND

EDITED BY
Norman Muir
and
Douglas Bell

THE MEDICAL and DENTAL
DEFENCE UNION of SCOTLAND
2002

ACKNOWLEDGEMENTS

This book is the product of the vision and foresight of Dr Ian Simpson, the Chief Executive and Secretary of the MDDUS. It was his idea to give substance to the occasion of the centenary birthday of the MDDUS, by producing a history of medical defence, as seen through the experiences of doctors and dentists throughout the UK.

The book has been compiled from the historical archives of the MDDUS and anecdotal contributions and essays from individual doctors, dentists and lawyers. Without the work, over a number of years, of Dr Douglas Bell, our Medical Archivist and Mr Ian Rattray, our Dental Archivist, there would have been no historical foundations on which to construct this history. I am also indebted to Dr Iain Macdonald, whose knowledge of medical history proved an invaluable asset. Likewise, Dr Henry Noble and Dr Rufus Ross of the history of dentistry group at Glasgow University provided a fund of information and knowledge on dental historical developments.

During the compilation of the history, we enjoyed unfailing enthusiasm, support and assistance from a wide cross-section of the medical and dental membership of the MDDUS throughout the UK. It is true to say that without the active co-operation and dedication of the many contributors, the mosaic of the content would have been considerably less colourful. The support the book project received from members and staff of The Royal College of Physicians of Edinburgh, The Royal College of Surgeons of Edinburgh, The Royal College of Physicians and Surgeons of Glasgow, The Royal College of Physicians and The Royal College of Surgeons of England was particularly appreciated.

The progress of the book through its draft stages has been supported throughout, in a variety of ways, by the staff of the MDDUS, ranging from the Medical and Dental Advisers to the secretarial and administrative staff. Each has played his or her part in what may be regarded as a successful outcome. Our legal advisers from Shepherd & Wedderburn of Edinburgh and RadcliffesLeBrasseur of London have also continued to keep us on the straight and narrow path of legal probity.

It is well nigh impossible to catalogue the individual contributions in any detail, however I am particularly grateful to the authors of the various essays, which have gone to make up the fabric of the book. They are listed in chapter order. I should also like to thank all those who took the time and trouble to send in written or illustrative contributions to the book and those who helped, advised and gave the benefit of their knowledge throughout the drafting process. They are also listed separately in alphabetical order. The book is indeed a sum of its parts.

Finally, I should like to thank Dr Gail Gilmartin for her support and guidance during the drafting of the book, Maureen Park of the University of Glasgow for her invaluable assistance and advice as an historian of art in medicine and Anne Chambers who, in addition to her routine medical defence work, found sufficient time to type out innumerable drafts and essays with much grace and good humour.

Norman Muir
Editor

The Medical and Dental Defence Union of Scotland
Mackintosh House
120 Blythswood Street
Glasgow
G2 4EA

Published by The Medical and Dental Defence Union of Scotland 2002

ISBN 0-9542251-0-4

Printed and bound in the UK by L&S Litho Printers/Designers Ltd, Glasgow

PREFACE

The quote by Lord Denning during a judgement in a Court of Appeal case in 1954 has a reality, which stands the test of time and, despite advances in modern medical science and technology, will remain a feature of every medical and dental procedure for the foreseeable future:

> *Medical science has conferred great benefits on mankind, but these benefits are attended by considerable risks. Every surgical operation is attended by risks. We cannot take the benefits without taking the risks. Every advance in technique is also attended by risk. Doctors, like the rest of us, have to learn by experience, and experience often teaches in a hard way.*

The process of litigation to seek compensation is a natural consequence of the disappointment felt by patients, when a medical or dental procedure fails to achieve the desired result. Inevitably, it is the practitioner who employed the procedure, who is featured in the process. In this climate of despair, accompanied by media publicity, the MDDUS ensures a fair hearing for the medical or dental practitioner, until the outcome of the case is decided.

It is not widely appreciated that, throughout its history, members of the MDDUS, as representatives of a caring profession, have made proper provision for the compensation of victims of medical and dental accidents and have established significant funds to ensure the appropriate care of these patients.

There are other facets to medical defence. In earlier days, it would have been inconceivable that doctors and dentists would abrogate their professional ethos and skill in letting patients down by slipshod practice. Recent history has shown that a very small percentage of both professions have been found guilty of such an offence and, in the case of Shipman, guilty of mass murder, a heinous breach of care and trust. There must therefore be constant vigilance that practitioners act and procedures are applied, in accordance with the law and remain within it.

The MDDUS has, over the last one hundred years, exercised a watchful eye on all these facets of medical and dental practice and will continue to foster public confidence and trust in doctors and dentists, the vast majority of whom have always practised their science and art for the general good of their patients.

Mr Peter Edmond, CBE TD
Chairman

Mackintosh House

CONTENTS

FOREWORD

The history of the Medical & Dental Defence Union of Scotland has charted its path through the medico-legal minefields of the past one hundred years. It was a century dominated by the catastrophes of war and famine, but the overwhelming feature was the explosion of knowledge through mass-media communication, brought about by advances in science and technology. Access to information and expectation of cure have defined the rise of medico-legal activity in the last forty years. Medical and dental advances in treatment and procedures have raised the anticipation of a failsafe health system among the general public. When this has not been realised, a volatile mix of patient expectation, knowledge and legal process has resulted in medical litigation. Although the tide of medical litigation is riding high, the instances of culpability of medical negligence remain low.

The MDDUS is the youngest of the three major medical defence organisations in the UK. It was formed to meet the needs of practitioners in Scotland, practising under Scots law. However, over the century it has gained in size and influence and embraced the legal systems of both England and Scotland. The membership is now spread throughout the UK. Nine doctors and one dentist took the initiative in May 1902 to form the MDDUS and to agree its constitution. At the time, there was no rush to join the fledging society. At the end of its first year, only 468 practitioners had been persuaded to pay the 10/- annual subscription. Now the membership exceeds 22,000 and a general practitioner subscription is currently £2,350.

Medical defence is neither passive nor protectionist. The MDDUS has paramount responsibilities in helping to maintain optimum standards, the integrity of medical and dental practice, and safeguarding the professional rights of an individual practitioner in the event of patient complaint. Any charge or claim against the professional reliability of a doctor or dentist is a complex issue, which is judged over a considerable period of time and depends to a large extent on the judgement of peer review of procedures and practices. The professional indemnity of an individual during the process, is an indisputable entitlement, until the case is concluded.

Medico-legal cases are expensive to resolve and inevitably take a considerable time through the courts. The Bolitho case in England took thirteen years to reach a conclusion. During the period of complaint and possible progression to litigation, a practitioner will require support and advice from a variety of medical and legal sources, co-ordinated by his or her defence organisation and will labour under the stress of the situation, particularly if under suspension by a health authority. The raison d'être for the MDDUS remains as strong today as at its formation.

This is the story of the MDDUS, the events and individuals that shaped it, the needs which it met and the contrasts between its founding and its present position in the medical, dental and legal world.

We are indebted to Mr Norman Muir without whom this book would never have been created. His tact, enthusiasm and tenacity have all resulted in the text, which you now have before you.

Dr Ian G. Simpson
Chief Executive and Secretary

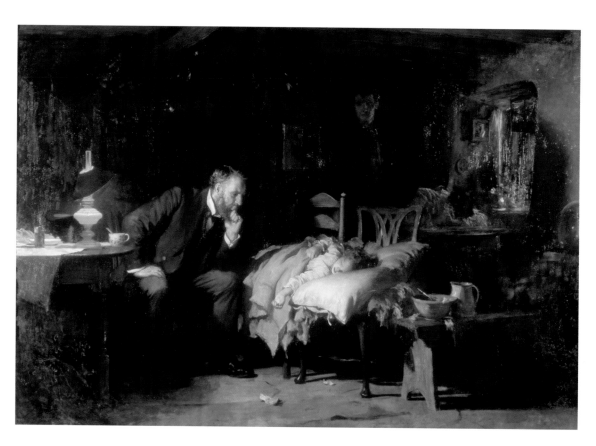

Sir Luke FILDES
(1844-1927)
The Doctor   exh.1891
Oil on canvas
©Tate, London 2001

The Doctor was inspired by the death
of Fildes' son Phillip on Christmas
morning 1877. Fildes had been deeply
impressed by the dedication of their
family physician, Dr Murray, during
his son's illness. This is a painting of
hope, however, for the dawn breaking
through the cottage window is a sign
the child will survive.

The Scene is Set

No member of the profession, however long he may have enjoyed immunity from attack and however confident he may be of the care with which he discharges his duties, can claim to be free from charges and claims made against him. Such claims are made when they are least expected and deserved.

Dr Robert W. Forrest, Convener
The Medical and Dental Defence Union of Scotland
1902-1910

Introduction

The Medical and Dental Defence Union of Scotland opened for business in May 1902, as the youngest of the three principal medical defence organisations in the UK. In the past one hundred years, the MDDUS has kept pace with accelerating scientific advances in medicine and dentistry, with increasing patient expectation and with a myriad of ethical and legal developments. Its ethos has remained the promotion of high standards of medical and dental practice and the support of the professional interests of its members, in the face of a spiralling rise in legislation and patient litigation.

The MDDUS was formed to meet the needs of doctors and dentists caught up in this surge of activity. In fact, many of its members exerted considerable influence on, and helped to fashion, the direction and subsequent outcome of events. As a consequence, this account of its history is bound closely to the national context in which this activity took place and the broad historical background of both professions.

Developments

The foundations for these professional and legislative developments had been laid in the nineteenth century. Anaesthesia and aseptic techniques expanded the boundaries of surgery. Improved sanitation and vaccination began to make an impact on infectious diseases. The public provision of health care for the poor resulted from Poor Law reform. Population migration into crowded towns and cities created deteriorating living conditions, which led to the Public Health Acts. These Acts gave rise to Medical Officers of Health in every local authority throughout the land by the end of the nineteenth century. For the medical and dental professions, the Medical Act of 1858 and the Dentists Act of 1878 began to put the regulation of both on a more formal basis.

Important developments were also taking place in medical science. In November 1895, Röntgen announced his discovery of X-rays, which were brought into use in Glasgow Royal Infirmary early in the following year. Radium, discovered by the Curies in 1898, was used in the treatment of carcinoma in 1903. Aspirin had been produced and named under patent by Bayer in 1899, after some seventy years in development. More advances were to follow.

Harrington's Clockwork Dental Drill

Letters patent were granted 22 April 1864 to George Fellows Harrington 1812-1895 – surgeon dentist of Ryde, Isle of Wight
drawing Laura Cameron-Jackson
The Royal College of Surgeons of Edinburgh

While some doctors were eager to embrace the new technologies of the twentieth century, others had reservations. One doctor, writing in *The Lancet* in 1902, denounced the new binaural stethoscope. He extolled the virtues of the wooden monaural instrument, invented some eighty years earlier by Laennec, which the binaural stethoscope had almost entirely supplanted. For good measure, he took a poor view of the undue weight being attached to laboratory methods of diagnosis, which could only result in, "an unsound, unpractical, theoretical type of clinician".

The invention of the foot-operated drill in 1871 by James Beall Morrison, an American dentist, opened a new era in dentistry. However, dental practice remained primitive by today's standards. A new student would look on as more senior students treated patients, until he would be allocated his first unsuspecting patient. Students would place their bag of instruments on the floor beside the dental chair in the manner of a plumber's kit and chairs were raised or lowered by means of a ratchet mechanism. No local anaesthetic was considered safe to use and extractions were carried out with "cold steel" forceps [Ross 1999].

Regulation of the Professions

Until 1858, there was no legal definition of a qualified medical practitioner. Eleven universities, nine medical corporations, and the Archbishop of Canterbury were entitled to award medical qualifications. Educational standards varied widely and qualifications were not universally accepted.

Edinburgh had become a leader in world medicine in the 18th century and developed the Edinburgh Pharmacopoeia, which eventually became the British Pharmacopoeia. Many of the early physicians from the Royal College of Physicians of Edinburgh were instrumental in setting up the Edinburgh Medical School.

The Faculty of Physicians and Surgeons of Glasgow claimed an ancient right to license the practice of surgery in a large area in and around Glasgow. In 1815, the Faculty obtained a judgement prohibiting four doctors, one from each of the Scottish universities, from practising surgery in that area. Despite a number of legal skirmishes the legitimacy of the Faculty position, upheld at one stage by the House of Lords, remained intact until the Medical Act of 1858 resolved the matter [Lambert 1963; Mackie 1954].

This confusing situation was considered by a number of Parliamentary Select Committees and subsequently Private Members' Bills were introduced in the mid 1850s to rectify it. These led eventually to the Medical Act of 1858. The new General Medical Council, established by the Act, had been intended to have powers to re-shape medical education and enforce a uniform minimum standard. This ran into opposition from some of the professional bodies, which succeeded in reducing the powers given to the Council [Lambert 1963]. The Act was nevertheless important in providing the term "medical practitioner" with a legal definition and in establishing a Medical Register of practitioners. The Act was, in due course, amended to increase the powers of the General Medical Council.

The regulation of the medical profession had two other aims. The first was to enable the public to identify legitimately qualified practitioners and the nature of their qualifications. The second was to deter the significant number of "quacks" from debasing the medical profession.

In a paper in the *British Medical Journal*, Dr Jean Scott drew attention to the Census of 1841, which showed that, of 34,000 persons practising medicine at the time, less than 11,000 were qualified to do so. This highlighted the extent to which the formal registration of practitioners was necessary. In addition, the first indications of change in the status of women aspiring to a medical career were also becoming apparent. Dr Elizabeth Blackwell, the first woman medical graduate in America, became the first woman doctor to register with the newly created General Medical Council in 1859. She had a long association with Scotland and is buried at Kilmun, Argyll [Scott 1984].

Dentistry was considered briefly in the 1858 Act. The Odontological Society of Great Britain was instrumental in the insertion of an amending clause that authorised the Royal College of Surgeons of England to introduce the Licentiate in Dental Surgery diploma in 1860. This was the first step towards recognition of dentistry as a profession. A forum for debate on the future direction of the dental profession was provided by various dental journals at the time. *The British Quarterly Journal of Dental Surgery* and *The Forceps* were the first of their kind in Europe and acted as springboards for the crusaders in the profession, who sought to organise and regulate dentistry. Without their influence, the formation of the various dental societies could well have been delayed even further.

The Dentists Bill of 1878 prompted robust opposition from the medical profession. This focused on the use of the terms, "dental surgeon" and "surgeon dentist" in the draft and the stipulation that medical practitioners who wished to practise dentistry had to have their names entered on the proposed Dentists Register.

This requirement was vehemently attacked in the medical publications. *The Lancet* observed that, "fully qualified physicians and surgeons were now to be on the same list with all the advertising quacks and unqualified dentists, who may be in practice at the same time". After a stormy passage, the Act finally received the Royal Assent on 22 July 1878. The main provisions of the Act established, a General Medical Council Register of persons entitled to practise dentistry; the responsibility of the Medical Council to supervise and improve dental education; the protection of the titles "dentist" and "dental practitioner"; and rendered it lawful for surgical colleges and academic bodies to examine candidates and grant LDS diplomas.

In dentistry, the first British woman to be awarded a diploma by the Royal College of Surgeons of Edinburgh was Lilian Lindsay in 1895. The first Scotswoman, Williemina Simmers, who was awarded a diploma by the Faculty of Physicians & Surgeons of Glasgow in 1901, followed her. Miss Simmers experienced great difficulty passing her final examinations. On her first attempt she failed one subject and had to retake the year. At her second attempt, she again failed the same subject. Her father went to see the examiner in the subject, who informed him, "I have two sons entering the profession and as long as I am the examiner in this subject, your daughter will fail"! The next time, with a different examiner, Miss Simmers finally qualified [Fothergill nd].

The Boer War

Tented hospital in South Africa
The Royal College of Physicians and Surgeons of Glasgow

The war in South Africa ended in May 1902, just as the MDDUS was being established. It was the first major conflict involving the British Army since the Crimea. Despite the fifty-year gap in providing medical support to large-scale military deployments, doctors served with distinction as civilian and military medical officers in the support medical services. Tented field hospitals of 1,000 beds followed the progress of the war and Dr Andrew Balfour of Edinburgh, a civilian medical officer with the Field Force, wrote of the rigours of medical life under canvas and the treatment of "Typhoid Tommy".

Professor Henry Clark, Professor of Surgery at St Mungo's College, Glasgow, who also served as a civilian surgeon, wrote of the hazards of poor sanitation and the heavy pollution of rivers and wells. In an account of experiences in South Africa, he bore witness to the Boer marksmanship, at ranges of 800-900 metres, in a remarkable medical case:

A lieutenant of the Sherwood Foresters saw a comrade struck down by a wound in the abdomen and at once took up the wounded man to carry him out of the line of fire. He had picked him up off the ground and carried him a few steps, when he was himself struck by a bullet, which passed in through the ala of the nose of one side and out at the other, and then entered the head of the man he was carrying and caused instantaneous death.

The patient casebook of Dr Archibald Young, later to become a Vice President of the MDDUS, clearly indicated the considerable damage caused by gunshot wounds at long range. It also highlighted the growing dependence on, and routine use of, X-ray photographs in the detection and removal of bullets lodged in the wounded [Young 1910]. Dr Young was a pioneer in the operative treatment of fractures, by bonding the broken bones with metal plates. Another Scot, Major William Babtie a native of Dumbarton and a graduate of Glasgow University, was awarded the Victoria Cross at the battle of Colenso, for his courage in attending the wounded during the battle.

The outstanding medical feature of this war was the high incidence of enteric or typhoid fever among the troops. Over the three years, there were 57,684 cases including 8,022 deaths. Immunisation was relatively ineffective at that time but was much more successful in the First World War when there were only 20,139 cases with 1,191 deaths, although ten times as many troops were at risk [Currie 1930]. The disparity in numbers between the non-battle casualties and the battle casualties in the Boer War, illustrated that both medicine and dentistry had an increasingly important role in maintaining the health of the armed forces [Table 1.1].

Table 1.1

Soldier Casualties of the Boer War

Battle Casualties

Killed	7,293
Wounded	19,457

Non-Battle Casualties

Died of Injury or Disease	13,682
Sick or Injured	390,444

Note: The proportion of battle casualties to non-battle casualties among soldiers was 1:15 [Mitchell and Smith 1931]

The Boer War also marked an important event in dental history when Frederick Newland-Pedley was selected to accompany a voluntary hospital unit to Cape Town in 1900. He was the first dentist to treat British troops on active service, providing most of the dental equipment at his own expense. After strong representation from the British Medical and Dental Associations to the Secretary of State for War, four dental surgeons were sent to South Africa in 1901. In addition, two further dentists were appointed to the Army at home with a salary of 20/- a day. They were required to provide their own instruments and proved, not surprisingly, quite inadequate to deal with the demand for dental treatment.

The *British Dental Journal* in 1903 published an account of an acute dental problem, vouched for by a front-line officer in South Africa. A Militia Battalion of the Cheshire Regiment, one of the last to be embodied, was sent to South Africa. The soldiers suffered severely from gastric and intestinal troubles attributed to badly chewed food. A general medical inspection was ordered. The inspection revealed an absence of "grinding" teeth among the men. As a result, orders were given for the immediate supply of mincing machines to the troops, two machines per company [Ross 1994].

Royal Concerns

A century ago, in common with today, striking items of medical news commanded public attention. As the date of the Coronation of King Edward VII approached, it was announced that the King would give a dinner for five hundred thousand of his poorer subjects, for which he would pay. The prospect reminded *The Lancet* of anxieties it had expressed about a similar function at the time of Queen Victoria's Diamond Jubilee, when it asked, "If it would be wise to gather together so many of those whose mode of life made them prone to contract and disseminate infection?" Additionally, there was the awful prospect that the metropolis might be, "...inundated from all parts of the kingdom with every scoundrel and loafer and provincial tramps"!

Such concerns about the Coronation were soon overshadowed by a more startling development. The King developed acute appendicitis. This condition had been recognised in the later years of the nineteenth century by doctors in the United States, where the term "appendicitis" had been proposed in 1886. On 24 June 1902, an official bulletin announced that King Edward VII had been operated upon by Sir Frederick Treves, his Serjeant Surgeon. The Coronation had to be postponed.

This created a popular demand for the operation that had apparently saved the King's life. Sir William Macewen of Glasgow was among those who tried to still the more extravagant anxieties aroused by appendicitis and to resist the trend to carry out unnecessary surgery. He is said to have remarked that, "Physicians awoke to their responsibilities and surgeons to their opportunities" [Bowman 1942]. Sir William, a student of Lister, sought to take Lister's work forward by trying to achieve aseptic conditions in the operating theatre. He was a general surgeon in the days before there

Sir William Macewen
The Royal College of
Physicians and Surgeons of
Glasgow

was any appreciable specialisation within surgery and he became one of the world's most famous surgeons of the period. As a result of successful aseptic practices, he was able to pioneer aspects of brain surgery and surgery of the spine, which are now highly specialised fields of surgery in their own right.

Medical Practice

By 1902 the motor car had arrived and *The Lancet* published letters under the heading "Motor Cars for Medical Men". In January, Dr T Pritchard Roberts in St Albans recommended "the genuine geared Benz", to his colleagues. However, the motor car was not yet sweeping all before it. The Cortland Wagon Company of Covent Garden advertised their new "Cortland Broughamette", specially designed for the medical profession. It was hung on high tempered steel springs and had solid rubber tyres. The body was, "very roomy and upholstered in good taste". Nevertheless, it would be easy to forget that there were many doctors who could not aspire to the opulence of a horse and carriage or a new-fangled motor car but had to be content pedalling themselves around on a bicycle.

The Cortland Broughamette
drawing Laura Cameron-Jackson
The Lancet

The Medical Directory for 1902 listed 3,645 doctors in Scotland. At first glance, doctors of today might feel that the shape of the profession in 1902 was vaguely recognisable with surgeons, physicians, and general practitioners. On closer examination, they would find that, although the divisions were in some respects less rigid, there was a lack of career structure, defined postgraduate training opportunities and stable incomes in the early years.

The Lancet described the relationship between general practitioners and consulting surgeons or physicians as "very delicate" [Lancet 1902]. On the one hand, general practitioners were apprehensive about surgeons or physicians accepting direct approaches from patients, or failing to refer patients back to them when their specialist skills were no longer needed. On the other hand, young consulting surgeons or physicians could be faced with great difficulty in establishing themselves. Work could be hard and remuneration small, until time and experience brought referrals from general practitioners. The advantage of private means to the aspiring consulting surgeon or physician was not infrequently mentioned.

Many of the specialties of today did not exist or were not recognised in 1902. Obstetricians and gynaecologists were in a curious position. Argument could rage over whether an obstetrician and gynaecologist was a physician or a surgeon. The issue in the background was, of course, how far an obstetric physician, as he was often called, should undertake major surgical operations in the course of his practice. In some hospitals, such patients requiring major surgery were routinely referred to surgical colleagues.

Sir James Young Simpson
A son of Bathgate
Obstetric Physician
The Scotsman

At Lincoln County Hospital, the gynaecologist, Dr J Stitt Thomson, a graduate of St Andrews and a Fellow of the Royal College of Surgeons of Edinburgh, arranged to remove a patient's ovary. He gave due notice. When the patient was in theatre and about to be anaesthetised, two of his surgical colleagues entered and protested. In this instance, the Governors supported the gynaecologist and resolved that he could treat his patients by operation or otherwise [Thomson 1902; Lancet 1902].

Anaesthesia was scarcely recognised as a specialty and there was concern about the lack of systematic teaching of the subject to medical students. It was claimed that this often amounted to no more than a single lecture given, often perfunctorily, by a surgeon. Students were shown how to give chloroform by "rule of thumb" and were said to desire more and better teaching [Jarvie 1902]. Expansion of the scientific and technical basis of medical practice later in the century led to increasing specialisation.

In 1902, most general practice was undertaken privately but the state was involved to an extent that may now seem surprising. This had arisen from the provisions of the Poor Law. Prior to the reform of that Law, there had been charitable provisions in some localities for the medical care of the poor, but these lacked uniformity and continuity. In England, the Poor Law Amendment Act of 1834 permitted the provision of "Outdoor Medical Relief", which led to the appointment of salaried medical officers. In Scotland, the Poor Law Amendment Act of 1845 stipulated that parochial boards were to appoint a properly qualified medical man to attend the inmates of the poorhouse and to assign him a reasonable salary. For the first time, these Poor Law medical arrangements created a situation in which a section of the population had a statutory entitlement to medical care, government had a statutory duty to ensure that it was provided, and contracts had to be made by Poor Law Authorities with medical practitioners for that purpose.

Towards the end of the nineteenth century, criticisms were being voiced about these Poor Law medical arrangements. There was an emphasis on patient care at home, but Poor Law authorities were coming under increasing pressure to provide proper hospital accommodation in which better facilities could be provided as medical knowledge advanced. Glasgow led the way with an ambitious scheme and was the only authority in Scotland that erected Poor Law Hospitals on sites detached from the general poorhouses [Kinnaird 1987].

Clubs and Societies

One criticism of the Poor Law arrangements, which could not be easily dismissed, was that they did nothing to help those whose incomes were low, but not quite low enough to qualify for Poor Law benefits. Medical insurance and sickness benefits were offered by Friendly Societies and by various kinds of Clubs, to those who could afford the membership. The Societies and Clubs made contracts with doctors to treat their members, which often involved heavy workloads but very modest fees for the doctors.

Some of the Clubs were organised on a very large scale and their activities gave rise to bitter feelings among doctors. The main source of resentment was that the Clubs refused to set any upper income level for subscribers. This could result in the majority of the population receiving their medical care through charity, the Poor Law, Friendly Societies and Club sources. This suited the Clubs, which drew income from administering the arrangements. In a report in *The Lancet,* it was calculated that 75% of the entire population of Leicester escaped the necessity of paying medical fees. A Club medical officer of the Walsall Medical Association, an amalgamation of Friendly Societies, paid 6,115 visits and gave 13,025 consultations to Association members during 1895; for this work he received a salary of £168 [Lancet 1902]. Doctors felt that most of their work was being done at levels of remuneration that were not intended to cover the majority of the population.

Incident at Ballachulish

There were also Clubs organised on an employment basis and disputes could arise between employers and workers. A notable incident arose at the Ballachulish Slate Quarries where the salary of the medical officer was paid out of deductions from the wages of the workmen. The medical officer in post resigned in June 1900, and Dr Lachlan Grant was appointed in his place. His contract included a condition that his service at the quarries would terminate on a month's notice. He would then also be required to cease general practice in the district.

In July 1902, the company dismissed Dr Grant. The reason for his dismissal was never made clear, but at one point the company referred to an increase, since his employment, of 50% in the premium charged by the insurance company, with whom the Slate Company insured their men. Two men had recently been seriously injured; Dr Grant had provided injury certificates and the insurance company had to pay compensation.

The workmen expressed their confidence in Dr Grant and formed a new medical committee, which confirmed him as their medical officer. The company insisted, however, on its right to choose a medical officer. Their case was upheld by the Court of Session and subsequently on appeal. Work at the quarries ceased, as the company tried to force the workers to accept a new agreement that would deprive them of any say in the choice of a medical officer.

While Dr Grant was considering an appeal to the House of Lords, the dispute ended suddenly in December 1903, when the company conceded the right of the workmen to appoint the medical officer. Dr Grant remained

Dr Lachlan Grant
The Royal College of Physicians and Surgeons of Glasgow

in post and the restriction on practising in the district, if he ceased to be the quarry medical officer, was removed. The *British Medical Journal* hailed this as, "A victory for the men and for Dr Lachlan Grant whom they have so staunchly supported throughout". The company had lost a year's business, the men had lost a year's wages and at least one hundred and fifty of the workforce were known to have left the district [BMJ 1902; 1903].

Medical Conditions

The workload of doctors in practice in 1902 differed from the workload of doctors today for several reasons. Some conditions such as coronary thrombosis, which are familiar now, were not generally recognised in 1902. Indeed it was not until the late 1920s, that Dr A. Rae Gilchrist of Edinburgh Royal Infirmary first described coronary thrombosis in a number of papers. Lack of specific and effective treatments often meant that patients who today may expect to be returned to full health, or to be maintained successfully on continuing treatment, did not survive for long. Alternatively, a condition, which would now be treated effectively in the early acute stage, could pass into a chronic phase and continue for a long period. Syphilis provided an outstanding example of this. Effective treatment was not available in the early years of the twentieth century and the disease frequently manifested itself in a variety of serious chronic conditions in later life. These could incapacitate the patient and be a substantial burden on the facilities for long-term care.

Sir Luke FILDES
(1844-1927)
Awaiting admission to the casual ward 1874
Oil on canvas
Royal Holloway, University of London/
Bridgeman Art Library

This is one of several paintings by Fildes that illustrate themes of social injustice. The picture shows a line of homeless people applying for tickets to shelter for a night in the casual ward of a workhouse. The original compostition had appeared as an illustration by Fildes in the first edition of the Graphic magazine in December 1869.

Although the great epidemic diseases had declined throughout Europe in the second half of the nineteenth century, transmissible diseases still made a substantial contribution to the workload of doctors. In spite of vaccination, the United Kingdom was never completely free from smallpox. Typhus fever was still prevalent in the Highlands and Islands and there were occasional outbreaks elsewhere.

Typhoid fever was also found from time to time. By 1906, it was known that typhoid could give rise to a carrier state in which an infected individual, who had apparently returned to good health, would continue to be a source of infection. Scarlet fever and diphtheria had both declined in significance during the later years of the nineteenth century, but they were still responsible for a substantial amount of illness and death, particularly among children. The use of diphtheria antitoxin, which began about 1894, brought about a steady reduction in deaths from that disease. However, these still averaged 857 a year throughout the period 1911-1915 [Ferguson 1958].

Tuberculosis was not a notifiable disease in 1902. However, the death rate at the beginning of the century was 224 per 100,000 of the population, which gives a striking indication of the pervasiveness and persistence of this disease in society. Non-pulmonary forms of the disease, much of it of bovine origin spread by infected milk, were also widespread and troublesome. Compulsory notification of pulmonary tuberculosis was introduced in 1912, and the non-pulmonary forms became notifiable in 1914 [Clayson 1987; Ferguson 1958].

Concern was also growing about the health of school children, the care of expectant mothers, standards of midwifery, control of tuberculosis, and the availability of medical care for those unable to afford it. There was, more significantly, a developing conviction that remedial action could and should be taken to address those concerns.

Dental Practice

The disastrous state of the nation's teeth was clearly documented in dental journals in the last decade of the nineteenth century. A report in the *British Journal of Dental Science* stated:

...it is a melancholy fact that the teeth of the lower middle and lower classes of Society are as a rule hopelessly decayed and past redemption long before the limits of middle age are reached. ...

William Macpherson Fisher of Dundee was a tireless advocate of the role that dentistry should be playing in the field of public health. In 1885, at the Annual General Meeting of the British Dental Association at Cambridge, he argued that the standard of the dental health of the nation could only be raised by the compulsory attention to the treatment of children's teeth. Fisher believed that every child should have a dental examination on entry to, and occasionally throughout, school life. Families on low incomes would be assisted with the cost of payment. He put the scale of the task clearly in context, when he stated that, "Where one person may require medical treatment, ten needed dental treatment" [Lindsay 1933]. He also drew attention to the recruitment of men in Dundee for the Royal Naval Reserve, in which one in four was rejected because of insufficient, decayed or bad teeth [Fisher 1885].

Millbank School Dental Inspection
The Curator BDA Museum

George Cunningham, a powerful ally of Fisher, continued the attack on the deplorable condition of children's teeth. Cunningham presented a paper to a Cambridge Conference on "The Condition of School Children's Teeth" in 1892, in which he noted that dental caries was one of the most widely

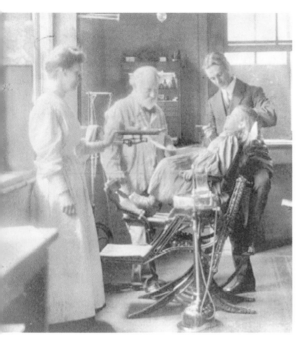

Dr George Cunningham
from left to right: Surgery
maid, Dr Cunningham, Mr
Gant, school dentist
The Curator BDA Museum

prevalent diseases of childhood. He linked the high medical rejection rates in the Armed Forces, on dental grounds, with prevention and care of children's teeth [Cunningham 1892]. Sir James Crichton-Browne, the Chairman of the Conference, stated in his opening address that:

It is impossible to believe that the British Empire would have become what it is today if among those hardy Norsemen who pushed up their keels on the shore at EbbsFleet and entered upon the making of England there had been only one set of sound teeth in every ten...no nation has ever climbed to pre-eminence on carious teeth...it behoves a [nation]...to look to its teeth, and to keep them, not less than its weapons, bright and sharp.

Public Health Legislation

The Education Act in 1907 contained discretionary powers to provide medical and dental treatment to schoolchildren in England and Wales, but it was not until 1918 that these powers became mandatory. The position was similar in Scotland, although local authorities were not allowed to offer dental treatment to schoolchildren until 1913. At the time, the School Dentists Society listed around two hundred schools and institutions, served by either part-time or full-time dentists, throughout the country [Ross 1994].

Pressure for public health reform led, in England, to the Public Health Act of 1848. The Public Health (Scotland) Act followed in 1867. Further legislation ensured that, by the 1890s, every local authority in Britain had a Medical Officer of Health and a Sanitary Inspector as the nucleus of a Public Health Department. This provided local administrative machinery, which the government could use to implement reforms and to introduce new services. Much of the progress in the first half of the twentieth century, which will be described later, was achieved by the government giving particular powers to, or imposing specific duties upon, local authorities.

Litigation and Medical Defence

These legislative changes and advances in medical science increased patients' expectations of accurate diagnoses and survival after surgery and other forms of treatment. Nevertheless, dissatisfaction about the outcome of treatment is not an entirely modern development. Examples can be found in earlier times.

In 1786, Christina, the wife of John Kennedy, died at Auchteraw near Fort Augustus a day or two after giving birth to her second son. Dr Donald McDonald, who practised in Fort Augustus for many years, had attended her during the birth of her child. Her husband apparently declined to pay

Dr McDonald's account for attendance on his wife. This became the subject of litigation and Dr McDonald found himself challenged over the competence of his treatment. A letter, which he wrote on 20 March 1795 to Campbell Mackintosh, a lawyer in Inverness, has survived:

Dear Sir,

I this day received your favr ... you desire of having the number of visits made ... specified. I can by no means comply with, as I never keeped a regular account of them from the supposition that I had to deal with a gentleman who would pay his medical acctt...

...That Mrs Kennedy died in Child bed is a fact not denied, but how far I was culpable... I leave to be determined by Drs Robertson or Kennedy or the surgeon at Ft Willm. when desired to whom I shall most willingly give an account of my procedures...[National Archives of Scotland [a]].

This illustrates two of the fundamental issues woven into present day litigation. The first is the need for adequate records. The second is the part that the opinions and assessments of other doctors must play in determining whether or not the standard of care provided, was adequate.

Until the end of the eighteenth century, when Jenner's much safer vaccination was introduced, it was the practice to inoculate live smallpox in the hope of inducing a mild form of the disease and so create a defence against encounters with a more virulent form. The practice was a risky one but, on balance, was accepted as beneficial.

In 1794, Alexander McDonald, a doctor practising in Knoydart inoculated some children against smallpox. Among them were two children of Duncan McDonald, a farmer on the north shore of Loch Nevis. Duncan McDonald apparently refused to pay the doctor's account and was threatened with legal action. He wrote on 12 July 1794 to Alexander Macdonell, a lawyer in Inverness, asking that he defend him:

Sir, youl see by the Inclosed that I am charged for Inoculating two of my children without either my order or the mother of my Children's leave... the Pox being of a bad kind he killed one of my children beside many more Children in the Country he neither gave Drugs nor the least attendance in their sickness so I therefore think instead of him charging me I might make him pay very Dear but I beg of you Sir that youl send me your advice ... [National Archives of Scotland [b]].

Duncan McDonald identified three issues that are relevant to this day; consent, the safety of the material used and failure to attend and treat patients. These issues are still being addressed in courts all over the world.

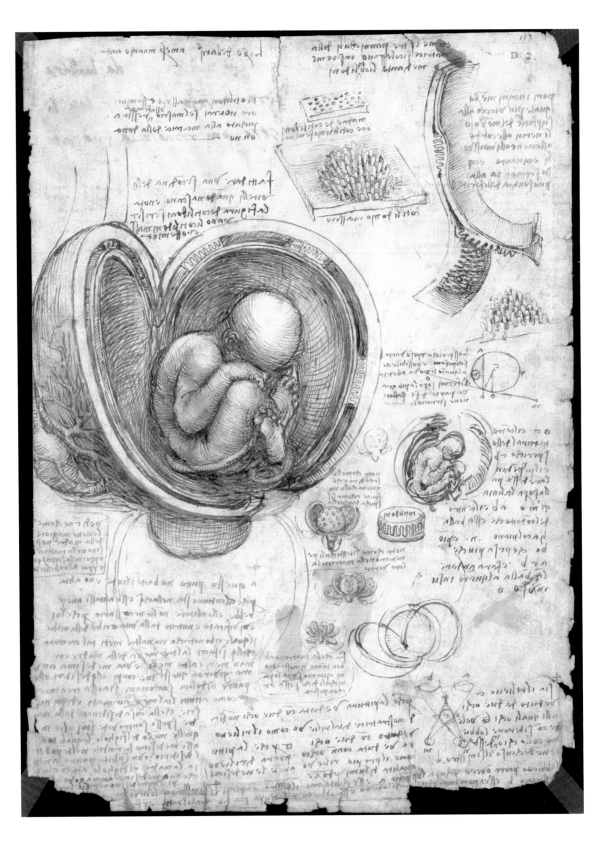

The Founding of the MDDUS

Professional Disquiet

During the 1880s, a number of cases were brought against medical practitioners in England by their patients, who accused them of such offences as lack of due care and attention, gross negligence and unethical behaviour. Many of these cases were frivolous and, though unsuccessful, gave great concern both to the practitioners involved and the medical profession in general.

A leading article in the *British Medical Journal* appeared under the heading, "Vexatious prosecutions of medical men". It referred to a charge of manslaughter brought against two Dulwich practitioners, Drs Bower and Keates. The charge followed the death of a child. The case was dismissed by the Magistrate, who remarked that this was a case of, "...persecution not prosecution". The article voiced the mounting alarm within the medical profession. At a meeting held in the house of Sir William Jenner, the President of the Royal College of Physicians of London, attended by many eminent doctors, it was unanimously agreed to form a committee to collect subscriptions to defray the sizeable legal expenses incurred by both practitioners [BMJ 1883].

About the same time, Jenner was even more concerned at what befell Dr David Bradley of Chesterfield, who was sentenced to two years in prison with hard labour for an alleged assault on a female patient. The outcome was considered to have been a grave miscarriage of justice and subsequently the Home Secretary exercised his authority to grant Dr Bradley a free pardon after he had served eight months of his sentence. In a speech of gratitude to doctors for their support, at a subsequent dinner in his honour, Bradley said he had been urged to employ an expert medical witness in his defence [BMJ 1885]. However, his solicitor had overruled him!

The funds Jenner helped to raise, assisted all three doctors to re-establish themselves in practice. Furthermore, he wrote at the time:

Opposite:

LEONARDO da Vinci
(1452-1519)
The foetus and linings of the uterus C.1511-13
Pen and ink with wash, over red and black chalk
The Royal Collection
©2001, Her Majesty Queen Elizabeth II

In the winter of 1511-12 Leonardo collaborated on human dissections with Marcantonio della Torre, the professor of anatomy at Pavia University. This sheet of drawings was probably compiled over several years. Although inaccurate in certain details, the drawing of the foetus is considered one of the most outstanding medical images ever produced.

*...every member of the profession must feel a deep personal interest, for any
medical man, whether consultant or practitioner, might be placed in the same
position at any moment.*

These were not isolated incidents and it soon became apparent that doctors could not always expect to rely on the financial support of colleagues, when faced with the expense of court cases. One solution to the predicament came from seven laymen, "two solicitors and five gentlemen", who were signatories to the Memorandum instituting the Medical Defence Union in London on 23 October 1885. Membership was only offered to the medical profession. Dentists were ineligible for membership unless medically qualified and their names were entered on the Medical Register. In 1892, some members resigned and established a rival organisation, the London and Counties Medical Protection Society. Overtures for the amalgamation of the two organisations were made a year later, but ultimately the negotiations were abandoned in 1896 [Forbes 1948].

The first evidence of concern in Scotland appeared in 1895, when the Scottish Medical Defence Association Limited was formed in Edinburgh. It ceased to exist in 1899 and there is apparently no record of its activities. There was also legal pressure on some members of the medical profession in the west of Scotland, around this time, for employing unqualified dispensary assistants in their dispensaries, in breach of the Pharmacy Acts. A number of doctors were fined [Jenkinson 1993].

In 1901, medical men in Scotland must have had the hazards of practice brought home to them by a case in the Court of Session in Edinburgh. It was an action for damages by John Farquhar, an Edinburgh provision merchant, against Dr Donald Murray of Leith. Farquhar had called on the doctor on 14 April 1900 complaining of a scratched finger. Dr Murray diagnosed erysipelas. He instructed the patient to poultice the finger with linseed and oatmeal as part of the treatment, until he called again. However, Dr Murray went off on holiday.

Twelve days later, Mr Farquhar was attended by a locum doctor, who was unaware of the earlier treatment. He indicated that the poultice treatment had been persisted with for too long. He prescribed other treatment and continued to attend Mr Farquhar. By the middle of May, the locum and Dr Murray, who had returned from his holiday, agreed that Farquhar's finger would have to be amputated. When the case came to Proof (Hearing of Evidence), three of the four Judges agreed that the case could not be dismissed without an inquiry into the allegation of negligence on the part of Dr Murray.

This action took place less than a year before the inaugural meeting of the MDDUS and probably served as a salutary warning to the members of the medical profession in Scotland that they were not immune to the charges of negligence in practice, as were being experienced by their

*An amputation set of
surgical instruments,
mid-19th century*
The Royal College of
Physicians and Surgeons of
Glasgow

*A Lister Carbolic Spray,
late 19th century*
on a table from the Lister
Ward of the Royal Infirmary,
Glasgow
The Royal College of
Physicians and Surgeons of
Glasgow

colleagues in England. Throughout the years, Scots law had evolved parallel to, but separate from, English law and retained its own traditions and institutions. In 1902, the medical and dental professions in Scotland must have felt that their needs would be better understood and served by a Scottish defence organisation, whose unique knowledge of Scots law would be to their advantage.

The Establishment of the MDDUS

On 1 May 1902, the Memorandum and Articles of Association of the Medical and Dental Defence Union of Scotland were published. A meeting followed twelve days later, in a room of the Religious Institution at 200 Buchanan Street, Glasgow, at 8.30 p.m. The Religious Institution, now buried beneath the red brick of the Buchanan Galleries, was a sombre four-storey sandstone building, blackened by the grime, soot and fog of industrial Glasgow. It was owned by John McCallum, Booksellers, whose shop occupied the ground floor. The source of the religious connotation is unknown. It may have stemmed from a determination on the part of the proprietors to let the room only to those who could be relied upon to refrain from "strong drink, dancing and singing" on the premises. The temperate, founder members of the MDDUS would, doubtless, have abided by these criteria!

Nine doctors and one dentist attended the meeting. All were practitioners in Glasgow [Table 2.1].

Table 2.1

Founder members of the MDDUS

Dr Robert W. Forrest   Dr John Adams

Dr Robert Crawford   Dr George Balfour Marshall

Dr Andrew N. McGregor   Mr Alex P. Robertson

Dr Alexander Barr Pollock   Dr James Anderson Robertson

Dr John Wright   Dr Robert Wilson

Dr Robert W. Forrest
First Convener
drawing
Laura Cameron-Jackson

Dr Robert W. Forrest, the most experienced of the group, was unanimously elected President, a designation later changed to Convener. Dr Forrest enjoyed an extensive practice and was a man of wide interests. Along with his brother William, also a doctor, he took a keen interest in physics. In the mid-1880s, they lived in Glasgow in proximity to John Stewart MacArthur, a chemist who was devoting much of his time to experiments in gold recovery. The three men are credited with the discovery of the MacArthur-Forrest Cyanide Process in 1887, which increased the success rate of gold extraction from ore from around 70%, up to 95%. The experiments took place in the basement of the brothers' medical practice in Glasgow [GMJ 1920].

Their discovery is reckoned to have saved the gold mining industry in South Africa from extinction since, at that time, the economic viability of the gold mines was dangerously low. It is also interesting to speculate on the effect this had on South Africa as events led up to the Boer War. Certainly, immigration to South Africa was stimulated by the revitalisation of the mines and the economic support to the war from the mine revenues would have been considerable. MacArthur had a favourite story of how the newspapers of a Canadian town greeted his arrival with the headline, "Man Who Caused the Boer War visits..."

After the election of Dr Forrest, it was agreed that the ten founder members would act as an Executive Council and it was also agreed that dental practitioners would be added to the list of the members of the Council, underlining the emphasis which the founders of the MDDUS put on the incorporation of qualified and registered dentists within its organisation. Mr William Findlay, Solicitor, was appointed Law Agent and Mr William Young, Secretary and Treasurer. Finally, it was agreed that a general circular to the professions in Scotland, inviting membership, would be prepared and issued in the near future.

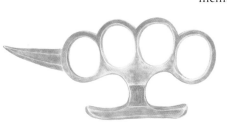

Knuckle Duster
carried by Frederick Smith
dentist in Chesterfield on his
weekly cab ride to branch
practice in Alfreton 1862-1912,
as a defence against
highwaymen.
drawing
Laura Cameron-Jackson
The Royal College of Surgeons
of Edinburgh

The British Dental Journal stated in February 1903:

We are requested to note the establishment of this Society [the Medical and Dental Defence Union of Scotland] *for the fundamental differences between Scottish and English law and judicial procedures seemed to furnish adequate reason for the foundation of a purely Scotch Union.*

The stage had been set to face a future of continued professional and legislative developments with confidence, as membership increased and the MDDUS gained knowledge and experience in its professional abilities.

Formative Years

In May 1903, its first anniversary, there were four hundred and sixty eight members throughout Scotland, with one hundred and fifteen in Glasgow, forty-six in Edinburgh, thirteen in Aberdeen, twelve in Dundee and two hundred and eighty two provincial members outside these four cities. The first Annual General Meeting was held on Friday 18 December 1903. The Annual Report described progress made to date. It noted that the MDDUS had started in a very modest way with twenty-six members, but word of its formation and the services and benefits it offered had spread rapidly. At the Meeting in December, membership had increased to five hundred and thirty nine members.

The financial position was not particularly sound. The revenue account showed an income of £231 18s 3d and a credit balance of £135 17s 5d. These modest amounts seemed to have been adequate to sustain the commitments of the MDDUS at the time. The Report also gave details of twenty-one cases, of which most only required advice.

In one instance, a doctor had been called upon to attend the confinement of a young married woman who had given birth after seven months of marriage. Shortly afterwards, the doctor was visited by a member of the local Kirk Session, who asked the doctor to provide a certificate stating whether or not the child had been conceived in wedlock. The doctor declined to be a party to this apparent persecution and was supported in his stance by the MDDUS Council. The incident illustrated that the shadow of the Stool of Repentance still hung over some parishes in early 20th century Scotland.

Many requests for advice were far outside the responsibility of the MDDUS. One member wrote, "My horse knocked down a child. The Coachman was not at fault. As I am now threatened by an action for damages, does this come within the provisions of membership?" Another doctor, hurrying to visit a patient on his bicycle, knocked down and injured a person and expected support to settle the case brought against him. The Council decided that, since there was no professional principle involved in either case, the members had to arrange for their own defence.

Early 20th century German silver-handled letter opener representing the stages of toothache, extraction and fitting of artificial dentures
drawing
Laura Cameron-Jackson
The Royal College of Surgeons of Edinburgh

Women in the Professions

In both the medical and dental professions women struggled to gain an equal status with their male counterparts. At the time of the MDDUS formation there were some two hundred women doctors in the UK, a number that doubled in the succeeding decade and increased thereafter. Prejudice and male chauvinism deterred all but the most determined and dedicated individuals. It is therefore not surprising that the early female practitioners were strong characters and notable practitioners. Dr Jean Scott who has conducted considerable research into the subject of women in medicine has pointed to the first female general practitioner in Scotland, Dr Sophia Jex-Blake, as an indication of this. Dr Jex-Blake founded the first women's dispensary in Edinburgh. This was followed in 1901 by a second one in the city founded by Dr Elsie Inglis, arguably the most notable of Scotland's early women doctors.

As in medicine, women who aspired to a career in dentistry had to face considerable opposition from within the profession itself. In the footsteps of the pioneers such as Lilian Lindsay, women began to achieve entry to dentistry courses and gain gradual acceptance. At the annual meeting of the Odonto-Chirurgical Society in Edinburgh in 1906, it was agreed to amend the constitution. This would allow women, legally qualified to practise dentistry, to be admitted to membership. By 1912, thirteen women had obtained their LDS qualification in Scotland, six in Glasgow and seven in Edinburgh [Ross 1994].

The First Case

The first MDDUS legal case surfaced in 1903. It was an action in which Mrs Margaret Gillies of Stewarton sued Dr John Cunningham, a local general practitioner, for £1,000 damages; a considerable sum of money in those days. The case arose out of his alleged treatment of her husband, who had died after being given chloroform for a manipulation procedure on his shoulder carried out at the patient's home. The MDDUS sub-committee formed to consider the case reported that the member had not handled the case discreetly, but added that in their view the death was the result of an accident.

It then transpired that Dr Cunningham had applied for MDDUS membership on the same day that he had received notice of the action to be taken against him. The tragic incident had taken place some months earlier. This ended the MDDUS formal involvement with the case, although its Law Agents, Turnbull and Findlay, were retained by Dr Cunningham as his local agents.

However, the facts of the case gave an interesting insight to the practice of medicine and the application of anaesthetics at the time. The evidence given by Mrs Gillies and the doctor on the circumstances leading up to the fatal administration of chloroform on Sunday 13 July 1902 was contradictory in many respects. Nevertheless, there was agreement that Mr Gillies, a fit and healthy joiner in his forties, had fallen through a hatch and injured his left shoulder some months previously. He consulted Dr Cunningham and a diagnosis of shoulder adhesions was made. Subsequently, Dr Cunningham advised manipulation under chloroform.

The operation duly went ahead. Mrs Gillies persuaded her son, Andrew, and his friend to assist. Mr Gillies stripped to the waist and was given some whisky to steady his nerves. He went upstairs to a bedroom and lay

Junker's Chloroform Inhaler
used up to the First World War.
The Royal College of Physicians and Surgeons of Glasgow

down on a couch. Dr Cunningham saturated a towel in chloroform and placed four fingers of each hand between the towel and his patient's face, forming a bridge. He began to count and Gillies replied. When "30" was reached, the towel was discarded and the operation was performed - a simple, abrupt raising of the arm.

The doctor then noted that the patient was not recovering from the chloroform and started artificial respiration. Another doctor was eventually sent for and, when he arrived, asked Dr Cunningham if he had any stimulant, such as strychnine or ether, with him. Dr Cunningham went to his house to collect some. On his return he gave an injection of ether, to no effect. Artificial respiration was given for forty minutes before Mr Gillies was declared dead.

At the trial, expert witnesses agreed that death was due to syncope, although they were unsure how this had occurred in an otherwise healthy man. The Judge remarked that, "there was untruthfulness somewhere", in that the evidence of the two parties was irreconcilable. He then left it to the Jury to decide whom to believe. He also pointed out that the law on the matter was that a person was not liable in the exercise of his profession for a mere mistake, or a mere failure, which might cause injury to another. There must be what, in Scotland, was called gross negligence and, in England, crass negligence. The Jury, after an absence of forty-five minutes, returned a unanimous verdict in favour of Dr Cunningham on all counts.

Dental Dilemmas

The Dentists Act of 1878 did not specifically prohibit the practice of dentistry by unregistered persons. All sorts of "quacks" and charlatans could still continue to advertise and practise their spurious skills so long as they did not imply that they were registered under the Act or qualified to practise dentistry. Following its incorporation in 1880, the British Dental Association continually drew attention to the deficiencies in the regulation of dentistry and actively pursued the prosecution of the increasing numbers of shady operators, posing as registered and qualified practitioners.

The MDDUS played its part in protecting the public and upholding the standards of ethical practitioners. Some cases were considered by its newly constituted Dental Committee, chaired by Mr J Austen Biggs, a former Dean of Glasgow Dental Hospital. It was resolved to obtain the opinion of an eminent Counsel in Edinburgh, as to whether convictions could be secured under the Dentists Act. The sincerity and enthusiasm of the three dental members of the Committee can be measured by their willingness to pay the cost of the consultation out of their own pockets.

Mr Alexander P. Robertson, one of the three, made the first complaint on the list against a former employee of the same surname, Robert

Robertson, who had worked for him eighteen years previously. The employee had issued a handbill in Uddingston in which he stated that he was a dental surgeon and had lately worked with Mr Robertson. Counsel stated, that in his opinion, a prosecution could be brought against the man for advertising himself falsely as a surgeon dentist in the handbill. Counsel's advice was sound and the prosecution succeeded. Robert Robertson was fined £5 with £1 2s 6d expenses, while Mr Alex P. Robertson, no doubt, breathed a sigh of relief!

A Scottish Dental Surgery of the late 19th century
The equipment and instruments on display are representative of the period. These include the dental chair and cabinet c.1890, spitoon c.1900, which would contain disinfectant in the base and dental foot engine to facilitate the preparation of cavities in carious teeth.
drawing
Laura Cameron-Jackson
The Royal College of Surgeons of Edinburgh

However, there were often considerable inconsistencies in the verdicts and penalties arrived at by the judiciary in similar cases. Judges interpreted the 1878 Act in the light of their personal views and opinions. There were significant problems caused by unregistered dentists and Dr Rufus Ross [1994] has given several instances of prosecutions brought against illegal practice, not all of which were successful. "There was intense antagonism", he wrote, "between the registered and unregistered and, in the early years of the century, there was further competition in the shape of limited companies springing up all over the country and specialising in extracting teeth and supplying dentures."

A prosecution reported in *The Dental Surgeon* of 12 November 1904 and cited by Dr Ross, illustrated an example of such a company. Oscar Farkasch, carrying on business at the Hygienic Institute, Elmbank Street, Glasgow, was charged under the Dentists Act. He was not on the Dentists Register and pleaded not guilty to the charges against him. Farkasch said that he was not a dentist himself and had never claimed to be, although there were as many as one hundred and fifty employees in his company.

Having considered the evidence the Sheriff stated, with regret, that he found that the prosecution had failed in their complaint. It would have been in the public interest if people like Farkasch could be suppressed, but the Dentists Act did not prohibit practice by unregistered persons. If it had done, it would have applied to Farkasch.

The 1878 Act was neither a strong safeguard for the public, nor a protection for the registered practitioner. It was finally shown to be quite ineffectual in the case of Bellerby, Heyworth and Bowen. This was a test case on behalf of unregistered dentists, in which a successful prosecution had resulted from false advertisement. Subsequently, the House of Lords upheld an Appeal against the verdict. This decision was seen at the time as a severe setback to the cause of dentistry. An article in the *British Dental*

Journal of May 2nd 1910 referred to the decision as, "...a public misfortune and a serious blow to the prestige and status of our profession..." The situation was not to be resolved until the passage into law of the Dentists Act 1921.

Armistice at Bridge of Earn

In the early part of the century, it was becoming clear that the esteem in which medical men had previously been held was diminishing. Patients began to realise that doctors were also subject to human failings and fallibility and started to adopt more critical attitudes to their treatment and indeed the behaviour of their doctors. The Council Minutes of 30 October 1906 stated, "This is a painful case." It was certainly a jackets-off, no-holds-barred, slanging match which had developed between the doctor in Bridge of Earn, a quiet country village near Perth and a patient's daughter, Marion, whom he claimed had maligned him. She had said that he spent all his time attending the rich, but neglecting the poor. Roused to fury, the doctor responded to this defamation by calling the girl, "A harlot and a whore and a damned whore". Whereupon Marion, not to be outdone, had yelled, "You are a drunkard and your name is a by-word in the village".

The Council of the MDDUS decided that the Secretary should be sent to Bridge of Earn with the objective of seeking an armistice. He visited both warring factions and successfully persuaded both to exchange apologies in writing. Alas, the break in hostilities was short-lived! Marion again wrote, withdrawing her apology and seeking damages of £500. As the case was clearly going to be protracted, the solicitor and the doctor's own agents advised that a small sum might be tendered to Marion. The doctor agreed to a payment of £10. Marion accepted this and peace settled once more on Bridge of Earn!

Lunacy Case

There were a number of references to lunacy cases in the early Minutes. Patients raised actions against doctors involved in the original certification and committal. The case that caused most trouble to the MDDUS was that of Purves v. Drs Gilchrist and Carswell. Doctor Marion Gilchrist was the first woman to obtain a medical degree from a Scottish University, at Glasgow in 1894. Both doctors were alleged to have conspired with the patient's wife to arrange his committal. It was also alleged that no examination to determine the patient's mind was made prior to his committal to hospital.

The MDDUS agreed to defend the action on behalf of the two doctors, although neither was a member at the time of the committal. They had only joined when the action was threatened. As a result both

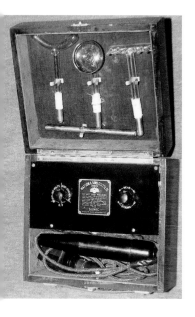

Sunic machine
The Sunic Machine was
designed to produce high
frequency currents for
therapeutic use.
Recommended by the
manufacturers for the
treatment of some fifty
medical conditions. These
included shaving wounds,
bust development and
paralysis. The machine
literature prudently warned
not to use it in the bath!
Dr John MacDonald

doctors provided written undertakings to refund any charges for costs. This arrangement broke with precedent. The Council had always determined only to defend those who were current members. However it was deemed to be an important case and one in which the MDDUS should be involved.

In January 1904, the patient had been released from the Mental Hospital following a successful appeal to the court. The Sheriff stated that one of the certifying practitioners, in fact the general practitioner of the patient's wife, had failed to consult the patient's own medical practitioner prior to taking certification action. The certifying practitioner had not been aware that the patient had his own medical practitioner. The Sheriff pronounced that the man should be released.

The Proof was set for 7 November 1905 in the Court of Session. Many medical practitioners and other witnesses were cited for the defence, including Sir Henry Littlejohn, eminent in medical jurisprudence at the time. After a month, the Edinburgh agent was already seeking legal fees of £300. The MDDUS was unfortunately unable to meet such an amount and could only send £275; an illustration of its precarious financial basis in those early years. Judgement was eventually given in favour of the defendants, both of whom wrote to the MDDUS expressing their gratitude for all that had been done on their behalf.

Costs totalled £949 18s 1d. A sum of approximately £560 had been raised by public subscription, leaving the balance to be paid by the doctors equally, in accordance with their prior undertaking. An argument developed over the payment of the outstanding balance. One doctor settled immediately, while the other denied any obligation. Concern about the dispute mounted and even involved the Lord Provost of Glasgow who attempted to intervene on the recalcitrant doctor's behalf. The debt was finally cleared in December 1906 [MDDUS 1904].

The case did have one early benefit. In 1908, the MDDUS issued all members with certificates, to be signed by the relatives of those they were seeking to have committed, prior to the completion of a certifying procedure. This would effectively indemnify certifying practitioners against similar actions in the future. This device was only adopted after failure to persuade the authorities responsible for the management of lunacy cases, to make appropriate arrangements to protect doctors in such cases.

A further important point was raised by Dr Thomas Clouston, an expert witness in the case, who stated that the finances of the MDDUS were in no state to undertake the defence and indemnity of members in long and expensive legal cases. This observation did not receive due action at the time. It was only some years later that re-insurance was accepted as the obvious and advisable safeguard.

Motoring Realities

The early motor car proved to be a great boon to doctors. Although not totally reliable, it was usually faster than either the horse or the bicycle. It was also much more prestigious, but expensive to buy, maintain and fuel! The Chancellor of the Exchequer had not been slow to recognise the tax-raising potential of petrol. A few years after the MDDUS had been established, he proposed, in a Finance Bill, to levy a duty on petrol. The Secretary was directed by the Council to circulate a letter to all Scottish Members of Parliament, making strong representations against the proposed tax and emphasising the punitive financial effect it would have on medical practitioners. The issue was raised in the House of Commons, as a result of which doctors were granted exemption from the entire duty on petrol used for the purposes of their profession, prior to 1 January 1910 and one half of the duty after that date [MDDUS 1909].

Motorised members sought help from the MDDUS on other various matters. Dr John Cameron of Fortrose complained that his car had not lived up to his expectations and had frequently broken down. He alleged that the guarantee he had been given by the motor dealer had been infringed and asked the MDDUS for assistance in his claim against the firm. The Council declined involvement as this was regarded as a commercial rather than a professional matter.

Muddy roads and farm tracks played havoc with the immaculate paintwork of new vehicles, which prompted Dr Taylor of Perth to write on behalf of several worried colleagues when the local council determined to levy a special rate for water used to wash cars. Dr Robert Zuill of Dunfermline was similarly dismayed when his local council proposed the same action as Perth. They wanted the MDDUS to take the matter up with the councils concerned. However under the Burgh Police Act, local authority councils were legally entitled to levy such rates, unjust though they seemed to be. The new water rate would have to be paid.

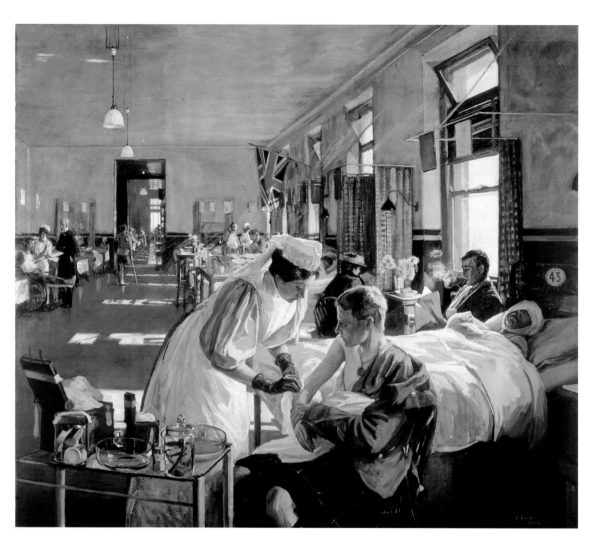

Sir John LAVERY
(1856-1941)
**The First Wounded in London Hospital,
August 1914** 1915
Oil on canvas
Dundee Arts and Heritage, McManus
Galleries

Although born in Belfast, Lavery was brought
up in Ayrshire and is best known as one of the
Glasgow Boys. This painting, his first of the
Great War, was issued as a photogravure and
sold in aid of the hospital's work. In 1917
Lavery was appointed an Official War Artist by
the Department of Information.

Health, Welfare and Conflict

The Welfare Revolution

Sir Alexander Macgregor, a former Medical Officer of Health for Glasgow, whose recollections went back to the early years of the twentieth century, said that the period from 1905 to 1914 was often described as "The Welfare Revolution" [Macgregor 1967]. Additional responsibilities were given to the Public Health Departments of local authorities, a new National Health Insurance Scheme was introduced and bold new arrangements were inaugurated in the Highlands and Islands.

Early efforts to reduce infant mortality were concentrated on the encouragement of breast-feeding and the provision of safe cow's milk for artificially fed infants. The Notification of Births Act of 1907, which required the notification of all births to the Medical Officer of Health within thirty-six hours, assisted these efforts. This brought infant welfare within the responsibility of the Public Health Departments and made it possible for Health Visitors to make home visits and provide a measure of supervision and encouragement of safer feeding practices.

Concern about the practice of midwifery had resulted in the Midwives Act of 1902, which established the Central Midwives Board in England, with powers to issue and cancel certificates to midwives and to regulate training, examination and practice. The Midwives (Scotland) Act of 1915 belatedly made similar provision for Scotland. In both cases, local supervision fell to the Public Health Departments.

The high number of volunteers for the South African War, who had been rejected as physically unfit, created some alarm in military circles. There were gloomy thoughts about whether this implied a progressive loss of national physical fitness. This anxiety gave rise to several official inquiries, which, in turn, led to legislation to provide the systematic medical examination of school children and treatment, when necessary, for the children of poor parents. Most local authorities used the services

of their Medical Officers of Health and his staff to provide the new
school health services.

Tuberculosis

At the beginning of the twentieth century, tuberculosis was still a major
disease. For much of the 19th century, it had been regarded as mainly
an hereditary predisposition. But in 1882, Koch proved that the
disease was due to infection, and the medical profession and health
authorities had to come to terms with the implications of that triumph
of German bacteriology.

There was a long-established public health responsibility to take measures
to prevent the spread of infectious diseases and to provide hospital facilities
for isolation and treatment. Some local authorities introduced voluntary
notification of tuberculosis and this was soon followed by regulations
making it compulsory for all forms of tuberculosis to be notified to
the Medical Officer of Health. The fever hospitals, which then existed,
were quite incapable of dealing with such an enormous new responsibility.
The same applied to voluntary hospitals. In Great Britain there were a
few sanatoria on the German or Swiss models. These were private
institutions and could only help a favoured few. Therefore, a long-term
approach was needed.

In Edinburgh, Dr Robert (later Sir Robert) William Philip had foreseen
the main problem and by the turn of the century his scheme was in
operation, administered by a charitable trust. This, in due course, became
the Royal Victoria Hospital Tuberculosis Trust. Philip's scheme, in
brief, was a graduated system of co-ordinating prevention and treatment.
Two types of institution were needed. The first was the Dispensary, later
the Chest Clinic, where general practitioners could refer patients for
diagnosis and assessment. The whole family, not just the patient, was the
unit for care. Continuing supervision after discharge from hospital was
assured, and health education maintained, especially in the prevention of
the spread of infection.

The second element of the scheme was the sanatorium or the hospital for
in-patient treatment. The first such sanatorium was the Royal Victoria
Hospital in Edinburgh. This was the place for "active treatment". This
meant a fresh air routine, winter and summer alike; windows were open
all the year round. The graduated system of rest in bed, graduated exercise
and work, was always with the benefit of fresh air. At that time, the great
majority of patients who were discharging tubercle bacilli succumbed
within two years; the direct attack on the bacillus was still fifty years or
so in the future. Meantime, the physician had to exercise his ingenuity in
combating symptoms and in relieving the distress of the dying.

During the early years of the century, the co-ordinated Edinburgh scheme
developed steadily. At the same time, other voluntary committees in Great

Britain were also attempting to raise funds in order to meet their local needs. One committee in Dumfriesshire deserves, perhaps, belated recognition. In 1904, a newly qualified lawyer was appointed to the committee. He immediately pointed out to the committee members that, since tuberculosis was an infective disease, the prevention of the disease and hospital care of sufferers were the responsibility of the Local Authority and a clear charge on the public rates under the Public Health (Scotland) Act 1897. The Committee was quite startled and referred the matter to Edinburgh for the consideration of the Local Government Board. In 1906, the Board confirmed the Dumfries contention. By that time, however, the Edinburgh scheme was attracting the attention of the Government.

In 1911, the Finance Act and the National Insurance Act provided that the treatment and care of all insured persons became a national responsibility. As far as tuberculosis was concerned, the Edinburgh scheme was recommended as a model for the whole country. However, progress had to be deferred until the First World War was over. A consequence of the development of services to prevent and treat tuberculosis was the recruitment by public health authorities of medical staff for this purpose. These became identified as Tuberculosis Officers and, later, as specialist chest physicians.

Growing Responsibilities

Syphilis was giving rise to particular concern, but the appearance of Salvarsan (Erlich's 606) in 1910 had offered a prospect of much more effective treatment than had previously been available. In 1916, a Royal Commission, which examined the prevalence of venereal diseases and the provision for diagnosis and treatment, recommended that local authorities should establish centres for the early diagnosis and treatment of these diseases. The Government issued regulations requiring all local authorities to implement the recommendations of the Royal Commission [Currie 1930; MacGregor 1967]. As in the case of tuberculosis, public health authorities recruited medical staff for this new responsibility, leading eventually to the creation of the specialty now recognised as Genito-Urinary Medicine.

Thus, in little more than a decade, the public health authorities had been given by the Government an impressive range of new responsibilities for personal services, which were intended to serve a preventative purpose. In later years Government would add more such responsibilities as further needs were identified, particularly when it could be argued that effective measures had become available and could be introduced.

National Health Insurance

Parallel to these developments, it was becoming evident that the cost of health provision for those on low incomes was rapidly becoming an issue. The National Insurance Act of 1911 was a wide-ranging measure, which included compulsory insurance against sickness, unemployment and disablement as well as the provision of medical treatment and attendance. The driving force behind this measure was David Lloyd George, Chancellor of the Exchequer. He became convinced that the State had to do more to assist the poorer sections of the community, taking as his model the type of state-supported health insurance scheme already operating in Germany. The administration of the scheme was entrusted to ad hoc authorities set up for this purpose.

In Scotland, a body called the National Health Insurance Commission was established in Edinburgh and local insurance committees were appointed. The Act did much to make medical care more widely available, but it had important limitations. Its provisions were available only to employed persons with incomes up to a modest maximum, originally set at £160 per annum. Dependants were not eligible, which meant that mothers and children were not provided with medical care, nor were the self-employed eligible for any of the benefits, regardless of income level.

The medical services were mainly those provided by general practitioners. Insured persons were free to join the list of patients of any participating general practitioner, who would then be paid an annual fee by the insurance committee administering the scheme in his or her area. Hence, "capitation fee" became a familiar phrase, as did, "on the panel" derived from the name given to the list of participating doctors. The Act was passed in December 1911. However discussions with the medical profession, which were sometimes acrimonious and mainly about remuneration, took a further year before the new service commenced in January 1913 [Hogarth 1987].

The arrangements did, however, stand the test of time and when the National Health Service was introduced in 1948, the general practice provisions were essentially an extension of these arrangements to the whole population, regardless of income or employment status. One apparently modest provision of the 1911 Act was particularly far-sighted. A small amount of the funds contributed, a penny for each insured person, was to be set aside for medical research. The committee set up to administer this fund was the forerunner of the Medical Research Council [Macgregor 1967].

The Highlands and Islands Medical Scheme

The new National Health Insurance Scheme brought little benefit to the Highlands and Islands, because it focused on wage earners and most of the population of the Highlands and Islands were self-employed in occupations such as crofting and fishing. The Poor Law medical service had also brought limited benefit because there were many parishes without any qualified medical practitioner to undertake the necessary duties. Many of the population who lived on the land were poor in cash terms, but did not qualify for relief under the Poor Law.

From the middle of the nineteenth century a series of reports drew attention to the inadequacy of medical services in the Highlands and Islands. Several features discouraged the improvements emerging elsewhere. A sparse population and the large geographic area played a part, but the overwhelming problem was widespread poverty. This made it difficult for doctors to earn a reasonable living, except possibly in the few towns of any size. An inquiry undertaken by the Royal College of Physicians of Edinburgh between 1850 and 1852 provided a vivid and sympathetic record of the situation at the time.

Last of the Crofts
Fort Augustus

Highland Folk Museum
Kingussie and Newtonmore

It drew attention to the rigours of the Highlands, experienced by physician and patient alike. It described the case of an injured workman whose leg had been crushed while building a wall. His companions rowed him on a thirty-six hour journey in an open boat to find a doctor, who amputated the leg successfully. Doctors were accustomed to exposure to wet and stormy sea conditions and walking many miles over open moorland to reach their patients. Dr Somerled Fergusson, later to be a redoubtable proponent of improvements in medical services in the Highlands and Islands, recalled as a young boy in the 1930s being sent out by his mother to accompany his GP father practising in Ardnamurchan. It was her belief that her husband would take fewer risks in the boat crossing Loch Sunart to visit his patients, if his son was with him.

The Medical Officers of Health appointed by new county councils under the Local Government (Scotland) Act of 1889 confirmed the situation in their Annual Reports. Dr Ogilvie Grant of Inverness-shire drew attention on several occasions to the large tracts of the country without any resident medical practitioners. He pointed out that the great bulk of the people, while not paupers, were so poor that they could not pay for medical attendance. Therefore a medical man could not reasonably be expected to undertake long, arduous, and even dangerous journeys, in the knowledge that he would not be paid.

The introduction of the National Health Insurance Scheme finally made the contrast with the rest of the country intolerable. An inquiry, under the chairmanship of Sir John Dewar, took extensive evidence, investigated conditions in a series of visits, and produced a bold, radical plan by 1912. Its introductory paragraph was a statement given to the inquiry by a Rona fisherman:

It is just the Portree doctor we have, and he must come in a boat, and in the winter time he cannot come. We may possibly have to wait a fortnight for

*him, and the patient will be suffering pain all that time. It is quite possible
that the patient may die without seeing a doctor at all.*

The plan proposed that medical and nursing services were to be subsidised
by the state, doctors guaranteed a minimum salary and their cost of travel
to remote patients reimbursed. The necessary legislation was passed within
eight months and the Highlands and Islands (Medical Services) Board was
set up in 1913 to administer the new scheme. In 1919, its functions were
transferred to the new Scottish Board of Health, and in 1929 to the
Department of Health for Scotland, but the Highlands and Islands
Medical Scheme remained a distinct and even cherished entity.

Some of the promising early momentum was lost because of the outbreak
of war in 1914; restrictions on expenditure remained for some years after
the war. However, by the middle of the 1920s a start was made on
implementing other broader measures envisaged by the Dewar
Committee. Money was provided for improvements to hospital services,
for houses for doctors and for nurses, for telephone and transport costs,
and even for an air ambulance. In the days before the National Health
Service, the Highlands and Islands Scheme was probably the only
comprehensively planned and managed health service in the country
[Hamilton 1987; Ferguson 1948; Ferguson 1958; Blackden 1998].

Taking Stock

In 1912, membership of the MDDUS stood at 1,215, with an entrance
charge of 10/- and an annual subscription of 10/-. During the period a
large number of threatened actions were intimated but, after consideration
and action by the Council, only a few reached the courts. This seemed
to confirm that the MDDUS demonstrated a stronger challenge to claims
for damages than if the matter had fallen on a single practitioner. There
were a disproportionate number of applications for assistance from dental
members, compared to medical members. This, according to Sir Hector
Cameron, President of the MDDUS, was exactly what he would have
expected. Looking back on his professional life, he observed, "When we
come to such things as teeth, eyes and lunacy, complaints are prolific."

In the Census of 1911, the number of Scots who declared their main
occupation to be dentistry amounted to 1,395. However, the Dentists
Register for the same year contained only 431 names, which indicated
that the number of unregistered dentists at the time numbered at least
964. The overall figure of registered dentists in Britain totalled 4,883,
which gave a dentist to population ratio of 1:9,291 [Ross 1994].

Malpractice cases were significantly outnumbered at the time by requests
for advice on all sorts of questions unrelated to professional activity. The
MDDUS advised and arbitrated on numerous incidents of slander, articles
of libel, partnership disputes, breaches of contract between practitioners,

territorial rights between practitioners, payment of overdue fees and the scale of fees to be charged. The advice even extended to members in making income tax returns!

The MDDUS had to come to terms with the self-imposed restriction at its formation, as a defence organisation solely for medical and dental practitioners practising in Scotland under Scots law. Scottish medical and dental schools are, by tradition, net exporters of their graduates outside Scotland. Thus, the two English-based defence organisations had an understandable interest in recruiting Scottish graduates of each profession likely to practise in England. Equally, the migration of medical and dental practitioners throughout the UK gave rise to members of the English defence organisations coming to practise in Scotland, who might then wish to become members of the MDDUS. The result was that the MDDUS changed its policy to offer membership to these practitioners and also agreed to continue the membership of Scottish members who had moved south of the border. There was, however, no active effort to recruit members outside the borders of Scotland.

The Growing Dental Problem

Around this time, prosecution of contraventions of the Dentists Act 1878 highlighted some of the worst excesses of treatment by unqualified dentists. Many cases were brought as civil actions for damages by patients, although this was only a small fraction of the actual total. One of the most notorious culprits was the Hygienic Institute, which had branches all over Scotland. A patient, James Lawson, sued it for £500 on the grounds that, during an operation to remove seventeen teeth, he had suffered a broken jaw and severe lacerations to his mouth. The teeth had been removed to make room for a set of artificial teeth. His general health had been so seriously affected and the formation of his mouth so altered, that it was unlikely he could ever be fitted for false teeth. The Sheriff found that the injuries were the result of the incompetence, carelessness, or negligence, by the Institute and awarded Lawson £100 with expenses [Ross 1994].

In 1910, an official report for the Government identified the four different types of non-qualified practice.

- Chemists who practised dentistry.

- Dental companies and other institutes, which practised from town to town through agents, who canvassed house-to-house and advertised in the local Press. They utilised rented hotel rooms and charged high fees.

- Unqualified dentists who advertised so-called "American Dentistry". They would often settle in a district and sometimes build up large practices.

- Itinerant "quacks", who were evident on market days and enjoyed a considerable trade in the extraction of teeth and sale of medicines, pills, etc. [Ross 1994].

1914-1918 War

The First World War was declared on 4 August 1914. An early indication of its future impact on medical and dental members was the postponement and subsequent abandonment of a case against a member for the alleged negligent extraction of teeth, due to the absence on war service of Dr George Edington, an expert witness. Nevertheless, the MDDUS continued to deal with the incongruous nature of medico-legal life at this momentous time. A claimant's solicitors wrote asking for the refund of the cost of a set of teeth made for her deceased daughter a few years previously! A further case involved Dr Thomas Grant of Blantyre, who notified the Council of an action against him by a Mr Quinn for alleged improper and immoral conduct with a female patient. The Council was willing to arbitrate on the issue and an appointment was made, but Mr Quinn failed to appear. Some time later, Dr Grant reported that Mrs Quinn had informed him that the claim was entirely without foundation and had been concocted at the instigation of her husband, who was now dead!

It was not long before the serious business of recruitment of civilian practitioners to the Royal Army Medical Corps (RAMC) began. There was a ready response from medical practitioners to accept temporary commissions in the RAMC, but the conflicting demands of the civil and military medical services soon led to attempts to regulate the flow of medical men from civil to military life. The first step in this direction was taken by Dr James Hamilton of Hawick, as Chairman of the Scottish Committee of the British Medical Association. A Scottish Medical Service Emergency Committee was formed to provide Medical Officers for the Army, taking account of the needs of the civil population and the need to look after the interests of individual doctors during their absence on military service. This initiative was followed by a similar Committee formed in London to deal with the Metropolitan area, which was subsequently extended throughout the United Kingdom [MacPherson 1921].

The Scottish Emergency Committee put forward a scheme for recruiting Medical Officers in three

SIR ALEXANDER SIMPSON

Sir Alexander Simpson was one of the first Presidents of MDDUS and served as such for thirteen years. He was the nephew of Sir James Young Simpson, the pioneer of chloroform as a general anaesthetic. Sir Alexander was elected to succeed his uncle in the Chair of Midwifery, Edinburgh, in 1870. He had studied widely at home and abroad and for the next thirty-five years he dominated Edinburgh obstetrics and gynaecology. He was one of a group of professors who, at the time, made the medical teaching at Edinburgh University known and respected worldwide. He received many honours and was knighted in1906. He met an untimely end in 1916. He was knocked down and killed by a motor car in Edinburgh, which had been blacked-out because of the threat of Zeppelin raids.

groups; those under 45, to be commissioned for General Service as Lieutenants RAMC; those between the ages of 45 and 55, as Lieutenants for the Home Service, locum tenens, or part-time military and civilian work; and those over 55, for part-time and locum tenens work. Compulsory military service came into force in January 1916 and by January 1917, more than half the medical profession had been called up for military service. The shortage of qualified medical men of ages suitable for the RAMC, especially younger men, for service with regimental and field medical units, became more and more acute as the war went on, a situation only relieved when the United States of America lent its support.

There had been unofficial contact between the Director General of the Army Medical Service and the Surgeon General of the United States Medical Service, which resulted in the despatch during April 1917 of six base hospital units and a considerable number of individual Medical Officers. This prompt and generous support was emphasised by the agreement that the Medical Officers would be placed at the disposal of the British military authorities. The American hospital units were selected from some of the best-known medical schools in the United States, each school contributing the personnel of one unit. The six represented were the Presbyterian Medical School and the Universities of Cleveland, Harvard, St Louis, Philadelphia, and Chicago [MacPherson 1921].

It was decided that each British General Hospital should adopt the name of the Medical School of the American unit assigned to it, thus the Presbyterian Medical School took over No. 1 General Hospital and the others became, the 9 (Cleveland) General Hospital; 11 (Harvard) General Hospital; 12 (St Louis) General Hospital; 16 (Philadelphia) General Hospital; and 18 (Chicago) General Hospital. They continued to support the British forces for the remainder of the war until early 1919, when they were gradually withdrawn to the United States. At the peak, some six hundred and forty nine US Medical Officers were drafted to regimental and field medical units of the British Army during the war [MacPherson 1923].

Many recruits appeared for voluntary enlistment at the beginning of the war, but were rejected because of poor dental health. At first there was a tendency to relax the dental standard, but this had to be re-considered owing to the bad state of teeth in men sent to units in the field. The British Dental Association, dental surgeons and dental institutions throughout the country volunteered to treat, without payment, the men rejected because of dental defects. Arrangements were made, empowering a Medical Officer examining recruits to send men who could be made fit by dental treatment to dental surgeons and dental institutions in the neighbourhood of the recruiting office. Men were flooding to join the armed forces and an Arbroath doctor who was inundated by the number of medical examinations asked MDDUS advice on the fee he should charge. He was told that the Government had settled disputed claims on the basis of 2/6 per head for the first sixteen recruits and 2/- per head thereafter, in any one day.

There were no dentists included with the British Expeditionary Force when it deployed to France in August 1914. Ironically, in the early part of the war, dentistry was not classified as one of the exempted professions [Marlborough 1995]. In contrast, dental support within Dominion and American troops was much more advanced and on a more extensive scale. This situation swiftly changed when, during the battle of the Aisne in September 1914, General Sir Douglas Haig suffered severe toothache, which had to be treated by a French dentist. As a consequence, a telegram was sent to the War Office asking for dentists, who then began to arrive in the theatre of operations in some numbers before British troops left the Aisne! [MacPherson 1923]. A list of dentists was subsequently prepared to act as honorary consultants in dental surgery to the military hospitals. In due course, this led to the recognition of dentistry as a special branch of the army medical organisation.

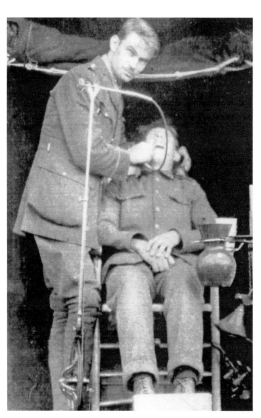

*An Army Dentist of the
First World War*

Curator Army Medical Services
Museum

The number of Dental Officers gradually increased to four hundred and sixty three in December 1916 and continued to increase year by year until the total reached eight hundred and forty nine at the time of the Armistice in November 1918 [MacPherson 1921]. They were dispersed throughout the various theatres of war. William Donald Anderson, Dean of the Glasgow Dental Hospital, was commissioned in the rank of major and sent to organise the dental services in the Middle East.

Medical accounts of the war in the MDDUS archives are in short supply, however Dr Osborne Mavor provided an insight. He was to achieve distinction in quite different fields, as a consulting physician, a leading dramatist under the pseudonym of James Bridie and lastly on the battlefields of Northern France. He put his literary talent to good use in overcoming censorship in his letters home. His device was to place two exclamation marks at the end of a sentence. In the following sentence the initial letters of the words would spell out his location.

He related one occasion when he was wakened by his sergeant with the words, "I have to report, Sir, that this dressing station is being consistently shelled," to which Mavor replied, "Well, in that case I'd better get up"! He then spent the time outside with his companions smoking cigarettes while salvoes of shells exploded all around them. He was to spend more than a year in and around Ypres, during which time he witnessed a chlorine gas attack drifting across the French sector. It cut a swathe four miles wide in the Allied lines, occupied only by the dead and dying. Ypres was rendered almost defenceless, but continued to be heavily contested for almost three years. In one particular day of high surgical intensity, his dressing station attended to 1,315 casualties between 3.00 p.m. and 4.30 a.m. the following day. Although he had retired from medical practice in order to concentrate on his work as a playwright, Dr Mavor rejoined the RAMC in 1939 and served for a further four years [Mavor 1988].

The MDDUS continued to support its members enlisted in the armed forces, as well as those in civilian practice, to the best of its ability during the conflict. The high level of recruitment of medical and subsequently dental members to the forces led to minimal representation at Annual General Meetings. In 1916, only two members attended, so the election of office bearers was conducted by post. As a gesture of patriotism, the MDDUS invested all available funds in War Loans and, in an exercise of economy, the Annual Report was sent with a halfpenny stamp instead of the customary penny stamp! Its reputation was far-reaching. A cablegram was received from a Dr Cooke, serving in Alexandria, Egypt asking the Council's assistance in obtaining his "liberation" from active service after his term of duty had been completed. The Secretary had correspondence with the War Office and the Scottish War Emergency Committee with the satisfying result that the War Office agreed to "liberate" him and he subsequently sailed for Britain. Closer to home, the Council also considered a request by dental members in seeking an exemption from military service for dental mechanics, this time without success.

British stretcher bearers
Passchendaele 1917

The Imperial War Museum

The experiences of Sir Stanley Davidson in the conflict indelibly coloured his future distinguished career as Professor of Medicine at Edinburgh University. Although he was two years into his studies, he enlisted as a combatant officer, notwithstanding the fact that he had had a kidney surgically removed prior to enlistment. He witnessed the tragic aftermath of the first chlorine gas attack and the stretcher casualties suffering from chemical broncho-pneumonia lining the length of railway platforms, prior to their evacuation to hospitals. He was twice wounded; the second time he lay in the open for twenty four hours before regaining consciousness in a gas gangrene ward in Boulogne Base Hospital. After a rehabilitation that lasted two years, he resumed his medical studies and graduated from Edinburgh. His subsequent career took him to Aberdeen as the first full-time Professor of Medicine, where he formed a close partnership with Sir John Boyd Orr and became interested in various aspects of nutrition, the management of nutritional anaemias, the study of immunology and quite separately the recognition of Weil's Disease among the fish workers at Aberdeen harbour.

Sir Stanley SPENCER
(1891-1959)
**Travoys with Wounded
Soldiers Arriving at a
Dressing Station at Smol,
Macedonia** 1919
Oil on canvas
Imperial War Museum,
London

Commissioned by the Ministry
of Information, Spencer's
painting records his personal
memory of an attack on
Machine Gun Hill made by the
22nd Division about the
middle of September 1916. He
witnessed the wounded being
brought to the dressing
station on mule-drawn
stretchers. Spencer painted it
in his family home at
Cookham. Berkshire.

The most poignant story to emerge from within the corporate valorous service given by MDDUS members throughout the war concerned Colonel Donald James Mackintosh, the Medical Superintendent of the Western Infirmary in Glasgow. He had been invalided out of the Army after two years of service and had to learn that his only son, Lieutenant Donald Mackintosh of the Seaforth Highlanders, had been killed in an action, which gained him the award of a Victoria Cross. Colonel and Mrs Mackintosh received the Victoria Cross from the King in July 1917. On the occasion of the hospital's Jubilee in 1925, the Western Infirmary Nurses League dedicated two stained glass windows in the hospital's Alexander Elder Memorial Chapel to the memory of Lieutenant Mackintosh, VC, as an appreciation of his father's support for the nursing profession [MacQueen and Kerr 1974].

Scottish Women's Hospitals

The First World War opened up employment opportunities for women in medicine and dentistry, which had previously been monopolised by men. The prevailing prejudice of the time was unable to prevent Dr Elsie Inglis from assisting the war effort. The experience she had gained in opening the women's hospital in Edinburgh must have proved invaluable in her subsequent initiative, which established her fame. At the outbreak of the war she formed The Scottish Women's Hospitals for Home and Foreign Service to supplement the medical support for the Allied forces. A number of the female members of the MDDUS joined this notable enterprise. The hospitals were staffed entirely by women in the role of doctors, nurses, cooks, ambulance drivers, etc. The Scottish Women's Suffrage Movement office in Edinburgh became the headquarters of the organisation established by Dr Inglis and it received matching volunteer support from the Suffrage movement in England. The formation of the Scottish Women's Hospitals soon drew in volunteers from America, Australia and Canada to staff the hospital units, the first of which were ready for deployment within months of the declaration of war.

This remarkable achievement was overshadowed by the refusal of the British War Office to accept Dr Inglis' offer of the first hospital unit formed. The decision was inexplicable in the face of the significant deficiencies the military authorities faced in providing medical staff and equipment for the Army. In contrast however, rapid acceptance of the offer came from France, Belgium and latterly Serbia, Russia and the Red Cross. Seven hospital units were formed. The 1st hospital unit was set up at Royaumont in Dec 1914 and remained there throughout the war. The 2nd hospital unit sailed for Salonika in the

A Scottish Women's Hospital

The Royal College of Physicians and Surgeons of Glasgow

same period and was set up at Kragujevac. The 3rd hospital unit sailed from Cardiff in April 1915 on its way to Serbia, but was called to help out at Malta and eventually reached Valjevo. A German advance caused a retreat of the forces there and those of the hospital unit who stayed were taken prisoners and eventually repatriated. The 4th hospital unit left Liverpool in the autumn of 1915 for Archangel, Odessa and Mejidia. The 5th hospital unit was formed from a party that had set out in Aug 1915 to help those remaining at Valjevo, but they were too late and went with the Serbian refugees to Corsica, to set up a hospital. The 6th hospital unit, known as the American unit, had Dr Agnes Bennett as CMO as well as Australian and New Zealand medical staff. It went to Salonika and set up a hospital at Ostrova. The 7th hospital unit went to Villers Cotterets in France in the spring of 1917 and had to be evacuated in May 1918.

Eventual official recognition of the Scottish Women's Hospitals' contribution came in the form of a despatch from General Sir George Milne, Commander-in-Chief British Forces Salonika, which read, "I desire to take this opportunity of expressing my admiration of the work of the Scottish Women's Hospitals Organisations serving with the Serbian Army".

For her part, Dr Elsie Inglis had an eventful war. She was taken prisoner in Serbia when the Austro-German forces overran the country and after some months she and the hospital unit were repatriated to Britain. At the

Dr Elsie Inglis
1864-1917
Medical Pioneer
The Scotsman

request of the Serb authorities, she returned to Russia to work with the Serbian Division attached to the Russian army. The unit sailed for Archangel and proceeded south. The fortunes of war turned and the hospital was forced to retreat. Afterwards, it supported both the Russian and Serbian forces until the end of the war. In 1918, the unit embarked at Archangel en route to Newcastle, but, by this time, Dr Inglis was ill and her condition worsened during the voyage. She died on arrival at Newcastle on 26 November.

Dr Katherine Macphail qualified in medicine at Glasgow in 1914 and immediately volunteered to go out to Serbia with the first of the units of the Scottish Women's Hospitals. The young doctor succumbed to a typhus epidemic in which two sisters and another member of staff died. She recovered sufficiently to be invalided back to Britain to recuperate, but then returned under the auspices of the Red Cross to Serbia until the war ended. In Serbia the unit built up a 650-bed hospital, which treated the wounded from the battles against the Austrians. After the war, Dr Macphail was awarded the Freedom of Coatbridge, but again returned to Serbia to found a children's hospital. The national authorities bought the hospital and, with the proceeds, Dr Macphail opened a new Anglo-Yugoslav children's hospital where children with tuberculosis could be treated.

The Second World War forced Dr Macphail and her secretary Miss Murphy to leave Yugoslavia, however she returned to Kamenica after the war to find the hospital intact with the Scottish Lion Rampant still outlined on the tile floor. The hospital reopened in 1946, but after thirty years it was time for Dr Macphail to retire. She was awarded the highest Order of St. Sava by President Tito but refused a pension. He insisted on making her a gift of £2,000, which she used in the establishment of an international children's home in Switzerland. The British Government also recognised her services with the award of an Officer of the Order of the British Empire.

Despite the growing numbers of women taking up medicine as a career and the exploits of the notable pioneers before and during the war, the official view remained ambivalent. In his GMC presidential address in 1916, Sir Donald MacAlister praised, "The admirable services rendered by women doctors," and commended the appeal to, "All women practitioners who are physically fit for such duty". Four years later in 1920, he warned female practitioners that, "Their services

---

PROFESSOR WILLIAM STEPHENSON

Professor William Stephenson served the MDDUS with distinction as one of its inaugural presidents from 1902 until 1919, when he died aged eighty-one. He had been appointed Professor at the University of Aberdeen in 1875 and was a paediatrician as well as an obstetrician, a traditional linkage at the time. He was considered one of the best teachers of obstetrics and gynaecology in the country and contributed extensively to medical and scientific journals. These papers were marked by the same sound judgement and practical insight that formed a feature of his oral instruction. The community and the School of Medicine were much indebted to him for what has been described as his "unoffending pertinacity", in his long and ultimately successful fight to establish a sick children's hospital and a maternity hospital in Aberdeen.

were less in demand; they would have difficulty in obtaining suitable opportunity; Disappointments may be encountered" [Scott 1984].

It is little wonder therefore, that women doctors began organising their collective responsibility. A number of associations had been established throughout the country since the late nineteenth century and it had become obvious that these regional associations would have to combine and speak with one voice. Thus, in 1917, the Medical Women's Federation was formed as a national body to promote education, study and practice, raise the status of women in all branches of medicine and secure equality of opportunity.

At the time there was no representation of women doctors on the GMC and it was not until a Federation Council meeting in 1924, that a motion was passed to take steps to secure a woman nominee for election to the GMC. Support for this initiative came from the BMA who worked with the Federation Council to nominate a medical woman candidate. The choice fell on Dr Christine Murrell, a prominent member of the BMA Council. In the autumn of 1933 she was duly elected to the GMC. Sadly her health failed and she died in October of that year without formally taking her seat on the Council. There was no immediate successor. Subsequent negotiations in the years ahead saw the number of elected members of the GMC increase, which consequently allowed the BMA to ensure that, in future, one of its nominees would be a woman. Thus, in 1955, Dr Janet Aitken, CBE MD became the first elected woman to sit on the GMC, thirty years after the initial motion of the Medical Women's Federation in 1924 [Scott 1988].

Progress and Practice

Dentists Act 1921

Legislative developments concerned with the 1878 Dentists Act had started during the latter stages of the First World War. The Act had failed comprehensively to curb the growing number of unqualified and unregistered persons practising their brand of primitive, unskilled and downright dangerous dentistry. Furthermore, the public had no ready means of distinguishing between the competent dentists and charlatans. In the early years of the 20th century there was little recognition of the need for formal education in dentistry. The majority of entrants to the profession were educated by a variety of unsatisfactory methods of apprenticeship, involving neither formal teaching nor examination. In 1915, the Acting Registrar of the General Medical Council wrote expressing concern that few practising dentists were registered under the Dentists Act of 1878.

The majority of those practising during the first two decades of the century realised that the provisions of the Act were more of a hindrance than a help towards financial prosperity as a dentist. Under the Act, they would be required to pay for a relatively expensive education and examinations, in order to register as a Dental Surgeon. They would then be prohibited from advertising their skills and, in return, would receive almost no protection from unqualified and unregistered colleagues who could advertise freely with little restriction. These unqualified and unregistered dentists increased greatly in number before the 1921 Dentists Act.

The need for reform became apparent to the Government. During the war, on the 12 July 1917, the Lord President of the Privy Council appointed the Acland Committee, named after its chairman, to examine the Dentists Act 1878. It was to investigate, "...the extent and gravity of the evils of dental practice by persons not qualified under the Dentists Act". Members of the Council of the MDDUS gave evidence before the

Opposite:

Jean FOUQUET
(c.1420-1481)
The Martyrdom of St Apollonia c.1450
Book illumination
Musée Condé, Chantilly

Apollonia (died AD 249), deaconess of Alexandria, is patron saint of dentists and is invoked against toothache. According to the 4th century Bishop of Alexandria, her teeth were broken by an angry mob before she was burned alive for her faith. Her symbol of martyrdom is usually a molar held in a pair of pincers.

Committee in London and arranged meetings of practitioners in
Edinburgh and Glasgow to discuss dental health, the control of the
profession and the rights of practitioners.

The Committee published its Report on 5 February 1919, after nearly two
years of deliberation. It made a number of recommendations, the first of

Table 4.1

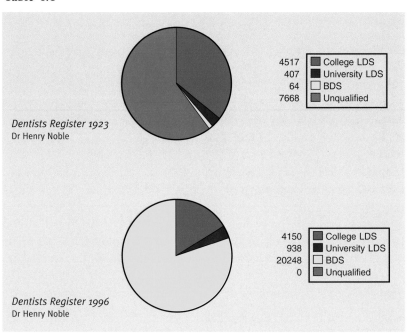

Dentists Register 1923
Dr Henry Noble

4517	■ College LDS
407	■ University LDS
64	□ BDS
7668	■ Unqualified

Dentists Register 1996
Dr Henry Noble

4150	■ College LDS
938	■ University LDS
20248	□ BDS
0	■ Unqualified

which was legislation. Dental practice by unqualified persons should be
prohibited under penalty and a Register kept of qualified persons, who had
undergone a proper dental education and passed the qualifying
examinations. However this would have removed the livelihood of
unregistered practitioners and, furthermore, made it impossible for a large
proportion of the population to obtain dental treatment. Additionally, many
unregistered practitioners, e.g., members of the Incorporated Dental Society,
were practising ethically and had invested capital in premises, equipment
and staff. It was therefore proposed that any unregistered person, who had
been engaged continuously in the practice of dentistry for five of the seven
years before the date of the Report, would be entitled to have their name
entered on the Dentists Register. This compromise was reluctantly
incorporated in the 1921 Act and, as a result, qualified practitioners formed
some 40% of those named in the 1923 Register [Table 4.1].

A most important recommendation of the Acland Committee was that a
Statutory Dental Board would govern the profession under the auspices
of the General Medical Council. The Committee was also anxious to
ensure the provision of students in sufficient numbers to meet the adequate

needs of the nation and made recommendations about the curriculum and the cost of a course of study. It suggested the award of State Scholarships and that State Aid should be given to Dental Schools. Each registered practitioner paid an annual fee of five guineas to the Dental Board of the United Kingdom. The money went towards maintenance of the Register as well as towards scholarships and grants for equipment, libraries and publications. In 1928, it also provided assistance towards the appointment of a professor and two lecturers in dental subjects in each Dental School; a significant contribution which is seldom recognised.

The Minister of Health, Dr Christopher Addison, introduced the Dentists Bill to Parliament in December 1920. It proceeded through the various subsequent Parliamentary stages during which the Dental Legislation Committee of the MDDUS scrutinised the clauses. MDDUS Council members, Dr John Towart and Mr Alex Macgregor, gave evidence to the Parliamentary Standing Committee, assisted by Mr McQuiston, KC, MP, who had agreed to represent the rights of Scottish dentists in Parliament. The Bill passed into Law on 28 July the following year and became the Dentists Act 1921, thereby constituting dentistry a closed profession.

Initially, the Council of the MDDUS agreed to offer membership to all practitioners admitted to the Register under the new Act. However, after correspondence with the Registrar of the Dental Board, the London and Counties Medical Protection Society and the General Accident Insurance Company, this decision was rescinded in March 1922 [MDDUS 1922]. It was decided that only those possessing diplomas and university degrees would be eligible for membership. Thus, it was not until 1940 that "Dentists 1921", the unqualified persons on the Register, were admitted to the MDDUS and then only when proposed and seconded by members of at least three years standing. The first "Dentist 1921" to apply for membership was Mr John Anderson of Burnside, who joined in December 1940 [MDDUS 1940].

Consolidation

There were moves for change in national medical arrangements. In 1919, the Ministry of Health was established in England and a newly formed Scottish Board of Health took over all the health responsibilities of several national bodies in Scotland. In the same year the Secretary for Scotland, Robert Munro, heralded new arrangements for supervising public health as, "... a definite recognition by the State of the paramount importance of the health of the people, and of the urgent necessity for consolidating all activities for the permanent improvement of the health of the people" [National Archives of Scotland].

In pursuit of that positive development, some significant reports on health care facilities were produced. In 1920, the Ministry of Health's Consultative Council under the chairmanship of Lord Dawson of Penn produced its

Interim Report on the Future Provision of Medical and Allied Services. This was, in effect, an outline of a national health service in which domiciliary services based on primary health centres would feature. In December that year, a Consultative Council of the Scottish Board of Health under the chairmanship of Sir Donald MacAlister delivered an even more progressive interim report entitled, "A Scheme of Medical Service for Scotland". It proposed a central role for the general practitioner in a further expansion of public provision. The National Health Insurance scheme would include dependent members of the families of insured workers and there would be access to publicly provided specialist, consultant, and domiciliary nursing services. It was eloquently described by *The Scotsman* as, "A report born out of due season" [Brotherston & Brims 1987; Hogarth 1987].

Four years later, the Scottish Board established a Hospital Services Committee under the chairmanship of Lord Mackenzie, "… to inquire into and report upon the extent and nature of the inadequacy of the present hospital and ancillary services in Scotland…" In 1926 the Committee reported that because of shortage of beds, "… many persons in Scotland … are unable to get at the proper time the hospital treatment which they need". They proposed that 3,600 extra beds should be provided in the voluntary hospitals and recommended a Treasury grant of half of the capital cost. No such grant was forthcoming and by 1939 only 1,809 additional beds had been provided. It is interesting to note, in passing, that in order to consider the adequacy of beds, the Committee found it convenient to divide Scotland into five regions, centred on Inverness, Aberdeen, Dundee, Edinburgh and Glasgow [Brotherston & Brims 1987; Kinnaird 1987]. This regional concept was to become firmly established as the way forward for hospital services.

Tuberculosis

The battle against tuberculosis continued. In the years between the two World Wars, the tuberculosis service of the country, more or less on the Edinburgh model, became well established under Local Authority control. There were two developments during this period. Firstly, there was the attempted direct attack on the tubercle bacillus by chemotherapy. The drug involved was Sanocrysin, but the results were very disappointing.

The second development was to encourage healing by imposing rest on the affected part. For the respiratory system this meant collapsing the lung; for the locomotor system it meant immobilising the affected bones or joints. The most commonly practised treatment for the lungs was by therapeutic pneumothorax - the introduction of a cushion of air round the lungs. Provided that cases were properly selected, good collapse obtained and carefully maintained, the results were excellent. Early discharge from hospital and even return to work became possible.

These developments led to more permanent forms of surgical collapse involving rib resection. In those days, these were more hazardous undertakings, however good the surgical technique might have been. In the event, with careful pre-operative assessment and with post-operative measures such as physiotherapy, results steadily improved.

The Discovery of Insulin

The discovery of insulin in 1921 made the treatment of diabetes possible. Until then all that doctors could offer patients with insulin-dependent diabetes was the "starvation diet" advocated by F.M. Allen. It imposed a ruthless regimen of near-total starvation upon the unfortunate victims, who might survive for two years or so, before their malnourished bodies succumbed to death from ketoacidosis.

Insulin was discovered in the laboratory of Dr John James Rickard Macleod, professor of physiology at the University of Toronto. Macleod was born in Scotland and graduated in medicine at Aberdeen, where he returned in 1928 as Regius Professor of Physiology. His reputation lay in carbohydrate physiology. Frederick Banting, a young orthopaedic surgeon, obtained a position in Macleod's laboratory and Charles Best, then a medical student, was assigned to him.

Professor John Macleod
The Librarian Aberdeen
Medico-Chirurgical Society

Under Macleod's supervision, Banting and Best discovered that chilled extracts of pancreas would lower blood glucose in diabetic dogs. James Collip, a trained biochemist, joined the work at the end of 1921 and developed procedures to prepare a pure extract, free from toxic contaminants. On 23 June 1922, an extract was injected into Leonard Thompson, a boy aged 14 years who was dying of diabetes. His blood glucose fell to normal, ketonuria was abolished and the era of "insulin" therapy began. At Macleod's suggestion, the extract was termed insulin, after the Latin root for islet cells in the pancreas. In 1923, the Nobel Prize was awarded to Banting and Macleod. A meticulous and scholarly account of this phenomenal discovery has been given by Professor Michael Bliss of Toronto [Bliss 1996].

The first Diabetic Department in Britain opened in Edinburgh Royal Infirmary in 1922. Its first patient - and the first person anywhere in the country to receive insulin - was a diabetic doctor who received his first injection in August of that year [Kelnar 1995]. Hard on his heels came a distinguished doctor and longstanding member of the MDDUS, Dr Sam Davidson consultant paediatric surgeon, who was treated with insulin from 1924 until his death in February 2000.

Insulin became generally available from 1924 creating a new and welcome situation. Patients with diabetes had a more favourable prognosis. There were, however, two difficulties. Firstly, patients had to purchase supplies of insulin, for the rest of their lives. The Government responded with a short Act enabling local authorities to issue insulin free of charge to persons who were suffering from diabetes and who required such assistance [Macgregor 1967]. Secondly, perhaps too much was expected of insulin treatment, although it was usually successful. Some problems remain, and in the last decade of the 20th century the MDDUS processed forty claims of negligence regarding the diagnosis and treatment of diabetes.

Future Visions

An action with prophetic implications for the future medico-legal interests of the medical profession and the defence organisations occurred in 1924. It had been brought by a Mr Harnett against Dr Bond, a Commissioner in Lunacy and Dr Adam, the manager of a House for the Reception of Lunatics. The Hearing in the King's Bench Division of the High Court lasted for three weeks and examined an action for damages for alleged conspiracy, assault and false imprisonment. The jury returned a verdict in Harnett's favour and awarded a sum of £25,000 damages.

In view of this judgement and the unprecedented sum awarded, the Secretary of the MDDUS wrote to the two other defence organisations to investigate the effect on indemnity insurance. The scale of the award was such that defence organisations had neither the insurance cover, nor the reserve funds to cope, under existing arrangements. The BMA was also concerned and decided to call a conference of interested parties to study the implications of the case and to keep watch on the forthcoming appeal. An appeal by Dr Adam was allowed and a new trial was ordered in the case of Dr Bond. In the end, the original judgement in favour of Mr Harnett was reversed, much to the relief of the defence organisations, who now saw no reason to take urgent steps to increase their indemnity insurance or subscriptions.

Two and a half years later, a further case arose which demonstrated that court actions did not cease with the death of the individual against whom a case had been brought. It concerned alleged negligence and had been raised in the Court of Session by Duncan Carmichael, a dairyman married with five children, against Dr Alexander Miller the Medical Superintendent of Belford Hospital, Fort William. The case continued for over three years and it occupied much of the MDDUS time during its progress through the courts.

Mr Carmichael's son, Duncan, was certified as suffering from scarlet fever and on the instructions of Dr Miller and, it was claimed, without Mr Carmichael's consent, the boy was removed to Belford Hospital. He remained in hospital for over eight weeks. On his return home it

---

DR GEORGE BALFOUR MARSHALL

Dr Marshall died after a short illness in January 1928. He was one of the original founders of MDDUS and had served as Convener from 1917 until the time of his death. He was born in Edinburgh in 1863, the son of a goldsmith. He graduated MB CM with honours in 1890 and four years later he received the MD with Honours and was admitted to the Fellowship of the Royal Faculty of Physicians and Surgeons of Glasgow. His career lay in the specialties of obstetrics and gynaecology and he studied at Dublin, Jena and Berlin, before succeeding Dr J. K. Kelly in the Gynaecological Wards at the Glasgow Royal Infirmary. He lectured at the Western Medical School and at St. Mungo's College, and in 1921 he succeeded Dr Robert Jardine as Professor of Obstetrics.

was noted that he had a severe discharge from his ear. Shortly afterwards, his brother John and sister Sarah were admitted to hospital suffering from diphtheria, from which Sarah died one week later. Two weeks later, another son, Dougall, was sent to hospital with diphtheria. A swab from the discharge in Duncan's ear demonstrated the presence of diphtheria bacilli and it was claimed that Duncan had contracted diphtheria while in hospital and had subsequently infected the other children.

Dr Miller's defence team argued that the bacilli from Duncan's ear were non-virulent and that Sarah's death was due to delay in seeking treatment for her condition. Dr Miller died in January 1928, but the case continued against his Executors. The case was concluded on 23 December the following year with the Lord Ordinary, Lord Fleming, finding in favour of Dr Miller and awarding expenses to him. The MDDUS Council did not take action to recover these expenses.

Takeover Challenge

Dr John Towart became Convener of the MDDUS in 1928 and almost immediately faced the threat of an external takeover. At a Council meeting in April that year, a letter was received from Mr William Findlay resigning his position as Secretary, Treasurer and Legal Adviser with the MDDUS. The resignation was accepted. A short time later, a letter was received from the same Mr Findlay and his law firm, McClure & Co., offering to purchase the MDDUS on behalf of the Surgical and Medical Protection Union of London Limited. The offer was briefly considered at two meetings of the Council and unanimously rejected.

A further development followed quickly. Findlay, McClure & Co. wrote again enclosing a requisition for a Special General Meeting to consider the purchase offer, which they were entitled to do in accordance with the MDDUS constitution. The Meeting was held on 13 June and the motion was again rejected unanimously by the membership. Messrs. Findlay, McClure & Co. made a final attempt in 1933. Findlay's previous position would have given him access to the roll of members and he used this to effect by circulating literature, which advertised the advantages of a "Scottish Medical Defence Union Limited" and invited applications for membership. Advertisements also appeared in the Edinburgh and Glasgow newspapers. The MDDUS response was to write to all its members seeking their views. It resulted in an almost unanimous rejection of the Findlay approach, which ended any further interference [MDDUS 1933].

Developments in Health Policy

In 1926, the Mackenzie Committee on Hospital Services had proposed that responsibility for hospital services for the sick poor be transferred from the Poor Law authorities to the local authorities. The purpose was to facilitate full co-operation between the voluntary hospitals and the statutory authorities. The Local Government (Scotland) Act 1929 brought these changes into effect and some very large general hospitals, particularly in the cities, now became the responsibility of the Public Health Departments. In several of these hospitals, arrangements were made with universities to create departments and establish teaching facilities.

The Scottish Board of Health gave way to the new Department of Health for Scotland in 1929. The new Department was optimistic that the reorganisation of Local Government under the 1929 Act and the new health powers given in that Act would lead to greater co-ordination of health service provision [Brotherston & Brims 1987]. The theme of co-ordination would continue to be an influence during the approach to a National Health Service.

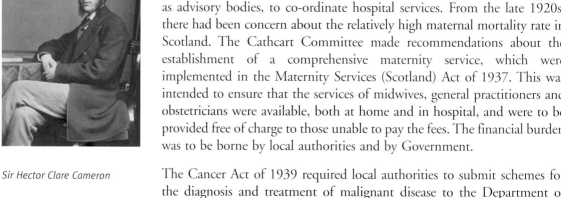

SIR HECTOR CLARE CAMERON

Sir Hector Cameron had been invited to become President of the MDDUS in 1902, but declined, due to his membership of the GMC. When this terminated, he became President of the MDDUS from 1906 - 1928. He arrived in Glasgow to study medicine at the time Joseph Lister assumed his appointment as Regius Professor of Surgery and Surgeon to the Royal Infirmary. Lister and Cameron became firm friends and close working colleagues. Lister departed to Edinburgh to continue his work, but Cameron decided to stay on in Glasgow. He became full Visiting Surgeon to the Royal Infirmary and subsequently Professor of Clinical Surgery at the Western Infirmary. During his Presidency of the Faculty of Physicians and Surgeons of Glasgow, he received a knighthood from Queen Victoria. Sir Hector died in 1928.

In 1936, the Cathcart Committee advocated the development of a national health policy. It emphasised the central role of the general practitioner and wanted to see co-ordination with child welfare, school health and other services. It proposed regional hospital service committees, representing voluntary and statutory hospitals as advisory bodies, to co-ordinate hospital services. From the late 1920s, there had been concern about the relatively high maternal mortality rate in Scotland. The Cathcart Committee made recommendations about the establishment of a comprehensive maternity service, which were implemented in the Maternity Services (Scotland) Act of 1937. This was intended to ensure that the services of midwives, general practitioners and obstetricians were available, both at home and in hospital, and were to be provided free of charge to those unable to pay the fees. The financial burden was to be borne by local authorities and by Government.

Sir Hector Clare Cameron

The Cancer Act of 1939 required local authorities to submit schemes for the diagnosis and treatment of malignant disease to the Department of Health. The outbreak of war limited the implementation of the Act, although interim schemes were discussed with a few authorities [Brotherston & Brims 1987]. It is, however, interesting that, in the light of the way in which the National Health Service was to be organised a few years later, local authorities were to be used to formulate and implement these schemes.

A Bygone Age

Pressure of business was on the increase in the MDDUS in 1933 to such an extent that the Secretary was authorised to purchase a filing cabinet for correspondence! Another red-letter day in MDDUS history occurred in December three years later. The office acquired a typewriter. Prior to that date, all minutes were recorded in clearly legible manuscript; thereafter minutes appeared in typescript, but much less succinct!

The conduct of MDDUS business was not solely concerned with serious medico-legal problems. A member was advised that if he could prove the urgency of the case he was travelling to in his car, when charged with exceeding the speed limit, he should go to the police authorities and lay the facts before them. In a later case, a doctor who was stopped for speeding, was asked for his name and address. When the police officer realised he was a member of the medical profession he said, "Ah, doctor, you will be hurrying to attend a patient?" "No, officer" he replied, "You must do your duty, I am a pathologist and my patients are all dead." The policeman, impressed by the high principles and probity of the culprit, waved him on!

> ## PROFESSOR JOHN ALEXANDER KYNOCH
>
> Professor Kynoch died in June 1931. He was President of MDDUS for twenty-seven years. He was born at Forres in 1863 and attended Edinburgh University, graduating MB CM in 1887. He specialised in midwifery and gynaecology and attended the universities of Berlin, Vienna, Bonn and Munich. The conjoint medical school of St. Andrews University was established at Dundee in 1898 and he was appointed its first Professor of Midwifery. He became Obstetric Physician and Gynaecologist to the Dundee Royal Infirmary. He was Dean of the Faculty of Medicine at St. Andrews for many years and became Emeritus Professor of Obstetrics at the University of St. Andrews, which also conferred upon him the degree of Doctor of Laws. He was a Fellow of the Royal Colleges of Physicians of Edinburgh and Surgeons of Edinburgh.

Professor Archibald Young of Boer War fame was now the Vice President of the MDDUS and he and Dr Joseph G. McCutcheon, a member of Council, were appointed Deputy Lieutenants for the County of Glasgow in March 1937. Mr Alexander Macgregor, the Honorary Treasurer, intimated that his other professional duties precluded his attendance at the monthly meetings held on the last Friday of the month. As a consequence he tendered his resignation, but he was held in such high regard by the MDDUS that the meetings were changed to the third Friday of each month, to accommodate him and ensure his continued service to MDDUS. He remained in that office for the next twenty-six years. Both he and Dr Livingstone Lowden were presented with Coronation Medals in June 1937.

General Practice in the 1930s

The 1930s bore the brunt of the aftermath of the First World War and the economic depression, which followed hard behind. MDDUS members of both professions were deeply involved in the life of the community and their recollections of the life and times of the period provide a vivid image of medical and dental history.

Dr Alan Large recollected that his father's practice was in a county town in central Scotland, the economy of which was based on coal mining, brewing, light engineering, farming, and woollen manufacturing. As a result of this diversity of employment, the slump of the thirties did not affect the community as badly as it might have done. Nonetheless, the queues outside the labour exchange seemed endless. The sights of an empty sleeve, or a trouser leg pinned up and its wearer on crutches, were not uncommon legacies of the war and accidents in the pits.

The common major illnesses, such as diphtheria, Bright's Disease (acute glomerulonephritis) rheumatic fever, scarlet fever, tuberculosis, or pneumonia, meant a lot of worry and hard work and the list of therapeutically active drugs was woefully small to treat them. Aspirin, apart from its use as an analgesic, was often the mainstay, arsenicals and bismuth for syphilis, insulin in crude form for diabetes, phenobarbitone for the epileptic,

---

DR JOHN TOWART

Although Dr Towart had been re-elected Convener, at the Council Meeting following the Annual General Meeting in October 1932, his death took place during the following month. His valued and faithful service to the MDDUS was recorded and his beneficial influence on the work of the Council was gratefully acknowledged. John Towart was born on 14th July 1867 in Glasgow and passed the Scottish Colleges triple qualifications, making him LRCP Ed, LRCS Ed, LRFPS Glasgow, in 1893. He practised as a dental surgeon at 15 Woodside Crescent, Glasgow, until his death.

---

etc. Liver extract for pernicious anaemia came in about this time, but Dr Large's wife remembered her grandmother having to take half a pound of raw liver mixed with a glass of sherry daily.

Sulphanilamide and sulphapyridine ("M & B 693" - prepared by May & Baker) arrived in the early 1940s and made a miraculous difference to the treatment of infection. In these pre-chemotherapeutic and antibiotic days, pneumonia was a major killer for which there was no effective remedy. The doctor would call two or even three times a day awaiting " the Crisis", having to balance the need to support the patient and the family against the fear of the family thinking he might be building up a big bill. Ill health could lead to a great deal of financial worry. Dr Large remembered his father's distress after he had been called to see a two year old dying of diphtheria. When he asked why he had not been sent for earlier he got the answer, "I hadnae the money, doctor".

The ordinary run of the mill activity of dealing with mounting bills was responsible for Dr Large being taught to drive a motor car! His father and uncle, two brothers in practice, abhorred the idea of professional debt collectors, as they felt that employing them would destroy the relationship they had with their patients. At the same time they had to live. Therefore medical bills, which had risen beyond the capability of families to pay, were repaid at a minimum payment of sixpence per week. The result was every Saturday afternoon, the gardener would appear in his best suit, bearing a little black book and the young Large would drive him round the practice to collect the sixpences. Everyone was happy; the patient relieved of worry, the gardener with some extra cash, the doctor paying his own bills, and Dr Large, still to this day with a clean licence, after the good instruction from the gardener!

In midwifery, home delivery was the rule. However, often there was no doctor "booked", it cost £4 and consequently there was no antenatal care.

There were times when not even a midwife attended, but merely a "howdie wife", a totally untrained woman. Dr Matthew Dickson recollected that the "howdie wife" attended the poorest of pregnant women and always managed to produce plenty of boiling water, a fresh towel and a new cake of soap. A Mrs Freckleton, whose hands were as rough as a shoemaker's rasp, cleaned off vernix very efficiently - the baby's skin glowed!

Relations between the GP and specialist seemed warmer in those days and domiciliary consultations were carried out with full ceremony, with the family doctor introducing Dr or Mr 'X', who had been asked to come and help with his opinion. Dr Large's father was fortunate to have two wealthy and neurotic families as patients, who demanded a specialist opinion at the drop of a hat. The great man would come down, at the fee of a guinea a mile, see the patient and then come to the Large home for a cup of tea. "Now Stanley, who do you really want me to see?" he would say. The real patient might be a miner with a back problem, or a mill worker with a cardiac lesion, or a woman with a possible recurrent carcinoma.

> **PROFESSOR GEORGE M. ROBERTSON**
>
> At the April 1932 Council meeting it was announced that Professor G. M. Robertson had died in his sixty-ninth year. He was born in India, the son of a Colonel in the Indian Army, educated at Madras College in St. Andrews and studied medicine at Edinburgh, where he graduated MB ChB in 1885. In 1910 he succeeded Sir Thomas Clouston as Physician Superintendent of the Royal Morningside Asylum for the Insane, later to be called, the Royal Edinburgh Hospital for Mental and Nervous Disorders. In 1919 he became the first Professor of Psychiatry in the University of Edinburgh. Professor Robertson made numerous contributions to the literature of his special subject and took particular interest in transforming asylums into hospitals, where mental disorder was treated on much the same lines as physical disease.

Dr James Kelly Swanston was a medical student in Edinburgh in the 1930s and an aspiring racing motorcyclist, thus on maternity cases he would collect the Nurse in his motor cycle sidecar and set off. A typical case would be at the top of a tenement, eight flights up a stone staircase. The bedroom had bare boards and the only furniture a large iron double bed, where mother was lying surrounded by several children. There were no sheets or blankets, only a straw mattress covered with newspapers.

His first appointment after graduation in 1934 was as one of twenty-one housemen in the Royal Infirmary in Edinburgh, who all worked gratuitously, because it was considered an honour to work in such a prestigious place. The only money they earned was from completing insurance claims, from which they had to pay two pounds a month to augment Mess funds. His next hospital appointment was as House Surgeon in Harrogate General Hospital. Two Surgeons looked after 140 beds and all the Out-Patient Clinics, on a salary of £3 per week. At Harrogate, he did his first tracheotomy, a case of Vincent's Angina. By keeping the tube cleared with a feather the patient did very well! At the time, leeches were still used for eye conditions, "cupping" for backache and subcutaneous oxygen for rheumatism.

Dr Swanston was a regular competitor in the TT races on the Isle of Man and enjoyed success on his fifth appearance by finishing second in the

Junior and winning the Senior in record time. One of the other competitors had come off in practice and suffered very superficial abrasions, which Dr Swanston dressed and told him to report the accident to the race organisers. The competitor did this, telling them that he had seen Dr Swanston, but that he needed to see a real doctor!

After several assistantships he bought a share in a practice in Thirsk. The going rate for purchase of a share in a practice was about eighteen months salary, which made things difficult financially. The surgery was behind the house; a long waiting room with benches and chairs, where there were three stock bottles, one for coughs, one for nerves, and one for stomach complaints. An old farmer used to attend regularly and if somebody was seated in his accustomed chair he would stand in front of him or her until they moved, saying, "That is my seat"!

Dr Kelly Swanston
after his triumph on the Isle of
Man

Dentistry in the 1930s

Overshadowing every aspect of life in Britain during this period was the gloom and despondency of economic depression, which developed in the aftermath of the First World War, exacerbated by the stock-market collapse on Wall Street. Britain was experiencing a financial crisis and had announced that it had abandoned the gold standard, leading to a devaluation of 30% in the value of sterling. Following pay cuts of 25% for police, teachers, the armed forces and cuts in unemployment benefit, there were riots in many parts of the country and a mutiny by naval ratings at Invergordon.

The majority of dentists relied on the fees earned under the National Health Insurance scheme. In 1930, there was now a scale of fees. 7s 6d was the fee for a filling, with a maximum of 12s for any one tooth. Extractions with a local anaesthetic attracted a fee of 2s 6d. The fee for a "full clearance" of upper and lower teeth was £1 2s 6d. The maximum fee for the provision of upper and lower dentures was £5 10s, reduced from £6 in 1926.

Malpractice under the insurance scheme by dentists was fairly common. The Reference Committee of the Dental Benefit Scheme dealt with infringements under a number of headings; false statements on the estimate form as to fees charged, forging the insured person's signature in the declaration of completion, claiming payment for treatment not executed, claiming payment for dentures not delivered, unsatisfactory treatment, etc.

Misconduct of dentists was treated severely. Philip Henry, a Licentiate in Dental Surgery, Edinburgh and also of Glasgow, was charged with, among other matters, excessive advertising by displaying the words "Dental Surgery" in large letters on four windows, canvassing patients of a former employee and notifying patients that he was opening a new surgery. He was found guilty of infamous conduct and his name was removed from the Register.

There was a dire need for a comprehensive dental service. The 7th Annual Report of the Department of Health for Scotland for 1935 noted that nearly 70% of children examined, had dental defects. If confirmation was needed, it came from the House of Commons. In a reply to a question, Mr Duff Cooper, Secretary of State for War, listed some of the causes of rejection of potential recruits in 1936. The highest incidence was due to diseases of the middle ear, including deafness. In second place came deficient dentition and dental decay. This was identical to the situation described in a report from the Director General of the Army Medical Services thirty-three years earlier in 1903.

The Long Arm of Coincidence

Dr John Nicholson graduated in 1935 and was on his first house job at Sutton and Cheam hospital. A young male patient was admitted to have a hernia operation. It was the custom in those days to stay in hospital after such an operation for a fortnight. At the end of this period, the young man was duly discharged in the morning, to return home. He had very distinctive features, with very red hair and a moustache.

The same evening about 8 o'clock, Dr Nicholson was called to Casualty because there been a motor cycle road traffic accident and a young man had been brought in unconscious with a head injury. The Night Sister and the doctor began to clean him up and both recognised the individual as the man who had been discharged that morning. His rucksack lay on the floor with his initials on it, which tallied with the name they remembered. The doctor felt very annoyed and planned to give him a piece of his mind.

At that stage, he and the Night Sister decided to take a look at his abdomen to check the hernia wound. To their consternation, there was no sign of a recent operation scar. They could make no sense of it, until a junior night nurse came in and said that he was a twin brother! The twins were identical and could rarely be told apart. To further confuse the issue, this twin had borrowed both his brother's rucksack and his motorcycle - and then was brought into the same hospital, the same day that his twin had been discharged. Such is the long arm of coincidence.

In November 1938, the prospect of war was now accepted as more than just a threat. A contributor to the correspondence columns of the *British Dental Journal* reflected this view. It was suggested that wearers of complete or partial dentures should ensure they were wearing their dentures before putting on their gas masks. He said that failure to do so could result in a leakage of gas into the mask. On a more formal note, the Representative Board of the BDA decided to draw up a scheme for the protection of practices of those absent on war service. This scheme gave rise to considerable controversy concerning the division of income between the locum and the absentee dentist. This had been fixed at 75% to the locum and 25% to the absentee dentist. Once again the *British Dental Journal* became the focus for the inevitable exchanges, often outspoken and sometimes derogatory:

... In our enthusiasm to protect the practices of those called upon to perform National Service, we have overlooked the fact that the scheme presented is tantamount to a reduction of over 25% of fees charged by acting practitioners. The present NHI dental benefit scheme is now not only inequitable - it is economically impossible.

Details were published in the *British Dental Journal* regarding conditions of service and remuneration for temporary commissions in the dental branches of the Armed Forces. On entry, pay in the Royal Air Force and Army would be £456 rising after one year to £632 in both the Services. The Royal Navy would also accept dentists, but being the Senior Service had different rates of pay. Entry as a Temporary Surgeon Lieutenant would attract a salary of £361 19s 2d. An extra £55 was available if the Officer was not "victualled". In addition, married officers over the age of thirty were eligible to an extra 4s 6d per day, marriage allowance.

The Glasgow Dental Hospital and School continued to treat an increasing number of patients up to the outbreak of the war and from 1932 to 1939 a total of 570,024 patients attended for treatment. On the teaching side, student numbers also increased from one hundred and ten in 1933 to two hundred and seven in 1939. Arrangements were made with the Royal Dental Hospital in London to accommodate their third and fourth year students in Glasgow, should their evacuation from London be necessary.

The two other Scottish dental schools continued to expand both treatment of patients and training of dental students. The Incorporated Edinburgh Dental Hospital and School, under Dean William Guy, increased the numbers of patients treated. In 1930, 29,261 operations were carried out. This included 6,406 extractions, 5,356 with general anaesthetics. A chronic shortage of funds was an ever-present concern affecting the dental hospitals. All had difficulty in making ends meet and, in the 1934 Annual Report, the secretary of the Edinburgh Dental Hospital reported that income had exceeded expenditure by only £5 2s 8d. The situation improved in 1936 when the secretary was able to report a surplus of just over £684, including the proceeds of a "Dental Hospital Flag Day" which realised £379 7s 2d collected by students, employees and members of the families of the dental profession in Edinburgh. By 1938, the total number of operations in the hospital had increased to 51,884 of which 21,090 were extractions.

Dundee Dental Hospital had opened in 1914 and the School was added two years later. One of the first two students to qualify as Licentiates in Dental Surgery was Dr William Tattersall, who was later to become Convener of the MDDUS from 1963 until 1970. The 1930 Report showed that 6,761 treatments were performed on 7,832 patients at an average cost per patient of 2s 9d. The number of students on the roll was 23. Lack of finance, as elsewhere, was a significant factor and the Report stated that The Dundee Dramatic Society and the Ladies of the Entertainment Committee helped to reduce the deficit on the accounts to just over £254. By 1939, the total number of treatments had risen to 17,480, with 20,118 visits by patients.

The two decades from the First World War proved to be a mixture of fortunes for the medical and dental professions and the MDDUS. Recovery from the effects of war was a slow process overshadowed by the worldwide economic depression. In the latter part of the 1930s, a sense of déjà vu arose from the need to prepare for another approaching conflict.

A Time of War

The Second World War

Britain declared war against Germany on 3 September 1939. An MDDUS Council meeting was held twelve days afterwards. The attention of the meeting focused on the approval of grants to medical and dental practitioners called up to the Forces and to assist with the preservation of their practices. It was decided to suspend the subscriptions of members serving in the Forces for the duration of the war. The suspension of subscriptions was eventually withdrawn on 5 August 1948, having made deep inroads into MDDUS funds.

On this issue, a letter was received from the Secretary of the British Dental Association requesting information on the MDDUS policy concerning the subscriptions of members on war service. The Association asked if a statement might be made about it in the *British Dental Journal*. The Council agreed to provide the information required, but felt that caution should be exercised in publicising it, in case it should have a detrimental effect on relations with the other defence organisations.

As a result of the increasing menace of air raids, the Council considered it vital that the register of members and records should be protected against possible destruction by bombing. It was decided that a duplicate register should be obtained and lodged elsewhere and the Advisory and Finance Committee recommended that a photographic record of the register should be made immediately and that this should be kept up to date. The Treasurer was empowered to spend not more than £10 per annum to accomplish this necessary safeguard.

The drawn-out processes of governmental procedure were amply demonstrated at the Council meeting on Friday 17 January 1941, when Mr Alexander Macgregor the Treasurer, was congratulated on receiving the OBE in belated recognition of his work in organising the Dental Health Benefits Scheme after the 1914-18 war! Twelve cases were

Opposite:

Francisco GOYA
(1746-1828)
The sleep of reason produces monsters
1796-98
Etching and aquatint
The Wellcome Library, London

Goya published this image in a set of 80 satirical prints *Los Caprichos* (The Caprices). Goya had originally intended it as the title page of a print series on dreams. The figure is thought to be Goya himself, haunted by the creatures of nightmares. The image links artistic creation with the irrational unconscious.

considered at the Council meeting on 21 February 1941, including one in which a member had reported that a girl patient aged fifteen was found to be eight months pregnant and he wished to know whether he had a duty to report this fact to the police. It was agreed that he should not, as he had no definite knowledge of the girl's precise age, but that he should inform the parents verbally that, if the patient's age as stated was correct, it was their duty to inform the police.

PROFESSOR ARCHIBALD YOUNG

The death of Professor Archibald Young occurred on July 23rd 1939 at the age of sixty-five. He studied in Berlin, Breslau and Heidelberg and served as a civil surgeon during the South African War. In 1902, he was an Assistant Surgeon to the Western Infirmary in Glasgow and assisted Sir William Macewen, whom he succeeded in the Regius Chair of the University. During WW I, he advanced his reputation with work on nerve injuries and became an authority on plastic surgery and numerous surgical treatments. In 1926, he received the Honorary Fellowship of the American College of Surgeons, the American Surgical Association and the Academy of Surgery in Philadelphia. He was also elected a member of the Rome Academy of Medicine and Surgery and made an honorary MD of the University of Strasbourg.

PROFESSOR CARSTAIRS CUMMING DOUGLAS

At the October 1940 Council meeting, the untimely death of Professor C. C. Douglas was announced. He had been tragically killed in a street accident at the gates of Anderson College. He was born in Kirkcaldy and educated at George Watson's College and Edinburgh University, where he graduated MB CM with first class honours in 1890. In 1896 he took the MD of Edinburgh with Honours and, in 1906, a DSc in Public Health. His interests were wide ranging. In 1899 he was elected Professor of Medical Jurisprudence, at Anderson College, Glasgow. This was combined with appointments, at various times, as Pathologist to the Royal Maternity Hospital, Glasgow, Bacteriologist to the Counties of Argyll and Stirling and Examiner in Medical Jurisprudence and Public Health to the University of Aberdeen and the Scottish Conjoint Board.

Wartime Experiences

MDDUS members entered military service in all three Services and in all theatres of war during the six years of conflict. It is only possible to record a sample of the fascinating experiences and memories collectively gained during the period. At the end of the war, 1,883 MDDUS members were serving in the Forces, out of a total membership of 5,463.

Professor Ronald Girdwood. Professor Ronald Girdwood volunteered for military service. In 1943 he found himself despatched to the Far East theatre of war in India and Burma. En route in a convoy off the coast of Algeria he witnessed at first hand one of the biggest troop transport disasters of the war as the adjacent ship to his, the Rohna, with 2,232 mainly American troops on board, was bombed and sunk with the loss of 1,149 lives.

His experience of blood diseases and the sternal puncture needle he had taken with him soon made him a valuable addition to the medical support in India. Towards the conclusion of the war in 1945 he found himself treating the effects of war imprisonment on prisoners suffering from malnutrition and varying degrees of blindness from vitamin deficiency. Girdwood had available to him a stock of crude liver extract with which he had been treating epidemic sprue. He used this with some success in an attempt to improve the vision of blinded prisoners who had just been released.

One of those who suffered from lasting deterioration of his eyesight as a result of the conditions of imprisonment was Stanley Pavillard, a RAMC doctor known in the POW camps as the "Bamboo Doctor" because of his skill in improvising intravenous transfusions for severe dehydration, using bamboo, glass jars and stethoscope tubing. Ronald Girdwood came across numerous instances of such ingenuity in the face of adversity; the radio receiver built into an Army water bottle, the discovery of which would have meant execution for the owner; and the sabotage of the Burma-Thailand 'Death Railway' bridges by hollowing-out the wooden supports and filling them with white ants, to ensure their eventual collapse.

Pavillard drip

When a new patient was admitted we placed him on the ground and started to administer intravenous salines at once. This was often difficult since his veins had usually collapsed as a result of dehydration caused by copious vomiting and diarrhoea. We could not locate a vein with our fingertips we had to cut the skin in an approximate fashion where we knew there ought to be a vein and then patiently to dissect the tissues around the vein until it was exposed. The best vein for this purpose was the one on the inner aspect of the foot just above the ankle bone. Once the vein was located a linen thread was passed under it and it was eased clear of the wound; a hollow bamboo needle was pushed into the vein and tied with the thread and then connected by means of a rubber tube to the saline bottle. The operation was carried out without any local anaesthetic but fortunately the shocked and collapsed condition of the patients was as good as any anaesthetic.

[Pavillard 1960]

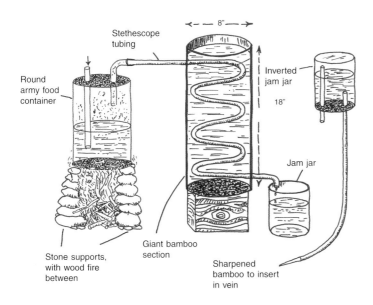

Bamboo Drip
drawing
Laura Cameron-Jackson
Anita Pavillard

61

The war brought its own rewards for Girdwood. A whirlwind courtship, engagement and marriage compressed into two weeks to an Army nurse, laid the foundation of a union, which celebrated its 50th anniversary in 1995. His wife remained in India while he continued his duty in Burma, but communications were so bad between the two locations that mail between them had to be sent via Edinburgh! During his long and distinguished career he became Dean of the Faculty of Medicine of Edinburgh University and subsequently President of the Royal College of Physicians of Edinburgh.

Dr John Barr. As a major in the RAMC, Dr John Barr had an eventful war, which took him and his Field Ambulance from the North African landings through Tunisia and subsequently the Italian campaign, ending the war in southern Austria. His reminiscences of war began at the Thibar Monastery, used as a Casualty Clearing Station during the Tunisian campaign, by the Field Ambulance. The medical staff soon realised the monastery produced a very passable red wine. As the campaign progressed, the monastery was left to the rear. One day, Dr Barr decided to travel back to get a further wine supply for the unit. On arrival at the monastery gates, he made his way to the building, which held the wine press. At the door stood a monk in white habit and red fez. Dr Barr approached him and, in his best French, asked if he could have some wine for the Field Ambulance. The monk looked at him for a minute and then said in English, "What part of Glasgow do you come from?" It transpired that Father McGinley originally hailed from Parliamentary Road in the city!

During the battle for Tunis, the Field Ambulance had its HQ and Main Dressing Station in a large farmhouse in Medjez-el-Bab. A large cactus hedge enclosed the house and garden. In the middle of the hedge was a gate leading to the desert. One night after a long operating session dealing with casualties, Dr Barr went out into the garden for some fresh air. As he approached the gate, a heavily armed German soldier confronted him. The German pointed down to the ground and then with a wave of his hand disappeared with the rest of his patrol into the night. Lying outside the gate was a badly wounded German soldier, who became yet another successful operating statistic of the night.

Unexploded German mortar bomb removed from the leg of an Indian soldier, 1943 Dr A.W. Raffan

The Field Ambulance supported Allied troops in the battle for Monte Cassino and a forward field dressing post lay some six hundred yards from the front line in full view of German observation posts. There was no interference in the transportation of allied casualties from the battlefront. One day, under cover of a white flag, two German medical orderlies from the monastery approached the medical post and asked for the loan of 12 blankets. With traditional reluctance the quartermaster handed over the blankets. The blankets were returned a week later, however, much to the chagrin of the quartermaster, one was missing! The campaign in Italy moved north and the Field Ambulance eventually found itself in South Austria, where Dr Barr finished his war and returned home to take up general practice.

Dr Thomas Reilly. Dr Thomas Reilly was the first member of his family to study medicine. He put up his plate in Bonnybridge in 1933 and, with the exception of the war, served his community as a GP continuously until he retired at the age of seventy. He enlisted for war service in 1940 and was posted to Edinburgh. After some months he became restless for action and was sent to join the 51st Highland Division, en route from Liverpool to the Middle East. The convoy sailed towards Iceland, to reduce the risk of submarine attack. In a dense freezing fog, a collision occurred between the Warwick Castle, on which he was embarked, and her sister ship the Windsor Castle. It badly damaged the Warwick, which lost half her lifeboats and most of her bow. The Warwick limped into Halifax, Nova Scotia, after two weeks of pumping water out of the ship and dropping depth charges to clear the ice. Eventually, he arrived in Cairo.

Dr Reilly replaced the wounded Medical Officer of the 1st Battalion Royal Sussex Regiment and stayed with them for the next three years. He took part in the battle of Wadi Akirit and was decorated in the field with the Military Cross, for his distinguished conduct during the battle, by General Oliver Leese. It was a frontal attack in the foothills and casualties were heavy. The battalion mortar platoon commander was wounded and Dr Reilly had to receive an instant mortar course in how to fire mortars to alleviate the immediate situation, with mixed results for friend and foe!

The following day, a sudden barrage of shells left dead and wounded everywhere. With three ambulances, the regimental medical staff managed to get all the wounded out to the evacuation point. Dr Reilly was dressing the leg wound of a casualty, with the Padre assisting, when a mortar strike blew Reilly clear of the ground and over his casualty. He was winded, apart from some slight superficial shrapnel wounds. As he came to, he found the Padre unconscious with a large lump on his chin, but otherwise unharmed, as was his casualty. Dr Reilly's mid-air flight had caused his army boot to catch the Padre on the chin and lay him out!

The Allied advance continued through Sicily and Southern Italy where ferocious fighting took place, especially at Monte Cassino. On one occasion a barrage of fire inflicted very heavy casualties and the stretcher-bearers were pinned down. Once again Dr Reilly had to call upon his mortar instruction from the Wadi Akirit battle to provide covering fire and allow his stretcher-bearers to get back with their casualties. When the fighting started at Cassino, the battalion numbered some 1,000 men and 32 officers; six weeks later, it consisted of 151 men and 8 officers.

A casualty evacuation at sea involving HMS Uganda
Professor David Watt

Dr David Watt. During the war, dentists were added to the complement of ships carrying in excess of 1,000 crew. David Watt of Edinburgh found himself on board HMS Uganda, which saw action on the Malta convoys and in North Africa and Sicily. It was during the Sicily operations that Uganda took a direct hit amidships from a bomb. The impact explosion narrowly missed the dental surgery and presented a moment to remember for the young dentist and his patient undergoing treatment at the time. Apart from her own casualties, Uganda took on board casualties from a nearby hospital ship and David Watt treated the facial injuries. Uganda was patched up and limped from the Mediterranean for repair in Pensacola, USA at a maximum speed of six knots. David Watt went on to enjoy a distinguished career as a Professor of Dentistry at Edinburgh in his research specialties, materials and metallurgy.

Dr Martin Nichols. Dr Martin Nichols was captured during the retreat to Dunkirk and after a few months was sent with some other doctors and medical staff to set up a prisoners' hospital at Hildburghausen in Thuringia. There were six POW hospitals in Thuringia housing prisoners of every nationality. The Red Cross supplied every British and American prisoner a food parcel per week on an amazingly regular basis from mid 1941-1944. Invalid comfort parcels with special light food and medical equipment were also invaluable. The nursing of the numerous Russians dying of starvation and advanced tubercle would have been quite impossible without them. The Red Cross supplied much of the instruments and drugs used by the medical staff. They also administered the repatriation of the wounded, which only took place when it was possible to balance the number of Allied and German prisoners involved.

Dr Nichols finally ended up as camp medical officer at Stalag Luft 1 at Barth, in Pomerania, on the Baltic coast. The camp held 10,000 men, mainly British and American aircrew. There were twenty surgical and forty medical beds in the wooden-hutted hospital, which was exceedingly difficult to heat in winter. There was a small electric autoclave and an instrument steriliser for sterilizing bowls. Sterile water was provided from big pots and pans boiling on a stove. The theatre staff had a unique composition. There were no medical orderlies, so Dr Nichols started off with aircrew sergeants.

A rear gunner gave the anaesthetics, a navigator was his assistant and a Spitfire pilot became the theatre sister. After a dentist arrived, the rear gunner became a dental orderly and eventually did all the fillings.

They dealt with the acute abdomen, many hernias, peripheral nerve repairs, some orthopaedic work, occasional abdominal emergencies and all the many problems associated with wound surgery. In 1945, when the Allied armies approached from east and west, the camp guards melted away. The Russians arrived and the POWs awaited evacuation. In the meantime, there were some remarkable additions to the work. Each day, there were queues of women, often with prams, coming for consultation because their own doctors had decamped when the guards went. Three and a half years of captivity ended when Flying Fortresses and Lancasters evacuated the camp [Nichols 1951]. Martin Nichols was later to become a distinguished neuro-surgeon at Aberdeen.

Mr Sandy Flockhart. Sandy Flockhart qualified in dentistry in 1939 and subsequently volunteered for military service just after Dunkirk. He trained as a paratrooper and joined the staff of 133 Parachute Field Ambulance as a paratroop dentist. He was taught anaesthetic techniques, including blind intubation, at Lincoln Military Hospital. At the time he did not appreciate how important this part of his training was to prove in the near future.

The staff of the Field Ambulance deployed, as part of Operation Market Garden, to Arnhem in the Netherlands. As a member of a surgical team of twenty personnel, Flockhart parachuted from a Dakota aircraft with his 60-lb. kitbag tied to his ankle, while he clutched a stretcher bundle containing blankets, stretchers, plasma, saline and transfusion sets. The parachute drop was off target due to a malfunction of the warning light at the door of the aircraft and the team descended in their parachutes from 400 feet through heavy gunfire.

Members of the British surgical team finally surrendering at Oosterbeek, with wounded patients, Sandy Flockhart, extreme left

Their target was Oosterbeek, which involved a cross-country march of four miles from the dropping zone. At Oosterbeek, a dentist's surgery was commandeered and the team began to operate on casualties. Their first case was a Polish glider pilot whose leg had been shot away above the knee and required amputation. Sandy was the anaesthetist. During a crucial part of the surgery, the handsaw snapped halfway through dividing the femur. There was no spare saw. At that point, the lighting also failed and the Padre lit the grim scene with a hand torch. The surgeon snapped the rest of the femur with a resounding crack. The Padre fainted and light was lost again. Despite these calamities, the operation was completed successfully.

The battle raged around the surgical team location. Ground positions were won, lost, and then won again. The surgical team was captured by a German Panzer unit, but allowed to continue to look after casualties of both sides during this confusing situation. Shortly afterwards the Germans lost control and the team were no longer prisoners. The senior medical officer, who was also a dentist, Dr Graeme Warrack from Edinburgh, found himself liaising with the German Panzer Group for medical and surgical supplies. The team worked under the most trying conditions with so much gunfire around, that all the windows of the building were knocked out to reduce the risk from flying glass. Finally, the Germans succeeded in holding the area and the surgical team became prisoners of war.

After a couple of days in solitary confinement, Flockhart was despatched to a camp deep in Germany, losing in the process of interrogation his logbook containing all his anaesthetics details. He is still resentful at the loss of the book, since it might have allowed him to claim an "honorary" Diploma in Anaesthetics, on discharge from the Services! In the prison camp he teamed up with an excellent New Zealand dentist and took an active interest in dental mechanics. He also spent much of his time making prosthetic eyes and even a nose out of acrylic material. On release and demobilization he resumed his golfing activities and reached a standard to compete in the Open Golf Championship of 1946. He subsequently went on to win the Scottish Amateur Championship two years later.

Post-war Health Services

Pre-war developments had been pointing the way to greater public provision of health services. The war of 1939-1945 forced the pace and created a situation in which there could be no return to previous arrangements. Immediately pre-war, the Cabinet had agreed to the provision of emergency hospital accommodation in the event of wartime air attack [Levitt 1992]. The resulting Emergency Hospital Scheme provided 16,574 additional beds in Scotland. Just over half were in new annexes added to existing institutions, but seven completely new hospitals were built.

Fortunately, casualties did not arise in the numbers anticipated and by 1942 some of the beds in the emergency hospitals were being used to relieve the pressure on voluntary hospitals and to reduce their long waiting lists [Kinnaird 1987]. Thomas Johnston, the wartime Secretary of State, recorded with pride that by April 1945 the waiting list of 34,000 patients on the books of the voluntary hospitals had been cleared! [Johnston 1952]. The emergency hospitals, funded directly by central government, had earned themselves an important place as part of the hospital service. It would have been unthinkable, if not impossible, to abandon them. Some were to have remarkably long lives.

In October 1941, the Government announced its intention to introduce a comprehensive health service as soon as possible after the war [Kinnaird

1987]. At the end of 1942, the Beveridge Report on Social Insurance and Allied Services based its recommendations on the important assumption that a comprehensive health service would be made available to all [Brotherston & Brims 1987].

The Hetherington Committee, established by the Secretary of State for Scotland, sought a method that would enable all hospitals, whether managed by local authorities or as individual voluntary hospitals, to co-operate within a comprehensive administrative arrangement. In their Report in August 1943 they envisaged a regionally organised hospital service overseen by five advisory Regional Councils on which all relevant interests including the local authorities would be represented [Kinnaird 1987].

In February 1944, The White Paper, "A National Health Service", outlined the Government's proposals as they stood at that time. It included a particularly telling comment on hospital services:

The hospital and specialist services have grown up without a national or even an area plan... The tendency in the modern development of medicine and surgery is towards specialist centres - for radiotherapy and neurosis for example - and no one hospital can be equally equipped and developed to suit all needs, or to specialise equally in all subjects. The time has come when the hospital services have to be thought of, and planned, as a wider whole... [Ministry of Health, Department of Health for Scotland 1944].

Further discussions and negotiations with the interested parties developed these proposals into the structure of the National Health Service introduced in 1948. In Scotland, all hospitals became the responsibility of five Regional Hospital Boards nominated and funded by the Secretary of State. Teaching hospitals were included in these arrangements. This differed from the position in England where separate arrangements were made for the management of teaching hospitals.

The arrangements for general practitioner services were similar to those in the long established National Health Insurance Scheme, with the important difference that they were now available to the whole population. Administration became the responsibility of new bodies called Executive Councils, which resembled the former insurance committees. Local authorities remained responsible for the control of infectious diseases and for environmental health matters. They were given statutory responsibility for the provision of a variety of services in the community, which included district nursing, domiciliary midwifery, and home helps.

Joint Council Initiatives

In 1944, an initiative was proposed by the MDDUS to establish a common code of medico-legal practice, guidance on current medical issues, proposed amendments to the Medical Acts and an exchange of information of mutual interest among the three medical defence organisations in the UK. The first tentative suggestion about the possibility of setting up a Joint Co-ordinating Committee with the other organisations was made at the April 1944 meeting of the Council. By June, it was proposed to write to the other organisations to consider the matter [MDDUS 1944].

This produced a favourable response and an exploratory meeting was arranged in London on 26 January 1945. Four representatives from each organisation attended. Dr Andrew Allison, Mr Alexander Macgregor, Dr John Beck and Mr William Tattersall, two doctors and two dentists, represented the MDDUS along with the Secretary and Solicitor. At the conference, it was recommended that each defence organisation should retain its individuality. Further subjects for discussion would include the pooling of information, the establishment of guidelines for joint action on professional matters and that the differentiation from insurance companies would be maintained.

The first formal meeting of the Co-ordinating Committee took place on 2 November 1945 under the chairmanship of Sir Ernest Rock-Carling. It was agreed that proceedings would be strictly advisory and that minutes of meetings would be presented regularly to the respective Councils. The Committee considered the correspondence between the Medical Defence Union and the London and Counties Medical Protection Society relating to an important issue concerning two of their medical practitioners who had appeared before the GMC as a result of complaints by the Ministry. In both cases the doctors had had the charges against them previously considered by the local insurance committees. Both were fined and one had his name removed from the list of insurance practitioners. Afterwards the Ministry referred the cases to the GMC.

In effect, both practitioners concerned were victims of double jeopardy and the Ministry had acted both as judge and prosecutor by imposing the original fine, then by referring the case for further possible punishment. Such practices were held to be totally unreasonable and unfair. The situation was considered by the Co-ordinating Committee and the BMA. As a result, the strongest representations were made to the GMC that complaints, based solely on alleged professional negligence, or a breach of terms of service of insurance practitioners, should be deferred until the GMC had received the opinion of Counsel.

A further proposal from the GMC was discussed, in which members of defence organisations would resign their membership while acting as members of the GMC. The Co-ordinating Committee decided to send a letter in the name of the three organisations to the President of the GMC suggesting that, during the hearing of any penal case, members of council of the GMC who were members of the defence organisations should not be required to withdraw unless requested to do so by one of the parties in the case.

In 1946, the MDDUS found itself in the enviable position of passing on its cumulative knowledge to another defence organisation. Since its formation, the MDDUS had offered membership to both doctors and dentists. The MDDUS Secretary reported that the Medical Defence Union, for the first time, was considering the admission of dentists and that he had had a letter from its Secretary asking about the MDDUS experience with dental members [MDDUS 1946].

Norman ROCKWELL
(1894-1978)
**Norman Rockwell Visits a Family
Doctor**   1947
Oil on canvas
Norman Rockwell Museum,
Stockbridge, Mass.
Printed by kind permission of
Norman Rockwell Family Trust.
©1947 Norman Rockwell Family
Trust

For 47 years the American artist Norman
Rockwell designed covers for *The
Saturday Evening Post*. In the 1940s *A
Family Doctor* was included in a series of
country life images for inside the
magazine. The doctor was George Russell
MD, for many years the country doctor in
the small town of Arlington, Vermont,
where Rockwell lived from 1939 to 1953.

Catalysts of Change

The National Health Service

On the morning of Monday, 5 July 1948, a four page buff-coloured pamphlet arrived by post at every house in the land. This announced the introduction of the National Health Service:

...It will provide you with all medical, dental and nursing care. Everyone - rich or poor, man, woman or child - can use it or any part of it. There are no charges, except for a few special items. There are no insurance qualifications. But it is not a "charity". You are all paying for it, mainly as taxpayers, and it will relieve your money worries in time of illness.

The NHS Booklet issued to soldiers returning to civilian life at the end of the war

Dr Douglas Garvie

For men and women leaving H.M. Forces to live in the United Kingdom

The New NATIONAL HEALTH SERVICE

5th July, 1948 onwards

What is the new National Health Service? How do you get it?

It will provide you with all medical, dental, and nursing care. Everyone—rich or poor, man, woman or child—can use it or any part of it. There are no charges, except for a few special items. There are no insurance qualifications. But it is not a "charity". You are all paying for it, mainly as taxpayers, and it will relieve your money worries in time of illness.

Choose Your Doctor Now You will be entitled to all usual advice and treatment from a family doctor. Your dealings with your doctor will be personal and confidential. You will visit his surgery or he will call on you as may be necessary. The difference is that the doctor will be paid by the Government out of funds provided by everybody.

Choose a doctor, as soon as you have obtained your National Registration Identity Card, by completing the special form (E.C.13) attached to this pamphlet and handing the form to the doctor of your choice. Many will choose their pre-service doctor. Any doctor can decline to accept a patient. If one doctor cannot accept you, ask another or ask to be put in touch with one by the new "Executive Council" which has been set up in your area (you can get its address from the Post Office).

After you have been accepted by a doctor your Executive Council will send you a medical card. If you want to change your doctor you can do so at any time without difficulty. If you need a doctor when away from your home district, you can go to any doctor who is taking part in the new arrangements. You will not have to pay.

For any further information about these arrangements ask at the offices of the local Executive Council.

Maternity Services An expectant mother can have the services of a doctor who undertakes maternity work (whether he is her usual doctor or not), and of a midwife, as well as general care before and after confinement. If her usual doctor does not undertake maternity work, he, or the Welfare Centre, will put the expectant mother in touch with another doctor. It will be the doctor's responsibility, with the midwife, to give all proper care and (if he considers it necessary or is called in by the midwife) to be present at the confinement.

Hospital and Specialist Services You will also be entitled to all forms of treatment in general or special hospitals, whether as an in-patient or as an out-patient. These include, for instance, maternity care, sanatorium treatment, care of mental health, and *all surgical operations*.

The help of consultants and specialists of all kinds will be made available to you as national resources allow, whether at hospital, at special health centres, or at your home.

Your doctor will arrange this help when you need it.

Hospital charges are not payable in the new scheme. Where accommodation permits, however, you can pay something for greater privacy (for example, in single rooms or small wards). Or, if you do

The introduction of the National Health Service was a defining moment in the medical and dental health care of the United Kingdom, but searches of the Minutes of the MDDUS reveal little more than three brief and non-committal references to what was happening. The MDDUS Council of the day were scrupulous in their non-partisan acceptance of this major change for both professions, whatever their personal opinions might have been. This low-key response of the Council was the opposite of the widespread disapproval and condemnation felt and expressed by the medical and dental professions to the introduction of the Act, despite the worthiness of its aim.

The 1947 Annual General Meeting of the British Dental Students Association at Leeds addressed by Aneurin Bevan (second from left) The History of Dentistry Research Group, University of Glasgow

The *British Medical Journal* had previously voiced formal disapproval of the scheme and in a leader in a February 1948 issue, it revealed the results of a poll among over 50,000 members of the medical profession in Britain, in which 43,013 completed the voting papers. A 90% ratio of the votes cast expressed disapproval of the Act in its present form. This was underlined by a further finding of the poll, which indicated that, in any case, 22,000 would refuse to take service under the Act [BMJ 1948].

The dental profession reacted in a similar fashion and Mr Aneurin Bevan, the Minister of Health, in an unprecedented move addressed the 1947 Annual General Meeting of the British Dental Students Association in Leeds. It was an indication of the sensitivity of the situation and his desire and need to mollify the next generation of dental practitioners.

National newspapers urged the Government to compromise in the face of all this opposition.

The Times wrote:

The Minister of Health must give due weight to this remarkable expression of feelings.

The Yorkshire Post hoped:

...this impressive demonstration of feeling will convince the Minister of Health of the need to seek a settlement by compromise.

The Glasgow Herald considered:

... a workable health service will be forthcoming only at the cost of concessions of a more definite nature than the Government have seen their way to make so far.

The principal cause of concern centred on the perceived threat to individual and intellectual freedoms and on the likely excessive demands on the medical and dental professions, from a service offered free to the entire population. A spirit of reconciliation and compromise gradually filtered through the negotiations and eventually carried the day. An

Amending Bill was introduced in the House of Commons to take account of many of the concerns raised by the medical and dental professional bodies. The necessary adjustments to the Act were made and all major professional opposition abated. Nevertheless, on the 5 July, *The Scotsman* delivered a parting shot with the comment:

Yesterday was Independence Day and today as it were the doctors lose their freedom. From now on those of them who have chosen to throw in their lot with the Minister of Health become Bevan boys...

In contrast, the Health Service Act was greeted with enormous enthusiasm by the public at large. There was a high demand for dentures, spectacles, hearing aids and surgical supports. The dental profession was inundated with prospective patients. Queues formed outside GP and GDP premises. In one Fife town, the GP turned up for his evening surgery and hoped that the queue outside his surgery was for the cinema, a short distance away. He was to be disappointed!

Funding Problems

A month after the introduction of the new National Health Service, the Department of Health for Scotland submitted a memorandum on a Capital Investment Programme for the Hospital and Specialist Service. It pointed out that this had previously been a matter for individual and independent hospital authorities, either municipal or voluntary. It would now, however, be possible to have complete integration of the hospital building programme, to secure new building where need was most urgent. After a modest beginning in 1948, up to £2,000,000 was forecast for spending in 1949, £2,350,000 in 1950, £2,850,000 in 1951, and £2,850,000 in 1952 [Levitt 1992]. By early 1949, it was becoming clear that the initial estimates for 1949-50 were too low.

Demands on some of the general medical and dental practitioner services had been seriously under-estimated. In the hospital service there was difficulty in finding reliable figures of past experience on which to base future estimates, and undertakings had been given to improve salaries and wages.

The search for possible economies and for additional sources of revenue was becoming more pressing. The possibility of charging for prescriptions and for spectacles was mooted. Levying a "hotel charge" on hospital in-patients, which had been a tentative suggestion in the Beveridge Report, was considered, but administrative difficulties were recognised. Some patients might be given priority in the provision of services. For example, dental services might be cut back to cover only important groups such as mothers and children. The Secretary of State for Scotland recognised that measures along these lines would mean that the Government must admit publicly, with all its political consequences, that they were deserting the concept of a universal free service [Levitt 1992]. Nevertheless, in October 1949, the Government agreed to a substantial reduction on public investment in response to the devaluation of sterling. The capital building programme, which had scarcely begun, was already in jeopardy.

There were similar troubles over dental running costs. During the years leading up to the Second World War, demand for dental treatment was limited to a narrow range of treatment. A few well-organised high street dental practices prospered, but there was hardship among the majority of dental practices, with the average dentist earning £400 per annum. The large proportion of the population called up for military service during the war, discovered the free entitlement to medical and dental treatment and transposed expectation of this entitlement to their civilian life after demobilisation. Thus, the original estimate by the Friendly Societies that only 17% of the population might demand dental treatment became, in reality, a demand from almost 100% of the population for dental services. The high demand on the dental services, both for dentures and conservative treatment had to be financed and a series of economy measures were introduced. These were, a ceiling on earnings, a new scale of fees representing a reduction of 25% and, in 1951, a requirement that all patients receiving dentures pay approximately half the cost.

Joint Committee Meetings

Meetings of the Joint Co-ordinating Committee, with representatives from the three defence organisations, continued. A question of procedure was discussed, in which a claim might be made against a practitioner who was a member of more than one defence organisation. In cases where the respective Councils agreed either to defend or settle, the MDDUS would handle the case if it arose in Scotland and the appropriate English organisation if in England. Costs and damages would be shared equally. If the defence organisations disagreed on the settlement policy adopted, it would be left to the member to select a defence organisation, who would take full responsibility for the conduct of the case.

At a further meeting in October 1948, the work of the committee dealt with the fragility of needles used for medical and surgical purposes and the agreement that had been reached on the standardisation of needle calibre, after much argument with the manufacturers of surgical apparatus. The Joint Co-ordinating Committee also considered the admission to membership of foreign medical practitioners who were temporarily resident in this country for postgraduate study and who were registered. After some debate, it was agreed that foreign practitioners should be admissible to membership of the defence organisation concerned.

Domestic Matters

The Annual Report of the MDDUS for 1949 stated that there was no sign of any decrease in the number of claims for negligence. During the year, a case was brought in the South East of England, which was to prove the most expensive to date in the MDDUS history. It involved a radiotherapist who had given treatment to two women. Apparently, he had taken up a new hospital appointment and failed to check the dosage figures for deep X-ray therapy. Both patients received an excessive dose, as a result of which, one of the patients died. The other lived, but suffered severe lung damage and her left arm became virtually useless [MDDUS 1949].

The Senior Counsel, Mr Hylton Fost QC, did not consider that either claim could be successfully defended and advised that they should both be settled. An out-of-court settlement was concluded at £4,100 for the patient who died and £10,710 for the survivor. This large settlement was taken into account by the MDDUS insurance company when renewing its policy and the premium was subsequently doubled from 2s 3d per member to 4s 6d. The excess payable by the MDDUS was increased from £2,500 to £5,000. The case highlighted a number of claims in connection with deep X-ray therapy and raised the question of a differential subscription rate for members administering this treatment. The Joint Co-ordinating Committee, however, decided not to support any differential rate.

A Joint Co-ordinating Committee meeting in Glasgow, on the 10 October 1951, investigated the question of the examination of patients by a doctor before a general anaesthetic was administered in dental treatment. This was in response to what Professor John Glaister had said in a recent court case, that a dentist should never administer an anaesthetic, until he held a certificate from a medical practitioner stating the patient was fit to be anaesthetised. It was not an opinion, which found support among the Committee membership, and it was agreed that no move would be made by the defence organisations to publish advice to members on this issue. Nevertheless, the Association of Anaesthetists had become concerned about the increasing number of legal actions involving its members and sought information on cases involving anaesthetic mishaps from the MDDUS files.

Media Matters

Relationships between the three defence organisations remained close and professional, although media commentators in the south sometimes overlooked the existence of the youngest organisation in the north. During a television programme in March 1954 Max Robertson, a distinguished presenter, informed his viewers that there were only two defence organisations in the country. An indignant MDDUS Council set the matter straight immediately and received prompt acknowledgement of the mistake from the BBC [MDDUS 1954]!

Jubilee Year

The MDDUS reached its Jubilee on 1 May 1952 and the Council considered how this occasion could be celebrated in an appropriate but modest way. Eventually, a decision was taken to hold a dinner party attended by Council members, Solicitors and the Secretary. This was duly held in the New Club in Glasgow on 13 January 1953. The day of reckoning came at the February meeting when the participants were told that the cost of their night out, £67 8s 11d - (£4 9s 11d each) - would be deducted from their fees [MDDUS 1952].

At the fiftieth annual general meeting, Professor Thomas Munro, the President, requested that the Secretary read a letter of resignation on his behalf. He had been President for twenty-one years. He expressed his appreciation of the support he had received from the Council during his long term of office.

Gathering Momentum

The first faint stirrings of change in health care and its medico-legal consequences started to become evident in the early 1950s. The novelty of free access to family doctors and dentists and the seemingly unlimited provision of free medicines and appliances, greatly increased the demands and expectations of patients. Easy access for patients to hospital consultancy services was a welcome development. At the same time, a barrier was created between the general practitioner and hospital services. X-ray, laboratory and physiotherapy services were only available through a hospital consultant; often clinically unnecessary, but a procedural necessity.

The family doctor saw patients, made a diagnosis on the basis of history and clinical examination before giving advice, prescribing treatment or explaining management to the patient, who would remain convinced that advice without a prescription was a deprivation of treatment. When a doctor might advise a consultant opinion, an appointment could be arranged there and then by telephone. The appointment was invariably almost immediate, or at most, within a few days. Increasingly, the family doctor became a purveyor of large numbers of prescriptions, National Health Insurance certificates and letters to specialists.

Doctors with an average size list of NHS patients conducted open surgeries and would see about twenty patients every morning and more than that in the evening. The "Consulting Hour" usually lasted a good deal longer and took place twice a day, five or six days a week. In between, the doctor fitted in as many as twenty home visits, day and night, often more in the winter. The elderly were visited regularly on a routine basis. Some doctors added domiciliary midwifery to an already busy day. It was not unusual to leave a crowded waiting room to attend a confinement, only to return an hour or two later and find patients still waiting.

By the late 1950s, hospital appointments were made by completing a hospital proforma and usually occurred within two to three weeks. Limited use of radiology - straight X-rays - and laboratory services became more available. The absence of a collecting service for specimens/samples became another chore for the GP, but at least the relevant reports did arrive within two to three days, representing a distinct advance in general health care.

Hunter v Hanley

In the midst of this state of flux, there arose a MDDUS medico-legal case, which became the first of a small number of landmark judgements concerning medical care and competence. In the early 1940s, John Hanley, an Arts student at Glasgow University, visited the anatomy department of the medical school. The scene made a deep impression and convinced the Arts student to change his vocation to medicine.

From this quirk of fate arose the subsequent historic legal judgement of medical negligence in Scotland. *Hunter v Hanley* in 1955 [SC 1955] and its counterpart judgement in England some two years later, *Bolam v Friern Hospital Management Committee* [All ER 1957], established the test for medical negligence adopted by both Scottish and English courts, which is still in use today.

Dr Hanley qualified in April 1947 and moved to a mining community practice in Durham, where the main health problems were chronic bronchitis and broken bones. The mainstay of treatment for bronchitis was penicillin and "M&B 693" and fractures were sent off to the local infirmary. Patient consultation was carried out within earshot of all the other patients. A strip of curtain material, a foot wide, hung from a rail attached to the wall. It served to provide the only concession to privacy and confidentiality. The curtain rail was swung at right angles to the wall and behind the tiny strip of material, the patient undressed and presented him or herself for examination.

Dr Hanley returned to Glasgow, as the NHS was being introduced and set up his practice surgery at 686 Gallowgate. Within a few years, he was joined by his brother, who obtained a practice about two hundred yards away. Weekend rosters were set up and another practice joined in, so that life became somewhat easier. A further innovation of the brothers was the establishment of an appointment system. Neighbouring GPs scoffed and warned that the Hanleys would never get another private patient if NHS patients were allowed appointments, hitherto a preserve of the private patient.

Mrs Jemima Hunter had been under treatment for some time with chronic pulmonary symptoms and had been seen on a fairly frequent basis by Dr Hanley and his partner. A course of twelve injections of penicillin in September 1951 was followed up by a further course of twelve injections in November, because her condition had failed to improve. Dr Hanley administered both courses of treatment.

On the twelfth and final injection of the second course of treatment, Dr Hanley gave the penicillin injection in full and began to withdraw the needle. It broke and lodged in the patient's right buttock in the upper outer quadrant. The needle used was a No. 16, suitable for hypodermic intravenous and intra-muscular injection. At that stage of his practice he was a veteran of some 2,000 injections. Dr Hanley informed Mrs Hunter immediately what had happened, gave her a letter of explanation to the hospital and sent her off to the Accident & Emergency Department at Glasgow Royal Infirmary.

It may have been fright, induced by an over-emphasis of the danger the needle posed, or a third party, which led Mrs Hunter subsequently to take legal action against Dr Hanley. After the incident she had thanked Dr Hanley and stated that she realised what had happened was purely accidental and due to no fault of his. However the doctor on duty at the hospital implied that the needle could go all through her body and get to her heart and kill her, in order, presumably, to ensure her compliance with her treatment. Mrs Hunter immediately came back to Dr Hanley and told him. He tried to reassure her, with no success. Mrs Hunter sought legal advice and qualified for legal aid to pursue her claim for damages of £2,500.

The advice, which Dr Hanley received all those years ago from the professor of medico-legal studies at medical school, to join a medical defence organisation, now stood him in good stead. He had joined the MDDUS and, on receipt of his court summons, the MDDUS took over. A trial by jury was held in July 1954 and a unanimous verdict was returned for Dr Hanley. However there was an immediate motion for a new trial on the grounds that the jury had been misdirected.

On the 4 February 1955, Lord President Clyde sat in consideration of the motion and delivered the now famous judgement on the establishment

Dr John Hanley
the Hanley Family

of liability by a doctor. Its clarity has established a set of criteria for professional skill and standard of care, which remain valid today:

It must be proved that there is a usual and normal practice;

It must be proved that the defender has not adopted that practice;

It must be established that the course the doctor adopted is one which no professional man of ordinary skill would have taken if he had been acting with ordinary care.

Despite his judgement, Lord Clyde directed that the verdict in the first trial could not stand and ordered a new trial. The subsequent trial concluded in 1956 and once again Dr Hanley was found not liable by the jury to pay Mrs Hunter damages.

Dr Hanley remained in general practice for several years after the trial. However, years of running up steep tenement stairs carrying a midwifery bag in one hand and a general bag in the other encouraged Dr Hanley to seek a different career option and he gained a Diploma in Public Health and subsequently went on to enjoy a career in that specialty. History does not relate when the offending syringe needle was removed from Mrs Hunter. Despite several attempts to remove the needle, it remained deep in her right buttock, certainly until the time of the trials some four years after the initial incident.

Bolam

The test that established the criteria in assessing medical negligence in England evolved from the court case, *Bolam v Friern Hospital Management Committee* in 1957, in which a judgement was handed down in favour of the hospital [All ER 1957]. In 1954, John Hector Bolam a salesman was admitted to Friern Hospital on 29 April suffering from mental illness. He was discharged on 30 July but was re-admitted on 16 August with a persistence of his depression. He was advised by a consultant to undergo electro-convulsive therapy. He signed consent to the treatment, but was not warned of the risk of fracture, albeit that the risk was very small. On the 19 August, he was treated with electro-convulsive therapy. He received a further course of treatment on the 23 August when he sustained the dislocation of both hip joints and fractures of the pelvis.

Neither relaxant drugs, nor manual control were used, although nurses were in attendance throughout the treatment. The use of relaxant drugs would have excluded the risk of fracture. However, among those skilled and experienced in this form of therapy, there were two bodies of opinion, one of which favoured the use of relaxant drugs or manual control as a general practice; the other considered that the use of such drugs was attended by mortality risks and confined their prescription to cases where there were particular reasons for their use.

Bolam sued the hospital for negligence in the administration of treatment and in failing to warn him of the risk involved, before treatment. The case centred on the question of professional skill. In the summing up the jury was directed:

... a doctor is not guilty of negligence, if he has acted in accordance with a practice accepted as proper by a responsible body of medical men skilled in that particular art. The test is the standard of the ordinary skilled man exercising and professing to have that special skill...it is sufficient if he exercises the ordinary skill of an ordinary competent man exercising that particular art.

In the judgement, the principles established in the *Hunter v Hanley* case were quoted in corroborative support and the two cases have ruled supreme in the test of medical negligence ever since. There was a visionary undertone in the judge's direction to the jury, when he quoted from a judgement by Lord Denning in similar circumstances at the Court of Appeal [All ER 1954]:

...we should be doing a disservice to the community at large if we were to impose liability on hospitals and doctors for everything that happens to go wrong. Doctors would be led to think more of their own safety than the good of their patients...We must insist on due care for the patient at every point, but we must not condemn as negligence that which is only a misadventure.

Medical science has conferred great benefits on mankind, but these benefits are attended by considerable risks. Every surgical operation is attended by risks. We cannot take the benefits without taking the risks. Every advance in technique is also attended by risk. Doctors, like the rest of us, have to learn by experience, and experience often teaches in a hard way.

National Service

The 1950s was a time of conscription for the country. Young men were called up for national military service and the MDDUS was faced with the situation of providing indemnity cover for young doctors and dentists serving their conscription, particularly overseas. The MDDUS Council agreed to provide full cover for all National Service and Short Service doctors and dentists provided the period of service did not exceed five years. The indemnity cover extended to claims arising in courts abroad without any extra subscription or additional insurance premium.

The incidence of medical negligence was low, although there was a recurring emergence of problems associated with administering anaesthetics, particularly in dentistry. In military circles at least, the dentist had a clear role in such matters. Professor Paul Geissler experienced an emphasis on extractions and anaesthesia during his training at the Edinburgh Dental School. He was called up for national service and posted to Germany at the height of the Cold War. On postings abroad, the dentist was responsible not only for the dental health of the troops but also their families. The overall dental state was, by and large, poor. Thus, there were fairly regular general anaesthetic sessions for extractions.

Initially the Medical Officer of the medical centre, also a National Service officer, was booked to provide the anaesthetics. However, it appeared that at the time medical students did not receive much general anaesthetic training so the sessions were very fraught and his services were quickly dispensed with. From then on, Professor Geissler gave the general anaesthetic and his civilian dental colleague extracted the teeth. Had the situation escalated to a hot war it was quite clear that army dentists would have been employed as field anaesthetists, as indeed they were at Arnhem, in the experience of Sandy Flockhart.

Conditions and Comforts

General practice in the 1950s remained a demanding occupation with a close affinity to local communities. Dr Alistair Riddell entered general practice as an assistant with a view on 1 January 1956. At the time, obtaining a post in practice was very difficult, but Dr Willie Davie, in Castle Street, Glasgow was looking for a partner and the post would meet Riddell's needs for a few months. He was to stay for over 39 years!

Co-operation between practices in his area was minimal and among local stories was the one about pneumonia, in which there was lobar pneumonia, broncho-pneumonia, and Dr "X" pneumonia, so-called because he made excessive diagnoses of pneumonia, for which there was a payment for notification. Infant mortality remained high and the most common cause of death was certified as infection, although the benefits of antibiotics were evident after 1945 and life expectancy increased. Abortions were a problem and incomplete abortions were very common. Tuberculosis was rife.

The 50 Yard Dash

Haemorrhoidectomies were not always mundane procedures failing to catch the interest of audiences in the Surgical Operating Theatre....at least not when Mr Frank E.Jardine Consultant Surgeon in Edinburgh Royal Infirmary in the 1940's was the operator. When "piles" were to be treated by him, the Gallery was usually full and there were two lines of medical students lining the corridor outside. The reason? "Frankie" used the method of "clamp and cautery". Long-handled clamps with blades about 2" long, metal on the upper surface and bone on the under surface to prevent accidental skin burns, were applied around the base of each haemorrhoid.

The cautery was achieved by means of soldering irons heated to red heat on the kitchen stove of Ward 19 about 50 yards away. When the desired heat was achieved and the great man was ready, relays of medical students ran down the corridor each brandishing an iron aloft, presenting it to the surgeon poised waiting to sear off the offending tissue. Perhaps half a dozen irons were required for each patient. The results were good - no bleeding no infection and early discharge of the patient. Today it may all seem unsophisticated, but it worked and... it was good theatre!

In a West Riding of Yorkshire practice, Doctor Gerry McGlone's starting salary was £1,000 per annum as an assistant in a mining community with two pits in the practice area. There were in excess of 14,000 persons on the practice list supported by the three partners. Dr McGlone's family was initially housed in a council house allocated by the local council as an inducement to attract a young doctor into the area. He drove a Ford Popular car and his weekly grocery bill amounted to £5. The family's first night in the house was disturbed by a lot of rumbling and banging. In the morning they awoke to find the coal cellar full of coal, their first experience of the kindness and generosity of the local people.

The miners worked hard and played hard. If a miner was off work and able to provide a doctor's certificate, he would collect his full pay plus any bonus payments. However, absences of one day were common and were not covered by the NHS certificate. The private certificates were blue and known as blue notes. They cost one shilling. One miner introduced such a certificate to his foreman, who had trouble reading the doctor's writing, "What were you off with - all I can see is a stroke?" "Well that's what I was off with," came the quick reply!

The main surgery of the practice was described as, "an out-patient clinic in hospital". The reality was that the doctors stood some distance apart at a long desk and the patients formed a queue behind each doctor. Those patients who required examination were sent to another room. The practice employed a practice nurse, an innovation of its time and the practice secretary had two large, very thick ledgers where all persons on the practice list were noted. It was very comprehensive and extremely well cross-referenced.

Penicillin, only by injection at the time, was heralded as miraculous. A glass syringe had its plunger removed and the barrel and plunger, wrapped in lint, were boiled up in a pot of water, together with a couple of needles. The penicillin was made up by injecting sterile water into a small bottle containing the penicillin powder, which was dissolved in the water, drawn up into the syringe and injected deep into the patient's buttock. The advent of a long-acting penicillin - Penidural - lasting 24 hours was a godsend to general practice. The most important drugs available to the GP in the 1950s were digoxin, morphine, nikethamide (coramine) and phenobarbitone, which was used to treat epilepsy and included in any medicine where a calming effect was required.

Almost all antacid mixtures contained phenobarbitone. Barbiturates were very extensively used both as sedatives and hypnotics. Sleeping tablets were liberally prescribed and, although there was concern about addiction to codeine, especially linctus codeine, doctors seemed oblivious to the addiction to barbiturates. Similarly, when amphetamines arrived and were used to treat obesity, they were prescribed for years without it being recognised that their treatment had no effect on the patient's obesity and that potential amphetamine addicts were being created.

Doctors were still writing their own prescriptions in full, using minims, fluid ounces, grains and grammes. The oedema in congestive heart failure was treated with mercury-based mersalyl, given by injection. It prolonged the life expectancy of the patient, as far as the heart was concerned, but it may have compromised kidney function. The advent of the first oral diuretic was a major step forward in the treatment of congestive heart failure.

Ascites was a familiar condition and was treated at home using a trocar and cannula to drain the abdomen. Under local anaesthetic a small incision was made in the abdominal skin usually in the right iliac fossa - trocar and cannula were inserted through the abdominal wall. The trocar was removed and fluid drained via the cannula. This brought great relief to the patient and allowed him to die peacefully. Terminal care was very basic with a liberal use of morphine, diamorphine and sedatives.

An interesting anomaly existed between the NHS in England and in Scotland. In England, a GP making up a morphine /cocaine mixture for the terminally ill, called Brompton's Mixture, or Cocktail, could legitimately add whisky or brandy to the prescription. This was not allowed in Scotland!

Dentistry Comes of Age

The dental profession experienced many subtle, yet significant, changes in the decade of the 1950s as the profession gradually settled down to a peacetime existence under an NHS controlled by the Government. Some did not accomplish these changes without difficulty. Oral history recorded that a fighter pilot, who resumed a career as a dental student, intermittently experienced sufficient restlessness to cause him to offer his services as a fighter pilot to the Israeli Air Force in the desert conflict and to the American Air Force in the Korean War!

Dental Schools, as well as their medical counterparts, experienced an influx of ex-service mature students who overshadowed somewhat the more junior output from the fifth and sixth years of secondary schools. This could be very refreshing to the lecturing staff accustomed to a normally submissive class of young hopefuls. However, discipline could be tricky when a transgressor was known to have been a Squadron Leader, or a Commanding Officer of legendary fame. This was, however, just the opening gambit in a process that would lead to great change in the status and perceived authority of all concerned in the delivery of university education.

The idea that, by the end of the century, the Professor chosen to be Dean and Director of Dental Education would normally retire after occupying a six-year term in a rotational post and would only be appointed after consultation with lecturers, representatives of the student body and others, would have been unthinkable in the 1950s. Anyone appointed to a university lectureship was granted security of tenure until normal retirement. In choosing between a clinical and a non-clinical post, it was relevant to keep in mind that clinical Professors would have to retire at sixty-five years of age, whereas non-clinical Professors could continue to seventy years of age or later. The terms "redundancy" and "early retirement" were certainly not associated in one's thinking with any university appointment.

A reasonable income in general dental practice under the National Health Service, was assured practically anywhere in the country provided that there was a population of from 2,000 to 5,000 on the doorstep. This encouraged many newly qualified young practitioners to set up single-handed practices. The aim of the dental curriculum in those days was to turn out practitioners capable of independent practice from the outset and many planning authorities, rebuilding or creating communities, encouraged this procedure.

The establishment of Local Dental Committees, Regional Dental Officers and many other more senior posts in an enlarged Department of Health, also encouraged some senior and many more junior dental practitioners to support the profession in administrative ways, which had not been necessary previously. The dental schools and universities also enlarged their teaching staff and many young dentists discovered that an academic career was an alternative to general dental practice. It offered success and promotion, dependent on the quality of research work undertaken. This, in turn, led to the organisation in 1953 of a British Division of the North American International Association for Dental Research. This provided the main platform for an explosion in dental research among all the UK dental schools, which had immeasurable consequences for the dental health of the population by the end of the century.

In 1956, the dental profession became self-governing with the introduction and passing of the Dentists Act 1956. One of the principal purposes of the Act was to form the General Dental Council, which would regulate the professional standards of dentistry. However close links were to continue with the GMC on matters of professional education and examinations. The MDDUS was in close consultation with the Dental Board, particularly in regard to the disciplinary procedure rules, during the transition of the Bill through Parliament. An irony of the Bill was the time it took to come to a conclusion. It had been prepared in 1950, but with a change in government at the time, it was withdrawn until its final presentation six years later [Hansard 5s, 545:1349-1350].

Dentistry was essentially a very buoyant profession in the 1950's. It ranked highly as a career, in which a reasonable financial future was secure. The teaching staffs in dental schools were growing and many schools were considering enlargement or complete renewal of their premises. More young women were applying for entry to the profession, although they seldom amounted to a quarter of the annual intake. A note of satisfaction entered the medico-legal environment when a dentist, who had been the subject of a claim, sent a letter of thanks to the MDDUS stating that he wished to double his subscription in future! Sadly this philanthropic gesture had to be declined with thanks.

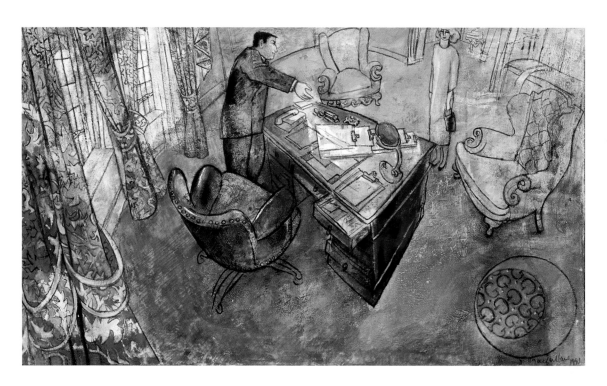

Susan MACFARLANE
(b.1938)
The Consultant   1991-5
Oil on canvas
Reproduced by kind permission of Susan
Macfarlane and A Picture of Health Ltd.

In 1991 the English artist Susan Macfarlane was
invited by Dr Geoffrey Farrer-Brown, a consultant
histopathologist, to observe the work done at his
London laboratories. Her subsequent visits to
Princess Grace Hospital and Gloucester Royal
Hospital resulted in a series of paintings and
drawings of breast cancer care *A Picture of Health*.
This is the first image in the series.

Advances and Specialties

Geriatric Medicine

The mid-20th century was a time when additional clinical and surgical specialties were beginning to emerge. The care of the elderly became such a specialty and has subsequently carried significant medico-legal risk in its practice. British geriatrician specialists have made a remarkable contribution to improvements in the standards of care for older patients. The point has been made by James Williamson, Professor Emeritus at the University of Edinburgh, that for several decades in the second half of the twentieth century, Britain was regarded as the leader in the field of geriatrics.

It all started with Dr Marjorie Warren in the 1930s, when she was appointed consultant physician at West Middlesex Hospital and found her responsibilities included numerous "chronic wards", which housed some seven hundred "incurable" patients. This was a common arrangement in such old municipal hospitals. In many instances, the physician thus designated would be summoned to certify death and to provide the necessary certificate, but had little prior involvement with the patients. Dr Warren's interest was aroused by these "incurables" and she set about assessing their individual medical and social needs. She found gross inefficiency, with large numbers of patients incorrectly categorised, often with no diagnosis.

She first established that a large number of patients were incorrectly categorised as requiring continuing hospital care. Many others, given appropriate diagnostic and therapeutic attention, recovered sufficiently to leave hospital and return home, or go to more suitable forms of care. Most importantly, Dr Warren demonstrated that well planned and expertly delivered rehabilitation frequently enabled restoration of some degree of useful function, even in very old and frail subjects and often this allowed these patients to leave hospital. Today's young doctors and nurses may find it difficult to realise what a revolutionary concept this was at the time. Many unpromising patients, such as stroke victims, benefited from the type of rehabilitation developed and practised by Dr Warren. Prior to this, most stroke victims were confined to bed and suffered the consequences of pressure sores and limb contractures, ending in an undignified and miserable death.

The lessons that were learned, led to the formulation of several basic principles, among which were, full diagnostic inquiry and assessment, ward design and furniture to cater for the frail and elderly and training and education in the field of geriatric medicine. This set the scene for British geriatric medicine and, by the mid-1940s, a small group of physicians had joined Dr Warren's crusade. With the introduction of the National Health Service, it was possible for Hospital Boards across the nation to appoint consultants and to establish what were then called, Geriatric Assessment Units. This led to great improvement in standards of care and the number of units increased rapidly. However, the demand outstretched the provision of resources.

The attitude of the medical profession, with a few notable exceptions, was generally unhelpful, sometimes even hostile and, at best, there was apathy. This was inevitable, given the exciting new discoveries and triumphs of medical science at the time. For the geriatricians, 100% success meant enabling the frail old patient to move unaided, to rise from bed, chair and toilet and to be continent. Such a patient can return to the community with some degree of independence and retain some dignity, but these modest indices of success tended not to attract doctors and nurses to work in geriatric medicine, so recruitment to the discipline was a huge problem.

In the early 1950s, the crusade came to Scotland and active departments were set up in Glasgow, Dundee and Aberdeen with such figures as Oswald Taylor Brown (Glasgow and Dundee), Ferguson Anderson (Glasgow), Leslie Wilson (Aberdeen) and R. G. Wilson (Perth), who founded the first day hospital in Scotland. It was critical to get the study of geriatrics into the undergraduate medical curriculum, but the early attempts were largely unsuccessful. It was therefore a great achievement in 1965 when Glasgow University established the first Chair in Geriatric Medicine, since when no fewer than five of the thirteen Presidents of the British Geriatric Society have been Glasgow graduates.

This was the start of a great academic and educational surge in geriatric medicine, with Britain in the forefront of that discipline. Work on the prevention of disability took place in Glasgow with the formation of consultative clinics, while research was published in Edinburgh on unreported disability at home. This led to closer links with general practice, which was likewise undergoing revolutionary change, following the GPs' Charter of 1965. Within a few years, every medical school had its Department of Geriatric Medicine, often with its own Chair. Colleges of Nursing were moving in the same direction and the most gratifying change in the 1970s and 1980s was the improvement in knowledge, skills and attitudes towards the proper management of older patients by young doctors and nurses.

The Tuberculosis Service

Intractable illnesses were also becoming the focus of improved treatment and drugs to combat their effects. The old adversary, tuberculosis, was one of these. The tuberculosis service had now become part of the National Health Service. As a result, the Government provided funding and the new administration allowed a rapid expansion of the tuberculosis service. By 1956, despite the quite serious setbacks of the wartime period, the number of tuberculosis beds actually exceeded the waiting lists.

Meantime, a revolution in pharmacology was taking place. The work of Fleming and then of Florey had fully demonstrated the value of penicillin in certain bacterial infections and hopes had been widely centred on finding a similar agent to combat tuberculosis. In 1944, Selman Waksman an American soil microbiologist, produced a substance having an in vitro bacteriostatic effect on the tubercle bacillus, which he called "Streptomycin". Years of careful research followed, with clinical trials and, with memories of Sanocrysin in mind, much caution. Serious problems of side effects and microbial resistance emerged and it was discovered that combined treatment with para-amino salicylic acid and isoniazid, or suitable alternatives, was essential and had to be continued over long periods of time.

The chief architect of combined therapy in the country was Professor (later Sir John) Crofton in Edinburgh. Crofton maintained that if the correct combination of drugs was selected and patients co-operated fully in following the prescribed treatment, 100% success was a reasonable target. The effects of this revolution were quite remarkable. New patients could often readily be treated at home. Some might not even have to stop work.

Patients who had active disease found that their stay in hospital was significantly shortened and they were quickly found to be no longer sources of infection. At the beginning of the 20th century there were 224 deaths from tuberculosis for every 100,000 of the population in the UK. At the present day, the figure is 1 per 100,000. It may well be concluded that, in this country, tuberculosis has been controlled but not yet eradicated. There are remaining problems, which pose serious difficulties. If patients also become infected with the human immunodeficiency virus, the perils are very obvious even in countries with well-developed health services.

The Royal College of General Practitioners.

The treatment of disease and illness was not the only change experienced at the time. General practice also felt a certain vulnerability. "The overall

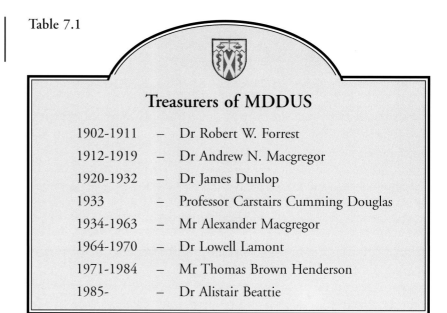

Treasurers of MDDUS

1902-1911	–	Dr Robert W. Forrest
1912-1919	–	Dr Andrew N. Macgregor
1920-1932	–	Dr James Dunlop
1933	–	Professor Carstairs Cumming Douglas
1934-1963	–	Mr Alexander Macgregor
1964-1970	–	Dr Lowell Lamont
1971-1984	–	Mr Thomas Brown Henderson
1985-	–	Dr Alistair Beattie

state of general practice is bad and still deteriorating", wrote Dr Joseph Collings, an Australian working as a Research Fellow at Harvard in a paper published in *The Lancet* [Collings 1950]. Predictably, Collings' paper caused offence to general practitioners, although subsequent surveys did much to redress the claims [Hadfield 1953; Taylor 1954]. It is of interest that Collings found that although standards were generally poor, they were higher in Scotland than England, particularly in the Highlands and Islands, which undoubtedly benefited from the medical scheme inaugurated in 1913. Many general practitioners had returned from the Second World War to predominantly single-handed practices in poor premises with no ancillary help, or attached nursing staff. Open access by general practitioners to hospital investigations was non-existent and treatment was largely empirical. Much time was given to completing "panel" certificates.

The Hospital Service was securely funded for the first time and developed accordingly. In contrast, many general practitioners were overwhelmed by patient demand, poor working conditions, long hours of work and a perverse and inadequate system of remuneration. They became increasingly demoralised and were perceived by many in the medical profession to be second-class citizens. There had been previous attempts to form an organisation in support of general practitioners, however these failed largely because of the opposition of the Royal Colleges of Physicians and Surgeons [Gray 1992]. At the end of the Second World War the idea of a college for general practitioners was mooted again and discussion was aided by a number of important reports published around this time, notably the Goodenough Report of the interdepartmental committee on medical schools and the Cohen Report on general practice and the training of GPs.

An important part in the development was played by a general practitioner from Lanarkshire, Dr George MacFeat, who wrote a letter to the *British Medical Journal* in 1951, suggesting a "Royal College of General Practitioners" [Hunt 1983; MacFeat 1951]. As a result of that letter, Dr John Hunt, was invited to a meeting of the General Practice Review Committee of the General Medical Services Committee of the BMA. Also at the meeting was Dr Fraser Rose from Preston, who served on the GMSC and the Council of the BMA. Their representations were received favourably.

After the meeting, John [later Lord] Hunt, a pillar of the medical establishment in London with an extensive private practice, and Fraser Rose, a general practitioner with an NHS practice in the industrial North West of England, jointly submitted a letter to the *British Medical Journal* seeking, "...to collect evidence upon [the foundation of]...a possible College of General Practice" [Rose and Hunt 1951]. They said that general practitioners had felt disadvantaged when the NHS was being negotiated and that there was a need for an organisation to represent the academic interests of the largest group of medical practitioners. Their letter received a very positive response and, six weeks later, John Hunt was invited to dinner by Sir Russell Brain, then President of the Royal College of Physicians, and advised that the three Royal Colleges of Physicians, Surgeons and Obstetricians and Gynaecologists felt that there was no need for a College of General Practitioners, but that they would support a Joint Faculty of General Practice.

Fortunately the Colleges' view did not prevail and in February 1952 a Steering Committee was formed under the Chairmanship of Sir Henry Willink, a former Minister of Health. The Committee worked quickly and effectively and, on 19 November 1952, the Memorandum and Articles of Association of the College of General Practitioners were signed. The Steering Committee had judged the mood of the profession exactly and this was confirmed by over a thousand individual applications for membership of the College by the middle of January 1953. There were also many expressions of support from other branches of medicine.

A number of distinguished Scottish general practitioners were influential in the early development of the College, including Ian Grant, of Glasgow, the Second President of the College; John Henderson from Pitlochry, a member of the Foundation Council and first Chairman of the Scottish Council of the College; Richard Scott of Edinburgh, the first Professor of General Practice in the United Kingdom; and Drs Willie Fulton and Willie Gardner of Glasgow, who became members of the First Scottish Council of the College. Lowell Lamont, a general practitioner in Edinburgh, was the first Chairman of the Court of Examiners of the College. He was particularly active in the MDDUS, becoming a member of Council, Honorary Treasurer and finally Convener in 1970.

William HOGARTH
(1697-1764)
Bedlam, plate 8 from
A Rake's Progress 1763
Engraving
Hunterian Art Gallery,
University of Glasgow

Hogarth's hero, Tom Rakewell,
ends his days in the notorious
Bedlam Hospital where he is
chained to the walls, a sign
that he was a 'pauper lunatic'.
Originally a hospice of St
Mary of Bethlehem, Bedlam
became London's asylum in
1547. Visitors, such as the
well-dressed ladies in this
print, paid to be entertained
by the antics of the patients.

In recent years, Drs Alastair Donald, Douglas Garvie and Brendan Sweeney, have served on the Councils of both organisations, maintaining the close links between the MDDUS and the Royal College of General Practitioners. The College obtained its Royal Charter in 1972 and now has over eighteen thousand members. It is influential in the areas of medical education, research and the maintenance of standards, all of which are of direct significance to the medico-legal interests of the MDDUS.

Mental Health

The most pronounced change in all the medical development of the 1950s was arguably in the field of mental health, which gave every indication of having been neglected. Before the Second World War there were only two chairs of psychiatry in the country, one in London, the other in Edinburgh. The first lunacy case in the early history of the MDDUS, which caused financial and professional alarm at the time, was indicative of the complex, medico-legal issues raised by the illness. The feeling in Parliament was that Scotland generally took the lead in teaching psychiatry in its medical schools and Edinburgh was credited with devoting three times as long to teaching the specialty than any other university in the UK. Deficiencies in the teaching of psychiatry flew in the face of the estimate at the time that 45% of all hospital beds in the country were occupied by patients suffering from some form of mental disorder [Hansard 5s, 598:728].

At the time, the care of the mentally ill was beginning to change but had not yet fully emerged from the attitudes, fears and the legislative influence of the Victorian era. Care and treatment were largely associated with the large county mental hospitals and mental health legislation consisted of two separate series of Acts of Parliament; the Lunacy and Mental Treatment Acts, which applied to the mentally ill, and the Mental Deficiency Acts.

The county asylums had their origins at the beginning of the nineteenth century when a decision was taken to create a new form of publicly funded provision for pauper and criminal lunatics to remove them from inappropriate accommodation in prisons and workhouses [Jones 1991]. Between 1811 and 1842 the first county asylums were set up in England and Wales. In Scotland, a total of seven Royal Asylums were built between 1781 and 1859 and, following the 1857 Lunacy (Scotland) Act, nineteen additional district asylums had been built by 1910. In 1950, the organisation and culture of these institutions had basically not changed since their foundation, but they had become increasingly over-crowded and, by 1930, their population numbered 140,000.

As it had been for most of the previous century, the typical mental institution in 1950 was in the charge of a physician superintendent, who was provided with a substantial house in the grounds, or accommodated in a wing of the hospital. Favoured and reliable long-stay patients acted as servants to him and his family, to assist, or even act as, his domestic staff and he had the benefit of fresh produce from the hospital farm. The farm was incorporated in the design of most asylums, partly to provide an early form of occupational therapy for inmates, but also to make the institution self-sufficient in the production of milk, meat, vegetables and other necessities.

Generally, the institution was divided into a male side in the charge of a Senior Hospital Medical Officer and a male Chief Nurse. The female side had a Senior Hospital Medical Officer and a Matron. Every weekday they would carry out their morning round of the wings and wards where the patients were housed, received deferentially by the "attendants", still in uniform, but about to become nurses with a training based on the *Red Book* on mental nursing produced by the Royal Medico-Psychological Association, the predecessor of the modern Royal College of Psychiatrists.

The majority of the patient inmates were in wards depending on sex, age and form of disorder or disturbance. Some hospitals still had incontinence wards and there would be special provision for the care of the physically ill. There was a high morbidity in these institutions and when the staffing improved in the 1950s, many undiagnosed physical disorders were revealed. Most hospitals had beds in open wards, with very limited space for patients' belongings. Virtually all patients received some form of sedation. Paraldehyde was extensively used, particularly in "mental deficiency" hospitals and the use of this drug to induce mass sedation and compliance in patients continued well into the 1960s. Barbiturates were popular and widely used as hypnotics.

However, during the decade, a change was taking place. There was, for instance, a decline in the diagnosis of catatonic and hebephrenic sub-types in the presentation of schizophrenia, a change not entirely due to the introduction of the phenothiazines in about 1957 [Hare 1988]. A decline

in the diagnosis of schizophrenia may also be explained by improvements
and refinements in diagnosis. This was a period when the doors of mental
hospitals began to be unlocked, the use of insulin coma therapy was
quickly abandoned and electro-convulsive therapy was administered in a
controlled manner, with the use of anaesthetics and muscle relaxants. It
also witnessed the introduction of the new anti-depressant drugs, new
ideas about community care and the concept of the therapeutic
community. A privileged few received individual and private care for their
neurotic problems from psychoanalysts, if they could afford it, but this
was only really available in the major cities.

"Mental defectives" were a separate group housed in their own
institutions, which became hospitals and were provided with special
schools. Prior to 1959, they were still dealt with under the Mental
Deficiency Act of 1913 and were classified as idiots, imbeciles,
feebleminded, or morons and moral imbeciles. During the decade 1950-
1960, improvements for this group tended to lag behind the changes
introduced for the mentally ill, despite repeated attempts to foster a new
approach with a new classification – "mental deficiency" became "mental
subnormality" and later "mental handicap", to be followed in 1983 by
"learning disability".

The asylum had officially become a hospital with the passing of the Mental
Treatment Act 1930, which gave recognition to mental illness as a true
illness and brought its treatment a step closer to the mainstream of
medicine. "Lunacy" and "lunatics" became outdated terms, although their
use lingered on in common parlance for decades afterwards. Indeed, this
period saw the opening of admission wards, for the treatment of
psychiatric conditions in general hospitals and the establishment of
outpatient clinics. But the culture changed very little. Whereas previously
all the patients were detained under legislation, now some patients could
be admitted voluntarily and the first steps were taken towards recognising
that mental illnesses are illnesses in the same way that physical disorders
are, although the stigma that has been associated with such conditions is
still deeply rooted in British culture today.

The turning point in changing attitudes towards mental ill health and
learning disability was the establishment of the Royal Commission on the
Law relating to Mental Illness and Mental Deficiency in 1954, under the
chairmanship of Lord Percy of Newcastle [Royal Commission 1957].
Legislation, concerning those with various degrees of mental illness and
disability, had started in the late eighteenth and early nineteenth centuries.
Apart from Acts, which dealt solely with property or with criminal
lunatics, over twenty Acts of Parliament were passed in the eighty-three
years from 1808 to 1891, dealing with the care of mentally disordered
patients in public or private institutions. During this period there were
four consolidations of the law, the last being the Lunacy Act 1890. In the

sixty-five years from 1891 to the establishment of the Royal Commission, there were seven Acts and extensive amendments introduced by way of other Acts, but there was no complete restatement or consolidation of this branch of the law.

The Royal Commission sat from 1954 until 1957 and not only led to the consolidation of the numerous Lunacy, Mental Treatment and Mental Deficiency Acts into one statute, but introduced a new and modern philosophy into legislation. This reflected the modern, humane approach to the care of these patients, based upon an ability to receive treatment and a developing awareness of their civil rights. Until this time, legislation had assumed that such patients must be legally detained in custody, in order that they might receive care and treatment.

From 1930, mental hospitals could admit voluntary patients, but they were required to be well enough to sign an application form expressing a positive wish to receive treatment. All other patients were admitted using procedures authorising detention, a process known as "certification". The Royal Commission Report observed that:

Many people think that only patients who are permanently deranged or dangerous are 'bad enough' to be certified, and that certification carries with it some social or moral stigma.

From the medical point of view, there was often little or no difference between their illness and that of a voluntary patient. Doctors were keenly aware of the distinction between these two groups of patients and of the undesirable consequences of certification. To avoid it, they sometimes went to considerable lengths to encourage, and occasionally even assist, patients to sign the application form for voluntary admission for their own good, to avoid the stigma of "certification".

The Commission laid down an important principle for the future, which continues as a cornerstone of modern mental health legislation. The

James GILLRAY
(1757-1815)
The Gout 1799
Etching and aquatint
The Wellcome Library,
London

Few images of illness are more striking than this print by Gillray, one of England's greatest caricaturists. It perfectly illustrates the four cardinal signs of gout inflammation as listed by the Roman physician Celsus – fever, pain, redness and swelling. It is possible that Gillray himself suffered from gout.

95

Commission recommended that the law should be changed so that, whenever possible, suitable care may be provided for mentally disordered patients with no more restriction of liberty or legal formality than would be applied to people who need care because of other types of illness, disability or social difficulty. In future, compulsory powers should be used only when positively necessary to override the patient's own unwillingness, or the unwillingness of his relatives, for the patient's own welfare or for the protection of others. However, fear and prejudice have continued to stigmatise those who suffer from psychological disturbances of mental health. Half a century later, after the Commission Report, the Royal College of Psychiatrists considered it necessary to launch a campaign to expose and combat stigma, which still continued in society at large. "Certification" is a term that lingers, but is now largely replaced by an equally inelegant new verb, "to section".

The basic tenets of the Royal Commission's Report and the provision of proper safeguards to protect against the abuse of powers of detention, were enshrined in the Mental Health Act 1959 and the Mental Health (Scotland) Act 1960, which resulted from the Report. They continued as the foundation of the Mental Health Act 1983 and the Mental Health (Scotland) Act 1984.

These Acts gave many potential benefits to psychiatric patients, but it was to take several decades to change the relationship between carers and the cared-for. Following the introduction of the 1959 and 1960 Acts, substantial funds directed towards mental health; physical conditions for patients were improved and more nurses and doctors were trained and employed. This was also the era of the psychiatric social worker, who was attached to the psychiatric unit and carried out valuable work in the process of rehabilitation. Many patients benefited and lived reasonably comfortable lives in those large hospitals. Many were cared for so well that care in the community, which was to be introduced in later years, was not always an improvement for them.

But the years following the 1950s, when the old Board of Control was abolished, were also characterised by a series of major inquiries into the alleged ill-treatment of patients in hospitals in England and numerous lesser inquiries, which revealed serious failures of hospital management in the care of patients with chronic conditions, the elderly and the mentally handicapped; in short, those who were most vulnerable and unable to represent themselves [Martin 1984]. In Scotland, the standard of the mental hospitals and the quality of psychiatric practice were generally higher than was the case in England, e.g., consultant psychiatrists in Scotland were often Fellows or Members of one of the Scottish Royal Colleges of Physicians and inquiries into unsafe practice were seldom necessary.

The way forward was to adopt the problems of mental disorder and disability as serious subjects for academic study and, during this period, departments of psychiatry began to be established in British medical schools. By 1960 there were some half dozen or more professors of psychiatry; psychiatric research was beginning to influence psychiatric care; and new psychological approaches such as learning theory and behaviour therapy were emerging. Child psychiatry, which up to that time was provided by local authorities from child guidance clinics, began to become established in NHS hospitals.

Offenders, suffering from mental disorder, benefited from other legislative change during this time. The 1959 and 1960 Mental Health Acts allowed hospital orders to be made as an alternative to imprisonment for seriously mentally ill offenders and transfers between prison and hospital to be made for the treatment of convicted prisoners, where this was necessary. Capital punishment was the subject of intense debate and review. It was restricted in England by the Homicide Act 1957, which introduced the notion of diminished responsibility, a feature of Scots law since the early nineteenth century. The law relating to insanity and fitness to plead to a criminal charge was changed by the Act of 1964.

The protection and welfare of those suffering from mental health problems is likely to remain an important issue in the future. The Mental Welfare Commission in Scotland and the Mental Health Act Commission in England exist to give protection to this vulnerable group by supervision and inspection. However, despite regulation and supervision, the medico-legal pitfalls associated with mental health are likely to continue to prevail.

Dental Clinical Practice

Prior to 1948, general dental practice in the UK was essentially treatment-orientated, especially concerned with the relief of pain, extractions, the provision of dentures and some restorative care for a minority of the population. With the advent of the free NHS dental service in 1948 and the great demand for treatment, there was a considerable need for extractions and dentures. This radical treatment approach arose from a number of factors, such as, the previous need of care that had not been met and a tradition that teeth were expendable, as they could constitute a focus of septic infection damaging the patient's general health. Furthermore, the new artificial teeth made of synthetic resins were more easily prepared and more attractive in appearance than the older vulcanite and porcelain dentures.

In 1955, the new high-speed air turbine dental drill was introduced. This facilitated cavity preparation at a time when more patients were requiring

The Barrel of Teeth at Glasgow Dental Hospital
In regular use up to the early 1950s, in which all extracted teeth from the extraction surgeries and the theatre were placed for student training purposes.
The History of Dentistry Research Group, University of Glasgow

restorative dentistry. The increasing demand for dentures, extractions and fillings meant that dentists were working long hours, increasing productivity, but with a system of remuneration that was producing dissatisfaction and stress. The system was based on an item of treatment scale that rewarded the fast worker, took no account of quality, and positively discouraged painstaking diagnostic treatment-planning and a continuing care approach. The profession, overall, received no financial recognition for increased productivity because total earnings were limited, while the volume of treatment was "open-ended".

In 1963, the General Dental Services Committee appointed a Sub-Committee under the Chairmanship of Mr William R. Tattersall, who was Chairman of the Representative Board of the British Dental Association and also Convener of the Council of the MDDUS. The brief was to explore alternative methods of remuneration for dental practitioners. The Tattersall Report of 1964 recommended radical changes based on a capitation payment for the routine maintenance of dental fitness, plus payment by scale of fees for dentures and the more complex items of treatment. The Report was widely appreciated, but it was not possible to obtain the agreement of both general dental practitioners and the Government to a completely new approach at that time, although in 1990, a system of payment for continuing care for adults and capitation fees for children was introduced.

PROFESSOR THOMAS KIRKPATRICK MUNRO

Professor Thomas Munro, President of the MDDUS from 1931 to 1952, died on 17th January 1958. He qualified in Arts and Medicine at Glasgow University in 1888 and, after a period of study abroad, returned as Pathologist of the Royal Infirmary, Glasgow. He became Professor of Medicine and Dean of the Medical Faculty at St. Mungo's College and in 1913, he became Regius Professor of Practice of Medicine at Glasgow. His major literary work, The Manual of Medicine, was published in 1903 and went into five editions. He was an authority on Sir Thomas Browne and had a remarkable collection of the editions of Religio Medici. Another book, The Physician As Man of Letters, Science and Action, was published in 1933. In 1937, the university conferred on him the Honorary Degree of LLD.

Medico-legal Snapshots

Medico-legal matters continued to proliferate, during the 1950s. They are noteworthy for their variety and scope.

There were two negligence claims associated with dental anaesthetics in 1956. One arose from the death of a patient, following a total extraction of teeth. The cause of death was the inhalation of a dental sponge. Attempts to clear the airway failed. The MDDUS Council suggested to dental members that, in all cases where dental sponges or throat packs were used, these should be provided with tapes of sufficient length to ensure their retrieval and so avoid a similar accident in the future.

A member had written in 1957, regarding the dilemma posed when there was an indication that children of Jehovah's Witnesses needed blood transfusion, when consent for surgery had been obtained on the condition that no blood transfusion would be given. It was agreed that, if the procedure was to be one of choice, the surgeon should refuse to operate. If the operation was to be of an emergency nature, it would not be unreasonable for the doctor to order a transfusion as a life-saving procedure and that the parents should be advised accordingly.

A pathologist contracted pulmonary tuberculosis and claimed compensation under the Industrial Injuries Act. His claim was refused on the grounds that his contact with tubercular material was not "close and frequent". An appeal to the Industrial Injuries Commissioner by the MDDUS was successful.

An MDDUS dentist extracted ten teeth, instead of two, from an eight-year-old girl. She and her mother had answered to the wrong name when called from the waiting room. A report by an orthodontist was reasonably favourable and an agreed settlement was negotiated.

A doctor conducted an arthrodesis on the wrong knee of a patient. The knee had been prepared by nursing staff for the operation and the doctor proceeded before realising his mistake. The MDDUS Council took the view that there was no defence in such a case and that responsibility lay with the surgeon. The claim was settled.

A surgeon operated on a patient on whom he had conducted an operation three years previously. At the second operation he found a swab clearly left there at the first operation. Although the surgeon had been assured the original swab count was correct, the MDDUS and the hospital in question, shared an ex-gratia payment to the patient.

The NHS in Practice

By 1960, the NHS was justifiably felt to be a success, although Beveridge's forecast that costs would fall as health improved, had already been shown to be unrealistic. Post-war advances had to be paid for and prescription charges came as early as 1951. Free health care for all had an immediate impact on doctors and patients, but there was slow change. Modern premises, ancillary help, appointment systems and group practices were still the exception.

Such changes in practice that happened, were unplanned and haphazard. Minor surgery was unpaid and ceased, except for stitching lacerations. Midwifery remained a major responsibility, but home births became less frequent. Many forward-looking GPs did modernise at personal cost, but the pay structure penalised innovation. There was unrest among GPs who felt that they were being left behind in that increasingly prosperous decade. In urban districts, small lock-up surgeries, where the doctor "sat" twice daily, were the norm and a busy session might attract several dozen patients. Many sought repeat prescriptions or insurance "lines", renewable at short intervals.

The rest of the day was spent on visits with regular calls on the elderly and chronic sick. Where doctors' lists were large, emergencies often disrupted the routine and obstetrics were a frequent cause. Midwives and GPs usually took total responsibility for antenatal care and labour and many women never saw a consultant unless for serious complications. The night watch waiting for the delivery was common and the local hospital flying squad was a useful back up. Gynaecological investigation was minimal before the era of cervical smear tests and contraceptive advice was the province of a few female pioneers.

Consultants, many of whom were pre-NHS veterans and individuals of colourful personality, were happy to come out at any time to visit a patient at home. It was almost unheard of for the GP not to be present and valuable professional relationships often resulted. Experience, rather than technology, was on offer, but for a heart problem there would be heavy mains ECG equipment with three leads.

MR ALEXANDER MACGREGOR

The death of Alexander Macgregor on September 7th 1963, at the age of eighty-nine, robbed the MDDUS of one of its eminent and respected members. He had been Honorary Treasurer since 1934, the longest serving office-bearer in MDDUS history. After the First World War, he was largely responsible for organising the Dental Health Benefits Scheme and he received an OBE in 1941. The British Dental Association honoured him with a Vice-Presidency of the Association in 1944 and he was appointed Chairman of the Committee that amalgamated the three dental societies under the parent body of the BDA. He also served on the Board of Management of the Glasgow Dental Hospital. He died in the same year he learnt to type, in order to write a book on dental caries for the general public.

There were no deputising services although some inter-practice rosters existed. With no modern conveniences such as pagers, mobile telephones or telephone answering machines, it was hard to keep in touch while on call and telephones were rare in some housing estates. Life could be hectic, night and day. In autumn 1957, influenza swept Britain and the acute demand nearly caused a breakdown in the NHS. Disposables, (syringes, gloves and instruments) were not yet available and sterilisation was time-consuming and probably ineffective, though cross-infection was seldom reported. Re-used needles became blunt and hooked. Few pathological specimens were taken except blood for grouping and haemoglobin levels in pregnancy. The Rhesus factor hazard to unborn babies was known, but the news had not reached some practices.

When the NHS was introduced, treatment in general practice was principally empirical and palliative. Insulin for controlling diabetes had been available since the twenties. Pernicious anaemia sufferers relied on regular liver extract injections, before cyanocobalamin was introduced. Sulphonamides and antibiotics, led by sulphapyridine and penicillin, had recently brought almost magical cure for many infections. Therapeutic advances transformed treatment and antibiotics multiplied in variety. Isoniazid made triple therapy for tuberculosis available from 1952 and emptied the sanatoria, while immunisation for diphtheria and polio saved many lives. Antihistamines had been introduced and corticosteroids, a mixed blessing, became popular in local form for eczema and psoriasis. Older doctors continued with their own personal formulae for cough bottles, stomach powders and "rubs", written in "dog Latin", allowing the local pharmacist to exercise his dispensing skills, while the patient had no means of knowing what he or she was getting. Some were understandably popular, like the iron tonic, "Vin ferri cit." (iron and cheap sherry), much in demand at Christmas!

The drug companies had already marketed many drugs in more convenient form. Regulation, other than for narcotics, was minimal, and GPs had almost total freedom in prescribing. Barbiturates were universal treatment for insomnia and "nerves" until the first tranquillizers appeared. Amphetamines were for slimming and the combination of the two in Drinamyl, known as "Purple Hearts" because of their original shape, was popular for anxiety or depression. Largactil (chlorpromazine) was a genuine early advance in the treatment of psychoses.

Representatives from drug companies were typically middle-aged men carrying a sample and a blotter, until the workforce increased with many younger recruits. Reputable firms gave a vital service, while others had a slicker approach with inducements that later bordered on bribery, giving the industry a bad name. There was no *MIMS* and no *Pulse*, nor its sister journals. In 1959, nearly all prescriptions were hand-written during consultation, many were repeat prescriptions issued in the consulting room without further consultation or examination.

The Watershed of Legislation

The 1960s personified an age of youth and vitality compared with the previous decade. Standards of living had risen and the population was better fed and clothed. Education was giving youngsters a chance to stay longer at school and consequently a more favourable access to university and college education. The introduction of the non-fiction paperback book and the widespread growing influence of television made the public more knowledgeable. The NHS had largely overcome public concern on health issues. Scientific research and development, embodied in the first manned space flight, followed later by the first landing on the moon, were in the ascendancy. Perhaps the most significant medical advance in research came with the contraceptive pill for women.

Legislation

Much current medical law derived from a surge of legislation in the 1960s. Twelve major items of legislation, with a bearing on medicine and dentistry, were passed into law as Acts of Parliament. This compared with a corresponding two Acts in the 1950s and one in the 1940s [Table 8.1 (over)]. The legislation ranged from the Suicide Act of 1961, making it no longer a crime to commit, or attempt to commit suicide, to the Health Service and Public Health Act of 1968, the first amending legislation of the NHS Act of 1948, the complexity of which was illustrated by its seventy-four clauses. This particular legislative activity caused a deep sense of dissatisfaction among general practitioners in 1965 over pay and conditions of service. At one stage, 17,000 practitioners put in notices of resignation from the NHS, which were only withdrawn after a year of negotiated agreement.

The Medicines Act 1968 took account of the major changes in the development of new medicines and the danger of not bringing potentially harmful side effects to the notice of doctors. The thalidomide tragedy in 1962 provided the most alarming and serious example and a Committee on Safety and Drugs worked for four years to establish standards for

Opposite:

Albrecht DÜRER
(1471-1528)
Melencolia I 1514
Engraving
Hunterian Art Gallery,
University of Glasgow

Dürer published this print in 1514, the year of his mother's death. Melancholy, one of the four temperaments, was characterised in the Hippocratic tradition by depression affecting those of superior intelligence including artists. 'Melencolia' wears a wreath of the water-plant 'levisticum officinalis Koch', recommended in the 16th century as a cure for excessive melancholy.

Table 8.1
Acts of Parliament
Growth of Principal Legislation affecting Medical Defence

1940s	1	NHS Act 1948.
1950s	2	Dentists Act 1956; Mental Health Act 1959.
1960s	12	Mental Health (Scotland) Act 1960; Suicide Act 1961; Human Tissue Act 1961; Public Health Act 1961; Limitation Act 1963; Abortion Act 1967; NHS Family Planning Act 1967; Health Service & Public Health Act 1968; Medicine Act 1968; Children & Young Person Act 1969; Medical Act 1969; Family Law Reform Act 1969.
1970s	10	National Health Service (Ombudsman) Act 1973; Prescription and Limitation Act 1973; Fatal Accident Inquiry Act 1976; Congenital Disabilities Act 1976; Damages (Scotland) Act 1976; National Health Service Act 1977; Medical Act 1978; National Health Service (Scotland) Act 1978; Protection of Children Act 1978; Vaccine Damage Payments Act 1979.
1980s	15	Limitation Act 1980; Mental Health Act 1983; Mental Health (Scotland) Act 1984; Data Protection Act 1984; Dentists Act 1984; Anatomy Act 1984, Surrogacy Arrangements Act 1985; Hospital Complaints Procedure Act 1985; Legal Aid (Scotland) Act 1986; Legal Aid Act 1988; Access to Medical Reports Act 1988; Coroner's Act 1988; Health and Medicines Act 1988; Human Organ Transplants Act 1989; Children Act 1989.
1990s	14	Access to Health Records Act 1990; Human Fertilisation and Embryology Act 1990; NHS and Community Care Act 1990; NHS Authority Indemnity Scheme against Medical Negligence 1990; Age of Legal Capacity (Scotland) Act 1991; Health Service Commissioners Act 1993; Health Authorities Act 1995; Medical (Professional Performance) Act 1995; NHS (Amendment) Act 1995; Children (Scotland) Act 1995; NHS (Primary Care) Act 1997; Data Protection Act 1998; Human Rights Act 1998; Health Act 1999.
2000s	4 ...	Civil Evidence Act 2000; Electronic Communication Act 2000; Adults with Incapacity (Scotland) Act 2000; Health and Social Care Act 2001.

safety and quality of medicines and a drug-licensing scheme. A Medicines Commission would take over from the GMC, the statutory duty it had held for over a hundred years, to prepare and publish the British Pharmacopoiea. The growth in drug prescription, in the twenty years of the NHS up to 1968, was referred to during the Parliamentary debate. The cost of prescribing non-proprietary drugs had remained steady at about £10m per year, within the NHS. In the same period, the cost of prescribing proprietary drugs had risen from just under £10m to £78m [Hansard 5s, 758:1600-1711].

The Family Law Reform Act of 1969, whose purpose was to make three important changes in family law, had in one of its clauses an issue of consent that was to return to public debate in later years. It concerned consent of persons over the age of 16 to medical and dental treatment. The consensus view was prevalent that the right to professional and ethical secrecy went hand-in-hand with the ability to provide consent to treatment. The clause was designed to make clear that any person over the age of 16 was able to give a valid consent to any treatment and that likewise, children of 16 could forbid the doctor to inform their parents or teachers of their physical condition.

Nevertheless, in medico-legal terms, the 1960s were dominated by two major items of legislation, the NHS (Family Planning) Act and the Abortion Act, both of which received Royal Assent in 1967. In a sense, they embodied the spirit of the times in which freedom of expression and the empowerment of women in contraception and family planning, were powerful factors. The development of medical science and changes in Coroner's Court proceedings were also of major importance, but it was the issue of abortion, particularly illegal abortion, that took centre stage.

Aberdeen Initiatives

In the first half of the 20th century, many women died in pregnancy and labour, particularly in cities where awful conditions of poverty and social deprivation existed in the slums. The experience had a profound effect on Professor [later Sir Dugald] Baird in his early career and when he was appointed to the Regius Chair of Midwifery in Aberdeen, just before 1939, he set out to look at the influences brought to bear on childbearing. Sir John [later Lord] Boyd Orr was Director of the Rowatt Institute in Aberdeen and had been appointed by Winston Churchill to supervise food rationing. Boyd Orr sought the help of Baird to determine the food requirements of pregnant women. Although some work had been done to ascertain the effects of food supplementation in pregnancy, little was known about the basic requirements. A team was set up to study the nutritional aspects of pregnancy.

A unified records system for the total obstetric population of Aberdeen and, eventually, the Grampian area was set up. Baird also created total clinical coverage for the pregnant women of the area. It thus became possible for what were probably unique epidemiological studies to be undertaken. He collected together and inspired an international staff including sociologists, nutritionalists, endocrinologists, physiologists, statisticians as well as obstetricians, who, under his direction, showed the influence of lifestyle and physical characteristics on reproductive performance. Much original work was done on the epidemiology and other aspects of such conditions as pre-term birth, haemorrhage, hypertension and diabetes, as well as the determination of physiological norms in pregnancy.

The provision of custom-built research wards and laboratories by the Medical Research Council greatly facilitated the work. As well as an observed reduction in maternal mortality, perinatal mortality was also falling. From these epidemiological studies it was possible to identify and classify the causes of perinatal mortality. In the field of obstetrics and perinatal medicine in general, Baird was influential in ensuring that audit of clinical performance was carried out, thus aiding the continuing improvement in standards in all clinical areas.

Sir Dugald Baird
The Librarian Aberdeen
Medico-Chirurgical Society

In a paper entitled "A Fifth Freedom", Baird underlined his abiding philosophy by adapting the four freedoms expressed in a speech by Franklin Roosevelt in 1941 [Baird 1965]:

In the future days, which we seek to make secure we look forward to a world founded upon four essential freedoms.
The first is freedom of speech and expression.
The second is freedom of every person to worship God in his own way.
The third is freedom from want.
The fourth is freedom from fear.

And I [Baird] *would suggest that it is time to consider a fifth freedom – freedom from the tyranny of excessive fertility.*

It was not surprising that, with Baird's encouragement and inspiration, many of his team became professors and heads of department throughout the world.

Abortion

Abortion has been a highly contentious subject over many decades of history and provoked extremes of passion on both sides of the argument. In spite of this, the law relating to its regulation in the 1960s remained framed within the Offences Against the Person Act of 1861. Although the 1861

Act contained very severe punishments to deter abortion, ranging from death, to penal servitude for life, transportation and whipping, the traffic in abortion did not seem to diminish, nor were the perpetrators deterred.

The call for reform of the 1861 Act began in the 1930s from groups as diverse as judges, women's organisations and medical bodies. This led to the appointment of a Government Inter-Departmental Committee chaired by Lord Birkett who spoke of:

...the urgency of the problem of the misery and heartbreak which at present prevail, of the need for clear thinking on the problem, and of the strong necessity for making the law clear and intelligible and in accordance with public opinion - the only ultimate sanction of the law.

The application of the 1861 Act remained unchallenged in England until 1938, when a case arose in the Central Criminal Court, which focused attention on the need to review the law. It concerned a criminal assault by a soldier on a young girl under the age of fifteen. As a result, she became pregnant. Mr Alex Bourne, an obstetric surgeon and gynaecologist at St Mary's Hospital Paddington, terminated the pregnancy on the grounds of rape. Bourne appeared at the Court to answer the charge of unlawfully procuring the miscarriage of a woman, contrary to section 58 of the Act.

Judge Macnaghten's ruling in the case hinged on the use of the word "unlawfully" in the indictment. He ruled that its use in the statute implied that there might be such a thing as the lawful procurement of an abortion and it is said that this ruling was the law on abortion, until the 1967 Act came into force. Bourne was subsequently acquitted of the offence, having argued at his trial that the abortion was necessary to protect the mental health of his patient.

Medical Differences

Ian MacGillivray, Baird's senior lecturer, was appointed to the chair of St Mary's Hospital, Paddington in 1961, where he established an academic department of Obstetrics and Gynaecology. Until then his experience of abortion was mainly with the "battered old multips", women who had four or more children, to whom Baird had offered abortion and sterilisation, in order that they might be free of excessive childbearing. Professor MacGillivray was appalled by the plight of pregnant women and girls in the Paddington and Marylebone areas, who had been referred to him by general practitioners.

He had a passing acquaintance with Bourne, whose court case had raised the profile of the abortion issue. He understood the motivation which had driven Bourne to such a course of action. Many of the women whom MacGillivray confronted were in desperate straits and threatened suicide if they were denied an abortion. Others suffered the complications of "back-street" abortions and were often gravely ill, a result of haemorrhage, infection and renal failure. He therefore set about aborting the unwanted pregnancies of these desperate women, thereby catapulting himself into the centre of the abortion debate.

There was considerable acrimony among obstetricians at the time. In Scotland, the debate raged between two Regius Professors, Dugald Baird in Aberdeen and Ian Donald in Glasgow. In England, there was a longstanding debate between Professor Ian MacGillivray at St Mary's and Professor Hugh McLaren of Birmingham. In simple terms, these opposite approaches stemmed from a compassion for the mother, as opposed to compassion for the foetus. However, this was a debate involving its members, which the MDDUS chose to view impartially from the sidelines. The introduction of the Abortion Act did little to reconcile these opposite and individual attitudes.

The Act

The social, medical and moral dilemmas caused by the termination of unwanted pregnancies were a recurring theme throughout MDDUS history. Nevertheless, it was the practical reality of dealing with unwanted pregnancies that caused concern among the medical profession. Particular dismay was felt at the consequences of back-street abortions that had gone wrong, leading to permanent damage, or death, to the patient. It is difficult to estimate the number of illegal abortions conducted in any one year. The number varied according to reports on the subject.

A survey conducted by National Opinion Polls, around the time the David Steel Bill was under discussion, on behalf of the Abortion Law Reform Association, assessed that a minimum of 40,000 abortions took place each year. However, there was common agreement that the trade involved many more thousands of women throughout the country. An indication of the extent of human misery can be gauged from the following table, which indicates the sharp drop in the number of offences for procuring illegal abortions after the introduction of the Abortion Act [Table 8.2].

Table 8.2

Offences recorded by the police for procuring illegal abortion in England and Wales

Years	Average number per year
1960-1964	276
1965-1969	242
1970-1974	84
1975-1979	9
1980-1984	3
1985-1989	4
1990-1994	3

[Macfarlane et al. 2000]

The issue of abortion reform remained an unstructured subject until the Act was raised as the Medical Termination of Pregnancy Bill, sponsored by David [later Lord] Steel, a junior Member of Parliament, as a Private Member's Bill. It had the support of an all-party group of Members of Parliament. The Bill sought to create a positive state of the law, whereby two practitioners could lawfully balance the rights and conditions of the mother against the assumption of the right of the foetus to develop to full life. David Steel also argued that if the Bill became law, it would become possible for a patient to consult her family doctor freely about the pregnancy. This was an important provision because the subject was cloaked in such secrecy and legal uncertainty, that the last person with whom the woman would wish to discuss her situation would be the family doctor.

The controversial nature of the legislation ensured an extended passage through Parliament. It took well over a year of discussion and amendment before the Bill received Royal Assent. During the period, there was some question that the Bill might run out of time and David Steel had to approach the Leader of the House, Richard Crossman, to make a case for more time. Crossman poured him a large whisky and the young Member embarked on his justification for a time extension. Absentmindedly, Richard Crossman poured the young man a further helping, this time of brandy! In the interests of his case, David Steel drank the potent mixture without complaint or comment and gained reward in the allocation of additional time in the parliamentary programme.

A final amendment to the Bill was a change in name from the Medical Termination of Pregnancy, to that of the Abortion Act. It was passed by Parliament with a large majority, receiving Royal Assent in October 1967 and came into force on 27 April 1968. Although the Act removed some of the anomalies and illegalities concerned with abortion, the moral and ethical dimensions remained, with the doctor at the centre of the decision process. The MDDUS recognised the significance of the issue and joined its fellow defence organisations at a special meeting of the Joint Co-ordinating Committee to discuss the Abortion Act. After the meeting, the MDDUS published a comprehensive booklet on the Act, which provided clear advice and supportive guidance on the procedures to be followed and, in particular, the conscientious objection to the treatment, by the practitioner.

David Steel
The Scotsman

Aberdeen was referred to as the abortion capital of Britain in the 1960s and a study of abortion in the North East of Scotland was carried out at the end of the decade. It showed that there had been a change in the climate of abortion, from multiple child bearing in uncertain domestic and low income situations, to a new demand by young, healthy, middle-class girls who had adopted the prevailing sexual freedoms, without adequate contraceptive knowledge [Horobin 1973]. This finding was probably reflected in the rest of the country.

A Royal Commission of Inquiry, the Lane Committee, was set up in 1971 to look at the effectiveness of the Act. The MDDUS was invited to submit evidence to the Committee on its experiences. The subsequent report found that the gains facilitated by the Act more than outweighed any disadvantages and that, despite vociferous opposition from opponents, parliamentary and public opinion remained in support of it. The abortion rate has increased over the years for a variety of reasons, although there are marked differences in the rates across the country [Table 8.3].

Table 8.3

Increase of Legal Abortions in Great Britain

Year	Scotland	England and Wales
1968	1,544	22,332
1978	7,451	111,851
1988	10,128	168,298
1998	12,424	177,871

[Macfarlane et al. 2000]

Developments in Family Planning

In an interesting association of events, in the same Parliamentary session in which the Medical Termination of Pregnancy Bill was being debated, a parallel Bill concerned with Family Planning was being processed. The National Health Service (Family Planning) Act of 1967 had its origins during the week of the outbreak of the General Strike of 1926, when Lord Buckmaster moved a resolution in the House of Lords which sought to remove all obstacles to the introduction of birth control in maternity and child welfare centres. The resolution was passed. It defined responsible parenthood as:

a legitimate and essential concern of the public service and that there was a wider need of advice and prescription for those who wisely desire to achieve the aim of planned parenthood.

The subsequent Act empowered Health Boards and Authorities to make family planning advice available to nursing mothers on medical grounds, but few took any action. It was left to voluntary organisations, especially the Family Planning Association, to develop services by setting up open-access clinics throughout the country. These clinics were used almost exclusively by married women and the majority had to pay for services and contraceptive supplies, although payment for both was often waived.

There were two principal reasons for the emergence of the Family Planning Bill, the forecast increase in the British population as a continuation of the tradition of the large family and the increased number of illegitimate births. It was estimated that the number of illegitimate births per 1,000 unmarried women between 15-44 years of age, had increased from 10.2 in 1950 to 19.9 in 1964 and that mothers bearing illegitimate babies were going down the age scale [Hansard 5s, 741:935-1020]. The Bill also sought to redress the lack of training among doctors in offering contraceptive advice and to make its provisions applicable to unmarried as well as married women.

The evolution of Family Planning provided a classic illustration of the issues of consent and confidentiality. It also demonstrated the potential for litigation as contraceptive methods and materials failed to meet the expectations demanded of them. The term "birth control" was coined in America in 1914 and Marie Stopes, who was born in Edinburgh and trained as a botanist at Liverpool, opened the first clinic in UK in London in 1921. Other clinics followed, in Glasgow in 1926 and in Edinburgh in 1933. Their real purpose was concealed by euphemistic names such as, "Edinburgh Mothers' Welfare Clinic". The medical profession, on the whole, resisted the concept of birth control. This view was reflected by the GMC, BMA, the College of Obstetricians and Gynaecologists and in official publications, although there were notable exceptions such as Lord Dawson of Penn and Professor Dugald Baird.

Forensic Dentistry

An indication of the increased prominence now accorded to scientific dental evidence followed the discovery on 6 August 1967 of the strangled body of a fifteen-year-old girl in a Biggar cemetery. The assailant was eventually identified and convicted by the comparison between certain features of his dentition and their marks, caused when he had bitten the breast of the victim. This was the first time in Scotland that a man charged with murder had been identified by a bite mark. Dr Warren Harvey and members of staff of the Glasgow Dental Hospital and School were complimented upon the clarity and quality of the novel dental evidence linking the bite mark to the dentition, without which the prosecution could not have proceeded [Harvey et al 1968].

Changing Attitudes

In 1952, the rules were changed and women, "about to be married", were seen at Family Planning Clinics. In many cases, they were required to provide evidence, such as banns of marriage, as proof of their true intent. But changing attitudes to premarital chastity led to demands for contraceptive services for all unmarried women who wished them and the first Brook Clinic opened in London in 1964 specifically for this purpose. Around this time, laparoscopy had been developed to the point at which it was possible to offer short-stay hospitalisation for sterilisation. Family planning services became free at clinics in England in 1967 and a year later in Scotland, but contraceptive supplies still had to be paid for.

It is anomalous that, with the Abortion Act of 1967, termination of pregnancy became free under the NHS, yet the majority of women in Scotland still had to pay for contraception and it was not until 1970 that the Family Planning Association officially provided contraception, irrespective of marital status. The problem of providing contraceptives for girls less than sixteen years of age, particularly if they did not want their parents informed, soon followed.

A Department of Health & Social Security Circular in 1974 advised that, if contraception was in the girl's best interests, this was for the doctor to decide and the girl did not need to tell her parents. This was challenged in a celebrated case by Mrs Victoria Gillick in 1982. She lost and, after appeal and counter-appeal, the House of Lords decided that the Circular advice was not unlawful. It explained, however, that every effort should be made to persuade the girl to inform her parents. It also served as a reminder of the importance of confidentiality in any family planning consultation.

A completely free family planning service at clinics and hospitals came with the reorganisation of the NHS in 1974 and extended to primary care in 1975. Thus, over a decade, family planning services were revolutionised, so that in the UK there existed the first completely free universally available family planning service in Western Europe. It is still government policy that services should be "open-access" to both men and women from a variety of sources, to ensure freedom of choice. Women are free to seek contraceptive advice from a GP other than the one with whom they are registered. GPs providing contraceptive care are on a contraceptive list and are identified by a "C" after their name on the local register of family doctors.

More contraceptive advice is now provided by primary care teams and hospitals, than by Family Planning clinics. This has meant that the role of the clinic has changed and the larger ones in particular, are used as centres of expertise for referral of problems and provision of special services. In 1993, the Royal College of Obstetricians & Gynaecologists established the Faculty of Family Planning and Reproductive Health Care, as a result of which programmes of education for doctors have become much more comprehensive.

The two principal methods of reversible fertility control, that remain under the control of women, are the Pill and the Intra-Uterine Device. The rhythm method had been given approval by Papal Encyclicals in 1930 and 1968, which stimulated research into improving its effectiveness and making it more acceptable to those who wanted to use it for a variety of reasons.

The work of Gregory Pincus at the Worcester Institute led to the use of the combined Pill, which became available in UK in 1961, transforming the lives of millions of women by making available to them effective contraception not related to the act of intercourse and under their control. For the first time, a woman could plan her life around if and when to have a baby. There is little evidence that the Pill actually encouraged premarital intercourse, but it did make it much safer. The social consequences were immense and the role of women in society, in the professions and in business was transformed.

Female sterilisation and vasectomy have become increasingly popular over the past thirty years for couples who have decided either to complete their families, or not to have children at all. Counselling and consent are of paramount importance in explaining the procedures involved, the risks and benefits, failure rate and the question of irreversibility. Failure of tubal occlusion and vasectomy are common causes of litigation. Abortion should never be seen as an alternative to contraception, the two should function in parallel. However, despite advances in the development of legislation and medical research, Family Planning remains a high profile area of medicine in medico-legal matters.

The Home Front

As far as the MDDUS was concerned, the 1960s represented a decade of increasing indemnity payments and insurance premiums. Costs, including legal charges, added weight to the reluctant recommendation that annual membership subscriptions should be raised. It was decided to raise the subscriptions in 1966 for members practising medicine to £6; members practising dentistry to £4; and new medical and dental graduates to £3. On the positive side, the membership continued its steady increase and stood at 9,455 doctors and dentists. It was a sign of the times, however, that medico-legal activity was on the increase and in July 1967 the MDDUS Council agreed changes in the administration of its organisation. It was agreed that the MDDUS should have a permanent office and staff, a medical secretary, a part-time joint secretary, two typists and two clerks. Dr James Patterson was appointed medical secretary of the MDDUS with effect from 1 February 1968.

In the same month, an approach was made to the MDDUS by the Medical
Defence Union in England for some form of co-operation or
amalgamation. The MDDUS agreed to discuss the situation on the firm
understanding that this discussion indicated no commitment. One month
later, a comparable approach was made by the second English defence
organisation, the Medical Protection Society, for similar discussions,
suggesting a closer liaison but not amalgamation. The negotiations which
resulted, came to nothing and the subject was left open, although the
MDDUS made it clear that their position was to co-operate with both
the English defence organisations, rather than singling out one for special
preference and that there would be no amalgamation with any other
organisation for the foreseeable future [MDDUS 1968].

The question of the administration of anaesthetics in dental surgeries
continued to surface periodically. An anaesthetic death was reported, in
which a medical member administered a general anaesthetic for the
extraction of teeth. At the Fatal Accident Inquiry, the pathologist reported
that death was due to anoxia, but he was unable to be precise about the
actual cause of death. The agents used were nitrous-oxide and air. The
MDDUS stated that this was not a recognised safe practice and had to be
regarded as an outmoded technique. The subsequent claim was settled for
£5,000 with costs. The member was advised that the MDDUS might not
see its way to indemnify him, if he utilised this technique in the future
[MDDUS 1966]. The issue of the dentist acting as his or her own anaesthetist
also arose around this period. The MDDUS view was that it seemed
improper for a dentist to act in this way in regard to general anaesthesia,
although there were some doubts if this should apply to intravenous
anaesthesia. After a demonstration of the techniques involved, it was agreed
that the advice to members would state that a dentist should not act as
operator/anaesthetist during treatment.

Preventive Dentistry

The early days of the NHS had seen a growing interest in preventive
dentistry. This at first focused on dietary improvements, such as
individual control of cariogenic sugary snacks between meals and the
public health measure of water fluoridation. The spectacular reduction
in dental caries in children, reported from test cities in USA, led to
support for its introduction in UK. In Scotland, fluoridated water
was introduced in Kilmarnock in 1955 with beneficial results. Sadly,
due to public concern about possible ill-effects orchestrated in a number
of high profile public campaigns by the anti-fluoridation lobby, the
project was discontinued in 1961. During the 1960s, fluoride was
added to toothpastes and this was to become a major factor in reducing
dental diseases, although its influence was not fully appreciated until
the end of the 1970s. However, the problem remained of the many

children who lived in deprived circumstances where toothpaste was not available or affordable; situations where water fluoridation would have been most effective.

In 1972, the first national survey of Adult Dental Health in Scotland was published. This revealed the consequences of the radical treatment approach prevalent in the early days of the NHS. The results showed that 44% of adults aged sixteen and over had lost all their natural teeth. These disturbing figures were to herald the search for, and the implementation of, the new preventive methods that were to become available. These would gradually change the attitude of the profession and population towards a more conservative and preventive approach with a continuing programme of care for individual patients. However this virtual revolution in the approach to general dental practice required the re-education of the clinicians, nurses, specialists and above all the educators themselves. This would take time and a change of attitude towards continuing postgraduate education.

Susan MACFARLANE
(b.1938)
First Day of the Future   1991-5
Oil on canvas
Reproduced by kind permission of Susan
Macfarlane and A Picture of Health Ltd.

This painting is from the series on breast
cancer *A Picture of Health*. The artist records:
"Still sore from the operation the previous day,
the young woman tells me about the various
hand exercises she must do to loosen the arm
muscles. A quiet time and we talked of her
children. Gloucester Cathedral gleams in the
afternoon sunlight".

Emerging Issues

The appearance of complex and innovative medical procedures coincided with technological advances in transplantation surgery and human fertilisation. This was reflected in a further period of intense activity in medical legislation and litigation. The legislation pointed to a number of emerging issues such as compensation, standards of professional conduct and ethics and the investigation of complaints, which, among other themes, would establish the future pattern for medical defence. Advances in medical sciences were balanced by litigation, as high-risk, innovative treatments failed to meet the expectation of their original purpose.

The Glasgow Coma and Outcome Scales

The development of intensive care in the 1960s and of computed tomography scanning in the 1970s led to an increased interest in the management of severe head injuries. In the early 1970s, the Department of Neurosurgery at the Institute of Neurological Sciences initiated international studies of the treatment and outcome of severe head injuries, with data from centres in the Netherlands and the USA sent to Glasgow for computer analysis. It soon became clear that there were no satisfactory terms by which to classify either the severity of injury, or the nature of the outcome.

Professor Bryan Jennett and his team decided to devise a scale of impaired consciousness that could be reliably used by, not only neurosurgical experts, but also junior medical staff and nurses. Ambiguous terms were rejected. During a trial period they compared observations on the same patient by senior and junior doctors across a range of specialties and by nurses.

In terms that caused the least disagreement between observers, they published a simple three-part scale, which has come to be known as the Glasgow Coma Scale or GCS. This records eye opening, motor responses and verbal performance, for which there are 4, 6 and 5 possible levels respectively. When these are given numbers, higher for better and lower for more impaired responses, their addition gives a range of scores from 15 for normal consciousness to 3 for deep, unresponsive coma. Severity of injury can then be expressed as the score immediately after injury, but preferably after resuscitation, because hypoxia and hypotension can depress the conscious level and make the brain damage seem worse than it really is. Severity can also be defined by how long the patient remains in coma - defined as eyes closed, not obeying commands and not uttering recognisable words.

In research, the GCS is of value in exploring the relationship between severity of injury and outcome, making it possible to devise prognostic models and to assess the effect of alternative management regimes on improving outcome. At the practical level of patient care, the GCS has proved useful in two ways. It offers a common language for describing the patient in communications between paramedics, rescue services and the hospital; also between personnel in different hospitals or departments when transfers are being discussed; and between doctors and nurses as they change shifts. The scale is also useful in monitoring the progress of patients as they improve or deteriorate. A lowering of this score often indicates complications that call for urgent intervention. For monitoring purposes, the patient's state on the three parts of the scale is usually plotted by nurses, like a temperature chart, at the bedside.

Terms describing outcome after brain damage were also previously confusing – "good, fair, poor, practical or worthwhile". The Glasgow Outcome Scale has 5 categories - dead, vegetative, severely, or moderately disabled and good recovery. Although both these scales were originally devised in the context of research on head injuries, they have been widely adopted for many kinds of acute brain insults. These include stroke, poisoning and intracranial haemorrhage or infection [Teasdale and Jennett 1974; Jennett and Bond 1975]. The scales have been translated into many languages and are familiar to TV audiences in the dialogue of numerous medical dramas and soap operas.

Medical Reforms and Procedures

The period also saw the start of a process of change in the conduct of General Medical Council professional business. The Medical Act of 1969 sought to modify the financial and disciplinary powers of the GMC. In the first instance it required an annual fee from a doctor for the retention of his or her name on the Register, as an additional source of income. The second element, concerned with discipline, wished to add suspension to the existing powers of the GMC. The Act was passed in July.

The process continued. Lord Walton of Detchant, a former President of the GMC, had a long and distinguished association with the GMC, spanning seventeen years from 1971 to 1989 and it was at his first meeting in November 1971 that a fateful decision was made. Doctors, who failed to pay the newly introduced annual registration fee to the Council, should be removed from the Medical Register. The decision led to a massive professional outcry, orchestrated by the several hundred doctors whose names were erased. The cry, "no taxation without representation", was regularly heard. The profession recognised that the Council's membership was dominated by the appointed members, representing the universities with medical schools, the royal colleges and faculties. The twelve elected members were very much in a minority. It made a persuasive case for reform.

In consequence, the Government decided to establish the Merrison Royal Commission, which recommended a complete restructuring of the GMC to ensure that it should include a majority of members elected from the entire UK medical profession. Sir John (later Lord) Richardson, a consultant physician at St Thomas's Hospital, presided over the eventual acceptance and implementation of the recommendations of the Merrison Commission, during his term as President of the GMC from 1975-1982. A short enabling Bill, designed to deal solely with the constitution of the Council, was introduced into the House of Lords.

Lord Hunt of Fawley, of RCGP fame, introduced a number of amendments when the Bill was debated in the Lords. These received government support allowing the Medical Act of 1978 to enter the Statute

Conveners of MDDUS

1902-1910	–	Dr Robert W. Forrest
1910-1917	–	Dr John Adams
1917-1928	–	Dr George Balfour Marshall
1928-1933	–	Dr John Towart
1933-1940	–	Dr Carstairs Cumming Douglas
1940-1943	–	Dr Joseph Glaister McCutcheon
1943-1962	–	Professor Andrew Allison
1962-1970	–	Dr William Richard Tattersall
1970-1980	–	Dr Lowell Lamont
1980-1991	–	Dr Andrew Allison
1991-2001	–	Mr Peter Edmond

Chairman

2001-	–	Mr Peter Edmond

Book. This established a new Council with fifty elected and forty-five appointed members, seven of whom would be lay members to represent the public interest. From the beginning, the contribution made by these lay members was impressive, one of the most notable in the early days was Sir Brynmor Jones, Vice-Chancellor of Hull University, but there were many others who gave outstanding service.

Subsequently, Lord Walton was elected to the Health Committee, newly established under the 1978 Medical Act and became convinced that many of the doctors appearing before the Professional Conduct Committee were not, in fact, guilty of serious professional misconduct but were suffering from ill health, whether due to alcoholism, drug addiction, or other causes. The new Health Committee had similar powers to those of the GMC Conduct Committee, with the exception that, while it could suspend a doctor's registration if it appeared that the health of the doctor was sufficiently impaired to put patients at risk, it did not have the power to erase the individual from the Register.

Under the newly established health procedures however, a mechanism was quickly devised whereby doctors, reported to the Council as suffering from a health problem, were invited to be examined by two nominated psychiatrists or physicians. They could, in addition, seek a consultant psychiatrist or other appropriate doctor to examine them on their own. If the subsequent reports suggested a particular course of action, then the doctor was advised to undertake treatment under the supervision of a psychiatrist or physician, who was then asked to prepare regular reports. These were submitted to a member of Council nominated as the Preliminary Screener for health, who subsequently monitored their progress.

Dr Philip Connell and, subsequently, Professor Neil Kessel fulfilled these responsibilities very conscientiously and many ill doctors were effectively rehabilitated and eventually able to return to practice. Any doctor failing to collaborate with these procedures, or one whose progress under supervision was unsatisfactory, could be brought before the Health Committee and might then have conditions attached to his or her registration, such as a ban on practice in a clinical discipline, or, in appropriate cases, registration could be suspended for a finite period. Plainly, these procedures were much more compassionate in dealing with sick doctors, and were very effective in protecting the public. Unlike the hearings of the Professional Conduct Committee, these proceedings were always held in camera though, of course, doctors could be accompanied by a friend, and many, if not all, were given legal representation during the proceedings. The conduct procedures were essentially fair and well-conducted by the officers of the Council, the Council's solicitor and those Counsel whom he briefed, as well as by the defence organisations acting for the doctor.

Lord Walton was duly elected President of the GMC in 1982. He assumed the chairmanship of the Preliminary Proceedings Committee (PPC), established under Council in order to determine complaints that raised issues of serious professional misconduct and might in consequence require the attendance of the doctor before a formal hearing of the Conduct Committee. That responsibility meant he was required to see most of the complaints received against doctors from members of the public, from persons acting in a public capacity, such as an officer of a health authority, or from other doctors.

About a quarter of complaints from patients related to treatment under the NHS, and these complainants were advised by a member of the office staff to submit their complaint first to the relevant NHS authority, either in hospital, or in general practice, as it was the Council's policy not to investigate a complaint under consideration by another authority. A substantial number of complaints were unfounded.

There remained a batch of complaints, perhaps as many as one hundred and fifty in any year, which at least raised the possibility that a doctor might be guilty of serious professional misconduct. These were referred to the PPC for consideration. Any criminal convictions were similarly reported. The same action was taken in cases, which suggested that the doctor's health might possibly be sufficiently impaired to put patients' welfare at risk. At the PPC, with two lay members present, and a QC and the Council's solicitor in attendance, all convictions were considered first.

A single conviction, for instance involving driving with only a little more than the prescribed level of alcohol on the breath, would invariably lead to a warning letter. However, a very high level of alcohol was usually regarded as indicative of a potential health problem and, in such cases, the doctor's fitness to practise was normally investigated under the health procedures. All convictions were considered in the light of observations made by the doctor or defence organisation, or a solicitor acting on his or her behalf, before any decision was then made. Similar decisions were taken in relation to complaints alleging serious professional misconduct. In any one year, about a hundred doctors would receive warning letters of varying severity, and some thirty to forty cases would be referred to the Conduct Committee for a formal hearing. Almost always, there were ten to twelve doctors each year whose problem was not so much one of alleged misconduct but one related to ill health. A national welfare and counselling service for sick doctors was established, which has continued to function since that time.

During the period, substantial changes were made in the Council's *Blue Book* which gave advice on professional conduct and discipline, new advice on standards of medical care and an attempt to define good standards of medical practice. Advice on issues such as confidentiality affecting medical authors was substantially revised, as was that on abortion and the offering of advice on contraception to young people under the age of 16. Later still, as the problem of AIDS became increasingly prominent, explicit advice to the profession was necessary over testing for HIV infection.

The Contemporary Scene

The Health Service Ombudsman, independent of both Government and the NHS, came into being in 1973 to investigate complaints from members of the public, alleging that they had suffered from a failure of service within the NHS. It was not until later that it became possible to consider complaints about family health service practitioners, or the exercise of clinical judgement. Since then, more than fifty percent of the Ombudsman's work has become concentrated on these aspects. At the root of many a complaint are two primary issues. One is a failure to communicate between the parties concerned and it is quite clear that the onus of responsibility for simple, clear and unambiguous explanation rests with the doctor or dentist. The second issue is the recording and retention of contemporaneous medical records. If either aspect is overlooked or incomplete, subsequent problems develop.

The claims paid by the MDDUS continued to increase and during 1975 amounted to £144,483, the largest in its history. It was also reported that both the English organisations had determined their new subscriptions at £40 for medical and £20 for dental members, as from 1 June 1976. It was agreed that the subscriptions for the MDDUS would be set at £35 per medical member and £16 for a dental member. In his remarks at the Annual General Meeting, held on 19 March 1976, the Convener observed that the increase in the size and number of claims and awards was giving concern to all three defence organisations [MDDUS 1975].

Legislation was also being set in place to take account of the innocence of victims. The Congenital Disabilities (Civil Liability) Act 1976 had its origins in the thalidomide tragedy. It was resolved that children born with disabilities, believed to be due to fault or negligence, would have an unequivocal right to seek compensation through the courts. In many ways, it was the rapid advances made in medical research that was the cause of the problem. New procedures, products and so forth, thought to be wholly beneficial, could turn out to have unforeseen medical side effects. The Act encompassed the application of drugs, any situation in which pregnant women were put at risk, involving injury to an unborn child, impure blood transfusions and state-of-the-art medical science, such as artificial insemination and the use of sperm banks. Another close relation, the Vaccine Damage Payments Act of 1979, followed the 1976 Act. It ensured payment from public funds in cases of severe disability that occurred from the results of vaccination.

In 1977, the MDDUS membership comprised 10,233 doctors and 1,973 dentists and, in that year, the organisation received seven hundred and thirty seven written requests for advice or assistance and one hundred and twenty three claims were intimated. Telephone requests for advice averaged ten calls per day [MDDUS 1977].

Prisoner No. 7 in Spandau

There are few occasions in life when moments of history present themselves. One such occasion involved Mr Peter Edmond, the present chairman of the MDDUS. During his distinguished medical career, he was called upon to treat Rudolph Hess in Spandau Prison, Berlin during the Cold War. Hess remains a controversial figure, with his flight to Britain to sue for peace in 1941 and the debate, which continues to surround his identity.

Hess was born in Egypt in 1894 and was fluent in English as a boy. In the First World War, he fought in the first battle of the Somme and received the Iron Cross 2nd Class and, at a later date, the Iron Cross 1st Class. During his infantry service he received three wounds, which became of great significance years later. In June 1916, he suffered gunshot wounds of the left hand and arm and a second wound to the left arm one year later, in July 1917. In August 1917, he suffered the most serious injury, a low velocity rifle wound to the left side of his chest exiting through his shoulder.

As a Territorial Officer, Peter Edmond went to BMH Hanover as a locum consultant surgeon, but almost immediately was posted to BMH Berlin. He later returned to Hanover. Unexpectedly, he was directed back to Berlin. On arrival, he was taken to the British Embassy for a political briefing on Hess, who was to be his patient. It was necessary to know the consequences of any misadventure, especially the prisoner's untimely demise. This was a very disturbing start to any clinical experience and certainly the only time in Mr Edmond's career when detailed consideration of a fateful outcome took precedence over the actual clinical issues. It was appropriate that he had a note from the Secretary of the MDDUS allowing him to operate anywhere in the world!

Hess had remained in Spandau, in spite of moves for his release, long after the other prisoners had been freed. He was seen as a figurehead of the Nazi regime and it was necessary to make detailed arrangements for his possible demise before any treatment was contemplated. Consequently, plans were made for a senior pathologist to be immediately available, a cremation to follow and the immediate destruction of Spandau prison. There was to be no memorial to the Third Reich.

For pre-operative assessment it was necessary to investigate Hess fully and Mr Edmond was able to demonstrate that the prisoner did have all the evidence of old gunshot wounds (and the residual metallic pieces) in chest and arm. He also had the supportive evidence from Dr Hunter Cummack, who had examined Hess on his capture in 1941.

Happily, for Peter Edmond's story and his personal record, Hess survived for a further ten or more years, living in virtual solitary confinement. He remained guarded in turn by the four Allied powers at enormous expense and died on 17 August 1987 by his own hand. All the detailed plans were immediately put into action and carried out to the letter. The bulldozers moved in and Spandau was razed to the ground.

Patient Concerns

A particularly unusual claim by the widow of a patient was reported to the MDDUS Council during 1980. The patient in question had completed a proposal form for a life assurance of £45,000 in early January and the company sent his GP a medical report to complete, as the applicant's medical practitioner. He did not complete the report. Three reminders later, the report had still not been completed. The patient was unfortunately killed in a motor accident in May. The widow's solicitors claimed that if the medical report had been completed and returned to the assurance company as requested, the patient's estate would now have benefited from the policy. They asserted that the delay was inordinate and unreasonable and claimed payment of £45,000 for the deceased's estate.

The GP could find no excuse for the delay in completing the required report. In addition, he could find no clinical evidence from the patient's medical records, which would either have prevented him from giving a satisfactory report, or have prejudiced the issue of a life policy. An action was brought to Perth Sheriff Court, but the Sheriff rejected the claimant's argument. However, three years later, after substantial amendment of the case, the claimant was allowed to return to the Sheriff Court. The Sheriff dismissed the part of her claim that there was a "contractual duty" to complete the report, but allowed a "Proof Before Answer", in that the doctor was negligent in failing to respond to numerous requests for action. Eventually, the case was settled out of court for £10,000.

An unusual, but less expensive, dental case was brought to the attention of the Council in the same year. A forty-five year old man presented to a dentist, complaining of pain in the upper left second premolar and first molar area. At the time, the dentist was particularly busy working between two surgeries, because his partner was on holiday. On examination, the second premolar and first molar on each side of the upper jaw all proved to be in a carious state but, because he was so busy, the member decided to deal only with the two teeth, which appeared to be causing the pain. He administered a local anaesthetic and then left the room to attend the other surgery.

DR WILLIAM RICHARD TATTERSALL

Dr Tattersall studied dentistry at Edinburgh Dental Hospital. In 1914, he enlisted and was wounded in action and invalided out of the army. He resumed his studies at Dundee Dental Hospital and, in 1918, became one of the first Licentiates in Dental Surgery of the University of St Andrews. He joined the visiting staff of Dundee Dental Hospital and became Lecturer in Dental Surgery and Pathology in 1929. In 1937, He was appointed Lecturer in Dental Jurisprudence, providing the first course on that subject in the UK. In recognition of his services to St Andrews, he received an Honorary Degree of Doctor of Laws. His record of service to the British Dental Association was equally distinguished. He served two terms as President and eleven years as Chairman of the Representative Board.

On his return, he passed a probe up the side of the affected teeth to test for anaesthesia. The patient did not react and he then extracted both teeth slowly and carefully. When he turned to clear up, he was astonished to hear the patient remark, "Tell me, why did you numb one side and then extract the teeth from the other side?" The amazed dentist asked, "Wasn't it sore?" The patient replied "No, not really". The dentist, somewhat shaken, then removed the anaesthetised teeth on the other side. Fortunately, this stoical patient was not disposed to make any claim against the absent-minded dentist.

Domestic Milestones

In the early 1980s, there was also a considerable change in the organisation of the MDDUS reflecting the substantial upsurge in medical litigation. An increase of staff became a necessity to deal with the workload. In addition, the trends already established in earlier years in the very costly settlement of claims, had the inevitable knock-on effect of increased subscriptions for the indemnity of both doctor and dentist members.

Thus, Dr Andrew Barr and Dr Joyce Watson joined the staff as additional Deputy Medical Secretaries; Mr Ian Stevenson became the full-time Controller of Finance; Mr James Whitelaw and Mr Ian Rattray were appointed part-time Dental Secretaries; and Mr John MacDonald was made deputy to Mr Robert H. Dickson, the MDDUS solicitor. A further milestone was reached in 1984, when Dr Elizabeth McSwan became the first lady member elected to serve on the Council.

In April 1984, the King Edward Memorial Hospital in Port Stanley, the Falkland Islands, was destroyed by fire and eight people lost their lives. An immediate public inquiry was set up and the senior medical officer contacted the MDDUS and asked for assistance. Within seventy-two hours, Mr Robert Dickson, now Sheriff of South Strathclyde, Dumfries and Galloway at Airdrie, was ready to leave for Port Stanley, where he spent a week in support of the doctor. The inquiry found that she had acted properly in attempting to bring the inadequate fire precautions at the hospital to the attention of the authorities. She was exonerated from any blame.

Legislative Controls

The right of access to information took further shape with the introduction of the Data Protection Act 1984, that took account of the electronic office and the right of a patient to know whether personal information was held. Access could be denied under a caveat of, "likely to cause serious harm", but a start had been made in enhancing the rights of the patient in this regard. Subsequent Acts of Parliament in the decade, were to be equally far-reaching in their fields. A further Dentists Act in 1984, consolidating the law relating to the training, registration and disciplining of dentists, and a Surrogacy Arrangements Act 1985, which prohibited the operation of commercial surrogacy agencies and their advertising, added their contribution to an environment of increasing control and regulation.

However, the most notable legislation concerned the introduction of the Hospital Complaints Procedure Act of 1985, which obliged health authorities to establish a complaints procedure for hospital patients and to make them aware of such a procedure. There was a view, expressed by Professor Andrew Mathews of St George's Hospital, London that:

The better a patient is informed about his treatment and about the way that he is being looked after in hospital, the less is his reliance on pain-killing drugs and the quicker his cure.

Certainly, many complaints arose out of a sense of frustration that doctors were unwilling to discuss, or provide information on, a medical condition. In 1983, a total of 19,000 written complaints were received by the NHS, which represented one complaint for every 3,000 episodes of treatment [Hansard 6s, 73: 1384].

Internal Changes

The MDDUS moved to new offices at 144 West George Street, Glasgow in late 1986. At the first Council meeting in the new premises, the

Convener informed the meeting that it was with the deepest regret and sadness that his first duty was to notify the death of the Secretary, Dr James "Pat" Patterson, on 9 December 1986. James Patterson was the first holder of the Secretary post at the MDDUS and was due to retire at the end of the year.

Dr Ian Simpson, an Aberdeen graduate, took up the post as Secretary in succession to Dr Patterson on 1 January 1987. He had spent nine years on the Secretariat of the Medical Defence Union in London and thus came

---

DR JAMES PATTERSON

had a distinguished career, which started with a B.A. in law at Oxford. He saw service in the Royal Armoured Corps during the Second World War, when he was awarded the Military Cross in the North African Campaign and a Bar to this distinction at Monte Cassino in Italy. During the final Monte Cassino battle, he was badly wounded and lost his right leg. Thereafter, he qualified as a doctor in 1950 at Glasgow University and proceeded from house officer posts to general practice and then to his appointment with MDDUS. He became immensely knowledgeable in medico-legal matters and his loss was felt deeply by many friends in both professions and by all those who benefited from his kindness and understanding.

---

to Glasgow with a wealth of knowledge and experience in the field of medical defence. He faced the reality of medico-legal situations, which threatened to stifle initiative and progress. In financial terms, the indemnity and adverse costs paid out by the MDDUS in 1987 amounted to £1,778,752, although on the positive side, membership continued to grow steadily and stood at 15,910 members. By the middle of the 1980s the frequency of claims had steadily increased from approximately 6 claims per thousand members to an estimated 10.9 per thousand in 1987. This proportion was projected to increase to 12.3 per thousand in 1988. The average cost per claim was calculated to be £29,600 in 1987, although this disguised the wide disparity among individual claim settlements.

Medical Performance

During the 1980s, there was continued criticism of the General Medical Council from both television and newspapers, centred on a few cases appearing before the Conduct Committee. A typical example would be where the alleged facts of specific instances of bad practice were found not proven, but, clearly, the defendant doctor had been seriously deficient in his or her daily medical practice. Obviously, public interest required an explanation and, if possible, a solution.

When Lord Kilpatrick of Kincraig became President of the GMC in February 1989, this problem was acute and an analysis had to made. "Fitness to practice" was to be enlarged from conduct and health procedures to include performance procedures. A mechanism was required in order to identify evidence of serious deficiency in the pattern of a doctor's medical practice, when there was no evidence of serious professional misconduct.

The first major point in the analysis was, that to allege a deficient pattern of practice on a daily, monthly and yearly basis required some method of obtaining evidence, which did not exist in criminal courts of law. "Conduct" procedures of the GMC had followed the Rules of Evidence of the Criminal Court, since the inception of the GMC. As in the Criminal Court, the case was heard adversarially through verbal evidence given by witnesses, who were subject to cross-examination. Such a method could only deal with specific events, which might amount to serious professional misconduct.

The solution in the analysis came from the "health case" procedures. When they began, it was clear that evidence of impairment of health could not be judged on the day of the hearing of the Health Committee. It was accepted that assessment by professional experts of a doctor's health over a period of weeks, months, or years, would be adduced in evidence. Accordingly, the same should apply in finding evidence of a pattern of medical practice. It was also concluded that this assessment would not measure competence, but performance. The public were not interested in what a doctor could do, often in a test situation, but what he did on a daily basis.

After the analysis, the next requirement was extensive consultation to persuade both the profession and the public of the necessity for such new procedures. All the various medical organisations, including the British Medical Association, the Royal Colleges and medical defence organisations were consulted. So far as the public were concerned, political parties and the Government were their obvious representatives. Also consulted were the Privy Council and the Law Lords. The latter were particularly interested as the analysis and the proposed solutions might be applicable to the legal profession.

The political administration of the day totally accepted the analysis and, in 1992, the GMC made a formal request of the Government to find primary legislation time to amend the Medical Acts to allow Performance Procedures. After nearly three years, the GMC was told that if there was all party support for this change, Parliamentary time would be made available. Extensive consultation with Members of the Houses of Commons and Lords had already taken place and all party support was given to the GMC and its recommendations. An amendment to the Medical Act subsequently became law in October 1995, just after Lord Kilpatrick demitted his Presidency of the GMC.

Further Legislation

During the decade, legislation continued in full flow. Further Acts of medico-legal interest became law. One in particular, the Access to Medical Reports Act 1988, continued the momentum to enable an individual to gain access to their medical information. This Act established the right of an individual to gain access to reports, relating to them, provided by practitioners for employment or insurance purposes. It was an overwhelmingly popular measure. A survey poll conducted at the time registered 86% of the public in favour.

A second Act drew attention to one of the fastest growing areas of government expenditure at the time, that of legal aid. The legal aid scheme was now in its fortieth year. The first twenty years had seen an annual expenditure of never more than £10 million per year, which helped about 150,000 people. At the time of the introduction of the 1988 Bill, this had risen to an annual rate of £450 million and about two million people had received help in England and Wales [Hansard 6s, 132: 884]. Furthermore, the growing impact of medical science heralded the introduction of the Human Organ Transplants Act of 1989, which prohibited commercial dealings in human organs intended for transplantation and restricted the transplant of organs between persons who were not genetically related.

The Access to Health Records and the Human Fertilisation and Embryology Acts of 1990, each typified the themes of the decade; an increased access to medical information and health records by the individuals concerned and a continued regulation of medical scientific progress. There is every indication that the medical profession in general supported the access to information legislation. The Greater London Association of Community Health Councils at the time surveyed opinion among their GPs, who commented:

…Complete access to the records gives the patients trust and confidence in their general practitioners. Good general practice is a partnership between patients and doctors.

The Human Fertilisation and Embryology Act proposed statutory regulation of certain types of infertility treatment, which had raised important scientific, medical, ethical, legal and social issues. It was of primary interest to general practitioners who might be consulted by those involved, at the outset of treatment. The birth of the world's first "test-tube baby" in Oldham, as a result of in vitro fertilisation, ushered in a new era in the treatment of infertile couples and was examined by Baroness Warnock in a committee of inquiry. The inquiry included in its investigations the research involving human embryos, leading to the introduction of the Bill in November 1989.

Crown Indemnity

In 1989, the Government announced that it intended to introduce Crown Indemnity for hospital and community health doctors and dentists. This Indemnity did not extend to general medical and dental practitioners. The announcement came as a surprise to the medical defence organisations, although the escalating costs of medical negligence and consequently defence organisations' subscriptions had given cause for concern to the Government, the professions and to the defence organisations themselves in recent years.

The introduction of the New Zealand system of no-fault compensation was advocated by certain politicians and by the BMA. It was seen as an answer to the problem of compensating patients, who had suffered ill effects following medical intervention. But no system of funding, sufficient to meet the enormous demands of such a scheme had, as yet, been devised and the estimates of its costs were very high. There was no unanimity among the medical defence organisations, on the grounds that it would not be a conclusive answer to the complex question of medical indemnity. The suggestion was shelved.

After months of discussion, it was hoped that the Government's proposals regarding Crown Indemnity might soon be notified. In fact, the Minister of Health arbitrarily announced that Crown Indemnity for all hospital and community doctors and dentists would take effect on 1 January 1990, less than two months after the most recent discussions. The MDDUS and its fellow defence organisations were faced with the transfer of assets assessed by the Government Actuary to finance Crown Indemnity and cover the estimated liabilities of £75,000,000. After some hard bargaining, a compromise was reached in 1992.

The level of dental litigation did not drop with the change to Crown Indemnity and the prospect of a high profile action caused by the professional malpractice of a dental member was the catalyst for the appointment of the MDDUS first full-time dental secretary, Mr Hugh Harvie. Also, in a continuing effort to educate and advise its members, the MDDUS established three specialist advisory panels to give advice and guidance in their particular areas. The Dental Advisory Panel had already been established and approval was given for setting up a General Practitioner Advisory Panel and a Hospital Advisory Panel.

> The MDDUS also instituted the award of Honorary Fellowship in 1990. There were six initial recipients of the award.

At the Annual General Meeting held at the Ninewells Hospital, Dundee in December 1991, the Convener, Dr Andrew Allison, retired after eleven years service. Mr Peter Edmond succeeded him. Furthermore, membership of the MDDUS opened up to all UK medical and dental graduates in 1992. This ended any previous restriction to membership and placed the MDDUS on an equal footing with the other two medical defence organisations.

90th Birthday

In June 1992, the MDDUS celebrated its 90th birthday and a reception to mark the occasion was held at the Burrell Collection attended by representatives from all fields of medicine and dentistry. The gathering was addressed by Mrs Janice Webster, who spoke on the subject of the integration of the medical and dental professions into the European Community and by Lord Abernethy, one of Scotland's senior judges, who spoke on the vital part that the MDDUS had played in the conduct of medical negligence cases during the past ninety years.

After more than ninety years of renting accommodation in various parts of Glasgow, the MDDUS decided to buy its own building and accommodate the increasing number of staff under one roof. Mackintosh House in Blythswood Street, Glasgow, was purchased. The building had been designed by the famous architect Charles Rennie Mackintosh, who used its drawing room while he designed the renowned Glasgow School of Art building. The move to Mackintosh House took place in February 1994 and The Right Honourable Lord Fraser of Carmyllie, QC, Minister of State at the Scottish Office officially opened the office and unveiled a commemorative plaque.

Mackintosh House
drawing
Laura Cameron-Jackson

MDDUS Coat of Arms

The MDDUS was granted a coat of arms by the Lord Lyon King of Arms. The St Andrews Cross represented its Scottish roots, the Scales of Justice and the Serpent on the Shaft, the legal and medical aspects of the MDDUS, and a zigzag line denoting teeth, represented the dental members.

Reflections and Reforms

Rising Costs

Despite the introduction of Crown Indemnity, the expense of medical defence to the MDDUS continued to rise in the early 1990s. The major reasons were the costs of legal representation at Fatal Accident Inquiries, Coroner's Inquests, disciplinary hearings and the support of members at GDC and GMC Inquiries. Fees for providing legal representation on such occasions were, on average, £1,000 per day excluding those for expert opinion, or the attendance of experts, although in a notable case before the GMC Professional Conduct Committee, the total bill was in excess of £60,000. In further large claim settlements, a GP case was settled for £20,000 with adverse costs of £12,000 and MDDUS legal costs of £8,000. A dental claim was settled for £1,500 and its associated legal bill was in excess of £3,000 [MDDUS 1993].

There was also an overall increase in the number of claims in the private medical sector. The claims made against dental members had also increased by a worrying 15%. The number of clinical cases considered by the Council was now considerably reduced, as this aspect of medico-legal work was now undertaken by the GP and Dental Advisory Panels. The Hospital Advisory Panel, which consisted of many distinguished practitioners from a wide spectrum of specialties, was also of immeasurable help. These functional developments helped the MDDUS to keep pace with the rapidly changing face of medical defence.

The Head of the MDDUS Medical Division, Dr Bill Mathewson, reported that, in 1996, the average cost of GP claims was £30,000, the least expensive being £41.50 and the most expensive £436,000. In the Dental Division, Mr Harvie announced that claims against one member now numbered 114, with an estimated value of £20,000 each. Thus, a sum in excess of £2million would be required to cover this liability. Another dental practitioner, whose name had been erased from the Dental

Opposite:

Vincent van GOGH
(1853-1890)
Portrait of Dr Paul Gachet
1890
Oil on canvas
Musée d'Orsay, Paris

In May 1890, two months before his death, Vincent van Gogh settled in Auvers-sur-Oise where his physician, Dr Paul Gachet, was an amateur artist. Gachet had a homeopathic practice in Paris. Van Gogh wrote: "I have found a perfect friend in Dr Gachet, something like another brother – so alike are we physically, and mentally, too."

Register, had seventeen claims intimated against him, of which seven had been settled relatively modestly for between £1,500 and £2,000 each. The third most worrying and unusual case concerned a dentist charged with seventy three offences, seventy of which related to the Forgery and Counterfeiting Act. The dentist was eventually sentenced to a one-year term of imprisonment [MDDUS 1996].

Services Medicine and Dentistry

In times of peace, it is sometimes overlooked that a number of medical and dental members of the MDDUS continue to serve in the medical services of the armed forces. The MDDUS tradition of representation and support for its armed forces members has been constant from the time of its founding.

Since the Second World War, the armed services have been involved in conflicts throughout the world, most notably Korea in the early 1950s. A member of the MDDUS, Dr A. M. Ferrie was taken prisoner in Korea and his bank, not unexpectedly, was having difficulty in getting in touch with him for financial instructions on his professional commitments. The Council agreed that Ferrie's membership should continue without payment until his return and that the same concession should apply to others in the same predicament.

*Regimental Medical
Officer Accommodation –
Korea*
Dr Neil Stirling

Medical services were influenced by the UN experience in Korea and, later, the American experience in Vietnam. The advent of helicopter evacuation meant that rapid casualty evacuation to forward medical facilities was feasible. Previously fatal injuries on the battlefield became potentially salvageable as resuscitation knowledge improved, along with increased technological advancement. In fields such as vascular surgery, it was the stimulus for developing new methods of treatment for the wounded serviceman that led to major advances in civilian practice.

Falklands Campaign

The UK's first major military experience since Korea was the 1982 Falkland Islands conflict. This was an amphibious campaign fought thousands of miles from home bases and required a major logistic effort. Medically, it required much careful thought with doctors appointed to all the deployed ships; enhancement of medical logistic elements; deployment of surgical teams; and the acquisition and rapid refit of SS Uganda, a school cruise liner, as a Hospital Ship. The first casualties were aboard ships damaged by bombing, strafing and Exocet missile attack. Casualties aboard ship were initially treated within the surgical facilities afloat. It was only after a remarkable landing and advance, that a field hospital could be established at San Carlos Bay, named the "Red & Green Life Machine" reflecting the colours of the Parachute Regiment and Royal Marine berets, whose medical staff manned it.

All those who arrived there alive, left alive - a remarkable feat in itself. Evacuation was not easy from such a distant area of the world, but a fleet of hydrographic ships were converted into "ambulances" and ferried the wounded to Uruguay, where long distance evacuation was continued by RAF medical teams. Battlefield commanders became increasingly aware of the value of first class medical care, especially as the world's media were reporting the campaign via satellite to a nightly television audience at home. The true horrors of war were visible for all to see and the pictures of wounded soldiers and sailors being evacuated from the Royal Fleet Auxiliaries, Sir Galahad and Sir Tristam at Bluff Cove, after both ships were severely damaged in a bombing raid on 8 June 1982, were unforgettable. The British population expected the standard of medical care for servicemen to be no less than that received at home, despite their deployment many thousands of miles from the UK. This would influence medical planning for future campaigns in the Gulf and former Yugoslavia.

Battle surgery in the field – Ajax Bay, Falkland Islands 1982
Dr Rick Jolly, OBE

Gulf Campaign

The country was soon to be involved in another major campaign with Iraq after the invasion of Kuwait in the early 1990s. This was as part of a large UN-sponsored force based mainly in Saudi Arabia. Once again commanders' awareness of medical issues in relation to the media, led to the early deployment of vast medical facilities sponsored by the major combatant countries and others. The state of the defence medical services was such that large numbers of reserves were called up and deployed to field hospitals established in the desert. Back in the UK, Health Authorities were poised to prepare for the arrival of mass casualties once the major battle commenced, as the capabilities of service hospitals had reduced to such a level that they would never have been able to cope. The threat of biological or tactical nuclear weapons resulted in rapid mass inoculation to protect servicemen against an unusual combination of pathogens. Other troops spent large periods of the build up to the campaign under the potential threat of nuclear attack in protective clothing, by it's nature, unsuitable for wear in the desert climate, which showed the problems of fighting in this strange environment.

DOCTOR LOWELL LAMONT

A long-serving member of the MDDUS, Dr Lowell Lamont died on 18th February 1994 aged ninety-three. He was born in Paisley in 1900 and graduated in medicine from Glasgow University in 1928. He and his wife went to South Africa as medical missionaries for a number of years, returning to Scotland to take up general practice. He became Chairman of the South East Scotland Faculty of the RCGP and then Provost. He was also on the Scottish Council of the College and subsequently became Vice Chairman and then Chairman, which made him a member of the Central Council of the College. He became a member of Council of the MDDUS in 1942, Honorary Treasurer for six years and finally Convener for ten years. He was elected one of the first Honorary Fellows of the MDDUS.

The campaign was thankfully short and with very few casualties. The medical facilities mainly dealt with normal non-battle disease, illness and trauma that might be expected during any campaign. It was only after return from the Gulf that its legacy presented itself. Veterans began to complain of "Gulf War Sickness", a debilitating series of symptoms that have baffled the medical community, despite attempts by the defence medical services, the US Surgeon General's Department and the Medical Research Council to isolate a cause. Many causes have been postulated, including the combinations of less-researched vaccinations, depleted uranium in armour piercing shells and chemical release from the fires of burning oil wells in liberated Kuwait. None has been shown to be the clear cause.

This type of symptom is being seen more often during modern warfare. Similar symptoms were seen in the more recent campaigns in the former Yugoslavia. More research is required into this syndrome, which may have been initially considered by commanders to be similar to "shell shock" in the First World War. In like fashion, military psychiatrists have begun to recognise that "post traumatic stress disorder" needs to be considered in servicemen who become ill often a long time after a conflict is over. Effective methods of treatment need to be developed in conjunction with civilian colleagues.

The diminution in medical services has been seen clearly over the last six years where defence medical staff have deployed in support of UN missions in Bosnia, Kosovo, and Rwanda, and UK missions in Sierra Leone. The frequency of deployment takes military surgeons, anaesthetists, nurses and other staff away from their new NHS practice all too frequently and, despite financial incentives and recruitment campaigns, the number of doctors and specialists remain low in the defence medical services. This would seem to indicate that reliance will continue to be placed on civilian medical and dental resources and staff to fill such gaps in the future.

The Ombudsman

Changes in 1996, which allowed the Ombudsman to consider complaints about either family health service practitioners or their clinical judgement brought GPs into contact with the Ombudsman for the first time and the scope and depth of the investigations came as a shock to some. When the Ombudsman started to look at issues of clinical judgement, he appointed a number of clinical advisers, two hospital advisers, one GP and one GDP adviser and a number of others. In addition to these advisers, external general practice professional advisers were appointed for investigations involving issues of clinical judgement.

The standards, which are applied when a report is produced, are what a patient has the right to expect as fair and reasonable in the circumstances. Account is taken of published guidelines, including those of the National Health Executive, GMC, GDC, BMA, BDA and the Royal Colleges.

In 1998-1999, there were 2,869 complaints received by the Ombudsman's office - an 8% increase on the previous year. There were 119 investigations completed, of which 35 were about the actions of GPs (14 about clinical judgement) and 10 were about the actions of community dental practitioners (9 about clinical judgement). The statistics, though small, reflected a continuing trend of complaint, which showed no sign of abating and a growing pressure, to resolve the delay and cost of the increased number of court cases, began to take tangible shape.

PROFESSOR ROBERT MCWHIRTER, CBE

Robert McWhirter died in Edinburgh on October 24th 1994. His radiological training began in Cambridge, with the work of Lord Rutherford. It continued at St Bartholemews Hospital London, where he first became involved in the treatment of breast cancer using radium needles. In 1935, he moved to Edinburgh Royal Infirmary and in 1936 took charge of the X-ray Department. During this period he continued his research into the management of breast cancer, eventually transforming international opinion. In 1946 he was appointed to the Forbes Chair of Medical Radiology at Edinburgh. During a busy career he served as Warden and subsequently President of the Faculty of Radiologists and in 1963 was honoured by the award of CBE for his services to radiology and oncology. He was elected a Fellow of the Royal Society of Edinburgh.

Proposals for the Reform of Civil Justice

In July 1996, HMSO published Lord Woolf's proposals for the reform of civil justice. The proposals, "Access to Justice", were set out in a 370-page report accompanied by a book of draft rules. The object of the proposals was to reduce the delays and cost of civil litigation, and thus make civil justice more widely available. The most important single principle was that the court should take a more active role in the management of civil litigation, thus cases would proceed at a pace set by the court, rather than at a pace chosen by the parties or their lawyers. The lavishness, or economy, of the procedures adopted would be determined by the court, not the parties and it would be proportionate to the sums of money or the nature of the issues, which were at stake.

The detailed proposals included the development of pre-action protocols to facilitate the investigation of matters in dispute, the exchange of information and, where possible, the achievement of settlement before any litigation. A "fast track" for dealing with smaller and more

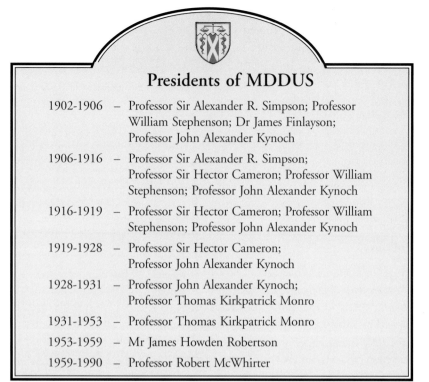

Presidents of MDDUS

1902-1906	–	Professor Sir Alexander R. Simpson; Professor William Stephenson; Dr James Finlayson; Professor John Alexander Kynoch
1906-1916	–	Professor Sir Alexander R. Simpson; Professor Sir Hector Cameron; Professor William Stephenson; Professor John Alexander Kynoch
1916-1919	–	Professor Sir Hector Cameron; Professor William Stephenson; Professor John Alexander Kynoch
1919-1928	–	Professor Sir Hector Cameron; Professor John Alexander Kynoch
1928-1931	–	Professor John Alexander Kynoch; Professor Thomas Kirkpatrick Monro
1931-1953	–	Professor Thomas Kirkpatrick Monro
1953-1959	–	Mr James Howden Robertson
1959-1990	–	Professor Robert McWhirter

straightforward cases, within the monetary band £3,000 to £10,000, would be created. Most cases below £3,000 would be dealt with by a more informal small claims arbitration procedure.

Cases above the fast track would proceed on a "multi-track". The type of management that the court provided would depend upon the nature and complexity of the case. In the heavier cases, there would be both a case management conference and a pre-trial review. At the case management conference, the court would identify key issues; explore the scope for alternative dispute resolution, or settlement; order appropriate disclosure of documents; give directions as to the evidence to be adduced; and set a timetable for the case. At the pre-trial review, the court would identify the issues to be tried and set a programme and budget for the trial.

In respect of cases destined for settlement, early settlement would be encouraged by a number of means. The most important innovation was the "claimant's offer to settle". If this offer was refused and, subsequently, the defendant did no better at trial, then the defendant would have to pay substantial extra interest. Disclosure of documents to opposing parties would be limited to documents that really mattered. The present rules of discovery can involve litigants in massive costs and generate huge bundles of documents, which are never referred to. Steps would be taken to limit adversarial expert evidence to those cases where it was necessary and to secure that the expert evidence given was impartial.

Medical negligence litigation was singled out for special attention because it was an area in which problems had arisen most acutely. Particular issues were the disproportion between costs and damages, excessive delay and too many cases being inappropriately contested. Thus, one whole chapter of the twenty-chapter report was devoted to medical negligence. Medical negligence cases would be tried by judges who had some expertise in the field, to speed up the trial and give them greater authority to manage cases. The concept of the Woolf Report was greeted generally with enthusiasm.

> ### Dr MATTHEW C.K. FINLAYSON
>
> Matthew Finlayson died on 13 November 1996. On the outbreak of the Second World War, he was called up but managed to obtain leave to sit his final examinations. A written paper in surgery was done to the accompaniment of an air raid over Edinburgh, when the Forth Bridge was attacked. He saw service in North Africa and the campaigns in Sicily and Italy. After the war, he established a practice in Edinburgh. As a general dental practitioner he sat and passed the Fellowship in Dental Surgery in 1955. In June 1967, he was co-opted to the Council of the MDDUS and gave wise, practical and authoritative advice until he retired in 1990. The Council later conferred on him an Honorary Fellowship in recognition of his service.

Bolitho

The House of Lords judgement in 1997 in the *Bolitho & Others v City and Hackney Health Authority* case aroused considerable medico-legal interest [All ER 1997] and clearly demonstrated the time delay in resolving medical cases. The case took thirteen years to conclude the litigation. Patrick Bolitho, aged two years, had been admitted, discharged and re-admitted to St Bartholomew's Hospital with croup. When respiratory difficulties alarmed the Paediatric Nurse, she called for the Senior Paediatric Registrar to attend. The doctor failed to do so. Patrick's breathing difficulties worsened, then eased for a time, but finally the child collapsed. He suffered cardiac arrest, severe brain damage and subsequently died.

The Hospital conceded that it was negligent for the doctor to have failed to attend and the argument therefore shifted from negligence to causation. The claimant's case was that Patrick should have been intubated. Five experts supported that view. Their opinion was that Patrick suffered a gradual decline into hypoxia. The three defence experts were of the opposite opinion. Their view was that Patrick's decline was sudden, that the crisis occurred because of a blockage of mucus. Intubation, they said, is an invasive procedure requiring anaesthetic, to which risks of morbidity and mortality attach.

Notwithstanding that evidence, the trial judge admitted that he found the case argued by the claimant's Counsel to be persuasive. He found:

Intubation was the safe option, whatever was suspected as the cause or even if the cause was thought to be a mystery ...

but then the judge went on to say:

The difficulty of this approach ... was that in effect it invited me to substitute my own views for those of the medical experts.

The trial judge found for the defence, as did the Court of Appeal, by a majority. In the House of Lords, the leading judgment was given by Lord Browne-

Wilkinson. He held that the trial judge and the majority in the Court of Appeal were correct. The interest aroused by the case lay in the comments made by Lord Browne-Wilkinson as to the testing of expert opinion:

...The Court is not bound to hold that a Defendant Doctor escapes liability for negligent treatment or diagnosis just because he leads evidence from a number of medical experts who are genuinely of the opinion that the Defendant's treatment or diagnosis accorded with sound medical practice...

He then referred to earlier cases and continued:

...The use of these adjectives, responsible, reasonable and respectable all show that the Court has to be satisfied that the exponents of the body of opinion relied upon can demonstrate that such opinion has a logical basis. In particular, in cases involving as they often do the weighing of risks against benefits the Judge before accepting a body of opinion as being responsible, reasonable or respectable will need to be satisfied that ... the experts have directed their minds to the question of comparative risks and benefits and have reached a defensible conclusion on the matter.

It reaffirmed the authority of a trial judge to evaluate the merits of expert medical opinion and to test that opinion for its rationality, its reasonableness and its logic, in the context of a risk benefit analysis of a case. In doing so, it re-confirmed both the *Hunter v Hanley* and *Bolam* judgements in determining the question of medical negligence. Nevertheless, the decision did mean that medical expert opinion must be exhaustively tested in pre-trial conferences, to ensure the highest quality. If expert evidence failed to convince, judges now had express encouragement from the House of Lords to reject it.

Fellows of MDDUS

1990	–	Dr Matthew C.K. Finlayson; Mr Thomas Brown Henderson; Dr Lowell Lamont; Professor William Arthur Mackey; Dr Archibald McDougall; Professor Robert McWhirter.
1991	–	Dr Andrew Allison; Professor Alexander Stuart Douglas.
1994	–	Professor Wallace Foulds.
1995	–	Professor Sir Donald Campbell; Dr John K. Davidson.
1997	–	Mr Donald Butchart; Dr Alistair Donald; Mr Robert Pringle.
1999	–	Mr Jimmy Graham; Dr Elizabeth McSwan.
2002	–	Dr Douglas Bell; Dr Douglas Garvie; Mr Ian Rattray.

The progress, or lack of it, of *Bolitho* through the courts illustrated an important fact. The wheels of justice grind exceedingly slow. Patrick Bolitho died in St Bartholomew's Hospital on 16 January 1984. It was not until 13 November 1997 that the doctors and Health Authority finally learnt that the claim arising from the death of the two-year old had failed. While thirteen years is an exceptionally long time for a court case to reach final resolution, it is indicative how slow the legal process can be. In the Scottish case of *Comber v Greater Glasgow Health Board*, seventeen years passed between the mishap and the hearing of evidence in relation to it. If, as happened in *Bolitho*, there is an appeal this can add more years to the delay.

In Scotland, the terms of the Prescription & Limitation (Scotland) Act 1973 allow a person three years to initiate court proceedings. In England, the Limitation Act 1980 also permits three years to do the same. In each case, the time is measured from the date on which he or she knows, or ought to have known, that there has been an injury due to negligence and the person or Health Board responsible for the fault can be identified. The consequences of a medical or dental mishap may not become apparent for a considerable time and it is only when they become evident, that the clock will start to run. Even those who fail to raise proceedings in good time can seek leave of a court to proceed late, if it is just and equitable that the permission should be given. In England, an additional period of four months is allowed for service of the writ and this can add further to the delay.

> **Mr DONALD G.M. BUTCHART**
>
> Mr Donald Butchart, a former member of the Council and Management Committee of the MDDUS died on 2 December 1999, after a short illness. He qualified LDS at St Andrews University in 1949. In 1985, he was awarded a Masters Degree in Dental Science for the important contribution he had made in the field of dental materials. He was a lifelong member of the MDDUS and was Chairman of the Dental Advisory Panel between 1992 and 1999. Away from dentistry Donald Butchart raised his family with pride in their achievements. A keen fisher and gardener, he had an encyclopaedic knowledge and was always willing to offer guidance to those less gifted in these arts with unfailing courtesy and good humour.

In cases involving children, the period may, in certain circumstances, not start until the child has reached the age of eighteen and can sue in person. Thus, in *Purryag v. Greater Glasgow Health Board*, a young lady, who claimed she had been damaged at birth, was able to sue the doctors involved, eighteen years later. Her claim failed, but not due to the lapse of time. Had she succeeded, she would have received eighteen years worth of interest on the value of her damages.

Susan MACFARLANE
(b.1938)
Radiotherapy   1991-5
Oil on canvas
Reproduced by kind permission of Susan
Macfarlane and A Picture of Health Ltd.

This image, from *A Picture of Health*,
illustrates the simulation room, where precise
measurements of the areas to receive
radiotherapy are made. The success of this
series of paintings, when first exhibited in
1995, has led to the founding of the charity
A Picture of Health Ltd.

Radiation Medicine

Discovery

The discovery of X-rays was arguably one of the most important breakthroughs in the history of medicine, because it made so many other things possible. It opened a window to what goes on inside the body and its development led to the saving of countless thousands of lives through early detection of tuberculosis, breast and other tumours, and cardiovascular disease. The public now have high expectations and radiology has become a frontline specialty, much involved in medical litigation.

Wilhelm Röntgen presented his historic paper on X-rays at Wurzburg in November 1895. He subsequently wrote to only two people in Britain, Lord Kelvin at Glasgow, for whom Röntgen had the highest esteem, and Professor Shuster of the Physics Department at Manchester University. At the time, the Royal Infirmary was the only Glasgow hospital to have an electricity supply, so Kelvin took the discovery there. Dr John Macintyre quickly grasped the possibilities of the "New Light" and had Britain's first hospital X-ray department up and running in March 1896. John Macintyre achieved many "firsts" with the new capability; an X-ray of a kidney stone, a coin in the gullet, and a spectacular cineradiograph showing the movement of a frog's leg [Calder 2001]. In 1900, he was chosen as the fourth President of the Röntgen Society and introduced as, "one of the chief pioneers of the practical application of Röntgen rays to medicine and surgery".

Development

The medical profession had no doubt about the importance of the discovery. Throughout Britain, many medical men and physicists, even a vicar, enthusiastically experimented with X-rays; the speed of development was quite staggering. Early X-ray photographs were produced at

Edinburgh's Royal Infirmary by Dawson Turner; by George Pirie in Dundee; and James Mackenzie Davidson, an ophthalmologist in Aberdeen who was later knighted, invented the Davidson Localiser for foreign bodies in the eye [Burrows 1986]. This was popular with ophthalmologists and used by the British Army in South Africa and subsequently in the First World War. He was later appointed consultant surgeon to the X-ray Department at Charing Cross Hospital. Throughout the country, those teaching hospitals with electrical departments, e.g., the London and St Bartholomew's, soon produced X-ray photographs and others were soon to follow.

A number of Scottish doctors became notable authors in the specialty. In 1899, Donald McIntosh, the Medical Electrician at Glasgow's Western Infirmary, produced one of the first radiology textbooks – An Atlas of Skiagraphy. Robert Knox of Edinburgh, who succeeded Sir Archibald Reid as the radiologist to the King's College Hospital, subsequently published two classic books on radiography and radiotherapy in 1917. The Reid-Knox Hall in the British Institute of Radiology is named after both men.

Sylvanus Thompson, a brilliant applied physicist repeated Röntgen experiments in 1896 and mobilised doctors' enthusiasm for the new clinical method. He set up a committee in 1897 named the Skiagraphic, or X-ray Society. This was soon re-named the Röntgen Society. In 1917 the British Association for the Advancement of Radiology and Physiotherapy (BARP) was founded. In 1924, it changed its name to the British Institute of Radiology. Three years later it amalgamated with the Röntgen Society, as the British Institute of Radiology [Thomas 1995]. This is the world's oldest radiology society. It has medical, industrial and scientific membership and is unique in providing such a forum. Initially, in the mid-1930s Scottish Radiology was a branch of the British Institute and it was not until 1946 that the Scottish Radiological Society held its first meeting [Calder 2001].

Martyrs Memorial Hamburg

It records the names of 169 radiologists from a number of nations, who were killed by exposure to X-ray and Radium radiation.

Philips Medical Systems

Radiation Hazards

The biological effects of X-rays were soon recognised and used initially to treat skin disease – the beginning of radiotherapy. Soon, large numbers of patients were referred for treatment for a variety of conditions. Radium became available and proved a more effective source of radiation. Little was known of the dangers of X-rays and protection was unknown, but the risks soon became apparent. Early radiologists used their own hands as controls, repeatedly putting them in the primary X-ray beam, in an attempt to obtain the best X-ray photographs. Many radiologists lost fingers, some developing radiation burns and fatal carcinomata. The Martyrs Memorial at St George's Hospital, Hamburg has recorded the names of all who died from X-rays; British radiologists included Dawson Turner of Edinburgh, George Pirie of Dundee and James Riddell of Glasgow [Thomas 1995]. Such was the concern, that the early radiological societies had radiation safety committees, but it was not until 1928 that the International Commission on Radiological Protection was formed. There is a continuing development of the understanding of radiation effects and hence control of radiation hazards, the latest being the concept of Controllable Dose.

The need to improve standards in radiology and radiotherapy became vital. Sir Archibald Reid, who earned his knighthood in the First World War for mobilising radiology services, was convinced that training in radiology was required. In conjunction with Mackenzie Davidson, he established training and an examination in radiology. The British Associations of Radiologists and Radiotherapists combined to form the Faculty of Radiologists in the Royal College of Surgeons of England in 1939. This Faculty became the Royal College of Radiologists with separate Faculties of Clinical Radiology and Clinical Oncology in 1975.

Litigation in Radiology

Deep X-ray therapy caused most claims in early years. The MDDUS Annual General Meeting of 1935 commented, "Members are reminded of the value of X-ray records and of the necessity of keeping careful records of treatment and appointments, essential for the corroboration of contemporary evidence in the handling of cases." In 1948, the Minutes of the Annual Meeting stated, "matters which give rise to claims were damage to tissues following X-ray treatment." The following year the most expensive claim up to that time was settled and in later years, claims against radiologists became increasingly frequent. Within the USA, radiologists are currently the fourth or fifth among specialties most frequently sued. However, in the UK, it is not common for clinical radiologists to be the subject of legal action. The pattern of radiological negligence has changed little over recent years [Craig 1997].

The defence of an error in X-ray diagnosis is based on a decision whether the error is negligence or a mistake. The following case is a good example where, by applying the test of *Hunter v. Hanley*, failure to recognise a minimal X-ray abnormality was considered a mistake and successfully defended. A twelve-year-old girl injured her hip while skiing in the Cairngorms, a fractured femur was suspected. Following clinical examination and X-rays, three specialists, the clinician at Accident & Emergency, an orthopaedic registrar, and the consultant radiologist, decided there was no fracture and considered the X-rays to be normal.

The girl rejoined her school party, but did not ski and later returned home. The pain in her hip became increasingly severe and sadly a subsequent X-ray showed severe osteonecrosis of the femoral head. Review of the original X-ray showed that a slipped femoral epiphysis had been missed.

An action was raised against the consultant radiologist and the Health Board, claiming negligence in failing to make the diagnosis. The claimant called two distinguished orthopaedic surgeons as expert witnesses and the defence called a consultant radiologist. While the experts all agreed, with the benefit of hindsight, the original X-ray showed a slipped femoral epiphysis, opinions then differed quite markedly. The orthopaedic surgeons took the view that even quite junior orthopaedic trainees would be expected to observe this minimal displacement and that any orthopaedic registrar missing such a lesion, "would be sacked"! They also implied that, when interpreting bone radiographs, orthopaedic surgeons were every bit as good, or even better, than radiologists.

The radiologist on the other hand, said that, although evident in hindsight, this sort of minimal abnormality could easily be overlooked and he pointed out that picking it up at the time of the original report would be a, "Good Spot". Observer error is a recognised problem when reporting large numbers of Accident & Emergency X-rays, where most are normal. The case was successfully defended. The judge took the view that a consultant general radiologist was better placed than a consultant orthopaedic surgeon to say what another competent and diligent consultant general radiologist would or would not observe. The judge also commented that neither of the two expert witnesses called by the claimant was a radiologist.

Bernhard S ALBINUS
(1697-1770)
Fourth Order of the Muscles 1749
Plate IV from *Tables of the Skeleton and Muscles of the Human Body*
Special Collections Department, Glasgow University Library

The artist Jan Wandelaar collaborated with Albinus on the original 28 plates for the *Tables*. It was his idea to place the skeletons in a landscape. The female rhinoceros in Plate IV was studied by Albinus in 1742. This pirated edition, with plates by Charles Grignon, appeared in London two years after its first publication in Leiden in 1747.

Radiologists can easily miss minimal abnormalities on X-rays, which are often obvious with hindsight and many authoritative papers report failure to detect small radiological abnormalities in the lungs and bones. Such observer error is a human factor and is accepted as a real problem. Dr Oscar Craig, in his 1989 Knox lecture to the Royal College of Radiologists, reviewed a survey of three hundred and sixty cases. Analysis showed that 78% concerned skeletal trauma and missed fractures and dislocations. The most common involved the cervical spine, the scaphoid and the neck of the femur. Fractures of the scaphoid can be easily missed, frequently leading to litigation. Craig described the scaphoid as, "the most expensive bone in the body" [Craig 1997]. Missed dislocations commonly involve the tarsus, the carpus and posterior dislocation of the shoulder. Dr John K. (Jake) Davidson (Consultant Radiologist) and Mr Jimmy Graham (Consultant Orthopaedic Surgeon) found a similar pattern in an MDDUS review of one hundred and twenty seven accident and emergency cases between 1981 and 1985.

The most serious and indeed most expensive cases have involved missed fractures of the cervical spine, which can result in a disastrous paraplegia. Good quality radiographs, which define all seven cervical vertebrae, are absolutely vital and many cases have frequently required computed tomography and other studies to define fractures and dislocations. Other recurring errors have involved trauma to soft tissues, where a failure to X-ray may lead to the non-detection of foreign bodies, including glass, in the eye. An increasingly common cause of litigation is the missed early breast carcinoma, by the misinterpretation of a mammogram. In chest X-rays, a hilar mass or a collapsed lung can be overlooked and, even when reported, there may be a failure to suggest further imaging studies.

Modern Imaging

Since Röntgen's discovery, the specialty has steadily developed with a wide range of sophisticated imaging techniques - angiography, interventional radiology, ultrasound, nuclear medicine, magnetic resonance imaging and computed tomography, in which two scientists, Allan Cormack and Sir Geoffrey Hounsfield, shared a 1979 Nobel Prize for its practical invention.

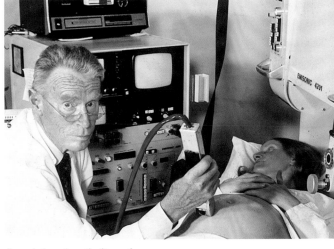

Dr Ian Donald
conducting an ultrasound scan on his prospective grandchild.
Dr J. K. Davidson

In the late 1960s, Ian Donald, Professor of Obstetrics in Glasgow, was very much the driving force in the clinical application of ultrasound. The early images were poor but Donald, ridiculed by his colleagues, persisted with his brilliant work. With considerable foresight he believed ultrasound's future lay in the wider field of radiology. In this he was ably supported by Dr John K. (Jake) Davidson, Head of the Department of Radiology at the Glasgow Western Infirmary. So began an innovative association between the two specialties, in which Dr Pat Morley also played a leading part.

John Mallard, Professor of Medical Physics in Aberdeen, began the work that ultimately led to magnetic resonance imaging, in the early 1960s. He used electron magnetic resonance to study normal and malignant tissue samples. It was found that tumours gave different signals from normal tissues, which meant that, if the team could form images from the signals, they might "see" the tumours by an imaging contrast. In March 1974, the team succeeded in obtaining the first ever image of a whole mouse, showing some perceivable anatomy. This was the starting pistol for a race to make imaging work between six teams, four in the UK and two in the USA.

The Aberdeen team spent a year obtaining a grant of £30,000 from the Medical Research Council and then set to work for the next five years. It was not until the spring of 1980 that a breakthrough was accomplished and the first patient was imaged under the care of Dr F.W. Smith, in August that year. The discovery created enormous interest and companies began to spend millions of dollars a year on research and development. By 1985 there were hundreds of MRI units in use in the USA, Japan and Germany, while in the UK there were fewer than ten! Professor Mallard has received many international awards for his work, most recently Honorary Membership of the British Institute of Radiology.

The Aberdeen Magnetic Resonance Imager 1979-1980
The magnetic field was provided by the four black horizontal coils. The radio frequency and field gradient coils were wound around the circular former within which the patient lay. The patient in the photograph is Dr J.M.D. Hutchison, one of the main designers.
Professor John Mallard

Non-ionising radiation, e.g., ultrasound and magnetic resonance, is generally reckoned to be safer than ionising radiation. There remains concern, especially in some consumer groups, that we have still to see the deleterious effects of these imaging methods, especially as it is known that such effects can skip generations. Scientific evidence of effects exists at high dose levels for both, but not at levels used in diagnostic work.

Modern Radiology

Digital Imaging is a recent method of handling and archiving images, often known as PACS, Picture Archiving and Communication Systems. The quality and interrogation of digital X-ray images have distinct medico-legal implications, especially the degree of manipulation, both possible and necessary. Storage in many ways will become easier, but with the vast number of images that are obtained in some procedures, for example cardiac catheter studies, it may in fact prove necessary to store such images off-line, or only keep selected views on the PACS system. In Angiography and Interventional Radiology, procedural problems can occur such as, post-angiography thrombosis, embolism or haemorrhage and adverse reactions to the contrast medium can be fatal. Thankfully with the improvement in contrast media over the last few years, these are now quite rare.

Interventional Radiology is relatively new and has enjoyed remarkable success, managing abdominal and thoracic aneurysms, draining abscesses, controlling bleeding, etc., under X-ray control by precise injection of clotting material, balloon dilation, etc. Stent placement is rapidly finding its place in the treatment of strictures, both in vessels and the gastrointestinal tract. This is very much a high-risk area, in which impeccable techniques and well-trained radiologists are of fundamental importance. Serious complications can occur; metal guide wires and catheter tips may break and become lodged in various organs; vessels can haemorrhage, rupture or thrombose; stents can migrate or become blocked. Thus a new radiologist-patient relationship is required in which informed consent is of fundamental importance [Allison 1997]. Not only does the doctor require a full understanding of the risks to the patient and that the patient understands these risks, but also the doctor has a duty to minimise risks to him or herself and other staff. This is an area that could become a source of litigation for the future.

The NHS Breast Screening Programme

The volatile balance between the benefits of medical scientific procedures, patient expectation and the threat of litigation is very evident in the screening programme for breast cancer. Breast cancer is the most common cancer to affect women in the UK, excluding skin cancers and remains a high profile feature of medical litigation. Each year, there are approximately 24,000 new cases and about 15,000 deaths from the disease. It is the cause of 25% of female cancer deaths. It is rare before the age of 25 years, increases steadily to age 50, tends to slow slightly until 65, but then the increase in risk with age is resumed. This biphasic effect is typical of countries at high-risk and is thought to be due to hormonal changes around the menopause.

There is considerable variation in breast cancer incidence throughout the world, which is at least partly related to affluence. It is most common among the American white population and among northern Europeans. England and Wales are marginally lower than Scotland and the lifetime risk, to age 80, of a woman in the UK is of the order of 1 in 10. Mortality is also high in the UK. This is in contrast to Asian populations, such as Japan.

Evidence had been accumulating from various trials that screening for breast cancer by mammography could improve mortality from the disease. Foremost amongst the papers published in the 1970s was that of Shapiro and colleagues, who initiated the New York Health Improvement Plan study in 1963, a randomised controlled study offering annual mammography and clinical examination for four years to 31,000 women aged 40-64 years, whilst a further 31,000 served as controls. A clear survival advantage was demonstrated in screened women especially for those with impalpable lesions.

The Swedish Two Counties Trial recruited from 1977-1981 and was a randomised control study of 163,000 women over forty years of age resident in Kopparberg and Östergotland counties. In Kopparberg, women were randomly allocated to screening with two controls; in Östergotland, each had one control. Early results indicated an improvement in mortality of 31% amongst women offered screening in the 40-74 year age group, especially those over fifty years of age. The design of the Two Counties trial was so robust and the results so convincing that the study remains the gold standard of what can be achieved by screening. The first results of the trial were published in *The Lancet* in 1985.

In the UK, a trial of the early detection and treatment of breast cancer was a multi-centre trial of mammography, clinical examination and breast self-examination. Edinburgh contributed a randomised control arm to this trial, which would eventually add confirmation that mammography was a suitable and reliable method for screening the breast. This trial led to the Forrest Committee Report of 1987, which had been commissioned by the Government in 1985. The Committee considered that there was sufficient evidence to recommend national screening by mammography.

Introduction of Screening

In late 1987, a rolling programme to introduce screening throughout the UK began. At the time, only about one third of health authorities had mammography facilities, while expertise in taking, and the interpretation of, mammograms was limited. An extensive recruiting and training programme had to be introduced. During the time the programme was designed, screening centres with their attendant mobile mammography units were set up and a comprehensive quality assurance programme was put in place. The programme became fully operational in 1991 and by 1994 all eligible women had been invited to take part [Table 11.1]. There are now about one hundred individual screening programmes throughout the UK and there are plans to extend the age of invitation for women from 65 to 70 years, which should be in place by 2004.

Table 11.1

UK Screening Activity 1998/99		
Women Invited	Women Screened	Cancers Detected
1,699,727	1,290,126	8,771
		(6.24 per 1,000 screened)

In the foreseeable future, there will be a general shortage of radiologists, especially those wishing to take up mammography. One explanation for this unwillingness is the spectre of litigation if abnormalities are missed or misdiagnosed. In a recent survey, more than 70% of radiologists involved in breast screening said they were concerned or very concerned about litigation, as opposed to 9% involved in general radiological work.

A Helping Hand

Prior to the start of the NHS, hospitals depended to a great extent on voluntary donations from charitable funds and the fund-raising efforts of celebrities. Among these was Sir Harry Lauder, who raised funds for a new X-ray room in a hospital. Sir Harry was invited to open this new facility and agreed to undergo the first X-ray, by having his hand X-rayed. He signed the radiograph.

Sir Harry was immensely popular, during the First and Second World Wars. He performed for frontline troops and in hospitals. He lost his only son, Captain John Lauder of the Argyll and Sutherland Highlanders, killed in action in 1916. He raised £1 million, a very considerable sum in these days, to found the Harry Lauder Fund for disabled war servicemen.

Sir Harry was a great favourite of Winston Churchill, for whom his songs were the utmost inspiration. As a young schoolboy, Dr John (Jake) Davidson was present at Edinburgh's Usher Hall when Winston Churchill received the Freedom of the City in 1942, after the fall of Singapore. At the ceremony, Sir Harry gave a rousing performance of Chuchill's favourite songs.

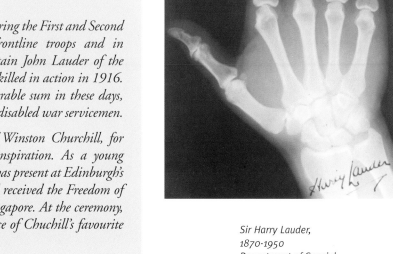

Sir Harry Lauder, 1870-1950 Department of Special Collections (Jimmy Logan Theatre Collections)

Glasgow University Library

Sport and Exercise Medicine

From Volunteer to Specialist

Over the last ten to fifteen years of the 20th century, sport has become increasingly commercial and competitive and has attracted growing public attention, which is fuelled by frequently speculative media coverage of events and individuals. The intrusion of sponsorship, as well as financial inducements into sport, has also raised many complex ethical issues in which the doctor may find himself or herself playing a central role. Issues such as consent, confidentiality and the doctor/patient relationship have come under increasing professional as well as public pressure in this process. It is hardly surprising therefore that the emerging specialty of Sports Medicine has had to ensure a sound professional, ethical and medico-legal basis for its practice.

The medical and dental professions have always enjoyed a close affinity with sport. This link has traditionally been established at university, where medical and dental students have participated in a wide range of sporting activities. Following graduation, doctors tend to drift between sports until they find one that suits their professional commitments and interests. Alternatively, many doctors volunteer to provide "touchline" medical support to maintain a link with their former teammates, the club of which they were members and the sport they enjoyed. Doctors, who turn out to support their children participating in sport at school or in a club, may also provide touchline medical support. These volunteer touchline doctors will come from a wide range of clinical backgrounds and the majority will have had little or no recent experience of first aid, or the management of the likely injuries or illnesses that can occur during the sporting activity. Accordingly, volunteer touchline doctors are frequently in the very difficult position of going along to a sporting event for the fun of the occasion or to support a family member, while at the same time a host club or venue expects them to provide medical services almost on a "Good Samaritan" basis.

Opposite:

Dr Stephanie Cook M.B.E.
Gold Medallist Women's
Modern Pentathalon
Sydney Olympic Games
2000

Gautier Deblonde

The doctor who is invited by an employer, school or other organisation to undertake pre-employment/pre-participation medical examinations on a professional or amateur sportsman/woman/child must ensure that they

School rugby
Glasgow High School

Dr Rob Hendry

follow a standardised approach. The medical should include a detailed examination of the musculo-skeletal system, which is appropriate to the particular sport. Some doctors delegate this assessment to a suitably experienced physiotherapist, especially if their experience of musculo-skeletal assessment is not great. Careful documentation of the history and examination as well as further investigations or requests for a specialist second opinion must be clearly documented. In professional sport, the doctor's opinion may influence multi-million pound contracts as well as players' insurance requirements. A high standard of medical examination can also work to the benefit of the athlete by identifying treatable, potentially lethal, or disabling conditions such as anaemia, exercise-induced asthma, a cardiac abnormality, or an unstable joint. Recent examples in international football include diagnosis of a defective aortic valve in an international football player as part of his pre-employment contract with Inter Milan, one of the major clubs of Italian and international football. The player subsequently underwent open-heart surgery and returned to international football a year later. In another situation, Manchester United delayed signing a player for a year while he received treatment for an unstable knee at his parent club and regained full fitness.

Standards

Civil law protects society against poor clinical standards on the basis of "probability" rather than applying the test for criminal law, which is "beyond all reasonable doubt". Liability in any given case will be judged by the standards applicable to that specialty and the level of knowledge at the time the incident occurred. In current legal practice, duty of care is defined as, "the standard of the ordinary skilled man or woman exercising and professing to have that special skill." This standard of care requires doctors professing expertise or providing services in Sport and Exercise Medicine to be able to demonstrate their competence by ensuring that they are well trained and are maintaining their professional development and continuing medical education in what is a rapidly developing specialist field of knowledge.

The doctor involved in Sport and Exercise Medicine is subject to the standards set by the GMC, outlined in their many recent directives covering the duties of a doctor, including maintaining good medical practice, confidentiality, ethics and the prescribing of performance-enhancing drugs. These standards apply to all aspects of NHS, private, and voluntary clinical practice and therefore to paid or unpaid contributions by a doctor practising Sport and Exercise Medicine. Participants in sport or exercise are not patients on whom doctors can try out "little experiments", neither are they patients who can be offered second-class standards of care. Evidence-based medicine applies to sport and exercise.

Doctors in sport can sometimes find themselves in conflict with their athletes, who are prepared to risk everything to overcome injury, train harder and improve their performance. Athletes are susceptible to every rumour or advert about new treatment options, dietary supplements - especially vitamins and minerals, and performance-enhancing gimmicks or magic formulae. Athletes frequently need to be protected from themselves, their coaches and their sponsors. Any doctor trying to persuade an international rugby forward that a balanced diet based on 60% carbohydrate with five or more daily portions of fruit and vegetable, excluding alcohol, the frying pan and T-bone steaks will have to present a very convincing case! Trust between the athlete and doctor is essential before the athlete will respect advice about diet and lifestyle.

Other spheres of clinical practice in which there has been increasing recent interest are the prescription of exercise for rehabilitation following injury or illness, as well as the recommendation of exercise programmes to enhance health. Sport invariably involves training and competition with an associated risk of injury or illness. The promotion of exercise for rehabilitation and health should be prescribed in such a manner that it is free of any risk to the patient or individual concerned, irrespective of their current state of health, whether they are able-bodied, disabled, or have learning disabilities.

The standards of clinical and ethical practice applied to Sports and Exercise Medicine do not vary from the standards relating to any other field of medical endeavour. Any breach in the application of these well-established clinical standards will be measured against a series of clearly defined medico-legal principles:

* That there has been a duty of care between the doctor and injured party,
* That a breach of that duty of care occurred,
* That the breach of care caused harm and that harm was reasonably foreseeable.

The "Good Samaritan" act undertaken by a doctor spectating at an event to which he or she was not invited with a view to providing any form of medical care, is a straightforward provision of a duty of care on the basis of first aid similar to a doctor attending a patient taken ill or being injured on a flight, or at an accident. In these circumstances the doctor is advised to err on the side of caution particularly if recommending the athlete to return to the event after, for example, an apparently minor head knock or joint sprain. The injured athlete is always liable to a more serious second injury.

The doctor/patient relationship, which is based on an activity, event, or venue rather than within the more traditional NHS, private or specialist clinic, is akin to the provision of Occupational Health Medicine services for exercisers or sports participants, or circumstances that apply when dealing with special groups, e.g., expeditions or the Armed Forces. These relationships involve third parties where consent and confidentiality should be agreed prior to the event, with the coach, employers or sponsors. Maintaining confidentiality in high profile sport can be a challenge particularly with live television and microphones at the touchline creating and feeding the constant public interest through the media.

> ### Case Study – Sports Medicine
>
> *A 21-year-old professional footballer employed by an English First Division team was referred by the club physiotherapist to a consultant general and vascular surgeon. Prior to the referral, the footballer had complained intermittently, for some eighteen months, of calf pain on exercise. He was seen and treated privately by the surgeon, in conjunction with a consultant radiologist. He was noted to have a lack of peripheral pulses below the femoral pulse on the affected side and was investigated by means of arteriography. This showed occlusion of the popliteal artery at the level of the knee with associated occlusion of the origins of the anterior tibial, peroneal and posterior tibial arteries.*
>
> *The decision was taken to proceed to pulse spray thrombolysis and balloon angioplasty. The initial angioplasty was unsuccessful and a further angioplasty was carried out, which caused a rupture in the tibial artery requiring vein patch repair. Although the patient's symptoms initially improved, they recurred some months after surgery. At that point, the patient was told he had no future as a professional footballer and that further surgery would not be helpful.*
>
> *The patient issued claims against the football club, the surgeon and the radiologist. The claim against the club failed and an appeal was unsuccessful. The unexpected dismissal of the claimant's case against the football club left a costly situation.*
>
> *The claim was continued against the clinicians. There was a considerable variation in expert opinion as to what extent his*

treatment may have failed, either to alleviate, or indeed exacerbate, his condition. The MDDUS experts held that there was no breach of duty of care and, that on the balance of probabilities, his condition from the outset was such that he would not have been able to continue a career as a footballer without treatment. However, there were sufficient differences of opinion among the experts, related to the clinical findings, the choice of treatment and causation arguments, for defence Counsel to have advised that there were significant litigation risks.

Following considerable consultation in conference with experts and Counsel it was decided to seek a settlement out of court without admission of liability. £270,000 was paid in settlement and the claimant's legal costs amounted to £300,000. The case from start to finish lasted six years.

Accountability

It is essential that doctors do not allow third parties to influence their opinion on player/patient management. Doctors should carefully document any medical advice that is given, bearing in mind that the player/patient or their employers may, for whatever reason, choose to disregard medical advice. Doctors cannot just shrug their shoulders, because they may be held accountable some time in the future. Many doctors in Sport and Exercise Medicine believe they can remain aloof from these pressures by providing an honorary or unpaid service. This is not the case. Any doctor who accepts an invitation to attend and provide clinical or advisory services to a sports body, event, team or individual has immediately acknowledged that he or she is providing a duty of care. The unpaid doctor should also remember that any gift such as a uniform, equipment, tickets, or a privilege such as car parking or hospitality, could be interpreted as a contract with financial implications.

In order to perform at the highest level successfully and consistently, elite and professional athletes push their bodies to their physical limits, and frequently train and compete knowing they carry injuries. They constantly take risks with their health and engage in activities that, in later life, may cause ill health such as degenerative change in a heavily worked joint. They are almost routinely required to weigh up the potential risks to their health, their ability to perform despite injury, against the possible personal, social and financial gain. An athlete's career in most disciplines is very short and the chance to prove one's ability at the highest level, e.g. the Olympics, may only happen once in a lifetime. The personal sacrifices individuals will make to reach this level are enormous. It is in this context that the decision to recommend that an athlete withdraws from competition is made.

If an injury is not severe enough to prevent competition, but could potentially cause permanent damage, e.g., a runner with a tibial stress fracture, the doctor and athlete must make a decision based on the athlete's full knowledge of the potential consequences of competing, independent of the pressure of coaches, team mates and family. This decision is important for the doctor because he or she may then be required to "collude" with the decision to compete, by considering whether the provision of pain-killing injections or medicine is ethical. Needless to say, the circumstances must be well documented.

Sports physicians frequently debate rights and wrongs in this grey area and an individual case can rarely be decided on the basis of exact precedent. A prior established relationship with the athlete and coach might help to make a decision satisfactory to all. Involvement of the athlete's customary physiotherapist or doctor may also be valuable. Although one has to accept that at the elite level such decisions are commonplace, this should not lead the doctor to lose perspective and regard sporting glory as more important that the individual athlete's welfare, particularly in a team situation.

Safe Approaches

Any doctor, who has agreed to participate with a particular sport team event, whether on a one-off or continuing basis, must establish a safe approach at an appropriate standard equivalent to NHS, private, or specialist clinical practice. The doctor's first priority is to establish and maintain medical records. In addition, the doctor should:

- Know the rules of the game and the associated injury or illness pattern
- Clarify relationships with the players, management, the media, sponsors
- Clarify responsibilities for crowd control and drug testing
- Establish a good record system, which will range from pre-participation medicals to documentation of injury or illness and rehabilitation programmes
- Identify and minimise risks such as in the climatic or playing environment
- Ensure that appropriately qualified, experienced and insured personnel, as well as suitable facilities, are available for treatment and support, to facilitate the saving of life and limb, first aid, rescue and transport to hospital
- Ensure appropriate and reliable communications are available
- Prepare in professional terms for responsibilities equivalent to an appointment in an A & E Department compounded by

dealing with a physically and psychologically demanding industry, i.e. sport

- Ensure a competency at cardio-pulmonary resuscitation

- Join an appropriate specialty association and attend the relevant training programmes

- Undertake an audit of clinical practice, reviewing medical records and assessing them against evidence-based medicine standards

- Participate in research and consider taking higher training in the form of a diploma or degree

- Ensure adequate insurance, particularly if not a General Practitioner

- Non-General Practitioner doctors should be supported by their medical defence organisation

The General Medical Council has also recently supported worldwide efforts to reduce the abuse of drugs in sport by issuing a statement confirming that they would consider any doctor, identified as having promoted the use of performance-enhancing drugs in sport, to have breached the ethical standards laid down by the General Medical Council and the individual would therefore be liable to disciplinary proceedings.

The difficulty arises where an athlete tells a doctor in confidence about the use of a banned substance. The doctor is in danger of breaching ethical standards, whether he or she informs the authorities and therefore breaches confidentiality, or keeps the patient's confidence,

International Ladies Hockey, Scotland v Argentina

SNS Group

implicitly condoning or supporting the athlete's actions. There is no straightforward answer to this, but doctors who feel strongly one way or the other should consider making this position clear in advance to athletes and support staff in their care. In reality, this position rarely occurs and an athlete who confides in a doctor can often then be persuaded that the best course of action is to "come clean" or stop the use of banned drugs, particularly once the full implications of their actions have been discussed. Any doctor in need of guidance should consider discussing the position with another experienced sports health professional, such as a senior sports physician or sports psychologist.

Any doctor involved in the care of competitive adult sport should be familiar with doping control regulations. Even at quite a low amateur level, testing occurs and penalties for positive tests are potentially harsh. A number of "over the counter" medicines, herbal preparations and dietary supplements contain banned substances. If an athlete unwittingly takes these, this does not form an acceptable defence in the event of a positive test. Details of all IOC doping classes and banned or restricted substances are available from UK Sport. Some sports have individual variations in their list, to include sport-specific, performance-enhancing drugs. The doctor should be aware of these differences and team doctors should regard educating athletes on this subject as part of their role. On a practical note, it is sometimes easier to provide a limited list of acceptable drugs for common complaints such as sore throat, headache etc., than explain the various drug categories, or list the hundreds of banned drugs.

In addition to doping classes, the doctor, particularly in elite sport, must be familiar with the procedure by which a urine, or blood sample for dope-testing is obtained. The doctor, or, in his or her absence, the coach or physiotherapist, will usually take the role of "accompanying official", staying with the athlete to provide support during testing. The procedure by which sampling officers handle the test is very carefully laid out to prevent tampering and no departure from this protocol should be accepted. Any failure to follow procedure may form the basis of an appeal on behalf of the athlete, should the sample test positive. The accompanying official should note and point out any irregularities and either document these on the sampling form, or refuse to sign that part of the form, which confirms that all parties are happy with the test procedure. Doctors involved in sports where ergogenic aids could be in use should be familiar with those substances most likely to be abused and their potential adverse effects. This can help with informing and educating athletes and understanding the significance of related medical signs or symptoms, should they occur.

Gymnastics

SNS Group

Ethical guidelines for doctors involved in Sport and Exercise Medicine have been published by the World Medical Authority, the Medical Commission of the International Olympic Committee and the Fédération Internationale de Médecine du Sport. Doctors practising Sport and Exercise Medicine would need to be aware of these guidelines.

Regrettably, the guidelines rarely specifically direct the doctor to promote the prevention of illness or injury by encouraging audit and research, the identification of persistent offenders, or harmful patterns of training and play that can occur, particularly in contact sport. In addition, very little guidance is given to the identification of suitable activities in sport or exercise for children and individuals with learning difficulties, handicap or disabilities.

In the United Kingdom and Ireland, the Specialist Training Authority, the Joint Committee for Postgraduate General Practice Training and the Academy of Medical Royal Colleges set standards of medical practice. The Academy of Medical Royal Colleges established, in 1998, the Intercollegiate Academic Board for Sport and Exercise Medicine. This Board has been given the responsibility of approving basic and higher specialty training programmes in Sport and Exercise Medicine. A number of universities have also developed higher degree courses, which can be undertaken on a full-time, part-time or distance-learning basis. Doctors involved in this developing specialty would be well advised to join a relevant specialty association such as the British Association of Sport and Exercise Medicine, which was established in 1953 by Lord Arthur Porritt and Sir Adolphe Abraham, both previous Olympic athletes. The Scottish Committee of BASEM was set up in 1964 and has subsequently held major international congresses in 1986 (Gleneagles) and 1998 (Peebles).

Guidelines

The doctor in sport will face many dilemmas with regard to the delegation of authority. This situation may arise because of involvement of a doctor in the training grades who offers his or her services. This individual doctor's experience and insurance must be reviewed before any form of delegation can take place. Delegation of authority by a doctor to members of the professions allied to medicine, such as Chartered Physiotherapists, should again be based on knowledge of the individual's professional qualifications, experience and insurance status.

Doctors should be aware that the qualifications of some individuals, who typically providing para-medical support, such as masseurs, are not standardised or well-regulated. In addition, the name "physiotherapist" is not protected and can be used by anyone. Only a chartered physiotherapist (MCSP) will have completed the full four-year graduate course. Courses for other therapists vary from several years to several

Husky team training
Sled Dog Racing is one of the fastest growing sports in the UK. Keith Johnson is currently the United Kingdom Sled-dog Champion in the four-dog class and has held the Scottish Championship title for two years. He uses a variety of breeds in his dog team, Siberian Huskies, Cumbrian Trail Hounds and German short-haired Pointers. British 'mushers' are now able to compete abroad using their own dogs, now that the quarantine regulations have been changed.

Dr George Fernie

days. It is conversely the case, that many newly qualified chartered physiotherapists have very little experience of work in sport and although this does not strictly present a legal risk, it should be borne in mind when delegating decision-making to an individual. Doctors should also investigate the implications of delegating responsibility for care of athletes abroad, to doctors either from the UK or, who are based locally. The differences in medical defence cover and liability between countries need to be clarified.

Concerns

Following the Hillsborough disaster, the definition of the role of the Crowd Doctor significantly advanced the concept of improved safety for spectators. The responsibilities undertaken by a Crowd Doctor at a venue and the relationship between the Crowd Doctor and the Police, First Aid and Ambulance services are sufficiently complex for the doctor concerned to require specialist training. However, it is important to stress that the role of Crowd Doctor is not the same as that of the Team Doctor and both roles should not be combined, as has sometimes been the case in the past.

The Michael Watson v British Boxing Board of Control court case and subsequent legal appeal has established the principle that the governing bodies of sport are responsible for ensuring the safety of participants in potentially dangerous sporting activities. Accordingly, there is a need for governing bodies in sport and their medical advisers to undertake research into significant injuries or illnesses arising during their particular sport, to help establish safety guidelines for the future.

A further area of concern in sport that has recently been highlighted is the abuse of children and young adults in sport and exercise by both over-training and sexual exploitation. Every doctor must be alert to these potential problems.

Opportunities

Opportunities and responsibilities now exist for doctors to seek full or part-time professional employment specialising or sub-specialising in Sport and Exercise Medicine. The British Medical Association has recently published a booklet entitled, *Doctors' Assistance to Sports Clubs and Sporting Events*, giving advice on the responsibilities of doctors participating in Sport and Exercise Medicine. It is not inconceivable that doctors of the future will be able to work as fully trained NHS specialists in Sport and Exercise Medicine, based in hospital or community medicine, as well as in primary care or the private sector. The Government has recently developed a series of UK national and regional Institutes of Sport, which will seek to employ highly qualified doctors with a significant experience in Sport and Exercise Medicine. In addition, professional sports organisations and clubs will also expect the highest standards from their medical staff. The journey by doctors from amateur to professional, from volunteer to specialist, continues to gain a momentum to the benefit of the public, patients and sports participants.

Doctors in Sport and Exercise Medicine can enjoy stimulating, challenging and fun professional opportunities. The doctor in sport must "prepare for performance" as conscientiously as any athlete striving for excellence, or any exerciser striving to improve their physical fitness. The job satisfaction is brilliant when you see the disabled participating, the frail walking, the young and old exercising, and the athlete achieving.

Dame Barbara HEPWORTH
(1903-1975)
Concourse   1948
Oil on wood
Reproduced by kind permission of the
President and Council of the Royal College of
Surgeons of England

In 1947 the sculptor Barbara Hepworth began a
series of drawings and paintings inspired by visits to
operating theatres in Exeter and London hospitals.
Concourse was painted for her friend, the
orthopaedic surgeon Norman Capener, who had
operated on her daughter. Hepworth depicts herself
sketching on the extreme left of the composition.

Plastic Surgery

Introduction

Plastic surgery has evolved over the years to include the rapid growth and popularity of cosmetic surgery. In this field, operations are performed purely for the sake of appearance, often for perceived deformities, which are really within the limits of normal. Patient expectation of success is counter-balanced by the limitations of technique and the fact that no surgical operation is without some risk. If patient satisfaction is not realised, the surgeon is quite likely to become subject to litigation. The result is that this type of surgery features prominently on the list of high-risk specialties.

The term plastic surgery was introduced by the German surgeon Eduard Zeis in 1838 after careful consideration of a number of different terms, which were being used. He defined it as, "That part of surgery which is concerned with the living replacement of missing parts" [Zeis 1838]. At that time, this implied using the looseness or elasticity of the skin, which would enable a piece of skin to be freed by one or more incisions still retaining a blood supply and then be transferred to a nearby defect. Study of the literature around Zeis' time showed that this definition applied precisely to the many operations performed, mostly on the face, and which are frequently described in the surgical literature of the first half of the 19th century.

Historical Background

Accounts of such procedures can be found many years before the 19th century and most were concerned with partial or complete loss of the nose. Three thousand years ago the Indian surgeon, Susruta, repaired these defects by transferring flaps from the cheek or the forehead [Gupta 1835-36]. Later, in the 15th and 16th centuries, Italian surgeons, Branca and Tagliacozzi, repaired noses by flaps taken from the upper arm. In this technique, the arm had to be strapped to the head until the flap had healed on the nasal defect and after about three or four weeks it could be detached from the arm. However, these operations seem to have been performed less and less frequently and, in the 19th century, few of such operations seem to have been carried out.

The early 1800s brought a great increase in the number of operations, which fitted entirely into Zeis' classification. German surgeons, Graefe and Diffenbach, were the most prominent followed by the French surgeons, Delpech, Roux and Nélaton. In England, Joseph Carpue described three cases of repair of noses by the Susruta method, but otherwise, there seems to have been little interest in the United Kingdom. What does seem quite extraordinary is the number of these operations performed at a time when neither anaesthesia nor antiseptics were available. Langenbeck even operated on a cleft palate.

Some surgeons, for example Dupuytren, advised against such operations because of the high risks and danger of complications, even death, presumably mostly from infections. The introduction of anaesthesia in the 1850s immediately increased the number of operations, which could be performed but the risk of infection after operations persisted until the introduction of antiseptics by Lister in Glasgow in 1865, and of asepsis by Macewen, also in Glasgow, in 1879, made it possible to operate with the expectations of healing without infection.

It was about this time that the development of free skin grafting, taking a piece of skin completely freed from the body and applying it to a raw area, was successfully accomplished. It was Reverdin, a young intern in a Paris hospital in 1869, who showed that it was possible to transplant pieces of skin by free transfer if they were small and thin [Reverdin 1869]. These small pieces of skin would survive and from them epithelium would grow out to resurface the whole area. His grafts were taken by lifting upwards a tiny cone of skin with the point of a needle and cutting off the apex with a scalpel. He originally described these as epidermic grafts, but in fact it is impossible to cut a graft of epidermis only, by such a method; these grafts always contained some dermis. The idea was to use multiple small grafts that were scattered on the raw area, rather like spreading seed on a surface to make a lawn. Later, it was shown that it was possible to take a thin shaving of skin with a razor and cut this into small pieces, which were scattered on the raw area with the same result. This technique caused less damage to the donor area.

Some time afterwards, Thiersch demonstrated that it was not only possible to transfer small grafts successfully, but that a large thin sheet of the partial thickness of the skin could be cut off using a long straight razor and that this could be applied to a raw area, to which it would adhere and be incorporated in a permanent cover; in other words, the graft would "take" [Thiersch 1874; 1886]. Also, the donor area would heal spontaneously and leave little deformity. This technique of split skin grafting was a major advance and greatly improved the treatment of large areas of skin loss, such as burns, but for various reasons, it did not realise its full potential until many years later.

A few years after these events, in 1875, Wolfe, an ophthalmic surgeon, who was working in Glasgow after a period in Aberdeen, showed that as long as all fat was carefully removed from the deep surface of an intact piece of skin it could be transferred as a free skin graft and would survive [Wolfe 1875]. This graft had the advantage that it did not contract in the same way as split thickness grafts, but it had the disadvantage that it created a defect at the donor site, the same size as the original defect. Wolfe took his original grafts for eyelids from the upper arm, where the skin was loose enough for the defect to be closed by suture. Subsequently, the grafts were taken from the cranial surface of the pinna, because the defect could be closed by suture at the expense only of making the post auricular sulcus more shallow. It had the additional advantage that the skin of the graft was thin and supple and was a good match to the eyelid skin.

Advances

By the end of the 19th century, advances in anaesthesia and asepsis had made it possible for surgeons in general to extend the scope of their activities and, at this time, most of their efforts were directed to abdominal and orthopaedic surgery. Plastic surgery operations were largely ignored. Even the surgeons who had developed these techniques, such as Thiersch and Langenbeck, remained mostly occupied with general surgery and the plastic procedures formed only a small part of their practice.

It seems unfortunate that it should have taken the stimulus of a war for plastic surgery to develop as a separate speciality and to bring about rapid developments. The First World War was fought with many new weapons of much greater destructive power than any previous war and the medical services of the armies were soon faced with the problem of dealing with many men with severe facial wounds. No surgeon had any experience of treating these conditions. The British Army Medical Services, therefore, appointed a young Major called Harold Gillies to find out whatever knowledge was available from other surgeons working in the war zone and then to return to England to set up a department at the Cambridge Military Hospital at Aldershot. Gillies had previously been working in London as an ENT Surgeon.

It soon became obvious that the accommodation at Aldershot was insufficient for the number of patients and the department was then transferred to a separate hospital, the Queen's Hospital at Sidcup. This establishment grew ultimately to accommodate 1,000 patients, who were almost exclusively suffering from wounds of the face. Because these injuries frequently involved fractures of the jaw, it was necessary for Gillies to work in close cooperation with dental surgeons and, of these, King and Kelsey-Fry were particularly prominent.

Development of Techniques

The British team was later joined by surgeons from Canada, Australia and New Zealand and later, when the Americans entered the war, a group of American surgeons led by Vilray Blair, who had a particular influence on the development of free skin grafting when he returned to America after the end of the war. As a result of his experiences, Gillies published a book, which showed that, in addition to the local flaps of his predecessors, he now explored the use of transferring large flaps of tissue from the chest or abdomen in stepwise procedures [Gillies 1920].

At each step, one end of the flap being healed was secured by a large enough attachment to ensure an adequate blood supply. Most of the flap was sewn into a tube to eliminate the raw surface and was termed a tubed pedicle flap. Thus, a tubed flap from the abdomen could have one end attached to the wrist and when this was healed the flap could be separated from the abdomen and transferred, for instance, to the face and finally released from the wrist and spread out to cover the defect.

Gillies' pictures illustrated that wounds were initially allowed to heal spontaneously with the inevitable distortion caused by scar formation and that plastic surgery was then used to correct the deformity. The most important change that has taken place over the years is that plastic surgery is now used as part of the initial treatment of the wound, so that further damage is not allowed to occur and the deformity is minimised. This is particularly important in burns of the face. Gillies showed some of the earliest cases of pilots burned when their aircraft caught fire and the bad results which followed when early operation was not possible.

Intratracheal anaesthesia was an important development during this period and greatly increased the possibilities for plastic surgery. The endotracheal tube developed by McGill at Sidcup was so successful that, although it may have been refined, the general design is still retained in present day tubes. When the end of the war came, the majority of the surgeons who had been involved in this work felt that the techniques that had been developed were all very well for wartime practice, but had very little relevance to civilian practice. They therefore returned to the established specialties, abdominal surgery, orthopaedic surgery, ear nose and throat surgery and so on.

Surgical Skills

A much wider range of techniques was now available than those covered by the original definition of Zeis and a separate surgical discipline had been created, which was more properly entitled, "Plastic and Reconstructive Surgery". Gillies foresaw that these techniques had great application to many of the conditions seen in civilian practice; not only injuries of the face, but injuries of other parts of the body and also congenital deformities, cleft lip and palate, and the deformities created during the treatment of malignant disease. At the end of the war, Gillies was joined by a young surgeon, Thomas Pomfret Kilner. When they were demobilised, Gillies and Kilner, with McGill as Anaesthetist and Kelsey-Fry as Dental Surgeon, set up in practice in London. Gillies was knighted in 1920 and had an appointment at St Bartholomew's Hospital, Kilner at St Thomas's Hospital.

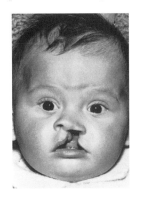 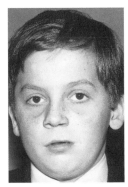

Cleft Lip and Palate Deformity
The left photo shows a child with complete unilateral cleft lip and palate. The lip was repaired at 3 months of age and the palate at 6 months. The right hand photo is the child aged 12 years old when the permanent teeth have erupted. Irregularity of incisor teeth and deformity of the nasal septum will need correction.

Mr Ian Muir

Kilner's contribution in the 1920s was particularly in the field of lip and palate surgery and his work and teaching greatly improved the treatment of these deformities in the whole of Britain and, indeed, has had great influence on practice up to the present day. Gillies and Kilner were joined in 1929 by Archibald McIndoe and, in 1930, by Rainsford Mowlem, both young New Zealanders, who had come to England to further their surgical training and had decided to stay on. These four worked closely in London, but also made visits to the large cities in the Midlands and the north, particularly Birmingham and Manchester. They formed the nucleus for the development of plastic surgery and virtually all the surgeons practising plastic surgery in the United Kingdom are either the pupils of one or other of these men, or pupils of their pupils.

In the London teaching hospitals, the tradition persisted for many years of the general surgeon who could do everything and although Gillies, Kilner and later McIndoe and Mowlem all had appointments to different teaching hospitals, the opportunity for them to operate as plastic surgeons in these hospitals was very limited. The London County Council, however, which was very far sighted, provided facilities, first at one hospital and then another and finally in St James's Hospital at Balham just south of the Thames, where they established not only a well-staffed Accident Department under William Gissane, but also a self-contained Plastic Surgery unit, which set the pattern for the plastic surgery units one sees in the United Kingdom today.

By the 1930s, when this unit was established, Kilner had largely broken away from the other three and the St James unit had Gillies, McIndoe and Mowlem on the staff. The three also worked together in private practice so that by the late 1930s they, working together and Kilner working independently, were the only four surgeons in Britain who confined their practice to plastic surgery. Visits of the four surgeons to the provincial areas made contacts with a number of younger surgeons who were interested to learn the techniques, so that in centres such as Newcastle, Manchester, Leeds and Birmingham a number of surgeons came to spend some of their time in plastic surgery, often covering only one field such as cleft lip or palate, but still carrying out general surgery as well. The future opportunities for full-time practice in plastic surgery appeared to be limited and few young surgeons were interested in taking up such a career full-time. It seems that even those who expressed interest in doing so were discouraged by the established experts who said that they could not see the need for any more full-time plastic surgeons.

When the Second World War broke out, there were in Britain the four fully trained plastic surgeons, a similar number of general surgeons with some plastic surgery experience and a few juniors in training. This time, with the experience of the previous war to guide them, the Government anticipated the necessity for plastic surgery services and, under the guidance of Gillies and Kelsey-Fry, the Ministry of Health sent each of the four to establish a plastic surgery centre within reach of, but at some distance from, London to avoid interruption by the expected air raids. Sir Harold Gillies went to Basingstoke, Kilner, temporarily to the Ministry of Pensions hospital at Roehampton and then to Stoke Mandeville Hospital at Aylesbury, McIndoe to East Grinstead and Mowlem to St Albans.

Only McIndoe's unit was a purpose-built unit, which had been set up by the Canadian Red Cross in 1939. The others were in rapidly adapted accommodation. The Gillies and Mowlem units were in mental hospitals, from which the original inhabitants had been evacuated. These units were to deal with military and civilian casualties and, in quiet periods, to treat the conditions that normally occur in civilian practice. It was an interesting feature of these units that, although they dealt to a large extent with service casualties, the senior surgeons never took military rank and remained civilians. They immediately started training military doctors who went back to establish units in the Army, Navy and Air Force, at home and abroad, for the initial treatment of battle casualties, particularly facial wounds and burns. McIndoe's unit became famous for its treatment of RAF aircrew, who had sustained burns when their aircraft caught fire. He showed how early plastic surgery was vital to preserve function and appearance.

Small units were also established in civilian hospitals, particularly those where a part-time surgeon had been working. Thus, units were established in England, in Gloucester, Newcastle and Manchester and later in Scotland, Bangour for Edinburgh and Ballochmyle for Glasgow. The actual accommodation was usually in single story hutted buildings, which were erected in 1939 and 1940 under the government's Emergency Medical Services scheme.

No great tradition of plastic surgery existed in Scotland, but there was extensive experience of burning injuries. In Glasgow, a separate burns ward had operated continuously since 1833 as part of a general surgical charge in the Royal Infirmary. Dunbar in 1933 wrote an excellent review of the activities of this ward over one hundred years [Dunbar 1934]. In the early 1940s, the Government became concerned about the number of burn injuries that occurred in the fighting in North Africa. These were caused by the ignited fuel of tanks and other vehicles and also in aircraft. They therefore asked the Medical Research Council to look into aspects of the future treatment of these burns and the Council decided to evaluate the use of two new substances, which had recently become available, human blood plasma for the treatment of burn shock and sulphanilamide for the control of streptococcal infection.

The Research Council assembled a team in 1942 to carry out research over a period of two years and to use the Glasgow burns unit for this purpose. Leonard Colebrook, the distinguished bacteriologist, led the team and a young surgeon, Thomas Gibson, was appointed to work full-time as the clinical member. The report of this work was published in 1945 and was a milestone in the treatment of burns [Medical Research Council 1945]. Gibson's findings of the way to use plasma to treat shock in burn patients were the foundation on which all subsequent work was based. His findings remain valid to this day. The use of sulphanilamide in dressings showed that streptococcal infection, which was rampant in burns wards in spite of antiseptics, could be controlled. When penicillin became available, this was used in the same way. It was later superseded by other antibacterial substances because, although penicillin remained active against streptococci, other organisms continued to cause trouble.

It was at this time that Gibson found it necessary to use grafts from the father of a badly burned child, on two separate occasions. It was not expected that the grafts would remain permanently, but it was noted that the second set of grafts were rejected more rapidly than the first. This became known as the second set reaction. Gibson reported these findings to Leonard Colebrook who thought that this was important enough to persuade the Research Council to send for Peter Medawar, who was then working on the problems of homo-graft rejection in Oxford. Medawar was convinced enough of the findings to repeat the observations in experimental animals and these led to the conclusions that the rejection was due to an immune reaction. Medawar's publication led to a Nobel Prize for him but Gibson appears to have had little recognition, although the original observations and probably the original hypothesis were undoubtedly his own.

171

Edinburgh

As in the English experience, the Government made early moves to provide plastic surgery services in Scotland, and in Edinburgh, they had a young surgeon who was ideally suited to lead a team. Alastair Wallace had spent time in Canada in research at McGill University, and, on his return to Edinburgh, he met and was much influenced by W. C. Wilson, who was

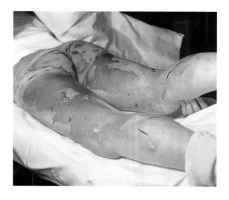

then senior lecturer in the Professorial Surgery Department, and had much experience with burned children in the Hospital for Sick Children. Wallace then spent some time at the Strangeways Laboratory in Cambridge and was encouraged to increase his interest in plastic surgery. He studied with Gillies, Kilner, McIndoe and Mowlem in the London area and was thus well suited to take the post as consultant when the Bangour unit, some miles west of Edinburgh, opened in 1941. Accommodation for adults was provided in the hutted hospital. Accommodation for children was provided at the Children's Hospital.

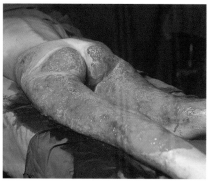

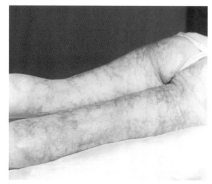

Wallace's achievements were twofold. He was able to analyse problems and set out the answers in a clear logical fashion, which could be easily understood and were of great value to people who were not managing large numbers of burns. His second, and perhaps his greatest contribution, was in the unsensational, but enormously important, work in the prevention of burns, particularly in children. In the 1950s and 1960s, it was rare in a burns unit not to have at least one and sometimes more girls, who had sustained severe burns from their clothes catching alight on unguarded fires. These burns caused many deaths and left severe deformity in those who survived. Wallace was successful in persuading the Government to pass legislation to ban manufacturers from making children's dresses and nightdresses from flammable material and secondly to prohibit the sale of unguarded electrical and gas fires. The effect of this has been outstanding and long-lasting. For instance, in the last ten years in the Aberdeen unit, there has not been a single child with severe burns from clothing catching alight.

Wallace also had many other interests, associated with burns and plastic surgery, outside the clinical field. He was Editor of the British Journal of

Severe Burns
Top left, Severe burns of thighs in a teenage girl whose skirt of flammable material (later banned) caught fire. Lower left, after dead skin of full thickness burns has separated – healthy granulation. Lower right, after raw areas have been covered by split skin grafts taken from the undamaged skin of the front of the thighs. This shows how extensive areas of skin loss can be re-epithelialised, by partial thickness grafts, whose donor areas will heal spontaneously – a graphic example of the Thiersch procedures.

Mr Ian Muir

Plastic Surgery from its inception in 1948 until 1969, during which it commanded the highest respect in its field. He was also active in promoting international co-operation in the treatment of burns and was prominent in promoting the foundation of the International Society for Burn Injuries in 1970. He had long wished to move from the rather primitive accommodation at Bangour to better facilities preferably near the academic departments in Edinburgh. On at least two occasions he was promised this, but, in truth, he was rather too kind and gentle a person allowing himself to be overcome by more aggressive personalities. The move from Bangour came in 1992, eight years after Wallace's death, to a hospital in Livingston, still some distance from the academic department in Edinburgh.

Tayside

In Angus and Fife, now the Tayside region, there was no formal provision for plastic surgery until 1956 when the Dundee Hospital Group asked Alastair Wallace to provide part-time services. Outpatient and operating facilities were provided at Dundee Royal Infirmary and at Bridge of Earn Hospital, near Perth. The number of patients listed for in-patient treatment rapidly increased and, in 1960, a self-contained plastic surgery unit was established at Bridge of Earn Hospital. John Kirk, previously senior registrar at Bangour, was appointed consultant. During the 1960s the work of the unit increased, particularly in the numbers of burns cases, and, since there was no plastic surgery service in Aberdeen at that time, the Aberdeen surgeons transferred serious burn cases, particularly children, to Bridge of Earn. When these children later came for review, after a plastic surgery service has been established in Aberdeen, the very high quality of the surgery, which had been carried out at Bridge of Earn was commented upon.

A second consultant, Arthur Morris, was appointed in 1970. In 1974, a new University Hospital was opened at Ninewells, which made available space at the Dundee Royal Infirmary. One of the wards underwent what John Kirk described as a "modest conversion" and a number of beds were provided for plastic surgery. Later, a separate burns unit of eight beds was established and, in 1986, all surgery had been transferred to Dundee and the Bridge of Earn closed.

Aberdeen

Except for ophthalmology and ear, nose and throat, there was very little specialisation in the surgical field until shortly after the end of the war in 1945. Plastic surgery was covered by different surgeons in established departments of general surgery. In 1969, the north-east regional hospital board established a plastic surgery department in Aberdeen. Ian Muir, who was consultant at the North-West Metropolitan Regional Plastic

Surgery Centre at Mount Vernon Hospital and at the West Middlesex Hospital, became the first consultant.

Muir had a special interest in the treatment of burns and particularly in the use of modern air conditioning to provide the optimum environment

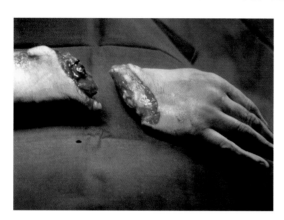

for burned patients. He also had an interest in the treatment of cleft lip and palate deformities in children and had been appointed a Hunterian Professor at the Royal College of Surgeons of England for his work in this field. The accommodation for adults was initially in a Nightingale-type ward at Woodend Hospital, part of the teaching hospital group, but a single specially air-conditioned room was constructed to continue the work on burns.

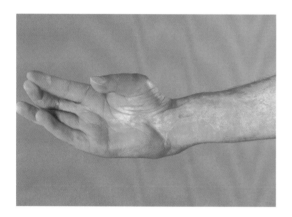

Building on the teaching hospital site at Foresterhill had been almost continuous since the early 1960s and, in 1986, accommodation was provided for the plastic surgery department to move to the Foresterhill site. It was possible to modify one of the wards to provide a burns unit which had an intensive care room, five further beds, a dressings room and an operating theatre. Only the intensive care room was reserved exclusively for burned patients and both the five beds and the operating theatre could be used in conjunction with the main ward. This flexible unit proved highly successful and economic. It was severely tested soon after its completion in 1988 when the Piper Alpha oil platform disaster occurred. Eleven badly burned men were admitted for treatment, but it has to be remembered that one hundred and fifty persons died on the platform and, if it had been possible for more of those to have been rescued, the strains on the burns unit would have been immense.

Re-implantation of a Hand Completely Amputated in an Accident
This rare injury occurred in 1972 and was possibly the earliest of such procedures in the United Kingdom. It was caused by an accident involving a paper guillotine. Final function both in movement and sensation was good enough for the man to return to work about a year later. The lower photo was taken in November 2001.

Department of Medical Illustration, University of Aberdeen

Provision for children remained at the Children's Hospital, which is on the same campus. Here, it has been possible to establish a team for the treatment for cleft lip and palate children who come from as far afield as Orkney and Shetland. This team consists of the surgeon, an orthodontist, an oral surgeon, an otologist and a speech therapist. Although the plastic surgery unit is small compared with the bigger units for Glasgow and Edinburgh, its existence as an integral part of a major teaching hospital and its closeness to the academic department has been of enormous value. Both Ian Muir and Colin Rayner who joined him in 1977 were interested in basic research problems and had great co-operation, particularly from the departments of developmental biology, cell pathology and medical physics in their research, chiefly into the healing of burns, other injuries and problems of scar formation.

Glasgow

The burns unit stayed at the Royal Infirmary but, in line with the practice in England, the Government decided to establish a plastic surgery unit within reach of, but safely away from, Glasgow. This was done in a hutted-type hospital, which had been built at Ballochmyle in Ayrshire in 1940. Nothing seems to be known about the original staffing of this unit or its work and it is possible that there was no young general surgeon with knowledge of, or interest in, plastic surgery. Whatever the reason, the unit was closed and then re-opened in 1944 when the young surgeon, John Scott Tough, was appointed as its Director.

Tough had been working as a general surgeon at Stracathro Hospital, an emergency medical services hospital in Angus, and had met Gillies there. Gillies was a keen fly fisherman and an excellent golfer and made many trips to North-East Scotland in the course of these pursuits before the war. He knew many of the surgeons in the Aberdeen area and at Stracathro. It was on a visit to Stracathro at the request of one of the ENT surgeons that he met Tough. Gillies was aware of the vacancy in Ballochmyle and thought that Tough would be a good choice to fill it. He therefore arranged for him to have a crash course in plastic surgery in the London area with himself, McIndoe and Mowlem. On his return, Tough took up his duties at Ballochmyle in 1944 and set out to organise the plastic surgery service in the West of Scotland. He was undoubtedly an excellent administrator with a clear view of his objective, which was finally to have a single large purpose-built, self-contained department in Glasgow to serve the whole of the population of West Scotland, about 2.5 million people.

The construction of the new building and the movement of all facilities to Canniesburn occupied the remainder of his professional life. It involved periods of using accommodation at different times, in the Royal Infirmary, the Western Infirmary, and vacant buildings at Canniesburn Hospital, itself a satellite of the Royal Infirmary, until finally in 1967 the new unit at Canniesburn was complete. The whole process was made more difficult by the fact that, for much of the time, Tough and his senior consultant colleagues did not see eye to eye.

After his two years with the Medical Research Council, Gibson had joined the Army. In 1947, he returned to Glasgow and was appointed consultant surgeon in the Department of Plastic Surgery. He was of a similar age to Tough and of comparable experience. However, it appeared that Tough behaved like the old "Surgeon-in-Charge" of a previous generation who expected all those appointed after him to be completely subservient, even in respect of individual patients.

As a result, Gibson devoted more of his time to his academic interests, partly in the department of Sir Charles Illingworth, Regius Professor of Surgery in the University of Glasgow and partly in the University of Strathclyde in its Department of Bioengineering.

A somewhat similar situation developed when Jack Mustardé was appointed the third consultant in 1953. Mustardé had previously been an ophthalmologist before going into plastic surgery and became internationally known for his expertise in reconstructive surgery of the eyelids and orbit. From the beginning, Mustardé exiled himself to Ayrshire and had little connection with Canniesburn. Unfortunately, these disagreements between the consultants meant that when a strong unified voice was needed in negotiations, this was not forthcoming. In addition, there was strong opposition from other quarters, particularly Sir Charles Illingworth. It says much for Tough's ability in negotiating, that the move to the new large purpose-built unit was finally accomplished.

In addition to his administrative achievements, Tough was also an excellent operative surgeon and the clinical work went from strength to strength. Ian McGregor made great improvements in the results of treatment of cancers of the head and neck, which became even better when micro-vascular techniques made it possible to carry out transfers of skin and bone in single stage procedures. The centre also became actively involved with post-graduate teaching courses and junior appointments were much sought after by surgeons in training.

An association with Canniesburn gave rise to one of the most remarkable stories of modern plastic surgery. Ian Jackson joined the Plastic Surgery Department at the Royal Infirmary as a Senior House Officer in 1959, at the time when Tough was the consultant in charge, Ian McGregor was a consultant, and William Henry Reid was Senior Registrar. Jack Mustardé visited on a Friday to see patients. In the move to Canniesburn, the oral and maxillofacial surgeons moved at the same time. The department was headed by Steven Plumpton and its strengths lay with the maxillofacial prosthodontists, Walter Smith and Matthew Orr. There was not the luxury of sophisticated reconstructions and many of the head and neck patients had to rely on prostheses. Although these were made out of acrylic, they were absolutely superb. Steven Dobbie, another oral surgeon, came up from Ayrshire to provide his specialised assistance.

Shortly after the move, Dr Jackson went off on a Fellowship to further his studies in cleft lip and palate. He spent time in Uppsala, Göteborg and then to Germany to visit the well-known oral surgeons in Hamburg, Stuttgart and Dusseldorf. He then attended Obwegeser, who was becoming the most authoritative maxillofacial surgeon in Europe and perhaps the world. During the latter three months of his Fellowship, he had very little money left and solved the problem of accommodation by buying a tent for he and his family to live in for the remainder of his time.

He returned to find a Canniesburn which attracted a stream of visitors from all over the world. Its staff produced an array of textbooks in the plastic surgery specialty. Ian Jackson produced a book on local flaps, which has become a handbook for Residents and Registrars, worldwide. Ian McGregor's book is also very popular, particularly in the UK and Europe and has now been taken over by his son. Jack Mustardé wrote what was virtually the classic handbook of eyelid and orbital surgery. Tom Gibson continued to work with the bioengineers. The Bioengineering Department, under Bobby Kenedi, developed many concepts of tissue expansion and management of cartilage.

Another development was the organization of craniofacial surgery, which was set up by Jackson and "Rab" Hide, who had been classmates at university. This was the first centre of its type in the UK, probably only the second or third centre in Europe, which went from strength to strength, dealing not just with congenital deformity, but also with malignancies and other pathologies concerning the cranial base. From that, came the first organized textbook in craniofacial surgery, a co-operative work involving Ian Jackson in Glasgow, Linton Whitaker in Philadelphia, Ian Munro in Toronto, and Ken Salyer in Dallas.

David

One of the visitors to Canniesburn was Carlos Navarro, a very experienced individual, particularly in the area of cleft lip and palate. He invited Ian Jackson to go to Lima to do some craniofacial surgery, since none had ever been done there. Jackson went to Lima with Duncan Ferguson, his anaesthetist and did several craniofacial cases under very difficult conditions. One evening, about 11:00 p.m., having just finished a very difficult craniofacial case, Jackson came out and saw a small boy sitting, sucking a lollypop. The strange thing about this small boy was that the lollipop stick came out of the centre of his forehead, because he had no upper jaw. He was, in effect, a lower jaw with eyes. He had been "stolen" from the Children's Hospital by a Swiss social worker, who heard that Jackson was in town and felt that he could do something, because no one was doing anything for the child in Lima. She was told that something could by done for the child, but not in Peru.

There was nothing further, until one day a note came to say that the social worker was trying to get the boy, David, out of Peru and bring him to Glasgow. Jackson wrote to Archbishop Tom Winning of Glasgow for financial help to cover all the medical treatment. The Archbishop agreed. David arrived with the Swiss social worker, who immediately went back to Switzerland, and the Jackson family were left with a tiny boy, about three years old, who could speak no English and had lost the whole central portion of his face. He had no nose, no upper jaw, no palate - simply a big hole and his teeth could come up between his eyes.

So began a long, interesting and challenging story for David and the Jackson family. David began a course of operations under Jackson, funded by the Health Service and from funds raised by the good Archbishop. It was a slow process. At the time, there was no microsurgery, tissue was simply moved around. Slowly, with good fortune and some misfortunes, a face was gradually built up for David.

David

The Jackson family

When Jackson moved to the Mayo Clinic in 1979, David moved with the family and the Clinic allowed Jackson to continue treatment free of charge. Gradually, Jackson and his staff were able to build David a mid-face with a nose and an upper jaw. Doctor Branemark from Sweden who devised the system, which is now used worldwide to allow teeth to be placed in the jaw with little metal pegs, operated on David at the Mayo Clinic and managed to put pegs in his upper jaw and so give him teeth. This was a great day for David. Around that time, the Jacksons were able to adopt David and he joined the Jackson family. There was a great celebration in which the Cardinal of Peru took part.

Subsequently, Dr Jackson moved to Detroit where David had further treatment. In Detroit, David went through Art School and has recently graduated and gone off to seek fame and fortune in California.

Cosmetic Surgery

By the 1930s, the development of new techniques meant that the original description of plastic surgery in the mid 1800s covered probably only a minority of operations and that the whole field could be described more accurately by the term, reconstructive surgery. Any disease process, or deformity may involve an abnormal appearance and one objective of an operation, e.g., for a cleft lip, or removal of a nevus, is to improve appearance. However, from the mid 1900s onwards, there has been an increasing demand for change purely for reasons of appearance, particularly facial features. Some of the objectionable features one would accept as actually ugly, but, increasingly, complaints are made of those which are within the normal range of appearance.

These conditions include minor nasal deformities, wrinkling and sagging skin of the eyelids and cheek, excesses of fat in the region of the hips, abdomen and abnormalities of the breast, either too large or too small. It is now possible to improve these unwelcome appearances by operations, which are correctly entitled cosmetic or aesthetic procedures. Unfortunately, they are still in common parlance referred to as plastic surgery operations and are often thought by the general public to comprise the most part of the work of plastic surgeons. Thus, the more rewarding reconstructive operations are undervalued.

It may be hazardous to say, since so many similar statements in the past have been subsequently proved to be completely wrong, but it seems likely that now the possibilities created by the development of microsurgical techniques have been exploited, further advances in techniques in the near future may seem unlikely. Improvements in the foreseeable future are likely to come from the cellular biology field, which will increase the scope both of auto-transplantation and homo-transplantation. It has already been shown that it is possible to grow skin epidermal cells in culture and cause them to multiply at a faster rate than can be achieved in the intact body.

Thus, if a burned patient has insufficient donor areas to provide grafts for the whole of a burned surface, it should have been possible to take epidermal cells (keratinocytes) from a small auto-graft, multiply them in culture and then seed them on to the raw area. Unfortunately this apparently simple technique has not been successful but, more recently, it has been possible to provide a non-cellular dermal layer on which the keratinocytes can be seeded to produce a continuous sheet, which can be handled and transferred to the patient. In addition to skin cells, Wheatley in Aberdeen has shown that it is possible to grow blood vessel cells while others have shown that it is possible to grow cartilage cells in culture.

Transplantation of skin cells from other persons has remained extremely difficult. Long-term survival of solid organ transplants (kidney, heart, liver) are now well established. However skin grafts provoke a strong rejection reaction. Whether more recent knowledge about stem cells will produce improvement in the homo-grafting field is not yet known, nor whether it is possible to isolate stem cells from children or adults.

Robert C HINCKLEY
(1853-1941)
First Operation Under Ether   1881-1894
Oil on canvas
Boston Medical Library, Francis A. Countway
Library of Medicine

This painting records the events of 16 October 1846
when John Collins Warren, Professor of Surgery at
Harvard Medical School used ether as an anaesthetic
in a surgical operation. The patient, Gilbert Abbot,
had a tumour removed from the left side of his jaw.
The setting was the amphitheatre – later called "the
Ether Dome" – in the Massachusetts General
Hospital.

Chapter 14

Anaesthesia

The first case dealt with by the fledgling MDDUS just after its formation concerned a death associated with anaesthesia. It was an early indication that this specialty would continue to occupy a place among the high-risk branches of medicine and dentistry in the following years and so it has proved. Despite considerable advances and sophisticated practices, anaesthesia continues to present medical defence with some of its more challenging problems.

The injunction "primum non nocere" applies to all medicine and in surgical anaesthesia it is an absolute. The process contributes to cure but is not, of itself, curative. It is a physiological trespass. Thus, a death under anaesthesia always attracts scrutiny. For many years in the twentieth century, Procurators Fiscal in Scotland were to be informed of any death within twenty-four hours of anaesthesia, and most of the subsequent enquiries led to autopsy. Such official concern was not always so focused. A great-grandfather was admitted to the Royal Infirmary of Edinburgh for what would nowadays be classified as "intermediate" surgery. When relatives called later in the day to enquire about progress, the Ward Sister was waiting to advise that he had died. The explanation was, "He just did not take the anaesthetic well". Three generations had the indelible impression that grandfather had disgraced the family!

In the first half of the twentieth century the principal recognised causes of "anaesthetic" death were aspiration of teeth or other foreign bodies, regurgitation with aspiration of stomach contents to the lungs, and "status lymphaticus", a mythical diagnosis, which featured in the text books until the early 1950s. Asphyxia probably accounted for the vast majority of deaths from aspiration and probably the cases of "status lymphaticus" too. Hypoxia was likely to have accompanied most apparently successful general anaesthetics, because there was little understanding of the clinical significance of cyanosis. It was not until the late 1950s, when modern concepts and measurements were applied to the study of arterial oxygenation, that the need for adequate concentrations of inspired oxygen began to be taught. Most babies at the time were delivered while their mothers breathed the analgesic "gas and air". The standard apparatus for this was designed to deliver 50% nitrous oxide in air, so that the maternal inspired oxygen was only 10%. Few, if any, of these practices were the subject of litigation and the gas and air routine continued almost as standard until the early 1960s.

Developments

The Second World War marked a watershed in anaesthetic practice. Up to then, the only specialist practice on any scale was for thoracic surgery of tuberculosis. War was a stimulus to anaesthesia for major trauma, including problems of major sepsis (mainly before antibiotics) and blood loss. Chest and brain injuries were growing challenges. Curare was introduced in Canada in 1942 and intravenous induction just before the war. Injudicious administration of both types of drug killed some patients, although proper use saved many others, who would not have survived under earlier methods.

In Britain the use of neuromuscular blockers had developed to what was known as the Liverpool Technique, in which anaesthesia was induced in a heavily premedicated patient with thiopentone, followed by a relatively large dose of neuromuscular blockers, the trachea intubated and the lungs ventilated artificially with a nitrous oxide in oxygen mixture. Although there was then no means of systematic measurement of blood pH or partial pressure of carbon dioxide pCO_2, hyperventilation of the lungs was part of the method, contributing to the required state of unconsciousness. The dangers of hypocapnia for organ blood flow were not fully realised until the 1970s. Nevertheless, compared with the days of ether and chloroform, the new methods allowed faster and arguably safer recovery; neuromuscular blockers also allowed surgical access to body cavities with a quality of muscle relaxation previously unimagined. All of this provided the essential infrastructure for the development and practice of modern surgery.

Local anaesthesia was under a cloud in the early 1950s after an action for negligence on the part of two patients, Mr Wooley and Mr Roe who featured on the same operating list and who suffered paraplegia in association with subarachnoid ("spinal") anaesthesia [Cope 1954]. No satisfactory explanation for the disaster was ever uncovered. Even more serious, but seemingly less dramatic, most doctors and dentists were casual in the use of infiltration or topical local anaesthesia without, in many cases, knowledge of the toxicity of the drugs, the factors affecting their systemic uptake, the recommended maximum doses, the existence of transmucosal uptake as a phenomenon, the risk to endarteries from adrenaline-containing solutions (loss of fingers etc.), or what to do if any of these problems presented as a clinical emergency. There was an annual loss of life, but few examples of public inquiry or litigation.

Bodkin Adams, a general practitioner from Eastbourne who also practised in anaesthetics, appeared at the Old Bailey, in 1957 charged with murdering an elderly female patient who had been overdosed with morphine. It was a public perception that he had a number of very wealthy ladies as patients, who were besotted by him and his attention to them as a doctor. In most cases, he stood to benefit substantially from their wills. The trial elicited enormous public interest and everyone assumed that Bodkin Adams was guilty [BMJ 1957]. In the end, he was acquitted. A film drama based on the case, attributed the result to the arrogant and condescending behaviour of a leading Crown witness, a distinguished pharmacologist whose performance alienated both the judge and the jury. Subsequently, Bodkin Adams' name was struck from the Medical Register for offences concerning dangerous drugs. He held a diploma in Anaesthetics of the Conjoint Board (RCP Lond. and RCS Eng.) and was a member of the Association of Anaesthetists. His name was removed from the lists of the Association, but he took his diploma to the grave [BMJ 1983].

Anaesthesia in the 1960s

By 1961, there were a number of important factors to consider, the unnoticed exhaustion of the oxygen cylinder (the Bosun warning device had only recently been introduced and not all anaesthetic machines carried one), migration of a tooth, throat pack etc. to the bronchial tree, aspiration of regurgitated material, pressure on peripheral nerves in the arm, leg or face from malposition of the unconscious patient and corneal damage. Thiopentone (at least as a 5% aqueous solution) accidentally injected to an artery - typically the brachial - instead of a vein, was a predictable cause of arterial thrombosis with loss of the distal part of the limb.

Epidural local anaesthetic analgesia in labour was introduced to British obstetrics in the 1960s and is now an established feature of maternity services. Although there have been both pro and anti-epidural lobbies, there is no doubt that, for those who wish it, epidural analgesia has facilitated civilised management of many labours, second only in its benefits to the introduction of inhalation anaesthesia for difficult delivery. The legal issue centres on post-delivery persisting back pain in a few patients. In spite of much study, a clear cause has not been found. For the time being, it can only be described as an inevitable, if small, risk which should always be made clear to the patient before the epidural puncture is made. Sadly, not all doctors remember to do that.

The Drummond-Jackson Case

Stanley Drummond-Jackson was a dentist who practised in Wimpole Street. His clinical expertise was never in doubt, but he had great ambition for a technique of dental anaesthesia with intermittent injections of the oxybarbiturate methohexitone. It was presented by Drummond-Jackson as a "safe" method, requiring trained judgement as to the timing of the increments. Having published widely on the method, he also taught it to others, principally under the auspices of the Society for the Advancement of Anaesthesia in Dentistry, which he had helped to found and of which he was a leading member. A group of clinical researchers, from the Department of Anaesthesia and other departments at the University of Birmingham, studied what they believed to be the technique, with measurement of cardio-respiratory variables and a method for assessing laryngeal competence during and immediately after the procedure. This allowed them to conclude that the physiological trespass might be considerable, and even dangerous. Their report was published [BMJ 1969].

The same issue of the Journal carried an unsigned editorial (subsequently attributed to Dr A. H. Galley, of King's College Hospital) that further criticised the method. Drummond-Jackson sued both the Birmingham team, and also the BMA, as publishers of the Journal, claiming that he had been libelled with significant damage to his previously high professional reputation. He challenged the ability of the investigators to reproduce his technique accurately and fairly. The case ran for several weeks in the summer of 1972, and again in the autumn after the summer recess. Many of the leading anaesthetists of the day enjoyed the cachet of being called as witnesses. In addition, Drummond-Jackson was supported by some very important figures who had been treated by him, including Sir John [later Lord] Hunt. Eventually Mr Justice Ackner, the Judge, was instrumental in obtaining a settlement [BMJ 1972]. Drummond-Jackson withdrew his action, the two sides met their own costs, and the medical defence organisations involved, picked up the huge bill.

Tracheal Intubation

A technique for tracheal intubation was first described by Sir William Macewen in the late 19th century and both tracheal and bronchial intubation, the latter in thoracic surgery, were used increasingly in the 1920s and 1930s. The availability of neuromuscular blockers, particularly the short-acting suxamethonium, made tracheal intubation easier and more desirable. It protected the airway, facilitated Intermittent Positive Pressure Ventilation, and freed the hands of the anaesthetist. Trainees in the 1960s were taught that there was no patient who could not be intubated (except perhaps someone with advanced cervical spondylosis), but that did not take account of the problems of teeth getting in the way, perhaps because at the time the vast majority of patients were edentulous! Nevertheless, inadvertent misplacement of a tracheal tube to the oesophagus and leaving it there, in a patient who is unable to breath spontaneously has become a growing source of legal problems. There are many diagnostic techniques for establishing where the tube lies, which should prove failsafe. The ultimate reassurance today is a continuous airway CO_2 recording.

However, in at least one court, there has been argument about the authenticity of the record. The axiom, "when in doubt take it out", applies to both tracheal tube and the more recent laryngeal mask airway anaesthesia. In a crisis, the patient's safety can be assured in most cases, by lung ventilation via a facemask, or better still spontaneous breathing. Fibre optic techniques to assist tracheal tube placement can be planned nowadays in cases of anticipated difficulty.

Awareness During Anaesthesia

The use of "light" anaesthesia with neuromuscular blockers and nitrous oxide was heavily dependent for achieving unconsciousness, on opiate premedication, lingering tissue levels of thiopentone, and hypocapnia. In the 1970s, fashion, and to some extent, evidence led away from all three to more rapidly metabolised drugs and eucapnic levels of ventilation. In some obvious respects the physiological and pharmacological basis of change was understandable, but it led to such light levels of anaesthesia that the problem of awareness and recall emerged.

The first high profile case of consciousness during anaesthesia was that of Mrs Ackers who, in 1985, successfully brought an action against Wigan Health Authority [MedLR 1990]. She received £12,000 for "pain, suffering and loss of amenity" plus £1,775 for future psychiatric treatment. It would appear that, although paralysed during Caesarean section, in 1981, the settings of the lung ventilator were inappropriate and Mrs Ackers received room air instead of the planned anaesthetic gas mixture. Various complaints of awareness followed the intense publicity given to Mrs Ackers and continue to occur. Most are more complex than the Ackers case.

Unless there is clear evidence or admission of a clinical error, a complaint is difficult to sustain. A patient can be easily confused in the course of discussion of the case as between what is in fact recalled and what has been induced as a result of questions based on the profile of other cases. Many of the cases occur from obstetric anaesthesia where there may have been a deliberate intention to minimise doses of potential respiratory depressants in the interests of the baby. Some patients will present with difficulty in bonding with the baby or a breakdown in aspects of the marital relationship. Others may develop phobias relating to hospitals, operations, or anaesthetics. Thus the recall problem is not just confined to the day of the event; the psychological sequelae may be protracted.

Inadequate anaesthesia in any type of case will be accompanied by a variety of clinical responses, - hypertension, tachycardia, sweating, movement of eyebrows, limbs, tongue, side-to-side head movement, "bucking" on the tracheal tube with attempts to extrude it, and tightening of muscles at the operation site. Indeed, it is difficult to believe that such a major problem could arise without the anaesthetist and all onlookers becoming concerned. Yet in many cases coming to review, the record is suspiciously devoid of clues if, in fact, unacceptably light anaesthesia has occurred. If a complaint is made by a patient, say within twenty four hours of the procedure, it would seem sensible for a respected independent party to obtain a written, signed statement from each observer regarding anything untoward.

Anaesthesia and Dentistry

In the mid 19th century, general anaesthesia was used for dental procedures more than for any other type of surgery. The first successful public demonstration of anaesthesia, in Boston, USA, in October 1846 was by W.T.G. Morton who was a dentist, and the first anaesthetic given in London, in December of the same year, was at the hands of James Robinson, also a dentist. For many of the succeeding years countless dental anaesthetics were administered successfully and in dental schools emphasis was laid on the teaching of anaesthesia. Some single-handed practitioners acted as both an operator and anaesthetist. This was clearly both unsafe and technically difficult and most responsible practitioners engaged a colleague to provide the anaesthesia.

By the late 1960s, genuine concerns were being expressed about the standards and safety of anaesthesia in the dental surgery. However to refer patients with acute toothache from outlying locations to hospital for dental treatment was considered inconvenient, although some dental practices specialised in dental anaesthesia. Some of them employed medically qualified anaesthetists. It is perhaps pertinent to note that in some of the high profile anaesthetic tragedies that have occurred in the dental surgery, medically qualified anaesthetists administered the anaesthetics. One of the problems was the inadequacy of the domestic surgery in the high street compared with the resources of a modern, fully staffed hospital. This continued to trouble the leaders of both dentistry and anaesthesia and it was probably inevitable that there has been inter-disciplinary bitterness from time to time.

Sadly, what it is hoped will be the last case of this type of anaesthetic tragedy occurred recently in a dental clinic at Edinburgh. Following a Fatal Accident Inquiry, the Sheriff delivered an incisive and informed determination, which would be a fitting epitaph to outmoded practices. The medically qualified anaesthetist, who was not a specialist, and a dentist have had their names removed from their respective professional registers.

Sedation for Endoscopy

The development of fibre optic techniques has brought better and more comfortable diagnostic methods in a variety of specialties. Whereas, for example, anaesthetist-involvement in oesophagoscopy or bronchoscopy was essential for "rigid" endoscopy, these new methods allowed the gastroenterologist or thoracic physician to work alone. However, the need for sedation, coupled with the lack of training in the use of appropriate drugs, caused an alarming number of "near misses" and an indeterminate number of fatalities. The belated publication of guidelines on sedation for various endoscopic procedures, including guidance on facilities for monitoring and resuscitation, and on levels of support staff, may have reduced the significance of these serious problems.

In future decades, we can expect to see a continuing evolution of surgical anaesthesia as a more sophisticated, technically complex, but much safer practice. The early specialist anaesthesia for thoracic surgery in the years before the Second World War was followed by other specialisms in anaesthesia for neuro-surgery, obstetrics, paediatrics, cardiac surgery and, more recently, ambulatory surgery and anaesthesia for trauma. In the USA, an increasing number of anesthesiologists are professing the specialty of "peri-operative care". Growing numbers of doctors may confine their work to just one of these areas of practice.

A further development for anaesthetists away from the operating room includes intensive care and pain therapy. Neither of these is exclusive to anaesthesia, but in both cases anaesthetists represent the majority of the specialist staffing. Again, some doctors are exclusively devoted to such activity. These developments, in addition to bringing great benefit to patients, bring new issues of risk, which are certain to be reflected in medico-legal considerations in the future.

Edvard MUNCH
(1863-1944)
The Sick Child   1907
Oil on canvas
©Tate, London 2001

From 1885 the theme of the sick child became a life-long obsession for the
Norwegian artist Munch. In his youth he had watched as both his mother
and his favourite sister Sophie succumbed to tuberculosis. Munch uses
intense colours and dramatic imagery to convey his sense of grief.

Medical Genetics

Research into human genes entered the public domain in the 1990s and opened up a "Pandora's box" of future medical litigation and ethical issues. The science is too new at this stage to do much more than speculate on the future outcome. However the prospect of human engineering in its many forms is a daunting example of the recurring situation, in which advances in medical science bring in their wake a myriad of medical defence issues. These will bring a range of new challenges to the MDDUS in the coming century.

The Genome Project

The aim of the Human Genome Project, which began in 1990, was to determine the sequence of the human genome in an attempt to identify all the genes that make up a human being. This is an immense project. The DNA sequence is composed of 3 billion base pairs containing enough information to code for between 100,000 and 300,000 genes. The human genome is estimated to contain between 50,000 and 100,000 genes and progress in its sequencing has been extremely impressive. The first draft of the Project became available in 2000.

There is no doubt that the application of advances in our knowledge of genetics will transform the practice of medicine and have considerable impact on the medico-legal landscape. Identification of the genes associated with a single gene disorder will afford an opportunity for earlier diagnosis and many diseases of multi-factorial aetiology will be shown to have a genetic linkage, as has already been proved with diabetes, asthma and hypertension.

We may be able to design a new classification of diseases based on the biochemical and physiological mechanisms involved, not on the symptoms that a patient presents, allowing at-risk patients to be identified early, when asymptomatic. Genetic knowledge will allow at-risk individuals to be targeted, with treatment designed to take account of genetic factors that may influence its success or failure. It is likely that some common psychiatric and neurological illness will be found to have a genetic component and identifying this will enable a clearer analysis to be made of the environmental factors that trigger such conditions.

In general, advances in genetic knowledge will produce a better understanding of the biochemical and physiological mechanisms of disease processes, enabling more rational targeting of interventions, not merely drugs to provide control of symptoms. The detection, prevention and treatment of disease are, therefore, on the brink of a revolution and it is impossible to over-estimate the importance both for society and the medical profession, of advances in medical genetics.

Implications

The implications of this revolution, in the face of such impressive scientific advances, sound a cautionary note and advise a pause for reflection. It is important to realise that the possession of genetic information has significant ethical implications and will present individuals and society as a whole with difficult decisions. Discussion of these implications throughout society, and not simply within the medical and scientific community, is essential. It is already possible to screen for some genetically linked or genetically determined diseases. The gene for cystic fibrosis has been identified and screening can be carried out so that adults can make informed reproductive decisions and, if a carrier couple is identified, prenatal diagnosis is possible with the offer of a termination if the baby is affected.

Two genes for breast cancer, BRCA1 and BRCA2, have been identified. These relate only to familial breast cancer, 5% of the total, so they are a poor predictor at population level. Women can currently be tested for these genes and, presumably, predictive genetic testing will soon be possible in female foetuses with a strong family history of breast cancer. It is estimated that 80% of women carrying one of these genes will develop breast cancer at some stage in their lives. However, we have no knowledge of what stage in these lives the gene will be expressed. The current clinical picture suggests that a woman will have three, four, or more, decades of healthy life before the clinical presentation of a tumour.

This raises a number of questions, which remain to be addressed. There is the question of the normality or abnormality of the foetus, identified as carrying the breast cancer gene. There is the question of the termination of such a pregnancy. A young girl, identified as carrying one of the breast cancer genes, will have to be informed at some stage of her life of the risk and offered treatment, such as early bilateral mastectomy or lifelong Tamoxifen. There may be a requirement for regular screening to enable early detection of the tumour. Screening may soon be readily available for colonic and ovarian cancer and similar questions will emerge.

The understanding of the concepts of health, disease and normality will have to be re-examined. At a fundamental level, society may have to redefine what is understood by notions of normality. Disability is a social construct and society will have to define how far it is prepared to tolerate deviation from such a socially determined norm. There is a risk that the availability of pre-natal diagnoses for a large number of diseases will produce a change in attitude to parenthood, with parents demanding a right to have a perfect baby. This could be called the commodification of babies - the concept of babies as commodities with only the perfect product being acceptable. In this brave new world, parents will be encouraged and possibly forced, eventually, to consider the consequences of reproductive choice, with a pressure to abort affected foetuses. In this scenario, bringing the less than perfect child into the world will be considered socially irresponsible.

Issues of Debate

Genetic and environmental influences contribute to the development of disease in a mutual and inter-connected fashion. Thus, even if the genetic influences affecting a disorder are well understood, there will be a degree of variability in expression of the symptoms and outcome observed, depending on environmental factors. There is a potential danger that an emphasis on genetic determinism will promote a reductionist view of the human condition, with both an under-estimation of the role of the environmental factors and reduced efforts at environmental modification.

The possibility is raised of genetic discrimination and stigmatisation of the symptomless ill. There is already evidence of public misunderstanding of carrier status. The House of Commons Science and Technology Committee on Human Genetics stated, "a US scheme to identify asymptomatic carriers (sickle cell trait) backfired because of racial overtones, poor public education, inadequate counselling, and genetic stigmatisation with large numbers of carriers being denied health insurance or employment".

Enthusiasts point to a future in which advances in genetic science will transform medicine, with pre-symptomatic diagnosis, targeting of at-risk individuals, and more rational interventions including somatic cell gene therapy. An alternative view, however, suggests that, not for the first time in the history of medicine, diagnostic techniques have outstripped therapeutic possibilities. We now face a more profound problem in which the human intellect has outstripped our current moral and ethical framework of thinking. It is imperative that the widest possible public debate of the implications of advances in medical genetics is encouraged, to allow for the construction of a framework to help solve the dilemmas that will result from this new knowledge. Ultimately, this framework must be of a multi-dimensional form because no single model can be applied to all categories of genetic knowledge. For example, the lessons we have learned from single gene disorders do not necessarily apply to susceptibility disorders, nor should we attempt to impute commonly recognised traits from dominant or recessive conditions, such as high levels of predictability or certainty, to conditions in which genes may have no more a causal role in the onset of disease than non-genetic factors.

Susan MACFARLANE
(b.1938)
The Waiting Room 1991-5
Oil on canvas
Reproduced by kind
permission of Susan
Macfarlane and A Picture
of Health Ltd.

In this early image from the
series *A Picture of Health*,
Susan Macfarlane has shown
the patient waiting to undergo
further investigations. The
artist had tried to convey the
sense of loneliness felt by the
patient. She writes: "The
panes of glass showing open
doorways behind the patient
indicate the unknown
experience to come."

The Dilemmas of Genetic Disclosure

The aphorism that "information is power" has never been more true than in the context of genetic information. Rapid advances in genetic research have provided a plethora of genetic tests, making it possible to test for 95% of the most common genetic conditions and a host of other rare disorders. Yet, in the main, these advances have not been accompanied by cures or therapies. It is possible to generate significant amounts of information about a patient's genetic constitution and correspondingly that of his blood relatives, but there is little that can currently be done with this information in the way of preventing or alleviating ill health.

This is not to say that nothing can be done with the results of genetic tests. It is often argued that a number of other uses can be made of this information. It can, for example, assist people to prepare for the onset of disease. Similarly, genetic knowledge can assist in the making of important life-changing decisions. A decision to reproduce, or not to reproduce, is a more informed decision if taken in the light of all available material information. A risk of passing on genetic disease to one's progeny is a material factor to be considered. For reasons such as these, it has often been argued that relatives of a person who has been tested for genetic disease have a valid claim to know the results of such a test.

There are then a number of persons with an interest in knowing genetic information, but there is a responsibility to oversee future access and control issues. There may be consequences as a result of freer access and so it is likely to be health care professionals, and particularly those involved in primary care, who will be expected to assume the mantle of regulating the flow of genetic information. This is especially true in the case of GPs who are family doctors and who feel a duty to the family as a whole. But, the consequences of wider dissemination of genetic information are currently unclear.

A Question of Knowledge

Genetic information is seen to be unique for a number of reasons, not least of which is the fact that it reveals personal data about a number of individuals and not simply one individual. It is on this basis that family members frequently claim a "right to know", but the basis of such a right is in question. Certainly, it cannot be the law, for few jurisdictions have addressed the issues thrown up by advances in genetics and the UK has not enacted any legislation in the field. Thus, as is so often the case, law must take its lead from ethics and appropriate legal responses must be informed by justified ethical argument. Any basis for a "right to know" must, therefore, be found in ethical discourse.

The ethical basis for a "right to know" could be found in a number of areas. The principle of respect for autonomy dictates that an individual's wishes and choices be respected, and this is true as much for an individual's personal information as it is for his/her bodily integrity. However, in the context of familial genetics, an appeal simply to the principle of autonomy does not help. The wishes of a relative to know, should not trump the wishes of a person who has been tested not to disclose the information in question, or vice versa. They cannot do so, and hence the resolution of the problem cannot be found in an appeal to autonomy alone.

The principles of non-maleficence and beneficence, that is, of the duty not to do harm and to strive to do good wherever possible, come into focus. Certainly, if a cure or treatment is available the claim of family members to know information becomes stronger. But in the light of the current therapeutic shortfall, no effective intervention will be on hand for many familial genetic traits. Yet, it is tempting to argue that disclosure should nonetheless occur, given that it can avoid the "harm" of ill-preparedness or the "harm" to choice if, for example, repro-ductive decisions are subsequently taken by relatives in the absence of full information.

It is necessary to proceed with caution in this realm of argument. For, while such forms of harm might undoubtedly be avoided in certain cases, the possibility that harm might be caused in other circumstances by unsolicited approaches to relatives cannot be ignored. Empirical evidence has shown that the disclosure of un-asked-for information about future ill health, when nothing can be done to alleviate the future suffering, can be a significant burden for many people.

In one US survey concerning young men diagnosed with Huntington's disease, it was shown that the suicide rate for their group was four times the national average for a comparable unaffected group. Similarly, in Sweden in the early 1970s, a nation-wide programme of screening infants for alpha$_1$-antitrypsin deficiency had to be abandoned after follow-up studies showed that more than half of the families with affected children suffered adverse psychological consequences, some of which continued for five to seven years. Evidence such as this must lead to the conclusion that it can no longer be assumed that it is always better to know. Indeed, it questions whether people have an interest in not knowing information about themselves in certain circumstances, or even whether they have a right not to know.

Disclosure

The treatment of familial genetic information is affected by this realisation. It means that the health care professional who finds him or herself at the centre of a dilemma about disclosure should consider the full range of factors, including the possible interest or "right" not to know. Moreover, the use of the language of "rights" is potentially dangerous because "rights" can easily conflict, and in the current context this could put the GP in a very difficult position. If the law adopts the language of "rights" it could lead to duties of disclosure being imposed, which could conflict directly with other duties such as the duty of confidentiality. A GP, who simultaneously owes a duty of confidentiality to a person who has been tested and a duty of disclosure to the relatives of that person, is in a very unenviable position indeed. For this reason it is preferable to speak of "interests" in information, which can be assessed in the overall balance.

At present, the law only offers a discretion to GPs to breach confidentiality in the most rare of circumstances, and principally when significant harm to third parties can be avoided. Thus, for the GP who faces a dilemma of disclosure in the context of genetics, he or she must identify a relevant "harm" and be prepared to justify his or her conduct subsequently. In all cases, the full range interests must be carefully weighed in the balance.

While few could deny that the avoidance of physical harm or even death is anything other than justifiable, other forms of "harm" such as psychological harm or harm to choice, are less easily avoided, and indeed disclosure can lead to harm itself. In such cases, the justification for disclosure falls away to a very large extent. The recognition of an interest in not knowing raises the level of debate to a more sophisticated level.

Unfortunately, it does not make the task of the GP any easier. It does, however, help to ensure that the response to advances in genetics is a responsible one. And, while the interest in not knowing seems to endorse the adage that "ignorance is bliss", it also fosters an understanding of the full potential consequences of actions when dealing with highly sensitive personal information.

John BELLANY
(b.1942)
Bonjour, Professor Calne   1988
Watercolour
Aberdeen Art Gallery and Museums.
Reproduced by kind permission of
John Bellany

On 30 April 1988 Sir Roy Calne performed
a liver transplant on the Scottish painter
John Bellany. After moving from intensive
care, Bellany used a shaving mirror to help
make a series of self-portraits charting his
very personal response to the operation
and his recuperation.

Chapter 16

A Duty of Disclosure
(Rogers v Whitaker: Australia)

There are relatively few medico-legal judgements in national courts of law, which achieve international standing. *Hanley* and *Bolam* are examples from the UK. Nevertheless, there are indications that judgements from other jurisdictions can be influential in certain circumstances. The most significant court decision for medical practitioners in Australia in recent times, *Rogers v Whitaker*, handed down by the High Court of Australia [CLR 1992], may well have a future impact on the medico-legal situation in the UK.

In this case, the High Court rejected the *Bolam* principle in the context of a doctor's duty of disclosure and affirmed the patient-centred approach to what information must be disclosed to patients contemplating medical or dental treatment. For medical and dental practitioners, that decision not only represented unwanted regulation of the conduct of their profession, but also has been difficult to translate into practice.

In 1983, in anticipation of returning to work after spending three years caring for her injured son, 46 year old Maree Whitaker decided to have an eye examination by way of a check up. She had had a penetrating injury to her right eye at the age of nine, which had left her almost totally blind in that eye. She was referred by her general practitioner to an ophthalmic surgeon who prescribed reading glasses and also referred her to Dr Christopher Rogers, another ophthalmic surgeon who specialised in anterior segment surgery, for possible surgery on her right eye.

Mrs Whitaker saw Dr Rogers in May 1984. He told her that he could improve the appearance of her right eye and probably also restore its sight by removing scar tissue that remained as a result of the earlier injury. Mrs Whitaker was "keenly interested" in the outcome of the surgery and "incessantly questioned" Dr Rogers about it. At a second consultation, three weeks later, Mrs Whitaker agreed to have the operation, which was carried out on 1 August 1984. There was no improvement in Mrs

Whitaker's right eye following the surgery, and unfortunately she went on to develop sympathetic ophthalmia affecting her left eye which, by the beginning of 1986, had left her virtually totally blind.

Mrs Whitaker commenced proceedings against Dr Rogers in 1986, the principal complaint being that Dr Rogers failed to warn her of the risk of sympathetic ophthalmia. She claimed that, had she been warned of this risk, she would not have gone ahead with the operation.

Dr Rogers did not warn Mrs Whitaker of the risk of sympathetic ophthalmia. Nevertheless, the expert opinion, obtained on behalf of Dr Rogers, was that the occurrence of sympathetic ophthalmia after anterior segment eye surgery was in the order of 1 in 14,000, and that Dr Rogers could not be criticised for failing to warn Mrs Whitaker of such a remote risk. On the basis of this opinion and in light of the law as it stood at the time, it was considered that there were good prospects of successfully defending the claim.

The trial took place in 1990. The experts called on behalf of Mrs Whitaker gave evidence that their practice was to disclose the risk of sympathetic ophthalmia to patients, but conceded that there was a responsible body of professional opinion that favoured non-disclosure. Despite this evidence, the trial judge found that the practice of non-disclosure did not conform to, "the standard of reasonable care demanded by the law" and therefore that Dr Rogers had breached his duty of care to Mrs Whitaker in not warning of the risk. The trial judge awarded Mrs Whitaker A$808,564.38 in damages.

Dr Rogers appealed to the Australian Court of Appeal, which upheld the trial judge's findings. Dr Rogers then appealed to the High Court.

The High Court

There was no issue that Dr Rogers was under an obligation to exercise reasonable care and skill in treating Mrs Whitaker and that this extended to the provision of advice about risks. The question before the High Court was whether Dr Rogers' failure to advise Mrs Whitaker of the risk of sympathetic ophthalmia was, as found by the trial judge, a breach of his duty of care.

It was argued on behalf of Dr Rogers that the principle derived from the English decision *Bolam v Friern Hospital Management Committee* should apply in the context of a doctor's duty to warn a patient of risks [All ER 1957]. The provision of advice to patients was a medical matter to be judged according to the standards of the profession. In other words, if, in treating Mrs Whitaker, Dr Rogers acted in accordance with responsible professional practice, then he was not negligent simply because there was a contrary responsible practice.

By contrast, it was argued on behalf of Mrs Whitaker that whether Dr Rogers had been negligent was for the court to decide and, in so deciding, the court should not defer to medical experts and the practice of the profession. If *Bolam* applied, it was argued, that would be the end of patient autonomy in the medical context and would revive medical paternalism.

In its decision, the High Court affirmed that a medical practitioner has a duty to exercise reasonable care and skill in the examination, diagnosis and treatment of patients and the provision of information. However, the Court held that there was a fundamental difference between diagnosis and treatment on the one hand, and the provision of advice and information on the other.

A patient's choice to undergo medical treatment was "meaningless" unless it was made on the basis of relevant information and advice. Rejecting the *Bolam* principle, the High Court held that whether a patient has been given all the relevant information was not a question which depended on medical standards or practices. No special medical skill was involved in disclosing the information; rather, "the skill is in communicating the relevant information to the patient in terms which are reasonably adequate for that purpose, having regard to the patient's capacity to understand the information."

Affirming that it was for the Court to decide whether a practice was reasonable, as in *Sidaway v Governors of Bethlem Royal Hospital* [All ER 1985], the High Court held that it was open to the trial judge to find Dr Rogers negligent despite the expert evidence. It was not a defence to an action in negligence for failure to warn, to argue that the doctor was not negligent because he or she acted in accordance with the practice, "accepted at the time as proper by a responsible body of medical opinion". As to the relevance of expert medical evidence, the High Court stated that:

... while evidence of acceptable medical practice is a useful guide for the courts, it is for the courts to adjudicate on what is the appropriate standard of care, after giving weight to the paramount consideration that a person is entitled to make decisions about his life.

The High Court's findings in respect of the content of a medical practitioner's duty to provide information borrowed heavily from earlier decisions. Approving the Canadian Supreme Court's decision of *Reibl v Hughes* [CSCR 1980], the High Court held that:

... a doctor has a duty to warn a patient of a material risk inherent in the proposed treatment; a risk is material if in the circumstances of the particular case, a reasonable person in the patient's position, if warned of the risk, would be likely to attach significance to it or if the medical practitioner is or should reasonably be aware that the particular patient, if warned of the risk, would be likely to attach significance to it.

The High Court agreed that the following factors referred to by Chief Justice King of the South Australian Supreme Court in its decision of *F v R* [SASR 1983], must be considered by a medical practitioner in deciding whether to disclose a risk of the procedure:

- The nature of the matter to be disclosed
- The nature of the treatment
- The patient's desire for information
- The temperament and health of the patient
- The general surrounding circumstances

Patient-centred Approach

Rogers v Whitaker reflected the increasing recognition at common law of patient autonomy as a fundamental principle in medical decision-making. While the High Court's decision was not the one those representing Dr Rogers were hoping for, with hindsight the decision was not surprising.

High Court Australia

Developments both in Australia and overseas in the years prior to the decision being handed down, signified a movement away from medical paternalism towards a more patient-centred approach.

Since the 1960s there has been a gradual development in North America in particular, of the "patients' rights movement" and a concomitant erosion of the traditional doctor-patient relationship which tended to be based on the maxim, "doctor knows best". The oft-cited United States case of *Canterbury v Spence* handed down in 1972 marked the beginning of judicial recognition of the shift from the professional standard towards a patient-centred one [US App DC 1972]. The Canadian Supreme Court followed suit in 1980 in the case of *Reibl v Hughes*, which, as noted earlier, was approved by the High Court in *Rogers v Whitaker*.

In Australia, the South Australian Supreme Court's 1983 decision of *F v R*, also approved by the High Court, saw the judicial expression of patient-centred sentiments for the first time in an Australian jurisdiction. In 1989, the Australian, Victorian and New South Wales Law Reform Commissions published a report entitled, "Informed Decisions about Medical Procedures". Referring in particular to the decision of *F v R*, the report prophetically stated, "The *Bolam* test would not be applied by Australian courts". The report recommended that guidelines be introduced to assist doctors in advising their patients about treatment options, which, "…should emphasise not only that doctors should give information to patients but that doctors should focus on the patient's needs in deciding what information should be given".

Impact on Medical Practice and Claims against Doctors

The impact of the High Court's decision on medical practice has been significant. *Rogers v Whitaker* is considered by the medical profession and medical defence organisations in Australia to have imposed an onerous responsibility on medical practitioners to warn of risks associated with a proposed treatment or procedure. Indeed, Justice Kirby of the High Court has described the duty to warn as, "A rigorous legal obligation"; breaches of which the court treats seriously.

In *Rogers v Whitaker*, the High Court considered the obligation on a medical practitioner to disclose information to patients in the context of risks associated with proposed treatment. However, it is generally accepted and advised that a medical practitioner's duty of disclosure extends to the nature of the proposed treatment and the availability of alternative forms of treatment, as well as the risks and complications. The greater the risk of harm, and the more serious it is likely to be, the more information is required. However, there is no necessity to warn of speculative risks or, "Remote serious risks … yet to be established as real".

Translating this into practice is another matter. Despite the passing of almost a decade since the High Court's decision, medical practitioners are still uncertain as to precisely what the law requires them to tell patients, and how to attend to this in a busy clinical practice. Thus, compliance with the law continues to present significant challenges to doctors practising in Australia today. It requires doctors to be vigilant in keeping up to date with developments in their area of practice, and to develop and maintain effective communication skills so that they can advise patients appropriately without inadvertently discouraging them from treatment.

Claims against medical practitioners now almost invariably contain allegations of failure to warn or disclose information. The focus in most of these types of claims is now on the adequacy and extent of any warnings and other information given to the patient/claimant, and whether the alleged material information or risk was known at the time of the events, i.e., the subject of the claim. Expert medical evidence is relevant to, but not conclusive of, what warnings should have been given. However, it is in respect of the issue of whether a risk was known to the medical profession at the relevant time that expert medical evidence still has a significant role to play in claims involving allegations of failure to warn.

Causation

Although the High Court did not deal with it in *Rogers v Whitaker*, the issue of causation is one of the particular challenges currently facing medical defence organisations and their lawyers in medical negligence cases. Causation in this context has two aspects, first, whether the claimant would have gone ahead with the surgery, and, secondly, whether the failure to disclose information had led to the alleged damage.

In Australia the test for whether a claimant would have gone ahead with treatment is a subjective one. In other words, the question is not what a hypothetical reasonable patient, or the reasonable patient in the position of the particular patient, would have done, but whether the particular patient would have accepted the treatment. This is in contrast to the position in other jurisdictions such as Canada. Failure of the claimant to give evidence of what he or she would have done, had he or she been warned of the relevant risk will be fatal to the claimant's case.

Because of the subjective test it is difficult to defend a case purely on the basis of causation. While the courts have recognised the problems of hindsight, and affirmed that it is necessary to refer to the surrounding circumstances in determining whether to accept or reject the claimant's evidence on causation, this is often a difficult hurdle for defendants. This is despite recent comments such as those of Justice McHugh of the High Court:

In practice there is likely to be little difference in the application of the subjective and objective tests in medical issue cases. Human nature being what it is, most plaintiffs will genuinely believe that, if he or she would or might have avoided the injury, the option would have been taken. In determining the reliability of the plaintiff's evidence in jurisdictions where the subjective test operates, therefore, demeanour can play little part in accepting the plaintiff's evidence. It may be a ground for rejecting the plaintiff's evidence. But given that most plaintiffs will genuinely believe that they would have taken another option if presented to them, the reliability of their evidence can only be determined by objective factors, particularly the attitude and conduct of the plaintiff at or about the time when the breach of duty occurred.

The second aspect of causation referred to above was considered by the High Court in its 1998 decision of *Chappel v Hart* [CLR 1998]. This case involved complex legal issues concerning whether a failure to disclose information caused damage to the claimant, what injuries and disabilities flowed from the failure to advise of the relevant risk, and what position the claimant would have been in had the appropriate advice been given. The decision is made more complicated by the fact that there are separate judgments by each of the seven members of the High Court.

The decision has caused consternation amongst the medical profession, as it has been widely misunderstood as imposing on medical practitioners a duty to advise patients of their own statistics in relation to procedures, and to refer patients to more experienced surgeons. This is not the case, although there is some suggestion in the judgment to this effect.

This misunderstanding has led to many claims against doctors in the area of failure to warn alleging not that the claimant would not have gone ahead with the operation, but rather that the claimant would have sought further information or a second opinion. Trying to determine what position the claimant would then have been in, had the warning been given, presents particular challenges to those representing both sides in claims of this nature.

Conclusion

Rogers v Whitaker has had a significant impact on the practice of medicine in Australia. Failure to warn is almost invariably pleaded in medical negligence claims against medical practitioners. Yet despite the passing of almost a decade since the decision was handed down, medical practitioners are still uncertain as to the extent of their obligations to their patients in this area. Consequently, medical defence organisations in Australia have developed professional development programs for practitioners, which deal with this and other issues. However, despite doctors being concerned about the content of their obligations in this respect, the decision in many ways merely confirms matters that are fundamental to good medical practice, namely the requirement to keep up-to-date with developments in the relevant practice area, and to communicate effectively with patients.

Hans HOLBEIN the Younger
(1497/8-1543)
**Henry VIII handing to Thomas Vicary the Act of
Union between Barbers and Surgeons of England**
1541
Oil on paper
Reproduced by kind permission of the President and
Council of the Royal College of Surgeons of England

The German artist Holbein was working for Henry VIII of
England by 1536. This painting records an historic event in
British surgery, the amalgamation of the Companies of
Barbers and Surgeons in 1540. Members of the Court of
Assistants look on as the King hands the Act of Union to
Thomas Vicary, the first Master of the United Company.

Governance and Regulation

Clinical Governance

The introduction of clinical governance increased the scope of the existing responsibilities of the MDDUS in looking after the professional interests of members. Clinical governance as a concept appeared in the Government's first policy statements on the NHS following the 1997 election. Widely portrayed as a radical rolling back of the previous administration's internal market approach, the idea of managing for quality in the NHS may have seemed to many doctors to be less of a radical rethink than a statement of the self-evident. The NHS was approaching its half-century and for the first thirty-five or so years it had been not so much managed as administered.

But general management in the NHS had been a reality for fifteen years and the basics of governance, the distinction between executives and non-executives on Trust Boards and Health Boards, were still in place. The values of the NHS were enduring and the commitment of professional staff to the concept of a comprehensive health system, free at the point of use and funded out of general taxation, was assured. The policy statements dwelt on the fact that clinical governance was going to be built on the principles of corporate governance.

The concepts of corporate governance have evolved over the last decade and, hence, clinical governance in the NHS cannot be considered in isolation. Major forces in society, globalism, consumerism, the emergence of the primacy of the individual, and the information revolution have all contrived to shape the way industry, commerce and society are organised and governed. Previously accepted but unwritten rules about "the way we do things around here", internal codes and the quiet word behind the scenes have all been swept away as unacceptable and outdated. They are now regarded as, at best, elitist and prone to bias and, at worst, sexist, racist, bigoted and socially exclusive.

Companies and governments alike have felt the "power of the people" and there is no authority now, which is not answerable directly to public opinion and its proxy, the media. There is an expectation of probity, of openness, of accountability, of transparency and of accessibility at every level. A series of reports, starting with the Cadbury report and proceeding through Greenbury, Hempel and Turnbull, have progressively widened and defined the responsibility of boards and their directors. In a nutshell, the latest in the series, the Turnbull Report, simply stated that shareholders and stakeholders in a listed company should have the reasonable expectation that their board will ensure that all decisions are accessible and are taken in an open and transparent way, that those responsible are accountable and that the future of the company is assured to levels consistent with the type of enterprise by the management of all risks including risks to reputation. New risk management structures have evolved to give effect to these functions.

In particular, external financial audit is now supplemented by new internal audit procedures. Board-level audit committees monitor and report on the way companies manage risk. This is often achieved by contracting the task to third party risk management specialists, but sometimes through internal risk management divisions. New rules are being drawn up for the appointment, training and accountability of directors. New penalties, including possible revisions to the law of manslaughter to introduce a new criminal offence of corporate manslaughter, will no doubt sharpen board-level debate about issues around risks to health and safety as it affects products, processes, customers and the workforce.

These are the principles of corporate governance, which clinical governance is supposed to mirror. The NHS has to measure up against these standards. Even though there is no question of the NHS being forced to comply for commercial reasons, there can be no case for maintaining standards of governance in the NHS, which are less than those demanded in line with best practice elsewhere. NHS Boards, at whatever level, must ensure probity, openness, accountability and transparency of decisions. They must take all reasonable steps to manage all risks, clinical and financial, as well as risks to reputation.

Confidence, some would say faith, in the doctors, nurses and health care system looking after them, is a vital element in every patient's recovery. NHS Trusts are aptly named. Within this context, clinical governance includes any process which assures an NHS Board and, through them, the public that all reasonable steps are being taken to maximise benefit and to minimise risk in the clinical process.

Systems

There have, in many senses, been four NHS systems in the UK for many years but formal devolution since 1997 has widened the policy differences in the different administrations. The new parliament in Scotland and the Assemblies in Wales and Northern Ireland have added a new dimension of accountability to clinical governance. For the purposes of the centenary history, the approach in Scotland is explored. The White Paper, "Designed to Care", introduced the concept of clinical governance to the NHS in Scotland. A Working Group was set up, chaired by the Chief Nursing Officer which produced guidance to support Trusts and Boards in the implementation of clinical governance with effect from April 1999. Trusts were thus made responsible explicitly for the quality of care delivered, in the same manner as they were already responsible for their stewardship of public monies. Chief executives became accountable for the discharge of this duty, as they were also accountable for proper use of resources.

The way in which Trusts were to deliver their new responsibilities was left as flexible as possible. Issues relating to the quality of clinical care would be expected to feature prominently on Trust and Board agendas, and to form complementary and equal strands alongside financial and probity issues in their accountability. To achieve this, and in line with best corporate governance practice, mechanisms for the delivery of clinical governance would have to be integrated into the existing management structures of the organisation. Clinical governance was to become an integral and integrated part of mainstream business.

The guidance was prescriptive only in relation to one aspect of organisational structure. Each Board was to put in place a Clinical Governance Committee. Consistent with the analogous internal audit committee in the corporate world, this body was not tasked with the delivery of clinical governance. It was to be responsible for oversight of clinical governance within the organisation in order to assure the Board that all was well. In that regard its role was to be similar to that of the Financial Audit Committee in overseeing financial governance. The guidance attempted to make clear what clinical governance was and, perhaps more importantly, what it was not, as follows:

Clinical governance as such is about the governance of the Health Service, and thus about accountability and about structures and processes. However, it will only achieve the desired outcomes of improved quality of care and public reassurance about standards of care, if it is underpinned by a wide range of activities most of which require to be owned and led by clinicians individually and collectively. Clinical governance is not the sum of all these activities; rather it is the means by which these activities are brought together into a structured framework and linked to the corporate agenda of NHS bodies.

Implementation

A number of myths persist about what clinical governance is and is not. It is neither synonymous with the term "clinical effectiveness", nor is it solely about identifying "poorly performing clinicians", though both those activities support it. Clinical governance is about:

...creating a culture where the delivery of the highest standard possible of clinical care is understood to be the responsibility of everyone working in the organisation and is built upon partnership and collaboration within health care teams and between health care professionals and managers.

...introducing structures and processes which assure Boards that this is happening whilst at the same time empowering clinical staff to contribute to the improvements of standards, and involving patients and the public in this process.

Clinical governance was implemented in Scotland against a background of Trust re-configuration. Much of the initial focus was, not surprisingly given this context, on the structures that required to be established. There was confusion in some quarters about the process of delivering clinical governance and further guidance was therefore issued to the service in June 2000 clarifying the respective roles in clinical governance of:

Clinical Governance Committees	- Overseeing role
Trust management, including clinicians involved in management.	- Delivering role
Staff involved in clinical effectiveness	- Supporting role
Clinicians and support staff	- Practising role

In addition, a monitoring template was issued for completion by Trusts and Boards so that a picture could be obtained of progress.

A number of national initiatives provide external benchmarking and advice to Trusts and Boards to support the delivery of clinical governance. Scottish Intercollegiate Guidelines Network (SIGN) recommendations and reports of national audits are two examples on the clinical effectiveness front. In addition, the work of the Clinical Standards Board for Scotland will increasingly provide information for Trusts and Boards about the clinical quality of their service provision - both in terms of standards - what they should be aiming for - and in terms of peer review - what they are currently delivering. The standards will be generic as well as condition specific. Clinical risk management underpins the delivery of clinical governance. The Clinical Negligence and Other Risks Indemnity Scheme, better known as CNORIS, was launched in April 2000 and has taken forward the development of clinical and non-clinical risk management working closely with the Clinical Standards Board for Scotland.

In parallel with developments in clinical governance are measures to ensure that individual clinicians are performing to generally acceptable standards.

The GMC is introducing five-yearly revalidation of all doctors in the UK, and this will be complemented with annual appraisals by NHS management. All doctors will need to show that they are keeping up to date by being part of continuing professional development programmes, and evidence of this will be part of the GMC's revalidation process. Where it is considered by Trust management or others that a doctor poses a potential risk to patients or the public, the GMC now has an "Interim Orders Committee" which can order a doctor's immediate suspension from the Medical Register while his case is being considered under the GMC's Fitness to Practise procedures. Investigation of clinical services by the Clinical Standards Board for Scotland may reveal failings of individual doctors within that service. This is something that the Trust Medical Director will then have to pursue. Conversely, individual annual appraisals may indicate difficulties within a particular Trust's clinical service, which management will then need to address.

The development of clinical governance in Scotland faces another challenge. A major plank of the recently published paper, "Our National Health: A Plan for Action a Plan for Change", issued by the Scottish Executive on 14 December 2000 is to streamline the management of the Health Service in Scotland through the creation of new unified Health Boards directly responsible for the management of the Trusts in their areas. Clear guidance has been provided on the consequential arrangement for corporate and clinical governance within these new structures to ensure the highest standards of corporate governance within the NHS Scotland.

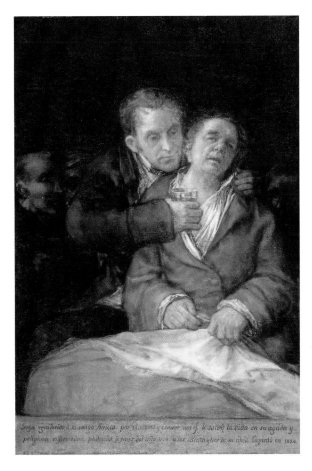

Francisco GOYA
(1746-1828)
Self Portrait with Dr Arrieta 1820
Oil on canvas
The Minneapolis Institute of Arts

In 1819, at the age of 73, Goya suffered a severe illness from which he did not expect to recover. However, he was nursed back to health by his doctor, Don Eugenio García Arrieta. The painting is inscribed "in gratitude, for his friend Arrieta: for the care and attention with which he saved his life".

Changes in Professional Regulation

For the first time since the days of "quack" doctors in the nineteenth century, the British public, led by the media and the Government, has suspended its automatic trust in the medical profession. The inevitable effect of several cases, including that of the Bristol paediatric cardiac surgeons who misled parents about the chances of their children's survival, Dr Harold Shipman's unexplained serial murders of his patients in general practice, and Alder Hey Hospital's failure to seek informed consent for the removal and preservation of body organs, has been to raise questions about the profession's ethical and moral values. The Lord Chief Justice has warned that courts are too quick to assume that "doctor knows best" and Sir Donald Irvine, lately President of the GMC, has attacked the profession for excessive secrecy and lack of respect for patients.

The GMC has also been criticised for being complacent, over-protective of doctors and slow to respond to complaints. In fairness, it was the GMC who addressed the problem of the Bristol surgeons when local arrangements had failed, and it had already obtained new legislation to allow it to investigate and deal with poorly performing doctors. The organisation is in the process of reform to further increase lay representation, whilst making the Council itself smaller and more responsive.

Since its foundation in 1858, the GMC has had the powers to investigate specific cases of alleged misconduct by doctors. In 1980, it introduced health procedures to protect patients from sick doctors whilst also aiming to rehabilitate the doctor if possible. In 1997, it introduced its Professional Performance Procedures, which enable the GMC to consider cases where, even if a doctor had not committed an offence of serious professional misconduct, he or she put patients at risk because of a pattern of poor performance as a doctor [Table 17.1].

Table 17.1. Definition of seriously deficient performance

A departure from good medical practice – whether or not it is covered by current GMC guidance – that is sufficiently serious to call into question the doctor's registration.

A doctor's registration is called into question when there is repeated or persistent failure to comply with the professional standards appropriate to the work being done by the doctor, particularly where this places patients, or members of the public, in jeopardy. This may include repeated or persistent failure to comply with the GMC's guidance in '"Good Medical Practice".

Procedures

Since they were introduced, the number of cases considered under the Performance Procedures has increased exponentially. There were 10 in 1998, 26 in 1999 and 170 in 2000. Each assessment costs about £15,000 and there is a sufficient range of assessors to enable assessment of a doctor in virtually any medical discipline, from general practice to forensic pathology or occupational medicine.

A team of at least two medical assessors and one lay assessor, selected nationally and trained by the GMC, visit the doctor's place of work to assess his or her performance in practice [Table 17.2] as Phase 1 of the assessment.

Table 17.2. Assessment of Performance (Phase 1)

- Initial interview
- Site visit to place of work
- Review of medical record keeping
- Case based orals, based on doctors own cases
- Third party interviews with clinical and non-clinical colleagues
- Observation of actual practice
- Summary interview

Although it is not part of the assessment itself, the doctor in question completes a portfolio, which provides background information, available to the visiting team. It describes the doctor's circumstances of practice, experience, continuing professional development and standard setting / audit activities. It also includes rating scales that describe the doctor's familiarity with and confidence in managing a list of diseases and procedures relevant to his or her specialty.

Phase 1 takes at least two days and includes, if possible, direct observation of the doctor at work - if the doctor has not been suspended from work and the presence of assessors is acceptable to patients and would not put them at risk. The assessors inspect at least fifty medical records and interview the doctor about some of them. Thus, the doctor can demonstrate to the assessors how he or she actually manages their own patients, and describe clinical thinking and decision-making.

The assessors interview at least twelve third parties - five of whom can be nominated by the doctor. The complainant, usually a Health Authority or Trust, but sometimes a patient, has a right to be interviewed as well. Interviewees may include medical colleagues, nurses, managers, pharmacists, or others with direct knowledge of the doctor's performance. All interviews are structured, chaired by the lay assessor and transcribed by a stenographer. Transcripts are sent to the doctor for comment.

Phase 2, is held after an interval and in a hospital or university clinical skills laboratory and assesses the doctor's competence - what he or she can do [Table 17.3].

Table 17.3. Assessment of Competence (Phase 2)

- Written knowledge test
- Clinical skills test
- Simulated practice
- Observed history taking, clinical examination and structured discussion of findings and proposed management with real patients.

The doctor undertakes a written knowledge test and clinical and communication skills tests. Simulated practice may be observed with either patients or manikins. Manikins, upon which a doctor can demonstrate physical examination or surgical skills, are widely used in undergraduate and postgraduate education and their range and authenticity are improving all the time. Wherever possible, all Phase 2 tests have been piloted using volunteers from the same specialty. There is no pass / fail mark as such, but the assessors use volunteers' scores as reference data when they write their report.

The assessors' report is sent to the GMC, which uses it to decide whether it is necessary to limit or suspend the doctor's registration and whether to recommend remedial education. If necessary, there is a formal hearing of the Committee on Professional Performance. Remedial education is the responsibility of the doctor, not the GMC. The doctor is advised to contact the regional Postgraduate Dean or Director of Postgraduate General Practice Education and can be reassessed after a period of remedial education.

Experience so far has been that assessors have identified important areas of potential improvement in every doctor who has been assessed, including well-regarded volunteers. There is little data about normal error rates in medical practice but, where data are available, an error rate of about 10% is typical. The BMJ covered the topic in depth in a symposium and special issue of the journal in March 2000.

We all make mistakes, but other organisations seem to be better at running systems that protect the public from disaster when errors occur. Airlines are commonly quoted as examples of good practice. Like the NHS, many airlines are large, complex organisations responsible every day for thousands of human lives. There are sufficient checks and balances in airline procedures to ensure that, when errors occur, they only rarely lead to tragedy. Too many NHS systems and procedures are inadequate or ignored, leading to repeated errors such as intrathecal injection of intravenous drugs.

Balance

Most airlines look after their staff in a way that NHS employees can only dream about. For example, they insist that staff rest at appropriate intervals and provide an effective occupational health service. They encourage reporting of "near miss" accidents and learn from them. Although the NHS aspires to a "no blame" culture, its systems encourage its employees to conceal their mistakes. Patients would be better served if the NHS culture genuinely encouraged openness and honesty about mistakes and failures so that everyone could learn from them and do better next time.

The interaction and balance between the performance of individual practitioners and the conditions and systems in which they operate is complex. The GMC Performance Procedures focus on defects in individual doctors, but it is often system failures that lead to patients being harmed. For example, NHS systems should have identified and dealt with problems in Bristol earlier than they did. Clinical governance in the National Health Service, where Chief Executives are responsible for clinical standards in their organisations, should help to ensure improved patient care, as should the GMC's revalidation proposals, in which all doctors have to demonstrate their fitness to practise every five years. A proportion of doctors will be referred from revalidation into the Performance Procedures, which act as a "backstop" for the protection of patients. However, this will perpetuate the belief that poor practice can be eliminated by discarding the "bad apples".

This approach ignores the reasons why doctors are poorly performing; poor selection, inadequate education and continuing professional development, lack of an effective occupational health service etc. Diminishing trust in the medical profession and increasing litigation against doctors are symptoms of cultural changes in society. If they lead to increased humility and less arrogance in the medical profession, they may be beneficial. But if lack of trust leads to more litigation, using up valuable resources to compensate a few at the expense of many, it is likely to adversely affect the health of the nation.

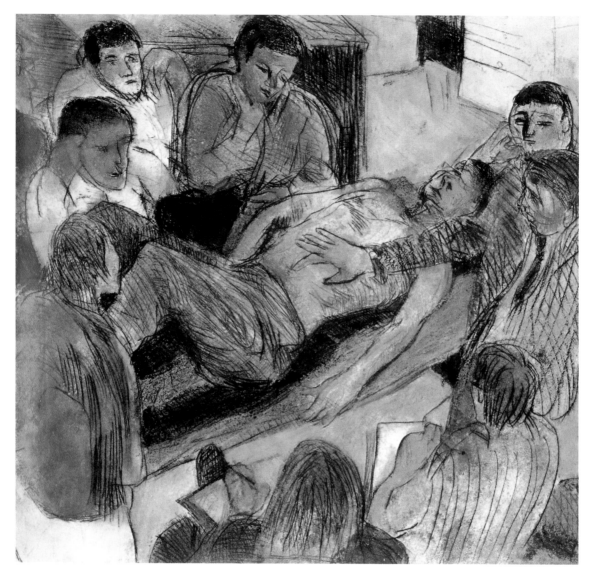

May H LESSER
Second Year: Introduction to Clinical Diagnosis
1974
Colour drypoint engraving
Reproduced by kind permission of May Lesser

For more than thirty years May Lesser's art has been inspired by medicine. She is the daughter, wife and mother of physicians, and has worked extensively in American medical centres. For this print, from the series *The Art of Learning Medicine*, the artist followed a class of medical students through their training at Tulane University School of Medicine, New Orleans.

Medical Defence and Ethics

Medical Defence

The indemnity support that medical defence organisations offer medical and dental practitioners is still widely interpreted as a closed-shop protection of both professions, which will fly in the face of logic and the legal process to shield poor practice and individual incompetence. This has never been the case. While we are proud of our Scottish origins, the MDDUS has a vested interest in maintaining high standards of medical and dental practice across the entire United Kingdom. The old adage, "Prevention is better than Cure", could not be more apt than in the context of medical negligence matters.

Individual practitioners are at their most vulnerable when their professional actions are called to account. A medico-legal case is conducted over a long period of time and involves the due processes of law and expert professional testimony. Despite a sea change in the attitude of the professions, there is still an inherent delay in our legal systems, such that the average time to reach settlement of a case continues to be in the region of five years and legal costs remain factors of considerable concern. This may improve in England and Wales as the effects of the Woolf Reforms are felt. The worries and misgivings experienced by the practitioners a century ago, which led to the founding of the MDDUS, are as valid today as they were at the time. The only differences are of scale in an increasingly litigious environment and the modern "blame culture" society. Without defence organisations, it would be difficult to envisage the continuation of the health service in its present form.

The Contemporary Medico-Legal Scene

The MDDUS exists to assist and advise its members. The scope of medico-legal practice is very wide-ranging and covers a broad variety of medico-legal subjects. One of the prime reasons for a member to join may be the provision of indemnity so that, when faced by a civil claim for negligence, legal costs and any settlement are covered by the indemnity. However, many NHS hospital practitioners are members, although they have no requirement for indemnity because their work in hospital is covered by NHS Indemnity. The MDDUS provides medico-legal advice and support across a broad spectrum, including disciplinary matters relating to professional conduct, medical legislation, mediation and education. Where legal representation is appropriate, that also is provided. All of this means that members can be secure in the knowledge of obtaining expert advice and help whenever necessary, with no worries regarding unforeseen or escalating costs of legal advice.

Table 18.1.

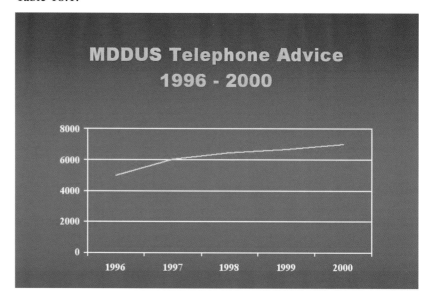

In all situations, the MDDUS must use the professional requirements for modern practice as the basis for any advice provided. Occasionally, members do make mistakes, most often because of human error; others knowingly take inappropriate risks and must face the consequences. In all situations members receive frank and honest advice regarding the standards of their actions and the likely consequences. Invariably, legal representation is provided, as determined by a particular process, but all such services are discretionary and, in extreme cases of repeated and wilful bad practice, these have on occasions been withheld.

There are many calls for advice in relation to complaints [Table 18.1]. This may be at the outset of the NHS Complaints Procedure; it may be in relation to non-NHS complaints, e.g., the private sector; or in relation to complaints addressed to the General Medical Council and the General Dental Council, both in general terms about the procedures involved and in specific terms about an individual case. If a member faces a negligence claim the MDDUS is usually contacted as a matter of urgency, in connection with the investigation and any legal steps that may be required. The range of legislation which affects the medical profession is extensive and on the increase. Advice is sought on a variety of legislative matters such as the Human Rights Act, the Data Protection Act and the Adults with Incapacity (Scotland) Act.

A considerable number of queries arise on professional guidelines, which originate from the General Medical Council, the General Dental Council and the National Health Service. Members also seek help in situations that may require legal representation, e.g., Coroner's Inquests, Fatal Accident Inquiries and other public inquiries.

Members call when they feel they have a difficulty. Occasionally, a member may call because he or she is upset and simply wants someone to talk to. A member once rang after being in a minor car accident, realising that the MDDUS could not assist but would provide a sympathetic ear! In general terms, however, most calls are relevant to medico-legal work, such as, "Living Wills", more properly referred to as "Advance Directives", and the withdrawal or withholding of treatment. Unfortunately, there is also an increasing tendency for members to require assistance in relation to criminal matters directly related to their professional activity. Members have faced charges of culpable homicide and manslaughter, however, to date, none of the MDDUS members involved in such cases has been found guilty. Although rare, the serious nature of allegations of sexual impropriety in the course of clinical practice may ultimately result in a custodial sentence. The MDDUS offers regular advice to members on the importance of chaperones.

The most helpful advice, when problems occur, is to keep matters in context and proportion. Thereafter, specific and practical guidance can be offered, such as reviewing reports and letters, or clarifying an area of legislation. Many members have a good knowledge of what a situation demands and ring for more reassurance. Occasionally, the belief or opinion held may be quite wrong and require timely correction!

Complaint

Patient dissatisfaction with some aspect of medical or dental treatment lies at the root of complaint. This has been a recurring theme throughout the century to the present day. Treatment that has gone wrong, or failed to live up to expectation, has raised the question of the professional competence, or otherwise, of the practitioner and, in pursuit of the answer, patients have sought redress through the processes of law.

The current NHS Complaints Procedure has now been in place since 1996 and, whilst the initial stages are kept informal, there is nonetheless formal and specific guidance available. The ethos behind this route of

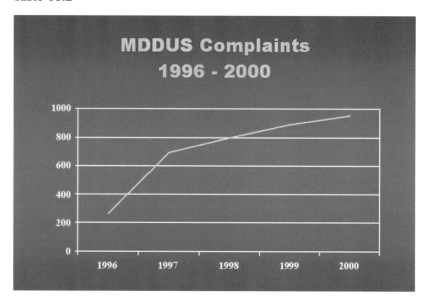

accountability was that there should be a non-adversarial, fact-finding process. Although this pre-dated clinical governance, it fits in well with the concept and the opportunity to learn from critical incidents. When an initial written or oral complaint is made, the doctor or dentist is invited to comment. Many seek advice about the drafting of their response. Some are concerned about offering a full apology, or a forthright explanation, particularly if an error has been made [Table 18.2].

However, professional guidance is very clear that doctors and dentists must be honest with their patients. The MDDUS always encourages a candid explanation of what has transpired and an apology, if appropriate. At this stage, it is often helpful to meet informally with the patient or complainant, to discuss their concerns and to try to seek local resolution. In those situations, where patients remain dissatisfied, they are entitled to ask for an Independent Review, which may or may not be granted. A Review will produce a report with recommendations. The whole of the process is not disciplinary, though in the case of GPs the report is often passed on to the Local Referral Committee to see if the matters complained of should result in disciplinary action. Alternative dispute resolution has found great favour with the legal profession in recent years and its principles are applied within the NHS Complaints Procedure.

At the conclusion of the Independent Review Panel, when the

MR JAMES WHITELAW

Jim Whitelaw died on the 3rd August 2000. He was a successful general dental practitioner in Glasgow who devoted the latter part of his career to passing on his skills and experience to students and younger colleagues. His quick-witted humour made him a popular and memorable figure. He qualified LDS from the Glasgow Dental Hospital in 1947 and served for two years in the RADC in post-war Berlin. He returned to Glasgow and practised for twenty-seven years. During this time he became a visiting teacher at the Glasgow Dental Hospital and in 1977, he was appointed to the General Practice Unit. On his retirement he served for five years as a part-time Dental Adviser to the MDDUS guiding and supporting colleagues with medico-legal problems.

report has been finalised, if either party, i.e., the complainant or the doctor or dentist, believes that there has been unfairness, or the Complaints Procedure has been badly applied, the Health Service Ombudsman may be asked to review the case. The Ombudsman will not re-open every matter referred, but only those where there appears to be a difficulty, which occurs in 10% of referrals. Throughout this process, members often experience a range of emotions and may be very distressed, particularly in circumstances where they feel they have provided exemplary care. The private sector does not have its own separate complaint procedure and does not come under the NHS Complaints Procedure. However, many private organisations now run a parallel system and the MDDUS offers similar advice and support to the member involved.

Professional Conduct

Many complainants now refer matters to the GMC [Table 18.3] or GDC [Table 18.4]. Indeed, the respective Councils may be the first port of call for a complainant. At one time, if a complaint reached that level, it would be of a serious nature, but now complaints vary widely from the relatively trivial to issues of serious professional misconduct. If correspondence on a case is received from either Council, all MDDUS members are advised to seek advice on the likely processes involved and an assessment of the seriousness of the situation. At the present time, the General Medical Council reviews professional practice in one of three sub-groups - Professional Conduct, Performance, or Health and, in many cases, solicitors are instructed for detailed and expert legal input. If a matter proceeds to a hearing, legal representation will include the instruction

Table 18.3

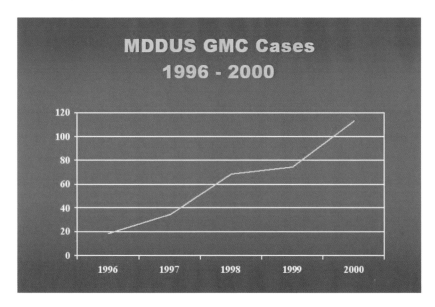

of Counsel with appropriate expertise and experience of the General
Medical Council.

Table 18.4

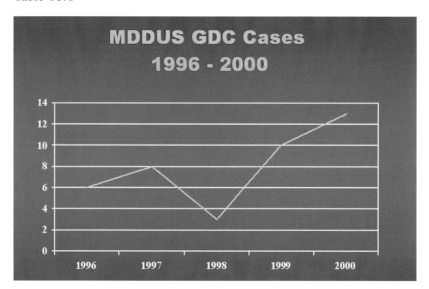

GMC and GDC complaints are especially distressing for members because
of the obvious link to registration. The way in which the current system
operates means that many medical cases reach the Preliminary Proceedings
Committee and members involved invariably have visions of ultimately
being struck off the Medical Register. The minimum period of erasure for
a doctor is now five years and this, in the majority of cases, results in the
loss of the doctor's career. The impact of such a possibility is quite profound.
In many cases, the risk of erasure actually occurring is extremely small,
though members suffer the same stress and require reassurance accordingly.
No member can rest entirely easily until the whole process is concluded,
usually in the form of a warning letter, and often many months after the
initial complaint has been made. Unfortunately, GMC processes always
involve the issue of such a warning letter and the retention of material on
file for two to three years, even when the doctor has not been found guilty
of any misconduct. The whole procedure has an unpleasant feeling, which
many members believe is tantamount to a form of double jeopardy.

Negligence Trends

Negligence has a well-known colloquial meaning, but, in relation to civil
claims it is clearly and legally defined. There are three hurdles in relation
to negligence claims and the claimant must clear each before being
successful. Firstly, it must be established that there was a duty of care; in
most medical settings this is easily accomplished. Secondly, it must be
shown that there was a breach of that duty. Currently, the tests remain
much as they have been in the past. *Hunter v. Hanley* [SC 1955] remains

the test case in Scotland. In England and Wales, *Bolam v. The Friern Hospital Management Committee* [All ER 1957] remains the legal yardstick. The third hurdle is the proof that harm resulted from the breach of duty, i.e., causation and in many cases this can be very difficult for a claimant to prove, on the balance of probabilities.

Latterly, since the judgement of *Bolitho* [All ER 1997] the role of the court has been reinforced, when it comes to accepting expert testimony.

Of the many claims intimated to the MDDUS, a high percentage do not proceed beyond the initial inquiry and investigation. Nevertheless, the majority of cases will involve legal advice and representation. Similarly, expert opinions are required both on liability and causation. Claims are made on an occurrence basis and if a claim materialises when a member has retired, or died, MDDUS continues to represent the individual with no financial penalty for that individual or his or her estate.

The number of negligence cases has escalated significantly over recent years. It is difficult to find centralised information about negligence claims, but the table below has been formulated after counting the cases reported in Butterworths Medico-Legal Reports and the cases reported in "Medical Negligence Case Law" by Nelson-Jones & Burton in 1990. The graph shows there was a sharp rise in the cases listed from 1980-1990 and between 1990 and 1995 the cases in Butterworths increased by over 400% [Table 18.5]. There is currently much public debate about the impact of negligence claims. These are perceived as persecutory by the profession and practitioners worry about disciplinary consequences if they have made an error or a large claim leads to close scrutiny of their work. There is also much talk regarding the "blame culture", however, no obvious and

Table 18.5

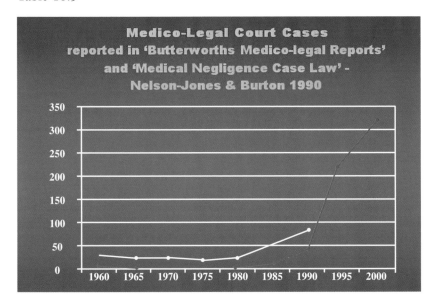

clear solution has yet been put forward. Claimants are also often dissatisfied about facing a lengthy and expensive legal process.

The cost of negligence to the NHS in England is escalating and everyone is dissatisfied when legal costs significantly exceed settlement. A large part of the NHS budget is spent on claims. Recent figures for 1999/2000 show that the NHS in England paid out nearly £400 million in clinical negligence costs, whilst the total NHS budget in England was just over £40 billion. The National Audit Office has also reported that legal costs were more than the damages awarded in 44% of cases.

There is no doubt that dealing with negligence, in general practice, hospital, or the private sector, is financially burdensome, yet those receiving settlement undoubtedly deserve compensation and those lawyers dealing with claims clearly must be paid. No-fault compensation is often held out as a preferred model for compensation in that it would be quick and simple, costs could be more easily controlled and with "no-fault" would come "no blame". However, this may fail to address the issue of individual culpability.

In medical cases, it can be extremely difficult to separate disease progression from harm due to inappropriate care, so the issue of causation persists. In no-fault schemes, settlements are often at a lower level with concomitant concerns that patients who suffer serious harm are not adequately compensated, though perhaps this is the price for a simpler and less expensive system. Also of concern is the tendency to see an increase in criminal charges in countries with a no-fault scheme. If medical mishaps occur, it is important that those involved are fully aware and clear about their individual responsibilities. If this does not happen, other routes may be used to ensure accountability, such that disciplinary procedures or even criminal prosecution may be invoked.

The Government will be attempting to address these thorny issues in a White Paper expected in 2002. Reforms may well result. These will coincide with the MDDUS Centenary and could mark a substantial turning point in the history of medical and dental defence.

Medical Errors

Patients may perceive an error in their management when, in fact, none has occurred. The resulting dissatisfaction can then lead to involvement in protracted procedures and processes for all concerned. It is not unusual for complainants to embark on all routes of accountability, even though the NHS Complaints Procedure ceases if notification of a claim is made. Complainants can, of course, await the outcome of the Complaints Procedure before pursuing a claim or bringing the matter to the attention of the General Medical Council.

If, when a situation is reviewed, errors in management may become apparent and should always be admitted. However, detailed debate may continue if any aspect of the situation is subject to dispute. The importance of a genuine expression of regret cannot be over-emphasised, but this should not constitute an admission of legal liability. Errors have relevance to complaints, claims, public inquiries and disciplinary action. The Press may also become interested and be quick to act if there is a prospect of an interesting story. Examples of the reporting of medical mishaps can be found on an almost daily basis in newspapers and it is not unknown for the GMC to ask for observations, simply on the basis of a media report. Sometimes these stories are misleading, even in circumstances where there has been a full and public disclosure of the facts of the case, e.g., if there has been a Fatal Accident Inquiry or Inquest.

It is not unusual for newspapers to report the most emotive and dramatic statements made by the relatives, to the exclusion of the medical situation that prevailed under the circumstances. The result is an unbalanced report, which ignores the medical facts of the case. This state of affairs gives little or no opportunity of redress. Some newspapers do try to portray matters in a more balanced way, after a patient has been in contact making allegations of poor treatment. However, without specific consent from the patient concerned, where information is not already within the public domain, discussion of the case would amount to a breach of confidentiality, so doctors are frequently left unable to make any response. Unprofessional newspaper reporting can be unnecessarily damaging and distressing, particularly in relation to the formal routes of accountability which a doctor or dentist may face in the course of events.

Many members seek advice when they become aware of a significant error. If an error is of sufficient magnitude, it will be immediately apparent, e.g., operations carried out on the wrong side, drug administration errors, anaesthetic errors, etc. Unfortunately, some of these cases have very serious consequences. If corrective measures can be taken, they should be done as quickly and efficiently as possible. If an error has occurred, it is important to notify those with a legitimate interest, most clearly the patient and their close carers, usually the doctor's or dentist's immediate manager or senior and, in the case of a fatality, the Coroner or Procurator Fiscal. Clear and contemporaneous records need to be kept and appropriate reports produced.

Most medical practitioners are aware of the list of reportable deaths that need to be brought to the attention of the Procurator Fiscal or Coroner. In Scotland, at the present time, any death in which a complaint is involved should be reported to the Procurator Fiscal. The MDDUS provides support and advice on the procedures and processes involved and take a view as to whether or not legal advice or representation is necessary.

The Coroner's Court England and Wales

The Coroner has to hold an inquest within the district of his jurisdiction, in the event of a violent or unnatural death or a sudden death from an

223

Table 18.6

MDDUS Coroner's Inquest Cases
1996-2000

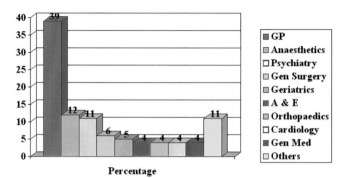

Percentage

unknown cause. An inquest must also be held if a person has died in prison. The inquest is held in a Coroner's Court, which is open to the public and the Press. The public can be excluded from an inquest or part of an inquest if it is in the interest of national security. The inquest is a fact-finding exercise. It is not a trial, but an inquisitorial process. There are no parties; there is no defence; there is no prosecution; and no one is charged. The inquest is not a method of apportioning guilt [Table 18.6].

Formerly, the Coroner's Court had the power to commit a person for murder, manslaughter, or infanticide. This power was abolished in 1977. It is mandatory for the Coroner to have a jury in certain situations, e.g., a death in prison, in police custody or on railway property, etc. The jury will consist of not more than eleven members and not less than seven and the Coroner, at the completion of his summing up, will in the first instance seek a unanimous verdict. If this cannot be reached, a majority verdict will be allowed but the minority must not exceed two.

The certification and registration of death, especially if there is the possibility of a post mortem, which may on some occasions be followed by an inquest, can be very stressful to relatives. The post mortem is frequently viewed as an anathema and families often consider the inquest a traumatic and unnecessary ordeal, as well as an invasion into their privacy and grief. However, there are certain other situations where relatives and interested parties would welcome the post mortem as an effort to prove or disprove a homicide, or some form of negligence.

The certification of death first became formalised with the Birth and Deaths Act 1836. The Act had two main purposes, to facilitate the legal proof of death and to produce more accurate mortality statistics, which were sorely needed in order to record the trends of disease in the community at large. It required the registration of every death in England and Wales.

It was the registration of uncertified deaths, which gave rise to most anxiety from the medico-legal point of view. Registration of the death was a passport to an easy passage through the formalities of regular disposal of the body. The registration of uncertified deaths without further investigation constituted a serious defect in the safeguards against the concealment of homicide. In 1858, the proportion of all deaths, which were registered as uncertified, amounted to 11% of total deaths [Registrar General 1860]. In 1885, the Registrar General stated that in the absence of a medical certificate from a registered medical practitioner or a certificate from the Coroner, the cause of death should be entered on the best information available, if necessary, on the basis of information contained in a certificate from an unregistered practitioner. Indeed, certificates were accepted from unqualified midwives and chemists [Brodrick 1971].

1893 became an important milestone in the continuing saga of the thorny problems concerning the inadequacies of the certification of death and the disposal of bodies. A select committee of Parliament was set up to inquire into the existing laws and their many loopholes, in order to allay public concern. In cases of stillbirth death, there was some suspicion that death in infancy could escape inquiry if it was accepted as a stillbirth. It was recommended that no death should be registered without a certificate stating the cause of death from a duly registered medical practitioner or a Coroner, after inquest. Before the medical certificate was issued, the medical practitioner should have personally inspected the body in order to establish the fact of death as well as its cause. Stillbirths should be treated the same way as deaths generally. There were other recommendations regarding the disposal of bodies and that burials should only be permitted by an order of the Registrar [Brodrick 1971].

In spite of these recommendations, little concerted action was taken until the Birth and Death Certification Act of 1926 made it unlawful to dispose of a body before either a Registrar's or Coroner's Certificate had been issued. It required stillbirth to be registered and imposed restrictions on the disposal of the bodies of stillborn children, as well as imposing certain controls on the movement of bodies into or out of England and Wales.

The Brodrick Report

On the 17 March 1965, a warrant of appointments was issued in Parliament appointing a committee to review the law and practice relating to the issue of medical certificates on the cause of death, the disposal of dead bodies and the law and practice relating to Coroners and Coroners Courts. Mr

---

IAN LAIDLAW STEVENSON

Ian Stevenson was the Financial Controller of the MDDUS from 1984 until 1993. He died suddenly at his home on 1 November 2000. He was educated at Glasgow Academy where he was an excellent rugby player and an equally good cricketer. He played for his school and also for Clydesdale Cricket Club and was a keen member of the Academy's OTC. He saw service as a paratrooper in Europe, the Middle East and the Far East, before being demobbed at the end of 1947. He was a very popular figure within the organisation and saw many changes in the way in which the MDDUS activities expanded during his time, starting in St Vincent Street, moving to West George Street and ultimately retiring from Mackintosh House.

Norman Brodrick QC was appointed Chairman and gave his name to the report, which had taken the committee almost seven years to complete. It was finally submitted to Parliament on the 10th November 1971. It was a most searching report, which looked at the very many aspects of Death Certification.

The Brodrick Report contained no less than 114 recommendations. The past thirty years have highlighted how many of the recommendations were admirable and immensely practical. Many recommendations have been slowly implemented in a variety of ways, such as, Coroner's Rules and Amendments, The Criminal Law Act of 1978, Local Government Acts, etc. It is also equally true to state that some of the recommendations have been modified and that a number have not as yet been implemented.

The death certificate had been looked upon by the public as providing the authoritative and genuine truth as to the cause of death. It had been thought of as the safety net against the possibility of secret homicide. The Brodrick Report stated:

Our general conclusions are that the risk of secret homicide occurring and remaining undiscovered as a direct consequence of the state of the current law on the certification of death has been much exaggerated and that it has not been a significant danger at any time in the past 50 years.

The present death certificate allows "old age" to be given as a cause of death provided the person was over seventy years. Dr K. Kafetz expressed the view that persons aged seventy - seventy five should not be classed as elderly [BMJ 2001]. He commented:

... Few doctors who work with elderly people are unable to give a specific cause of death even for patients over ninety-five. I use 'old age' only for those few patients over eighty-five (no more than one a year), who make an active decision to fade away and in whom disease has been excluded by physical examination, blood tests, basic radiology and psychiatric examination. The time has come to restrict or even abolish use of this cause of death on certificates.

In the wake of the Shipman Saga with its startling disclosures of his secret multi-homicide activity, there have been inevitable questions raised concerning the rules and regulations of death certification and cremation. Shipman's criminal conduct was able to escape discovery for a very long period of time and, despite the number of deaths, he evaded detection. The safeguards to protect the public from such abhorrent and totally unprofessional behaviour appeared to be ineffective. Thus, it is to deter any possible future medical maverick that the current regulations should be strengthened and modified.

A more accurate definition is required for the statement, "Attended to in his or her last illness". The obscurity of the term has been unresolved ever since its first appearance in the Act of 1836. It was stated in evidence before the select committee on death certification that a High Court Judge had ruled that "attendance" implied at least two attendances on the deceased, one of which must have been given within eight days of death [Havard 1960]. The regulations should state the number of times the doctor had attended the deceased and over what period. It is equally important that the attendance must be related to the final cause of death.

There is no obligation for a doctor to report a death to the Coroner, although, in practice, doctors do so in situations of doubt or suspicion. However, in the case of the death of any person who has been attended in his last illness by a registered medical practitioner, the practitioner is obliged to sign and transmit to the Registrar of Births and Deaths, a certificate stating to the best of his knowledge and belief the cause of death [Jervis 1993]. Jervis goes on to make comment on this obligation; it is strictly an obligation to notify the cause of death and not the fact.

Certification of death undoubtedly will need some modifications and new guidelines. However there must be care not to rush into changes of such magnitude, which could result in an oppressive regime both for the medical profession and other associated agencies.

Fatal Accident Inquiry

In Scotland, the Procurator Fiscal has responsibility for the investigation and prosecution of crime and the investigation of sudden deaths, under the Fatal Accident and Sudden Deaths Inquiry (Scotland) 1976 and the Fatal Accident and Sudden Deaths Inquiry (Scotland) Rules 1977. The two functions are related since, in investigating deaths, one of the concerns of the Procurator Fiscal is to eliminate the risk of undetected homicide or breaches of statutory duties of care. However, it is the duty of the office to investigate all sudden, suspicious, accidental, unexpected and unexplained deaths, whether or not the circumstances include any element of criminality.

The Procurator Fiscal acts impartially and in the public interest. The mandate is to ascertain the true circumstances of a death. Investigations initiated by the Procurator Fiscal may be sufficient in themselves to establish the innocent circumstances of a death. These may provide evidence to warrant prosecution for murder or culpable homicide, for breaches of health and safety legislation or for contraventions of the Road Traffic Act. Alternatively, the circumstances may be such as to warrant the holding of a Fatal Accident Inquiry [Table 18.7 (over)].

A Fatal Accident Inquiry is held in public, on the application of the Procurator Fiscal to the Sheriff Court for the area in which the circumstances of the death were most closely related. Such action is mandatory in cases where it appears that the death occurred as a result of an accident in the course of the deceased's employment or occupation, or

Table 18.7

MDDUS Fatal Accident Inquiry Cases
1996-2000

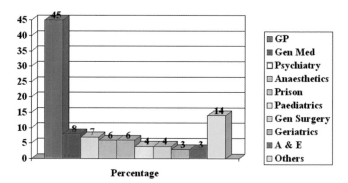

Percentage

if the death occurred while the deceased was in legal custody. The category that is most likely to affect members of MDDUS is the Inquiry deemed to be in the public interest. Other categories would include deaths resulting from road traffic accidents where the condition of the road or quality of signposting is an issue, deaths that may have resulted from a defect in a medicinal product or lack of medical care, deaths resulting from the abuse of controlled drugs and, of course, deaths resulting from major disasters such as Lockerbie. In other cases, a Fatal Accident Inquiry will be held at the discretion of the Lord Advocate, on the grounds that a death was sudden, suspicious, unexplained, or occurred in circumstances that gave rise to serious public concern.

Intimation of a Fatal Accident Inquiry goes to the deceased's next-of-kin and any other person having an interest, or upon whom there is a likelihood of responsibility for the accident or death. In addition, the Procurator Fiscal must also advertise the hearing in two newspapers, one a national daily, the other a local daily. Witnesses to the Inquiry will then be cited by means of a written citation, served by recorded delivery or by a police officer. If a witness fails to attend, there is provision in the rules for the Sheriff to grant a warrant to apprehend and bring the witness to court.

Fatal Accident Inquiries are held before a single Sheriff, sitting without a jury. Although it is the duty of the Procurator Fiscal to adduce all evidence regarding the circumstances of death, the deceased's next of kin is also entitled to appear, to be represented and lead evidence. This also applies to any person the Sheriff is satisfied has an interest. In practice those who do tend to appear, or arrange for representation, are the next of kin and those who may be at risk of being criticised in relation to the circumstances of death.

At the conclusion of the evidence, the Sheriff is obliged to make a finding of where and when the death or accident resulting in the death took place. He must also determine the cause. The Sheriff then has the discretion to state in his finding the reasonable precautions, if any, whereby the death or the accident resulting in death might have been avoided. He can also state the defects, if any, in any system of work that contributed to the situation. Finally, he can make a finding on, "any factors which are relevant to the circumstances of the death". It is not necessary for the evidence upon which the Sheriff based any of his findings to be corroborated.

A Fatal Accident Inquiry is not a criminal trial. The evidence led at the Inquiry may tend to show responsibility attaching to one individual or organisation and the Sheriff's determination may reflect that. However the Sheriff's determination is not admissible in evidence in any other civil or criminal proceedings arising from the circumstances of the death. In the majority of cases, most deaths do not raise issues of public concern. The proportion of deaths reported to the Procurator Fiscal, which result in an Inquiry is very small. In 2000/2001, out of a total of 13,685 deaths reported to Procurators Fiscal across Scotland, only 79 resulted in Fatal Accident Inquiries.

Ethics

The ethical dimensions of medicine and dentistry are as important in medical defence deliberations as high professional standards and good practice. The application of ethics has been ingrained in both professions since their origins, although the heightened emphasis on the subject in recent years belies this longevity. Ethics do not offer easy definition, or criteria, on which to base judgement. In its simplest form, it is an examination of the rights and wrongs of professional conduct, ideals that are not imposed by formal standards or by the application of the law.

Although the essence of ethics is embodied in the Hippocratic Oath, it was not until the eighteenth century that it developed a form in the moral and intellectual concept of the practice of medicine. Since the formulation of the Oath in the fifth century BC, issues embodied within it, such as confidentiality and respect for life from its conception, continue to be relevant in modern day medical practice. The man credited as the architect of professional medical ethics in the English-speaking world was John Gregory of Aberdeen [McCullough 1998]. He studied medicine at Aberdeen, Edinburgh and Leiden before returning to Aberdeen as Professor of Philosophy. It was during the mid-1700s, that he formulated his ideas on medical ethics, in which the judgement, knowledge and experience of the individual physician are the central components that remain in force to the present day.

Advances in medical science have promoted the frequency and complexity of ethical debates. The intravenous drip technique for feeding, introduced in 1926 and subsequent developments, such as blood plasma transfusion, made it possible for comatose patients to be fed and nourished much more easily than any previous methods. This created, in turn, prolongation of life issues.

Decisions to Limit Life-Extending Treatment

Since the development of intensive care units and the technologies of mechanical ventilation, dialysis and tube-feeding, it has become possible to save and sustain the lives of patients with previously fatal conditions. Some such patients need life support only temporarily and then recover. For others, these technologies simply prolong the process of dying. Some who survive are left dependent on technology and with very poor quality of life. Inevitably, a view emerged that doctors were sometimes doing more harm than good and the phrases, "death with dignity" and "a life worse than death" began to be heard.

Ethicists emphasise that treatment is justified only when the benefits are greater than the burdens and that the patient's views on this balance are paramount. Every mentally competent patient has the right to refuse treatment, either its initiation or continuation, even if it is life-saving or life-sustaining, provided that the consequences of such refusal are understood. It is unlawful for a doctor to ignore an expression of autonomy by a patient, either contemporaneously or in a previous advance directive.

The treatments that may be limited include cardiopulmonary resuscitation, admission to or continued stay in an intensive care unit, emergency surgery, mechanical ventilation, artificial nutrition, dialysis, blood transfusion and the use of drugs such as antibiotics, anti-cancer agents and cardiac stimulants or anti-arrhythmics.

The decision to limit treatment most often arises in one of three circumstances. The most common is when a previously healthy patient develops critical illness - usually due to trauma, heart attack, stroke or infection. In such patients an initial trial of treatment is almost always justified. The second is a predictable relapse or progression in a patient already suffering chronic illness, such as advanced cancer, organ failure or AIDS. The third arises in a patient in a relatively static state of poor quality of life such as Persistent Vegetative State (PVS), or advanced dementia.

The decision to withhold or withdraw treatment from a previously healthy patient taken suddenly ill is made largely on the grounds that treatment is considered unlikely to be successful in saving life, or if it is, that death would be only temporarily postponed. Patients with such critical illness are seldom able to participate in the decision-making, but families will always be consulted about the patient's attitude to such a life-threatening situation. The decision has to be made by the doctor because, legally, no relative or friend can consent to or refuse treatment for an adult incompetent patient, except in Scotland under the terms of the Adults with Incapacity (Scotland) 2000.

Difficulty arises in patients in a relatively stable state such as PVS or advanced dementia. A decision not to treat acute infections with antibiotics or to use cardio-pulmonary resuscitation for a crisis is relatively readily made, after consultation with the relatives. When patients with advanced dementia begin to refuse to accept food, it is relatively uncontroversial to decide not to initiate tube-feeding, which can be regarded as an intrusive intervention that brings no ultimate benefit to the patient. More difficult are patients in the vegetative state, because they are already being tube-fed, although it is agreed that there is no moral or legal distinction between withholding and with-drawing treatment [Jennet 2002].

It is now held by many authorities that the vegetative state can be considered to be permanent twelve months after a head injury or six months after a non-traumatic brain insult. It is morally and legally acceptable to discontinue tube-feeding on the grounds that this is non-beneficial treatment that a doctor is under no obligation to provide. Although many members of the public, doctors and nurses indicate in questionnaires that they would not wish to be kept alive in this state, it is only a minority of the families of such patients who agree to discontinuation of treatment.

DR ANDREW ALLISON

Dr Andrew Allison died on 20th May 2001 in the Scottish Borders. He was consultant physician at the Southern General Hospital, Glasgow from 1950 to 1978, a Fellow of the British Medical Association and Honorary Fellow of the Medical and Dental Defence Union of Scotland. He was the son of Professor Andrew Allison, the forensic medical expert. He enjoyed a long professional association with the MDDUS. He was elected to its Council in 1967 and subsequently became Convener, a post he held from 1980 to 1991. In this appointment, he carried on a unique family tradition, established by his father, who had been Convener between 1943 and 1962. Between them they formed a family connection in the appointment, spanning thirty years.

Since the Bland case in 1992 [BMLR 1993], it has been necessary to apply for a High Court declaration before withdrawing artificial nutrition and hydration from vegetative patients. In England, Wales and Northern Ireland, the Official Solicitor represents the patient and will usually commission an independent second expert medical opinion. Several cases have gone through the English courts since Bland, usually attracting little publicity and often with an interdict (injunction) against identifying the patient or the hospital. Many cases have been decided in the American courts (including one appeal to the US Supreme Court). In the last decade, US judges have emphasised that the court should be used only when there is a dispute to settle. Recent reports from the Law Commissions in England and in Scotland recommend that a less formal method of decision-making should be devised in the UK.

In Scotland, it is not necessary to apply to the High Court for a declarator, the Scottish equivalent of a declaration, before withdrawing artificial nutrition and hydration from vegetative patients. In the Law Hospital case [SC 1996], it was explained that it is competent to apply by petition to the

Court of Session for authority to discontinue treatment for vegetative patients. When such petition proceedings are raised, the Court will appoint an advocate to act as curator to the patient, to ensure that the interests of the patient are fully considered by the Court. There is, however, no requirement that such authority must be sought in every case and if doctors act in accordance with BMA Guidelines, good medical practice and with the full agreement of the relatives it would be inconceivable that there would be any legal repercussions. It is very important that neither medical staff, nor relatives involved in these tragic situations, should contemplate that there would be any possibility of criminal proceedings, if they had behaved responsibly and in accordance with sound medical practice.

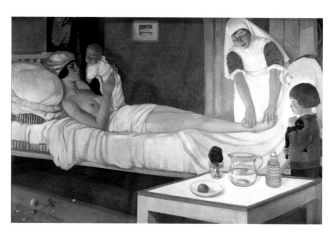

Cecile WALTON
(1891-1956)
Romance 1920
Oil on canvas
Scottish National Portrait
Gallery, Edinburgh

Cecile Walton was the daughter of the Glasgow Boy E. A. Walton. In 1914 she married Eric Robertson and both became members of the Edinburgh Group of artists. In this memorable image of maternity, she has represented herself stretched out on a bed and holding up her newborn son, Edward, while a nurse washes her feet.

Judges dealing with individual cases have emphasised that there is a clear distinction between "letting die" and "killing". Ethicists likewise have mostly recognised a clear distinction between a decision to limit treatment so as to let nature take its course, and a deliberate act to end life.

It is not simply the criteria used in selecting patients for the withdrawal of therapy, but also the methods by which treatment is discontinued. MDDUS has had involvement in such cases either by advising on the interpretation of guidelines, or assisting the doctor in respect to a criminal inquiry.

Advances in Ethics

It was the advances in the transplantation of human organs and human tissue, which propelled bioethics to the top of the ethical debate in the 1960s, from which it has not since been displaced. Subsequent medical advances have raised ethical questions on human fertilisation and embryology issues between the 1970s and 1990s, which, in turn, has led to the emergence of medical genetics, which now undergo their own ethical scrutiny and resolution.

The Human Fertilisation and Embryology Authority (HFEA) was set up in 1991 as a regulatory body for clinical treatment utilising in vitro fertilisation or donor insemination and research involving human embryos. It has additional functions to inform both the general public and those seeking treatment and to lead debate on the associated ethical and social issues. The HFEA has considered and consulted on many contentious issues, such as pre-implantation diagnosis, cloning and the production of a healthy baby for sibling treatment, where life-saving transplant material is required. All of these developing areas, in which the HFEA has a central role, will have a substantial impact on society and the indications are that there will be considerable growth in these aspects of medicine in the future, accompanied by their associated ethical dilemmas.

The MDDUS follows the development of such issues very closely. It is as easy to fall foul of ethical negligence as it is of medical negligence. Two of the key issues in medical negligence are consent and confidentiality and both have an equal importance and bearing on the practice of medical ethics. The underlying principle of non-maleficence, doing no harm to someone who is willing, is an essential component of consent in medical treatment. The counterbalance to this principle is that every medical patient of sound mind has the right to determine what is to be done with his or her own body and that this right carries certain responsibilities. The position between is bridged by the information and agreement necessary to satisfy both sides of this doctor-patient equation. Consent binds the legal and ethical requirements of medicine.

In the patient-doctor relationship, there has also been a change from the paternalism of the past to a more modern partnership, in which health decisions are made on a mutually agreed basis. The prima facie moral principle of autonomy underpins good modern medical practice. Partnership brings with it more than agreement, it also brings mutual responsibility for any decision that has been reached. This would seem to imply that consent might well develop into a shared responsibility between doctor and patient. Nevertheless, it will remain incumbent on the doctor or dentist to ensure that the patient's understanding of alternatives to and inherent risks in the proposed treatment is as comprehensive as possible.

Medicine and dentistry remain inexact sciences. Outcomes cannot be guaranteed and difficulties during procedures remain a constant risk. Against this background of uncertainty, the information on which consent is based is never likely to be exhaustive and complete and any expressed risks may dissuade patients from undergoing the proposed treatment. However, the danger in incomplete consultation to obtain consent, is shown by the 1972 American court case in which a doctor was held not to have reasonably met his obligation to disclose information on risks, by a failure to disclose to his patient, a chance of paralysis from a laminectomy, based on the results of all laminectomy operations conducted, in the order of 1 in 14,000 [US App C 1972].

The traditional relationship between doctor and patient is private and confidential. It underpins the trust between both parties and the ability of the doctor to provide effective treatment from inclusive information on the case in question. Absolute confidentiality is not enjoyed between doctor and patient such as is found in the solicitor and client relationship, which is shielded by legal privilege. In recent years, legislation on the disclosure of information has enshrined patients' right of access to manual and computer-produced medical records. In addition, patients must give consent to the disclosure of personal medical information in reports required by employers, etc. The legislation also included the extension of the right of access to those with a familial responsibility and those who have been granted consent by the patient. Traditional confidentiality becomes strained under these circumstances and the dilemma of disclosure is not solely a medical consideration. The strict insistence on these rights to information denies the duty of discretion to the doctor and may be an impediment to protecting sensitive matters of medical care, which may cause harm to the patient. Although a doctor's duty of confidentiality extends beyond death, the approach has had to be modified because the Access to Health Records Act 1990, which remains valid in such circumstances, permits disclosure to a variety of third parties.

Ethical issues continue to proliferate in the practice of medicine and dentistry, as more and more research continues into biotechnology and gene therapy. Medical ethics have also broadened to include bioethics and the swift expansion of knowledge in life sciences has created an increasing range of bioethical problems. These impinge on a number of disciplines, e.g., science, law and medicine, which demonstrate that the resolution of medical ethics issues is a matter that requires an inter-disciplinary approach. Despite this, the sense of moral judgement on which the individual doctor or dentist depends is personal, yet it is part also of a communal sense of right and wrong within his or her profession, fashioned by the tradition of service and association with colleagues. The key component in practical medical ethics is a balanced partnership with effective communications between patient and doctor.

Legislation and Medical Defence

Legislation continues to impinge on medical defence as British society becomes more sophisticated and European-oriented. The European Convention on Human Rights sought to protect certain freedoms, which were embodied into the Human Rights Act of 1998. It was the first major Bill on Human Rights for 300 years. The standards that set the European convention were largely drafted by Britain in the late 1940s and Britain was the first country to ratify the convention in March 1951. However, since these were set out in an international convention, the individual had to look to the European court at Strasbourg to interpret and give effect to them. In essence, the Act brought home from the European court, the ability of British people to argue for their rights in British courts without inordinate delay or cost. Prior to the Act, an appeal in 1992 would have cost, on average, £30,000 and taken five years to get an action into the European court in Strasbourg. Several of the Articles of the Act will have significant effect on medico-legal affairs in the future.

In a similar fashion, data protection has continued to affect both the medical and dental professions. The Data Protection Act 1998 implemented a directive on data protection that was agreed in the European Union in 1995. It covered both manual and computerised records with special safeguards for the processing of sensitive personal data and individual rights to gain access to information. It also instituted a Data Protection Register for users. The implications for practitioners of both professions are obvious and the Bill brought within its scope records covered by the Access to Health Records Act 1990, except for deceased patients.

This sampling of legislation at the start of a new century seems to give a clear indication that the legislative trend affecting the medical and dental professions, begun in the 1960s, will continue to maintain its comparatively high level of activity.

Practitioners at the beginning of the 20th century were not likely to face legal challenge, although they perceived a need for assistance that was undoubtedly heightened by a few high profile cases. Over the last one hundred years, not only has the rate of claims accelerated, so has the complexity of the medico-legal interface. Legislation directly related to medical practice has increased, especially in the latter half of the 20th Century. Accountability, regulation and governance have all become part of the day-to-day practice of medicine and dentistry. As a result, disciplinary processes are increasingly complex and complaints procedures have been introduced.

During the first fifty years, the vast majority of MDDUS members would never encounter any medico-legal difficulties. That is no longer the case and any doctor or dentist in modern practice will be faced with medico-legal queries or challenges quite frequently in their practice. Legislation and disciplinary processes will continue to change, develop and grow. At one time, a practitioner could have had a good working knowledge of medical law to assist their clinical activities. This is now not possible. Medical law is developing into such a complex specialty in its own right that MDDUS provides advisory services twenty-four hours a day. Medical progress has brought increased legislation and regulation to the professions. Medical technology also raises new ethical dilemmas and problems. These affect every practitioner and it is the responsibility of the MDDUS to keep up to date with every aspect of medicine and medical law in order to play a pivotal role in giving member practitioners access to current information throughout the year. There is no doubt that medical defence is an essential feature in medical and dental society and will continue to support efficient and expert practice in the 21st century.

Change at the GMC

These have been anxious times for doctors. A recent series of worrying and highly public clinical failures has shaken the profession and the structures through which it operates, raising fundamental questions about the culture and safety practices of both the medical profession and the NHS. The public reaction to these events has fuelled momentum for change in the regulation of doctors and for the modernisation of the NHS. An old-fashioned, inefficient GMC has undoubtedly been part of the problem. But even more worrying is the NHS itself, which, as the report by Ian Kennedy and his team into the adverse events at the Bristol Royal Infirmary indicated, has suffered from organisational, management and cultural failings that have jeopardized the safe care of patients [Bristol Inquiry 2001].

Against this background, over the last five years, substantial changes have been taking place. These are being taken forward through a new framework for clinical standard-setting and service delivery, the National Institute for Clinical Excellence and the National Service Frameworks. In hospitals, the principles of effective quality management are starting to be applied to the every day clinical processes in clinical governance. There is also external institutional quality assurance in the form of the Commission for Health Improvement and the Clinical Standards Board in Scotland.

The regulation of individual health professionals by the profession itself, is a key part. Good, safe, care is heavily dependent on doctors, their competence, ethical values, attitude to patients, honesty and commitment. However, despite consistent and continued trust in doctors [BMA/MORI Poll 2001], the trust in the system that regulates them has been seriously eroded. The GMC has realised this and unprecedented structural and constitutional modifications are taking place. These will enable the GMC to be more open and transparent, as well as more effective, fair and efficient in the discharge of its functions.

Opposite:

Alonso de SEDANO
(late 15th century)
Saints Cosmas and Damian performing surgery c.1495
Oil on wood
The Wellcome Library, London

The brothers Cosmas and Damian, patron saints of doctors and surgeons, were 4th century martyrs in Syria. Here they are performing their most famous miracle, the first transplant surgery. They amputated the cancerous (or ulcerated) leg of "a devoted servant of the martyrs", replacing it with the healthy leg of a dead Ethiopian.

Reform

The GMC remained largely unchanged for over a century until the 1970s, when questions about purpose and function began to emerge. The first substantial attention paid to its activities came in the form of the Merrison Committee, which was established in the wake of a revolt by the medical profession over the introduction of the retention fee. The committee did not question professional self-regulation. It stated that the essence of a profession is that it should be composed of people with specialist skills and knowledge that the public wants to use and affirmed that the maintenance of a register of competent practitioners by the profession should represent a contract with the public [Merrison 1975]. It did, however, lay considerable criticisms at the door of the GMC and the outcomes produced the groundwork for reforms that came into force under the 1978 Medical Act. These changes included:

The GMC Nameplate at Great Portland Street
The GMC

- New structures, which included a larger General Council with an Executive Committee.
- Giving the GMC the ability to be more positive in raising the standard of education.
- The introduction of more robust procedures for overseas doctors.
- Expansion of guidance on standards, set out in the *Blue Book* [GMC 1979].
- The creation of the Health Committee for handling sick doctors.
- Revision of the complaints machinery.

Although changes, made in the light of the Merrison Inquiry, went some way towards satisfying the Government, the profession and the public that professional self-regulation could work, many of the GMC's problems were just beginning. The public's expectations of what medical regulation was and should be, were changing rapidly. With the rise of a consumer-focused culture and the increased availability of health care information, especially through developments in information and communication technologies, patients no longer wanted a paternalistic and one-way relationship with their doctor. More and more patients wanted to be fully informed and involved as assertive participants in their own health care. They also wanted, and indeed started to demand, reassurance that doctors were up to date, fully competent and safe to practise. For many, the GMC reflected attitudes, which appeared increasingly out of date and unduly protective of doctors, rather than patients.

The changes in public expectations paralleled significant changes within medicine itself. As Chantler pointed out, "Medicine used to be simple, ineffective and relatively safe. Now it is complex, effective and potentially dangerous" [Chantler 1999]. Continuing and accelerating scientific and technological advance began, in many ways, to outstrip professional development and the ability of the NHS to support a quality medical service through the production of good reliable data and good systems. There was also a move towards ever more narrow technical skills in the specialties and, at the same time, a move towards a more holistic approach in general practice. This resulted in a widening gap between the two fields. Doctors' attitudes, communication skills, and the way they related to colleagues tended to fall in between. It was from within this shifting context that the GMC began to make fundamental philosophic changes to its policies, working towards a new professionalism in medicine and re-establishing the basis of its original contract with the public.

In the past, the GMC had focused principally on discipline. It was now to adopt the role of fostering standards of good practice for all doctors, by defining the attributes of a good doctor, rather than focusing on defining what would amount to serious professional misconduct. Revision of the *Blue Book*, post-Merrison, was the first step, but the most radical change came in 1995 with the introduction of *Good Medical Practice* [GMC 2001]. For the first time there were explicit generic standards for what was expected of a doctor. Similarly, *Tomorrow's Doctors* made explicit recommendations as to what skills and knowledge should be encompassed in undergraduate medical education [GMC 1993].

George CRUIKSHANK
(1792-1878)
The Cholic
Coloured lithograph
Glasgow Museums

The English illustrator and caricaturist, Cruikshank, produced several prints depicting the agony of ill health. While no remedy is offered for colic the cause of the illness is alluded to in the picture hanging behind the patient – an overweight woman is shown drinking in her bedroom.

Another major shift in thinking for the GMC came with the introduction of performance procedures. The conduct procedures could deal only with specific, usually serious, incidents and were unsuitable for dealing with patterns of deficient professional practice. The first stages in the development of what are now the Performance Procedures began in 1989, but it was not until later that the Medical (Professional Performance) Act 1995 was passed, to become operational in 1997. For the first time, poor or unsafe clinical performance was now regarded as within the GMC's scope, rather than in a kind of "no man's land".

Additionally, perhaps one of the most decisive shifts towards a modern, more inclusive GMC was the increase in lay membership, signalling the emergence of a professional/public partnership in the regulation of medicine. Today, a quarter of the Council is comprised of lay members, who provide an active and invaluable contribution to the work of the Council at all levels. In July 2001, the Council agreed that, after a review of its structure, constitution and governance, a smaller, more efficient body of thirty-five members should be established, at least 40% of whom will be lay members.

The Present

This brings the subject up to date and to some of the most fundamental changes to happen to the GMC in its 150-year history. Changes, which will help not only to address many of the concerns about it being isolated, bureaucratic, and protective of doctors, but also to take on the difficult task of driving medical culture further in the direction of more openness and accountability.

The job of the GMC is to set the framework for effective professional practice. It needs to make sure that all doctors on the Medical Register can demonstrate that they have the qualities that the public expects of a registered medical practitioner, in particular that they are competent, reliable and capable of forming good relationships with their patients and colleagues. Today there is a coherent strategy for implementation that has four main components.

Professional Standards

For the first time, the GMC has set out the principles of good medical practice and linked them directly to a doctor's registration. *Good Medical Practice* was a landmark in the development of explicit professional standards. Medicine, and the social and cultural landscape within which it operates, is not static but continues to be updated and reviewed on a regular basis. The second edition was published in 1998, the third in the summer of 2001. The booklet has attracted international interest and is now being used in twelve countries and translated into languages that include Japanese and Albanian. Many medical schools now also incorporate the fundamentals of its contents into student graduation ceremonies. The Royal Colleges and Faculties have already, or are currently interpreting, its principles in the context of their own specialties, to underpin specialist training, continuing professional development and for use in revalidation.

Education

The Education Committee of the GMC is responsible, under the Medical Act, for setting and maintaining the high standard of undergraduate medical education in the UK and of medical student assessment. *Tomorrow's Doctors,* the committee's current Recom-

mendations on Undergraduate Medical Education, published in December 1993, contains an explicit range of guidelines concerning the form and content of the curriculum. A new version is about to be
published, bringing it up to date and allowing it to reflect changes since the last publication, such as, changes in the legal and ethical basis of medicine, multi-professional working, and preparing students for practice in a multi-cultural society. The most significant change made in the new edition will allow the professional standards and behaviour set by *Good Medical Practice* to be delivered through undergraduate medical education.

Revalidation

The Medical Register is the foundation of the system of medical regulation and it is in this area that the GMC is making some of the most fundamental changes; changes that are likely to have the greatest impact on patient safety. Until now, registration has been a historical record of the qualifications needed to join the Register. In 1999, the Council decided that this was no longer sufficient. Instead registration should be an up to date statement of a doctor's fitness to practise, which is directly linked with the professional standards of practice set out in "*Good Medical Practice*".

The GMC in session in the Council Chamber

The GMC

In May 2001, the Council agreed that the model for revalidation was sufficiently developed and that the GMC should ask the Government for the legislation that will provide an enabling framework for implementation. In due course, the GMC will issue guidance to recommend that doctors produce information in the form of a "revalidation folder" submitted at five yearly intervals to a "revalidation group" appointed by the GMC. The group will include two doctors and one lay person and will decide whether it can recommend to the GMC that the doctor's registration be revalidated. In most cases, the background material for this folder will be provided by the annual appraisal being introduced across the NHS. The NHS has agreed that appraisal should cover the seven headings of *Good Medical Practice*.

A similar approach is being taken with institutions outside the NHS. For example, arrangements have been agreed with the medical services of the armed forces. In the private sector, there are moves towards an understanding with private hospital providers that the renewal of hospital privileges would be based on a review, set against the template of "*Good Medical Practice*". With revalidation, there is a coherent approach, focused on local clinical quality assurance, which is systematic and based on the booklet. The new process will be consistent with effectiveness and underpinned by fitness to practise procedures.

Fitness to Practise

The fourth component of the new strategy is a review of the fitness to practise procedures. The purpose is to be fair, objective, transparent and free from discrimination, when dealing with doctors whose registration is brought into question. This covers not only the scope for small-scale changes but also whether the whole legal structure is fit for its purpose.

The need for change has become increasingly manifest. There has been a threefold increase in complaints since 1995, i.e., 1,500 in 1995, to 4,500 in 2000. In recent years, the on-going public scrutiny of professional regulation, outlined earlier, has come to a head with the Professional Conduct Committee's inquiry into complaints about paediatric cardiac surgery in Bristol, the case of gynaecologist Rodney Ledward and the shocking case of Harold Shipman. Concern inside and outside the profession focused on the need for effective action to be taken swiftly on emerging problems and that all agencies, concerned with the safe delivery of medicine, work together to protect the public. Scrutiny has also raised concerns about the effectiveness and consistency of processes, especially decisions taken at an early stage. A 1999 report by the Policy Studies Institute contained proposals for making those initial stages more consistent and demonstrably fair to all doctors [Allen 2000].

A number of changes have already been initiated:

Introduction of service standards
At the end of June 2001, 74% of cases received since 1 July 2000 had met the standard of being either closed with an explanation or, referred on to the next substantial stage, within six months.

Increased number of recruits to Professional Conduct Committee (PCC)
74 extra members, 47 lay and 27 medical, from outside the GMC have been members recruited and fully trained to sit on the PCC panels.

Increased number of PCC hearings
The number of PCC hearings for 2001 was more than double the number in 2000.

Creation of Interim Orders Committee (IOC)
The IOC has given the GMC the power to restrict or suspend a doctor's registration quickly, pending investigation, if it is justified in the public interest to do so. The IOC came into force on 3 August 2000, the first meeting was held on 17 August 2000 and during 2000, the IOC considered 72 cases.

There is still much to do. The GMC is in the process of reviewing the initial stages of the complaints procedures to avoid duplication of effort and to foster consistency in decision-making. There is also a proposed separation of functions, which will secure procedural safeguards, preventing the involvement by the same personnel at both the investigation and adjudication stages. With the recent introduction of the European Convention on Human Rights through the Human Rights Act, these changes are a vital step towards fairness, openness and uniformity.

The review also extends to looking at the standard of proof currently used by the PCC and examining at what level of seriousness the use of a criminal standard of proof is justified. There has been full consultation on all of these issues and there is a general consensus on the way forward with many of them. Within such a complex sphere of policy development there are, of course, still areas where more work is needed. If the GMC's strategy is implemented successfully, the professionalism of doctors will be enhanced and many of the anxieties, felt by doctors and patients alike, alleviated.

Saturn
NASA and the NSSDC Photo Gallery

Hubble observes a new Saturn Storm

This NASA Hubble Space Telescope image of the ringed planet Saturn shows a rare storm that appears as a white arrowhead-shaped feature near the planet's equator. The east-west extent of this storm is equal to the diameter of the Earth (about 7,900 miles). Hubble provides new details about the effects of Saturn's prevailing winds on the storm.
The storm was imaged when Saturn was 904 million miles from the Earth. The picture is a composite of images taken through different color filters within a 6 minute interval to create a "true-color" rendition of the planet. The Hubble images are sharp enough to reveal that Saturn's prevailing winds shape a dark "wedge" that eats into the western side of the bright central cloud. The planet's strongest eastward winds (clocked at 1,000 miles per hour from analysis of Voyager spacecraft images taken in 1980-81) are at the latitude of the wedge.
Reta Beebe (New Mexico State University), D. Gilmore, L. Bergeron (STScI), and NASA

Future Perspectives

The Changing Face of Medicine

Medicine over the last one hundred years has specialised in many different ways and along many different avenues. No longer do we have an anaesthetist, now we have anaesthetists specialising in neonatal surgery, cardiac surgery, intensive care, transplants, and so on. As these sub-specialties have developed so have the levels of skill amongst the specialists involved. This has led to the development of many high-risk procedures, which even a decade ago would not have been contemplated. League tables are now being produced comparing one hospital with another. Unfortunately these comparisons are not often as accurate or as reliable as they might be, because adequate consideration is not always given to the fact that specialist hospitals take on cases of a much higher risk than hospitals of a more general nature. This, however, is not always understood by the public and can lead to an increased expectation of the service provided by general hospitals, which, in fact, should only be available through the specialised units. This, in turn, leads to more claims, more complaints and more dissatisfaction amongst the general public.

Although the public may now surf the Internet and obtain more detailed information about the health care services, they do not always understand that specialised health care may not be available in their area. It may be necessary to travel some distance to obtain the level of care to which they feel they are entitled. In some respects, the medical profession must carry its own share of the blame for this, in that it is often reported in the Press that a certain type of surgery, or treatment has recently been developed, which will answer all the problems of patients suffering from a particular disease. Unfortunately, this is usually proved to be in small areas of clinical practice, in very specialised cases and at the hands of a very few experienced practitioners. However, it leads the population at large and particularly those suffering from that particular condition to develop high expectations of a cure, or a better prognosis than they might otherwise have had. When they find that such a prognosis is not available and a cure is not round the corner, they may react badly. Again, this is understandable but it does bring further problems for medical practitioners, particularly those who have no knowledge or experience of this new "cure".

Gone are the days when patients were admitted to hospital and were prepared to do whatever they were told was necessary, in order to achieve a good outcome for their problem. Nowadays they expect full information, full consultation and full participation in their treatment. In many ways, this is to be accepted by the profession but it is very often difficult, bearing in mind that the patients are not always as well informed as they think they are and refuse to accept the information provided by their specialist practitioners.

Difficulties arise in situations where the more specialised the treatment, the more expensive it is likely to be, the more staff are likely to be involved and the costs involved may not be acceptable to the Government, or to the various health organisations. The Government has been accused of postcode provision of services and the new Human Rights legislation may well have some bearing on this as cases are put forward to the courts arguing that every patient has the right to the same level of treatment, irrespective of where they live within the UK. Unfortunately, with the financial resources available to the health service, this is not always feasible. It would seem very likely that more and more specialisation in very highly specialised units will be the norm and patients will have to travel some distance to obtain this specialised treatment. This may, in fact, reduce the risk to these patients, because the practitioners carrying out the treatment will be seeing many cases of this particular type and thereby build up an enviable expertise in dealing with them. It will mean that the general attitude of the public will have to be re-educated to appreciate that health care at its optimal level, available on everyone's doorstep, is now unrealistic and impractical as far as finance and medical expertise are concerned.

The Changing Face of Dentistry

Dentistry has also become more specialised during the last century. As well as oral surgery, orthodontics and restorative dentistry, there are now specialists in maxillofacial surgery, periodontology, endodontics, paediatric dentistry, oral medicine and pathology. The majority of dentists, about 80% of the profession, still work in general dental practice and an increasing number of those may have a specialist interest. During the last thirty years, there have been major changes in the incidence of dental disease and dental care. Dental caries has undergone a marked reduction among children and periodontal disease can generally be controlled. Health education and prevention is the basis in dental care of the young, rather than the regular inspection and fillings regime that often led to extractions and dentures. Scottish statistics of the period reveal a drop in the number of fillings and extractions, whereas crowns, bridges and veneers show a marked increase. According to the Scottish Dental Practice Board, in the period from 1966 to 2000, annual treatments for crowns have risen from 7,005 to 138,749; bridges from 7 to 15,075; and, since 1988, when they became available on the NHS, veneer treatments have risen to 23,077.

There is an increasing awareness that dentistry has become oral health care which cannot be separated from health care in general. The dentist is progressively more concerned with influencing patients' behaviour and encouraging individual involvement in prevention by home care, with regular, less frequent, visits to the dentist for inspection, treatment and care. Nevertheless, there is still a need for restorative dentistry and repair work for the adult and elderly sections of the community. The modern dentist is also more involved in the early detection and treatment of oral cancer and pre-cancerous lesions and oral manifestations of systemic disease such as AIDS and infections. Furthermore, the dentist is providing dental care for an increasing number of patients, many of whom may be receiving systemic drug therapy and are medically compromised.

The broadened scope of the dentist has, as its main purposes, prevention or early diagnosis. The dentist has been trained to make clinical decisions on the basis of the history, the lifestyle and clinical examination of the patient and in knowing what is normal and what is abnormal. In those ways, the dentist has not only to be manually and technically skilled, but also able to utilise the methods of the oral physician.

Dentists are conscious of what can be achieved by the preventive approach to disease. They are becoming involved in encouraging healthy lifestyles and the promotion of health in general. Dentists in many countries are providing this type of health promotion. Some large companies have screening programmes for their employees. They include breast screening, cervical cytology, oral examinations, etc. The patient data on history and lifestyles are interchangeable between the programmes. However, these are only the early stages in developing co-ordinated primary care involving doctors, dentists and other health care professionals. There are important opportunities for further development and research in this area.

Health Care Changes

The establishment of the Scottish Parliament has vested the responsibility for the provision of health care services in Scotland in that Parliament. So far, the changes in health care provision in Scotland have been very few, but it is still early in the life of the Parliament. Scotland has always enjoyed an excellent reputation for its high level of health care and no doubt the Holyrood government will ensure that this tradition is continued.

247

One of the major elements of concern at the beginning of this new millennium is the development of risk assessment and risk management. The Westminster and Holyrood governments are promoting these as key areas along with clinical governance. If they are properly implemented and funded, then they could assist the development of better health care and reduce the incidence of claims and complaints against the practitioners who work within the system.

One of the worrying areas is the proliferation of committees, working parties, sub groups, etc., within the health care services. More and more clinicians are becoming involved in these committees and groups and this means that they have less time to give to patient care. The Government is looking very carefully at the regulation of health professionals and is proposing to introduce a council for the regulation of health care professionals working within the health care services. Added to the various other groups that are involved in supervising the health care services, one might wonder whether the situation has now been reached where the supervisors are supervising themselves and being supervised, in turn.

It is to be hoped that this proliferation will be short-lived and that the committees and working parties will provide the solutions to the various problems of delivering first class health care, thereby allowing clinicians in the medical and dental professions to get on with the work for which they are properly and appropriately trained. The professions must have a say in the running of the health service but their prime role is the care of patients. The combination of committee and clinical responsibilities can be very difficult, particularly when finances and resources are limited.

Challenges

As the MDDUS faces the beginning of its second century of service to members it faces challenges, which its forebears in 1902 could never have anticipated. Advances in science and technology and the continuing revolution in information access and dissemination continue to have major implications for the medical and dental professions. They have to be taken account of, if professional independence is not to be regarded as dated and out of tune with modern society. Patients are no longer the passive recipients of care, but well-informed participants in their treatment choices and this has altered the doctor-patient relationship. Medical litigation remains on the increase and associated costs have escalated.

Modern health care is a complex field in a changing National Health Service and the development of medical ethics has demonstrated that medical science will continue to raise challenging issues which may require adjudication. Rapid developments and innovation in medical and dental practice over the years have necessitated changes in the structure and function of the component parts of the NHS and successive governments have struggled to balance costs with effective treatment. This, in turn, has brought stress and pressure of change to the very point of health care delivery. It is particularly evident in the upsurge of medical legislation in the past thirty years or so. In addition, recent high profile cases of medical misdemeanour have led to an unwarranted general attack on the professional ability of the professions. This has caused a sense of alienation and of being undervalued within clinical establishments. There is a real danger to the standards of health care in the country if this trend continues.

Patient expectation has risen steadily alongside consumer expectation generally. This has been fuelled by the wider dissemination of medical information, particularly the high focus that is given to new emerging techniques and treatment procedures. The general population has become more litigation-conscious due to a variety of factors - media attention to claims and large settlements, lawyers advertising their services, access to free advice, Patients' Charter, NHS Complaints Procedure, to name a few. Legal aid provided the finance to pursue the majority of medical negligence claims although the criteria, both financial and merits-based, are now much more stringent. Added to the further factors of a state of flux in the NHS, the numerous accountability structures and procedures that have been set in place for both professions and the present "blame culture" in society, it is not difficult to see the continuing importance to the individual practitioner of his or her medical defence organisation.

Members of the Council and Management Committeee of the MDDUS 2001

1. Dr William Chambers
2. Dr Donald Pearson
3. Professor Ray Newton
4. Mr Douglas Harper
5. Dr Douglas Garvie
6. Dr Brendan Sweeney
7. Mr Eric Battison
8. Professor Robert Wood
9. Dr Douglas Bell
10. Dr Judith Chapman
11. Dr William Matthewson
12. Dr John Garner
13. Dr Ian Anderson
14. Dr Ian Simpson
15. Mr Peter Edmond
16. Professor David Wray
17. Mr Colin Slevin
18. Mr Hugh Harvie
19. Mr Martin Lees
20. Dr Alistair Miller
21. Dr Alistair Beattie
22. Professor Forrester Cockburn
23. Mr Alexander Matthewson
24. Dr Bernice Muir
25. Dr David Watts
26. Dr Graham Buckley
27. Mr George Bennet

Litigation and Legislation

In 1948, the MDDUS paid out £787 in settlements of medical litigation; in 1996, claim settlements had risen to £2,755,000. From 1948 until the end of 1989, all doctors and dentists had to look to a professional indemnity organisation to provide the necessary indemnity cover. On 1 January 1990 the Government introduced the NHS Indemnity Scheme, which now provides indemnity for all doctors and dentists working in the hospital and community sectors. General practitioners are still required to provide their own indemnity, although with the introduction of salaried

GPs employed by Trusts and the development of Primary Care Trusts and Groups this may well change.

The MDDUS experience of hospital-based claims almost disappeared in 1990 following the introduction of NHS indemnity, however this has been substantially replaced by hospital and community doctors and dentists utilising the other services provided by the MDDUS in disciplinary and GMC/GDC matters, Fatal Accident Inquiries and Coroner's Inquests. There has also been an increased interest in the private sectors of medicine and dentistry. No-fault compensation has been considered several times by different governments, but no scheme has yet been devised which would appear to have any signs of a successful outcome. Both the General Medical and General Dental Councils have progressively increased their powers to deal with practitioners who have under-performed, are ill or have misbehaved. This, in turn, has had significant consequences for the MDDUS in an increased demand from members for advice and representation.

Legislation, which understandably lags behind medical science, has also changed the face of medical defence over the century. After the comparative calm of the first fifty years, the 1960s decade saw a significant increase in medical legislation, or legislation closely associated with the practice of medicine, which contained a strong ethical dimension, such as the Abortion and Human Tissue Acts. Each subsequent decade seems to have had a distinctive legislative theme. The 1970s reflected the retrograde effects of medical science in such Acts as Congenital Disabilities and Vaccine Damage and the rising tide of patient complaint. The 1980s reflected the growing ethical dimension in such Acts as Surrogacy and Organ Transplantation and the start of the drive on privacy of information. The 1990s continued the theme of information access and disclosure while bioethics gained ground with human fertilisation, organ transplant and the prominent emergence of genetics and gene therapy. The future is likely to see the emergence of a European influence on medical legislation, such as a continued focus on human rights. The electronic age will continue to impact on the security of medical information and records and medical science will continue to strain the ethical dimensions of its boundaries.

Much comment has been made in this record of a century of service, on the changes that have occurred in the professions during this period. The changes in the medico-legal scene over the last few decades have been greater than for many years and there are no signs that the rate of change is likely to decrease within the next decade. Much of this is due to increased patient awareness, access to very highly specific information through the Internet, and other forms of electronic communication. There now exists a much better educated population in general than existed at the outset, when the MDDUS took its first faltering steps and it has taken some time for the medical and dental professions to realise this. The problem is, that the population has not as yet been able to look critically at computer information and analyse whether or not that information is relevant to them. Education of the population in this area is therefore likely to be vital if they are to be able to use the service effectively and efficiently.

It is difficult to believe that medical litigation in its current format will continue for very many more years but, human nature being what it is, it is likely that there will always be a perceived need to retaliate in some way or another against the person or the system, which is believed to have caused harm. Introduction of no-fault compensation will not alleviate the patient's desire to "punish" the clinical professional, whom they feel caused them pain and suffering, no matter the compensation. The present tort system is by no means ideal but, as yet, no one has come up with a suitable alternative. Mediation, arbitration, Independent Review Panels have all been considered but none, as yet, has proved to be the ideal solution. A great deal of money, which could otherwise be usefully directed towards an increased level of excellence in health care, is currently being diverted to compensate a very small number of patients for the harm they have suffered. Whilst everyone is entitled to compensation for any harm, the fact that this may, in itself, be causing harm to others because they cannot get the level of service that they need, has not been fully understood and appreciated.

Since its founding, the MDDUS has been at the centre of the impact of legislation, ethics and scientific advance on both professions. It has participated fully in the debates and decisions, which have resulted. Its members have assumed positions of professional responsibility within all the governing bodies of medicine and dentistry and have been party to many of the medico-legal legislative developments which have passed into law. Medical and dental science will continue to challenge the current legislative and ethical parameters that govern them and, with a century of experience in practice behind it, the MDDUS will continue to uphold the best traditions of both medicine and dentistry.

Chapter Essayists

Chapters
1-4

Dr Douglas Bell, FRCP Ed FFOM

Professor Christopher Clayson, CBE MD FRCP FRCP Ed Hon
FRCP Ed Hon FACP Hon FRACP Hon FRCPS Glasg Hon FRCGP

Dr Somerled Fergusson, MBE FRCGP DObst RCOG

Dr Alan Large, FRCGP

Dr Angus MacCuish, MD FRCP Ed FRCP Glasg

Dr Iain Macdonald, CB MD FRCP Ed

Mr Ian Rattray, MBE BA LDS

Dr Rufus Ross, LDS RCPS Glasg BA (Hons) PhD

Dr Jean Scott, MD FRCPath DStJ

Dr J. Kelly Swanston, LRCP Ed LRCS Ed LRCPS Glasg

Chapter 5

Dr John B. Barr, MBE MB ChB

Mr Sandy Flockhart, LDS

Professor Ronald Girdwood, CBE MD PhD FRCP FRCP Ed
FRCPath FRSE Hon FACP Hon FRACP

Dr Thomas Reilly, MC MB ChB KStJ

Dr Martin Nichols, MBE ChB FRCPS Glasg

Professor David Watt, BDS FDS PhD

Chapter 6

Professor Paul Geissler, DDS FDS DRD FRCS Ed

Dr John Hanley, LRCP LRCS Ed LRFPS Glasg

Dr Gerald C. McGlone, LRCP Ed LRCS Ed LRCPS Glasg

Dr Henry Noble, PhD FDS

Dr John Alistair Riddell, OBE FRCGP

Chapter 14   Professor Alastair A. Spence, CBE MD FRCA

Chapter 15   Dr Brendan Sweeney, MA FRCGP
             Dr Graeme Laurie LLB PhD
Chapter 16   Georgina Haysom, BSc LLB (Hons) Sydney LLM (Bioethics) McGill

Chapter 17   Dr E. M. Armstrong, FRCP Ed FRCP Glasg FRCGP
             Dr Jim Cox MD FRCP Ed FRCGP

Chapter 18   Dr Gail Gilmartin MB ChB MPhil
             Sir Montague Levine, Kt FRCP(I) FRCGP LRCP&S(I) DMJ[Clin]
                 Hon DSc City
             Professor Bryan Jennett, CBE MD FRCS
             Dr C. George M. Fernie, MB ChB MPhil MRCGP Dip[For Med]
             Mr Rupert Jackson, QC
             The Lord Mackay of Drumadoon, QC LLM

Chapter 19   Sir Donald Irvine, CBE MD FRCGP

Chapter 20   Dr Ian Simpson MB ChB FRCP Ed MRCGP Dip[Soc Med]
             Professor Sir David Mason, CBE BDS MB ChB MD FDSRCPS
                 Glasg FRCS Glasg FRC Path FDSRCS Ed FFDRCSI Hon FDS
                 RCPS Glasg Hon DDS Wales Hon LLD Dundee Hon FRCS Ed
                 Hon DSc Western Ontario D Univ Glasg FRSE

Contributors to the History

Mr Alexander Adam, FRCS, Hon Librarian, Aberdeen Medico-Chirurgical Society, University of Aberdeen

Dr E. M. Armstrong, FRCP Ed FRCP Glasg FRCGP, Chief Medical Officer, Scottish Executive

Mrs Sheila Baumann, Medical and Dental Defence Union of Scotland

Dr John B. Barr, MBE MB ChB

Mr James Beaton MA ALA FSA (Scot), Librarian, The Royal College of Physicians and Surgeons of Glasgow

Dr Douglas Bell, FRCP Ed FFOM, Medical Archivist, Medical and Dental Defence Union of Scotland

Dr E.S. Blackadder VRD FRCP Ed FRCPS Glasg MRCGP FFOM DObst RCOG

Professor Robert Bluglass, CBE FRCPsych FRCP

Mr John A.D. Cameron BDS DGDP (UK), Medical and Dental Defence Union of Scotland

Dr Graham Carey MB ChB FRCA MRCGP Dip[Com Child Health], Medical and Dental Defence Union of Scotland

Kathy Cerminara, Assistant Professor of Law, Shepard Broad Law Center, Nova Southeastern University, Florida

Anne Chambers, Medical and Dental Defence Union of Scotland

Professor Christopher Clayson, CBE MD FRCP FRCP Ed Hon FRCP Ed Hon FACP Hon FRACP Hon FRCPS Glasg Hon FRCGP

Dr Stephanie J. Cook MBE MA(Cantab) BM BCh(Oxon)

Dr Robert H. Corbett, DMRD Eng

Dr Charlotte Cowie MB BS Dip[Sport Med] Dip[M-S Med] MLCOM

Dr Jim Cox MD FRCP Ed FRCGP

Dr John K. Davidson, OBE MD FRCP Ed FRCP Glas FRCR Hon FACR Hon FRACR

Dr Matthew Dickson MB ChB

Sheriff Robert H. Dickson, Sheriff of South Strathclyde, Dumfries and Galloway
at Airdrie

Mr Simon Dinnick, RadcliffesLeBrasseur

Liz Dunbar, Medical and Dental Defence Union of Scotland

Mr Peter Edmond CBE TD, Chairman, Medical and Dental Defence Union of
Scotland

Cathy Ferguson, Medical and Dental Defence Union of Scotland

Dr Robert Somerled C. Fergusson, MBE FRCGP DObst RCOG

Dr C. George M. Fernie, MB ChB MPhil MRCGP Dip[For Med], Medical and
Dental Defence Union of Scotland

Mr A. S. Flockhart, LDS

Dr Douglas Garvie, OBE FRCGP

Professor Paul R. Geissler, DDS FDS DRD FRCS Ed

Dr Gail Gilmartin MB ChB MPhil, Medical and Dental Defence Union of
Scotland

Professor Ronald Girdwood, CBE MD PhD FRCP FRCP Ed FRCPath FRSE
Hon FRACP Hon FACP

Mr John Griffiths, Shepherd & Wedderburn WS

Mr Andrew M. Hadden, BDS MPhil MGDS RCPS Glas, Medical and Dental
Defence Union of Scotland

Mr Christopher Hale BA (Hons)

Dr John McD. Hanley, LRCP LRCS Ed LRFPS Glas

Mr Andrew Harry Hamilton

Mr Hugh Harvie BDS FDS RCS Ed FDS RCPS Glasg Dip[For Med], Medical
and Dental Defence Union of Scotland

Georgina Haysom BSc LLB (Hons) Sydney LLM (Bioethics) McGill
United Medical Protection, Australia

Sir Donald Hamilton Irvine, CBE MD FRCGP

Professor Carol Henderson, The Shepard Broad Law Center, Nova Southeastern
University, Florida

Dr Robert A. Hendry MB ChB M Phil MBA MRCGP DRCOG, Medical and
Dental Defence Union of Scotland

Dr Ian T. Jackson, MD FRCS FACS Hon FRACS Hon DSc Glasg, St. Louis

Mr Rupert Jackson, QC

Professor Bryan Jennett, CBE MD FRCS

Professor P. F. Jones MA FRCS FRCS Ed

The Lord Kilpatrick of Kincraig, CBE MD Hon FRCP Ed

Dr Alan H. D. Large FRCGP

Dr Graeme Laurie, LLB PhD Department of Law, University of Edinburgh

Sir Montague Levine, Kt FRCP(I) FRCGP LRCP&S(I) DMJ[Clin] Hon DSc City

Dr Nancy B. Loudon, OBE FRCP Ed FSFP

Dr John D. D. Loudon, OBE FRCS Ed FRCOG FFFP

Dr Angus MacCuish MD FRCP Ed FRCP Glasg

Dr Iain S. Macdonald, CB MD FRCP Ed

Dr John MacDonald, FRCGP DObst RCOG

The Lord Mackay of Drumadoon, QC LLM

Professor Ian MacGillivray, MD FRCP Glasg FRCOG, Emeritus Regius Professor
of Obstetrics and Gynaecology, University of Aberdeen

Professor E. McC. McGirr, CBE MD DSc FRSE FRCP
FRCP Ed FRCPS Glasg

Dr Gerald Corbett McGlone, LRCP LRCS Ed LRFPS Glasg

Fiona Mackie, Medical and Dental Defence Union of Scotland

Mr Donald A. D. Macleod FRCS Ed FRCP Ed, Honorary Medical Adviser to
the Scottish Rugby Union, Vice President, The Royal College of Surgeons of
Edinburgh

Karl Magee, MA Dip Arch Stud RMSA, Archives and Special Collections, Mitchell
Library, Glasgow

Professor William G. Manderson MD FRCP FRCPS Glasg Hon LLD

Dr J.S. Manson MB ChB AFOM

Professor Sir David Mason, CBE BDS MB ChB MD FDSRCPS Glasg FRCS
Glasg FRCPath FDS RCS Ed FFDR CSI Hon FDS RCPS Glasg Hon DDS Wales
Hon LLD Dundee Hon FRCS Ed Hon DSc Western Ontario D Univ Glasgow FRSE

Dr William B. Mathewson MB ChB MPhil FRCP Ed FRCGP Dip(For Med)
Dip[GM], Medical and Dental Defence Union of Scotland

Professor Ronald H.M. Mavor CBE FRCPS FRSA

Dr Berenice B. Muir MB ChB FRCR

Mr Ian Fraser Kerr Muir MBE VRD FRCS FRCS Ed

Dr Roderick F. Neilson MB ChB FRCP MRCPath Dip[For Med], Medical and
Dental Defence Union of Scotland

Dr Martin Nichols MBE MB ChB FRCPS Glasg

Dr Henry W. Noble, PhD FDS, History of Dentistry Research Group, University
of Glasgow

Dr Malcolm Nicholson, Wellcome Unit for the History of Medicine, University
of Glasgow

Dr John Nicolson MB ChB FRCS Ed

Mrs Carol Parry BA DAA, The Royal College of Physicians and Surgeons of
Glasgow

Miss Fiona Paterson, Shepherd & Wedderburn WS

Miss Anita Pavillard

Mr G. A. Piper VRD FDS RCS Ed

Dr A. W. Raffan TD FFA RCS

Contributors to the History

Mr Ian J. Rattray, MBE BA LDS, Dental Archivist, Medical and Dental Defence Union of Scotland

Dr Thomas Reilly, MC MB ChB KStJ

Professor John Richmond, CBE MD FRSE FRCP FRCP Ed FRCS Ed FRCPS Glasg Hon FACP Hon FRACP

Dr J. Alistair Riddell, OBE FRCGP

Dr James Rodger BA BSc (Hons) MBA FRCP Ed FRCGP, Medical and Dental Defence Union of Scotland

Dr Rufus Ross, LDS RFPS Glasg BA (Hons) PhD, History of Dentistry Research Group, University of Glasgow

Dr Jean Scott, MD FRCPath DStJ

Dr Ian G. Simpson MB ChB FRCP Ed MRCGP Dip[Soc Med], Chief Executive and Secretary, Medical and Dental Defence Union of Scotland

Mr Colin Slevin, MA CA Medical and Dental Defence Union of Scotland

Professor Alastair A. Spence, CBE MD FRCA

Capt (retd) Peter Starling, Curator, Army Medical Services Museum

Rt Hon The Lord Steel of Aikwood KBE MSP, Presiding Officer, The Scottish Parliament

Dr Peter Stewart MB ChB

Dr James Kelly Swanston, LRCP Ed LRCS Ed LRCPS Glasg MRCGP

Dr Brendan Sweeney, MA FRCGP, Medical and Dental Defence Union of Scotland

Surgeon Commander Alasdair J. Walker, FRCS RN

The Lord Walton of Detchant, Kt TD MA MD DSc FRCP F.Med.Sci.

Andrew Watt MD FRCS

Professor David Watt BDS FDS PhD

Professor James Williamson CBE FRCP Ed DSc Professor Emeritus, University of Edinburgh

References

Chapter 1. - The Scene is Set

Bowman, A. K. 1942. *Life and Teaching of William Macewen*. London: William Hodge & Co.

British Medical Journal. 1902. 2: 625-626. *The Ballachulish Quarry Company and its Medical Officer*.

– – –. 1903. 1: 100, 162-163, 626. *The Ballachulish Quarry Company and their Medical Officer*.

– – –. 1903. 2: 45-46, 328-329, 1092, 1605. *The Ballachulish Quarriers and their Medical Officer*.

Clayson, Christopher. 1987. In *Improving the Common Weal: Aspects of Scottish Health Services 1900-1984*. McLachlan, G. ed. Edinburgh: Edinburgh University Press.

Cunningham, George. 1892. "Cambridge Conference on the Condition of Children's Teeth." *British Dental Journal* 13: 582-583.

Currie, J. R. 1930. *A Textbook of Hygiene*. Edinburgh: E & S Livingstone.

Ferguson, T. 1958. *Scottish Social Welfare*. Edinburgh: E & S Livingstone.

Fisher, William, Macpherson. 1885. "Compulsory Attention to the Teeth of School Children." *British Dental Journal* 6: 585-593.

Fothergill, Margaret I. Letter to Professor Sir David Mason, n.d. History of Dentistry Research Group, University of Glasgow Dental Hospital and School.

Jarvie, Nicol. 1902. "The Teaching of Anaesthetics." *The Lancet* 1: 122.

Kinnaird, J. 1987. In *Improving the Common Weal: Aspects of Scottish Health Services 1900-1984*. McLachlan, G. ed. Edinburgh: Edinburgh University Press.

References

Lambert, R. 1963. *Sir John Simon 1816-1904.* London: MacGibbon & Kee.

Lancet, The. 1902. 1: 38. *The Consultant and the General Practitioner.*

– – –. 1902. 1: 979. *The Obstetrician – Physician or Surgeon?*

– – –. 1902. 1: 58-59. *The Organisation of the Profession – Popular Errors in regard to Club Practice.*

Lindsay, Lillian. 1933. *A Short History of Dentistry.* London: John Bale, Sons and Danielsson, Ltd.

Mackie, J. D. 1954. *The University of Glasgow 1451-1951.* Glasgow: Jackson, Son & Co.

Mitchell, T.J., Smith G.M. 1931. *History of the Great War: Medical Services - Casualties and Medical Statistics of the Great War.* London: HMSO.

National Archives of Scotland, Edinburgh. Fraser-Mackintosh Collection:

    (a). GD: 128/54/11/5.

    (b). GD: 128/54/10/9.

Ross, M. R. 1994. "The Development of Dentistry: A Scottish Perspective circa 1800-1921." Ph.D. diss., Department of Scottish History, University of Glasgow.

Ross, M. R., ed. 1999. "Recollections of a Dental Student 1899." *History of Dentistry Research Group University of Glasgow Dental Hospital and School Newsletter,* No. 5 (October).

Scott, Jean, M. 1984. "Women and the GMC." *British Medical Journal* 289: 1764-1767.

Thomson, J. Stitt. 1902. "The Obstetrician - Physician or Surgeon?" *The Lancet* 1: 1138.

Young, Archibald. 1910. *Papers of Archibald Young 1873-1939.* Royal College of Physicians & Surgeons of Glasgow, Archives: 39/3/9 March - June 1900.

Chapter 2. - The Founding of the MDDUS

British Medical Journal. 1883. 2:1207, 1211. *Vexatious Prosecutions of Medical Men.*

– – –. 1885. 2: 272, 1177-8. *The Case of Dr Bradley.*

Forbes, Robert. 1948. *Sixty Years of Medical Defence.* Cambridge: W. Heffer and Sons Limited.

Glasgow Medical Journal. 1920. 93: 19-20. *Obituary Dr Robert Wardrop Forrest.*

Jenkinson, Jacqueline. 1993. *Scottish Medical Societies 1731-1939.* Edinburgh: Edinburgh University Press.

MDDUS Minute Papers. 1904. *Minute Book No. 1*. May 1902 – Dec 1908.

– – –. 1909. *Minute Book No. 2*. Jan 1909 – Apr 1918.

Ross, M. R. 1994. "The Development of Dentistry: A Scottish Perspective circa 1800-1921". Ph.D. diss., Department of Scottish History, University of Glasgow.

Chapter 3. - Health, Welfare and Conflict

Blackden, Stephanie. 1998. *From Physicians' Inquiry to Dewar Report: A Survey of Medical Services in the West Highlands and Islands of Scotland, 1852-1912*. Part 1. Proceedings of the Royal College of Physicians of Edinburgh 28: 51-66.

Currie, J. R. 1930. *A Textbook of Hygiene*. Edinburgh: E & S Livingstone.

Ferguson, T. 1948. *The Dawn of Scottish Social Welfare*. Edinburgh: Nelson.

Ferguson, T. 1958. *Scottish Social Welfare*. Edinburgh: E & S Livingstone.

Hamilton, D. 1987. In *Improving the Common Weal: Aspects of Scottish Health Services 1900-1984*. McLachlan, G. ed. Edinburgh: Edinburgh University Press.

Hogarth, J. 1987. In *Improving the Common Weal: Aspects of Scottish Health Services 1900-1984*. McLachlan, G. ed. Edinburgh: Edinburgh University Press.

Macgregor, A. 1967. *Public Health in Glasgow 1905-1946*. Edinburgh: E. & S. Livingstone.

MacPherson, Major General Sir W.G. 1921. *History of the Great War; Medical Services General History*. Vol. 1. London: HMSO.

– – –. 1923. *History of the Great War; Medical Services General History*. Vol. 2. London: HMSO.

MacQueen, Loudon and Kerr, Archibald, G. 1974. *The Western Infirmary 1874-1974*. London and Glasgow: John Horn Ltd.

Marlborough, H. S. 1995. "The Emergence of a Graduate Dental Profession 1858-1957." Ph.D. Thesis, University of Glasgow.

Mavor, Ronald. 1988. *DR MAVOR and JAMES BRIDIE Memories of James Bridie*. Edinburgh: Canongate Publishing Limited.

Ross, M. R. 1994. "The Development of Dentistry: A Scottish Perspective circa 1800-1921". Ph.D. diss., Department of Scottish History, University of Glasgow.

Scott, Jean, M. 1984. "Women and the GMC". *British Medical Journal* 289: 1764-1767.

Scott, Jean, M. 1988. "Women and the GMC: The Struggle for Representation." *Journal of the Royal Society of Medicine*. Vol. 81.

Chapter 4. - Progress and Practice

Bliss, M. 1996. *The Discovery of Insulin.* Toronto: McClelland & Stewart.

Brotherston, J. & Brims, J. 1987. In *Improving the Common Weal: Aspects of Scottish Health Services 1900-1984.* McLachlan, G. ed. Edinburgh: Edinburgh University Press.

Hogarth, J. 1987. In *Improving the Common Weal: Aspects of Scottish Health Services 1900-1984.* McLachlan, G. ed. Edinburgh: Edinburgh University Press.

Kelnar, C.J.H. 1995. *Childhood and Adolescent Diabetes.* London: Chapman and Hall.

Kinnaird, J. 1987. In *Improving the Common Weal: Aspects of Scottish Health Services 1900-1984.* McLachlan, G. ed. Edinburgh: Edinburgh University Press.

Macgregor, A. 1967. *Public Health in Glasgow 1905-1946.* Edinburgh: E. & S. Livingstone.

MDDUS Minute Papers. 1922. *Minute Book No. 3.* Apr 1918 – July 1926.

– – –. 1933. *Minute Book No. 4.* Sep 1926 – Apr 1935.

– – –. 1940. *Minute Book No. 6.* Jun 1940 – Dec 1944.

National Archives of Scotland, Edinburgh. HH1/472.

Chapter 5. - A Time of War

Brotherston, J. & Brims, J. 1987. In *Improving the Common Weal: Aspects of Scottish Health Services 1900-1984.* Edited by G. McLachlan. Edinburgh: Edinburgh University Press.

Johnstone, T. 1952. *Memories.* London: Collins.

Kinnaird, J. 1987. In *Improving the Common Weal: Aspects of Scottish Health Services 1900-1984.* Edited by G. McLachlan. Edinburgh: Edinburgh University Press.

Levitt, I. ed. 1992. *The Scottish Office, Depression and Reconstruction 1919-1959.* Edinburgh: Scottish Historical Society.

Ministry of Health, Department of Health for Scotland. 1944. *Scotland A National Health Service.* CMD 6502. London.

MDDUS Minute Papers. 1944. *Minute Book No. 6.* Jun 1940 – Dec 1944.

– – –. 1946. *Minute Book No. 7.* Jan 1945 – Dec 1946.

Nichols, W. Martin. 1951. *Presidential Address: Detained Personnel.* Zodiac Journal Vol. 2: No 3. Aberdeen University Medical Society: Aberdeen.

Pavillard, Stanley. S. 1960. *Bamboo Doctor.* London: Macmillan & Co. Ltd.

Chapter 6. - Catalysts of Change

All England Law Reports. 1954. 2: 131-143. *Roe v Ministry of Health and Others Woolley v Same.*

– – –. 1957. 2: 118-128. *Bolam v Friern Hospital Management Committee.*

British Medical Journal. 1948. 1: 347. *38,534 Doctors Disapprove.*

Hansard Parliamentary Debates. 1956. 5th ser., vol. 545, cols. 1349-1350.

Levitt, I. ed. 1992. *The Scottish Office, Depression and Reconstruction 1919-1959.* Edinburgh: Scottish Historical Society.

MDDUS Minute Papers. 1949. *Minute Book No. 9.* Nov 1948 – Sep 1950.

– – –. 1952. *Minute Book No. 11.* Apr 1952 – Dec 1953.

– – –. 1954. *Minute Book No. 12.* Jan 1954 – Jan 1956.

Session Cases 1955. SC 200: 204-205. *Hunter v Hanley.* [Scots Law Times Reports. 1955. 213-218].

Chapter 7. - Advances and Specialties

Collings, J.S. 1950. "General Practice in England Today: A Reconnaissance." *The Lancet* 1: 555-585.

Gray, D.J.P. 1992. *Forty Years On.* London: Atalink.

Hadfield, S. 1953. "A Field Survey of General Practice." *British Medical Journal* 2: 683-706.

Hansard Parliamentary Debates. 1959. 5th ser., vol. 598, col. 728.

Hare, E.H. 1988. "Schizophrenia as a recent disease." *British Journal of Psychiatry* 149: 554-561.

Hunt, J.H. 1983. *Past attempts to found a College of General Practitioners one and a half centuries ago.* In *A History of the Royal College of General Practitioners.* Lancaster: MTP Press Limited.

Jones, K. 1991. *The culture of the mental hospital.* In *150 years of British psychiatry, 1841-1991.* Berrios, G.E., Freeman, H. eds. London: Gaskell Press.

MacFeat, G. 1951. "The Family Doctor." *British Medical Journal* 2: Supplement, 1-3.

Martin, J.P. 1984. *Hospitals in trouble.* Oxford: Blackwell.

References

Rose, F.M. and Hunt, J.H. "College of General Practice." *British Medical Journal* 2: 908.

Royal Commission Report. 1957. *Royal Commission on the Law Relating to Mental Illness and Mental Deficiency 1954-1957.* Cmnd 169. London: HMSO.

Taylor, S. 1954. *Good General Practice.* London: Oxford University Press.

Chapter 8. - The Watershed of Litigation

Baird, Dugald. 1965. "A Fifth Freedom". *British Medical Journal* 2: 1141-1148.

Hansard Parliamentary Debates. 1967. 5th ser., vol. 741, cols. 935-1020.

Harvey, W. Butler, O. Furness, J. and Laird, R. 1968. The Biggar Murder, Dental, Medical, Police and Legal Aspects. *Journal of the Forensic Science Society.* Vol. 8: No. 4.

Horobin, Gordon. ed. 1973. *Experience with Abortion: A Case Study of North East Scotland.* Cambridge: Cambridge University Press.

Macfarlane, Alison, et al. 2000. *Birth Counts. Statistics of pregnancy & childbirth.* Vol. 2 Tables. Second Edition. London: The Stationery Office.

MDDUS Minute Papers. 1966. *Minute Book No. 18.* Mar 1966 – Sep 1967.

– – –. 1968. *Minute Book No. 19.* Oct 1967 – Feb 1969.

– – –. 1968. 5th ser., vol. 758, cols. 1600-1711.

Chapter 9. - Emerging Issues

Teasdale, G. and Jennett, B. 1974. "Assessment of coma and impaired conscious: a practical scale." *The Lancet* 2:81-84.

Hansard Parliamentary Debates. 1985. 6th ser., vol. 73, col. 1384.

– – –. 1988. 6th ser., vol. 132, col. 884.

Jennett, B. and Bond, M. 1975. "Assessment of outcome after severe brain damage: a practical scale." *The Lancet* 1:480-484.

MDDUS Minute Papers. 1975. *Minute Book No. 26.* May 1975 – Jun 1976.

– – –. 1977. *Minute Book No. 28.* Sep 1977 – Oct 1978.

All England Law Reports. 1997. 4:771-780. *Bolitho v Hackney Health Authority*.

MDDUS Minute Papers. 1993. *Minute Book No. 39.* Nov 1987 – Oct 1995.

MDDUS Management Committee. 1996. *Book No. 2.* Mar 1993 – Dec 1997.

Chapter 11. - Radiation Medicine

Allison, D. 1997. *Medico-legal issues in diagnostic radiology: Ethical issues and informed consent in interventional radiology.* In *Diagnostic Radiology: A Textbook of Medical Imaging*. 3rd edn. Grainger, R.G. and Allison, D. eds. Edinburgh & New York: Churchill Livingstone.

Burrows, E.H. 1986. *Pioneers & Early Years: A History of British Radiology.* Alderney: Colophon Press.

Calder. J.F. 2001. *A History of Radiology in Scotland 1896-2000.* Edinburgh: Dunedin Academic Press.

Craig, J.O.M.C. 1997. *Medico-legal issues in diagnostic radiology: Litigation in clinical radiology in the United Kingdom.* In *Diagnostic Radiology: A Textbook of Medical Imaging*. 3rd edn. Grainger, R.G. & Allison, D. eds. Edinburgh & New York: Churchill Livingstone.

Thomas, A.M.K. 1995. *The Invisible Light. 100 years of Medical Radiology.* Oxford: Blackwell Science.

Chapter 12. - Sports and Exercise Medicine

No references

Chapter 13. - Plastic Surgery

Dunbar, J. 1934. "Review of the burn cases treated in the Glasgow Royal Infirmary during the past hundred years (1833-1933) with some observations on the present day treatment." *Glasgow Medical Journal* 122: 239-255.

Gillies, H.D. 1920. *Plastic surgery of the face.* Oxford: Oxford University Press.

Gupta, Sri Madhusu dana. ed. 1835-1836. *The Susrata or System of Medicine taught by Dhanwantari and composed by his disciple Susrata.* Calcutta.

References

Medical Research Council Special Report Series No. 249. 1945. *Studies of Burns and Scalds (Reports of the Burns Unit, Royal Infirmary, Glasgow 1942-1943)*. London: HMSO.

Reverdin, J-L. 1869. "Epidermic grafts." *Bulletin Soc. Impérial de Chirurgie*. 2nd ser. Vol. 10: 493, 511. Paris. 1969.

Thiersch, C. 1874. "The microscopic changes in skin grafted onto granulation tissue." *Verhandl. Deutsche Gesellsch. Chir*. 3: 69.

– – –. 1886. "On skin grafting." *Verhandl. Deutsche Gesellsch. Chir*. 15: 17.

Wolfe, J.R. 1875. "A new method of performing plastic operations". *British Medical Journal* 2: 360.

Zeis, Eduard. 1838. *Handbuck der plastichen Chirugie*. Berlin.

Chapter 14. - Anaesthesia

British Medical Journal. 1957. 1 :712, 771, 828, 889,954. *Bodkin Adams Trial*.

– – –. 1969. 3: 165-166. *Management of Respiratory Failure*.

– – –. 1972. 4: 372-374. *End of Dentist's Libel Action*.

– – –. 1983. 2: 223. *Bodkin Adams Obituary*.

Cope, R.W. 1954. "The Woolley and Roe Case. Woolley and Roe versus the Ministry of Health and others". *Anaesthesia* 9: 249-270.

Medical Legal Reports. 1990. 2: 232. *Ackers v Wigan Health Authority*. QBD (Russell J) 06/06/85.

Chapter 15. - Medical Genetics

No references

Chapter 16. - A Duty of Disclosure

All England Law Reports. 1957. 2: 118-128. *Bolam v Friern Hospital Management Committee*.

1985. 1: 643-666. *Sidaway v Governors of Bethlem Royal Hospital*.

Canadian Supreme Court Reports. 1980. 2: 880. *Reibl v Hughes*.

Commonwealth Law Reports. 1992. 175: 479. *Rogers v Whitaker*.

– – –. 1998. 195: 232. *Chapel v Hart*.

South Australian State Reports. 1983. 33: 189. *F v R.*

United States Appeals Court D.C. 1972. 464: F. 2d 772, 150 U.S. App. D.C. 263. *Canterbury v Spence.*

Chapter 17. - Governance and Regulation

No references

Chapter 18. - Medical Defence and Ethics

All England Law Reports. 1957. 2: 118-128. *Bolam v Friern Hospital Management Committee.*

– – –. 1997. 4: 771-780. *Bolitho v Hackney Health Authority.*

British Medical Journal. 2001. 322: 993. *Letter by Kalman Kafetz Consultant physician for elderly people Whipps Cross Hospital, London.*

Brodrick. 1971. *Report of the Committee on Death Certification and Coroners.* p11: 2.09. London: HMSO.

– – –. P11: 2.10.

Butterworth Medico-Legal Reports 1993. 12: 64-143. *Airedale NHS Trust v Bland.*

Havard, John, David, Jayne. 1960. *The detection of secret homicide: a study of the medico-legal system of investigation of sudden and unexplained deaths.* London: Macmillan.

Jennett, B. 2002. *The Vegetative State: Ethical and Legal Dilemmas.* Cambridge: Cambridge University Press.

Jervis. 1993. *Jervis on the office and duties of coroners: with forms and precedents.* 11th Ed. 5.18. Mathews Paul and Foreman John. London: Sweet & Maxwell Ltd.

McCullough, Lawrence, B. 1998. *John Gregory and the Invention of Professional Medical Ethics and the Profession of Medicine.* Dordrecht: Kluwer Academic Publishers.

Registrar General. 1860. *Report of Registrar General of Births and Deaths.*

Session Cases 1955. SC 200: 204-205. *Hunter v Hanley.* [Scots Law Times Reports. 1955. 213-218].

– – –. 1996. SC 301. *Law Hospital NHS Trust v Lord Advocate.* [Scots Law Times Reports. 1996. 848-867].

United States Appeals Court D.C. 1972. 464: F. 2d 772, 150 U.S. App. D.C. 263. *Canterbury v Spence.*

Chapter 19. - All Change at the GMC

Allen, I. 2000. *The Handling of Complaints by the GMC: A Study of Decision-making and Outcomes.* London: Policy Studies Institute.

BMA/MORI Poll. 2001. *Doctors win overwhelming vote of confidence from public.* http://www.mori.com/polls/2001/bma2001.shtml

Bristol Royal Infirmary Inquiry, The. 2001. *The Report of the Public Inquiry into children's heart surgery at the Bristol Royal Infirmary: 1984-1995.* London: HMSO.

Chantler, C. 1999. "The role and education of doctors in the delivery of health care." *The Lancet* 353: 1178-81.

General Medical Council. 1979. *Professional Conduct and Discipline.* London: GMC.

– – –. 1993. *Tomorrow's doctors.* London: GMC.

– – –. 2001. *Good Medical Practice 3rd edition.* London: GMC.

Merrison, A.W. 1975. *Report of the Committee of the Inquiry into the Regulation of the Medical Profession.* London: HMSO.

Chapter 20. - Future Perspectives

No references

Index

Greetings from the General Chairman,

On behalf of the Institute of Electrical and Electronic Engineers, its Neural Networks Council, and the Organizing Committees of the Second IEEE International Conference on Fuzzy Systems and the 1993 IEEE-International Conference on Neural Networks, it is my pleasure to welcome the participants of FUZZ-IEEE'93 and ICNN'93 to its beautiful venue. We trust that the natural beauty of the Bay Area and the cosmopolitan atmosphere of San Francisco will provide a most congenial background to your professional activities.

I felt most honored when Jim Bezdek, in the Spring of 1991, recommended my appointment to head a major conference in the field where both of us have spent most of our professional careers. About one year later, when I was entrusted, once again, with the responsibility to organize another major meeting I must confess that I felt rather elated but also very worried at the magnitude of the task that lay ahead.

Now that both FUZZ-IEEE'93 and ICNN'93 have been successfully planned and organized, I am most happy to have disregarded those apprehensions and to have engaged, for the past year, in the coordination of a major technological event that brings together two major disciplines that are redefining our notions of modeling, learning, and system analysis. Beyond sharing common objectives related to the understanding and control of complex systems, fuzzy logic and neural networks have been successfully applied in combination to treat many important problems—-a fact that should be obvious to the readers of these Proceedings. I cannot find words to express my satisfaction to have contributed to this first combined gathering of specialists of both fields.

As I surmised last year, the secret to this success rested on the selection of a competent team to coordinate the multiple details of such a complex event. The ability to organize such a pioneering meeting, to prepare its records both in conventional and compact-disk formats, to prepare a videotape detailing the state of the art, to secure the participation of interested researchers and exhibitors attests to their ability and dedication.

I am most thankful to all members of the Advisory Boards, Organizing Committees, and Program Committees of FUZZ-IEEE'93 and ICNN'93 for their continued help and support. Special recognition goes to Aviv Bergman, who helped to conceive and supported the production of our video program, Wei Xu for his timely advice and dedicated effort on behalf of our exhibits program, Jim Bezdek for his trust and for his single-handed organization of the tutorial program, Richard Tong, who kept and keeps tracking our finances, Camerone Welch for her dedication and superb communication skills, and Andy Worth, who coordinated our student volunteers. I am also most thankful to Nomi Feldman and her team at Meeting Management, who gave us indispensable logistic and organizational support and who handled significant crises in a most competent manner. I am particularly proud of the support provided by my family, specially by my wife Susana, who helped tirelessly to assure that the data would be duly recorded and that the mail would leave on time, and to my son Gabriel, who took care of the art work production. Ann Burgmeyer and Janet Romano of IEEE Publishing Services, Reed Carlstrom and John Sands of Young Minds, Inc. made sure that Conference Proceedings would be prepared in the short time that our schedule allowed and, by efficient performance and judicious advice, greatly simplified my task. I am also thankful to Peter-Wiesner and Beth Murray of the IEEE Educational Activities Board and to Ossama Khatib, of Stanford University, Paul Marca and his staff at the Stanford Instructional Television Network for their help with our video documentary and to Perry Sensi of IEEE Conference Services for his help and advice.

I want to acknowledge Russ Eberhart, Bob Marks, Jim Bezdek and all members of the Neural Networks Council for their trust and encouragement. I am indebted to John Lowrance, Ray Perrault, and the management of SRI International, who have strongly supported my research endeavors and, particularly, my efforts to organize these meetings. I am most grateful to Shiro Usui and Elie Sanchez, who were invaluable, as ICNN'93 Program Cochairs, to coordinate the details of this world wide project.

I cannot find words to tell of my deep enduring gratitude to Piero Bonissone and Hamid Berenji, who worked closely with me to assure the quality of our program, and with whom, I am happy to say, I will continue to collaborate in upcoming IEEE events. And, finally, to Lotfi Zadeh, who gave us so much guidance and encouragement through the years.

Enrique H. Ruspini
General Chairman, FUZZ-IEEE'93 and ICNN'93

1993 IEEE International Conference on Neural Networks
San Francisco Hilton Hotel, San Francisco, California
March 28 — April 1, 1993

General Chairman: Enrique H. Ruspini

Program Cochairmen: Hamid R. Berenji, Elie Sanchez, Shiro Usui

Sponsored by the IEEE Neural Networks Council with the cooperation of the European Neural Networks Society and the Japan Neural Networks Society

IEEE Neural Networks Council Constituent Societies:

IEEE Circuits and Systems Society
IEEE Communications Society
IEEE Computer Society
IEEE Control Systems Society
IEEE Engineering in Medicine and Biology Society
IEEE Industrial Electronics Society
IEEE Industry Applications Society
IEEE Information Theory Society
IEEE Lasers and Electro-Optics Society

IEEE Oceanic Engineering Society
IEEE Power Engineering Society
IEEE Robotics and Automation Society
IEEE Signal Processing Society
IEEE Social Implications of Technology Society
IEEE Systems, Man, and Cybernetics Society

Advisory Board

Shun-ichi Amari
James Anderson
George Bekey
James C. Bezdek
Yves Burnod
Leon Cooper
Russell C. Eberhart
Rolf Eckmiller

Jerome Feldman
Marcus Feldman
Kunihiko Fukushima
Robert Hecht-Nielsen
John Holland
Charles Jorgensen
Teuvo Kohonen
Clifford Lau

Carver Mead
David Rumelhart
Bryan Skyrms
Lawrence Stark
Allen Stubberud
Phillip Treleaven
Bernard Widrow

Program Committee

Kazuyuki Aihara
Igor Aleksander
Luis B. Almeida
Gerry Andeen
Charles Anderson
James Anderson
Andreas Andreou
Panos Antsaklis
Jacob Barhen
Behnam Bavarian
Hamid R. Berenji
Aviv Bergman
James C. Bezdek
Herve Bourlard
Donald E. Brown
Joan Cabestany
David Casasent

Silvano Colombano
Rui de Figueiredo
Michel Dufosse
Russell C. Eberhart
Jay Farrell
Jerome Feldman
William Fisher
Walter Fontana
A.A. Frolov
Toshio Fukuda
Charles Glover
Karl Goser
Dan Hammerstrom
Mohamad H Hassoun
Jeanny Herault
John Hertz
David Hislop

Akira Iwata
Michael Jordan
Charles Jorgensen
Leslie P. Kaelbling
James Keller
Pratap Khedkar
Shinzo Kitamura
Bart Kosko
John Koza
Clifford Lau
Caro Lucas
Robert J. Marks
Jerry Mendel
E. MicheliTzanakou
W. Thomas Miller
Melanie Mitchell
Sei Miyake

A.F. Murray
Jean-Pierre Nadal
Takashi Nagano
Kumpati S. Narendra
Robert Newcomb
E. Oja
Andras Pellionisz
P. Peretto
L. Personnaz
Alberto Prieto
Dimitri Psaltis

Herbert Rauch
Tom Ray
Max B. Reid
Michael Roth
Elie Sanchez
Jude Shavlik
Bing Sheu
Shigeru Shinomoto
John Shynk
Patrick K. Simpson
Noboru Sonehara

Donald F. Specht
Allen Stubberud
Noboru Sugie
Shiro Usui
David White
Halbert White
Ronald Williams
Takeshi Yamakawa
Eiji Yodogawa
Shuji Yoshizawa
Steven W. Zucker

ORGANIZING COMMITTEE

Publicity: Hamid R. Berenji

Tutorials: James C. Bezdek

Exhibits: Wei Xu

Finance: Richard Tong

Volunteers: Andrew Worth

Press/Public Relations: Camerone Welch

Video Documentary: Aviv Bergman

1993 IEEE INTERNATIONAL CONFERENCE ON NEURAL NETWORKS

San Francisco Hilton Hotel, San Francisco, California

March 28–April 1, 1993

Table Of Contents
VOLUME I

Monday, March 29, 1993, 8:30–10:00 AM

Joint FUZZ-IEEE '93 and ICNN '93 Plenary Session
Chairman: Enrique H. Ruspini, SRI International

Monday, March 29, 1993, 11:00 AM–12:30 PM

NEW LEARNING ARCHITECTURES I

RECURRENT NEURAL NETWORKS I

SENSORIMOTOR, BIOLOGICAL AND CEREBELLUM MODELS I

OTHER APPLICATIONS OF NEURAL NETWORKS I

HARDWARE IMPLEMENTATIONS I

* Not available at time of printing

* Not available at time of printing

POSTER PAPERS

MONDAY, MARCH 29, 1993

NEW LEARNING TECHNIQUES

CONTROL AND ROBOTS

SUPERVISED LEARNING

* Not available at time of printing

VOLUME II

TUESDAY, MARCH 30, 1993, 8:30–10:00 AM

PLENARY SESSION

TUESDAY, MARCH 30, 1993, 11:00 AM–12:30 PM

NEW LEARNING ARCHITECTURES III

INVITED SESSION:

FROM NEUROBIOLOGY TO ARTIFICIAL NEURAL NETWORKS
Chairman and Organizer: Andras Pellionisz, NASA Ames Research Center

SENSATION AND PERCEPTION

OTHER APPLICATIONS OF NEURAL NETWORKS II

HARDWARE IMPLEMENTATIONS II

Not available at time of printing

* *Not available at time of printing*

NEURO-FUZZY SYSTEMS, HYBRID SYSTEMS

ASSOCIATIVE MEMORIES

OPTIMIZATION

GENETIC ALGORITHMS

RECURRENT NEURAL NETWORKS

* Not available at time of printing

VOLUME III

* Not available at time of printing

WEDNESDAY, MARCH 31, 1993, 2:00–3:30 PM

NEURO-CONTROL III

INVITED SESSION:

REVERSE ENGINEERING
Chairman: Lawrence W. Stark, University of California, Berkeley

PROBABILISTIC NEURAL NETWORKS

ASSOCIATIVE MEMORIES III

HYBRID (NN AND EXPERT SYSTEMS) III

APPLICATIONS TO PATTERN RECOGNITION III

Not available at time of printing

OTHER APPLICATIONS OF NEURAL NETWORKS

Not available at time of printing

Not available at time of printing

THURSDAY, APRIL 1, 1993, 2:00–3:30 PM

NEURO-CONTROL IV

* Not available at time of printing

Things You Haven't Heard about the Self-Organizing Map

Teuvo Kohonen

Helsinki University of Technology

Laboratory of Computer and Information Science

Rakentajanaukio 2 C, SF-02150 Espoo, Finland

Abstract— This presentation has been inspired by two new findings. First, it quite recently turned out that the Self-Organizing Map (SOM) algorithm can be related to a biological neural network in many essential known details; even a cyclic behavior automatically ensues from a simple nonlinear neural model, whereby these cycles correspond to the steps of the discrete-time SOM algorithm. Second, compared with the other traditional neural-network algorithms, the SOM alone has the advantage of tolerating a very low accuracy in the representation of its signals and synaptic weights; this has been proven by simulations. Such a property ought to be shared by any realistic neural-network model. While the SOM can thus be advanced as a genuine neural-network paradigm, it has also been shown in this presentation how the basic algorithm can be generalized and made more efficient computationally in several ways.

I. INTRODUCTION

The *Self-Organizing Map (SOM)* [1,2] is a neural-network model that usually implements a peculiar nonlinear "projection" from the high-dimensional space of sensory or other input signals onto a two-dimensional array. This mapping often automatically finds and displays characteristic features or other abstractions from the raw data.

There exist many kinds of such maps in the brain. The SOM then has a twofold role in neural-network research: first, it models certain brain structures in idealized form, and second, it can be used for many practical applications to visualize interrelationships in complex data, such as process states.

The SOM belongs to the competitive-learning category of neural-network algorithms. Its cells usually form a two-dimensional array, and in principle at least, they receive the same input information in terms of a spatial activity pattern. Every cell acts as a selective decoder of a different pattern, by comparison of its weight vector with the input vector. Learning of the proper weight vector values is somewhat similar to high-dimensional regression, where a finite number of *reference vectors*, corresponding to the weight vectors, is adaptively placed into the input signal space to approximate to the samples. During adaptation, the corrections made in the reference vectors of neighboring cells in the array are correlated, as if the set of reference vectors formed an elastic net in the signal space. Self-organization means that this net becomes oriented and adaptively assumes a form by which it best describes the input vectors *in an ordered, structured fashion*.

I start this presentation with an overview of the SOM algorithms, pointing out how they look in different metrics.

Since most of the neural-network research is still based on software methods, a new idea to compute the SOM is introduced in this paper. The so-called *Batch Map algorithm* is a parameter-free and very fast version of the SOM. With special unsymmetric weighting of the learning rate at the borders of the map, this algorithm can be made to follow time-variable density functions accurately and very fast; a straightforward application is in telecommunications engineering, in the adaptive detection of discrete signal states.

An attempt to generalize the SOM for arrays of *operators* that may not even be differentiable with respect to any parameters is also made.

This paper was actually inspired by two important new findings. First, although these algorithms are usually advanced only as effective computational methods without reference to biology, it has recently turned out that the "short-cut" SOM algorithms may not be so abstract and nonbiological after all: there seems to exist a rather detailed *physiological interpretation* of the SOM process, which is described by system equations, the solutions of which behave very similarly with those of the "short-cut" SOM. Second, we have recently carried out extensive simulations on high-dimensional speech data, whereby it also turned out that the vector-quantization methods (to which the SOM belongs) tolerate *very coarse numerical accuracies*, three or four bits. This result too favors the SOM as a biological model and might be particularly interesting to researchers aiming at *analog hardware implementation* of artificial neural networks.

II. MANY DIFFERENT ALGORITHMIC DESCRIPTIONS OF THE SOM

A. The "Dot-Product Map"

Let us start with an algorithmic model that may have its biological counterpart in the brain as explained in Sec. IV. This algorithm is related to a two-dimensional array of interacting cells as depicted in Fig. 1.

Signal inputs to the cells of the SOM network can be defined in many ways. Consider first that the cells are activated in proportion to the dot product $m_i^T x$, where $x \in \Re^n$ is the input data vector, and $m_i \in \Re^n$ the reference vector of cell i, respectively.

In Sec. IV we shall show how a *Winner-Take-All (WTA) function* can be implemented by a simple distributed network. Its effect is to find the cell c ("winner") for which the activation is highest, i.e.,

$$m_c^T x = \max_i \{m_i^T x\} . \tag{1}$$

During learning, the corrections on adjacent cells are made to depend on their *relative distances*, and the degree of interaction is defined by the function $h_{ci}(t)$ below. The idealized updating or "learning" rule relative to (1) is expressed in discrete-time coordinates as

$$m_i(t+1) = \frac{m_i(t) + h_{ci}(t) \cdot x(t)}{\text{Norm of the numerator}} \tag{2}$$

where $h_{ci}(t)$ is the so-called (scalar-valued) *neighborhood function* relating to the "winner" and another arbitrary cell i in the array. This function has high values when $\|i - c\|$ is small and decreases with increasing distance. It

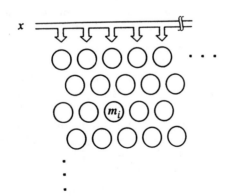

Fig. 1. Layout of a Self-Organizing Map.

has been shown that self-organization is most effective if the average width of $h_{ci}(t)$ decreases during the course of learning.

For a high learning power of this version of the SOM, $h_{ci}(t)$ for $i = c$ ought to assume rather high values during the first steps, say, $\gg 1$. Naturally the process also works for low $h_{ci}(t)$, although slower, whereby we can use the approximate series expansion of (2),

$$m_i(t+1) \approx m_i(t) + h_{ci}(t) \cdot [x(t) - m_i(t)m_i^T(t)x(t)] . \tag{3}$$

This law will be found similar to the one discussed in Sec. IV.

B. The "Euclidean-Distance Map"

While above the matching criterion and updating were referred to dot products of high-dimensional vectors, an almost similar self-ordering process is implemented in high-dimensional Cartesian coordinates by the following pair of equations:

$$\|x - m_c\| = \min_i\{\|x - m_i\|\} , \tag{4}$$

$$m_i(t+1) = m_i(t) + h_{ci}(t)[x(t) - m_i(t)] . \tag{5}$$

In this algorithm we must have $0 < h_{ci}(t) < 1$. The reference vectors $m_i(t)$ are not normalized. This may be the most familiar version of the SOM.

C. The SOM for a General Differentiable Distance Measure

Let now $d(x, m_i)$ be a general distance measure between x and m_i in the signal space. Assume that $d(x, m_i)$ is differentiable with respect to m_i. The "winner" is defined by

$$c = \arg \min_i\{d(x, m_i)\} . \tag{6}$$

Let us next introduce a global objective or weighted-error function

$$E = \int \sum_i h_{ci} f(d(x, m_i))p(x)dx , \tag{7}$$

where some function f of the quantization error $d(x, m_i)$ is first weighted by the neighborhood function h_{ci} and then averaged; here $p(x)$ is the probability density function of x. It has to be emphasized that in the following discussion, E need not be a potential function. If we would know an effective method for to minimize E, we could accept the optimal values of the m_i as a solution that would represent a generalized SOM. A severe problem is caused, however, by the subscript c being not constant but variable, $c = c(x; m_1, \ldots, m_k)$, where k is the number of all reference vectors, as discussed in depth in [4]. Therefore the solution method chosen here, the *Robbins-Monro stochastic approximation* [4, 5] only finds approximate optima. The class of these solutions has been studied with mathematical rigor and especially the convergence properties are thoroughly known. In applying this method we first define the *sample function* $E_1(t)$:

$$E_1(t) = \sum_i h_{ci}(t) f(d(x(t), m_i(t))) . \tag{8}$$

An approximate solution is then obtained as the last term of a sufficiently long sequence defined by

$$m_i(t+1) = m_i(t) - \lambda(t) \text{grad}_{m_i(t)} E_1(t) , \tag{9}$$

where $\lambda(t)$ defines the step size, or learning rate. The learning rate sequence must always fulfil the following conditions:

$$\sum_{t=0}^{\infty} \lambda(t) = \infty , \quad \sum_{t=0}^{\infty} \lambda^2(t) < \infty . \tag{10}$$

Notice that "optimization" in this method only means "local gradient" steps, not the steepest descent in the E "landscape."

For instance, if $d(x, m_i) = ||x - m_i||$ and $f(d) = d^2$, and we denote $\alpha(t) = 2\lambda(t)$, we obtain the "Euclidean Distance" SOM algorithm written as

$$m_i(t+1) = m_i(t) + \alpha(t) h_{ci}(t)[x(t) - m_i(t)] . \tag{11}$$

Naturally, $\alpha(t)$ can be combined with $h_{ci}(t)$.

Although the Robbins-Monro method is only approximate, it anyway facilitates derivation of various practical algorithms with different choices of f and d. For instance, in applications one might often want to experiment with different Minkowski metrics [1]. In particular, for hardware reasons, the Minkowski metric with power 1 (the so-called city-block or Manhattan distance) is sometimes used in learning circuits. Above we would then have $f(d) = d = \sum_j |\xi_j - \mu_{ij}|$, where $x = (\xi_1, \ldots, \xi_n)^T$ and $m_i = (\mu_{i1}, \ldots, \mu_{in})^T$, and the "optimal" (actually, almost optimal) adaptation rule relating to this metric would read

$$\mu_{ij}(t+1) = \mu_{ij}(t) + h_{ci}(t) \cdot \text{sgn}[\xi_j(t) - \mu_{ij}(t)] . \tag{12}$$

The learning rate $h_{ci}(t)$ must now be normalized in a different way than in the previous cases, to guarantee a proper convergence.

D. The "Batch Map" Algorithm

The following observation leads to further computational simplification of the "Euclidean Distance" SOM algorithm. In the convergence limit every $m_i = m_i^*$ must satisfy the equilibrium condition

$$E\{h_{ci}(x - m_i^*)\} = 0 , \tag{13}$$

whereby, in the averaging over the x space, the subscript c of the "winner" is a function $c = c(x; m_1^*, \ldots, m_k^*)$. An alternative way of writing (13) is

$$m_i^* = \frac{\int h_{ci} x p(x) dx}{\int h_{ci} p(x) dx} , \tag{14}$$

where $p(x)$ is the probability density function of x. It has to be noted that m_i^* has thereby not been solved explicitly; the index c on the right side still depends on x and all the m_i^*. Nonetheless (14) may be regarded as an expression from which the m_i^* can be solved *iteratively*, as shown shortly.

It has further been shown [1, 2] that the following simple definition of h_{ci} is effective enough in practice and saves much computing time: $h_{ci} = 1$ if i belongs to some *topological neighborhood set N_c* of cell c in the cell array, whereas otherwise $h_{ci} = 0$. With this h_{ci} there follows

$$m_i^* = \frac{\int_{V_i} x p(x) dx}{\int_{V_i} p(x) dx} , \tag{15}$$

where V_i means the following domain of values of x: Let some cell c be selected by values of x that belong to domain V_c around c, and let N_c be the topological neighborhood set of c (as referred to cell indices). If cell i is a common member of several neighborhood sets N_c, the union of the corresponding V_c is then called V_i. In [1] it was called the "influence region of cell i," i.e., *the set of those values of x that directly, or indirectly through the neighborhood function, select cell i for updating.*

Both (14) and (15) are already in the form in which the so-called *iterative contraction mapping* used in the solving of nonlinear equations is directly applicable. If z is an unknown vector that has to satisfy the equation $f(z) = 0$, then, since it is always possible to write the equation as $z = g(z)$, the successive approximations of the root can be computed as a series $\{z_n\}$ where

$$z_{n+1} = g(z_n) . \tag{16}$$

We shall not discuss any convergence problems here. If there would exist any, they can be overcome by the so-called Wegstein modification of (16). The iterative process in which a number of samples of x is first classified into the respective V_i regions, and the updating of the m_i^* is made iteratively as defined by (15) and (16), can be expressed as the following steps. The algorithm dubbed "Batch Map" resembles the familiar K-means algorithm [3], where all the training samples are assumed to be available when learning begins. The learning steps are defined as follows:

1. For the initial reference vectors, take, for instance, the first K training samples, where K is the number of reference vectors.

2. For each map unit i, collect a list of copies of all those training samples x, whose nearest reference vector belongs to the topological neighborhood set N_i of unit i.

3. Take for each new reference vector the mean over the respective list.

4. Repeat from 2 a few times.

This algorithm is particularly effective if the initial values of the reference vectors are already roughly ordered, even though they would not yet approximate to the distribution of the samples. It should be noticed that the above algorithm contains no learning-rate parameter; therefore it seems to yield stabler asymptotic values for the m_i than the original SOM. We shall revert to this algorithm in Sec. III.

Definition of the size of the neighborhood set N_i can be similar as in the basic SOM algorithms. "Shrinking" of N_i in this algorithm means that the neighborhood size is decreased while the steps 2 and 3 are repeated. At the last iterations, N_i may contain the element i only, and the last steps of the algorithm are then equivalent with the K-means clustering.

E. The SOM for Operators with Nonobservable Parameters or Nondifferentiable Similarity Measures

The SOM philosophy can actually be much more general than discussed so far. For instance, in a two-dimensional array it is possible to associate with each cell any complex *operator*, like a filter for dynamic signals, whereby the filter parameters may not directly be observable or controllable. Still it would be possible to run an input sequence $\{x(t)\}$ through each filter and compare the integrated responses; the cell with the maximum integral or energy of response can be characterized as the "winner". But how can we make such cells learn, to develop an *ordered* SOM?

The solution to this problem is a kind of "evolution" or "natural choice" that resembles the genetic algorithms. Let us denote the operator associated with cell i in the array by F_i. Denote the input information, eventually a process, by X. The "winner" with respect to X is now denoted by F_c. In the first method we assume that new candidates or versions for the F_i operators called G can

be generated easily; for instance, if they belong to some category that is parametrized, by a random choice of the parameters one can easily generate one or several candidates G, although these parameters were not observable later on. During one "learning" step, the same input process X is operated by both the F_i and a number of tentative G, and among these tests one eventually finds the best operator G_c that is better (in terms of some criterion) than F_c. Then F_c is *replaced* by G_c *with a probability* P, where P corresponds to the learning rate $h_{cc}(t)$ in the other SOM models. Moreover, every other F_i (or eventually operators in a bounded neighborhood N_c around cell c) will similarly be replaced by G_c with the probability $h_{ci}(t)$. These replacements shall be statistically independent, i.e., the decisions concerning replacements in the neighboring cells are drawn independently, but with the given probabilities.

It may also be self-evident that the F_i and G must somehow be *normalized*. For instance, one might require that the impulse responses of every F_i and G should have the same integral or energy.

If the operators are so complex that their on-line generation as described above is time-consuming, one may keep up another table, eventually a nonordered linear list that contains precomputed operators denoted by G_j. The G_j list can also be updated with new items intermittently. In order that the "learning" procedure explained below were gradual enough, it is important that the size of the G_j list is all the time much greater than the size of the F_i array, so that the G_j list contains plenty of gradual intermediate cases of the F_i. Now X is operated by every F_i and every G_j, and the best matches in the two tables, according to some criterion, are indexed by c in the F_i array, and by d in the G_j list, respectively. Assume that the G_d functional of X represents a better match than the F_c functional of X. The substitution of F_c and its neighbors by G_d is then made as explained in connection with the first method.

It might turn out that this kind of operator array, without preprocessing, were directly applicable, e.g., to the recognition or analysis of time-domain signals such as continuous speech. Filters sensitive to temporal features might be defined, e.g., as linear or nonlinear recursive expressions of the time-domain samples. The input process X might be taken from a sufficiently long time interval that extends over a few phonemes, to take the temporal context effects into account, too. The next sample X would then be taken from another interval that *overlaps* with the previous one, etc. In this way the different cells of the map become trained, say, to different *sequences* of the speech waveforms, in analogy with the methods reported in [12].

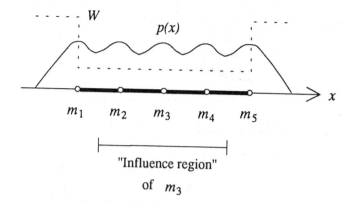

Fig. 2. One-dimensional SOM with five reference "vectors" m_i that approximate to the probability density function $p(x)$, and delineation of the weighting function W.

III. ELIMINATION OF BORDER EFFECTS AND APPLICATION OF THE BATCH MAP TO TELECOMMUNICATIONS

In the transmission of digitally encoded signals, the discrete signal states are often represented by amplitude modulation. In the QAM (quadrature amplitude modulation) method, the same frequency channel transmits two carrier waves that have a relative phase shift of 90 degrees. If each carrier has k possible discrete amplitude states, the whole channel can transmit one of k^2 digital states at a time. Such discrete signal states form a k by k lattice in a two-dimensional signal space. A SOM array, with k^2 reference vectors, can be made to follow and detect (demodulate) such signal vectors: if the signals are corrupted by noise and time-variable transmission properties of the channel, the SOM follows the corrupted states adaptively, and each of its cells acts as a decoder of the respective signal state. In practice, the SOM must be preceded by an equalizer, which first compensates for the general transfer properties of the channel, whereby the SOM can be used to control the equalizer [6]. In the present context, however, we shall omit the equalizer and concentrate on the problem of adaptive detection.

Consider first a single carrier wave that is amplitude-modulated by one of k discrete states. Consider also a one-dimensional SOM with k reference "vectors" (scalars) $m_i(t) \in \Re$; each of the $m_i(t)$ can be made to follow one particular signal state. One property of the simple SOM, which is harmful in this application, is occurrence of border effects, on account of which the $m_i(t)$ do not accurately approximate to $p(x)$, the density function of input. The compensation method used in [6] was not yet quite effective. Contrary to that, the solution presented in this paper seems to be very close to ideal.

Inspection of Fig. 2 may facilitate understanding of the reason for the border effects. Let every cell of the SOM have two neighbors, except one at the ends. For instance, the "influence region" of cell i ($i > 2$ and $i < k - 1$) (or the range of x values that can affect cell i) is $R_i = [\frac{1}{2}(m_{i-2} + m_{i-1}), \frac{1}{2}(m_{i+1} + m_{i+2})]$. In the asymptotic equilibrium, according to (13), every m_i must coincide with the centroid of $p(x)$ over the respective R_i. The definition of the "influence regions" near the borders of the SOM is different, however, and therefore the m_i do not approximate to $p(x)$ everywhere in the same way.

In computing the centroids, it is now possible to provide the x samples with *conditional weights* W that depend on index i and the relative magnitude of x and m_i. This weighting can be used both in the old stepwise SOM algorithm (with the given definition of the neighborhood set N_c), and with the Batch Map, too. In the former case, the weight should be applied to the learning rate α, not to x. For to guarantee stability, one must then have $\alpha W < 1$, so this trick is not applicable during the first steps when α is still large. In the Batch Map algorithm, however, the x samples are always weighted directly, so no such restriction exists. Henceforth we assume that the Batch Map is used.

The following rules may first sound a bit complicated, but they are simple to program, and in practice they are also very effective and robust in eliminating the border effects to a large extent. Assume that the m_i values are already ordered.

Weighting Rule for the One-Dimensional SOM:

In updating, each x sample is provided with weight W. Normally $W = 1$, but $W > 1$ for the border (end) cells in the case that x is bigger than the biggest m_i or smaller than the smallest m_i, AND when the updating of the border cell (but not of its neighbors) is due.

Consider the special case that $p(x)$ is *uniform* over some connected domain of x and zero outside it. It may then be easy to deduce on the basis of Fig. 2 and the Weighting Rule that if we select for the special weight a value of $W = 9$, all the m_i will become equidistant in the asymptotic equilibrium; then they describe $p(x)$ in an unbiased way. Naturally, for other forms of $p(x)$, we should take other values for W. In those practical cases that occur in signal detection, however, the default value $W = 9$ compensates for the most part of the border effects in general.

It is possible to eliminate the border effects *totally*, if after a couple Batch Map iterations the neighborhood set N_i is replaced by i, i.e., having a couple of simple K-means iterations at the end. It is known that the K-means clustering is unbiased for static data, but it cannot be used to follow stochastically occurring time-variable signal states as such, because it does not "notice" if one signal state does not occur for some time; the algorithm tries to approximate to the rest of the states (cf. Fig. 3). The Batch Map algorithm, on the contrary, is more stable, because when any m_i is updated, the neighboring m_i values are updated, too, which has a regularizing effect on the m_i. The m_i are thus much less sensitive to missing signal states. Combination of a couple weighted Batch Map iterations and a couple K-means iterations is robust and usually leads to a totally unbiased result, as demonstrated in Fig. 3 (b).

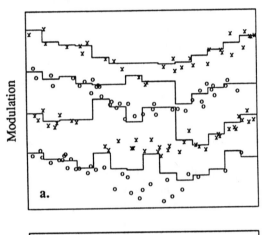

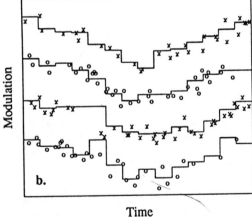

Fig. 3. (a) Demonstration of how the K-means algorithm tries to follow signal states. The discrete signal values were corrupted by noise and sinusoidal variations. A few iterations of the K-means clustering were run on each successive interval that consisted of ten signal samples, randomly distributed among four signal states. It is discernible that the K-means algorithm is prone to miss signal states. (b) The same demonstration for two iterations of the Batch Map followed by two iterations of the K-means algorithm. The number of errors has radically reduced.

In the QAM method with a two-dimensional SOM, the weighting rules are slightly different. While we used, say, the value of $W = 9$ for the end cells in the one-dimensional array, in the updating of the two-dimensional array we must have a different weight W_1 for the corner cells, and another value W_2 for edge cells that are not in the corner. Inside the array, the weight is equal to unity.

Weighting Rules for the Two-Dimensional SOM:

> The value W_1 is applied if both of the following two conditions are satisfied: *A1.* The value of x is in one of the four "outer corner sectors," i.e. outside the array and such that the m_i of some corner cell is closest. *A2.* Updating of this selected m_i (but not of any other of its topological neighbors) is due.
>
> The value W_2 is applied if both of the following conditions are satisfied: *B1.* The value of x lies outside the m_i array, but the closest m_i does not belong to any corner cell. *B2.* Updating of the selected edge cell or any of its topological neighbors, which must be one of the edge cells (eventually even a corner cell) is due.

If $p(x)$ in the two-dimensional signal space were uniform over a square domain and zero outside it, it will be easy to deduce, in analogy with the one-dimensional case, that for equidistant equilibrium distribution of the m_i values we must have $W_1 = 81$, $W_2 = 9$. Again, for other $p(x)$ the compensation is not total with these weights. Then, as earlier, the Batch Map process may be run a couple iterations, followed by a couple K-means iterations. Such a combination of methods is again both robust and unbiased and follows the two-dimensional signal states very effectively.

IV. PHYSIOLOGICAL INTERPRETATION OF THE SOM

It is possible to ask just how "neural" the SOM algorithms are. The same question could be posed about the other traditional feedforward and feedback "neural networks", too, the analytical descriptions of which are developed further in the computational than in the biological direction. Therefore it may be of special interest to note that the SOM can be related to a biological neural network in many essential details, as shown below.

A comprehensive discussion of this new physiological SOM model can be found in [7]; let only its main features be reviewed here.

A. The WTA Network

Consider a planar neural network (Fig. 4) where each cell receives input from some external sources, and the cells are

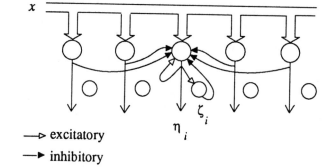

$\longrightarrow$ excitatory

$\longrightarrow$ inhibitory

Fig. 4. Simplified model of a distributed neural network (cross section of a two-dimensional array). Each location consists of an excitatory principal input neuron and an inhibitory interneuron that feeds back locally. The lateral corrections between the principal input neurons may or may not be made via interneurons.

further interconnected by abundant lateral feedbacks. In the simplest case the same set of input signals is connected to all cells in this piece of network.

Assume that the output activity η_i (spiking frequency) of the input neuron i in the network is described [7, 8] by

$$d\eta_i/dt = I_i - \gamma(\eta_i) \, , \qquad (17)$$

where I_i is the combined effect of all inputs, i.e. afferent inputs as well as lateral feedbacks, on cell i embedded in the layered network. Let $\gamma(\eta_i)$ describe the net effect of all loss or leakage effects that oppose to I_i. This is an abbreviated way of writing: since $\eta_i \geq 0$, (17) only holds when $\eta_i > 0$, or when $\eta_i = 0$ and $I_i - \gamma(\eta_i) \geq 0$, whereas otherwise $d\eta_i/dt = 0$.

If we write $I_i = I_i^e + I_i^f$, where the superscript e means "external" or afferent input, and f the lateral feedback, respectively, then in the simplest model we have

$$I_i^e \;=\; m_i^{\mathrm{T}} x = \sum_j \mu_{ij}\xi_j \; , \qquad (18)$$

$$I_i^f \;=\; \sum_k g_{ik}\eta_k \; . \qquad (19)$$

Here $x = (\xi_1, \xi_2, \ldots, \xi_n)^{\mathrm{T}} \in \Re^n$ again means the input data vector, or the vector of signal activities on a set of axons that is assumed to be connected in parallel to all cells of this network, and $m_i = (\mu_{i1}, \mu_{i2}, \ldots, \mu_{in})^{\mathrm{T}} \in \Re^n$ is redefined to be the corresponding vector of synaptic strengths of cell i. The $g_{ik} \in \Re$ describe effective lateral coupling strengths of cells in the planar array. For simplicity, it is assumed that g_{ii} is independent of i, and the $g_{ik}, k \neq i$ are mutually equal.

In the above system of equations, the only and rather general further restrictions shall be $\mu_{ij} > 0$, $\xi_j > 0$ (i.e.,

the external inputs are mainly excitatory), $g_{ii} > 0$, $g_{ik} < 0$ for $k \neq i$, $|g_{ik}| > |g_{ii}|$, $\gamma > 0$, and $d^2\gamma/d\eta^2 > 0$.

Starting with arbitrary (nonnegative) different m_i and $\eta_i(0) = 0$, the output η_c of that cell for which $m_i^{\mathrm{T}} x$ is maximum ("winner") will converge to an asymptotic high value, whereas the other η_i, $i \neq c$ tend to zero. This convergence property and the uniqueness of the winner can be proved mathematically [7].

As this network must respond to new inputs continually, the output state $\{\eta_i\}$ must be *reset* before application of a new input. In this model resetting is done automatically by providing each cell with an extra local inhibitory integrating feedback loop, eventually through an interneuron with feedback variable ζ_i (Fig. 4) described by the system equation

$$d\zeta_i/dt = b\eta_i - \theta \, , \qquad (20)$$

where b and θ are scalar parameters. Also here we must state that (20) only holds if $\zeta_i > 0$, or if $\zeta_i = 0$ and $b\eta_i - \theta \geq 0$, whereas otherwise $d\zeta_i/dt = 0$. The complete equation corresponding to (17) reads

$$d\eta_i/dt = I_i - a\zeta_i - \gamma(\eta_i) \, , \qquad (21)$$

where a is another scalar parameter.

This WTA circuit operates in *cycles* like a multivibrator, and each cycle can be thought to correspond to one discrete-time phase in (2) or (3). Normally the input is also thought to be changed at each new cycle; however, if the input is steady for a longer time, the next cycle selects the "runner-up", after which the "winner" is selected again, etc.

The cyclic operation of this WTA circuit is illustrated in Fig. 5.

B. Almost-Hebbian Learning

Most neural-network models, in one way or another, make use of the synaptic adaptation law named *Hebb's hypothesis*. If ξ is a presynaptic signal and η the output (spiking) activity of a neuron, the efficacy (strength, weight) of the synapse is thereby assumed to increase in proportion to $\xi\eta$.

At least two severe problems have now to be mentioned. First, since $\xi, \eta \geq 0$, then the efficacy can only grow or stay constant. In order that adaptation be reversible, some extra stabilizing term or terms should be subtracted from $\xi\eta$. Second, one has to take into account that neural cells are usually ramified, and the postsynaptic effect (proportional to η) must be propagated unattenuated even to the most distal branches and synapses.

If it is essential, as it seems, that the plasticity (modifiability) of a synapse is a function of the cell's output, then the quickest and most uniform retrograde messenger for this information would be a chemical agent that is

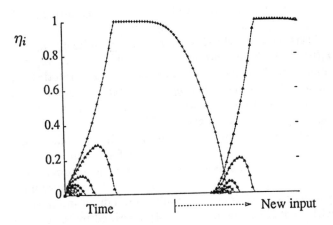

Fig. 5. Demonstration of the WTA function provided with automatic reset. The first inputs were applied at time zero. New inputs were applied as indicated by the dotted arrow. The network consisted of 20 cells, and the inputs $I_i^e = m_i^T x$ were selected as random numbers from the interval (0, 1). The g_{ii} were equal to 0.5 and the $g_{ij}, i \neq j$, were -2.0, respectively. The loss function had the form $\gamma(\eta) = 0.1 \ln \frac{1+\eta}{1-\eta}$; other simpler laws can also be used. The feedback parameters were $a = b = 1, \theta = 0.5$. The network operates as follows: The first "winner" is the cell that receives the largest input; its response will first stabilize to a high value, while the other outputs tend to zero. When the activity of the "winner" is temporarily depressed by the dynamic feedback, the other cells continue competing. The solution was obtained by the classical Runge-Kutta numerical integration method, using a step size of 10^{-5}.

produced in proportion to the postsynaptic activity and spreads back to the synaptic sites extracellularly. As a matter of fact, plenty of experimental evidence for such agents, of which the most primary one is nitric oxide (NO), has accumulated in a couple of recent years (cf., e.g., [9]). Among the numerous chemicals that are present at the cells, there probably also exist other similar factors, which have not yet been detected, however. Such chemicals can spread evenly over the cells' surfaces, even in their most distal branches.

An even more important aspect of the above diffuse chemical interaction is that due to diffusion, the postsynaptic chemical messenger can also affect *nearby* cells, not only the active cell itself. This property is central in the SOM process where the "winner", or the cell with the highest activation, is supposed to control adaptation in its *neighboring cells*, too. Attempts to explain such an interaction through collateral synaptic control have not been particularly successful, and one must also note that the anatomy of the biological neural networks is not isotropic enough for to define a symmetric neighborhood function $h_{ci}(t)$. If, on the other hand, the lateral interaction during learning were implemented by diffuse chemical substances, its geometric form would be rather isotropic, independent

of the microanatomy of the network, and thus very beneficial for the SOM process.

We are now ready to set up the adaptation equation corresponding to (2) or (3), which we write:

$$d\mu_{ij}/dt = (\xi_j - \lambda \mu_{ij} \sum_r \mu_{ir} \xi_r) \sum_l h_{il} \eta_l , \qquad (22)$$

where λ and h_{il} are system parameters. This equation can be justified in the following way. The rate of change of the synaptic efficacy, $d\mu_{ij}/dt$, is *modulated* by $\sum_l h_{il}\eta_l$, a weighted sum of the activities of the nearby cells, which describes the strength of the diffuse chemical effect of cell l on cell i; h_{il} is a function of the distance of these cells. Synaptic changes shall be proportional to ξ_j like in the Hebb synapses, but their reversibility is guaranteed by the active "forgetting" effect, or disturbance due to the adjacent synapses. Typically, forgetting effects are proportional to the variable itself (here μ_{ij}), and if the disturbance caused by synaptic site r is mediated through the postsynaptic potential, such an effect must further be proportional to $\mu_{ir}\xi_r$. Naturally this effect would be some function of the distance between sites j and r, too, but for simplicity we "compartmentalize" a subset of synapses that are located near each other, and approximately act as one collectively interacting set. If the interaction between synapses is mediated chemically, say, by nitric oxide, the size of such an interacting synaptic subset at the cell is then roughly defined by the diffusion length of this chemical.

If we now think that the factor $\sum_l h_{il}\eta_l$ corresponds to the time-variable neighborhood function $h_{ci}(t)$ in the SOM algorithm, if we realize that only the speed of the ordering process depends on this factor, and if we further assume that the range of index r defines those input signals that are regarded to constitute the input vector x relating to this particular ordering process, then (22), which is expressed in continuous time, and (3), which is a discrete-time approximation, can easily be found equivalent.

The most important message of the above discussion is that it motivates biologically the following "idealized" features of the SOM theory: 1. A natural, robust way for the implementation of the WTA function. 2. A realistic interpretation of the Hebb-like law of synaptic plasticity. 3. Automatic normalization of *subsets* of synaptic vectors. 4. A natural explanation of the lateral interaction (neighborhood function) between neurons in learning.

A more rigorous discussion of the physiological SOM model can be found in [7].

V. Using Low-Accuracy Signals in Vector Quantization

The SOM and the *Learning Vector Quantization (LVQ)* [1, 2] are two "neural network" algorithms that are closely related. Learning in the SOM is unsupervised, while the LVQ is a supervised method. The cells in the SOM interact (during learning) in the lateral direction, while the LVQ cells are updated independently. In principle, both the SOM and the LVQ could be used for pattern recognition (classification); however, if supervised learning is possible, the LVQ is usually two to three times more accurate.

It is a general notion that the traditional neural-network algorithms need a numerical accuracy of three to four decimal digits. It will now be shown that the LVQ and SOM tolerate much worse accuracies.

The experiments reported in this section were actually performed by the LVQ, but similar results may be obtained for the SOM, too. In short, it has been shown that if the dimensionality of the m_i vectors is high (> 100), their component values *during classification* (or determination of the "winner") can be approximated by as few as three or four *bits*, without noticeable reduction in recognition accuracy. Thus, if learning is made off-line, preferably with a higher accuracy, the approximations of the m_i values can be loaded onto very simple hardware devices. The low accuracy demands also make it possible to apply special solutions, such as replacement of arithmetic circuits by precomputed tables or memories, from which the values of the classification functions can be *searched* rapidly.

One of the problems studied in our laboratory over the years has been speech recognition, whereby we have collected a large database of Finnish speech. The speech states are represented every 10 ms by 20 cepstral coefficients [10]. To someone unfamiliar with this task it may not be quite clear how much statistical variance the same phonemes, even for the same speaker, may have. For this reason, increasing accuracy in feature detection, e.g., in cepstral amplitude detection is reasonable only up to a certain limit, whereas increasing the number of different feature variables is much more effective in improving statistical accuracy [11, 12]. For instance, picking the cepstral coefficients from the 220-ms "time window" (Fig. 6) and concatenating them into a 140-dimensional feature vector yields an about 14-fold accuracy in phonemic recognition compared with recognition of single 20-dimensional feature vectors.

It is now demonstrated in the present paper that (i) a very similar recognition accuracy is achievable, although the feature *amplitudes* are *quantized* to a few, say, eight or 16 levels, (ii) with such a quantization, a very high computing power is achievable in decisions, using quite

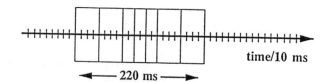

Fig. 6. Time window for phonemes.

conventional circuit technology but unconventional architectures.

First we evaluate how much the phonemic recognition results are reduced if the component values of the feature vectors, and those of the reference vectors are represented in a quantized scale. These figures describe the *average* accuracy taken over all the Finnish phonemes (for a single speaker): even /k/, /p/, and /t/ were recognized individually!

The quantization levels were selected to be equidistant, and the level values were set experimentally to approximate to the dynamic range of the cepstral coefficients. (Determination of optimal quantization levels for each vectorial component separately by the so-called scalar quantization, i.e., minimizing the average expected quantization errors was also tried, but the results were not much different.)

The cases studied were: (i) 20-dimensional input feature vectors formed of the coefficients of single cepstra taken over 10 ms intervals and using 200 reference vectors, (ii) 140-dimensional input feature vectors taken from the "time window" (cf. Fig. 6) and using 2000 reference vectors, respectively.

TABLE I
EFFECT OF QUANTIZATION: RECOGNITION ACCURACY, PER CENT

No. of bits	No. of quantization levels	Dimensionality of input and number of reference vectors	
		20 times 200	140 times 2000
1	2	50.1	90.1
2	4	72.1	97.3
3	8	82.6	98.7
4	16	84.9	99.0
Floating-point computing accuracy		85.9	99.0

The basic and most frequently computed expression in classification, based on vector quantization methods (such as the SOM or the LVQ) is

$$c = \arg \min_i \left\{ \sum_{j=1}^n (\xi_j - \mu_{ij})^2 \right\} \quad . \qquad (23)$$

Here the ξ_j are the components of vector x, and the μ_{ij} the components of vector m_i, respectively. It is to be noted that if the ξ_j and μ_{ij} are quantized, there exists only a finite and generally rather small number of their discrete-value combinations, for which the function $(\xi_j - \mu_{ij})^2$ can be tabulated completely. For instance, with 3-bit accuracy such a table contains 64 rows, and with 4 bits, 256 rows, respectively.

The curled-bracket expression in (23) may be computed by tabular search depicted in Fig. 7, whereas the $\min_i(\cdot)$ operation could best be left to software. The ξ_j and μ_{ij} can be loaded from a bus into the buffers, from which they are read cyclically. The expressions $(\xi_j - \mu_{ij})^2$ may be added in a fast accumulator, from which the result can be copied into the bus. Counting of loop indices, reading the arguments, and performing the table-look-up can be done by an autonomous control circuit of this hardware. If we have k reference vectors with dimensionality n, and T is the length of the clock cycle, then the computing time is roughly $k \cdot n \cdot T$. For instance, for the 140×2000 array and a typical clock frequency $1/T = 66$ MHz, classification time would be 4.2 msec.

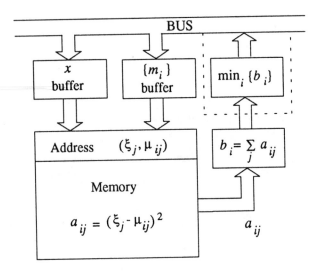

Fig. 7. Block scheme of the pattern-recognition architecture that makes use of tabular search in the evaluation of the classification function.

VI. AVAILABLE SOFTWARE

Recently, two software packages, the LVQ_PAK and the SOM_PAK, were released by us. They are available free of charge at the Internet address cochlea.hut.fi (130.233.168.48).

The LVQ_PAK contains near-Bayesian pattern recognition methods, whereas the SOM_PAK can be used, e.g., for the visualization of complex process states.

REFERENCES

[1] T. Kohonen, *Self-Organization and Associative Memory*, 3rd ed. Heidelberg: Springer, 1989.

[2] T. Kohonen, "The self-organizing map," *Proc. IEEE*, vol. 78, pp. 1464-1480, September 1990.

[3] J. Makhoul, S. Roucos, and H. Gish, "Vector quantization in speech coding," *Proc. IEEE*, vol. 73, pp. 1551-1588, 1985.

[4] T. Kohonen, "Self-organizing maps: optimization approaches," in *Artificial Neural Networks*, T. Kohonen, K. Mäkisara, O. Simula, and J. Kangas, Eds. Amsterdam: Elsevier (North-Holland), 1991, vol. 2, pp. 981-990.

[5] H. Robbins and S. Monro, "A stochastic approximation method," *Ann. Math. Statist.*, vol. 22, pp. 400-407, 1951.

[6] T. Kohonen, K. Raivio, O. Simula, and J. Henriksson, "Start-up behaviour of a neural network assisted decision feedback equalizer in a two-path channel," *Proc. IEEE Int. Conf. on Communications* (Chigago, Ill., USA, 1992) pp. 1523-1527.

[7] T. Kohonen, "Physiological interpretation of the self-organizing map algorithm," *Neural Networks*, in press.

[8] T. Kohonen, "An introduction to neural computing," *Neural Networks*, vol. 1, pp. 3-16, 1988.

[9] M. S. Fazeli, "Synaptic plasticity: on the trail of the retrograde messenger," *Trends in Neuroscience*, vol. 15, pp. 115-117, 1992.

[10] K. Torkkola et al., "Status report of the Finnish phonetic typewriter project," in *Artificial Neural Networks*, T. Kohonen, K. Mäkisara, O. Simula, and J. Kangas, Eds. Amsterdam: Elsevier (North-Holland), 1991, vol. 1, pp. 771-776.

[11] T. Kohonen, "New developments of Learning Vector Quantization and Self-Organizing Map," in *SYN-APSE'92, Symposium on Neural Networks; Alliances and Perspectives in Senri 1992* (Osaka, Japan, 1992).

[12] J. Mäntysalo, K. Torkkola, and T. Kohonen, "LVQ-based speech recognition with high-dimensional context vectors," *Proc. ICSLP, 1992 Int. Conf. on Spoken Language Processing* (Banff, Alberta, Canada, 1992) vol. 1, pp. 539-542.

A NEW ACCELERATION TECHNIQUE FOR THE BACKPROPAGATION ALGORITHM

Xiangui Yu, Nan K. Loh, William C. Miller
Department of Electrical Engineering, University of Windsor
Windsor, Ontario, N9B 3P4, Canada

Abstract--This paper presents an adaptive momentum algorithm which can update the momentum coefficient automatically in every iteration step. The basic idea comes from the optimal gradient method used in the standard backpropagation algorithm. Because of the very complex nonlinear structure in the multi-layer feedforward neural network, it is very difficult to obtain the optimal gradient vector by analytical methods, but it can be proven that the optimal gradient vectors in two successive iteration steps are orthogonal. Based on this property one can use the Gram-Schmidt orthogonalization method to ensure the orthogonality of the successive gradient vectors. The result of this process is equivalent to adding a momentum term to the standard backpropagation algorithm and the momentum coefficient is updated automatically in every iteration. Numerical simulations show that the adaptive momentum algorithm not only can eliminate possible divergent oscillations during the initial training, but can also accelerate the learning process and result in a lower error when the final convergence is reached.

I. INTRODUCTION

The backpropagation algorithm has become the standard algorithm used for training multilayer feedforward neural networks [5],[11]. It is based upon the gradient descent method which minimizes the sum of the squared errors between the actual and the desired output values. Although the gradient descent algorithm used in conjunction with the backpropagation strategy is capable of providing reasonable estimates of the weighting vectors, like other gradient descent techniques, the backpropagation algorithm converges very slowly, even for medium sized network problems [2],[3],[4]. In the standard backpropagation algorithm, the learning rate parameter is selected as a constant. The larger this constant, the larger the changes in the weights. In practice, the learning rate is chosen as large as possible without leading to oscillation, so as to offer the most rapid learning. One way to increase the learning rate without leading to oscillation is to include a momentum term which effectively filters out any high frequency variations of the error space. This is very useful in error spaces containing long ravines that are characterized by sharp curvature across the ravine and a gently sloping floor [5]. In practice, the use of a momentum term implies a constant fine-tuning of the learning parameters and thus an algorithm to automatically adjust their values would be desirable.

This paper proposes a new acceleration technique for the backpropagation algorithm. The aim is to choose the learning rate which tends to minimize the number of iteration steps required. Since the error function is also a function of the learning rate parameter in every iteration step, one can select an optimal learning rate parameter to make the error function reach a local minima in every iteration. But since the error function is usually a very complex nonlinear function with respect to the learning rate the optimal learning rate can not be determined by analytical methods. Using a one-dimensional minimization technique is also not useful. After studying the optimal gradient method one finds that for the optimal gradient algorithm, the two gradient vectors in the successive iteration steps are orthogonal. Thus, we derive a new method to replace the one dimensional optimization process of the learning rate parameter, *i.e.*, in every iteration we make the current gradient vector perpendicular to the vector of the previous iteration. The simplest method to make the two successive gradient vectors perpendicular to each other is the Gram-Schmidt orthogonalization method. After using this method, a new algorithm can be derived that is equivalent to a momentum algorithm, but in the new algorithm the momentum coefficient is updated automatically. Extensive numerical simulations have shown that this algorithm is fast in converging to a local minima. For given initial weights, the new algorithm converges to one local minima faster than the constant momentum method and the mean squared-error is also smaller in the convergence results.

The paper is organized as follows: In Section II the standard backpropagation algorithm is reviewed and some earlier works on acceleration techniques are reported. In Section III the optimal gradient method is described. The Gram-Schmidt orthogonalization method is utilized. A new algorithm is derived, based on the orthogonal properties of two successive gradient vectors, that is equivalent to the adaptive momentum method. In Section IV simulation results for the new algorithm are presented. In Section V the conclusions are presented.

II. STANDARD BACKPROPAGATION ALGORITHM

Let $E(\ )$ denote the total squared error function to be minimized by a given network, let $w(\ )$ denote the weight vector, which includes all weights and threshold values. $E(w)$ is defined as:

$$E(w) = \sum_{p=1}^{P} \sum_{j=1}^{L} (y_{jp}^{[L]} - d_{jp})^2 \qquad (1)$$

where d_{jp} is the desired output for jth output neuron corresponding to the pth input pattern, $y_{jp}^{[L]}$ is the corresponding actual output.

In its basic form, the weight updating rule of the backpropagation algorithm can be written as:

$$w(n+1) = w(n) - \eta \cdot \frac{\partial E}{\partial w(n)} \qquad (2)$$

where n identifies the update epoch and η is the learning rate parameter. From the above algorithm it is evident that the backpropagation algorithm is a supervised learning technique. It compares the responses of the output units to the desired response and readjust the weights in the network so that the next time the same input is presented to the network, the network's response will be closer to the desired response. In other words, in the backpropagation algorithm the weight update is performed in the direction that yields a maximal error reduction. The convergence speed is also related to the learning rate parameter η, if η is small, the algorithm will closely approximate the gradient path, but convergence will be very slow since the gradient vector must be calculated many times. On the other hand, if η is large, convergence will be initially very fast, but the algorithm will oscillate about the optimum [5]. Thus, it is clear that some mechanism must be found for reducing the learning rate parameter as the optimum value is approached. In general, large steps are desirable far away from the optimum with decreasing step size as oscillations are about to occur. In 1987 Chan and Fallside [1] proposed an adaptation rule for the learning rate parameter that is based on the cosine value of the angle between the two gradient vectors in the successive iterations. In their algorithm, the momentum term is also updated, however, their technique can drive the learning rate parameter to a very small value. In 1986 Sutton [2] proposed a method which can increase or decrease the learning rate parameter according to the number of sign changes observed in the partial derivation of the error function relative to the corresponding weight. This method was also studied by Jacobs extensively [3]. In 1989 Silva [4] proposed another similar method which chose the learning rate in every connection based on the sign changes in the partial derivation of the error functions relative to the corresponding weight. If the sign remained the samethe corresponding learning rate is multiplied by a constant greater than unity; if the sign changed multiply by a constant less than unity. The significant feature of this adaptation rule is its exponential nature. The convergence process can increase or decrease each learning rate parameter by several orders of magnitude in a few iterations.

Although these *ad hoc* methods are often employed successfully, there is one method for choosing the step size which tends to minimize the number of iteration steps required. This method is called the optimal gradient method. In the following section a new method that is based on the properties of the optimal gradient method is presented.

III. The Derivation Of The Adaptive Momentum Algorithm

The basic idea for the optimal-gradient method is as follows: at the $(n+1)$th iteration step, the weight vector $w(n+1)$ changes along the gradient direction $\frac{\partial E}{\partial w}$ defined at $w(n)$, i.e., $\frac{\partial E}{\partial w(n)}$, until the objective function $E(w(n+1))$ reaches at a local minima. Since the objective function $E(w(n+1))$ would increase if $w(n+1)$ continued past this point (local minimum), a new gradient determination $\frac{\partial E}{\partial w(n+1)}$ could be made at $w(n+1) = w(n) - \eta \cdot \frac{\partial E}{\partial w(n)}$. This method tends to reduce the number of iteration steps taken. However, the amount of computation is increased due to the one dimensional minimization problem which must be solved in each iteration to determine each new learning rate η. The problem can be written as

$$\min_{\eta} E\left(w(n) - \eta \cdot \frac{\partial E}{\partial w(n)} \right) \qquad (3)$$

which is a function of η only, when $w(n)$ is specified. The necessary condition for this minimum is:

$$\frac{\partial E(w(n+1))}{\partial \eta} = 0$$

or

$$\frac{\partial}{\partial \eta} E\left(w(n) - \eta \cdot \frac{\partial E}{\partial w(n)} \right) = 0 \qquad (4)$$

Since $E(w(n+1))$ is usually a very complex nonlinear function of the learning rate η, it can not be solved by an analytical method. The one dimensional minimization with respect to learning rate η must be performed by some approximation methods and the amount of computation at each iteration step is increased due to this minimization process.

For a multilayer feedforward neural network, it is very difficult to obtain the optimal learning rate η using a one dimensional optimization method. However, one can derive an improved method based on the properties of the above optimal-gradient algorithm. One property is that the gradient vectors in two successive iteration steps of the optimal gradient algorithm are orthogonal. From (4) it is very easy to check this property:

$$\frac{\partial E(w(n+1))}{\partial \eta} = \left(\frac{\partial E(w(n+1))}{\partial w(n+1)} \right)^T \cdot \frac{\partial w(n+1)}{\partial \eta}$$

$$= \left(\frac{\partial E}{\partial w(n+1)}\right)^T \cdot \frac{\partial E}{\partial w(n)} = 0 \qquad (5)$$

which is the required relation for orthogonality.

It is very difficult to obtain the optimal learning rate η by analytical methods, but equation (5) is a necessary but not sufficient condition for an optimal gradient method. For example, one can compute the gradient vector according to the standard backpropagation algorithm, making the next gradient vector perpendicular to the previous one in every iteration in order to meet the necessary condition of the optimal gradient method. Although this method can not minimize the number of iteration steps, it can accelerate the learning process. One of the easiest methods to implement the orthogonal requirement is the Gram-Schmidt orthogonalization method. Suppose the gradient vector at iteration step n-1 is $\frac{\partial E}{\partial w(n-1)}$. According to the standard backpropagation algorithm the computed gradient vector at iteration step n is $\frac{\partial E}{\partial \overline{w}(n)}$ and the new gradient vector at iteration step n can be calculated by Gram-Schmidt method as:

$$\frac{\partial E}{\partial w(n)} = \frac{\partial E}{\partial \overline{w}(n)} - \frac{\left(\frac{\partial E}{\partial \overline{w}(n)}\right)^T \cdot \frac{\partial E}{\partial w(n-1)}}{\left(\frac{\partial E}{\partial w(n-1)}\right)^T \cdot \frac{\partial E}{\partial w(n-1)}} \cdot \frac{\partial E}{\partial w(n-1)} \qquad (6)$$

substituting (6) into (2), one has:

$$w(n+1) = w(n) - \eta$$

$$\cdot \left(\frac{\partial E}{\partial \overline{w}(n)} - \frac{\left(\frac{\partial E}{\partial \overline{w}(n)}\right)^T \cdot \frac{\partial E}{\partial w(n-1)}}{\left(\frac{\partial E}{\partial w(n-1)}\right)^T \cdot \frac{\partial E}{\partial w(n-1)}} \cdot \frac{\partial E}{\partial w(n-1)} \right)$$

$$= w(n) - \eta \cdot \frac{\partial E}{\partial \overline{w}(n)}$$

$$+ \eta \cdot \frac{\left(\frac{\partial E}{\partial \overline{w}(n)}\right)^T \cdot \frac{\partial E}{\partial w(n-1)}}{\left(\frac{\partial E}{\partial w(n-1)}\right)^T \cdot \frac{\partial E}{\partial w(n-1)}} \cdot \frac{\partial E}{\partial w(n-1)}$$

From (2),

$$w(n) - w(n-1) = -\eta \cdot \frac{\partial E}{\partial w(n-1)}$$

Let

$$\alpha(n) = -\frac{\left(\frac{\partial E}{\partial \overline{w}(n)}\right)^T \cdot \frac{\partial E}{\partial w(n-1)}}{\left(\frac{\partial E}{\partial w(n-1)}\right)^T \cdot \frac{\partial E}{\partial w(n-1)}} \qquad (7)$$

Then

$$w(n+1) = w(n) - \eta \cdot \frac{\partial E}{\partial \overline{w}(n)} + \alpha(n) \cdot (w(n) - w(n-1)) \qquad (8)$$

Obviously the above algorithm is similar to the momentum method, but here the momentum coefficient $\alpha(n)$ is adapted according to (7) in every iteration step. As is known, the function of the momentum term is to effectively filter out high frequency variations of the error space, especially when the error space contains long ravines that are characterized by a sharp curvature across the ravine and a gently sloping floor [5]. Since the sharp curvature tends to cause divergent oscillations across the ravine, the momentum term filters out the high curvature and thus allows the effective weight steps to be bigger. However, for a given system one has no idea of the properties of the error space and the optimal criteria to select the value of the momentum coefficient is not known. When the coefficient is too small it can not eliminate the divergent oscillation caused by the sharp curvature existed in the error space. If it is very large, it would be expected to degrade performance and lead to greater misadjustment. In effect, because of the increased misadjustment there is essentially no improvement in convergence speed [7], [10]. In the adaptive momentum algorithm, the momentum coefficient is updated in every iteration step in order to satisfy the necessary condition of the optimal gradient vector. When the algorithm is near convergence, $\alpha(n)$ is nearly zero, then the algorithm is equivalent to the standard backpropagation algorithm.

IV. NUMERICAL SIMULATIONS

Extensive numerical simulations have been carried out for the adaptive momentum algorithm. Due to space limitations only two examples will be given here. The first problem is concerned with the design a two layer feedforward neural network for use in an intelligent optical sensor. The network was designed with 23 input nodes, 3 hidden neurons in the first layer and 3 output neurons in the second layer. The output from an integrated photosentive array is combined with external tolerance adjustment signals and the resultant signals are the inputs signals to the neural network. The outputs of the neural network act as a control vector for a process control. The training set contains 380 input-output pattern pairs and a mean squared error is used as the comparison criteria. Both the constant and adaptive momentum algorithms are used to train this network. Both algorithms are started from the same initial weights with values that are randomly changing from -2.0 to 2.0 and the training patterns are selected in exactly the same order.

1159

Figure 1. shows the how the mean squared error is minimized as a function of the iteration number for three cases. The upper curve corresponds to the standard backpropagation algorithm with no momentum term and is designated as case (b). The middle curve represents an algorithm with a constant momentum term equal to 0.8 and designated as case (a). The lower curve that converges to smallest value of mean squared error was obtained using the adaptive momentum algorithm based on equation (7). The results of twenty different training runs have been averaged together, while the initial values of the weighting coefficients are changed from one run to the next. All the results were obtained by using the same training pattern pairs in every run. In order to observe the convergence properties more clearly the vertical axis in Figure 1. represents $\log_{10}$ M.S.E. and the horizontal axis represents the number of iterations.

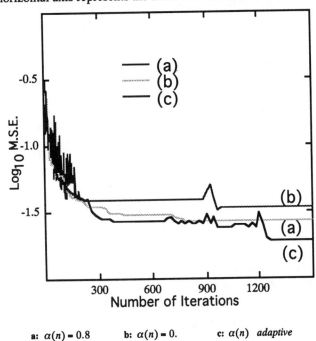

a: $\alpha(n) = 0.8$ b: $\alpha(n) = 0.$ c: $\alpha(n)$ adaptive

Fig. 1: Learning curves for different momentum

It is observed that the convergence trajectory for the standard backpropagation algorithm can be highly oscillatory during the initial phase of the convergence. It is also noted that the convergence speed is faster when the momentum coefficient α is larger and that a smoother learning curve is possible when the adaptive momentum algorithm is used. It is also observed that with an increase in the momentum value the mean squared error at convergence will also be also increased. However, for the adaptive momentum algorithm, the final error is less than the case of $\alpha(n) = 0$ or for a constant momentum term. It can be seen in Figure 2. how the momentum coefficient, $\alpha(n)$, as computed using equation (7) varies as a function of the iteration number associated with the learning process. When the iteration number is small (<200) the momentum coefficient $\alpha(n)$ can be relatively

large, however, when the algorithm is near convergence the incremental change in the momentum coefficient is very small value, almost zero, and thus the proposed algorithm essentially becomes the standard backpropagation algorithm without a momentum term.

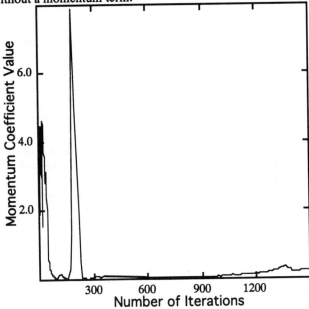

Fig. 2: Momentum updating in the learning process

The second problem considered is a neural network realization of a logic circuit with the truth table shown in Table I. The logic circuit has a 4-bit input and a 2-bit-output and was not based on a Boolean expression but rather the input-ouput relationships were randomly generated by a computer [11]. Figure 3. shows the learning process using backpropagation algorithms with both adaptive and constant momentum coefficients. The neural network realization contains one hidden layer with 6 neurons. $\eta = 0.9$ is used in both algorithms and $\alpha = 0.7$ is used as the constant momentum coefficient. Figure 3. shows how the backpropagation algorithm is accelerated when the momentum coefficient $\alpha(n)$ is varied at every iteration.

TABLE I
A FOUR-INPUT TWO-OUTPUT PROBLEM

Input	Output
0 0 0 0	0 0
1 0 0 0	0 1
0 1 0 0	0 0
1 1 0 0	0 0
0 0 1 0	1 0
1 0 1 0	0 0
0 1 1 0	1 0
1 1 1 0	1 1
0 0 0 1	0 0
1 0 0 1	1 1
0 1 0 1	0 1
1 1 0 1	0 0
0 0 1 0	1 0
1 0 1 1	1 1
0 1 1 1	0 0
1 1 1 1	0 0

It should be noted that the adaptive momentum algorithm will not obtain a global minimum for arbitrary initial values of the weights. Its main advantage is to accelerate the convergence of the standard backpropagation algorithm in reaching a certain local minimum, where this local minimum may be different from the one reached by a constant momentum algorithm.

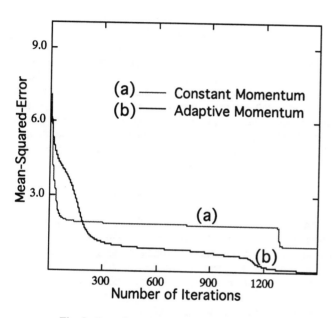

Fig. 3: Learning process for the logic network

V. CONCLUSIONS

An adaptive momentum algorithm for training multilayer feedforward neural network has been introduced. The momentum term has been computed in accordance with equation (7). The use of an adaptive momentum term tends to eliminate the divergent oscillations in the M.S.E. produced during the initial iteration steps associated with the standard backpropagation algorithm. The final M.S.E. when convergence was reached was also found to be smaller. For a given convergence criteria, the adaptive momentum algorithm was also found to reach convergence in a fewer number of iterations. The proposed algorithm was tested on two different application problem. The simulation results also show the better convergence speed and final smaller mean-squared-error properties of the adaptive momentum algorithm over simply using a constant momentum term.

ACKNOWLEDGMENT

This research project was carried out with the support and funding of the Natural Sciences and Engineering Research Council (Canada) and Ortho-McNeil Inc. of Don Mills, Ontario.

REFERENCES

[1] L. W. Chan, and F. Fallside, "An Adaptive Training Algorithm for Backpropagation Networks", *Computer Speech and Language*, Vol. 2, September - December, 1987

[2] Richard S. Sutton, "Two problems with Backpropagation and other Steepest-Descent Learning Procedures for Networks", *Proceedings of the 8th Annual Conference of the Cognitive Science Society*, 1986, pp. 823-831

[3] R. Jacobs, "Increased Rates of Convergence through Learning Rate Adaptation", *Neural Networks*, Vol. 1, No. 4, 1988

[4] Fernando M. Silva, and Luis B. Almeida, "Acceleration Techniques for the Backpropagation Algorithm". *Neural Networks, EUTSDIP Workshop 1990*, Feb. 15-17, 1990, pp. 110-119

[5] D. Rumelhart, D. Hinton, and G. Williams, "Learning Internal Representations by Error Propagation", In D. Rumelhart and F. McCelland, eds., *Parallel Distributed Processing*, Vol. 1, Cambridge, MA, MIT Press, 1969

[6] R. Lippmann, "An Introduction to Computing with Neural Nets", *IEEE ASSP Mag.* Vol. 4, April 1987, pp. 4-22

[7] J. J. Shynk and S. Roy, "Analysis of a Perceptron Learning Algorithm with Momentum Updating", in *Proc. IEEE Int. Conf. Accost., Speech, Signal Processing*, Albuquerque, NM, April 1990, pp. 1377-1380

[8] J. J. Shynk and S.Roy, "Convergence Properties and Stationary points of a Perceptron Learning Algorithm," *Proc. IEEE*, Vol. 78, October 1990

[9] J. R.. Glover, Jr., "High Order Algorithms for Adaptive Filters", *IEEE Trans. Commun.*, Vol. COM27, January 1979, pp. 216-221

[10] S.Roy and J.J. Shynk, "Analysis of the Momentum LMS Algorithm", *IEEE Trans. Acoust., Speech, Signal Processing*, Vol. 38, No. 12, December1990, pp. 2088-2098

[11] T. S. Chang and K. A. S. Abdel-Ghaffar, "A Universal Neural Net With Guaranteed Convergence to Zero System Error", *IEEE Trans. on Signal Processing*, Vol. 40, No. 12, December 1992, pp. 3022-3031

Fuzzy Function Learning with Covariance Ellipsoids

Julie A. Dickerson and Bart Kosko

Department of Electrical Engineering–Systems
Signal and Image Processing Institute
University of Southern California
Los Angeles, California, 90089-2564

Abstract - This paper shows how first and second order statistics can estimate fuzzy rules and sets from input-output data. The fuzzy system approximates the function by covering its graph with fuzzy patches in the input-output state space. The neural quantizer system uses unsupervised competitive learning to estimate the local centroids and covariances of pattern classes. The covariance matrix of each random quantization vector defines an ellipsoid around the centroid of the pattern class. The ellipsoids define fuzzy patches or rules that cover the graph of the function. Regions of sparse data give rise to large ellipsoids or less certain rules. The approximation error falls as the number of patches grows. Ellipsoidal covariance learning estimated the control surface for a car velocity controller.

I. FUZZY RULES AS ELLIPSOID REGIONS

Higher order correlations can estimate nonlinear non-Gaussian systems from noisy sample data [7,8]. Competitive learning quantizes vectors in local statistical averages. The neural adaptive vector quantization (AVQ) system, which uses unsupervised competitive learning, asymptotically estimates higher order statistics of sample data. These statistics apply to non-Gaussian and nonlinear problems.

We used second order statistics to learn the fuzzy sets and rules for an additive fuzzy system. Competitive learning estimated the unknown probability density function that underlied the data and that described the distribution of patterns in R^n. Adaptive vector quantization systems converge exponentially quickly to pattern class centroids [6]. Competitive learning laws can asymptotically estimate the local conditional covariance matrix for a pattern class.

The covariance matrix defines an ellipsoid in the input-output space. These ellipsoids approximate the fuzzy rules that in turn approximate the function. Projections of the ellipsoids onto the axes form the fuzzy sets. When many patches overlap, we compute a histogram of the projections. This estimates the density of ellipsoids or patches along each axis and combines the information in the ellipsoids. Peaks in the distribution center the fuzzy associative memory (FAM) cells. Clusters of synaptic vectors in the state space give the fuzzy rules. We used this method to estimate the control surface for a car velocity controller.

II. FUZZY SYSTEMS

Additive fuzzy systems can uniformly approximate any continuous or measurable function [5]. This gives model-free estimation of functions. A fuzzy system stores a set of associations of the form "If antecedent conditions hold, then consequent conditions hold". These associations store expert knowledge or learned rules between system variables. Each fuzzy association defines a patch or a Cartesian product of input-output fuzzy sets. The fuzzy system approximates the function by covering its graph with fuzzy patches and averaging patches that overlap. A fuzzy rule maps input set **A** to output set **B**. The simplest fuzzy rule associates output fuzzy set **B** with an input fuzzy set **A** and defines a fuzzy associative memory (FAM) map from the input fuzzy sets A_i to the output fuzzy set B_i. The FAM maps similar input fuzzy sets to similar output fuzzy sets. This reduces to the rule "IF X=A, THEN Y=B". Additive fuzzy systems fire all rules in parallel and add the scaled output sets B_i to get the output set **B**.

Defuzzification of **B** gives a number or a control signal. Centroidal defuzzification with correlation product inference[6] gives the output control signal as the ratio

$$y_k = \frac{\sum\limits_{i=1}^{N} c_i\, w_i\, I_i\, m_{B_i}(x_k)}{\sum\limits_{i=1}^{N} w_i\, I_i\, m_{B_i}(x_k)} \qquad (1)$$

where w_i is the sum of the rule weights for the ith set, I_i is the area, and c_i is the centroid of the ith output set B_i. m_{B_i} is the scaling value for the output set B_i.

The Caltrans PATH Program supported this research (Agreement #20695 MB).

III. DENSITY ESTIMATION WITH COMPETITIVE LEARNING

A. Unsupervised Competitive Learning

Neurons compete for the activation from input patterns. The winning neuron learns the input pattern. The p synaptic vectors $\mathbf{m}_j$ define the p columns of the synaptic connection matrix $\mathbf{M}$. $\mathbf{M}$ interconnects the n input neurons in the input field F_X to the p competing neurons in the output field F_Y: $\mathbf{y} = \mathbf{x}^T \mathbf{M}$. Nonnegative signal functions S_i and S_j map the activations x_i and y_j into bounded monotone increasing signals $S_i(x_i)$ and $S_j(y_j)$. Competitive synapses learn only when the jth neuron "wins" and $S_j(y_j)$ is positive:

$$\dot{\mathbf{m}}_j = S_j\left(y_j\right)\left[\mathbf{S}(x) - \mathbf{m}_j\right] \tag{2}$$

where $\mathbf{S}(x) = (S_1(x_1), \ldots, S_n(x_n))$ and $\mathbf{m}_j = (m_{1j}, \ldots, m_{nj})$. A steep logistic signal function,

$$S_j\left(y_j\right) = \frac{1}{1 + e^{-cy_j}} \tag{3}$$

with a large $c > 0$, approximates a binary win-loss indicator for the jth pattern class. The jth F_Y neuron wins the competition at time t if $S_j(y_j) = 1$; it loses if $S_j(y_j) = 0$.

In the discrete case we use a stochastic difference equation:

$$\mathbf{m}_j(k+1) = \mathbf{m}_j(k) + c_k\left[\mathbf{x}_k - \mathbf{m}_j(k)\right]$$
if the jth neuron wins

$$\mathbf{m}_j(k+1) = \mathbf{m}_j(k) \tag{4}$$
if the jth neuron loses

Estimators have covariances. Centroids provide a first-order estimate of how the unknown probability density function $p(\mathbf{x})$ behaves in the regions $\mathbf{D}_j$. Local covariances give a second-order estimate. Competitive learning laws can asymptotically estimate the local conditional covariance matrices $\mathbf{K}_j$:

$$\mathbf{K}_j = E\left[\left(\mathbf{x} - \bar{\mathbf{x}}_j\right)\left(\mathbf{x} - \bar{\mathbf{x}}_j\right)^T \mid \mathbf{D}_j\right] \tag{5}$$

At each iteration we estimate the unknown centroid $\mathbf{x}_j$ as the current synaptic vector $\mathbf{m}_j$. In this sense $\mathbf{K}_j$ becomes an error conditional covariance matrix. This leads to the stochastic difference-equation algorithm[6]:

$$\mathbf{K}_j(k+1) = \mathbf{K}_j(k) + d_k\left[\left(\mathbf{x}_k - \mathbf{m}_j(k)\right)\left(\mathbf{x}_k - \mathbf{m}_j(k)\right)^T - \mathbf{K}_j(k)\right]$$
if the jth neuron wins

$$\mathbf{K}_j(k+1) = \mathbf{K}_j(k) \tag{6}$$
if the jth neuron loses

for the synaptic vectors. $\mathbf{K}_j(k+1)$ converges to the local conditional covariance matrix [6].

Adaptive vector quantization (AVQ) systems adaptively cluster pattern classes in a state space. Stochastic competitive learning systems are neural AVQ systems. The algorithms estimate the unknown probability density function $p(\mathbf{x})$ that underlies the data. Competition reduces to nearest neighbor classification. The AVQ system compares the current vector random sample $\mathbf{x}(t)$ with the p columns of the synaptic connection matrix $\mathbf{M}$. If the jth synaptic vector $\mathbf{m}_j(t)$ is closest in Euclidean distance, then the jth neuron wins in (4). The competitive synaptic vectors converge exponentially quickly to pattern-class centroids [6]. At equilibrium the average synaptic vector $E[\mathbf{m}_j]$ equals the jth centroid. Centroid estimation requires that the competitive signal approximate the indicator function of the locally sampled pattern class $\mathbf{D}_j$ with a near binary win-loss function.

The following procedure describes the algorithm for competitive AVQ density estimation.[4]

Competitive AVQ Algorithm

1. Initialize: $\mathbf{m}_i(0) = \mathbf{x}(i)$, $i = 1, \ldots, p$.

2. For a random data sample $\mathbf{x}(t)$, find the closest or "winning" synaptic vector $\mathbf{m}_j(t)$:

$$\left\| \mathbf{m}_j(t) - \mathbf{x}(t) \right\| = \min_i \left\| \mathbf{m}_i(t) - \mathbf{x}(t) \right\| \tag{7}$$

where $\| \mathbf{x} \|^2 = x_1^2 + \ldots + x_n^2$ is the squared Euclidean norm.

3. Update the winning synaptic vector $\mathbf{m}_j(t)$ with (4) and its local covariance estimate $\mathbf{K}_j(t)$ with (6).

We scale the components of the data sample $\mathbf{x}(t)$ so that all features have equal weight in the distance measure [2].

B. Product-Space Clustering for Fuzzy Rule Estimation

Ellipsoidal covariance learning finds the fuzzy rules and sets from the system input-output data. The covariance estimates define ellipsoids in the q-dimensional input-output state space (Fig. 1), where $q = n + p$ for n inputs to the fuzzy system and p outputs of the fuzzy system. The covariance ellipsoid is the locus of all $\mathbf{x}$ that satisfy

$$c^2 = \left(\mathbf{x} - \mathbf{m}_j\right)^T \mathbf{K}_j^{-1}\left(\mathbf{x} - \mathbf{m}_j\right) \tag{8}$$

The eigenvalues of $\mathbf{K}_j^{-1}$ are $\lambda_1, \ldots, \lambda_q$. The eigenvalues and eigenvectors of the positive definite matrix $\mathbf{K}_j^{-1}$ define an ellipsoid in q-space [10]. The eigenvectors orient the

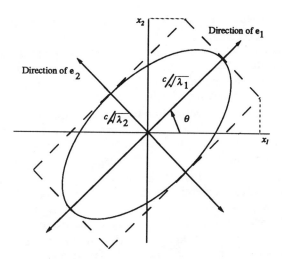

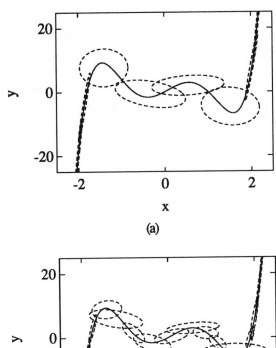

Fig. 1. Each covariance matrix defines an ellipsoid around the centroid. The eigenvalues of $\mathbf{K}_j^{-1}$ define the length of the axes. The axes point towards the eigenvectors.

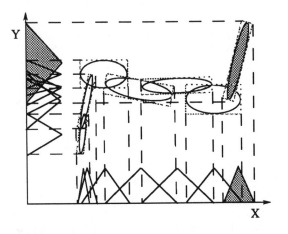

(a)

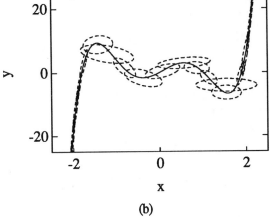

(b)

Fig. 3. The approximation of $f(x)=3x(x-1)(x-1.9)(x+0.7)(x+1.8)$ improves as the number of ellipsoids grows. (a) 10 ellipsoids cover the graph. (b) 20 ellipsoids cover the graph.

Fig. 2. The projection of each ellipsoid onto the axes of the input-output state space defines a fuzzy set and fuzzy association or rule between the inputs and the outputs.

ellipsoid. The Euclidean half-lengths of the axes equal $c/\sqrt{\lambda_1}$, $\ldots$, $c/\sqrt{\lambda_q}$. The ellipsoid in (8) implies that $\mathbf{K}_j$ is positive-definite. If not, the ellipsoid concentrates on a lower dimensional hyperplane and this method can fail. We assume that $\mathbf{K}_j$ is positive-definite.

The covariance ellipsoids relate local changes in the input-output space. The projections of the ellipsoid onto the input and output axes bound the fuzzy sets. We used symmetric triangular sets centered at the centroid (Fig. 2). Most unimodal sets will work. The ellipsoid itself defines a fuzzy association or patch or rule between the inputs and the outputs. Figure 3 shows the covariance ellipsoids for different numbers of quantizing vectors. A quantizing vector "hops" more in regions where data is sparse and so gives rise

to larger ellipsoids or less certain rules. Tightly clustered data gives rise to smaller ellipsoids or more certain rules.

To simplify the calculations we inscribed the ellipsoid in a hyperrectangle. The hyperrectangle had 2^q vertices at ($\pm c/\sqrt{\lambda_1}, \ldots, \pm c/\sqrt{\lambda_q}$). The unit eigenvectors define *direction cosines* for each axis of the ellipse. The *direction cosine* is the angle between the eigenvector and the axis [3]. The projection of the jth hyperrectangle onto the ith axis is the interval ∂_{ji}:

$$\partial_i = [m_i - c(|\cos\gamma_{i1}|/\sqrt{\lambda_1} + \ldots + |\cos\gamma_{iq}|/\sqrt{\lambda_q}),$$
$$m_i + c(|\cos\gamma_{i1}|/\sqrt{\lambda_1} + \ldots + |\cos\gamma_{iq}|/\sqrt{\lambda_q})] \quad (9)$$

This interval defines the base of the triangular fuzzy sets in each of the input and output dimensions. Figure 4 shows how fuzzy ellipsoids can approximate a fifth-order polynomial. More synaptic vectors give a more accurate

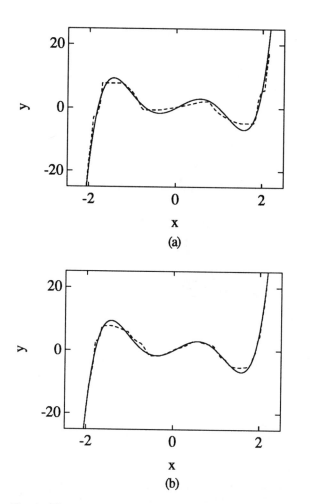

(a)

(b)

Fig. 4. The approximation of $f(x) = 3x(x-1)(x-1.9)(x+0.7)(x+1.8)$ improves as the number of ellipsoids grows. (a) Fuzzy system output for 10 patches. (b) Fuzzy system output for 20 patches.

approximation. Figure 5 shows the mean squared error as the number of synaptic vectors grows.

C. Histogram Density Estimation

When the data fall in many pattern classes, we estimate the density of the projections along the axes of the state space. Competitive learning estimates the unknown probability density function $p(\mathbf{x})$ that describes the distribution of patterns in the input-output state space (realizations of random vector $\mathbf{x}$). The synaptic quantizing vectors track the data. Where sample vectors are dense or sparse, synaptic vectors tend to be dense or sparse. This gives a nonparametric estimate of the density in the state space.

Even in low probability regions there must be enough synaptic vectors to estimate the pattern class statistics. Rare events may be as important as equilibrium events for system performance and stability. This method needs data or expert

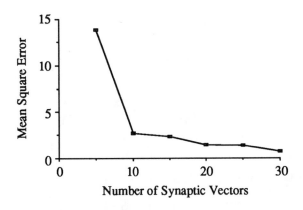

Fig. 5. More fuzzy patches better approximate the function. Mean squared error falls as the number of patches grows.

rules for these rare events. A large number of fuzzy rules and sets results if each synaptic vector counts as a rule.

Histogram estimation [2] gives a nonparametric estimate of a probability density. We sum the weighted triangular projections of the ellipsoids to form the histogram:

$$p_i(x_k) = \sum_{j=1}^{Q} b_{ij}(x_k)$$

(10)

Q is the number of synaptic vectors. $b_{ij}(x_k)$ is the triangular projection of the jth ellipsoid on the ith axis at x_k. Figure 6 shows this technique applied to each axis. The peaks of the distribution are the centers of the fuzzy sets in each dimension. We partition the state space along this grid and count the number of synaptic vectors in each cell. Clusters of synaptic vectors form a rule [4]. Different values of the ellipsoid scaling constant c change the size of the projections on the axis. Larger values of c smooth the data. Small values of c give more resolution in areas where there are many synaptic vectors.

IV. ESTIMATION OF CAR VELOCITY CONTROL SURFACE

In this section we use competitive AVQ and the histogram method to estimate the control surface for a throttle controller for a sport utility vehicle. In [1] we defined a simple control system for velocity in car platoons. The inputs to this system are

$$\Delta v_i(t) = v_{Platoon} - v_i(t)$$

(11)

$$a_i(t) = a_i(t)$$

(12)

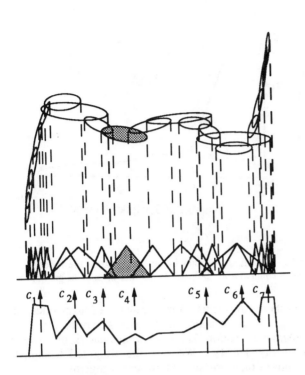

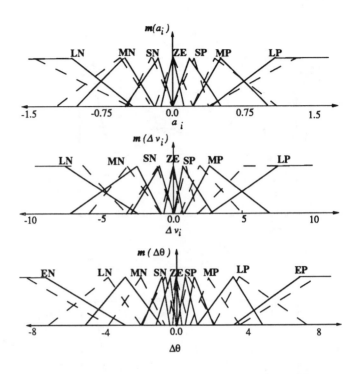

Fig. 7. Comparison of the fuzzy sets for the velocity controller. The solid lines are the original sets for cars. The dashed lines are the AVQ determined sets for a truck.

Fig. 6. Large numbers of ellipsoids estimate the underlying density $p(\mathbf{x})$ from the data. First we project the ellipsoids onto an axis. The sum of these projections forms a histogram. The peaks in this distribution give the centers of the FAM cells (shown by the arrow).

$v_i(t)$ and $a_i(t)$ are the velocity and acceleration of the ith car at time t. $v_{Platoon}$ is the desired velocity of the platoon. The output of the system is the change in throttle angle $\Delta\theta_i$. The controller allows the car to maintain a constant velocity and change velocity. We tested the fuzzy controller with the dynamic car model in [9]. That study assumed a flat straight horizontal road surface with no perturbing forces such as wind. Equations 13 and 14 give the car model:

$$m_i\, a_i = m_i\, \xi_i - K_{d_i}\, v_i^2 - d_{m_i} \tag{13}$$

$$\dot{\xi}_i = -\frac{\xi_i}{\tau_i(v_i)} + \frac{\theta_i}{m_i\, \tau_i(v_i)} \tag{14}$$

Equation 13 comes from Newton's Second Law($F=ma$). The term $m_i\xi_i$ denotes the tractive engine force that the wheels apply. The variables a_i and v_i represent the acceleration and velocity of the car. $K_{d_i}v_i^2$ and d_{m_i} are the aerodynamic and mechanical drag forces. m_i is the total mass of the car and cargo. τ_i is the engine time lag. The input to the system, θ_i, comes from the throttle, which produces changes in the rate of acceleration or jerk.

The leader velocity controller in [1] generated 7500 training samples in 200 trajectories for the sport utility vehicle. The training vectors (a, Δv, $\Delta\theta$) defined points in the three dimensional input-output space. An adaptive vector quantizer with competitive learning clustered the data and computed its local statistics. The AVQ system had 450 synaptic vectors or local pattern classes. The sum of the ellipsoid projections onto each axis of the state space gave a histogram of the density of the pattern classes. We chose seven sets in each of the input dimensions. The center of each FAM rule cell matched a peak in the histogram. The boundaries of the FAM rule cells lay at the midpoints between the histogram peaks.

We then partitioned the state space into possible rule patches and found the rules by counting the number of synaptic vectors in each cell. Clusters of synaptic vectors in the FAM cell defined the rules[4]. We chose seven sets in each of the input dimensions. Figure 7 shows the fuzzy sets for the FTC and the system based on ellipsoidal learning. The sets for the truck are larger and coarser than those for the smaller and lighter cars. Figure 8 shows the control surfaces for the original system and the adaptive system. The adaptive fuzzy system had a higher peak value and a steeper control surface. Figure 9 shows the results of changing the platoon velocity for the truck using both controllers. The controller based on ellipsoidal covariance learning had no overshoot. The hand-designed controller in [1] overshot the desired value. Velocity overshoot leads to unsafe situations in platoons of cars separated by 2 meters.

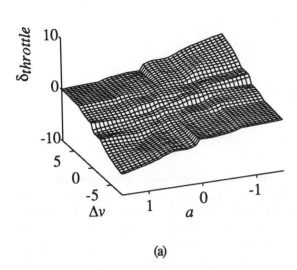

(a)

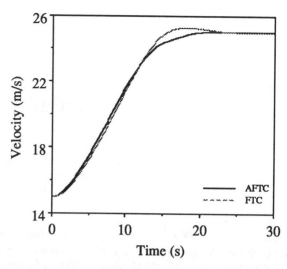

Fig. 9. Comparison of the hand-designed fuzzy throttle controller in [1] and the adaptive controller for sport-utility vehicles. Ellipsoidal covariance learning found the fuzzy rules and sets.

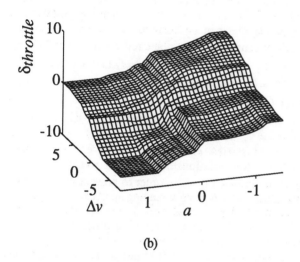

(b)

Fig. 8. Covariance ellipsoids estimate the control surface for a car velocity controller. (a) Control surface for hand-designed controller. (b) Control surface for AVQ designed controller. Ellipsoidal covariance learning found the fuzzy rules and sets.

V. CONCLUSIONS

Unsupervised ellipsoidal learning offers a new way to find a fuzzy system using only data from a human driver or other controller. Ellipsoidal learning works for any control system when input-output data is available as in the control of many biological or engineering or economic processes. Future research will compare how well supervised and unsupervised learning find the optimal ellipsoids and rules for fuzzy systems.

REFERENCES

[1] Dickerson, J.A., Kosko, B., "Fuzzy Longitudinal Control for Car Platoons," in *Modern Tools for Manufacturing Systems - Proceedings of the International Workshop on Emerging Technologies for Factory Automation*, August 1992.

[2] Fukunaga, K., *Introduction to Statistical Pattern Recognition*, Electrical Science Series, Academic Press, Inc., Harcourt Brace Jovanovich, Publishers, 1972.

[3] Hildebrand, F.B., *Advanced Calculus for Applications*, Second Edition, Prentice-Hall, Englewood Cliffs, 1976.

[4] Kong, S.G., Kosko, B., "Adaptive Fuzzy Systems for Backing up a Truck-and-Trailer," *IEEE Transactions on Neural Networks*, vol. 3, No. 2, pp. 211-223, March 1992.

[5] Kosko, B., "Fuzzy Systems as Universal Approximators," in review; an early verson appears in *Proceedings of the 1st IEEE International Conference on Fuzzy Systems(FUZZ-IEEE FUZZ92)*, pp. 1153-1162, March 1992.

[6] Kosko, B., *Neural Networks and Fuzzy Systems*, Prentice-Hall, Englewood Cliffs, 1992.

[7] Mendel, J.M., "Tutorial on Higher-Order Statistics (Spectra) in Signal Processing and System Theory: Theoretical Results and Some Applications," *Proceedings of the IEEE*, vol 79, No 3, pp 278-305, March 1991.

[8] Nikias, C., Raghuveer, M.R., "Bispectrum Estimation: A Digital Signal Processing Framework," *Proceedings of the IEEE*, vol 75, pp. 869-891, July 1987.

[9] Sheikholesam, S., Desoer,C.A., "Combined Longitudinal and Lateral Control of a Platoon of Vehicles: A System Level Study," *PATH Technical Memorandum*, 91-3, 1991.

[10] Strang, G., *Linear Algebra and Its Applications*, Second Edition, Academic Press, 1980.

Learning in the Hypercube

Volnei A. Pedroni and Amnon Yariv

Dept. of Electrical Engineering and Applied Physics
California Institute of Technology, 128-95
Pasadena, CA 91125 USA

Abstract — We present a discussion on learning from a geometric point of view, with the main purpose of obtaining ways of pre-estimating the weights and thresholds of a neural network and analyzing the corresponding effects on the learning procedure speed.

I. INTRODUCTION

Simply put, the learning problem considered here can be viewed as follows. Given a neural network structure and a task to be learnt (for example, a set of sample points to be classified into groups), find a set of weights w and a threshold t for each neuron in the structure such that the expected function is performed within certain tolerance parameters, while keeping the structure size as small as possible. The learning algorithm is then the procedure for trying to reach such numbers. We can draw the following *geometric* analogy to the above. A single threshold neuron can be viewed as an unit that implements a hyperplane in an E-space, partitioning it into two regions. The weights (synapses) define the orientation of the plane (the vector w is perpendicular to it), while the threshold defines its relative position (Fig.1). So, if a feedforward NN is specified, for example, a certain number of hyperplanes are automatically placed in the space, whose positions and orientations depend only upon the weights and thresholds chosen. It is the learning algorithm's task to move these planes around until (hopefully) the specified function is implemented.

There are three main issues to be considered here. First, given a certain architecture and a task to be learnt, what size of network to chose. Second, which learning algorithm gives better performance for a particular task. Finally, where to locate the hyperplanes in the very first place. The first two issues have received very intense attention in the literature, while learning is frequently chosen to be started from random weights. We discuss in this paper the learning problem from a geometric viewpoint, with the main purpose of pre-estimating the position of the hyperplanes and analyzing its effects on the learning speed of conventional learning algorithms, like back propagation [1].

Let us consider a space where $m \leq 2^n$ n-bit points are distributed and we wish to separate them into two groups (dichotomy computation) by means of a feedforward neural network of linear threshold neurons. So, as all the points are located at vertices of a hypercube of dimension n, they can be represented by vectors with components (-1,1), all with same length $\sqrt{n}$. If there is in the space a separable cluster of points, it is admissible that the summation of all the vectors representing those points will point to somewhere around their center of gravity. Therefore, it is also admissible that this vector and the vector of the weights $w=w_1w_2...w_n$ are somehow related, since w is perpendicular to the hyperplane that separates those elements. To illustrate this idea, let us consider n=3. For any set of linearly separable points, i.e., a set of points that can be correctly classified by just one plane, there is an equivalent plane represented by $w^+ = \Sigma_i x_i^+$ or by $w^- = \Sigma_i x_i^-$, where $x^+ = (x|f(x)=1)$ and $x^- = (x|f(x)=-1)$, while $M^+ = \{x^+\}$ and $M^- = \{x^-\}$. In the example of Fig.1, $M^+ = \{(1,1,1), (1,1,-1), (-1,1,1)\}$ and $M^- = \{(1,-1,-1), (1,-1,1), (-1,-1,1), (-1,-1,-1), (-1,1,-1)\}$. Hence, $w^+ = (1,3,1)$. If we make $w=w^+$, with t=2, we readily obtain a plane that correctly classifies all the points given. For higher dimensions, this relationship becomes weaker, but it is possible to improve on w^+ in order to prevent the vector w^+ and the ideal vector w from spreading apart excessively.

The method presented here is mainly intended as a discussion tool. If used as a learning procedure, the final network size would be about minimum for clustered or layered spaces (Fig.2), but it could be much bigger than minimum for more intricate distributions. Since the Vapnik-Chervonenkis dimension grows with the number of neurons in the hidden layer [2],[3], this would make generalization less likely to occur. A simple reference number one could

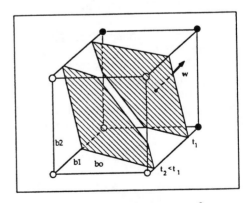

Fig. 1. A set of linearly separable points in E^3. The vector w defines the orientation of the hyperplane, while t defines its relative position.

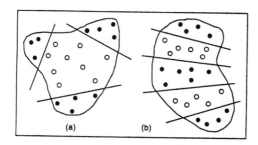

Fig. 2. (a) Clustered and (b) layered spaces.

watch for is $2^n/n^2$ neurons in the hidden layer, in which case the average minimum number of bits needed to represent the network is still below its information capacity. This number is about the same as $e.m/((e+n)\log_2 m)$, a lower bound on number of neurons required for the NN to be able to learn arbitrary functions [4].

II. PROCEDURE

The basic procedure can be described as follows. First, a center of gravity is estimated. Based on its vector w^+, the first neuron is designed, which will correspond to a hyperplane separating a certain number of training data points belonging to one of the sub-sets, say M^+. Next, this hyperplane is slightly moved until it rests on (contains) as many elements belonging to the other group (M^-) as possible. If there still are elements of M^+ to be separated, a second hyperplane is added to the network, and so on, until all the elements are correctly classified. These neurons constitute the hidden layer of the network. An output element is then added in order to produce the system's output.

The method is presented in two versions. In version 1, each neuron separates (collects) as many elements belonging to one same sub-set as possible, being so appropriate for computing dichotomies on clustered spaces, like the symbolic one illustrated in Fig.2(a). For layered spaces (Fig.2(b)), version 2 gives better performance, since each new neuron added to the network acts on the opposite sub-set from the one considered by the previous neuron.

Version 1:
a) Design of the first neuron of the hidden layer:
. estimate a center of gravity(1) and determine $w_1^+ = \Sigma_i x_i^+$;
. make $w_1 = w^+$;
. make $t = \max(w_1, x_i^-)$;
. make $w_1 = \Sigma_i x_i^+$ for all x^+'s such that $(w_1, x_i^+) > t$;
. repeat last two steps until w_1 stabilizes;
. move hyperplane until it contains as many elements of M^- as possible (2); call this w_1^{++} and t_1;

. construct neuron 1, with $w = w_1^{++}$ and $t = t_1$.
b) Design of neurons 2 through k of hidden layer:
. remove from M^+ all the x^+'s separated by neuron 1. If there still are points x^+'s left, repeat (a) for the new set.
. construct neuron 2, with $w = w_2^{++}$ and $t = t_2$;
. repeat this until the set of points left coincides with M^-.
d) Design of the output neuron:
. the output neuron acts as an OR threshold gate. So, make $w_i = 1$ ($i = 1, 2, ..., k$) and $t = -(k-1)$.

Version 2:
a) Design of the first neuron:
. same as (a) above.
b) Design of neurons 2 through k:
. same as above, but acting on M^- and M^+ alternately.
c) Design of the output neuron:
. the output neuron acts as a collect/remove threshold unit. Therefore, one choice for the weights is $(-2)^{k-i}$ if k=odd, or $-(-2)^{k-i}$ if k=even, with i representing the neurons $1, 2, ..., k$ of the hidden layer, and threshold $t = -(w_1 + w_2 + ... + w_k + 1)$.

In the next section, we apply this procedure to a pair of well-known problems and discuss its effects on learning speed.

III. APPLICATION EXAMPLES

Example 1: Parity Detection

This problem consists of detecting whether the number of bits of a certain type in a vector is even or odd. This is equivalent to the multi-dimensional XOR problem, which consists of, given a reference element, separating in one group all the elements whose Hamming distance d from it is odd and in the other all those whose d is even. The XOR problem has been considered a hard problem for many learning algorithms, since they often get trapped in local minima. As this space is perfectly organized in layers (Fig.2(b)), it turns out that version 2 yields the optimal

---

(1) If one neuron suffices to compute a dichotomy, it follows from previous discussions that $w^+ = \Sigma_i x_i^+$ is a good initial approximation for w. If, however, multiple neurons are necessary, as it is generally the case, it implies that the space has multiple centers of gravity. One trivial way of breaking the space into sub-regions is by observing that, in a fully specified space, two elements can only belong to the same sub-set of points if each one has Hamming distance d=1 from at least one other element in that sub-set. Also, if a set is a degenerate one, that is, $w^+ = w^- = 0$, it has at least two centers of gravity, and complements (d=n) are on opposite sides. So, we can take one element from the set (normally one with an intermediate weight will do better) and list all the elements with d=1 from it. We can repeat the procedure for the second element in the list, and so on, but lists bigger than n will tend to degrade the results.

solution (minimum size), with k=n neurons in the hidden layer and only n iterations. Let us consider, as an example, n=16, with $x_{ref}=(x_1,x_2,...,x_{16})=(1,1,...,1)$. Using version 2, we obtain neuron 1 with $w_1=(1,1,...,1)$ and t=n-1=15, which separates only x_{ref}. Next, we get $w_2=(1,1,...,1)$ and t=n-3=13 for neuron 2, which separates the element already separated by the first neuron plus all the elements with d=1 from it. Repeating the algorithm, we obtain the third neuron, with $w_3=(1,1,...,1)$ and t=n-5=11. This neuron again separates all the elements already separated by the others plus all those with d=2 from x_{ref}. Proceeding in this way, it results k=n=16 neurons in the hidden layer, all with $w=x_{ref}$ and t=n-2i+1 (i=1,2,...,n). Geometrically speaking, this NN implements a set of n hyperplanes, all parallel to each other and perpendicular to the main diagonal of the hypercube that passes through the origin and the reference element and all separated from one another by a distance $2/\sqrt{n}$ ($\Delta t=2$). The output neuron has to produce an output=1 for the first neuron in the hidden layer, since it is separating an element from

M^+ (collect), so $w_1=1$. The second synapse of the output neuron has an opposite (remove) function, since the second neuron in the hidden layer is adding elements from M^- to the set, so $w_2=-1$. Repeating this, we obtain w=(1, -1,1,-1,...,1,-1) for the output unit. Its threshold is t=-1, since k is even (t=0 if n were odd). This result is illustrated in Fig. 3. (Notice that the numbers used above for the output neuron were slightly different from those in the description of version 2 of the procedure; this was only possible because each new hyperplane introduced here separated not only a new group of points but all the points already separated by the previous neurons as well.)

Example 2: Symmetry Detection

This problem, for n=6, was considered in a discussion on the back-propagation algorithm [1]. As mentioned there, the learning required 1,425 sweeps through the set of 64 possible input vectors. Geometrically speaking, this problem is harder than the previous one, though, no matter what the dimension of the space is, it can always be solved with just two neurons in the hidden layer and one output neuron (so, minimum size is k=2). Let us analyze the case of n=4 first. We start by constructing the sub-sets M^+ and M^-. As all the elements in M^+ have d≥2 from each other, we choose to work on M^-, even though it is bigger than M^+. We obtain $w^-=0$. Thus, we pick one element from M^- (say -1-1-11) and break the space into partial regions, from what we obtain w^- =(-4,2,-2,4). Applying then version 1 results $w_1=w^-$ and t=1. For the second neuron, we obtain $w_2=-w_1$, with t=1 again. As there are no points left, this concludes the design of the hidden layer (k=2). The output unit has w=(1,1) and

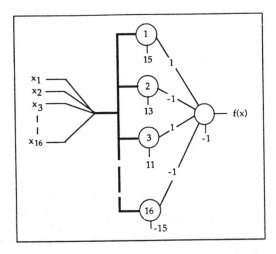

Fig. 3. Multi-dimensional XOR implementation.

---

(2) A very simple way of sliding the hyperplane to the position where it contains as many elements of M^- as possible is by looking at all the x^-'s that produce $(w,x^-)=t$ as well as at the x^- that produces the scalar product closest to t. Say this difference is Δt. Then we determine in how many positions the components of the first group of x^-'s vectors above are equal, at the same time that they differ from those of the latter x^-. Say this number is p. To those positions in w we can add $\Delta t/2p$ or $-\Delta t/2p$, depending on whether the components of the latter x^- in each of those positions is a 1 or a 0, respectively. This process can be repeated until no other vector satisfies the conditions above.

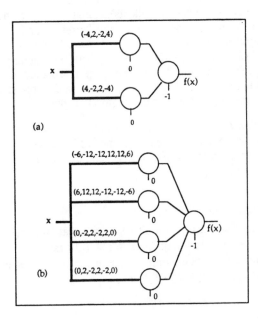

Fig. 4. Symmetry detection implementation (a) n=4, (b) n=6.

1170

t=-(k-1)=-1 (version 1). Therefore, for n=4 only one iteration per neuron was necessary for 0% error and minimum size was obtained. Fig. 4(a) shows this NN.

Let us consider now the case of n=6. Here, M^+ has 8 elements, while M^- has 56. Again, $w^-=0$. Hence, we pick an element from M^- (say -1-1-1111) and break the space, applying then version 1, which produces $w_1=(-6, -12, -12,12,12,6)$ and $w_2=-w_1$, with 60/64=94% of the points correctly classified. Applying then these numbers to the back propagation algorithm, less than 100 epochs are now needed for the NN to learn the symmetry detection function. (Notice that, if we keep applying the former procedure to this example until all the points are correctly classified, what will always eventually happen, a k bigger than minimum is obtained (k=4, Fig.4(b)), which is often the case.)

IV. CONCLUSIONS

It is conceivable that even a rough preliminary evaluation of the position of the hyperplanes will improve the learning process. It is also conceivable that in spaces with well-defined geometric properties the information inherently contained in the training data set can be somehow helpful in making such an evaluation. In this paper, we discussed the subject and showed basic alternatives for doing so, from which we concluded that, depending on the configuration of the space, geometric tools can indeed lead to improvements.

REFERENCES

[1] D. E. Rumelhart, G. E. Hinton, R. J. Williams, "Learning representations by back- propagating errors", Nature, vol. 323, 1986, pp. 533-536.

[2] E. B. Baum, D. Haussler, "What size net gives valid generalization?", Neural Computation, 1989, pp.151-159;

[3] Y. S. Abu-Mostafa, "The Vapnik-Chervonenkis dimension: Information versus complexity in learning", Neural Computation, 1989, pp.312-317.

[4] E. B. Baum, "On the capabilities of multilayer perceptrons", J. Complexity, 1988, pp.193-215.

Learning Trajectories
with a Hierarchy of Oscillatory Modules

Pierre Baldi* and Nikzad Benny Toomarian
Jet Propulsion Laboratory
California Institute of Technology
Pasadena, CA 91109

Abstract—To this date, the most successful approaches to learning has been the back-
propagation method. Although very powerful
on relatively simple problems, theoretical analysis
and simulations show that this approach breaks
down as soon as sufficiently complex problems are
considered. To overcome this fundamental limitation, we suggest a hierarchical and modular approach, directly inspired from biological networks,
whereby a certain degree of structure is introduced
in the learning system. This approach is applied to
a simple example of trajectory learning of a semi-
figure eight. The ideas involved, however, extend
immediately to more general computational problems.

I. INTRODUCTION

Learning is a fundamental ability of biological systems.
Understanding its principles is also key to the design of
intelligent circuits, computers and machines of various
kinds. To this date, the most successful approach to learning, from an engineering standpoint, has been the back-
propagation approach [12] or gradient descent approach.
In this framework, in the course of learning from examples, the parameters of a learning system, such as a neural
network, are adjusted incrementally so as to optimize, by
gradient descent, a suitable function measuring, the performance of the system at any given time. Although very
powerful on relatively simple problems, theoretical analysis and simulations, (see [4-5]), show that this approach
breaks down as soon as sufficiently complex problems are
considered. Gradient descent learning applied to an amorphous learning system is bound to fail. To overcome this
fundamental limitation, we have suggested a hierarchical
and modular approach, directly inspired from biological
networks, whereby a certain degree of structure is introduced in the learning system. The basic organization of
the system consists of a hierarchy of modules. The lowest

*and Division of Biology, California Institute of Technology

levels of the hierarchy serve as primitives or basic building
blocks for the successive levels. A very concrete example
is described next for the basic problem of trajectory learning in neural networks (see also [9] and [13]). The ideas
involved, however, extend immediately to more general
computational problems.

II. TRAJECTORY LEARNING

Consider the problem of synthesizing a neural network
capable of producing a certain given non-trivial trajectory.
To fix the ideas, we can imagine that the model neurons
in the network satisfy the usual additive model equations
(see, for instance, [1] and [6])

$$\frac{du_i}{dt} = -\frac{u_i}{\tau_i} + \sum_j w_{ij} f(u_j) + I_i \qquad (1)$$

The learning task is to find the right parameter values, for
instance for the synaptic weights w_{ij}, the charging time
constants τ_i and the amplifiers gains, so that the output
units of the network follow a certain prescribed trajectory
$u^*(t)$ over a given time interval $[t_0, t_1]$. For instance, a
typical benchmark trajectory in the literature is a circle
or a figure eight. Networks such as (1) have been successfully trained, although through lengthy computer runs,
on figure eights using a form of gradient descent learning for recurrent networks [10-11,14]. Consider now the
problem of learning a more complicated trajectory, such
as a double figure eight (i.e. a set of four loops joined at
one point). Although the task appears only slightly more
complicated, simulations show that a fully interconnected
set of units will not be able to learn this task by indis-
criminate gradient descent learning on all the parameters.
Thus a different approach is needed.

III. MODULAR HIERARCHICAL APPROACH

Biology seems to have overcome the obstacles inherent to
gradient descent learning through evolution. Learning in
biological organisms is never started from a tabula rasa.
Rather, a high degree of structure is already present in

the neural circuitry of newly born organisms. This structure is genetically encoded and the result of evolutionary tinkering over time scales several times larger than those of continental drift. Little is known of the interaction between the prewired structure and the actual learning. One reasonable hypothesis is that complex tasks are broken up into simpler modules and that learning, perhaps in different forms, can operate both within and across modules. The modules in turn can be organized in a hierarchical way, all the way up to the level of nuclei or brain areas. The difficult problem then becomes how to find a suitable module decomposition and whether there are any principles for doing so (in particular, the solutions found by biology are probably not unique). One trick used by evolution seems to have been the duplication, by error, of a module together with the subsequent evolution of one of the copies into a new module somehow complementary of the first one. But this is far from yielding any useful principle and may, at best, be used in genetic type of algorithms, where evolutionary tinkering is mimicked in the computer. Whether in our search of solutions to complex problems we can avoid or significantly accelerate a long evolutionary process for each problem remains to be seen.

We have taken inspiration from these ideas, to tackle the problem of creating specific complex trajectories in a neural network. Although it is difficult at this stage to keep a close analogy with biology, it may be useful to think of the problem of central pattern generation or motor control in natural organisms. In order to construct a neural network capable of producing a double figure eight, we are going to introduce a certain degree of organization in the system prior to any learning. The basic organization of the system consists of a hierarchy of modules. Related but different ideas on hierarchical and modular decomposition, applied to a different class of problem, can be found in [7-8]. In this particular example, each module can be viewed essentially as an oscillator. The modules, in turn, are organized in a hierarchical way. For the time being, all the modules within one level of the hierarchy control the output of the modules located in the previous layer.

At the bottom of the hierarchy, in the first level, one finds a family of simple and possibly independent modules, each one corresponding to a circuit with a small number of units capable of producing some elementary trajectory, such as a sinusoidal oscillation. In the case of the additive model, these could be simple oscillator rings with two or three neurons, an odd number of inhibitory connections and sufficiently high gains [2-3]. Thus, in our example, the first level of the hierarchy could contain four oscillator rings, one for each loop of the target trajectory. The parameters in each one of these four modules can be adjusted, by gradient descent or random descent or some

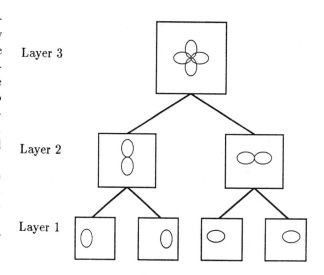

Figure 1: Symbolic representation of a modular and hierarchical network for double figure eight.

other optimization procedure, in order to match each one of the loops in the target trajectory.

The second level of the pyramid should contain two control modules. Each one of these modules controls a distinct pair of oscillator networks from the first level, so that each control network in the second level ends up producing a simple figure eight (see fig .1). Again, the control networks in level two can be oscillator rings and their parameters can be adjusted. In particular, after the learning process is completed, they should be operating in their high-gain regimes and have a period equal to the sum of the periods of the circuits each one controls.

Finally, the third layer, consist of another oscillatory and adjustable module which controls the two modules in the second level so as to produce a double figure eight. The third layer module must also end up operating in its high-gain regime with a period equal to four times the period of the oscillators in the first layer. In general, the final output trajectory is also a limit cycle because it is obtained by superimposition of limit cycles in the various modules. If the various oscillators relax to their limit cycles independently of one another, it is essential to provide for adjustable delays between the various modules in order to get the proper harmony among the various phases. In this way, a sparse network with 20 units or so can be constructed which can successfully execute a double figure eight. The importance of the effects of delays and adjustable delays in these architectures and their ubiquitous presence in natural neural systems has also lead us to conduct an analytical study of the effect of delays on neural dynamics (especially oscillatory properties) and learning

[3]. The main result there is that delays tend to increase the period of oscillations and broaden the spectrum of possible frequencies in a quantifiable way. A recurrent back-propagation learning algorithm can be derived for adjustable delays.

There are actually different possible neural network realizations depending on how the action of the control modules is implemented. For instance, if the control units are gating the connections between corresponding layers, this amounts to using higher order units in the network. The number of layers in the network then becomes a function of the order of the units one is willing to use. Alternatively, one could assume the existence of a fast weight dynamics on certain connections governed by a corresponding set of differential equations.

In the terminology used in [7-8], the four oscillators in the first level can be regarded as four experts, each one of them being knowledgeable about one of the four loops of the double figure eight. In their framework, the two output units of the network would be linear combinations of the corresponding outputs of the experts. The weights of the linear combinations, would come from the outputs of a gating network which has access to some input, for instance a representation of periodic time. The weights form a Gibbs distribution. These authors propose a back-propagation scheme to train the entire architecture simultaneously in a supervised way. Successful training should lead both to proper experts and proper Gibbs distribution which select only one of the experts at a time, in the right order. It remains to be seen if their algorithm can be used dynamically.

It is clear that this approach which combines a modular hierarchical architecture together with some simple form of learning can be extended to general trajectories. At the very least, one could always use Fourier analysis[1] to decompose a target trajectory into a superimposition of sinusoidal oscillations of different frequencies and use, in the first level of the hierarchy, a corresponding large bank of oscillators networks (although this decomposition may not be the most economical). One could also use damped oscillators to perform some sort of wavelet decomposition. Although we believe that oscillators with limit cycles present several attractive properties (stability, short transients, biological relevance...), one can conceivably use completely different circuits as building blocks in each module. Another observation is that the problem of synthesizing a network capable of certain given trajectories is more general than what would seem at first sight. In fact, any computation can be viewed as some sort of trajectory in the state space of a computing device, whether digital or analog.

The modular hierarchical approach leads to architectures which are more structured than fully interconnected networks, with a general feedforward flow of information and sparse recurrent connections to achieve dynamical effects. The sparsity of units and connections are attractive features for hardware design; and so is also the modular organization and the fact that learning is much more circumscribed than in fully interconnected systems. In these architectures, some form of learning remains essential, for instance to fine tune each one of the modules. This, in itself, is a much easier task than the one a fully interconnected and random network would have been faced with. It can be solved by gradient or random descent or other methods. Yet, fundamental open problems remain in the overall organization of learning across modules and in the origin of the decomposition. In particular, can the modular architecture be the outcome of a simple internal organizational process rather than an external imposition and how should learning be coordinated in time and across modules (other than the obvious: modules in the first level learn first, modules in the second level second,...)? How successful is a global gradient descent strategy applied across modules? How can the same modular architecture be used for different trajectories, with short switching times between trajectories and proper phases along each trajectory?

IV. EXAMPLE OF NUMERICAL SIMULATIONS

The learning paradigm, presented in the preceding section, can be applied to the problem of learning a figure eight trajectory. Results referring to this problem can be found in the literature [10,14]. We assumed that the desired trajectory of a semi-figure eight is composed of two circles and given by:

$$D_1 = C_1\,[x_{10} + cos(t)] \ + \ (1 - C_1)[y_{10} - cos(t)] \quad (2a)$$

$$D_2 = C_1\,[x_{20} + sin(t)] \ + \ (1 - C_1)[y_{20} + sin(t)] \quad (2b)$$

in which C_1 is a square wave with a period of 4π, given by the following equation;

$$C_1 = sign[sin(t/2)] \quad (3)$$

and $x_{10}, x_{20}, y_{10}, y_{20}$ are the coordinates of the center of the left and right circles respectively. Plotting D_1 vs. D_2 will produce the desired semi-figure eight, as shown in fig. 2.

The basic module of the hierarchical approach for this trajectory is a simple oscillatory ring network with four

---

[1] Actually, in classical Fourier analysis, functions are expressed as superposition of sinusoidal oscillations with evenly spaced frequencies over the entire real line. This decomposition is not very "neural" and should be replaced by one where the frequencies of the oscillations are concentrated in a relatively narrow band, but can take arbitrary values within this band.

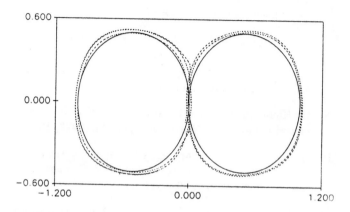

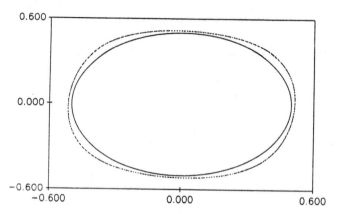

Figure 2: Desired semi-figure eight (solid line) and the one produced by the network (dashed line).

Figure 3: Desired circle (solid line) and the one produced by the basic module in the first layer (dashed line).

neurons. The activation dynamics of each unit in the module is given by:

$$\frac{du_i}{dt} = -\frac{u_i}{\tau_i} + w_{i-1}V_{i-1} \quad i = 1, \cdots, 4 \qquad (4)$$

where $V_0 = V_4$ and V_i is the output of neuron i given by;

$$V_i = tanh(\gamma_i\, u_i) \qquad (5)$$

An odd number of inhibitory connections is required for stable oscillations [2]. At this stage for simplicity, we assume that $w_i = w$ for $i = 1, 3, 4$, $w_2 = -w$ and $\tau_i = \tau, \gamma_i = \gamma$ for $i = 1, \cdots, 4$. The module is trained to produce a circle through a sinusoidal waive with period of 2π. Following the analysis in [2], the initial value of the network parameters, i.e., w, τ and γ are set to one at the beginning of the learning procedure. To update the network parameters, a gradient descent algorithm based upon the forward propagation of the error is used [15]. After the training, the network parameters converge to the following values, $w = 1.025, \tau = 0.972$ and $\gamma = 1.526$. With these values, after a brief transition period, the module converges to a limit cycle where each unit has a quasi-sinusoidal activation. The phase shift between two consecutive neurons is about $\pi/4$. Therefore, plotting the activity of neuron 1 and 3 in the module against each other will produce a circle which is close to the desire one as illustrated in Fig. 3.

At the second level of the hierarchy is the control module. This module is also chosen to be a simple oscillatory ring network with four neurons. This network is operating in the high gain regime and its period is twice that of the basic modules, i.e., 4π. The network parameters at the

beginning of the learning are set to $w = 0.9, \gamma = 10$, and $\tau = 2.58$.

The overall network has two output at any time, Z_1 and Z_2. Their value is given by:

$$Z_1 = 0.5\{[1 + VC(1)] \cdot [x_{10} + VN1(1)] + [1 - VC(1)] \cdot [y_{10} + VN1(3)]\} \qquad (6a)$$

$$Z_2 = 0.5\{[1 + VC(1)] \cdot [x_{20} + VN2(1)] + [1 - VC(1)] \cdot [y_{20} + VN2(3)]\} \qquad (6b)$$

in which $VN1(i)$ and $VN2(i)$ are the output of ith neuron in the first and second modules in the first level of the hierarchy, respectively, where $VC(1)$ is the output of the first neuron in the control module. Figure 4 shows the semi-figure eight obtained be plotting Z_1 vs. Z_2.

The convergence time of different modules to their limit cycle may vary. Therefore, it is essential to have a synchronization mechanism that aliens the activity of different units at various modules and levels. One such mechanism that has been adapted in this example is based upon time delays. The value of these delays is adjusted by using gradient descent approach such that the network outputs are in harmony with the desired output.

V. CONCLUSIONS

In conclusion, a new hierarchical approach for supervised neural learning of time dependent trajectories is presented. The modular hierarchical methodology leads to architectures which are more structured than fully interconnected networks, with a general feedforward flow of information and sparse recurrent connections to achieve dynamical effects. The sparsity of the connections as well as the modular organization makes the hardware implementation of the methodology very easy and attractive.

ACKNOWLEDGMENTS

This research was carried out at the Center for Space Microelectronics Technology, Jet Propulsion Laboratory, California Institute of Technology under contract with the National Aeronautics and Space Administration. Support for the work came from agencies of the U.S. Department of Defense, including Air-Force Office of Scientific Research and Army's APO techbase program.

REFERENCES

[1] S. Amari, "Characteristics of random nets of analog neuron-like elements," *IEEE Transactions on Systems, Man and Cybernetics*, Vol. **SMC-2**, 5, 643-657, 1972.

[2] A. Atiya and P. Baldi, "Oscillations and synchronization in neural networks: an exploration of the labeling hypothesis," *International Journal of Neural Systems*, Vol. **1**, 2, 103-124, 1989.

[3] P. Baldi and A. Atiya, "How delays affect neural dynamics and learning," *IEEE Trans. On Neural Networks*, in Press, 1993. unpublished.

[4] P. Baldi, " Learning in dynamical systems: gradient descent, random descent and modular approach," JPL Technical Report, California Institute of Technology, 1992.

[5] S. Geman, E. Bienenstock and R. Doursat, "Neural networks and the bias/variance dilemma," *Neural Computation*, Vol. **4**, 1-58, 1992.

[6] J. J. Hopfield, "Neurons with graded response have collective computational properties like those of two-state neurons," *PNAS USA*, Vol. **81**, 3088-3092, 1984.

[7] R. A. Jacobs, M. I. Jordan, S. J. Nowlan and G. E. Hinton, "Adaptive mixture of local experts," *Neural Computation*, Vol. bf 3, 79-87, 1991.

[8] M. I. Jordan and R. A. Jacobs, "Hierarchies of adaptive experts," *Neural Information Processing Systems*, Vol. bf 4, J. Moody, S.Hanson and R. Lippmann Eds., Morgan Kaufmann, 1992.

[9] D. Kleinfeld, "Sequential state generation by model neural networks." *PNAS*, Vol. **83**, 9469-9473, 1986.

[10] B. Pearlmutter, "Learning state space trajectories in recurrent neural networks," *Neural Computation*, Vol. **1**, 2, 263-269, 1989.

[11] F. J. Pineda, "Generalization of back-propagation to recurrent neural networks," *Physical Review Letters*, Vol. **59**, 19, 2229-2232, 1987.

[12] D. E. Rumelhart, G. E. Hinton and R. J. Williams, "Learning internal representations by error propagation," *Parallel Distributed Processing*, Rumelhart, D. E. and McClelland, J. L. eds. MIT Press, 1986.

[13] H. Sompolinsky and I. Kanter, "Temporal association in asymmetric neural networks," *Physical Review Letters*, Vol. **57**, 22, 2861-2864, 1986.

[14] N. B. Toomarian and J. Barhen, "Learning a trajectory using adjoint functions and teacher forcing," *Neural Networks*, Vol. **5**, 3, 473-484, 1992.

[15] R. J. Williams and D. Zipser, " A learning algorithm for continually running fully recurrent neural networks," *Neural Computation*, Vol. bf 1, 2, 270-280, 1989.

Neural Network Construction Using Multi-Threshold Quadratic Sigmoidal Neurons

Cheng-Chin Chiang and Hsin-Chia Fu
Department of Computer Science and Information Engineering
National Chiao-Tung University
Hsinchu, Taiwan 300, R.O.C
Fax: 886-3-572-4176

Abstract— This paper proposes a new type of neurons called *Multi-Threshold Quadratic Sigmoidal* neurons. In cooperation with Single-Threshold Quadratic Sigmoidal neurons, the Multi-Threshold Quadratic Sigmoidal neurons can be used to construct multilayer neural networks to dichotomize arbitrary dichotomy defined on any given training set. For such constructed neural networks, we prove that the number of required hidden neurons is only one fourth of those of networks with the standard architecture (feedforward, Heaviside activation function), which is often assumed in theoretical studies.

I. INTRODUCTION

Recently, many researchers [7, 1, 4, 5] have studied the recognition capability of feedforward neural networks. In general, the main results obtained in these studies are the derivations on the lower or upper bounds on the number of hidden neurons required to learn the recognition of a given training set S with fixed number of training patterns. For examples, Huang *et al.* [4] have proved that a feedforward network with at most $k-1$ hidden neurons which use heaviside activation function can dichotomize arbitrary dichotomy defined on an any training sets with k training patterns. Sontag [7] also proved that if the direct input-to-output connections or the continuous sigmoid activation function is used, then the recognition capability can be doubled. In other words, a network with k hidden units can dichotomize arbitrary dichotomy defined on any training sets with at least $2k$ training patterns.

In [2], we proposed a new activation function called *Quadratic Sigmoid Function* (QSF). We refer a neuron which use the Quadratic Sigmoid activation function as *Single-Threshold Quadratic Sigmoidal* neuron because there is an extra parameter which we named *threshold* in each neuron (to be described lat-

ter). In this paper, an extended type of neurons called *Multi-Threshold Quadratic Sigmoidal* neurons are proposed to improve the capability of multilayer neural networks. By using this type of neurons, a multilayer neural network can dichotomize any training set with fewer hidden neurons than the conventional sigmoidal neural networks. As a matter of fact, we will prove that a multilayer neural network can be constructed with one Multi-Threshold Quadratic Sigmoidal output neuron and $k+1$ Single-Threshold Quadratic Sigmoidal hidden neurons to dichotomize any dichotomy defined on an arbitrary training set with at least $4k+1$ training patterns.

The rest of this paper is organized as follows. In Section 2, we formally define the Multi-Threshold Quadratic Sigmoidal neurons and present a hybrid single-hidden-layer neural networks based on the composition of Multi-Threshold Quadratic Sigmoidal neurons and Single-Threshold Quadratic Sigmoidal neurons. In Section 3, the construction of the hybrid networks for arbitrary dichotomy problems are presented through the theoretical studies on their capability. Finally, Section 4 provides some conclusions and suggestions for future works on this research.

II. MULTI-THRESHOLD QUADRATIC SIGMOIDAL NEURONS

In [2], we have ever proposed an improved activation function called *Quadratic Sigmoid Function* (QSF) for multilayer neural networks. In our simulations, the multilayer neural networks with Single-Threshold Quadratic Sigmoidal neurons have been applied to continuous-valued function approximations and obtained satisfactory results such as faster learning and good generalization capability, etc. However, we still cannot prove that a neural network with Single-Threshold Quadratic Sigmoidal neurons has more powerful recognition capability than a conventional sigmoidal neural network (network with sigmoid activation function) so far. Hence, in this paper, we extend the Single-Threshold Quadratic Sigmoidal neurons to another type of neurons to improve the capability. This new type of neurons are called *Multi-Threshold Quadratic Sigmoidal* neurons. In the following, we formally define the Multi-Threshold Quadratic Sigmoidal neurons.

Each Multi-Threshold Quadratic Sigmoidal neuron, say neuron i, contains n weights ($w_{i,j}$, $1 \leq j \leq n$), one bias ($w_{i,0}$), and $n+1$ thresholds ($\theta_{i,j}$), where n denotes the input degree of the neuron i. Within each Multi-Threshold Quadratic Sigmoidal neuron, the extended QSF is used as its activation function. Let vectors $\mathbf{w_i} = (w_{i,0}, w_{i,1}, \ldots, w_{i,n})$, $\Theta_\mathbf{i} = (\theta_{i,0}, \theta_{i,1}, \ldots, \theta_{i,n})$. and let vector $\mathbf{x}$ represent the input augmented input vector, i.e., $(1, x_0, x_1, \ldots, x_n)$. The extended QSF is then defined as:

Extended QSF:

$$f(net_i, \Theta_\mathbf{i}) = \frac{1}{1 + exp(net_i^2 - g(\Theta_\mathbf{i}, \mathbf{x}))}, \quad (1)$$

where $net_i = \mathbf{w_i}\mathbf{x} = w_{i,0} + \sum_{j=0}^n w_{i,j} x_j$. The function $g(\Theta_\mathbf{i}, \mathbf{x})$ is called *thresholding function* and is defined as:

$$g(\Theta_\mathbf{i}, \mathbf{x}) =$$

$$\begin{cases} \theta_{i,m} & \text{if } \tau < x_m = \max_{1 \leq j \leq n}\{x_j\} \text{ and} \\ & m = \min\{k | x_k = \max_{1 \leq j \leq n}\{x_j\}\} \ (2) \\ \theta_{i,0} & \text{otherwise,} \end{cases}$$

where τ is a very small positive constant specified by user. In the original QSF, since each neuron has only one threshold (say θ_i) instead of $n+1$ thresholds, thus, the thresholding function $g(\theta, \mathbf{x})$ of a QSF is simply taken as $g(\theta, \mathbf{x}) = \theta_i$. In other words, the QSF is defined by:

$$\textbf{QSF:} \quad f(net_i, \theta) = \frac{1}{1 + exp(net_i^2 - \theta)}. \quad (3)$$

From Eq.(1) and Eq.(3), we can see that both Multi-Threshold Quadratic Sigmoidal neurons and Single-Threshold Quadratic Sigmoidal neurons contain quadratic terms in their activation function (net_i^2). Thus, both Multi-Threshold Quadratic Sigmoidal neurons and Single-Threshold Quadratic Sigmoidal neurons can exhibit second-order characteristics as conventional second-order neural networks [3]. The second-order property is very helpful for a network in solving nonlinearly-separable problems such as XOR, Parity problems.

With the Multi-Threshold Quadratic Sigmoidal neurons, we can use them to construct multilayer neural networks. There are many methods for construction. For examples, we can use Multi-Threshold Quadratic Sigmoidal neurons for all neurons in all layers, or use Multi-Threshold Quadratic Sigmoidal neurons for some selected layers and other types of neurons such as Single-Threshold Quadratic Sigmoidal neurons or sigmoidal neurons for other layers. In this paper, we will consider only the single-hidden-layer networks with one Multi-Threshold Quadratic Sigmoidal neuron in output layer and Single-Threshold Quadratic Sigmoidal neurons in hidden layer. Assume that the input layer, hidden layer and output layer are the 0th, 1th and 2th layer, respectively. Thus, $w_{i,j}^{(l)}$ ($j \neq 0$ and $l = 1, 2$) can be used to represent the weight which connects the ith neuron at the lth layer and the jth neuron at the $(l-1)^{th}$ layer. The bias of the ith neuron at the lth layer can be denoted as $w_{i,0}^{(l)}$. For each hidden neuron, since it is a Single-Threshold Quadratic Sigmoidal neuron which contains only one threshold, we use $\theta_i^{(1)}$ to denote the ith hidden neuron's threshold. For the Multi-Threshold Quadratic Sigmoidal output neuron, we use the vector $\Theta^{(2)} = (\theta_0^{(2)}, \theta_1^{(2)}, \ldots, \theta_h^{(2)})$ to represent its multiple thresholds, where h is the number of hidden neurons.

III. Construction of Neural Networks for Arbitrary Dichotomy Problems

Before presenting the construction of the hybrid single-hidden-layer neural networks for arbitrary dichotomy problems, another activation function called *Quadratic Heaviside* function has to be introduced first. The Quadratic Heaviside function is an extension of conventional Heaviside funcion and is defined as:

Quadratic Heaviside:

$$\mathcal{H}_q(\mathbf{w_i}\mathbf{x}, \theta_\mathbf{i}) = \begin{cases} 0 & \text{if } \theta_\mathbf{i} - (\mathbf{w_i}\mathbf{x})^2 < 0, \\ 1 & \text{if } \theta_\mathbf{i} - (\mathbf{w_i}\mathbf{x})^2 \geq 0. \end{cases} \quad (4)$$

If we use $\mathcal{H}(x)$ to denote the conventional Heaviside function, i.e., $\mathcal{H}(x) = 0$ for $x < 0$ and $\mathcal{H}(x) = 1$ for $x \geq 0$, then we can rewrite $\mathcal{H}_q(\mathbf{w_i}\mathbf{x}, \theta_\mathbf{i})$ as

$$\mathcal{H}_q(\mathbf{w_i}\mathbf{x}, \theta_\mathbf{i}) = \mathcal{H}(q(\mathbf{w_i}\mathbf{x}, \theta_\mathbf{i})), \quad (5)$$

where $q(\mathbf{w_i}\mathbf{x}, \theta_\mathbf{i})$ is defined as $\theta_\mathbf{i} - (\mathbf{w_i}\mathbf{x})^2$. According to the definition of Quadratic Heaviside function in Eq.(4), we can easily obtain the following lemma.

Lemma 1 *For any positive constant k,*

$$\mathcal{H}_q(\mathbf{w_i}\mathbf{x}, \theta_\mathbf{i}) = \mathcal{H}_q(k\mathbf{w_i}\mathbf{x}, k^2\theta_\mathbf{i}), \qquad \text{for all } \mathbf{x}.$$

Let $\sigma(x)$ be the sigmoid function, i.e., $\sigma(x) = \frac{1}{1+exp(-x)}$. Then we also can prove the following lemma.

Lemma 2 *Given an error tolerance $\epsilon > 0$,*

$$|\sigma(x) - \mathcal{H}(x)| \leq \epsilon, \qquad for\ |x| \geq |\log(\frac{1-\epsilon}{\epsilon})|.$$

Proof. For $x < 0$, $\sigma(x)$ must be less or equal to ϵ, i.e., $\frac{1}{1+exp(-x)} \leq \epsilon$. Thus, it is easy to derive that $x \leq -\log(\frac{1-\epsilon}{\epsilon})$. On the other hand, for $x \geq 0$, $\sigma(x)$ must be larger or equal to $1 - \epsilon$, i.e., $\frac{1}{1+exp(-x)} \geq 1 - \epsilon$. Thus, we derive $x \geq \log(\frac{1-\epsilon}{\epsilon})$. Therefore, we conclude that for $|x| \geq |\log(\frac{1-\epsilon}{\epsilon})|$, $|\sigma(x) - \mathcal{H}(x)| \leq \epsilon$. $\square$

It is obvious that the Quadratic Heaviside function can be regarded as the discontinuous version of the Quadratic Sigmoidal function. Thus, similar to the Multi-Threshold Quadratic Sigmoidal neurons, we can also define the extended Quadratic Heaviside function for another type of neurons called *Multi-Threshold Quadratic Heaviside neurons* as follows:

Extended Quadratic Heaviside

$$f(\mathbf{w_i x}, \Theta_i) = \begin{cases} 0 & \text{if } g(\Theta_i, \mathbf{x}) - (\mathbf{w_i x})^2 < 0 \\ 1 & \text{if } g(\Theta_i, \mathbf{x}) - (\mathbf{w_i x})^2 \geq 0 \end{cases} \quad (6)$$

The thresholding function $g(\Theta_i, \mathbf{x})$ is defined as:
$g(\Theta_i, \mathbf{x}) =$

$$\begin{cases} \theta_{i,m} & \text{if } \tau < x_m = \max_{1 \leq j \leq n}\{x_j\} \text{ and} \\ & m = \min\{k | x_k = \max_{1 \leq j \leq n}\{x_j\}\} \\ \theta_{i,0} & \text{otherwise}, \end{cases} \quad (7)$$

where all denotations are the same as those in Eq.(1).

In the following, we will first propose the construction method for networks containing Quadratic Heaviside neurons in hidden layer, one Multi-Threshold Heaviside neuron in output layer and direct input-to-output connections. Then, we extend the results to the feedforward networks with Single-Threshold Quadratic Sigmoidal neurons in hidden layer and with one Multi-Threshold Quadratic Sigmoidal neuron in output layer.

Without loss of generality, we will reduce the input dimensions of dichotomy problems to 1 since we always can find a vector $\mathbf{v}$ whose inner products with all the elements of the finite training set S are distinct. Then, the original training set S can be replaced by the set (say S') of these inner products. Precisely, let S consist of the distinct vectors $\mathbf{u_1}, \ldots, \mathbf{u_p}$, where $\mathbf{u_i} \in \Re^n$. Since the solution set for $\mathbf{v}$ is $\Re^n - \bigcup_{i \neq j}\{\mathbf{s} | \mathbf{s} \cdot (\mathbf{u_i} - \mathbf{u_j}) = 0, \mathbf{s} \in \Re^n\}$ which can not be empty, the vector $\mathbf{v}$ always can be found.

Thus, the new training set S' becomes $\{y_i | y_i = \mathbf{v u_i}, 1 \leq i \leq p\}$. Suppose that a network with h neurons in its first hidden layer can dichotomize a given dichotomy defined on S'. Let the weights of these h hidden neurons be $w_1, w_2, \ldots, w_h$ ($w_i \in \Re$). Then, it is obvious that the network also can dichotomize the corresponding dichotomy defined on S if we replace the weights of these h hidden neurons as $w_1 \mathbf{v}, w_2 \mathbf{v}, \ldots, w_h \mathbf{v}$.

For the purpose of convenience, let us assume that $y_1 < y_2 < \ldots < y_p$, where $y_i \in S'$, and take any dichotomy (S_-, S_+) on the original training set S. This induces a partition of the set of y_i's into two subsets, corresponding to values $\mathbf{v u_i}$, $u_i \in S_+$ and $\mathbf{v u_i}$, $u_i \in S_-$. We shall assume that y_1 is of the first subset since we always can find a vector $\mathbf{v}$ for this purpose. Now, we can prove the following theorem.

Theorem 1 *Given a training set $S = \{y_1, y_2, \ldots, y_{4k+1} | y_i \in \Re, 1 \leq i \leq 4k + 1\}$. A single-hidden-layer network with at most k Quadratic Heaviside neurons in hidden layer, one Multi-Threshold Quadratic Heaviside neuron in output layer, and direct input-to-output connections can be constructed to dichotomize arbitrary dichotomy defined on S.*

Proof. Let us use the notation "$I_i < I_j$" for intervals to mean that $x < y$ for all $x \in I_i$ and all $y \in I_j$. Let $I_1 < I_2 < I_3 < I_4 < I_5 < \ldots < I_{4(k-1)+1} < I_{4(k-1)+1} < I_{4(k-1)+3} < I_{4(k-1)+4} < I_{4k+1}$ be closed subintervals of $\Re$. Denote $I^+ = \bigcup_0^{2k} I_{2i+1}$, $I^- = \bigcup_0^{2k} I_{2i}$. If we can construct a single-hidden-layer network with at most k Quadratic Heaviside neurons in hidden layer, one Multi-Threshold Quadratic Heaviside neuron in output layer, and direct input-to-output connections such that the network outputs '1' for $x \in I^+$ and outputs '0' for $x \in I^-$, then the proof can be completed. Assume that $\alpha_0 < I_1 < \beta_0 < I_2 < \gamma_0 < I_3 < \gamma_0' < I_4 < \beta_0' < I_5 < \alpha_1 < \ldots < \alpha_i < I_{4i+1} < \beta_i < I_{4i+2} < \gamma_i < I_{4i+3} < \gamma_i' < I_{4i+4} < \beta_i' < I_{4(i+1)+1} < \alpha_{i+1} < \ldots < \alpha_{k-1} < I_{4(k-1)+1} < \beta_{k-1} < I_{4(k-1)+2} < \gamma_{k-1} < I_{4(k-1)+3} < \gamma_{k-1}' < I_{4(k-1)+4} < \beta_{k-1}' < I_{4k+1} < \alpha_k$. Let $\mathbf{w_i} = (w_{i,0}, w_{i,1})$ denote the weight vector (including bias) of the ith Quadratic Heaviside hidden neuron, and $\theta_i^{(1)}$ denote the threshold of the ith Quadratic Heaviside hidden neuron. Also let $\mathbf{u} = (u_0, u_1, \ldots, u_k)$ and $\Theta = (\theta_0^{(2)}, \theta_1^{(2)}, \ldots, \theta_k^{(2)})$ denote the hidden-to-output connection weight vector and the threshold vector of the Multi-Threshold Quadratic Heaviside neuron, respectively. Besides, use v to denote the direct input-to-output connection weight. Thus, the output of this network can be formulated by:

$$O = f(u_0 + v \cdot x + \sum_{i=1}^{k} u_i \cdot h(w_{i,0} + w_{i,1}x, \theta_i)), \quad (8)$$

where $x \in \Re$ is the input and $f()$ denotes the extended Quadratic Heaviside function (See Eq.(6)) and $h()$ denotes the Quadratic Heaviside function (See Eq.(4)). Now, let us set the parameters of this network as: $u_0 = 0$, $u_i = -\frac{\gamma_{i-1}+\gamma'_{i-1}}{2}$, $v = 1$, $\theta_i^{(2)} = (\frac{\gamma'_{i-1}-\gamma_{i-1}}{2})^2$, $w_{i,0} = -\frac{\beta_{i-1}+\beta'_{i-1}}{2}$, $w_{i,1} = 1$, and $\theta_i^{(1)} = (\frac{\beta'_{i-1}-\beta_{i-1}}{2})^2$, for $1 \le i \le k$. Thus, given an input x in the interval $(\beta_{i-1}, \beta'_{i-1})$, it is easy to prove that only the ith hidden neuron will output '1' and other hidden neurons output '0'. Therefore, according to Eq.(8) and the definition of the thresholding function $g()$ defined in Eq.(7), the output of the output neuron becomes

$$O = f(x - u_i, \Theta),$$
$$= \begin{cases} 1 & \text{if } \gamma_{i-1} \le x \le \gamma'_{i-1}, \\ 0 & \text{if } \beta_{i-1} < x < \gamma_{i-1} \text{ or } \gamma'_{i-1} < x < \beta'_{i-1}. \end{cases}$$

In other words, if $x \in I_{4i+3}$ then the network outputs '1'; if $x \in I_{4i+2}$ or $x \in I_{4i+4}$, the network outputs '0'.

For x in I_{4i+1}, we can see that no hidden neuron will output '1'. Thus, if we set the parameter τ of the thresholding function as any positive constant, then the output of the output neuron becomes

$$O = f(x, \Theta),$$
$$= \begin{cases} 1 & \text{if } -\sqrt{\theta_0^{(2)}} \le x \le \sqrt{\theta_0^{(2)}}, \\ 0 & \text{otherwise.} \end{cases}$$

Thus, if we set $\theta_0^{(2)} = \max\{\alpha_0^2, \alpha_k^2\}$, then we can prove that for all x in I_{4i+1} ($1 \le i \le k$), the network outputs '1'. Therefore, we can conclude that for $x \in I^+$, the network outputs '1' and for $x \in I^-$, the network outputs '0'. $\square$

Theorem 1 have provided the constructive method of a non-feedforward network for any dichotomy problems defined on any given finite training set. In the following, we proceed to extend the results to the feedforward networks which use Single-Threshold Quadratic Sigmoidal hidden neurons and Multi-Threshold Quadratic Sigmoidal output neurons. Before the extension, it is necessary to introduce the following lemmas first.

Lemma 3 Let $\Phi(\mathbf{wy}, \theta)$ denote a Quadratic Sigmoid function, where $\mathbf{w} = (w_0, w_1)$ and $\mathbf{y} = (1, x)$.

Given a compact domain $C \subset \Re - \{\frac{\sqrt{\theta}-w_0}{w_1}\}$ and an error tolerance $\epsilon > 0$,

$$|\Phi(\lambda\mathbf{wy}, \lambda^2\theta) - \mathcal{H}_q(\mathbf{wy}, \theta)| \le \epsilon,$$
$$\text{as } \lambda \ge \sqrt{\frac{|\log(\frac{1-\epsilon}{\epsilon})|}{m}}, \text{ for all } x \in C,$$

where $m = \min(\{|\theta - (w_0 + w_1 x)^2| \, |x \in C\})$.

Proof. Since the Quadratic Sigmoid function $\Phi(\mathbf{wy}, \theta)$ can be regarded as a variant of Sigmoidal function, i.e., $\Phi(\mathbf{wy}, \theta) = \sigma(\theta - (w_0 + w_1 x)^2)$, where $\sigma(x)$ denotes the conventional sigmoidal function. Thus, according to Lemma 2, we obtain that

$$|\sigma(\lambda^2\theta - (\lambda w_0 + \lambda w_1 x)^2) - \mathcal{H}(\lambda^2\theta - (\lambda w_0 + \lambda w_1 x)^2)| \le \epsilon,$$

Let $m = \min(\{|\theta - (w_0 + w_1 x)^2| \, |x \in C\})$. Since x can not be $\frac{\sqrt{\theta}-w_0}{w_1}$, thus $m > 0$. Therefore, the above equation can be rewrite as

$$|\Phi(\lambda\mathbf{wy}, \lambda^2\theta) - \mathcal{H}_q(\lambda\mathbf{wy}, \lambda^2\theta)| \le \epsilon, \quad (9)$$
$$\text{as } \lambda \ge \sqrt{\frac{|\log(\frac{1-\epsilon}{\epsilon})|}{m}}, \text{ for all } x \in C.$$

By Lemma 1, we obtain that

$$|\Phi(\lambda\mathbf{wy}, \lambda^2\theta) - \mathcal{H}_q(\mathbf{wy}, \theta)| \le \epsilon, \quad (10)$$
$$\text{as } \lambda \ge \sqrt{\frac{|\log(\frac{1-\epsilon}{\epsilon})|}{m}}, \text{ for all } x \in C,$$

where $m = \min(\{|\theta - (w_0 + w_1 x)^2| \, |x \in C\})$. $\square$

Corollary 1 Let $\Psi(\mathbf{wy}, \Theta)$ and $\Omega(\mathbf{wy}, \Theta)$ denote an Extended Quadratic Sigmoid function and an Extended Quadratic Heaviside function respectively, where $\mathbf{w} = (w_0, w_1, \ldots, w_n)$, $\Theta = (\theta_0, \theta_1, \ldots, \theta_n)$ and $\mathbf{y} = (1, y_1, y_2, \ldots, y_n)$. Given a compact set $C \subset \Re^n - \bigcup_{j=1}^{n}\{(x_1, x_2, \ldots, x_n)|\theta_j - (w_0 + \sum_1^n w_i x_i)^2 = 0\}$ and an error tolerance $\epsilon > 0$,

$$|\Psi(\lambda\mathbf{wy}, \lambda^2\Theta) - \Omega(\mathbf{wy}, \Theta)| \le \epsilon, \quad (11)$$
$$\text{as } \lambda \ge \sqrt{\frac{|\log(\frac{1-\epsilon}{\epsilon})|}{m}}, \text{ for all } \mathbf{y} \in C,$$

where $m = \min(\bigcup_{j=1}^{n}\{|\theta_j - (w_0 + \sum_1^n w_i y_i)^2| \, |(y_1, y_2, \ldots, y_n) \in C\})$.

Lemma 4 Let vector $\mathbf{y} = (1, x)$ and $\mathbf{w}_c = (c, 0)$ be a weight vector in $\Re$ such that $\frac{\partial \Phi(\mathbf{w}_c\mathbf{y}, \theta)}{\partial net} = \mu \ne 0$, where $net = \mathbf{wy} = w_0 + w_1 x$. Let $C \subset \Re$ be a compact domain. There exists a weight $\mathbf{w}_\lambda = (c - \frac{c}{\lambda}, \frac{1}{\lambda})$, such that

$$\lim_{\lambda \to \infty} \frac{\lambda}{\mu}[\Phi(\mathbf{w}_\lambda\mathbf{y}, \theta) - \Phi(\mathbf{w}_c\mathbf{y}, \theta)] + c = x,$$

for all $x \in C$.

Proof. For the purpose of convenience, let $f(net, \theta)$ denote the Quadratic Sigmoid function, where $net = \mathbf{wy} = w_0 + w_1 x$. Thus, $\Phi(\mathbf{w}_c \mathbf{y}, \theta) = f(c, \theta)$. Since $\frac{\partial \Phi(\mathbf{w}_c \mathbf{y}, \theta)}{\partial net} = \mu \neq 0$, thus

$$\lim_{\lambda \to \infty} \frac{f(c + \frac{x-c}{\lambda}, \theta) - f(c, \theta)}{\frac{x-c}{\lambda}} = \mu \neq 0.$$

Rearranging the above equation, we obtain that

$$\lim_{\lambda \to \infty} \frac{\lambda}{\mu}[f(c + \frac{x-c}{\lambda}, \theta) - f(c, \theta)] + c - x = 0.$$

In other words, there exists a weight $\mathbf{w}_\lambda = (c - \frac{c}{\lambda}, \frac{1}{\lambda})$, such that

$$\lim_{\lambda \to \infty} \frac{\lambda}{\mu}[\Phi(\mathbf{w}_\lambda \mathbf{y}, \theta) - \Phi(\mathbf{w}_c \mathbf{y}, \theta)] + c = x, \quad \square$$

for all $x \in C$.

With the above lemmas, the following theorem can be proved.

Theorem 2 *Given a finite training set $S = \{y_1, y_2, \ldots, y_{4k+1} | y_i \in \Re, 1 \leq i \leq 4k+1\}$. A single-hidden-layer network with at most $k+1$ Single-Threshold Quadratic Sigmoidal neurons in hidden layer and one Multi-Threshold Quadratic Sigmoidal neuron in output layer can be constructed to dichotomize arbitrary dichotomy defined on S.*

Proof. Consider each Quadratic Heaviside hidden neuron i in the network constructed in Theorem 1.

Since $\frac{\sqrt{\theta_i^{(1)}} - w_{i,0}}{w_{i,1}} = \frac{\sqrt{(\frac{\beta'_{i-1} - \beta_{i-1}}{2})^2 - (-\frac{\beta'_{i-1} + \beta_{i-1}}{2})^2}}{1} = \beta'_{i-1}$, and we have assumed that β'_{i-1} is not contained in any interval I_i for $1 \leq i \leq 4k+1$ in Theorem 1, thus, according to Lemma 3, each term of Quadratic Heaviside function $(h(w_{i,0} + w_{i,1}x, \theta_i))$ in Eq.(8) can be replaced by a Single-Threshold Quadratic Sigmoidal neuron with activation function $\Phi(\lambda \mathbf{wy}, \lambda^2 \theta)$, for large enough λ. Let h_i denote the output of the ith hidden neuron. In the proof of Theorem 1, we have seen that for any input in $\bigcup_{i=1}^{k} \{I_{4i+2} \bigcup I_{4i+3} \bigcup I_{4i+4}\}$, one and only one hidden neuron will output '1'. Thus, the term $g(\Theta, \mathbf{y}) - (\mathbf{wy})^2 = \theta_i^{(2)} - (x - u_i)^2$, where $\mathbf{y} = (1, x, h_1, h_2, \ldots, h_k)$, and $\mathbf{w} = (u_0, v, u_1, u_2, \ldots, u_k)$. Since $\theta_i^{(2)} = \frac{\gamma'_{i-1} - \gamma_{i-1}}{2}$ and $u_i = -\frac{\gamma'_{i-1} + \gamma_{i-1}}{2}$. In addition, we have also assumed that γ'_{i-1} and γ_{i-1} are not contained in any interval I_i for $1 \leq i \leq 4k+1$ in Theorem 1, i.e., $x \neq \gamma'_{i-1}$ and $x \neq \gamma_{i-1}$. Thus, $\theta_i^{(2)} - (x - u_i)^2$ cannot be zero. Similarly, for any input in I_{4i+1}, no hidden neuron outputs '1'. Hence, the term $g(\Theta, \mathbf{y}) - (\mathbf{wy})^2 = \theta_0^{(2)} - x^2$, where $\theta_0^{(2)} = \max\{\alpha_0^2, \alpha_k^2\}$. Since both α_0 and α_k are not contained in any interval I_i for $1 \leq i \leq 4k+1$ in Theorem 1, $\theta_0^{(2)} - x^2$ cannot be zero. Thus, by Corollary 1, we also can use a Multi-Threshold Quadratic

Sigmoidal neuron to replace the Multi-Threshold Quadratic Heaviside output neuron of the network constructed in Theorem 1. For the linear term, $v \cdot x = 1 \cdot x = x$, in Eq.(8), according to Lemma 4, thus we can use another Single-Threshold Quadratic Sigmoidal neuron to approximation this linear function. In conclusion, we can use $k+1$ Single-Threshold Quadratic Sigmoidal neurons to implement the function of the k Quadratic Heaviside hidden neurons and the linear function, and use one Multi-Threshold Quadratic Sigmoidal neuron to implement the function of the Multi-Threshold Quadratic Heaviside output neuron. $\square$

In Sontag's work [7], he had proved that the upper bound on the number of hidden neurons required by a feedforward sigmoidal network for dichotomizing a training set with $2k$ training patterns is k. For the Multi-Threshold Quadratic Sigmoidal networks, according to Theorem 2, only at most $\lceil \frac{k}{2} \rceil$ Multi-Threshold Quadratic Sigmoidal hidden neurons are enough. Let us compare the Multi-Threshold Quadratic Sigmoidal networks with the conventional sigmoidal networks in terms of the number of free parameters. Suppose that the input dimension is n. Given a training set with $4k+1$ training patterns, then the Multi-Threshold Quadratic Sigmoidal network requires at most $(k+1)(n+2) + 2(k+1)$ free parameters. However, the sigmoidal network requires at most $2k(n+1) + (2k+1)$ free parameters. Thus, for problems with large input dimensions (n is large), the upper bound on the number of required free parameters for Multi-Threshold Quadratic Sigmoidal networks is only a half of that of sigmoidal networks. For training set with large number of training patterns (k is large), the ratio between the upper bounds on the numbers of required free parameters for Multi-Threshold Quadratic Sigmoidal networks and sigmoidal networks is $\frac{n+4}{2n+4}$. Thus, the improved ratio (say ξ) for the Multi-Threshold Quadratic Sigmoidal networks is $\frac{6}{5} \leq \xi < 2$.

IV. CONCLUDING REMARKS AND FUTURE WORKS

In this paper, a new type of neurons called Multi-Threshold Quadratic Sigmoidal neurons are proposed. Using a Multi-Threshold Quadratic Sigmoidal neuron in output layer and k Signle-Threshold Quadratic Sigmoidal neurons in hidden layer, a neural network can be constructed to dichotomize arbitrary dichotomy defined on any training set with at least $4k+1$ training patterns. Thus, in comparison with the networks with standard architectures (feedforward and Heaviside activation function) [7], we can say that the Multi-Threshold Quadratic Sigmoidal neurons have improved the recognition capability of single-hidden-layer neural networks by a factor of 4. As a matter of fact, a version of backprop-like learning algorithm for Multi-Threshold Quadratic Sigmoidal neural networks is very similar to the conventional backprop learning algorithm [6] except some modifications. We do not present this learning algorithm here due to the space limitation. However, research into the following two interesting topics on the Multi-Threshold Quadratic Sigmoidal neural networks is still undergoing:

- Capability studies on more complicated architectures such as non-feedforward networks, networks with more layers, or networks with Multi-Threshold Quadratic Sigmoidal neurons in hidden layers.

- Practical application studies on Multi-Threshold Quadratic Sigmoidal neural networks.

REFERENCES

[1] E.B. Baum and D. Haussler. What size net gives valid generalization? *Neural Computation*, 1:151–160, 1989.

[2] C.C. Chiang and H.C. Fu. A variant of second-order multilayer perceptron and its application to function approximations. In *IJCNN '92*, pages III:887–III:892, Baltimore, Maryland, 1992.

[3] C.L. Giles and T. Maxwell. Learning, invariance and generalization in high-order neural networks. *Applied Optics*, 26:4972–4978, 1987.

[4] S.C. Huang and Y.F. Huang. Bounds on the number of hhidden neurons in multilayer perceptrons. *IEEE Transactions on Neural Networks*, 2(1):47–55, 1991.

[5] N. J. Nilsson. *Learning Machines: Foundation of Trainable Pattern-Classifying Systems*. McGraw-Hill Book Company, New York, 1965.

[6] D. E. Rumelhart, J. L. McClelland, and the PDP Research Group. *Parallel Distributed Processing (PDP): Exploration in the Microstructure of Cognition (Vol. 1)*. MIT Press, Cambridge, Massachusetts, 1986.

[7] E.D. Sontag. On the recognition capabilities of feedforward nets. Technical Report Report SYCON 90-03, SYCON-Rutgrs Center for Systems and Control, Department of Mathematics, Rutgers University, New Brunswick, NJ 08903, April 1990.

The Problem of Learning Long-Term Dependencies in Recurrent Networks

Yoshua Bengio[†], Paolo Frasconi[‡], and Patrice Simard[†]
†AT&T Bell Laboratories
‡Dip. di Sistemi e Informatica, Universitá di Firenze

Abstract— **We are interested in training recurrent neural networks to map input sequences to output sequences, for applications in sequence recognition or production. In this paper, we present results showing that learning long-term dependencies in such recurrent networks using gradient descent is a very difficult task. We show how this difficulty arises when robustly latching bits of information with certain attractors: the derivatives of the output at time t with respect the unit activations at time 0 tends rapidly to 0 as t increases for most input values. In such a situation, simple gradient descent techniques appear inappropriate and we suggest to consider alternative optimization methods and architectures.**

I. INTRODUCTION

A recurrent network has *cycles* in its graph that allow it to keep information about past inputs for an amount of time that is not fixed a-priori, but rather depends on its weights and on the input data. In contrast, static networks, even if they include delays (e.g., as in Time-Delay Neural Networks), have a finite impulse response and can't store a bit of information for an indefinite amount of time. The type of recurrent networks studied here can be used either for sequence recognition or production: units are not usually clamped. Instead, the dynamics of the network are non-autonomous. Hence the recurrent network transforms an input sequence (e.g., speech spectra) into an output sequence (e.g., degrees of evidence for phonemes), while taking into account contextual information in a flexible way. In this paper, we restrict our attention to discrete-time dynamical systems.

Although recurrent networks can in many instances outperform static networks [1], they appear more difficult to train optimally. Earlier experiments indicated that their parameters settle in sub-optimal solutions which take into account short-term dependencies but not long-term dependencies [2]. Similar results were obtained by Mozer [7]. It was found that back-propagation was not sufficiently powerful to discover contingencies spanning long temporal intervals. In this paper, we present experimental and theoretical results in order to further the understanding of this problem, i.e., of the conditions in which gradient descent in the output error is inappropriate to train a non-autonomous recurrent network. We begin in Section ii, by presenting a minimal problem for such recurrent networks. Being able to learn this task is a necessary condition for any recurrent network and learning algorithm applied to sequence recognition problems involving long-term context. It requires

1. a system that is able to store one or more bit of information for an arbitrary duration,
2. that is resistant to background noise,
3. and that is learnable[1].

In Section iii, theoretical results are presented showing that when trying to satisfy conditions (1) and (2) above, the magnitude of the derivative of the state of a dynamical system at time t with respect to the state at time 0 decreases exponentially as t increases. We show how this makes the back-propagation algorithm (and gradient descent in general) inefficient for learning of long term dependencies in the input/output sequence, hence failing condition (3) for sufficiently long sequences.

II. A MINIMAL PROBLEM FOR RECURRENT NETWORK

This minimal task is designed as a test that must necessarily be passed in order to satisfy the three conditions enumerated above. For this task, a dynamic system is to learn discriminating between two different sets of sequences, whose class is only determined by the values of the input on a fixed number L of time steps at the beginning of each sequence of length T. If we allow sequences of arbitrary length, then the problem can be solved only if the network is able to latch information about the initial input values. The input u_t for this system can be thought of as the weighted sum of the outputs of a subnetwork directly interfaced with the actual inputs. Hence we can regard u_t as values which can be tuned by gradient

---

[1]Given external targets, it can compute variations of its inputs and parameters necessary to approach those targets.

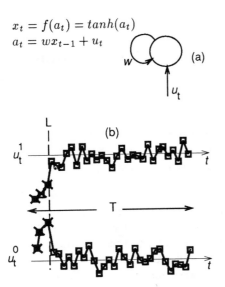

$$x_t = f(a_t) = tanh(a_t)$$
$$a_t = wx_{t-1} + u_t$$

(a)

(b)

Figure 1: a) Latching neuron. b) Sample input sequences after successful learning (free parameters are marked with small crosses).

descent. The problem is thus stated as follows. The system has one input u_t and one output x_t (at each discrete time step t). The initial inputs u_t^k $t \leq L$ are learnable parameters whereas u_t is zero mean gaussian noise for $t > L$. $k = 0$ or $k = 1$ for the two classes (0 and 1) of sequences. Optimization is based on the cost function $C = (x_T^0 + \bar{x})^2 + (x_T^1 - \bar{x})^2$ with $\bar{x}$ a target close to 1 for the last time step T. Although very simple, this example can provide insights on the behavior of more complex networks. The ability of learning the free input values is a measure of the effectiveness of the gradient which would be propagated further back if the neuron were connected to the output of another subnet.

We performed experiments on this task with a single recurrent neuron, as shown in fig. 1a. This recurrent neuron can latch information if $w > 1/f'(0)$ [3],[4]. Two types of trajectories are considered for this system, for the two classes ($k = 0$, $k = 1$):

$$\begin{aligned} x_t^k &= \tanh(a_t^k) \\ a_t^k &= w \tanh(a_{t-1}^k) + u_t^k \qquad t = 1 \ldots T \\ a_0^0 &= a_0^1 = 0 \end{aligned} \qquad (1)$$

The recurrent weight w is also learnable. The solution for $T \gg L$ requires to adapt $w > 1$ to produce two stable attractors $\bar{x}$ and $-\bar{x}$. The free input parameters must yield the state of the neuron towards $\bar{x}$ or $-\bar{x}$ in order to robustly latch a bit of information against the input noise. Note that a linear network would not be resistant to noise in such a situation.

In fig. 1b we show two sample input sequences. A set of simulations were carried out to evaluate the effectiveness

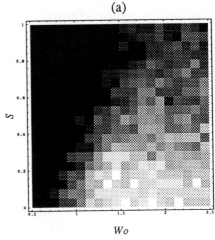

(a)

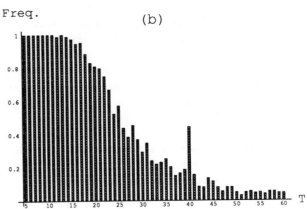

Freq. (b)

Figure 2: Experimental results for the illustrating problem. a) Density of convergence with respect to the initial weight w_0 and the noise variance s (white $\Rightarrow$ high density), with $L = 4$ and $T = 20$. b) Frequency of convergence with respect to the sequence length T, ($s = 0.2, w_0 = 1.25$).

of back-propagation on this simple task. In a first experiment we investigated the effect of the noise variance s and of different initial values w_0 for the self loop weight. A density plot of convergence is shown in fig. 2a, averaged over 18 runs for each of the selected pairs (w_0, s). It can be seen that convergence becomes very unlikely for large noise variance or small initial values of w. $L = 3$ and $T = 20$ were chosen in these experiments. In fig. 2b, we show instead the effect of varying T, keeping fixed $s = 0.2$ and $w_0 = 1.25$. In this case the task consists in learning only the input parameters u_t. When T becomes large it is extremely difficult to attain convergence. These experimental results show that even in the very simple situation where we want to robustly latch on 1 bit of information about the input, gradient descent on the output error fails for long term input/output dependency, for most initial parameter values.

III. Gradient Loss: Analysis

In this section, we attempt to understand better why the gradient with respect to the weights often ignores the contributions due to long term dependencies in the input/output sequences. Let us consider the non-autonomous discrete-time map with additive inputs

$$a_t = M(a_{t-1}) + u_t \qquad (2)$$

and the corresponding autonomous dynamics

$$a_t = M(a_{t-1}) \qquad (3)$$

where a_t and u_t are n-vectors representing respectively the system state and the external input[2] at time t. In the next subsection, we find that the problem mentionned in the previous section occurs when $\frac{\partial x_t}{\partial x_\tau} \to 0$ as $t - \tau$ increases, with $\tau < t$. Furthermore, we argue that this is a common situation, when the network is used to "robustly latch" on bits of information, i.e., when its dynamics are restricted to one of several basins of attraction while being resistant to input noise.

A. Latching in a basin of attraction

Here we will argue that in certain conditions of network dynamics that we will define as "robust latching", the derivatives of a_t with respect to a_0 tend to decrease rapidly as t increases, for most initial conditions a_0 and for inputs that do not disturb the latching condition. This situation is the essential reason for the difficulty in using gradient descent to train a dynamical system to model long-term dependencies.

Definition 1 *A set of points E is said to be* invariant *under a map M if $E = M(E)$.*

Definition 2 *A* hyperbolic attractor *is a set of points X invariant under the differentiable map M, such that $\forall a \in X$, all eigenvalues of $M'(a)$ are less than 1 in absolute value.*

An attractor X may contain a single point (fixed point attractor), a finite number of points (periodic attractor), or an infinite number of points (chaotic attractor). Note that a stable and attracting fixed point is hyperbolic for the map M, whereas a stable and attracting periodic attractor of period l for the map M is hyperbolic for the map M^l. For a recurrent net, the kind of attractor depends on the weight matrix. In particular, for a network

---

[2] A dynamic system with non-additive inputs, e.g., $a_t = N(a_{t-1}, u_{t-1})$, can be transformed into one with additive inputs by introducing n additional state variables and corresponding inputs. The $2n$-vector state is $x_t = (a_t, y_t)$ where $a_t = N(a_{t-1}, y_{t-1})$ (i.e., with 0 inputs) and $y_t = u_t$ (i.e., with the 0 map).

defined by $a_t = W \tanh(a_{t-1}) + u_t$, if W is symmetric and its minimum eigenvalue is greater than -1, then the attractors are all fixed points [6]. On the other hand, if $\|W\| < 1$, the system has a single fixed point attractor at the origin.

Definition 3 *The* basin of attraction *of an attractor X is the set $\beta(X)$ of points a converging to X under the map M, i.e., $\beta(X) = \{a : \forall \epsilon, \exists l, \exists x \in X \text{ s.t. } \|M^l(a) - x\| < \epsilon\}$.*

Definition 4 *We call $\Gamma(X)$ the* reduced attracting set *of a hyperbolic attractor X the set of points y in the basin of attraction of X, such that $\forall l \geq 1$, all the eigenvalues of $(M^l)'(y)$ are less than 1.*

Lemma 1 *For a hyperbolic attractor X, $X \subset \Gamma(X) \subset \beta(X)$.*

Definition 5 *A network is* robustly latched *at time t_0 to X, one of several hyperbolic attractors, if a_{t_0} is in the reduced attracting set of X under a map M defining the autonomous network dynamics.*

Again, for the case of non-autonomous dynamics, it remains robustly latched to X as long as the inputs u_t are such that $a_t \in \Gamma(X)$ for $t > t_0$. Let us now see why it is more robust to store a bit of information by keeping a_t in $\Gamma(X)$.

Theorem 1 *Assume x is a point of $\mathbf{R}^n$ such that there exist an open sphere $U(x)$ centered on x for which $\|M'(z)\| > 1$ for all $z \in U(x)$. Then there exist $y \in U(x)$ such that $\|M(x) - M(y)\| > \|x - y\|$.*

Proof: By hypothesis and definition of norm, $\exists\ u$ s.t. $\|u\| = 1$ and $\|M'(x)u\| > 1$. The Taylor expansion of M at x for small value of λ is:

$$M(x + \lambda u) = M(x) + M'(x)\lambda u + O(\|\lambda u\|^2) \qquad (4)$$

Since U(x) is an open set, $\exists\ \lambda$ s.t. $\|O(\|\lambda u\|^2)\| < \lambda(\|M'(x)u\| - 1)$ and $x + \lambda u \in U(x)$. Letting $y = x + \lambda u$ we can write $\|M(y) - M(x) - M'(x)\lambda u\| = \|O(\|\lambda u\|^2)\| < \lambda\|M'(x)u\| - \lambda$ or $-\|M(y) - M(x) - M'(x)\lambda u\| + \|M'(x)\lambda u\| > \lambda$. This implies using the triangle inequality $\|M(y) - M(x)\| > \lambda = \|x - y\|$. $\square$

This theorem implies that for a hyperbolic attractor X, if a_0 is in $\beta(X)$ but not in $\Gamma(X)$, then the size of a ball of uncertainty around a_0 will grow exponentially as t increases. Thus the system would not be resistant to input noise. In contrast, the following results show that if a_0 is in $\Gamma(X)$, it is guaranteed to remain within a certain distance of X when the input is bounded.

Definition 6 *A map M is* contracting *on a set D if $\exists \alpha \in [0, 1)$ such that $\|M(x) - M(y)\| \leq \alpha\|x - y\|\ \forall x, y \in D$.*

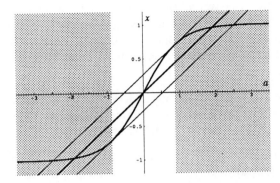

Figure 3: Reduced attracting set (shaded area) in the monodimensional case, for $w = 2$. The heavy line represents the equation $a = wx$. The two light lines represent the equations $a = wx \pm u^*$, where $u^* = 0.532$ is the maximum absolute value of the input to guarantee information latching (cf. [3],[4]).

Theorem 2 *Let M be a differentiable mapping on a convex set D. If $\forall x \in D$, $|M'(x)| < 1$, then M is contracting on D.*

Proof: See [8].

Theorem 3 *Suppose a network is robustly latched to X, starting in state a_0, and the inputs u_t are such that for all $t > 0$, $\|u_t\| < b$ and $\forall y \in D_t$, $|M'(y)| < \lambda < 1$, where D_t is a ball of radius b around a_t. Then for $t > 0$, a_t must be in a ball of radius of less than $\frac{b}{1-\lambda}$. Furthermore, for $t \to \infty$, this ball intersects X.*

Proof: Let us denote by ρ_t the radius of the "uncertainty" ball $\Phi_t = \{a : \|\tilde{a}_t - a\| < \rho_t\}$ in which we are sure to find a_t, where $\tilde{a}_t$ gives the trajectory of the autonomous system. By Lagrange's mean value theorem and convexity of Φ_t, $\exists z \in \Phi_t$ s.t. $\|M(x) - M(y)\| \le |M'(z)|\|x - y\|$, but $|M'(z)| < \lambda$ by hypothesis. Then by the contraction theorem (2), we have $\rho_0 = 0$, $\rho_1 = b$, $\rho_2 = \lambda b + b$, $\rho_t = \lambda \rho_{t-1} + b$. Hence for $t > 0$, $\rho_t = b \sum_{i=0}^{t-1} \lambda^i = \frac{b(1-\lambda^t)}{1-\lambda}$, thus $\lim_{t \to \infty} \rho_t = \frac{b}{1-\lambda}$. To show how Φ_t intersects with X when $t \to \infty$, consider a point c_t in Φ_t obtained from a point c_{t-1} in Φ_{t-1} by setting $c_t = M(c_{t-1})$. c_t must converge to X, hence the conclusion. $\square$

The above results justifies the term "robust" in our definition of robustly latched network: as long as u_t is such that a_t remains in the reduced attracting set of a hyperbolic attractor X, a_t is guaranteed to remain within a distance $\frac{2b}{1-\lambda}$ of some point in X. On the other hand, outside $\Gamma(X)$ but in $\beta(X)$, M is not contracting, it is expanding, i.e., the size of a ball of uncertainty grows exponentially with time.

Theorem 4 *If the input u_t is such that a network remains robustly latched on attractor X after time 0, then $\frac{\partial a_t}{\partial a_0} \to 0$ as $t \to \infty$.*

Proof: By hypothesis and definitions 4 and 2, $\left\| \frac{\partial a_\tau}{\partial a_{\tau-1}} \right\| = |M'(a_{\tau-1})| < 1$ for $\tau > 0$, hence $\frac{\partial a_t}{\partial a_0} \to 0$ as $t \to \infty$ $\square$.

The above results show that when storing one or more bit of information in a way that is resistant to noise, the gradient with respect to past events rapidly becomes very small in comparison to the gradient with respect to recent events. In the next section we discuss how that makes gradient descent on parameter space (e.g., the weights of a network) inefficient.

B. Effect on the Weight Gradient

According to the above results, in state-space regions with strong attractors (with basins of attraction), the behavior of the network resembles that of a multi-valued analog switch (or latch). The input can push the state into one of several basins of attraction. Once in a basin of attraction, it stays there if or until a sequence of inputs pushes it out. If the network is robustly latched on one of these attractors, the derivatives of the cost function at time t with respect to the state at an earlier time rapidly tend to 0 as t increases.

Let us consider the effects of these conditions on the derivatives of a cost C_t at time t with respect to parameters of a dynamical system, say a neural network with weights W:

$$\frac{\partial C_t}{\partial W} = \sum_{\tau \le t} \frac{\partial C_t}{\partial a_\tau} \frac{\partial a_\tau}{\partial W} = \sum_{\tau \le t} \frac{\partial C_t}{\partial a_t} \frac{\partial a_t}{\partial a_\tau} \frac{\partial a_\tau}{\partial W} \quad (5)$$

Suppose we are in the condition in which the network has robustly latched. Hence for a term with $\tau \ll t$, $\left\| \frac{\partial C_t}{\partial a_\tau} \frac{\partial a_\tau}{\partial W} \right\| \to 0$. This term tends to become very small in comparison to terms for which τ is close to t. This means that even though there might exist a change in W that would allow a_τ to jump to another basin of attraction, this effect is not taken into account. This is because the effect of a **small** change in W would be felt mostly on the near past (τ close to t). For example, if between the time the system is latched (say time 0) and the time the stored bit is used (say time t) the inputs are noisy, the gradient contribution for time 0 tends to be insignificant in comparison to the contribution for intervening times. Worse, if the intervening events are not noise but represent other input events that can influence later outputs, the system can learn these short-term dependencies but will probably fail to learn the long-term dependencies.

C. Generalization to a Projection of the State

The results in the above subsections can be generalized to the case when a projection $P a_t$ of the state a_t converges to an attractor under a map M. Let P and R be orthogonal projection matrices such that

$$a_t = P^+ z_t + R^+ y_t$$
$$z_t = P a_t; \quad y_t = R a_t \qquad (6)$$
$$P R^+ = 0; \quad R P^+ = 0$$

where A^+ denotes the right pseudo-inverse of A, i.e. $A A^+ = I$. Suppose M is such that P can be chosen so that z_t converges to an attractor Z with the dynamics $z_t = M_P(z_{t-1}) = P_t M(P^+ z_t + R^+ y_t)$ for any y_t. Then we can specialize all the previous definitions, lemmas and theorems to the subspace z_t. When we conclude with these results that $\frac{\partial z_t}{\partial z_0} \to 0$, we can infer that $\frac{\partial a_t}{\partial a_0} \to R^+ \frac{\partial y_t}{\partial y_0} R$, i.e., that the derivatives of a_t with respect to a_0 depend only on the projection of a on the subspace Ra. Hence the influence of changes in the projection of a on the subspace Pa is ignored in the computation of the gradient with respect to W, even though non-infinitesimal changes in Pa could yield very different results (jumping into a different basin of attraction).

D. Alternative Approaches

This section helped us understand better why training a recurrent network to learn *long range* input/output dependencies is a hard problem. Gradient-based methods appear inadequate for this kind of problem. We need to consider alternative systems and optimization methods that give acceptable results even when the criterion function is not smooth and has long plateaus. Global search methods such as simulated annealing can be applied to such problems, but they are generally very slow. One way to help in the training of recurrent networks is to set their connectivity and initial weights (and even constraints on the weights) using prior knowledge. For example, this is accomplished in [4] and [5] using prior rules and sequentiality constraints. Another approach is to look for algorithms that can yield desired changes in parameters even when the map is non-differentiable. Such an approach is explored in the next section.

IV. A Trainable Flip-Flop

The goal of this section is to propose a new kind of unit designed to meet the 3 conditions listed in the introduction, at least for the minimal problem presented in Section II. The idea is to have a unit whose function is not necessarily differentiable but for which condition (3) (learnability) is still satisfied. Since no gradient exists for such a unit, the variations that should be submitted to the input to induce the desired variation of the output should be computed discretely. In the simplest case, the unit has one internal state and one input. Its time behavior is described by:

$$x_{t+1} = f(x_t, u_t) \qquad (7)$$

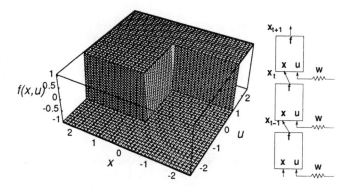

Figure 4: Left: Map $f(x, u)$ for the trainable flip-flop. Right: unfolding in time of the trainable flip-flop with its inputs x_t and u_t and its output $x_{t+1} = f(x_t, u_t)$.

A simple function f which exhibit noise resistance and can store one bit of information is shown in figure 4 and defined as follows:

$$f(x, u) = \begin{cases} 1 & \text{if } |u| < 1 \text{ and } x \geq 0 \\ & \text{or if } u \geq 1 \\ -1 & \text{otherwise} \end{cases} \qquad (8)$$

This unit satisfies criterion (1) and (2) of the introduction. For learning (criterion (3)), we have to compute the variation of Δf with respect to Δx and Δu. The variation of f with respect to the variation of x can be easily infered from Eq. 8 or from figure 4 :

$$\Delta f_x(\Delta x, x, u) = \begin{cases} 2 & \text{if } |u| < 1, \ x < 0, \ x + \Delta x \geq 0 \\ -2 & \text{if } |u| < 1, \ x \geq 0, \ x + \Delta x < 0 \\ 0 & \text{otherwise} \end{cases}$$
$$(9)$$

From which we can infer a "backpropagation" rule in time:

$$\Delta x(\Delta f) = \begin{cases} k_{x,1} - x & \text{if } |u| < 1, \ x < 0, \ \Delta f = 2 \\ -k_{x,2} - x & \text{if } |u| < 1, \ x \geq 0, \ \Delta f = -2 \\ 0 & \text{otherwise} \end{cases}$$
$$(10)$$

Where $k_{x,1}$ and $k_{x,2}$ are positive constants. Assuming the additional constraint $x \in \{-1, +1\}$, this system simplifies to:

$$\Delta x(\Delta f, u) = \begin{cases} \Delta f & \text{if } |u| < 1 \\ 0 & \text{otherwise} \end{cases} \qquad (11)$$

Note that this is a recursive rule for backpropagating *targets* in time, $\Delta x_t = \Delta x_{t+1}$ if $|u_t| < 1$ and 0 otherwise. In other words, the Δf signal is passed down to earlier times for as long as the flip-flop was in the final state. Similarly, the variation of f with respect to the variation of u can be easily infered from Eq. 8 or from figure 4 :

$$\Delta f_u(\Delta u, x, u) =$$

$$\begin{cases} 2 & \text{if } x < 0 \,,\ u < 1 \,,\ u + \Delta u > 1 \\ & \text{or } x > 0 \,,\ u < -1 \,,\ u + \Delta u > -1 \\ -2 & \text{if } x < 0 \,,\ u > 1 \,,\ u + \Delta u < 1 \\ & \text{or if } x > 0 \,,\ u > -1 \,,\ u + \Delta u < -1 \qquad (12) \\ 0 & \text{otherwise} \end{cases}$$

From this we can compute the variations Δu

$$\Delta u(\Delta f, x, u) =$$
$$\begin{cases} 1 - u + k_1 & \text{when } x < 0 \,,\ u < 1 \,,\ \Delta f = 2 \\ -1 - u + k_2 & \text{when } x > 0 \,,\ u < -1 \,,\ \Delta f = 2 \\ 1 - u - k_3 & \text{when } x < 0 \,,\ u > 1 \,,\ \Delta f = -2 \quad (13) \\ -1 - u - k_4 & \text{when } x > 0 \,,\ u > -1 \,,\ \Delta f = -2 \\ 0 & \text{otherwise} \end{cases}$$

Where each k_i is a positive constant. When used in a network, the rule becomes recursive, that is, Δu_t is computed from $\Delta x_{t+1}, x_t, u_t$. The learning rates for each Δu_t are weighted by the probability of contribution. Lets assume for the sake of illustration that the flip-flop has ended in state $+1$ at time T, that the target state was -1 and that $|u_t| < 1$ for $T - n < t \le T$ and $u_{T-n} > 1$. There are two ways of udating u_t to get the correct answer. Either $u_t < -1$ for some t in $T - n < t \le T$ or $u_{T-n} < 1$. The learning rate should therefore be weighted by $0.5/n$ for $T - n < t \le T$ and by 0.5 for $t = T - n$.

In order to adapt the threshold to the external level of noise and signal, the input to the unit is scaled by a weight w that can also be learnt using the target on u. Experiments were performed with this system on the minimal task described in Section II. Sequence lengths were varied from 10 to 100 by increment of 10 and zero-mean uniform noise with levels from 0.2 to 1.0 by increment of 0.2. We found the algorithm to converge in more than 99% of these cases (within a maximum of 100 epochs), independently of the noise level and the sequence length, in average within 4.6 epochs. This is in contrast to the recurrent sigmoid trained with backpropagation which was sensitive to the noise level and for which the probability of convergence decreased rapidly when increasing sequence length (as shown in Figure 2).

V. Conclusion

Recurrent networks are very powerful in their ability to represent context, often outperforming static networks [1]. However, we have presented theoretical and experimental evidence indicating that in many circumstances, simple gradient-based optimization of an error criterion may be inadequate to train them. There remains theoretical questions to be considered, such as whether the problem with simple gradient descent discussed in this paper would be observed with chaotic attractors that are not hyperbolic. A better understanding of the problem underlying the loss of information in the gradient may help us designing more efficient algorithms and/or architectures for recurrent neural networks. In fact, based on the specifications required to solve a minimal problem for such algorithms, we have introduced a new type of unit with its learning algorithm, that could learn to store one bit of information for an indefinite duration while being resistant to input noise. In any case, the results of this paper strongly suggest that different training algorithms should be considered for recurrent networks. Solutions to the challenge presented here to learning long-term dependencies with dynamical systems such as recurrent networks may have implications for many types of applications for learning systems, e.g., in language related problems, for which long-term dependencies and the use of context are essential in order to take correct decisions.

References

[1] Y. Bengio, "Artificial Neural Networks and their Application to Sequence Recognition," Ph.D. Thesis, McGill University, (Computer Science), 1991, Montreal, Qc., Canada.

[2] Y. Bengio, R. De Mori, G. Flammia, and R. Kompe, "Global Optimization of a Neural Network - Hidden Markov Model Hybrid," *IEEE Transactions on Neural Networks*, vol. 3, no. 2, 1992, pp. 252–259.

[3] P. Frasconi, M. Gori, and G. Soda, "Local Feedback Multilayered Networks", *Neural Computation* 3, 1992, pp. 120–130.

[4] P. Frasconi, M. Gori, M. Maggini, and G. Soda, "Unified Integration of Explicit Rules and Learning by Example in Recurrent Networks," *IEEE Trans. on Knowledge and Data Engineering*, in press.

[5] C.L. Giles and C.W. Omlin, "Inserting Rules into Recurrent Neural Networks", *Neural Networks for Signal Processing II, Procedings of the 1992 IEEE workshop*, (eds. Kung, Fallside, Sorenson and Kamm), IEEE Press, pp. 13-22.

[6] C.M. Marcus, F.R. Waugh, and R.M. Westervelt, "Nonlinear Dynamics and Stability of Analog Neural Networks", *Physica D* **51** (special issue), 1991, pp. 234-247.

[7] Mozer M.C., "Induction of multiscale temporal structure", Advances in Neural Information Processing Systems 4, (eds. Moody, Hanson, Lippman), Morgan Kauffmann, 1992, pp. 275-282.

[8] Ortega J.M. and Rheinboldt W.C. *Iterative Solution of Non-linear Equations in Several Variables and Systems of Equations*, Academic Press, New York, 1960.

Practical Considerations for Kalman Filter Training of Recurrent Neural Networks

G. V. Puskorius and L. A. Feldkamp
Research Laboratory, Ford Motor Company
Suite 1100, Village Plaza
23400 Michigan Avenue
Dearborn, Michigan 48124
Email: gpuskori@smail.srl.ford.com   lfeldkam@smail.srl.ford.com

Abstract— Although the potential of the powerful mapping and representational capabilities of recurrent network architectures is widely recognized by the neural network research community, general recurrent neural networks for application studies have not been widely used, possibly due to the relative ineffectiveness of existing gradient-based training algorithms. Recent developments in the use of extended Kalman filter algorithms for training recurrent networks may provide a mechanism by which these architectures will prove to be of practical value. This paper presents an overview of a decoupled extended Kalman filter (DEKF) algorithm for training of recurrent neural network architectures with special emphasis on application to control problems. We discuss qualitative differences between the DEKF algorithm, which only performs updates to a recurrent network's weight parameters, and a recent EKF formulation by Williams [1, 2] that performs parallel estimation of both the network's weights and recurrent node outputs.

I. INTRODUCTION

The extended Kalman filter (EKF) has served as the basis for a number of recent neural network training algorithm studies. The EKF can be thought of as a gradient-based, on-line information processing algorithm that is used for smoothing, filtering or predicting the states of a nonlinear dynamical system. Singhal and Wu [3] demonstrated that the global EKF (GEKF) could be used to train layered feedforward networks by treating the weights of the network as an unforced nonlinear dynamical system with stationary states. Alternatively, an identical algorithm is derived by using the method of linearized recursive least squares to infer the weights of a static feedforward network [4]. Although this global approach demonstrates fast learning as a function of number of presentations of training data, the training time per instance scales as the

square of the number of weights in the network, hence rendering the algorithm impractical for many problems. A number of researchers have investigated simplifications to GEKF for the training of multilayer perceptrons [5, 6]. In [5], we show that an effective and efficient training algorithm can be achieved by ignoring the interdependencies of mutually exclusive groups of weights, thereby leading to lower computational complexity and storage per training instance. This decoupled EKF (DEKF) algorithm was demonstrated to exhibit faster training, both in terms of number of presentations of training data and in total training time on a serial processor, than a standard implementation of backpropagation for problems in pattern classification and function approximation. Furthermore, the classification and mapping performance of DEKF-trained networks was usually found to be substantially superior to that of networks trained by standard backpropagation.

Current research efforts have focussed on the use of the EKF as a training algorithm for recurrent neural network architectures. Training of recurrent network architectures by either real time recurrent learning (RTRL) [7] or backpropagation through time (BPTT) [8] usually requires that very low learning rates be employed due to the inherent correlations between successive node outputs that lead to an underlying eigenvalue structure that is ill conditioned. On the other hand, the EKF is a second order algorithm that in effect processes and uses information about the shape of the training problem's error surface for updating the states of the system, thereby providing an effective mechanism for dealing with temporal and spatial correlations in input signals and successive node outputs in recurrent neural networks.

The use of EKF as a training algorithm for recurrent neural networks was first explored by Matthews [9] with application to signal processing problems. Williams [1, 2] provides a detailed analytical treatment of EKF training of recurrent neural networks, and suggests that a ten-fold decrease relative to RTRL in the number of presentations of training data is achieved for some simple finite state machine problems. In contrast to the EKF formulation of Singhal and Wu for feedforward layered networks, the training problems as treated by Matthews and Williams provide for parallel estimation of both network states (i.e., recurrent node outputs before they are used as inputs at the next time step) and parameters (i.e., the network's trainable weights). This approach is one of many ways of performing simultaneous state and parameter estimation for dynamical systems (e.g., see Anderson and Moore [10]). Livstone et al. [11] have also explored the use of parallel state and parameter estimation for radial basis function networks with feedback connections. Although this development appears promising, we restrict the remainder of our discussion to recurrent networks with sigmoidal or linear node output functions.

In earlier work, independently of Matthews and Williams, we had extended the DEKF formulation for feedforward layered networks to network architectures with recurrent connections [12, 13]. The DEKF formulation for recurrent neural network architectures differs from that of the parallel EKF formulation in two fundamental ways. First, the DEKF formulation assumes that the interdependence of disjoint weight groups can be ignored. This simplification has the effect of reducing the computational and storage requirements for the measurement update portion of DEKF relative to the parallel EKF. The second difference is that state estimation is **not** performed in our DEKF formulation, although weights of the recurrent network architecture are trained. We discuss below what we perceive to be the relative advantages and disadvantages of performing parallel state and parameter estimation, as opposed to performing parameter estimation alone, by EKF-based training algorithms.

We are primarily interested in using recurrent neural networks for control applications, both for identification of nonlinear dynamical systems and for the synthesis of nonlinear dynamical feedback controllers. The use of recurrent neural networks as system identification networks and feedback controllers offers a number of potential advantages over the use of static layered networks. Recurrent neural networks provide a means for encoding and representing internal or hidden states, albeit in a potentially distributed fashion, which leads to capabilities that are similar to those of an *observer* in modern control theory. Recurrent network architectures provide increased flexibility for the filtering of noisy inputs. Recurrent neural network feedback controllers may be less sensitive (i.e., more robust) than static feedforward controllers to changes in plant dynamics and parameters. A recurrent neural network controller can be trained to simultaneously provide state-space control and observer capabilities within a homogeneous architecture. We have observed all of these benefits in our application-oriented

studies, and believe that these behaviors emerged largely due to the use of an effective recurrent neural network training procedure based on an extended Kalman filter algorithm. We elaborate below on some of the practical issues involved in the use of EKF methods for the training of recurrent neural networks.

II. EKF Algorithms for Parameter Estimation

Derivation of an EKF algorithm for the estimation of a feedforward layered network's weights was first provided by Singhal and Wu [3]. Later, a recursive linearized least squares derivation was developed by Douglas and Meng [4]. Since the resulting algorithms are essentially equivalent, we will simply refer to these algorithms as parameter-based EKF training algorithms. We view the neural network training problem as a parameter estimation problem, and treat the training of purely feedforward networks and recurrent network architectures in a uniform fashion. The major difference in applying parameter-based EKF algorithms for the training of weights in feedforward and recurrent network architectures lies in the computation of the ordered derivatives of network outputs with respect to the trainable weights. Once the derivatives are computed, as we describe below, the same parameter-based EKF training algorithm applies to either class of network architecture.

Assume a general neural network architecture with arbitrary interconnectivity, potentially including both feedforward and feedback connections. The neural network training problem is formulated as a weighted least squares minimization problem, where the error vector is the difference between differentiable functions of the network's node outputs and target values for these functions. Let the target vector at time step n be given by $\mathbf{d}(n) = [d_1(n)\, d_2(n)\, \cdots\, d_{N_c}(n)]^T$, and let the vector $\mathbf{h}(n) = [h_1(\mathbf{y}(n))\, h_2(\mathbf{y}(n))\, \cdots\, h_{N_c}(\mathbf{y}(n))]^T$ denote a vector of differentiable functions (potentially nonlinear) of the network's outputs $\mathbf{y}(n)$. N_c is the number of components of the cost function which is given by $E(n) = \frac{1}{2}\boldsymbol{\xi}(n)^T \mathbf{S}(n) \boldsymbol{\xi}(n)$, where $\mathbf{S}(n)$ is a user-specified nonnegative definite weighting matrix, and where $\boldsymbol{\xi}(n) = \mathbf{d}(n) - \mathbf{h}(n)$. The network's trainable weights are arranged into a M-dimensional vector $\mathbf{w}(n)$, and the estimate of the weight vector at time step n is denoted by $\hat{\mathbf{w}}(n)$. The Kalman recursion requires that, in addition to maintaining and updating estimates of the network's weight vector $\hat{\mathbf{w}}(n)$, it is also necessary to maintain and update a matrix that is called the *approximate error covariance* matrix, given by $\mathbf{P}(n)$, which is used to model the correlations or interactions between each pair of weights in the network. At the beginning of training (time step $n = 0$), the weight vector is initialized to small random values (e.g., of magnitude less than 0.1), and the matrix $\mathbf{P}(0)$ is initialized as a diagonal matrix with component values on the order of 10^2. At the nth time step, the input signals and recurrent node activations are propagated through the network, and the functions $\mathbf{h}(n)$ are computed. The error vector $\boldsymbol{\xi}(n)$ is calculated, and the gradients of each component of $\mathbf{h}(n)$ are formed with respect to the weights of the network, evaluated at the current weight estimates $\hat{\mathbf{w}}(n)$; these derivatives are arranged into the M-by-N_c matrix $\mathbf{H}(n)$. Then the weight vector and approximate error covariance matrix are updated by the following GEKF recursion:

$$\mathbf{A}(n) = \left[(\eta(n)\mathbf{S}(n))^{-1} + \mathbf{H}(n)^T\mathbf{P}(n)\mathbf{H}(n)\right]^{-1}, \quad (1)$$

$$\mathbf{K}(n) = \mathbf{P}(n)\mathbf{H}(n)\mathbf{A}(n), \quad (2)$$

$$\hat{\mathbf{w}}(n{+}1) = \hat{\mathbf{w}}(n) + \mathbf{K}(n)\boldsymbol{\xi}(n), \quad (3)$$

$$\mathbf{P}(n{+}1) = \mathbf{P}(n) - \mathbf{K}(n)\mathbf{H}(n)^T\mathbf{P}(n) + \mathbf{Q}(n). \quad (4)$$

This formulation includes a scalar learning rate parameter $\eta(n)$ whose role is similar to that of the learning rate in gradient descent training. The overall learning rate of this EKF algorithm is determined by the scalar $\eta(n)$ and the relative scaling of the components of the weighting matrix $\mathbf{S}(n)$. The EKF recursion also requires the computation of an intermediate matrix $\mathbf{A}(n)$, for which a matrix of size N_c must be inverted at each time step, and of the Kalman gain matrix $\mathbf{K}(n)$, which determines the extent to which the weight estimates and approximate error covariance matrix are changed. Finally, $\mathbf{Q}(n)$ is a diagonal matrix which provides a mechanism by which the effects of process noise are included in the Kalman recursion. The use of a nonnegative $\mathbf{Q}(n)$ matrix tends to increase the training algorithm's effective learning rate and helps the algorithm avoid local minima, as demonstrated in [5].

The matrix $\mathbf{S}(n)$ is described above as a nonnegative definite matrix. For problems in neural controller training, it may be desirable to impose constraints on the desired behavior of the overall system. Jordan [14, 15] describes how the effects of constraints are included in the cost function $E(n)$ for gradient-descent training of neural controllers by allowing $\mathbf{S}(n)$ to be a function of the evaluations of the functions $\mathbf{h}(n)$. In general, if a *configurational* constraint is satisfied at time step n (e.g., the value of $h_i(\mathbf{y}(n))$ falls within a desired range), then the corresponding component of the error vector and derivatives of the function $h_i(\mathbf{y}(n))$ should not contribute to the updates of $\hat{\mathbf{w}}(n)$ and $\mathbf{P}(n)$. The constraint is imposed by introducing zero values into the appropriate columns and rows of the weighting matrix $\mathbf{S}(n)$ for time step n. However, since equation (1) requires the inverse of $\mathbf{S}(n)$, we reformulate the Kalman recursion to remove this mathematical difficulty. Defining $\boldsymbol{\xi}^*(n) = \mathbf{S}(n)^{\frac{1}{2}}\boldsymbol{\xi}(n) = \mathbf{S}(n)^{\frac{1}{2}}\mathbf{d}(n) - \mathbf{S}(n)^{\frac{1}{2}}\mathbf{h}(n) = \mathbf{d}^*(n) - \mathbf{h}^*(n)$ yields the cost function $E(n) = \frac{1}{2}\boldsymbol{\xi}^*(n)^T\boldsymbol{\xi}^*(n)$. Then the GEKF algorithm is given by

$$\mathbf{A}^*(n) = \left[\eta(n)^{-1}\mathbf{I} + \mathbf{H}^*(n)^T\mathbf{P}(n)\mathbf{H}^*(n)\right]^{-1}, \quad (5)$$

$$\mathbf{K}^*(n) = \mathbf{P}(n)\mathbf{H}^*(n)\mathbf{A}^*(n), \quad (6)$$

$$\hat{\mathbf{w}}(n{+}1) = \hat{\mathbf{w}}(n) + \mathbf{K}^*(n)\boldsymbol{\xi}^*(n), \quad (7)$$

$$\mathbf{P}(n{+}1) = \mathbf{P}(n) - \mathbf{K}^*(n)\mathbf{H}^*(n)^T\mathbf{P}(n) + \mathbf{Q}(n), \quad (8)$$

where the scaling matrix $\mathbf{S}(n)$ is now distributed into both the scaled error vector $\boldsymbol{\xi}^*(n) = \mathbf{S}(n)^{\frac{1}{2}}\boldsymbol{\xi}(n)$ and the scaled derivative matrix $\mathbf{H}^*(n) = \mathbf{H}(n)\mathbf{S}(n)^{\frac{1}{2}}$. Although the two formulations are mathematically equivalent, the latter formulation gracefully handles the effects of configurational constraints.

The computational requirements of the GEKF recursion are dominated by the need to store and update the approximate error covariance matrix $\mathbf{P}(n)$. GEKF's computational complexity is $O(N_c M^2)$ and its storage requirements are $O(M^2)$. The DEKF recursion is easily derived from the global recursion by assuming that the interactions between different weight estimates can be ignored. This simplification introduces many zeroes into the global approximate error covariance matrix. Furthermore, if we assume that the weights can be decoupled so that the weight groups are mutually exclusive of one another, then the matrix $\mathbf{P}(n)$ can be arranged into block diagonal form. Let g refer to the number of such weight groups. Then, the vector $\hat{\mathbf{w}}_i(n)$ refers to the estimated weight parameters of group i, $\mathbf{H}_i^*(n)$ is the submatrix of ordered derivatives of the functions $\mathbf{h}^*(n)$ with respect to the weights of group i, $\mathbf{P}_i(n)$ is the approximate error covariance matrix modeling the interactions between the weights of group i, and $\mathbf{K}_i^*(n)$ is the Kalman gain matrix for the ith weight group. Note that the concatenation of the vectors $\hat{\mathbf{w}}_i(n)$ forms the vector $\hat{\mathbf{w}}(n)$, and the global matrix $\mathbf{H}^*(n)$ is composed of the individual submatrices $\mathbf{H}_i^*(n)$. With this convention and simplifying assumption, the DEKF recursion is given by

$$\mathbf{A}^*(n) = \left[\eta(n)^{-1}\mathbf{I} + \sum_{j=1}^{g}\mathbf{H}_j^*(n)^T\mathbf{P}_j(n)\mathbf{H}_j^*(n)\right]^{-1}, \quad (9)$$

$$\mathbf{K}_i^*(n) = \mathbf{P}_i(n)\mathbf{H}_i^*(n)\mathbf{A}^*(n), \quad (10)$$

$$\hat{\mathbf{w}}_i(n{+}1) = \hat{\mathbf{w}}_i(n) + \mathbf{K}_i^*(n)\boldsymbol{\xi}^*(n), \quad (11)$$

$$\mathbf{P}_i(n{+}1) = \mathbf{P}_i(n) - \mathbf{K}_i^*(n)\mathbf{H}_i^*(n)^T\mathbf{P}_i(n) + \mathbf{Q}_i(n). \quad (12)$$

One should immediately note the striking similarity of the decoupled and global recursions. Note that a single global matrix $\mathbf{A}^*(n)$ is computed based on contributions from all of the approximate error covariance submatrices and ordered derivatives. It is also noteworthy that in the limit of a single weight group ($g = 1$), the decoupled Kalman recursion reduces exactly to the GEKF algorithm.

The computational complexity and storage requirements for the DEKF algorithm can be significantly less than those of the GEKF recursion. For g disjoint weight groups, the computational complexity of DEKF becomes $O(N_c^2 M + N_c \sum_{i=1}^g M_i^2)$, where M_i is the number of weights in group i, while the storage requirements become $O(\sum_{i=1}^g M_i^2)$. Note that this complexity analysis does not include the computational and storage requirements for the matrix of ordered derivatives. In particular, in the case of recurrent network architectures, the computational complexity of the derivative computations can be significant, as we describe below. For the purposes of this paper, we are interested in a DEKF algorithm for which the weights are grouped by node (i.e., the weights connecting inputs to a node are grouped together). We call this node-decoupled EKF (or NDEKF for short).

III. RECURRENT NETWORKS AND DERIVATIVE COMPUTATIONS

We consider neural network architectures that are specified by a generalized version of the *recurrent multilayer perceptron* (RMLP) architecture described in [16]. A general RMLP architecture consists of layers of nodes arranged in a feedforward fashion, where the nodes of a given layer may be connected to one another through trainable feedback connections with a unit time delay. Network architectures ranging from purely feedforward multilayer networks without recurrent connections to a recurrent network consisting of a single layer of nodes, all completely interconnected, can be specified by a generalized RMLP architecture. Between these extremes are network architectures consisting of layers of nodes, with some feedback connections between nodes within a given layer.

The following notation is employed in order to describe the derivative computations for RMLP architectures. A RMLP network is assumed to consist of L layers of nodes, with N_i processing elements in layer i (N_0 is the length of the input vector). Each processing element of the network is characterized by two indexes, one referencing the layer to which the node belongs and the other referencing the node number within the layer. A vector of input signals or node outputs is denoted by $\mathbf{y}_i(n) = [y_{i,1}(n)\ y_{i,2}(n) \cdots y_{i,N_i}(n)]^T$, where $0 \le i \le L$. Provisions for a bias input are made by constructing an augmented representation for the vectors $\mathbf{y}_i(n)$: $\bar{\mathbf{y}}_i(n) = [y_{i,0}(n)\ \mathbf{y}_i(n)]^T$, where the bias input $y_{i,0}(n)$ is usually set to unity. Two vectors of weights are generally associated with each processing element of the network, corresponding to the feedforward connections (including the bias weight) and to the feedback connections. Weight vectors are denoted by $^h\mathbf{w}_{i,j}$, where the subscript i refers to the layer to which the node belongs ($1 \le i \le L$), the subscript j refers to the node number within layer i ($1 \le j \le N_i$), and the superscript h refers to the layer from which the connection is made. The superscript h takes on only one

of two values for the RMLP architectures considered here: $h = i - 1$, for which the weight vector consists of feedforward weights that connect the previous layer's augmented output vector $\bar{\mathbf{y}}_{i-1}(n)$; and $h = i$, for which the weight vector consists of recurrent weights that connect the ith layer's time-delayed output vector $\mathbf{y}_i(n-1)$. The form of the feedforward weight vector for the jth node of the ith layer is given by $^h\mathbf{w}_{i,j} = [^hw_{i,j,0}\ ^hw_{i,j,1} \cdots ^hw_{i,j,N_h}]^T$, where $h = i - 1$; similarly, the form of the recurrent weight vector for the jth node of the ith layer is given by $^i\mathbf{w}_{i,j} = [^iw_{i,j,1}\ ^iw_{i,j,2} \cdots ^iw_{i,j,N_i}]^T$. With this notation, assuming complete interconnectivity, the weighted input to the jth node of the ith layer at time step n is given by

$$x_{i,j}(n) = {}^{i-1}\mathbf{w}_{i,j} \cdot \bar{\mathbf{y}}_{i-1}(n) + {}^i\mathbf{w}_{i,j} \cdot \mathbf{y}_i(n-1)$$

$$= \sum_{k=0}^{N_{i-1}} {}^{i-1}w_{i,j,k} y_{i-1,k}(n) + \sum_{k=1}^{N_i} {}^iw_{i,j,k} y_{i,k}(n-1) , \quad (13)$$

and the output of the jth node of the ith layer at time step n is given by $y_{i,j}(n) = F_{i,j}(x_{i,j}(n))$, where $F_{i,j}(\cdot)$ is the node's output function.

A general rule for computing the ordered derivatives (or *total* partial derivatives) of the outputs of a RMLP network with respect to its trainable weights can be formulated based upon three fundamental observations. First, the ordered derivative of the output of a node in the ith layer with respect to a weight in the gth layer (either recurrent or feedforward) is zero when the gth layer follows the ith layer: $\partial y_{i,j}(n)/\partial\ ^hw_{g,u,v} = 0$ for $g > i$. Second, the ordered derivative of the output of a node in the ith layer with respect to a weight in the same layer is obtained by a generalization of the RTRL rule for a recurrent network with complete interconnectivity. Third, the ordered derivative of the output of a node in the ith layer with respect to a weight in the gth layer when the gth layer precedes the ith layer is a function of the ordered derivatives of the outputs of nodes from both the $(i-1)^{th}$ and i^{th} layers with respect to the same weight. From these observations we derive the following general formula for computing the ordered derivative of an arbitrary node's output with respect to an arbitrary weight for RMLP architectures:

$$\frac{\bar{\partial} y_{i,j}(n)}{\bar{\partial}\ ^hw_{g,u,v}} = \left(\frac{1 + \delta_{i,g} + \mathrm{signum}(i-g)}{2} \right)$$

$$F'_{i,j}(x_{i,j}(n)) \left\{ (1 - \delta_{i,g}) \sum_{k=1}^{N_{i-1}} {}^{i-1}w_{i,j,k} \frac{\bar{\partial} y_{i-1,k}(n)}{\bar{\partial}\ ^hw_{g,u,v}} \right.$$

$$\left. + \gamma(n) \sum_{k=1}^{N_i} {}^iw_{i,j,k} \frac{\bar{\partial} y_{i,k}(n-1)}{\bar{\partial}\ ^hw_{g,u,v}} + \delta_{i,g}\delta_{j,u} y_{h,v}(n+i-h-1) \right\},$$

$$(14)$$

where $\gamma(n)$ is a derivative discount factor that exponentially decays the effects of recurrent derivatives from time long past. The value of $\gamma(n)$ is usually set equal to or slightly less than unity. This equation is a compact representation of the derivative formulation as derived by Parlos et al. [17] for RMLP architectures.

The derivative computations as described above assume RMLP architectures of multiple layers of nodes, where all nodes within a layer are interconnected with one another. If an RMLP architecture consists of both recurrent and purely feedforward layers, then the derivative computations can be performed more efficiently by performing backpropagation of derivatives through the feedforward layers, and combining this information with the feedforward derivative computations through the recurrent layers. One can visualize the form that these calculations would require by considering the sensitivity circuits for systems consisting of both feedforward layered networks and models of linear dynamical systems as described by Narendra and Parthasarathy [18, 19].

Our principal interest is in the use of recurrent neural networks for control applications where a RMLP network is used in a feedback loop to control a nonlinear dynamical system. In this case, in addition to the internal recurrence within the RMLP controller, there is also external recurrence in the form of plant outputs used as controller inputs. Because of this external feedback loop, the ordered derivative of a node's output with respect to any weight of the RMLP network is generally nonzero. For RMLP architectures used as feedback controllers, the derivative computations of equation (14) become

$$
\frac{\bar{\partial} y_{i,j}(n)}{\bar{\partial}\,{}^h w_{g,u,v}} = F'_{i,j}(x_{i,j}(n)) \left\{ \sum_{k=1}^{N_{i-1}} {}^{i-1}w_{i,j,k} \frac{\bar{\partial} y_{i-1,k}(n)}{\bar{\partial}\,{}^h w_{g,u,v}} \right.
$$
$$
\left. + \gamma(n) \sum_{k=1}^{N_i} {}^i w_{i,j,k} \frac{\bar{\partial} y_{i,k}(n-1)}{\bar{\partial}\,{}^h w_{g,u,v}} + \delta_{i,g}\delta_{j,u} y_{h,v}(n+i-h-1) \right\}.
$$

(15)

The vector $\mathbf{y}_0(n)$ consists of the unit time delayed dynamical system's outputs, for which derivatives with respect to controller weights are generally nonzero, and optionally external reference inputs. Note that the derivative computations for an RMLP architecture for which there are feedback paths from system outputs to network inputs generally require increased computational resources, since storage and computation of the ordered derivatives of the outputs of all recurrent nodes with respect to all trainable weights of the network are required.

IV. Parallel State and Parameter Estimation with EKF

The EKF formulations of Matthews [9] and Williams [1, 2] perform both state and weight updates for recurrent net-

work architectures. The parallel estimation of states and parameters leads to an EKF algorithm that has a number of significant differences from the parameter-based EKF algorithm described above. We summarize some of these differences for a recurrent network architecture consisting of a single layer of completely interconnected nodes, and discuss implications of these differences for practical applications. We concentrate on Williams' EKF formulation for comparative purposes.

The parallel EKF algorithm treats the state vector as the concatenation of the recurrent node outputs with the weight parameter vector. Thus, it is convenient to decompose the approximate global error covariance matrix into four distinct blocks: $\mathbf{P}_1(n)$ models the interactions between the recurrent node outputs, $\mathbf{P}_4(n)$ models the interactions between the weights of the network, and $\mathbf{P}_2(n) = \mathbf{P}_3(n)^T$ models the cross correlations between the network's weights and recurrent node outputs. The submatrices $\mathbf{P}_1(n)$ and $\mathbf{P}_4(n)$ lie along the diagonal of $\mathbf{P}(n)$, while $\mathbf{P}_2(n)$ and $\mathbf{P}_3(n)$ fill the off-block diagonal parts of $\mathbf{P}(n)$. The submatrix $\mathbf{P}_4(n)$ is equivalent to the entire matrix $\mathbf{P}(n)$ in the parameter-based EKF recursion defined above.

In applying the parallel EKF recursion, there are two distinct steps, the *time* and *measurement* updates. The time update step involves propagating input signals and time-delayed recurrent node outputs through the recurrent network, computing the linearized dynamics, and propagating the error covariance. The linearized dynamics are provided by computing the *partial* derivatives of recurrent node outputs with respect to both the recurrent node outputs from the previous time step and the network's weight estimates. These partial derivatives, which are **not** recursively defined as a function of ordered derivatives from the previous time step, are then used to propagate the error covariance matrix. The net effect of these steps is that the ordered derivatives of recurrent node outputs with respect to the network's weight parameters (i.e., the RTRL data structure) become embedded in the submatrices $\mathbf{P}_2(n)$ and $\mathbf{P}_3(n)$. However, these ordered derivatives are coupled with the evolution of the error covariance matrix and do not appear to be directly accessible. On the other hand, for the parameter-based EKF formulation, the ordered derivatives of network outputs with respect to network weights are computed by the RTRL algorithm as a function of these derivatives from the previous time step. Thus, the parameter-based and parallel formulations effectively compute the same ordered derivatives, but these derivatives become embedded in the approximate error covariance matrix for the parallel formulation.

There are a number of potential advantages to performing the full parallel EKF formulation as opposed to only estimating the parameters. First, the additional computational cost for state estimation is negligible, since the computational complexities and storage requirements of the two global EKF formulations along with the corresponding derivative computations are identical (for N nodes, $O(N^4)$). In addition, it may also be convenient to perform some decoupling of the weights in either formulation. This would involve ignoring the interdependencies of mutually exclusive groups of weights, thereby leading to a block-diagonal structure for the submatrix $P_4(n)$ in the parallel formulation. Although weight decoupling does not reduce the order of the computational time complexity for either formulation, the grouping of weights by node has the effect of reducing the storage requirements to $O(N^3)$. The parallel EKF formulation may also exhibit superior performance to the parameter-based formulation because of the cross coupling of estimated states and parameters. Furthermore, the parallel EKF formulation has additional user-settable training parameters such as initial diagonal values for the covariance submatrix $P_1(0)$ and the corresponding noise covariance matrix $Q_1(n)$ that can be used to tune the training algorithm. Finally, Williams points out that the parallel formulation has theoretical appeal since it provides a principled generalization of the *teacher forcing* mechanism that is often employed in recurrent network training by gradient descent.

Although the parallel EKF formulation has a number of appealing characteristics, we have identified some apparently unresolved difficulties in its practical application. The first difficulty arises for those training problems in which there are multiple trajectories or sequences, as opposed to a single continuous trajectory of training signals. With each new trajectory, the submatrices $P_2(n)$ and $P_3(n)$ are initialized to null matrices, which has the effect of initializing to zero values the ordered derivatives of node outputs with respect to network weights. On the other hand, there is generally no need to reinitialize the submatrix $P_4(n)$ (although occasional reinitializations may be useful for escaping poor local minima). The major difficulty arises in deciding how to reinitialize the submatrix $P_1(n)$ at the beginning of a new sequence of inputs. Upon the completion of training with the parallel formulation, if the submatrix $P_1(n)$ has not converged to a matrix that is nearly zero, then the question arises as to whether it is necessary in deployment to perform some aspect of Kalman filtering of the recurrent node outputs to achieve the same level of mapping performance as observed during training.

Perhaps the most critical obstacle in the practical application of the parallel EKF formulation for real-time training of recurrent neural networks is the coupling of the RTRL data structure with the approximate error covariance matrix. This coupling appears to preclude the use of computationally efficient methods for approximating or computing the necessary ordered derivatives in real

time. A potentially useful alternative to computing the ordered derivatives in the forward direction as described by equations (14–15) for the parameter-based EKF algorithms is to approximate these derivatives by truncated backpropagation through time [20]. In addition, Sun et al. [21] describe a promising new algorithm for computing the necessary ordered derivatives based upon a Green's function method that has $O(N^3)$ complexity, which is the same order of complexity as the weight and covariance update portions of a node-decoupled EKF algorithm for recurrent network architectures. The derivatives computed by either of these two methods could be directly used by the parameter-based EKF formulations, while it is not obvious how the parallel EKF formulation would be able to take advantage of these efficiencies.

V. Summary and Conclusions

The parameter-based DEKF algorithm offers a superior alternative to simple gradient descent algorithms such as RTRL and BPTT for training of recurrent neural networks. We have demonstrated that the parameter-based DEKF algorithm is capable of training the weights of recurrent neural networks for a wide range of problems, including simple finite state machines, system identification and control problems, often with results superior to those achieved with the simpler gradient descent methods [12, 13]. We have also shown in simulation that recurrent neural network feedback controllers can be trained to provide excellent control for a variety of automotive subsystems, including control of active suspension [22], anti-lock braking [23], and engine idle speed [24]. These control problems exhibit a number of troublesome characteristics such as process nonlinearities, nonstationary dynamics, unobserved disturbances, time-varying time delays, hidden states, and asynchronous sampling. Interestingly, recurrent neural control architectures of modest complexity (on order of 10 nodes and 100 weights) were found to be sufficient for providing good control for these problems. We have also been able to apply the same training procedure to recurrent networks of larger size [13]. We have found that the imposition of *smoothness* constraints [14, 15] on the computed control signals during training can be conveniently handled in the parameter-based DEKF formulation by including additional terms in the cost function. This constraint is particularly useful for preventing oscillatory behavior in the control signals for dynamical systems with significant time delays.

We have provided here a qualitative comparison of parameter-based EKF algorithms with a parallel state and parameter EKF formulation for the training of recurrent network architectures. Although we have found that the parameter-based EKF algorithms exhibit good performance for many problems, we acknowledge that some classes of problems may benefit from a parallel EKF estimation scheme. Further work is required to address some of the apparently unresolved difficulties described above for practical application of the parallel EKF formulation.

REFERENCES

[1] R. J. Williams (1992a). *Some Observations on the Use of the Extended Kalman Filter as a Recurrent Network Learning Algorithm*, (Technical Report NU-CCS-92-1). Boston: Northeastern University, College of Computer Science.

[2] R. J. Williams (1992b). Training Recurrent Networks Using the Extended Kalman Filter. In *International Joint Conference on Neural Networks* (Baltimore 1992), vol. IV, 241–246.

[3] S. Singhal and L. Wu (1989). Training Multilayer Perceptrons with the Extended Kalman Algorithm. In *Advances in Neural Information Processing Systems 1*, (Denver 1988), ed. D. S. Touretzky, 133–140. San Mateo, CA: Morgan Kaufmann.

[4] S. C. Douglas and T. H.-Y. Meng (1991). Linearized Least-Squares Training of Multilayer Feedforward Neural Networks. In *International Joint Conference on Neural Networks* (Seattle 1991), vol. I, 307–312.

[5] G. V. Puskorius and L. A. Feldkamp (1991). Decoupled Extended Kalman Filter Training of Feedforward Layered Networks. In *International Joint Conference on Neural Networks* (Seattle 1991), vol. I, 771–777.

[6] S. Shah, F. Palmieri and M. Datum (1992). Optimal Filtering Algorithms for Fast Learning in Feedforward Neural Networks. *Neural Networks 5*, 779–787.

[7] R. J. Williams and D. Zipser (1989). A Learning Algorithm for Continually Running Fully Recurrent Neural Networks. *Neural Computation 1*, 270–280.

[8] P. J. Werbos (1990). Backpropagation Through Time: What It Does and How to Do It. *Proceedings of the IEEE 78*, no. 10, 1550–1560.

[9] M. B. Matthews (1990). Neural Network Nonlinear Adaptive Filtering Using the Extended Kalman Filter Algorithm. In *Proceedings of the International Neural Networks Conference* (Paris 1990), vol. I, 115–119.

[10] B. D. S. Anderson and J. B. Moore (1979). *Optimal Filtering*. Englewood Cliffs, NJ: Prentice-Hall.

[11] M. M. Livstone, J. A. Farrell, and W. L. Baker (1992). A Computationally Efficient Algorithm for Training Recurrent Connectionist Networks. In *Proceedings of the 1992 American Control Conference* (Chicago 1992), vol. II, 555–561.

[12] G. V. Puskorius and L. A. Feldkamp (1992). Recurrent Network Training with the Decoupled Extended Kalman Filter Algorithm. In *SPIE Vol. 1710 Science of Artificial Neural Networks* (Orlando 1992), 461–473.

[13] G. V. Puskorius and L. A. Feldkamp (1992). Model Reference Adaptive Control with Recurrent Networks Trained by the Dynamic DEKF Algorithm. In *International Joint Conference on Neural Networks* (Baltimore 1992), vol. II, 106–113.

[14] M. I. Jordan (1989). Supervised Learning and Systems with Excess Degrees of Freedom. In *Proceedings of the 1988 Connectionists Summer School* (Pittsburgh 1988), eds. D. Touretzky, G. Hinton and T. Sejnowski, 62–75. San Mateo, CA: Morgan Kaufmann.

[15] M. I. Jordan (1989). Generic Constraints on Underspecified Target Trajectories. In *International Joint Conference on Neural Networks* (Washington D.C. 1989), vol. I, 217–225.

[16] B. Fernandez, A. G. Parlos, and W. K. Tsai (1990). Nonlinear Dynamic System Identification Using Artificial Neural Networks (ANNs). In *International Joint Conference on Neural Networks* (San Diego 1990), vol. II, 133–141.

[17] A. G. Parlos, A. Atiya, K. T. Chong, W. K. Tsai, and B. Fernandez (1991). Dynamic Learning in Recurrent Neural Networks for Nonlinear System Identification. Submitted for publication.

[18] K. S. Narendra and K. Parthasarathy (1990). Identification and Control of Dynamical Systems Using Neural Networks. *IEEE Transactions on Neural Networks 1*, no. 1, 4–27.

[19] K. S. Narendra and K. Parthasarathy (1991). Gradient Methods for the Optimization of Dynamical Systems Containing Neural Networks. *IEEE Transactions on Neural Networks 2*, no. 2, 252–262.

[20] R. J. Williams and J. Peng (1990). An Efficient Gradient-Based Algorithm for On-Line Training of Recurrent Network Trajectories. *Neural Computation 2*, 490–501.

[21] G.-Z. Sun, H.-H. Chen and Y.-C. Lee (1992). Green's Function Method for Fast On-line Learning Algorithm of Recurrent Neural Networks. In *Advances in Neural Information Processing Systems 4*, (Denver 1991), eds. J. E. Moody, S. J. Hanson and R. P. Lippmann, 333–340. San Mateo, CA: Morgan Kaufmann.

[22] L. A. Feldkamp, G. V. Puskorius, L. I. Davis. Jr., and F. Yuan (1992). Neural Control Systems Trained by Dynamic Gradient Methods for Automotive Applications. In *International Joint Conference on Neural Networks* (Baltimore 1992), vol. II, 798–804.

[23] L. I. Davis, Jr., G. V. Puskorius, F. Yuan and L. A. Feldkamp (1992). Neural Network Modeling and Control of an Anti-Lock Brake System. In *Proceedings Intelligent Vehicle '92 Symposium* (Detroit 1992), 179–184.

[24] G. V. Puskorius and L. A. Feldkamp (1993). Automotive Engine Idle Speed Control with Recurrent Neural Networks. To appear in *Proceedings of the 1993 American Control Conference* (San Francisco 1993).

Constructive Learning of Recurrent Neural Networks

D. Chen[a], C.L. Giles[a,b], G.Z. Sun[a], H.H. Chen[a], Y.C. Lee[a], M.W. Goudreau[b,c]

[a]Institute for Advanced Computer Studies
University of Maryland
College Park, MD 20742

[b]NEC Research Institute
4 Independence Way
Princeton, NJ 08540

[c]Department of Electrical Engineering
Princeton University
Princeton, NJ 08544

Abstract— Recurrent neural networks are a natural model for learning and predicting temporal signals. In addition, simple recurrent networks have been shown to be both theoretically and experimentally capable of learning finite state automata [Cleeremans 89, Giles 92a, Minsky 67, Pollack 91, Siegelmann 92]. However, it is difficult to determine what is the minimal neural network structure for a particular automaton. Using a large recurrent network, which would be versatile in theory, in practice proves to be very difficult to train. Constructive or destructive recurrent methods might offer a solution to this problem. We prove that one current method, Recurrent Cascade Correlation, has fundamental limitations in representation and thus in its learning capabilities. We give a preliminary approach on how to get around these limitations by devising a "simple" constructive training method that adds neurons during training while still preserving the powerful fully recurrent structure. Through simulations we show that such a method can learn many types of regular grammars that the Recurrent Cascade Correlation method is unable to learn.

I. INTRODUCTION

Recurrent Neural Networks have been studied extensively, because of their ability to store and process temporal information and sequential signals; for a summary of these issues see [Hertz 91, Narendra 90]. For example recent studies have shown that various order recurrent networks are able to infer small regular grammars from grammatical examples [Cleeremans 89, Giles 92a, Watrous 92].

For the purpose of good generalization, Occam's Razor would likely conclude that a small a network as possible would give the best generalization; this is also in keeping with the results of systems theory [Ljung 87]. [Alon 91] has given an upper limit on the size of a first order network needed to represent a regular grammar or a state automaton. However, in practice, we often do not have enough information about the nature of the target sequence in order to decide the network size before training. In addition for a particular problem, a much smaller network than that given by the theoretical upper bound solution usually exists.

One way to solve this problem is to train different size networks and find the smallest one that learns the training sequences. In practice this can be very time consuming since each different network is trained independently and there are too many different network architectures to choose from.

Another problem associated with recurrent networks is that the training scales badly with both network and problem size. The convergence can be very slow and training errors are not always guaranteed to reduce to previously defined tolerances. By using constructive training methods, one can hope that the neural network could possibly build itself little by little, and speed up the whole training process. In this paper, we show that an existing constructive method, Recurrent Cascade Correlation, has fundamental limitations. We propose an alternative method which eliminates these limitations and give some encouraging preliminary training results.

II. SIMPLE DRIVEN RECURRENT NETWORK

For our purposes a simple driven recurrent neural network consists of three parts (figure 3). We term the recurrent network "driven" to denote that it responds

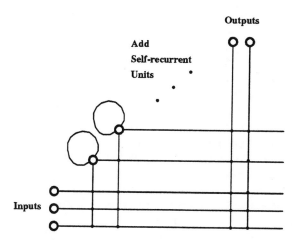

Figure 1: Recurrent Cascade-Correlation Network. The hidden neurons are self-recurrent, and only connect to previously existing neurons.

temporally to inputs. The hidden recurrent layer is activated by both the input neurons and the recurrent layer itself. The output neurons are in general activated by the input and recurrent neurons or, in a special case, by only the recurrent neurons.

Connections between layers can be first, second, or even higher orders; see [Giles 92a, Pollack 91, Sun 90, Watrous 92] for more discussion. In general, the updating rule can be written as,

$$\mathbf{S}^{t+1} = \mathcal{F}(\mathbf{W}, \mathbf{S}^t, \mathbf{I}^t)$$
$$\mathbf{O}^{t+1} = \mathcal{G}(\mathbf{U}, \mathbf{S}^t, \mathbf{I}^t).$$

where $\mathbf{I}^t, \mathbf{S}^t, \mathbf{O}^t$ are the values of input, recurrent and output neurons at time step t and $\mathbf{W}, \mathbf{U}$ are the respective connection weights. The typical learning rule uses gradient decent [Williams 89] to adjust the weights $\mathbf{W}, \mathbf{U}$ so as to minimize the error function:

$$E = \sum_t (\mathbf{T}^t - \mathbf{O}^t)^2.$$

III. "Simple" Constructive Learning

In general a constructive method dynamically changes the network structure during the training - [Gallant 86], [Hanson 90] and for a summary of other methods [Hertz 91]. In addition to the normal updating rule and learning rule of the neural network, a constructive training scheme also requires:

1. a criterion for when the changing takes place,

2. how to connect the newly created neurons to the existing system,

3. how to assign initial values to the newly added connections.

(For simplicity we ignore methods which are both constructive and destructive.) To speed up the training, we hypothesize that in addition to these criteria we must also satisfy the principle that the network preserves previously acquired knowledge *while* the network is changing. Previous work where a priori knowledge such as rules are encoded directly into recurrent networks have shown this to be the case [Frasconi 91, Giles 92b]. Various constructive learning schemes have been proposed for feed-forward networks [Ash 89, Fahlman 90, Gallant 86]. These methods find a minimal structure for the problem and reduce the computational complexity. However, to our knowledge little work besides [Fahlman 91] has focused on recurrent networks.

A. Limitations of the Recurrent Cascade-Correlation Architecture

[Fahlman 91] proposed a constructive training method — a Recurrent Cascade-Correlation (RCC) network (Figure 1). Regardless of the training procedure, this network can be topologically viewed as in Figure 2. It differs from a fully connected recurrent network in the sense that the recurrent connection of the old neurons to the newly added neurons are restricted - *i.e.* nonexistent. Even though this self recurrent restriction simplifies the training (each neuron can be trained sequentially), it *significantly* restricts the representational power of the network. We will show that this type of structure with a *sigmoid updating function* is **not** capable of representing all finite state automata.

To understand the limitations of RCC, we first examine the hard-limit threshold case, where each neuron is only allowed to take on binary values, *e.g.* $\{0, 1\}$ or $\{-1, 1\}$. Suppose we have a constant input sequence, say all 1's. The activation function of the first neuron S_1 then simplifies to

$$S_1^{t+1} = \Theta(W_{11} * S_1^t + \theta_1),$$

where Θ is the threshold function and the constant input term I is implicit. It is easy to verify that under such an update function, S_1 will either remain constant or oscillate at each time step between the two values $0, 1$ or $-1, 1$, since S_1 only depends only on its value at the previous time step. We define this oscillation at each time step as an oscillation of period 2. Oscillations that occur at two or more time steps have a period greater than 2, and a constant value is a period 1 oscillation. An example of all such sequences of period 2 or less is: $\{0000000\cdots, 1111111\cdots, 0101010\cdots\}$.

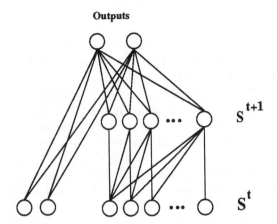

Outputs

Inputs **Hidden units with self recurrent connections**

Figure 2: Re-drawing of RCC in figure 1.
The input and output neurons are connected to all hidden recurrent neurons. The hidden neurons are not fully connected to each other.

The activation function for the nth RCC neuron S_n can be written as

$$S_n^{t+1} = \Theta(W_{n1} * S_1^{t+1} + W_{n2} * S_2^{t+1} + \cdots + W_{nn} * S_n^t + \theta_n).$$

Or,

$$S_n^{t+1} = \Theta(\Lambda + W_{nn} * S_n^t), \qquad (1)$$

where

$$\Lambda = W_{n1} * S_1^{t+1} + W_{n2} * S_2^{t+1} + \cdots + W_{n(n-1)} * S_{n-1}^{t+1} + \theta_n.$$

We prove this by induction. Assume $S_1, \cdots, S_{n-1}$ at each time step all oscillate with period 2 or remain constant. As Λ is a linear function of $S_1, \cdots, S_{n-1}$, it will at most oscillate at period 2. If Λ remains constant all the time, then S_n will be a constant or oscillate at period 2, the same as for S_1. If Λ oscillates at period 2, then by examining all 14 possible mappings of equation 1 (see Appendix), we find that S_n can only oscillate at period 2 or remains constant all the time. This proves that the binary RCC structure is not be able to represent or to simulate all possible finite state machines, *e.g.* a machine consists of part that has period greater that 2 under a same input. It can also be shown that for an analog RCC network with a constant input signal, the activities of the recurrent neurons will asymptotically become either constant or oscillate at period 2. [There results hold for both first and second order recurrent neural networks. See [Pao 89] for a discussion of order and [Lee 86] for order in recurrent networks.]

It is arguable that the analog RCC network can have more complex dynamics during the transient period. However, a typical finite state automaton can accept infinitely long strings. Thus, the RCC type of network structure (with sigmoid thresholds) will fail at some point (beyond the transient period) after a periodic input sequence is presented. For example, numerical simulations have shown the RCC network is unable to learn the simple double parity grammar. The number of added neurons grow as a function of the longest string length of the training examples!

It should be noted that the sigmoid type updating function is *essential* to the above proof. If the activity function is Gaussian or another non-monotonic shape, or if the activity function is of high order in terms of the hidden neurons, i.e. based on terms such as $S_i * S_j$; much more complicated behavior can occur and the above conclusions may not hold.

B. Simple Expanding Recurrent Neural Network

In order to get around the interconnect restriction imposed by RCC, we propose a very simple scheme to dynamically construct a recurrent network. In this method, the network is the same as the simple driven recurrent structure discussed in Section II. In this method the number of neurons in the recurrent layer is allowed to expand whenever needed. The only criterion for expansion is that the network spend some time learning. As the network is always fully-connected, it does not have the restriction of RCC. Theoretically it has been shown that a fully connected recurrent network is capable of representing any finite state automaton [Minsky 67].

The importance of using a priori knowledge in neural network learning has been described by many, see for example [Towell 90, Giles 92b, Frasconi 91]. We further assume that it is important to effectively maintain some of the networks knowledge acquired during training. To do this we require the network to be expanded smoothly, *i.e.* the newly added weights should remain zero or very small random numbers. Thus, the new network behaves very similar to the old one immediately after the expansion.

First, we present a simple example of the above method. For our example we train a recurrent neural network to be a deterministic finite state automaton. For training we use a second-order fully-recurrent neural network that uses full gradient, real-time recurrent learning [Williams 89]. For detail description see [Giles 92a]. We examine if the network can take advantage of its previous knowledge. We first train the network to learn a 10-state randomly generated deterministic finite state automaton (DFA) (figure 4) as in [Giles 92c]. We use the incremental training method, where the network reads through

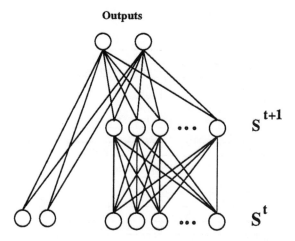

Outputs

S^{t+1}

S^t

Inputs   **Hidden fully connected recurrent units**

Figure 3: Fully recurrent neural network.
The input and output neurons are connected to all
hidden recurrent neurons.

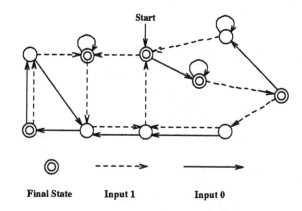

Final State   **Input 1**   **Input 0**

Figure 4: A 10-state finite state automaton, which is
randomly generated.

the ordered training samples until the accumulated error
exceeds the preset value or all training samples are classified correctly. When training with a fixed size 8 neuron fully-recurrent network, the network converged in 72
epoches after using 10000 positive and negative training
examples. However, if we train a similar network with
only 7 recurrent neurons for 150 epoches first and then
expand the network to 8 recurrent neurons, the network
takes only 32 more epoches to converge. Here an epoch
is defined as a training cycle in which the network starts
again at the beginning of the training samples after finding 5 errors. This indicates that the network does take
advantage of previous knowledge and converges faster
than a network with no a priori knowledge and random
initial weights.

Choosing the criterion for when the network expands
is very important. A simple method is to determine if the
training error reaches the local minimum. More complex
methods based on entropy measure, network capacity, or
neuron activity distribution would be more feasible.

In other preliminary experiments, we add one more
neuron to the recurrent layer after every 50 epoches, until the network learns all the training samples. This is a
very simple constructive criterion; a more sophisticated
constructive criterion might generate a smaller network.
In training very small grammars (those of [Tomita 82]),
we found that the constructive method converges very
fast when the network size grows up to the minimal size
required. However the convergence speed was not sig-

nificantly less than that obtained by training the corresponding fixed size networks. This is understandable
since for a very simple problem, the fixed size network
can learn the training samples very quickly assuming a
large enough network is provided. However, by avoiding training all different size networks, the constructive
method does appear to save time in finding the smallest
size network for each of these grammars.

IV. CONCLUSIONS

We presented some preliminary results on a "simple"
constructive learning method for recurrent neural networks. This method relies on using some of the knowledge of a partially trained neural network, and more importantly, expands the network in a fully recurrent manner. The constructive learning method permits the network to build itself up from scratch. This type of training
method is necessary when only very limited information
about the problem to be solved is available. The recurrent cascade-correlation network is certainly a step in
the right direction, but it is incapable of representing
and thus learning many finite state automata. The simple constructive method proposed avoids the limitations
of Recurrent Cascade-Correlation (RCC) networks. We
illustrate this method by learning some small grammars
of Tomita and a randomly generated 10-state grammar.
The reason this simple constructive method outperforms
RCC easily explained - the full recurrence of the growing network is preserved. Admittedly, the experiments
described are preliminary. Further experiments might
show inherent limitations in such a "simple" method,
such as uncontrolled neuron growth. Other questions are
what are good criteria for expansion? What amount of
"captured" knowledge is necessary for effective learning?
However, the lesson of maintaining the full recurrence in

the "added" neurons seems an important one, especially if the full representational power of the recurrent network is needed.

APPENDIX BINARY RECURRENT CASCADE CORRELATION NETWORK

Without loss of generality, assume the binary neuron is either 0 or 1. Recall equation 1,

$$S_n^{t+1} = \Theta(\Lambda + W_{nn} * S_n^t).$$

If Λ oscillates with period 2, *i.e.*

$$\Lambda = \begin{cases} \lambda_1 & \text{if } t = \text{odd} \\ \lambda_2 & \text{if } t = \text{even} \end{cases}$$

we can list all possible outcomes of the above equation.

Λ	S^t	S^{t+1}	possible sequences
λ_1	0	0	
λ_1	1	0	00000000···
λ_2	0	0	
λ_2	1	0	10000000···

Λ	S^t	S^{t+1}	possible sequences
λ_1	0	1	
λ_1	1	0	01010101···
λ_2	0	0	
λ_2	1	0	10010101···

Λ	S^t	S^{t+1}	possible sequences
λ_1	0	0	
λ_1	1	1	00000000···
λ_2	0	0	
λ_2	1	0	11000000···

Λ	S^t	S^{t+1}	possible sequences
λ_1	0	1	
λ_1	1	1	01010101···
λ_2	0	0	
λ_2	1	0	11010101···

Λ	S^t	S^{t+1}	possible sequences
λ_1	0	0	
λ_1	1	0	00101010···
λ_2	0	1	
λ_2	1	0	10101010···

Λ	S^t	S^{t+1}	possible sequences
λ_1	0	1	
λ_1	1	0	01010101···
λ_2	0	1	
λ_2	1	0	10101010···

Λ	S^t	S^{t+1}	possible sequences
λ_1	0	1	
λ_1	1	1	01010101···
λ_2	0	1	
λ_2	1	0	10101010···

Λ	S^t	S^{t+1}	possible sequences
λ_1	0	0	
λ_1	1	0	00000000···
λ_2	0	0	
λ_2	1	1	10000000···

Λ	S^t	S^{t+1}	possible sequences
λ_1	0	0	
λ_1	1	1	00000000···
λ_2	0	0	
λ_2	1	1	11111111···

Λ	S^t	S^{t+1}	possible sequences
λ_1	0	1	
λ_1	1	1	01111111···
λ_2	0	0	
λ_2	1	1	11111111···

Λ	S^t	S^{t+1}	possible sequences
λ_1	0	0	
λ_1	1	0	00101010···
λ_2	0	1	
λ_2	1	1	10101010···

Λ	S^t	S^{t+1}	possible sequences
λ_1	0	1	
λ_1	1	0	01101010···
λ_2	0	1	
λ_2	1	1	10101010···

Λ	S^t	S^{t+1}	possible sequences
λ_1	0	0	
λ_1	1	1	00111111···
λ_2	0	1	
λ_2	1	1	11111111···

Λ	S^t	S^{t+1}	possible sequences
λ_1	0	1	
λ_1	1	1	11111111···
λ_2	0	1	
λ_2	1	1	11111111···

Two combinations of S^{t+1}

Λ	S^t	S^{t+1}	Λ	S^t	S^{t+1}
λ_1	0	0	λ_1	0	1
λ_1	1	1	λ_1	1	0
λ_2	0	1	λ_2	0	0
λ_2	1	0	λ_2	1	1

are not listed above. This is because the linear threshold function cannot solve the XOR problem. It is easy to see that the sequence of S will either be a constant or oscillate at period 2.

REFERENCES

[Alon 91] N. Alon, A.K. Dewdney, T.J. Ott, Efficient simulation of finite automata by neural nets, *J. A.C.M.* 38, p. 495 (1991).

[Ash 89] T. Ash, Dynamic Node Creation in Backpropagation Networks, it Connection Science, vol 1, No. 4, p. 365 (1989).

[Cleeremans 89] A. Cleeremans, D. Servan-Schreiber, J. McClelland, Finite State Automata and Simple Recurrent Recurrent Networks, *Neural Computation*, 1(3), p. 372 (1989).

[Fahlman 90] S.E. Fahlman, C. Lebiere, The Cascade-Correlation Learning Architecture, *Advances in Neural Information Systems 2*, D.S. Touretzky (ed), Morgan Kaufmann, San Mateo, Ca, (1990).

[Fahlman 91] S.E. Fahlman, The Recurrent Cascade-Correlation Architecture, in *Advances in Neural Information Processing Systems 3*, R.P. Lippmann, J.E. Moody, D.S. Touretzky (eds), Morgan Kaufmann, San Mateo, Ca., p.190 (1991).

[Frasconi 91] P. Frasconi, M. Gori, M. Maggini, G. Soda, An Unified Approach for Integrating Explicit Knowledge and Learning by Example in Recurrent Networks, *Proceedings of the International Joint Conference on Neural Networks* IJCNN-91-SEATTLE, Vol. I, p. 811, (1991).

[Gallant 86] S.I. Gallant, Three Constructive Algorithms for Network Learning, in *Proceedings, 8th Annual Conference of the Cognitive Science Society*. p. 652 (1986)

[Giles 92a] C.L. Giles, C.B. Miller. D. Chen, H.H. Chen, G.Z. Sun, Y.C. Lee, Learning and Extracting Finite State Automata with Second-Order Recurrent Neural Networks, *Neural Computation*, 4(3), p. 393 (1992).

[Giles 92b] C.L. Giles, C.W. Omlin, Inserting Rules into Recurrent Neural Networks *Neural Networks for Signal Processing II, Proceedings of the 1992 IEEE-SP Workshop*, S.Y. Kung, F. Fallside, J. Aa Sorenson C.A. Kamm (eds), IEEE92TH0430-9, p.13 (1992).

[Giles 92c] C.L. Giles, C.B. Miller. D. Chen, G.Z. Sun, H.H. Chen, Y.C. Lee, Extracting and Learning an Unknown Grammar with Recurrent Neural Networks, *Advances in Neural Information Processing Systems 4*. J.E. Moody, S.J. Hanson and R.P. Lippmann (eds), Morgan Kaufmann, San Mateo, Ca., (1992).

[Hanson 90] S.J. Hanson, Meiosis Networks, in *Advances in Neural Information Processing Systems 2*, D. Touretzky (ed), Morgan Kaufmann, San Mateo, Ca., p.533 (1990)

[Hertz 91] J. Hertz, A. Krogh, R.G. Palmer, *Introduction to the Theory of Neural Computation*, Addison-Wesley, Redwood City, CA., p. 163 (1991).

[Lee 86] Y.C. Lee, G. Doolen, H.H. Chen, G.Z. Sun, T. Maxwell, H.Y. Lee, C.L. Giles, Machine Learning Using a Higher Order Correlational Network, *Physica D*, Vol.22-D, No.1-3, p. 276 (1986).

[Ljung 87] L. Ljung, *System Identification - Theory for the User*, Prentice-Hall, Englewood Cliffs, N.J. (1987).

[Minsky 67] M.L. Minsky, *Computation: Finite and Infinite Machines*, Ch 3.5, Prentice-Hall, Englewood Cliffs, N.J. (1967).

[Narendra 90] K.S. Narendra, K. Parthasarathy, Identification and Control of Dynamical Systems Using Neural Networks, *IEEE Trans. on Neural Networks*, Vol. 1, No. 1, page 4 (1990).

[Pao 89] Y-H. Pao, *Adaptive Pattern Recognition and Neural Networks*, Addison-Wesley Publishing Co., Inc., Reading, MA (1989).

[Pollack 91] J.B. Pollack, The Induction of Dynamical Recognizers, *Machine Learning*, vol 7, p. 227 (1991).

[Siegelmann 92] H.T. Siegelmann, E.D. Sontag, On the computational power of neural nets, in *Proc. Fifth ACM Workshop on Computational Learning Theory*, Pittsburgh PA, ACM Press, p. 440 (1992).

[Sun 90] G.Z. Sun, H.H. Chen, C.L. Giles, Y.C. Lee, D. Chen, Connectionist Pushdown Automata that Learn Context-Free Grammars, *Proceedings of the International Joint Conference on Neural Networks*, IJCNN-90-WASH-DC, Lawrence Erlbaum, Hillsdale, N.J., Vol I, p. 577 (1990).

[Tomita 82] M. Tomita, Dynamic Construction of Finite-state Automata from Examples Using Hillclimbing. *Proceedings of the Fourth Annual Cognitive Science Conference* p. 105 (1982).

[Towell 90] G.G. Towell, J.W. Shavlik, M.O. Noordewier, Refinement of Approximately Correct Domain Theories by Knowledge-Based Neural Networks, *Proceedings of the Eighth National Conference on Artificial Intelligence*, Boston, MA, p. 861, (1990).

[Watrous 92] R.L. Watrous, G.M. Kuhn, Induction of Finite-State Languages Using Second-Order Recurrent Networks, *Neural Computation* 4(3), p.406 (1992).

[Williams 89] R.J. Williams, D. Zipser, A Learning Algorithm for Continually Running Fully Recurrent Neural Networks, *Neural Computation*, Vol.1, No.2, p.270, (1989).

An unsupervised learning rule for vector normalization and gain control

Marc M. VAN HULLE*
Department of Brain and Cognitive Sciences
Massachusetts Institute of Technology
Cambridge, MA 02139, USA

Abstract— A neural network model is proposed with linear processing units and an unsupervised learning rule for normalizing input vectors drawn from a given probability distribution. After training the network, the gain with which the inputs are sampled is set at such a level that it yields a fixed mapping between the root of the average squared norm of the input vectors and the norm of the processing unit's outputs. Three cases of normalization are considered. The adaptive network simultaneously performs error correction and recalibration. Finally, it is shown that our learning rule solves the dual problem of Oja's single-unit unsupervised learning rule.

I. PROBLEM STATEMENT

Normalization usually involves keeping a fixed relation between a set of variables and the present value of a metric defined over them. In neural networks, normalization has been invoked in both learning and optimization applications [1,2,3,4,5] for two major reasons: First, unsupervised learning schemes using a plain Hebbian learning rule often fail to converge without some weight normalization after each weight update (as *e.g.* in [6]). Competitive learning schemes often work best with pre-normalized inputs [3], or else use some weight normalization step to determine the winning neuron (following the scalar product metric, see *e.g.* [7] and Kohonen's rule [2] in case of a linear network implementation) or to prevent the weights from growing without bound [8]. In case of supervised learning, input normalization is used as a preprocessing technique to ensure zero-error convergence for constructive algorithms [9,10], and as a way to accomodate both open and closed decision regions in the same network [10,11,12]. Second, the limited dynamical range to which nonlinear units respond requires the system to adapt itself to the current in-

put distribution. Light adaptation [13,14,15] and contrast adaptation [16] are notorious examples of this type of normalization (see also [1]). Adaptation can be regarded as a simple example of a system's ability to perform *recalibration*: the capacity of a system to change and readjust itself to environmental perturbations. In addition, the system must display the ability to readjust itself following perturbations of its internal variables, *i.e.* to perform *error correction*. In network terminology, recalibration and error correction are generally referred to as robustness against (internal and external) perturbations.

Several unsupervised learning rules exist that yield normalized weight vectors [2,17,18,19,20] or normalized input vectors [1]. (We will treat both from a common standpoint.) However, in this contribution, we consider an additional requirement for normalization: the output vectors must be *proportional* to the input vectors, at least after convergence. More formally, normalization is defined here as maintaining a fixed relation between an average metric M on the input signal $\xi = [\xi_i]$ and the output $V = [V_i]$. If c denotes the fixed relation, then the gain W of the system is always set at $W = c/M$. In particular, M equals the root of the average squared Euclidian norm of a set of N input vectors ξ^μ with $\mu = 1, ..., N$. We will show how a simple unsupervised learning rule can successfully perform normalization of inputs drawn from an arbitrary probability distribution. In the following three sections, three cases will be considered. First, the general multi-dimensional case with N input vectors. Here the learning rule is introduced and its convergence shown. Then two special cases are considered: 1) vector normalization and 2) uni- and multi-dimensional normalization called *gain control*. The former considers the convergence of the rule towards a unit-length vector in case $N = 1$. The relevant ability here is error correction. The latter refers to the case of a time-varying input. The relevant ability is recalibration. It is shown under what condition our rule leads to similar results as Ullman and Schechtman's rule [21], a rule introduced for modelling perceptual phenom-

*E-mail: marc@psyche.mit.edu Present address: Laboratorium voor Neuro- en Psychofysiologie, K.U.Leuven, Campus Gasthuisberg, Herestraat, B-3000 Leuven, BELGIUM

ena associated with visual adaptation. The correspondence with Oja's single-unit unsupervised learning rule [17] is established. It is then argued that our rule solves the dual problem of Oja's rule. Finally, due to its simplicity and genericness, our rule could easily be integrated into network models that require explicit weight- or input normalizations. This way, one could avoid invoking an algorithmic step in an otherwise self-organizing network model and perform normalization "on line" and, hence, facilitate implementation in neural hardware.

II. GENERAL MULTI-DIMENSIONAL CASE

Consider a network of n linear units with output $V = [V_i]$, $i = 1, ..., n$, receiving input from a vector ξ^μ with components ξ_i^μ, $i = 1, ..., n$. Assume that there are N such vectors ξ^μ, $\mu = 1, ..., N$, and that they comprise a set Ξ, *i.e.* the network's environment; the input vectors could be drawn from a multivariate probability distribution $P(\xi)$. The output of the network is a weighted version of the input:

$$V^\mu = W\xi^\mu, \tag{1}$$

with W a positive scalar called gain. After seeing enough elements of the set Ξ, W should converge to a value representing a fixed mapping between the root of the average squared Euclidian norm of the input vectors and the Euclidian norm of the output vectors V:

$$W = \frac{c}{\sqrt{<\sum_i \xi_i^{\mu 2}>_\mu}}, \quad \text{so that} \tag{2}$$

$$|V| = W\sqrt{<\sum_i \xi_i^{\mu 2}>_\mu} = c, \tag{3}$$

with c the desired fixed value and with $<.>_\mu$ the average taken over the elements of the set Ξ. Note that the ξ^μ are weighted equally though in general a probability $P(\xi^\mu)$ could be inserted in the definition. The learning rule we propose for the modification of W during each training step is

$$\Delta W = \eta(cW - \sum_j V_j \xi_j^\mu W^2) = \eta(cW - \sum_j \xi_j^{\mu 2} W^3)$$

$$= \eta(cW - |\xi^\mu|^2 W^3) \tag{4}$$

with η the learning rate. We further put $c = 1$ without loss of generality. The mathematical advantage of this rule is that there is an associated cost function:

$$C = -0.5 \sum_\mu W^2(1 - 0.5 |\xi^\mu|^2 W^2) \tag{5}$$

so that the average of ΔW corresponds to gradient descent on the cost surface C:

$$<\Delta W>_\mu = -\eta \frac{\partial C}{\partial W} = \eta \sum_\mu W(1 - |\xi^\mu|^2 W^2). \tag{6}$$

To prove the normalization capacity of the learning rule, we consider the average of ΔW at equilibrium:

$$<\Delta W>_\mu = 0 = <\eta W(1 - \sum_i \xi_i^{\mu 2} W^2)>_\mu \tag{7}$$

from which follows that:

$$W = \frac{1}{\sqrt{<\sum_i \xi_i^{\mu 2}>_\mu}}. \tag{8}$$

As with most learning algorithms either an incremental or a batch update scheme is possible. In the former, W is updated after the presentation of each input sample; in the latter, W is updated after the average change $<\Delta W>_\mu$ is determined. We will consider both possibilities in this contribution. Figures 1A and B show the results of a computer simulation using batch update on a set of N samples drawn from a 2D Gaussian distribution. The starting value of W is 0.01 though any positive value yields the same end-result. However, larger starting values lead to faster convergence. Evidently, for negative starting values, W converges to $-\frac{1}{\sqrt{<\sum_i \xi_i^{\mu 2}>_\mu}}$. Finally, since output normalization (eq. (3)) is performed without requiring square root and devision, but only analog multiplication, our rule is amenable to an easy neural hardware implementation.

III. VECTOR NORMALIZATION

In this special case, a single vector ξ^μ is applied to a network comprising n units. W then simply converges to the inverse of the Euclidian norm of ξ^μ. Hence, the Euclidian norm of the output vector of the network, V, converges to unity as well:

$$|V|^2 = \sum_i V_i^2 = \sum_i W^2 \xi_i^{\mu 2} = W^2 \sum_i \xi_i^{\mu 2} = \frac{\sum_i \xi_i^{\mu 2}}{\sum_i \xi_i^{\mu 2}} = 1. \tag{9}$$

This way, the output vector V returns the normalized input vector ξ^μ. The starting value of W may be any nonzero value: the norm will always converge to unity. The error correction ability is easily verified: If for the converged network $W = \frac{1}{|\xi^\mu|}$ is replaced by $W = \frac{1}{|\xi^\mu + \varepsilon|}$ where ε is some internal error, we can easily verify that if ε increases W, $\Delta W < 0$ and if it decreases W, $\Delta W > 0$, so that the effect of the error is indeed corrected. Finally, an example of vector normalization is given in Fig. 2.

IV. GAIN CONTROL

A. Uni-dimensional case

We now consider the case in which there is a single unit and a single but time-varying input signal. The set Ξ can now be regarded as an ordered set of samples taken from a time-varying signal $\xi[t]$ at discrete time steps $t \equiv \mu$

A

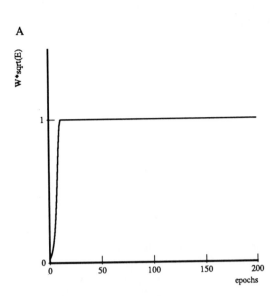

B

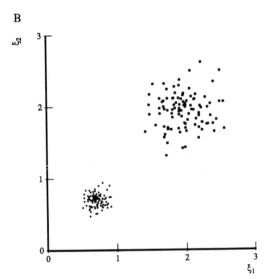

Figure 1: Normalization performance during 200 batch updates (epochs) on 100 samples drawn from a 2D Gaussian. A. Evolution of normalization performance is expressed in terms of $W[epoch]\sqrt{E}$ with $E = \mathrm{E}\{\xi_1^2 + \xi_2^2\}$ and which is known *a priori*. Convergence towards unity is complete within 12 epochs. The remaining error is negligible and only limited by the number representation used. The learning rate $\eta = 0.5$; the starting value of W is 0.01. B. Distribution of the 100 samples before (large dots) and after normalization (small dots). The original distribution is centered around (2,2) and has a standard deviation of 0.25 in both dimensions.

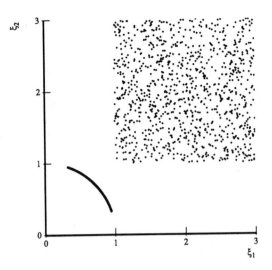

Figure 2: Vector normalization of 1000 samples distributed uniformly in the square $\{\xi_1 \in [1,3]; \xi_2 \in [1,3]\}$. After normalization, the sample vectors lie on the circle segment the arc of which spans the original sample distribution. For each sample vector, convergence is complete after 15 iterations. The error is only limited by the number representation used. The learning rate $\eta = 0.5$; the starting value of W is 0.01.

with equal time intervals between subsequent time steps. The sampled time signal is assumed to obey a stationary probability distribution $P(\xi[t])$. The gain is updated after the presentation of each input sample (incremental update scheme) and converges to

$$W = \frac{1}{\sqrt{<\xi^{\mu 2}>_\mu}} = \frac{1}{\sqrt{<\xi[t]^2>_t}}. \qquad (10)$$

This means that although the network is memoryless, it ensures a gain setting over time at a level for which the root of the average squared measured signal is mapped onto a fixed unity level ($c = 1$). This ability is called *gain control* in this context.

The recalibration property is then reflected by the capacity of the system to adapt W when the environment Ξ changes: Ξ's with different $<\xi^2>$'s lead to different W's. The crucial aspect of recalibration is the speed with which this occurs. Clearly, the speed increases with η, the learning rate, though too large values of η lead to more or less pronounced oscillations in W. The addition of a momentum term dampens these oscillations but at the expense of a much slower convergence rate. We found it more useful to lower η for such cases then to resort to a momentum term and have an extra parameter in the network.

Interestingly, our rule can lead to similar results as Ullman and Schechtman's rule (referred to with subscript U)

$$\triangle W_U = \eta(c_U - W_U \xi), \qquad (11)$$

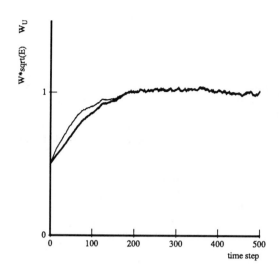

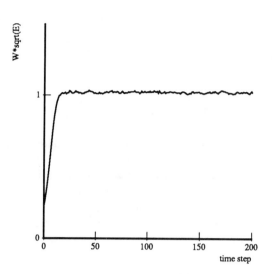

Figure 3: Evolution of gain normalization performance on a 1D time signal (incremental update scheme). Comparison between our rule (thick line) and Ullman and Schechtman's rule (thin line). As described in Fig. 1 of [21], the time signal $\xi[t]$ is a random variable distributed uniformally in the interval [1,2], the learning rate $\eta = 0.01$, the fixed mapping level $c_U = 1.5$, and the gain W_U is initialized at 0.5. The vertical axis is expressed in $W\sqrt{E}$ units for our rule, with $E = \text{E}\{\xi^2\}$, and gain units W_U for Ullman and Schechtman's rule. The gain W has been initialized so as to start the iterations from the same position on the vertical axis as Ullman and Schechtman's rule; fixed mapping level $c = 1$. The average relative error is defined as $\mid 1 - W[t]\sqrt{E}\mid$ and equals 0.047 in the time interval [200,500]. The average relative error for Ullman and Schechtman's rule is calculated in a similar way as the average of $\mid 1 - W_U \mid$. The error is similar to ours. Both rules converge within 200 time steps.

Figure 4: Evolution of gain control performance on a 100 dimensional time signal $(\xi_1, ..., \xi_{100})$ (incremental update scheme). At each time step t, a signal component $\xi_i[t]$ is drawn from a (stationary) Gaussian distribution with standard deviation 0.25 and with a mean value drawn from a uniform distribution in the interval [0,4] at the onset. The average relative error is defined as in Fig. 3 and equals 0.026 in the interval [100,200]. Convergence is complete after 15 time steps. The learning rate $\eta = 0.2$; the starting value of W is 0.01.

for cases in which the variance of the probability distribution governing the time-varying input signal is small. To see this, we rewrite $< \xi^2 >$ as: $< \xi^2 > = \sigma_{\xi^2} + < \xi >^2$, with σ_{ξ^2} the variance on ξ; the gain of our network becomes at equilibrium (for $c = 1$): $W = \frac{1}{\sqrt{\sigma_{\xi^2} + <\xi>^2}}$, and in case σ_{ξ^2} is small it approaches: $W = \frac{1}{<\xi>}$, which is exactly the result of Ullman and Schechtman's rule (for $c_U = 1$). Figure 3 shows an example of this using their data and parameters (see caption of Fig. 3 for details). The result is indeed similar but our rule has the additional advantage that it can operate even for distributions with zero mean; we only need to have a nonzero $< \xi^2 >$ value. Hence our rule is more general than Ullman and Schechtman's rule.

B. Multi-dimensional case

We can easily extend the previous case to higher-dimensional input signals. Figure 4 shows an example in case of a 100 dimensional time signal. Notice the fast and correct convergence towards unity. Such a performance was not attainable with the multi-dimensional extension of Ullman and Schechtman's rule: for a 3D example input signal, the gain already converged towards 1.4 instead of the desired 1.0 (see their Fig. 4).

V. Correspondence with Oja's rule

In case of Oja's single-unit unsupervised learning rule [17] we have a single linear unit with input vector $\xi = [\xi_i]$, weight vector $W = [W_i]$ and output: $V = \sum_i W_i \xi_i$. The unit is trained on vectors ξ^μ drawn from an input distribution $P(\xi^\mu)$ and the rule for adapting the connection weights W_i is:

$$\triangle W_i = \eta V(\xi_i^\mu - V W_i) = \eta(V\xi_i^\mu - \sum_j W_j \xi_j^\mu V W_i). \quad (12)$$

1205

In our case, the network's outputs V_i change as:

$$\triangle V_i = \eta(W\xi_i^\mu - \sum_j \xi_j^{\mu 2} W^3 \xi_i^\mu) = \eta(W\xi_i^\mu - \sum_j V_j \xi_j^\mu W V_i) \tag{13}$$

with the adaptation performed by adjusting the gain W. Upon comparing both rules, we see that our W and V_i correspond to Oja's V and W_i, respectively. In other words, our network solves the dual problem: our rule determines the W that normalizes ξ^μ while Oja's rule determines the W_i that normalizes W. Indeed, at equilibrium, $| W | = 1$ with Oja's rule with W in the direction that maximizes $< V^2 > = < (\sum_i W_i \xi_i^\mu)^2 >$ (first principal component direction). Evidently, the results are completely different. Indeed, the equilibrium condition $< \triangle V > = 0$ corresponding to Oja's case would, in our case, imply that the average of W^2 would be equal to:

$$< W^2 > = \frac{< \xi_i^\mu >}{< \sum_j \xi_j^{\mu 2} \xi_i^\mu >}, \quad \forall i, \tag{14}$$

which is clearly different from Oja's corresponding result in V^2 and cannot be satisfied in general.

VI. Conclusion

In this contribution, we have introduced a learning rule that performs normalization in a multi-dimensional system in an adaptive way. Two special cases have been distinguished that focussed on two different aspects of robustness: error correction and recalibration. The advantages of our learning rule are: 1) the same rule leads to vector normalization or to gain control, depending on the nature of the network's input distribution; 2) normalization is performed without divisive components as is usually done; 3) the existence of a lower-bounded cost function which ensures convergence; and 4) normalization is proportional and works even if $< \xi^\mu >_\mu = 0$, as opposed to Ullman and Schechtman's rule. Finally, we have shown the correspondence of our rule with Oja's single-unit learning rule.

Acknowledgement

M.M.V.H. is a senior research assistant of the National Fund for Scientific Research (Belgium). He is also supported by a Fulbright-Hays grant-in-aid and a NATO research grant. He is on leave from the K.U.Leuven, Laboratorium voor Neuro- en Psychofysiologie, Campus Gasthuisberg, Herestraat, B-3000 Leuven, Belgium.

References

[1] S. Grossberg, "Adaptive pattern classification and universal recoding: I Parallel development and coding of neural feature detectors," *Biol. Cybern.*, vol. 23, pp. 121-134, 1976.

[2] T. Kohonen, *Self-organization and associative memory*, 3rd ed. Berlin: Springer, 1989.

[3] J. Hertz, A. Krogh, and R.G. Palmer, *Introduction to the theory of neural computation*. Reading MA: Addison-Wesley, 1991, ch. 9.

[4] J. Moody, and C. Darken, "Fast leaning in networks of locally-tuned processing units," *Neural Computation*, vol. 1, pp. 281-294, 1989.

[5] D.E. Van den Bout, and T.K. Miller, "Improving performance of the Hopfield-Tank neural network through normalization and annealing," *Biol. Cybern.*, vol. 62, pp. 129-139, 1989.

[6] J. Rubner, and K. Schulten, "Development of feature detectors by self-organization," *Biol. Cybern.*, vol. 62, pp. 193-199, 1990.

[7] G. Carpenter, and S. Grossberg, "A massively parallel architecture for a self-organizing neural pattern recognition machine," *Computer Vision, Graphics and Image Processing*, vol. 37, pp. 54-115, 1987.

[8] D.J. Willshaw, and C. von der Malsburg, "How patterned neural connections can be set up by self-organization," *Proc. R. Soc. Lond. B*, vol. 194, pp. 431-445, 1976.

[9] J. Saffery, and C. Thornton, "Using stereographic projection as a preprocessing technique for Upstart," *Proc. IJCNN'91, Seattle*, vol. 2, pp. 441-446, 1991.

[10] D. Martinez, M. Chan, and D. Estève, "Construction of layered quadratic perceptrons," *Proc. Neuro-Nimes'92, Nîmes, France*, pp. 655-665, 1992.

[11] G.D. Wilensky, and N. Manukian, "The projection neural network," *Proc. IJCNN'92, Baltimore*, vol. 2, pp. 358-367, 1992.

[12] T. Denoeux, and R. Lengellé, "Initialization of back-propagation neural networks with prototypes", *Neural Networks*, to appear.

[13] J.J. Koenderink, W.A. van der Grind, and M.A. Bouman, "Foveal information processing at photopic luminances," *Kybernetik*, vol. 8, pp. 128-144, 1971.

[14] D. Tranchina, J. Gordon, and R.M. Shapley, "Retinal light adaptation - evidence for a feedback mechanism", *Nature*, vol. 310, pp. 314-316, 1984.

[15] R. Chappell, and K.-I. Naka, "Sensitivity transformation for vertebrate vision," *Vis. Neurosci.*, vol. 6, pp. 371-374, 1991.

[16] I. Ohzawa, G. Sclar, and R.D. Freeman, "Contrast gain control in the cat's visual system," *Journal of Neurophysiology*, vol. 54, pp. 651-667, 1985.

[17] E. Oja, "A simplified neuron model as a principal component analyzer," *J. Math. Biol.*, vol. 15, pp. 267-273, 1982.

[18] E. Oja, "Neural networks, principal components, and subspaces," *International J. Neural Systems*, vol. 1, pp. 61-68, 1989.

[19] T.D. Sanger, "Optimal unsupervised learning in a single-layer linear feedforward neural network," *Neural Networks*, vol. 2, pp. 459-473, 1989.

[20] P. Földiák, "Adaptive network for optimal linear feature extraction," *Proc. IJCNN'89, Washington*, vol. 1, pp. 401-405, 1989.

[21] S. Ullman, and G. Schechtman, "Adaptation and gain normalization," *Proc. R. Soc. Lond. B*, vol. 216, pp. 299-313, 1982.

Is LVQ Really Good for Classification? – An Interesting Alternative

W. Poechmueller, M. Glesner, H. Juergs
Darmstadt University of Technology
Institute for Microelectronic Systems
Karlstrasse 15
D-6100 Darmstadt, Germany

Abstract — **Nearest neighbor classifiers are well-known classifiers in the world of application oriented engineers. Their benefits are simplicity, model free classification and good performance. Learning vector quantization (LVQ) developed by Kohonen is a neural network based method to find a good set of reference vectors to be stored as a nearest neighbor classifier's reference set. In this paper an efficient method of finding reference vectors along class boundaries instead of finding vectors representing class distribution, as LVQ does, will be described. A quantitative comparison with LVQ is done.**

I. INTRODUCTION

Nearest neighbor classifiers are simple model free classifiers that are easy to handle an show good classification results even compared with neural network methods [1]. Thereby, a set of vectors with wellknown class affiliation serves as a reference set to classify unknown vectors.

In the following, two tests will be used to benchmark algorithm performance. *Test 1* consists of linearly distributed two-dimensional vectors belonging to two nonoverlapping classes. *Class 1* (500 vectors) lies in area $(0.1, 0.1) \times (0.4, 0.9)$ with a small satellite in area $(0.8, 0.7) \times (0.9, 0.8)$ (see Fig. 1 left). Gaussian distributed vectors belonging to two classes, however, are used in *Test 2*. Thereby, 150 vectors of *Class 1* are restricted to a rather small area around center $(0.6, 0.6)$ with a variance of $\sigma_1^2 = 0.2$, whereas vectors of *Class 2* (1500 vectors) are spread widely around center $(0.4, 0.4)$ with variance $\sigma_2^2 = 8.0$ (see Fig. 1 right). Thus, both classes are overlapping with *Class 1* being completely embedded in *Class 2*. In subsequent figures vectors belonging to *Class 1* are represented by small crosses and vectors from *Class 2* are indicated by small rectangles.

II. LEARNING VECTOR QUANTIZATION

Learning Vector Quantization (LVQ) is an adaptive algorithm proposed by Kohonen [4] to find an optimal set of reference vectors for classification purposes. Thereby, during learning, reference vectors are shifted into an optimal position, whereas during recall a nearest neighbor classification technique is used. In the original approach from Kohonen, reference vectors are shifted from a random initial distribution to a final position that describes the probability density function $p(\vec{x})$ of the set X of n-dimensional training vectors $\vec{x} \in I\!R^n$. Thus, an optimal placement of reference vectors is a placement such that the local point density of reference vectors $\vec{w}^k$ (i.e. the number of $\vec{w}^k$ falling in a small volume $I\!R^n$ centered at the observed point $\vec{x}$) is as close as possible to the probability density function of the vectors in the training set [4]. Derived from this idea, with the modification of punishing wrong classifications, an algorithm for reference vector adaptation is given by

$$\vec{w}_{t+1}^k = \begin{cases} \vec{w}_t^k + \alpha 1_t \left[\vec{i}_t - \vec{w}_t^k \right] \\ \quad \text{if } ||\vec{i}_t - \vec{w}_t^k|| \text{ min. and } cl(\vec{w}_t^k) = cl(\vec{i}_t) \\ \vec{w}_t^k - \alpha 2_t \left[\vec{i}_t - \vec{w}_t^k \right] \\ \quad \text{if } ||\vec{i}_t - \vec{w}_t^k|| \text{ min. and } cl(\vec{w}_t^k) \neq cl(\vec{i}_t) \\ \vec{w}_t^k \qquad \text{else} \end{cases}$$

(1)

with k-th reference vector $\vec{w}_t^k$, learning parameters $\alpha 1_t$ and $\alpha 2_t$ (which may be constants or functions of time indicated by index t), and currently applied input vector $\vec{i}_t$ [4] ($cl(\vec{w}_t^k)$ returns the class vector $\vec{w}_t^k$ is belonging to). Several main disadvantages can be observed by applying this algorithm:

1. The fact that a winning reference vector moves away leaving other reference vectors back which thus will never get a chance to win.

2. Using an LVQ-algorithm, the number of reference vectors for each class has to be defined in advance (no adaption of number of reference vectors to actual needs).

3. LVQ-algorithms place reference vectors to copy the probability distribution of training vectors. However, this is not a very efficient method in combination with a nearest neighbor classification method

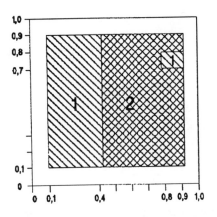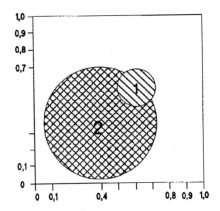

Fig. 1: *Test* 1 (left) and *Test* 2 (right) used as benchmarks for algorithm performance

during recall phase. The more reference vectors are used to represent a class with sufficient accuracy, the more reference vectors will be placed in the class center especially if training vectors are distributed similar to a gaussian distribution (which seems to be a realistic assumption for many practical problems) and only few at class boundaries.

4. The LVQ-algorithm is computational intensive.

In the following, these problems will be referenced as *Problem 1* through *Problem 4*. All these effects may be found in the two tests sketched in Fig. 2. *Test 1* was performed with all 16 reference vectors (8 per class) initialized near the origin. *Problem 1* is obvious since only one reference vector belonging to *Class 2* moved through *Class 1* area into *Class 2* and no reference vector of *Class 1* was able to cross *Class 2* area to reach the small satellite of *Class 1*. Not more than 3 *Class 1* reference vectors moved into *Class 1* area. A total of 12 reference vectors remains in the origin and does not contribute to form class boundaries as accurate as possible. Even a random initialization of reference vectors before learning cannot solve this problem since most of the vectors in wrong class areas after initialization will either be forced to leave the input vector space or remain in wrong class areas. For *Test 2* an initialization with random distributed reference vectors was chosen (right part of Fig. 2). Reference vectors moved into correct positions, however, 8 reference vectors are too many to represent *Class 1* but too few to represent *Class 2* (*Problem 2*). All reference vectors of *Class 1* are forced together but cannot be placed in one point due to respective repulsion (thus, *Class 1* area becomes too large). To cope with this problem, Kohonen recommends to form classification boundaries by using a weighted Voronoi tesselation (vector distances are weighted by average inverse distances of reference vectors at class borders). Then, class borders are formed by Appollonian hyperspheres but this means more complex computations during recall [4].

The mentioned drawbacks are wellknown and devia-

tions of the basic LVQ-algorithm emerged trying to compensate some of the most severe problems. To cope with *Problem 1* deSieno proposed to include a punishment for reference vectors winning too often [3]. Thereby, a punishment of winning reference vector is done by adding a punishment distance b_k to distance $d_k = d(\vec{i}_t, \vec{w}_t^k) = ||\vec{i}_t - \vec{w}_t^k||$ between currently applied training vector $\vec{i}_t$ and neareast reference vector $\vec{w}_t^k$. This punishment is calculated as

$$b_k = \epsilon_t \cdot d_{kmax} \cdot (N \cdot p_k - 1) \qquad (2)$$

with ϵ_t influencing punishment strength, d_{kmax} an estimated normalization factor, N the number of reference vectors per class, and p_k the winning frequency of reference vector k. Winning frequency p_k is calculated by

$$p_{k,t+1} = \begin{cases} (1-\gamma) \cdot p_{k,t} & \text{if } cl(\vec{w}_t^k) \neq cl(\vec{i}_t) \\ (1-\gamma) \cdot p_{k,t} + \gamma & \text{if } cl(\vec{w}_t^k) = cl(\vec{i}_t) \end{cases} \qquad (3)$$

with γ a constant. The adaptation of the winning reference vector is then done according to

$$\vec{w}_{t+1}^{inclass} = \begin{cases} \vec{w}_t^{inclass} + \alpha 1_t \cdot (\vec{i}_t - \vec{w}_t^{inclass}) \\ \qquad \text{if } \vec{w}_t^{inclass} = \vec{w}_t^{glob} \\ \vec{w}_t^{inclass} + \alpha 2_t \cdot (\vec{i}_t - \vec{w}_t^{inclass}) \\ \qquad \text{if } \vec{w}_t^{inclass} \neq \vec{w}_t^{glob} \end{cases} \qquad (4)$$

and

$$\vec{w}_{t+1}^{glob} = \vec{w}_t^{glob} - \alpha 3_t \cdot (\vec{i}_t - \vec{w}_t^{glob}) \text{ if } cl(\vec{w}_t^{glob}) \neq cl(\vec{i}_t). \quad (5)$$

Thereby, $\alpha 1_t$, $\alpha 2_t$, and $\alpha 3_t$ are learning rates, $\vec{w}_t^{inclass}$ is the nearest reference vector to input vector $\vec{i}_t$ belonging to the same class $(cl(\vec{w}_t^{inclass}) = cl(\vec{i}_t))$, and $\vec{w}_t^{glob}$ is the nearest vector to $\vec{i}_t$ regardless its class affiliation.

This algorithm reduces *Problem 1*, now all 16 reference vectors are used to represent classes, but cannot avoid the other problems as may be seen from the examples sketched in Fig. 3. Still the satellite area of *Class 1* is not found

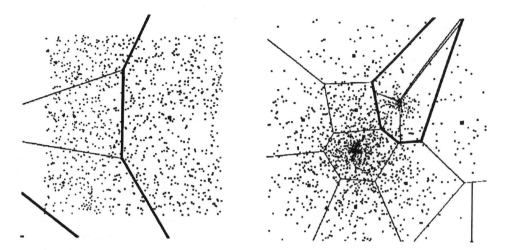

Fig. 2: Behaviour of original LVQ-algorithm on *Test 1* (reference vectors initialized near the origin) and *Test 2* (random initialization of reference vectors)

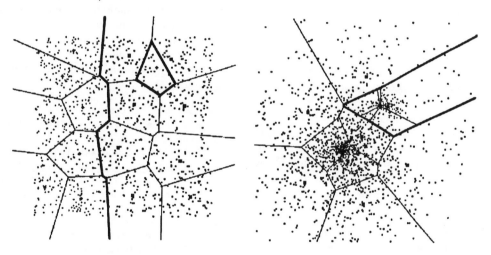

Fig. 3: *Test 1* (left) and *Test 2* (right) with deSieno's algorithm

in *Test 1* and *Class 1* area is too much extended in *Test 2* (*Problem 2*). Furthermore, in both, *Test 1* and *Test 2*, some reference vectors do not contribute in building class boundaries. This is the case if a vector's Voronoi cell does not touch the class boundary. After learning this vector does not affect classification and thus is an unnecessary load (*Problem 3*).

To comply more with Bayes' philosophy, Kohonen proposed a refinement of the LVQ-algorithm called LVQ 2 [4], [2]. Thereby, a window of certain width is defined around the midplane between two class distinct reference vectors $\vec{w}^i$ and $\vec{w}^j$. If $cl(\vec{w}^i)$ is the nearest class but $\vec{i}$ belongs to $cl(\vec{w}^j) \neq cl(\vec{w}^i)$ where $cl(\vec{w}^j)$ is the next-to-nearest class and if $\vec{i}$ falls into the window around midplane, reference vector adaptations are then made according to

$$\vec{w}^i_{t+1} = \vec{w}^i_t - \alpha 1_t \cdot \left(\vec{i}_t - \vec{w}^i_t\right) \qquad (6)$$

$$\vec{w}^j_{t+1} = \vec{w}^j_t + \alpha 1_t \cdot \left(\vec{i}_t - \vec{w}^j_t\right) \qquad (7)$$

$$\vec{w}^k_{t+1} = \vec{w}^k_t. \qquad (8)$$

However, this algorithm results only in a refinement of reference vector placement and thus in a refinement of class boundaries. Furthermore, applying it for many iterations, the placement may become even worse. Therefore, in practical applications a combination of LVQ with punishment (Equations 2-5) and LVQ 2 is used. Such a combination of 20000 learing steps of LVQ proposed by de Sieno followed by further 10000 training steps of LVQ 2 were applied to benchmarks *Test 1* and *Test 2* (with random initialization before learning). The results were similar to those depicted in Fig. 3.

To cope with problems caused by a predefined fixed number of reference vectors for each class (*Problem 2*) Poirier et al. proposed a modified LVQ algorithm that dynamically increases the number of used reference vectors if the closest reference vector $\vec{w}^{inclass}$ belonging to the same class as the currently applied input vector $\vec{i}$ is too far away ($d(\vec{w}^{inclass}, \vec{i}) \geq \sigma$) [5]. This reduces *Problem 2* since the number of reference vectors per class or class cluster is adapted as requested by local demand. Furthermore, it is more efficient with respect to the nearest neighbor classification philosophy since more reference vectors will be placed near class boundaries. The reason for that is that most wrong classifications causing the creation of a new reference vector will occur near class boundaries, thus reducing *Problem 3*. However, the creation of a new reference vector can make previously generated vectors superfluous which then should be deleted. This is not done by the algorithm so it will not work optimally with respect to *Problem 3*. Dynamic Vector Quantization (DVQ) is reported to work better than LVQ 2 [5].

III. DATA REDUCED NEAREST NEIGHBOR PHILOSOPHY

In this section we want to present a "learning method" for nearest neighbor classification which is well suited for this type of classifier. Since the nearest neighbor of a vector to be classified decides about its class affiliation, it would be an unnecessary load to store vectors in a nearest neighbor classifier's reference set that are far away from class boundaries. To store only vectors near to class boundaries, we took the algorithm described subsequently. As in the LVQ simulations we used the Euclidean distance as metric. Vectors near class boundaries are then found by the following simple algorithm:

```
1:  copy all training vectors in training list
2:  initialize reference vector list (empty)
3:  set training list pointer on first element in
       training list
4:  take element where training list pointer is
       pointing to and classify it
5:  if classification is correct goto 6
       else insert training vector into
       reference vector list
6:  increase training list pointer (now pointing on
       next element)
7:  if not end of training list goto 4
8:  set reference list pointer on first element in
       reference list
9:  remove the vector where reference list pointer
       is pointing at and classify removed vector
10: if vector is not classified correctly it
       must be reinserted in reference list
11: increase reference list pointer (now pointing
       on next element)
12: if not end of reference list goto 9
13: if no reference list change and no training list
       change between lines 2 and 12 goto 14
       else goto 3
14: end
```

This algorithm is similar to DVQ in that way that reference vectors are dynamically created (inserted in reference list) in steps 4 through 7 if wrong classifications occur but we are generating a new reference vector in any case regardless of a threshold distance $d(\vec{i}, \vec{w}^k) \neq \sigma$. However, during steps 9 through 11 we delete old reference vectors which became unnecessary by the creation of new reference vectors. This is a very efficient method to avoid unnecessary reference vectors placed in class centers. Fig. 4 shows the application of this algorithm to *Test 1*. With a simple reduction many vectors near to class boundaries are found (19 vectors belonging to *Class 1* and 18 belonging to *Class 2*) which then may be stored as a nearest neighbor classifier's reference vectors (left part of Fig. 4). Through this procedure not only a data reduction is obtained but also generalization effects since the class boundary is now formed by fewer vectors. However, the number of reference vectors to be stored may further be decreased by exploiting a feature of the reduction algorithm. The more separated two classes are (the larger the distance between them is) the less will be the number of remaining vectors after reduction. Now in *Test 1*, classes may be separated by eliminating vectors in the boundary region by a cleaning algorithm.

```
1:  copy all training vectors in training list
2:  set training list pointer on first element
       of training list
3:  look for k nearest neighbors of vector where
       training list pointer is pointing at
4:  if j (majority) of k nearest neighbors belong
       to other class than observed vector, then
       mark vector
5:  if not end of training list then increase
       training list pointer and goto 3
6:  delete all marked vectors
```

We eliminated all vectors which are not having at least 8 neighbors belonging to their own class in the scope of their next 10 nearest neighbors. Applying the reduction algorithm to the remaining, cleaned vector set results in the situation depicted in the right part of Fig. 4. Only 5 vectors belonging to *Class 1* and 6 vectors belonging to *Class 2* represent the classes. Very good generalization is obtained. The Voronoi tesselation shows only some few vectors of the underlying training set on the wrong side of the formed class boundaries, which is a result of generalization. Also the test with a recall set shows nearly the same classification performance as the reference vectors in the left part of Fig. 4 (see Table 1).

Unfortunately, problems with simple pure reduction occur if classes overlap. Then, many vectors in the overlapping region will be stored as may be seen from the left image of Fig. 5, forming a complexly shaped class boundary. There, the reduction algorithm was applied to benchmark *Test 2*. Again the previously described cleaning method helps to solve the problem.

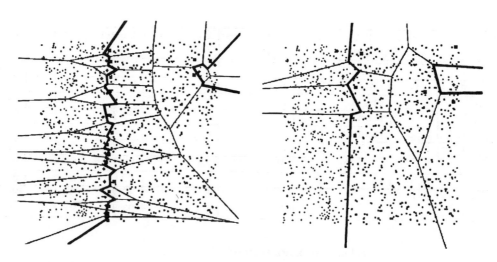

Fig. 4: Reference vector reduction algorithm (left) and combined cleaning/reduction algorithm (right) applied to *Test 1*

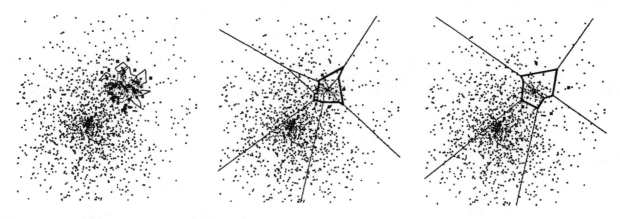

Fig. 5: Application of cleaning and reduction algorithms on data from *Test 2*

By first applying this cleaning algorithm and then the reduction algorithm very good results may be obtained. Fig. 5 shows in its center image the result obtained by first cleaning (all vectors eliminated which do not have at least 3 neighbors belonging to their class within their next 5 nearest neighbors) and then reducing training data from *Test 2*. The result are 5 reference vectors belonging to *Class 1* and 6 reference vectors belonging to *Class 2*. Generalization and the number of reference vectors finally found may be influenced by cleaning parameters. In the right part of Fig. 5 we eliminated all vectors that did not have at least 12 neighbors of the same class within the scope of their next 15 nearest neighbors during the cleaning phase. This results in a wider cleaning of the overlapping area with a wider separation of remaining vector classes. After applying the reduction algorithm there remained only 2 vectors of *Class 1* and 5 vectors of *Class 2*. The numerical classification results of the recall set can be taken from Table 1.

IV. A QUALITATIVE AND QUANTITATIVE COMPARISON TO LVQ

The proposed reduction algorithm generates reference vectors only if needed and locates them near to class boundaries. If classes are widely separated only few vectors will be stored up to an extreme of only one reference vector per class if there is a large distance between classes, whereas the class boundary is built up with fine granularity by many vectors if the classes are facing each other with very short distance. By means of the cleaning algorithm the distance between classes may be increased or overlapping areas erased, thus reducing the number of reference vectors (compare left and right part of Fig. 4) to be stored and thus increasing generalization. Only two parameters must be chosen in the "cleaning" procedure, namely the majority proportion in the k-nearest neighbor search whether to mark or not a vector, which will be deleted later and the size of the environment where the algorithm is looking for neighbors. This is a big difference

Algorithm	Clean	Initiali-zation	Test	References Class 1	References Class 2	Correct Class 1	Correct Class 2	Correct total
LVQ	-	origin	1	8	8	96.0	76.4	86.7
LVQ	-	random	2	8	8	99.3	91.0	91.8
LVQ (de Sieno)	-	origin	1	8	8	94.2	92.0	91.0
LVQ (de Sieno)	-	random	2	8	8	99.3	92.6	93.2
LVQ (d.S.)/LVQ 2	-	random	1	8	8	95.3	93.8	94.5
LVQ (d.S.)/LVQ 2	-	random	2	8	8	96.6	92.5	92.9
Reduction	-	-	1	19	18	98.7	98.4	98.5
Clean/Red.	8-10	-	1	5	6	99.6	97.2	98.3
Clean(few)/Red.	3-5	-	2	5	6	87.2	97.4	96.5
Clean(much)/Red.	12-15	-	2	2	5	93.3	97.2	96.8

Table 1: Numerical simulation results

to more elaborate LVQ-algorithms as LVQ from deSieno or LVQ 2, where many parameters influence algorithm behaviour. Furthermore, the described reduction and cleaning algorithms were much faster than LVQ in our simulations. Convergence of reduction was always obtained after few iterations (4-8 iterations). In our simulations we used the NeuralWorks Professional II/Plus environment with the following parameters to simulate LVQ networks:

LVQ: $\alpha 1 = \alpha 2 = 0.05$, 20000 learning steps

LVQ (deSieno): $\alpha 1 = 0.05$, $\alpha 2 = \alpha 3 = 0.04$, $\gamma = 0.001$, $\epsilon = 0.3$, 20000 learning steps

LVQ 2: $\alpha 1 = \alpha 2 = 0.02$, window width $0.4 \cdot ||\vec{w}^i - \vec{w}^j||$, 10000 learning steps

For numerical results we independently generated a training and a recall set of vectors with the same statistical parameters, each.

In the following we will regard numerical simulation results obtained by applying previously described algorithms to data from *Test 1* and *Test 2*. Recall sets generated independently from training sets served to obtain recall results stated in Table 1. Column *Clean* of this table gives the cleaning parameter if cleaning was used. A parameter of e.g. *8-10* means that each vector, which does not have at least 8 neighbors belonging to its class in its 10 neighbors comprising vicinity, will be deleted.

In all cases total classification accuracy of LVQ-algorithms was inferior to that obtained by our simple algorithms. We also changed the number of reference vectors of LVQ networks, however this did not improve results. Major problem of LVQ in *Test 2* is that the rather small *Class 1* area becomes too large if represented by several reference vectors adapted by LVQ technique (which may easily be recognized from good *Class 1* recognition but very bad *Class 2* results compared with our approach). Even LVQ simulations with 30 reference vectors per class did not yield better results but showed clearly a wasteful placement with many reference vectors located in class

centers or far away from class boundaries. In addition we evaluated the total correct classifiction rates of some conventional classifiers. We obtained 91.7% (*Test1*) and 82.7% (*Test2*) with an Euclidean distance classifier, 91.8% (*Test1*) and 82.5% (*Test2*) with a Mahalanobis classifier, 93.0% (*Test1*) and 90.9% (*Test2*) with a linear polynomial classifier and 95.4% (*Test1*) and 90.5% (*Test2*) with a quadratic polynomial classifier.

All described algorithms may work on data of arbitrary dimensions using an arbitrary metric for vector comparison.

REFERENCES

[1] C. Windsor (editor), *The Performance of Neural Network and Conventional Algorithms in the Classification of Generic Representations of some Real Problems*, Internal Report ANN90R02 of ESPRIT Project 2092 "ANNIE", January 1990

[2] T. Kohonen, J. Kangas, J. Laaksonen, K. Torkkola, *LVQ-PAK: The Learning Vector Quantization Program Package*, Technical Report from the LVQ Programming Team of the Helsinki University of Technology, Laboratory of Computer and Information Science, Rakentajanaukio 2 C, SF-02150 Espoo, Finland, 31 January 1992

[3] D. DeSieno, "Adding a Conscience to Competitive Learning", *Proceedings of the Second Annual IEEE International Conference on Neural Networks*, Volume 1, 1988

[4] T. Kohonen, *Self-Organization and Associative Memory*, Third Edition, Springer, 1989

[5] F. Poirier, A. Ferrieux, "DVQ: Dynamic Vector Quantization - An Incremental LVQ", *Proceedings of the International Conference on Artificial Neural Networks ICANN'91*, Volume 2, pp. 1333-1336, Helsinky, 1991

Fast Non-Linear Dimension Reduction

Nandakishore Kambhatla and Todd K. Leen
Department of Computer Science and Engineering
Oregon Graduate Institute of Science and Technology
19600 N.W. von Neumann Drive, Beaverton OR 97006-1999

Abstract—

This paper presents a new algorithm for non-linear dimension reduction. The algorithm builds a *piece-wise linear* model of the data. This piece-wise linear model provides compression that is superior to the *globally linear* model produced by principal component analysis. On several examples the piece-wise linear model also provides compression that is superior to the *global non-linear* model constructed by a five-layer, autoassociative neural network. Furthermore, the new algorithm trains significantly faster than the autoassociative network.

I. Introduction

Pattern recognition systems typically involve high-dimensional feature vectors. However, classifiers that receive high-dimensional feature vectors can be slow to train, and may generalize poorly due to the large number of model parameters. These problems can be ameliorated by dimension-reduction techniques.

Dimension reduction techniques aim to map high-dimensional feature vectors onto lower-dimensional vectors, maintaining sufficient information to discriminate between object classes. This is achieved by identifying and reducing statistical redundancy in the original feature set.

Principal component analysis (PCA) is a classical statistical technique used for data analysis and dimension-reduction. In PCA dimension reduction, the original n-dimensional space is projected onto the m-dimensional *linear subspace* $(m < n)$ spanned by the eigenvectors of the data's correlation or covariance matrix corresponding to the largest eigenvalues [1, 2, 3, 4]. One can choose the target dimension m by specifying the tolerable mean square error (MSE) in the reduced representation.

Since PCA is based on second moments it is un-able to detect and eliminate higher-order redundancies in the data. In effect, the PCA projection models the original data as an m-dimensional Gaussian *signal* plus $n - m$ *noise* degrees of freedom. The components of the dimension-reduced vectors form global coordinates on the m-dimensional hyperplane spanned by the principal correlation eigenvectors. The original n-dimensional data vectors lie *near* this hyperplane in a least MSE sense.

This global, linear subspace model can fail to be optimal in several ways. As a simple example, suppose that the data lies on, or near, a *curved* p-dimensional submanifold of R^n. Projecting the data onto a p-dimensional *linear* subspace can result in a large error in the representation. To achieve a low error one must increase the target dimension to m, with $m > p$. Thus, one is forced to represent the data in a space of higher dimension than the number of intrinsic degrees of freedom (p in this example). Under such circumstances, *non-linear* dimension reduction can provide better compression than PCA.

This paper presents a new algorithm for non-linear dimension reduction. The basic idea is to construct a *locally linear* model of the input data. We demonstrate that our locally linear model can produce more accurate encodings than both PCA and the *global nonlinear* model produced by a five-layer autoassociative network. Furthermore, the locally-linear model can be significantly quicker to train than the autoassociative network.

II. Global Nonlinear Dimension Reduction

Several researchers [5, 6, 7] have used three-layer feedforward autoassociative networks to perform dimension reduction. These networks consist of an input layer that receives the raw data vectors $x \in R^n$, a hidden layer with $m < n$ nodes, and an output layer whose node activities we denote by $x' \in R^n$. The network weights and biases are trained by error backpropagation with the target outputs equal to the inputs $x' = x$. If the training is successful, the network approximates an identity mapping on the set of input vectors. Since the hidden layer has *fewer* nodes than the input and output layers, the network is forced to develop a compact (i.e. lower dimensional) representation of the data in the hidden layer.

For three-layer networks, auto-associative training is equivalent to a PCA projection. Baldi and Hornik [8] consider three-layer auto-associative networks with *linear* node activation. They show that the transformation performed by the trained network is an orthogonal projection onto the space spanned by the leading m eigenvectors of the input's covariance matrix. Bourlard [9] and Funahashi [10] extend this work, showing that even with *non-linear* nodes in the hidden layer a three-layer autoassociative network cannot achieve compression superior to PCA.

Recently, several researchers have realized that *five-layer* autoassociative networks *can* improve on PCA [11, 12, 13, 14]. These networks have three hidden layers. The first and third hidden layers of nodes have non-linear response, and are referred to here as the *mapping layers*. The $m < n$ nodes of the second hidden layer have linear response. The activities of these nodes form the compressed representation. We refer to this layer as the *representation layer*.

The activities of the nodes in the representation layer form coordinates on a, generally curved, submanifold of the input space. The second mapping layer maps these coordinate values back into R^n. The network must pick these coordinate mappings to cover the entire domain of the input data. We thus refer to five-layer autoassociative networks as a *global, nonlinear* compression technique.

III. LOCALLY LINEAR DIMENSION REDUCTION

An alternative to laying down a single *global* coordinate system that covers a submanifold of the input space is to lay down *local* coordinate patches; with each patch responsible only for a small region of the input space. If the regions are small enough, then one can locally approximate the data manifold as a hyperplane. Within such regions, PCA is sufficient. This suggests a *locally linear* model for the data. [1]

A. VQPCA

In our implementation we use a vector quantizer (VQ) to define the regions for the local PCA. The disjoint regions defined by the VQ are called *Voronoi cells*. We use

a standard competitive learning algorithm [17, and references therein] with Euclidean distortion measure, to train the VQ. The training algorithm places reference vectors (network weights) at the mean of the data points that fall in each Voronoi cell. We also implemented the partitioning using a hierarchical multi-stage vector quantizer [18]. The advantage of a multi-stage architecture is that we effectively obtain N Voronoi cells by training fewer than N weights. For example, using a two stage vector quantizer with N weights in each level, we effectively obtain N^2 Voronoi cells by training only $2N$ weights. We refer to the hybrid algorithm of clustering and local PCA as VQPCA.

To summarize, the model is constructed in two phases:

1. Train a VQ with N reference vectors, or weights, $(r_1, \ldots r_N)$.

2. Perform a *local* PCA within each Voronoi cell. For each cell V_i, the local covariance matrix $CM_i \equiv E_i[\,(x - r_i)(x - r_i)^T\,]$ is computed, where the expectation is over all training vectors that fall in V_i. Compute the eigenvectors $(e_1^i, \ldots, e_n^i)$ for each CM_i. [2]

Finally, a target dimension m is chosen (identical for all V_i). Each data point $x \in V_i$ is projected onto the leading m eigenvectors of CM_i to give local linear coordinates $z = (e_1^i \cdot x, \ldots, e_m^i \cdot x)$.

The compressed representation for each data point x consists of the index i of the Voronoi cell in which x falls, together with the m component vector z. The data is reconstructed from this representation according to

$$x' = r_i + \sum_{k=1}^{m} z_k\ e_k^i. \tag{1}$$

We use the MSE to assess the accuracy of the compressed representation. To facilitate interpreting the error as a percentage of the signal strength, we report a normalized MSE defined as

$$\mathcal{E}_{norm} = \frac{E\left[\,\|x - x'\|^2\,\right]}{E\left[\,\|x\|^2\,\right]} \tag{2}$$

where the expectation $E[\cdot]$ is over the points in the data set.

IV. EXPERIMENTAL RESULTS

In this section we compare the performance of VQPCA with five-layer networks (hereafter referred to as 5LNs),

---

[1] While this work was in progress, we became aware of the use of *local* PCA in several related contexts. Broomhead [15] suggests the use of local PCA, together with scaling arguments, to determine the dimension of signals arising from chaotic dynamical systems. In earlier work, Fukunaga [16] proposed an interactive algorithm that uses a local PCA to find the intrinsic dimension of data sets. The goal of our work is to provide dimension reduction of data using an algorithm that develops a locally linear data model.

[2] We computed the eigensystems using standard matrix techniques [19]. Alternatively one could use a neural network algorithm such as that given in [20].

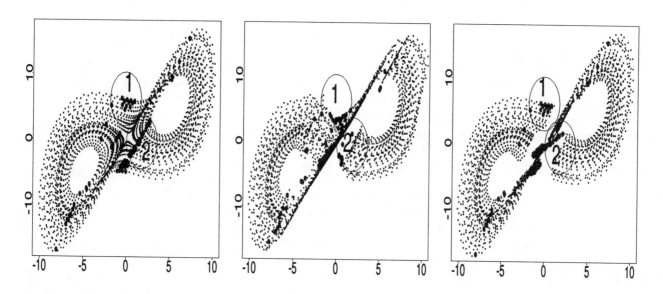

Figure 1: Lorenz attractor data : (a) Original data set, (b) Reconstructed data set from a 5LN-BFGS encoding and (c) Reconstructed data set from a VQPCA encoding. The darker points are those for which the 5LN had its squared error greater than 1.5.

and with PCA (computed from the data's covariance matrix) The first example is a low-dimensional problem that graphically contrasts compression using global coordinates with compression using local coordinates. The other examples deal with compression of speech signals.

We compare the algorithms in terms of the reconstruction errors and training times. All errors reported in this section are in terms of $\mathcal{E}_{norm}$ defined in (2). The 5LNs are trained using conjugate gradient descent (hereafter referred to as 5LN-CGD) or a quasi-Newton second order method (the BFGS algorithm [19]; hereafter referred to as 5LN-BFGS). We use the same number of nodes in both the mapping layers (first and third hidden layers) in order to limit the search in the space of network architectures. The optimal value of the number of nodes in the mapping layers, is estimated by varying it over a range of values, and choosing the value for which the test set error is lowest. Similarly, we estimate the optimal number of Voronoi cells for VQPCA by varying it over a range of values and then choosing the value for which the test set error is lowest. We implement the clustering for VQPCA using a flat VQ or a hierarchical multistage VQ.

A. A Geometrical Example

In this example, data from numerical integration of the Lorenz equations [21] (3-dimensional vectors) is compressed to a 2-dimensional representation. Figure 1(a) shows a two dimensional view of 2800 points on an orbit asymptotic to the attractor. Over much of the attractor, the data is well-located by two coordinates. However in

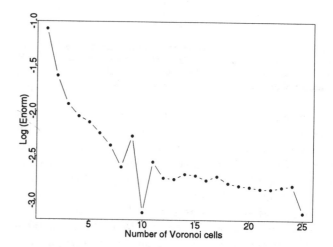

Figure 2: The variation of the logarithm of the reconstruction error $\mathcal{E}_{norm}$ (log base 10) with respect to the number of Voronoi cells for VQPCA for the Lorenz data set.

the region where the two spiral wings of attractor join, the data more nearly fills 3-space. In this transition region the orbits become inclined to the plane of each wing.

We ran experiments with 5LNs (both 5LN-CGD and 5LN-BFGS) configured as 3-mp-2-mp-3, with mp varying from 5 to 50 in increments of 5. We obtained the smallest reconstruction error $\mathcal{E}_{norm}$ with $mp = 15$ for a 5LN trained with the BFGS algorithm. For VQPCA, we varied the number of Voronoi cells from 1 to 25, and obtained the least error with 10 Voronoi cells. However the error with 10 Voronoi cells was anomalously *low* (see Figure 2), and we are therefore reporting the error for VQPCA with 22 cells.

Figure 1(b) shows the data reconstructed from a 2-dimensional representation generated by a 5LN (5LN-BFGS) with 15 nodes in the mapping layers. The 5LN fails to obtain an accurate encoding for the points lying near the transition regions between the two wings of the attractor. For example, it is clear from the figure that the 5LN fails badly in the regions marked 1 and 2. The 5LN attempts to cover the attractor with a single 2-dimensional coordinate system. In the transition regions, the data more nearly fills 3-space, so the encoding has a high error here. This geometric distortion is not limited to the transition regions, but spreads into the wings. This is clearly seen in Figure 1(b). Presumably this spreading occurs because the transformations constructed by each layer of the network are smooth.

Architecture	$\mathcal{E}_{norm}$	Training Time (in seconds)
PCA	0.08345	5
5LN	0.00266	8,330
VQPCA	0.00139	56

Table 1: Reconstruction errors and training times for a 2-D compression of the Lorenz data set by different architectures. The 5LN (5LN-BFGS) reported here had 40 nodes in the mapping layers, while the VQPCA reported here was with 22 Voronoi cells.

As seen in Figure 1(c), VQPCA does much better. This is because it is a purely local procedure, so the mismatch between the 2-dimensional model and the structure of the data in the transition regions does not affect the encoding in the adjacent regions. Hence for all the Voronoi cells except the ones which lie right in the transition regions, the compression is very accurate. This advantage is reflected in the errors $\mathcal{E}_{norm}$ reported in Table 1. The table also reports the time (in Sparc 2 cpu seconds), required to construct the encoding model. Note the tremendous time advantage of VQPCA, relative to the 5LNs.

B. Speech Compression

In these set of experiments, we compress speech signals using VQPCA, 5LNs and PCA. The data sets consist of the vowel portions extracted from the isolated utterances of letters and continuous speech. Each input vector consists of the lowest 32 discrete Fourier transform (DFT) coefficients (spanning the frequency range 0-4kHz), time-averaged over the central third of the sonorant (sounds produced solely by the vibration of the vocal chords).

It is widely recognized that sonorants are distinguished by the frequencies of the lowest *three* resonances of the vocal tract, called formants. A compressed encoding of

two or three dimensions should be able to capture the formant frequencies. We therefore conducted experiments compressing the 32-dimensional input data down to 2 and 3 dimensions.

We varied the free parameters in the algorithms over a range of values, and estimated the optimal value by a value for which the test set error was lowest. For 5LNs trained with conjugate gradient descent (5LN-CGD), we varied the number of nodes in the mapping layers from 5 to 50 in increments of 5. However for 5LNs trained with the second order method (5LN-BFGS), the increased amount of storage space required makes it non feasible for larger networks. Hence, for 5LN-BFGS, we varied the number of nodes in the mapping layers from 5 to 25 in increments of 5. All errors reported for 5LNs are the best of three runs with different random initializations for the weights.

Similarly, we varied the number of Voronoi cells for VQPCA from 1 to 50. For the multistage VQPCA (VQPCA-MS), we used a configuration of N weights in the first level and N weights in the second level (denoted by NxN). This effectively results in a partitioning of the input space into N^2 Voronoi cells. In the experiments described below, we varied N from 2 to 10.

B.1. The ISOLET database

The first data set that we used consists of isolated utterances of the letters A,E,F,O and R, spoken by both males and females, from the ISOLET database [22]. The training set contained 225 utterances. The test set contained 75 utterances from speakers not represented in the training set.

Tables 2 and 3 summarize the relative performance of PCA, 5LN (CGD and BFGS) and VQPCA with flat and multi-stage clustering in terms of compression accuracy, and training times. We note that using VQPCA-MS, we obtained an error .6-.8 times the error obtained by using the 5LNs (either 5LN-CGD or 5LN-BFGS). Moreover, training the VQPCA-MS was 16-48 times faster than training the 5LNs (5LN-CGD or 5LN-BFGS). In separate

Architecture	$\mathcal{E}_{norm}$	Training Time (in seconds)
PCA	0.0623	5
5LN-CGD	0.0566	2,609
5LN-BFGS	0.0523	3,845
VQPCA	0.0352	866
VQPCA-MS	0.0349	80

Table 2: Reconstruction errors (for the test set) and training times for 2-D compression of the ISOLET data. The 5LN-CGD had 40 nodes in the mapping layers while the 5LN-BFGS had 10 nodes in the mapping layers. The VQPCA was with 46 Voronoi cells. The VQPCA-MS had a two-level 8x8 configuration.

Architecture	$\mathcal{E}_{norm}$	Training Time (in seconds)
PCA	0.04502	5
5LN (CGD)	0.04089	1,287
5LN (BFGS)	0.03795	2,910
VQPCA	0.03008	850
VQPCA-MS	0.03013	80

Table 3: Reconstruction errors (for the test set) and training times for 3-D compression of the ISOLET data. Both the 5LN-CGD and the 5LN-BFGS had 10 nodes in the mapping layers. The VQPCA was with 45 Voronoi cells. The VQPCA-MS had a two level 8x8 configuration.

experiments, we found that using the encodings generated by VQPCA with flat clustering, we were able to achieve a higher classification accuracy than with the encodings generated by 5LNs or PCA.

B.2. The TIMIT database

The second data set we used was from the TIMIT [23] database. The data set consists of the 12 monothongal vowels (/iy/, /ih/, /eh/, /ae/, /ix/, /ax/, /ah/, /uw/, /uh/, /ao/, /aa/, and /er/) extracted from continuous speech from both males and females. The diphthongs were excluded as they exhibit spectral change which makes them inappropriate to use in experiments using time-averaged spectral coefficients. The training set contained 1200 vectors. The test set contained 816 vectors taken from utterances spoken by speakers not represented in the training set.

Tables 4 and 5 summarize the relative performance of PCA, 5LN (CGD and BFGS) and VQPCA (with various clustering schemes) in terms of compression accuracy, and training times. We note that training the VQPCA-MS was 12-136 times faster than training the 5LNs (5LN-CGD or 5LN-BFGS). Moreover, using VQPCA-MS, we obtained an error of .6-.7 times the error obtained by using 5LN-CGD or 5LN-BFGS. In separate experiments, we again

Architecture	$\mathcal{E}_{norm}$	Training Time (in seconds)
PCA	0.00606	11
5LN (CGD)	0.00619	2,107
5LN (BFGS)	0.00561	12,663
VQPCA	0.00362	1,454
VQPCA-MS	0.00350	168

Table 4: Reconstruction errors (for the test set) and training times for 2-D compression of the TIMIT data. The 5LN-CGD had 20 nodes in the mapping layers while the 5LN-BFGS had 10 nodes in the mapping layers. The VQPCA was with 50 Voronoi cells. The VQPCA-MS had a two level 9x9 configuration.

Architecture	$\mathcal{E}_{norm}$	Training Time (in seconds)
PCA	0.00473	11
5LN (CGD)	0.00480	2,861
5LN (BFGS)	0.00440	22,879
VQPCA	0.00325	2,086
VQPCA-MS	0.00311	168

Table 5: Reconstruction errors (for the test set) and training times for 3-D compression of the TIMIT data. The 5LN-CGD had 15 nodes in the mapping layers while the 5LN-BFGS had 20 nodes in the mapping layers. The VQPCA was with 43 Voronoi cells. The VQPCA-MS had a two level 10x10 configuration.

found that using the encodings generated by VQPCA with a flat clustering, we were able to achieve a higher classification accuracy than with the encodings generated by 5LNs or PCA.

V. Discussion

We have presented a new hybrid algorithm (VQPCA) for non-linear compression. VQPCA approximates the data distribution with a set of local hyperplanes. The location and the distribution of this set captures the large scale, non-linear structure of the data, while coordinates on the hyperplanes capture the local variations.

We have compared VQPCA with five-layer networks, and with PCA. For the examples that we presented, both of the non-linear techniques (VQPCA and five-layer networks) have a definite advantage over PCA for accurate compression. In general, the advantage offered by a *non-linear* technique will depend on the structure of the data. Our results indicate that VQPCA can generate more accurate encodings, and can take significantly less time to train, than five-layer networks.

Issues that remain to be explored include establishing criteria for selecting the number of Voronoi cells and the target dimension. Information theoretic criteria can presumably be used to select these parameters. Allowing compression to different dimensions in different Voronoi cells should further enhance the efficiency of compression for storage/transmission purposes.

Acknowledgements

We would like to thank Professors Ronald Cole and Mark Fanty for continued interest in this work, and for access to speech data and tools.

References

[1] Satosi Watanabe. Karhunen-Loeve expansion and factor analysis, theoretical remarks and applications. In *Transactions of the 4th Prague Conference on Information Theory, Statistical Decision Functions and Random Processes*, pages 645–660, 1965.

[2] S Watanabe. Feature compression. In J. T. Tou, editor, *Advances in information Systems Science, vol. 3*, pages 63–111. Plenum, 1970.

[3] P.A. Devijner and J. Kittler. *Pattern Recognition, a Statistical Approach*. Prentice / Hall, Englewood Cliffs, New Jersey, 1982.

[4] E. Oja. *Subspace Methods of Pattern Recognition*. John Wiley & Sons Inc., New York, 1983.

[5] Garrison W. Cottrell and Janet Metcalfe. EMPATH: Face, emotion, and gender recognition using holons. In R. Lippmann, John Moody, and D. Touretzky, editors, *Advances in Neural Information Processing Systems 3*, pages 564–571. Morgan Kauffmann, 1991.

[6] Garrison W. Cottrell, Paul Munro, and David Zipser. Learning internal representations from gray-scale images: an example of extensional programming. In *Proceedings of the Ninth Annual Cognitive Science Society Conference, Seattle, Wa*, pages 461–473, 1987.

[7] B.A. Golomb, D.T. Lawrence, and T.J. Sejnowski. Sexnet: A neural network identifies sex from human faces. In R. Lippmann, John Moody, and D. Touretzky, editors, *Advances in Neural Information Processing Systems 3*, pages 572–577. Morgan Kauffmann, 1991.

[8] Pierre Baldi and Kurt Hornik. Neural networks and principal component analysis: learning from examples without local minima. *Neural Networks*, 2:53–58, 1989.

[9] H. Bourlard and Y. Kamp. Auto-association by multilayer perceptrons and singular value decomposition. *Biol. Cyb.*, 59:291–294, 1988.

[10] Ken-ichi Funahashi. On the approximate realization of identity mappings by three-layer neural networks. Technical report, Toyohashi University of Technology, Department of Information and Computer Sciences, 1990. Translation of Japanese paper in Denshi Joho Tsushin Gakkai Ronbunshi, Vol. J73-A, No. 1, 1990, pp 139-145.

[11] Shiro Usui, Shigeki Nakauchi, and Masae Nakano. Internal color representation acquired by a five-layer neural network. In O. Simula T. Kohonen, K. Makisara and J. Kangas, editors, *Artificial Neural Networks*. Elsevier Science Publishers, North-Holland, 1991.

[12] E. Oja. Data compression, feature extraction, and autoassociation in feedforward neural networks. In *Artificial Neural Networks*, pages 737–745. Elsevier Science Publishers B.V. (North-Holland), 1991.

[13] Mark A. Kramer. Nonlinear principal component analysis using autoassociative neural networks. *AIChE Journal*, 37:233–243, 1991.

[14] Aran Namphol, Mohammed Arozullah, and Steven Chin. Higher order data compression with neural networks. In *Proceedings of the IJCNN*, pages I 55–I 59, June 1991.

[15] D. S. Broomhead. Signalprocessing for nonlinear systems. In Simon Haykin, editor, *Adaptive Signal Processing, SPIE Proceedings Vol. 1565*, pages 228–243. SPIE, July 1991.

[16] Keinosuke Fukunaga and David R. Olsen. An algorithm for finding intrinsic dimensionality of data. *IEEE Transactions on Computers*, C-20(2):176–183, 1971.

[17] Stanley C. Ahalt, Ashok Krishnamurthy, Prakoon Cheen, and Douglas Melton. Competitive learning algorthms for vector quantization. *Neural Networks*, 3:277–290, 1990.

[18] Biing-Hwang Juang and A.H. Gray Jr. Multiple stage vector quantization for speech coding. In *Proceeding of the IEEE International Conference on Acoustics and Signal Processing*, pages 597–600, 1982.

[19] W.H. Press, B.P. Flannery, S.A. Teukolsky, and W.T. Vetterling. *Numerical Recipes – the Art of Scientific Computing*. Cambridge University Press, Cambridge / New York, 1987.

[20] T. Sanger. An optimality principle for unsupervised learning. In D.S. Touretzky, editor, *Advances in Neural Information Processing Systems 1*. Morgan Kauffmann, 1989.

[21] John Guckenheimer and Philip Holmes. *Nonlinear Oscillations, Dynamical Systems, and Bifurcations of Vector Fields*, volume 42 of *Applied Mathematical Sciences*. Springer-Verlag, 1983.

[22] Ron Cole, Yeshwant Muthusamy, and Mark Fanty. The ISOLET spoken letter database. Technical Report CSE 90-004, Oregon Graduate Institute of Science & Technology, March 1990.

[23] W.M. Fisher and G.R. Doddington. The darpa speech recognition research database : specification and status. In *Proceedings of the DARPA Speech Recognition Workshop*, pages 93–99, Palo Alto, CA, 1986.

Error potentials for self-organization

Tom M. Heskes and Bert Kappen

Department of Medical Physics and Biophysics,

University of Nijmegen, Geert Grooteplein 21,

6525 EZ Nijmegen, The Netherlands,

e-mail: tom@mbfys.kun.nl

Abstract— **We give an error potential for self-organizing learning rules. The gradient of this error potential leads to the well-known learning rule of Kohonen, except for the determination of the "winning" unit. The existence of an error potential facilitates a global description of the learning process. A one-dimensional topological map is treated as an example.**

I. Introduction

Sensory maps are a crucial first step in the information processing of the brain. The external information is represented in a orderly, topology-preserving manner, i.e., neighbouring units in the sensory map represent similar inputs. The formation of these maps is a process of self-organization for which several learning paradigms have been suggested [1, 2]. The proposal of Kohonen [3] does not aim at the modelling of all biological details, but tries to capture the most important features of self-organizing processes. Basically, this algorithm works as follows. Given a certain input vector from the environment, the unit with the smallest Euclidian distance to this vector is called the "winner." The weight vector of this unit and, to some extent, its neighbouring units, are moved towards the input vector. After this learning step, another input vector is drawn at random from the environment, etcetera. The properties of this learning procedure are studied in great detail [4, 5, 6]. Recently, a lot of effort is devoted to the search for an energy function that is minimized by the learning rule [7, 8, 9]. The existence of such an energy function or error potential facilitates a description of the global performance of the learning procedure [10]. The best possible state is the global minimum of the error potential, undesired (meta)stable configurations are simply local minima. In self-organizing learning rules

This work was partly supported by the Dutch Foundation for Neural Networks and the Canon Foundation in Europe.

possible local minima are topological defects like twists and kinks [11].

The definitions in Sec. II will be used in Sec. III to investigate whether it is possible to find an error potential for the original Kohonen learning rule. In Sec. IV we go the other way around. We start with a well-defined error potential and try to derive an on-line learning procedure. An example, kinks in a one-dimensional map, will be treated in Sec. V. Implications and further lines of research are discussed in Sec. VI.

II. The learning procedure

The network consists of n units labeled $1, \ldots, i, \ldots, n$. To each unit we ascribe an m-dimensional weight vector $\vec{w}_i$. The combination of all weight vectors is the N-dimensional state vector $\mathbf{W} = (\mathbf{w}_1, \ldots, \mathbf{w}_i, \ldots, \mathbf{w}_n)^T$, so $N = n \times m$. An on-line learning procedure, a repetition of the following three steps, takes care of the adaptation of this state vector.

1. *Pick an input vector from the environment.*

   This is why the learning procedure is called on-line: the network state is adjusted at each presentation of a training pattern. The environment Ω is a set of m-dimensional input vectors $\vec{x}$ with probability density function $\rho(\vec{x})$. The average of an arbitrary function $q(\vec{x})$ with respect to this environment Ω is written

$$\langle q(\vec{x}) \rangle_\Omega \stackrel{\text{def}}{=} \int d^m x \, \rho(\vec{x}) \, q(\vec{x}) \,.$$

2. *Determine the winning unit.*

   We ascribe a "winning error" $g_i(\mathbf{W}, \vec{x})$ to each unit i. The unit with the smallest winning error is the "winner." For Kohonen's learning rule the winning error is the Euclidian distance between the input vector and the weight vector of the unit, i.e.,

$$Kohonen: \quad g_i(\mathbf{W}, \vec{x}) = \frac{1}{2} \left\| \vec{x} - \vec{w}_i \right\|^2 \,. \quad (1)$$

For a nice mathematical description of this determination of the winner, we define, for any arbitrary vector $\mathbf{q}$, the following average with respect to the winning error (for notational convenience we will drop the arguments $\mathbf{W}$ and $\vec{x}$)

$$\langle\langle q\rangle\rangle_\beta \stackrel{\text{def}}{=} \frac{\sum\limits_{i=1}^n q_i \exp[-\beta g_i]}{\sum\limits_{i=1}^n \exp[-\beta g_i]} . \qquad (2)$$

In the limit $\beta \to \infty$ only the components with the smallest winning error survive, i.e.,

$$\langle\langle q\rangle\rangle_\infty \stackrel{\text{def}}{=} \lim_{\beta\to\infty} \langle\langle q\rangle\rangle_\beta = \frac{\sum\limits_{i=1}^n q_i \delta_{g_i,g_{\min}}}{\sum\limits_{i=1}^n \delta_{g_i,g_{\min}}}$$

$$\text{with} \quad g_{\min} \stackrel{\text{def}}{=} \min_i g_i . \qquad (3)$$

So, $\langle\langle \ldots\rangle\rangle_\infty$ stands for a "winner-take-all" mechanism with respect to the winning errors $g_i(\mathbf{W},\vec{x})$. This special average $\langle\langle q\rangle\rangle_\infty$ depends on $\mathbf{W}$ and $\vec{x}$ not only through $q_i(\mathbf{W},\vec{x})$, but also through the winning errors $g_i(\mathbf{W},\vec{x})$, which is important for differentation and integration. That part of the environment for which unit i is the winner is called the "receptive field" of unit i.

3. *Adapt the network state such that the local error of the winning unit becomes smaller.*

Apart from the winning error, we also ascribe a "local error" $e_i(\mathbf{w},\vec{x})$ to each unit i. The learning rule is written formally

$$\Delta\mathbf{W} = \eta\,\mathbf{F}(\mathbf{W},\vec{x}) = -\eta\,\langle\langle \nabla e(\mathbf{W},\vec{x})\rangle\rangle_\infty , \qquad (4)$$

where η is the learning parameter and ∇ denotes the gradient with respect to the network state $\mathbf{W}$. This fairly cryptical and unusual definition of the learning rule becomes clearer if we write Kohonen's learning rule in these terms. We choose the local error

$$Kohonen: \quad e_k(\mathbf{W},\vec{x}) = \frac{1}{2}\sum_{i=1}^n h_{ki}\,\|\vec{x}-\vec{w_i}\|^2 . \quad (5)$$

The matrix with components h_{ij} defines the topological structure between the units. Usually, h_{ij} is a decreasing function of the distance between the

units i and j in the topological map. The learning rule (4) now yields

$$Kohonen: \quad \Delta\vec{w_i} = \eta\,h_{\kappa(\mathbf{W},\vec{x})i}(\vec{x}-\vec{w_i}) ,$$

with $\kappa(\mathbf{W},\vec{x})$ the winner, the unit with the smallest Euclidian distance between its weight vector and the input vector.

There are two closely related questions we would like to answer. The first question will be discussed in Sec. III, the second one in Sec. IV.

1. Is it possible to write the average learning rule (4) as the gradient of some global error potential, i.e., can we find a function $E(\mathbf{W})$ such that

$$\langle\langle\langle \nabla e(\mathbf{W},\vec{x})\rangle\rangle_\infty\rangle_\Omega = \nabla E(\mathbf{W})\,?$$

2. Does the gradient of a global error potential of the form $E(\mathbf{W}) = \langle\langle\langle e(\mathbf{W},\vec{x})\rangle\rangle_\infty\rangle_\Omega$ lead to a self-organizing on-line learning rule, i.e., can we find learning rules $\mathbf{D}_i(\mathbf{W},\vec{x})$ such that

$$\nabla\langle\langle\langle e(\mathbf{W},\vec{x})\rangle\rangle_\infty\rangle_\Omega = \langle\langle\langle \mathbf{D}(\mathbf{W},\vec{x})\rangle\rangle_\infty\rangle_\Omega\,?$$

III. DOES THERE EXIST AN ERROR POTENTIAL FOR KOHONEN LEARNING ?

To investigate whether there exists an error potential for Kohonen's learning rule or, more general, an error potential for learning rules of the form (4), we have to calculate the derivative of the average learning rule

$$\mathbf{F}(\mathbf{W}) \stackrel{\text{def}}{=} \langle\mathbf{F}(\mathbf{W},\vec{x})\rangle_\Omega .$$

The difficult part in calculating this derivative is the contribution of the winner-take-all mechanism. That is why we introduced the winner-take-all mechanism as a special limit of a weighted average with respect to the winning error. Using shorthand notation $\partial_\mu F_\nu \stackrel{\text{def}}{=} \partial F_\nu(\mathbf{W},\vec{x})/\partial W_\mu$, etcetera, we have

$$\partial_\mu F_\nu = -\partial_\mu \lim_{\beta\to\infty}\left\langle\langle\langle \partial_\nu e\rangle\rangle_\beta\right\rangle_\Omega = -\lim_{\beta\to\infty}\left\langle\partial_\mu\langle\langle \partial_\nu e\rangle\rangle_\beta\right\rangle_\Omega .$$

Here it is allowed to interchange the gradient and the limit, but *not* to interchange the gradient with respect to $\mathbf{W}$ and the average with respect to the winning errors $g_i(\mathbf{W},\vec{x})$, which is a function of $\mathbf{W}$. The gradient can be calculated using the definition (2). We obtain

$$\partial_\mu F_\nu = -\left\langle\langle\langle \partial^2_{\mu\nu}e\rangle\rangle_\infty\right\rangle_\Omega +$$
$$\lim_{\beta\to\infty}\beta\left\langle\left\langle\left\langle\left(\partial_\nu e - \langle\langle\partial_\nu e\rangle\rangle_\beta\right)\left(\partial_\mu g - \langle\langle\partial_\mu g\rangle\rangle_\beta\right)\right\rangle\right\rangle_\beta\right\rangle_\Omega .(6)$$

The average learning rule is the gradient of some error potential if and only if $\partial_\mu F_\nu = \partial_\nu F_\mu$. Obviously, the first term in (6) is symmetric. The second term is symmetric if and only if the local error is a monotonic function of the winning error, i.e., *if and only if the local error also determines the winning unit*. In fact, we might as well say that the local error must be equal to the winning error, since any monotonically increasing function of the winning error is totally equivalent to the winning error itself in the limit $\beta \to \infty$. So, only if the local and winning error are equal, the learning procedure (4) can be interpreted as a (stochastic) way to minimize a well-defined error criterion. The Kohonen choices (1) and (5) do not satisfy this requirement, except in the limit of no lateral interaction $h_{ij} = \delta_{ij}$.

IV. DOES AN ERROR POTENTIAL LEAD TO AN ON-LINE LEARNING RULE ?

Here we do not ask whether it is possible to find an error potential corresponding to an existing learning rule, but we start with a well-defined error potential and try to derive a learning rule from it. An obvious choice for the error potential is

$$E(\mathbf{W}) \stackrel{\text{def}}{=} \langle\langle\langle e(\mathbf{W}, \vec{x})\rangle\rangle_\infty\rangle_\Omega , \qquad (7)$$

i.e., the local error of the winning unit, averaged over the whole environment. A similar error potential is suggested in [12]. It can be interpreted as a transmission error between neural layers [13]. The derivative of the error potential (7) obeys

$$\nabla E = \langle\langle\langle\nabla e\rangle\rangle_\infty\rangle_\Omega -$$
$$\lim_{\beta\to\infty} \beta \left\langle \left\langle\left\langle \left(e - \langle\langle e\rangle\rangle_\beta\right)\left(\nabla g - \langle\langle\nabla g\rangle\rangle_\beta\right)\right\rangle\right\rangle_\beta \right\rangle_\Omega . \quad (8)$$

The first term is exactly the learning rule (4) averaged over the environment Ω. It is difficult (see [8]), to interpret the second term as the average of an on-line learning rule. Therefore we would like to get rid of it. For some combinations of $\mathbf{W}$ and $\vec{x}$ there is just one winner, say k. In this case

$$\lim_{\beta\to\infty} \left\langle\left\langle \left(e - \langle\langle e\rangle\rangle_\beta\right)\left(\nabla g - \langle\langle\nabla g\rangle\rangle_\beta\right)\right\rangle\right\rangle_\beta =$$
$$(e_k - e_k)(\nabla g_k - \nabla g_k) = 0 .$$

However, there exist combinations of $\mathbf{W}$ and $\vec{x}$ for which there are two (or more) winning units, say k and l, with $g_k(\mathbf{W}, \vec{x}) = g_l(\mathbf{W}, \vec{x}) = g_{\min}(\mathbf{W}, \vec{x})$, so, with $\vec{x}$ exactly on the boundary of the receptive fields of unit k and l. Then we have

$$\lim_{\beta\to\infty} \left\langle\left\langle \left(e - \langle\langle e\rangle\rangle_\beta\right)\left(\nabla g - \langle\langle\nabla g\rangle\rangle_\beta\right)\right\rangle\right\rangle_\beta =$$
$$\frac{1}{4}(e_k - e_l)(\nabla g_k - \nabla g_l) .$$

This "boundary term" is zero if either $e_k = e_l$ or $\nabla g_k = \nabla g_l$. This second possibility is clearly not true for the Kohonen learning rule and is hard to satisfy in general. So, the only way to exclude boundary terms is to ensure that on these boundaries the local errors are equal. The conclusion is that the second term in (8) vanishes if and only if

$$g_i(\mathbf{W}, \vec{x}) = g_j(\mathbf{W}, \vec{x}) \Rightarrow e_i(\mathbf{W}, \vec{x}) = e_j(\mathbf{W}, \vec{x}) \quad \forall_{i,j,\mathbf{W},\vec{x}} .$$

We arrive at a similar conclusion as above: the gradient of an error potential of the form (7) leads to an on-line learning rule *if and only if the local error also determines the winning unit*.

In the meantime, we have proved that we may interchange taking the derivative and determining the winner, i.e., that

$$\langle\langle\langle\nabla e(\mathbf{W}, \vec{x})\rangle\rangle_\infty\rangle_\Omega = \nabla \langle\langle\langle e(\mathbf{W}, \vec{x})\rangle\rangle_\infty\rangle_\Omega ,$$

if the local error and the winning error are equal, i.e., if $e_i(\mathbf{W}, \vec{x}) = g_i(\mathbf{W}, \vec{x})$. With this particular choice, the on-line learning rule (4) performs stochastic gradient descent on the error potential (7). For the rest of the paper, we will choose the local error and the winning error equal to Kohonen's local error (5). The resulting learning rule is equal to Kohonen's learning rule except for the determination of the winning unit.

V. AN EXAMPLE: KINKS IN ONE DIMENSION

We consider a one-dimensional map consisting of three units. The weight vector is written $\mathbf{w} = (w_1, w_2, w_3)^T$. The input probability distribution obeys

$$\rho(x) = \theta(x)\,\theta(1 - x) ,$$

i.e., x is drawn with equal probability from the interval $[0, 1]$. The lateral interaction matrix h with components h_{ij} is defined

$$h = \frac{1}{1 + \sigma} \begin{pmatrix} 1 & \sigma & 0 \\ \sigma & 1 - \sigma & \sigma \\ 0 & \sigma & 1 \end{pmatrix} .$$

It is normalized such that $\sum_j h_{ij} = 1 \; \forall_i$. σ gives the strength of the interaction between neighboring units in the map. $\sigma = 0$ means no lateral interaction.

Ordered configurations are called "lines." One of them, denoted by (123) since $w_1 < w_2 < w_3$, is drawn schematically in Fig. 1(a). The other one is (321), i.e., w_1 and w_3 are exchanged. There are four different disordered configurations called "kinks:" (132), (213), (231), and (312). The first one is sketched in Fig. 1(b).

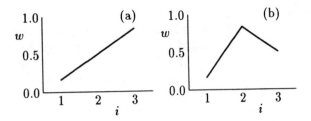

Figure 1: Configurations in a one-dimensional map. (a) Line. (b) Kink.

By numerical calculations, it can be proved that for $\sigma < \sigma^* \approx 0.082$ the error potential (7) has six minima: two lines are global minima, four kinks are local minima. At $\sigma = \sigma^*$ the local minima disappear and only two global minima remain.

We would like to picture how the error potential changes by going from the local to the global minimum. To get rid of two degrees of freedom, we bring in the following constraints. These are based on the fact that at a minimum always one of the weights is approximately equal to 1/6, the second to 1/2, and the third to 5/6. So, at the minima, the sum of the weights and the sum of the squared distances between the weights are approximately constant,

$$\begin{cases} w_1 + w_2 + w_3 \approx \frac{3}{2}, \\ (w_2 - w_1)^2 + (w_3 - w_2)^2 + (w_3 - w_1)^2 \approx \frac{2}{3}. \end{cases}$$

Combining these constraints (''$\approx$'' is replaced with ''$=$''), $\mathbf{W}$ is totally parametrized by the angle ϕ,

$$\begin{cases} w_1(\phi) = \frac{1}{2} - \frac{2\sqrt{3}}{9}\cos\phi, \\ w_2(\phi) = \frac{1}{2} + \frac{\sqrt{3}}{9}\cos\phi - \frac{1}{3}\sin\phi, \\ w_3(\phi) = \frac{1}{2} + \frac{\sqrt{3}}{9}\cos\phi + \frac{1}{3}\sin\phi. \end{cases}$$

In terms of ϕ, the lines and the kinks are positioned as follows.

minimum	line	kink	kink	line	kink	kink
configuration	(123)	(213)	(231)	(321)	(312)	(132)
ϕ	$\pi/6$	$\pi/2$	$5\pi/6$	$7\pi/6$	$3\pi/2$	$11\pi/6$
phase	1/12	1/4	5/12	7/12	3/4	11/12

The error potential as a function of the ''phase'' $\phi/(2\pi)$ is plotted in Fig. 2 for $\sigma = 0$, 0.04, 0.08, and 0.12. At $\sigma = 0$ all minima are equally deep. For $\sigma > 0$, symmetry is broken: the kinks have a higher error potential than the lines. Eventually, the disordered local minima disappear.

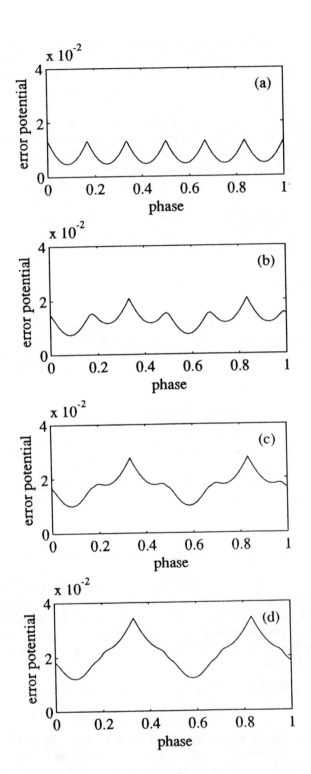

Figure 2: The error potential E as a function of the ''phase'' $\phi/(2\pi)$ for different values of the interaction strength σ. (a) $\sigma = 0$. (b) $\sigma = 0.04$. (c) $\sigma = 0.08$. (d) $\sigma = 0.12$.

VI. Discussion

In this paper an error potential and corresponding learning rule for the self-organization of topological maps are derived. The resulting learning rule is exactly equal to the one proposed by Kohonen, except for the determination of the winning unit. The disadvantage of our learning rule is that the determination of the winning unit is computationally more expensive. (The Euclidian distances, which require $n \times m$ multiplications, must be multiplied with the lateral interaction matrix h. This requires $n \times |h|$ extra multiplications, with $|h|$ the number of nonzero lateral connections for one unit.) The advantage is that we know exactly what error potential is minimized by the learning procedure. Furthermore, the existence of an error potential facilitates a global description of the learning process. The lower the error potential, the "better" the network state. Fixed points of the learning dynamics are minima of the error potential [14]. Local minima of the error potential correspond to topological defects, like kinks in one-dimensional maps or twists ("butterflies") in two-dimensional maps. Global minima are perfectly ordered configurations.

Results from a general study concerning learning in neural networks with local minima [10] can be applied to calculate transition times between different minima. In this context it means that we can calculate the transition times from topological defects to perfectly ordered configurations, i.e., the (average) time it takes to remove a kink in a one-dimensional map or to unfold a twist in a two-dimensional map [15]. Other research aims at the derivation of cooling schedules for the learning parameter that guarantee convergence to the global minimum of the error potential [16].

Acknowledgment

We would like to thank Dr. Andrzej Komoda for stimulating discussions.

References

[1] C. von der Malsburg. Self-organization of orientation sensitive cells in the striate cortex. *Kybernetik*, 14:85–100, 1973.

[2] A. Takeuchi and S. Amari. Formation of topographic maps and columnar microstructures. *Biological Cybernetics*, 35:63–72, 1979.

[3] T. Kohonen. Self-organized formation of topologically correct feature maps. *Biological Cybernetics*, 43:59–69, 1982.

[4] M. Cottrell and J. Fort. A stochastic model of retinotopy: a self-organizing process. *Biological Cybernetics*, 53:405–411, 1986.

[5] H. Ritter and K. Schulten. On the stationary state of Kohonen's self-organizing sensory mapping. *Biological Cybernetics*, 54:99–106, 1986.

[6] H. Ritter and K. Schulten. Convergence properties of Kohonen's topology conserving maps: fluctuations, stability, and dimension selection. *Biological Cybernetics*, 60:59–71, 1988.

[7] V. Tolat. An analysis of Kohonen's self-organizing maps using a system of energy functions. *Biological Cybernetics*, 64:155–164, 1990.

[8] T. Kohonen. Self-organizing maps: optimization approaches. In T. Kohonen, K. Mäkisara, O. Simula, and J. Kanga, editors, *Artificial Neural Networks*, pages 981–990, Amsterdam, 1991. North-Holland.

[9] E. Erwin, K. Obermayer, and K. Schulten. Self-organizing maps: ordering, convergence properties and energy functions. *Biological Cybernetics*, 67:47–55, 1992.

[10] T. Heskes, E. Slijpen, and B. Kappen. Learning in neural networks with local minima. *Physical Review A*, 46:5221–5231, 1992.

[11] T. Geszti. *Physical models of neural networks*. World Scientific, Singapore, 1990.

[12] S. Luttrell. Self-organisation: A derivation from first principles of a class of learning algorithms. In *International Joint Conference on Neural Networks*, volume 2, pages 495–498. IEEE Computer Society Press, 1989.

[13] H. Ritter, K. Obermayer, K. Schulten, and J. Rubner. Self-organizing maps and adaptive filters. In E. Domany, J. van Hemmen, and K. Schulten, editors, *Models of neural networks*, pages 281–306, Berlin, 1991. Springer.

[14] T. Heskes and B. Kappen. Learning processes in neural networks. *Physical Review A*, 44:2718–2726, 1991.

[15] T. Heskes. Transition times in self-organizing maps. *Submitted to Biological Cybernetics*, 1992.

[16] T. Heskes, E. Slijpen, and B. Kappen. Cooling schedules for learning in neural networks. *Submitted to Physical Review E*, 1992.

INTELLIGENT FMS SCHEDULING USING MODULAR NEURAL NETWORKS

Luis Rabelo[1], Yuehwern Yih[2], Albert Jones[3], and George Witzgall[4]

[1]Department of Industrial and Systems Engineering, Ohio University, Athens, Ohio 45701

[2]School of Industrial Engineering, Purdue University, West Lafayette, Indiana 47907

[3]AMRF, National Institute of Standards and Technology, Gaithersburg, Maryland 20899

[4]P.O.Box 14805, Stanford University, Stanford, California 94309

Abstract-- A scheme for the scheduling of Flexible Manufacturing Systems (FMS) has been developed which divides the scheduling function into four different steps: candidate rule selection, transient phenomena analysis, multicriteria compromise analysis, and learning. This scheme is based on a hybrid architecture which utilizes neural networks, parallel Monte-Carlo Simulation, genetic algorithms, and induction mechanisms. This paper investigates the candidate rule selection process, which selects a small list of scheduling rules from a larger list of such rules. A modular architecture (i.e., expert networks) is utilized due to the contextual information and different performance criteria involved. Neural network development issues are given for different input/output schemes, different paradigms such as Cascade Correlation and Backpropagation, and training techniques. The modular architecture provides neural structure flexibility to achieve desired generalization and interpretable representation levels.

I. INTRODUCTION

In the past two decades, manufacturing systems have moved toward more and more automated production, a larger variety of products, and smaller lot sizes. To efficiently and effectively control such manufacturing systems, intelligent, computer-based decision aids are needed.Typically, decisions (such as schedules) are generated from the knowledge contained in a knowledge base.

The first step in developing the required knowledge base is knowledge acquisition. In most cases, knowledge sources are "human experts" who describe or explain the process of decision making. However, there is a problem with FMS scheduling due to the lack of available expertise. Because of this, we often resort to a "computer-based expert" to help us analyze the impact of scheduling rules on system performance. In this approach, simulation results can be used to form the knowledge base through inductive learning processes. However, with more than 100 commonly used heuristic rules, it is impractical to study all the rules and their combinations through simulation.

To shorten the lead time for developing intelligent scheduling aids, it is imperative that the knowledge acquisition process be quick and easily refined, as new knowledge becomes available. In addition, this process must fit into an overall framework for real-time scheduling. We adopt a four phase framework [9,16]. In phase one, a small set of candidate scheduling heuristics is selected based on a quick analysis of the "system". In phase two, a more detailed analysis of the selected rules is performed using discrete-event simulation. In phase three, a genetic algorithm is used to improve the schedules from phase two. Then, in phase four, inductive learning techniques are utilized to "learn" from those decisions. In this paper, we will concentrate on phase one, that is, the initial rule selection process and its implementation using modular neural networks.

II. GENERIC INTELLIGENT CONTROLLER

This research is built upon the generic framework of the intelligent controller proposed by Davis et al. [5] as shown in Figure 1. This framework has its foundations in Albus et al. [1], Jones and McLean [8], and Jones and Saleh [10]. It performs four production management functions: assessment, optimization, execution, and monitoring.

The Assessment Function (AF) formulates the planning and scheduling problems facing the controller based on three sets of inputs (see Fig. 1). The first set is specified by the supervisor and includes assigned tasks, priorities, due dates, and any other constraints or performance measures. The second set is the feedback from the Monitoring Function (MF) that describe the current system state and the projected system response with current control rules. The third input comes from the Optimization Function (OF) indicating the current status of its attempts to generate "feasible/optimal" solutions. The AF specifies the performance criteria for each optimization problem to be considered by the OF. In addition, the AF constructs constraints to be imposed as part of those optimization problems.

This research is supported by a grant from the National Institute of Standards and Technology.

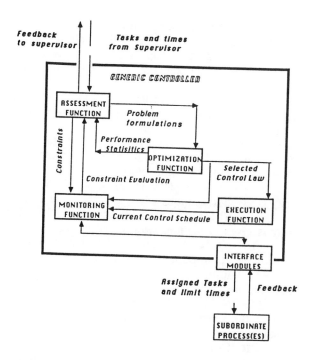

Figure 1.   Generic Control Architecture

The OF is responsible for selecting a run-time production plan and scheduling rule. The production plan is selected from those feasible plans passed down by the AF. In general, there are no a priori limitations on the choice of scheduling rules, but the framework allows for this if it is desirable. The selection is made which optimizes the current set of performance measures. In addition, the OF must deal with violations of the scheduled start/finish times and any other constraints imposed by the Assessment Function. In this paper, we concentrate on a method for implementing the OF which we describe in the next section.

The Execution Function (EF) implements the decision rules selected by the OF. Currently, it is envisioned to work as follows. Using the current state of the system, it does a single pass simulation using the selected production plan and scheduling rule to compute the starting and finishing times for each task. In addition, when minor deviations from these times are envisioned, it can try to restore feasibility using techniques such as perturbation analysis or match-up scheduling [10].

Lastly, the MF updates the system state using feedback from subordinates, and evaluates proposed subordinate responses against the current set of imposed (from the AF) and computed (by the OF) constraints. During error recovery, the MF acts as an expediter.

III. FRAMEWORK OF RULE SELECTION AND IMPROVEMENT

The learning-based framework consists of four phases explained as follows.

After receiving the production constraints and performance criteria from the Assessment Function, an initial candidate rule selector will be activated. Based on the desired system performance, the rule selector will select candidates that are more likely to fulfill the requirement and pass them to the simulation phase. Neural networks are proposed for this step due to their real-time and learning capabilities.

The simulation phase uses the candidates selected in the first phase and any additional constraints from the AF to generate feasible schedules. These simulations are initialized to the current state of the system. The performance of each schedule is evaluated against the imposed criteria. Those schedules performing well based on the criteria will be selected as the basis for further improvement in the third phase.

Phase three is responsible for improving the quality of schedules when possible. This phase is needed because it is very unlikely to have a single scheduling heuristic that can optimize all the objectives (some of which can be negatively correlated) simultaneously. In this phase, new schedules are generated based on those good schedules passed from the second phase by using GA. This process of regeneration iterates until no significant improvement is found. This is the schedule that is implemented by the EF.

At the conclusion of the improvement phase, one "good" schedule has been generated for the current system and performance measures. We would like to learn from this experience to avoid a repeat of the process the next time similar conditions arise. To extract the scheduling strategy, we propose to use an inductive learning algorithm- Trace-Driven Knowledge Acquisition (TDKA) [15]. This algorithm results in the representation of the strategy as a rule base. The result will be a new heuristic which can be placed in the knowledge base and which can be used the next time the candidate rule selection module is invoked.

IV. RULE SELECTOR DEVELOPMENT

The first step in this process is to select a small list of candidate scheduling rules from a larger list of such rules using neural networks.   Due to the large number of variables involved in generating a feasible and "near-optimal" schedule in real-time, it can be prohibitively difficult to formulate a mathematical model to reflect the functional relationship between the system state variables and the criteria to be optimized.   The neural network(s) should be designed to have as input the "state of the system" and the desired performance criteria. The output of the neural network(s) would consist in a quantitative evaluation of the multiple available scheduling policies.

The following sub-sections describe the FMS environment utilized and the development of the candidate rule selector for one of the workstations.

A. Simulation Environment

This subsection explains the FMS cell model, scheduling rules selected, and the performance criteria utilized in the simulation studies.

Physical Model. A Computer-simulated model consisting of a workstation that is member of a cell with five workstations and one material handling robot was developed in the C programming language (see Fig. 2). This cell is able to produce seven different types of products. Each product type has its own arrival behavior, process plans, processing time distributions, and set up dependencies. There are buffers among the workstations and one input and one output buffer for the cell. The robot is responsible for transporting jobs from the input buffer to workstations sequentially and eventually to the output buffer. Jobs arrive at the cell randomly and the batch size is one.

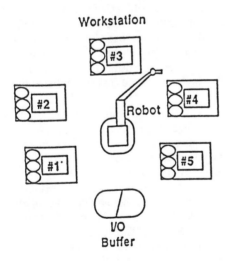

Figure 2. A five-Workstation Cell

Scheduling Rules Selected Several rules where selected due to their utilization and acceptance by the industry and previous scheduling studies:

SPT (Shortest Processing Time) where the jobs with the least expected processing times have the highest priority.

LPT (Largest Processing Time) where the jobs with the largest expected processing times have the highest priority.

FIFO (First In First Out) in which the highest priority is given to the jobs that arrived earliest.

LIFO (Last In First Out) in which the highest priority is given to the jobs that arrived latest.

SST (Shortest Setup Time) where the jobs with the least expected setup times have the highest priority.

LST (Largest Set Up Time) where the jobs with the largest expected set up times have the highest priority.

SPST (Shortest Processing and Setup Times) where the jobs with the least expected processing and setup times have the highest priority.

LPST (Largest Processing and Setup Times) where the jobs with the largest expected processing and setup times have the highest priority.

EDD (Earliest Due Date) in which the highest priority is given to the jobs with the nearest due date.

LDD (Latest Due Date) in which the highest priority is given to the jobs with the latest due date.

mSLACK (Minimum Slack Time) where the jobs with the least amount of slack time (available time before due date-time for remaining operations) have the highest priority.

MSLACK (Maximum Slack Time) where the jobs with the maximum amount of slack time have the highest priority.

CR (Critical Ratio) where the highest priority is given to the job with the smallest ratio, calculated at time t, as follows:

$$CR_i = (due\ date_i - t)/remaining\ processing\ time\ of\ job_i\ at\ time\ t.$$

Performance Measures For these studies several performance measures were selected due to their importance in industrial scheduling problems. Selected performance measures are:

a. Maximum Flowtime (Fmax) where the goal is to minimize the maximum flowtime (the amount of time a job spends in the system) of the jobs to be scheduled.

b. Mean Flow time where the goal is to minimize the mean flow time of the jobs to be scheduled.

c. Maximum Tardiness (Tmax) where the goal is to minimize the maximum tardiness (the amount of time by which a job exceeds its due date, or zero otherwise) of the jobs to be scheduled.

d. Mean Tardiness where the goal is to minimize the mean tardiness of the jobs to be scheduled.

e. Work-In Process Inventory where the goal is to maintain low inventory levels.

f. Resource Utilization where the goal is to maintain a desired level of resource utilization.

g. Throughput where the goal is to maintain a desired level of production in the system.

B. Modular Neural Networks

To optimize the neural structures and to avoid the complexity of the multi-criteria decision making process, a modular neural network architecture is utilized (Initial studies emphasized the utilization of a single unit without achieving "reasonable" generalization levels). Different networks, each one is an expert in a specific performance measure, are utilized to select the best rules according to the system status (see Figure 3). A gating network is utilized in order to weight the output of each network based on the system status and the performance criteria desired as follows [6,7]:

$$Y = \sum_i g_i \, o_i$$

where **Y** is the output of the system, g_i is the ith output of the gating network, and o_i is the output of expert network **i**.

Jacobs et al. [6,7] have developed powerful competitive learning modular schemes. Their architectures perform task decomposition. Our implementation is simpler because the task decomposition is known in advance and the gating network is only trained to moderate the output of each expert network based on the performance criteria desired. The objective function (**E**) of the gating network is [6]:

$$E = \|d - \sum_i g_i o_i\|^2$$

where o_i is the output vector of expert **i** for a specific case (data sample), p_i is the proportional contribution of network **i** to the output of the system (**Y**), and **d** is the desired output vector.

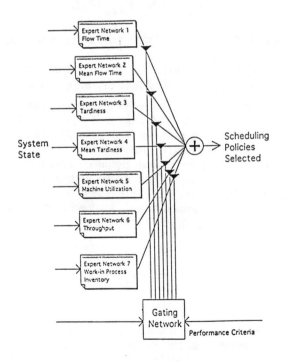

Figure 3. Modular Neural Networks Architecture

C. Paradigms for Rule Selection

These investigations are mainly developed on standard backpropagation to implement the expert networks and cascade correlation to implement the gating networks. Initial studies utilized other supervised paradigms such as Radial Basis Functions, and Cascade Correlation[5] for the expert networks. However, backpropagation yielded higher generalization levels. On the other hand, for the gating network several paradigms yielded good results. Cascade Correlation was selected due to its learning speed and simpler architecture.

Using Backpropagation. The training process using backpropagation is a difficult problem. One needs to find an appropriate architecture (e.g. number of hidden units, number of hidden layers etc.), adequate size and quality of training data, a satisfactory input scheme, satisfactory initialization (e.g initial weights), learning parameter values to speed up convergence, and to avoid over-training effects. In this research several approaches were utilized in order to achieve fast convergence and select an appropriate architecture.

Architecture Design
The methodology used in this research to select an appropriate architecture is based on the steps of the "heuristic search" algorithm of Moody and Utans [13] with some differences in our implementation. First, a minimum hidden units architecture is selected according to "reasonable" RMS and Maximum Output errors. Second, sensitivity analysis is utilized to prune input variables. Third, the final architecture is achieved by a weight prunning training process.

a) Number of Hidden Units: To help find an appropriate number of hidden units an interactive addition of nodes was performed. A new node is added to the hidden layer(s) if the root mean square (RMS) error curve has flattened out to an unacceptable level [2]. This process is stopped when the desired performance has been achieved.

b) Eliminating Input Variables: To test which inputs are more significant to the network several approaches could be utilized. It is possible to to evaluate the significance of each input by examining their impact on the output. This was done by utilizing a measure of the impact expressed as [13]:

$$\text{Impact of } I_i = 1/N \sum \text{ASE}(1/N \sum I_{ij}) - \text{ASE}(I_i)$$

where I_{ij} is the ith input of the jth training sample, **N** is the total number of training samples, **ASE** is the average square error. After that, several models are evaluated by utilizing v-fold cross-validation by deleting input variables in order of increasing impact.

c) Weight Prunning Techniques: Several weight prunning techniques could be utilized. It is possible to utilize the second derivatives for each weight $(\partial^2 E_p/\partial w^2_{ij} (w_{ij})^2)$ of a trained network and measure its effect on the training error as performed by Optimal Brain Damage [12]. This will lead to a evaluation/re-training process due to the elimination of the weights with the lower score. Other techniques emphasizes on the addition of a weight decay term to the objective function. The weight decay term could penalizes large weights [11], intermediate weight values [14], or even weight and output values [3].

Convergence Behavior

To speed convergence behavior, the dynamic selection of parameters such as learning rates and momentum factors were utilized.

Results

The utilization of this training methodology provided neural structures with a higher generalization level. As an example, the results for the expert network that selects the rules that minimize Maximum Flow Time is chosen. A training file of 600 data samples and testing file of 200 data samples were utilized.

a) **Selection of Hidden Units:** The interactive addition of nodes was utilized and an architecture of 4 hidden units was achieved in several trials.

b) **Eliminating Input Variables:** The elimination of input variables was performed. However, numerous trials had to be done. 5-fold validation was utilized and many retraining sessions were performed. An initial scheme with 40 inputs was reduced to 30 inputs. Improvements in generalization (as tested with unseen data) were achieved as shown in tables 1 and 2.

TABLE I.

Results of several trials for 40/4/13 architectures

RMS Training Error (Average)	0.03527
RMS Testing Error (Average)	0.06026

Results of several trials for 30/4/13 architectures

RMS Training Error (Average)	0.03991
RMS Testing Error (Average)	0.05705

c) **Weight Elimination:** The elimination of weights was performed as described by Weigend et al. [14]. This technique has the following objective function:

$$E_p = 1/2 \sum (t_i - o_{il})^2 + \lambda \sum (wi/wo)^2/(1 + (wi/wo)^2)$$

Where the parameter λ represents the relative importance of the $(wi/wo)^2/(1 + (wi/wo)^2)$ term and therefore encouraging the reduction of weights. This weight elimination process increased the performance of the networks as shown in table II. However, this increase in performance was not so dramatic as with the elimination of inputs. Weight elimination reduced the number of weights by a small quantity (e.g., 11 weights in average). Qualitatively, the final networks developed were able to predict the best five rules (a very difficult performance), 95% of the time.

TABLE II.
Results of several trials using weight elimination

RMS Training Error (Average)	0.04011
RMS Testing Error (Average)	0.05579

Using Cascade Correlation. Cascade Correlation is a constructive scheme [5]. The hidden units are cascaded one after another until the network yields the desired performance. For each new hidden unit, the correlation (S) between the new unit's output and the residual error signal is maximized as follows:

$$S = S_j |S_p (b - b_{ave}) (E_{p,j} - E_{ave})|$$

where j is the network output where the error is measured, p is the training pattern, b is the output of the candidate unit, E_j is the residual error at the output unit j, and b_{ave} and E_{ave} are the values of b and E_j averaged over all the patterns. The weights are then changed such that S is maximized. The process is repeated until there is no longer an improvement in S. Finally, the candidate unit is added to the active network as a hidden unit with its input weights frozen and outputs connected, to the output layer units. The final architecture has 5 hidden/layer units. It provided a higher level generalization architecture without having to be trained for a long period of time.

V. EXAMPLE

Here we consider an scheduling example to illustrate the modular architecture performance. The goal of this task is to generate a schedule for the system status and performance criteria imposed by the cell controller to the workstation as explained above.

Current Time = 285
Previous Job Type executed: 3
Batch Size = 10

Job Number	Job Type	Arrival Time	Processing Time(mean)	Due Date
1	1	246	4	283
2	6	249	6	310
3	6	251	6	310
4	2	252	4	286
5	3	257	5	309
6	1	257	4	299
7	3	263	5	313
8	7	265	5	313
9	3	277	5	325
10	6	281	6	340

Degree of Importance	Performance Measure
Very important (10)	Maximum Tardiness(9←→10), Mean Flow Time(9←→10)
Not important (1)	Mean Tardiness(0←→1), Maximum Flow Time(0←→1)
	WIP(0←→1), Resource Utilization(0←→1)
	Throughput(0←→1)

Modular Neural Network(Ranking according to predicted performance)

Max F-time Expert 1	Mean F-time Expert 2	Max Tard. Expert 3	Mean Tard. Expert 4	W.I.P. Expert 5	Res. Util. Expert 6	Throughput Expert 7	Gating Network
EDD	SST	EDD	SPT	CR	SST	SST	SST
FIFO	SPST	FIFO	EDD	EDD	SPST	SPST	SPST
CR	SPT	CR	SST	SST	SPT	SPT	EDD
mSlack	EDD	mSlack	SPST	SPST	LPT	LPT	FIFO
SST	mSlack	SST	mSlack	mSlack	LDD	LDD	CR
SPST	CR	SPST	CR	SPT	MSlack	LIFO	mSlack
SPT	FIFO	SPT	FIFO	FIFO	LIFO	LIFO	SPT
LPT	LPT	LST	LPT	LST	EDD	EDD	LPT
LST	LDD	LPT	LIFO	LIFO	FIFO	FIFO	LST
LPST	MSlack	LPST	LDD	LPT	mSlack	mSlack	LDD
LDD	LIFO	LDD	MSlack	LDD	CR	CR	MSlack
MSlack	LST	MSlack	LST	MSlack	LPST	LPST	LIFO
LIFO	LPST	LIFO	LPST	LPST	LST	LST	LPST

Figure 4. A Scheduling Example

The candidate rule selector implemented, using a modular neural network, uses the system status and the performance criteria in order to select a small set of candidates from the 13 rules available. Each expert network in parallel ranks all rules. However, the gating network, based on the performance criteria, will give a higher weight to the expert networks that minimize Maximum Tardiness and minimize Mean Flow Time (See Fig. 4). The networks developed in the C programming language take on average less than 20 mS (486 PC @ 33 MHz) to give an answer to the problem.

VI. CONCLUSIONS

The utilization of the training techniques for backpropagation were able to provide networks with a higher level of generalization capabilities. The utilization of a modular architecture allowed the improvement of individual networks which because of their expertise did not use the same set of inputs and data samples. Therefore, the modular architecture yielded a higher generalization level and quicker training sessions. These preliminary results of our on going research are encouraging. Neural networks might be the right technique for candidate rule selection. However, we have to remember that after this process the GA will create a "new rule" based partially on these initial schedules. Finally, the induction process will make the entire structure evolve and simplify the process for the future.

REFERENCES

[1]. Albus, J., McCain, H. and Lumia, R., "NASA/NBS Standard Reference Mode for Telerobot Control System Architecture," NIST Technical Note 1235, National Institute of Standards and Technology, 1989.

[2]. T. Ash, "Dynamic Node Creation," Technical Report, ICS, University of California-San Diego, 1989.

[3]. Chauvin, I., "Dynamic Behavior of Constrained Back-Propagation Networks," Advances in Neural Information Processing Systems 2, pp. 642-649, 1990.

[4]. Davis, W., Jones, A. and Saleh, A., "A generic architecture for intelligent control systems," Computer Integrated Manufacturing Systems, to appear.

[5]. Fahlman, S. and Lebiere, C., The Cascade-Correlation Learning Architecture, Technical Report CMU-CS-90-100, February 14, 1990,

[6]. Jacobs, R., Jordan, M., and Barto, A., Task Decomposition Through Competition in a Modular Connectionist Architecture: The What and Where Vision Tasks, COINS Technical Report 90-27, 1990.

[7]. Jacobs, R., Jordan, M., Nowlan, S., and Hinton, G., "Adaptive Mixtures of Local Experts," Neural Computation, Vol. 3., No.1, 1991.

[8]. Jones, A. and McLean, C., "A Production Control Module for the AMRF," Proceedings of the International Symposium on Computers in Engineering, Boston, MA, August, 1985.

[9]. Jones, A. and Rabelo, L., "Real-Time Decision Making Using Neural Networks, Simulation, and Genetic Algorithm," Proceedings of the International FAIM'92 Conference, Fairfax, VA, 1992.

[10]. Jones, A. and Saleh, A., "A Multi-level/Multi-layer Architecture for Intelligent Shop Floor Control," IJCIM, Special Issue on Intelligent Control, 3, 1, 60-70, 1990.

[11]. Krogh, A. and Hertz, J., "A Simple Weight Decay Can Improve Generalization," Advances in Neural Information Processing Systems, 4, pp. 950-957, 1992.

[12]. Le Cun, Y., Denker, J. and Solla, S., "Optimal Brain Damage," Advances in Neural Information

[13]. Moody, J. and Utans, J., "Principle Architecture Selection for Neural Networks: Applications to Corporate BOND Rating Prediction," Advances in Neural Information Processing Systems 4, pp. 683-690, 1992.

[14]. Weigend, A., D. Rumelhart, B. Huberman, "Back-Propagation, Weight Elimination and Time Series Prediction," CONNECTIONIST MODELS: Proceedings of the 1990 Summer School, Morgan Kaufmann Publishers, pp. 105-116, 1990.

[15]. Yih, Y., "Trace Driven Knowledge Acquisition for Expert Scheduling System, Ph.D. dissertation, University of Wisconsin-Madison, December, 1988.

[16]. Yih, Y.and Jones, A., "Candidate Rule Selection to Develop Intelligent Scheduling Aids for Flexible Manufacturing Systems (FMS)," Proceedings of the Second US/GERMAN Conference on New Directions for Operations Research in Manufacturing, to appear in 1993.

Application of neural networks to fluorescent diagnostics of organic pollution in natural waters

Yuri V.Orlov, Igor G.Persiantsev, Sergey P.Rebrik
Microelectronics Department, Nuclear Physics Institute,
Moscow State University, Moscow, 119899, Russian Federation
E-mail on Internet: orlov@compnet.msu.su

Abstract—Use of a neural net allows one to build a sea water pollutant rapid diagnosis system. The neural net classifies sea water pollutant on the basis of its total luminescent spectroscopy (TLS) spectrum and is insensitive to the dissolved organic matter (DOM) spectrum variations. Gradual complication of task during learning is used to reach the minimal decision threshold value. The net gives an adequate answers to presentation of a mixture of pollutants spectra or spectra of unknown substances. Three-step determination of pollutant concentration comprises classification of a pollutant by basic net, its identification by auxiliary net, and concentration determination by linear neural net with a typical accuracy of 0.05 ppm. It is shown that use of a net with two hidden layers for classification of TLS-spectra of low resolution allows one to achieve classification thresholds close to those of standard TLS-spectra.

I. INTRODUCTION

Identification of a pollutant is a key problem in the field of rapid diagnosis of organic pollution of natural and technogeneous environment. In the total luminescent spectroscopy (TLS) method [1] every mixed condition of water environment corresponds to a two-dimensional TLS-spectrum (spectral signature), which is a matrix of emission intensity recorded in coordinates of excitation and emission wavelengths. For the fluorescent diagnostics of organic pollution an excitation range of 240-360 nm was used, and the spectral response was registered in the 200 nm wide window, red-shifted by 10 nm against the excitation wavelength. The standard size of the intensity matrix was 25 x 40 elements. The catalogue of potential natural water pollutants includes more than 50 samples (reference spectra of solutions and emulsions of pollutants in bidistilled water).

The pollutant samples classification made according to the similarity of their spectral images is given in Tables I–III. It turned out that such classification is in good correlation with the pollutant's physical and chemical properties. Fig.1 (a,b) presents spectra of substances from one class, while Fig.1 (c,d) demonstrates some typical spectra of substances, belonging to other classes.

In general the signature depends on the geographical region and is subject to seasonal change. In Figs.2a and 2b dissolved organic matter (DOM) spectra of the coastal zone of the Baltic and the North Sea are shown. The DOM type catalogue includes 7 samples mainly from the Baltic and the North Seas. The Raman Scattering Signal (RSS) of water molecules is dominant in fluorescence spectra of water with low DOM concentration (Fig.2c). The bidistilled water spectrum is shown in Fig.2d. Typical spectra of polluted sea water are shown in Fig.3.

Thus the recognition of a pollutant is hampered by the following: (a) camouflaging of the pollutant spectrum by the variable DOM spectrum and (b) the dependence of the TLS-spectrum shape on concentrations of the pollutant and DOM.

II. TRAINING PROCEDURE OF THE NEURAL NET

A well-known multi-layer feed forward neural net [2] and the backpropagation algorithm [3] were used.

To train the neural net we used 16 pollutant spectrum samples divided into 6 classes, different DOM spectra, and the RSS spectrum of water. The additive feature of the pollutant fluorescence signal, DOM fluorescence, and RSS allowed to synthesize the training spectrum for the concrete concentration of the pollutant just before presenting spectrum to the neural net. All spectra were normalized to unity at the point of maximum intensity.

The net was trained to determine the class of the pollutant. As spectra are normalized to unity in maximum, the spectrum for every mixture is determined only by the ratio of DOM and pollutant concentration (neglecting RSS of water). It is more convenient to use the pollutant's spectrum portion (PSP) in the overall spectrum instead of the pollutant's concentration. The resulting spectrum (without taking normalization into account) is given by:

$$S_i = PSP \cdot P_i + (1 - PSP) \cdot D_i,$$

where the i index corresponds to the i-th point in the spectrum and P_i and D_i are the intensities of the pollutant spectrum and DOM spectrum at that point.

Certain problem arises with the training process. The neural net must have a step-shaped dependence of the output neuron's activity on the PSP. It is clear that the PSP threshold value for which the pollutant's class determination is possible is not known beforehand. A too high threshold value will result in the underuse of the net's possibilities, and a too low value will confuse the net during the training process, as it will be expected to give an answer when necessary input information is absent. To solve this problem we introduced the following training schedule: at the beginning the net was trained on pure samples, including those of pure sea water, i.e. PSP = 1 or 0. At PSP = 0 all neurons should have zero activity; for PSP = 1 the activity of the neuron responsible for a given class is maximal (=1). After reaching a sufficiently high percentage of correct classifications (we had set a goal of 98% correct out of 100 presentations), the network weights are saved and the training set is modified : the net is given either the spectrum of pure water (PSP=0) or a spectrum of a randomly chosen pollutant, with a PSP also taken at random in the range 0.7-1. The learning goes on until the desired percentage of correct classification is reached. Then the lower PSP limit in the presented spectra is slightly decreased. Apparently, there exists the lowest PSP at which the percentage of correct classification can be maintained on the given level. The net weights obtained for this PSP are used for further data processing.

DOM spectra of the Baltic sea, the coastal North sea, the open water North sea, and spectrum of bidistilled water were used for training. This way the net was made insensitive to variations of DOM spectra.

III. CLASSIFICATION OF TLS-SPECTRA OF STANDARD SIZE

TLS-spectrum of standard size (SSS, 25x40 points) was presented to 1,000 input neurons; in the hidden layer there were 32 neurons, completely connected to the neurons of the input layer. In the output layer, that was completely connected to the hidden layer, the number of neurons corresponded to the number of classes into which the pollutant catalogue was divided.

Cumulative error was not used in the training process, the moment was equal to 0.9, training speed varied from 0.1 to 0.025. The number of single presentations after which decreasing the PSP did not allow the net to reach the desired percentage of correct classifications was about 4,000, and the lowest PSP limit was 0.2. The neural net was emulated on an IBM PC/AT-12MHz computer, equipped with a 80287 co-processor. A full training cycle required about 8 hours.

To test the neural net we used spectra, synthesized out of pollutants and DOM spectra that were not presented before (Table II), as well as real pollutant spectra recorded in sea water in the presence of DOM (Table III). When spectra of pure sea water (the first three spectra in Table II) were processed by neural net, the noise amplitude at the output layer did not exceed 0.1. This value was used to define threshold of the correct classification. A pollutant was considered to be correctly determined when the corresponding neuron's activity exceeded twice the maximum amplitude of the output noise, and exceeded the other neurons activity not less than two times. The threshold of correct classification, determined for the synthesized spectra, is shown in Tables I and II in the "Threshold for SSS" column. Typical value of the threshold is close to the lowest PSP limit reached in the training process.

All the test spectra from Table III, for which the pollutant's class is known, were classified by the neural net without mistakes. For other spectra from Table III, taken from a water body previously known to be polluted, the net classification indicates the possible presence of a pollutant. Unfortunately we had no alternative method to check the classification results.

To determine minimal detectable pollutant concentration, one needs DOM and pollutant spectra recorded at standard device sensitivity. The RSS can be used for the sensitivity standardization. Unfortunately, in many cases the pollutant's spectra and the RSS strongly overlap, and it is not possible to determine the RSS amplitude correctly. A high level of fluorescence signal also decreases the accuracy of normalization by the RSS.

As the pollutant detection threshold depends on the DOM concentration in water, two values of the threshold in concentration units are given in Tables I, II for the spectra that could be normalized to the RSS. The lower values correspond to the total absence of DOM, and the higher values were obtained for extremely high DOM concentrations (10 mg/l of organic carbon) typical for coastal zones of closed seas, i.e. in the most unfavorable conditions for diagnostics.

We tested the neuroclassifier on mixtures of pollutants and for all PSPs exceeding the threshold value the neural net did detect the presence of pollution. However, determination of the components classes is typically possible at higher PSP values and not in every case. Still, simultaneous activity of a number of output neurons can be used to detect situations where the system is responding to a complex signal.

At times it is necessary to know not only the class, but also the concentration of the pollutant. As each class contains a number of pollutants spectra with different fluorescence efficiencies, the identification of pollutant must precede the determination of concentration. This task can be solved by first classifying the pollutant by basic net. From a second, an auxiliary network, trained to identify the pollutants belonging to the determined class, is used. (We used a net similar to the one described above, but its hidden layer had from 4 to 8 neurons, and the size of output layer was equal to the number of pollutants in the given class.) Finally a neural net consisting of a single neuron with a linear output function determines concentration of the identified pollutant. Spectra in relative (i.e. normalized to the RSS) units were presented at the input of the neuron (the intensity was normalized to unity at the RSS maximum). Concentrations of the pollutant and DOM used to synthesize the spectrum were varied randomly in a wide range and the output neuron was trained to give the pollutant's concentration in ppm units (parts per million). Such nets were trained for a number of samples belonging to different classes. The training process took about 500 presentations. It was found out that such a simple net can determine the concentration with the accuracy of $+/- 0.02$ ppm.

IV. CLASSIFICATION OF TLS-SPECTRA OF DIMINISHED SIZE

Initially the registration of TLS-spectra of standard size was provided by a CCD. During further development of spectrometer it was suggested to use more efficient photo-electron multiplier with 20 channels of registration. So an important question arises - whether a neural network is able to classify spectra successfully if the amount of input information is significantly reduced (by one half in our case)?

TLS-spectra of diminished size (SDS, 25x20 points) were formed by averaging of adjacent points in SSS. We used different configurations of neural networks with one hidden layer (the number of hidden neurons varied from 32 to 64). In all cases thresholds of correct classification have increased 1.5-2.5 times (compared to those of SSS), while some of spectra of pure water were classified as polluted.

We also tried to use SDS formed from a left half of SSS (it is the most informative part of TLS-spectra of most pollutants), but the absence of its right half, where maximum of DOM fluorescence and total maximum at low pollutant concentration are located, does not allow to estimate the degree of water pollution, and all spectra of pure water were classified as polluted one.

As a next attempt to classify SDS we have used a net with two hidden layers of 32 neurons each. Every consequent layer was fully connected to the previous one. SDS were formed by averaging of SSS. Typical number of learning presentations increased from 4000 (for a net with one hidden layer) to 12000. As the computational cost of one presentation was approximately halved, the classification time also halved, so the learning time increased only 1.5 times. Thresholds of correct classification and limits of minimal detectable pollutant concentration for this net are presented in Tables I and II in the "Threshold for SDS" column. One can see, that this net has classification thresholds of SDS close to those of the net with one hidden layer in the case of SSS classification.

V. CONCLUSIONS

The neural net suggested in this paper is able to classify sea water pollution on the basis of its TLS (total luminescent spectroscopy) spectrum.

Learning is based on the gradual complication of classification task, what is attained by iterative decreasing of a pollutant concentration in presented mixtures. Also, during this procedure the minimal PSP (pollutant's spectrum portion) value for which the net can still be trained is reached.

The neural net is made insensitive to the DOM spectrum variations.

A typical minimal detectable PSP value is 0.2. This value corresponds to a pollutant concentration of 0.5-10 ppm for a high DOM concentration in water (10 mg/l of organic carbon), i.e. in a situation most difficult for diagnostics.

The net is capable of giving adequate answers when spectra corresponding to a mixture of two pollutants or spectra of unknown substances are presented. Simultaneous activity of a number of output neurons can be used to detect complex situations.

A three-step procedure is used for determination of pollutant concentration : at first basic net classifies a pollutant, then an auxiliary net corresponding to the determined class identifies a pollutant. Finally a linear neural net determines concentration of pollutant with a typical accuracy of 0.05 ppm; variations of the DOM spectrum shape and amplitude in reasonable limits do not affect the neural net's functioning.

It is shown that a net with one hidden layer can not classify TLS-spectra of low resolution, while addition of a second hidden layer allows to achieve classification thresholds close to those of standard TLS-spectra.

ACKNOWLEDGMENT

The authors would like to thank S.M.Babichenko and L.V.Poryvkina for providing the TLS-database and for helpful discussions of the work.

REFERENCES

1. A.E.Dudelzak, S.M.Babichenko, L.V.Poryvkina, K.U.Saar, "Total luminescent spectroscopy for remote laser diagnostics of natural water conditions", Appl. Opt., vol.30, no. 4, pp.453-458, 1991.

2. Lippmann R.P., "An Introduction to Computing with Neural Nets", IEEE ASSP Mag., vol.3, no.4, pp. 4-22, 1987.

3. Rumelhart D.E., Hinton G.E., and Williams R.J., "Learning Internal Representations by Error Propagation", *In: Parallel Distributed Processing: Explorations in the Microstructures of Cognition*, vol.1: Foundations, MIT Press, 1986, pp. 318-362.

TABLE 1. Training patterns

PATTERN	Classification	Threshold for SSS		Threshold for SDS	
		PSP	ppm*	PSP	ppm*
Baltic sea DOM	-	-	-	-	-
Bidistilled water	-	-	-	-	-
Pas - de - Kale DOM	-	-	-	-	-
Central part of North sea DOM	-	-	-	-	-
Belorussian crude oil Y-02	A	0.1	0.15-0.75	0.11	0.09-0.75
Perm crude oil O-73	A	0.11	0.13-0.5	0.14	0.1-0.65
Diesel oil LS-05	A	0.08	-	0.08	-
Compressor oil K-12-59	B	0.2	0.8-10.0	0.18	0.43-5.0
Transmission oil TEP-15-48	B	0.13	0.6-5.0	0.13	0.36-3.6
Residual oil	B	0.17	0.5-3.0	0.17	0.25-2.3
Unrefined machine oil SHF-68	C	0.14	0.5-4.0	0.11	0.25-3.5
Shale oil (medium fraction)	C	0.14	-	0.14	-
Diesel oil M-10B-67	C	0.14	0.5-2.5	0.07	0.12-1.6
Turbine oil T-30-66	D	0.13	0.08-0.75	0.14	0.04-0.9
Petrol fraction (oil-shale)	E	0.17	-	0.11	-
Gas turbine oil (oil-shale)	E	0.2	-	0.14	-
Timol	F	0.14	-	0.18	-
5-metil-2-etil-rezorcin	F	0.13	-	0.17	-
Rezorcin	F	0.11	-	0.14	-
Phenol	F	0.13	-	0.17	-

TABLE 2. Testing patterns

PATTERN	Classification	Threshold for SSS		Threshold for SDS	
		PSP	ppm*	PSP	ppm*
Baltic sea DOM	-	-	-	-	-
South of North sea DOM	-	-	-	-	-
Skagerrak DOM	-	-	-	-	-
Kaliningrad crude oil M-06	A	0.11	0.14-0.75	0.14	0.11-0.75
Siberian crude oil P-01	A	0.1	0.09-0.4	0.13	0.07-0.45
Diesel oil AV-87	A	0.1	-	0.13	-
Kerosene	A	0.13	0.75-3.0	0.18	0.55-4.2
Cylinder oil C-11-33	B	0.14	1.0-10.0	0.14	0.45-4.0
Industrial oil I20-A60	B	0.17	0.75-5.0	0.2	0.33-3.6
Shale oil (heavy fraction)	C	0.14	-	0.14	-
Transformer oil TF-31	D	0.13	0.05-0.5	0.14	0.03-0.6
Petrol AI-93	E	0.4	-	0.2	-
2-metil-rezorcin	F	0.13	-	0.17	-
5-geptil-rezorcin	F	0.14	-	0.18	-
4-geptil-rezorcin	F	0.2	-	0.26	-
5-metil-rezorcin	F	0.13	-	0.17	-
Stirol	F	0.13	-	0.17	-
Para-c-rezorcin	F	0.14	-	0.18	-

• The limits correspond to the DOM concentration variance in the range of 0.1-10 mg/l of organic carbon.

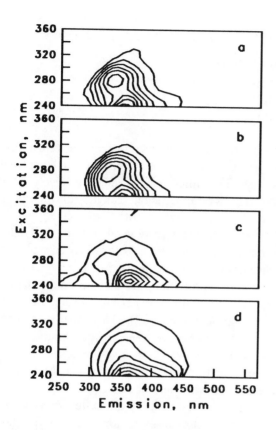

Fig. 1. Some examples from spectral catalog of pollutants:
a— Siberian crude oil,
b— Diesel oil,
c— Turbine oil,
d— Shale oil.

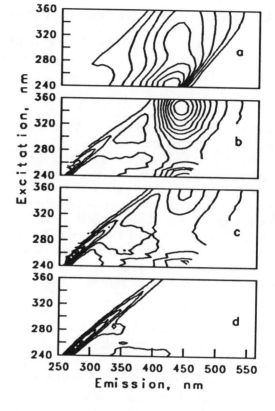

Fig. 2 Spectra of Dissolved Organic Matter (DOM) :
a—Gulf of Finland,
b—central part of English Channel,
c— central part of the North Sea,
d— bidistilled water.

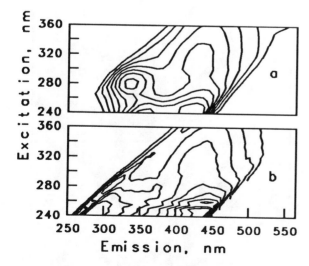

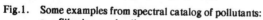

Fig. 3 Typical spectra of polluted water of the Baltic Sea:
a— water polluted by Siberian crude oil (see Fig. 1a),
b— water with unknown pollutant.

TABLE 3. Independent testing patterns

PATTERN	Classification
Siberian crude oil P-01	A
Perm crude oil 0-73	A
Turbine oil T-30-66	D
Petrol AI-93	E
	Network class
Baltic Sea (polluted water)	C
Baltic Sea (polluted water)	C
Baltic Sea (polluted water)	C
Baltic Sea (polluted water)	C
Baltic Sea (polluted water)	C
Kattegat (polluted water)	C

Classification of Chromosomes using a Combination of Neural Networks

Phil A. Errington and Jim Graham.
Department of Medical Biophysics,
University of Manchester, Oxford Road,
Manchester, M13 9PT, UK

Abstract– Visual analysis of microscope images containing chromosomes is an important clinical task in pre–natal diagnosis and cancer monitoring. In developing computer vision systems for analysing chromosomes images, a central task is the classification of the 46 chromosomes into 24 groups. We describe a combination of multi–layer–perceptrons for classifying isolated chromosomes and demonstrate that these perform as well as, or significantly better than a well developed statistical classifier. We suggest a method for using a competitive network to take advantage of constraints on the assignment of chromosomes to groups as a means of improving the classification rate.

I. INTRODUCTION.

The genetic material of all higher organisms is contained in a number of constituent parts of the organism's cell nuclei called chromosomes. At certain parts of the cell cycle these chromosomes exist as separate bodies which, appropriately stained, may be made visible under high resolution microscopy. Fig. 1 shows the appearance of a cell at the metaphase stage in which the chromosomes have been stained so that each exhibits a series of bands along its length (G–banding). The banding pattern, together with the chromosome length and centromere position (Fig. 2) can be used to assign the 46 chromosomes of a normal human cell into 24 groups (22 pairs of "autosomes" and two sex chromosomes: a pair of X chromosomes in the case of a female or an X and a Y chromosome in the case of a male) [15]. This classification by inspection (karyotyping) is a skilled and important task in pre–natal diagnosis of genetic abnormality and in diagnosis and monitoring of cancer. There has been considerable interest over many years in automating the analysis of chromosome images by computer vision [2], [5], [12], [13], [14]. A central issue in the development of automated systems is the specification of measurable features representing the banding pattern which cope with the considerable variability in banding appearance between cells. A range of features have been used for this purpose [2], [6], [7], [8], [12], [13], [16], [17], [21], usually derived intuitively and consequently lacking robustness to changes in preparation techniques.

An artificial neural network offers the possibility of an adaptable classifier for chromosomes [10]. Of particular interest are the feature extraction properties such models exhibit, which allow unrefined information to be presented to the classifier rather than specific intuitively defined features. This is reflected in our classification approach, as we use an artificial neural network to extract features from the raw grey level banding profile taken along the length of the chromosome. This profile is relatively easy to extract from chromosome images (Fig. 2). Additionally we use two other features representing the chromosome length and the position of its centromere (a characteristic constriction in the chromosome, see Fig. 2). This paper presents and compares the performance of an artificial neural network with a statistical classifier and discuses how the performance of the network classifier may be enhanced with the use of further neural networks.

Three extensive data sets of annotated measurements from G–banded chromosomes are used in our study, originating in Copenhagen, Edinburgh and Philadelphia. These have been used in previous classification studies using statistical methods [7], [16], [17], [21]. They cover a range of data quality, each set consisting of a large number

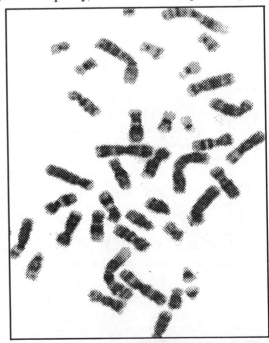

Fig. 1. An image of a metaphase cell showing G–banded chromosomes.

This work is supported by the UK Science and Engineering Research Council, Grant 90310105.

TABLE I

DETAILS OF THE THREE CHROMOSOME DATA SETS USED.

Dataset	Tissue of Origin	Digitization method	No. in set	Data quality
Copenhagen	Peripheral blood	Densitometry from photographic negatives	8106	Good
Edinburgh	Peripheral blood	T. V. Camera	5469	Fair
Philadelphia	Chorionic villus	CCD line scanner	5817	Poor

of chromosome density profiles extracted from images of cells in the metaphase stage of cell division.

Of the three data sets the Copenhagen set is considered the highest visual quality, as its chromosomes were carefully measured by densitometry of photographic negatives from selected cells of high quality. The other two data sets were taken from routine material with no attempt to remove measurements errors arising from overlapped or bent chromosomes. The Philadelphia set is considered the poorer of these two, as the nature of the slide preparation method results in direct chorionic villus samples providing cells of significantly poorer visual quality than in the case of peripheral blood. Details of the three data sets appear in Table I. It should be noted that the chromosomes are all from normal human cells and not from those exhibiting abnormalities. Such cells are expected to contain 46 chromosomes of 24 classes. These 46 chromosomes consist of 22 pairs of classes 1 to 22, with either one X and one Y chromosome (in male cells) or a pair of X chromosomes (in female cells).

II. Classification Of Chromosomes

In our approach, classification takes place in two stages. The first involves classification of a chromosome independent of other chromosomes in a cell. For this task the Multi-Layer Perceptron (MLP) was selected. The bulk

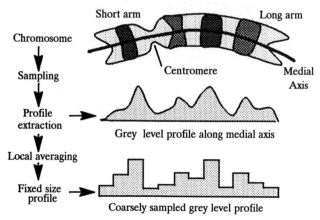

Fig. 2. An example of an extraction of a fixed length profile from a chromosome

of our work has been to modify and optimise classifiers built from this design of neural network.

During all classification experiments we use both a training and test set of data. Each of these sets is selected from approximately half of the data set under study. Two experiments are conducted, one with one half of the full data set as training data and then in a subsequent experiment as test data. Similarly the role of the other half of the data set is reversed. The classification rates we present are the mean classification rates over the two experiments.

III. First Stage Classification Using A MLP

A. Network Training Algorithm.

Preliminary work had shown the MLP to be a promising classifier for chromosome data [10] compared with other network topologies. For training our MLPs we chose a modification of the back-error propagation algorithm of Rummelhart, Hinton and Williams [19]. Our modification of the standard algorithm as described in [19] involves the use of a gradual reduction in gain (or learning rate). Initially the gain value in our network is set at a standard value (e.g. 0.1). As training proceeds two measures are monitored to select when a decrease in the gain term is required. These measures are the network classification error rate for the training data and the sum of the output node error signals for all of the training examples. The gain term is halved if the classification error rate does not decrease after 4 passes of the training data through the network. The gain is also halved if the sum of error signals increases by 10% over that observed on the previous pass of the training data set. This second measure (which is a scaled measure of the r.m.s. error between desired and actual outputs) prevents the network weights oscillating wildly with too high an original gain value, it is unlikely that such increases in the summed error signal will occur after the first few training passes.

The gain reduction mechanism permits larger values of gain to be initially used to allow considerable alteration in network weights, while allowing smaller more refined adjustments later in training for optimal classification performance. Fig. 3 shows a typical training curve for network error and classification performance using Copenhagen data.

Other algorithms (reviewed in [4]) have not yet been investigated for our MLP training, if training time becomes an issue it may be necessary to adopt one of these.

B. Use of the MLP for Chromosome Classification.

The number of samples in the banding profile of individual chromosomes in the data sets varies considerably. Profiles with up to 140 samples are present,

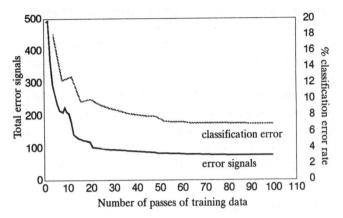

Fig. 3. The reduction in total error signals and classification error rate with training

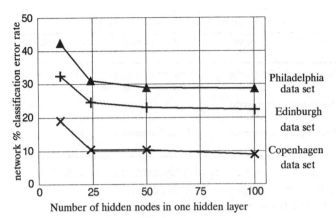

Fig. 5. The variation in classification performance of networks with different numbers of hidden nodes in one hidden layer

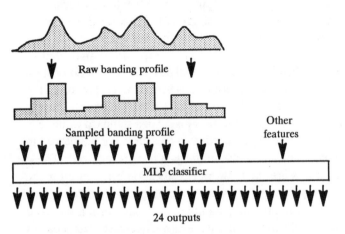

Fig. 4. Presentation of classification features to the MLP

although most profiles have approximately 90 samples. To maintain consistent inputs to the MLP the chromosome profiles are scaled to a constant length and local averaging used to produce a fixed number of averaged samples along the chromosome length (Fig. 4). These averaged inputs are presented to the MLP input nodes. If extra features are used these are presented alongside the banding profile at extra input nodes.

The network is trained so that the highest output denotes the category of the input pattern. As there are 24 classes of chromosome, 24 output nodes are required. A variable number of hidden nodes are used in one or two layers (see below).

C. Optimisation of the MLP Classifiers.

We have conducted a number of experiments to optimise our MLPs, using banding samples as the only inputs. The first stage of the optimisation involved testing the sensitivity of a particular network topology to changes in the value of the gain and momentum parameters. After varying the values of these parameters between 0.1 and 0.9 (involving 81 separate experiments in two halves) it was discovered that

medium and high values of gain (greater than 0.6) and high momentum (e.g. 0.8, 0.9) resulted in unstable classifiers, while if the gain value was initially low (0.1) near optimal classification performance could be achieved with the entire range of momentum values. The result of the experiment was to select the best combination, in terms of training time efficiency, of gain and momentum which produces optimal classification performance. This combination was found to be an initial gain of 0.1 and a constant momentum value of 0.7.

Selection of an optimal topology for our problem was the next task. Although there are theoretical guide-lines to the number of hidden nodes required for a classification problem [1], [9], [20], these involve knowing something about the expected variability of the input data. As chromosome classification requires the network to cope with highly variable data, we selected the optimal topology for the MLP by experimentation.

Topology testing was performed with a fixed number of input nodes accepting banding inputs and 24 output nodes, one for each class of chromosome. Fifteen input samples were presented to the inputs as these had proved effective at representing the banding profile information in a preliminary study [10]. A variety of topology combinations of hidden nodes were tried. Initially a single hidden layer of nodes was used, with topologies involving 10, 24, 50 and 100 hidden nodes. The performance of these classifiers is shown in Fig. 5, which shows that the classification performance increases with increasing network complexity. Experiments with a second layer of hidden nodes were also conducted to evaluate the effect of their extra discriminating ability. The number of nodes in the first layer was set at 100 to reflect the best performing single hidden layer network. The results of trying 10, 24, 50 and 100 nodes in a second hidden layer is shown in Fig. 6. This

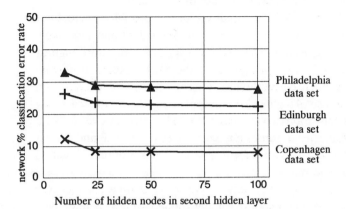

Fig. 6. The variation in classification performance of networks with a first hidden layer of 100 nodes and different numbers of nodes in a second hidden layer..

shows that there is very little variation in performance with increasing numbers of second hidden layer nodes. This is interesting as the training and classification times of the larger nets are far greater than those with fewer hidden nodes.

D. Classification Performance.

Once a good choice of topology and network parameters were made, the main advance in the performance of the classifier was achieved by including two extra features representing the length and centromere position. The centromere divides the chromosome into a long 'arm' and a short 'arm'. The ratio of the length of the short arm to that of the whole chromosome is called the centromeric index, and can be used as a representation of the centromere position, which varies depending on chromosome class. Length values are normalised to remove the effects of considerable inter–cell variation.

Three methods of including the centromeric index and length features were tried. The first involved each feature as an extra input along with banding inputs in a large MLP. The second used both features along with the banding information, but by far the most effective method was the use of an MLP pre–classifier (see Fig. 7).

Using the centromere position and chromosome length alone it is possible to classify the chromosomes into 7 broader groups, corresponding to the 'Denver' classification [3]. The pre–classifier was built to perform

this broader classification, accepting the two features as inputs and producing likelihoods of membership of the 7 broader groups as outputs. This 7 group information was passed, together with the banding inputs, to a second MLP trained to produce the 24 class classification.

The optimisation of the MLP pre–classifier was performed in a similar manner to that discussed above; a number of topologies involving 2 inputs and 7 outputs were tried. The best performing of these topologies and their performance at classifying the 24 chromosome classes into the corresponding 7 Denver groups is shown in Table II.

The performances of the three inclusion methods for the centromere position and length features are shown in Table III, which indicates that a succession of two MLPs, the first performing a broad classification, later refined by a second using extra data, can out perform a single large MLP working on all the data.

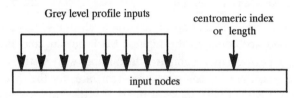

Method 1 : Profile plus single feature

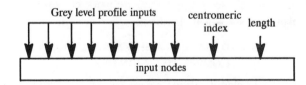

Method 2 : Profile plus pair of features

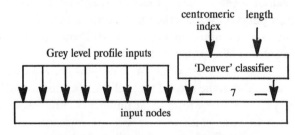

Method 3 : Profile plus pre–classified features

Fig. 7. Different methods of inclusion of the centromeric index and length features.

TABLE II

CLASSIFICATION ERROR RATES FOR THE BEST DENVER CLASSIFIERS USED
FOR PRE-CLASSIFICATION

Data set	Network Topology	Error rate for classifying into 7 groups
Copenhagen	2–14–7	5.4%
Edinburgh	2–14–7	10.1%
Philadelphia	2–14–7	14.6%

TABLE III

CLASSIFICATION ERROR RATES OF NETWORKS USING 15 GREY LEVEL
BANDING INPUTS WITH DIFFERENT REPRESENTATIONS OF CENTROMERE
AND LENGTH FEATURES.

Features Used	Data set		
	Cop.	Edi.	Phi.
Banding pattern alone	8.8%	22.3%	28.6%
Banding and normalised length	8.4%	19.4%	27.6%
Banding and centromeric index	7.7%	21.0%	26.5%
Banding, length and centromeric index	6.9%	18.6%	24.6%
Banding, and 'Denver' groups	5.8%	17.0%	22.5%

Using this combination of classifiers, chromosomes are classified according to the highest MLP output, and the overall performance compares favourably with statistical classifiers. Table IV compares the error rates for the three data sets we use with those of the best statistical classifier working under context free conditions on the same data [17]. As can be seen the neural network classifier out-performs this statistical classifier.

IV. SECOND STAGE CLASSIFICATION USING A COMPETITIVE NETWORK

The first classification stage works on individual chromosomes classified in isolation; no contextual information is used. The approach also relies on the highest MLP output representing the correct class of chromosome; information contained in the other MLP outputs is not considered. We propose to use a second stage of classification where the other MLP outputs are examined and used. Also in the second stage of classification we wish to apply context in the form of the number of chromosomes expected in each class when a cell of chromosomes is

classified. We are investigating the application of a competitive network to both of these tasks.

From an MLP's output vector it is possible to select not only the most likely class, but secondary and less likely classes, using the second highest output, the third highest etc [18]. By considering all the MLP outputs, it may be possible to correctly classify chromosomes mis–classified on the basis of highest MLP output alone. To test the feasibility of this approach we have trained a competitive network using chromosomes mis–classified by the MLP and used it as a post–classifier for a separate test set of mis–classified chromosomes.

The competitive network we chose to use is a single layer topology of competitive nodes trained using a 'Winner Take All' algorithm. Each node receives the same input vector and compares this to its pattern of weights (which initially are random). The node with a pattern of weights closest to the input pattern is designated the winner. During training, winning nodes alter their weight values so that they are closer to their inputs. After a period of training each node has specialised to represent a class of similar input vectors (those for which it 'won'), and can be labelled with the class(es) of these vectors. The nodes can then be used to classify input vectors, the class of each vector being decided by the label of the winning node. The vectors we use are those produced at the 24 output nodes from the MLP first stage classifier. At present no lateral inhibition or Kohonen neighbourhoods [11] are used, each winning node updating only its own weights. It may be necessary to introduce some form of refinement near class boundaries as it becomes clear how the subclasses lie in weight space.

The results of classifying mis–classified chromosomes from the Copenhagen, Edinburgh and Philadelphia data sets, using a competitive network are presented in Table V.

The performance of this classifier is encouraging. It shows that, even when the highest value in the MLP output vector does not correspond to the true class, the entire vector contains information which allows classification to be made. However the classifier is not attempting to classify all chromosomes, only those mis–classified by the MLP. It is possible to train other competitive nodes to classify

TABLE IV

COMPARISON OF CLASSIFICATION ERROR RATES FOR A NEURAL
NETWORK CLASSIFIER USING BOTH BANDING AND DENVER GROUP
INPUTS WITH A HIGHLY OPTIMISED PARAMETRIC CLASSIFIER.

Data set	Classification error rate.		Significance of Improvement
	Network	Parametric [17]	
Copenhagen	5.8%	6.5%	2% level
Edinburgh	17.0%	18.3%	5% level
Philadelphia	22.5%	22.8%	Non significant

TABLE V

PERCENTAGE OF CHROMOSOMES MIS-CLASSIFIED ON THE BASIS OF
MLP OUTPUT WHICH ARE CORRECTLY CLASSIFIED BY A COMPETI-
TIVE NETWORK TRAINED ON MIS-CLASSIFIED CHROMOSOMES.

Data set	Percentage of chromosomes correctly classified	
	Training data	Unseen data
Copenhagen	48.0%	23.1%
Edinburgh	42.1%	30.4%
Philadelphia	43.4%	31.7%

chromosomes correctly classified by the MLP. The nodes classifying these may then be included with nodes classifying mis–classified chromosomes. Combining 'correct' trained and 'error' trained competitive nodes in this manner, we have so far only managed to achieve a classification performance equivalent to selecting the highest MLP output as the correct class.

Our experiments involving the application of context to the classification of chromosomes also make use of a competitive network. The contextual constraint is that a cell of 46 chromosomes will possess 2 chromosomes each of classes 1 to 22, with either one X and one Y chromosome or a pair of X chromosomes. Application of this constraint has been shown to effect an improvement in the performance of statistical classifiers, [22].

We are currently investigating methods of applying this constraint using a competitive network. One method currently under consideration is to to classify all the chromosomes in a cell using a competitive network pre–trained to recognise MLP output vectors. A mechanism of penalising and rewarding competitive nodes according to how well they match the contextual constraints is applied in the winner take all competition. Nodes winning too few chromosomes in classification should therefore receive more, while those winning too many chromosomes should receive less.

V. Conclusions

Overall the application of trainable neural networks for chromosome classification has proved effective. The first stage of classification involving 2 MLPs out–performs a highly optimised statistical classifier working with the same data and splitting mechanisms [17]. We have begun investigations into the use of competitive networks in a second classification stage, with emphasis on applying contextual constraints for classifying all the chromosomes in a cell. Results so far are equivocal.

Acknowledgments

This work was greatly facilitated by the exchange of materials and ideas available within the Concerted Action of Automated Cytogenetics Groups supported by the European Community, Project No. II.1.1/13. We are grateful to Jim Piper of the MRC Human Genetics Unit, Edinburgh for permission to reproduce some of his results.

References

[1] E. B. Baum. "On the capabilities of multilayer perceptrons." *Journal Complexity* Vol 4 pp 193–215, 1988.

[2] K. R. Castleman and J. Melnyk. "An automated system for chromosome analysis– final report." *Internal document* No. 5040–30. Jet Propulsion Laboratory, Pasedena, Texas 1976.

[3] "Denver Conference. A proposed standard system of nomenclature of human mitotic chromosomes." *Lancet* Vol 1 pp. 1063–1065, 1960.

[4] S. E. Fahlman. "Faster learning variations on back–propagation: an empirical study." in *Proceedings Connectionist Models Summer School*, 1988, pp 38–51.

[5] J. Graham. "Automation of routine clinical chromosome analysis I, Karyotyping by machine." *Analytical and Quantitative Cytology and Histology*, Vol. 9 pp. 383–390, 1987.

[6] G. H. Granlund. "Identification of human chromosomes using integrated density profiles." *IEEE Trans. Biomed. Eng.* Vol. 23 pp. 183–192 1976.

[7] E. Granum. "Application of statistical and syntactical methods of analysis to classification of chromosome data." in *Pattern Recognition Theory and Application*, Kittler J. Fu KS, Pau LF, eds. NATO ASI (Oxford), Reidel, Dordreht, 1982, pp 373–398.

[8] F. C. A. Groen, T. K. Ten Kate, A. W. M. Smeulders and I. T. Young. "Human chromosome classification based on local band descriptors." *Pattern Recognition Letters* Vol. 9. pp. 211–222, 1989.

[9] S.C. Huang and Y. F. Huang. "Bounds on number of hidden neurons in multilayer perceptrons." *IEEE Trans on Neural Networks*, Vol. 2 pp. 47–55. 1991.

[10] A. M. Jennings. "Chromosome Classification Using Neural Nets," *MSc Thesis*, University of Manchester, U.K. 1990.

[11] T. Kohonen. "Self–Organisation and Associative Memory," *Series in Information Sciences*, Vol 8. Springer–Verlag, Berlin–New York–Tokyo, 1984. 2nd ed. 1988.

[12] R. S. Ledley, P. S. Ing and H. A. Lubs. "Human chromosome classification using discriminant analysis and Bayesian probability." *Comput. Biol. Med.* 10:209–218, 1980.

[13] C. Lundsteen, T. Gredes, E. Granum and J. Philip. "Automatic chromosome analysis II. Karyotyping of banded human chromosomes using band transition sequences." *Clin. Genet.* Vol. 19 pp. 26–36 1981.

[14] C. Lundsteen, T. Gerdes and J. Maahr. "Automatic classification of chromosomes as part of a routine system for clinical analysis." *Cytometry* Vol. 7 pp. 1–7, 1986.

[15] Paris Conference (1971), "Standardization in Human Cytogenetics." *Original Article series*, 8:7. The National Foundation, New York 1972.

[16] J. Piper and E. Granum. "On fully automatic feature measurement for banded chromosome classification." *Cytometry* 10:242–255, 1989.

[17] J. Piper. "Aspects of chromosome class size classification constraint," *CAACG Interlab meeting and Topical Workshop on High–level Classification and Karyotyping, Approaches and Tests*, University of Aalborg, 13–14 March 1991.

[18] D. W. Ruck, S. K. Roggers, M. Kabrisky, M. E. Oxley and B. W. Suter. "The Multilayer perceptron as an approximation to a Bayes Optimal Discriminant Function," *IEEE Trans Neural Networks*, Vol. 1 pp. 296–297. 1990.

[19] D. E. Rummelhart, G. E. Hinton and R. J. Williams. "Learning Internal Representations by Error Propagation." in *Parallel Distributed Processing: Explorations in the Microstructures of Cognition*. Rummelhart DE and McCelland JL (eds.), Vol. 1 Foundations, MIT Press, Cambridge, MA, 1986, pp. 318–362.

[20] M. A. Sartori and P. J. Antsaklis. "A Simple Method to Derive Bounds on the Size and to Train Multilayer Neural Networks." *IEEE Trans on Neural Networks*, Vol. 2 pp. 467–471, 1991.

[21] M. G. Thomason and E. Granum. "Dynamically programmed inference of Markov networks from finite sets of sample strings." *IEEE Trans. PAMI* Vol 8 pp. 491–501, 1986.

[22] M. K. S. Tso, P. Kleinschmidt, I. Mitterreiter and J. Graham. "An efficient transportation algorithm for automatic chromosome karyotyping." *Pattern Recognition Letters* Vol. 12 pp. 117–126, 1991.

Two-bit Weights Are Enough To Solve Vehicle License Recognition Problem

F. Lisa
J. Carrabina
C. Pérez-Vicente
N. Avellana
E. Valderrama

Centre Nacional de Microelectrònica
Universitat Autònoma de Barcelona
08193 Bellaterra. Barcelona.
SPAIN
Tel. +343 5802625
Fax +343 5801496
E.mail. neures@cnmvax.uab.es

Abstract - This paper describes the construction of a system that recognizes vehicle license numbers using feed forward neural networks, once they have been extracted using classical methods. The system has been trained and tested on real-world data. In order to reduce the total amount of memory required and increase the process speed, an additional step has been added to the learning algorithm that produces low precision weights {+1,0,-1}. The network obtained after this training process has a similar behaviour to those networks using floating point representation for weights. A special hardware accelerator has been developed to achieve high speed recognition.

I. INTRODUCTION

Image recognition is one of the fields of research where neural networks shows a higher degree of competitiveness against the classical methods, due to the requirements of high speed processing of large amount of data. Parallelism, inherent in neural network processing, could be more efficient for these purposes.

Vehicle license recognition is usually viewed as a two step process: segmentation of the image and recognition of each symbol. This scheme is still the same in both the classical and the neural approaches.

In the segmentation process, the starting image, usually represented as a grey scale, is processed until the isolation of several binary images representing individual symbols. The main problem is the difficulty in extracting the vehicle license number under conditions of changeable and uneven illumination, so that one part of the license plate is darker than the other parts, besides the problem of getting the image from the vehicle.

Several methods are used in order to obtain binary images. This methods mainly deal with the choice of the threshold between the two states. Otsu's method [1] obtains the threshold after inspecting a grey level histogram of the image, whereas later improvements uses a variable threshold to overcome uneven illumination problems. These methods require several iterations through the whole image, and this makes them slower without parallelism.

Neural Network Approaches to solve image segmentation use several kernels which represent features of image such as edges, corners or others obtained through the training process. The presence of these features can be computed in parallel for all of them in a portion of the image. Using specialized neural network chips, AT&T system can process 32*32 pixels in parallel [2]. For an image of 512*512 pixels, they need 256 executions of the recall phase of the network. Very simple one-layer networks, with 20 input units, suffice to determine the presence of a character from the feature representation.

The symbols obtained from the segmented image are in a fixed window ranging from 5*8, to 20*20 in [3], so that compression or expansion should be necessary before the recognition phase. This is true for both the classical approach, mainly consisting in the evaluation of the Hamming distance to the different patterns, and the neural approach.

There are different neural approaches ranging from those that operate over the whole image, to the ones that use feature extraction. The methods that deal with the whole image, that are of small size, use classical feedback networks (i.e. Hopfield networks or BAM networks), or feed forward networks (i.e. multilayer perceptron networks trained with the backpropagation algorithm). In these cases, images usually do not come from real images, since compression process highly degrades their quality.

For large size windows, these methods are not useful since the size of the network becomes to large for the most powerful learning algorithms. The most common way to proceed is to use a two-step approach. There is a first step for the extraction of basic features, and a second step for the recognition of the set of features.

The highest degree of parallelism is achieved with the smallest resolution for weight and state values, which is specially useful for analog chips but also for the digital ones since the throughput can be increased. This requires a slightly different learning scheme in order to obtain this set of weights. In the case of the AT&T chip [3], weights are represented by 6 bits and states by 3, and it can process 1000 characters per second.

II. NETWORK TOPOLOGY.

The system developed at our laboratories focuses on the recognition of characters of vehicle licenses. These characters came from a segmentation process that uses a non-neural method developed at the Centre de Tractament D'imatges at the UAB [4]. This method is a knowledge-based algorithm that warranties the correct segmentation of the images independently of the position and orientation of the vehicle.

Our network receives an image of 20x30 binary pixels for each character. We use a two-level strategy to reduce the complexity of the learning process. Our basic goal is to obtain low resolution weights for the whole network and, therefore, to reduce the processing time and complexity.

The first step lies in the extraction of features from the image using a three layer network. Since car plates have specific font characters, the set of features could be reduced (42 units in the F2 layer) and it is reasonable to write them by hand, simplifying the learning process. The first layer (F1) detects variations of the basic features, and the second groups them. The corresponding weights are binary and the activation functions are hard-limiter. The neurons in layer F1 have a very high threshold and behave like multi-input "and" gates. Layer F2 has the opposite behaviour and we can see them as "or" gates.

The second step is a feed forward network whose input are features, and with an output for every class (34 classes are considered). There is a hidden layer with 100 units. Fig. 1 shows the structure of the network. A special learning algorithm used to obtain low-resolution weights is explained further below.

The connectivity degree between layers I, F1 and F2 is very reduced due to the locality of the features being extracted. The two last layers are fully connected but, as we will see later, they have low-precision weights (+1, 0 or -1).

III. THE LEARNING RULE.

The method used to train the network is derived from the well-known backpropagation algorithm [5]. The main addition to this algorithm is that it looks for low resolution weights (-1, 0, +1) that are optimal in terms of computational cost; they allow higher degree of parallelism, faster execution, less

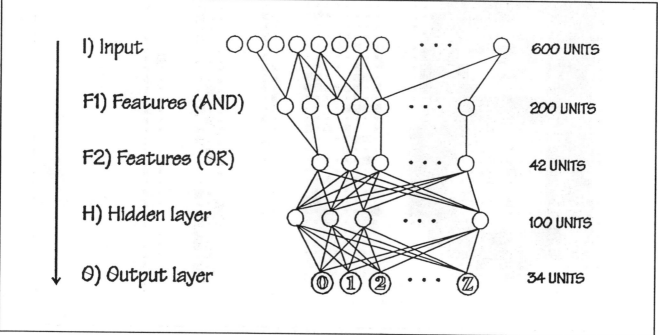

Fig. 1. Topology of the network.

memory and simpler resources. The algorithm described in [6] introduces a penalty term to the backpropagation cost function that drives the learning evolution to local minima, verifying the constraints imposed to the set of weights. The cost function can be expressed as follows:

$$Ep = E_1 + E_2$$

where E1 is the cost function used in the backpropagation method (the squares of the differences between the actual and the desired output value), and E2 is a function with local minima in the desired weight values:

$$E_2 = \sum_{ij} w_{ij}^2 (w_{ij}^2 - 1)^2$$

According to backpropagation methodology, we evaluate the gradient for this function:

$$\Omega = -\frac{\partial E_1}{\partial W_{ij}} = -6W_{ij}^5 + 8w_{ij}^3 - 2w_{ij}$$

This expression is added to the backpropagation rule obtaining the following learning rule:

$$\Delta_p w_{ij}(n+1) = (\delta_{p_j} O_{p_i} + \lambda \omega) \eta + \alpha \Delta_p w_{ij}(n)$$

where η is the learning rate, α is the momentum factor and λ is a constant which determines the effect of the penalty.

In the first iterations we set $\lambda=0$ to insure that the network learns, using high resolution weights. When the network is stable, the value of λ is increased until we obtain a set of weights verifying all the constraints.

Finally we obtain a network composed of low-resolution weights and also simpler activation functions (fig. 2). After training with sigmoid functions, discrete weights allow us to simplify the activation function to a look-up table function with two bits of resolution for the hidden layer, and to a step function for the output layer.

Training and simulation programs were developed in the Rochester Connectionist Simulator environment [7] using a general-purpose Sun Sparcstation II.

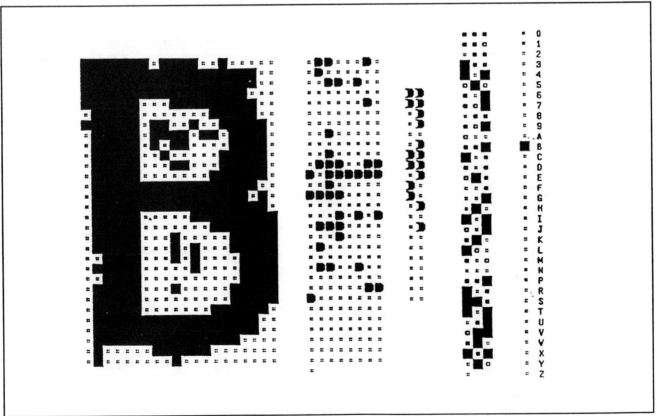

Fig. 2. Exmaple of the process of a pattern by the network.

IV. HARDWARE IMPLEMENTATION

Neural networks with low resolution weights can be processed through very simple resources. If the number of weights is small, analog computations produce a very high speed [3]. If it is large and weights require external memory, digital processing can also be used. In this case the main limitation to the process speed is the number of input/output pins in the processor [8], since computational resources are logical gates.

The final configuration of our network has 10000 two-bit weights and 976 neurons, so we decided to implement a digital processor, the NDN4. This processor can use an already developed PC board specialized in dealing feedback networks [8], by only changing the CPU. This board is able to store up to 2K neurons and 4Meg weights with a system clock of 48Mhz. Nevertheless this ASIC can be easily adapted to work in an image processing environment.

V. RESULTS

The database used to train the network is composed of 438 images from real world; this means that there is noise produced by external factors (dirt, degradation,..) or by the image processing itself (distortion,...). A sample of this set is shown in fig. 4. The solution for floating point weights (using backpropagation) was obtained after about 4 hours of CPU

(118000 presentations), whereas the rest of the learning process up to the obtaining of two-bit weights took about five days. After learning, the network failed to recognize 4 patterns of the training set (0.9%). The way the system was designed, promotes the rejection of patterns (no neuron of the output layer active), more than missclassification (activation of non-correspondent neurons). The test set was composed of 215 images; 2 of them were misclassified and 8 rejected (4.5% total error).

Using simulation programs, the process speed is 10 characters per second, whereas with the system above described, it is possible to process 10000 characters per second. As usual in this kind of systems, the process speed is mainly restricted by the segmentation process.

VI. CONCLUSIONS

In this paper we show that it is possible to solve real problems using neural networks with low resolution weights, by making more effort in the learning phase. These networks can be easily implemented in hardware through simple (and cheap) resources, and introduced in a specific image processing system.

In the vehicle license recognition problem, we deal with images of 20*30 pixels, showing that large dimensions for input layers are not so important restrictions for the implementation of neural networks.

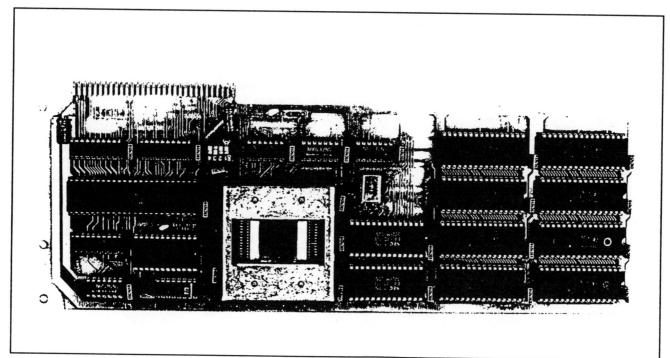

Fig. 3. The NDN4 board.

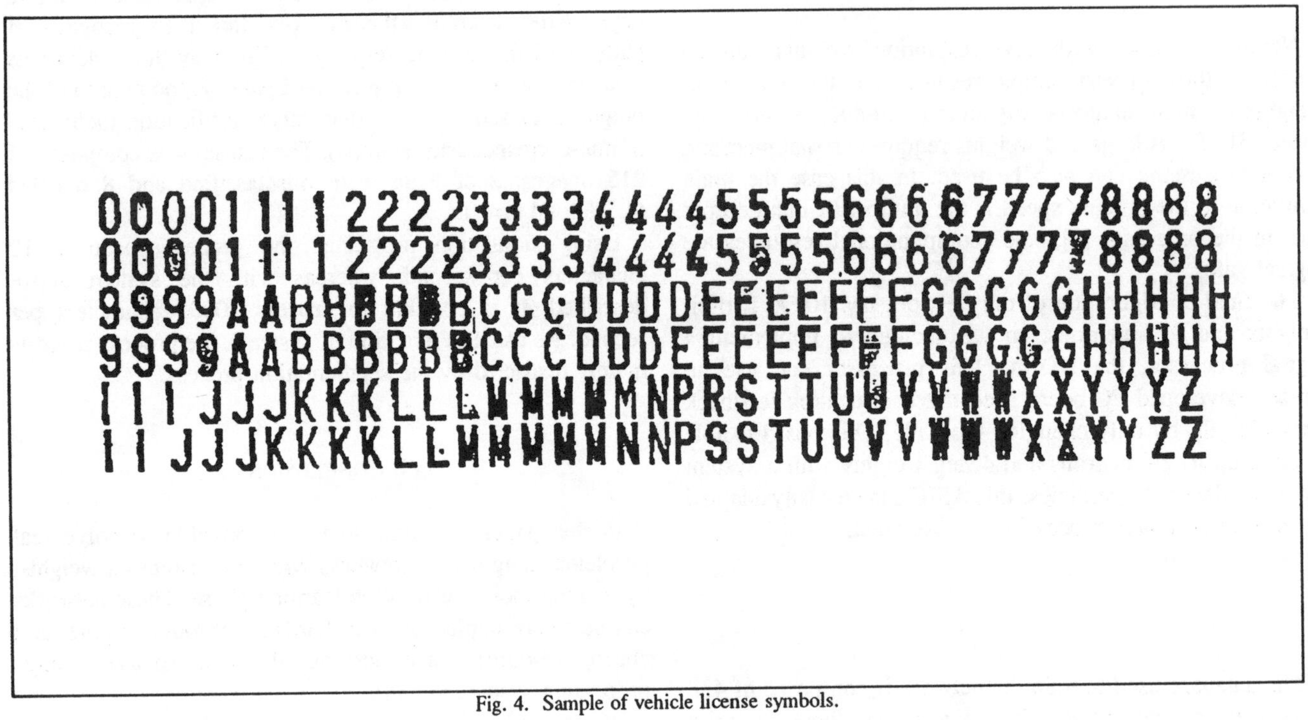

Fig. 4. Sample of vehicle license symbols.

ACKNOWLEDGMENT

This work was sponsored by the spanish Comision Inteministerial de Ciencia y Teconología (CICYT), project TIC91-1049-C02-01.

REFERENCES

[1] N. Otsu, "An automatic threshold selection method based on discriminant and least square criteria". Trans. IECE of Japan, Vol. J63-D, N.4, pp 349-355, 1980.

[2] H.P. Graf et al. "Recent developments of electronic neural nets in the US and Canada". Proc of the 2nd Intl. Conference on Microelectronics for Neural Networks. Munich, pp. 471-488. March 1991.

[3] B.E. Boser et al. "An analog neural network processor and its application to high-speed character recognition". Proc. of Int. Joint Conf. Neural Networks, pp I-415 - I-420, July 1991.

[4] J. Massa. "Detecció Automàtica de Matrícules en un entorn obert". Master Dissertation. Universitat Autònoma de Barcelona. September 1991.

[5] D.E. Rumelhart, G.E. Hinton and R.J. Williams. "Learning internal representations by error propagation", in PDP, vol 1, pp. 318-362. MIT press, 1986.

[6] C.J. Pérez-Vicente, J. Carrabina and E. Valderrama. "Discrete learning in feed-forward neural networks". International Journal on Neural Systems, vol.2, no.4 1991 pp. 323-329.

[7] N.H. Goddard et al. "Rochester Connectionist Simulator". Technical Report 233. October 1989.

[8] J. Carrabina. "High speed/capacity VLSI neural networks". PhD Dissertation. Universitat Autònoma de Barcelona. September 1991.

An Analog Wavelet Transform Chip

R. Timothy Edwards   Michael D. Godfrey*

ISL, Dept. of Electrical Engineering
Stanford University
Stanford, California 94305

Abstract— This paper describes the theory and implementation in subthreshold analog CMOS technology of a circuit which performs continuous wavelet decompositions of a one-dimensional (e.g., audio) input. The analog wavelet outputs are the output of a logarithmically scaled bank of bandpass filters; each band is sampled at a rate proportional to the Nyquist rate of the highest frequency content of that band. The result is a matrix of discrete points describing the input signal as a function of both frequency and time. The filter function of each band is gaussian shaped in order to best resolve the uncertainty relation between time and frequency at each sampled point.

I. INTRODUCTION

The authors have designed and built a chip which performs continuous wavelet transforms on its input using analog subthreshold CMOS circuits fabricated in a standard process.

The Continuous Wavelet Transform (CWT) performed by the chip is an analog filtering function similar to what is known as the Gabor spectrogram [1]. It is not to be confused with the Discrete Wavelet Transform (DWT), although the result of both transforms is a similar time-frequency description of a signal. That description is shown graphically in Fig. 1. The DWT produces this result by starting with a block of discrete data and performing successive high- and low-pass digital filtering. The filtering is repeated on the low-pass output in order to band-pass the signal in a series of stages called "dilations." Each dilation divides the frequency space of the current interval in half while doubling the time span, thus keeping the time-frequency product constant. The CWT divides a signal into a set of logarithmically-scaled frequency bands by passing it through a bank of bandpass filters. The simplest and most natural form of the bandpass filter is a

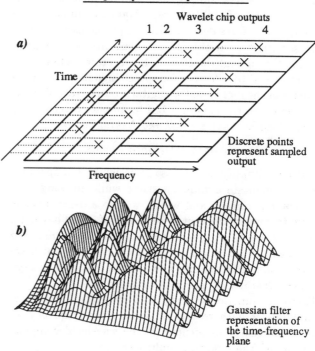

Frequency-Time Representation

Fig. 1. Output sampling and frequency-time representation of the input.

gaussian-shaped function,

$$f(\omega) = e^{-\omega^2/2\sigma^2} \tag{1}$$

which is also gaussian-shaped (and therefore effectively bandlimited) in the time domain. A few other useful filter functions have been investigated in [1, 2]. The CWT as described is merely a band equalizer; in order to produce the most efficient description in terms of the time-frequency uncertainty relation, each frequency band is sampled at a rate proportional to its bandwidth. The result is that each rectangle in the time-frequency plane has an equal

*This chip was designed by T. Edwards under the direction of M. Godfrey, and fabricated by Zilog Corporation of Campbell, California. Zilog provided the funding for this project.

area representing the effective time and frequency bandwidths of the gaussian filter (with some overlap).

Fig. 1a shows how proper sampling of the transform outputs creates a set of points which best describes the input signal as a function of both time and frequency. If the filter bands are sampled in the binary-tree fashion shown and the channels are centered on a $\log_2$ scale, the samples can be easily time-division multiplexed into a single output stream. Fig. 1b is a representation of the gaussian filter functions which produce each sampled value.

This chip was built as an alternative to using a computer or DSP system to perform the same transform; the advantages of this approach are reduced size and power consumption. The resulting analog implementation is inflexible in terms of ability to reprogram the function performed, and requires dealing with the problems of temperature sensitivity, variable process parameters, and noise injection throughout the circuit. However, we believe that the circuit will be effective for speech signals and will be smaller and cheaper than the digital alternatives. The circuit is based on the Analog VLSI techniques described by Carver Mead in *Analog VLSI and Neural Systems* [3].

II. Complex Demodulation

In order to simplify the process of designing bandpass filters that maintain a gaussian shape while allowing variable center frequency and width, we use a demodulation process to convert the center frequency of each filter band to zero before filtering; the result is that each required bandpass filter is reduced to two lowpass filters which are relatively simple in design. This process is known as *complex demodulation* [4] and is described below.

The input function is designated by $f_{in}(t)$. In order to demodulate it with respect to some given frequency ω_c (one of the center frequencies of the wavelet decomposition), we use the following multiplication:

$$f_{out}(t) = 2LPF\left(f_{in}(t)(\cos\omega_c t + i\sin\omega_c t)\right). \quad (2)$$

Since the low-pass filter $LPF(\cdot)$ is assumed to be real, and $f_{in}(t)$ is real, then the output $f_{out}(t)$ must necessarily be complex-valued, and can be represented by

$$f_{out}(t) \equiv f_{real}(t) + if_{imag}(t). \quad (3)$$

Therefore,

$$f_{real}(t) = 2LPF\left(f_{in}(t)\cos\omega_c t\right) \quad (4)$$

and

$$f_{imag}(t) = 2LPF\left(f_{in}(t)\sin\omega_c t\right). \quad (5)$$

In other words, the "real" and "imaginary" parts are both results which are easily obtained by multiplying the input

by two sinusoids which are 90° out of phase with each other.

Each part (sine and cosine) of the demodulation process produces a new signal which contains the sum and the difference of the original and "carrier" frequencies. Since we are demodulating the carrier frequency down to zero, we are interested only in the difference, so we low-pass filter the function to get rid of the part containing the sum of the two signal frequencies. The remaining difference does not differentiate between signals on one side or the other of ω_c since ω_c is now at zero and negative frequencies have no physical meaning. However, this information is preserved in the relationship between $f_{real}(t)$ and $f_{imag}(t)$, as shown by the exact reconstruction below.

In order to remodulate the signal back to its original frequency, we perform the following multiplication:

$$\hat{f}_{in}(t) = f_{out}(t)(\cos\omega_c t - i\sin\omega_c t). \quad (6)$$

This is the same function as the demodulation (2) except for the change in sign. We multiply out the real and imaginary parts of this equation to get a purely real result, which is the reconstruction of the original input:

$$\hat{f}_{in}(t) = f_{real}(t)\cos\omega_c t + f_{imag}(t)\sin\omega_c t. \quad (7)$$

Here the signs have worked out such that the remodulating sinusoids have exactly the same phase relation as the demodulating sinusoids. Note that no low-pass filter is needed for reconstruction. In the instance of the continuous wavelet transform, the low-pass filter for the demodulation can be combined with the gaussian filter of the transformation.

III. Wavelet Gaussian Function

The design of the circuit which approximates a gaussian filter (as described by Grossman [1]) is based on a probabllity argument. Because the signals are first demodulated, it is only necessary to create one half of a gaussian centered around zero. When the signals are remodulated to their respective center frequencies, this low-pass filter will behave as if it were reflected symmetrically across the modulation frequency, becoming a band-pass filter with gaussian characteristics.

Equation (8) describes the filter we designed:

$$H(s) = \frac{V_{out}}{V_{in}} = \left(\frac{1}{\tau s + 1}\right)^n. \quad (8)$$

This filter consists of a cascade of n follower-integrator sections in series. Although (8) converges to a delta function in the limit as $n \to \infty$ for constant τ, it can be shown that when τ is replaced by an expression which maintains constant bandwidth, the transfer function approaches the gaussian function (1) as $n \to \infty$. A proof of this equation can be found in [5] which shows that the gaussian shape is an example of the central limit theorem; in other words, it is a result of the use of cascaded stages and is relatively independent of the shape of the filter.

For n sections in cascade, the relationship between τ and σ from (1) is

$$\sigma = \frac{1}{\tau \sqrt{n \ln(2)}}. \tag{9}$$

Due to considerations of signal-to-noise ratio, and the ability to generate a given constant τ from a voltage applied to the follower-integrators, we chose a cascade order of five sections. The circuit is shown in part in Fig. 2.

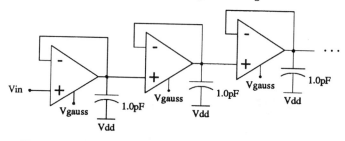

Fig. 2. Three cascaded stages of a filter approximating a half-gaussian function.

The center frequencies of the filters in the filter bank are spaced on a $\log_2$ scale. Assuming speech-quality bandwidth for the input signal, we decided that six outputs would be sufficient, giving typical center frequencies of 9kHz, 4.5kHz, 2.25kHz, 1.125kHz, 562.5Hz, and 281.25Hz. The center frequency of the highest-frequency filter is determined by an oscillator which can be generated either on-chip for a voltage-controlled frequency, or off-chip for a stable frequency. The center frequencies of the rest of the filters are determined by dividing down the oscillator appropriately.

The bandwidth of each gaussian filter is set automatically with respect to the others with the exception of the first and last filters, which have widths adjustable using two control voltages **VgaussH** and **VgaussL**. In terms of the transfer function (8) for the filter, the parameters τ of the highest- and lowest-frequency filters are fixed by these control inputs. τ should be calculated to assure that the width of each gaussian is proportional to the value of the center frequency.

IV. THE VOLTAGE-CONTROLLED OSCILLATOR

A. The Hysteretic Inverter

This circuit, shown in Fig. 3, is the low-power analog VLSI equivalent of the latch. The circuit is a transconductance amplifier with a positive feedback connection. The

Schematic

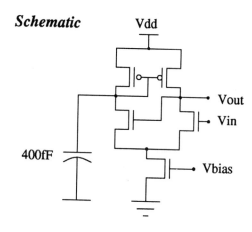

Symbol

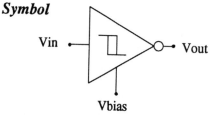

Fig. 3. The hysteretic inverter/latch circuit.

capacitor prevents large voltage swings on the side opposite the output, and so prevents the circuit from sticking in a latched state. The bias voltage **Vbias** is set appropriately to place the transistor in the subthreshold region. The limited amount of current prevents the circuit from switching very fast, so it can only be used in instances where slow switching time is acceptable. In the wavelet transform, it is used to produce the oscillatory output for the modulators, so its highest rate for intended applications is on the order of 10 kHz. The switching points of the hysteretic inverter are close to power and ground, and are a weak function of **Vbias**.

B. Voltage-Controlled Oscillator

Fig. 4 shows the voltage-controlled oscillator (VCO) used in this circuit. The VCO operates using the principle that the saturated current output of wide-range amplifier **(A1)** produces an almost perfectly linear rise in the voltage on the capacitor at its output. When that voltage reaches a critical value, the hysteretic inverter flips states, reversing the values on the inputs to amplifier **(A1)**. Consequently, charge is pulled off of the capacitor and the voltage drops linearly until reaching the critical low value which causes the hysteretic inverter to change state again. The frequency of the output **Vout (cosine)** is dependent on the time required for the capacitor to charge and discharge, which is dependent on the current drive of the amplifier, which is controlled by the bias voltage **Vf**. The

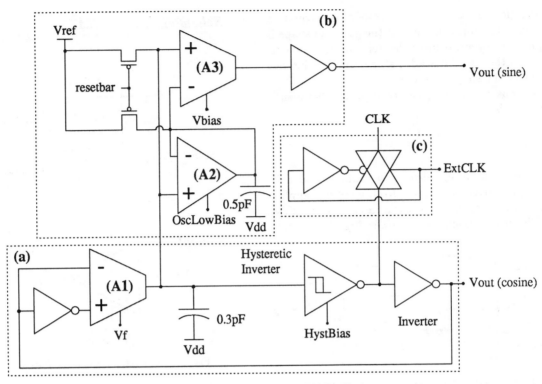

Fig. 4. Low-power voltage-controlled oscillator.

two inverters in the main part of the circuit (a) ensure a clean square wave at the output.

The +90° phase-shifted square wave output is produced by a simple feed-forward adaptive circuit (b). A follower-integrator amplifier (A2) tracks the average value of the input, which in this case is the triangle wave produced by the charging/discharging capacitor of the main oscillator (a). This midpoint value is compared to the actual value of the triangle wave using a high-gain amplifier (A3) which then acts as a signum function. The result is a square wave output which is quarter cycle behind the main oscillator output. The value of **OscLowBias** should be set to ensure a slow adaptation. The digital inverter at the output of the circuit ensures a clean square wave signal.

The frequency f of the oscillator is proportional to the exponential bias voltage **Vf**.

V. WAVELET CHIP SLICE

Due to the parallel nature of the analog wavelet computation, this chip is easily created using abutting slices of circuitry. There are twelve slices in all, each containing the logic to divide down an incoming clock (oscillator) signal, low-pass filter the oscillator to produce a smooth sine (or cosine) wave, multiply this modulating signal with two different inputs (one of them for the signal decompo-

sition part of the transform, the other for the reconstruction half), filter the decomposition result with a gaussian-shaped function, and aggregate (average) the reconstruction result with the result from all other slices to produce a final result. The slices alternate between those producing sine wave modulating signals and cosine wave modulating signals (defined by their phase relation to one another). Each sine-cosine pair of slices receives the same value of **Vgauss** for the gaussian filter. This value is tapped off of a long polysilicon resistor which reaches across all the filter banks and has fixed endpoint values.

A block diagram of the entire Wavelet Transform chip is shown in Fig. 5.

VI. CHIP SPECIFICATIONS

- Power Supply: +5V DC ±5%

- Input mean value: 2.5V ±0.5V

- Input p-p amplitude: 0.4V

- Input frequency range: 80Hz to 10kHz

- Number of output channels: 12 (6 pairs)

- Silicon area: $1.96 \times 10^6 \mu m^2$ (in 2.0 micron CMOS process)

- Chip package: 68-pin PLCC

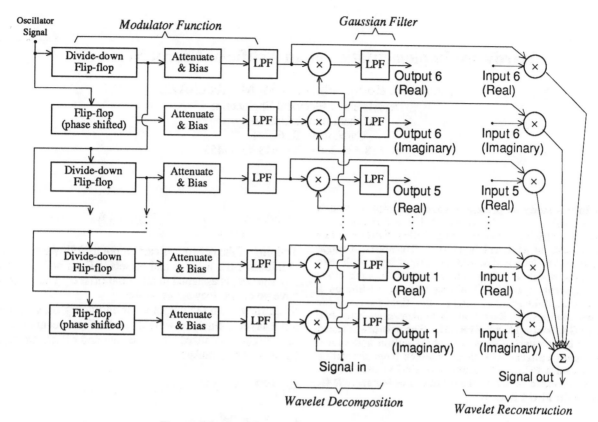

Fig. 5. Wavelet Transform Chip block diagram.

REFERENCES

[1] A. Grossmann, R. Kronland-Martinet, and J. Morlet, "Reading and understanding continuous wavelet transforms," *Wavelets: Time-Frequency Methods and Phase Space*. Springer-Verlag, 1989, pp. 2–20.

[2] R. Bracewell, "Adaptive chirplet representation of signals on time-frequency plane," *Electronics Letters*, vol. 27, no. 13, pp. 1159–1161, June 1991.

[3] C. Mead, *Analog VLSI and Neural Systems*. Reading, MA: Addison-Wesley, 1989.

[4] C. Bingham, M. D. Godfrey, and J. W. Tukey, "Modern techniques of power spectrum estimation," *IEEE Trans. Audio and Electroacoustics*, vol. 15, no. 2, pp. 56–66, June 1967.

[5] W. McC. Siebert, *Circuits, Signals, and Systems*. Cambridge, MA: The MIT Press, 1986, pp. 496–497.

Hardware Implementation of an Artificial Neural Network

Nazeih M. Botros, Ph.D., and M. Abdul-Aziz
Department of Electrical Engineering
Southern Illinois University
Carbondale, IL 62901.
Tel: 618-536-2364 Fax: 618-453-7455

Abstract-In this study we present a hardware implementation of a fully digital and fully interconnected feed forward back-propagation artificial network using Xilinx FPGAs. The network consists of an input layer with five nodes, a single hidden layer with four nodes, and an output layer with two nodes. These nodes are fully interconnected to each other between adjacent layers. Training is done off-line on a conventional digital computer where the final values of the weights are obtained. Each node is implemented with two XC3042 FPGAs and a 1K x 8 EPROM. The network is tested successfully by comparing the values of the output nodes for a different input patterns with those obtained from simulating the network on a PC. The number of FPGAs used can be significally decreased as well as the speed can be increased if 4K or higher family FPGA is used.

I. INTRODUCTION

In recent years, implementation of Field Programmable Gate Arrays (FPGA) in realizing complex hardware system has been accelerated. The relatively low cost and easiness of implementation and reprogramming of FPGA offer attractive features for the hardware designer in comparison with the VLSI technology [1]. Field programmable gate arrays are high density ASICS that can be configured by the user. They combine the flexibility of gate arrays with desktop programmability.

The artificial neural network implemented in this study is a three-layer back-propagation network. See Figure 1. The network is used to classify selected input patterns. It consists of 3 layers: an input layer with 5 nodes, a hidden layer with 4 nodes and an output layer with 2 nodes. The network is selected due to its high performance as a classifier and the easiness of its training procedure [2]. The input to the network is a continuous valued vector $x_1, x_2, \ldots\ldots x_5$.
The output of the network is the class of the current input. The output of node j, y_j, is calculated as follows:

$$y_j = f\left[\left(\sum_i w_{ij} y_i\right) - \theta_j\right] \quad\ldots\ldots\ldots(1)$$

Where θ_j is the offset (bias) of node j, W_{ij} is the weight of the connection between node j and node i, and the function f is the sigmoid non-linearity:

$$f(\alpha) = \frac{1}{1+e^{-\alpha}} \quad\ldots\ldots\ldots\ldots(2)$$

Training of the network is carried out as follows:
i) Initialize the weights and offsets. Each node, except the input nodes, is assigned to an initial offset. The input nodes have no offset; they act as buffers.
ii) Starting from the output layer and going backward to the input layer, adjust the weights and offsets recursively until the weights stabilized. The weights and offsets are adjusted by using the formulas:

$$W_{ij}^{new} = W_{ij}^{old} + \mu \,\varepsilon_j\, x_i \quad\ldots\ldots\ldots(3)$$

$$\theta_j^{new} = \theta_j^{old} + \mu\, \varepsilon_j\, 1 \quad\ldots\ldots\ldots(4)$$

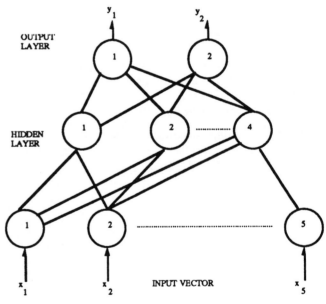

Figure 1. The Artificial Neural Network

Where μ is the gain factor and is assumed to be 0.5, ε_j is the error. In this study, the weights are considered stabilized if the value of each new weight is greater than 95% of its previous(old) value. If node j is an output node, then
$$\varepsilon_j = y_j\, (1-\, y_j\,)(d_j - y_j\,)\ldots\ldots\ldots(5)$$
Where d_j is the desired output of node j and y_j is the actual output. The desired output for all output nodes is set to zero

except for the node that corresponds to the current input training set which is set to 1, [2]. If node j is a hidden node, then:

$$e_j = y_j (1 - y_j) \sum_k e_k W_{jk} \dots\dots\dots(6)$$

Where k is over all nodes in the layers above node j.

II. GENERAL ARCHITECTURE

Figure 2 shows the general architecture of the network. The input layer consists of five nodes (neurons), the hidden layer of four nodes and the output layer of two nodes. These nodes are fully interconnected to each other between adjacent layers. Training is done by off-line simulation of the network on a PC. The final values of weights are obtained at the end of training session. The input layer does no processing but simply buffers the data. The nodes in the other layers first form a weighted sum of their inputs. The 8-

bit input to the hidden and output nodes y_i, is multiplied by 8-bit signed weights W_{ij} to form 16-bit signed product. The products (five in the hidden and four in the output layer) and a 16-bit signed bias value θ_j are accumulated into a 20-bit sum. The sum can be expressed as : $\left[\left(\sum_i w_{ij} y_i \right) - \theta_j \right]$.

The 20-bit sum in the accumulator is then scaled to a 10-bit value. The 10-bit scaling is selected because it is the minimum number of bits that can be retained without deteriorating the accuracy of the sum. This 10-bit scaled sum serves as the address of a 1K x 8 EPROM where a sigmoid activation function f is realized as a lookup table. The activation function produces an 8-bit output. Two's complement number system is employed to handle the multiplications and additions of negative numbers. This

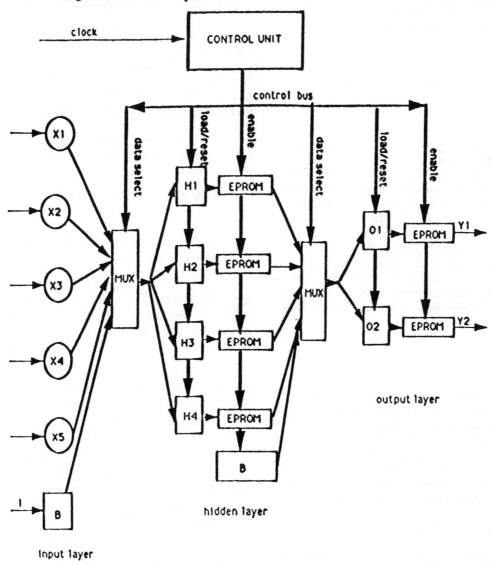

Figure 2. General Architecture of the Network.

1253

output can be expressed as: $f\left[\left(\sum_i w_{ij} y_i\right) - \theta_j\right]$ where

$f(\alpha) = \dfrac{1}{1 + e^{-\alpha}}$. Figure 3 shows a schematic diagram of the processing flow for the hidden node. Each node in the network is built by two XC3042 FPGAs and a 1K by 8 EPROM. The first FPGA carries input latches and multipliers. The second carries a 20 bit fast adder/accumulator circuit and a scaling logic. These two FPGAs compute the weighted sum of five inputs (four in the output layer) and the bias value and then scale the result. The EPROM holds the activation functions for the node. The system clock is 4 MHz which is the maximum speed that could be achieved due to the use of slower EPROMs and two FPGAs per node. The entire network is driven by a micro programmed controller The controller generates a proper sequence of signals to control the timing for both layers. Computations for nodes of the same layer are done in parallel.

III. DETAILS OF THE ARCHITECTURE

Multiplication

Since the weights and biases are contants (pre-determined), multiplication of any number with them can be done in a look-up table fashion The CLBs (Configurable Logic Blocks) of the FPGA are programmed to realize these look-up tables. Multiplying an 8-bit number by an 8-bit constant produces a sixteen bit product. The 8x8 multiplication is broken into two-8x4 multiplications and one addition. The most significant partial product (8x4) is shifted by four bits before adding it to the least significant partial product. The shift is realized by physically shifting (routing) the most significant bits. One CLB is used to generate two bits of the product. The twelve bits of the partial product are generated by using six CLBs.

Summation

The next task performed by the nodes is to produce the sum of the partial products into a single 20-bit sum. The 20 bits are selected so that no overflow can happen. A 20-bit fast carry look-ahead adder is designed to carry out the summations. Each node in the hidden layer adds up ten 16-bit partial products and a bias into a 20-bit positive edge triggered accumulator to produce a single sum. The output nodes perform the same but for eight partial product.

Scaling and Activation Function

The final task performed by the nodes of hidden and output layers is the scaling and the application of activation (sigmoid) function. The final result of addition of all the

partial products and the bias value is stored in a 20-bit accumulator. An investigation of the behavior of the sigmoid function shows that it saturates to approximately 1.0 when $\alpha \geq +7$ and saturates to approximately 0.0 if $\alpha \leq -8$. Accordingly the 20-bits is scaled to 9 bits.

Control Unit

A separate micro programmed controller drives the entire circuit. Two 4-bit asynchronous TTL counters are cascaded to generate the addresses for the control memory. The counters are driven by a 4 MHz system clock. The asynchronous clear inputs of the counters are connected to a push button switch. the ENP of the least significant counter is connected to the Q output of a JK flip flop whose Preset & Clear inputs are driven by two control signals produced by the control memory. See figure 4.

IV. RESULTS

The network is simulated by software and same input patterns are applied to both the software and the hardware network. In both cases the outputs are calculated. Table 1 shows the outputs and y_2 of both networks. See Figure 1. As shown in this table the hardware network (Hard W.) performs correctly. The hardware implementation computes 4 million interconnections (approx. 70,000 decisions) per second. This speed allows the implementation of the network in real-time applications.

V. DISCUSSION AND CONCLUSION

We have presented a successful hardware implementation of a simple artificial neural network. The implementation can be expanded to realize more complex networks. Reconfigurability and adaptability are the main features of the hardware. For a new application only the weights, biases and scaling parameters need to be re configured on the CLBs without changing the basic design. It is easily expandable just by adding more nodes with the same design.

Xilinx FPGAs and other alike FPGAs are found feasible and efficient tools for the design of neural nets. They offer acceptable densities without the cost and length design cycles of full custom circuits. Their reconfigurability and desktop programmability allow to make design changes at user's terminal, thereby avoiding the fabrication cycle times and non-recurring engineering charges. Although (due to our limited funds) the use of two XC3042 FPGAs (50 MHz) and a 1K x 8 EPROM (450ns) per node makes the network bulky, we found that its size and speed can be greatly improved by using higher density FPGAs. FPGA XC3090 can easily accommodate the circuits in the two XC3042 used in this study. It will also significantly reduce the size as well as increase the speed by eliminating the 55ns (approx.) delay between the I/O pins of two FPGAs. RAMs can be

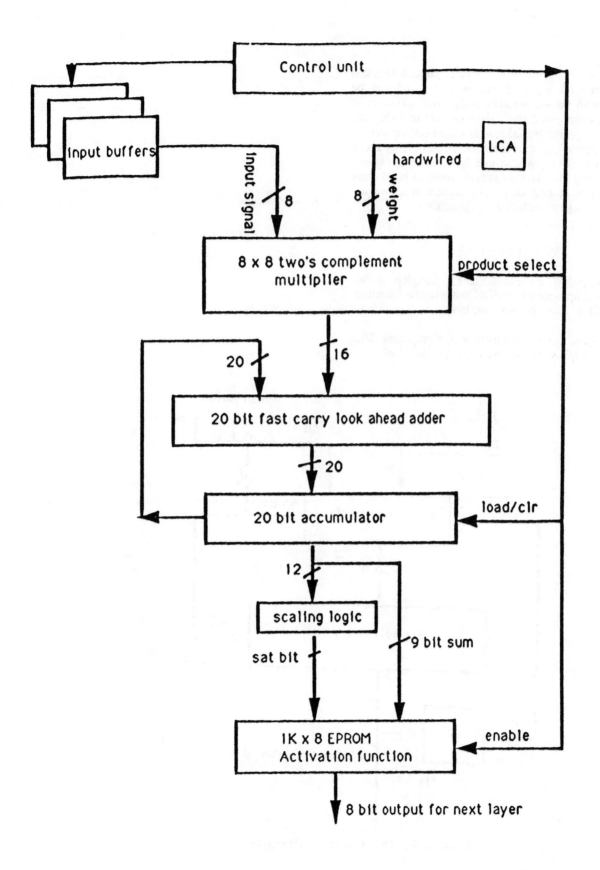

Figure 3. Schematic of digital neuron (hidden unit)

1255

implemented inside the 45K FPGA series. These RAMs can be programmed for sigmoid lookup tables and can be downloaded with the bit stream during configuration, to further increase the speed and reduce the size to 1 chip per node. Use of pipeline techniques in each node as well as between successive layers of the network and higher speed EPROMs and FPGAs can also greatly increase the speed. Very high density FPGAs may provide room to build more than one neuron in one chip. At present time we are modifying the design to include on-chip training.

VI. REFERENCES

[1] C. E. Cox, and W. Ekkehard Blanz, " Ganglon- A Fast Hardware Implementation of a Connectionist Classifier, " IEEE-CICC Phoenix, Arizona, 1991.

[2] R. Lippmann, " An Introduction to Computing With Neural Nets," IEEE-ASSP, Magazine, 4-22, April 1987.

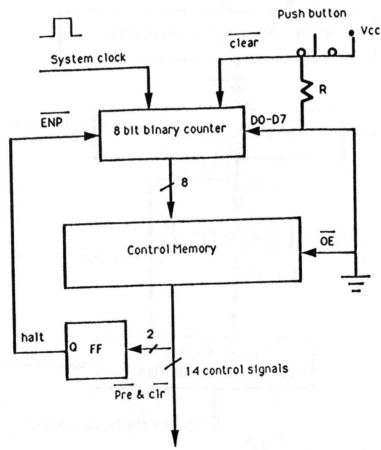

Figure 4. The Control Circuit

Test Patterns					Output Y1 Soft W. Hard W.		Output Y2 Soft W. Hard W.	
7	20	30	48	58	.98967	.99218	.00806	.00781
3	6	19	21	59	.99620	1	.01530	.01562
14	26	39	45	50	.98967	.99218	.00806	.00781
5	19	7	29	37	.98967	.99218	.00806	.00781
10	18	29	53	61	.98967	.99218	.00806	.00781
40	35	31	27	20	.03114	.03125	.95791	.96003
75	66	50	41	19	.03114	.03125	.95791	.06093
31	20	15	8	1	.03114	.03125	.95791	.96093
62	50	55	67	70	.74267	.74218	.20795	.20312
40	32	22	44	14	.03114	.03125	.95791	.96093
20	86	54	38	97	.98967	.99218	.00806	.00781
16	8	4	2	1	.03115	.03125	.95791	.96093
1	2	4	8	16	.99499	.99218	.01258	.01562
19	27	89	34	63	.98967	.99218	.00806	.00781
19	27	89	63	34	.56162	.51562	.41332	.40625
63	34	89	27	19	.03114	.03125	.95791	.96093
34	63	89	27	19	.03114	.03125	.05791	.96093
200	180	100	80	5	.03114	.03125	.95791	.06093
200	180	100	5	80	.03114	.03125	.95791	.96093
5	80	100	180	200	.98967	.99218	.00806	.00781
8	4	1	16	4	.60804	.60937	.42076	.40625

Table 1. Results of Software and Hardware Networks

A Neural Network Systems Component

Dean Mueller and Dan Hammerstrom

Adaptive Solutions, Inc.

1400 NW Compton Drive Suite 340

Beaverton Oregon 97006

Abstract - This paper presents a CMOS device designed to interface the CNAPS™-1064 neural processor IC to traditional computing environments. The encapsulation of flexible I/O models and sequencer control into a modular architecture enables the creation of systems across a wide spectrum of performance capabilities.

I. Introduction

Adaptive Solutions' mission is to leverage the combination of state-of-the-art VLSI, and the non-linear, adaptive capabilities of neural networks to provide a quantum leap in our capability to perform pattern recognition and control applications. This objective is met by optimizing a VLSI architecture for the problem domain at hand. The CNAPS (Connected Network of Adaptive Processors) system provides orders of magnitude improvement in performance at the cost of traditional microprocessor-based systems. We believe this performance increase translates directly to vastly improved solutions for pattern recognition (such as speech, OCR, and image processing) and control problems.

We have chosen artificial neural networks (ANN) as our primary model, since the essence of our approach is to provide general applicability for implementing data transformations (such as from an image scan to the ASCII representation of a character). These transformations are extremely complex and often involve time-varying, non-linear functions. The non-linear capabilities and adaptive nature of ANNs make them a natural for these types of tasks. However, for most applications the neural network is a small part of a larger system which generally involves more traditional computations such as Fourier transforms, Markov models, rule-based knowledge, image segmentation, etc.

Consequently, the CNAPS architecture is not limited to neural networks but has been designed to meet the needs of an entire range of associated problems. It is not a general-purpose computer, but it is reasonably general-purpose within the target domain. By restricting the range of applicability, simplifications are possible that allow an inexpensive implementation of a parallel processor system with a significant boost in performance. Low cost, in turn, is essential because of the pervasive nature of the problems we are trying to solve and the situations where such solutions are required.

Crucial to the CNAPS strategy is the ability to provide low-cost program and I/O control of the CNAPS processor array and to encapsulate this functionality efficiently into a single piece of silicon. In addition, a traditional, digital co-processor-like interface to the CNAPS system is essential for the target applications of this processor. This paper presents the design of the CSC — the CNAPS Sequencer Chip — which performs this function.

A common criticism of neural network chips is that their designs often represent local optimizations with little thought given to the larger system context in which these devices must operate. The CSC is a *systems* component and was designed with the larger system in mind. It has two objectives, to control the CNAPS processor array and to interface the array efficiently to the larger digital world. The CSC provides efficient control of CNAPS programs. In addition, it is a powerful I/O processor which simultaneously controls system input and output. The CSC operates as a building-block component and can interface directly to external I/O devices and to other CSCs, allowing large, complex systems to be created. It also can control external input and output devices interfacing directly with the CNAPS processor array chips, increasing the usable I/O bandwidth of the CNAPS system. Finally, and most importantly, integrating the entire I/O control and sequencing functions into a single chip enables low-end CNAPS systems to be created easily and inexpensively.

The CSC functionality and its simple, clean interface is critical to the deployment of real world pattern recognition and neural network applications executing on CNAPS. We believe that the CSC is the first neural network *systems* component. This paper presents the CSC architecture and design methodology.

II. CNAPS System Architecture

To appreciate the functionality of the CSC, an understanding of a general CNAPS system architecture is helpful. A CNAPS application development system consists of a control subsystem and a CNAPS subsystem as shown in Fig. 1. The control subsystem is responsible for downloading programs, data I/O support, debugging services, diagnostics, and interfacing to other hardware peripherals. In this type of full-function environment, the CP could be a microprocessor controller board with RAM, ROM, and various other hardware interfaces to control system-level, real-time functions. However, the control subsystem implementation

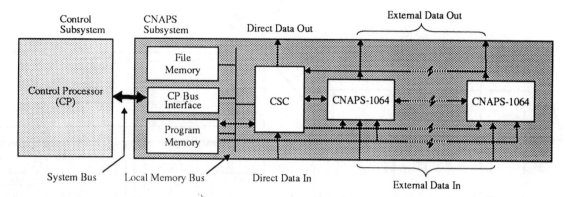

Fig. 1 System Architecture and CNAPS Subsystem Architecture

depends on the extent of the functionality required in the application. For a simple end-use application, the CP may be very simple, or it may not exist at all. With the help of a small state machine and some ROM, the CSC can implement an auto-boot function that tests the system, loads the application program, and begins execution without any external assistance.

The CNAPS subsystem executes the CNAPS program. A block diagram of the basic architecture is shown in Fig. 2. The subsystem consists of three types of interfaces to external systems: the CP interface, the Direct Data interface, and the External Data interface. The CP interface is required to interface to the larger compute system. The Direct and External interfaces access stream data independent of the system memory bus. These interfaces may allow higher access rates than the system bus, as well as the benefits of off-loading system traffic. The architecture of the CNAPS subsystem can be broken down into a few basic modules: an interface to the CP, the DRAM file memory space, a SRAM program memory space, the CSC, and an array of Adaptive Solutions CNAPS-1064 multi-processor ICs.

The CP bus interface links the local bus and the system bus. It is also configured to map the CNAPS subsystem into the larger control and memory space. This interface can be a slave only, or a master/slave depending on the application. Master capability is mandatory if the CNAPS program requires data that is outside the range of local file memory. The CNAPS subsystem can be easily adapted to different compute environments by simply modifying the CP interface block to be compatible with the target system bus.

The various memory spaces in the CNAPS subsystem are connected to a local memory bus. A local, synchronous memory bus was implemented so that the CSC could perform high-speed memory access to the local data memory without contending for the system memory bus. The major units on this bus are: File memory, Program memory, the CSC, and the CP interface. The DRAM file memory is a slave device used to store data locally in the CNAPS subsystem. This memory can hold input or output data files and can be accessed by the CP or the CSC.

The SRAM program memory is a slave device that must be downloaded with programs before execution can begin. It is accessed by the CP over the local memory bus, but when a CNAPS program is executing, it is accessed by the CSC over an independent address and data bus. This lets the CSC access an instruction from the program memory on every clock cycle independent of the traffic on the local memory bus.

The CSC accesses a 64-bit instruction from program memory on every cycle. Thirty-two bits of each instruction are decoded by the CSC to specify sequencer operation and I/O control. The other 32 bits are broadcast to control the CNAPS array processing nodes. As a slave on the local memory bus, the CSC can be accessed by the CP to initialize various state. As a master, it can read or write to local memory while it executes a CNAPS program. The CSC also interfaces to the CNAPS-1064 to supervise the data and instruction flow to/from the array.

Each CNAPS-1064 IC is a VLSI device that contains an array of 64 digital signal processor-like processing nodes (PNs). The processing nodes are arranged in a SIMD (single instruction, multiple data) configuration using broadcast interconnect [1]. The architecture of each PN is general enough for classical digital signal processing and pattern recognition, but is optimized for neural network applications.

One of the major advantages of the CNAPS system is its ability to perform feature extraction [2] as well as pattern recognition on the same system. The CNAPS system has been effectively used for speech recognition [3] as well as for speaker identification applications [4]. The system has also been effective for high speed image processing applications such as Kanji character recognition [5].

The PN architecture, as shown in Fig. 2, has proven to be very suitable for many types of applications. Two input buses are supplied to the array: the PNCMD Bus and the IN Bus. The PNCMD Bus contains the 32-bit instruction and the IN Bus contains the 8-bit data broadcast to all PNs. The OUT Bus allows any PN to output data under the control of the CSC. In addition to the parallel broadcast buses, each processor is interconnected to its nearest neighbor by a one-

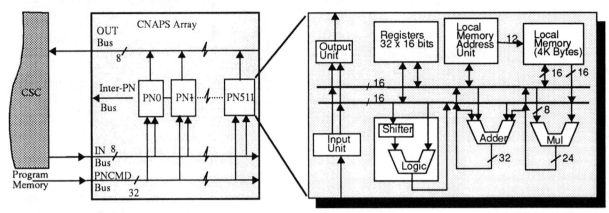

Fig. 2 The CNAPS Array and PN Architecture

dimensional Inter-PN Bus.

Each PN contains 4K bytes of memory and its own address generation logic to access the local memory. The multiplier, ALU, and dual internal buses provide an efficient architecture for high-speed sum-of-products execution. Signed 8-, 16-, or 32-bit integer arithmetic is supported by these units. The input and output units support 8- or 16-bit communication to the rest of the array. When operating at 20MHz, each 64-processor chip is capable of performing 1.28 billion connections per second. When executing the Back Propagation algorithm, each chip performs 210 million updates per second [6]. ANNs are implemented by mapping neurons into physical or virtual PNs. All processors execute a multiply-accumulate in a single cycle. A PN can place its output on the OUT Bus, and the CSC will broadcast this value to the IN Bus where it is available to all PNs in the next network layer. Each PN will broadcast its output in turn implementing n^2 connections in n clocks [1].

The broadcast SIMD structure allows for easy expansion of the array beyond a single chip. Multiple CNAPS-1064 chips can be connected to create larger systems without the concept of distinct chip boundaries. However, the user must know the number of PNs in the system when programming.

III. CSC Operation and Architecture

The master state-machine in the CSC is shown in Fig. 3.

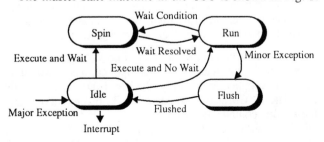

Fig. 3 CSC State Machine

When IDLE, the CSC does not execute a CNAPS program, and the entire internal state is accessible from the local memory bus. When instructed to do so, the CSC moves to RUN mode and begins executing instructions. When RUNning, the CSC may require mastership of the local memory bus. Various wait conditions such as a wait-for-data cause the CSC to SPIN until the wait is resolved. When a minor condition occurs that stops execution, the CSC will first flush the file memory output buffers before entering IDLE. There are also some major exceptions that can occur that will cause the CSC to enter the IDLE state without flushing the buffers. When the CSC returns to IDLE, it issues an interrupt, and the CP can query the status register to determine the cause of termination.

The CSC contains the five major modules shown in Fig. 4. Each of these units has control lines to communicate with each other, as well as a global data bus that connects all blocks and allows instruction-controlled data transfer between the units. In addition to these functions, there are mode registers, profile counters, and other miscellaneous functions that are beyond the scope of this paper. There has been much discussion so far about interfacing to the local bus, sequencing instructions, and I/O processing, the three major blocks in the CSC. In addition to these functions, there is also a 64x32 register file and a 32-bit ALU. These two structures, along with the CSC's ability to perform internal data transfers, enable complex address control and file structure maintenance. Each of the three major functional units will now be discussed.

A. The Control Processor Interface (CPIF)

The interface to the local memory bus functions as a basic master/slave memory interface with interrupt capability. The internals of the CSC are highly accessible and observable by the CP because most CSC internal state is mapped into the bus. The CPIF controls these accesses by acting as a slave on the local bus. In addition to providing a pathway into the internal state, this interface contains command and status

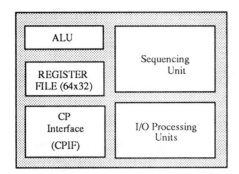

Fig. 4 CSC Block Diagram

registers that allow the CP to start, stop, or query the status of the CSC at any time. Before executing a CNAPS program, the CP sets up the CSC by initializing various state and pointers to file memory data input and output space. The CP then issues a command to the command register and CNAPS execution begins.

When the CSC is executing CNAPS programs, it may become master of the local bus to access file memory or locations in the larger system memory space. The interface is responsible for taking requests from the I/O processing unit, arbitrating for the local memory bus, and controlling the access. This interface is capable of transferring data at the maximum combined I/O rate of the CNAPS-1064. As the program executes, a number of conditions can occur that cause the CSC to halt execution and issue an interrupt. The status registers in this interface can be read at any time to determine the cause of the interrupt or to monitor the internal modes and status of the CSC.

B. Sequencing Unit

The sequencer unit controls the activity of the CNAPS array interface by executing instructions that specify sequencing and I/O control. The 16-bit program counter can address 64K, 64-bit instructions. Thirty-two bits of the instruction are sent to the array, while the other half is sent to the CSC to dictate sequencer and data flow control. The sequencer and I/O control blocks work together to supply synchronized instruction and data flow to the CNAPS array.

There are two distinct types of CSC commands: those that control the program sequencing and data I/O flow (sequencer), and those that cause intra-CSC data transfers (DATAXFR). Sequencer commands support breakpoints, CP system calls, conditional looping with eight different loop registers, literal loading into various sequencer registers, a single level jump and return, and control of I/O source and destination. The various conditional instructions can test the loop register, ALU output tests, CNAPS arbitration, and OUT Bus status.

The DATAXFR instruction group allows the user to specify direct or indirect data transfers within the CSC. This includes access to most internal state, the register file, and the ALU. This instruction type is useful for transferring data that has been loaded from the program into sequencer

registers to some other place such as the I/O pointers or the CNAPS array itself. Since the DATAXFR instruction uses some of the fields normally used to control I/O and sequencer operation, default functions are implied.

C. I/O Processing Units

The I/O processing units for the IN Bus and OUT Bus are designed to allow a variety of data flow paths to interact with and be synchronized to the CNAPS array. Each CSC instruction contains fields that specify the I/O type for that specific instruction. These fields, along with some control registers, are used to control the actions of the I/O processors.

In defining the types of I/O support, the primary goal is to use data at the maximum rate allowed by the CNAPS array, to support traditional file and stream data flow from DRAM, and to support stream data flow that is independent of the memory bus. Another integral factor in solving the instruction/data synchronization problem is the ability for the I/O processing units to block instruction flow and pause the array if data is required but not yet available, or if the instruction calls for data output, but there is no room. In this case, the I/O units instruct the master mode control to SPIN on the current instruction until the wait is resolved. When SPINning, even though the sequencer and array are stalled, the I/O units will continue to operate with the CSC-external interfaces to resolve the wait condition.

Fig. 5 shows a block diagram of the I/O datapaths in the CSC. This diagram illustrates the possible sources for the IN Bus and the various destinations for the OUT Bus. A portion of the CNAPS array is also shown for clarity. The IN Bus data on any particular CNAPS chip can come from five possible sources: External, Direct, Constant register, Out-In pipe, or File memory. There are four possible destinations for data on a CNAPS chip's OUT Bus: External, Direct, File memory, and the Out-In pipe. The Out-In pipe actually latches the OUT Bus on every instruction, independent of the use of the other destinations. Only one of the other destinations can be specified at one time. Each I/O processing unit type will now be briefly described.

The 16-byte input and output queues that access file memory can transfer data at 40MByte/sec, which is the maximum combined I/O rate of the CNAPS-1064. In addition to the data buffers themselves, there are also address generation and control functions. This includes address pointers, counters, byte counters, and bounds detection to fully control file memory access. The buffers perform sequential access from a user-defined starting point, which allows auto-increment access to sub-portions of data that randomly exists in a larger data set. This capability is useful in an image application for scanning the region of interest, or for sliding templates or windows in a pattern recognition application. When maintaining file structures, the various pointers can be saved in the register file, manipulated in the ALU, and restored by the program, so the CSC can emulate a large number of *virtual* channels.

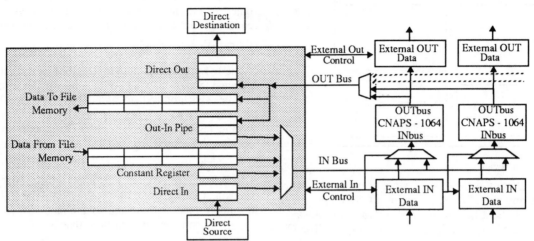

Fig. 5 CNAPS I/O Datapaths

The Direct I/O channels consist of two (one for input, one for output) 8-bit parallel interfaces. These direct data paths are used in applications where data does not come from file memory, but rather from a separate CSC data port. Access to this data by the CNAPS array is synchronized by the CSC. The Directin interface accepts data at 20MBytes/sec and routes it to the IN Bus. The Directout interface takes data from the OUT Bus at 20MBytes/sec and applies it to the Direct output port. A simple synchronous handshake interface allows multiple CSC systems to connect directly and operate in a loosely synchronized, data dependent manner.

The external I/O is a control interface that allows independent, remote data transfer to/from each CNAPS-1064 in the array, thus permitting multiple external datapath channels to/from each CNAPS-1064. Such a system, when used with multiple CNAPS-1064 chips, could provide the data rates required for high-resolution continuous video processing. When instructed to use external data, the CSC asserts the control lines to an external multiplexor that allows the remote device to place data on the IN Bus or take data from the OUT Bus. This is just a control interface; data are not transferred through the CSC. A burst mode supports external data transfers on every clock cycle. Each external channel supports a 20MBytes/sec transfer rate; the total maximum data rate depends on the number of external channels. The maximum rate is $(20M * n)$ where n is the number of external channels. For example, an 8-chip system with 8 external in and 8 external out channels can transfer data at 320MByte/second.

In addition to the three sources listed above, the user can indicate that the IN Bus be driven from the constant register, or that the data on the OUT Bus are fed back around to the IN Bus. This data wrap-around allows recursive neural networks or feedforward neural networks to be implemented efficiently on the CNAPS array. For a feedforward network, one layer transmits its outputs while the next layer in the network computes its outputs.

IV. Design Technology and Methodology

The CSC is implemented in a 240-pin MQFP package using a 95K gate array in a 0.8 micron double-metal CMOS process. The design methodology used to develop the CSC relies heavily on simulation and a top-down design flow. A high-level simulator was written in C that allowed clock-accurate simulation of the architecture. It is fully integrated with Adaptive Solutions' software products, providing the ability to accurately simulate the CP and CNAPS system concurrently. This simulator is used for software and architecture development and is considered the "golden" simulator for the system.

The CSC was designed by creating an RTL-level description in Verilog. A behavioral-level model was created for the CNAPS subsystem so that the CSC could be verified in its native environment. The Verilog CNAPS subsystem was tested by running programs on the C simulator and capturing transactions for application to the Verilog simulation. A run-time comparison technique is used to compare the idealistic realm of architecture simulation against a real hardware implementation. Random "throttles" control the models to allow the transactions to take place randomly. This creates the ability to superimpose asynchronous random data rates, random bus contention, and random halt and restart functions while performing robust validation against the architectural simulator. This technique was instrumental to the success of the CSC design in an environment dominated by unknown data/control rates and distributions.

Synthesis tools were used to create a gate-level implementation from the RTL-level model. This gate implementation was verified in the same system as the RTL-level model. A static timing analyzer was used to verify chip timing with the ASIC vendors library. After the design was complete, automatic test insertion and test pattern generation were used to implement internal serial scan and JTAG.

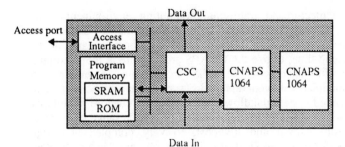

Fig. 6 Low-cost Application Engine

V. A Spectrum of CNAPS System Configurations

The system configuration shown in Fig. 1 is typical of a high-performance application development system. The CSC was designed to support a wide range of systems that could be much bigger, or much smaller than this example. To give the reader a feeling for the flexibility of the system, two different systems will now be described.

The configuration shown in Fig. 6 shows a small system that could be designed for a specific end-use application. It contains 2 CNAPS-1064 chips (128 processors) running at 20MHz. This system is capable of performing 2.56 billion connections (multiply-accumulates) per second and 420 million connection updates per second. Notice that the CP interface has been replaced by a simple access port for special-purpose access only. It is not required for normal operation and could be used for diagnostics or for downloading EPROM software updates. Also notice that there is no File memory in this system. Instead of getting data from a file memory, data is accepted from an acquisition

system into the Direct input port of the CSC. Likewise, data is pumped out via the Direct out interface. Each of these ports can maintain a transfer rate of 20MByte/second.

On system power-up, the CSC executes from ROM to perform diagnostics and load the application software into SRAM program memory. The CSC can immediately start performing the application software loop. The program will expect data from the Direct input port and will block on any instruction that requires data if data does not exist. As soon as data is available, the CSC continues execution. This provides the capability to perform real-time computations in a data stream environment. If the Access Interface shown here is replaced with PC bus converter logic or a SCSI interface, an external device could control or interact with the application. A low-cost implementation designed with a popular interface can bring impressive computational power to the consumer market.

The basic architecture can be easily expanded to support large, high-performance systems with flexible dataflow configurations. The system shown in Fig. 7 consists of four CNAPS arrays. Each array contains 8 CNAPS-1064s with direct and external I/O support. Operating at 20MHz, such a system would provide 2048 processors computing 40 billion connections per second. It is useful for compute intensive, high-bandwidth applications where the problem can be broken down into independent programs and process levels with point-to-point data communication between each level.

Each CNAPS array requires a CSC to control the array. This example shows two such arrays per local memory bus. This is just an arbitrary choice, the number of CSCs on any

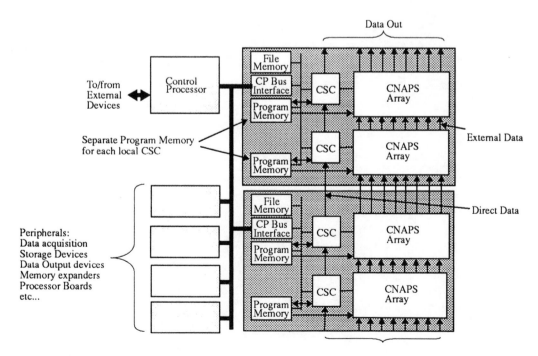

Fig. 7 Complex Multi-level CNAPS Configuration

local bus depends on the memory structure, the bus loading, and the target frequency. Each CSC has its own program memory to allow independent programming in each array. The CSCs that are attached to the same local bus have high-speed access to the same file memory. Such a scenario is useful in applications that require independent processing but share the same data. Semaphores can be used to synchronize access to shared data files.

The CSCs can also initiate transfers across the system bus to allow access to alternate memory spaces, data acquisition boards, or other system devices. Such a configuration is useful when data is shared across the system, as long as the bandwidth/traffic load does not impose an unacceptable limit on the performance of the CNAPS array.

The CSCs are connected to each other via the Direct data ports. These ports allow data to be transferred between CSCs without the use of the system or local bus. Communicating between levels is accomplished by allowing instruction blocking on the data until the communicating neighbor is synchronized, thus allowing data transfer between levels. In addition to communicating between CSCs, these ports could also be used to communicate with a data acquisition system or some other data output device. A similar configuration is used to connect the external interfaces together for high-bandwidth requirements such as high-end image applications.

VI. *Summary*

Adaptive Solutions has successfully achieved its goal of creating a device to efficiently interface the CNAPS architecture to traditional computing environments. The CSC provides a simple co-processor interface that can be easily adapted to different target environments and, at the same time, utilize the CNAPS architecture at the maximum performance possible. The architecture is simple and modular, with general data I/O support that can be adapted to varied system dataflow models. The architecture modularity allows efficient implementation of a wide range of systems from simple and low-cost, to very complex and high performance applications. This development is a significant step towards the deployment of truly high performance neural networks and other highly parallel algorithms into the computing and application mainstream.

References

[1] Hammerstrom, D., "A VLSI srchitecture for high-performance, low-cost, on-chip learning", Proceedings IJCNN June 1990.

[2] Skinner, T., "Speech signal processing on a neurocomputer", Proceedings of ICSLP 1990.

[3] Holt, J., Skinner, T., and Nguyen, N., "Automating operator services using automatic speech recognition", Proceedings of IEEE Asilomar Conference 1992.

[4] Skinner, T., Holt, J., and Nguyen, N., "Automatic identity confirmation at Adaptive Solutions", *Speech Technology*, Vol. 5, no. 4 1991.

[5] Togawa, F., Ueda, T., Aramaki, T., Tanaka, A., "Receptive field neural network with shift tolerant capability for Kanji character recognition", IJCNN, Singapore, Nov 1991.

[6] McCartor, H., "Back propagation implementation on the Adaptive Solutions neurocomputer chip", Advances in Neural Information Processing Systems, Vol. 3, pp. 1028-1031, Morgan Kaufmann, 1991.

PROCESS MODELS AND NETWORK COMPLEXITY

Edward A. Rietman and Robert C. Frye
AT&T Bell Laboratories
600 Mountain Avenue
Murray Hill, NJ 07974

and Earl R. Lory
AT&T Bell Laboratories
PO Box 900
Princeton, NJ 08540

Abstract -- We have used a neural network to model a plasma etching system. The network was trained from a large data base generated from actual CMOS production runs. We describe one aspect of this model, which predicts the amount of over-etching into the underlying oxide during silicide gate patterning. Comparing networks of varying complexity, we find that large, complex networks, which perform better on the task of learning the training data, do not necessarily perform as well on verification. We have used the neural network model to extract information regarding the relative influence of various process variables and signatures in the etching process. For such procedures, small, simple networks often prove to be better and more accurate.

I. INTRODUCTION

One of the main objectives of modeling a process is to learn something about it, perhaps by identifying the key parameters that influence it. Another is for control, either as an on-line monitor or for use in a feedback controller. In this paper, we discuss a neural network process model for plasma etching during gate formation in microelectronic circuits. Modeling this particular process is useful for the above reasons, but it is an especially interesting example because it illustrates the importance of choosing networks of appropriate complexity for a given modeling task.

Plasma etching is a process in which a chemical layer is etched from a substrate by a highly reactive ionized gas. Because of the reactive nature of this gas it is possible to perform chemical reactions that are far from thermodynamic equilibrium without exposing the reacting surfaces to high temperatures. Furthermore, the sheath potential of the plasma at low pressures will accelerate the ions perpendicular to the etching surface. Ion impact accelerated chemistry preferentially etches the horizontal surfaces to produce the anisotropic etching necessary for

submicron geometries. The gases in the plasma are chosen such that they produce volatile products after reacting with the film to be etched. This procedure is called "dry etching" in comparison to older technology, "wet etching", which uses a liquid etch solution. The process we are modeling is a TaSi plasma etch used for CMOS gate formation. Tantalum silicide, like many metal silicides, is refractory and has low resistivity. These material properties make it an excellent choice for gate material where further processing steps involve high temperatures. The etch chemistry and process have been described by Curtis and Brunner (1989) and van Roosmalen *et al.* (1991).

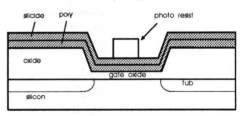

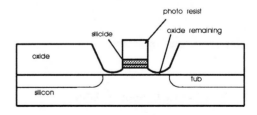

Figure 1: CMOS gate formation.

Figure 1 is a diagram of the CMOS structure before and after the etch. The thickness of the oxide remaining next to the gate must be greater than some minimum. If over-etching occurs it will have an adverse effect on the resulting device's performance. One of the objectives of our model is to predict the remaining thickness of this oxide after the etch.

II. PROCESS DESCRIPTION

We built a neural network plasma etch model from a production database. The project focused specifically on a Drytek Quad plasma etcher in an AT&T microelectronics factory. This etcher is used for TaSi etch in the CMOS gate formation step. The model uses mean values of various monitored process variables on the etch machine to predict wafer attributes of the end product. An abstract model of this type could have a major impact on modeling other systems for cybernetic and closed loop control.

The Drytek quad plasma etcher has two pairs of etch chambers, a robotic handler and a load lock chamber. The TaSi/poly etching consists of two etch processes under different chemistries. A wafer starts in one chamber and undergoes a fast etch of the TaSi. It is then transported to another chamber for a slow etch of the polysilicon using a different set of etch gases and conditions than in the first chamber. Two wafers can be etched simultaneously. We used a single network to model both pairs of chambers on a single machine.

Table 1

| Model Inputs: | |
TaSi etch	Poly etch
applied rf	applied rf
pressure	pressure
dc bias	dc bias
gas 1 (flow rate)	gas 1 (flow rate)
gas 2	gas 2
gas 3	gas 3
gas 4	gas 4
end time	end time
over etch time	over etch time

Model output: oxide thickness

Table 1: Network input variables.

The plasma etch process is controlled by an applied rf power, gas flow rates, chamber pressure and etch time. All but the last of these variables are pre-set and maintained by closed-loop control. The etch time is determined by in-situ end-point detectors. Some of the signatures produced by this process are the induced dc-bias, reflected rf power and the emission spectrum from the plasma glow. The gas flow rates into the plasma reactor, the pressure and the applied rf power are measured many times during the etch process.

Their mean values and standard deviations are automatically entered into a production database. Values are recorded for each parameter for each of the four chambers. During processing a wafer is rapidly etched in the first chamber using chemistry that has a high etch rate for TaSi and polysilicon but poor selectivity towards oxide. The second chamber uses chemistry with a high poly etch rate and high selectivity towards oxide. The pre-etch and post-etch wafer attributes are entered into a second production database. By querying these databases with a relational language we collected a relation of input/output vectors representing the model. The input/output vectors for the neural network model consisted of the flow rates for the gases, the applied rf power, pressure, reflected rf-power, induced dc-bias, pre- and post-etch oxide thickness and several fields to act as keys. These inputs to the network are summarized in Table 1. The output for the model was the oxide thickness. We collected a total of 1744 input/output vectors from actual production runs. We used a randomly chosen subset of 200 of these vectors for verification, and the remainder for training.

The pre-etch oxide thickness between the gate structure and the field oxide has a mean thickness of $208\,\text{Å}$ with a standard deviation of $5\,\text{Å}$. This is the as-grown oxide. The post-etch oxide thickness, measured at the center of the wafer, has a mean thickness of $153.2\,\text{Å}$ with a standard deviation of $12.9\,\text{Å}$.

III. NETWORK ARCHITECTURES

The development of a neural network architecture is analogous to choosing an optimal subset of regressor variables for a statistical model. Since we have no analytical formalism for this task, we generally rely instead on trial and error. Scores of networks must be tried with different numbers of nodes in the hidden layer(s) and different learning rates. In our initial experiments we started with one hidden layer of hyperbolic tangent neurons and changed both the number of nodes in this layer and the learning rate. The criterion for preferring a particular architecture was its ultimate performance on the learning data. The final version of this network, which we will call the "complex" network, had 33 neurons in its hidden layer and one linear output neuron to represent the oxide thickness. The learning curve and a histogram showing the network's performance on the verification data are shown in Figure 2. The standard deviation of the error, roughly $9\,\text{Å}$, is smaller than the $12.9\,\text{Å}$ standard deviation in the database, indicating that the network's predictions are better than simply guessing the mean on each trial.

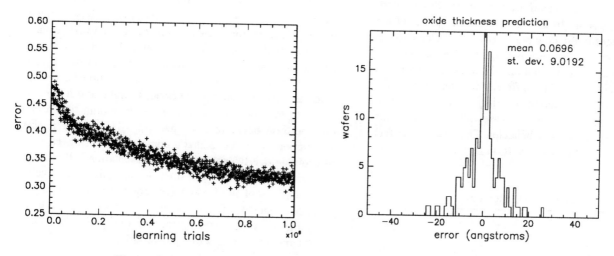

Figure 2: Learning curve and verification performance for the complex network.

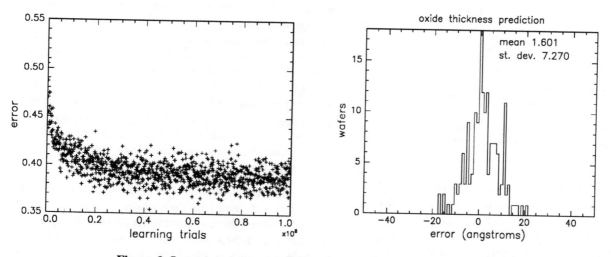

Figure 3: Learning curve and verification performance for the simple network.

We evaluated the network's sensitivity to each of its input variables by finding the partial derivative of the output with respect to each input assuming an average input vector. This procedure determines the relative importance of each of these variables in determining the final oxide thickness. The results of this analysis made it clear to us that the model developed by the "complex" network was not consistent and, therefore, was not reliable. We trained the same network several different times, changing only its random seed to set the starting point for the weights. In all cases, the results were similar to those shown in Figure 2, but the sensitivity was quite different in every case. We conjectured that the network architecture was overly complex, resulting in a classifier, rather than a true model.

To address this problem, we chose a different criterion for the architecture optimization. Since the objective was to evolve a "simple" network, we reduced the number of neurons in the hidden layer until we observed an appreciable degradation in the ultimate error for the training data. Figure 3 shows the results of this procedure for a network with only 5 neurons in its hidden layer. By comparison with Figure 2, it does not do as well in learning the training data, but it is better at predicting the oxide thicknesses in the verification set, predicting the oxide thickness with a standard deviation of about 7.3Å. This level of accuracy is particularly impressive in light of the fact that the incoming oxide thickness is only known to within 5Å.

An example of the sensitivity analysis for this network is shown in Figure 4. In this example, the response of the model to changes in the flow rate of one of the etch gases is shown. Each axis in this plot is normalized to its standard deviation, and is computed holding all other input variables at their average value. The different data markers on the plot correspond to different training runs started from different random seeds. In this case, all three networks converged to a very similar behavior. This leads us to feel more confident that the network is, in fact, learning to truly model the process.

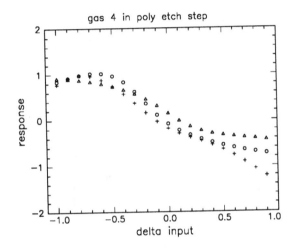

Figure 4: Sensitivity analysis example.

This kind of analysis is a useful way to identify the important variables in a complex process. Figure 5 shows a relative ranking of the sensitivity of the model's output to variations in each of its inputs. The sensitivity is the change in output with respect to each input evaluated at an average operating point. In Figure 5, each of the variables has been normalized to its standard deviation. As we might expect, variations in the TaSi etch part of the process are much less important than variations in the polysilicon etch. In addition, the key parameters identified in the polysilicon etch agree well with those identified by experienced process engineers in the plant, further reinforcing our confidence in the validity of the model.

IV. DISCUSSION

We have compared the performance of the neural network model to that of traditional, statistical modeling methods. The complex model showed a correlation to the ideal response of 0.51, and the simple model showed a correlation of 0.68 . For comparison, an additive statistical predictor model resulted in a correlation value of 0.45.

The most interesting feature is that the complex model, when tested by sensitivity analysis gave widely different response curves for each training of the network from a different random seed. This suggests that constructing a neural network for minimum training error is not necessarily good practice for all process models. Overly complex networks may prove easier to train, and it is often tempting to choose a large network, assuming that it can only perform better than a small one. The danger in this assumption, however, is that a complex network is capable of evolving overly sophisticated representations. It may, in fact, simply become a classifier -- recognizing particular configurations of input variables rather than developing a consistent model of the process. A small network is incapable of such sophisticated behavior, and can only exhibit simple responses to input variations.

Two process models analogous to ours have recently been reported. Mocella *et al.* (1991) and Himmel *et al.* (1992) discuss plasma etch models constructed from neural networks. The Mocella *et al.* model is for a polysilicon etch. Its inputs are rf-applied power, pressure, magnetic field, gas flow, and temperature of the wafer. The output of the model is etch rate of the polysilicon, oxide etch rate, induced current and voltage. (These voltage and current values are derived from the reflected rf power. The phase angle is also extracted but, not used in the modeling.) The data set was developed from a statistical design experiment and consisted of 34 input/output records. Their simple network with 5 inputs, 8 nodes in one hidden layer and 4 outputs had 160 connections.

Himmel *et al.* (1992) also built a neural network polysilicon etch model. In their model the inputs were the applied rf power, the reactor pressure, the electrode gap, and the flow rate of three gases. Their network had six inputs, six hidden neurons and four outputs giving the polysilicon etch rate, the uniformity of the etching, and the selectivity of the etch to oxide and resist. The neural networks were trained by the back-propagation algorithm with a data set of 53 vectors from a statistical design experiment. Their network had 144 connections.

In general, a network with N hidden, sigmoidal neurons can exhibit 2^N binary states. It is capable of classifying its input vectors into as many as 2^N distinct categories. In practice, most networks do not approach this maximum, but it is clear that the complexity of behavior exhibited by a layered neural network escalates rapidly with network size. If the network is capable of recognizing each of its inputs as a unique class, it is likely to "memorize" rather than "learn". The likelihood of training a classifier, rather than a true model, is especially high for networks trained with design experiment data, since the experiments are intentionally

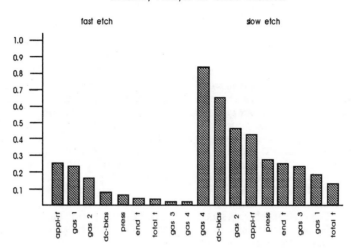

Figure 5: Relative response to various process variables.

chosen to distribute the input vectors uniformly throughout the volume of the input space. When developing a model, as opposed to a classifier, it is important to keep the network small in relation to the training data base. In our problem, for example, the complex network with 33 hidden neurons is capable of distinguishing as many as 8.6 billion classes. The simple network, with 5 hidden neurons, can distinguish 32. Generally, in developing a model, for M training examples the network should not exceed about $\log_2(M)$ hidden neurons in size.

In contrast to classification, modeling with neural networks is a process more similar to curve fitting (c. f. Denker *et al.*, 1987). The hidden neurons act as a set of basis functions, and the weights as a set of adjustable parameters. Again, as with classifiers, there is a relationship between the network size and the size of the database. As in curve fitting, it is important that the number of training examples be larger than the number of adjustable parameters, *i.e.* weights. If this condition is not satisfied, the problem is under-constrained. Whenever possible, we try to ensure that the training data base size is at least three time greater than the number of weights in the network. Clearly, it is sometimes impractical to satisfy this constraint, particularly in situations where the data base has to be generated experimentally.

ACKNOWLEDGMENTS

This work was conducted in partial fulfillment of the requirements for a Doctorate of Philosophy (for E. A. R.) from the Eurotechnical Research University, Hilo Hawaii.

We acknowledge database support from Ron Mohn, Milton Beachy, Dean Fresonke, Allen Woodard and Tom Harry. Helpful conversations were provided by Lynn Keen, Steve Neston, Dave Friedman, Yann Le Cun and John Denker. We thank Sherwin Kahn and Rick Gottscho for support of this research.

REFERENCES

[1] B. J. Curtis, and H. R. Brunner, "The Reactive Ion Etching of Tantalum Silicide/Polysilicon Bilayers in Silicon Tetrachloride and Hydrogen Chloride", J. Electrochem. Soc. **136** (5), 1463-1468 (1989).

[2] J. Denker, D. Schwartz, B. Wittner, S. Solla, R. Howard, L. Jackel, and J. Hopfield, "Large Automatic Learning, Rule Extraction, and Generalization", Complex Systems, **1**, 877-922 (1987).

[3] C. D. Himmel, B. Kim, G. S. May; "A Comparison of Statistically-Based and Neural Network Models of Plasma Etch Behavior", Simicon West, '92, San Francisco, June (1992).

[4] M. T. Mocella, J. A. Bondur, and T. R. Turner, "Etch Process Characterization Using Nerual Network Methodology: A Case Study", SPIE Proceedings, Vol. 1594, (1992).

[5] A. J. van Roosmalen, J. A. G. Baggerman, and S. J. H. Brader, *Dry Etching for VLSI*, Plenum Press, New York, (1991)

A Multi–Layer Kohonen's Self–Organizing Feature Map for Range Image Segmentation

Jean Koh and Minsoo Suk
Department of Electrical and Computer Engineering
Syracuse University
Syracuse, NY 13244 – 1240, USA

Suchendra M. Bhandarkar
Department of Computer Science
University of Georgia
Athens, GA 30602 – 7404, USA

ABSTRACT — The goal of range image segmentation is to partition a range image represented by a two–dimensional pixel array into geometric primitives so that all the image pixels are grouped into clusters with a common geometric representation or property that could be used by higher–level cognitive processes. This paper proposes and describes a self–organizing neural network for range image segmentation. The Multi–Layer Kohonen's Self–Organizing Feature Map (MLKSFM) which is an extension of the traditional single–layer Kohonen's Self–Organizing Feature Map (KSFM) is seen to alleviate the shortcomings of the latter in the context of range image segmentation. The problem of range image segmentation is formulated as one of vector quantization and is mapped onto the Multi–Layer Kohonen's Self–Organizing Feature Map (MLKSFM). The Multi–Layer Kohonen's Self–Organizing Feature Map (MLKSFM) is currently implemented on the Connection Machine CM–2 which is a fine–grained SIMD computer. Experimental results using both, synthetic and real range images are presented.

I. INTRODUCTION

Vision can be considered as an information processing activity. The two distinct goals of computer vision are modelling and understanding human visual perception and developing machines capable of visual sensing and interpretation of their environment. The work presented in this paper is directed towards the second goal, i.e. computer vision from a more practical point of view. In recent years, there has been a rapid increase in computer vision research using range images as input data. This is primarily due to the recent advances in range sensing technology that has resulted in the availability of fast, accurate, reliable and economical range sensors. A range image can be looked upon as an array of pixels wherein each pixel value encodes the depth or the distance of a point on a visible scene surface from the range sensor. In contrast, an intensity image is an array of brightness values. Techniques for deriving 3–D structure from 2–D intensity images such as shape from shading, shape from texture, shape from motion etc. tend to be ill–posed due to the large number of factors encoded in the pixel brightness value such as surface geometry, surface reflectance, surface texture, scene illumination, etc. Range image formation, on the other hand, is conceptually a simpler process encoding just the surface geometry and the range sensor characteristics. The pixel values in the range image directly approximate the three dimensional shape of the corresponding visible object surfaces in the field of view. Thus, recognizing objects from their three–dimensional geometric shape is much easier using range images than using intensity images.

Computer vision seen as an information processing task is the process of successive construction of representations at various abstraction levels. Representations and processing in computer vision are usually grouped into two broad but overlapping stages. Low-level vision, or early vision, deals mainly with the measurement and extraction of iconic attributes, such as edge detection, segmentation, feature extraction, and description. High–level vision deals with the use of general and domain–specific knowledge for the interpretation of data. Image segmentation, which is the main focus of this paper, is one of the most fundamental information processing steps in low–level vision. In computer vision, the grouping of an image into regions exhibiting one or more homogeneous characteristics results in a segmented image. This is perhaps the most comprehensive domain–independent analysis of the image. The goal of range image segmentation is to partition the image based on the simplest possible 3–D surface primitives i.e. smooth surface regions and surface discontinuities. Therefore, most surface segmentation techniques can be classified as either edge–based or region–based depending on whether they emphasize the detection of surface discontinuities or the detection of smooth surface regions respectively.

The basic idea behind edge–based range image segmentation techniques is to detect and classify range image pixels that signify surface discontinuities and classify them as one of : (1) *Jump Edges* (Fig.1(a)) which signify discontinuities in range, (2) *Crease Edges* (Fig.1(b)) which signify continuity in range but a discontinuity in the surface normal and (3) *Curvature Edges* (Fig.1(c)) which signify a continuity in range and surface normal but discontinuity in curvature. One of the primary drawbacks of edge–based segmentation techniques is the inevitable fragmentation of the edges. If the edges are fragmented or discontinuous, they must be linked using a heuristic technique. For this reason, edge–based segmentation techniques have proved to be less popular than region–based segmentation techniques.

The central idea behind region–based range segmentation techniques is to estimate the surface curvature at each range pixel and cluster range pixels with homogeneous surface curvature properties to form smooth surface regions. There are two broad categories of region–based segmentation techniques: (a) region–growing techniques and (b) feature vector clustering techniques. In region growing techniques, an analytical surface is fitted in a local neighborhood surrounding a range pixel followed by spatial grouping of homogeneous pixels [1]. Although range image segmentation by region growing is popular, it has some shortcomings:

(a) Jump Edge　　(b) Crease Edge　　(c) Curvature Edge

Fig. 1. Range edge types

(a) a good criterion for merging and splitting adjacent regions is needed and (b) it is possible for object surfaces to be oversegmented or undersegmented.

Segmentation techniques based on feature vector clustering assign a feature vector based on surface curvature properties to each range image pixel. The image segmentation problem, in this case, can be treated as one of feature vector quantization. Feature vector quantization is a process of partitioning an n-dimensional feature vector space into M regions so as to minimize a criterion function based on overall quantization distortion when all the points in each region are approximated (or represented) by the representative vector $\underline{X_i}$ associated with that region. Finding an optimal solution to the feature vector quantization problem necessitates a training process which involves learning the probability distribution of the input data. Learning, in this case, involves the following steps:
For each vector in the feature vector space:
(1) Identify the best representative feature vector from the current set of representative feature vectors.
(2) Update the representative feature vector to incorporate the current feature vector.
The basic idea behind clustering techniques for range image segmentation is to gather similar feature vectors and to separate dissimilar feature vectors [2,3]. Clustering techniques treat feature vectors simply as patterns in a high-dimensional space. Thus, the resulted clusters are not guaranteed to be spatially connected unless feature vectors include positional information. Image segmentation by region growing guarantees that each segment is connected in the image while image segmentation by clustering does not. The other problem with clustering techniques is that the number of regions required by the clustering algorithm, is not known in advance. Prespecifying a large number of regions results in an oversegmented image. Choosing too few cluster centers results in improper clustering of dissimilar feature vectors. Moreover, deciding what features should constitute the feature vector is also an important issue that needs to be addressed. The selection of an appropriate clustering algorithm is also important because different clustering techniques tend to produce different clusters.

Neural networks are ideally suited for computer vision applications due to their inherent parallelism. Many different aspects of visual perception are inherently parallel and distributed in nature, and can be modelled by appropriate neural networks. Some of the previous work in image segmentation include Geman and Geman [4], Hurlbert and Poggio [5], and Grossberg and Mingolla [6].

II. MULTI-LAYER KOHONEN'S SELF-ORGANIZING FEATURE MAP

The purpose of this paper is to describe a neural network structure suitable for the task of image segmentation and also the associated learning procedure. We also demonstrate the performance of the network with a few selected experimental results. It is well known that the task of image segmentation is basically a vector quantization problem [7, 8]. Also well known is the fact that the Kohonen's Self-Organizing Feature Map (KSFM) can be used for vector quantization [9]–[11]. However, as will be shown here, the original single-layer KSFM is not adequate for image segmentation. In this paper, we extend the single-layer KSFM to a Multi-Layer KSFM. The associated learning procedure for the multi-layer network will also be described.

A typical KSFM structure is shown in Fig. 2. It consists of two layers, a layer of input nodes and a competitive layer consisting of neural units. A weight vector is associated with each connection from the input layer to a neural unit. The neural units in the competitive (and cooperative) layer are organized in a regular geometric structure such as a two-dimensional mesh. The units are interconnected with their local neighbors and these connections could be excitatory.

2.1. KSFM for Range Image Segmentation

As mentioned previously, the segmentation problem could be treated as a feature vector quantization problem. Range image segmentation can be interpreted as a mapping from the pixels in an input image $\{z = f(x, y)\}$ of size N_x by N_y, to a set of M regions $R = \{R_i : 1 \le i \le M\}$. Let us suppose that the KSFM is used to identify or learn this mapping. In the case of intensity image segmentation, only the feature vectors consisting of position and intensity, $\underline{x} = (x, y, f(x, y))$, can be used [12]. Since range images are an explicit representation of the scene surface geometry, the segmentation of range images should be based on homogeneity criteria that incorporate geometrical properties of 3-D surfaces. A homogeneous region in range images can be bounded by three types of edges, jump edges, crease edges, and curvature edges. Jump edges occur when an object occludes another object or when a part of an object occludes itself. Therefore, we need to incorporate positional information as one of features in the feature vector in order to use jump edges as one of the decision boundaries in clustering or vector quantization. Since most natural object faces are bounded by crease edges and curvature edges, we also need unit surface normal and invariant surface curvature values as features in order to use crease edges and curvature edges, respectively, as decision boundaries between clusters. Among the invariant surface curvatures, the mean and Gaussian curvatures have been the most widely used [1]. Using the KSFM for clustering alleviates the characteristic problem of lack of spatial connectivity between clusters or regions. This is because of the topology preserving property of the KSFM. Although the KSFM does not guarantee preserving the exact connectivity relationship between clusters or regions, it preserves the topological neighborhood relationship in input vector space to the greatest extent possible.

The components of the input range vector and the unit surface normal vector, and the mean and Gaussian curvature values are presented to the input layer, pixel by pixel,

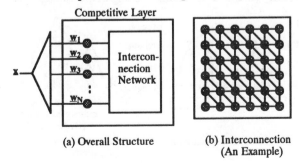

(a) Overall Structure   (b) Interconnection
(An Example)

Fig. 2. The network structure of KSFM.

as a four–way–partitioned eight–dimensional vector $\underline{x}_i = (x, y, z; n_x, n_y, n_z; H; K)$, where the (n_x, n_y, n_z) is the unit normal vector at the point (x, y, z) on the three–dimensional surface. H and K are the mean and Gaussian curvatures respectively at the point (x, y, z). Ideally on the completion of learning, each neural unit in the competitive layer should be made sensitive to a single region, where the weight vector $\underline{w}_j = (w_x, w_y, w_z, w_{nx}, w_{ny}, w_{nz}, w_H, w_K)$ of each unit is the representative vector of a region where (w_x, w_y, w_z) are the coordinates of the center of the region in the three–dimensional space, (w_{nx}, w_{ny}, w_{nz}) is the representative unit normal vector of the region and w_H, w_K are the representative mean and Gaussian curvature values of the region which are close to the average of the mean and Gaussian curvature values respectively where the average is taken over all the pixels in the region. The number of neural units in the competitive layer should be close to the number of regions desired. It is usually not possible to determine the number of regions M, i.e. the size of the set R, a priori. This makes the use of original single layer KSFM for image segmentation rather difficult because one does not have direct control over the number of regions which might result from image segmentation when a single–layer KSFM is used. This is a significant shortcoming of the single–layer KSFM since the number of regions is very much dependent on the scene content and cannot be accurately determined a priori.

The segmentation process can also be interpreted as one of data abstraction where R is the final abstraction of an input image. Let us consider a hierarchical approach to segmentation. The first level segments an input image into M_1 regions. These regions are the first level abstraction of the input image. The process is repeated resulting in M_2, M_3, ... regions until the highest level of abstraction is reached which corresponds to the trivial case consisting of a single region covering the entire input image. Thus a tree called an *abstraction tree* containing all levels of abstraction can be generated as shown in Fig. 3 (a). Each node in the tree represents a subregion at a particular level of abstraction. We may regard the abstraction tree as the final outcome of the segmentation process thus representing the highest domain–independent abstraction of the input data. If it is necessary to generate the segmented image, we can expand the nodes of the tree starting from the root until some stopping criterion is met. Regions corresponding to the *closed* nodes represent the final segmented image as illustrated in Fig. 3 (b). We note that the image segmentation using a single–layer KSFM would produce an abstraction of the input image at a *prespecified* (and somewhat arbitrarily chosen) abstraction level. On the other hand, the segmented image pro-duced by the MLKSFM would consist of regions belonging to different levels of abstraction, thus overcoming a significant shortcoming of segmentation techniques based on clustering. This makes sense since different levels of abstraction are needed for different parts in the image depending on the local scene content. In fact, the abstraction tree contains all levels of abstraction.

2.2. MLKSFM

The Multi–Layer KSFM (MLKSFM) is organized as a pyramidal structure consisting of multiple layers of single–layer KSFM's. Input data arrives at the lowest layer and information flows to the higher layers in a strictly feed–forward manner. Output from any given layer is converted into the input for the next layer by a buffer unit. The number of units in a layer decreases at each successive level resulting in a pyramidal structure. The number of representative vectors to be formed in a layer is proportional to the number of neural units in the layer. Thus, in a layer at a higher level which has a smaller number of neural units, each weight vector represents a larger cluster, or a higher level of abstraction of the input data. We show that the MLKSFM supports hierarchical image segmentation.

2.2.1. Preprocessing

The input feature vector $(x, y, z; n_x, n_y, n_z; H; K)$, for every pixel in a scene is computed and provided to the MLSKFM. The feature vector is computed directly from a range image using window operators, which are fixed–weight feed–forward networks. The unit normal vector at pixel x, $\underline{n}_x$ is given by:

$$\underline{n}_x = \frac{\frac{\partial x}{\partial u} \times \frac{\partial x}{\partial v}}{\| \frac{\partial x}{\partial u} \times \frac{\partial x}{\partial v} \|}$$

In this paper, we use two 5x5 equally weighted least squares derivative estimation operators, D_u and D_v, which are given by:

$$D_u = \underline{d_0} \cdot \underline{d_1}^T,$$
$$D_v = \underline{d_1} \cdot \underline{d_0}^T,$$
$$where\ \underline{d_0} = 1/7 [\ 1\ 1\ 1\ 1\ 1\ ]^T,$$
$$\underline{d_1} = 1/10 [\ -2\ -1\ 0\ 1\ 2\ ]^T.$$

The mean and Gaussian curvatures are computed using the technique suggested in [2, 3]. A simple estimate of surface curvature at pixel p in the direction of pixel q, is given by:

$$k(p, q) = \frac{\| \underline{n}_p - \underline{n}_q \|}{\| \underline{p} - \underline{q} \|} \times s(p, q) ,$$

$$where\ s(p, q) = 1, if\ \| \underline{p} - \underline{q} \| \le \| (\underline{n}_p + \underline{p}) - (\underline{n}_q + \underline{q}) \|,$$
$$= 0,\ otherwise.$$

$\underline{n}_p$ and $\underline{n}_q$ are the unit normal vectors at points p and q, respectively. This definition makes two assumptions – one, that the underlying surface is smooth and the other that q is close enough to p so that the arc length can be adequately approximated by the Euclidean distance. $s(p, q)$ is a sign factor such that if two surface normals, $\underline{n}_p$ and $\underline{n}_q$ at pixels p and q approach each other, the curvature has negative value indicating a concave surface, else the curvature has a positive value indicating a convex surface. Let $W(p)$ be the pixels in the neighborhood of pixel p. The mean curvature, H and

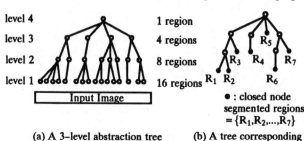

(a) A 3–level abstraction tree   (b) A tree corresponding to the segmented image

Fig. 3. Abstraction tree.

1272

Gaussian curvature, K are given by:

$$H = \frac{(k^{\min}(p) + k^{\max}(p))}{2},$$

$$K = (k^{\min}(p) \times k^{\max}(p)),$$

$$\text{where } k^{\min}(p) = \min_{q = \Omega(p)} [k(p, q)],$$

$$k^{\max}(p) = \max_{q = \Omega(p)} [k(p, q)].$$

In this paper, we use a 3x3 neighborhood, i.e. only 8 nearest neighbor pixels are considered when computing the mean and Gaussian curvatures. These computations can be replaced by the receptive field of a column structure composed of MAXNETs, MINNETs and fixed–weight networks. Each pixel provides it's position vector and unit normal vector computed as shown above. Each curvature computing unit receives these inputs from a center pixel and it's 8 nearest neighbors, and computes a curvature value. The MAXNET and MINNET collect the curvature values to find the maximum and minimum curvature values. The last units, the multiplying unit and the averaging unit compute H and K, respectively using the maximum and the minimum curvature values from the MAXNET and MINNET.

2.2.2. Structure

The Multi–Layer KSFM consists of multiple competitive layers. The input layer receives input from the external world and propagates the input to all neural units in the first competitive layer. Competitive learning takes place, and the weights are converted and propagated to the next layer as input to that layer. The same process is repeated until the top layer is reached. A higher layer contains a smaller number of neural units as compared to a lower layer.

Without loss of generality, we can assume that the input is a square image of size N_f by N_f, and neural units in each competitive layer are organized into square arrays. We further assume that the size of competitive layers are 1x1, 2x2, 4x4, ..., NxN where $N = 2^n$ is the size of the first layer and $N = N_f/2$. This is similar to the quadtree or pyramid data structure in image processing. However, the present structure is much more flexible than the quadtree. In the present structure, a parents node can have an arbitrary number of child nodes and the shapes of the resulting region represented by a node can be arbitrary. This is in contrast to the quadtree wherein a parent node must have four child nodes with the resulting regions having a *boxy* appearance. The structure of the MLKSFM is illustrated in Fig. 4. Fig. 5 shows the structure of a typical competitive layer.

2.2.3. Learning

Learning in each layer consists of two phases. The first phase determines the winning neural unit for weight adjustment. The second phase adjusts weight vectors. We use, in this paper, a modification of the original learning algorithm proposed by Kohonen [13] to give separate weights to the position vector, the unit normal vector, and the two curvature values in feature space.

Weighted Euclidean Distance Measure : There are three sources of information in a feature vector – the contribution

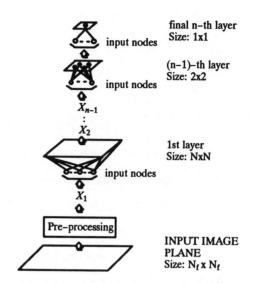

Fig. 4. The structure of multi–layer KSFM.

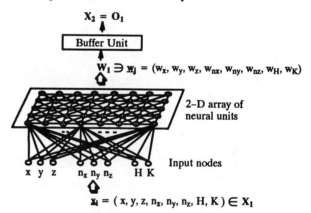

Fig. 5. A typical competitive layer (the first layer).

from the position vector, $\underline{x}_p = (x, y, z)$, the one from the unit normal vector, $\underline{x}_n = (n_x, n_y, n_z)$, and the one from the curvature values, H and K. To control the extent of contribution from each source, the Euclidean distance measure in the KSFM is modified. We use the linear combination of four separate Euclidean distance measures from the position vector, the unit normal vector, and the two curvature values, H and K :

$$d(\underline{x}_i, \underline{w}_j) = a \|\underline{x}_p - \underline{w}_p\| + b \|\underline{x}_n - \underline{w}_n\| + c |H - w_H| + d |K - w_K|,$$

where $0 \le a, b, c, d \le 1$,

$$\underline{x}_i = (x, y, z, n_x, n_y, n_z, H, K) = (\underline{x}_p; \underline{x}_n; H; K),$$

$$\underline{x}_p = (x, y, z),$$

$$\underline{x}_n = (n_x, n_y, n_z),$$

$$\underline{w}_j = (w_x, w_y, w_z, w_{nx}, w_{ny}, w_{nz}, w_H, w_K)$$

$$= (\underline{w}_p; \underline{w}_n; w_H; w_K),$$

$$\underline{w}_p = (w_x, w_y, w_z),$$

$$\underline{w}_n = (w_{nx}, w_{ny}, w_{nz}).$$

We call this a weighted Euclidean distance measure. With this measure, we can control the relative dominance of each term. The abstraction tree, however, can be used for many different purposes in high–level vision. One application of the abstraction tree is to produce segmented images.

III. Experimental Results and Discussions

The multi–layer KSFM was simulated on the Connection Machine (CM–2). The Connection Machine is a fine-grained SIMD computer with a hypercube interconnection topology which can also be configured as a mesh. Each neural unit at one layer is assigned to a virtual processor in the CM–2. All the neural units perform their functions simultaneously. This configuration is specially advantageous for finding a minimum distance and updating the weight vectors. The distances from the weight vectors of neural units to a given input vector are calculated simultaneously on a layer. Due to the nearest neighborhood connections among processors and special connections among processor columns and rows, it takes just one instruction to find the minimum distance. However, the speed–up achievable by the massively parallel computer is limited since the KSFM learning procedure is inherently sequential i.e. based on examining one input vector at a time. After learning, input for the next layer is extracted from the winning neural units. The geometry of the CM processors is changed to that of the next stage and the learning process is repeated.

All input images used in this experiments vary in size from 160x80 pixels to 240x240 pixels. The real range images are produced by the Technical Arts 100X White scanner at the Pattern Recognition and Image Processing Laboratory at Michigan State University, East Lansing, Michigan. The White scanner is a triangulation–based laser range sensor, which is the reason why the real range images used in this experiments suffer from shadows. The first competitive layer has neural units arranged as a 16 by 16 array, the second layer 8 by 8, the third layer 6 by 6, the fourth layer 4 by 4, the fifth layer 3 by 3, and the top layer 2 by 2.

We used the weight ratio $a : b : c : d = 1 : 10^{-2} : 10^{-1} : 10^{-5}$ for the modified Euclidean distance measure. During our experiments, all the input images were found to contain objects that did not have too many complex surfaces so that the Gaussian curvature was not necessary to segment them, and using the magnitude of the mean curvature was much more effective than using the mean curvature values directly. Thus, the Gaussian curvature was not used, i.e. d was almost zero and the magnitude of the mean curvature was used instead of the mean curvature value. A segmented image is generated by traversing the abstraction tree in a breadth-first manner from the root node i.e. a node is expanded if the variances of range values, mean curvature magnitude values, and normal vectors of the pixels in the regions exceeds a threshold value, otherwise the node is labelled as a closed node and is not expanded any further. Note that the resulting segmented image usually contains regions from different abstraction levels. One can define a more sophisticated tree traversal criterion depending on the nature of the image. Note further that for many applications, an abstraction tree itself may be the final outcome of the segmentation and may be directly propagated as input to the high–level vision processes. However, since with the images we used in our experiments, all the closed nodes occur at the same level in the abstraction tree, the abstraction tree itself has been omitted.

We carried out a series of experiments using both synthetic and real range images containing various surfaces such as polygonal, cylindrical, conical, and spherical surfaces to see the effects of various image characteristics on the final seg-mentation using the MLKSFM. Fig. 6 shows all intermediate results in the process of segmentation, and is organized as three columns and six rows. The three columns show the range values, the magnitude of the mean curvature, and the direction of unit normal vectors, respectively, while the first row shows these values for an input range image and the rest of the rows show these values, respectively, for the first layer, the second layer, and so on. For convenience of display, the range values are converted to intensity values from 0 to 255, the mean curvature magnitude values are scaled down appropriately to the maximum value 255, and the unit normal vectors are projected onto a plane (X–Y) to display their directions. All the results from the layers are mapped back to the input image coordinates where each pixel location shows the value of the particular neural unit to which the pixel is mapped on completion of learning. In the first column, the white contours represent boundaries between segmented regions.

Segmentation results on some selected examples are shown in Fig. 7. For each object, an input image and a final segmentation result are displayed. Note that the small circular noise-like regions and the two lines dividing the objects in the scene containing multiple objects are due to the lack of data in the input range images. The above experiments demonstrate the utility of the MLKSFM for range image segmentation, both in concept and in practice.

VI. Conclusions

Neural networks are ideally suited for computer vision applications due to their inherent parallelism. This paper has considered the use of neural networks for an important low–level computer vision problem, namely, range image segmentation. Since image segmentation can be considered as a vector quantization problem, it is natural to consider the use of the Kohonen's Self–Organizing Feature Map. However, it turned out that the original single–layer net was inadequate for image segmentation. The network was extended to include multiple competitive layers which were organized as a pyramid. The new extended net supports hierarchical range image segmentation producing various levels of image abstraction. The result which includes all intermediate levels of abstraction is organized as an *abstraction tree*. The experimental results were positively favorable in demonstrating the utility of the MLKSFM for range image segmentation.

References

[1] P. Besl and R.C. Jain, "Segmenting through variable order surface fitting." *IEEE Trans. on Pattern Anal. and Machine Intell.*, vol. 10, no. 2, pp. 167–192, 1988.

[2] D.J. Ittner and A.K. Jain, "3–D surface discrimination from local curvature measures." *Proceedings of IEEE Computer Vision and Pattern Recognition Conference*, pp. 119–123, 1985.

[3] R. Hoffman and A.K. Jain, "Segmentation and classification of range images," *IEEE Trans. on Pattern Anal. and Machine Intell.*, vol. 9, no. 5, pp. 608–620, 1987.

[4] S. Geman and D. Geman, "Stochastic relaxation, Gibbs distributions, and the Bayesian restoration of images," *IEEE Trans. on Pattern Anal. and Machine Intell.*, vol. 6, no. 6, pp. 721–741, 1984.

[5] S. Grossberg and E. Mingolla, "A neural network architecture for preattentive vision: multiple scale segmentation and regularization. *Proceedings of IEEE the First International Conf. on Neural Networks*, vol. 4, pp. 177–184, 1987.

[6] A. Hurlbert and T. Poggio, "A network for image segmentation using color," in *Advances in Neural Information Processing Systems*, vol. 1, D.S. Touretzky, Ed. Morgan Kaufmann Publishers, 1989, pp. 297–304.

[7] J. Bryant, "On the clustering of multidimensional pictorial data," *Pattern Recognition*, vol. 11, pp. 115–125, 1979.

[8] M.M. Trivedi and J.C. Bezdek, "Low–level segmentation of arial images with fuzzy clustering," *IEEE Trans. on Syst. Man, Cybern.*, vol. 16, no. 4, pp. 589–598, 1986.

[9] H. Ritter and K. Schulten, "Topology conserving mappings for learning motor tasks," in *Neural Networks for Computing, Proceedings of AIP Conference*, vol. 151, J.S. Denker, Ed. pp. 376–380, 1986.

[10] G. Martinelli, L.P. Ricotti, and S. Ragazzini, "Nonstationary lattice quantization by a self–organizing neural network," *Neural Networks*, vol. 3, no. 4, pp. 385–393, 1990.

[11] E. Mcdermott and S. Katagiri, "Phoneme recognition using Kohonen networks," *Proceedings of ATR Neural Net Workshop*, July 1988.

[12] M. Suk and J. Koh, "Image segmentation using multi–layer Kohonen's self–organizing feature map," *Progress in Neural Networks*, vol. 4, Ablex Publishing Co., in press.

[13] T. Kohonen, *Self–Organization and Associative Memory*, 2nd ed., Springer–Verlag, 1988.

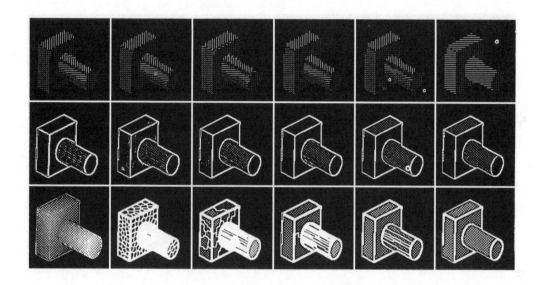

Fig. 6. Segmentation of the column.

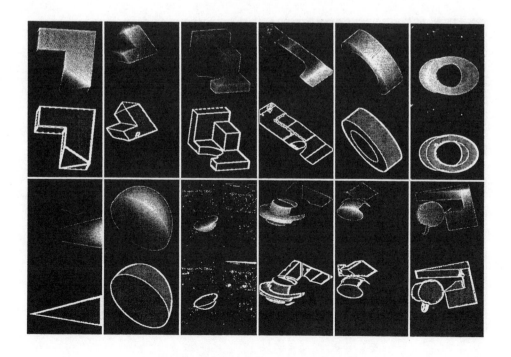

Fig. 7. Segmentation results of variable objects.

[6] A. Hurlbert and T. Poggio, "A network for image segmentation using color," in *Advances in Neural Information Processing Systems*, vol. 1, D.S. Touretzky, Ed. Morgan Kaufmann Publishers, 1989, pp. 297–304.

[7] J. Bryant, "On the clustering of multidimensional pictorial data," *Pattern Recognition*, vol. 11, pp. 115–125, 1979.

[8] M.M. Trivedi and J.C. Bezdek, "Low-level segmentation of arial images with fuzzy clustering," *IEEE Trans. on Syst. Man, Cybern.*, vol. 16, no. 4, pp. 589–598, 1986.

[9] H. Ritter and K. Schulten, "Topology conserving mappings for learning motor tasks," in *Neural Networks for Computing, Proceedings of AIP Conference*, vol. 151, J.S. Denker, Ed. pp. 376–380, 1986.

[10] G. Martinelli, L.P. Ricotti, and S. Ragazzini, "Nonstationary lattice quantization by a self-organizing neural network," *Neural Networks*, vol. 3, no. 4, pp. 385–393, 1990.

[11] E. Mcdermott and S. Katagiri, "Phoneme recognition using Kohonen networks," *Proceedings of ATR Neural Net Workshop*, July 1988.

[12] M. Suk and J. Koh, "Image segmentation using multi-layer Kohonen's self-organizing feature map," *Progress in Neural Networks*, vol. 4, Ablex Publishing Co., in press.

[13] T. Kohonen, *Self-Organization and Associative Memory*, 2nd ed., Springer-Verlag, 1988.

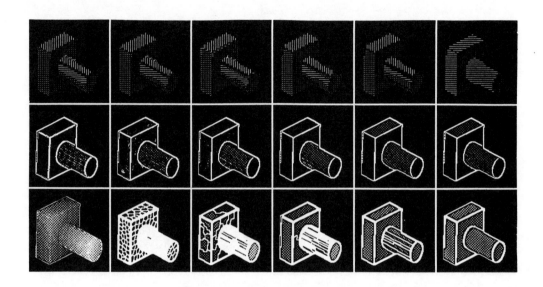

Fig. 6. Segmentation of the column.

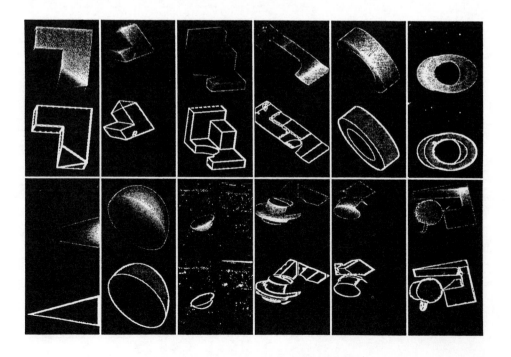

Fig. 7. Segmentation results of variable objects.

Segmentation of Medical Images Through Competitive Learning

Atam P. Dhawan and Louis Arata

Department of Electrical and Computer Engineering
University of Cincinnati, Cincinnati, OH 45221

Abstract-In image analysis applications, segmentation of gray-level images into meaningful regions is an important low-level processing step. Various approaches to segmentation investigated in the literature, in general, use either local information of gray-level values of pixels (region growing based methods, for example) or the global information (histogram thresholding based methods, for example). Application of these approaches for segmenting medical images with large structural information often does not provide satisfactory results. We present a novel approach to image segmentation that combines local contrast as well as global feature information. The presented method adaptively learns useful features and regions through the use of a normalized contrast function as a measure of local information and a competitive learning based method to update region segmentation incorporating global information about the gray-level distribution of the image. In this paper, we present the framework of such a self-organizing feature map, and show the results on simulated as well as real medical images.

1. INTRODUCTION

Medical images are usually characterized by faded features utilizing a narrow distribution of gray-levels. Because of this reason, medical images often suffers from low contrast that can be further degraded by the noise introduced in the process of imaging. In addition, medical image often exhibit very rich structures with textured details. The examples of such class of images include mammograms, images of skin-lesions, brain images, and ultrasound images. In general, for computerized analysis of medical images, a sequence of segmentation, feature extraction and feature classification operations is applied. The standard image processing and segmentation techniques, related to computer vision, are often found inadequate for medical image analysis applications because of their characteristic nature of low contrast and rich structure [1].

Most of the conventional image segmentation techniques either use the local or global information of gray-levels. Since features are not sharply defined in medical images and may have textured details or structures which may be degraded by the presence of noise, it is important to use the local contrast information as well as the overall distribution of gray-levels for obtaining meaningful regions.

This work was supported by the NIH grant CA49976.

Image segmentation to partition the image into meaningful regions is an essential step in image analysis. A large number of algorithms with many approaches have been investigated [2-4]. These approaches include histogram based methods, edge and boundary detection based methods, region growing based methods, and linear feature based methods. The image segmentation can be considered as a clustering process in which pixels are classified belonging to a specific region based on their gray-level values and spatial connectivity. Obviously such region formation is affected by both local information, i.e. the gray-level values of the neighborhood pixels, and global information, i.e. the overall gray-level distribution of the image. The histogram based segmentation methods make use of global information to find best thresholds to classify pixels into regions. On the other hand region growing based methods make use of local information to grow a region around a given pixel through clustering. While region extraction and segmentation is subjective to biological vision systems, it is important to include both information to obtain meaningful regions which can interpreted successfully by the high-level analysis.

In this paper, we present a two-dimensional self-organizing feature map based approach that incorporates both local and global information about the gray-level distribution of the image and learns the useful features of the image to provide meaningful regions. The presented approach uses the concept of competitive learning [4,5] the overall gray-level distribution of the image as global information. It also uses a contrast measure as a local information defining the homogeneity of the region. In the next sections, we will present the framework of the proposed self-organizing feature map and show the results on simulated as well as real medical images. In particular, we will show the results of the proposed segmentation on images of skin-lesions and mammographic images of microcalcifications. In our applications under research, analysis of skin-lesion and mammographic-microcalcifications images are directed, respectively, towards the early diagnosis of skin cancer [7-8], and breast cancer [9].

2. SELF-ORGANIZING FEATURE SEGMENTATION MAP

As briefly described above, the main objective of the self-organizing feature map based segmentation algorithm is to learn and form regions using both local and global information of the image. This is accomplished by using the local contrast information as a local measure and a competitive region formation scheme as a global measure. These two aspects combined together provides a controlled smoothing affect in region formation process even in highly textured images. Features leading to region formation are identified by using the contrast and conductivity through the local region growing processes which are controlled by a competitive process utilizing the gray-level distribution of the image. The Segment Feature Map for image segmentation is implemented using two layered structure as shown in Figure 1. The adaptive region growing process to extract feature region is implemented through an input layer representing the original gray-level image. These regions are then learned in the output layer through competitive learning as the segment feature map.

A. Feature Adaptive Region Growing Process

Around each pixel in the image, two local regions, called center and surround regions, are grown. These regions are grown using a fixed square shaped neighborhood or a feature shape adaptive neighborhood criterion [9]. In the first case, the neighborhoods are grown around a pixel as the areas of 3X3, 5X5, 7X7, and so on, pixels. Thus, the initial seed pixel itself represents the center region (1X1 pixel) in the first step; and the surround region is represented by the 3X3 pixels region. In the next step, 3X3 pixel region becomes the center region and 5X5 pixel region (centered around the seed pixel) represents the surround region. If the region growing process is continued, the next center and surround regions would be represented, respectively, by 5X5 pixel and 7X7 pixel regions. In the second option of using feature shape adaptive neighborhood criterion,, the pixels in the eight-connected neighborhood region of the center region are only accepted in surround region if their gray-level values fall within the allowed range. The allowed range of gray-level values for inclusion in the surround region is computed from the gray-level value of the seed pixel using a percentage threshold by which the seed gray-level value can be varied to provide the allowed range [see 9 for more details]. For example, if the central pixel value is 100, and the percentage threshold is 10, then the allowed gray-level range is 90 to 110. Thus, in the first step of region growing process with the center region of 1X1 pixel, all pixels in the 3X3 neighborhood region around the seed pixel are examined to the form the surround region. Only those pixels falling in the allowed range are included in the surround region yielding a feature adaptive shape (Figure 2). The pixels contiguous to the last region are examined for inclusion in the next surround region. Regardless of the selection of the shape option of region growing, the process of region growing is stopped when the stopping criterion (as defined below) is met.

Let us assume that at an instant t, N_C and N_S represent the number of pixels in the center (C) and surround (S) neighborhoods around the seed pixel (i,j). The contrast function value is re-computed at each step of region growing using new center and surround regions. At any specific step, the contrast function value, $\mathbf{K}(\mathbf{i},\mathbf{j})$, is defined as

$$K(i,j) = \frac{\sum_{l,m \in S} |\bar{x}_c(i,j) - x(l.m)|}{N_s}$$

where

$$\bar{x}_c(i,j) = \frac{\sum_{u,v \in C} x(u,v)}{N_c}$$

where x(l,m) is the gray-level value of the original image at the pixel (l,m).

B. Segment Feature Map

As shown in Figure 1, the proposed architecture of the self-organizing feature map consists of two layers: the input layer and the output layer. The original image is realized as the input layer of the network. The output layer provides the learned and mapped features. Initially, all pixels in the output layer of the feature map are provided with a constant value.

During the region growing process, a distance measure from the center region of the input layer to the corresponding region learned in the output layer is computed. The value of the distance measure is allocated to the initial seed pixel of the input layer. The distance measure, D(i,j), is computed by the following expression.

$$D(i,j) = \frac{\sqrt{\sum_{u,v} \{\frac{\sum_{l,m \in W} x(l,m)}{N_w} - y(u,v)\}'}}{N_w}$$

where y(u,v) is the gray-level value of the segment map of the output layer at the corresponding pixel (u,v); W is the union set of center (C) and surround (S) regions; and N_W is the number of pixels in the region W.

An overall score, Z(i,j), is awarded to the seed pixel by the following relationship.

$$\mathbf{Z}(\mathbf{i},\mathbf{j}) = \alpha \mathbf{K}(\mathbf{i},\mathbf{j}) + \beta \mathbf{D}(\mathbf{i},\mathbf{j})$$

where K(i,j) the contrast function value at the termination of region growing process, and α and β are the weights which determine the contribution of the contrast function and distance measure in computing the overall score.

During the adaptive region growing process around a selected seed pixel of the input layer, the overall score Z(i,j) is computed at each step. Each time the center and surround regions are grown, new score Z(i,j) is compared with the old Z(i,j) and a percentage increase or decrease is computed. If this percentage is within a threshold, called 'allowance' A, the region growing process is continued until the size of the center region reaches to the largest allowed size which may be set a priori based on the nature of the image and image size. When the percentage of change in overall score crosses the allowance value, the region growing process is stopped and an error update is computed using the center and surround regions of the previous step. The error update, E(i,j), for the old N_W region of the segment map of the output layer is computed as

$$E(i,j) = \min_{u,v} \left\{ \frac{\sum x(l,m)}{N_w} - y(u,v) \right\}$$

where the sign of E(i,j) is chosen to reduce this difference for each y(u,v).

C. Competitive Selection of Seed Pixels for Learning Segment Feature Map

Initially all pixels in the output layer are set to a constant value. The adaptive regions are grown around each pixel in the input layer and the corresponding score Z(i,j) is computed (for each pixel). The resulting Z array containing all scores is sorted from smallest to largest value. This ensures that the regions are sorted on the basis of local homogeneity. Since the image size may be large, the competition for selection of starting pixel (in successive iterations) from the whole image may result the dominance of a specific area of the image in segment feature map. To avoid this biasing effect in learning the segment feature map, the Z array is divided into a specific number of segments (we used eight) of equal length contiguous sections. These sections were randomly selected to provide the next starting pixel for computing the error update for the corresponding pixels in the output layer. The pixel chosen from the selected section of the array is the first pixel in the section which has not yet been assigned an error update. This is the mechanism by which the competition among regions is implemented. The pixel, thus selected, becomes the starting seed pixel of the new region growing operations. Once the new region growing process is stopped by comparison of with successive Z(i,j) values, the error update E(i,j) is computed and assigned for all pixels in the W region of the output layer. The selected seed pixel in the Z array is marked with a flag that the error updates for this seed pixel have been assigned. After all pixels in the input layer are selected through the Z array and the respective error update are assigned, the respective pixels in the output layer are updated by a small fraction values computed from the assigned E(i,j) values. Thus, the gray-level values of the output layer pixels are updated as

$$y_{\_}(i,j) = y_{\_}(i,j) + \gamma E(i,j).$$

In our experiments, we used γ=0.05.

For pixels from overlapped regions which are assigned multiple error updates are only updated by the value which has the minimum absolute value. This completes one iteration. In the next iteration, the Z array is re-sorted based on the last iteration scores. The sections are randomized again. The first pixel of the selected section which has not yet been assigned an error update in the current iteration, is selected as the seed pixel for the new region growing operation, and the process continues as described above till the final segment map is obtained.

D. The Segment Feature Map Algorithm

The segment feature map algorithm as described above uses a competitive pixel selection procedure to select a seed pixel in the input layer and then grows adaptive regions around the seed pixel to compute a contrast function value. In addition, the average pixel value of the grown region of the input layer is compared with the corresponding pixels in the output layer to compute a distance measure. Both contrast function and distance measure are used to obtain a score which is assigned to the seed pixel. All pixels are sorted in an array and divided into some pre-defined (we used eight) sections for avoiding bias in learning segment feature map. A seed pixel is selected from the competition among the pixels in the same section of the array. The selected pixel is subjected to the new region growing process to compute an error update. Once all pixels are analyzed for computing the error updates, the gray-level values of the output layer pixels are updated by a fraction of the assigned error update values. The process continues for another iteration till a segment feature map is learned. One way to know when to stop the iteration process is to check the gray-level histogram of the learned image after each iteration. The presence of peaks and their separation are indicators of the regions learned in the segment feature map image. If sufficient peaks are obtained, the iteration process may be stopped. We observed that the iteration stopping criterion is depended on the nature of the input image, and the approximate desired number of segmented regions. Since this subjective on the application, any specific iteration stopping criterion will not be discussed here.

The segment feature map algorithm is given below in pseudo-code.

```
for iteration ITERATION =1 to #ITERATION
begin
        compute Z(i,j) for all pixels (i,j) in the input image
        sort Z(i,j) array from lowest to highest value
        randomize array in mutually exclusive and
                exhaustive sections
        while pixels with unassigned errors E(i,j), remain
        begin
                select next seed pixel from the selected
                        section of the array
                repeat
                        grow regions around the seed pixel
                until % change of Z > allowance A
                compute and assign E(i,j)
        end
        update segment feature map based on E(i,j)
end.
```

3. RESULTS AND DISCUSSION

The above described segmentation method was applied on images of skin-lesions and mammographic micro-calcifications. To demonstrate the ability of the algorithm to learn useful features, a synthetic test image simulating a lesion embedded in the surrounding tissue of four different density values was created. As shown in Figure 3, the synthetic test image contains four uniform gray regions and one moderately textured region in the middle. The gray level histogram of this region overlaps two of the other regions. As can be seen from the histogram, because of this overlap,

1279

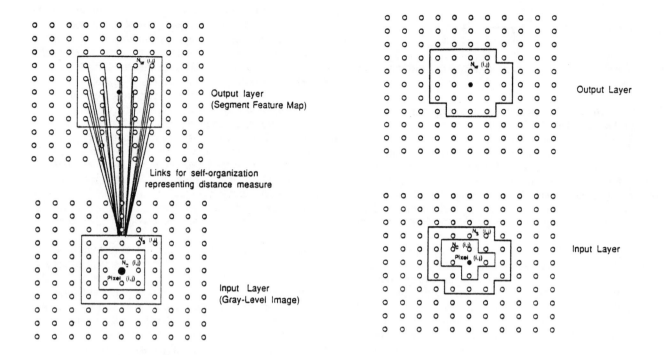

Figure 1. The structure of the self-organizing segment feature map for image segmentation. The square shaped neighborhoods are shown for computing the contrast and distance measure values.

Figure 2. The definition of the feature shape adaptive neighborhoods used in the region growing process..

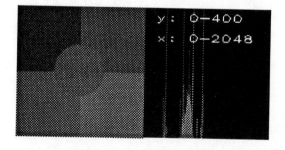

Figure 3. A test image. The histogram of the test image is shown at the right.

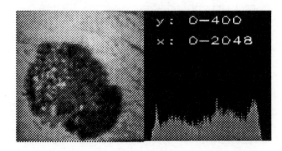

Figure 4. An image of malignant skin-lesion with histogram at the right. This image has 1256 connected regions.

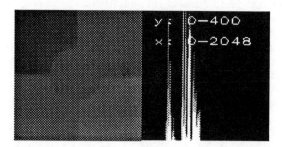

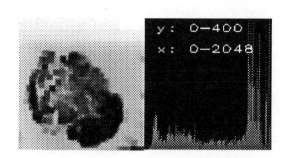

Figure 5. The segmented test image of Figure 3 using square neighborhoods. The histogram of the segmented image is shown at the right.

Figure 6. The segmented test image of Figure 4 using square neighborhoods. The histogram of the segmented image is shown at the right.

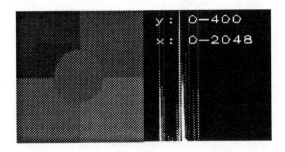

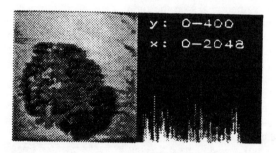

Figure 7. The segmented test image of Figure 3 using feature based adaptive neighborhoods. The histogram of the segmented image is shown at the right.

Figure 8. The segmented test image of Figure 4 using feature based adaptive neighborhoods. The segmented image has 729 connected regions. The histogram of the segmented image is shown at the right.

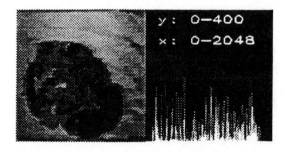

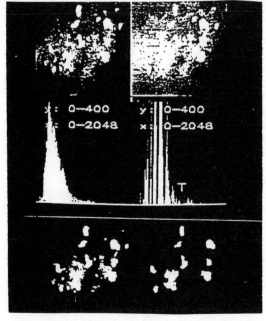

Figure 9. The segmented test image of Figure 4 using feature based adaptive neighborhoods. Error updates are used over the corresponding N_c region of the output layer only. The segmented image has 298 connected regions. The histogram of the segmented image is shown at the right.

Figure 10. Top left: a digitized mammogram with microcalcifications. Middle left: the histogram of the original digitized image. Bottom left: the extracted microcalcification areas using the selective threshold. Middle right: the histogram of the learned image. Bottom right: The extracted microcalcification areas using the threshold T selected from the histogram of the learned image.

thresholds to segment the middle region can not be obtained directly from the histogram. A real textured image is an image of a cancerous skin lesion (Figure 4). This image presents a particularly challenging segmentation problem because of the dense histogram.

The effectiveness of this method is demonstrated for these images by an examination of the histograms and the number of connected regions produced by a thresholded image both before and after application of the segmentation method. Figures 5 and 6 show results of the proposed method for which the three neighborhoods described above were square in shape (as shown in Figures 1 and 2). The artifacts produced by this affect are evident, however, it is clear that the network produced a segmentation with a histogram whose distribution provides well separated peaks for easy threshold selection for identification of regions. In case of skin-lesion image (Figure 6), useful meaningful features are provided by the well defined peaks on the right of the histogram which represents the bright regions in the skin-lesions. It can be seen that these regions are representative segments of smoothed textured features seen on the left of the original image (Figure 4). The characterization of these regions provides meaningful description of changes in color, density and the surface pigmentation pattern of the lesion. It should also be noted that small noise-like variations which may be interpreted as very find texture in the original image (in particular the black area at the right side of the lesion, and the background) are well smoothed out in the segmented image. Thus, the presented segmentation map controls the unnecessary regions. Only one black large region can be seen at the right side of the segmented image (Figure 6) with very few regions in the background.

To address the problem of artifact to obtain a better segmentation, image feature shape adaptive neighborhood [9] (Figure 2) was used instead of square neighborhood. Figures 7-9 show results of the segmentation network using the feature shape adaptive neighborhood method. Smoothing of the textured regions is apparent in these images. Figure 7 shows the results of segmentation of the test image. The histogram shows reasonable separation of the 5 identifiable regions in the segmented image. Histogram multi-level thresholding followed by connected-component labeling yielded 549 distinct regions for the original image and 30 distinct regions for the segmented image. The extreme reduction in the number of segments in the textured region is apparent. Figure 8 shows the results of segmentation network with error updates over N_W region. The results of segmentation network with error updates over N_C only is shown in Figure 9. It can be easily noted from a comparison of Figure 8 and 9 that Figure 9 provided a coarser segmentation with less number of regions. These regions are very close to the visual interpretation of the original image shown in Figure 4. The analysis of connected regions yielded 1256 regions in the original image, 729 in the segmented image shown in Figure 8, and 298 in the final segmented image shown in Figure 9.

For another application of detection of breast cancer, we segmented an image of mammographic microcalcifications.

Mammographic microcalcifications often provides a very low contrast and faded features. Figure 10 shows the original image at the top left with the histogram shown at the middle in the left column. It can be seen from the histogram that no clear threshold can be obtained for microcalcification areas. The extracted microcalcification areas using the best threshold, that could be obtained by interaction, is shown at the bottom of the left column. The learned segmentation map is shown at the top-right with its histogram shown at the middle of the right column. This histogram presents several well separated peaks for several features in the image. The threshold selection for this histogram is clear and marked as T. Using this threshold, the extracted microcalcification areas are shown at the bottom right. These microcalcification areas were evaluated by expert physician and judged to be accurate.

4. CONCLUSION

We have presented a novel approach to image segmentation which is based on the concepts of competitive learning and integrating the local and global information about the features present in the image. Such an integration provides an efficient mechanism to learn about the gray-level features of the image to the extent where homogeneous regions can be grown with a reasonable amount of smoothing. The network can be implemented more efficiently on an appropriate hardware with parallelization

5. ACKNOWLEDGMENTS

This work was supported in parts by the NIH grant CA49976. Authors are deeply grateful to Thomas Dufresne, Prashanth Kini and Charles Peck, III for many valuable suggestions and discussions related to this work.

6. REFERENCES

[1] A.P. Dhawan, "A review on biomedical image processing and future trends", Computer Methods and Programs in Biomedicine", vol. 31, pp. 141-183, 1990.
[2] R.M. Haralick and L. G. Shapiro, Image Segmentation Techniques, Comp. Vision, Graphics, and Image Processing, Vol. 29, pp. 100-132, 1985.
[3] J.S. Weska, A survey of threshold selection techniques, Comp. Graphics, and Image Processing, Vol. 7, pp. 259-265, 1978.
[4] S. Zucker, Region growing; childhood and adolescence, Comp. Graphics and Image Processing, Vol. 5, pp. 382-399, 1976.
[5] T. Kohonen, Self-Organization and Associative Memory, Springer-Verlag, NY, 1988.
[6] D. E. Rumelhart, and J.L. McClelland, Parallel Distributed Processing, Vol.1, MIT Press, MA, 1988.
[7] A.P. Dhawan, "An expert system for early detection of cutaneous malignant melanoma using knowledge-based image analysis", Anal. Quant. Cytol. Hist., vol. 10, pp. 403-416, 1988.
[8] A.P. Dhawan and A. Sicsu, "Segmentation of images of skin-lesions using color and texture information of surface pigmentation", Comp. Medical Imaging and Graphics, vol. 16(3), pp. 163-177, 1992.
[9] A.P. Dhawan and E. Le Royer, "Mammographic feature enhancement by computerized image processing", Comp. Meth. Prog. Biomed., vol. 27, pp. 23-35, 1988.

NEURAL NETWORK BASED OBJECT RECOGNITION IN IMAGES

D. Z. Badal

Computer Science Department
University of Colorado, Colorado Springs, CO 80919
badal@sunshine.uccs.edu, (719)593-3332

Abstract - This paper describes an investigation of object recognition in images which is based on the following novel idea. We view the image not unlike the transparency obtained by overlaying several transparencies each containing a single object. Thus we take the view that any image is a composition of several atomic images. The atomic images contain only one object and they have the same size as composite images. We show that the neural networks trained on a small set of atomic images can recognize very large set of all possible composite images, including overlaping objects, with reasonable recognition rates. The paper also briefly discusses the research prototype of the postrelational DBMS CHINOOK being developed at the University of Colorado at Colorado Springs. CHINOOK is intended to manage databases of digitized images and digitized one-dimensional data as well as text and tables. CHINOOK is intended to support the retrieval of images by their content, possibly using the neural network based object recognition described in this paper.

1 Introduction

There is a need for next generation database technology which can support applications that are not traditional business data processing. Such new applications require different data types, different access methods, different optimization techniques, different architecture, different concurrency control and recovery, than the existing relational database technology. These new classes of non-traditional databases certainly include image databases. The image databases present a technological challenge in the following areas. First, the digitized images and particularly color images, even when compressed are large objects and thus they require novel storage technology like optical disk jukeboxes or some other direct access tertiary storage. From the database system point of view we need to develop the management of tertiary storage, i.e., we need to address

the storage data structures and buffering strategies to minimize the movement of data in a three level storage system. Second, we need to support retrieval of images by their content. This requires the recognition of objects in the images which is currently an open research problem. Third, the retrieval of images by their content requires new access structures, new query languages, new optimization techniques for image queries and perhaps new concurrency and recovery techniques as well.

2 Postrelational DBMS CHINOOK

At present time the first generation of several postrelational DBMS experimental systems are already implemented or are being implemented at universities and industrial R&D labs. These prototypes are intended to explore the new database technology for some of the new classes of applications. The first generation of these prototypes includes the STARBURST project at IBM Almaden Research Lab in San Jose [CHAN89, LEHM89]' the POSTGRES project at the University of California at Berkeley [STON88, STON90], the EXODUS project at the University of Wisconsin in Madison [CARE88, SHEK90, VAND91] and the ORION project at MCC in Austin [KIM88, KIM89]. None of these projects is addressing the image data management.

CHINOOK architecture, shown in Figure 1, is very different from the architecture of any current postrelational DBMS. The CHINOOK architecture is intended to be modular and scalable and it is also intended to support parallel and distributed execution. We also want to explore the most interesting issues first and to implement the prototypes of several CHINOOK modules independently of the rest of the system. For example, we are now concentrating on image system manager.

The CHINOOK system consists of four system managers for the image, text, 1D (digitized one dimensional data like voice or any other one dimensional signal data)

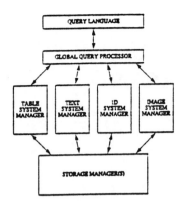

Figure 1: CHINOOK Architecture

and table (relation) data types. Each CHINOOK system manager is a query processor for a given data type and thus it will do query optimization. The top layer of CHINOOK consists of two sublayers - one is a database language and the other is a global query processor. The global query processor is intended to identify in the global queries the relational, text, image and 1D subqueries and to coordinate their execution by the individual system managers. The global query processor will also do global optimization which will involve the sequencing of relational, text, image and 1D subqueries. For example, the global query processor may decide to execute all subqueries in parallel or it may decide to execute the image subquery first, then a part of text subquery, then a part of table subquery and then it may execute the rest of the global query. The bottom layer of CHINOOK architecture consists of EXODUS storage manager [CARE86a,b] extended for tertiary storage. The tertiary storage in CHINOOK will consist of an erasable laser disk jukebox. We are investigating the issues of minimizing the movement of data between storage media, utilizing hard disk as a cache for the jukeboxes and the two-level buffering.

2.1 Image Management in CHINOOK

The current technology for image data storage and retrieval is to have an expert in a given domain, say marine biologist, look at raw images and create the key-word description of image content. Such description is then stored in the relational DBMS together with a pointer to the raw image. The raw images, which may be compressed, are stored either in the file system, DBMS itself if the system has long fields or on video laser disks. Such video disks can be either CD-ROM variety or they can be erasable video laser disks which became available about 3 years ago. The retrieval of images is then via keywords using the current relational DBMS capabilities. This approach is a reasonable solution for relatively small image databases as there is a need for human operator to create the image descrip-

tions. The obvious disadvantage of this approach is that it is not suitable for ultra large image databases and it does not support ad hoc queries in a sense that the image content may not be described completely or it may be described only from the domain expert's point of view.

The approach we are taking is to replace the key word description of images with an image signature which should a) be a compact representation of the image, b) describe the image either in terms of its features (like feature vector) or in terms of its content, c) be machine generated, d) be usable in spatial access methods for fast retrieval of images, and e) support ad hoc queries. The signatures satisfying these requirements are the basis of our approach to image management. The above stated requirements for image signatures mean that we want the raw images to be scanned by the signature extractor and then to store in DBMs the compressed images as well as their signatures with pointers to the compressed images. We are investigating several approaches to image signatures and in this paper we discuss one approach which is based on using neural network classifier to recognize objects in the images.

The typical approach taken in computer vision [KAST89, BROL89, JAGA89, GOOD89, PIZA89] is to construct automatically from a digital image a symbolic description or representation of the image which includes the identity and the structures of objects and their spatial and temporal relationships. The general paradigm for computer model-based vision is that such system works with stored models of objects or object classes it expects to see. The object recognition is by matching the features extracted from the image with features of the stored object model. The computer model-based vision involves multiple levels of representation and abstraction, from low (image representation - purely numeric), to intermediate, and to high (object or object-class models stored in the knowledge base). At the low level of vision the typical processing involves the extraction of homogeneous regions (collections of contiguous image data points with similar properties), edges and lines, 3D surface patches, motion information, etc. Such image descriptions are typically extracted without knowledge of the image content and they are stored at the intermediate level as named and typed symbolic entities or tokens. For example, each token may be an attribute-value pair describing the color and texture of a region or the length and contrast of a line segment. Additional tokens and token types can be created by grouping, splitting, or modifying existing tokens or by imposing hierarchical structures on the representation. The common task performed at this intermediate level is conceptual grouping which assembles related tokens into aggregate structures. The result of such grouping is a set of tokens that represents new image event and can possess properties not possessed by any of its components.

For example, the more abstract tokens include line groups that satisfy certain geometric properties and aggregates of regions and lines consistent with an object or object parts in the knowledge base. Usually the largest amount of data and processing occurs at the intermediate level. High-level knowledge is organized into object or object-class descriptions to facilitate recognition or image interpretation. The image interpretation is done by matching the stored object or object-class descriptions with symbolic representation of image features, i.e., by searching the intermediate and low levels of vision for the evidence of the object. The computer vision requires extensive image and symbolic processing for object (pattern) recognition. We were reluctant to follow the traditional computer vision approach not only because we are not computer vision experts but also because the people in the computer vision have been investigating the object recognition in images for some time now and this still remains an open research problem.

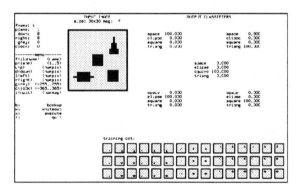

Figure 2: Composite test image with nonoverlaping objects

The traditional database approach to images is just to retrieve them efficiently from the database as single objects and not to bother with the recognition of objects. Our goal is to support ad hoc queries on images where we can specify the image content and we can retrieve the images efficiently. Thus we are addressing both problems - the recognition of objects and their spatial relationships in the images as well as the fast access to images. As we did not want to follow the computer vision approach we decided to investigate another approach which is based on neural networks. The principal idea we are pursuing is based on our view of image as a set of atomic images each containing a single object. We view the image not unlike the transparency obtained by overlaying several transparencies each containing a single object. Thus we take the view that any image is a composition of one or more atomic images. The atomic images and the composite images are of the same size - just like transparencies. Our reasoning is that if we can train the neural network(s) to recognize the atomic images and if so trained neural

network(s) can recognize any combination of atomic images then we can a) avoid all the processing required by computer vision approach, and b) we can support ad hoc queries on image content without explicitly training neural networks for all possible images we may like to retrieve. Thus the basic idea we are following is that by training the neural networks on the image "alphabet" (atomic images of objects we know of for a given application) will allow us to recognize image "words and sentences" (composite images containing more than one object). As far as we know this is the original approach not reported or investigated anywhere else at this time.

3 Results

In this section we report on work done during the past three months. We used the cascade-correlation (cascor) neural network architecture designed by Scott Fahlman from CMU [FAHL90]. The cascor architecture has variable topology in a sense that it generates as many one-element hidden layers as needed to train the network. The variable topology is perhaps one of the most important differences between the cascor architecture and the fixed topology backpropagation architecture. However, the main advantage of the cascor architecture is that it trains much faster than backpropagation architectures.

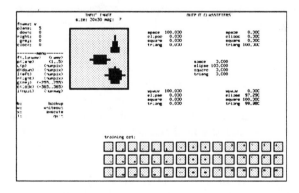

Figure 3: Composite test image with overlaping and nonoverlaping objects

In this paper we report the results of two investigations of atomic and composite images. The first investigation deals with training one net on forty five 30x30 pixel atomic images. Each atomic image contains in one of five positions (left up, right up, center, left down, right down) one of the three objects - ellipse, square and triangle. Each object in the training set has three gray levels and thus for example we have three atomic images with three ellipses in one position. An example of our graphical interface which shows the training set, the input composite image containing nonoverlaping objects only and the classifier output is shown in Figure 2.

We tested the network trained on 45 atomic images on all possible 1,024 composite images containing nonoverlaping objects only and we achieved 97% recognition rate which we consider truly remarkable.

Then we tested the same network on all possible combinations of overlaping objects, i.e., we tested the network on 3,125 test cases where we had three or four possible overlaping objects (spaces, space ellipse square, space ellipse triangle, space square triangle, and space ellipse rectanle triangle) in five possible positions. We achieved 50% recognition rate where all errors were solely due to spaces. We consider 50% recognition rate for overlaping objects very reasonable particularly in the context of very small training set and very large and very difficult (overlaping objects) testing set.

Figure 4: Face segments

An example of our graphical interface which shows the training set, the input composite image containing overlaping and nonoverlaping objects and the classifier output is shown in Figure 3.

The second investigation of atomic and composite images we report in this paper deals with the atomic images consisting of human face segments or slices. We segmented human face images into four atomic images each containing the hair and the forehead segment, the eyes segment, the nose segment and the jaws and mouth segment. The rest of the image was either black or white background. Then we tested thus trained networks on the composite images of each face consisting of all combinations of each face segments. Thus we did not test the networks on composite images consisting of face segments belonging to different people. An example of the four human face segments we used in this investigation is shown in Figure 4.

In this investigation we used eight faces each in six positions or views. We trained one network on 64 atomic images consisting of one view of the same face segment with either black or white background (4 face segments * 8 faces * 2 backgrounds = 64 atomic images). We tested the trained network on all composite images of each face in all 6 positions. The composite images had white background. The testing set consisted of 720 images (15 composites * 8 faces * 6 views). The composites are encoded as shown in the following table.

composite	1	2	3	4	5	6	7	8
hair								x
eyes				x	x	x	x	
nose		x	x			x	x	
jaws	x		x		x		x	
composite	9	10	11	12	13	14	15	-
hair	x	x	x	x	x	x	x	-
eyes				x	x	x	x	-
nose		x	x			x	x	-
jaws	x		x		x		x	-

We achieved the recognition rates [%] shown in the following table.

composite	1	2	3	4	5	6	7	8
recogniton	67	48	69	35	56	40	63	52
composite	9	10	11	12	13	14	15	total
recogniton	58	56	73	50	54	48	60	56

The recognition rates in the above table should be correctly interpreted in the context of the size and difficulty of the training and the testing sets. In that context the recognition rates are quite reasonable.

We also trained another network on 320 atomic images consisting of five views of the same face segment with either black or white background (4 face segments * 8 faces * 2 backgrounds * 5 views = 320 atomic images). We tested the trained network on all composite images of each face in all 6 positions. The composite images had white background. The testing set consisted of 720 images (15 composites * 8 faces * 6 views). We achieved the recognition rates [%] shown in the following table.

composite	1	2	3	4	5	6	7	8
recognition	92	90	85	15	90	69	44	77
composite	9	10	11	12	13	14	15	total
recognition	60	81	81	64	73	75	90	77

The recognition rates in the above table are good and of course that is due to a much larger training set. The data in the above table seem to suggest that the hair, nose and jaws alone give as good recognition as the nose and the jaws combined or as the whole face.

4 Conclusions

We feel that we are investigating a promising and original approach to the unresolved and very hard problem of recognition of objects in images. Our initial results are very encouraging. However, we are well aware that we are using small images (1K pixels) to test our ideas and it is not entirely clear how our approach will scale up for larger images - that is the next step we need to take. Also, it is clear to us that for larger images we either have to have substantially more computing power or we have to use some encoding scheme to decrease the size of the neural networks. However, we believe that eventually we will have specialized chips for what we are doing now in software.

5 Acknowledgements

The work reported in this paper was supported by the NSF grant IRI-9209025. The author wishes to acknowledge the contribution of research assistant Richard Simmons who implemented neural network experiments.

6 References

[BADA92] Badal, D.Z., "Neural Networks and Image Data Mnagement", Proceedings of the 3rd International Conference on Database and Expert Systems, Valencia, Spain, September 2-4, 1992, pp.191-197.

[BROL89] Brolio, J., et al., "ISR: A Database for Symbolic Processing in Computer Vision," COMPUTER, Vol. 22, No. 12, December 1989.

[CARE86a] Carey, M.J., et al., "The Architecture of the EXODUS Extensible DBMS: A Preliminary Report," Computer Science Tech Report No 644, University of Wisconsin at Madison, May 1986.

[CARE86b] Carey, M.J., et al., " Object and File Management in the EXODUS Extensible Database System," Computer Science Tech Report No. 638, University of Wisconsin at Madison, March 1986.

[CARE88] Carey, M.J., et al., "A Data Model and Query Language for EXODUS," Proc ACM SIGMOD 88, June 1988.

[CARE89] Carey, M. and Livny, M., "Parallelism and Concurrency Control Performance in Distributed Database Machines," Proc ACM SIGMOD89, June 1989.

[CHAN80] Chang, N.S. and Fu, K.S., "Query-by-Pictorial-Example," IEEE Transactions Software Engineering, Vol.6, November 1980.

[CHAN87] Chang, N.S., et al., "A Relational Database System for Pictures," Proc IEEE Workshop on Picture Data Description and Management, CS Press, 1977.

[CHAN89] Chang, W.W., and Schek, H.J., "A Signature Access Method for Starburst Database System," Proc VLDB 89, August 1989.

[COPE88] Copeland, G., et al., "Data Placement in Bubba," Proc ACM SIGMOD88, June 88.

[COTT87] Cottrell, G. W., Munro, P. and Zisper, D., "Image Compression by Back Propagation: An Example of Extensional Programming," University of California at San Diego, Institute for Cognitive Science Report 8702, February 1987.

[COTT88] Cottrell, G. W., "Analysis of Image Compression by Back Propagation," Workshop on Neural Architectures for Computer Vision, AAAI 1988.

[COTT88a] Cottrell, G. W. and Munro, P., "Principal Component Analysis via Back Propagation," Proc SPIE, Vol. 1001, Visual Communication and Image Analysis, 1988, pp. 1070-1077.

[COTT90] Cottrel, G. W. and Fleming, M., "Face Recognition Using Unsupervised Feature Extraction," Proceedings of the International

[CARE86a] Carey, M.J., et al., "The Architecture of the EXODUS Extensible DBMS: A Preliminary Report," Computer Science Tech Report No 644, University of Wisconsin at Madison, May 1986.

[CARE86b] Carey, M.J., et al., " Object and File Management in the EXODUS Extensible Database System," Computer Science Tech Report No. 638, University of Wisconsin at Madison, March 1986.

[CARE88] Carey, M.J., et al., "A Data Model and Query Language for EXODUS," Proc ACM SIGMOD 88, June 1988.

[CARE89] Carey, M. and Livny, M., "Parallelism and Concurrency Control Performance in Distributed Database Machines," Proc ACM SIGMOD89, June 1989.

[CHAN89] Chang, W.W., and Schek, H.J., "A Signature Access Method for Starburst Database System," Proc VLDB 89, August 1989.

[FAHL90] Fahlman, S. E., and Lebiere, C. "The Cascade-Correlation Learning Algorithm," CMU Technical Report, CMU-CS-90-100, February 1990.

[**GOOD89**] Goodman, A., et al., "Knowledge-Based Computer Vision - Integrated Programming Language and Data Management System Design," COMPUTER, Vol. 22, No. 12, December 1989.

[**JAGA89**] Jagadish, H.V. and O'Gorman, L., "An Object Model for Image Recognition,"

[**KAST89**] Kasturi, R., et al., "Map Data Processing in Geographic Information System," COMPUTER, Vol. 22, No. 12, December 1989.

[**KIM88**] Kim, W., et al., "Integrating an Object-Oriented Programming System with a Database System," Proc OOPSLA 88 Conference, May 1988.

[**KIM89**] Kim, W., et al., "Composite Objects Revisited," Proc ACM SIGMOD 89, June 1989.

[**LEHM89**] Lehman, T.J., and Lindsay, B., "The Starburst Long Field Manager," Proc VLDB89, August 1989.

[**PIZA89**] Pizano, A., et al., "Specification of Spatial Integrity Constraints in Pictorial Databases," COMPUTER, Vol. 22, No. 12, December 1989.

[**SHEK90**] Shekita, E. and Carey, M., "A Performance Evaluation of Pointer-Based Joins," Proc ACM SIGMOD90, June 1990.

[**STON88**] Stonebraker, M. and Rowe, L.(editors), "The Postgres Papers," University of California at Berkeley, Memorandum No. UCB/ERL M86/85, June 1987.

[**STON90**] Stonebraker, M., et al., "On Rules, Procedures, Caching and Views in Data Base Systems," Proc ACM SIGMOD90, June 1990.

[**VAND91**] Vandenberg, S. and DeWitt, D., "An Algebra for Complex Objects with Arrays and Identity," Proc ACM SIGMOD91, May 1991.

HOPFIELD-BASED ADAPTIVE STATE ESTIMATORS

Rahmat Shoureshi and S. Reynold Chu*
School of Mechanical Engineering
Purdue University
1288 Mechanical Engineering Building
West Lafayette, IN 47907-1288, U.S.A.
Phone: (317) 494-5639 FAX: (317) 494-0539

Abstract–Hopfield networks have been applied to the problem of system identification. Luenberger observers have long been used for estimation of unmeasurable states of linear systems. This paper presents mathematical derivation of an adaptive observer based on integration of the two techniques. Identification of unknown MIMO systems with noise corrupted measurements is described. Simulation results for different plant conditions are detailed.

INTRODUCTION

The Hopfield neural network model consists of a number of mutually interconnected processing units called neurons. Each neuron can be modeled as a nonlinear amplifier. The nonlinear input-output characteristic is typically specified by the following sigmoid function.

$$v_i = g(\lambda\, u_i) = s\left[\frac{2}{1+e^{\lambda u_i}} - 1\right] \qquad (1)$$

where u_i and v_i represent the input and output of the ith neuron and λ controls the slope (gain) of the function at $u_i = 0$. The continuous-time neural network model studied by Hopfield (1984) is governed by the following equation

$$\frac{du_i}{dt} + \frac{u_i}{r_i} = \sum_{j=1}^{n} T_{ij} v_j + I_i, \quad i = 1,2,...,n \qquad (2)$$

where T_{ij} is called the connection weight from the jth neuron to the ith neuron and I_i is the bias to the ith neuron. The energy function considered in the original work by Hopfield has the following form

$$J = -\frac{1}{2}\sum_{i=1}^{n}\sum_{j=1}^{n} T_{ij} v_i v_j - \sum_{i=1}^{n} I_i v_i + \frac{1}{\lambda}\sum_{i=1}^{n}\frac{1}{r_i}\int_{0}^{v_i} g^{-1}(v)dv \quad (3)$$

Notice that the last term in the above energy function can be neglected if high gain neurons are used, i.e. λ is sufficiently large compared to other terms. Then J is a quadratic function of v's. This motivates implementation of least-squares based estimation schemes on the Hopfield network.

As a major difference to the conventional applications of the Hopfield network, in this study time-varying weights are used. Therefore, the condition under which the Hopfield-based identification schemes converge must be investigated. Moreover, the problem of partial convergence due to nonunique parametrization of the observer have to be addressed. This discussion is presented in other publications by the authors (Shoureshi et al. 1992).

It is well known that Luenberger observers can generate asymptotic reconstruction of the state of a linear time-invariant system from the inputs and outputs of the system, provided that the system parameters are known. A natural extension of this problem is to estimate states of an unknown linear system and this falls into the study of adaptive observers (Narendra and Annaswamy, 1989). Among the various algorithms developed in the 70's to solve the problem of adaptive observer (see Chap. 4, Narendra and Annaswamy, 1989), Kreisselmeier (1977) distinguished his method from others by separating the state observation process from the parameter estimation process. This paper discusses simultaneous identification of entries of A and B matrices as well as estimation of unmeasurable states.

SYSTEM IDENTIFICATION WITH MEASURED STATES

Consider the linear dynamic system

$$\dot{\mathbf{x}} = A\,\mathbf{x} + B\mathbf{u} \qquad (4)$$

where $\mathbf{x}\,\varepsilon R^n$, $\mathbf{u}\,\varepsilon R^m$, and A and B are unknown matrices to be identified. Let the corresponding estimated matrices be $\hat{A}$ and $\hat{B}$, respectively. To avoid the need of measuring $\dot{\mathbf{x}}$, the proposed least-squares estimation scheme will be based on filtered signals from state-variable filters, as shown in Figure 1. In a state space form, the state-variable filters for $\mathbf{x}$ and $\mathbf{u}$ are described by

---

* Currently at Navistar Corporation

$$\dot{\mathbf{W}}_1 = \mathbf{W}_2, \qquad \mathbf{W}_1(0) = 0 \tag{5a}$$

$$\dot{\mathbf{W}}_2 = g_1 \mathbf{x} - g_1 \mathbf{W}_1 - g_2 \mathbf{W}_2, \qquad \mathbf{W}_2(0) = 0 \tag{5b}$$

$$\mathbf{x}_f = \mathbf{W}_1 \tag{5c}$$

$$\dot{\mathbf{n}}_1 = \mathbf{n}_2, \qquad \mathbf{n}_1(0) = 0 \tag{5d}$$

$$\dot{\mathbf{n}}_2 = g_1 \mathbf{u} - g_1 \mathbf{n}_1 - g_2 \mathbf{n}_2, \qquad \mathbf{n}_2(0) = 0 \tag{5e}$$

$$\mathbf{u}_f = \mathbf{n}_1 \tag{5f}$$

where g_1 and g_2 are chosen such that filters are asymptotically stable. Notice that each element of $\mathbf{x}$ and $\mathbf{u}$ utilizes by a second order filter. Define

$$\mathbf{C}_1 = \dot{\mathbf{x}}_f - A\mathbf{s}_f - B\mathbf{u}_f$$

Considering equations (5a-f) and the fact that $\dot{\mathbf{x}} - A\mathbf{x} - B\mathbf{u} = 0$, we have

$$\dot{\mathbf{C}}_1 = \mathbf{C}_2 = \dot{\mathbf{W}}_2 - A\mathbf{W}_2 - B\mathbf{n}_2 \tag{6a}$$

$$\dot{\mathbf{C}}_2 = \ddot{\mathbf{W}}_2 - A\dot{\mathbf{W}}_2 - B\dot{\mathbf{n}}_2$$

$$= g_1(\dot{\mathbf{x}} - A\mathbf{x} - B\mathbf{u}) - g_1(\dot{\mathbf{W}}_1 - A\mathbf{W}_1 - B\mathbf{n}_1)$$

$$- f_2(\dot{\mathbf{W}}_2 - A\mathbf{W}_2 - B\mathbf{n}_2)$$

$$= -g_1 \mathbf{C}_1 - g_2 \mathbf{C}_2 \tag{6b}$$

Clearly, equations (7a-b) describe an unforced system with some initial conditions, i.e., $\mathbf{C}_1(0) = 0$, $\mathbf{C}_2(0) = \dot{\mathbf{W}}_2(0) = g_0 \mathbf{x}(0)$. Thus, after some initial transients, the following equivalent system is obtained. Let the ith row of $\hat{A}$ and the ith row of $\hat{B}$ be $\hat{\mathbf{a}}_i^T$ and $\hat{\mathbf{b}}_i^T$, respectively.

Define

$$\phi = \begin{bmatrix} \mathbf{x}_f & 0 & \cdots 0 \\ \mathbf{u}_f & 0 & \cdots 0 \\ 0 & \mathbf{x}_f & 0 & \cdots 0 \\ 0 & \mathbf{u}_f & 0 & \cdots 0 \\ \vdots & \vdots & \vdots \\ 0 & 0 & \cdots & \mathbf{x}_f \\ 0 & 0 & \cdots & \mathbf{u}_f \end{bmatrix} \quad \theta = \begin{bmatrix} \hat{\mathbf{a}}_1 \\ \hat{\mathbf{b}}_1 \\ \hat{\mathbf{a}}_2 \\ \hat{\mathbf{b}}_2 \\ \vdots \\ \hat{\mathbf{a}}_n \\ \hat{\mathbf{b}}_n \end{bmatrix} \tag{7}$$

and the estimation error

$$\mathbf{e}_f = \dot{\mathbf{x}}_f - (\hat{A}\mathbf{x}_f + B\mathbf{u}_f) = \dot{\mathbf{x}}_f - \phi^T \theta \tag{8}$$

Then, from equation (8) the estimation error can be written as

$$\mathbf{e}_f = (A - \hat{A})\,\mathbf{x}_f + (B - \hat{B}))\,\mathbf{u}_f = \phi^T (\theta^* - \theta) \tag{9}$$

where θ^* is related to the rows of matrices A and B in the same way as θ is related to the rows of matrices $\hat{A}$ and $\hat{B}$.

Consider the following least-squares error criterion as the energy function

$$J(t) = \int_0^t \frac{1}{2} \mathbf{e}_f^T(\tau)\mathbf{e}_f(\tau) \left[\exp\left(-(t-\tau)/\mu\right)\right] d\tau \tag{10}$$

Notice that an exponentially decaying window with time constant μ is used in the above energy function. This window has the effect of emphasizing the most current estimation error and has a gradually fading memory of earlier errors. The discrete-time analog of the weighting term $\exp(-t/\mu)$ is referred to as the forgetting factor in the literature on time-series analysis (Söderström and Stoica, 1989). With such exponential weighting of the estimation error, we are able to track the changing parameters of a time-varying system. Substituting (9) into (10), a quadratic function of parameter vector θ is resulted, i.e.,

$$J(t) = \frac{1}{2}\theta^T \left[\int_0^t \phi(\tau)\phi^T(\tau)\exp(-(t-\tau/\mu)d\tau\right]\theta - \theta^T \tag{11}$$

$$\left[\int_0^t \phi(\tau)\dot{\mathbf{x}}_f(\tau)\exp(-(t-\tau)/\mu)dt\right]$$

$$- \frac{1}{2}\int_0^t \dot{\mathbf{x}}_f^T(\tau)\dot{\mathbf{x}}_f(\tau)\exp(-t-\tau/\mu)d\tau$$

Letting the output of each neuron represent one of the unknown parameters, and by comparing equations (3) and (11) the connection weights and biases of the Hopfield network can be represented as follows

$$T_{ij}(t) = -\left[\eta \int_0^t \phi(\tau)\,\phi^T(\tau)\exp(-(t-\tau)/\mu)d\tau\right]_{ij} \tag{12}$$

$$I_i(t) = \left[\eta \int_0^t \phi(\tau)\,\dot{\mathbf{x}}_f(\tau)\exp(-(t-\tau)/\mu)d\tau\right]_i \tag{13}$$

where $[\ ]_{ij}$ represents the element at the ith row and the jth column of the bracketed matrix, $[\ ]_i$ represents the ith element of the bracketed vector, and parameter η is the learning gain.

SYSTEM IDENTIFICATION AND STATE ESTIMATION

Consider the following state space model of a linear time-invariant system

$$\dot{\mathbf{x}} = A\mathbf{x} = B\mathbf{u}, \quad \mathbf{x}(0) = \mathbf{x}_0 \tag{14}$$

$$\mathbf{y} = C\mathbf{x}$$

where $\mathbf{x} \in R^n$, $\mathbf{u} \in R^m$, and $\mathbf{y} \in R^p$. Here, no information is available about matrices A and B except (C,A) is assumed to be an observable pair and C is given. To reconstruct states of the system, consider the family of observers of

1290

the form

$$\dot{\hat{x}} = \overline{A}\hat{x} + \hat{K}y + \hat{B}u, \quad \hat{x}(0) = \hat{x}_0 \quad (15)$$

where $\overline{A}$, the desired closed-loop system matrix, has a set of eigenvalues with real parts less than $-s(s>0)$. The above observer is parametrized on matrices $\hat{K}$ and $\hat{B}$. One particular set of parameters

$$\overline{A} = A - KC, \quad \hat{K} = K, \quad \hat{B} = B \quad (16)$$

gives the Luenberger observer. Although the eigenvalues of $\overline{A}$ can be arbitrarily assigned due to the observability of (C,A), existence of K has to be assumed. In other words, $A - \overline{A}$ is assumed to be in the row space of matrix C. Under this set of parameters, the state observation error, $\tilde{x}(t) = x(t) - \hat{x}(t)$, vanishes exponentially according to $\tilde{x}(t) = \exp(\overline{A}t)\tilde{x}_0$. In order to use the least-squares estimation process, an expression of estimation error which is linearly dependent on $K - \hat{K}$ and $B - \hat{B}$ is desired. In the following, such parametrization of $\tilde{x}(t)$ will be described.

Let I_n denote an $n \times n$ identity matrix, then, observer (15) can be rewritten as

$$\dot{\hat{x}} = \overline{A}\hat{x} + \sum_{i=1}^{p} \hat{k}_i y_i + \sum_{i=1}^{m} \hat{b}_i u_i = \overline{A}\hat{x} + \sum_{i=1}^{p} y_i I_n \hat{k}_i + \sum_{i=1}^{m} u_i I_n \hat{b}_i \quad (17)$$

where $\hat{k}_i$ is the ith column of matrix $\hat{k}$ and $\hat{b}_i$ is the ith column of matrix $\hat{B}$. Next, define the following state-variable filters

$$\dot{W}_i = \overline{A}W_i + y_i I_n, \quad W_i(0) = 0, \quad i=1,...,p \quad (18a)$$

$$\dot{P}_i = \overline{A}P_i + u_i I_n, \quad P_i(0) = 0, \quad i=1,...,m \quad (18b)$$

where $W_i \varepsilon R^{nxn}$, and $P_i \varepsilon R^{nxn}$. Then the estimated state vector, $\hat{x}$ can be written as

$$\hat{x}(t) = \left[W_{1...}, W_p, P_{1,...} P_m \right]\theta + \exp(\overline{A}t)\hat{x}_0 \quad (19)$$

where $\theta^t = \left[\hat{k}_{1,...}\mathbf{k}_p, \hat{b}_{1,} \cdots \hat{b}_m \right]^T$. Since the state estimation error of the Luenberger observer is $\tilde{x}(t) = \exp(\overline{A}t)\tilde{x}_o$, it follows from the relation $x(t) = \hat{x}(t) + \tilde{x}(t)$ that

$$x(t) = \left[W_1, \ldots, W_p, P_1, \ldots, P_m \right]\theta^* + \exp(\overline{A}t)x_0 \quad (20)$$

Subtracting (19) from (20), the state estimation error is

$$\tilde{x}(t) = \left[W_1, \ldots, W_p, P_1, \ldots, P_m \right]\theta^* - \theta + \exp(\overline{A}t)\tilde{x}_0 \quad (21)$$

Equation (21) clearly shows that the state estimation error can be separated into two parts. The first part, which is parameter induced error, is linearly dependent on the parameter mismatch. The second part is due to the state estimation error of the Luenberger observer.

Since the observer output is $\hat{y} = C\hat{x}$, then the output estimation error, $\tilde{y} = y - \hat{y}$, becomes

$$\tilde{y}(t) = y(t) - C\left\{ \left[W_1, \ldots, W_p, P_1, \ldots, P_m \right]\theta + \right.$$
$$\left. \exp(\overline{A}t)\hat{x}_0 \right\} = \phi^T(\theta^* - \theta) + C\exp(\overline{A}t)\tilde{x} \quad (22)$$

where $\phi^T = C\left[W_1, ..., W_p, ..., P_a, ..., P_m \right]$. Based on the output estimation error in the least-squares error criterion, the connection weights and biases of the Hopfield network would result from the following equations.

$$T_{ij}(t) = -\left[\eta \int_0^t \phi(\tau)\,\phi^T(\tau)\exp\left(-(t-\tau)/\mu\right)d\tau \right]_{ij} \quad (23a)$$

$$I_i(t) = \left[\eta \int_0^t \phi(\tau)\left[y(t) - C\exp(\overline{A}t)\hat{x}_0 \right] \right.$$
$$\left. \exp(-(t-\tau)/\mu)d\tau \right]_{ij} \quad (23b)$$

Notice that the term $C\exp(\overline{A}t)\hat{x}_0$ is estimated output of the Luenberger observer. As transients due to the initial state of the observer die out, the Hopfield network should be able to settle to the desired parameters. Also, identification of matrix A comes from identification of the feedback matrix K for the Luenberger observer, i.e., $A = \overline{A} + KC$. From equation (21), convergence of the state observation can be achieved after the convergence of parameter estimation process or convergence of the Luenberger observer, whichever comes later is reached.

ADAPTIVE STATE OBSERVATION WITH MEASUREMENT NOISE

In the above derivation, a scheme of adaptive state observation free from measurement noise was presented. However, in practice, measurements of the exact output variables may not be possible. Therefore, the accuracy of parameter estimation under noise corrupted measurements of output variables needs to be investigated. Consider the revised version of equation (14)

$$\dot{x} = Ax + Bu, \quad x(0) = x_0 \quad (24a)$$

$$y = Cx + w \quad (24b)$$

where w is the vector of measurement noise. No specific assumptions is made on w except it is bounded and has a zero mean. The observer still has the same form, i.e.,

$$\dot{\hat{x}} = \overline{A}\hat{x} + \hat{K}y + \hat{B}u, \quad \hat{x}(0) = \hat{x}_0$$

Assume there exists a matrix K such that $\overline{A} = A - KC$. Then, equation (24a) can be rewritten as

$$\dot{x} = \overline{A}x + Ky + Bu - Kw \quad (25)$$

With the same state-variable filters defined by equations (18a-b), $\mathbf{x}(t)$ can be expressed as follows

$$\mathbf{x}(t) = \left[\mathbf{W}_1, ..., \mathbf{W}_p, \mathbf{P}_1, \cdots, \mathbf{P}_m\right]\theta^* + \exp(\overline{A}t)\mathbf{x}_0 - (SI{-}\overline{A})^{-1}\mathbf{Kw} \quad (26)$$

where $S \triangleq \dfrac{d}{dt}$. On the other hand, representation of $\hat{\mathbf{x}}(t)$ remains the same, i.e.,

$$\hat{\mathbf{x}}(t) = \left[\mathbf{W}_1, \cdots, \mathbf{W}_p, \mathbf{P}_1, ..., \mathbf{P}_m\right]\theta + \exp(\overline{A}t)\hat{\mathbf{x}}_0 \quad (27)$$

Therefore, the output estimation error is

$$\tilde{y}(t;q) = C\tilde{\mathbf{x}} = \phi^T(\theta^* - \theta) + C\exp(\overline{A}t)\tilde{\mathbf{x}}_0 - C(SI{-}\overline{A})^{-1}\mathbf{Kw} \quad (28)$$

Notice that the last term represents a filtered noise. Therefore, even if $\mathbf{w}$ is frequently assumed to be uncorrelated white noise, $\tilde{y}$ is still influenced by a correlated noise. Let $\mathbf{n} = -C(SI{-}\hat{A})^{-1}\mathbf{kw}$. Consider the following least-squares error criterion with variable exponential weighting

$$J(t;\theta(t)) = \int_0^t \frac{1}{2}\tilde{y}^T(\tau;\theta(t))\tilde{y}(\tau;\theta(t)) \exp\left[-\int_t^t \frac{1}{\mu(v)}dr\right]d\tau \quad (29)$$

By solving $\dfrac{\partial J}{\partial \theta} = 0$, the estimated parameter vector can be resulted as following

$$\theta(t) = \theta^* + R^{-1}(t)\int_0^t \phi(\tau)(C\exp(\overline{A}\tau)\tilde{\mathbf{x}}_0 + \mathbf{n}) \exp\left[-\int_\tau^t \frac{1}{\mu(nu)}dr\right]d\tau \quad (30)$$

where

$$R(t) = \int_0^t \phi(\tau)\phi^T(\tau)\exp\left[-\int_\tau^t \frac{1}{\mu(r)}dr\right]d\tau$$

Notice that the second term on the right hand side of equation (30) represents the parameter estimation error caused by an initial state error and the measurement noise. Particularly, the integral term in (30) can be considered as the output of the following time-varying first order filter

$$\dot{S}(t) + \frac{1}{\mu(t)}S(t) = \phi(t)(C\exp(\overline{A}t)\tilde{\mathbf{x}}_0 + \mathbf{n}(t)) \quad (31)$$

Since matrix $\overline{A}$ is asymptotically stable, then as time increases only $\mathbf{n}$ will make significant contribution to the parameter estimation error. To reduce such fluctuation, larger values of μ should be selected such that the filter has narrower bandwidth and hence better noise rejection property. This can also be understood from the fact that the least-squares estimation with larger μ attempts to fit more data up to the present time and thus can average out more noise, particularly those at high frequencies.

However, increasing the value of μ will reduce the ability of the estimation scheme to track time-varying parameters. Therefore, it is beneficial to utilize variable exponential weighting such that a small value of μ is used initially to ensure fast parameter convergence and the value is increased gradually to improve robustness against noise. In addition, μ should also be reset to small values when significant output estimation error is detected. This can expedite forgetting of the old data. The following is a useful formula for time-varying μ.

$$\mu(t) = \mu_i + (\mu_f - \mu_i)(1 - \exp(t/\mu_0)) \quad \mu_f > \mu_i > 0, \mu_o > 0 \,(32)$$

where μ_i and μ_f are the initial and the final values of $\mu(t)$, respectively, and μ_o is the time constant of $\mu(t)$ approaching μ_f.

SIMULATION RESULTS

Two examples describing the cases with and without measurement noise are presented.

Example 1: Simulation of an adaptive observer with full state measurements has been performed on the following third order plant.

$$\dot{x} = \begin{bmatrix} -2 & 0 & 0 \\ 1 & -0.5 & 0.866 \\ 1 & -0.866 & -0.5 \end{bmatrix} x + \begin{bmatrix} 1 \\ 1 \\ 0 \end{bmatrix} u$$

$$y = \begin{bmatrix} 1 & 0 & 0 \\ 1 & 1 & 0 \\ 1 & 1 & 0 \end{bmatrix} x$$

Figures 2 and 3 show representative convergence of parameters and state estimates. Similar results have been obtained for remaining parameters and states.

Example 2: In this example the influence of measurement noise on the accuracy of parameter estimation by the adaptive observer is examined. Particularly, the effectiveness of variable rate forgetting factor over the fixed rate is demonstrated. The plant is described by the following equations.

$$\dot{x} = \begin{bmatrix} -2 & 0 & 0 \\ 1 & -0.5 & 0.866 \\ 1 & -.866 & -0.5 \end{bmatrix} x + \begin{bmatrix} 1 \\ 1 \\ 0 \end{bmatrix} u$$

$$y = \begin{bmatrix} 1 & 0 & 0 \\ 1 & 1 & 0 \\ 1 & 1 & 1 \end{bmatrix} x + \begin{bmatrix} 1 \\ 1 \\ 1 \\ 1 \end{bmatrix} w$$

Where w is a white noise added to all measurements. The following two schemes of exponential averaging are used:

fixed rate: $\mu = 0.4$ seconds

variable rate: $\mu_i = 0.2$ seconds

                 $\mu_f = 8.$ seconds

                 $\mu_o = 20$ seconds

Figures 4 through 6 compare estimations of three system parameters by these two schemes of averaging. The two schemes are almost equal in the initial convergence to the target values but the variable rate forgetting case clearly has the edge in noise immunity. The convergence of remaining parameters show similar results.

CONCLUSION

A major contribution of this paper is the development of a method for application of the Hopfield network in implementing a least-squares estimation of continuous-time linear dynamic systems in state space models. System identification without differentiating state variables and adaptive state observation of MIMO systems are demonstrated. Also, the influence of measurement noise on parameter estimation and state observation was analyzed. Variable rate of exponential averaging has been employed to achieve fast parameter convergence and robustness against noise. The resulting neural-based adaptive observer demonstrates a new generation of the Luenberger state estimators.

REFERENCES

[1] Chen, C.T. (1984), *Linear System Theory and Design*, Holt, Rinehart and Winston, New York, NY.

[2] Chu, S.R., R. Shoureshi, and M.F. Tenorio (1990), "Neural Networks for System Identification," *IEEE Cont. Syst. Mag.*, Vol. 10, No. 3, pp. 31-35.

[3] Hopfield, J.J. (1985) and D.W. Tank, "Neural Computation of Decisions in Optimization Problems," *Biol. Cybernetics*, Vol. 52, pp. 141-152.

[4] Hopfield, J.J. (1984), "Neurons with Graded Response Have Collective Computational Abilities Like Those of Two-State Neurons," *Proc. Natl. Acad. Sci.*, Vol. 81, pp, 3088-3092.

[5] Kreisselmeier, G. (1977), "Adaptive Observer with Exponential Rate of Convergence," *IEEE, Trans. Automat. Cont.*, Vol. AC-22, No. 1, pp. 2-8.

[6] Narendra, K.S., and A.M. Annaswamy (1989), *Stable Adaptive Systems*, Prentice Hall, Englewood Cliffs, NJ.

[7] Shoureshi, R., Chu, S.R., (1992), "Convergence Conditions on Hopfield-Based Adaptive Observers," submitted to *IEEE Trans. on Neural Networks*.

[8] Söderström, T. and P. Stoica (1989), *System Identification*, Prentice Hall, New York.

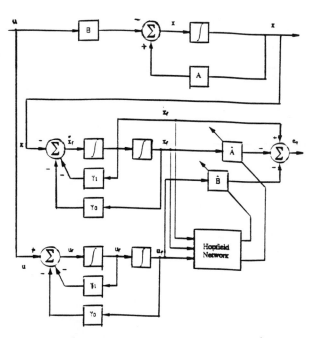

Fig. 1.   Identification of linear dynamic system using Hopfield network and state-variable filter.

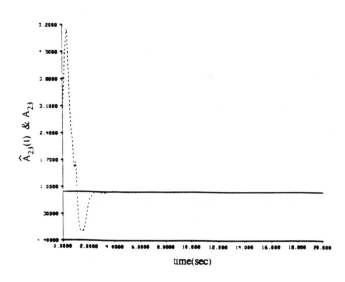

Fig. 2.   Identification of A_{23} by Adaptive Observer

1293

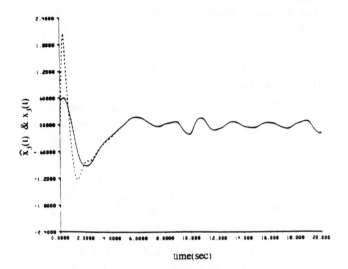

Fig. 3.   Estimation of $x_3(t)$ by Adaptive Observer

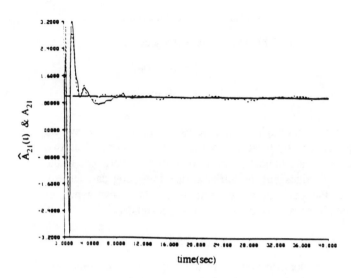

Fig. 4.   Identification of A_{21}: fixed rate forgetting vs. variable rate forgetting.

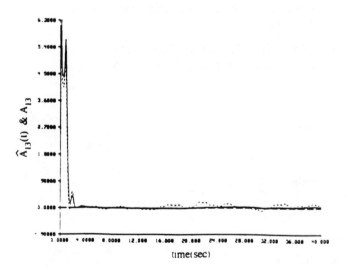

Fig. 5.   Identification of A_{13}: fixed rate forgetting vs. variable rate forgetting.

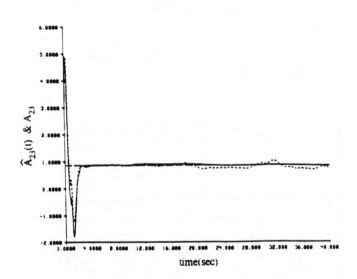

Fig. 6.   Identification of A_{23}: fixed rate forgetting vs. variable rate forgetting.

Design of Fault Tolerant Neurocontrollers Using Immunization Technique *

D.U. Ekong[†]   M.H. Abd-El-Barr[‡]   H.C. Wood[†]

[†]Dept. of Electrical Engineering   [‡]Dept. of Computational Science
University of Saskatchewan
Saskatoon, Canada S7N 0W0
Email: ekong@edison.usask.ca

Abstract— Recent developments in VLSI have resulted in hardware implementations of neural networks which offer reductions in size and computing time. Before hardware implementations of neural networks can be available commercially for use in areas such as control, it would be necessary to study the ability of a neural network to continue to give desired output in the presence of fault(s) in the network. Various techniques have been proposed for the design of fault tolerant neural networks. One technique involves the deliberate injection of possible faults into the network during the training phase. This paper presents simulation studies on the use of this technique, called Immunization technique, to improve the fault tolerance of neurocontrollers.

Keywords: Fault Tolerance, Neural Networks, Neurocontrollers.

I. INTRODUCTION

Artificial neural networks, or neural networks, have found applications in control systems because of their ability to learn and adapt to their environment. The objective of a control system is to provide an appropriate input to a physical process in order to get a desired output. The physical process to be controlled is known as the plant. A controller is required to generate the appropriate signal(s) that would drive the output of the plant to be equal to the desired output. If the controller is a neural network, it is called a neural controller or a neurocontroller.

Most neural controllers are simulated on computers [1] - [6], and the speed of these simulations depend on the computer used. With recent developments in VLSI, it is now possible to have hardware implementations of neural networks which offer reductions in size and computing time [7, 8]. Before these hardware implementations can be available commercially for use in areas such as control of chemical processes, or control of robots in a manufacturing environment, it is necessary to study their fault tolerance. The fault tolerance of a neural network is the ability of the network to continue to give the desired output in the presence of fault(s) in the network. A fault is defined as a defect that occurs in a neural network, which could result in erroneous results in the output of the neural network. Examples of faults include stuck-at faults, and deviations in nominal component values. Studies have been carried out on the fault tolerance of neural networks [9] - [13]. These studies have shown that the fault tolerance of of a neural network depends on the stored information and fault model used, and that fault tolerance must be built into the network. Fault models describe the type of faults that can occur in a system. Various techniques have been proposed to improve the fault tolerance of neural networks. One technique involves the injection of possible faults into the network during the training phase [10, 11]. This technique is called Immunization technique [10], because of the resulting improvement in the immunity of the network to these faults. This paper presents the design of fault tolerant neurocontrollers using the immunization technique.

II. CONTROL SYSTEM ARCHITECTURE

The control system architecture used is the specialized learning architecture, proposed by Psaltis et al. [1]. The objective of the control system is to drive the plant output to be as close as possible to the desired output. This is done by training the neural-based controller to provide appropriate signals needed to drive the plant. Fig. 1 shows the control architecture for a dynamical plant. Feedback from the plant output is required by the neural controller in order to learn the state of the plant [5, 14].

*Supported by NSERC with grants 7-70791 and A3976

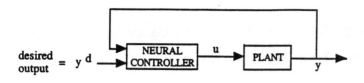

Figure 1: Control System Architecture

in order to learn the state of the plant [5, 14].

III. NEUROCONTROLLER TRAINING

The architecture used for each neurocontroller in this paper is the multi-layered perceptron, as shown in Fig. 2. It is trained to give the correct plant input that would drive the plant output to be equal to, or close to (within an acceptable error margin), the desired output value. Training involves adjusting the weights using the back-propagation algorithm [15] :

$$W_{ab}^m(k+1) = W_{ab}^m(k) + \eta \delta_a^m q_b^{m-1} + \alpha(W_{ab}^m(k) - W_{ab}^m(k-1)). \quad (1)$$

$W_{ab}^m(k)$ is the weight between neuron a of layer m and neuron b of layer $m-1$ at time k, while q_b^{m-1} is the output value of neuron b of layer $m-1$. δ_a^m is the error term of neuron a in layer m, while η is the learning rate, and α is the momentum gain used to control the rate of convergence. The error term for the hidden layers of the neurocontroller is [15] :

$$\delta_a^m = f'(X_a^m) \sum_n \delta_n^{m+1} W_{na}^{m+1}. \quad (2)$$

X_a^m is the weighted sum of the inputs of neuron a of layer m, and $f'(X)$ is the derivative of the activation function, $f(X)$, of the hidden layers.

In the specialized learning architecture, to calculate the error term of the neurocontroller output layer, δ_{ol}, the plant is treated as an additional unmodifiable layer. The error at the output of the plant is then propagated through the plant to the output layer of the neurocontroller by using the partial derivatives of the plant at its operating point to give, [1]:

$$\delta_a^{ol} = f'_{ol}(X_a^{ol}) \sum_i (y_i^d - y_i) \frac{\partial y_i}{\partial u_a}. \quad (3)$$

The ith element of the plant output is y_i, while y_i^d is the desired output. The output of neuron a of the neurocontroller output layer is u_a, while $f'_{ol}(X)$ is the derivative of the activation function, $f_{ol}(X)$, of the output layers.

IV. FAULT TOLERANT DESIGN

A typical design technique that is used to achieve fault tolerance in a system is to replicate the critical components

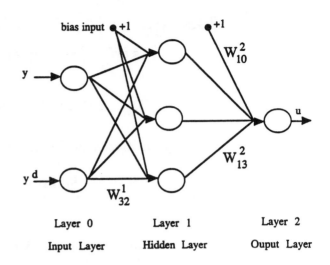

Figure 2: Neurocontroller

of the system. This replication technique does not guarantee fault tolerance in neural networks because training can result in dominant and redundant weights, with the locations of these weights varying if training is repeated with different initial conditions. Dominant weights have large magnitudes and the removal of these weights adversely affects the performance of the neural network. Redundant weights have smaller magnitudes and their removal does not adversely affect the fault tolerance of a network [11, 16]. To achieve fault tolerance, the training procedure must increase the ability of the neural network to tolerate faults.

The immunization technique utilizes the adaptive capability of a neural network to teach it how to compensate against possible faults, by training the network in the presence of those faults[10]. The fault model used in this paper is a deviation in the weight values. This is similar to the fault model that was used in [10], and it is considered to be a high-level generalized case of many possible faults in analog and digital implementations of neural networks. Deviations in weight values can be thought of as the weight being corrupted by noise. To synthesize the effects of hardware faults, and improve the fault tolerance of the neural network, noise is injected into the network during training by perturbing the weights.

Fault tolerance analysis is performed by measuring how much each weight can be perturbed about its nominal value before it causes the controlled plant to give output values which are outside a certain tolerance range. This is known as headroom analysis [10]. There are two extreme cases for a weight: it can have a very small headroom, or it can have a very large headroom. Slight changes in weights with small headrooms lead to errors in the output of the controlled plant, while changes in the values of weights with very large headrooms do not significantly affect the output of the controlled plant.

V. SIMULATIONS

Simulation studies include the use of the immunization technique to improve the fault tolerance of two neurocontrollers. The first neurocontroller is used to control a linear plant, while the second neurocontroller is used to control a non-linear plant. Both plants are single-input single-output (SISO) plants.

The neurocontroller in each example is a feedforward neural network with input, hidden, and output layers, as shown in Fig. 2. The input signals are the desired plant output, y^d, and the actual plant output, y. Each neuron in the input layer (layer 0) receives only one of these inputs and distributes it, through weights, to the neurons in the next layer without any further processing of the received signal. The activation function, $f(X)$, for each neuron in the hidden layer (layer 1) is $1/(1 + e^{-x})$, where x is the weighted sum of the inputs of a neuron. This is a sigmoid function which gives outputs in the range [0,1]. The neuron in the output layer (layer 2) has a similar sigmoid function which is multiplied by 10 to give outputs within the control input range of the plant. In addition to weighted inputs from other neurons, the neurons in the hidden and output layers have weighted bias inputs to enable them to find their threshold values, and hence aid convergence during training.

The neurocontroller for each plant was trained to give the correct input that would drive the plant output to the desired output, with an error range of ± 0.05. At the start of each training, the network was intialized with small random weights. Training was done using (1) to (3), with learning rate, η, equal to 0.2, for the neural network controlling the linear plant, and 0.15 for the neural network controlling the non-linear plant. The momentum gain, α, was 0.4 for both plants. The immunization technique was incorporated into the training process by perturbing the weights with randomly generated percentages which were less than or equal to 10% (10% noise), 25% (25% noise), and 50% (50% noise). For each neurocontroller, the same initial weights were used at the start of each training session, i.e., training without noise, with 10% noise, with 25% noise, and with 50% noise. The experiments were repeated with the momentum gain, α, set equal to zero, to study the effect of α on the fault tolerance of the two neurocontrollers. Different values of initial weights were also used to study how the choice of weights affects the fault tolerance of the neurocontrollers.

Example 1: The transfer function of the linear plant is $1/(1.5s + 1)$. To simulate this plant, a discrete system described by the linear difference equation

$$y(k + 1) = e^{-T/1.5}y(k) + (1 - e^{-T/1.5})u(k)$$

with the sampling interval, $T = 0.1$ secs., was used. This system has the same states and output as the plant [17]. Five training points (2.0, 4.0, 1.0, 3.0, 5.0), were used to train the neurocontroller for this plant. It was tested with twelve data points, (3.3, 1.2, 2.0, 5.0, 3.5, 4.0, 1.5, 2.8, 4.5, 3.0, 2.5, 1.0), which included both training and other data. The test points were also used in the headroom analysis of the neurocontroller.

Example 2: The transfer function of the non-linear plant is described by the difference equation [4]

$$y(k + 1) = \sum_{i=0}^{n-1} \beta_i y(k - i) + g[u(k)]$$

with $n = 1$, $\beta_0 = 0.8$ and $g[u(k)] = 1.5 \sin(\pi u(k))$, in this example.

The neurocontroller for the non-linear plant was trained with eleven points (0.5, 1.0, 2.0, 3.0, 4.0, 5.0, 4.0, 3.0, 2.0, 1.0, 0.5) and tested with thirteen data points (3.3, 1.2, 2.0, 5.0, 3.5, 4.0, 1.5, 2.8, 4.5, 3.0, 0.5, 1.0, 2.5), which were also used in the headroom analysis.

A. Simulation Results and Discussion

Figs. 3 to 5 show results of headroom analysis performed on the neurocontrollers, while Tables 1 to 3 show the respective weights. The headroom indicates the minimum percentage that a weight can be changed before it causes the difference between the desired output and the actual plant output to be outside the acceptable error range. The vertical axis of each graph represents the magnitude of the headroom, while the horizontal axis represents the respective weights. Weight W_{ab}^m would be represented on the graph as $Wmab$, where $Wmab$ is the notation for the weight between neuron a in layer m, and neuron b in layer $m - 1$. For example, $W132$ is the notation for the weight between neuron 3 in layer 1 (hidden layer) and neuron 2 in layer 0 (input layer). When b in W_{ab}^m is equal to zero, then W_{a0}^m represents the weight between neuron a in layer m and its bias input. For each weight, there are four bar graphs. The first graph represents training without noise, the second graph, training with 10% noise, the third graph, training with 25% noise, and the fourth graph represents training with 50% noise.

Fig. 3 shows the headroom analysis results of the neuron in the output layer (layer 2) of the neurocontroller for

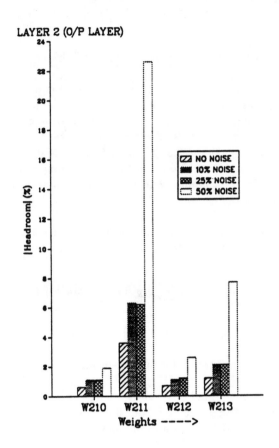

LAYER 2 (O/P LAYER)

Figure 3: Headroom of Output Layer for Linear Case

Table 1: Weights of the Neuron

| | WEIGHTS AFTER TRAINING WITH | | | |
	NO NOISE	10% NOISE	25% NOISE	50% NOISE
W210	3.5409	3.5826	3.5922	3.6599
W211	-1.3173	-1.3380	-1.3592	-1.4529
W212	-5.5624	-5.5952	-5.6179	-5.7228
W213	-3.1736	-3.2207	-3.2459	-3.3094

the linear plant. Table 1 shows the values of the weights after training. The results indicate a general improvement in the headroom, and hence the fault tolerance, of the weights of the neurons as a result of training with noise. For example, an increase in the magnitude of $W213$ as a result of training with 50% noise has resulted in an increase in the magnitude of the headroom from 1.2% to 7.7%. Trainings with 10% and 20% noise have also resulted in improvements in headroom, and hence fault tolerance, when compared with training without noise. The results for the remaining neurons in this example, which are given in Fig. 4 and Table 2, show that training with 10% and 25% noise have resulted in increases in magnitudes of the weights and headrooms of the neurons. This is in contrast with training with 50resulted only in increases in the magnitudes of the weights.

Fig. 5 and Table 3 respectively show the headroom analysis results and weight values of the neurocontroller for the non-linear plant. Only a small number of weights show improvements in headroom as a result of training with noise. Most other weights actually witness decrease in headroom values. Changes in initial weight values and noise percentages did not improve the headroom values.

B. Effect of Momentum Gain, α, and Change in Initial Weight Values

The momentum gain, α, was set to zero and the training process was repeated. The results for both the linear and non-linear plants showed longer training cycles, which is not surprising. There was an improvement in fault tolerance of the neurocontroller for the linear plant when compared with training with α equal to 0.4. The opposite is the case for the neurocontroller of the non-linear plant. In addition to a decrease in fault tolerance, this neurocontroller witnessed a decrease in its generalization capability when it was trained without noise.

Similar results as in previous simulations were obtained when the initial weights were changed in both neurocontrollers.

VI. CONCLUDING REMARKS

The simulation results have shown that the overall fault tolerance of a neural network used to control a linear plant can be improved when training incorporates the immunization technique. Fault tolerance was improved further when the momentum gain, α, was reduced from 0.4 to 0. The results for the neurocontroller of the non-linear plant are however different, with little or no improvement in fault tolerance of the weights when training incorporates noise. It may be that the architecture for the neurocontroller was unsuitable for the control of the non-linear plant.

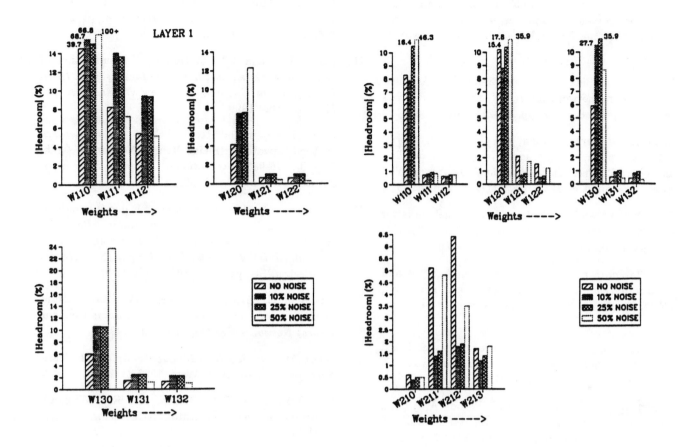

Figure 5: Headroom Results for Non-Linear Case

Figure 4: Remaining Headroom Results for Linear Case

Table 3: Weights of the Neurons

Table 2: Weights of the Neurons

	WEIGHTS AFTER TRAINING WITH			
	NO NOISE	10% NOISE	25% NOISE	50% NOISE
W110	0.1619	0.1646	0.1686	0.1835
W111	0.7464	0.7665	0.7890	0.8845
W112	-1.1969	-1.2073	-1.2156	-1.2495
W120	0.3885	0.3761	0.3707	0.3815
W121	2.8101	2.8343	2.8783	3.1505
W122	-2.9004	-2.9197	-2.9853	-3.2285
W130	0.4415	0.4387	0.4444	0.4678
W131	1.7523	1.7873	1.8287	2.0149
W132	-2.0796	-2.1047	-2.1540	-2.3298

	WEIGHTS AFTER TRAINING WITH			
	NO NOISE	10% NOISE	25% NOISE	50% NOISE
W110	-0.6862	-0.2318	0.1338	0.1436
W111	1.7281	1.7362	1.7720	1.8409
W112	-2.0667	-2.1050	-2.2151	-2.3009
W120	-0.4661	-0.2373	-0.1264	0.1274
W121	3.0792	2.2318	2.1854	2.3419
W122	-4.0413	-3.0256	-2.9483	-3.2229
W130	0.4202	-0.0661	-0.0610	0.3115
W131	1.0730	1.5124	1.6098	1.8113
W132	-1.3195	-1.7421	-1.7907	-2.0381
W210	-2.5496	-2.7820	-2.7917	-2.8036
W211	-3.1078	-2.7242	-2.6170	-1.6466
W212	-4.3481	-3.4450	-3.2678	-3.3430
W213	-2.7157	-2.3915	-2.2404	-2.1162

Future work includes a combination of the immunization and other software techniques with hardware techniques to improve the fault tolerance of neural networks.

REFERENCES

[1] D. Psaltis, A. Sideris, and A. Yamamura, 'A multi-layered neural network controller', *IEEE Control Systems Mag.*, vol. 8, no. 2, pp. 18–21, April 1988.

[2] E. Levin, R. Gerwitrzmann, and G.F. Inbar, 'Neural network architecture for adaptive system modelling and control', *Proc. Int. Joint Conf. on Neural Networks*, Washington, D.C., pp. 311–316, June 1989.

[3] D.H. Nguyen and B. Widrow, 'Neural networks for self-learning control systems', *IEEE Control Systems Mag.*, vol. 10, no. 3, pp. 18–23, April 1990.

[4] K.S. Narendra and K. Parthasarathy, 'Analysis and control of dynamical systems using neural networks', *IEEE Trans. on Neural Networks*, vol. 1, no. 1, pp. 4–27, March 1990.

[5] M. Saerens and A. Soquet, 'Neural controller based on back-propagation algorithm', *IEE Proc.*, vol. 138, pt. F, no.1, pp 55–62, Feb. 1991.

[6] M.M Gupta, D.H. Rao, and H.C. Wood, 'A learning and adaptive neural controller', *Proc. Int. Joint Conf. on Neural Networks*, Singapore, pp. 2380–2385, Nov. 1991.

[7] M. Yasunaga et al., 'A self-learning neural network composed of 1152 digital neurons in wafer-scale LSIs', *Proc. Int. Joint Conf. on Neural Networks*, Singapore, pp. 1844–1849, Nov. 1991.

[8] U. Ramacher, 'Guide lines to VLSI design of neural nets', in *VLSI Design of Neural Networks*, Ulrich Ramacher and Ulrich Rückert, Eds. Norwell, MA: Kluwer Academic, 1991, pp. 1–17.

[9] J. A. G. Nijhuis and L. Spaanenburg, 'Fault tolerance of neural associative memories', *IEE Proc.*, pt. E, vol. 136, no. 5, pp. 389–394, Sept. 1989.

[10] R.K. Chun and L.P. McNamee, 'Immunization of neural networks against hardware faults', *Proc. IEEE Int. Symp. on Cir. and Sys.*, New Orleans, LA, pp. 714–718, May 1990.

[11] Carlo H. Séquin and Reed D. Clay, 'Fault Tolerance in Feed-forward Artificial Neural Networks', Tech. Rep. TR-90-031, International Computer Science Institute, Berkeley, CA, 1990.

[12] V. Piuri, 'Continuous learning: A design methodology for fault-tolerant neural networks', *Proc. 3rd Int. Conf. on Industrial and Engineering Appl. of Artificial Intelligence and Expert Sys., IEA/AIE 90*, Charleston, SC, pp. 1019-1029, July 1990.

[13] J.H. Kim, C. Lurinsap, and S-K Park, 'Fault-tolerant artificial neural networks', *Proc. Int. Joint Conf. on Neural Networks*, Seattle, WA, July 1991.

[14] Jacek M. Zurada, *Introduction to Artificial Neural Systems*, St. Paul, MN: West, 1992.

[15] D.E. Rumelhart, G.E. Hinton, and R.J. Williams, 'Learning internal representations by error propagation', in *Parallel Distributed Processing: Explorations in the Microstructure of Cognition. Vol. 1: Foundations*, D.E. Rumelhart and J.L. McClelland, Eds. MIT, 1986.

[16] B.E. Segee and M.J. Carter, 'Fault tolerance of pruned multilayer networks', *Proc. Int. Joint Conf. on Neural Networks*, Seattle, WA, vol. II, pp. 447–452, July 1991.

[17] C.L. Phillips and H.T. Nagle, *Digital Control System Analysis and Design*, Englewood Cliffs, NJ: Prentice Hall, 1990.

An Adaptive-Topology Neural Architecture and Algorithm for Nonlinear System Identification

Girish Govind, and P.A. Ramamoorthy

ML # 30, Department of Electrical & Computer Engineering
University of Cincinnati, Cincinnati, OH 45221-0030

Abstract— Neural-based nonlinear system identification and control suffers from the problem of slow convergence, and selection of a suitable architecture for a problem is made through trial and error. There is the need for an algorithm that would provide an efficient solution to these problems. This paper presents one possible solution. Unlike the usual setup where backpropagation algorithm trains a fixed structure, in the algorithm presented in this paper, the network is built slowly in a step-by-step fashion. This evolving architecture methodology allocates a certain number of nodes that avoid training on outliers and at the same time, provide sufficient complexity for the approximation of a data set. Through simulation examples we show that this algorithm also exhibits faster convergence properties than the usual multi-layered neural network algorithms.

I. INTRODUCTION

In various engineering applications it is necessary to be able to model the input-output transfer function when only its input-output measurement data is given. This process of abstracting the relationships between inputs and outputs using only the data observed from the system is called system identification[1]. Most of the recent developments have been in the area of linear system identification where a linear structure is assumed for the model[1]. However most physical systems are nonlinear and thus a nonlinear model is required to get a globally valid model (true for all inputs) for a system.

Artificial neural networks models are composed of a highly interconnected mesh of nonlinear elements (neurons) whose structure is drawn from our current understanding of the biological neural system[2]. Several paradigms have been developed that have utilized different learning rules for training structures of these "biologically-inspired" neurons.

The main properties of multi-layered neural networks are:

- Ability to **learn** from experience.

- **Generalize** the performance over untrained inputs.

- **Abstract** relationships between signals.

- Capable of **arbitrary approximation** given sufficient number of neurons.

Neural networks have become of interest because of these abilities and have been used in several applications for performing various mappings. The properties outlined above are the same (the terminology *is* different) as those of interest to researchers in the area of system identification. But, although the above properties appear to be the solution to all the problems in conventional system identification, in actual practice there are other limitations that restrict their performance. For instance, convergence is not easily obtained in multi-layered networks and may take several hundreds of thousands of iterations[3]. Fine adjustment of the learning parameters and repeated presentations of the available data are required for satisfactory approximation. There is no method (or heuristic) to select the number of hidden nodes for a good approximation – less numbers can lead to an imprecise model, excess numbers can make the training very slow and provide poor generalization after training[4].

Thus, the multilayered neural network and the associated training algorithms available in the literature today are not a good solution to the nonlinear system identification problem. This paper describes an algorithm that has been developed for performing online adaptation of the weights. Unlike the backpropagation algorithm that trains a fixed structure, in this algorithm the network is built slowly in a step-by-step fashion. This evolving architecture methodology allocates a reasonable number of hidden nodes that would provide sufficient "degrees of freedom" for approximating a nonlinear system. Although the computational complexity of this algorithm per iteration could be higher than that of the standard backpropagation, it exhibits fast convergence. Also as the network is built during training, the complexity changes from iteration to iteration.

II. Nonlinear System Identification

System identification usually consists of two stages – *model selection*, and *parameter estimation*. In neural-based system identification, the selection of the number of hidden nodes corresponds to the model selection stage. The backpropagation algorithm utilizes gradient descent to determine the weights of the network and thus corresponds to the parameter estimation stage. Neural networks in system identification have not seen much change since they were first proposed by Lapedes and Farber[5] and also independently by us[6]. Extended offline training times have been used by researchers to get the network to converge even for simple problems but this also makes neural networks undesirable for practical engineering applications. Other researchers have begun using radial basis function networks which use a large number of radial basis functions usually taken from the data itself[7], CMAC (Cerebellar Model Articulation Controller)[8] which uses a very large amount of memory, or local approximation techniques that require the explicit storage of large amounts of data[9].

The next section presents the development of an adaptive neural algorithm that works quite differently from conventional designs. It has some similarities with another recent algorithm that performs model building combined with parameter estimation[10] but as will be shown with the chaotic prediction example, the presented algorithm is far more parsimonious in the number of parameters, and faster.

III. New Architecture & Algorithm

In a recent paper[4] it was discussed that the problem of approximation in a multilayer neural network with binary neurons is NP-complete. But as also pointed out in the same paper, this is the case only for a network with a fixed architecture. There-

fore, if a network can allocate more parameters it may be possible to solve the problem in polynomial time, and thus in this paper we use an evolving architecture strategy. We however restrict the scope of the presented algorithm to problems of nonlinear system identification where the input-output data is not binary.

The simplest node allocation strategy would be to add one node using every sample but this would not be optimal as in an online example the net would keep on growing. A different scheme is hence used where nodes are only allocated when really required and the nodes are adjusted for other data points. This is different from radial basis function networks where a certain number of datapoints are arbitrary selected to be the radial basis for the approximation and this basis is not adapted. The strategy of allocation and adaptation is also accompanied with a strategy for pruning as redundant or noncontributing nodes may be allocated while growing, or nodes may become so after adaptation. The next few paragraphs will provide some more detail about these new heuristics and in the next section these will be tested for some sample problems.

As can be seen from Figure 1, the architecture consists of two distinct parts. In the first part, a node with a gaussian bar[11] activation function is used. This function for the node is different from both the sigmoidal and the radial basis functions as it has a semilocal activation function. It has only one input and its output varies in the shape of a gaussian with respect to that input. Thus it can be considered as providing constant activation with respect to other inputs to the network. This nodal function has advantages in problems which have irrelevant inputs.

The second part in Figure 1, with larger empty circles represents multi-dimensional gaussian nodes which exhibit a gaussian variation along each of the input dimensions. More of each of these gaussian bar nodes as well as multi-dimensional gaussian nodes get allocated during the training procedure. The bold lines are weighted connections while the dashed lines are only performing distribution of the signals. The output stage is linear. This total structure is used as a model for approximating the problem at hand.

In the algorithm presented in this paper, not only are the parameters $\mu1$, $\sigma1$, $\mu2$, and $\sigma2$ adapted but so are the values $P(m)$ and Q.

Two parameters are very important for the allocation process – a variable threshold is used to

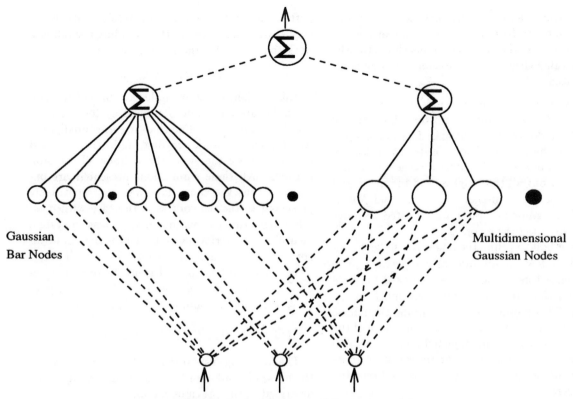

Figure 1: Architecture of the new model.

$$y_n = \sum_{m=1}^{M} \sum_{i=1}^{P(m)} w1_{nmi} exp(-\frac{(x_m - \mu1_{mi})^2}{\sigma1_{mi}^2}) + \sum_{k=1}^{Q} w2_{nk} H_k(x_1, x_2, \cdots, x_m)$$

where

$$H_k(x_1, x_2, \cdots, x_m) = \prod_{m=1}^{M} exp(-\frac{(x_m - \mu2_{km})^2}{\sigma2_{km}^2})$$

where the following notation has been used:

x_m – one of the M inputs
y_n – one of the N outputs
$w1$ – weights associated with Gaussian Bar nodes
$w2$ – weights associated with Multi-dimensional Gaussian nodes
$P(m)$ – number of gaussian bar nodes allocated for input m
Q – number of Multi-dimensional Gaussian nodes

decide when new nodes (Gaussian Bar or Multi-dimensional Gaussian) should be allocated. This threshold is set to a high value at the start of the simulation but is allowed to decrease slowly to a small value. Also a neighborhood parameter is used to discourage the allocation of Gaussian Bar and Multi-dimensional Gaussian nodes very near to each other. This neighborhood parameter is also started at a relatively large value and then slowly decreased to a small value as the simulation proceeds.

The complete detailed algorithm has not been

flowcharted here as it would require a lot more space but the main ideas behind it are given here. The allocation strategy is as follows:

1. If the modeling error at the output is greater than the variable error threshold value at the time, and the distance to the closest neighbor gaussian bar node is greater than the variable neighborhood threshold value then a new gaussian bar node is allocated.

2. If the modeling error at the output is greater than the variable error threshold value at

the time, and the distance to the closest neighbor Multi-dimensional Gaussian node is greater than the variable neighborhood threshold value then a new gaussian bar node is allocated.

It may seem that the two kinds of nodes would be allocated at the same instant for taking care of the high modeling error but this does not happen because of the neighborhood constraint. If the error is less than the threshold then no new structure is allocated but all the weights, and the mean and variances of the Gaussian Bar nodes and Multi-dimensional gaussian nodes are adjusted to move towards lowering the error.

The method to prune the nodes is also kept simple and of low computational complexity. The weighting factors $w1$, and $w2$ are checked to single out nodes that are not contributing much to the outputs. This method is used to prune the nodes. Other conditions to check for are – the mean of the gaussian functions being adjusted and moved outside the range of the signal or the gaussian function becoming just a spike i.e. variance becoming almost zero.

It is important to note that the above scheme is only a heuristic, like several other methods that are in use today to speed up the convergence. If conventional optimization techniques are used then the problem of training the multilayered neural network is very difficult. In fact most such attempts have used an approximation to the complete technique to reduce the computational complexity. The heuristics presented in this paper combine the stages of model selection and parameter estimation and work better than other training algorithms. The allocation and pruning schemes could be made more precise and complicated but then the training can no longer be done online in a reasonable time. For instance, Singular Value Decomposition can be used to identify even more of the redundant nodes in the network for pruning. Genetic Algorithms have been used by other researchers to get the absolute optimal network structure for problems but the key concept in this paper is to provide an algorithm of low computational complexity which builds a reasonable sized neural structure, not necessarily optimal. The evolving architecture methodology used here has some similarities with the tree-growing architecture used by Sanger[10] but the methodology there can lead to very large networks. In that algorithm, the network is grown at regular intervals and never pruned. Here the network is grown when desired, and pruned at regular intervals. This pruning procedure is very important as it improves generalization and also keeps the network size in check, thus yielding a small network that can solve the given problem.

IV. SIMULATIONS

In this section, three examples are provided. Two examples are on online nonlinear system identification, and one on online chaotic series prediction. All stepsize, network growing, and other selected parameters are the same throughout all the simulations. All these simulations presented are online and thus the same data was not repetitively presented to the network as is the case with most other algorithms. Consequently, just as in system identification, performance measures the offline algorithms are normally more exact than online ones – the results to be expected from the presented algorithm should not be compared for accuracy to those with offline training conditions.

System identification example 1

The following system (from [3]) is simulated and the network is allowed to grow using the algorithm described in the previous section.

$$y[k+1] = 0.8y[k] + (u[k] - 0.8)u[k](u[k] + 0.5)$$

Uniformly distributed random noise in the range [-1, 1] is used for the input $u[k]$. The modeling error is used to grow or adapt the network structure in an online fashion. As can be seen in figure 2 the network quickly learns the input-output mapping. The final network structure was $P(1) = 7$, $P(2) = 3$ for $u[k]$ and $y[k]$ respectively, and $Q = 50$. After this training, figure 3 shows the performance when the parameters of the network were kept fixed and the network is tested with the actual model data.

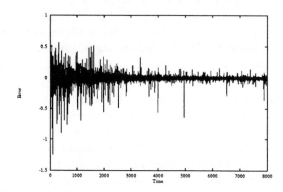

Figure 2: Example 1: Online training error.

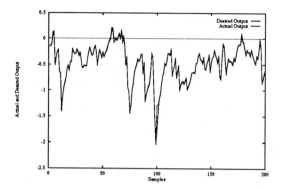

Figure 3: Example 1: Actual and Desired outputs after convergence.

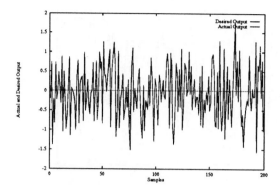

Figure 5: Example 2: Actual and Desired outputs after convergence for output 2

System identification example 2

The system in this example is a multi-input, multi-output one with four inputs and two outputs (from [3]).

$$\left[\begin{array}{c} y_1[k+1] \\ y_2[k+1] \end{array} \right] = \left[\begin{array}{c} \frac{y_1[k]}{1+y_2^2[k]} \\ \frac{y_1[k]y_2[k]}{1+y_2^2[k]} \end{array} \right] + \left[\begin{array}{c} u_1[k] \\ u_2[k] \end{array} \right]$$

The two inputs $u_1[k]$ and $u_2[k]$ are random uniformly distributed in the range [-1, 1]. This model corresponds to a $M = 4$, $N = 2$ model, and after convergence the structure has the P values as 6, 9, 11, and 5, and Q is 239. After the model has been constructed the network output was compared against the actual model outputs. These are shown in figure 4 and 5.

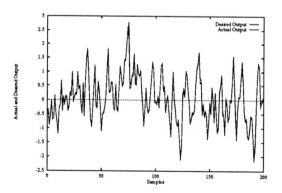

Figure 4: Example 2: Actual and Desired outputs after convergence for output 1

Chaotic prediction: Mackey-Glass ($\tau = 30$)

This is a classic benchmark problem for neural network training algorithms. This was first used by the Los Alamos nonlinear dynamics group and is now tested for by every known multi-layered training method.

$$\dot{x}(t) = \frac{0.2x(t-\tau)}{1+x^{10}(t-\tau)} - 0.1x(t)$$

A fourth-order Runge-Kutta is used to provide values of x at discrete time steps. The initial condition used is $x = 0.8$. This problem corresponds to a 6 input ($M = 6$), one output ($N = 1$) problem. The six inputs correspond to $x[t-6m]$, $m = 0..5$, and the desired output is $x[t+6]$. The actual series is plotted against the predicted series for a six-step ahead prediction in figure 6. Prediction for even further values can be made through iteration of the map. The network constructed here has a normalized performance index of 0.05 (this is square root of the ratio of error variance and series variance) which is almost as exact as the simulation by Sanger[10]. In that paper there were 20 sinusoidal basis functions used for each of the 6 inputs and 106 trees were constructed i.e. the total number of estimated parameters was over 12,000 from about 42,000 samples.

In contrast to that simulation, the algorithm presented in this paper constructed a network of P values as 6, 5, 5, 4, 7, and 6, and the value of Q was 43. Considering all the parameters this corresponds to about 700 parameters. Thus this algorithm is very parsimonious in the parameters. Figure 7 shows the evolution of this network structure.

V. Discussion & Conclusions

In this paper some heuristics have been presented that allow fast and online construction of nonlinear input-output maps from data. This algorithm would be very useful in engineering applications which require online performance – particularly

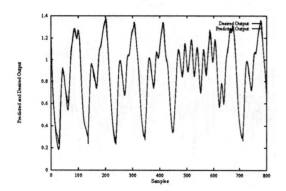

Figure 6: Mackey Glass: Actual & Desired output

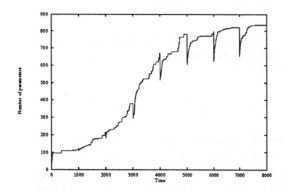

Figure 7: Mackey Glass: Evolution of the network

channel equalization, and nonlinear adaptive control.

REFERENCES

[1] S. Haykin, *Adaptive Filter Theory*. Englewood Cliffs, NJ: Prentice Hall, second ed., 1991.

[2] J. Hertz, A. Krogh, and R. G. Palmer, *Introduction to the theory of neural computation*. Reading, MA: Addison-Wesley, 1991.

[3] K. S. Narendra and K. Parthasarathy, "Identification and control of dynamical systems using neural networks," *IEEE Trans. on Neural Networks*, vol. 1, pp. 4–27, March 1990.

[4] E. B. Baum and D. Haussler, "What size net gives valid generalization," *Neural Computation*, vol. 1, pp. 151–160, 1989.

[5] A. Lapedes and R. Farber, "Nonlinear signal processing using neural networks: Prediction and system modeling," tech. rep., Los Alamos National Laboratory, 1987.

[6] P. A. Ramamoorthy, G. Govind, and V. Iyer, "Signal modeling and prediction using neural networks," in *International Neural Network Society First Annual Meeting*, (Boston, MA), September 1988.

[7] J. Moody and C. J. Darken, "Fast learning in networks of locally-tuned processing units," *Neural Computation*, vol. 1, pp. 281–294, January 1989.

[8] W. T. Miller, F. H. Glanz, and L. G. Kraft, "CMAC: An associative neural network alternative to backpropagation," *Proc. of the IEEE*, vol. 78, pp. 1561–1567, October 1990.

[9] J. D. Farmer and J. J. Sidorowich, "Exploiting chaos to predict the future and reduce noise," Tech. Rep. LA-UR-88-901, Los Alamos National Laboratory, Los Alamos, NM, March 1988.

[10] T. D. Sanger, "A tree-structured adaptive network for function approximation in high-dimensional spaces," *IEEE Trans. on Neural Networks*, vol. 2, pp. 285–293, March 1991.

[11] E. Hartman and J. D. Keeler, "Predicting the future: Advantages of semilocal units," *Neural Computation*, vol. 3, pp. 566–578, 1991.

SELF-TUNING ADAPTIVE CONTROL OF MULTI-INPUT, MULTI-OUTPUT NONLINEAR SYSTEMS USING MULTILAYER RECURRENT NEURAL NETWORKS WITH APPLICATION TO SYNCHRONOUS POWER GENERATORS

S.I. Sudharsanan
Advanced Development
IBM Corporation
Boca Raton, FL 33431

I. Muhsin and M.K. Sundareshan
Electrical and Computer Engineering
University of Arizona
Tucson, AZ 85721

Abstract – **A multilayer recurrent neural network-based approach for the identification and self-tuning adaptive control of multi-input, multi-output nonlinear dynamical systems is developed in this paper. An efficient on-line implementation of the control strategy, by a fast updating of the control actions to track the dynamical variations in the system, is facilitated by the recurrent neural network which is trained by a supervised training scheme that employs a simple updating rule. An application of this approach for the adaptive control of synchronous power generators under fault conditions is described and a quantitative performance evaluation is given to bring out certain important characteristic features of the neural network used for control.**

I. INTRODUCTION

Adaptive control of dynamical systems has received a major boost in recent years from the innovations and developments in neural network theory. Fundamental research in understanding the input-output function mapping capabilities of trained multilayer neural networks has provided an attractive alternative to classical methods of adaptive control, which essentially require an *à priori* defined mathematical model structure for the system. While the latter techniques have worked quite well with linear system models [1], extensions to nonlinear systems have not been very satisfactory [2], and neural network-based approaches are becoming highly popular in the design of adaptive control strategies for nonlinear dynamical systems.

Various schemes, differing in the way neural networks are employed in the implementation of the identification and control algorithms for realizing the adaptive control objectives, are presently being developed. For control problems where reference models are used to specify desired dynamical response, novel structures constructed from multilayer neural networks have been developed by Narendra and Parthasarathy [3, 4]. A different approach

that utilizes self-tuning mechanisms for control adaptation is proposed by Chen [5] using feedforward neural nets, and by Karakasoglu, *et al.* [6, 7] using recurrent neural nets. Application of similar ideas to the specific problem of modeling and controlling certain chemical process systems is also made in [8]. It must be emphasized that controllers designed using these approaches are considerably distinct from those designed using the more familiar "inverse dynamics" approach [9], where the primary objective is the design of a feedforward controller which takes over the entire control action once the training is completed; in contrast, the objective in the adaptive control approaches is to identify the nonlinear system dynamics in order to generate more general control laws (including, in particular, feedback control laws) for efficiently controlling the unknown dynamical system operating in an uncertain environment.

For an efficient on-line implementation of the adaptive control strategy, the identification of the system dynamics needs to be completed very quickly, and it is precisely in this regard that recurrent neural networks equipped with an appropriate training rule can offer very attractive features. The fast adaptation properties of these networks were exploited in the design of a self-tuning adaptive control strategy for the simple class of single-input single-output (SISO) systems and an implementation of this strategy for the decentralized control of a multijointed robotic manipulator executing complex trajectory tracking motions was discussed in [6, 7]. The SISO requirement, however, is a very restrictive one (in fact, several of the other approaches to neural network-based adaptive control mentioned earlier also impose similar restrictions in being applicable only to SISO systems). In this paper, we give a formulation of the adaptive control strategy for more general multi-input, multi-output (MIMO) nonlinear dynamical systems and identify an implementation architecture using multilayer recurrent neural networks. For a quantitative demonstration of the convergence performance of the neural net training and the adaptation performance of the self-tuning control algorithm, we examine a specific case study, *viz.*, control of a synchronous power generator under fault conditions. These systems are characterized by highly nonlinear dynamics and the presence of two inputs and two outputs, and offer significant challenges for designing satisfactory control strategies.

II. CONTROLLER ARCHITECTURE DESIGN

For a concise description of the design details, consider a discretized representation of the N-input M-output mapping behavior of the system to be controlled in the form

$$y_i(k+1) = \psi_i(Y_k^\psi, U_{k-1}^\psi) + \sum_{j=1}^N \phi_{ij}(Y_k^\phi, U_{k-1}^\phi)u_j(k), \quad (1)$$

for $i = 1, 2, \ldots M$, where

$$
\begin{aligned}
Y_k^\psi &= [Y^T(k), Y^T(k-1), \ldots Y^T(k-n_1+1)]^T \\
U_{k-1}^\psi &= [U^T(k-1), U^T(k-2), \ldots U^T(k-n_2)]^T \\
Y_k^\phi &= [Y^T(k), Y^T(k-1), \ldots Y^T(k-n_3+1)]^T \\
U_{k-1}^\phi &= [U^T(k-1), U^T(k-2), \ldots U^T(k-n_4)]^T
\end{aligned}
$$

and $Y(k) = [y_1(k), y_2(k), \ldots, y_M(k)]^T$, $U(k) = [u_1(k), u_2(k), \ldots, u_N(k)]^T$, with n_1, n_2, n_3 and n_4 being integers. The generality of this input-output representation provided by the arguments of the functions ψ_i and ϕ_{ij} being vectors of variable lengths, constructed from the past input and output data, needs a particular emphasis. Let us assume for the time being $M \geq N$.

Consider the control problem of finding $U(k)$ to track a desired output $Y^d(k+1) = [y_1^d(k+1), y_2^d(k+1), \ldots y_M^d(k+1)]^T$. If the functions ψ_i and ϕ_{ij} are known exactly, then the required control can be readily evaluated as

$$U(k) = [\Phi^T \Phi]^{-1} \Phi(Y^d(k+1) - \Psi) \quad (2)$$

where $[\Phi^T\Phi]^{-1}\Phi$ is the generalized inverse of $\Phi = [\phi_{ij}]_{i=1,2,\ldots M \text{ and } j=1,2,\ldots N}$ and $\Psi = [\psi_1, \psi_2, \ldots \psi_M]^T$. However, since ψ_i and ϕ_{ij} are not known, a neural-network based identification of each of these functions performed using the models

$$\hat{y}_i(k+1) = \hat{\psi}_i(Y_k^\psi, U_{k-1}^\psi, \mathcal{W}_{\psi_i})$$

$$+ \sum_{j=1}^N \hat{\phi}_{ij}(Y_k^\phi, U_{k-1}^\phi, \mathcal{W}_{\phi_{ij}})u_j(k),$$

for $i = 1, 2, \ldots M$, will be utilized. The set of weights, denoted by $\mathcal{W}_{\psi_i}$ of the neural network providing the function $\hat{\psi}_i$ (which approximates ψ_i) and the weights, denoted by $\mathcal{W}_{\phi_{ij}}$, of the neural network providing the function $\hat{\phi}_{ij}$ (which approximates ϕ_{ij}), are trained by a supervised scheme of minimizing the gradient of the error

$E(k) = \sum_{i=1}^M [y_i(k) - \hat{y}_i(k)]^2$. Once the training is completed, the control $U(k)$ can be obtained from

$$U(k) = [\hat{\Phi}^T \hat{\Phi}]^{-1} \hat{\Phi}(Y^d(k+1) - \hat{\Psi}) \quad (3)$$

where $\hat{\Phi} = [\hat{\Phi}_{ij}]_{i=1,2,\ldots M \text{ and } j=1,2,\ldots N}$ and $\hat{\Psi} = [\hat{\psi}_1, \hat{\psi}_2, \ldots, \hat{\psi}_M]^T$. The computation of $[\hat{\Phi}^T\hat{\Phi}]^{-1}$ in eq. (3) has to be done at every time-step. For small dimensional control signals, this is not computationally intensive. One possible problem is that the matrix $\hat{\Phi}^T\hat{\Phi}$ can become ill-conditioned or singular. In our experiments, we have often added a small scalar matrix (αI, where α is a small positive integer) to avoid singularities.

Eq. (3) gives the adaptive control law in the case when $M \geq N$. For the other case ($M < N$), computation of an appropriate control will in general be difficult following the technique described above.

An architecture for implementing the adaptive control laws stated above can be developed as follows. A distinct neural network for identifying each function ϕ_{ij} will be employed with inputs selectively chosen from the sets Y_k^ϕ and U_{k-1}^ϕ. Thus, a total of MN neural nets will be utilized for realizing $\hat{\Phi}$. However, the approximation of the N functions ψ_i can be integrated into one neural network which realizes $\hat{\Psi}$ and the inputs into this network are from the sets Y_k^ψ and U_{k-1}^ψ. Thus, the identification and control architecture for a two-input, two-output system (*i.e.*, $M = N = 2$) will utilize five networks in a scheme depicted in Fig. 1. The blocks denoted TD are tapped delays which give appppropriately delayed versions of the inputs and the outputs of the system in order to provide inputs to the neural networks.

III. NEURAL NET SELECTION AND A TRAINING SCHEME

Since each of the functions approximated in realizing $\hat{\Phi}$ and $\hat{\Psi}$ at a given instant is a static nonlinear input-output map, any multilayer neural network could be utilized for this purpose. Several investigators [10 - 12] have rigorously established that a three-layer feedforward net with one hidden layer can approximate virtually any nonlinear function of interest arbitrarily closely provided sufficient number of nodes are included in the hidden layer. However, as demonstrated in [13, 14], introduction of recurrent connections in the hidden layer of such a three-layer network can result in very significant benefits, such as reduction in the required number of hidden nodes for the same degree of approximation, superior training rates, etc., if the network is properly tailored. Hence, we shall employ a neural net with one input layer, one output layer, and one hidden layer consisting of n nonlinear neurons with recurrent connections, for approximating the mapping between a m-dimensional input vector $z(k) = [z_1(k), z_2(k), \ldots z_m(k)]^T$ applied at instant k and the corresponding p-dimensional steady-state output vector $\mathbf{q}(k) = [q_1(k), q_2(k) \ldots, q_p(k)]^T$. The network dynamics are described by

$$\dot{\mathbf{v}} = -\mathbf{v} + \mathbf{W}\xi(\mathbf{v}) + \mathbf{B}\mathbf{z}(k) \text{ and } \mathbf{q}(k) = \mathbf{H}\mathbf{v}^\star, \quad (4)$$

where $\mathbf{v} \in \Re^n, \xi(\cdot) : \Re^n \to \Re^n$ is a vector-valued function with sigmoidal elements, $\mathbf{W} \in \Re^{n \times n}, \mathbf{B} \in \Re^{n \times m}$ and $\mathbf{H} \in \Re^{p \times n}$ specify the interconnection weights. The architecture of the network is depicted in Fig. 2.

Explicit conditions for the convergence of the network dynamics to a stable equilibrium state and certain guidelines for tailoring the sigmoidal nonlinear functions in order to achieve a rapid exponential convergence are given in [13, 14]. When the network reaches a steady-state $\mathbf{v}^\star$ which is given by

$$\mathbf{v}^\star = \mathbf{W}\xi(\mathbf{v}^\star) + \mathbf{B}\mathbf{z}(k), \quad (5)$$

the output is read as $\mathbf{q}(k) = \mathbf{H}\mathbf{v}^\star = \mathbf{H}[\mathbf{W}\xi(\mathbf{v}^\star) + \mathbf{B}\mathbf{z}(k)]$.

Training of this network, $i.e.$, adaptive updating of the elements h_{ij}, ω_{ij} and b_{ij} of the matrices $\mathbf{H}, \mathbf{W}$ and $\mathbf{B}$ respectively, can be conducted in a supervised mode in order to approximate a given input-output mapping, $\mathbf{q}(k) = \mathcal{F}[\mathbf{z}(k)], k = 1, 2, \ldots$. A distributed approximate gradient updating scheme which affords a particularly simple implementation has been developed in [13] for minimizing the output error

$$E(k) = (\mathbf{q}_d(k) - \mathbf{q}(k))^T(\mathbf{q}_d(k) - \mathbf{q}(k)) \quad (6)$$

where $\mathbf{q}_d(k)$ denotes a desired output. The training algorithm can be briefly stated as

$$h_{ij}(k+1) = h_{ij}(k) + \mu_1 \sum_{\ell=1}^{p} q_{d\ell}(k) - q_\ell(k)v_i^\star,$$

for $\quad i = 1, 2, \ldots p,$

$$w_{ij}(k+1) = w_{ij}(k) + \mu_2 \sum_{\ell=1}^{p} (h_{\ell i}(k)[q_{d\ell}(k) - q_\ell(k)])\xi_j(v_j^\star),$$

for $i, j = 1, 2, \ldots n$, and

$$b_{ij}(k+1) = b_{ij}(k) + \mu_3 \sum_{\ell=1}^{p} (h_{\ell i}(k)[q_{d\ell}(k) - q_\ell(k)])z_j(k),$$

for $i = 1, 2, \ldots n$ and $j = 1, 2, \ldots, m$. In these equations, μ_1, μ_2, and μ_3 are appropriately selected updating gain parameters. An analytical proof of convergence of the training procedure and some useful guidelines for the selection of μ_1, μ_2 and μ_3 (by specifying bounds in terms of the size of the hidden layer n) to result in desired convergence rates are given in [13, 14]. It may be mentioned

that the desirable convergence properties of this training algorithm are rendered possible by a selection of moderately large gains for the sigmoidal nonlinear functions, which ensures that the equilibrium states of the network lie in the saturation range of these functions.

IV. APPLICATION: ADAPTIVE CONTROL OF POWER GENERATORS

An electrical power system consists of several generators and electrical loads connected to grids consisting of transformers, transmission lines, buses, and control equipment. The primary objective in power system control is to maintain a constant frequency (permitted variations $\leq 4\%$), constant terminal voltage (variations within $\pm 5\%$) and synchronism of generators during transient conditions. Deviations in system frequency indicate a lack of balance between active load and active generation, while deviations in terminal voltage indicate a lack of equilibrium between the load and the generated reactive power. Furthermore, during transient conditions caused by disturbances (external disturbances such as lightening strikes, wind, etc., or internal disturbances such as random load variations), the main concern is to maintain stability by keeping each generator in synchronism with the power system. The problem is compounded by the fact that under such transient conditions, one may expect a high degree of nonlinear behavior of the system.

Although several different control functions (ranging from the control of mechanical power sources, such as the turbine, to the control of various devices attached to the grid) together constitute the overall control for the power system, the control of the generator is considered the first line of defense in maintaining system stability. It has response times in the range of a fraction of a second. Due to its importance, sophisticated methods for the design of generator control mechanisms are often necessary. The two control strategies that are to be developed for satisfactory control of the generator are the excitation control (to regulate terminal voltage deviations) and the governor control (to regulate speed deviations) [15]. In this section, we outline the learning performance of the neural network scheme and the regulation performance of the adaptive control scheme when applied to this problem under fault conditions.

Dynamical models typically used in the analysis and design of synchronous power generators (details on such models can be found in [15, 16]) are very highly nonlinear if accurate representations of the underlying electrical and mechanical phenomena are included. While such models are too complex for designing adaptive controls directly, computer simulations of these models can be used as vehicles for generating the input/output data for training the neural networks, which can be used to build adaptive control architectures such as the present one described in Fig. 1. The two input signals in the present application are u_1 = torque applied to the generator shaft and u_2 = voltage applied to the field circuit, while the two outputs are y_1 = machine speed and y_2 = terminal voltage.

For implementing the neural network-based control scheme developed in the earlier sections, we begin by noting the correspondence between a discretization of the generator models described in [16] and the representation of the input-output behavior given by (1). Since the problem is a two-input two-output one, five three-layer neural nets, each consisting of three hidden layer nodes with recurrent connections (observe that the number of input and output nodes are specified by the problem), were employed for approximating the functions Ψ and Φ using the architecture depicted in Fig. 1. The sigmoidal nonlinear functions were selected as $\xi_i(v_i) = \frac{2}{\pi}\tan^{-1}(\frac{\pi\beta v_i}{2})$, with the gain $\beta = 40.0$. A computer simulation model of the generator was used for training the networks. With the initial weight selections of $\omega_{ii}(0) = -0.5 \; \forall \; i$, and $\omega_{ij}(0) = 0 \; \forall \; i \; \neq \; j, h_{ij}(0) = 0.1 \; \forall \; i$ and j and $b_{ij}(0) = 1 \; \forall \; i$ and j, the training algorithm (9) was implemented with $\mu_1 = 0.2, \mu_2 = 0.2$, and $\mu_3 = 0.0$.

With the generator running at an operating condition specified by the application of a reference input, pseudorandom binary sequence signals, with amplitude set at 30% of the reference input, were added to the reference input to ensure excitation of the system at several frequencies. Using 1000 data points created with desired output values for the chosen input values, the training was conducted over each cycle of 1000 data points in the real-time learning mode (*i.e.*, updating performed after the presentation of each data point). The mean squared error at the end of each cycle was computed, and the algorithm was run for several cycles. The convergence performance is depicted by the learning curve in Fig. 3, which indicates that the mean squared error reduces to less than 10^{-3} within only four cycles confirming the steep convergence of the identification process.

For evaluating the performance of the adaptive control scheme in the face of a fault occurrence, a three-phase short-circuit to earth at the sending end of one transmission line, which was cleared after 120 ms., was simulated. Figs. 4a, b, c and d depict the controller performance, from which the following conclusions can be drawn.

(i) The neural network-based control is capable of handling a highly transient condition induced by the fault occurrence and maintains a constant terminal voltage which is a high priority requirement at the supply terminal. It also ensures a very rapid settling time with little overshoot, as evident from Fig. 4a.

(ii) After the fault clearance, the reactive power very

rapidly converges to a steady-state value of 0.1 p.u. (Fig. 4b). This performance is considerably superior to that possible from conventional excitation control schemes.

(iii) A rapid damping of the rotor angle oscillations consequent to the fault and a quick re-establishment of synchronous speed (Fig. 4c) is observed. This performance, which enhances the synchronization of the generator with the rest of the power system, is once again better than what conventional governor control schemes can deliver.

(iv) Active power is kept within the required limits, and the plot in Fig. 4d depicts a swift and desirable response.

In addition to the application to the synchronous generator problem discussed here, an application of the presently developed recurrent neural network-based adaptive control scheme was also made to control a more complex turbogenerator system. For this system, a different way of designing a neural network-based controller has been reported very recently by Wu *et al.*, [17]. The performance delivered by the present scheme, tested under identical conditions, turned out to be signficantly better than the performance shown in [17]. Due to space limitations these results are not given in detail here; they can, however, be found in [16]. A fundamental difference that may be noted in comparison is that in the scheme proposed in [17], two neural networks, one used for identification of dynamics and the other for learning the control, are to be *trained sequentially*, whereas in the present scheme, control is applied instantaneously following the identification of dynamics (which is also completed more quickly due to the recurrent neural network architecture).

REFERENCES

[1] K. J. Astrom, "Adaptive feedback control," *Proceedings of the IEEE, Vol.* 75, No. 2, pp. 124-132, February 1987.

[2] S. Sastry and A. Isidori, "Adaptive control of linearizable systems," *IEEE Trans. on Automatic Control, Vol.* 34, No. 11, pp. 1123-1131, November 1989.

[3] K. S. Narendra and K. Parthasarathy, "Identification and control of dynamical systems using neural networks," *IEEE Trans. on Neural Networks, Vol.* 1, pp. 4-27, 1990.

[4] K. S. Narendra and K. Parthasarathy, "Neural networks and dynamical systems," *Int. Journal of Approximate Reasoning, Vol.* 6, pp. 109-131, 1992.

[5] F. C. Chen, "Backpropagation neural networks for nonlinear self-tuning adaptive control," *IEEE Control Systems Magazine, Vol.* 10, pp. 44-48, 1990.

[6] A. Karakasoglu, S. I. Sudharsanan and M. K. Sundareshan, "Identification and decentralized adaptive control of

robotic manipulators using dynamical neural networks," *Proc. 1991 Int. Joint Conf. on Neural Networks (IJCNN-91)*, Seattle, Washington, July 1991. (Also to appear in *IEEE Trans. on Neural Networks*.)

[7] A. Karakasoglu, S. I. Sudharsanan and M. K. Sundareshan, "Neural network-based identification and adaptive control on nonlinear systems: A novel dynamical network architecture and training policy," *Proc. 30th IEEE Conf. on Decision and Control*, Brighton, England, December 1991.

[8] N. V. Bhat, P. A. Mindelman, T. McAvoy and N. S. Wang, "Modeling chemical process systems via neural computation," *IEEE Control Systems Magazine, Vol.* 10, pp. 24-31, 1990.

[9] D. Psaltis, A. Sideris and A. Yamamura, "A multi-layered neural network controller," *IEEE Control Systems Magazine, Vol.* 8, pp. 17-21, 1988.

[10] G. Cybenko, "Continuous valued neural networks with two hidden layers are sufficient," *Math. Controls, Signal and Systems, Vol.* 2, pp. 303-314, 1989.

[11] H. Hornik, M. Strinchcombe and H. White, "Multi-layer feedforward networks are universal approximators," *Neural Networks, Vol.* 2, pp. 359-366, 1989.

[12] K. Funahashi, "On the approximate realization of continuous mappings by neural networks," *Neural Networks, Vol.* 2, pp. 183-192, 1989.

[13] S. I. Sudharsanan and M. K. Sundareshan, "Training of a three-layer recurrent neural network for nonlinear input-output mapping," *Proc. Int. Joint Conf. Neural Networks, IJCNN*, Seattle, Washington, 1991.

[14] S. I. Sudharsanan, "Equilibrium characterization for a class of dynamical neural networks with applications to learning and synthesis," Ph.D. Dissertation, ECE Department, University of Arizona, Tucson, Arizona, 1990.

[15] R. Bergen, *Power Systems Analysis*, Prentice-Hall: Englewood Cliffs, New Jersey, 1986.

[16] I. Muhsin, "Control of power systems using nonlinear transformations and neural networks," Ph.D. Dissertation, ECE Department, The University of Arizona, Tucson, Arizona, 1992.

[17] Q. H. Wu, B. W. Hogg and G. W. Irwin, "A neural network regulator for turbogenerators," *IEEE Trans. on Neural Networks, Vol.* 3, No. 1, pp. 95-100, 1992.

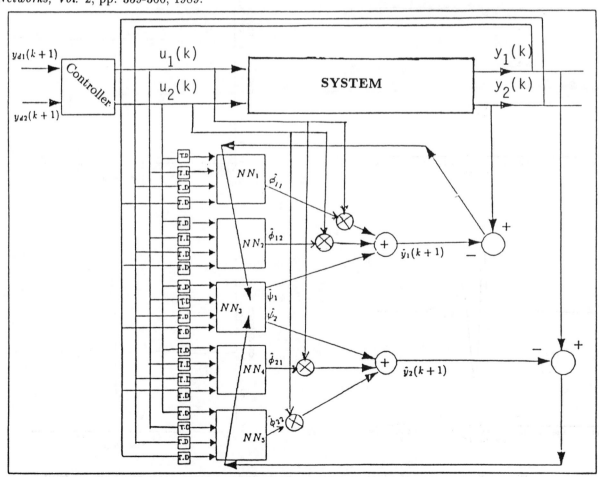

Fig. 1. Identification and control architecture

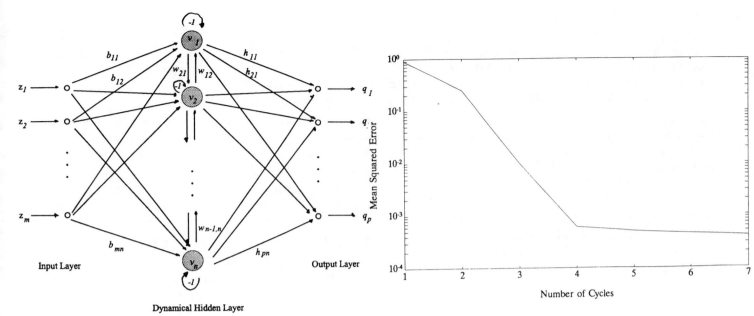

Fig. 2. Neural network architecture

Fig. 3. Convergence of training procedure

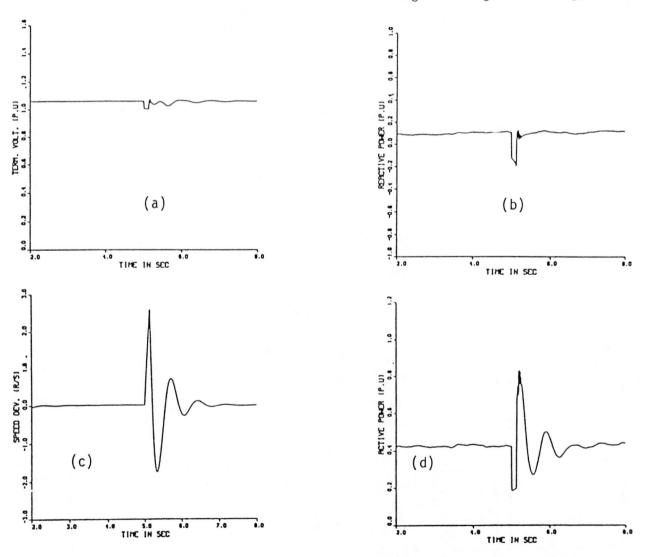

Fig. 4. Performance of adaptive control scheme under a three-phase short circuit fault

Neural Nets, Random Design and Reverse Engineering

Lawrence W. Stark
Neurology and Telerobotic Units
Bioengineering Graduate Group
University of California at Berkeley
481 Minor Hall
Berkeley, California 94720

I. Introduction

The goals of neural net research are several. The very name bespeaks

i) a biological aim. There are a number of examples of straight-forward model of biological systems from knowledge about its neural elements and behavior controlled by that neural system (or speculation regarding such behavior). Outstanding neurophysiological research is the Lettvin-McCulloch (1959) paper "What the frog's eye tells the frog's brain". This was, of course, based upon McCulloch-Pitts formal neuron theory that initiated the neural network concept (Fig. 1) [9, 10].

ii) An engineering goal for neural nets is to make machines that work and work well — that is accurately, predictably and robustly under changing conditions. A main advantage of the neural net as a machine is that it programs itself, and thus is designed by experience. The Perceptron of Rosenblatt is the outstanding and pioneering example of trainable neural nets functioning as pattern recognition devices [11, 15, 22].

iii) Bionics or biomimetics suggest that we can learn about a biological system that works in order to make an engineering copy of this machine or perhaps to make a better machine that will carry out the principles of the biological machine.

iv) Reverse engineering is related to the above. We wish to understand the workings of a natural biomachine designed by evolution to carry out a particular function. We then study an artificial network that has been trained to carry out this same function. We discover the actions of its artificial neural elements, especially the "hidden units". Thus, we may obtain insights as to how the natural net performs its role.

The aim of this paper in the Reverse Engineering session it introduces is to review some historical experiments and lead to the key stellar studies of reverse engineering to be presented by the Andersen group from the Massachusetts Institute of Technology (Fig. 6) [16, 24], and the Usui group at Toyohashi University, Japan (Fig. 7) [12, 20].

II. From Engineering Goals To Reverse Engineering

With simple engineering goal, neural nets can be considered as an engineering black box whose unknown design is considered satisfactory if its performance is satisfactory. A mechanical metaphor may be appropriate: — suppose we have a network of mechanical elements under the hood of an automobile. This mechanical net could be rewarded for forward motion when the accelerator pedal is depressed, and punished for backward motion or absence of forward motion. With some scheme to connect all these mechanical elements in all possible configurations and then to solidify connections that are active in a successful trial and to reduce connections during an unsuccessful trial, this mechanical net "should" eventually make a satisfactory car engine. What a nice automatic way to accomplish mechanical design! An example of this in the neural net field is Perceptron, either the old perceptron from the 1950's or 1960's or new perceptrons from the 1980's or 1990's. These now perform successful pattern recognition, and are being further developed to provide membership functions for fuzzy controllers.

For the reverse engineering paradigm we must also LOOK-UNDER-THE-HOOD and examine the actual mechanical design of the machine created. "Aha! It is a heat engine of type xyz." Reverse engineering to understand specific brain functions has at least two solid recent successful contributions by Andersen and by Usui. Here, nets have been created as models of specific parts of the nervous system. They were rewarded and punished for correct and incorrect behavior until they performed satisfactorily, thus achieving engineering goals. These two researchers then proceeded further with the reverse engineering paradigm. They explored the new particular mechanisms in the neural nets — neurons, synapses, weights and connections — to obtain clues to how neurons of particular parts of the nervous system do in fact function. There remains a logical problem because the uniqueness of the design solution is not guaranteed; still it is a potent approach.

III. MAMF, MULTIPLE ADAPTIVE MATCHED FILTER SCHEME

An early attempt in this direction was carried out by a 1960 MIT group [17, 18, 19, 23]. This MAMF approach to ECG diagnosis was an example of unsupervised learning equivalent to a neural net. This MAMF scheme is described in the figure legends illustrating figures 2, 3 and 4. However, there was no attempt to make an analogy at the neuronal level; the satisfactory performance of the MAMF scheme was at a level of adaptive brain function not yet even now understood in terms of neurons.

The MAMF scheme is of Eliashberg-Chomsky, E-C, order 1 (see Fig. 5 and also Eliashberg paper in this session) [2, 3, 4, 5]. It illustrates self-organization or learning without a teacher. In its adaptive phase it develops a) changes of synaptic weights or equivalent filter coefficients (winner take all tactics), b) changes of thresholds that protect against destructive modification, c) spontaneous generation of new filters either with random coefficients or as daughter filters (related to later development of genetic algorithms) and d) for initial preprocessing, such as time and amplitude warping. Adaptive filters for signal extraction from noise are to be contrasted with this scheme for signal extraction from a background of many similar signals. It was tested for feasibility on ECG and earlier on EEG data. According to Nilsson [13], it was the first piece-wise linear categorizer with the mode-seeking training rule. Grossberg and his school have redeveloped this scheme and used it to justify ART theories [7].

REFERENCES

[1] R.A. Andersen, G.K. Essick, and R.M. Siegel, "Encoding of spatial location by posterior parietal neuron," *Science*, vol. 230, pp. 456-458, 1985.

[2] N. Chomsky, "Three models for the description of language," *I.R.E. Transactions on Information Theory*, vol. IT-2, pp. 113-124, 1956.

[3] V. Eliashberg, "The concept of E-machine: On brain hardware and the algorithms of thinking," *Proceedings of the Third Annual Meetings of the Cognitive Science Society*, pp. 289-291, 1981.

[4] V. Eliashberg, "Context-sensitive associative memory: 'Residual excitation' in neural networks as the mechanism of STM and mental set," *Proceedings of IJCNN-89*, Washington, D.C., 1989.

[5] V. Eliashberg, "Universal Learning Neurocomputers" *Proceedings of the Fourth Annual Parallel Processing Symposium*, April 1990

[6] S. Goodman, and R. Andersen, "Microstimulation of a neural-network model for visually guided saccades," *Journal of Cognitive Neuroscience*, vol. 1, No. 4, pp. 317-326, 1989

[7] S. Grossberg, *Studies of Mind and Brain*, Boston: Reidel Press, 1982.

[8] J.Y. Lettvin, and H. Maturana, W. McCulloch, and W.H. Pitts, "What the frog's eye tells the frog's brain," *Proceedings of the I.R.E.*, vol. 47, No. 11, pp. 1940-1959, 1959.

[9] W. McCulloch, "A Heterarchy of values determined by the topology of nervous nets," *Bulletin of Mathematical Biophysics*, vol. 7 pp. 89-93, 1945.

[10] W. McCulloch, and W. Pitts, "A logical calculus of the ideas immanent in nervous activity," *Bulletin of Mathematical Biophysics*, vol. 5 pp. 115-133, 1943.

[11] M. Minsky, "Neural nets and the brain-model problem", Unpublished doctoral dissertation, Princeton University, 1954.

[12] S. Nakauchi, S. Usui, and S. Miyake, "A three-layered neural network model which simulates color-opponent processing," *Proceedings of the International Conference on Fuzzy Logic and Neural Networks*, pp. 481-484, 1990.

[13] N.J. Nilsson, *Learning Machines: Foundations of trainable pattern-classifying systems*, pp. 125-126, California: McGraw-Hill Inc., 1965.

[14] M. Okajima, L. Stark, G. Whipple, and S. Yasui, "Computer recognition techniques: Some results with real electrocardiographic data," *IEEE Transactions on Biomedical Electronics, BME*, vol. 10 pp. 106-114, 1963.

[15] F. Rosenblatt, *Principles of Neurodynamics*, Washington, D.C.: Spartan Books, 1962.

[16] D. Sankoff and J.B. Kruskal, editors. *Time Warps, String Edits, and Macromolecules: The Theory and Practice of Sequence Comparison*, Massachusetts: Addison-Wesley Inc., 1983.

[17] L. Stark, "Pattern recognition for electroencephalographic diagnosis", *Quart. Prog. Report No. 61, Research lab. of Electronics, M.I.T.*, pp. 215-219, 1961.

[18] L. Stark, M. Okajima, and G.H. Whipple, "Computer pattern recognition techniques: Electrocardiographic diagnosis," *Communications of the Association for Computing Machinery*, vol. 5 pp. 527-532, 1962.

[19] L. Stark, and J. Dickson, "Remote computerized medical diagnostic systems," *Computers and Automation*, vol. 14 pp. 18-21, 1965.

[20] S. Usui, S. Nakauchi, and S. Miyake, "Aquisition of the color-opponent representation by a three-layered neural network model," *Proceedings of this Conference*, 1993.

[21] J. Von Neumann, "First draft of a report on the EDVAC" Contract Report, Moore School of Electrical Engineering, University of Pennsylvania, June 30, 1945.

[22] B. Widrow, "Generalization and information storage in networks of Adaline neurons," in *Self-organizing systems. Washington, D.C.: Spartan Books*. Cambridge, MA: MIT Press, 1962.

[23] S. Yasui, G. Whipple, and L. Stark, "Comparison of human and computer electrocardiographic waveform classification and identification," *American Heart Journal*, vol. 68 pp. 236-242, 1964.

[24] D. Zipser, and R.A. Andersen, "A back-propagation programmed network that simulates response properties of a subset of posterior parietal neurons," *Nature*, vol. 331 pp. 697-684, 1988.

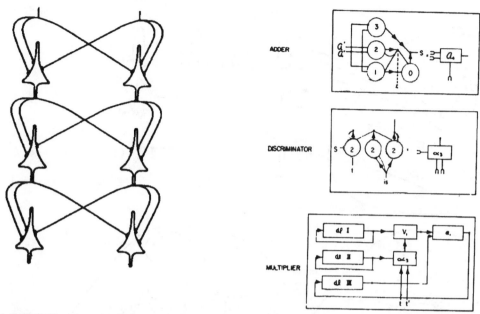

Figure 1   McCulloch-Pitts Formal Neurons

A small net of formal neurons (left) created by McCulloch and Pitts (1943); these were as "poverty stricken" so as to clearly illustrate the encompassing ability of a brain composed of such neurons. John Von Neumann (1945), after meeting McCulloch (on the train station at Princeton Junction!), used such neurons to depict the logical design of ALU operators of the EDVAC (right).

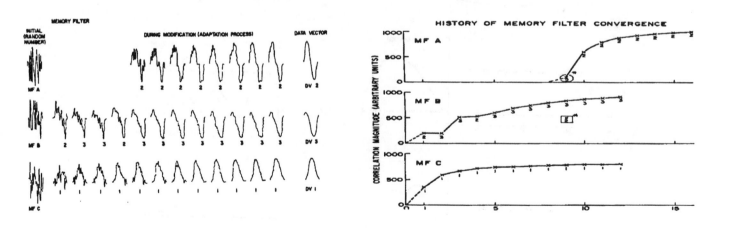

Figure 2   Multiple Adaptive Matched Filters; MAMFs

Above, MFs as they adapt; below, history of MF convergence. Original noisy library matched filters, MF A, B, C... (left upper); data vectors, DV 1, 2, 3... (right upper) produce a random sequence of events from successive data vector presentations. Adaptation or matching of original noisy library MFs at times proceeds smoothly (lower panels, both above and below) until with modification of coefficients to data events MF C approximate DV 1. Ordinate below is cross-correlation amplitude of MFs to DVs, abscissae are successive instances of filter modification.

At times, several DVs are accepted by a MF especially early in adaptation process (middle panels, both above and below); finally, although DV 2 is maximally matched to MF B (see box) and according to first order winner-take-all algorithm should be incorporated into MF B, its cross-correlation coefficient is below a rising threshold (not shown). A new library filter MF C is pressed into service (upper panel both above and below) [In another experiment, this could have been a daughter filter (see references to genetic algorithms in text)]. Now MF B and MF C each develop smoothly, showing convergent adaptation and thus separate DV 2 and DV 3. (From Stark, Okajima and Whipple, 1962).

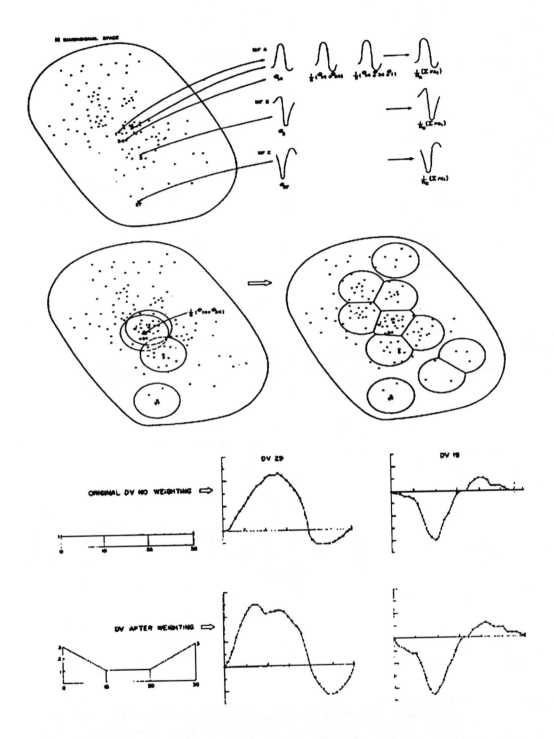

Figure 3 Feature Space View of Multiple Adaptive Matched Filters, MAMFs

As the matched filters adapt (upper right), they come to represent clusters of similar events in feature space (upper left and middle left). After adaptation they fill event space and are separated by hyperplanes (middle right).

An early example of "time warping" was accomplished by dividing the width of the QRS of the ECG into 31 equally spaced time samples (lower left), thus making the feature space (above) 31-dimensional. "Gain warping" or weighting of data vectors was also employed since the initial and ending aspects of the QRS apparently was deemed more informative by our medical experts (lower panels). (From Okajima, Stark, Whipple and Yasui, 1963).

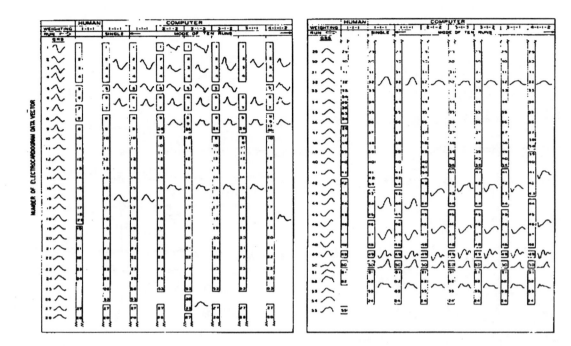

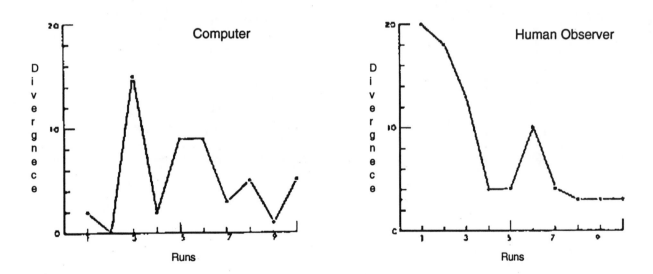

Figure 4 Classification by Humans and Computer

  Data vectors are 55 ECG QRS patterns presented in random and repetitive sequences. After self-organization by MAMF about a dozen classes were obtained (upper panels). Amplitude weighting (see column labels) influenced the classification obtained as did random order of presentation. For example, divergences (D, ordinate) from the modal classification of ten runs (T, abscissa) varied from 20 to 3 (lower left). Divergences in classifying a pattern were almost always to a neighboring cluster, so MAMF errors were similar to human ones.

  Human observers (skilled ECGers) also diverged from a modal classification (lower right). With cross-communication they were able to finally converge to between one and five discrepancies. (From Yasui, Whipple and Stark, 1964).

1317

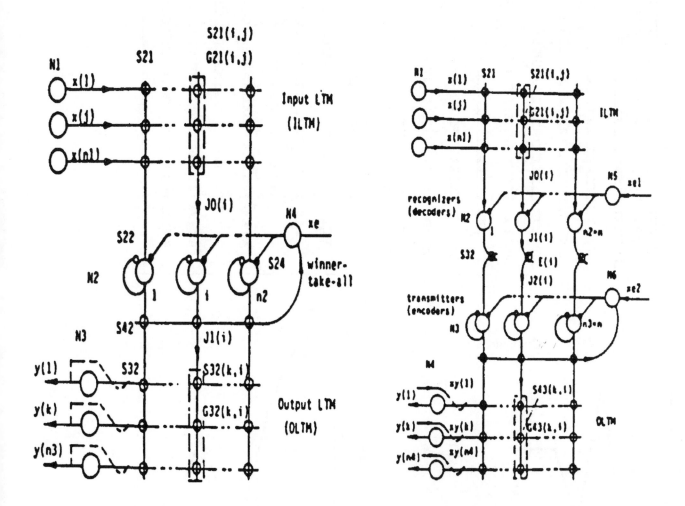

Figure 5   Eliashberg-Chomsky Orders for Intelligent Machines

     An analog neural network universal with respect to class of combinatorial machines (left); it is of order 4, since it is without memory; a finite state machine, without memory is more complex, but still of order 4 (right). A net with random access memory is of order 1 (and equivalent to a Turing machine). If a net possesses only stack memory it is of order 3.

     Note the use of PLA ,programmable logic array, formulation; this well-known circuitry introduces clarity when comparing neural nets of various structural complexities (see Eliashberg 1988, 1989, 1990).

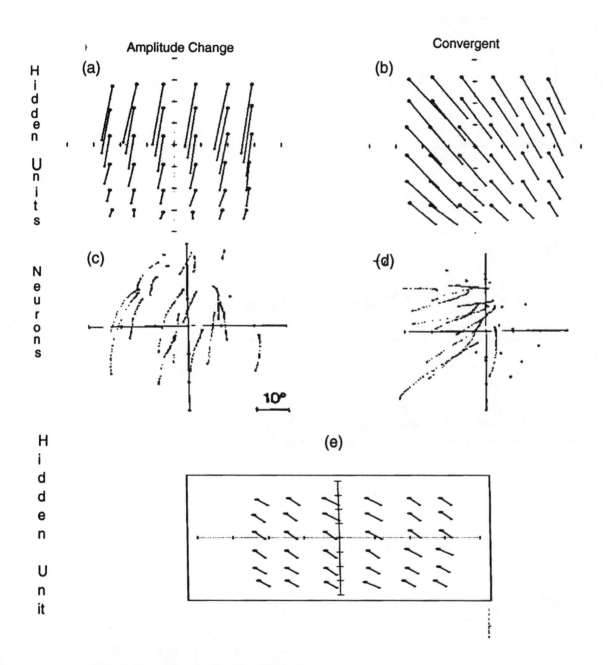

Figure 6   Reverse Engineering: Spatial Neuron Example

Spatial direction neural net has as input, eye-in-orbit (two 16 x1 vectors for HZ and VT), target-on-retina (an 8 x 8 retinal matrix), and for output target-in-space (an 8 x 8 spatial matrix that is head centered). Output is documented by a series of eye movement vectors to target-in-space from multiple retinal loci.

A model directrix with varying amplitudes (a) indicates influence of retinal locus on amplitude; a convergent directrix (b) maps influence of retinal locus on direction. Experimental values from parietal lobe spatial neurons yield (c) and (d) for comparison. Another model example wherein neither direction nor amplitude are influenced by retinal locus (e), could represent a motor command signal following non-linear interaction of the two inputs to yield output (modified from Goodman and Andersen, 1989; see other references [1, 24] to Andersen and Zipser).

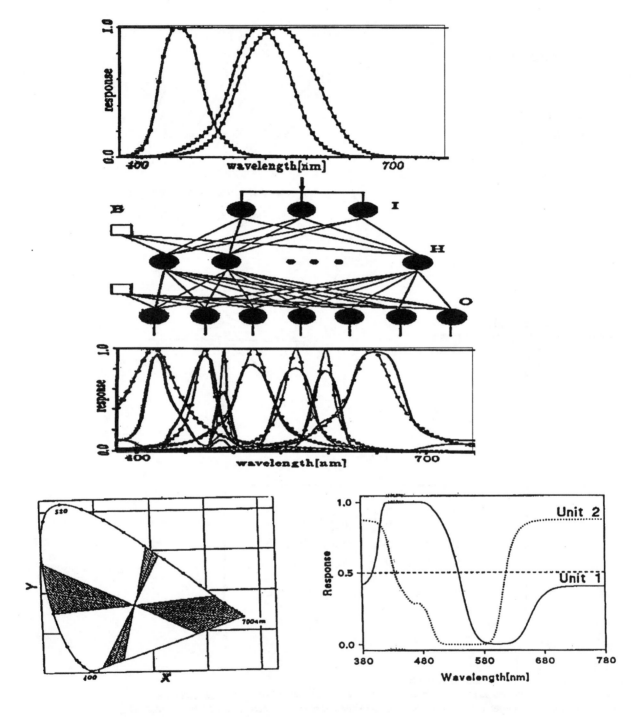

Figure 7   Reverse Engineering: Color Vision Example
    Color vision neural net with wavelengths of input layer red, green and blue cone-like neurons (upper). Network with input (I), hidden (H), and output (O) layers and their interconnections, including bias units (B) (upper middle). Wavelength definitions of output training set of seven color responses derived from cortical neurophysiological experiments; also, superimposed the converged output responses after training (middle lower).
    Confusion boundaries in color space of hidden layer neurons after training (lower left); with color responses of two hidden units, for a two H-unit model (lower right). (Modified from Usui et al., 1993, and Nakauchi et al., 1990).

The Role of Neural Networks in The Study of The Posterior Parietal Cortex

Pietro Mazzoni and Richard A. Andersen

Department of Brain and Cognitive Sciences
Massachusetts Institute of Technology
Cambridge, MA 02139
USA

Abstract—We review the use of a neural network model of a cerebral cortical area as an aid to understanding this area's function. The basic model is a feedforward multilayer network that learns to transform the coordinates of a visual stimulus from a retinocentric to a craniocentric reference frame using backpropagation. The similarity of certain features acquired by the model's components with the response properties of neurons in the posterior parietal cortex made the model a candidate for studying the cortical area's processing in an artificial system. An extension of the model to one that transformed retinal coordinates into body-centered ones predicted response properties that were later confirmed by neurophysiological experiments. Simulation of electrical stimulation of the model predicted a pattern of effects similar to the one later obtained by stimulation of a specific region of the parietal cortex. More importantly, study of the response properties of the model's units provided a simple explanation of how the parietal cortex might compute coordinate transformations and of why certain manipulations such as stimulation should produce the effects observed. The same algorithm for coordinate transformation was also obtained in an analogous network trained with a learning rule biologically more plausible than backpropagation. These results show that neural network modeling is a useful adjunct to the neurophysiological and psychophysical techniques we are using to study the function of the posterior parietal cortex.

I. INTRODUCTION

One of many uses of neural networks has been as models of neuronal ensembles that might give us some insight into the processing that neurons perform as a group. The approach in such studies, as in most modeling studies, is to construct a model that captures the features of a complex system that we believe are relevant to a particular function. One can then analyse, manipulate and modify the model with the hope of (1) gaining a further understanding of the system, (2) evaluating the role of various features in the system's function, (3) perhaps predicting other important features that could be observed experimentally, and (4)

predicting the system's response to various perturbations. As for any model, the network model that does incorporate some function or important feature of the neural system can then become a tool for expressing in explicit form various hypotheses and mechanisms related to the neural system. A neural network model developed in our laboratory has played the role we just described in our study of the posterior parietal cortex (PPC) of the primate brain. We will describe this model and its initial contribution to our understanding of the response properties of parietal neurons. We will then review the predictions produced by modifications and perturbations of the model, as well as the results obtained by similar manipulations and perturbations of the experimental system. The neural network model has so far helped not only to predict the system's behavior in various circumstances, but also to understand how its observed properties can subserve the computational functions attributed to this area of the brain.

II. THE POSTERIOR PARIETAL CORTEX: PRESUMED FUNCTION AND NEURONAL PROPERTIES

The posterior parietal cortex is thought to play an important role in the integration of sensory perception and motor behavior because lesions of this area cause impairments of spatial abilities and because its neurons are specifically active during sensory stimulation and particular motor acts (for a review, see [1]). One requirement of sensorimotor integration is the transformation of spatial locations across coordinate frames. In order to reach for an object, for example, the location of its image on the retina must be transformed to the coordinate frame in which hand movement commands are generated. These transformations are important for accurate spatial behavior because our sensory and motor organs can move relative to one another.

Early studies of the monkey's PPC revealed a group of neurons that responded to visual stimuli in an eye-position-dependent manner [2]. The portions of the visual field in which luminous stimuli elicited responses, i.e. their receptive fields, corresponded to particular retinal locations. As the trained monkey rotated its eyes to different locations the receptive fields maintained their shape and retinal location, but the neurons' responses were modulated by eye position. Such eye-position-modulated receptive fields were referred to as "spatial gain fields," because eye position acted as a gain of the visual response. A striking feature of these gain fields was that for a majority of the neurons the modulation was planar, i.e. proportional to the horizontal and/or vertical component of eye position, or had a planar component. The gain fields set PPC neurons apart from those of more peripheral visual areas, which encode strictly the retinal location of visual stimuli. However, PPC neurons do not code spatial locations unambiguously at the single cell level; rather, the code for a stimulus' spatial location is distributed across the population response. If individual neurons were actually invariant for locations in head-centered coordinates, for example, then their receptive fields should remain fixed to some location relative to the head, i.e. their responses should be independent of eye movements. Instead, the individual neurons' firing rate is an ambiguous signal for stimulus location, because a change in activity can be due to a movement of the stimulus as well as by an eye movement. Another special feature of these neurons is that their receptive fields are extremely large, covering as much as half the visual field. Such a large response area makes it difficult for the individual neuron to code stimulus location precisely.

III. THE ZIPSER-ANDERSEN MODEL

The properties of PPC neurons suggested that individual neurons were unlikely to subserve the spatial integration functions attributed to this cortical region. Being sensitive to both retinal location and eye position these neurons remained candidates for playing a role in computing spatial relationships, but a spatial code could only be obtained from the pooled activity of a group of these neurons. Zipser and Andersen developed a neural network to study how an ensemble of neuron-like model units might solve the coordinate transformation problem [3, 4]. The aim was to examine the properties of individual units that were trained to solve the problem as a group. If the brain was indeed encoding spatial locations in the distributed pattern of activity of many parietal neurons, then some features of the brain's algorithm might emerge in the model network too.

The Zipser-Andersen model was a three-layer feedforward network of units with sigmoid input-output functions. In the input layer a group of units encoded the retinal location of a punctate visual stimulus

and another group encoded eye position. Retinal location was encoded topographically, each unit having a two-dimensional receptive field of Gaussian profile centered at a given point in the receptive field. Eye position was encoded linearly in the units' activity, using a different slope and intercept for each unit. These inputs were modeled according to input signals actually available to neurons in the PPC. Units in the hidden layer received signals from all the input units and projected to all output units. The output layer was intended to code for the head-centered location of the visual stimulus. The task was thus to perform the vector addition of two positions, the stimulus' retinal position and the eye position, to obtain the location in a craniocentric reference frame. The output layer was trained to express head-centered locations in one of two formats: a receptive-field based one like the retinal input (topographic format) or a linear-function one like the eye position input (monotonic format). The network was trained to compute the coordinate transformation from a set of examples using backpropagation. After the network learned the task, its hidden units were found to respond to visual stimuli and to eye position very much like PPC neurons. Specifically, they had retinotopic visual receptive fields whose activity profiles were modulated by eye position, i.e. they had spatial gain fields, and these gain fields were largely planar. The receptive fields were also very large and smooth with one or a few eccentric peaks, and thus looked remarkably like those of PPC neurons.

The results of this simulation addressed several issues related to PPC function. First, it was shown that a layered network can learn to transform retinocentric coordinates into craniocentric ones using the input signals available to the PPC (whether the training signal required by backpropagation is available to the PPC is unknown, but see the discussion of the reinforcement-based model below). This result is consistent with the adaptability of spatial behavior (e.g., when the visual input is distorted by prisms) that persists throughout an animal's life. In fact, such adaptation is easily elicited precisely by training subjects with examples, as in the change in amplitude of eye movements to stimuli presented through distorting prisms. Second, the representation of the spatial signals that emerges at the hidden units' level as a results of learning to solve this problem is very similar to the representation of the same signals in PPC neurons. These neurons can thus play a similar role in the organism, i.e. build up an intermediate representation between input and output stages that is part of the coordinate transformation computation. The network demonstrates explicitly that units with PPC neurons' properties contain, as a group, a distributed representation of space that is sufficient for accurate localization. Such a distributed representation obviates the need for a topographic representation of head-centered space. The version of the model trained with the monotonic output format demonstrates that the distributed spatial representation of the hidden layer can appropriately drive a non-topographic code directly. This output layer could represent a set of motoneurons driving the eye muscles to orient the eye toward the desired spatial location. The adequacy of the hidden layer's representation to feed directly into a peripheral output could explain why such a topographic map of head-centered or body-centered visual space is generally not found in the cerebral cortex. Finally, and most importantly, the fact that training a neural network to perform coordinate transformations produced a hidden layer with properties like those of PPC neurons suggests that the network and the brain may employ a common strategy in solving the problem.

IV. AN EXTENSION OF THE MODEL: BODY-CENTERED COORDINATES

Having the problem's solution programmed in a network model made it possible to further investigate what algorithms the PPC may indeed be using through analysis and manipulations of the model. An immediate question was how locations could be coded in other coordinate frames. The transformation from retinal to head-centered coordinates has a natural application in the programming of eye movements, the eyes having to move to particular positions relative to the head. Large gaze shifts, however, are achieved by coupled movements of the eyes and head; in this case the target's position must be calculated in body-centered coordinates. Could the Zipser-Andersen network be modified to compute body-centered coordinates, and if so, what predictions would it make about the PPC?

Goodman and Andersen [5] added a group of units encoding head position to the input layer of the Zipser-Andersen network and trained this new network to produce body-centered locations at the output layer. The new units encoded head position using linear functions of the orientation of the head along various axes, roughly simulating the signals that neck muscles' proprioceptors might produce. The network was otherwise equivalent to the original one. It learned to compute the correct body-centered location given retinal, eye, and head position inputs. The hidden units were found to be sensitive to all three input types. They had retinotopic receptive fields modulated by both

eye and head position, each in a planar fashion. In other words, they developed planar "gaze fields," that is, linear modulation of visual responses along a particular direction of gaze, which is the sum of eye and head positions. Moreover, the "eye" gain field of a given hidden unit was always aligned (with the same direction and slope) with the same unit's "head" gain field. This was a natural solution for the network given the constraints of its architecture (the eye and head position inputs produced signals in very similar formats) and of the problem (eye and head position are indeed coupled for a given spatial position). The result suggested, however, that if the PPC subserves coordinate transformations beyond the head-centered reference frame and does so with an algorithm analogous to the neural network's strategy, then it should contain units with gaze fields similar to those of the network just described. Such units have recently been identified in the PPC [6]. Brotchie and Andersen trained monkeys to look in various directions by moving their eyes alone or by moving both their eyes and their head. A population of PPC neurons had visual responses modulated equivalently by eye or head position. These gaze fields were largely planar and the direction of eye and head position modulation was the same. This population was distinct from another group of PPC neurons whose visual responses were modulated by eye position alone. The locations of visual stimuli are thus presumably encoded in body-centered coordinates by the group of neurons with gaze fields and in head-centered coordinates by the neurons sensitive with only eye position gain fields.

V. HOW THE NEURAL NETWORK COMPUTES COORDINATE TRANSFORMATIONS

The addition of a head position input is only one example of the many manipulations that are possible once a neural network embodies a candidate of a biological solution to a problem. Various manipulations of this type led Goodman and Andersen [5] to a simple explanation of how the network performs coordinate transformations. Over the course of learning each hidden units develops a "preferred direction,", that is, a direction in its input space along which to maximally modulate its activity. This statement actually describes the general behavior of hidden units in most feedforward networks trained with examples. The preferred direction is expressed in the unit's weight vector. The units of the Zipser-Andersen network, receiving both retinal and eye position inputs, align their sensitivity in retinal space and in eye position space, and develop an eye position response field that approximates a plane oriented along what becomes the unit's preferred direction. Each hidden unit then extracts the components of the retinal and eye position vectors along its preferred direction and adds them. A hidden unit effectively collapses the multidimensional signal of the retinal and eye position units into two two-dimensional vectors, one for retinal and one for eye position. Each vector is then projected onto the unit's preferred direction. A single hidden unit's operation can thus be described as a sum of dot products, and is an elegant way of adding two vectors that are encoded in the activity of many input units. The preferred directions of the hidden units span the two-dimensional input space so that the retinal and eye position vectors are decomposed without losing information. Because these vectors' components are added at each hidden unit's input, the output of each hidden unit effectively consists of the component of the head-centered vector along the unit's preferred direction. These components are combined again at the output layer to give the head-centered vector that is the sum of the retinal and eye position vectors.

Understanding the algorithm discovered by the network model in these terms gives us a clearer view of how the brain might be solving the same problem. In this regard it is also useful to consider alternative solutions not employed by the network. One solution that the network does not choose is a look-up table in the hidden layer, with each hidden unit individually encoding the correct answer to each of the inputs in the set of training input-output pairs. It instead learns to perform the abstract computation of vector addition, as evidenced by its correct performance on novel pairs of retinal and position inputs. As the number of hidden units in the network is increased, a look-up table solution does indeed emerge. This observation suggests that a constraint on computational efficiency may be at work in the biological system's choice of solution.

The network also avoids solutions of the "shifter circuit" type [7], whereby a group of hidden units might set up retinal receptive fields that are gated at the output layer by the signals of another group of hidden units concerned with eye position alone. It seems instead a very common result that networks trained to minimize an error signal at the output layer develop distributed representations in their hidden units. The distributed representation of the same signals in the PPC suggests that the brain arrives at this solution due to constraints analogous to those imposed on the model network, e.g. training with an error signal a group of neurons highly interconnected to begin with. Moreover, a shifter circuit solution would have predicted not gaze field units to emerge when the head-position input was added, but rather a separate cluster of head-position units. Gaze field units are thus not a chance prediction of the model, but something to be expected from the way a trained layered neural network computes coordinate transformations. The observation of neurons with gaze fields in the PPC then supports the hypothesis that the neural network model embodies some of the important features of the nervous system's solution to the same problem.

VI. PERTURBING THE MODEL: SIMULATING ELECTRICAL MICROSTIMULATION

If theoretical analysis of the neural network's behavior suggests that this model captures some features of the brain's algorithm for coordinate transformations, then it may be instructive to introduce perturbations to the model and observe its behavior. We have mentioned that one use of transforming retinal coordinates into head-centered ones is to compute the orientation of the eyes required to direct gaze to a peripheral visual target. One symptom of parietal lesions is indeed difficulty in orienting gaze, and the PPC is directly connected with various centers controlling eye movements. Electrical stimulation of a cortical area is one way to test its role in the production of specific behavior, and stimulation of the PPC does produce eye movements [8, 9, 10]. Simulating electrical stimulation in the neural network made specific predictions concerning the metrics of eye movements that would be obtained if the neural network's output encoded the programmed endpoint of an eye movement [11]. These predictions were borne out by recent stimulation studies in the monkey [10].

The amplitude and direction of eye movements elicited from stimulation of a nervous system structure with the eyes starting at various orbital positions depends on how that structure represents spatial locations. Obtaining eye movements with metrics independent of the eye's initial position (fixed-vector pattern) suggests a coordinate frame centered on the eye, whereas amplitude and direction that vary with initial eye position so that the eyes are always moved to a single orbital position (convergent pattern) are consistent with a head-centered reference frame.

Goodman and Andersen [11] simulated the effect of electrical microstimulation by setting the output of a given hidden unit in a trained network to its maximum possible value and interpreting the new position encoded by the output layer as the endpoint of the eye movement presumed to result from the stimulation. This process was repeated for many initial eye positions, each of which was fed to the network's input layer. What we know about the way the hidden layer encodes spatial locations allows us to predict the pattern of eye movements to be obtained from the network. Because a hidden unit's activity encodes the component of the head-centered vector along the unit's preferred direction, maximal activation of that unit will shift the network's output along the unit's preferred direction. This direction is encoded in the unit's weights and so should not be affected by the values of the inputs; i.e., the direction of the eye movement will be independent of the starting eye position. The movement's amplitude, on the other hand, depends on how far from saturation the hidden unit is before stimulation. At starting eye positions whose vectors are orthogonal to the unit's preferred direction, the hidden unit will not be very active and maximal activation will produce a large shift in its output, giving a large-amplitude eye movement. At eye positions nearly parallel to the preferred direction the unit will be already very active and further activation due to stimulation will give only a small change in its output, and thus a small eye movement. Note that this aspect of the unit's behavior is not inconsistent, as it may seem at first, with the increase in a neuron's responsiveness to visual stimuli as the eye position moves in the direction of the neuron's gain field. This responsiveness cannot be compared with the saturating effect of microstimulation because the background firing rate also increases as the eye position changes.

This pattern of eye movements was indeed obtained by stimulation of most hidden units in a trained network [11]. The eye movements had very similar directions from all starting eye positions, but their amplitude decreased as the eye position was shifted along one direction. The direction of this amplitude decrease was very similar to the direction of the elicited eye movement, indicating that the saccades were getting smaller as the eye moved along the unit's preferred direction, as predicted. Another prediction made in this study was that stimulation of two sites in the PPC should produce a much more convergent pattern of eye movements than stimulation of either site alone. This pattern is what we expect from the vector sum of the saccades elicited from each site.

One of the stimulation studies in the monkey found a correspondence between eye movement types and anatomical subdivisions of the PPC [10]. Stimulation of the region that directly projects to eye movement centers and that is active during the programming of saccadic eye movements (the lateral intraparietal area) elicited a pattern of saccadic eye movements like those obtained from the neural network. The saccades were parallel but of decreasing amplitude as the starting eye position was moved in the direction of the elicited eye movement. Neurons in this area also have

spatial gain fields and could thus compute head-centered locations to drive eye movements much as the neural network does. This hypothesis is supported by the eye movements obtained from simultaneous stimulation of two separate sites: the pattern is much more convergent toward a circumscribed orbital region than in the case of single-site stimulation [12]. The neural network model thus correctly predicted the pattern of eye movements to be expected from stimulation of a PPC region that had been independently implicated in the control of eye movements. The stimulation studies would have been performed in the monkey whether or not any neural network model had existed or had made any predictions, as this technique has always been a classical neurophysiological tool for the study of nervous system structures. The particular effect predicted by double-site stimulation of the network at different starting eye positions did, however, prompt the experimenters to perform in the monkey this same experiment, which would not have been considered necessarily interesting otherwise. Moreover, the network provided an immediate and detailed explanation for why the eye movement pattern obtained—which suggests neither an oculocentric nor a craniocentric representation—should indeed be expected from an area encoding spatial locations using gain fields.

VII. BIOLOGICAL PLAUSIBILITY OF THE MODEL: THE REINFORCEMENT-BASED VERSION

The biological plausibility of the Zipser-Andersen model was an issue of concern because backpropagation, the learning algorithm used to train the model network, is an unlikely candidate as a biological learning mechanism. To address this issue Mazzoni et al. [13, 14] trained a neural network to perform the retinal to head-centered coordinate transformation using a reinforcement learning rule developed by Barto and Jordan (the associative reward-penalty, or A_{R-P}, learning rule, [15]). This algorithm adjusts the network's connections based on (1) a single error value computed from the network's overall performance, and (2) the local presynaptic and postsynaptic activity for each connection. It combines, in other words, a reinforcement signal with Hebbian updating of connection strength, and is thus biologically more plausible than backpropagation. The hidden units of this network developed gain fields and receptive fields virtually identical to those of the backpropagation-trained networks, suggesting that the networks' algorithm for computing coordinate transformations did not depend on the specific algorithm used. The reinforcement-based model not only helped to validate the analysis of the Zipser-

Andersen model as applicable to the study of the PPC, but also supported the idea that the PPC can learn to compute coordinate transformations from signals directly available to the nervous system.

VIII. CONCLUSIONS

The network model of PPC developed by Zipser and Andersen has revealed itself a valuable tool in our study of this cortical area's function. Like every useful model it embodies a few known features of the system being studied and it is helping us to understand why those features, and others that emerge from the model, are important for the system's computations. The model has predicted a few experimental results and has made it easy to put those results into an explicit theoretical context. The general approach has consisted of a combination of a novel modeling paradigm and a "reverse engineering" strategy of brain function investigation. A fundamental tenet of neurophysiology is that we can try to understand the functioning of the brain by observing the responses of its components to various stimuli and under various conditions. This method is a form of reverse engineering much like studying how a typewriter works by watching its parts move when someone presses the keys. The response properties of PPC neurons are complicated enough that reverse engineering applied directly to the brain was not sufficient, and a model was thus devised. A neural network was chosen as a model because it can program itself for an optimal solution given a problem (coordinate transformation) and a set of input and desired output signals (the signals that feed into the PPC and accurate spatial behavior, respectively). Reverse engineering was then applied to the trained neural network, with the advantage that the researchers could perform the manipulations necessary to understand the algorithm arrived at by the network. The properties and behavior of the biological network could thus be explained within a theoretical description of its processing function.

We believe the neural network has been a useful modeling paradigm for studies of the PPC especially because these studies addressed how neurons encode more than one parameter. Whereas most neurophysiological investigations so far have focused on the effect of varying one parameter at a time (a necessary first step for the study of any complex system), studies of an area thought to compute spatial relationships had to examine the interactions of several variables such as retinal location, eye position, and head position. It is not surprising then that the experimental data was not easily summarized by an intuitive scheme. The network model provided a framework for developing an intuition about the distributed representation of several variables. As more experiments address the encoding and interactions of several parameters in the nervous system, we expect neural networks to continue to fruitfully assist our investigations of nervous system functions.

REFERENCES

[1] R. A. Andersen, "Visual and eye movement functions of the posterior parietal cortex," *Annu. Rev. Neurosci.*, vol. 12, pp. 377-403, 1989.

[2] R. A. Andersen, G. K. Essick and R. M. Siegel, "Encoding of spatial locations by posterior parietal neurons," *Science*, vol. 230, pp. 456-458, 1985.

[3] D. Zipser and R. A. Andersen, "A backpropagation programmed network that simulates response properties of a subset of posterior parietal neurons," *Nature*, vol. 331, pp. 679-684, 1988.

[4] R. A. Andersen and D. Zipser, "The role of the posterior parietal cortex in coordinate transformations for visualmotor integration," *Can. J. Physiol. Pharmacol.*, vol. 66, pp. 488-501, 1988.

[5] S. J. Goodman and R. A. Andersen, "Algorithm programmed by a neural network model for coordinate transformation," *Proc. Int. Joint Conf. Neural Netw.*, vol. II, pp. 381-386, 1990.

[6] P. R. Brotchie and R. A. Andersen, "A body centred coordinate system in posterior parietal cortex," *Soc. Neurosci. Abst.*, vol. 17, pp. 1281, 1991.

[7] C. H. Anderson and D. C. Van Essen, "Shifter circuits: a computational strategy for dynamic aspects of visual processing," *Proc. Natl. Acad. Sci. U.S.A.*, vol. 84, pp. 6297-6301, 1987.

[8] H. Shibutani, H. Sakata and J. Hyvärinen, "Saccade and blinking evoked by microstimulation of the posterior parietal association cortex of the monkey," *Exp. Brain Res.*, vol. 55, pp. 1-8, 1984.

[9] D. D. Kurylo and A. A. Skavenski, "Eye movements evoked by electrical stimulation of area PG in the monkey," *J. Neurophysiol.*, vol. 65, pp. 1243-53, 1991.

[10] P. Thier and R. A. Andersen, "Electrical microstimulation delineates 3 distinct eye-movement related areas in the posterior parietal cortex of the rhesus monkey," *Soc. Neurosci. Abst.*, vol. 17, pp. 1281, 1991.

[11] S. J. Goodman and R. A. Andersen, "Microstimulation of a neural-network model for visually guided saccades," *J. Cog. Neurosci.*, vol. 1, pp. 317-326, 1989.

[12] P. Thier and R. A. Andersen, unpublished.

[13] P. Mazzoni, R. A. Andersen and M. I. Jordan, "A more biologically plausible learning rule for neural networks," *Proc. Natl. Acad. Sci. U.S.A.*, vol. 88, pp. 4433-4437, 1991.

[14] P. Mazzoni, R. A. Andersen and M. I. Jordan, "A more biologically plausible learning rule than backpropagation applied to a network model of cortical area 7a," *Cerebral Cortex*, vol. 1, pp. 293-307, 1991.

[15] A. G. Barto and M. I. Jordan, "Gradient following without backpropagation in layered networks," *Proc. IEEE Conf. Neural Netw.*, vol. II, pp. 629-636, 1987.

Color Opponency as the Internal Representation Acquired by A Three-Layered Neural Network Model

Shiro USUI and Shigeki NAKAUCHI

Department of Information & Computer Sciences,
Toyohashi University of Technology
1–1 Hibarigaoka Tempaku Toyohashi 441, JAPAN

Abstract—This paper discusses the color representation in the visual system through the analysis of a three-layered neural network model incorporating physiological evidences of color representation at the sensor level (broadband trichromatic representation by cones) and the perceptual level (narrowband color representation by color-coded cells in V4). We trained the model to perform a mapping between these color representations by back propagation algorithm and analyzed the acquired characteristics of the hidden units. It turned out that the hidden units learned characteristics similar to those of the color opponent cells found in fish retina and macaque LGN. It was concluded that the R-G and Y-B color opponent representations plays an essential role in color information processing through investigating the efficiency of color representation in the hidden layer and the capability of color discrimination task of the model.

I. INTRODUCTION

Recent progress in electrophysiological studies on color vision have revealed that there exist several color representations in the visual system; broadband trichromatic representation at the sensor level, broadband color opponent representation at the intermediate level[1][2], and narrowband color representation at the higher level[3]. A number of color vision models have been proposed to account such physiological observations on color representation in the visual system. Although these models might explain *how* color signal is transformed in the visual system, there are only a few attempts to explain the reasons *why* color information is represented in the visual system as it is.

This paper discusses the internal color representation in the visual system and relates it to a computational task of the color-coded cells, and to the parallel structure and distributed processing of the neural system. We here emphasize the importance of strategy of combining top-down and bottom-up approaches using neural network models to investigate the internal representation, which

strongly depends on the tasks to be achieved and also on the hardware[4]. Neural network models are different from the theoretical models or psychophysical models of the past because the neural network models both have a computational theory and include considerations about the hardware implementation level such as parallel structure and distributed processing. Neural network models should provide insights on both *what* real neural systems are doing and *why* they do so, by analyzing *how* it had designed the internal representation to perform a particular computational task.

In this paper, we trained a three-layered neural network model by means of a back propagation algorithm to transform the broadband trichromatic color representation of the three classes of cones in the retina, to a narrowband color representation of the color-coded cells in V4. After the learning process, such acquired characteristics of the hidden units in the hidden layer as spectral response properties and chromatic preferences were analyzed. We discuss relationships between the internal color representation at the hidden layer and the computational task to be learned.

II. METHODS

Figure 1 shows a schematic diagram of a three-layered neural network model which consists of 3 input units, 15 hidden units and 7 output units. The hidden and output units has sigmoidal input-output functions. Information from input units is transformed by the hidden layer to achieve the specific task to be learned. The number of hidden units was determined empirically and will be discussed later.

The input units correspond to three classes of cones (S,M and L cones) in the retina, which have broadband action spectra (s,m and l) derived from Smith-Pokorny[5] shown in Figure 1(a). The 7 output units, expressing the color-coded cells in V4, were designed to have the selectivities to the seven colors appearing in continuous spectral light. The action spectra of each output unit $c_k(\lambda)$ shown by thin curves in Figure 1(b) is represented by the

Lorentz curve. The peak wavelength and the bandwidth at half the maximum response of each output unit were defined according to psychological observations on the color appearance of monochromatic lights[6] and physiological observations on color-coded cells in V4[3], respectively.

We generated a set of 81 input-output data between 380 and 780nm at 5nm intervals shown by dots in Figure 1(a) and (b) for training the network. The back propagation algorithm[7] was used to train the network to perform a mapping from the broadband trichromatic representation at the input layer to the narrowband color representation at the output layer by minimizing the error between actual output of the network and the teaching data. Initial weight values were set to be random.

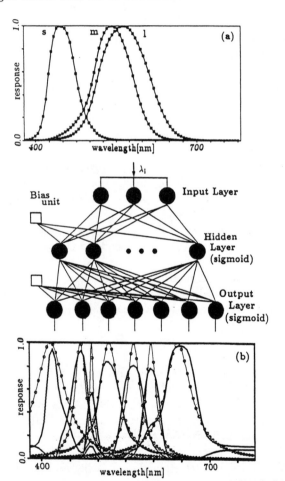

Figure 1. Structure of the neural network model and the response properties of input and output units. (a)broadband response curves of input units, (b)narrowband response curves of output units. Thin lines and thick lines represent training data and actual output of the network after learning, respectively. Each output unit has selectivities of seven-color appearance of rainbow. Curves are normalized between 0 and 1.

III. RESULTS

Spectral Responses of Hidden Units

Figure 1(b) (thick curves) shows the learned responses of each output units to training data (monochromatic lights) and indicates that the network learned the mapping sufficiently well. We examined the spectral response properties of 15 hidden units and classified them into six groups as shown in Figure 2. Type 1 and 2, Type 3 and 4 have similar properties with opposite signs and these curves can be interpreted as the color opponent representation of chromatic horizontal cells found in fish retina[1] or LGN cells of monkey[2]. Although we also had some bimodal-shaped curves such as Type 5 and 6, it will be shown in the next section that all these units can be characterized by their chromatic preference.

We can see that all of these curves are broad, that is, no hidden units are tuned for a specific wavelength. This means that the color discrimination was not realized at the hidden layer and the activitiy patterns of the hidden units could be interpreted as an intermediate representation for the narrowband color representation at the ouput layer.

Chromatic Preferences of Hidden Units

Monochromatic stimuli are often used in physiological and/or psychophyisical experiments because any monochromatic light of the fixed energy can be represented in terms of only its wavelength. However, the visual systems are usually exposed to mixed colors under natural environment. Recent physiological studies[8]−[9] examine the chromatic properties of cells using mixed colors to explore the neural color representation in detail. We here examined the responses of 15 hidden units to mixed colors as testing color stimuli which tell us the chromatic properties of hidden units. Since the cone responses to any mixed color are obtained from its spectral sensitivities, the chromatic response of each hidden unit can be caluculated.

Figure 3 shows the chromatic responses illustrated in the CIE xy-chromaticity diagram with contour lines. Mixed colors as testing data lie inside of the diagram, while the monochromatic lights as training data lie on the boundary of the diagram, namely spectrum locus. Each hidden unit responded selectively to the lights lying in the specific chromatic regions separated by lines, and shared the prefered chromaticity regions with other units.

This line corresponds to the "color confusion line" because responses on this line are the same; thus these colors are indistinguishable to a particular hidden unit. The direction of the color confusion line tells us the color preference of the individual hidden unit. To estimate the chromatic properties of the hidden units, we focused on the distribution of the directions of the color confusion lines.

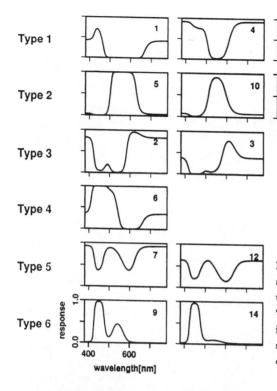

Type 1

Type 2

Type 3

Type 4

Type 5

Type 6

response 1.0 0.0

400   600

wavelength[nm]

Figure 2. Responses of 15 hidden units to monochromatic lights after learning. These curves were classified into six types due to redundancy of the number of the hidden unit. Type 1 and 2, Type 3 and 4 show similar shapes with opposite signs and can be interpreted as color opponent representation similar to spectral sensitivities of chromatic holizontal cells found in fish retina[1] or LGN cells of monkey[2].

A comparable physiological study[8] of chromatic response of LGN neurons of macaque has revealed that directions of the color confusion lines had a bimodal distribution as shown in Figure 4(a); each neuron corresponded to R-G or Y-B type, respectively. From a similar point of view, we examined the distribution of directions of the color confusion lines of the hidden units in the neural network model that developed in five learning trials with different initial weight sets. As a result, the distribution of the color confusion line of the hidden units was separated into two groups corresponding to R-G and Y-B types as shown in Figure 4(b); these are closely similar to the macaque LGN cells. It should be emphasized here that these properties of the hidden units were self-organized by learning rather than set directly into the network. We only provided the computational task and the training data to the network.

Evaluation of Color Representation at the Hidden Layer

The color opponent representation found in retina, LGN and the hidden layer must be favorable to the computational task of the visual system. In this section, we therefore probe the reason why the opponent color representation was acquired at the hidden layer by back propagation learning.

First, we examined the effect of the number of hidden units and the efficiency of the color representation at the hidden layer. To measure the efficiency of the internal color representation, the correlations of spectral responses of the hidden units for the networks having 2 to 15 hidden

units were analyzed.

Let $\phi_i(\lambda)$ (i=1 to n) be the spectral response of i-th hidden unit of the network with n hidden units. The correlation matrix $\mathbf{R_n}$ may be expressed as follows;

$$\mathbf{R}_n = \begin{pmatrix} r_{11} & \cdots & r_{1n} \\ \vdots & \ddots & \vdots \\ r_{n1} & \cdots & r_{nn} \end{pmatrix}$$

where

$$r_{ij} = \frac{\mathbf{E}[(\phi_i(\lambda) - \phi_i^m) \cdot (\phi_j(\lambda) - \phi_j^m)]}{\sqrt{\mathbf{E}[(\phi_i(\lambda) - \phi_i^m)^2] \cdot \mathbf{E}[(\phi_j(\lambda) - \phi_j^m)^2]}}, \quad \phi_i^m = \mathbf{E}[\phi_i(\lambda)]$$

Here, we define $|\mathbf{R_n}|$ as a redundancy measure for the internal color representation of the network with n hidden units as follows;

$$|\mathbf{R}_n| = \frac{1}{N} \sum_{i=1}^{n-1} \sum_{j=i+1}^{n} r_{ij}^2, \quad N = \frac{n(n-1)}{2}$$

Figure 5 shows the $|\mathbf{R_n}|$ for the networks with 2 to 15 hidden units (n=2 to 15). It was clearly shown that the two-hidden-unit model (n=2) acquired the most efficient (uncorrelated) internal color representation. Figure 6 illustrates the spectral response curves of hidden units in the two-hidden-unit model. Each unit could be interpreted as R-G and Y-B color opponent type similar to the chromatic horizontal cells found in fish retina[1] or LGN cells of monkey[2]. We confirmed that this property was

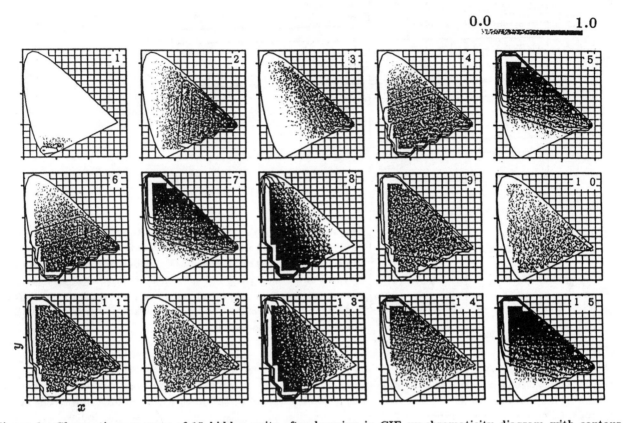

0.0   1.0

Figure 3. Chromatic responses of 15 hidden units after learning in CIE xy-chromaticity diagram with contour lines. Each unit prefers and shares the specific chromatic region to achieve the transformation from the broadband to the narrowband color representations.

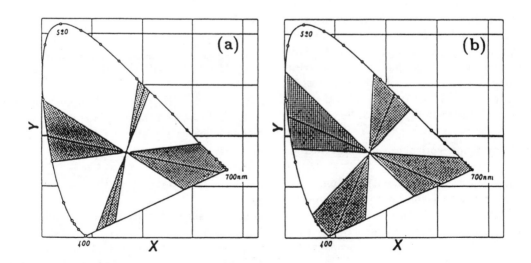

Figure 4. Mean directions (solid line) of color confusion line with standard deviations (shaded area) of (a)macaque LGN cells[8] and (b)learned hidden units. Both LGN cells and hidden units are classified into R-G and Y-B color opponent types.

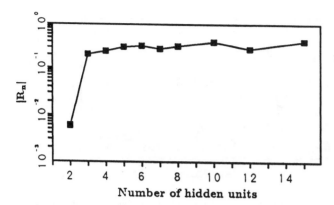

Figure 5. $|R_n|$ versus the number of hidden units of the network. The two-hidden-unit model acquired the most efficient (uncorrelated) internal representation.

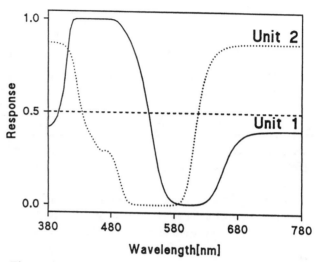

Figure 6. Spectral response properties of the hidden units in the two-hidden-unit model. Each curve was similar to the R-G and the Y-B color opponent responses recorded from the retinal horizontal cells of fish[1] or LGN cells of monkey[2]. This property was independent of the initial weight sets for the network learning.

independent of the initial weight set. This result thus suggests that the opponent color representation at the hidden layer was acquired as a result of reducing the redundancy of the broadband trichromatic color representation at the input layer and that the representation brought an efficient processing of the color information.

Next, we examined the capability of wavelength discrimination of the models. Figure 7 shows the response curves of output units of the one- and the two-hidden-unit models. The two-hidden-unit model had clearly distinguishable response peaks indicated by arrows in Figure 7(b), and thus the model discriminated the stimulus wavelengths while one-hidden-unit model did not as shown in Figure 7(a). Therefore, we can conclude that the opponent color representation also had an advantage for the color discrimination task.

IV. RELATED WORKS ON COLOR OPPONENCY

Usui et al.[14] proposed a wine-glass-type five-layered neural network model extracting the principal features of the Munsell colors. The network was trained to perform identity mapping on the set of the spectral reflectance curves of 1569 Munsell color chips. Analysis of the internal representation revealed that the spectral reflectance curve as the physical attribute of color can be represented efficiently in a 3-D feature space spaned by luminance and R-G and Y-B axes. Principal component analysis of cone signals have been done by Buchsbaum et al.[15], and it was pointed out that decorrelated signals provided by principal component analysis can be considered as the responses of the color opponent mechanisms in the retina.

Buchsbaum's work is close to our paper, but slightly different. Principal component analysis yields an optimal linear transformation in the sense of mimimum reconstruction error, while the network model proposed in this pa-

per achieves that optimal transformation in the sense of mimimum error of computational task to be learned, and the transformation the network model perform is nonlinear. Performance of principal component analysis is rather close to the wine-glass-type five-layer neural network in achieving identity mapping although the neural network can provide the nonlinear principal components of the input data set.

Usui et al.[16] showed that color opponency appears as a result of decorrelating broadband trichromatic color signals by anti-Hebbian learning and strongly relates to the color constancy. The decorrelating network also has another further potential in relating the computation of the color opponency to the biological mechanisms in real neural networks.

V. CONCLUSION

In this paper an attempt was made to explain the reason why the color opponent representation exists in the visual system. We adopted the strategy of combining both top-down and bottom-up approaches; that is, we constructed a three-layered neural network model whose specific task was to transform the broadband trichromatic color representation to a narrowband color representation.

Analysis of chromatic properties of the taught hidden units focused upon the directions of color confusion lines, revealed that these units have similar R-G and Y-B color opponent characteristics to those of the chromatic cells found in macaque LGN. It was found that the spectral re-

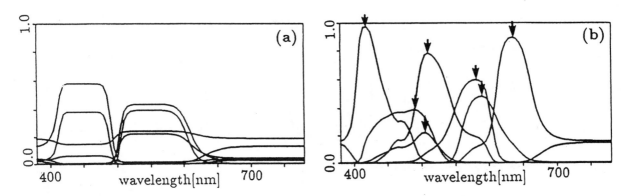

Figure 7. Capability of wavelength discrimination by (a) one-hidden-unit model and (b) two-hidden-unit model. One-hidden-unit model never achieve the seven-color discrimination task. However, the two-hidden-unit model with color opponent internal representation could discriminate the seven colors shown by arrows.

sponse properties of the two-hidden-unit model is the most efficient (uncorrelated) representation through investigating the redundancy of the activities among the hidden units; the two-hidden-unit model had optimum properties for the color discrimination task. Color opponent representation in the hidden layer was self-organized in the network to perform the computational task rather than designed by hand. Analysis of the internal representation in the hidden layer of the trained network provides insights into *what* real neural systems are doing and also *why* they do so.

This combined approach using the neural network models is not limited to the chromatic properties of neurons but may be extended to other problems including spatio-chromatic properties, namely color receptive fields, or to temporal-chromatic properties of neurons. Moreover, it may be indispensable in the future examinations of higher order brain mechanisms since internal representations or information coding schemes at the higher levels are considerd to be highly task-oriented.

Acknowledgment

We thank Dr.E.Yodogawa and Professor L.Stark for their valuable comments.

REFERENCES

[1] G.Mitarai, S.Usui and A.Takabayashi, "Particular type of chromatic responses and arrangement of all the horizontal cell types in the mugil retina", Biomedical Research **3**, 137–142 (1982).

[2] R.L.De Valois, "Contribution of different lateral geniculate cell types to visual behavior", Vision Res. **11**, 3, 383–396 (1971).

[3] S.Zeki, "The representation of colours in the cerebral cortex", Nature **284**, 3, 412–418 (1980).

[4] D.Marr, "Vision", San Francisco:Freeman (1982).

[5] V.C.Smith and J.Pokorny, "Spectral sensitivities of the foveal cone photopigments between 400 and 500nm", Vision Res. **15**, 161–171 (1975).

[6] L.M.Hurvich, "Color Vision", Sunderland:MA (1981).

[7] D.E.Rumelhalt, J.L.McClelland and the PDP Research Group, "Parallel Distributed Processing", MIT Press (1986).

[8] A.Derrington, J.Krauskopf and P.Lennie, "Chromatic mechanisms in lateral geniculate nucleus of macaque", J.Physiol. **357**, 241–265 (1984).

[9] P.Lennie, J.Krauskopf and G.Sclar, "Chromatic mechanisms in striate cortex of macaque", J.Neurosci. **10**, 2, 649–669 (1990).

[10] S.R.Lehky and T.J.Sejnowski, "Network model of shape-from-shading: neural function arises from both receptive and projective fields", Nature **332**, 2, 452–454 (1988).

[11] D.Zipser and R.A.Anderson, "A back-propagation network that simulates response properties of a subset of posterior parietal neurons", Nature **331**, 25, 679–684 (1988).

[12] A.Pouget and T.J.Sejnowski, "Neural models of binocular depth perception", Cold Spring Harbar Symposia on Quantitative Biology **55**, 765–777 (1990).

[13] Y.Uno, N.Fukumura, R.Suzuki and M.Kawato, "A neural network model for recognizing objects and planning hand shapes in grasping movements", Proc.SICE'92 (Kumamoto), IS17–1, 1261–1264 (1992).

[14] S.Usui, S.Nakauchi and M.Nakano, "Reconstruction of Munsell color space by a five-layer neural network", J.Opt.Soc.Am.A **9**, 4, 516–520 (1992).

[15] G.Buchsbaum and A.Gottschalk, "Trichromacy, opponent colours coding and optimum colour information transmission in the retina", Proc.R.Soc.Lond. **220**, 89–113 (1983).

[16] S.Usui, S.Nakauchi and Y.Miyamoto, "A neural network model for color constancy based on the minimally redundant color representation", Proc.IJCNN'92 (Beijing) **II**, 696–701 (1992).

A RELATIONSHIP BETWEEN NEURAL NETWORKS AND PROGRAMMABLE LOGIC ARRAYS

Victor Eliashberg
Universal Learning Systems, Palo Alto, CA

ABSTRACT. A useful relationship between some associative neural networks and programmable logic arrays (PLA) is discussed. The shown analogy helps to understand the properties of this class of neural networks as extensions of the properties of PLA's.

1. Introduction

Different versions of the following basic problem are often discussed in neural network literature:
PROBLEM 1. Given a set of input/output pairs (associations) $\mathbf{P}=\{(x^1, y^1), ...(x^n, y^n)\}$, where $x^i \in \mathbf{X}$, $y^i \in \mathbf{Y}$, and $\mathbf{X}$ and $\mathbf{Y}$ are the sets of binary or real input and output vectors, respectively, design a system implementing a function $f:\mathbf{X}\rightarrow\mathbf{Y}$ such that $y^i=f(x^i)$ for $i=1,...n$.
Let $\mathbf{X}_p$ be the set of input vectors that are included in the pairs (x^i, y^i) from $\mathbf{P}$. In the special case when $\mathbf{X}_p=\mathbf{X}$ and both $\mathbf{X}$ and $\mathbf{Y}$ are sets of binary vectors, Problem 1 can be solved with the use of a programmable logic device (PLD) known as a programmable logic array (PLA). In the more general case, when $\mathbf{X}$ and $\mathbf{Y}$ are sets of real vectors, Problem 1 can be solved with the use of different types of associative neural networks. Some such networks, having a general architecture similar to that of PLA's, are discussed in this paper.

2. Solution of Problem 1 with the use of a PLA

The basic architecture of a PLA is shown in Figure 1. The diagram uses the following notation:

x_i ($i=1,...m$)   is the i-th component of the input vector, where $x_i \in \{0, 1\}$; $x_i^+=x_i$ and $x_i^-=\overline{x}_i$.

g_{ij}^{x+} and g_{ij}^{x-} are, respectively, the conductivities of fuses between lines x_i^+ and x_i^- and the inputs of the i-th AND gate.

s_i is an auxiliary variable describing a similarity between input vector $x=(x_1,...x_m)$ and the vector represented by the conductivities of fuses.

d_i is the output of the i-th AND gate.

g_{ji}^y is the conductivity of the fuse between the output of the i-th AND gate and the input of the j-th OR gate.

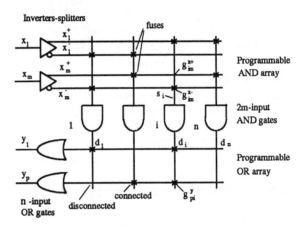

FIGURE 1. The basic architecture of a PLA

x_j	g_{ij}^{x+}	g_{ij}^{x-}	u_{ij}
$\times$	0	0	1
$\times$	1	1	0
0	0	1	1
0	1	0	0
1	0	1	0
1	1	0	1

$\times$ is ether 0 or 1

FIGURE 2. The table for calculating u_{ij} in Expression (1)

Using this notation the work of the PLA shown in Figure 1 can be described as follows:

$$s_i = \sum_{j=1}^{m} u_{ij} \qquad (i=1,...n) \qquad (1)$$

where u_{ij} is found using the table shown in Figure 2.

$$d_i = \begin{cases} 1 & \text{if } s_i = m \\ 0 & \text{otherwise} \end{cases} \qquad (2)$$

$$y_j = \sum_{i=1}^{n} g_{ji}^y \cdot d_i \qquad (j=1,...p) \qquad (3)$$

It is easy to verify that expressions (1) - (3) produce the same result as traditional logic expressions. That is, if input vector x matches the input fuse-vector of the i-th AND gate (vector g_i^x) then $d_i=1$ and the output fuse-vector of this gate (vector g_i^y) is retrieved as the output vector of the network (vector y).

NOTE: The first on-chip PLA was developed at IBM in 1969 and was referred to as a read-only associative memory (ROAM). The term PLA was introduced in 1970 by Texas Instruments (see [13]).

3. A Neural Network Solution of Problem 1

A simple neural network providing a solution of Problem 1 is shown schematically in Figure 3.

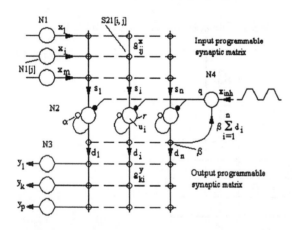

FIGURE 3. A neural network solution of Problem 1

Large circles with incoming and outgoing lines represent neurons with their dendrites and axons, respectively. Small white and black circles represent excitatory and inhibitory synapses, respectively. The network has three layers of neurons: input neurons N1, intermediate neurons N2, and output neurons N3. Neurons N2 have a global inhibitory feedback via neuron N4 and local excitatory feedbacks. It can be shown that in such a

network neurons N2 can compete via reciprocal inhibition in the *winner-take-all* fashion. A similar effect can be obtained in a network with lateral inhibitory feedbacks. Figure 3 uses the following notation:

Nk[j]   is the j-th neuron from set Nk.

Smk[i, j] is the synapse between neuron Nk[j] and neuron Nm[i].

x_j is the output of neuron N1[j].

g_{ij}^x is the gain of synapse S21[ij].

s_i is the net synaptic current of synapses S21[i, 1],.... S21[i, m]. s_i represents a similarity between input vector x and vector g_i^x (see expression (4) below).

d_i is the output of neuron N2[i].

q is the output of neron N4. This output is the sum of the feedback signal $\beta\Sigma d_i$ and an external signal x_{inh}.

β is the gain of synapse between any neuron from N2 and neuron N4.

τ is the time constant of any neuron from N2.

α is the gain of synapse providing local excitatory feedback for a neuron from N2.

g_{ki}^y is the gain of synapse between neuron N2[i] and neuron N3[k].

The following functional model of the network of Figure 3 was studied in [2] and [3]:

$$s_i = \sum_{j=1}^{m} g_{ij}^x \cdot x_j \qquad (4)$$

$$\tau \frac{du_i}{dt} + u_i = s_i + \alpha \cdot d_i - q \qquad (5)$$

$$d_i = \begin{cases} u_i & \text{if } u_i > 0 \\ 0 & \text{otherwise} \end{cases} \qquad (6)$$

$$q = \beta \cdot \sum_{i=1}^{n} d_i + x_{inh} \qquad (7)$$

$$y_k = \sum_{i=1}^{n} g_{ki}^y \cdot d_i \qquad (8)$$

Let all x_j and x_{inh} (and, therefore, all s_i) be step functions of time. Then, for all active neurons from layer N2 (the neurons for which $u_i > 0$), the solution of equations (5) - (7) can be represented in the following explicit form:

$$u_i = \frac{(s_i - s_{av})}{\alpha - 1}(e^{at} - 1) + (u_i^o - u_{av}^o)e^{at}$$

$$+ \frac{(s_{av} - x_{inh})}{1 + \beta \cdot n_1 - \alpha}(1 - e^{-bt}) + u_{av}^o \cdot e^{-bt} \quad (9)$$

where n_1 is the number of active neurons from N2, u_i^o are the values of u_i at $t=0$, and s_{av} and u_{av}^o are the average values of s_i and u_i^o for all active neurons from N2. That is,

$$s_{av} = \frac{1}{n_1}\sum_{i=1}^{n_1} s_i \quad (10)$$

$$u_{av}^o = \frac{1}{n_1}\sum_{i=1}^{n_1} u_i^o \quad (11)$$

Parameters a and b in e^{at} and e^{-bt} are as follows:

$$a = (\alpha - 1)/\tau \quad (12)$$

$$b = (1 + \beta \cdot n_1 - \alpha)/\tau \quad (13)$$

Let $1 < \alpha < 1 + \beta$. Then $a > 0$ and $b > 0$. According to expression (9), neurons N2[i] with $s_i > s_{av}$ increase their potentials u_i. Neurons N2[i] with $s_i < s_{av}$ decrease their potentials and switch off once $u_i < 0$. This reduces n_1 and increases s_{av} making $s_i < s_{av}$ for some additional neurons from N2. Eventually, only neurons with $s_i = \max(s_1, \ldots s_n)$ will have $u_j > 0$. It can be shown that this equilibrium is unstable if $n_1 > 1$. Therefore, in the presence of noise, at the end of the transient response there will be only one winner randomly selected from the set of neurons with the maximum level of s_i.
It was shown in [2] and [3] that the described neural model provides a solution of Problem 1.

4. PLA-like vs. Connectionist Notation

The drawing shown in Figure 3 uses a graphical notation similar to that employed in the area of programmable logic devices. It is my belief that this notation is more efficient than the connectionist notation employed in the majority of neural network publications. Figures 4 - 7 illustrate this point. Figure 4 displays the neural network corresponding to the ART1 model [5] using connectionist notation. In this notation each connection is represented by a separate line. One can hardly notice a similarity between this network and the network shown in Figure 3. This similarity is revealed in Figure 5.

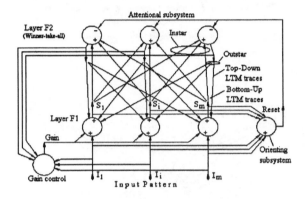

FIGURE 4. A connectionist representation of the ART1 model

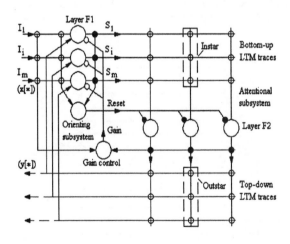

FIGURE 5. A PLA-like representation of the ART1 model.

Another illustration is provided by Figures 6 and 7. Figure 6a shows the architecture of the counterpropagation network (CPN) as it was presented in [7]. A different connectionist representation of the CPN architecture borrowed from [4] is shown in Figure 6b. Finally, a

PLA-like diagram corresponding to the same network is presented in Figure 7.

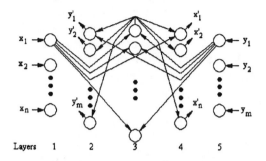

a)

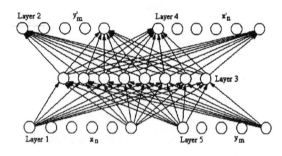

b)

FIGURE 6. Two connectionist representations of the CPN model

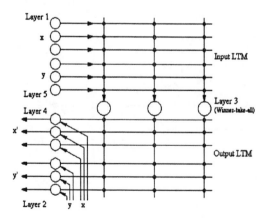

FIGURE 7. A PLA-like representation of the CPN model

5. History

As is known, the study of artificial neural networks (ANN) began with the classical work of McCulloch and Pitts [9]. Many interesting engineering and mathematical ideas inspired by this pioneering paper were introduced in the late forties, fifties and the sixties (Wiener [21], Hebb [6], Minsky [10], Kleene [8], von Neumann [12], Rosenblatt [15], Widrow and Hoff [19], Stark [18], Steinbuch [16], Anderson [1], and others).

In the late sixties, the notion of a "simple" model of brain hardware (such as the perceptron) became the target of sharp criticism on the part of the proponents of software-oriented AI [11]. As a result of this criticism, the ANN research lost much of its popularity and financing. Nowadays, the seventies are often referred to as the Dark Ages of neural networks.

The eighties and the early nineties witnessed a resurgence of interest in neurocomputing, so the nineties promise to bring many new and exciting results in this challenging area of research.

Unfortunately, the Dark Ages and the new renaissance have erased the memory about many good works that were done in the early days of ANN. Some old ideas have been rediscovered and given new names. Because of this situation it is appropriate to make the following historical references concerning the basic neurocomputing ideas mentioned in this paper.

1. The concept of a neuron as a similarity (match) detector appears in different forms in Rosenblatt [15], Widrow [20], Stark [18], and some other works of this period.

2. The concept of a programmable synaptic matrix ("Die Lernmatrix") has been promoted by Steinbuch [16].

3. The concept of the neuron layer with lateral (reciprocal) inhibition as the mechanism of the winner-take-all choice can be found in Reichardt and McGinitie [14]. The dynamics of the layer described by expressions (5) - (7) was studied in [2].

4. The basic PLA-like neural architecture shown in Figure 3 (two programmable synaptic matrices combined with the winner-take-all layer) can be found in [17], [2], [3].

I leave it to the reader to decide as to what extent such modern terms as "instar," "outstar," "top-down LTM traces," "bottom-up LTM traces," "adaptive resonance," "counterpropagation," and so on, contribute to the substance and clarity of the old ideas mentioned above.

AKNOWLEDGEMENT

I express my gratitude to Dr. L. Stark for inspiring discussions.

REFERENCES

[1] Anderson, J. A. A model for memory using spatial correlation functions. *Kybernetik 5: 113-119,1968.*

[2] Eliashberg, V. On a class of learning machines. *Proceedings of the Conference on Automation in the Pulp and Paper Industry, April 1967, Leningrad, USSR.: Proc. of VNIIB, #54, 350-398, 1969.*

[3] Eliashberg, V. The concept of E-machine and the problem of context-dependent behavior. *Txu 40-320, US Copyright Office, 1979.*

[4] Freeman, J.A, Skapura, D.M. Neural networks. Algorithms, applications, and programming techniques. *Addison-Wesley Publishing Company, 1991.*

[5] Grossberg, S. Neural networks and natural intelligence. *Cambridge, Ma: MIT Press, 1987.*

[6] Hebb, D.O. The organization of behavior. *New York: Wiley, 1949.*

[7] Hecht-Nielsen, R. Counterpropagation networks. *Proceedings of the IEEE First International Conference on Neural Networks, 1987.*

[8] Kleene, S. Representation of events in nerve nets and finite automata. *Automata Studies, (Annals of Mathematics Studies, no. 34), Prinston, 1956.*

[9] McCulloch, W.S. and Pitts, W. A logical calculus of the ideas immanent in nervous activity. *Bulletin of Matematical Biophysics, 5, 115-133, 1943.*

[10] Minsky, M. Neural nets and the brain-model problem. *Unpublished doctoral dissertation, Princton University, 1954.*

[11] Minsky, M. and Papert, S. Perceptrons. An introduction to computational geometry. *Cambridge, MA: MIT Press, 1969.*

[12] Von Neumann, J. The computer and the brain. *New Haven: Yale University Press, pp. 66-82, 1958.*

[13] Pellerin, D., Holley, M. Practical design using programmable logic. *Englewood Cliffs, New Jersey: Prentice Hall, 1991.*

[14] Reichardt W., McGinitieG. Zur Theorie der Lateralen Inhibition, *Kybernetik, B. 1, Nr. 4, 1962.*

[15] Rosenblatt, F.. The perceptron: a probabilistic model for information storage and organization in the brain. *Psychological Review 65: 386-408, 1958.*

[16] Steinbuch, K Die Lernmatrix. *Kybernetik 1, 36-45, 1961.*

[17] Steinbuch, K and Schmit, E. Adaptive system using learning matrices. *Biocybernetics in Avionics New Jork: Gordon and Breach, pp.751-768, 1967.*

[18] Stark, L. et al. Computer pattern recognition techniques: Electrocardiographic diagnosis. *Communications of the Associations for Computing Machinery, 5: pp.527-532, 1962.*

[19] Widrow, B. and Hoff, M.E. Adaptive switching circuits. *IRE WESCON Convention Record, New Jork: pp.96-104, 1960.*

[20] Widrow, B. Generalization and information storage in networks of Adaline neurons. *In selforganizing systems. Washington DC: Spartan Books, Cambridge, MA: MIT Press, 1962.*

[21] Wiener, N. . Computing machines and the nervous system. *Cybernetics, Cambridge, MA. MIT Press, pp. 116-132, 1948.*

MINIMUM DESCRIPTION LENGTH PRUNING
AND MAXIMUM MUTUAL INFORMATION TRAINING
OF ADAPTIVE PROBABILISTIC NEURAL NETWORKS

Waleed Fakhr and M.I. Elmasry
VLSI Research Group, Elect. & Comp. Eng. Dept.
University of Waterloo, Waterloo, Ontario, Canada, N2L 3G1

Abstract-The major problem in implementing artificial neural networks is their large number of processing units and interconnections. This is partly because their architectures are not optimal in size, where too many parameters are usually used when only few would suffice. In this paper we apply an approximated version of the minimum description length criterion "MDL" to find optimal size adaptive probabilistic neural networks "APNN" by adaptively pruning Gaussian windows from the probabilistic neural network "PNN". We discuss and compare both stochastic maximum likelihood "ML" and stochastic maximum mutual information "MMI" training applied to the APNN, for probability density estimation "PDF" and pattern recognition applications. Results on four benchmark problems show that the APNN performed better than or similar to the PNN, and that its size is optimal, and much smaller than the PNN.

1. INTRODUCTION

The backpropagation "BP" trained multilayer perceptron "MLP" estimates the Bayes decision boundaries between classes by estimating their posterior probabilities in the mean-square sense [1,2]. Although proved very successful in many classification applications, the BP trained MLP has several drawbacks. The Most serious drawback is that the MLP has the tendency to overfit training data when its architecture has more degrees of freedom, i.e., more free parameters, than necessary. Recently, many researchers have proposed various techniques to reduce the overfitting problem of the MLP [3-6]. Most of these techniques are based on the Bayesian inference approach, where smoothing priors for the model parameters are used during training. Even though employing smoothing priors, produces reduced variance estimates of the weights, there is no guarantee that any of the weights will actually go to zero so that it can be removed. In other words, the actual size of the MLP may remain unaltered.

On the other hand, the probabilistic neural network "PNN" [7], estimates the probability density function "PDF" for each class, then uses these estimates to implement the Bayes rule. The PNN, however, suffers from two major drawbacks. Firstly, all the training data must be stored, making the PNN

unattractive for implementation, as well as making it an inefficient representation of the data [8,9]. Secondly, the PNN lacks any form of corrective training, which is very useful in many classification applications.

In this paper we propose an adaptive neural network architecture which we call the adaptive probabilistic neural network "APNN" [10,11]. The initial APNN architecture is the PNN, and we adaptively reduce its size by removing Gaussian windows according to an approximated version of the minimum description length criterion "MDL" [8,9,12]. Doing this size reduction, we seek to find a minimum complexity PDF estimate for each data set, in the stochastic complexity sense [12]. After the pruning process is completed, stochastic maximum likelihood "ML" training is used to estimate the location and width of each Gaussian window for each class PDF separately. After the ML training the APNN can be used for both density estimation and classification. In many situations, however, the sum-of-Gaussian PDF model is not accurate, e.g., when the data clusters are not Gaussian in shape. To overcome this drawback, we propose to use stochastic maximum mutual information "MMI" corrective training to enhance the classification performance of the APNN.

2. MDL PRUNING OF THE APNN

Each class PDF in the APNN is modeled by:

$$F(X|C_j) = \frac{1}{\sum\limits_{i=1}^{N_j} a_i} \sum_{i=1}^{N_j} a_i \, \Phi_i \tag{1}$$

$$\Phi_i = \left(\frac{2\pi}{\alpha_i^2}\right)^{-p/2} \exp -\alpha_i^2 \sum_{n=1}^{p} (x_n - w_{ni})^2 \tag{2}$$

where N_j is the total number of training patterns for class C_j, p is the input pattern dimensionality, α_i is a width parameter for the ith window and a_i are integer parameters that take only $\{0,1\}$ value, where 0 indicate that the corresponding window Φ_i is removed and 1 indicates that it is included. In this paper we employ the Kullback-Leibler leave-one-out criterion [13] to find a suitable width for the windows of each class separately. For each class we assume equal α for all windows. The KL leave-one-out criterion is given by:

$$KL = \frac{1}{N_j} \sum_{i=1}^{N_j} Log\ F(X_i) \qquad (3)$$

where $F(X_i)$ is the probability density function when the window centered at the pattern X_i is not included:

$$F(X_i) = \frac{1}{N_j-1}[\sum_{n=1}^{N_j} \Phi_n]- \Phi_i \qquad (4)$$

A plot is made between the KL and α, and α value corresponding to maximum KL is taken. The KL criterion is used since it is a simple cross-validation criterion, which enhances the generalization capability of the network by making each Gaussian window extends its influence to its neighbors.

To prune the APNN, we apply an approximated version of the minimum description length criterion, as given by Rissanen [8,9]. The approximated MDL criterion for the APNN is given by:

$$- MDL = M = \frac{1}{N_j}[\sum_{i=1}^{N_j} LogF(X_i|C_j) - \frac{k_j}{2}LogN_j] \qquad (5)$$

where the first term between brackets is the log-likelihood, the second is the complexity-penalizing term, and k_j is the number of existing windows. In this paper we use the MDL criterion in (5) for pruning the APNN until a minimum of MDL (i.e. a maximum of M) is reached, and also as a performance criterion which indicates how good the PDF model is. The minimum description length criterion is employed since it can discover the closest probability distribution to the true one among many competing models [12]. During pruning the only adaptive variables are the a_i integer variables, which take only $\{0,1\}$ values, and at each step one window is removed, with the corresponding a_i is put to zero. The pruning steps are summarized in the following:

(1) Start with the KL-trained PNN, with all a_i equal one.

(2) Search for a_i which when put to zero results in the highest increase in M. Put this a_i to zero, i.e., remove the corresponding window.

(3) Re-adjust α value by using the KL criterion.

(4) Repeat steps 2 and 3 as long as M keeps increasing (or constant) at each step.

(5) After we reach the final architecture, we perform maximum likelihood "ML" training to enhance the PDF estimates. At this stage we allow all window parameters to adapt.

In applying the MDL, the window centers and widths are considered as fixed parameters for each competing model, hence the complexity of each model is proportional to the number of windows in that model by employing the factor $\frac{k_j}{2} LogN_j$. The MDL is closely related in that sense to the

Akaike criterion which employs a term k_j, however the MDL penalizes the number of parameters asymptotically much more severely [8].

3. STOCHASTIC MAXIMUM LIKELIHOOD TRAINING OF THE APNN

In applying the MDL, we restricted the centers of the windows to be fixed, and their widths to be equal at each pruning step. We also restricted the coefficients a_i to take binary value 0 or 1. These restrictions are tools to simplify the use of the MDL criterion, and to find the minimum number of windows needed in the model. The resultant pruned model's parameters however are not the ML estimates in the parameter space, and ML training can be used to obtain these estimates. Maximizing the Log-likelihood is equivalent to minimizing the Kullback-Leibler probabilistic distance between the modeled probability and the true one. The ML parameters are obtained by maximizing:

$$L = \sum_{C_j} Log\ F(X|C_j) \qquad (6)$$

with respect to the parameters of the model $F(X|C_j)$, where $\sum_{C_j}$ indicates the training data set of class C_j. Stochastic gradient-ascent maximization of L version is proposed, where the adaptation equations are:

$$\Delta a_i = \mu_a \frac{1}{\sum_{n=1}^{K_j} a_n\Phi_n} [\ \Phi_i - \frac{\sum_{n=1}^{K_j} a_n\Phi_n}{\sum_{n=1}^{K_j} a_n}\ ] \qquad (7)$$

$$\Delta \alpha_i = \mu_\alpha \frac{\Phi_i a_i}{\sum_{n=1}^{K_j} \Phi_n a_n} [\ \frac{p}{\alpha_i} - \alpha_i \sum_{m=1}^{p} (x_m - w_{mi})^2\ ] \qquad (8)$$

$$\Delta w_{mi} = \mu_w \frac{\Phi_i a_i}{\sum_{n=1}^{K_j} \Phi_n a_n} \alpha_i^2 [\ x_m - w_{mi}\ ] \qquad (9)$$

Where μ_a, μ_α and μ_w are learning rates which were chosen experimentally such that the likelihood function increases monotonically. It is to be noted that similar stochastic (Robbins-Monro), ML training was used in [14] for simple Gaussian mixtures, where convergence properties were discussed.

Up to this point we have used the APNN to estimate the PDF of the classes, where the quality of these estimates depend on the quality and quantity of the given data and the accuracy of the sum-of-Gaussians model. In many cases, the ML training is not the best training approach when the APNN is to be used as a classifier, for example, when the training data is poor both in quality and quantity, and/or when the PDF models do not closely approximate the true

PDFs. To enhance the classification performance of the APNN, MMI corrective training is proposed.

4. STOCHASTIC MAXIMUM MUTUAL INFORMATION TRAINING OF THE APNN

A tight upper bound on the Bayes error probability P(e) is given in [15]: $P_u(e) = I/2$, where "I" is the Equivocation. The mutual information "MI" is equal to "-I" plus a constant, hence maximizing MI directly minimizes the P(e) upper bound [10,11]. The MI involves integration over the data space, however to be able to use the criterion for training we rely on the large-sample approximation. The large-sample approximation of the MI for a 2-class case is:

$$MI = \frac{1}{N} [\sum_{C1} \frac{p1\, F(X|C_1)}{p1\, F(X|C_1) + p2\, F(X|C_2)} $$

$$ + \sum_{C2} \frac{p2\, F(X|C_2)}{p1\, F(X|C_1) + p2\, F(X|C_2)}] \qquad (10)$$

Where $\sum_{C_j}$ indicates the training data of class C_j, N is the total number of training data, and p1 and p2 represent the class prior probabilities, which can also be adaptive, subject to p1+p2=1, and we assume here that they are equal for simplicity. Similar to ML, we employ a stochastic gradient-ascent approximation to maximize MI with respect to the model parameters. The jth class model parameters are updated after each pattern according to:

$$\Delta a_i = Z_j\, \mu_a\, \frac{1}{\sum_{n=1}^{K_j} a_n} [\Phi_i - \frac{\sum_{n=1}^{K_j} a_n \Phi_n}{\sum_{n=1}^{K_j} a_n}] \qquad (11)$$

$$\Delta \alpha_i = Z_j\, \mu_\alpha\, \frac{\Phi_i a_i}{\sum_{n=1}^{K_j} a_n} [\frac{p}{\alpha_i} - \alpha_i \sum_{m=1}^{p} (x_m - w_{mi})^2] \qquad (12)$$

$$\Delta w_{mi} = Z_j\, \mu_w\, \frac{\Phi_i a_i}{\sum_{n=1}^{K_j} a_n} \alpha_i^2 [x_m - w_{mi}] \qquad (13)$$

Where for a 2-class case, Z_j is equal to:

$$Z_j = + \frac{F(X|C_k)}{F(X|C_j)\,(F(X|C_j) + F(X|C_k))} \qquad (14)$$

if the data pattern is from class C_j and the parameter is from the model $F(X|C_j)$, i.e., the same class, where $F(X|C_j)$ is that class PDF, and $F(X|C_k)$ is the other class PDF, and:

$$Z_j = - \frac{1}{F(X|C_j) + F(X|C_k)} \qquad (15)$$

if the data pattern is from the opposite class.

5. BENCHMARK PROBLEMS RESULTS

We have applied our proposed framework on four benchmark problems: 1.1 and 1.2 are 1-dimensional, and 2.1 and 2.2 are 2-dimensional. The training data used for the 1-dimensional case is 40 pattern/class, and for the 2-dimensional is 50 pattern/class. For testing, 10,000 pattern/class is used so that the verification results are statistically valid. For each problem we show the PDF estimation results by the PNN and the ML-trained APNN, compared to the true PDFs used. We then show the classification results of the PNN, the ML-trained APNN and the MMI-trained APNN compared to the theoretical optimal Bayes classifier performance. We also show the size of the PNN and the APNN compared to the optimal size in terms of the number of Gaussian windows required for the optimal Bayes classifier. We compared the PDF estimates by using the 10,000/class data points for testing, and calculating the average Euclidean distance between the estimated and the true PDFs, which we denote here by DPDF1 and DPDF2 for classes 1 and 2 respectively. In each table, "#error" denotes the number of misclassified patterns out of 20,000 test patterns, "%recog." denotes the % recognition rate, "%opt." denotes the % recognition relative to the optimal (included only if the optimal is not 100%), size1 and size2 are the number of windows in class-1 and class-2 networks respectively, and "NOT" denotes that this result is not included.

5.1. BENCHMARK PROBLEM 1.1

In this problem, each class PDF is composed of 2 uniform clusters of width=4, and centers at 2 & -6 for C1 and -2 & 6 for C2, i.e., the two classes are completely separable. The optimal size is 2 Gaussian windows per class, and a 100% recognition.

TABLE I: RESULTS OF PROBLEM 1.1

	PNN	ML-APNN	MMI-APNN	Optimal
Size1	40	2	2	2
Size2	40	2	2	2
DPDF1	0.0026	0.003	NOT	0.0
DPDF2	0.0028	0.0031	NOT	0.0
#error	565	611	347	0
%recog.	97.175	96.95	98.27	100

5.2. BENCHMARK PROBLEM 1.2

In this problem, each class PDF is composed of 2 Gaussian clusters, with centers at 2 & -6 for C1 and -2 & 6 for C2, and with different widths, where the two classes are highly overlapped with optimal recognition of only 86.8%, and optimal size of 2 Gaussian windows per class.

TABLE II: RESULTS OF PROBLEM 1.2

	PNN	ML-APNN	MMI-APNN	Optimal
Size1	40	2	2	2
Size2	40	2	2	2
DPDF1	0.0002441	0.0000674	NOT	0.0
DPDF2	0.000521	0.000387	NOT	0.0
#error	2723	2698	2700	2640
%recog.	86.39	86.51	86.5	86.8
%opt	99.53	99.67	99.65	100

5.3. BENCHMARK PROBLEM 2.1

This problem is a 2-dimensional generalized XOR, where the data values range between $\{-1,1\}$, class-1 is composed of 2 uniformly distributed clusters centered at (0.5,-0.5) and (-0.5,0.5) and class-2 is also composed of 2 uniform clusters at (0.5,0.5) and (-0.5,-0.5). This problem is completely separable, with an optimal recognition of 100% and optimal size of 2 Gaussian windows per class.

TABLE III: RESULTS OF PROBLEM 2.1

	PNN	ML-APNN	MMI-APNN	Optimal
Size1	50	2	2	2
Size2	50	2	2	2
DPDF1	0.0063	0.0059	NOT	0.0
DPDF2	0.0088	0.0089	NOT	0.0
#error	1331	1113	926	0
%recog.	93.35	94.44	95.37	100

5.4. BENCHMARK PROBLEM 2.2

This problem is a 2-dimensional generalized XOR, where class-1 is composed of 2 Gaussian distributed clusters centered at (0.5,-0.5) and (-0.5,0.5) and class-2 is also composed of 2 Gaussian clusters at (0.5,0.5) and (-0.5,-0.5). In this problem the classes are highly overlapped with an optimal recognition of only 75.5%, and the optimal size is also 2 Gaussian windows per class.

TABLE IV: RESULTS OF PROBLEM 2.2

	PNN	ML-APNN	MMI-APNN	Optimal
Size1	50	2	2	2
Size2	50	2	2	2
DPDF1	0.0036	0.00035	NOT	0.0
DPDF2	0.00322	0.00189	NOT	0.0
#error	5159	5070	5072	4900
%recog.	74.2	74.65	74.64	75.5
%opt.	98.28	98.87	98.86	100

6. CONCLUSIONS

(1) In all problems considered the optimal size is reached with the MDL pruning, starting from the PNN. The resulted APNN are much smaller in size than the PNN, which means a tremendous saving in implementation costs, and computational time.

(2) The APNN also has a much smaller stochastic complexity than the PNN, in other words, it is a more efficient representation of the data, or a more compact form of coding the data.

(3) Since the MDL criterion is based on asymptotic approximation of the stochastic complexity [8], it performs better for large data sets. We expect that it might fail to find the optimal number of clusters for more complex problems, with small data sets. In such cases, other approximations for the stochastic complexity should be used [16].

(4) On the other hand, if the data set is large, the MDL works well, and the optimal model for the given data is most likely found with the minimum number of windows, unlike the PNN, which increases in size with larger data sets.

(5) In classification, ML training was superior to MMI when the sum-of-Gaussians model matched the true class distributions, i.e., in problems 1.2 and 2.2, while the MMI training was superior in the other two cases when the true distributions were uniform not Gaussian.

(6) In PDF estimation, the ML-APNN is much better than the PNN when the true distributions are Gaussian sums, and they are almost equivalent in the other cases.

REFERENCES

[1] Robert Schalkoff; "Pattern Recognition, Statistical, Structural, and Neural Approaches", John Wiley & Sons, Inc., 1992.

[2] John Makhoul; "Pattern Recognition Properties of Neural Networks", IEEE-SP Workshop on Neural Networks for Signal Processing, Princeton, NJ, 1991, pp.173-187.

[3] Steven J. Nowlan, Geoffrey E. Hinton; "Adaptive Soft Weight Tying using Gaussian Mixtures", In J.E. Moody, S.J. Hanson and R.P. Lippmann (Eds.), Advances in Neural Information Processing Systems 4, Morgan Kaufmann, San Mateo CA 1992.

[4] Wray L. Buntine, Andreas S. Weigend; "Bayesian Back-Propagation", Complex Systems 5, 1991, pp.603-643.

[5] Mackay, D.J.C.; "A Practical Bayesian Framework for Backprop Networks", submitted to Neural Computation, 1991.

[6] John E. Moody; "Note on Generalization, Regularization, and Architecture Selection in Nonlinear Learning Systems", IEEE-SP Workshop on Neural Networks for Signal Processing, pp.1-10, 1991

[7] Donald F. Specht; "Probabilistic Neural Networks", Neural Networks, Vol.3, pp.109-118, 1990.

[8] Jorma Rissanen; "Stochastic Complexity in Statistical Inquiry", Series in Computer Science-Vol.15, World Scientific.

[9] Jorma Rissanen; "Density Estimation by Stochastic Complexity", IEEE Trans. on Information Theory, Vol.38, No.2, pp.315-323, March 1992.

[10] Waleed Fakhr and M.I. Elmasry; "Mutual Information Training and Size Minimization of Adaptive Probabilistic Neural Networks", ISCAS'92, San Diego CA, May 1992.

[11] Waleed Fakhr, M. Kamel and M.I. Elmasry; "Probability of Error, Maximum Mutual Information, and Size Minimization of Neural Networks", IJCNN, Baltimore MD, June 1992.

[12] Andrew R. Barron and Thomas M. Cover; "Minimum Complexity Density Estimation", IEEE Trans. on Information Theory, Vol.37, No.4, pp.1034-1054, July 1991.

[13] Keinosuke Fukunaga; "Introduction to Statistical Pattern Recognition", 2nd Ed., Academic Press, Inc. 1990.

[14] Tzay Y. Young and T. Calvert; "Classification, Estimation and Pattern Recognition", American Elsevier, 1974.

[15] Martin E. Hellman and Josef Raviv; "Probability of Error, Equivocation, and the Chernoff Bound", IEEE Trans. on Information Theory, Vol.16, No.4, pp.368-372, July 1970.

[16] Waleed Fakhr, M. Kamel and M.I. Elmasry; "Unsupervised Learning by Stochastic Complexity", Unpublished.

Receptive Field Estimation for Gaussian-Based Neural Networks

Mohamad T. Musavi

Electrical & Computer Engineering Department
5708 Barrows
University of Maine
Orono, Maine 04469 USA

Abstract - This paper offers a receptive field estimation technique to improve performance of Gaussian-based neural networks. In the standard approach a Gaussian function with the same receptive field (covariance matrix) is normally applied to every presentation of the data. This cannot guarantee the best performance of the network because it lacks the required degrees of freedom to preserve the local properties. In the proposed technique every local Gaussian has a different covariance matrix. These matrices are found by the Gram-Schmidt orthogonalization process as opposed to trial and error. The radial basis function (RBF) and the probabilistic neural networks (PNN) have been used to show the effectiveness of this approach.

I. INTRODUCTION

The kernel-based neural networks such as the radial basis function (RBF) [1, 2, 3, 4, 5] and the probabilistic neural networks (PNN) [6, 7, 8] have proven to be more time efficient than the conventional back-propagation (BP) type networks. The architecture for these kinds of networks is simple and consists of one hidden layer with kernel nodes and one output layer. Training is done by finding the parameters of the kernel functions, namely centers and receptive fields, and a set of coefficients that relates the kernel functions. The idea of training a feed-forward network on a layer by layer basis, without having the input signals go through complex and time consuming multi-hidden layer expansions, is indeed very appealing. This results in giving the network great speed especially in real time applications [9, 10, 11].

A problem in kernel-based networks that has not been given enough attention is the estimation of receptive fields of the local functions. The Gaussian function is a widely accepted choice of kernel by researchers. This is a legitimate choice because in reality there is very little to choose between the various kernels. It has been shown that the optimal solution for a kernel estimator, on the basis of a mean square error minimization, is the Epanechnikov kernel [12]. It has been also shown that the efficiency ratio between the Epanechnikov kernel and other kernels such as the Gaussian, Biweight, Triangular and Rectangular lies between 0.9295 and 1. Therefore, it is perfectly legitimate, and indeed desirable, to base the choice of kernel on other considerations, for example the degree of differentiability required or the computational effort involved. Assuming there is a general agreement on the choice of Gaussian kernel the question is then posed as: *"Which receptive fields or covariance matrices should be selected to achieve an optimal performance for a given problem and how do we find them?"*

To simplify the answer researchers use the same covariance matrix in the calculation of Gaussians at different regions of the input space. There are three shortcomings in their approach. First, there is only one covariance matrix as opposed to many covariance matrices. One single covariance matrix will not guarantee the optimal performance of the network even if the best covariance matrix is selected. Second, the covariance matrix Σ is normally selected proportional to the identity matrix, i.e. $\Sigma = \sigma^2 I$, hence the constant potential surface (CPS) is hypersphere and not ellipsoid. And finally, there is no identifiable approach for finding the receptive field and σ is normally selected by trial and error. The above observations have been also observed by Montana [13] in dealing with PNN. He suggested a modification of the PNN called the weighted probabilistic neural network (WPNN). In his approach he still applies only one covariance matrix for all data points but he assumes that this matrix is diagonal and that the eigenvalues are not equal. His technique falls short on providing a reliable approach for finding these eigenvalues.

In view of the former deductions we are proposing a methodology that will improve the generalization ability of Gaussian-based neural networks. The technique estimates an appropriate set of covariance matrices so that the best performance of the network can be achieved for the given training points. In this, many covariance matrices with ellipsoid CPS are utilized. The elements of the covariance matrices are found by the Gram-Schmidt orthogonalization process instead of trial and error. The proposed approach has been tested on RBF and PNN networks and improved performance has been achieved.

II. RECEPTIVE FIELD ESTIMATION

The underlying theory in all kernel-based classifiers is to estimate the desired output or the density of the input space from the given observations by linear combination of a set of local functions. In an RBF classifier this is given by:

$$y(\underline{x}) = \sum_{i=1}^{T} w_i \, \Phi_i \, (\|\underline{x}-\underline{c}_i\|) \qquad (1)$$

where $y(\underline{x})$ is the output, $\underline{c}_i$ is the i-th training pattern or the center of the i-th cluster, $\Phi_i(\|\underline{x}-\underline{c}_i\|)$ is the kernel function at the i-th node, w_i is the weight connecting the i-th kernel to the output node, and T is the total number of training patterns or clusters. The training consists of finding weights and an appropriate set of kernel functions and their parameters.

In a PNN classifier the treatment is similar except for the classification decision. For example in a two class (A and B) problem the densities of classes are found by:

$$f_A(\underline{x}) = \frac{1}{T} \sum_{i=1}^{T} \Phi_i \, (\|\underline{x}-\underline{c}_{ai}\|) \qquad (2a)$$

$$f_B(\underline{x}) = \frac{1}{T} \sum_{i=1}^{T} \Phi_i \, (\|\underline{x}-\underline{c}_{bi}\|) \qquad (2b)$$

where $\underline{c}_{ai}$ and $\underline{c}_{bi}$ are the training data points from class A and B respectively. The training in PNN is therefore that of again finding a set of appropriate kernel functions and their parameters. The classification decision is based on the Bayes rule. Assuming that $w_i = \frac{1}{T}$ for all i's, (1) and (2) would be identical.

It is noted that the major part of training an RBF, PNN and, in fact, any other kernel-based classifier is the selection of the kernel functions Φ_i. To simplify the matters researchers normally make the following three assumptions:

i) All kernels are the same,

$$\Phi_i \, (\|\underline{x}-\underline{c}_i\|) = \Phi \, (\|\underline{x}-\underline{c}_i\|). \quad \text{for} \quad i=1, 2, ..., T \qquad (3a)$$

ii) The kernel is Gaussian,

$$\Phi(\|\underline{x}-\underline{c}_i\|) = (2\pi)^{-\frac{M}{2}} |\Sigma|^{-\frac{1}{2}} \exp[-\frac{1}{2}(\underline{x} - \underline{c}_i)^T [\Sigma]^{-1} (\underline{x} - \underline{c}_i)]. \qquad (3b)$$

M is dimension of the input space and Σ is the covariance matrix.

iii) And that the covariance matrix is diagonal and has equal eigenvalues ($\Sigma=\sigma^2 I$),

$$\Phi \, (\|\underline{x}-\underline{c}_i\|) = (2\pi)^{-M/2} \sigma^{-M} \exp \left[- \frac{\|\underline{x} - \underline{c}_i\|^2}{\sigma^2} \right] \qquad (3c)$$

Using the above assumptions the problem of finding kernel functions is simply reduced to selecting the parameter σ that is referred to as the width in RBF literature and smoothing parameter in PNN. This parameter is normally found by trial and error. Note that since all eigenvalues are equal the constant potential surface (CPS) of Gaussian is hypersphere. It is evident that kernel functions should preserve the local properties of the input space and that the above assumptions will not satisfy this condition. Therefore, the network will not be able to achieve its optimal performance.

Now let us start with the general case and disregard all the above-mentioned assumptions. In that, the kernels are still Gaussian but for every training point the Gaussian is different. The Gaussian placed at $\underline{c}^i$ is:

$$\Phi_i(\|\underline{x}-\underline{c}_i\|)=(2\pi)^{-\frac{M}{2}} |\Sigma_i|^{-\frac{1}{2}} \exp[-\frac{1}{2}(\underline{x} - \underline{c}_i)^T [\Sigma_i]^{-1} (\underline{x} - \underline{c}_i)] \qquad (4)$$

Our goal is to estimate the covariance matrix in such a way as to minimize the overlapping of nearest neighbors of different classes to preserve local properties, as well as to maximize the generalization ability of the network. In general, the contour or the constant potential surface (CPS) of the Gaussian function is an ellipsoid in a multi-dimensional space. The actual CPS is controlled by Σ_i.

Therefore, the generalization of the classifier is determined by Σ_i. In order to obtain good generalization, the eigenvalues of the covariance matrix of each Gaussian should be as large as possible. While there is no problem if two functions belonging to the same class overlap each other, functions of different classes have to be separated to avoid any significant overlapping. So, the function is constrained by the locations of the nearest training patterns of the other class.

Let us decompose each covariance matrix as,

$$\Sigma = Q \Lambda Q^T \qquad (5)$$

where eigenvalues and eigenvectors are respectively the diagonal entries of Λ and the columns of Q. Since Σ is symmetric, all eigenvalues and their corresponding eigenvectors are real. The eigenvectors are the principal axes of the ellipsoid of the CPS and the square roots of eigenvalues define the lengths of the ellipsoid along these principal axes. To find the eigenvalues and eigenvectors the Gram-Schmidt orthogonalization procedure [14] is utilized. In a multi-dimensional space the equation for the j-th eigenvector $\underline{q}_j$ is [15]:

$$\underline{b}_j = (\underline{a}_j - \underline{c}_i) - \sum_{k=1}^{j-1} \underline{q}_k^T \, (\underline{a}_j - \underline{c}_i) \, \underline{q}_k \qquad (6a)$$

$$\underline{q}_j = \frac{\underline{b}_j}{\|\underline{b}_j\|} \qquad (6b)$$

in which $\underline{c}_i$ is the i-th training pattern, $\underline{a}_j$ is a pattern of opposite class which satisfies the projection criteria, given in (7), for all previously found (j-1) eigenvectors.

$$| \underline{q}_k^T (\underline{a}_j - \underline{c}_i) | < \| \underline{b}_k \| \qquad \text{for } k=1, 2, ..., j\text{-}1 \qquad (7)$$

Also the j-th eigenvalue can be found from :

$$\lambda_j = \frac{\| \underline{b}_j \|^2}{4r^2} . \qquad (8)$$

in which r is a probability measure specifying the overlapping of the local functions. Once eigenvalues and eigenvectors are known Σ_i and then $\Phi_i(\| \underline{x} - \underline{c}_i \|)$ can be found by (5) and (4) respectively.

III. TEST RESULTS

To show the effect of the receptive field estimation technique on the performance of kernel-based networks we have selected RBF and PNN networks and conducted different tests. In each category the proposed approach of finding covariance matrices has been used and the network performance has been compared with that of the standard approach. A two-dimensional (2-d) and an eight-dimensional (8-d) classification problems have been used to facilitate the graphical displays and also indicate the applicability in high dimensions. These problems have been generated by Gaussian random vectors. Without loss of generality it has been assumed that there are only two classes in each problem. In the 2-d problem the first class has zero mean random vectors with identity covariance matrix and the second class has mean vector [1 2] and diagonal covariance matrix with 0.01 and 4.0 entries. The distribution of training samples for the 2-d problem is shown in Fig. 1. The patterns of the first class have been indicated by "x" and the second class by dots ".". The patterns of the 8-d problem are Gaussian random vectors with equal mean vectors and identity (I) and four-identity (4I) covariance matrices.

Note that for any Gaussian distribution the optimal classifier is known to be a quadratic classifier given by:

$$\frac{1}{2} (\underline{x} - \underline{m}_1)^T [\Sigma_1]^{-1} (\underline{x} - \underline{m}_1) - \frac{1}{2} (\underline{x} - \underline{m}_2)^T [\Sigma_2]^{-1} (\underline{x} - \underline{m}_2)$$
$$+ \frac{1}{2} \ln \frac{|\Sigma_1|}{|\Sigma_2|} \underset{\text{class2}}{\overset{\text{class1}}{\lessgtr}} 0 \qquad (9)$$

where $\underline{m}_i$ is the mean vector of class i and Σ_i is the covariance matrix of class i. Applying (9) the optimal error rates for 10,000 samples of the 2-d and 8-d problems were found to be 6% and 9% respectively. These optimal values have been marked in our test figures for comparison.

To conduct our tests we selected 100, 150, 200, 250 and 300 training patterns along with 10,000 test patterns of each problem. The standard practice is to select σ by trial and error, therefore, we allowed σ to vary within a given range. For any given number of training patterns we then trained the standard RBF and PNN networks for different σs and tested the networks with the given 10,000 test patterns. The best error rates for each case was recorded. We then used our proposed technique to estimate the receptive fields for RBF and PNN networks. After testing the networks the error rates were again recorded for each case. These results were compared with the best error rates of the standard approach as shown in Fig. 2a-b and 3a-b for RBF and PNN networks respectively. Note that in all cases the proposed approach exhibits better error rates.

IV. CONCLUSION

A technique has been presented for receptive field estimation of Gaussian functions in kernel estimators. The technique has shown improvement on the performance of RBF and PNN networks.

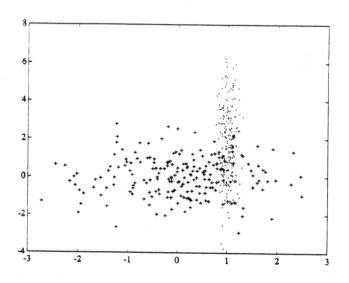

Fig. 1. The training points for the 2-d problem.

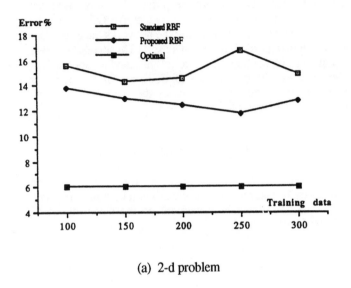

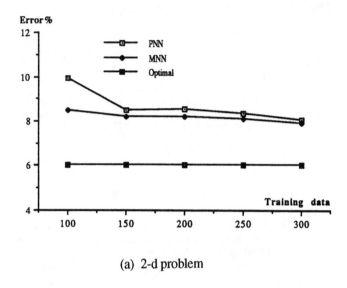

(a) 2-d problem

(a) 2-d problem

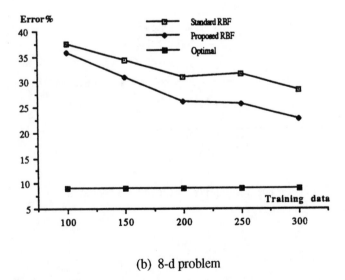

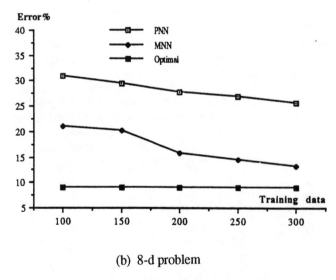

(b) 8-d problem

(b) 8-d problem

Fig. 2. The best performance of the standard RBF network compared with the performance of the proposed technique.

Fig. 3. The best error rates of the standard PNN compared with that of the proposed technique.

REFERENCES

[1] M.J.D. Powell, "Radial basis functions for multivariable interpolation: A review," in Algorithms for Approximation of Functions and Data, edited by J.C. Mason and M.G. Cox, pp. 143-167, 1987.

[2] C.A. Micchelli, "Interpolation of scattered data: distance matrices and conditionally positive definite functions," *Constructive Approximation*, 2, pp. 11-22, 1986.

[3] D.S. Broomhead and D. Lowe, "Multivariable functional interpolation and adaptive networks," *Complex Systems*, 2, pp. 321-355, 1988.

[4] J. Moody and C.J. Darken, "Fast learning in networks of locally tuned processing units," *Neural Computation*, 1, pp. 281-294, 1989.

[5] R.D. Jones, Y.C. Lee, W. Barnes, G.W. Flake, K. Lee, P.S. Lewis, and S. Qian, "Function approximation and time series prediction with neural networks," Proceedings of International Joint Conference on Neural Networks, I, pp. 649-665, 1990.

[6] D.F. Specht, "Probabilistic neural networks," *Neural Networks*, vol. 3, pp. 109-118, 1990(a).

[7] D.F. Specht, "Probabilistic neural networks and the polynomial adaline as complementary techniques for classification," *IEEE Transactions on Neural Networks*, vol. 1, no. 1, pp. 111-121, 1990(b).

[8] P.S. Maloney and D.F. Specht, "The use of probabilistic neural networks to improve solution times for hull-to-emitter correlation problems," San Diego: Int. Joint conf. on NN (IJCNN), I, pp. 289-294, 1989.

[9] S.S. Watkins and P.M. Chau, "A radial basis function neurocomputer with an analog input layer," Electrical and Computer Engineering, University of California at San Diego, La Jolla, CA 92093, and JPL, California Institute of Technology, Pasadena, CA 91109, 1992.

[10] S. Wolpert, M.J. Osborn, and M.T. Musavi, "A VLSI-based Gaussian kernel mapper for real-time RBF neural networks." IEEE 18th annual N.E. BioEngineering Conference, Kingston, RI, April 1992.

[11] T.P. Washburne, M.M. Okamura, D.F. Specht, and W.A. Fisher, "The Lockheed probabilistic neural network processor," Seattle: International Joint conference on Neural Networks, I, pp. 513-518, 1991.

[12] V.A. Epanechnik, "Nonparametric Estimation of a Multidimensional Probability Density," *Theory of Probability Application*, 14, pp. 153-158, 1969.

[13] D. Montana, "A weighted probabilistic neural network," Advances in Neural Information Processing Systems 4, edited by J.E. Moody, J. Hanson, and R.P. Lippman, pp. 1110-1117, Denver, Colorado, 1991.

[14] G. Strang, *Linear Algebra and its Applications*, New York: Academic Press, 1976.

[15] M.T. Musavi, W. Ahmed, K.H. Chan, K.B. Faris, and D.M. Hummels, "On the training of radial basis function classifiers," *Neural Networks*, Vol.5, pp. 595-603, 1992.

Invariance Constraints for Improving Generalization in Probabilistic Neural Networks

Hans G.C. Tråvén*

Studies of Artificial Neural Systems (SANS) research group

Department of Numerical Analysis and Computing Science (NADA)

Royal Institute of Technology (KTH)

S-100 44 Stockholm, Sweden

Abstract— **Neural networks can approximate any multivariate continuous mapping. In particular probabilistic neural networks can approximate class conditional densities in optimal (Bayesian) pattern classifiers. In natural pattern recognition applications, the size of the training set is always limited. This makes the approximation task difficult, especially so for a high-dimensional feature space. Invariance constraints can significantly simplify the task of density approximation. This paper presents a technique for learning invariant representations, based on a statistical approach to group invariance. Formally, we develop an iterative method for computing the maximum likelihood estimate to the parameters of an invariant mixture model. The method can be interpreted as a competitive training strategy for a radial basis function (RBF) network. It can be used for self-organizing formation of both invariant templates and features.**

I. Introduction

Feed-forward artificial neural networks with one hidden layer can approximate any multivariate continuous mapping to within any degree of accuracy [1, 2, 3]. Similar results are known for radial basis function (RBF) networks [4, 5, 6] as well as probabilistic neural networks (PNN) [7, 8]. In connection with *Bayes decision theory* these results warrants, at least theoretically, the use of such networks for approximating *class conditional densities* in optimal (Bayesian) pattern classifiers.

The problems encountered when applying artificial neural networks to natural pattern recognition tasks are however far from solved. In practice rarely enough training data can be obtained to determine the mapping (or class conditional densities) with an acceptable accuracy by such a direct approach. As in classical approximation the mapping is often only known for a finite number of irregularly spaced points and it is the task of the network to *interpolate* (or even *extrapolate*) it elsewhere. This is commonly referred to as that the network should have the ability of generalizing [9]. What constitutes good generalization is, however, largely determined by the application at hand. One interesting and useful method to improve generalization is to exploit a set of rules that encode some prior information about the expected approximation. Use of such *prior constraints* can significantly simplify the process of estimating probability density functions (pdfs). It should be mentioned that there is a potential danger in using prior constraints, since they restrict the set of possible solutions. If the assumptions are not valid the correct solution may never be found. However, there are several quite general constraints that can be used with advantage, such as smoothness, independence, in particular Markov properties and invariance.

In many natural pattern recognition applications, generalization implies that classifications should be *invariant* to the action of a transformation group. Invariant pattern recognition was also the basis for the criticism of the early *perceptron*. A perceptron can recognize any isolated (binary) figure in a fixed position [10]. However, a perceptron can only compute extremely trivial *predicates* when it is required that the predicate should be invariant to geometrical transformations like translation, rotation or dilation.

Recent neural network approaches to invariant pattern recognition have commonly either been of the type, *high order networks* [11, 12], the *Neocognitron* type [13], or *time delay neural networks* [14] or similar. This paper presents a statistical approach to group invariance. Section II contains a short review of some useful group theoretical concepts. In section III the invariant estimation problem is formulated and solved using an iterative *maximum likelihood* (ML) approach. Section IV contains re-

*The author is supported by a graduate position at the Royal Institute of Technology.

sults from a small character recognition application.

II. Group invariance and invariant distributions

A pdf $p(\mathbf{x})$ on a d-dimensional sample space $\mathbf{X}$ is called G-invariant if $p(\mathbf{x}) = p(g\mathbf{x})$ for each element g of a group G. One immediately recognize that $p(\mathbf{x})$ will contain regularities due to the invariance properties and that these regularities can be used to simplify the process of pdf estimation. In particular $p(\mathbf{x})$ will be constant within the *orbits* of $\mathbf{X}$ and samples from anywhere in the same orbit can be *pooled* to estimate this probability.

As an example consider the space of binary numbers. A pdf on this space has 2^d discrete entries (or $2^d - 1$ degrees of freedom). However, assume that the density is G-invariant when G is the discrete group of permutation matrices (this is for instance the case for the *parity function*). Then at most d of the entries will be unique, a significant reduction of complexity.

A standard procedure for constructing invariant densities is by averaging a noninvariant density (see e.g. [15]) $gp(\mathbf{x}) = p(g^{-1}\mathbf{x})$ over g with respect to the measure, on G.

$$p_1(\mathbf{x}) = \int_G gp(\mathbf{x})\nu(dg), \quad \int_G \nu(dg) = 1 \quad (1)$$

Here $\nu(dg)$ is the invariant probability measure on G which of cause is a multiple of the unique Haar measure. If $p(\mathbf{x})$ already is invariant this averaging has no effect, $p_1(\mathbf{x}) = p(\mathbf{x})$. In the context of artificial neural networks the use of invariant distributions were suggested already by Pitts and McCulloch [16].

The groups we are interested in are all finite discrete groups, for which $\nu(dg)$ has a uniform distribution, i.e. $\nu(dg) = dg$. If $\nu(dg)$ is uniform on G the pdf estimation task simplifies to estimating the pdf of a *cross section* $\mathbf{y}$ of $\mathbf{x}$. To be of interest this problem should be significantly simpler than the original problem. In practice, to estimate $p(\mathbf{y})$ from observations of $p(\mathbf{x})$ involves finding a random group element g_0 (for each sample), for which $\mathbf{y} = g_0^{-1}\mathbf{x}$, which can be quite difficult. However, the procedure is similar to a type of normalizing preprocessing frequently used in pattern recognition applications and can be quite useful [17, 18]. We will, however, pursue a different line of approach.

III. Maximum likelihood learning rule for invariant Gaussian Mixtures

A (noninvariant) multivariate normal (*or Gaussian*) pdf is completely determined by its mean, $\mu = E[\mathbf{x}]$ and covariance matrix $\Sigma = E[(\mathbf{x} - \mu)(\mathbf{x} - \mu)^T]$.

$$p(\mathbf{x}) = N(\mathbf{x}, \mu, \Sigma) =$$

$$\frac{1}{(2\pi)^{d/2}|\Sigma|^{1/2}}exp[-\frac{1}{2}(\mathbf{x} - \mu)^T \Sigma^{-1}(\mathbf{x} - \mu)] \quad (2)$$

It is well known [19] that the maximum likelihood estimate for these parameters (here donated with a hat) are $\hat{\mu} = \frac{1}{N}\sum_{k=1}^N \mathbf{x}_k$ and $\hat{\Sigma} = \frac{1}{N}\sum_{k=1}^N (\mathbf{x}_k - \hat{\mu})(\mathbf{x}_k - \hat{\mu})^T$, where N is the number of samples. We will now indicate how the maximum likelihood estimate for the same parameters can be derived when the examples are drawn from the invariant distribution $p_1(\mathbf{x})$, as defined by (1).

The log-likelihood of the samples can be written as

$$\log L = \sum_{k=1}^N \log p_1(\mathbf{x}_k, \mu, \Sigma). \quad (3)$$

With the intention of finding the supremum of this function, differentiate (3) with respect to μ and set the result equal to zero. After some amount of algebraic manipulation we get the following estimate for μ

$$\hat{\mu} = \frac{1}{N}\sum_{k=1}^N \frac{\int_G gp(\mathbf{x}_k)\mathbf{x}_k\nu(dg)}{p_1(\mathbf{x}_k)} =$$

$$\frac{1}{N}\sum_{k=1}^N \frac{\int_G gp(\mathbf{x}_k)\mathbf{x}_k\nu(dg)}{\int_G gp(\mathbf{x}_k)\nu(dg)}. \quad (4)$$

By differentiating (3) with respect to each component of Σ^{-1} and using some standard algebra on determinants we get a similar expression for $\hat{\Sigma}$.

$$\hat{\Sigma} = \frac{1}{N}\sum_{k=1}^N \frac{\int_G gp(\mathbf{x}_k)(\mathbf{x}_k - \hat{\mu})(\mathbf{x}_k - \hat{\mu})^T\nu(dg)}{\int_G gp(\mathbf{x}_k)\nu(dg)} \quad (5)$$

Unlike in the noninvariant case, the solution is regrettably not on closed form ($p(\mathbf{x})$ depends on μ). However, this was not expected considering the definition of $p_1(\mathbf{x})$ and it is in practice only a slight drawback. The equations (2)(4)(5) easily lends themselves to iterative as well as recursive (stochastic approximation) solutions. Empirical tests have shown the convergence to be quite fast.

So far we have only considered a statistical model with one multivariate Gaussian. We now proceed to a Gaussian mixture model. Mixture models can be viewed as statistical analogs to RBF networks (see e.g. [7, 20, 8]). We will assume that the individual components $\{\omega_1, \omega_2, ..., \omega_n\}$ of the mixture are invariant. This ensures that also the mixture model is invariant. The reverse is not always true. The mixture model is defined by

$$p_1(\mathbf{x}) = \sum_{i=1}^n p_1(\omega_i)p_1(\mathbf{x}|\omega_i), \quad \sum_{i=1}^n p_1(\omega_i) = 1 \quad (6)$$

where, as before

$$p_1(\mathbf{x}|\omega_i) = \int_G gp(\mathbf{x}|\omega_i)\nu(dg). \qquad (7)$$

When $p(\mathbf{x}|\omega_i) = N(\mathbf{x}, \mu_i, \Sigma_i)$ it can be shown that the maximum likelihood estimate for the parameters is

$$p_1(\omega_i) = \frac{1}{N}\sum_{k=1}^{N} p_1(\omega_i|\mathbf{x}_k), \quad p_1(\omega_i|\mathbf{x}) = \frac{p_1(\omega_i)p_1(\mathbf{x}|\omega_i)}{p_1(\mathbf{x})}$$

$$\hat{\mu}_i = \frac{\sum_{k=1}^{N} \frac{p_1(\omega_i)\int_G gp(\mathbf{x}_k|\omega_i)\mathbf{x}_k\nu(dg)}{\sum_{j=1}^{n} p_1(\omega_j)p_1(\mathbf{x}_k|\omega_j)}}{\sum_{k=1}^{N} p_1(\omega_i \mid \mathbf{x}_k)},$$

$$\hat{\Sigma}_i = \frac{\sum_{k=1}^{N} \frac{p_1(\omega_i)\int_G gp(\mathbf{x}_k|\omega_i)(\mathbf{x}_k-\hat{\mu})(\mathbf{x}_k-\hat{\mu})^T\nu(dg)}{\sum_{j=1}^{n} p_1(\omega_j)p_1(\mathbf{x}_k|\omega_j)}}{\sum_{k=1}^{N} p_1(\omega_i \mid \mathbf{x}_k)} \qquad (8)$$

To our knowledge this maximum likelihood estimation procedure for an invariant Gaussian mixture has not been published before. The proof is quite long but follows as a generalization of the proof for a single invariant Gaussian, indicated above, and the proof for a noninvariant Gaussian mixture, given in [8]. The estimator can also be derived as an application of the EM (expectation maximization) algorithm [21, 22], a general method for obtaining maximum likelihood estimates from incomplete data. The incompleteness in our case is twofold. First, we do not know the index of the component that generated a sample. Second, we do not know what transformation to apply to the sample to bring it back to its *normal form*.

These equations have an interesting interpretation when viewed as an unsupervised competitive training procedure for a PNN network (or Gaussian RBF network). The training procedure consists of two separate competitive processes. First there is the usual type of competition between units within the hidden layer to segregate which units are allowed to learn which patterns [23]. Second there is also competition between different transformations of the same pattern. This is easily seen in (4) where the contribution from different transformations of the same pattern is weighted with the probability of the transformed pattern.

From (1) and (3) it is apparent that the likelihood function is degenerate with respect to the action of the elements of G, i.e. there exists several "best" estimates for the parameters. However, in practice this just reflects the arbitrary nature of what to consider the normal form of a pattern. To better visualize the different steps in the training procedure we have written it up as an algorithm (Fig. 1). We have also developed a more "neural-like"

Choose initial values for
  $p_1(\omega_i), \hat{\mu}_i, \hat{\Sigma}_i \; ; \; i = 1..n$
repeat
  for all samples $\mathbf{x}_k$, $k = 1..N$ **do begin**
    for all transformations $g \in G$ **do begin**
      Compute (noninvariant) class-conditionals
        $p(g^{-1}\mathbf{x}_k|\omega_i)$ for all ω_i
  end
    Compute invariant class-conditionals,
      $p_1(\mathbf{x}_k|\omega_i) = \sum_{g \in G} p(g^{-1}\mathbf{x}_k|\omega_i)$
    invariant sample probability,
      $p_1(\mathbf{x}_k) = \sum_{i=1}^{n} p_1(\omega_i)p_1(\mathbf{x}_k|\omega_i)$
    and instantaneous parameter estimates
      $\hat{\mu}_i(\mathbf{x}_k) = \frac{p_1(\omega_i)\sum_{g \in G} g^{-1}\mathbf{x}_k p(g^{-1}\mathbf{x}_k|\omega_i)}{p_1(\mathbf{x}_k)}$
    and similar for $\hat{\Sigma}_i(\mathbf{x}_k)$.
    Compute posteriors by Bayes rule (normalize)
      $p_1(\omega_i|\mathbf{x}_k) = \frac{p_1(\omega_i)p_1(\mathbf{x}_k|\omega_i)}{p_1(\mathbf{x}_k)}$
  end
  Compute new priors by summing posteriors
    $p_1^+(\omega_i) = \frac{1}{N}\sum_{k=1}^{N} p_1(\omega_i|\mathbf{x}_k)$
  and new parameter estimates as
    $\hat{\mu}_i^+ = \frac{\frac{1}{N}\sum_{k=1}^{N} \hat{\mu}_i(\mathbf{x}_k)}{p_1^+(\omega_i)}$
  and similar for $\hat{\Sigma}_i^+$.
until convergence.

Figure 1: EM algorithm for invariant Gaussian mixtures.

stochastic-approximation-version of this algorithm, using an approach similar to the one in [8].

IV. RESULTS

We have tested the invariant ML estimator in a small printed character recognition application. The character patterns were obtained by scanning printed text of laser writer quality, using a resolution of 150 dpi. The character set consisted of 29 different upper case letters (A-Z, Å, Ä, Ö; the last three are national Swedish characters) in a 12 pt. Courier font. The text was machine segmented using a standard method based on local intensity histograms. Characters were centered within a rectangle, 14×21 pixels yielding a feature space with 294 dimensions. The equally large independent training and test sets consisted of 30 examples of each of the 29 characters. Fig. 2A show some examples of the preprocessed character patterns.

Recognizing printed characters from one fixed size font corresponds to recognizing an isolated figure in a fixed position. This is known to be a *linear predicate* [10] i.e. it can be solved by bisecting the feature space with a hyperplane or, in practice, by a one layer perceptron. A one layer RBF network with the same covariance matrix for

A

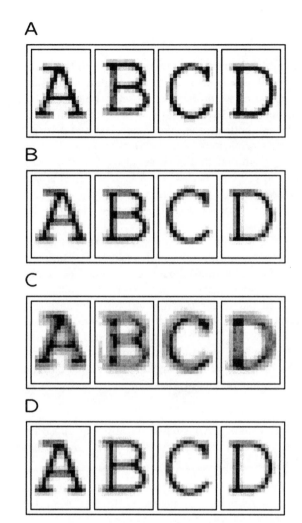

B

C

D

Figure 2: Examples of patterns and mean vectors estimated by noninvariant and invariant ML learning rules. A shows examples of some of the character patterns used for training. B and C shows examples of mean vectors (arranged to conform with the patterns) estimated using the standard noninvariant ML rule, before (B) and after (C) the training patterns had been transformed by random rigid translations. The mean vectors in D were also estimated from translated examples but this time using the invariant ML rule.

all units also has linear discriminant surfaces and should in principle be able to classify the patterns without errors. Fig. 2B shows examples of mean vectors obtained by a stochastic approximation to the standard noninvariant ML rule. The vectors are essentially templates matched to the different characters. A slight broadening of the lines in the characters can be observed and are probably caused by quantization errors introduced by the limited resolution. As predicted it was possible to classify the test set

with 0 % error rate using a Bayesian decision rule after training had been performed using the noninvariant ML estimator.

Zero error rate is only achieved if the characters are accurately located (or segmented) with respect to the paper plane coordinate system. Segmentation errors have the effect of permuting dimensions of the feature space. Although some regularity can be traced to correlations between nearby pixels (that tend to have the same value), there is no simple relation between segmentation errors and the distortions they introduce in feature space. Even small errors in the estimated paper plane position, can result in large "jumps" in feature space. We simulated segmentation errors by introducing random planar translations to the sample patterns. The translations were drawn from a rectangular distribution with a maximal distance of ± 1 pixel. The translations used cyclic boundary conditions, i.e. the space had a toroidal topology. Although the translations were quite small the error rate for a one layer RBF network trained and tested on patterns modified by this type of "invariant noise" was as large as 33 %. The performance quickly deteriorated as the maximal distance increased. Interestingly, the error rate was slightly higher if the network was trained on fixed patterns and tested on the translated patterns Fig. 2C shows examples of mean vectors estimated from translated patterns using the noninvariant ML rule. Visually the effect is similar to applying a "blurring" or diffusion operator to the original character.

The effects of invariant noise can be handled by using the invariant ML rule defined by (2)(4). The mean vectors estimated by this rule are shown in Fig. 2D. By using invariant densities as defined by (1) it was possible to classify also the patterns perturbed by translation noise with 0 % error rate.

The same set of patterns were used also to test the EM algorithm for invariant mixture densities. In this case the task was not classification but to develop invariant features useful as character descriptors. The features had a support of 5×5 pixels, i.e. small compared to the characters. To get interesting results it was necessary to sacrifice the uniform distribution of $\nu(dg)$ in favor of a rectangular distribution of translations also with a 5×5 pixels support. Although the features are thus only semi-invariant they turned out to be both more interesting and useful than the strictly invariant features. This also conforms with the general notion that a feature should have a localized response.

The feature set ($n = 16$) produced by a stochastic approximation to the noninvariant EM algorithm is shown in Fig. 3A. (The noninvariant EM algorithm is equivalent to the invariant rule when G contains only 1 element, see

A

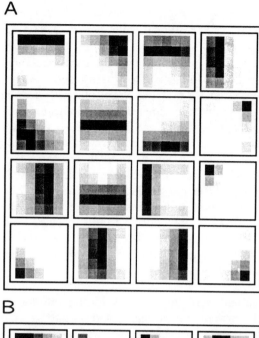

B

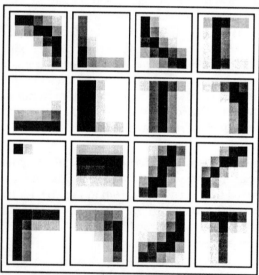

Figure 3: Features extracted by A, the noninvariant and B, the invariant EM algorithm for Gaussian mixtures

also [8].) The features are mainly horizontal and vertical lines at different positions. This is not surprising considering the frequency of horizontal and vertical lines in the training material.

The feature set produced by the invariant EM algorithm (Fig. 3B) showed a greater variety of descriptor types. In particular a number of useful geometric features not present in the previous set, like arcs, corners and T-junctions now appeared. The reason for the larger number of descriptor types is of course that most of the horizontal and vertical lines are now recognized as translations of the

same feature.

V. DISCUSSION

Several approximations can be made in (8) if the accuracy of the result is not critical. In particular, a decision directed approach would be to allow only the best matching transformation of each pattern to participate in learning. Heuristic methods that employ sequential matching of different transformations, e.g. by testing with a template, are not uncommon in the literature. The main advantage of the present method over such schemes is that it gives a well founded prescription for how the contribution from different transformations are to be weighted during learning.

The estimation procedure presented here is by no means intended to include all aspects of invariances. Rather its is aimed at handling small deviations such as segmentation errors that frequently occur in pattern recognition applications. In particular the method involves a testing of different transformations. If this task is to be manageable the order of G may not be too large. Still, its firm theoretical basis as a maximum likelihood estimate together with the property of being intuitively reasonable, makes it attractive for further studies.

REFERENCES

[1] G. Cybenko. Approximation by superposition of a sigmoidal function. *Math. Control Syst. Signals*, 2:303–314, 1989.

[2] K. Funahasi. On the approximate realization of continuous mappings by neural networks. *Neural Networks*, 2:183–192, 1989.

[3] K. Hornik, M. Steinchcombe, and H. White. Multi-layer feedforward networks are universal approximators. *Neural Networks*, 2(5):359–373, 1989.

[4] T. Poggio and F. Girosi. Networks for approximation and learning. *Proc. of the IEEE*, 78:9, 1990.

[5] E.J. Hartman and J.M. Kowalski. Layered networks with gaussian hidden units as universal approximations. *Neural Computation*, 2:210–215, 1990.

[6] D.S. Bloomhead and D. Lowe. Multi-variable function interpolation and adaptive networks. *Complex Systems*, 2:269–303, 1988.

[7] D.F. Specht. Probabilistic neural networks. *Neural Networks*, 3:109–118, 1990.

[8] H.G.C. Tråvén. A neural network approach to statistical pattern classification by semiparametric estimation of probability density functions. *IEEE Trans. Neural Networks*, 2(3):366–377, 1991.

[9] J. Denker, D. Schwartz, B. Wittner, S. Solla, R. Howard, L. Jackel, and J. Hopfield. Large automatic learning, rule extraction, and generalization. *Complex Systems*, 1:877–922, 1987.

[10] M. Minsky and S. Papert. *Perceptrons: An Introduction to Computational Geometry*. Morgan Kaufmann Publishers, Cambridge, MA, 1969.

[11] C.L. Giles and T. Maxwell. Learning, invariance, and generalization in high-order neural networks. *Applied Optics*, 26(23):4972–4978, 1987.

[12] S.J. Perantonis and P.J.G. Lisboa. Translation, rotation, and scale invariant pattern recognition by high-order neural networks and moment classifiers. *IEEE Trans. Neural Networks*, 3(2):241–251, 1992.

[13] K. Fukushima and N. Wake. Handwritten alphanumeric character recognition. *IEEE Trans. Neural Networks*, 2(3):355–365, 1991.

[14] K.J. Lang, A.H. Waibel, and G.E. Hinton. A time-delay neural network architecture for isolated word recognition. *Neural Networks*, 3:23–43, 1990.

[15] M.L. Eaton. *Group Invariance Applications in Statistics*. Institute of mathematical Statistics, Hayward, California, 1989.

[16] W. Pitts and A. McCulloch, W.S. How we know universals: the perception of auditory and visual forms. *Bulletin of Mathematical Biophysics*, 9:127–147, 1947.

[17] S. Kahan, T. Pavlidis, and H.S. Baird. On the recognition of printed characters of any font and size. *IEEE Trans. Pattern Analysis and Machine Intelligence*, PAMI-9(2):274–288, 1987.

[18] H. Sakoe and S. Chiba. Dynamic programming algorithm optimisation for spoken word recognition. *IEEE Trans. Acoustics, Speech and Signal Processing*, 26:43–49, 1978.

[19] T.W. Anderson. *An Introduction to Multivariate Statistical Analysis, Second Edition*. Weiley, 1984.

[20] S.J. Nowlan. Maximum likelihood competitive learning. In D.S. Touretzky, editor, *Advances in Neural Information Processing Systems II*, pages 574–582. Morgan Kaufmann Publishers, 1990.

[21] A.P. Dempster, N.M. Laird, and D.B. Rubin. Maximum-likelihood from incomplete data via the em algorithm. *J. Royal Statist. Soc. Ser. B (methodological)*, 39:1–38, 1977.

[22] R.A. Redner and H.F. Walker. Mixture densities, maximum likelihood and the em algorithm. *SIAM Review*, 26(2):195–239, 1984.

[23] D.E. Rumelhart and D. Zipser. Feature discovery by competitive learning. In D.E. Rumelhart and J.L. McClelland, editors, *Parallel Distributed Processing*. MIT Press, 1986.

BAYESNET: Bayesian Classification Network Based on Biased Random Competition Using Gaussian Kernels

Sukhan Lee [1,2,3]   Shunichi Shimoji [1]

Dept. of Computer Science[1] and EE-systems[2]
University of Southern California
Los Angeles, CA 90089-0781

Jet Propulsion Laboratory[3]
California Institute of Technology
Pasadena, CA 91009

Abstract — This paper presents a new neural network architecture referred to here as BAYESNET. BAYESNET is capable of learning the probability density functions (pdfs) of individual pattern classes from a collection of learning samples, and designed for pattern classification based on the Bayesian decision rule. Unlike the Parzen estimate, in BAYESNET, the pdf of a class is represented in terms of the sum of Gaussian subclass pdfs with unknown means, covariances and subclass probabilities that are to be determined through learning. The unique feature of learning the pdf of a class in BAYESNET is the random assignment of a sample of a class to subclasses: a sample is randomly assigned to a particular subclass for learning according to the probability of the sample to belong to individual subclasses. The property of Gaussian function provides efficient learning of parameters. It is shown that the learned parameters agree with those obtained by the maximum likelihood estimation of the sample set. To avoid local minima in parameter learning, biases of time decaying function are accounted in the subclass probability distribution. The simulation results show that BAYESNET achieves almost minimum error pattern classification for non-linear and non-separable pattern distribution.

I. INTRODUCTION

A pattern classification is practically an important problem arising in the domains of visual perception, object recognition and many others. In most domains, a pattern is composed of several features, and therefore, it is handled as a random vector generated according to the probability density function of the class it belongs to.

One of the most reliable statistical approaches of pattern classification is the Bayesian decision theory [1], which is known to yield the minimum error probability. The major problem is, however, the difficulty of formulating the probability density functions, or *pdfs*, of classes, which are explicitly used in the theory but usually unknown due to the lack of the complete system description and the occurrence of unexpected disturbance. Though a backpropagation network is reported to have the capability of attaining the Bayesian decision boundary by using a sample set [2, 3, 4] without knowing pdfs, the learning is generally slow and has a notorious deficit of falling in the lo-

cal minimum states. Therefore, it is indispensable to know pdf forms to obtain a reliable classification performance, which is achievable only by the direct application of the Bayesian decision theory.

When we have a large number of sample patterns together with their classes, two major methods for pdf estimation are known, nonparametric method and parametric method [1]. The network of nonparametric estimation using a Parzen window can be applied to a large class of pdf and has a fast learning capability, in which one pass of the sample set is often enough, but requires an enormous number of hidden units and thus a large cost of probability computation for classification [5]. In the other hand, the parametric estimation is fast for both of learning and classification due to the limited number of parameters.

Our learning scheme is also based on the parametric method using Gaussian mixtures as for formulating pdfs, where the parameters are embedded in a neural network architecture to be determined by the given samples. Though the parametric estimation has the approximation limitation, it is known that any continuous functions can be approximated by arbitrary accuracy if sufficiently many Gaussian functions are employed [6, 7, 8].

II. BAYESIAN NETWORK

In this section, we discuss on the background and the architecture of our neural network designed for pattern classification, referred to here as Bayesian Network or BAYESNET.

A. Bayesian Decision Theory and Parametric Estimation

In the domain underlying, we assume a pattern is composed of d features and represented as a random vector, $\mathbf{X} \in \Re^d$. Any pattern belongs to one of c classes where a collection of classes is described by $\Theta = \{\theta_1, \cdots, \theta_c\}$. Let "$\boldsymbol{x} \tilde{\in} \theta_i$" denote that "the pattern $\boldsymbol{x}$ belongs to the class θ_i."

Now for the observed pattern $\boldsymbol{x}$ of unknown class, the Bayesian decision theory determines that $\boldsymbol{x} \tilde{\in} \theta_s$, if the inequality

$$\Pr(\mathbf{X} \tilde{\in} \theta_s \mid \mathbf{X} = \boldsymbol{x}) \geq \Pr(\mathbf{X} \tilde{\in} \theta_i \mid \mathbf{X} = \boldsymbol{x}) \qquad (1)$$

holds for $\forall i \neq s$, assuming the equal cost of misclassification errors [1]. The decision rule can be rewritten using the Bayesian rule of a continuous distribution,

$$p_s(\boldsymbol{x})\,P_s \geq p_i(\boldsymbol{x})\,P_i \qquad (2)$$

where $P_i = \mathrm{Pr}(\mathbf{X}\tilde{\in}\theta_i)$ represents *a priori* probability of the class, or a *class probability*, and $p_i(\boldsymbol{x}) = pdf(\boldsymbol{x}|\mathbf{X}\tilde{\in}\theta_i)$ represents *a priori* pdf of the class, or a *class pdf*. Note that the probabilities satisfy $\sum_{i=1}^{c} P_i = 1$ and $\int p_i(\boldsymbol{x})\,d\boldsymbol{x} = 1$ for all i. Now what we need to know is the values of class probabilities and the function forms of class pdfs by analyzing a collection of observed patterns, $S = \{\boldsymbol{x}_1, \cdots, \boldsymbol{x}_n\}$, generated according to the probabilities.

The class probabilities can be relatively easily obtained if the set is large enough by counting the samples for the classes among all given samples. In the other hand, to find the class pdfs is difficult because they are functions of unknown form and no prior information is provided. One of the most frequently used methods to overcome the difficulty, called the *parametric method*, is to infer the probabilities by analyzing the sample set under a certain assumption on the forms of class pdfs. BAYESNET is also using the parametric estimation, assuming that a class pdf has a form of a Gaussian sum. Hereafter, let $\tilde{P}_i$ and $\tilde{p}_i(\boldsymbol{x})$ denote the estimations as $\tilde{P}_i \approx P_i$ and $\tilde{p}_i(\boldsymbol{x}) \approx p_i(\boldsymbol{x})$.

B. Gaussian Sum Estimation of Probability Density Function

In BAYESNET, the pdf of a class is estimated from the given learning samples so that we can apply Bayesian decision rule to achieve the minimum error pattern classification. To this end, a new method for estimating the pdf of a class is proposed: the pdf of class a, $\tilde{p}^a(\boldsymbol{x})$, is represented as the sum of m Gaussian functions, $\tilde{q}_i(\boldsymbol{x}; \boldsymbol{r}_i)$, $i=1,\cdots,m$, of unknown parameter vectors, $\boldsymbol{r}_i$, $i=1,\cdots,m$, that are to be trained from a collection of samples, S^a, belonging to the class a, such that

$$\tilde{p}^a(\boldsymbol{x}) = \sum_{i=1}^{m} \tilde{q}_i^a(\boldsymbol{x}; \boldsymbol{r}_i)\,\tilde{Q}_i. \qquad (3)$$

The Gaussian sum (3) is equivalent to saying that class a is composed of m subclasses with their pdfs and probabilities, referred to here as *subclass pdfs* and *subclass probabilities* respectively, represented as $\tilde{q}_i^a(\boldsymbol{x}, \boldsymbol{r}_i)$ and $\tilde{Q}_i^a$, $i=1,\cdots,m$. The unknown parameters of subclasses, $\boldsymbol{r}_i$ and $\tilde{Q}_i^a$, $i=1,\cdots,m$, are to be trained, using the sample set S^a, based on the iterative update of the current $\boldsymbol{r}_{ik}$ and $\tilde{Q}_{ik}^a$, $i=1,\cdots,m$, toward an equilibrium, at which the actual pdf of class a is realized.

For instance, as shown in Fig. 1, one dimensional sample set, S, is distributed on X axis, and the actual pdf of S, $p(x)$, over X is represented by the sum of two Gaussian functions $q_1(x)$ and $q_2(x)$: $p(x) = q_1(x)\,Q_1 + q_2(x)\,Q_2$. At the current state of training, the pdf of S is represented in terms of two Gaussian

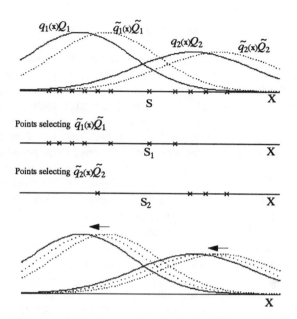

Fig. 1: In the top figure, the solid line shows the actual subclass pdfs and the dotted line shows the current estimations of the subclass pdfs. The training sample, S in the top, are partitioned into S_1 and S_2 as shown in the 2nd and the 3rd figures, according to the probability $\mathrm{Pr}(x_i \in S_1) = \tilde{q}_1(x_i)\tilde{Q}_1/(\tilde{q}_1(x_i)\tilde{Q}_1 + \tilde{q}_2(x_i)\tilde{Q}_2)$ and so on. Based on the new means and covariances for S_1 and S_2 respectively, the parameters are updated to obtain the new estimations as in the bottom figure.

functions $\tilde{q}_1(x)$ and $\tilde{q}_2(x)$: $\tilde{p}(x) = \tilde{q}_1(x)\,\tilde{Q}_1 + \tilde{q}_2(x)\,\tilde{Q}_2$. The parameters of $\tilde{q}_1(x)$ and $\tilde{q}_2(x)$, means and variances (m_1, σ_1^2) and (m_2, σ_2^2) respectively, as well as $\tilde{Q}_1$ and $\tilde{Q}_2$ are subject to incremental change in order to have $\tilde{p}(x)$ approach to $p(x)$.

The key feature of the proposed Gaussian sum estimation is the decomposition of S^a into m subclasses, $S_1^a, \cdots, S_m^a$. The decomposition is done by assigning each sample to one of m subclasses randomly according to the probability that the sample belongs to the particular subclass, where the probability is defined in terms of the current subclass pdfs $\tilde{q}_i(\boldsymbol{x})$, $i=1,\cdots,m$, and subclass probabilities $\tilde{Q}_i(\boldsymbol{x})$, $i=1,\cdots,m$. In other words, a subclass becomes the winner for a sample according to the probability that the sample belongs to the subclass. Fig. 1 illustrates the sample distributions for subclass 1, S_1, and subclass 2, S_2, respectively, after S is decomposed probabilistically into S_1 and S_2 based on the *selection probabilities*, $\mathrm{Pr}(x_i \in S_1)$ and $\mathrm{Pr}(x_i \in S_2)$ for all $x_i \in S$, where $\mathrm{Pr}(x_i \in S_j) = \tilde{q}_j(x_i)\tilde{Q}_j/(\tilde{q}_1(x_i)\tilde{Q}_1 + \tilde{q}_2(x_i)\tilde{Q}_2)$, $j = 1$ or 2.

For the subclass samples, $S_1^a, \cdots, S_m^a$, obtained from S^a, we can derive new parameter values for each subclass including means, variances and subclass probabilities. The update of parameters is based on the discrepancy between the current and the new parameter values: the current values are gradually changed toward the new parameter values. Fig. 1 illustrates the new means and variances computed from S_1 and S_2.

As shown later, the final parameter values obtained at an equilibrium state (i.e., the state when the update becomes zero) are equivalent to the solutions obtained by the maximum likelihood estimation. Furthermore, assuming that the actual pdf can be represented as the Gaussian sum, the actual parameter values become one of the stable equilibrium points, or vice versa. That is, the current parameter values of a small deviation from the actual parameter values guarantee to converge to the actual parameter values. In the case where the current parameter values are set far away from the actual parameter values, or the number of subclasses are set smaller than required, there may arise a local minima problem: the parameter values converge to one of the equilibrium states but we can not guarantee that they are the actual parameter values. To avoid the local minima problem, it is necessary to define a sufficient number of subclasses and set the initial parameter values appropriately. This problem may be resolved based on preclustering learning samples by known competitive learning scheme, such as RCCN[9], ART 2[10] or Entropy function [11], to obtain approximately the necessary number of subclasses and initial parameter values. In this case, BAYESNET plays a role of a fine tuner. Alternatively, we can adopt a certain bias of time decaying function in the probability of decomposing samples into subclasses, as will be described in detail later, to avoid zero subclass probabilities especially at the initial state of learning.

C. Parameters of BAYESNET

In more general case when there are c classes and d features for a pattern, the class pdf of the ith class is represented using subclass probabilities and subclass pdfs, as

$$\tilde{p}_i(\boldsymbol{x}) = \sum_{j=1}^{m_i} \tilde{q}_{ij}(\boldsymbol{x}) \tilde{Q}_{ij} \qquad (4)$$

where m_i is the number of subclasses of the class. The subclass pdf of the jth subclass of the ith class is assumed to have a multivariate Gaussian form as

$$\tilde{q}_{ij}(\boldsymbol{x}) = \frac{1}{(2\pi)^{d/2}|\tilde{\boldsymbol{\Sigma}}_{ij}|^{1/2}} \exp\left(-(\boldsymbol{x}-\tilde{\mathbf{m}}_{ij})^t \tilde{\boldsymbol{\Sigma}}_{ij}^{-1}(\boldsymbol{x}-\tilde{\mathbf{m}}_{ij})/2\right) \quad (5)$$

where $\tilde{\mathbf{m}}_{ij} \in \Re^d$ is an estimated mean and $\tilde{\boldsymbol{\Sigma}}_{ij} \in \Re^{d \times d}$ is an estimated covariance of the subclass, respectively.

The parameters are required to satisfy the constraints,

$$\sum_{i=1}^{c} \tilde{P}_i = 1$$

$$\sum_{j=1}^{m_i} \tilde{Q}_{ij} = 1 \quad \text{for} \quad \forall i \qquad (6)$$

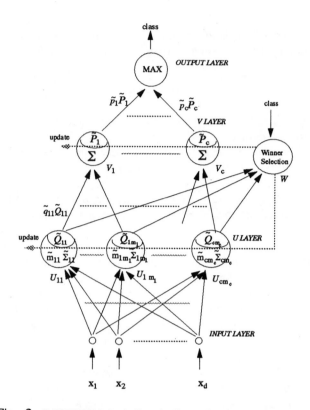

Fig. 2: BAYESNET is basically a feedforward network with two hidden layers. A pattern being presented to the input layer, the units in the U layer derive the probabilities for subclasses, and the units in the V layer compute the probabilities for classes. During learning, the Winner Selection unit selects the winner from the U layer. When the network is applied as a classifier, the output unit produces the final class by comparing the outputs from the V layer.

since $\int \tilde{p}_i(\boldsymbol{x})\, d\boldsymbol{x} = 1$ and $\int \tilde{q}_{ij}(\boldsymbol{x})\, d\boldsymbol{x} = 1$. In addition to them, the subclass covariances are positive definite. Now, the problem is reduced to find the appropriate values of the parameters, $\{\tilde{P}_i\}$, $\{\tilde{Q}_{ij}\}$, $\{\tilde{\mathbf{m}}_{ij}\}$ and $\{\tilde{\boldsymbol{\Sigma}}_{ij}\}$, by estimating the samples, $\{\boldsymbol{x}_1, \cdots, \boldsymbol{x}_n\}$.

D. Network Architecture

The architecture of BAYESNET is designed together with the learning and classification schemes to realize the parameter estimation following the idea described in the previous sections. Fig. 2 shows the network architecture. The network is trained by updating the parameters gradually based on the winner competition as LVQ system does [12], and also works as a pattern classifier after completion of learning. The network has four layers, the *input layer*, the *U layer*, the *V layer* and the *output layer*. Besides, the network is furnished with the *Winner Selection* unit, denoted by W, which is supposed to work only in the learning period.

The U layer consists of $(m_1 + \cdots + m_c)$ units, denoted by

U_{ij}, corresponding to each subclass. The unit U_{ij} stores three parameters, $\tilde{Q}_{ij}$, $\tilde{\mathbf{m}}_{ij}$ and $\tilde{\boldsymbol{\Sigma}}_{ij}$, to compute $(\tilde{q}_{ij}(\boldsymbol{x})\,\tilde{Q}_{ij})$ for the presented pattern using (5). The V layer consists of c units, denoted by V_i, corresponding to each class. The unit V_i stores a parameter $\tilde{P}_i$ to compute $(\tilde{p}_i(\boldsymbol{x})\,\tilde{P}_i)$ using (4). At each time of learning, a sample pattern is presented to the input layer and the class of the pattern is passed to the Winner Selection unit to select the winner unit from the U layer. Then the parameters are updated according to the update rules described later.

After completion of learning, a pattern classification for the presented pattern, $\boldsymbol{x}$, is processed as follows: receiving products $\{\tilde{q}_{ij}(\boldsymbol{x})\,\tilde{Q}_{ij}\}$ from the U layer, the units in the V layer derive products $\{\tilde{p}_i(\boldsymbol{x})\,\tilde{P}_i\}$. The products are compared at the output layer as the Bayesian decision theory suggests in (2), but using the estimated values instead, to decide the class of $\boldsymbol{x}$.

E. Learinig Scheme

Here describes details of the BAYESNET learning. In prior to learning, all parameters are initialized as

$$\tilde{P}_i = \frac{1}{c} \quad \text{for} \quad \forall i$$

$$\tilde{Q}_{ij} = \frac{1}{m_i} \quad \text{for} \quad \forall i, \forall j \qquad (7)$$

$$\tilde{\boldsymbol{\Sigma}}_{ij} = \mathbf{I}_{d \times d} \quad \text{for} \quad \forall i, \forall j,$$

where $\mathbf{I}_{d \times d}$ is a d by d identity matrix. The means, $\tilde{\mathbf{m}}_{ij}$, would be randomly initialized with the values in the possible range that patterns may exist. Note that the initialization relies that the variances are almost 1.0 for all components. A small degree of deviation is adjustable due to the adaptation capability of BAYESNET learning, but initialization procedure should be reconsidered if the deviation is too large, for example, a value may vary from 0 to 1000.

For each step of learning at time t $(t = 0, 1, \cdots)$, a learning sample $\boldsymbol{x}$ $(\tilde{\in} \theta_s)$ randomly selected from the sample set, is presented to the input layer, and the class θ_s is presented to the Winner Selection unit. Then, a winner is selected probabilistically from among $\{U_{ij}\}$. The probability that the unit U_{ij} is selected as a winner, is

$$\Pr(U_{sj} \text{ is selected}) = \frac{\tilde{q}_{sj}(\boldsymbol{x})\,\tilde{Q}_{sj}}{\tilde{p}_s(\boldsymbol{x})}$$

$$\Pr(U_{ij} \text{ is selected}) = 0 \quad \text{for} \quad \forall i \neq s, \forall j. \qquad (8)$$

That is, the winner is selected only from the units related to the given class, according to the product of the *current* subclass probability and the subclass pdf.

Once the winner is selected at time t, the parameters are updated as the usual competitive learning [9, 12]. The class probabilities are updated as

$$\tilde{P}_s(t+1) = \tilde{P}_s(t) + \alpha(t)\,(1 - \tilde{P}_s(t)) \qquad (9)$$

$$\tilde{P}_i(t+1) = \tilde{P}_i(t) + \alpha(t)\,(0 - \tilde{P}_i(t)) \quad \text{for} \quad \forall i \neq s.$$

For the winner unit, U_{sj},

$$\tilde{Q}_{sj}(t+1) = \tilde{Q}_{sj}(t) + \beta(t)\,(1 - \tilde{Q}_{sj}(t))$$

$$\tilde{\mathbf{m}}_{sj}(t+1) = \tilde{\mathbf{m}}_{sj}(t) + \gamma(t)\,(\boldsymbol{x}_s - \tilde{\mathbf{m}}_{sj}(t)) \qquad (10)$$

$$\tilde{\boldsymbol{\Sigma}}_{sj}(t+1) = \tilde{\boldsymbol{\Sigma}}_{sj}(t)$$
$$+ \delta(t)\,((\boldsymbol{x}_s - \tilde{\mathbf{m}}_{sj}(t))(\boldsymbol{x}_s - \tilde{\mathbf{m}}_{sj}(t))^t - \tilde{\boldsymbol{\Sigma}}_{sj}(t)).$$

For the non-winner units for the same class s, U_{sj},

$$\tilde{Q}_{sj}(t+1) = \tilde{Q}_{sj}(t) + \beta(t)\,(0 - \tilde{Q}_{sj}(t))$$

$$\tilde{\mathbf{m}}_{sj}(t+1) = \tilde{\mathbf{m}}_{sj}(t) \qquad (11)$$

$$\tilde{\boldsymbol{\Sigma}}_{sj}(t+1) = \tilde{\boldsymbol{\Sigma}}_{sj}(t).$$

For all other units, U_{ij}, all parameters are unchanged. The multipliers, $\alpha(t)$, $\beta(t)$, $\gamma(t)$, and $\delta(t)$, are all positive decreasing functions such as $\exp(-t)$. Note that the constraints on $\tilde{P}_i$, $\tilde{q}_{ij}$ and $\tilde{\boldsymbol{\Sigma}}_{ij}$ as in (6) are not violated by initialization or update rules.

F. Maximum Likelihood Estimation

The selection probability, denoted by $\tilde{w}_{ij}(\boldsymbol{x})$, that U_{ij} is selected as a winner when a learning sample $\boldsymbol{x} \tilde{\in} \theta_i$ is presented, was

$$\tilde{w}_{ij}(\boldsymbol{x}) = \frac{\tilde{q}_{ij}(\boldsymbol{x})\,\tilde{Q}_{ij}}{\tilde{p}_i(\boldsymbol{x})}. \qquad (12)$$

Using the selection probability for the update rules in (10) and (11), the parameters reach to a statistically equilibrium state when

$$(1 - \tilde{P}_i)\,P_i + (0 - \tilde{P}_i)\,(1 - P_i) = 0$$

$$\int (1 - \tilde{Q}_{ij})\,\tilde{w}_{ij}(\boldsymbol{x})\,p_i(\boldsymbol{x})\,d\boldsymbol{x}$$

$$+ \int (0 - \tilde{Q}_{ij})\,(1 - \tilde{w}_{ij}(\boldsymbol{x}))\,p_i(\boldsymbol{x})\,d\boldsymbol{x} = 0$$

$$\int (\boldsymbol{x} - \tilde{\mathbf{m}}_{ij})\,\tilde{w}_{ij}(\boldsymbol{x})\,p_i(\boldsymbol{x})\,d\boldsymbol{x} = 0 \qquad (13)$$

$$\int \{(\boldsymbol{x} - \tilde{\mathbf{m}}_{ij})(\boldsymbol{x} - \tilde{\mathbf{m}}_{ij})^t - \tilde{\boldsymbol{\Sigma}}_{ij}\}\,\tilde{w}_{ij}(\boldsymbol{x})\,p_i(\boldsymbol{x})\,d\boldsymbol{x} = 0$$

hold. Solving them to obtain

$$\tilde{P}_i = P_i$$

$$\tilde{Q}_{ij} = \int \tilde{w}_{ij}(\boldsymbol{x})\,p_i(\boldsymbol{x})\,d\boldsymbol{x}$$

$$\tilde{\mathbf{m}}_{ij} = \frac{\int \boldsymbol{x}\,\tilde{w}_{ij}(\boldsymbol{x})\,p_i(\boldsymbol{x})\,d\boldsymbol{x}}{\int \tilde{w}_{ij}(\boldsymbol{x})\,p_i(\boldsymbol{x})\,d\boldsymbol{x}} \qquad (14)$$

$$\tilde{\boldsymbol{\Sigma}}_{ij} = \frac{\int (\boldsymbol{x} - \tilde{\mathbf{m}}_{ij})(\boldsymbol{x} - \tilde{\mathbf{m}}_{ij})^t\,\tilde{w}_{ij}(\boldsymbol{x})\,p_i(\boldsymbol{x})\,d\boldsymbol{x}}{\int \tilde{w}_{ij}(\boldsymbol{x})\,p_i(\boldsymbol{x})\,d\boldsymbol{x}}.$$

The solutions above agree with those of the *Maximum Likelihood Estimation*, or MLE, that is, the solutions which maximize the probability of obtaining the sample set, assuming infinite number of samples [1].

If there given not many learning samples, it is possible to have the batch based update of the parameters, that is, update by the statistics of the sample set using (14) [11, 13]. On the contrary, sample-wise update as in BAYESNET is more practical when a lot of samples are provided, with the capability of on-line learning. Also it is possible to obtain a sample-wise update rule directly from the MLE solution (14), such as GC network [14]. In the network all Gaussian kernels are updated where the amount of change of a kernel is proportional to the corresponding probability (12). The network has, however, a possibility of local minima problem when two of the Gaussian kernels are exactly same at the initial state, though random selection in BAYESNET will eventually separate them away.

G. Biased Selection

Though the learning scheme of BAYESNET assures the convergence of parameters to those of MLE, the mutual correlations of the parameters in the equilibrium state (14) imply that the solutions may not be unique. Actually it is only guaranteed that the states are suboptimal.

To overcome the problem, we hire an idea of adding a bias for the winner selection [15]. The rules of selection and update, (8)-(11), indicate that once a unit wins, the unit will win in the higher probability for the next time. The tendency causes major local minimum problem, which degenerate the classification performance due to generation of dead units, more specifically, units whose subclass probabilities are zero. Therefore, some biases are added such that the units with lower subclass probabilities are favored for the winner selection in the early stages of learning, as

$$\Pr(U_{sj} \text{ is selected}) \quad \propto \quad \frac{\tilde{q}_{sj}(\boldsymbol{x}_s)\,\tilde{Q}_{sj}}{\tilde{p}_s(\boldsymbol{x}_s)}\frac{1}{\tilde{Q}_{sj}^{\epsilon(t)}} \qquad (\epsilon(t) \searrow 0)$$

$$\Pr(U_{ij} \text{ is selected}) \quad = \quad 0 \quad \text{for} \quad \forall i \neq s, \forall j \qquad (15)$$

for the place of selection probability (8). Since the effect of the bias decreases, the final equilibrium states are also assured to be those of MLE solutions.

III. SIMULATION

In the simulation following, BAYESNET was evaluated in two feature space with three classes, where each class is assumed to consist of three subclasses. Fig. 3 shows the sample distribution of classes and the final locations of the subclass means. Table I shows the values of class probabilities, etc., at the completion of learning. Table II shows the classification rates for BAYESNET and LVQ with/without biases. The means are well distributed in the range of each class to locate accurate class boundaries, yielding a high classification rate even close to the optimal case.

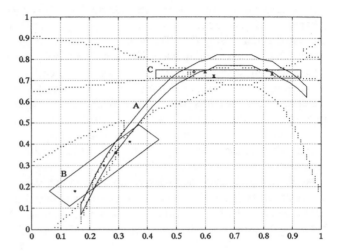

Fig. 3: There exists three classes, A, B and C. Samples of each class distribute uniformly in the specified region under $P(A) = 0.4$, $P(B) = P(C) = 0.3$. Three subclasses are prepared for each class in the network. The final locations of subclass means are represented by o for A, * for B and x for C. The small dots indicate the decision boundary obtained by the Bayesian decision theory. A sample set consists of randomly generated 1,000 patterns and totally 10 passes were provided using the biased selection.

The biased BAYESNET assigns positive subclass probabilities to all units, while the unbiased BAYESNET yields several dead units. Due to the adaptation capability of covariances, BAYESNET has the higher classification rates than those of LVQ.

IV. CONCLUSION

In this paper we proposed a new neural network architecture called BAYESNET for pattern classification based on the Bayesian decision rule. The pdf of a class is assumed to be of the

TABLE I: FINAL PARAMETER VALUES

Class Probabilities	Subclass Probabilities and Subclass Means	
$\tilde{P}(A) = 0.419$	$\tilde{Q}_{A1} = 0.33$	$\tilde{\mathbf{m}}_{A1} = (0.29, 0.36)$
	$\tilde{Q}_{A2} = 0.31$	$\tilde{\mathbf{m}}_{A2} = (0.81, 0.75)$
	$\tilde{Q}_{A3} = 0.36$	$\tilde{\mathbf{m}}_{A3} = (0.56, 0.74)$
$\tilde{P}(B) = 0.292$	$\tilde{Q}_{B1} = 0.27$	$\tilde{\mathbf{m}}_{B1} = (0.15, 0.18)$
	$\tilde{Q}_{B2} = 0.44$	$\tilde{\mathbf{m}}_{B2} = (0.25, 0.30)$
	$\tilde{Q}_{B3} = 0.29$	$\tilde{\mathbf{m}}_{B3} = (0.34, 0.41)$
$\tilde{P}(C) = 0.289$	$\tilde{Q}_{C1} = 0.30$	$\tilde{\mathbf{m}}_{C1} = (0.83, 0.73)$
	$\tilde{Q}_{C2} = 0.33$	$\tilde{\mathbf{m}}_{C2} = (0.60, 0.74)$
	$\tilde{Q}_{C3} = 0.37$	$\tilde{\mathbf{m}}_{C3} = (0.63, 0.72)$

TABLE II: Classification Rates and Number of Dead Units

Network Type	Classification Rate	Number of Dead Units
BAYESNET (biased, used in Fig. 3)	87.6%	0
BAYESNET (no bias)	84.8%	3
LVQ (biased)	76.6%	0
LVQ (no bias)	64.3%	3
Bayesian Decision Rule (Optimal)	91.4%	–

Gaussian sum and the parameters embedded in the network are determined using the sample set under nondeterministic winner selection. It was also stated that the parameters converge to MLE solutions, and the local minimum problem inherently existing in the solutions is partially resolved by adding biases to the selection probability. Though BAYESNET has the high classification performance with the theoretical background, it is strongly required to have the capability of determining the number of subclasses of each class for practical applications in the further study.

REFERENCES

[1] R. O. Duda and P. E. Hart, "PATTERN CLASSIFICATION AND SCENE ANALYSIS," *John Wiley & Sons*, 1973.

[2] D. W. Ruck, S. K. Rogers, M. Kabrisky, M. E. Oxley and B. W. Suter, "The Multilayer Perceptron as an Approximation to a Bayes Optimal Discriminant Function," *IEEE Transactions on Neural Networks*, Vol. 1, No. 4, Dec 1990.

[3] E. A. Wan, "Neural Network Classification: A Bayesian Interpretation," *IEEE Transactions on Neural Networks*, Vol. 1, No. 4, Dec 1990.

[4] S. Miyake and F. Kanaya, "A Neural Network Approach to a Bayesian Statistical Decision Problem," *IEEE Transactions on Neural Networks*, Vol. 2, No. 5, Sep 1991.

[5] D. F. Specht, "Probabilistic Neural Networks," *Neural Networks*, Vol. 3, pp. 109-118, 1990.

[6] H. W. Sorenson and D. L. Alspach, "Recursive Bayesian Estimation Using Gaussian Sums," *Automatica*, Vol. 7, pp. 465-479, 1971.

[7] D. L. Alspach and H. W. Sorenson, "Nonlinear Bayesian Estimation Using Gaussian Sum Approximations," *IEEE Transactions on Automatic Control*, Vol. AC-17, No. 4, Aug. 1972.

[8] E. J. Hartman, J. D. Keeler and J. M. Kowalski, "Layered Neural Networks with Gaussian Hidden Units as universal approximations," *Neural Computation*, Vol. 2, No. 2, pp. 210-215, 1990.

[9] S. Lee and S. Shimoji, "Radial Basis Competitive and Cooperative Network with Hierarchical Network Self-Organization for Bidirectional Many-to-Many Mapping," *IJCNN-92-Beijing*, 1992.

[10] G. A. Carpenter and S. Grossberg, "ART 2: Self-organization of Stable Category Recognition Codes for Analog Input Patterns," *Applied Optics*, Vol. 26, pp. 4919-4930, 1987.

[11] L. I. Perlovsky and M. M. McManus, "Maximum Likelihood Neural Networks for Sensor Fusion and Adaptive Classification," *Neural Networks*, Vol. 4, pp. 89-102, 1991.

[12] T. Kohonen, "Self-Organization and Associative Memory," *Springer-Verlag*, 1987.

[13] R. L. Streit, "A Neural Network for Optimum Neyman-Pearson Classification," *IJCNN-89-SanDiego*, 1989.

[14] H. G. C. Tråvén, "A Neural Network Approach to Statistical Pattern Classification by Semiparametric Estimation of Probability Density Functions," *IEEE Transactions on Neural Networks*, Vol. 2, No. 3, May 1991.

[15] D. DeSieno, "Adding a Conscience to Competitive Learning," *ICNN-88-NewYork*, Vol. I, pp. 117-124, 1988.

How Lateral Interaction Develops in a Self-Organizing Feature Map

Joseph Sirosh and Risto Miikkulainen

Department of Computer Sciences

The University of Texas at Austin, Austin, TX-78712

sirosh,risto@cs.utexas.edu

Abstract— A biologically motivated mechanism for self-organizing a neural network with modifiable lateral connections is presented. The weight modification rules are purely activity-dependent, unsupervised and local. The lateral interaction weights are initially random but develop into a "Mexican hat" shape around each neuron. At the same time, the external input weights self-organize to form a topological map of the input space. The algorithm demonstrates how self-organization can bootstrap itself using input information. Predictions of the algorithm agree very well with experimental observations on the development of lateral connections in cortical feature maps.

I. INTRODUCTION

Two-dimensional topological maps of sensory input are present in various cortices of the brain. They are believed to develop in a self-organizing process based on cooperation and competition between neurons [4, 13, 14]. The Self-Organizing Feature Map (SOFM) algorithm [5, 6] is a computational model of this process. The SOFM algorithm has been applied, for example, into modeling the development of retinotopy, ocular dominance and orientation preference in the visual cortex and somatotopy in the somatosensory cortex [9, 10, 11].

The SOFM algorithm is an abstraction, though biologically inspired. At each step of training, the algorithm finds the neuron whose input synaptic weights are closest to the current input vector and changes the input weights of all neurons in its neighborhood towards the input vector. The size of the neighborhood starts out large, but gradually decreases towards the end of training. The algorithm relies on an external supervisor to find the maximally active unit, and invokes an ad-hoc schedule for decreasing the neighborhood size.

To be biologically realistic, the SOFM algorithm should be reduced to local computations and interactions among neurons of the map. Proposed low-level models of SOFM

assume cooperative and competitive lateral interactions through excitatory and inhibitory connections [5, 8]. The lateral connections are non-modifiable and distinct from the external input connections. The connection weight profile in these models is shaped like a "Mexican hat", with short-range excitation and long-range inhibition. Similarly shaped lateral interaction is commonly found in many biological neural networks [5].

How does such lateral interaction arise? Enormous amounts of genetic information would be required to specify each synaptic weight of every neuron in a cortical map. Therefore, it is unrealistic to expect lateral interaction in such networks to be predetermined. All connections of a neuron should be modifiable, and there is no reason why the lateral interaction should have a uniform shape everywhere in the map. It makes sense to assume that the connections initially have random initial weights within a predetermined range. The question is, can these connections self-organize to form global order? Do the random-weight lateral connections develop a biologically realistic profile?

In this paper, we demonstrate through simulations that lateral connections can self-organize simultaneously with external input connections. In the process, the lateral interaction profile becomes a smooth "Mexican hat"-shaped function. The shape varies smoothly from neuron to neuron in the map depending on location. All connections can start out with random weights, and all connections are modified through a version of the Hebb learning rule.

II. THE SELF-ORGANIZING PROCESS

The computations for a self-organizing feature map with lateral connections are described below. The algorithm computes the activity of each neuron in a network as a weighted sum of the external input and refines the activity through lateral interactions between neurons. When the activity stabilizes, all connection weights are modified. The process is repeated for each input. Section A explains and motivates our neuron model. Sections B and C describe the network and the input, and section D delineates the equations and the computations.

A. The Neuron Model

Each neuron in the network is assumed to have three sets of inputs:

- excitatory input connections that supply external input to the neuron,

- short-range lateral excitatory connections from close neighbors in the map,

- long-range lateral inhibitory connections from within the map.

A connection has a characteristic strength (or weight), which may be any value between zero and a prescribed limit. In a real neuron, these limits would be a property of the synapse.

External inputs to primary cortical areas of the brain synapse differently from intracortical lateral connections [15]. It is possible that the external and lateral connections of the same neuron obey two different rules of weight modification. In our model, the two rules differ only in the normalization. The external connections are normalized to hold the sum of squares of the input weights constant, and the lateral (excitatory/inhibitory) connections are normalized to keep the sum of lateral (excitatory/inhibitory) weights constant.

In the primary cortices, most extrinsic afferents synapse in the dendritic spines of neurons [15]. The dendritic shafts sum the input from the spines approximately linearly. A rule of weight modification proposed by [12] appears realistic when applied to theses synapses. Oja's rule is an approximation of a Hebbian rule in which the synaptic weights are normalized to hold the sum of squares of the weights constant. We use the more general Hebbian rule (5) to modify the external input connections.

In a real neuron, excitatory and inhibitory synaptic transmission are mediated by different neurotransmitters and receptors. The two sets of synapses also have different morphology [15]. A neuron processes each set at different sites with different receptors and secondary messengers, and these resources are limited. It is reasonable to assume that the total synaptic weight for each set is fixed. When lateral connection weights are modified in our model, they are normalized so that the total excitatory weight and the total inhibitory weight are constant (refer to equation 3).

B. The Network

The feature map is a two dimensional $N \times N$ grid of neurons (Fig. 1). Each neuron connects to its neighbors within distance d with excitatory lateral connections and

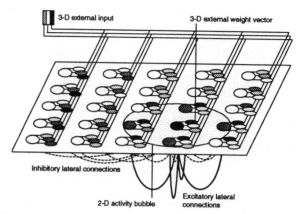

Fig. 1: **The laterally connected self-organizing feature map architecture.** Each neuron receives the same 3-dimensional input vector and computes an initial response based on the similarity with its external weight vector. The response then evolves through propagation along the lateral connections (only a few connections of the most strongly active unit are shown). After a stable activity bubble has formed, weights of the active units are adapted.

to all neighbors within $3d + 1$ with inhibitory connections. Lateral excitation weights are uniformly randomly distributed in the interval $(0, \gamma_e)$ within the excitation radius and are zero outside. Similarly, negative inhibition weights are distributed uniformly in the interval $(\gamma_i, 0)$ within the inhibition radius and are zero outside.

C. The Inputs

The input vectors must be normalized to prevent vectors with large norms from dominating the self-organizing process [8]. For this reason, the 2-D square area used as input in the simulations was laid on the surface of a unit sphere and represented in spherical coordinate system. In effect, such inputs are still 2-dimensional because the radius is constant. Each spherical input vector $(x_1, x_2, 1)$, $(-0.5 \leq x_1, x_2 \leq 0.5)$ was then transformed into a 3-dimensional cartesian vector $x = (\xi_1, \xi_2, \xi_3)$:

$$\begin{cases} \xi_1 = 1 \cdot \cos(x_1) \cos(x_2), \\ \xi_2 = 1 \cdot \sin(x_1) \cos(x_2), \\ \xi_3 = 1 \cdot \sin(x_2). \end{cases} \quad (1)$$

Corresponding to the three input components, each neuron (i, j) has three external input weights $\mu_{ij,h}$, $h = 0, 1, 2$.

D. The Computations

The external and lateral weights are organized through a purely unsupervised learning process. Input items are randomly drawn from the input distribution and presented to the network one at a time. At each training step, the neurons in the network start out with zero activity. The

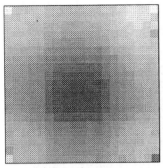 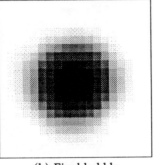

(a) Initial response   (b) Final bubble

Fig. 2: Focusing the response through lateral inhibition. The darkness of each square indicates the activity level of the corresponding unit in a 20 × 20 map.

initial response of each neuron η_{ij} in the map is based on a scalar product of the input and weight vectors:

$$\eta_{ij} = \sigma \left(\sum_h \mu_{ij,h} \xi_h \right), \qquad (2)$$

where the function σ is the familiar sigmoid activation function. The response evolves over time through lateral interaction. At each time step, the neuron combines external activation with lateral excitation and inhibition according to

$$\eta_{ij}(t) = \sigma \left(\sum_h \mu_{ij,h} \xi_h + \sum_{k,l} E_{kl,ij} \eta_{kl}(t - \delta t) + \sum_{k,l} I_{kl,ij} \eta_{kl}(t - \delta t) \right), \qquad (3)$$

where $E_{kl,ij}$ is the excitatory lateral connection weight on the connection from unit (k,l) to unit (i,j), $I_{kl,ij}$ is the inhibitory connection weight, and $\eta_{kl}(t - \delta t)$ is the activity of unit (k,l) during the previous time step. The activity pattern starts out as diffuse spread over a substantial part of the map and converges iteratively into a stable focused patch of activity, or activity bubble (Fig. 2). After the activity has settled, typically in a few iterations, the connection weights of each neuron are modified.

The lateral weights are modified by a Hebb rule, keeping the sum of weights constant:

$$\gamma_{ij,kl}(t + \delta t) = \frac{\gamma_{ij,kl}(t) + \alpha_L \eta_{ij} \eta_{kl}}{\sum_{kl} [\gamma_{ij,kl}(t) + \alpha_L \eta_{ij} \eta_{kl}]}, \qquad (4)$$

where η_{ij} stands for the activity of the unit (i,j) in the settled activity bubble, the γs are the lateral interaction weights ($E_{ij,kl}$ or $I_{ij,kl}$) and α_L is the learning rate for lateral interaction (α_E for excitatory weights and α_I for inhibitory). The larger the product of pre- and post-synaptic activity $\eta_{ij} \eta_{kl}$, the larger the weight change.

The external input weights are modified according to the normalized Hebbian rule:

$$\mu_{ij,h}(t + \delta t) = \frac{\mu_{ij,h}(t) + \alpha \eta_{ij} \xi_h}{\left\{ \sum_h [\mu_{ij,h}(t) + \alpha \eta_{ij} \xi_h]^2 \right\}^{1/2}}, \qquad (5)$$

which is otherwise similar to (4), but maintains the sum of squares of external weights constant.

Note that each computation is local to an individual neuron and its connections. The algorithm carries out local computations to achieve global self-organization of the map network. It does not require an external supervisory process.

III. SIMULATION RESULTS

The algorithm was applied into learning the 2-D structure of a uniform distribution on a square area. The simulations were performed on the Cray Y–MP 8/864 at the University of Texas Center for High-Performance Computing. Fig. 3 illustrates the external input weights of the neurons transformed back to the original spherical coordinates. The weight vectors are initially uniformly distributed on the input square. As the simulation progresses, the network unfolds, and the weight vectors spread out to form a regular topological map and to cover the input space. The course of this process is very similar to the standard SOFM algorithm. After a while, the network reaches a stable equilibrium. Further training causes small fluctuations about the stable equilibrium if the learning rate α is nonzero.

The lateral interconnection weights started random, but evolved into a very smooth "Mexican hat" profile around each neuron. Figures 4 and 5 show the lateral weights before and after training for a neuron at the center of the map. The lateral weights converged faster than the input weights, leading the self-organization. Both the input weights and lateral weights reached a stable dynamic equilibrium after sufficient training.

Interestingly, the lateral interaction profile is not uniform throughout the map, but exhibits boundary effects (Fig. 6). Because the units near the boundary do not have full neighborhoods, normalization of lateral weights results in profiles that are taller and asymmetric. The asymmetry is important because it affects the shape and location of activity bubbles. In simulations with uniform, predetermined interaction [8], activity bubbles formed away from the boundary even for input best stimulating a boundary neuron. In other words, the bubbles were representing the location of the best stimulus on the map incorrectly. In the new model, maximally active areas of the bubble correspond to best input response areas of the map even at the boundary. The shape of the activity bubble resembles the initial input activity, and the profile of

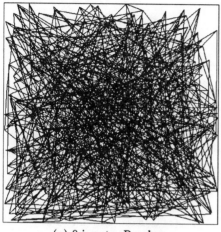 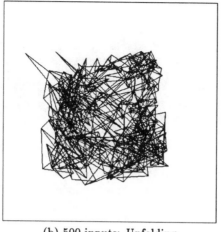 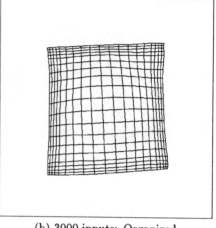

(a) 0 inputs: Random   (b) 500 inputs: Unfolding   (b) 3000 inputs: Organized

Fig. 3: **Self-organization of external input weights of a** 20×20 **map.** The square areas correspond to the input space. Each neuron is represented by its input weight vector plotted in 2D as a point inside the input square. Each neuron is connected to its four immediate neighbors, and the resulting grid depicts the topological organization of the neurons. An equilibrium is reached in about 3000 inputs. Additional inputs cause little change.

activity is very smooth within the bubble. The lateral interaction adapted to capture the smooth distribution of activity patterns on the map.

In the abstract feature map algorithm, metastable states such as twisted maps can form if the neighborhoods are initially too small [1]. The size of the activity bubble corresponds to the neighborhood size. The bubble size is determined by the radius and amount of lateral interaction. If these parameters are not large enough to make initial activity bubble sizes comparable to the size of the map, metastable states may form. The algorithm is robust within a fair range of parameters, and appropriate values can be easily determined.

IV. DISCUSSION

The new self-organization process described above has several important implications. It is a simulation of a realistic physical system that self-organizes based on purely local rules. If we were to actually construct "neurons" with properties described above and form a network as explained, the map would self-organize completely in parallel, without global supervision. This is in contrast to the abstract SOFM process, where the maximally responding unit is chosen through global supervision, and adaptation neighborhoods are reduced according to a preset schedule.

The shape of the lateral interaction is automatically extracted from the statistical properties of the external input. At each input presentation, the input vector is analyzed by the current state of the input weights and represented as an activity bubble on the map. The distribution of bubbles over time shapes the lateral weights, which in turn results in tighter and smoother activity bub-

bles and facilitates the self-organization of the external weights. The self-organization thus "bootstraps" by using external input information to establish the necessary cooperative and competive interactions.

Standard feature maps represent the topology of the input space by the network's grid-like layout. Units close by in the map represent input vectors nearby in the input space, and vice versa. In our model, the neighborhood relations are mediated by the lateral connections, and the model is not limited to strictly 2-dimensional topology. Units that are far apart on the map grid may still belong to the same neighborhood if they are strongly connected laterally. Such topologies are automatically learned as part of the self-organizing process. If several areas of the map are simultaneously active, long range connections between such areas will remain strong. These connections cause the units to behave as if they were neighbors on the map. This property is potentially very significant in representing complex high-dimensional input spaces. While lower-level sensory representation in the brain seems to be organized in 2-dimensional maps (such as retinotopic maps), it is possible that higher representations make use of long-range lateral connections to represent more complex similarity relationships [13]. The laterally connected feature map is a potential computational model for formation of such representations.

Standard SOFM has been used to model the development of input connections to neurons in the primary sensory cortices [9, 10, 11]. With the new algorithm, it should be possible to model the development of both lateral and external input connections in sensory cortices.

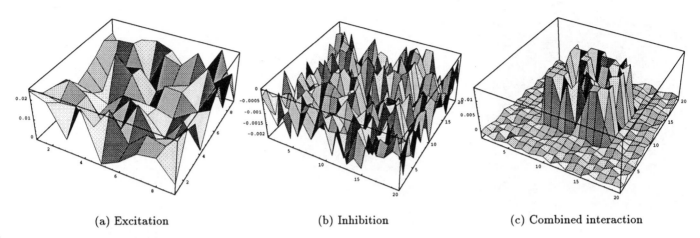

(a) Excitation   (b) Inhibition   (c) Combined interaction

Fig. 4: **Initial lateral interaction.** The lateral excitation and inhibition weights and the combined interaction profile are plotted for the neuron at position $(10, 10)$ in the 20×20 map.

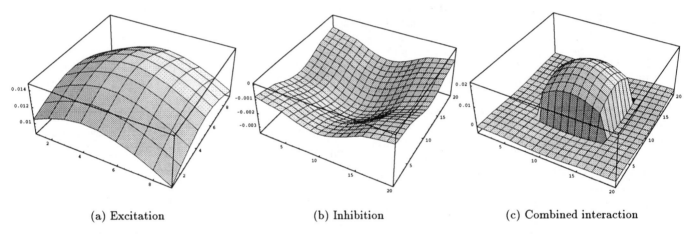

(a) Excitation   (b) Inhibition   (c) Combined interaction

Fig. 5: **Final lateral interaction.** A smooth pattern of excitation and inhibition weights has evolved, resulting in a smooth interaction profile.

It has recently been found that horizontal connections in the primary visual cortex mainly connect areas with similar functional properties, such as the same orientation sensitivity or ocular dominance [2, 3]. Assuming that average visual input excites similar feature detectors simultaneously, our model could give a computational account to this phenomenom. Specifically, (1) lateral connections between similar feature detectors strengthen due to correlated activity and (2) connections between dissimilar feature detectors weaken due to limited synaptic resources (through normalization). If weak connections are assumed to die off, the surviving connections would be those that link areas with similar functional properties.

The survival of horizontal connections in the primary visual cortex depend on correlated neuronal activity. If visual input to the cortex from both eyes of the cat is decorrelated by artificially introducing strabismus (squint-

eye) during development, lateral connections preferentially connect ocular dominance columns of the same eye [7]. In normal cats however, the connections prefer orientation columns of the same orientation specificity (as explained above). These results could be explained by the laterally connected model. In strabismic visual input there are more correlations among inputs from the same eye than between eyes. Ocular dominance columns representing the same eye would have highly correlated activity, and connections between them should strengthen. Other lateral connections should weaken due to normalization and eventually die off. Normally, images in the two eyes are very similar on the average, and have significant correlations. Similar orientation detectors in the cortex would have highly correlated activity irrespective of their ocular dominance. The stronger connections should then run between orientation columns of similar specificity.

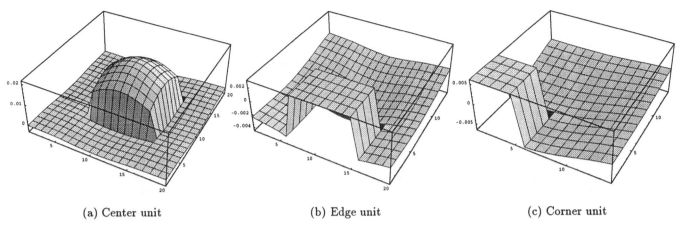

(a) Center unit	(b) Edge unit	(c) Corner unit

Fig. 6: Lateral interaction profiles at various locations of the 20×20 **map after training:** The profiles of neurons at $(10, 10)$, $(0, 10)$, and $(0, 0)$ are plotted. The profiles are tallest at the corner, shorter at an edge and shortest at the center. This is due to redistribution of synaptic weight by normalization.

V. CONCLUSION AND FUTURE WORK

Self-organizing models of cortical map development assume lateral interactions to be predetermined. We are not aware of other published work modelling the development of lateral connections in feature maps, biological or abstract. The algorithm presented here demonstrates simultaneous development of lateral interaction and self-organization of input weights. It is biologically motivated, and its predictions tie in very well with experimental observations in visuo-cortical maps.

Currently, the algorithm does not incorporate a mechanism to reduce the extent of lateral connections. The lateral connections of each neuron cover a substantial part of the map. This keeps the neuronal activity correlated over large distances and only the most significant variances in input (the ones that overcome the threshold of correlation; [9]) become represented. To capture features with lower variance, the extent of lateral connections must decrease gradually. We are currently working on an unsupervised mechanism for pruning lateral connections automatically. Research is also underway into constructing general models of cortical map development based on our algorithm.

REFERENCES

[1] E. Erwin, K. Obermayer, and K. J. Schulten. "Convergence properties of self-organizing maps," *Proceedings of the International Conference on Artificial Neural Networks* (Espoo, Finland). Amsterdam; New York: North-Holland, 1991, pp. 409–414.

[2] C. D. Gilbert, J. A. Hirsch, and T. N. Wiesel. "Lateral interactions in visual cortex," *Cold Spring Harbor Symposia on Quantitative Biology, Volume LV.* Cold Spring Harbor Laboratory Press, 1990, pp. 663–677.

[3] C. D. Gilbert and T. N. Wiesel. "Columnar specificity of intrinsic horizontal and corticocortical connections in cat visual cortex," *Journal of Neuroscience*, 9:2432–2442, 1989.

[4] D. H. Hubel and T. N. Wiesel. "Receptive fields and functional architecture in two nonstriate visual areas (18 and 19) of the cat," *Journal of Neurophysiology*, 28:229–289, 1965.

[5] T. Kohonen. *Self-Organization and Associative Memory*, 3rd ed. New York: Springer, 1989.

[6] T. Kohonen. "The self-organizing map," *Proceedings of the IEEE*, 78:1464–1480, 1990.

[7] S. Lowel and W. Singer. "Selection of intrinsic horizontal connections in the visual cortex by correlated neuronal activity," *Science*, 255:209–212, 1992.

[8] R. Miikkulainen. "Self-organizing process based on lateral inhibition and synaptic resource redistribution," *Proceedings of the International Conference on Artificial Neural Networks* (Espoo, Finland). Amsterdam; New York: North-Holland, 1991, pp. 415–420.

[9] K. Obermayer, G. G. Blasdel, and K. J. Schulten. "Statistical-mechanical analysis of self-organization and pattern formation during the development of visual maps," *Physical Review A*, 45:7568–7589, 1992.

[10] K. Obermayer, H. J. Ritter, and K. J. Schulten. Large-scale simulation of a self-organizing neural network. In *Proceedings of the International Conference on Parallel Processing in Neural Systems and Computers (ICNC)*. New York: Elsevier, 1990.

[11] K. Obermayer, H. J. Ritter, and K. J. Schulten. "A principle for the formation of the spatial structure of cortical feature maps," *Proceedings of the National Academy of Sciences, USA*, 87:8345–8349, 1990.

[12] E. Oja. "A simplified neuron model as a principal component analyzer," *Journal of Mathematical Biology*, 15:267–273, 1982.

[13] C. von der Malsburg and W. Singer. "Principles of cortical network organization," P. Rakic and W. Singer, Eds., *Neurobiology of Neocortex*, New York: Wiley, 1988, pp. 69–99.

[14] C. von der Malsburg. "Self-organization of orientation-sensitive cells in the striate cortex," *Kybernetik*, 15:85–100, 1973.

[15] E. L. White. *Cortical Circuits: Synaptic Organization of the Cerebral Cortex—Structure, Function, and Theory*, 1989. Boston: Birkhauser.

Quantization Effects of Hebbian-Type Associative Memories

Pau-Choo Chung[*], Yi-Nung Chung[**] and Ching-Tsorng Tsai[*]

*Department of Electrical Engineering, National Cheng Kung University
Tainan, Taiwan, R.O.C.
**Department of Electrical Engineering, Dai-Yeh Institute of technology
Changhwa, Taiwan, R.O.C.

Abstract- Effects of quantization strategies in Hebbian-Type associative memories are explored in this paper. The quantization strategies considered include two-level, three-level with a cut-off threshold, and linear quantizations. The two-level strategy is to clip positive interconnections into +1 and negative interconnections into -1. The three-level quantization uses the same strategy in turning the interconnections into +1 or -1, except that it is applied only to those interconnections having their values larger than a cut-off threshold. Those interconnections within the cutoff threshold are then set to zero. Results indicate that three-level quantization with a properly selected cut-off threshold gives network higher performance than two-level quantization. The performance of a network with linear quantization is also compared with a network with three-level quantization. It is found that the linear quantization, though preserves more network interconnections, does not significantly enhance network performance compared with the three-level quantization. Hence, it is convinced that the three-level binary quantization with an optimal threshold is a better choice when network implementations are considered.

I. INTRODUCTION

Hebbian-Type associative memory (HAM) has been and well-defined time domain behavior[1,2]. However, the real promise for applications of HAMs lies in specialized hardware. VLSI and opto-electronics are the two most prominent techniques being investigated for physical implementations. With today's integration densities, a large number of simple processors can be implemented inside a single chip together with the necessary interconnections to make a collective computing network. Presently several research groups have been devoted to the experiments with VLSI implementations and demonstrated several functioning units[3,4].

One of the first problems in the VLSI implementations of HAMs is the unexpectedly large synaptic area required as the number of stored patterns grows; since a synaptic weight computed accordingly to Hebb's rule may take any integer value between -M and +M when M patterns are stored. The quick growth of the required chip area with the increase of the number of stored patterns heavily obstruct physical usefulness of HAMs when network implementations are considered. Therefore, some way to reduce the range of interconnection values, or to quantize the interconnection values into a restricted range, is thus required.

As aforementioned, to reduce the range of interconnection values is an essential in VLSI implementations. Based on this concern, Verlaysen et al. [5] have presented a VLSI implementation technique for binary-interconnected (or clipped) associative memories with only three different interconnection values (+1, 0, -1). But, their discussion concerns mainly with the implementation techniques instead of network characteristics concerning various quantization strategies. In spite of the fact that Amit and Sompolinsky [6,7], using the spin-glass concept, have indicated that a clipped HAM actually retains certain capability of storage, their discussion is still relatively brief and restricted when the quantization techniques are concerned. Hence, a thorough exploration is still required.

In this paper, various quantization strategies for VLSI and opto-electronic implementations are explored based on the concepts of statistical neurodynamics. The quantization strategies considered include two-level, three-level with various cut-off threshold values, and linear quantizations. Results indicate that the three-level quantization preserves network capacity more than the two-level quantization strategy, especially when the quantization cut-off threshold is properly selected. Linear quantization which preserves the small to medium interconnections while truncates the large-valued interconnections into the nearest allowed large value is also investigated. We have found that preserving those small to medium interconnections does not significantly improve network performance. As a consequence, it would be good enough to just keep those interconnections having their original values beyond the optimal threshold, as the three-level quantization does.

This paper is organized as following. First, the concepts of Hebbian-Type associative memories are introduced in the next section. Followed is the analysis of two-level quantization strategy. Equations for estimating network performance using two-level quantization technique are derived. Network performances using three-level quantization and linear quantization strategies are explored in Section IV. Finally, discussion and conclusions are given in Section V.

II. HEBBIAN-TYPE ASSOCIATIVE MEMORIES

A Hebbian-type associative memory is constructed by

interconnecting a large number of simple processing units. For a network consisting of N processing units, or neurons, each neuron i, $1 \leq i \leq N$, receives an input from neuron j, $1 \leq j \leq N$, through a connection, or weight, T_{ij}. Assume that M binary valued vectors denoted by $x^k = [x_1^k, x_2^k, ..., x_N^k]$, $1 \leq k \leq M$, with each $x_i^k = +1$ or -1, are stored in the network. The connection matrix $T = [T_{ij}]$ for non-zero autoconnections (NZA) is obtained by

$$T_{ij} = \sum_{k=1}^{M} x_i^k x_j^k .$$

(1)

During network recall, when the probe vector, denoted as $x^f(t)$, is applied to the network at time t, after time step t+1 the state of neuron i evolves as

$$x_i(t+1) = F_h\left(\sum_{j=1}^{N} T_{ij} x_j^f(t) \right)$$

(2)

where $F_h()$ is the hard-limiting function defined as $F_h(x)=1$ if $x \geq 0$ and -1 if $x<0$.

The capacity of this type of network has been extensively studied by McEliece et al [8], Kuh[9] and Newman[10]. Wang, Krile and Walkup have also defined a unique parameter, C, for characterizing this type of network[11]. In Wang's results, the probability of a bit remaining in an incorrect state, no matter what its previous state is, has been characterized as $\phi(C)$, where $\phi(x)$, the standard error function, is represented as

$$\phi(x) = \frac{1}{\sqrt{2\pi}} \int_x^{\infty} \exp(-t^2/2)dt .$$

(3)

Later, Chung and Krile used this unique parameter to analyze the fault-tolerance capability of this type of network to interconnection faults[12-14]. From their analysis it can be easily seen that as the network evolution is approximated as a Gaussian distribution, the C parameter is related to the mean, S, and variance, σ^2, of the Gaussian distribution as $C=|S/\sigma|$ [11,12]. The mean value of the Gaussian distribution helps to "pull" a neuron to the correct state; hence, it is also called the signal value in the following analysis.

In our analysis, equations and simulation results are based on the following assumption: Each element in the stored vector, x_i^k, is considered to be an independent identically distributed random variable (i.i.d.) with equal probabilities of being +1 or -1. The mean of x_i^k is then zero and the variance is 1.

III. TWO-LEVEL QUANTIZATION

During the analysis following this paper, the interconnections to the inputs of neuron i are denoted as T_{i1}, T_{i2}, ..., T_{iN}. Furthermore assume that these interconnections are clipped into binary values S_{ij} with $S_{ij}=\text{sgn}(T_{ij})$, where

sgn() is defined as sgn(x)=1 if x>0, sgn(x)=0 if x=0, and sgn(x)=-1 if x<0, from (1) and (2), state evolutions of neuron i can be rewritten as

$$x_i(t+1) = F_h\left\{ \sum{}' S_{ij} x_i^f(t) \right\}$$
$$= F_h\left\{ x_i^f(t) + \sum_{j \neq i} S_{ij} x_i^f(t) \right\} .$$

(4)

Assume that the to-be retrieved pattern $x_i^{q'}$ is equal to +1. Then S_{ij} is related to the summation of the products of x_i^k and x_j^k for $1 \leq k \leq M$ as following:

$$S_{ij} = \text{sgn}(x_i^1 x_j^1 + x_i^2 x_j^2 + ... + x_j^{q'} + ... + x_i^M x_j^M)$$

(5)

Each term of $x_i^k x_j^k$, $1 \leq k \leq M$, $k \neq q'$, is a random variable with $P(x_i^k x_j^k=1)=0.5$ and $P(x_i^k x_j^k=-1)=0.5$. Given $x_j^{q'}=1$, from (5) there must be at least (M-1)/2 terms of $x_i^k x_j^k$ equal to 1 for S_{ij} to be greater than 0. Define [x] as the smallest integer which is greater than or equal to x. The conditional probabilities of S_{ij}, where $j \neq i$, are calculated as

$$P(S_{ij}=+1|x_j^{q'}=+1) = P(S_{ij}=-1|x_j^{q'}=-1)$$

$$= \left(\frac{1}{2}\right)^{M-1} \sum_{x=\left[\frac{M-1}{2}\right]}^{M-1} C_x^{M-1}$$

(6)

$$P(S_{ij}=-1|x_j^{q'}=+1) = P(S_{ij}=+1|x_j^{q'}=-1)$$

$$= \left(\frac{1}{2}\right)^{M-1} \sum_{x=\left[\frac{M-1}{2}\right]+1}^{M-1} C_x^{M-1},$$

(7)

where $C_a^b=b!/(a!(b-a)!)$. As we know that S_{ij} is independent of $x_j^f(t)$. Hence, following some manipulations, the probability of $S_{ij} x_j^f(t)$ equal to 1 can be obtained according to the following equation

$$P(S_{ij} x_j^f=+1) = P(S_{ij}=+1| x_j^{q'}=+1)P(x_j^{q'}=+1 \& x_j^f=+1)$$

$$+ P(S_{ij}=+1| x_j^{q'}=-1)P(x_j^{q'}=-1 \& x_j^f=+1)$$

$$+ P(S_{ij}=-1| x_j^{q'}=+1)P(x_j^{q'}=+1 \& x_j^f=-1)$$

$$+ P(S_{ij}=-1| x_j^{q'}=-1)P(x_j^{q'}=-1 \& x_j^f=-1).$$

(8)

The second item in each term of (8) is used to measure the probability of correct and incorrect bits. If we already know that neuron i has a correct input, for those remaining j such that $j \neq i$ there exist b incorrect bits. Since for those j such that

$j \neq i$, there is a total of N-1 terms, we would be able to obtain the following results:

$$P(x_j^{q'}=+1 \& x_j^{f}=+1) = P(x_j^{q'}=-1 \& x_j^{f}=-1) = \frac{N-1-b}{2(N-1)} \quad (9)$$

and

$$P(x_j^{q'}=+1 \& x_j^{f}=-1) = P(x_j^{q'}=-1 \& x_j^{f}=+1) = \frac{b}{2(N-1)}. \quad (10)$$

Hence, when neuron i has a correct input, from (6)-(10) the probabilities of $S_{ij}x_j^{f}(t)$ can be computed as

$$P(S_{ij}x_j^{f}(t) = +1)$$

$$= \left(\frac{1}{2}\right)^{M-1}\left\{ \sum_{x=\left[\frac{M-1}{2}\right]}^{M-1} C_x^{M-1} - \frac{b}{N-1}C_{[(M-1)/2]}^{M-1}\right\}. \quad (11)$$

Similarly, we can obtain

$$P(S_{ij}x_j^{f}(t) = -1)$$

$$= \left(\frac{1}{2}\right)^{M-1}\left\{ \sum_{x=\left[\frac{M-1}{2}\right]}^{M-1} C_x^{M-1} + \frac{b}{N-1}C_{[(M-1)/2]}^{M-1}\right\}. \quad (12)$$

Hence, when neuron i has a correct input, i.e., the ith bit in the probe vector is a correct bit, the mean and the variance of $S_{ij}x_j^{f}(t)$ can be computed as

$$\mu_c = E\{S_{ij}x_j^{f}(t)\} = \left\{ 1-\frac{2b}{N-1}\right\}\left(\frac{1}{2}\right)^{M-1}C_{[(M-1)/2]}^{M-1} \quad (13)$$

and

$$\sigma_c^2 = 1 - \mu_c^2, \quad (14)$$

respectively. Recalling from (4), it is obvious that, from our analysis, each term of $S_{ij}x_j^{f}(t)$ inside $\Sigma S_{ij}x_j^{f}(t)$ for $j \neq i$ is independent and identically distributed (i.i.d.). In the asymptotic case where the number of summation terms is large enough, $\Sigma S_{ij}x_j^{f}(t)$ for $j \neq i$ can be approximated to be a Gaussian distribution. The number of $S_{ij}x_j^{f}(t)$ for $j \neq i$ is N-1. Hence the mean of this approximate Gaussian distribution can be obtained as $(N-1)\mu_c$. Its variance can also be obtained as $(N-1)\sigma_c^2$. Therefore, the average ratio of signal to the standard deviation of noise is obtained as

$$C_c = \frac{1+(N-1)\mu_c}{\sqrt{(N-1)\sigma_c^2}} \quad (15)$$

for a correct bit.

On the other hand, when neuron i has an incorrect input, for those neurons js such that $j \neq i$, there exists b-1 incorrect inputs. Hence, the values in (9) and (10) are modified to be

$$P(x_j^{q'}=+1 \& x_j^{f}=+1) = P(x_j^{q'}=-1 \& x_j^{f}=-1) = \frac{N-b}{2(N-1)} \quad (16)$$

$$P(x_j^{q'}=+1 \& x_j^{f}=-1) = P(x_j^{q'}=-1 \& x_j^{f}=+1) = \frac{b-1}{2(N-1)}. \quad (17)$$

In this case, the probabilities of $S_{ij}x_j^{f}(t)$ are obtained as

$$P(S_{ij}x_j^{f}(t) = +1)$$

$$= \left(\frac{1}{2}\right)^{M-1}\left\{ \sum_{x=\left[\frac{M-1}{2}\right]}^{M-1} C_x^{M-1} - \frac{b-1}{N-1}C_{[(M-1)/2]}^{M-1}\right\} \quad (18)$$

$$P(S_{ij}x_j^{f}(t) = -1)$$

$$= \left(\frac{1}{2}\right)^{M-1}\left\{ \sum_{x=\left[\frac{M-1}{2}\right]+1}^{M-1} C_x^{M-1} + \frac{b-1}{N-1}C_{[(M-1)/2]}^{M-1}\right\}. \quad (19)$$

Therefore, the mean and variance of $S_{ij}x_j^{f}(t)$ are calculated as

$$\mu_i = \left\{ 1-\frac{2(b-1)}{N-1}\right\}\left(\frac{1}{2}\right)^{M-1}C_{[(M-1)/2]}^{M-1} \quad (20)$$

and

$$\sigma_i^2 = 1 - \mu_i^2, \quad (21)$$

respectively. Hence the average ratio of signal to the standard deviation of noise for an incorrect bit is obtained as

Table 1: Probability of direct convergence of networks using two-level quantization strategy.

P_{dc} (N,M,b)	(300,17) b=0	(300,17) b=3	(400,23) b=0	(400,23) b=4	(500,31) b=0	(500,31) b=5
theory	0.9378	0.9193	0.8972	0.8689	0.7886	0.7415
simulation	0.9365	0.9258	0.9150	0.8847	0.8156	0.7621

$$C_i = \frac{-1+(N-1)\mu_i}{\sqrt{(N-1)\sigma_i^2}}.$$

(22)

For a synchronous network, the updating of one neuron is independent of that of other neurons. Hence, the probability of direct convergence (or one-step correct recall), denoted as P_{dc}, for a two-level-quantized network can be obtained as

$$P_{dc}=(1-\phi(c_c))^{N-b}(1-\phi(c_i))^b.$$

(23)

Agreement with this equation has been established with Monte Carlo simulations, as shown in Table. 1 for networks with various (N,M)s. Form Table 1 it is easy to see that even when all of the interconnections of a HAM are clipped to +1 or -1, the network retains certain storage capability, which phenomenon has been mentioned in Amit and Sompolinsky's papers [6,7]. As we know that, from VLSI implementation point of view, clipping interconnections into +1 or -1 makes hardware implementation much easier. Therefore, (23) can be used for tradeoff calculation between network capacity and implementations.

IV. THREE-LEVEL QUANTIZATION WITH CUT-OFF THRESHOLD

Even though the possibility of clipping the interconnection values into +1 or -1 depending on the sign of the original interconnections has been demonstrated in the previous section, questions remain: if we could find some other ways to reduce VLSI complication but still retain network capability the most? As demonstrated in [15], certain interconnections actually keeps more informations than others. Therefore, those interconnections possessing scarce informations should be able to be discarded without affecting network performance much. In this section we would investigate the case where only those interconnections having their original values greater than a threshold, say D, are clipped to a fixed value S_{ij} with $S_{ij}=\mathrm{sgn}(T_{ij})$, where sgn() is

Table 3: Probability of direct convergence of networks having linear quantization.

cut-off value	D=5	D=7	D=9	D=11
P_{dc}	0.9738	0.9856	0.9914	0.9912

the sign function defined in the previous section. If we define a set A to be A={j: $|T_{ij}|$>D}, network evolutions of neuron i can be computed as

$$x_i(t+1) = F_h\left\{ x_j^f(t) + \sum_{j\in A\setminus\{i\}}' S_{ij}x_j^f(t) \right\}.$$

(24)

For those $S_{ij}=1$, the original T_{ij} must be greater than D. Network performances with various clip-off values Ds when (N,M)=(200,17) and (500,35) are illustrated in Table 2. When the clip-off threshold D is equal to 1, a network operates the same as that with two-level quantization technique. From Table 2 we can see that there exists an optimal cut-off threshold value D_{opt} which gives network not only better performance but also less interconnections than the two-level quantization strategy. Furthermore when this optimal cut-off threshold value is used, a network keeps most of its storage capability, i.e., its P_{dc} is compatible to that of original network before quantization. As we can see that, for the network with (N,M) equal to (200,17), the original network has its probability of correct recall equal to 0.982. When the optimal cut-off threshold 3 is applied, the network retains its capacity of 0.916. Alternatively, when (N,M)=(500,31), the original network has a Pdc equal to 0.996. When the optimal cut-off threshold 5 is applied, this network still retains its capability as high as 0.957. From this point of view, we are believed that the three-level quantization with an optimal threshold is a better choice when simplification of hardware implementations is considered. The validation of equations for estimating network Pdc using three-level quantization strategy is shown in [16].

Network performances using linear quantization technique are also obtained and listed in Table 3 for comparison. The quantization strategy is to set those interconnections greater than D to D, those smaller than -D to -D, and those in between remain unchanged. As we can see that though this strategy improve network performance some, the improvement is not significant. As a consequence, the results remain the three-level quantization to be the most prominent strategy when physical implementations are concerned.

Table 2: Probability of direct convergence of networks using three-level quantization strategy. (a) (N,M)=(200,17), b=0 with original Pdc=0.982, (b) (N,M)=(500,31), b=0 with original Pdc=0.996.

cut-off value	D=1	D=3	D=5	D=7
P_{dc}	0.7506	0.9159	0.8979	0.6791

cut-off value	D=1	D=3	D=5	D=7	D=9
P_{dc}	0.8156	0.9453	0.9572	0.9105	0.6961

V. DISCUSSIONS AND CONCLUSIONS

Networks quantized with various strategies are investigated in this paper. Quantization techniques used include two-level, three-level, and linear quantizations. Results in this paper indicate that a network with three-level quantization have better performance than the two-level quantization technique when a properly selected cut-off threshold is used. Therefore when binary quantization are used, three-level techniques with properly selected cut-off value should be adopted. Equations are also derived for estimating the probability of direct convergence of a quantized network. Simulation results show that our theoretical equations estimate network performance closely. Network performances using linear quantization technique are also demonstrated. We found that the linear quantization does not drastically improve network performance compared with the three-level quantization technique. Hence, when taking the tradeoff between hardware implementations and network performances into account, we are convinced that three-level binary quantization with optimal threshold should be a better choice.

REFERENCES

[1]   J.J. Hopfield and D.W. Tank, "Neural computation of decisions in optimization problems," Biol. Cybern., vol. 52, pp. 141-152, 1985.

[2]   D.W. Tank and J.J. Hopfield, "Simple optimization networks: A/D converter and a linear programming circuit," IEEE Trans. Circuit Syst., vol. CAS-33, pp. 533-541, 1986.

[3]   K.A. Boahen and P.O. Pouliquen, " A Heteroassociative Memory Using Current-Mode MOS Analog VLSI Circuits," IEEE Trans. Circuit & Systems, pp.747-755, May 1989.

[4]   M.K. Habib and H. Akel, "A Digital Neuron-Type Processor and Its VLSI Design," IEEE Trans. Circuit & Systems, pp.739-746, May 1989.

[5]   M. Verleysen, B. Sirletti, "A High-Storage Capacity Content-Addressable Memory and Its Learning Algorithm," IEEE Trans. Circuit & Systems, pp.762-766, May 1989.

[6]   H. Sompolinsky, "The theory of neural networks: The Hebb rule and beyond," in Heidelberg Colloquium on Glassy Dynamics Edited by J.L. Van Hermmen and I. Morgenstern, Springer-Verlag, June, 1986.

[7]   D.J. Amit, Modeling Brain Function: The World of Attractor Neural Networks, Cambridge University Press, 1989.

[8]   R.J. McEliece and E.C. Posner, "The capacity of the Hopfield associative memory," IEEE Trans. Information Theory, pp.461-482, July 1987.

[9]   A. Kuh and B. W. Dickinson, "Information capacity of associative memories," IEEE Tran. Info. Theory, vol.35, pp.59-68, January 1989,

[10]   C.M. Newman, "Memory capacity in neural network models: rigorous lower bounds," Neural Networks, vol.1. pp.223-238, 1988.

[11]   J.H. Wang, T.F. Krile, and J.F. Walkup, "Determination of Hopfield associative memory characteristics using a single parameter," Neural Networks, vol. 3, pp.319-331, May 1990.

[12]   P.C. Chung and T.F. Krile, "Characteristics of Hebbian-Type Associative Memories Having Faulty Interconnections," to appear in IEEE Trans. Neural Networks.

[13]   P. C. Chung and T. F. Krile, "Reliability Measures of Hebbian-Type Associative Memories with Faulty Interconnections," IJCNN, San Diego, CA, Vol.I, pp. 847-852, June 1990.

[14]   P. C. Chung and T. F. Krile, "Reliability Characteristics of Hebbian-Type Associative Memories in Network Implementations," IJCNN, Seattle, WA, Vol.II, pp. 363-368, July 1991.

[15]   J.H. Wang, T.F. Krile, and J. Walkup, "Reduction of Interconnection Weights in Higher Order Associative Memory Networks", IJCNN, Seattle, pp. II-177, July, 1991.

[16]   P.C. Chung, C.T.Tsai, and Y.N. Sun, "Characteristics of Hebbian-Type Associative Mempries with Quantized Interconnections", subbmited to IEEE Trans. Circuits and Systems.

Further Cross Talk Reduction of Associative Memory and Exact Data Retrieval

Yukio KUMAGAI[†]   Joarder KAMRUZZAMAN[†]   Hiromitsu HIKITA[††]

[†]Dept. of Compt. Scie. & Syst. Engg.,   [††]Dept. of Mech. Syst. Engg.

Muroran Institute of Technology

27-1 Mizumoto-cho, Mroran-shi, Hokkaido 050, JAPAN

Abstract - The analytical formulation of cross talk due to superposition, which is an essential concept of associative memory based on the outer product algorithm, has been presented in terms of Hamming distance between the memorized keys and the input key. The formulated result of cross talk becomes similar to the Krawtchouk polynomial which is often used in coding theory. Some noticeable properties of cross talk such as symmetricity, linear independency and cancellation characteristics etc. are derived by using the Krawtchouk polynomial. These properties are highly useful for reducing cross talk and make it possible to propose a new architecture of associative memory with less number of high order correlation cross products rather than the conventional one. The architecture proposed in this paper completely removes cross talk due to the memorized keys having odd number Hamming distance from the input key, and relatively large part of the remaining cross talk due to the memorized keys having even number Hamming distance from input key are also removed by utilizing the coding technique which constructs a simple error correcting Hamming code introducing relatively few redundancy. For achieving furthermore advanced exact recall single parity digit into each datum to be memorized is introduced. Comparative studies on exact data retrieval among these proposed architectures are carried out under nearly the same cost performance condition, i.e., nearly the same number of high order cross products used among these proposed architectures and the superior exact data retrieval ability of the proposed associative memory with Hamming code and parity digit are shown by computer simulation.

I. INTRODUCTION

An associative memory is defined as a mapping from an n dimensional vector $\mathbf{x} = \text{col}(x_1, x_2, \ldots, x_n)$ to an m dimensional vector $\mathbf{y} = \text{col}(y_1, y_2, \ldots, y_m)$ associated with it. Usually the components of these vectors are selected from a set $\{\pm 1\}$ since we can expect the cancellation effect by summing up. It has to be noticed that the concept of superposition is the most essential feature of neural associative memory and therefore this situation, i.e., superposition, has to be common in any new proposal to the extensions of associative memory or other neural network architecture. The outer product algorithm conventionally used is a quite simple memorization procedure of data and keys associated with it. But we have to take care of our attention that the outer product algorithm has an underlying rigorous theoretical background which has been established by Kohonen [1,2] and Amari [3,4]. The outer product algorithm is only the lowest order approximation of the pseudoinverse representation which is the converged result of neural networks consisting of the excitatory and inhibitory neurons trained by the Hebbian reinforced correlation learning rule [3,4],[5]. In this meaning, it seems to be true that the exact description of associative memory should be subjected to pseudoinverse representation associated with the learning data and keys. However, the realization of the pseudoinverse needs lots of preassigned higher order correlations, and the complex computation is required for determining the preassigned coefficients of a series expansion of pseudoinverse as shown in the von Neumann expansion formula, for example[23]. Nevertheless, the number of memorized pairs which could be exactly retrieved, i.e., storage capacity, is bounded to the dimension of space spanned by the keys to be used[1,2]. Obviously, this bound is too much low compared to the theoretically possible number. Based on these facts, extensions to the higher order correlation associative memory as a natural extension of the outer product algorithm have been attempted by many researchers under the belief that, by doing so, we could take some great advantages over the pseudoinverse, e.g., the simplicity of the memorization procedure, the mathematical insightness of the overall behavior of data retrieval and the easiness of incremental data memorization or deletion etc. In fact, a number of desirable results have been obtained[9]-[19], and the significant increment of storage capacity has been reported from many points of view, including modified associative memory recently re-examined by J.J.Hopfield[6], [12-19].

However, all the results of these researches concerned so far need monotonically increasing number of higher order cross product terms. This is a crucial issue for real implementation since such a method causes the well known combinatorial explosion. Thus we have attempted the direct computation of cross talk of associative memory that arises in response to an input key in terms of the mutual Hamming distance between the memorized keys and the input key, and devoted to the elucidating of the essential properties of cross talk[10]. Then we could successfully show that the analytically explicit formulation of cross talk is possible in terms of Hamming distance between the memorized keys and the input key in a quite similar functional form by using the Krawtchouk polynomial[7] which is often used in coding theory[8],[20]. Then it is easily shown that this finding is quite useful in devising how to cancel cross talk and how to construct a new associative memory architecture with reduced cross talk using fewer number of cross products than the conventional one [20].

The purpose of this paper is to summarize the results derived by our direct computation and some remarkable properties of cross talk. And furthermore it is intended to describe further advanced cross talk reduction by applying error detectable or correctable coding techniques into the previously proposed associative memory architecture [21,22]. In addition, in this paper, we introduce single parity digit into each datum vector to be memorized for achieving furthermore advanced exact data recall and avoiding increment of high order cross product to be used. We made a performance comparison between these proposed architectures and conventional one in terms of percentage of exact data retrieval. In order to make the comparison on the basis of retrieval cost performance, i.e., exactness of data recall v.s. the number of cross products used, all the architectures using nearly equal number of cross products were compared. Simulation results illustrate that the proposed architecture with Hamming code and parity digit achieves much better cost performance than the conventional one due to its superior ability on exact data retrieval.

II. DESCRIPTION OF ASSOCIATIVE MEMORY

Let $\mathbf{y}^{(i)}=\text{col}(y^{(i)}_1, y^{(i)}_2, ..., y^{(i)}_m)$, $\mathbf{x}^{(i)}=\text{col}(x^{(i)}_1, x^{(i)}_2, ..., x^{(i)}_n)$ denote the i-th pair consisting of an m dimensional datum vector and an n dimensional key vector to be memorized and $\mathbf{I}=\{i : i=1,2, ..., v\}$ the index set of the data and keys to be memorized.

Then the expression of the conventional associative memory based on the outer product algorithm including how to apply an input key and how to obtain the output is given as follows:

$$\mathbf{z}=F\{[\sum_{i=1}^{v} \mathbf{y}^{(i)} \otimes \mathbf{x}^{(i)}] \cdot \mathbf{x}\} \tag{1}$$

where $\otimes$ denotes an outer product operator, F denotes a signum function operating componentwisely, and $\mathbf{z}$, $\mathbf{x}$ are the m dimensional and n dimensional vectors, called the recalled output vector and the input key vector, respectively.

Now the expression of the extended high order correlation associative memory in which every vector is straightforwardly extended to the higher order correlational vector, is described as follows:

$$\mathbf{z}=F\{[\sum_{i=1}^{v} \mathbf{y}^{(i)} \otimes \mathbf{x}^{(i)}_{(\alpha)}] \cdot \mathbf{x}_{(\alpha)}\} \tag{2}$$

where $\mathbf{x}^{(i)}_{(\alpha)}$ denotes the i-th key's extension to higher order correlational vector up to order α whose components consist of nCk kinds of mutually disjoint cross products for k=0,1,...,α, and of total length $\sum_{k=0}^{\alpha}$ nCk. Similarly $\mathbf{x}_{(\alpha)}$ also denotes an input key's extended vector up to order α and its components are subjected to the same condition mentioned above. Throughout this paper, the following is assumed : the components of all these extended high order correlational vectors are arranged in certain preassigned order, e.g., lexicograghical order and each partitioned vector having length nCk is concatenated along with the ascendant order with respect to k (k=0,1, ..., α), and $\mathbf{x}^{(i)}_{(0)}$, $\mathbf{x}_{(0)}$ are set to 1.

III. FUNCTIONAL PROPERTIES OF CROSS TALK

In this paper, we devote to the direct computation described by expression (2) since this expression produces much more general functional form of expression (1) based on the outer product algorithm [10]. In the following, we summarize these computational results and elucidate the behavior of cross talk with respect to Hamming distance between the memorized keys and input key [20]. Throughout this paper, proofs are omitted because of limited space.

Proposition [1]: Let x be an arbitrarily chosen input key belonging to the set of the memorized keys. Then the output recalled by this input key can be described uniquely in terms of Hamming distance d between the memorized keys and this input key as follows:

$$\mathbf{z}=F\{\sum_{d=0}^{n} (\sum_{i_v(d) \in I^{(d)}} \mathbf{y}^{(i_v(d))}) \cdot H(d,\alpha;n) \}.$$

where

$$H(d,\alpha:n)=\sum_{k=0}^{\alpha} h(d,k;n), \qquad h(d,k:n)=\sum_{\zeta=0}^{d} (-1)^{\zeta} \, {}_d C_{\zeta} \cdot {}_{(n-d)} C_{(k-\zeta)}.$$

and the Hamming distance d is defined as follows:

$$d \equiv d(\mathbf{x}^{(i)} : \mathbf{x}) = (1/2) \sum_{j=1}^{n} |(x^{(i)}_j - x_j)|. \; \square$$

Here, the notation $\mathbf{I}^{(d)}=\{ i_v(d) : i_v(d) \in I \}$ (d= 0,1,... ,n) implies that the index set $\mathbf{I}$ ($\supseteq \mathbf{I}^{(d)}$) is uniquely partitioned into the mutually disjoint subset $\{\mathbf{I}^{(d)}\}_{d=0}^{n}$. Consequently, if we desire to recall the datum associated with the applied input key from all the superimposed items, both this desired datum and other data are uniquely decomposed depending upon the Hamming distance between the memorized keys and input key, but the recalled output is the mixture of desired datum and other undesirable data. Therefore, the following corollary is easily deduced:

Corollary [1]: Let $\mathbf{x}^{(i^*)}$ be an input key belonging to the set of the memorized keys and $\mathbf{y}^{(i^*)}$ be the corresponding datum. Then the recalled output z by applying the input key $x^{(i^*)}$ is uniquely decomposed as follows:

$$z=F\{y^{(i^*)} \cdot H(0,\alpha;n) + \sum_{d=0} (\sum_{i_v(d) \in I^{(d)}} y^{(i_v(d))}) \cdot H(d,\alpha;n) \}. \;\square$$

The latter quantity described above becomes just cross talk, since this would add the disturbance to the first quantity $y^{(i^*)}H(0,\alpha;n)$ which is desired one. Thus by using this expression, the quantitative behavior of data retrieval of associative memory can be explicitly explained. Therefore, the investigation of properties of $H(d,\alpha;n)$ is crucial. In the following, we summarize the properties of this function clarified in our study.

Proposition [2]: For $\forall \alpha,(\alpha=0,1,...,n)$, there holds $H(0,\alpha;n) > 0$. $\square$

Proposition [3]: For $\forall d\neq 0, \alpha\neq 0$, there holds $H(0,\alpha;n)>|H(d,\alpha;n)|$. $\square$

Remark [1]: Putting $\alpha=n$ in $H(d,\alpha;n)$, then $H(d,n;n)=0$.   for $\forall d \neq 0$ $\square$

Especially, Remark [1] implies that cross talk becomes zero when α is equal to n. Actually, this fact was pointed out by many researchers. However, this case employs all the possible higher order cross products. In general, this causes the combinatorial explosion. Therefore, this case is of no interest to us since it is highly desirable to construct associative memory of high exact data retrieval ability using cross products as few as possible.

Remark [2]: Stochastically, the number of key vectors of two valued elements attains maximum value around $d=n/2$. But for this region, $|H(d,\alpha;n)|$ is relatively small value as shown later in our numerical computation. $\square$

Now, the definition of the Krawtchouk polynomial [7,8] which is often used in the coding theory is as below:

$$K(d,k;n,q)=\sum_{\zeta=0}^{k} (-1)^{\zeta} \cdot {}_dC_\zeta \cdot {}_{(n-d)}C_{(k-\zeta)} \cdot (q-1)^{(k-\zeta)}. \;\square$$

Putting $q=2$, $k\geq d$, we notice the Krawtchouk polynomial: $K(d,k;n,2)$ is identical with $h(d,k;n)$. Several properties of this polynomial which are particularly useful in our study are summarized below:

Lemma [1]:

Property(1): The following symmetricity holds:

$$K(d,k;n,2)=(-1)^k \cdot K(n-d,k;n,2). \;\square$$

Property(2): The following orthogonality holds:

$$\sum_{d=0}^{n} {}_nC_d \cdot K(d,k;n,2) \cdot K(d,l;n,2)=\delta_{kl} \cdot {}_nC_k \cdot 2^n. \;\square$$

Property(3): The following relation of zeros of $K(d,k;n,q)$ holds:

$K(d,k;n,q)$ has k distinct real zeros on $(0,n)$; $\square$

If these are $v_1<v_2< ... < v_k$ an if $u_1<u_2< ... < u_{k-1}$ are zeros of $K(d,k-1;n,q)$,

then $0<v_1<u_1<v_2< ... < v_{k-1}< u_{k-1}< v_k < n.$ $\square$

Now, utilizing these properties of the Krawtchouk polynomial we drive some noticeable properties of cross talk, $h(d,k;n)$ and $H(d,\alpha;n)$ resulting from our computation [20]. The analysis of these properties provides us with important insights on cross talk reduction and based on that we propose a new associative memory architecture with reduced cross talk using fewer cross products than the conventional one.

Proposition [4]: For $\forall k,\alpha,(k,\alpha=0, ..., n)$, there holds:

$$h(n-d,k;n)=(-1)^k h(d,k;n), \;\; H(n-d+1,\alpha;n)=(-1)^\alpha H(d,\alpha;n). \;\square$$

$H(d,\alpha;n)$ for nonzero d strongly dominates the behavior of cross talk. In this meaning, $h(d,k;n)$ has to be called suitably as the component of $H(d,\alpha;n)$. It is worth mentioning that $|h(d,k;n)|$ has symmetricity w.r.t. $d=n/2$ while $|H(d,\alpha;n)|$ is symmetric within the interval $[1, n]$ with the center at $d=(n+1)/2$, i.e., in the truly cross talk's region, and $|H(0,\alpha;n)|$ corresponding to the desired datum is always greater than $|H(d,\alpha;n)|$ corresponding to nonzero d.

Proposition [5]: For $\forall d,(d=0, ..., n)$, there hold $h(d,n-k;n)=(-1)^d h(d,k;n)$.

For $\forall d,(d=1,2, ..., n)$, there hold $H(d,n-1-\alpha;n)=(-1)^{d-1} H(d,\alpha;n)$. $\square$

Corollary [2]: For $\forall d,(d=0,1, ..., n)$, there holds $\tilde{H}(d,n-\alpha;n)=(-1)^d \cdot H(d,\alpha;n)$.

where $\tilde{H}(d,n-\alpha;n)=\sum_{k=n}^{n-\alpha} h(d,k;n)$ $\square$

Remark [3]: For $\forall k(k,=1,2, ..., n)$, there holds $h(d,n-k;n)=h(d,n;n) \cdot h(d,k;n)$. $\square$

The above proposition and corollary state symmetricity of $h(d,k;n)$ and $H(d,\alpha;n)$ with respect to k and α for some fixed d. The first part of the proposition states symmetricity of the component $h(d,k;n)$ with respect to k for some fixed d. Particular emphasis has to be put on the fact arising due to this symmetricity that the components $h(d,k;n)$ for the extreme low and the corresponding higher order correlation (i.e., k and n-k) have the same magnitude but opposite sign for odd number d, and furthermore both components need equal number of cross products for their realization. Therefore, following corollary [2] which results from the first part of Proposition [5], we can propose a new architecture that simultaneously includes low and the corresponding extreme high order (i.e., the simultaneous inclusion of α-th and $(n-\alpha)$-th order, n being the highest order), and it is easily shown that this new associative memory architecture completely removes cross-talk due to the memorized keys having odd number

Hamming distance from the input key. The number of different kinds of cross products attains maximum value for high-order around n/2. Consequently the conventional high-order associative memory architecture, if necessary, might include the cross products for the order around n/2 up to the highest order n in order to achieve the desired performance. But those cross products are the last ones to be used in the proposed architecture and usually do not need to be included. Thus, compared to the conventional one, the proposed construction extremely reduces the number of cross products to be used and it also greatly facilitates the efforts for constructing the cross products (Remark [3]). In the following, we show these situations in the form of the proposition concretely:

Proposition [6]: For d,k = 0,1, ..., n, there holds:

$$(1/2) \cdot \{h(d,n-k;n)+h(d,k;n)\}=\begin{cases} 0 & \text{for odd number d,} \\ h(d,k;n) & \text{for even number d.} \end{cases}$$

For d=1,2, ..., n and α=0,1,..., n, there holds:

$$(1/2) \cdot \{H(d,n-1-\alpha;n)+H(d,\alpha;n)\}=\begin{cases} 0 & \text{for odd number d,} \\ H(d,\alpha;n) & \text{for even number d.} \square \end{cases}$$

Consequently, the following corollary is derived:

Corollary [3]: for d,α =0,1, ..., n, there holds:

$$(1/2) \cdot \{\widetilde{H}(d,n-\alpha;n)+H(d,\alpha;n)\}=\begin{cases} 0 & \text{for odd number d,} \\ H(d,\alpha;n) & \text{for even number d.} \square \end{cases}$$

Numerical computation results support the propositions, corollaries and remarks stated so far. Fig. 1(a) and 1(b) demonstrate these, exemplifying h(d,k;n), H(d,α;n) normalized by h(0,k;n), H(0,α;n), respectively for n=11. This illustrates the kinds of symmetricity, cross talk cancellation phenomenon, and concrete magnitude of cross talk.

Based on Corollary [3], we deduce the following proposition which describes the architecture of the proposed associative memory that employs less number of higher order cross products compared to conventional one [20].

Proposition [7]: Let $\widetilde{x}^{(i)}_{(n-\alpha)}$, $\widetilde{x}_{(n-\alpha)}$ be the i-th extended high order correlation vector and the extended input key vector, constructed using n to (n-α)-th order respectively. Then the associative memory described by the following expression:

$$z=F\{(1/2) \cdot [(\sum_{i=1}^{v} y^{(i)} \otimes x^{(i)}_{(\alpha)}) \cdot x_{(\alpha)} + (\sum_{i=1}^{v} y^{(i)} \otimes \widetilde{x}^{(i)}_{(n-\alpha)}) \cdot \widetilde{x}_{(n-\alpha)}]\}$$

make it possible to reduce completely cross talk due to the memorized keys having odd number Hamming distance between the memorized keys and input key. $\square$

Figure 2 demonstrates such behavior of cross talk of the proposed architecture, and this substantiates the properties of Proposition [7] and Corollary [3].

However, there still remains cross talk due to the memorized keys having even number Hamming distance between the memorized keys and input key. In the next step, we attempt to introduce error detectable or correctable coding techniques since cross talk has been explicitly formulated in terms of Hamming distance and the error detecting and correcting code has an inherent minimum Hamming distance. As stated previously, contribution to cross talk due to the memorized keys having small and large Hamming distance is relatively large [Fig.1]. Therefore, if the key vectors are coded by using error detectable and correctable coding technique such that the minimum Hamming distance is designed to be greater than the Hamming distance selected properly from those Hamming distances contributing relatively large parts of cross talk still remained, then we can construct an associative memory having no relatively large parts of cross talk corresponding to the Hamming distances less than the selected one [21]. But the use of coding technique introduces some redundancy into the key vectors and thereby, the number of cross product is also increased. If redundancy introduced is not few, cost performance would be rapidly deteriorated leading to combinatorial explosion of cross products since we deal with high order correlation associative memory.

From this point of view, we choose the single error correctable Hamming code with the minimum Hamming distance d_{min}=3. This coding includes relatively few redundancy as the length of code increases. Since the key vector to be coded is defined as the vector having the two valued components, we take the following 1:1 correspondence M from the two valued onto the binary ones:

$$M : \begin{cases} -1 \rightarrow 0, \\ 1 \rightarrow 1. \end{cases}$$

and we construct the Hamming coded key vector of total length N, subjecting to the conventional coding method under the modulo two operation. Thus, N is the minimum integer satisfying the following relation:

$$2^{(N-n)} \geq N+1$$

and the $x^{(i)}_{n+1}$, $x^{(i)}_{n+2}$, ..., $x^{(i)}_{N}$ to be newly added are determined over modulo two operation as follows:

$$x^{(i)}_{n+j} = M^{-1} f_j (M(x^{(i)}_1), M(x^{(i)}_2), ..., M(x^{(i)}_n)) \qquad \text{for j=1,2, ..., N-n, and i=1,2, ..., v,}$$

where f_j, (j=1,2, ..., N-n) denotes linear operators subjecting to the conventional way of constructing Hamming codes [24] and the notation M^{-1} implies the mapping $\{0,1\}$ onto $\{-1,+1\}$. The extended higher order correlation vectors of the coded keys are constructed in the similar way as described earlier. Now, denoting these Hamming coded key vectors by $\overline{\mathbf{x}}^{(i)}{}_{(\alpha)}$ and $\overline{\mathbf{x}}_{(\alpha)}$, then we can assert the following proposition.

Proposition [8]: Let $\overline{\mathbf{x}}^{(i)}{}_{(\alpha)}$ and $\overline{\mathbf{x}}_{(\alpha)}$ be the i-th extended high order correlation vector and the extended input key vector, applied Hamming coding, constructed from n to $(n-\alpha)$-th order respectively. Then the associative memory described by the following expression:

$$\mathbf{z}=F\{(1/2)\cdot[(\textstyle\sum_{i=1}^{v} \mathbf{y}^{(i)}\otimes\overline{\mathbf{x}}^{(i)}{}_{(\alpha)})\cdot\overline{\mathbf{x}}_{(\alpha)} + (\textstyle\sum_{i=1}^{v} \mathbf{y}^{(i)}\otimes\widetilde{\overline{\mathbf{x}}}^{(i)}{}_{(n-\alpha)})\cdot\widetilde{\overline{\mathbf{x}}}_{(n-\alpha)}]\} \tag{4}$$

make it possible to remove cross talk due to the memorized keys having odd d and also having d=2 and d=n-2 Hamming distance between the memorized keys and input key. $\square$

Figure 3 shows the behavior of cross talk in the proposed architecture applied Hamming code with n=11 and N=15. This show that relatively large part of cross talk corresponding to even d is eliminated.

In this paper, we furthermore introduce an even parity digit into each m dimensional vector datum $\mathbf{y}^{(i)}$, (i=1,2, ...,v). Denoting $\mathbf{y}^{(i)}$ with this even parity digit by $\widehat{\mathbf{y}}^{(i)}$, it is well known that we can detect the odd number of failed digits recalled unsuccessfully by observing the even parity of total digits of output vector $\mathbf{z}$ recalled. When the retrieval of data associated with the corresponding input key has been failed, through the observation of our computer experiment we can say empirically, that the absolute value of the net input corresponding to the unsuccessfully recalled digit is quite less than that of corresponding to the successfully recalled digit as it has been already pointed out by Widrow et al [23]. This architecture is represented by the following expression:

$$\widehat{\mathbf{z}}=F\{(1/2)\cdot[(\textstyle\sum_{i=1}^{v} \widehat{\mathbf{y}}^{(i)}\otimes\overline{\mathbf{x}}^{(i)}{}_{(\alpha)})\cdot\overline{\mathbf{x}}_{(\alpha)} + (\textstyle\sum_{i=1}^{v} \widehat{\mathbf{y}}^{(i)}\otimes\widetilde{\overline{\mathbf{x}}}^{(i)}{}_{(n-\alpha)})\cdot\widetilde{\overline{\mathbf{x}}}_{(n-\alpha)}]\} \tag{5}$$

where $\widehat{\mathbf{z}}$ is the output vector of length m+1 and subjected to the following digit correction algorithm:

[correction algorithm] (1): If the parity of recalled output $\widehat{\mathbf{z}}$ is the same as previously constructed even parity, we do not do anything;

(2): If the parity of recalled output $\widehat{\mathbf{z}}$ is not equal to the previously constructed even parity, the digit having least absolute value is altered its sign.

Exact data retrieval ability of the proposed architecture in (5) is compared with architecture in (4).

IV. COMPUTER SIMULATION AND DISCUSSIONS

Computer simulation was carried out in order to compare the ability on exact data retrieval between the proposed and conventional architectures. The architecture proposed with Hamming code, in general, make the length of vector longer due to introducing redundancy. Therefore by adjusting the extended high order correlation properly, the experiment has been done with keeping the condition that the total number of cross products used in each architecture is nearly equal. By doing so, we can evaluate the ability on exact data recall with nearly the same cost. The components of the data and keys are randomly generated with equal probability of occurring +1 and -1.

The experimental results are illustrated in Figure 4, 5 and 6. Conventional architecture, proposed architecture, proposed architecture with Hamming code and proposed architecture with Hamming code and parity digit are compared. Figure 4(a) shows performance comparison among the architectures in terms of percentage of exact recall and total number of failed pairs, using m=9 and n=11. Figure 5(a) shows the same type of comparison with single parity digit introduced in each datum to be memorized i,e., using m=9(10) and n=11. Comparison among the architectures are made with nearly equal number of cross products used and the proposed architectures use less order of correlation than the conventional one. This makes the comparison to be on cost performance basis. Comparison shows that the proposed architectures possess far better retrieval ability than the conventional one, and introduction of Hamming code and parity digit yields the best retrieval cost performance. Even when the number of memorized pairs is almost equal to the maximum possible number of stored pairs (in this experiment, 500 out of maximum possible 512), the proposed architecture with Hamming code and parity digit exactly recall 98% of the stored pairs whereas the conventional architecture recalls 93% as shown in Fig. 5(a). In this case, the number of failed pairs in the conventional architecture is 37 whereas that in our proposed architecture applied Hamming code is only maximum 9. This significant improvement of retrieval cost performance in the proposed architecture with Hamming code and parity digit is due to the substantial reduction of cross talk employed in its architecture. Another criterion of comparing the performance would be the number of failed components of recalled outputs. When an input key is failed to be exactly recalled, it is important how many components of the recalled output is different from the desired one. The number of failed components in the failed pairs is illustrated in Fig. 4(b), 4(c) and 4(d) without parity digit, and in Fig. 5(b), 5(c) and 5(d) with parity digit in the memorized data. In both the cases, i.e., with or without parity digit in the memorized data, the number of failed components is the largest in the conventional architecture, and the least in architecture with Hamming code as it is illustrated in the figures.

Simulation results shown in Fig. 4(b)-4(d) show that in conventional architecture there are failed pairs with in total 90 failed components whereas those in the proposed architecture with Hamming code are 46. Moreover, in the proposed architectures almost all of the failed pairs have only one failed component. This suggest that the introduction of single parity digit in the memorized data could further enhance the performance as illustrated by our simulation results in Fig. 5(a)-5(d). The benefit of introducing Hamming code in the proposed architecture is further exemplified in Fig. 6. Fig. 6(a) shows the substantial performance improvement and comparison of Fig. 6(b) and 6(c) also shows the significant reduction of the number of failed component in the proposed architecture with Hamming code. Observing all these results, we can say that the conventional architecture which needs monotonically increasing number of cross products has the worst exact data retrieval characteristics, especially the broadness being caused by the differences between the desired output and actually recalled output becomes much wider as the number of memorized pairs is increased. The proposed architecture, in construct to this, remains in relatively small variated region. This tendency becomes much better as we adopt the architecture proposed with the Hamming code. The exact data retrieval ability is the highest in the architecture proposed with Hamming coding and parity digit. However, the usefulness of the proposed idea or the introduction of error detectable and correctable coding techniques into the construction of associative memory is surely substantiated through our experiments.

V. CONCLUSION

In this paper, we have formulated explicitly cross talk of associative memory as the functional form of Hamming distance between the memorized keys and the input key. And we have elucidated some noticeable properties of cross talk by using the Krawtchouk polynomial. The properties described in this paper are not only highly useful for reducing cross talk but also make it quite worthwhile to devise a new architecture for further reducing cross talk. The associative memory architecture proposed in this paper eliminates not only cross talk due to the memorized keys having odd number Hamming distance from the input key but also the relatively large part of still remained cross talk having even number Hamming distance from the input key by introducing error detectable and correctable coding techniques. In addition, this proposed architecture considerably reduces the number of cross products to be used compared to the conventional high order associative memory. It can be highly appreciated that, only by adding single parity digit to each datum vector, we have achieved almost exact data retrieval in the proposed architecture with Hamming code. However, we must find out alternative method which is quite suitable for eliminating cross talk due to the memorized keys having even number Hamming distance from the input key since the Hamming-Code coding method presented in this paper is not useful for noise corrupted input keys. The construction of the suitable Liapnov function, suggested by J.J.Hopfield, and the extension to dynamical error correction system are quite significant problems which are currently being investigated with great enthusiasm.

REFERENCES

[1] T. Kohonen, "Correlation matrix memories", IEEE Trans. Comp. C-21., pp. 353-359, 1972.
[2] T. Kohonen, "Self-organization and Associative Memory", 2nd ed., Springer-Verlag: Berlin, 1988.
[3] S. Amari, "Neural theory of association and concept-formation", Biol. Cyber., 26., pp 175-185, 1977.
[4] S. Amari, "The Mathematical Theory of Neural Network", 2nd ed., (in Japanese), Sangyo-Tosyo: Tokyo, 1978.
[5] D. Hebb,"The Organization of Behavior", John Wiley: New York,1949.
[6] J. J. Hopfield, "Neurons with graded response have collective computational properties like those of two- state neurons", in Proc. Nat. Acad. Sci. (USA), 81., pp. 3088-3092, 1984.
[7] S. Szegoe, "Orthogonal Polynomials", Coll. Pub., 23, Amer. Math. Soc.: New York, 1959.
[8] J. H. van Lint, "Introduction to Coding Theory", Springer-Verlag: New York, 1982.
[9] Y. Kumagai, "Associative recall using storage redundancy", IECE Trans. J61-A.1., pp.76-77 (in Japanese),1978.
[10] Y. Kumagai, " Fundamental considerations on higher order correlation associative memory",Memoirs of Muroran Inst. of Tech., 37., pp 53-79 (in Japanese), 1987.
[11] P. Peretto et al.,"Long term memory storage capacity of multiconnected neural networks",Biol.Cyb.,54,pp. 54-63,1986
[12] P. Baldi P et al.,"Number of stable points for spin glasses and neural networks of higher orders",Phys. Rev. Lett.,58.,913-915,1987.
[13] R. J. Mceliece et al.,"The capacity of the Hopfield associative memory", IEEE Trans., IT-33, pp.461-482,1987
[14] A. Dembo, "On the capacity of the associative memories with linear threshold functions", IEEE Trans., IT-35., pp. 709-720, 1989.
[15] H.H. Chen et al.,"High order correlation model for associative memory", in Proc. AIP Conf. 151.,J.S.Denke(Eds), pp.86-99, 1986.
[16] Y. C. Lee et al., "Machine learning using a high order correlation network. Physica, 22D., pp. 276-306, 1986.
[17] D. Psaltis et al, "Higher order associative memory and the optical implementation", Neural Networks,1., pp.149-163,1988.
[18] X. Xu et al., "Constructing associative memories using neural network", Neural Networks, 33.,pp. 301-309,1990.
[19] P. K. Simpson ,"Higher-ordered and intraconnected bidirection associative memories", IEEE Trans., SMC-20, 3., pp.637-653, 1990.
[20] Y. Kumagai et al., "Artificial cross talk reduction of associative memory", in Proc. of Int. Joint Conf. on Neural Networks, IJCNN '92, Baltimore, U.S.A., p. II-153-159, 1992.
[21] Y. Kumagai et al.,"A novel architecture of high order associative memory with reduced cross talk", Artificial Neural Networks 2, I.Aleksander & J.Taylor(ed), North-Holland: Amsterdam, vol. 1, pp. 417-420, 1992.
[22] Y. Kumagai et al.,"Construction of High Order Correlation Associative Memory with Novel Retrieval Cost Performance", to be published in Proc. of 35th Midwest Symp. on CAS, Washington D.C.,USA.(Aug. 1992).
[23] B.Widrow et al.,"Layered Neural Nets for Pattern Recognition",IEEE Trans.,ASSP-36.,7.,pp.1109-1117,1988.
[24] C. R. Rao and S. K. Mitra, "Generalized Inverse of Matrices and its Application",John Wiley:New York,1971.
[25] W. W. Peterson, "Error-Correcting Codes", M.I.T. Press, 1968.

Acknowledgment- The authors are grateful to Prof. Honda of Dept. of Mathematics, Muroran Inst. of Tech., for helpful discussions, and Mr. H. Yoshida for helpful numerical computation and computer simulation.

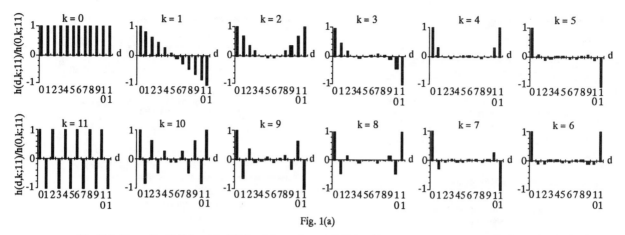

Fig. 1(a)

Fig. 1(a). Normalized h(d, k ; n) by h(0, k ; n) for m=9, n=11. |h(d, k ; n| is symmetric with respect to d and k . Especially in the latter case, it should be noticed that, for odd d, h(d, k ; n) for k and (n-k) are equal in magnitude but opposite in sign. This property plays an important role in designing higher order correlation associative memory with reduced cross talk.

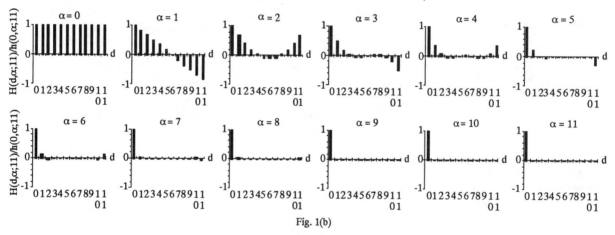

Fig. 1(b)

Fig. 1(b). Normalized H(d, α ; n) by H(0, α ; n) for m=9, n=11. H(0, α; n) > |H(d, α; n)| for any nonzero d and α. |H(d,α; n) | is symmetric with respect to d, attains comparatively lower value for d around n/2 and decreases monotonically with increasing α.

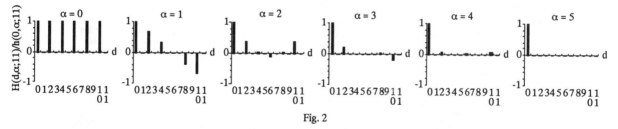

Fig. 2

Fig. 2. Behavior of cross talk of the proposed architecture. This shows the complete elimination of cross due to the memorized keys having odd Hamming distance from the input key.

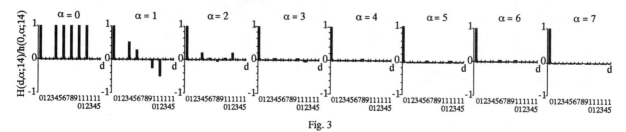

Fig. 3

Fig. 3. Behavior of cross talk of the proposed architecture with Hamming code. Relatively large part of cross talk due to memorized keys having even Hamming distance from input key (d=2 and 14) is eliminated.

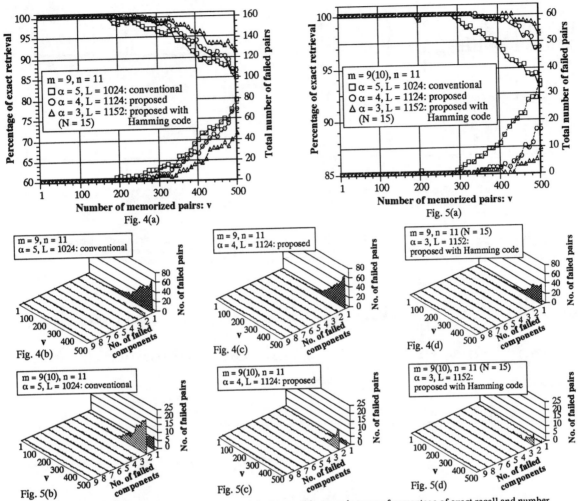

Fig. 4. (a) Comparison of retrieval ability among the three architectures in terms of percentage of exact recall and number of failed pairs. Number of failed components in the failed pairs against memorized pairs: (b) Conventional architecture (c) Proposed architecture (d) Proposed architecture with Hamming code. α is the order of extension, L is the number of cross products used in each architecture, and v is the number of memorized pairs.

Fig. 5. (a) Comparison of retrieval ability among the three architectures in terms of percentage of exact recall and number of failed pairs. Here, each architecture is constructed with single parity digit included in all the data to be memorized. Number of failed components in the failed pairs against memorized pairs: (b) Conventional architecture (c) Proposed architecture (d) Proposed architecture with Hamming code.

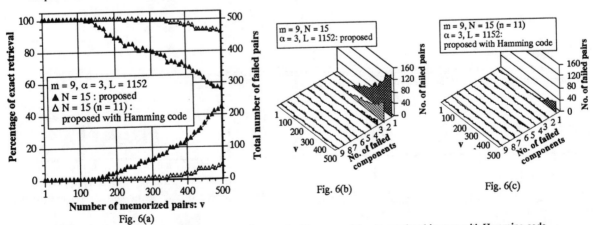

Fig. 6. (a) Performance comparison between the proposed architecture and the proposed architecture with Hamming code using exactly the same correlation order and number of cross products. Number of failed components in the failed pairs against memorized pairs: (b) Proposed architecture (c) Proposed architecture with Hamming code.

Convergence of Higher-Order Neural Networks
With Modified Updating

M. Vidyasagar
Centre for AI & Robotics
Raj Bhavan Circle, High Grounds
Bangalore 560 001, India
E-mail: sagar@yantra.ernet.in

Abstract In this paper, the problem of maximizing a general objective function over the hypercube $\{-1, 1\}^n$ is formulated as that of maximizing a *multilinear polynomial* over $\{-1, 1\}^n$. Two methods are given for updating the state vector of the neural network, called the asynchronous and the synchronous rules, respectively, that are natural generalizations of the corresponding rules for Hopfield networks with a quadratic objective function. It is shown that the asynchronous updating rule converges to a local maximum of the objective function within a finite number of time steps. However, the behavior of the synchronous updating rule is not well-understood. For this purpose, a *modified* synchronous updating rule is presented, that incorporates both *temporal as well as spatial* correlations among the neurons. For the modified updating rule, it is shown that, after a finite number of time steps, the network state vector goes into a limit cycle of length m, where m is the degree of the objective function.

1   Introduction

A vast majority of the current research into feedback neural networks has been focused on the so-called Hopfield networks, which are described by the evolution equation

$$x_i(t + 1) = \text{sign}\left[\sum_{j=1}^{n} w_{ij} x_j(t) + \theta_i\right], \ i = 1, \ldots, n,$$

(1)

where n is the number of neurons, $x_i(t) \in \{-1, 1\}$ is the state of neuron i at time t, w_{ij} is the weight of the interconnection from neuron i to neuron j, and $-\theta_i$ is the firing threshold of neuron i. Hopfield [1] defines the energy of the network as[1]

$$E = \frac{1}{2}\sum_{i=1}^{n}\sum_{j=1}^{n} w_{ij} x_i x_j + \sum_{i=1}^{n} x_i \theta_i,$$

(2)

and proves the following the property: Suppose $w_{ji} = w_{ij}$ for all i, j (symmetric interactions), and $w_{ii} = 0$ for all i (no self-interactions). Finally, suppose the neural states are updated *asynchronously*, as follows: At each (discrete) instant of time t, select an integer $i \in \{1, \ldots, n\}$ at random, compute $x_i(t + 1)$ in accordance with (1), but leave $x_j(t)$ unchanged for all $j \neq i$. In this mode of operation, it is true that

$$E[\mathbf{x}(t + 1)] \geq E[\mathbf{x}(t)],$$

(3)

where $\mathbf{x} = [x_1 \ldots x_n]^t$. Thus, in an asynchronous mode of operation, the neural network will eventually reach a fixed point of the network, that is, a vector $\mathbf{x}_0$ with the property that

$$\mathbf{x}(t) = \mathbf{x}_0 \Rightarrow \mathbf{x}(t + 1) = \mathbf{x}_0,$$

(4)

irrespective of which neuron is updated at time t. In [2], Goles *et al.* prove that, if the network is updated *synchronously*, that is, the states of *all* neurons are updated according to (1), then the network either converges to a fixed point, or else goes into a limit cycle of length two. See [3] for a unification of both convergence results, and [4] for a book-length treatment of the topic.

Therefore, in the case where it is desired to optimize a quadratic function of the form (2) over a finite set $\{-1, 1\}^n$, the behavior of the corresponding neural network (1) is well-understood. It is now known

---

[1] Actually, the energy function defined by Hopfield is the *negative* of this E, but this is a minor difference.

(see, e.g., [5]) that several NP-complete problems can be formulated as the minimization of a quadratic function of the type (2). However, there are situations in which it is more natural to use an objective function which is a polynomial of degree three or higher. One such example is given in [6], wherein the problem of checking whether of not there exists a truth assignment on a set of Boolean variables that makes each of a set of formulas true (commonly known as the "satisfiability problem" and the "original" NP-complete problem), is formulated as a minimization problem over the set $\{0,1\}^n$ where n is the number of literals, and the degree of the objective function is the length of the longest clause in the set of formulas. Another example is given in [7], wherein the problem of algebraic block-coding is formulated as that of maximizing a polynomial over $\{0,1\}^n$, and the degree of the polynomial is equal to the number of information bits.

The objective of the present paper is to state and prove a few convergence theorems for *higher-order* neural networks, which arise when the objective function $E(\mathbf{x})$ to be optimized is a polynomial of degree ≥ 2. In this case the updating rule (1) gets modified to

$$x_i(t+1) = \text{sign}\,\{\nabla E[\mathbf{x}(t)]_i\},\ i = 1,\ldots,n,\quad (5)$$

or, more compactly,

$$\mathbf{x}(t+1) = \text{sign}\,\{\nabla E[\mathbf{x}(t)]\}.\quad (6)$$

If some component of $\nabla E[\mathbf{x}(t)]$ equals zero, say $\nabla E[\mathbf{x}(t)]_i = 0$, then we define $x_i(t+1) = x_i(t)$. As in the case of a quadratic objective function, one can update the neural states either in an asychronous mode or a synchronous mode. The convergence of each type of operation is analyzed.

2 Updating Rules, Fixed Points and Local Maxima

In this section, we briefly study the problem of minimizing a polynomial $E(\mathbf{x})$ as $\mathbf{x}$ varies over the discrete set $\{-1,1\}^n$. Both the asynchronous as well the synchronous updating rules are studied. The relationship between fixed points (under each type of updating rule) and local maxima is explored. But first, a technical issue is laid to rest.

Given any polynomial E_p on $\Re^n$, there is an equivalent polynomial E such that $E_p(\mathbf{x}) = E(\mathbf{x})$ for all $\mathbf{x} \in \{0,1\}^n$, and such that no x_i appears with a power higher than one in $E(\mathbf{x})$. For example, consider the polynomial $E_p : \Re^4 \to \Re$ defined by

$$E_p(\mathbf{x}) = x_1^2 x_2 x_3 + x_1 x_2^3 x_4 + x_2 x_4 + x_3.\quad (7)$$

Then, because $x_i^2 = 1$ whenever $\mathbf{x} \in \{-1,1\}^n$, it is easy to see that if we define $E : \Re^4 \to \Re$ by

$$E(\mathbf{x}) = x_2 x_3 + x_1 x_2 x_4 + x_2 x_4 + x_3,\quad (8)$$

then $E_p(\mathbf{x}) = E(\mathbf{x})$ for all $\mathbf{x} \in \{-1,1\}^n$. Moreover, because no x_i appears with a power higher than one in $E(\mathbf{x})$, it is easy to see that $E(\mathbf{x})$ is an *affine function* of each x_i, for fixed x_j, $j \neq i$. For convenience, such a polynomial is hereafter referred to as a **multilinear polynomial**.

Lemma 1 Suppose $E : \Re^n \to \Re$ is a multilinear polynomial in the n variables $x_1,\ldots,x_n$. Then, specifying the values of $E(\mathbf{x})$ at the 2^n points in $\{-1,1\}^n$ determines E uniquely.

The proof is rather simple and is therefore omitted. Now we consider the two updating rules.

(a) Asynchronous Updating Rule In this updating, an integer $i \in \{1,\ldots,n\}$ is chosen at random, and the value of $x_i(t+1)$ is determined in accordance with (5).

(b) Synchronous Updating Rule In this updating, the states of *all* neurons are updated at each time instant t in accordance with (6).

The next lemma gives an alternate interpretation of asynchronous updating.

Lemma 2 Consider the following updating rule: At each instant of time t, choose an index $i \in \{1,\ldots,n\}$ at random. Replace $x_i(t)$ by $-x_i(t)$, and denote the resulting vector by $\mathbf{y}$. Set $\mathbf{x}(t+1) = \mathbf{y}$ if $E(\mathbf{y}) > E(\mathbf{x})$, and set $\mathbf{x}(t+1) = \mathbf{x}(t)$ otherwise. Then this rule is identical to the asynchronous updating rule of (5).

The proof is omitted because of space limitations.

Next, the concepts of fixed point and local maximum are introduced.

Definition 1 A vector $\mathbf{x}_0 \in \{-1,1\}^n$ is said to be a **fixed point** of the neural network with respect to the objective function E and a particular updating rule, if

$$\mathbf{x}(0) = \mathbf{x}_0 \Rightarrow \mathbf{x}(1) = \mathbf{x}_0\quad (9)$$

under that updating rule.

Note that, if the asynchronous updating rule is used, then a vector $\mathbf{x}_0$ must satisfy (9) irrespective of *which* index i is chosen, in order to qualify as a fixed point.

Definition 2 A vector $\mathbf{x} \in \{-1,1\}^n$ is said to be a **local maximum** of the objective function E if

$$E(\mathbf{x}) \geq E(\mathbf{y}),\ \text{for all } \mathbf{y} \in N(\mathbf{x}),\quad (10)$$

where $N(\mathbf{x})$ denotes the set of n vectors that lie at a Hamming distance of one from $\mathbf{x}$, that is, differ from $\mathbf{x}$ in exactly one component. It is said to be a **strict local maximum** if

$$E(\mathbf{x}) > E(\mathbf{y}) \text{ for all } \mathbf{y} \in N(\mathbf{x}). \quad (11)$$

Now we come to the main result of this section.

Theorem 3 Suppose E is a multilinear polynomial on $\Re^n$. Suppose $\mathbf{x} \in \{-1, 1\}^n$, and that no component of $\nabla E(\mathbf{x})$ is zero. Under these conditions, the following statements are equivalent:

1. $\mathbf{x}$ is a strict local maximum of E.

2. $\mathbf{x}$ is a fixed point under asynchronous updating.

3. $\mathbf{x}$ is a fixed point under synchronous updating.

Proof Let i be an arbitrary index from the set $\{1, \ldots, n\}$. If x_i is replaced by $-x_i$, then the change in E is

$$\Delta E = -2x_i[\nabla E(\mathbf{x})]_i. \quad (12)$$

Hence $\mathbf{x}$ is a fixed point under asynchronous updating if and only if

$$x_i = \text{sign } [\nabla E(\mathbf{x})]_i. \quad (13)$$

Clearly, (13) is also a necessary and sufficient condition for $\mathbf{x}$ to be a fixed point under synchronous updating.

In view of Theorem 3, the next result, which discusses the convergence of the neural network under asynchronous updating, is almost obvious.

Theorem 4 Suppose the network is operated under the asynchronous updating rule. Then the network converges to a local maximum in a finite number of time steps.

However, the behavior of the network under synchronous updating is not well-understood. In the next section, it is shown that, by *modifying* the synchronous updating formula, it is possible to say something about the convergence of the network.

3 Modified Synchronous Updating

In this section, we propose a modification of synchronous updating for higher-order neural networks. In the modified formula, the state of the network at time $t + 1$ depends on the state of the network at times $t, t-1, \ldots, t-(m-2)$, where m is the degree of the objective function. If the objective function is quadratic, then $m = 2$ and $m - 2 = 0$. In this case, the state of the network at time $t + 1$ depends only on its state at time t, and the updating formula reduces to (1). For higher-order objective functions, however, the updating formula makes use of the past states as well. Moreover, the interaction terms are products of up to $m-1$ terms. Hence the updating formula makes use of *temporal as well as spatial* correlation between neurons.

As a prelude to presenting the updating formula, we give a brief discussion on symmetric multilinear forms. Suppose we are given an objective function E, which is a multilinear polynomial of degree m. Then we can write

$$E(\mathbf{x}) = \sum_{k=1}^{m} E_k(\mathbf{x}, \ldots, \mathbf{x}), \quad (14)$$

where E_k is a homogeneous, symmetric, multilinear polynomial. Homogeneity means simply that E_k comprises all terms in E that are a product of *exactly k* terms of the form $x_{i_1} \ldots x_{i_k}$. Symmetry means that

$$E_k(\mathbf{x}_1, \ldots, \mathbf{x}_k) = E_k(\mathbf{x}_{\pi(1)}, \ldots, \mathbf{x}_{\pi(k)}), \quad (15)$$

for all permutations π of $\{1, \ldots, k\}$ into itself. If E_k is symmetric, it is easy to see that one can write

$$E_k(\mathbf{x}_1, \ldots, \mathbf{x}_k) = \mathbf{x}_1^t \, \bar{E}(\mathbf{x}_2, \ldots, \mathbf{x}_k), \quad (16)$$

where $\bar{E}(\mathbf{x}_2, \ldots, \mathbf{x}_k)$ is a homogeneous, symmetric, multilinear polynomial of degree $k - 1$.

For every homogeneous multilinear polynomial E_{hk} of degree k, there is an equivalent homogeneous *symmetric* polynomial E_k such that

$$E_{hk}(\mathbf{x}, \ldots, \mathbf{x}) = E_k(\mathbf{x}, \ldots, \mathbf{x}). \quad (17)$$

In fact, we can define

$$E_k(\mathbf{x}_1, \ldots, \mathbf{x}_k) = \frac{1}{k!} \sum_{\pi} E_{hk}(\mathbf{x}_{\pi(1)}, \ldots, \mathbf{x}_{\pi(k)}), \quad (18)$$

where the summation is over all permutations π of $\{1, \ldots, k\}$ into itself. The procedure is illustrated through an example.

Example 1 In [7], the problem of algebraic block-coding is formulated as an optimization problem over $\{-1, 1\}^n$. As a specific example, consider the so-called Hamming $(7, 4)$ code. In this case, $n = 7$, and the objective function is (see [7] for details)

$$E(\mathbf{x}) = x_1 x_2 x_4 x_5 + x_1 x_3 x_4 x_6 + x_1 x_2 x_3 x_7. \quad (19)$$

In this case, $E(\mathbf{x})$ is a homogeneous polynomial of degree 4. If we define

$$E_{h4}(\mathbf{x}, \mathbf{y}, \mathbf{z}, \mathbf{v}) = x_1 y_2 z_4 v_5 + x_1 y_3 z_4 v_6 + x_1 y_2 z_3 v_7, \quad (20)$$

then E_{h4} is not symmetric. It can be replaced by an equivalent symmetric polynomial as follows: Because of the complexity, the details are given only for the first term, namely $x_1 y_2 z_4 v_5$. There are $4! = 24$ ways of assigning subscripts 1, 2, 4, 5 to the symbols $\mathbf{x}, \mathbf{y}, \mathbf{z}, \mathbf{v}$. Write down all 24 possible combinations, add them up, and divide by 24. Thus

$$E_4(\mathbf{x}, \mathbf{y}, \mathbf{z}, \mathbf{v}) = \frac{1}{24}[x_1 y_2 z_4 v_5 + x_2 y_1 z_4 v_5 + \ldots + x_5 y_4 z_2 v_1]. \tag{21}$$

Symmetric versions of the other terms can be constructed in an entirely analogous manner.

Now we are ready to state the updating rule. Suppose the objective function $E(\mathbf{x})$ is a multilinear polynomial of degree m in $x_1, \ldots, x_n$. Then, without loss of generality, we can write

$$E(\mathbf{x}) = \sum_{k=1}^{m} E_k(\mathbf{x}, \ldots, \mathbf{x}), \tag{22}$$

where E_k is a homogeneous, symmetric, multilinear polynomial. Define $\bar{E}_k$ as before, namely by

$$E_k(\mathbf{x}_1, \ldots, \mathbf{x}_k) = \mathbf{x}_1^t \, \bar{E}_k(\mathbf{x}_2, \ldots, \mathbf{x}_k), \tag{23}$$

where $\bar{E}_k$ is a homogeneous, symmetric, multilinear polynomial of degree $k-1$. Note that

$$\nabla E_k(\mathbf{x}) = k \, \bar{E}_k(\mathbf{x}, \ldots, \mathbf{x}). \tag{24}$$

The idea behind the modified updating rule is rather simple, though the notation can become somewhat cumbersome. To state it, it is helpful to introduce the symbol $S(k, m)$. Given integers $m > k > 0$, let $S(k, m)$ denote the set of all k-tuples $(i_1, \ldots, i_k)$ such that

$$0 \leq i_1 < i_2 < \ldots < i_k \leq m - 1. \tag{25}$$

For example, $S(3, 5)$ equals

$$S(3,5) = \{(0,1,2), (0,1,3), (0,1,4), (0,2,3), (0,2,4),$$
$$(0,3,4), (1,2,3), (1,2,4), (1,3,4), (2,3,4)\}. \tag{26}$$

It is easy to see that the number of elements in $S(k, m)$ equals $m!/k!(m-k)!$.

Given an objective function of the form (25), we first define the constants α_k, $k = 1, \ldots, m$, by

$$\alpha_k = \frac{(m-k)!k!}{(m-1)!}. \tag{27}$$

For each k in $\{1, \ldots, m\}$, define the function $F_k(t)$ as follows: Let π vary over all elements of the set $S(k-1, m-1)$. For each π, define

$$F_{k,\pi}(t) = \bar{E}_k[\mathbf{x}(t - \pi_1), \ldots, \mathbf{x}(t - \pi_{k-1})], \tag{28}$$

and define

$$F_k(t) = \sum_{\pi \in S(k-1,m-1)} F_{k,\pi}(t). \tag{29}$$

Now the updating rule is as follows:

$$\mathbf{x}(t+1) = \text{sign}\left[\sum_{k=1}^{m} \alpha_k \, F_k(t)\right]. \tag{30}$$

Example 1 (Continued) For the function E_4 of (21) (which corresponds to just the first term of the objective function of (19)), we have

$$\bar{E}_4(\mathbf{y}, \mathbf{z}, \mathbf{v}) = \frac{1}{24} \begin{bmatrix} y_2 z_4 v_5 + \ldots + y_5 z_4 v_2 \\ y_1 z_4 v_5 + \ldots + y_5 z_4 v_1 \\ 0 \\ y_1 z_2 v_5 + \ldots + y_5 z_2 v_1 \\ y_1 z_2 v_4 + \ldots + y_4 z_2 v_1 \\ 0 \\ 0 \end{bmatrix}. \tag{31}$$

In this case, $m = k = 4$, so the set $S(3, 3)$ consists of the single element $(0, 1, 2)$. Therefore, from (29),

$$F_4(t) = \bar{E}_4[\mathbf{x}(t), \mathbf{x}(t-1), \mathbf{x}(t-2)]. \tag{32}$$

The constant α_4 equals 4, as can be easily computed. Hence the updating rule is

$$\mathbf{x}(t+1) = \text{sign}\{4\bar{E}_4[\mathbf{x}(t), \mathbf{x}(t-1), \mathbf{x}(t-2)]\}. \tag{33}$$

Notice that, if $\mathbf{x}(t-1)$ and $\mathbf{x}(t-2)$ are each replaced by $\mathbf{x}(t)$, the updating rule becomes

$$\mathbf{x}(t+1) = \text{sign}\{4\bar{E}_4[\mathbf{x}(t), \mathbf{x}(t), \mathbf{x}(t)]\}$$
$$= \text{sign}\{\nabla E_4[\mathbf{x}(t)]\}. \tag{34}$$

Thus the modification consists of the introduction of *time delays* in the gradient updating rule, in a systematic fashion.

It is left to the reader to verify that, if $m = 2$ so that the objective function is quadratic and has the form

$$E(\mathbf{x}) = \frac{1}{2}\mathbf{x}^t \mathbf{W} \mathbf{x} + \mathbf{x}^t \theta, \tag{35}$$

then the updating rule becomes

$$\mathbf{x}(t+1) = \text{sign}[\mathbf{W}\mathbf{x}(t) + \theta], \tag{36}$$

which is the familiar rule. Hence (30) is a "true" generalization of the Hopfield network.

What is the advantage gained by using the complicated updating rule (30) in place of the simpler gradient rule

$$\mathbf{x}(t+1) = \text{sign } \{\nabla E[\mathbf{x}(t)]\}? \qquad (37)$$

The principal advantage is that the dynamics of the system (30) can be analyzed precisely. This is the main result of this section, and indeed, of the paper. Before stating this result, a preliminary issue is resolved.

Definition 3 A vector $\mathbf{x}_0 \in \{-1, 1\}^n$ is said to be a **fixed point** of the system (30) if

$$\mathbf{x}(0) = \mathbf{x}(1) = \ldots = \mathbf{x}(m-2) = \mathbf{x}_0$$

$$\Rightarrow \mathbf{x}(t) = \mathbf{x}_0 \text{ for all } t \geq m - 1. \qquad (38)$$

This is just the standard definition of a fixed point, adapted for the fact that the right side of (30) contains some delayed terms.

Theorem 5 A vector $\mathbf{x}_0 \in \{-1, 1\}^n$ is a fixed point of (30) if and only if it is a fixed point of the gradient updating rule, that is, if and only if

$$\mathbf{x}_0 = \text{sign } [\nabla E(\mathbf{x}_0)]. \qquad (39)$$

Theorem 5 means that, even though there are time delays present in the updating rule (30), the fixed points are the same as those of the gradient updating rule. Combined with Theorem 3, this result means that, should the state vector of the network converge to a fixed point, this fixed point will be a local maximum of the objective function E, even though time delays are introduced into the updating rule.

Proof Suppose $\mathbf{x}_0$ satisfies (38), and suppose $\mathbf{x}(0) = \mathbf{x}(1) = \ldots = \mathbf{x}(m-2) = \mathbf{x}_0$. Then it follows from (28) that

$$F_{k,\pi} = \bar{E}_k(\mathbf{x}_0, \ldots, \mathbf{x}_0). \qquad (40)$$

Therefore, from (29),

$$F_k = \frac{(m-1)!}{(k-1)!(m-k)!} \bar{E}_k(\mathbf{x}_0, \ldots, \mathbf{x}_0), \qquad (41)$$

where the coefficient on the right side is the number of elements of the set $S(k-1, m-1)$. Now combining (27) and (41) shows that

$$\alpha_k F_k = k\bar{E}_k(\mathbf{x}_0, \ldots, \mathbf{x}_0) = \nabla E_k(\mathbf{x}_0). \qquad (42)$$

Finally,

$$\sum_{k=1}^{m} \alpha_k F_k = \sum_{k=1}^{m} \nabla E_k(\mathbf{x}_0) = \nabla E(\mathbf{x}_0). \qquad (43)$$

Therefore (38) is satisfied if and only if

$$\mathbf{x}_0 = \text{sign } [\nabla E(\mathbf{x}_0)], \qquad (44)$$

that is, if and only if $\mathbf{x}_0$ is a fixed point under the gradient updating rule.

Now we come to the main result.

Theorem 6 With the updating rule (30), there exists a finite integer N such that

$$\mathbf{x}(t) = \mathbf{x}(t-m), \text{ for all } t \geq N. \qquad (45)$$

Theorem 6 states that, with the modified updating rule, each trajectory of the neural network eventually goes into a limit cycle of length *exactly* equal to m, where m is the degree of the objective function. Observe that the theorem does not rule out the possibility that the network settles into a fixed point.

Proof Define a function $G(t)$ as follows:

$$G(t) = \sum_{k=1}^{m} \alpha_k \, G_k(t), \qquad (46)$$

where α_k is defined in (27), and $G_k(t)$ is defined as follows: Let π vary over $S(k, m)$, and define

$$G_{k,\pi}(t) = E_k[\mathbf{x}(t-\pi_1), \ldots, \mathbf{x}(t-\pi_k)], \qquad (47)$$

$$G_k(t) = \sum_{\pi \in S(k,m)} G_{k,\pi}(t). \qquad (48)$$

Now let us compute the quantity

$$\Delta G(t) = G(t+1) - G(t). \qquad (49)$$

It is claimed that

$$\Delta G(t) = [\mathbf{x}(t+1) - \mathbf{x}(t-m+1)]^t \left[\sum_{k=1}^{m} \alpha_k \, F_k(t) \right], \qquad (50)$$

where $F_k(t)$ is defined in (29). Suppose for the moment that (50) is true. Then, in view of (30), it follows that if $\mathbf{x}(t+1) \neq \mathbf{x}(t-m+1)$, then $\Delta G(t) > 0$. Moreover, the increase $\Delta G(t)$ can be bounded from below. In fact, $\Delta G(t)$ is at least equal to the magnitude of the smallest component of $\sum_k \alpha_k F_k(t)$. Since $\mathbf{x}(t)$ varies over a finite set, this quantity itself can be bounded from below, say by ϵ. Similarly, $G(t)$ can be bounded from above, say by M. Thus it follows that $\mathbf{x}(t+1) \neq \mathbf{x}(t-m+1)$ cannot happen more than $[M/\epsilon]$ times, that is, a finite number of times.

Thus the proof is complete if it can be shown that (50) holds. What we show instead is that

$$G_k(t+1) - G_k(t) = [\mathbf{x}(t+1) - \mathbf{x}(t-m+1)]^t F_k(t). \qquad (51)$$

Combined with (46), this is enough to establish (50).

To prove (51), we proceed as follows: Note that

$$\Delta G_k(t) = \sum_{\theta \in S(k,m)} E_k[\mathbf{x}(t - \theta_1 + 1), \ldots, \mathbf{x}(t - \theta_k + 1)]$$

$$- \sum_{\pi \in S(k,m)} E_k[\mathbf{x}(t - \pi_1), \ldots, \mathbf{x}(t - \pi_k)]. \quad (52)$$

If $\theta_1 \neq 0$, then there exists a π in $S(k, m)$ such that

$$(\theta_1 - 1, \ldots, \theta_k - 1) = (\pi_1, \ldots, \pi_k). \quad (53)$$

So the corresponding terms in the two summations cancel out. Similarly, if $\pi_k \neq m$, then there exists a θ in $S(k, m)$ such that (53) holds. So once again the corresponding terms in the two summations cancel out. Thus we are left with

$$\Delta G_k(t) = \sum_{\theta_1 = 0} E_k[\mathbf{x}(t - \theta_1 + 1), \ldots, \mathbf{x}(t - \theta_k + 1)]$$

$$- \sum_{\pi_k = m} E_k[\mathbf{x}(t - \pi_1), \ldots, \mathbf{x}(t - \pi_{k-1}), \mathbf{x}(t - \pi_k)] \quad (54)$$

However, since E_k is symmetric, we can write

$$\sum_{\theta_1 = 0} E_k[\mathbf{x}(t - \theta_1 + 1), \ldots, \mathbf{x}(t - \theta_k + 1)]$$

$$= [\mathbf{x}(t + 1)]^t H, \quad (55)$$

where

$$H = \sum_{\phi_2, \ldots, \phi_n) \in S(k-1,m-1)} \bar{E}[\mathbf{x}(t - \phi_2 + 1), \ldots, \mathbf{x}(t - \phi_m + 1)]$$

$$= F_k(t). \quad (56)$$

Similarly,

$$- \sum_{\pi_k = m} E_k[\mathbf{x}(t - \pi_1), \ldots, \mathbf{x}(t - \pi_{k-1}), \mathbf{x}(t - \pi_k)]$$

$$= [\mathbf{x}(t - m + 1)]^t F_k(t). \quad (57)$$

Combining (56) and (57) with (54) gives (51). This completes the proof.

4   Conclusions

In this paper, we have formulated the problem of maximizing a general objective function over the hypercube $\{-1, 1\}^n$ as that of maximizing a *multilinear polynomial* over $\{-1, 1\}^n$. We have given two methods for updating the state vector of the neural network, called the asynchronous and the synchronous rules, respectively, that are natural generalizations of the corresponding rules for Hopfield networks with a quadratic objective function. We have shown that the asynchronous updating rule converges to a local maximum of the objective function within a finite number of time steps. However, the behavior of the synchronous updating rule is not well-understood. For this purpose, we have *modified* the synchronous updating rule in such a way that it incorporates both *temporal as well as spatial* correlations among the neurons. For the modified updating rule, we have shown that, after a finite number of time steps, the network state vector goes into a limit cycle of length m, where m is the degree of the objective function.

References

[1] J. J. Hopfield, "Neural networks and physical systems with emergent collective computational capabilities," *Proc. Nat'l. Acad. Sci. (U.S.A.)*, Vol. 79, pp. 2554-2558, 1982.

[2] E. Goles, E. Fogelman and D. Pellegrin, "Decreasing energy functions as a tool for studying threshold networks," *Disc. Appl. Math*, Vol. 12, pp. 261-277, 1985.

[3] J. Bruck and J. W. Goodman, "A generalized convergence theorem for neural networks," *IEEE Trans. Info. Thy.*, Vol. 34, No. 5, pp. 1089-1092, Sept. 1988.

[4] Y. Kamp and M. Hasler, *Recursive Neural Networks for Associative Memory*, John Wiley, Chichester (U.K.), 1990.

[5] J. J. Hopfield and D. W. Tank, " 'Neural' computation of decision optimization problems," *Biol. Cybernet.*, Vol. 52, pp. 141-152, 1985.

[6] C. L. Masti and M. Vidyasagar, "A stochastic high-order connectionist network for solving inferencing problems," *Proc. Int. Joint. Conf. Neural Networks*, Singapore, p. 911-916, Nov. 1991.

[7] J. Bruck and M. Blum, "Neural networks, error-correcting codes, and polynomials over the binary n-cube," *IEEE Trans. on Info. Thy.*, Vol. 35, No. 5, pp. 976-987, Sept. 1989.

A Theory on a Neural Net with Non-Monotone Neurons

Hiro-F. Yanai† and Shun-ichi Amari††
† Department of Information and Communication Engineering, Faculty of Engineering,
Tamagawa University, Machida, Tokyo 194, Japan
†† Department of Mathematical Engineering, Faculty of Engineering,
University of Tokyo, Bunkyo-ku, Tokyo 113, Japan

Abstract—We show a theoretical equation on dynamical processes of a neural net consisting of neurons with two-stage nonlinear dynamics. The neurons have non-monotone response characteristics when parameters are chosen as such. By the exact solution, we prove the high performance of the auto-associative memory net consisting of non-monotone neurons within a general framework. Besides, we show a correspondence of the dynamical recalling processes of non-monotone neurons with the learning rule of orthogonal-projection type. Based on the correspondence, we can understand intuitively why non-monotone neurons are effective.

I. INTRODUCTION

In mathematical models of neural nets, it has been customary to use monotone neurons (monotonically responding neurons), *i.e.*, simple threshold elements or sigmoidal-function elements. In recent years, a couple of researchers have pointed out, by computer simulations or equilibrium state analyses, that non-monotone neurons make the auto-associative memory net more efficient in memorizing and recalling patterns (vectors) with a correlation-type synaptic connection matrix [1], [2], [3] (see [4] for optimal capacity of a non-monotone neuron free from the learning rule).

In a broader sense, non-monotone neurons could be placed in the discussion of time history of neurons, *i.e.*, hysteresis, refractory periods, *etc.* Although a non-monotone neuron is a novel concept, we can find a discussion on effects of history of a neuron in the work of Caianiello [5]. In that work he defined a neuron model whose response at time t is determined by a linear combination of responses of the neurons at $t-1$, $t-2$, ... On this line of formulation, we can deal with various kinds of history effects such as refractory periods or hysteresis [6], [7]. In rather simpler line of discussion like these, we can also find the work discussing effects of a response function of a continuous neuron model [8].

A non-monotone neuron employed here cannot be formulated by the model of Caianiello [5] in the sense that, in general, its internal state (membrane potential) cannot be expressed by any linear combination of neuron states.

In the present paper, we show exact solution on the dynamics of a neural net with non-monotone neurons whose response function is expressed by piecewise linear functions (In fact we are not dealing only with a non-monotone neuron in the sense that the neuron we will define contain a non-monotone neuron as just one of possible cases). By the theoretical solution we can unveil the "mysteriously" good effects of a non-monotone neuron when used in auto-associative memory nets [1].

Besides, we show a correspondence between the dynamical recall processes of a neural net with those neurons and the orthogonal-projection type learning processes. The orthogonal-projection type learning rule is a widely known procedure in which mutually interfering memory patterns are made orthogonalized into synaptic weights, resulting in the high performance when used together with monotone neurons [9], [10]. The key to improvement of the performance by the use of non-monotone neurons lies in the fact that the neurons are doing processes in just the same way as orthogonal-projection learning rule do in constructing synaptic weights in the learning process.

A non-monotone neuron would be more attractive if we note that the number of neurons in a net is, in general, much smaller than that of synapses. A net consisting of complex neurons and simple synapses is less complex than that consisting of simple neurons and complex synapses. This would be a new direction of neural net research that had been dealing mainly with complex synapses.

In the following, we define the model for use as the auto-associative memory net. Then we show exact equations for the dynamics of the net, comparing the theory with computer simulations, and prove that the performance of the net is optimized when the neuron is non-monotone. And then, we explain why a non-monotone neuron is effective by showing the correspondence of a non-monotone neuron with orthogonal-projection learning. Finally, we will discuss some possible development of our theory.

II. DEFINITION OF THE MODEL

We define an auto-associative memory net with two-stage nonlinear dynamics as

$$\mathbf{x}' = \mathrm{sgn}\big[\mathbf{W}\big(\mathbf{x} - f(\mathbf{W}\mathbf{x})\big)\big] \\ = \mathrm{sgn}\big[\mathbf{W}\mathbf{x} - \mathbf{W}f(\mathbf{W}\mathbf{x})\big] \tag{1}$$

where **x** is the initial state of the net and **x**′ the next state, whose ith components being the state of the ith neuron x_i and x_i' respectively (x_i, x_i' = +1 or −1). The matrix **W** is a synaptic weight matrix whose (i, j) component is a synaptic weight from jth neuron to ith neuron, w_{ij}. The function sgn is a simple threshold function, and f is a piecewise linear function specific to our model. The functions are defined as

$$\text{sgn}(u) = \begin{cases} 1 & (u \geq 0) \\ -1 & (u < 0) \end{cases}$$

$$f(v) = \begin{cases} a(v+h) - c & (v \leq -h) \\ 0 & (-h < v < h) \\ a(v-h) + c & (v \geq h) \end{cases} \quad (2)$$

where h and c are positive. Note that the above functions operate componentwise if u and v are vectors.

Their function shape is shown in Fig. 1. If we put $f(u) \equiv 0$, (1) represents a net with simple threshold elements. And if we put $a = 0$, the model is reduced to the non-monotone neuron originally proposed by Morita *et al.* [1]. Although the shape of f needs not to be restricted to that of (2), we confine ourselves to that family of functions for the convenience of theoretical analyses.

Rewriting (1) componentwise, we have

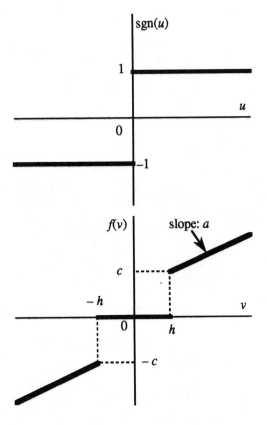

Fig. 1. Function shapes of sgn(u) and $f(u)$

$$x_i' = \text{sgn}\left[\sum_{j=1}^{n} w_{ij}\left(x_j - f(\sum_{k=1}^{n} w_{jk}x_k)\right)\right] \quad (3)$$

where $i = 1, 2, ..., n$ and n is the number of neurons in the net.

From the second line of (1), we can see that the dynamics of the neuron involve two stages. First the input strength **Wx** is computed and f is operated, then again **W** is operated, and finally the resultant vector is subtracted from the original **Wx**. To put it roughly, the neuron responds to the input non-monotonically if the parameter a in f is positive, although the response is not simple because the matrix **W** and a nonlinear function f is involved in the operation.

For synaptic weights, we adopt the correlation-type. From m memory patterns (column vectors)

$$\mathbf{s}_1, \mathbf{s}_2, ..., \mathbf{s}_\mu, ..., \mathbf{s}_m \quad (4)$$

the correlation-type synaptic weight matrix is defined by

$$\mathbf{W} = \frac{1}{n}\sum_{\mu=1}^{m}\mathbf{s}_\mu \mathbf{s}_\mu^T \quad (5)$$

where T denotes transposition. Or componentwise we have

$$w_{ij} = \frac{1}{n}\sum_{\mu=1}^{m}s_i^\mu s_j^\mu \quad (6)$$

where s_i^μ (= +1 or −1) is the ith component of $\mathbf{s}_\mu$. In the following discussion, we consider random memories: s_i^μ equals to +1 or −1 with equal probability.

III. Theory of the Dynamics

Description of exact dynamics of the auto-associative memory net is practically impossible for the reason that the number of necessary variables explodes as time goes by [11]. Therefore analyses of the long-time behavior (including the equilibrium) of the net rely on some approximation schemes such as replica symmetry (even in the case of simple threshold neurons). Here we shall evaluate the performance of the net by the exact analysis of one-step dynamics. (In the case of a non-monotone neuron, dynamics of the neuron is essentially two-step as can be seen by (1). In the same sense that the analysis of two-step dynamics of a simple neuron is exact, our one-step analysis of (1) is also exact.)

Calculations are made based on the method of statistical neurodynamics developed by Amari [12]. We consider, for the sake of simplicity, a zero-diagonal matrix, *i.e.*,

$$w_{ii} = 0 \quad (7)$$

1386

We assume the number of neurons n and memory patterns m are very large, then the dynamics of the net is described by a, h and c in (2) and two additional variables: similarity l and load ratio r. Similarity l is a measure of distance of the state of the net from the nearest memory pattern, which is defined by the scalar product of the state of the net $\mathbf{x}$ with the pattern, say $\mathbf{s}_1$:

$$l \equiv \frac{1}{n}\mathbf{s}_1 \cdot \mathbf{x} = \frac{1}{n}\sum_{i=1}^{n} s_i^1 x_i \qquad (8)$$

$l = 1$ means the state of the net exactly matches with the pattern. Load ratio is defined by

$$r = m/n \qquad (9)$$

We have derived exact theoretical equations for the dynamics of (1) for any combinations of l, r, a, h, and c. In the calculation, we evaluate the mean and the variance of the input $\mathbf{Wx}$, resulting in the signal term and the Gaussian noise. Similarly the signal and the noise term of $\mathbf{W}f(\mathbf{Wx})$ is evaluated under the condition that $\mathbf{Wx}$ is given – in other words, the variance of $\mathbf{W}f(\mathbf{Wx})$ and the covariance between $\mathbf{Wx}$ and $\mathbf{W}f(\mathbf{Wx})$. By the calculation we have seen that those terms are positively correlated, to put it roughly, when $a > 0$. Thus by the appropriate choice of the function parameters the signal to noise ratio of the whole input becomes greater than a simple neuron.

Here we just explain the calculation on error probability after one-step dynamics of (1) for the case f is linear, i.e., $h = c = 0$. We assume, without loss of generality, that all of the components of $\mathbf{s}^1$ is $+1$. Then the ith component of $\mathbf{Wx}$ is written as

$$(\mathbf{Wx})_i = l + N_i, \qquad N_i = \frac{1}{n}\sum_{j\neq i}\sum_{\mu\neq 1} s_i^\mu s_j^\mu x_j \qquad (10)$$

where N_i is a random variable subject to the Gaussian distribution. Using this equation, since n is large, we have

$$\left(\mathbf{W}^2\mathbf{x}\right)_i \cong l + \frac{1}{n}\sum_{j\neq i}\sum_{\mu\neq 1} s_i^\mu s_j^\mu\left(l + N_j\right) \qquad (11)$$

So we have

$$\begin{aligned}
\mathbf{Wx} &- \mathbf{W}f(\mathbf{Wx}) \\
&= \mathbf{Wx} - a\mathbf{W}^2\mathbf{x} \\
&\cong (1-a)l \\
&+ \underbrace{\frac{1}{n}\sum_{j\neq i}\sum_{\mu\neq 1} s_i^\mu s_j^\mu\left(x_j - al\right)}_{\equiv X} - a\underbrace{\frac{1}{n}\sum_{j\neq i}\sum_{\mu\neq 1} s_i^\mu s_j^\mu N_j}_{\equiv Y}
\end{aligned} \qquad (12)$$

The expectations, the variances and the covariance concerning X and Y are

$$\begin{aligned}
&\mathrm{E}[X] = 0, \qquad \mathrm{E}[Y] = rx_i, \\
&\mathrm{var}[X] = r(1 - 2al^2 + a^2l^2), \qquad \mathrm{var}[Y] = r(1+r), \\
&\text{and } \mathrm{cov}(X,Y) = r(1-al^2)
\end{aligned} \qquad (13)$$

Therefore we have the total variance of the noise term, and obtain the following theorem.

Theorem:

For $f(u) = au$, the probability of errors ε in the state $\mathbf{x}'$ is given by

$$\varepsilon = \frac{1+l}{2}\phi\left(\frac{(1-a)l - ar}{\sigma}\right) + \frac{1-l}{2}\phi\left(\frac{(1-a)l + ar}{\sigma}\right) \qquad (14)$$

where

$$\sigma^2 = r\left[1 - 2al^2 + a^2l^2 + a^2(1+r) - 2a(1-al^2)\right] \qquad (15)$$

and the function ϕ is an error integral defined by

$$\phi(u) = \int_u^\infty \frac{1}{\sqrt{2\pi}}\exp\left(-\frac{t^2}{2}\right)dt \qquad (16)$$

❑

The error probability ε and the similarity l' defined for $\mathbf{x}'$ just as (8) are related to each other by

$$\varepsilon = (1 - l')/2 \qquad (17)$$

Fig. 2 and Fig. 3 show relation between a and error probability ε by the one-step dynamics of (1). They are for $l = 1$, that is, the initial state of the net is set exactly to one of the memory patterns. In Fig. 2 computer simulations are shown with the theory. Theory agrees with the simulation perfectly. From the figures we can see that the performance of the net is better for $a > 0$ than for $a = 0$ (the simple threshold neuron) or $a < 0$. Since the positive a makes the neuron respond non-monotonically to inputs, this proves the superiority of a non-monotone neuron over a monotone neuron. For example, when there are 10^5 neurons, the net can store over 2×10^4 patterns without an error if a is set around 0.45, whereas if $a = 0$, over 10^3 errors appear in the same situation.

The reader may wonder if the above comparison of the performance is legitimate or not because (1) consists of two stages for $a \neq 0$ and one stage for $a = 0$. So we should note

1387

that by the two steps of dynamics of (1) with $a = 0$, error probability gets even greater than one step (see *e.g.*, [13]).

Since the derivation of the dynamical equation for the general function of f is very complicated, we will report on it in detail elsewhere. Here we just show a theoretical and a simulation results for another typical shape of function f, that is, for a stepwise function ($a = 0$). From Fig. 4 and Fig. 5, again, we can see the superiority of a non-monotone neuron over a monotone one if the parameters are appropriately chosen.

Then what is the optimal choice of parameters a, h and c for given r? Here we just mention that the minimum error probability is realized at parameter values around $h \approx c \approx 0$ (*i.e.*, when f is almost linear). This conclusion is obtained from the equation that is a generalization of *theorem* to general shapes of the function.

To measure the performance of auto-associative memory nets, the *capacity* (the maximum number of memory patterns that can be stably stored in the net) is often used. There are two definitions of the capacity [13]. The one is the *relative capacity* that allows erroneous bits, and the other is the *absolute capacity* that does not allow even a single error. The relative capacity of the net with monotone neurons is

widely known to be around $0.15n$ (*e.g.*, [13], [14]). Whereas, by the computer simulation, we can see that the relative capacity is over $0.30n$ if we put, for example, {$a = 0.4$, $c = h = 0$}, or {$a = 0$, $c = 0.5$, $h = 1$}.

For the absolute capacity, using the theorem, we can write down analytical results. The absolute capacity for function shape of $h = c = 0$ and $a \neq 0.5$ is given by

$$\left(\frac{1-a}{1-2a}\right)^2 \frac{n}{2\log n} \tag{18}$$

and in particular for $h = c = 0$ and $a = 0.5$ the capacity is

$$\frac{n}{\sqrt{2\log n}} \tag{19}$$

This shows a dramatic superiority of a non-monotone neuron ($a > 0$) over a monotone neuron ($a = 0$). Also when we put $a = 0$, the absolute capacity can be of the same order as (19) if we adjust parameters h and c suitably.

The results shown or mentioned above are for the condition $l = 1$, therefore the optimal parameters mentioned there are not

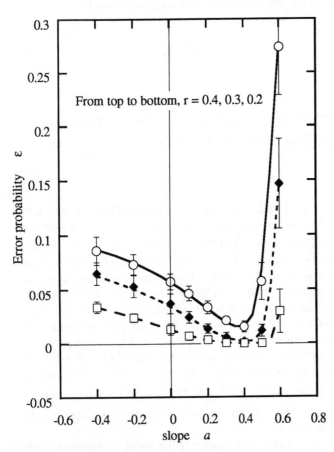

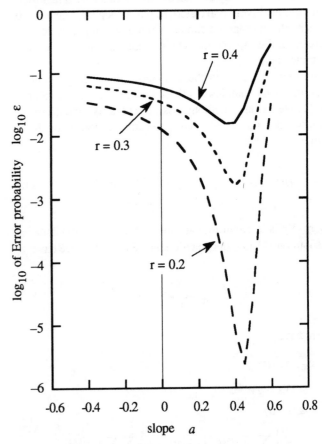

Fig. 2. Error probability ε as a function of a. Data points are from computer simulations with $n = 500$ for ten trials each, and bars indicate standard deviations. Lines are from the theorem.

Fig. 3 Log-plot version for the theoretical curves of Fig. 2.

necessarily applicable to cases where we consider initial conditions of $l < 1$, or multiple steps of dynamical recalls, or the non-zero diagonal components of the synaptic weight matrix.

IV. RELATIONSHIP WITH THE ORTHOGONAL-PROJECTION TYPE LEARNING

Let us prove the equivalence of the dynamics of a non-monotone neuron of linear f with the learning process of the orthogonal-projection type rule. The orthogonal learning is a rule to make non-orthogonal patterns into non-interfering patterns [9], [10].

We consider the orthogonal-projection type learning procedure with discrete time. Let a synaptic weight matrix at a certain time of learning be $\mathbf{V}$. Then the amount of change of the matrix by the presentation of a memory pattern $\mathbf{s}$ (column vector) is written as

$$\Delta \mathbf{V} = \alpha(\mathbf{s} - \lambda \mathbf{V} \mathbf{s})\mathbf{s}^{\mathrm{T}} \qquad (20)$$

where α and λ are positive constants. For appropriate choice of α and λ, the orthogonal-projection type learning theory

guarantees the convergence of the matrix to the desirable orthogonal-projection matrix by a sufficiently large number of iteration with respect to all memory patterns. Now consider one-step learning procedure. If we start the learning procedure from a correlation matrix of (5), the amount of change of the matrix by presenting all the memory patterns once for each is

$$\Delta \mathbf{W} = \sum_{\mu=1}^{m} \Delta \mathbf{W}_\mu = \alpha(\mathbf{I} - \lambda \mathbf{W}) \sum_{\mu=1}^{m} \mathbf{s}_\mu \mathbf{s}_\mu{}^{\mathrm{T}} \qquad (21)$$

where $\Delta \mathbf{W}_\mu$ denotes the change of the matrix by presenting the pattern $\mathbf{s}_\mu$, and $\mathbf{I}$ is a unit matrix. Here we suppose that the matrix does not change during the one-step learning procedure. The updated matrix $\mathbf{W}'$ by this procedure is written as

$$\begin{aligned} \mathbf{W}' &= \mathbf{W} + \Delta \mathbf{W} \\ &= \mathbf{W} + \alpha(\mathbf{I} - \lambda \mathbf{W})n\mathbf{W} \\ &= (1 + n\alpha)\left(\mathbf{I} - \frac{\lambda n \alpha}{1 + n\alpha}\mathbf{W}\right)\mathbf{W} \end{aligned} \qquad (22)$$

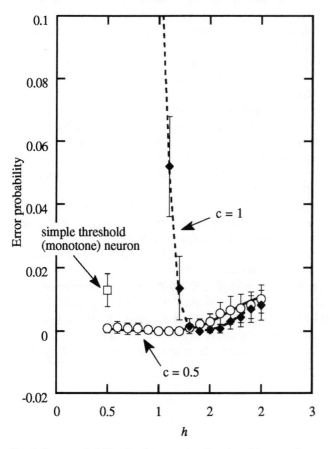

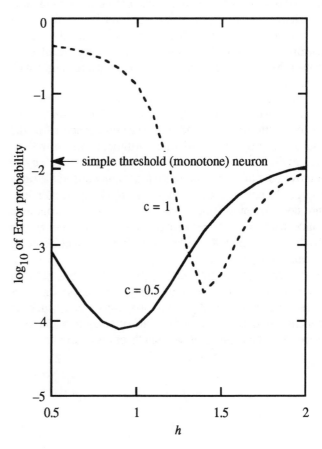

Fig. 4 Error probability for the stepwise function f, i.e. $a = 0$. $r = 0.2$. $n = 500$ for the simulation. Lines are from the theory.

Fig. 5 Log-plot version for the theoretical curves of Fig. 4.

where we used (5).

On the other hand, rewriting (1) for the case f is linear, we have

$$\mathbf{x}' = \text{sgn}\big[(\mathbf{I} - a\mathbf{W})\mathbf{W}\mathbf{x}\big] \qquad (23)$$

This equation describes the simple threshold dynamics with a synaptic weight matrix being $(\mathbf{I} - a\mathbf{W})\mathbf{W}$, which is a nearly orthogonalized version of the original matrix $\mathbf{W}$ for appropriate choice of the parameter a as we can see from (22). Thus a non-monotone neuron is equivalently doing a one-step orthogonalizing procedure in the course of dynamic recall. This explains why non-monotone neurons are effective for use in auto-associative nets.

V. SUMMARY AND DISCUSSION

We supplied a theoretical verification on the "mysterious" improvement of the performance of auto-associative memory nets with non-monotone neurons. To do so, we used the exact solution on the one-step recall process not only for the original non-monotone neuron model [1] but also for the more general two-stage nonlinear neuron model. Through the analysis, we discovered the inherent mechanism of auto-associative memory nets, hence we could derive the effects of response characteristics of higher-order dynamical neurons. We showed by our theory that the recall error probability is smaller with non-monotone neurons than with monotone neurons.

In addition to the analysis of the dynamics, we showed the correspondence between the dynamics of a non-monotone neuron with linear f and the learning process of the orthogonal-projection type rule. Although we showed no such explicit correspondence for a nonlinear f, the key to improvement of the performance is certainly due to the same nature. As investigated by Morita *et al.* [1], the continuous and non-piecewise-linear version of the non-monotone neuron works even better. Analysis of that model would be difficult. But again, the nature of the improvement would be the same (*cf.* [3]).

Now that we know the exact dynamics of a neural net with generalized neurons, we could apply our analysis to other types of neural nets than auto-associative nets, such as sequence associative nets. This line of study in addition to further developments of the present theory is under way.

REFERENCES

[1] Morita, M., Yoshizawa, S. & Nakano, K. (1990): Analysis and improvement of the dynamics of autocorrelation associative memory, *Transactions of the Institute of Electronics, Information and Communication Engineers of Japan,* vol. **J73-D-II**, pp. 232-242

[2] Morita, M., Yoshizawa, S. & Nakano, K. (1990): Memory of correlated patterns by associative neural networks with improved dynamics, *Proceedings of INNC-90-Paris*, pp. 868-871

[3] Yoshizawa, S., Morita, M. & Amari, S. (1992): Capacity and spurious memory of associative memory using a non-monotonic neuron model, in *Artificial neural networks,* **2**, ed. I. Aleksander and J. Taylor, vol. 1, pp. 445-448

[4] Kobayashi, K. (1991): On the capacity of a neuron with a non-monotone output function, *Network,* vol. **2**, pp. 237-243

[5] Caianiello, E. R. (1961): Outline of a theory of thought-processes and thinking machines, *Journal of Theoretical Biology,* vol. **2**, pp. 204-235

[6] Yanai, H.-F. & Sawada, Y. (1990): Associative memory network composed of neurons with hysteretic property, *Neural Networks,* vol. **3**, pp. 223-228

[7] Yanai, H.-F. & Sawada, Y. (1990): Effects of neuron property on the performance of associative memory networks, *Proceedings of the International Joint Conference on Neural Networks '90 (Washington)* **1**, pp. I-489–I-452, Lawrence Erlbaum Associates

[8] Yanai, H.-F. & Sawada, Y. (1990): Integrator neurons for analogue neural networks, *IEEE Transactions on Circuits and Systems,* vol. **37**, pp. 854-856

[9] Amari, S. (1977): Neural theory of association and concept-formation, *Biological Cybernetics,* vol. **26**, pp. 175-185

[10] Kohonen, T. & Oja, E. (1976): Fast adaptive formation of orthogonalizing filters and associative memory in recurrent networks of neuron-like elements, *Biological Cybernetics,* vol. **21**, pp. 85-95

[11] Gardner, E., Derrida, B. & Mottishaw, P. (1987): Zero temperature parallel dynamics for infinite range spin glasses and neural networks, *J. Physique,* vol. **48**, pp. 741-755

[12] Amari, S. (1974): A method of statistical neurodynamics, *Kybernetik,* vol. **14**, pp. 201-215

[13] Amari, S. & Maginu, K. (1988): Statistical neurodynamics of associative memory, *Neural Networks,* vol. **2**, pp. 63-73

[14] Yanai, H.-F., Sawada, Y. & Yoshizawa, S. (1991): Dynamics of an auto-associative neural network model with arbitrary connectivity and noise in the threshold, *Network,* vol. **2**, pp. 295-314

Adaptive Mixtures of Local Experts are Source Coding Solutions

Peter T. Szymanski and Michael D. Lemmon*
Department of Electrical Engineering
University of Notre Dame
Notre Dame, Indiana 46556 USA
(219)-631-5480

Abstract— Recent research in intelligent control uses Radial Basis Function Networks to learn and perform tasks. The networks adapt their outputs to produce desired controls. However, the method lacks rigorous quantitative analysis and a physical interpretation of the ideas present. Current research in intelligent control uses information theory to describe and quantify solutions to control problems. This approach lacks the flexibility as it relies solely upon a set of fixed outputs for control. This paper identifies the connection between the two approaches using a comparison of the two approaches. The main result is that the computation of the stochastic mapping in the adaptive mixtures approach is the same as the stochastic mapping in the source coding approach. This implies that the adaptive mixtures approach produces optimal mappings based on the analysis and results from source coding theory.

I. INTRODUCTION

Recent research in intelligent control using artificial neural networks has focused on the use of adaptive mixtures of local experts to learn and perform tasks[1, 2]. This approach consists of an ensemble of expert networks which compete for the right to respond to inputs. The experts are radial basis function (RBF) networks and use maximum likelihood estimation to adapt the means of the RBF's. The method maps a set of input vectors to a set of output vectors so as to minimize an error measure. However, this method lacks quantitative analysis in terms of optimality and convergence.

Current research in intelligent control using information theoretic techniques focuses on using *entropy*

and *distortion* measures to determine the appropriate control responses to inputs for a system to perform a task[3, 4]. This approach allows the quantification of the input and output in a consistent fashion. An information theoretic approach offers results on the optimality of input/output mappings in the form of the Shannon Bound. Finally, it provides Blahut's Algorithm as a means for computing optimal mappings for sets of fixed input and output vectors.

While appearing to be fundamentally different, the two approaches are very similar. Both use the same basic network structure with the main difference being the composition of the output agents. Both approaches use the same method to train networks to select output agents. This paper illustrates this connection. Additionally, it demonstrates concepts from information theory that aid in the analysis of neural networks.

Section II outlines the basic quantities involved and briefly describes the control network. Section III relates the control network to the adaptive mixtures approach and outlines the reasoning supporting this approach. Section IV presents the basics of the information theoretic approach and uses them in quantifying and optimizing network performance. Section V presents a comparison of the two approaches to highlight their similarity. Finally, the paper concludes in Section VI with a discussion of the findings.

II. PRELIMINARIES

Fig. 1 presents the basic control network. It consists of an ensemble of output agents which are moderated by a selection agent. The output agents receive input vectors and generate output vectors. The selection agent receives input vectors and selects one output agent to generate the response for the entire network.

The network takes as input some vector, $i \in V$,

*The authors would like to acknowledge the partial financial support of the National Science Foundation (IRI91-09298)

1391

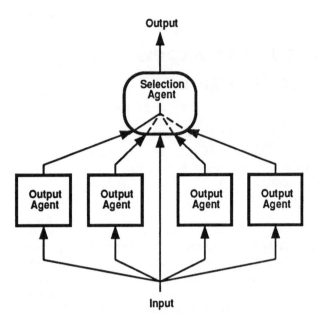

Output

Selection Agent

Output Agent **Output Agent** **Output Agent** **Output Agent**

Input

Figure 1: Basic Control Network

where $V \subset \mathbb{R}^n$. These vectors represent a system's perceptions of its environment which it receives via sensors. V has an associated distribution with $p_i = \Pr\{i \text{ occurs}\}$.

The output space for the network is $O \subset \mathbb{R}^m$. Let $D \subset O$ be the set of desired or target outputs. Each $i \in V$ has a desired output, $d_i \in D$, associated with it. Let $p_d = \Pr\{d \text{ desired}\}$ and $p_d = \sum_{i \in \{j \in V : d_j = d\}} p_i$. D represents the set of desired command or control vectors associated with the inputs in V that would produce optimal performance.

The set of vectors which the network is capable of producing is $M \subset O$. Let $p_\alpha = \Pr\{\alpha \text{ occurs}\}$, where $\alpha \in M$. These vectors are the actual control vectors that the network is capable of generating in response to inputs from V.

The collection of output agents is Φ. Each $\phi \in \Phi$ computes a mapping from $\phi(V) \to M$ that is independent of all of the other output agents. Each agent receives the same input as all the other agents, but each agent generates an individual output.

Finally, the selection or gating agent determines which output agent responds to a given input. The selection agent receives the same input as the output agents and stochastically chooses one of the output agents to respond. Let $Q_{\phi|i} = \Pr\{\phi \text{ chosen}|i \text{ occurred}\}$ be the probabilities that the selection agents use in choosing output agents.

III. ADAPTIVE MIXTURES APPROACH

An adaptive mixtures of local experts[1, 2] uses the basic network of Section II. Each output agent in this approach consists of an expert network. The implementation of the experts is similar to the RBF networks in [5]. The selection agent is a simple stochastic switch that uses the $Q_{\phi|i}$'s to determine the expert that responds to a given input.

Output agents are each multidimensional Gaussians with mean $\overline{\mu}_i$ and variance $\sigma_i^2 I$. The probability that output agent ϕ generates an output $\overline{o} \in O$ is

$$\Pr_\phi\{\overline{o}\} = k \exp\left(-\frac{1}{2\sigma_\phi^2}||\overline{o} - \overline{\mu}_\phi||^2\right) \quad (1)$$

where k is a normalizing constant. The total probability of output $\overline{o} \in O$ occurring is

$$\Pr\{\overline{o}\} = \sum_{\phi \in \Phi} q_\phi k \exp\left(-\frac{1}{2\sigma_\phi^2}||\overline{o} - \overline{\mu}_\phi||^2\right) \quad (2)$$

where q_ϕ is the total probability of choosing Gaussian ϕ.

The selection agent chooses an expert to produce an output based upon the current input. It bases its choice on the conditional probabilities $Q_{\phi|i}$. The agent computes these probabilities by

$$Q_{\phi|i} = \frac{\Pr_\phi\{d_i\}}{\sum_{\phi \in \Phi} \Pr_\phi\{d_i\}} \quad (3)$$

The selection agent generates a uniformly distributed random number and uses it in conjunction with the $Q_{\phi|i}$'s to choose an output agent.

An adaptive mixtures approach uses maximum likelihood competitive learning[5] to train the network. It trains the output agents and selection agent using gradient ascent of the likelihood function

$$L = \prod_{d \in D} \sum_{\phi \in \Phi} q_\phi k \exp\left(-\frac{1}{2\sigma_\phi^2}||d - \overline{\mu}_\phi||^2\right) \quad (4)$$

Since the use of logarithms simplifies manipulation of the equation, adaptive mixtures uses the log likelihood function. The gradient of the log likelihood function is simply the partial derivative of (4) taken with respect to the mean vectors

$$\frac{\partial \log L}{\partial \overline{\mu}_\phi} = \left[\frac{q_\phi \exp\left(-\frac{1}{2\sigma_\phi^2}||d - \overline{\mu}_\phi||^2\right)}{\sum_{\alpha \in \Phi} q_\alpha \exp\left(-\frac{1}{2\sigma_\alpha^2}||d - \overline{\mu}_\alpha||^2\right)}\right] (d - \overline{\mu}_\phi) \quad (5)$$

The result in (5) reveals how the network updates its selection of the Gaussians and the means of the

Gaussians themselves. Comparison of (3) with the bracketed term in (5) reveals that both the terms have the same form. In fact, substituting (1) into (3) and multiplying by q_ϕ yields the bracketed term. Thus, the conditional probabilities are the probabilities of each individual RBF generating the desired output normalized by the sum of all the individual probabilities.

The network updates the output agents by using (5) directly. By setting $\partial \log \mathrm{L}/\partial \overline{\mu}_\phi = 0$ and solving for $\overline{\mu}_\phi$, the formula for updating the means becomes

$$\overline{\mu}_\phi = \frac{\sum_{d \in D} Q_{\phi|d} d}{\sum_{d \in D} Q_{\phi|d}} \qquad (6)$$

which is simply the weighted average of the desired vectors taken over all the output agents.

IV. SOURCE CODING APPROACH

The information theoretic approach uses concepts from *Source Coding Theory*. Source coding theory[6] provides consistent measures for the network in Figure 1. The measures quantify the mapping from inputs to outputs and allow the optimization of the mapping with respect to an error measure.

The specifics of the network are now somewhat different than for the adaptive mixtures case. For simplicity, the network consists of agents as in [4]. The output agents are constant output devices that each generate only a fixed output $\overline{o}_\alpha \in M$. The output agents no longer require input since they have a fixed output.

The selection agent has the same definition as before. It uses the conditional probabilities $Q_{\overline{o}|i}$ to choose which output agent responds to a given input. The concern of the source coding approach is solely the determination of these $Q_{\overline{o}|i}$'s.

Source coding uses measures to quantify characteristics of the network's mapping. These measures are *entropy*, *distortion*, and *average mutual information*. Entropy describes the complexity, uncertainty, or information content of a set in a representationally independent fashion. Given a set X that has an associated distribution $p(x)$, where $x \in X$ the entropy of X is

$$H(X) = -\sum_{i=1}^{|X|} p(x) \log p(x) \qquad (7)$$

The source coding approach uses entropy to quantify the sets of input and output vectors. Using the notation from Section II, the input entropy is

$$H(V) \equiv H(p) = -\sum_{i=1}^{|V|} p_i \log p_i \qquad (8)$$

and the output entropy is

$$H(M) \equiv H(q) = -\sum_{\overline{o} \in M} q_{\overline{o}} \log q_{\overline{o}} \qquad (9)$$

In addition to quantifying the uncertainty of the input and output sets, source coding quantifies the performance of the mapping from input to output. Distortion, or error, measures the cost associated with encoding an input vector by some output vector. In the case of these control networks, the distortion for $i \in V$ is $E(\overline{o}, i) = ||d_i - \overline{o}||^2$, where $\overline{o} \in M$ is the network output. Average error, $\overline{E}(Q)$, is the expectation of the error over all the input and output combinations

$$\overline{E}(Q) = \sum_{\overline{o}, i} p_i Q_{\overline{o}|i} E(\overline{o}, i) \qquad (10)$$

Minimization of the average error guarantees good performance of the network.

Minimization of $\overline{E}(Q)$ is subject to constraints on $H(V)$ and $H(M)$ and depends upon relationships between $H(V)$ and $H(M)$ and between the entropies and $\overline{E}(Q)$. The first is the average mutual information (AMI) between sets V and M

$$I(V; M) \equiv I(p, Q) = \sum_{\overline{o}, i} p_i Q_{\overline{o}|i} \log \frac{Q_{\overline{o}|i}}{q_{\overline{o}}} \qquad (11)$$

AMI measures how well the output vectors provide information about the input vectors subject to the mapping from V to M. It is a non-negative quantity and is a lower bound to the entropies of the two sets being characterized.

$$\begin{aligned} 0 \leq I(p, Q) \leq H(p) \\ 0 \leq I(p, Q) \leq H(q) \end{aligned} \qquad (12)$$

If the choice of outputs tends to be independent of the inputs, the mutual information tends to be smaller $((Q_{\overline{o}|i} \approx q_{\overline{o}}) \rightarrow I(p, Q) \approx 0))$. If the choice of outputs is dependent on the input, AMI tends to be larger $((Q_{\overline{o}|i} \neq q_{\overline{o}}) \rightarrow I(p, Q) > 0))$. AMI measures the correlation between the outputs and the inputs. The greater the AMI, the better the encoding of inputs by outputs.

The second relationship is the *entropy-error function*. The entropy-error function (also known as the rate-distortion function in source coding[6] or the complexity-work function in [4]) relates AMI to $\overline{E}(Q)$ as

$$I(E) = \min_{Q \in Q_E} (I(Q)) \qquad (13)$$

Here Q_E is the set of all possible stochastic mappings from V to M that achieve the error level, E. In addition to relating mutual information and error, it identifies the specific $Q_{\overline{o}|i}$'s over the entire set of Q's which produce the given error level.

The entropy-error function is the *optimal performance theoretically achievable* (OPTA) by a network. It defines the set of optimal mappings ($Q_{\overline{o}|i}$'s) that satisfy different requirements on average error. $I(E)$ (also known as the Shannon Bound) has specific properties when the error function, $E(\overline{o}, i)$, is chosen appropriately. $I(E)$ is a convex-downward, monotonically decreasing function. It is also invertible, that is, if $I(\delta) = \epsilon$ then $E(\epsilon) = \delta$. This means that the function can be used to determine the minimum error associated with a given mapping of inputs to outputs, or it can determine the appropriate mapping ($Q_{\overline{o}|i}$'s) from inputs to outputs to meet certain error requirements.

The existence of this bound stems from the work done in Information Theory by Shannon[7]. Later work by Blahut[8] describes an algorithm that actually computes the bound at various locations. The algorithm exploits the convexity of the entropies to solve the constrained optimization problem implied by (13). For a given set of p_i's and $E(\overline{o}, i)$'s, it computes the value of the $Q_{\overline{o}|i}$'s, $I(Q)$, and $\overline{E}(Q)$ at various slopes. Formally, the algorithm is:

1. Begin with an initial estimate of $q_{\overline{o}}^{(0)}$ and set $m = 0$.

2. Compute $Q_{\overline{o}|i}^{(m)}$ for $q_{\overline{o}}^{(m)}$ by

$$Q_{\overline{o}|i}^{(m)} = \frac{q_{\overline{o}}^{(m)} e^{(sE(\overline{o}, i))}}{\sum_{j \in M} q_j^{(m)} e^{(sE(j, i))}} \quad (14)$$

where $s < 0$ is the slope of the bound at the point of interest.

3. Determine the distribution of the outputs

$$q_{\overline{o}}^{(m+1)} = \sum_{i \in V} Q_{\overline{o}|i}^{(m)} p_i$$

4. Evaluate $I(p, Q^{(m)})$ and $\overline{E}(Q^{(m)})$ and check for convergence. If convergence requirements have been met, stop. Otherwise, set $m = m + 1$ and go to step 2.

Repeated use of the algorithm with different values of s produces as much of the bound as required. For a single value of s, Blahut's Algorithm computes the optimal stochastic mapping $V \rightarrow M$.

V. COMPARISON OF METHODS

The two approaches are very similar. Both determine mappings from input vectors to output vectors that minimize an error function. The network implementation of each approach consists of an ensemble of output agents. In both cases, a selection agent moderates the choice of the appropriate output agent. However, it is the training of the selection agent that is most similar.

Both approaches train the selection agent by adjusting the conditional probabilities of selecting an agent given an input. In the mixtures approach, the adjustment occurs as a result of following the gradient of the log likelihood function. In the source coding approach, the adjustment follows as a result of the computation of the Shannon Bound. Regardless of the approach, the training is the same with the result being stated in the following theorem

Theorem V.1 *The update of the conditional probabilities, $Q_{\phi|i}$, in an adaptive mixtures network as described in Section III is equivalent to the update of the conditional probabilities, $Q_{\overline{o}|i}$, in a source coding network as described in Section IV.*

The proof of the theorem is simply to show that the bracketed term in (5) is equivalent (14). Begin by starting with

$$Q_{\phi|i} = \frac{q_\phi \exp\left(-\frac{1}{2\sigma_\phi^2} ||d - \overline{\mu}_\phi||^2\right)}{\sum_{\alpha \in \Phi} q_\alpha \exp\left(-\frac{1}{2\sigma_\alpha^2} ||d - \overline{\mu}_\alpha||^2\right)} \quad (15)$$

Recognize that q_ϕ is the probability of choosing an output agent in the adaptive mixtures network. Since the outputs of the source coding network are fixed, the probability of choosing one of these outputs is equivalent to choosing its output agent. Thus, $q_\phi = q_{\overline{o}}$. Substituting this into (15) yields

$$Q_{\phi|i} = \frac{q_{\overline{o}} \exp\left(-\frac{1}{2\sigma_\phi^2} ||d - \overline{\mu}_\phi||^2\right)}{\sum_{j \in M} q_j \exp\left(-\frac{1}{2\sigma_\alpha^2} ||d - \overline{\mu}_\alpha||^2\right)} \quad (16)$$

Setting $s = -\frac{1}{2\sigma_\phi^2}$ yields

$$Q_{\phi|i} = \frac{q_{\overline{o}} e^{s||d - \overline{\mu}_\phi||^2}}{\sum_{j \in M} q_j e^{s||d - \overline{\mu}_\alpha||^2}} \quad (17)$$

Finally, $\overline{\mu}_\phi$ is the output of agent ϕ. The adaptive mixtures approach assumes that the $\overline{\mu}_\phi$ is constant when it adjusts the conditional probabilities. Therefore, letting $\overline{\mu}_\phi = \overline{o}$ and substituting results in

$$Q_{\phi|i} = \frac{q_{\overline{o}} e^{s||d - \overline{o}||^2}}{\sum_{j \in M} q_j e^{s||d - j||^2}} \quad (18)$$

The right hand side of (18) is exactly $Q_{\bar{o}|i}$. Thus $Q_{\phi|i} \equiv Q_{\bar{o}|i}$. □

A number of points become apparent from the proof of the theorem. First, both networks select the output agent in the same manner. Conditional probabilities dictate which agent responds in both cases. However, in the mixtures approach, the output can take on any value while the source coding approach has only fixed outputs.

Secondly, the choice of the variance affects the parameter, s. Since s determines a point on the Shannon Bound, the choice of variance affects the resulting distortion of the network. Larger variances make s less negative resulting in greater distortion but simpler output mappings (i.e. the output has lower entropy). Smaller variances, which in the extreme correspond to fixed outputs, make s more negative resulting in lower distortion but higher output complexity (more agents are required to achieve better performance).

Finally, the equivalence of the updates of the conditional probability means that the results of the source coding approach apply to the adaptive mixtures approach. That is, Blahut's Algorithm computes optimal mappings in terms of the conditional probabilities between inputs and outputs. If the adaptive mixtures approach updates its probabilities so that they converge to the Shannon probabilities, it computes the optimal mapping for the current RBF network. However, this does not necessarily imply that the gradient ascent of the likelihood function actually achieves optimality, only that at each step in the training the mapping will be optimal for that configuration.

VI. DISCUSSION

The ideas presented in this paper serve to illustrate the similarities between two different approaches to control networks. Source coding theory and the concept of mixtures of adaptive networks both produce networks that have the same basic architecture. The only difference between the architectures is that the simpler source coding approach produces output vectors that are fixed and not functions of the inputs, while the mixtures approach produces adaptable outputs that are functions of the input.

Both types of networks have the same set of input and output vector sets. The same sort of probability distributions model the occurrence of vectors in both cases. One important result of this is that source coding and information theoretic techniques are applicable to the analysis of mixture networks. Source coding provides measures that quantify the networks in a consistent fashion. Results from source coding

then offer bounds that provide an additional insight into the performance of RBF networks, with the major result being that adaptive mixtures networks produce optimal mappings for the RBF networks at each training step.

The obvious differences between the approaches stem from the fact that the source coding approach has fixed output vectors while the output of mixture networks is dynamic. This suggests that the adaptive approach should be able to find better solutions to the problems because it can modify the outputs to reduce the error. However, it is not obvious because the global convergence of the mixtures approach is not proven. One approach to address the convergence to a globally optimal solution is the use of Monte Carlo methods, such as Simulated Annealing[9].

The comparison of the methods suggests that the error or distortion is controllable through the variance of the RBF's. By increasing or decreasing the variance, the mapping moves on the Shannon Bound, decreasing or increasing its error. This is similar to the idea of changing the number of agents in the source coding approach to allow increases or decreases of the entropy and the error.

Finally, the paper illustrates that each approach has contributions to be made to the other approach. The mixtures approach suggests an adaptive solution that is not present in the source coding approach. The source coding approach offers a proven analytical method for the mixtures approach. It also provides a physical interpretation to the quantities present in the mixtures approach, which should lead to a better understanding of both.

REFERENCES

[1] R. A. Jacobs and M. I. Jordan. A modular connectionist architecture for learning piecewise con trol strategies. In *Proceedings of the American Control Conference*, volume 2, pages 1597–1602, Boston, Massachusetts, 1991.

[2] R. A. Jacobs, M. I. Jordan, S. J. Nowlan, and G. E. Hinton. Adaptive mixtures of local experts. *Neural Computation*, 3:79–87, 1991.

[3] G. N. Saridis. Entropy formulation of optimal and adaptive control. *IEEE Transactions on Automatic Control*, 33(8):713–721, August 1988.

[4] P. T. Szymanski and M. D. Lemmon. Consistent measures and bounds for control policies. Technical Report ISIS-93-001, Department of Electrical Engineering, University of Notre Dame, January 1993.

[5] S. J. Nowlan. Maximum likelihood competitive learning. In *Advances in Neural Information Processing Systems 2*, pages 574–582. Morgan Kaufmann Publishers, Inc., San Mateo, California, 1990.

[6] R. M. Gray. *Source Coding Theory*. Kluwer Academic Publishers, Boston, Massachusetts, 1990.

[7] C. E. Shannon. A mathematical theory of communication. *Bell Systems Technical Journal*, 27:379–423,623–656, 1948.

[8] R. E. Blahut. Computation of channel capacity and rate-distortion functions. *IEEE Transactions on Information Theory*, IT-18(4):460–473, July 1972.

[9] S. Kirkpatrick, C. D. Gelatt, Jr., and M. P. Vecchi. Optimization by simulated annealing. *Science*, 220(4598):671–680, 1983.

Extraction of Semantic Rules
from Trained Multilayer Neural Networks

Raqui Kane   Maurice Milgram

LRP-CNRS, Université Paris-VI, 4 Place Jussieu

75252 Paris, CEDEX 05 France

Abstract—This paper describes methods to extract logical rules from trained multilayer neural networks. First we propose a general and theoretical method of logical rules extraction. This method is based on propositional logic and truth tables. To each logical unit of a trained neural network, we associate a truth table and therefore a logical rule. But before extracting rules, we need to make sure that the operation done by the unit is a logical one. Therefore, two approaches fulfilling this criterion are proposed. The first one consists of forcing the outputs of the units to be in {-1, 1}. This is done by adding a penalty term in the classical error function to minimize. An algorithm based on backpropagation (BP) is proposed. It is termed: the modified backpropagation constraining the ouput. The second approach consists of forcing each unit to realize only an elementary logical operation, namely AND($\land$), OR ($\lor$) or NOT ($\neg$), but not a combination of them. This is done by constraining weights and biases to be in a finite set of values. Three algorithms are proposed in this case. The first one is based on backpropagation, the second one on simulated annealing, the third one on simulated annealing and control by the gradient. Simulation results for these methods are reported.

I. Introduction

It is difficult to extract the information contained in a trained neural network. Indeed, the set of weights obtained after training the network is complex because it depends on all the changes made during learning. Rules extraction can be considered as a way of trying to understand trained neural networks. Some studies emerged in this field around 1986 as [1]. A first approach is to prune useless units in networks [2]. A second approach is to use statistical methods to cluster weights [3].

In this paper we propose to study the problem of logical rules extraction. Some people have tried to investigate this problem by using fuzzy logic [4], [5], and some by using propositional logic [6], [7]; but the proposed methods remain non general and only based on empirical results. We propose here a method of logical rules extraction. The analysis of the weights and bias coming to each logical unit after training enables us to find its truth table and therefore the logical operation realized. To get logical units during the training, we propose two approaches. First, we constrain the units of the network to be general logical operators, namely to be a combination of the elementary operators $\land$, $\lor$ and $\neg$. Second, we propose to constrain each unit to realize only an elementary logical operator, namely $\land$ or $\lor$ or $\neg$. For this, we constrain weights and biases to be in a finite set of values.

This paper is organized as follows: first, we propose a general and theoretical method of rules extraction from trained neural networks. Second, we propose a learning algorithm realizing constraints on the outputs of the units to make sure that logical operations have been realized. Finally, we propose three algorithms constraining each unit to perform only an elementary logic operator. Simulation results show the performance of these methods.

II. A Theoretical Method of Rules Extraction

A. The unit: a logical operator

We consider a unit i with n inputs $x_1^i \cdots x_n^i$ belonging to $S = \{-1(false), 1(true)\}$. The output of the unit is defined by the equation:

$$o^i = f(\sum_{j=1}^{n}(w_{ij} \star x_j^i - \theta_i) = f(a_i). \qquad (1)$$

where
f is a sigmoid function, for example: $f(x) = tanh(x)$, w_{ij} is the weight of the connection between units j and i, θ_i is the bias of unit i and a_i its activation.
We denote $W_i = \{w_{i1}, \cdots, w_{ij} \cdots, w_{in}\}$ the set of weights coming to i.

A unit i can be considered as a logical operator if its output is arbitrarily close to -1 or 1, namely if it is work-

*This work is supported by a grant from DRET.

ing in the saturated part of the sigmoid function. Then it can realize different logical functions: $\wedge$, $\vee$, $\neg$ or any combination of these functions.

There is an equivalence between the set of logical rules and the set of truth tables. Therefore, the condition for a unit to realize a particular logical rule is to satisfy its truth table.

lemma: Consider a unit i with a sigmoid function $f(x) = tanh(x)$, an activation a_i and an output o^i, then we have

$$a_i \geq 0.0 \Longleftrightarrow o^i = f(a_i) \geq 0.0. \quad (2)$$

B. The Construction of the truth tables

Consider a logical unit i, then $f(a_i)$ is arbitrarily closed to -1 or 1. W_i and θ_i are respectively the set of weights and bias coming to the unit i. The truth table of i is given by the following 2^n tables:

$S(\gamma_1)$	$\cdots$	$S(\gamma_n)$	$S(\gamma_1 \star w_{i1} + \cdots + \gamma_n \star w_{in} - \theta_i)$

Where the 2^n vectors $(\gamma_1, \cdots, \gamma_n)$ are elements of $V = \{-1, 1\} \times \cdots \times \{-1, 1\}$. S is the function sign.

Note: Consider a logical unit i of a trained neural network with its set of weights W_i and bias θ_i. The truth table of i is obtained by considering the truth values of its n inputs units j. To build its truth table, we need the following properties:

- The truth table of i is computed taking into account the truth values of its n connected inputs units j.

- To express that the information given by the logical unit j to the unit i is false (resp true), we have to multiply the output of j by -1 (resp 1), which means also to multiply w_{ij} by -1 (resp 1).

Therefore the truth table of i is given by:

truth value of units j					truth value of unit i
1	$\cdots$	j	$\cdots$	n	
+	$\cdots$	+	$\cdots$	+	$S(f(+w_{i1} + w_{i2} \cdots + w_{in} - \theta_i))$
−	$\cdots$	+	$\cdots$	+	$S(f(-w_{i1} + w_{i2} \cdots + w_{in} - \theta_i))$
$\cdots$	$\cdots$	$\cdots$	$\cdots$	$\cdots$	$\cdots$
−	$\cdots$	−	$\cdots$	−	$S(f(-w_{i1} - w_{i2} \cdots - w_{in} - \theta_i))$

As $S(f(a_i)) = S(a_i)$ (see lemma), then we obtain the truth table of i.

Let us take a very simple example: a 3 - 1 neural network, namely with 3 inputs units and 1 output unit. Fig. 1 shows the weights obtained after training.

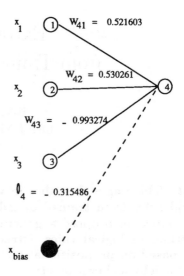

Fig. 1. Extracting rules from a trained network.

Weights of unit 3 are such that:

$$S(f(w_{41} + w_{42} + w_{43} - \theta_4)) = -$$
$$S(f(w_{41} - w_{42} + w_{43} - \theta_4)) = -$$
$$S(f(w_{41} + w_{42} - w_{43} - \theta_4)) = -$$
$$S(f(w_{41} - w_{42} - w_{43} - \theta_4)) = -$$
$$S(f(w_{41} - w_{42} + w_{43} - \theta_4)) = -$$
$$\vdots$$
$$S(f(-w_{41} + w_{42} + w_{43} - \theta_4)) = +$$

then, we obtain the truth table of unit 4. This unit realizes the logical rule: $(x_1 \wedge x_2) \vee \neg x_3$.

C. The rules extraction approach

It requires three main steps.

- We have to realize the learning step.

- We ensure that the unit is a logical operator, namely its output is arbitrarily close to -1 or 1. Then we build its associated truth table using the above construction.

- Once we have built the truth table of a logical unit, we have to interpret this rule. For example, we can express the logical rules in a normal conjunctive form.

III. Constraining the outputs of the units

Using this method, we are able to force all or some of the units of a network to be logical. We denote it MBPCO (modification of backpropagation constraining the ouput of the units). W is the union of the set of weights and biases of the network, and E(W) is the error function of the network to minimize.

In the BP framework, each unit computes the same transfer function, which is normaly a sigmoid function $tanh(\beta x)$, where β is an approximate value of the slope of the sigmoid. It is difficult to make an adequate choice for β to have outputs of units in {-1, 1}. Indeed, a great value of β can slow down the convergence of learning or even compromise it. Conversely, a small value of β doesn't ensure the desired property. To keep outputs of units in {-1, 1}, we propose to add a penalty funtion in the classical BP. The algorithm is the same as for the classical BP, but we add to the error function E(W) an extra term $P(W)$ that will force the outputs of the units to approach -1 or 1 during learning. Thus the function to minimize becomes $E'(W) = E(W) + \lambda P(W)$. Where λ is an adjustable parameter to get the best convergence property.

IV. Constraining the weights

We propose a method to constrain weights to be in {-1, 0, 1}. Reasoning with truth tables, we note that an adequate choice to force a unit i to be an $\wedge$ or $\vee$ operator is to set the following condition on its bias:

$$\theta_i = \epsilon \sum_{j=1}^{n} w_{ij}^2 - 1 \qquad (3)$$

Where $\epsilon = 1\,(resp -1)$ if the unit realizes an $\wedge\,(resp\,\vee)$.

We propose three learning algorithms keeping weights in {-1, 0, 1} during learning. For these algorithms, we denote E(W) the error function of the network to minimize, W and W' the union of the set of weights and biases of the network.

A. Modified simulated annealing (MSA)

Some parameters are used in this algorithm:
T is a temperature initialized to 5000. M and N are positive integers such that M $\leq$ N, and α is a constant in [0.800 0.999]. For simulations $\alpha = 0.9$.
The principle of the algorithm is based on classical simulated annealing. The main features follow:

1. Select randomly an initial set of weights in {-1, 0, 1}. Compute the resulting biases by means of (3) and choose their signs randomly.
   Select a great value for the initial temperature.

2. Select randomly a fixed number of elements of W. For each selected weight, do the following:

- Change the sign if it is a bias.
- Change the value of the weight in {-1, 0, 1} if it is not a bias and then compute the resulting bias. Compute the new cost $E(W')$, compute $\Delta = E(W) - E(W')$.

3. If $\Delta > 0$, change is accepted. If not, it is accepted with the probability $exp(-\Delta/T)$.

4. If M successul changes in W or N total changes in W have occured since the last change of temperature, we say that the equilibrium temperature has been reached, then we set the value of T to αT, where $\alpha \in [0.800\ 0.999]$.

5. If the new cost is more than δ (a small constant), then goto 2; else stop.

B. Simulated annealing controled by gradient (SACG)

This algorithm was proposed by [8]. The goal was to investigate an algorithm for learning ternary weights {-1, 0, 1} in perceptron with 3-valued connections. The main procedure is based on simulated annealing. Changes particularly appears in the thermal equilibrium procedure. Indeed, in this step, changes of weights are controled by signs of gradients. Therefore, the variation of the weights can be performed in two cases:

1. The gradient is positive and the weight is in {-1, 0}.

2. The gradient is negative and the weight is in {0, 1}.

The framework of the algorithm remains the simulated annealing. Only step 4 changes and becomes:

- Thermal equilibrium is reached if, given a W from step 3, there are no more changes possible computing the gradients of weights.

C. Modified BP constraining weights (MBPCW)

The algorithm is the same as for the classical BP, but we add to the error function E(W) an extra term Q(W) that will force weights to approach -1 or 0 or 1 during learning. Thus, the function to minimize becomes $E(W) + \lambda Q(W)$, where λ is a parameter to adjust to get the best convergeate property.

V. Simulation

A. Simulation of the MBPCO

One way to force an output of a unit to be near -1 or 1 is to put its activation in $]-\infty, -a] \cup [a, +\infty[$, where a is a number such that f(a) is close to 1. For simulations, we choose:

$$P(W) = \sum_{i \in C} (a_i - a)^2 \star (a_i + a)^2. \qquad (4)$$

C is the set of the units selected to be logical operators. Therefore, the outputs of the units approach $\{-1, 1\}$. Once we have ensured that all units are achieving logical operations, we analyse the weights and biases obtained after convergence. This analysis relies on the proposed theoretical method. To each unit corresponds the logical operation whose truth table is verified.

Example: We have trained a network whose architecture is 3 - 3 - 1, namely 3 layers with respectively 3 inputs units, 3 hidden units and 1 output unit, to learn $(x_1 \land x_2) \lor \neg x_3$. We present the extracted rules on the basis of weights after training in Table II. The rules are obtained by running recursively our truth-table-building method. Let us comment this example.

- for the first layer

  - for the first unit:
    The weights of this unit are such that

$$S(f(w_{11} + w_{12} + w_{13} - \theta_1)) \ = \ -$$
$$S(f(w_{11} + w_{12} - w_{13} - \theta_1)) \ = \ -$$
$$S(f(w_{11} - w_{12} - w_{13} - \theta_1)) \ = \ +$$
$$S(f(w_{11} - w_{12} - w_{13} - \theta_1)) \ = \ +$$
$$S(f(w_{11} - w_{12} + w_{13} - \theta_1)) \ = \ +$$
$$\vdots$$
$$S(f(-w_{11} + w_{12} + w_{13} - \theta_1)) \ = \ +$$

The truth table of unit 1 is obtained and the logical rule realized by this unit is $\neg x_1 \lor \neg x_2$.

  - for the second unit:
    Its logical truth table is built as above and the extracted rule is x_2.

  - for the third unit:
    Its logical truth table is built as above and the extracted rule is $\neg x_3$.

- for the second layer

  - for the fourth unit:
    We build its logical truth table and the extracted rule is $\neg x_1 \lor x_3$. This unit realizes the disjunction of its inputs $\neg(\neg x_1 \lor \neg x_2) \lor (\neg x_3)$, namely after transformation $(x_1 \land x_2) \lor \neg x_3$.

Fig. 2 shows the evolution of the training error with the training cycle for the BP and the MBPCO. The convergence time is approximately the same for the two algorithms. Fig. 3 shows the evolution of the outputs of the units in training. We notice that convergence towards -1 or 1 is reached in a reasonable amount of time.

TABLE I
RULES EXTRACTED ON THE BASIS OF WEIGHTS
AFTER TRAINING

Links from First To Second Layer		Links from Second to Third Layer
$w_{11} = -0.609765$		
$w_{12} = -0.869947$	$\neg x_1 \lor \neg x_2$	$w_{11} = -1.115160$
$w_{13} = 1.162060$		
$\theta_1 = 0.272822$		
$w_{21} = 0.333441$		$w_{21} = 0.064875$
$w_{22} = 1.855716$	x_2	$\neg x_1 \lor x_3$
$w_{23} = -0.270258$		
$\theta_2 = 0.003708$		$w_{31} = 0.722625$
$w_{21} = -0.669248$		
$w_{22} = 0.099231$	$\neg x_3$	
$w_{23} = -1.424752$		$\theta_1 = -0.645969$
$\theta_3 = 0.114358$		
Rule Extracted from NN		$(x_1 \land x_2) \lor \neg x_3$

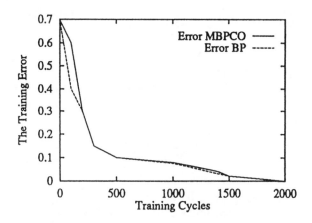

Fig. 2. Evolution of the error: Classical BP and MBPCO.

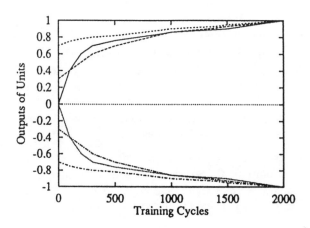

Fig. 3. Evolution of the ouputs of the units.

We have trained networks with different architectures to learn rules and results are satisfactory. We have extracted a great rate of accurate rules, but false rules also appeared. Their truth tables are closely related to the expected one. We have tested 20 networks with different architectures to learn various rules: The inputs are between 2 and 14 and the hidden layers between 1 and 5. The percentage of the extracted rules is reported in Table II. This method provides both performance and flexibility.

B. Simulation of the MSA, SACG and MBPCW

For the MBPCW, our choice of Q(W) corresponds to a differential juxtaposition of 5 paraboles.

$$
\begin{aligned}
P(x) = \quad & 8(x+1)^2 \chi(x)_{]-\infty;-\frac{3}{4}]} \\
& + (1 - 8(x+\frac{1}{2})^2)\chi(x)_{[-\frac{3}{4};-\frac{1}{4}]} \\
& + 8x^2 \chi(x)_{[-\frac{1}{4};\frac{1}{4}]} \\
& + (1 - 8(x-\frac{1}{2})^2)\chi(x)_{[\frac{1}{4};\frac{3}{4}]} \\
& + 8(x-1)^2 \chi(x)_{[\frac{3}{4};\infty[}
\end{aligned}
\tag{5}
$$

Where χ is the function defined by:

$$
\chi(x)_{[a;b]} = \begin{cases} 1.0 & \text{if } x \in [a;b] \\ 0.0 & \text{otherwise} \end{cases}
$$

For each of the three proposed methods, we have trained 40 networks with different architectures to learn different logical rules. The inputs are between 2 and 8 and the hidden units between 1 and 3. The results are summarized in Table II. We notice that false extracted rules are often tautological true rules namely, instead of extracting the expected rule, we extract a tautological true rule. This problem is related to the initialization of the neural network and to the local minima problems. The lowest rate of tautologically true rules extracted using so-constrained networks was obtained with the MBPCW.

TABLE II

PERCENTAGE OF EXTRACTED RULES FOR THE

MSA, SACG, MBPCW AND MBPCO

Method Used	Percentage of Accurate Rules	Percentage of false Rules
MSA	85 %	15 %
SACG	92 %	8 %
MBPCW	92 %	8 %
MBPCO	95 %	5 %

VI. CONCLUSION

In this paper, we have described a new theoretical method for rules extraction. This method, based on propositional logic and particularly on truth tables, enables us to extract logical dependencies from trained neural networks. We have proposed two approaches: the first one is to extract from each unit a combination of elementary rules. One algorithm based on BP has been proposed. The second one enables us to extract from each unit only one elementary operation. Three algoritms have been proposed. For all these algorithms, convergence is reached in a reasonable amount of time, even if it is reached faster using the first approach. This result is quite normal because constraints are lighter in the first approach. Simulations have shown the quality, the comprehensibility and the accuracy of the extracted rules, even if tautological true rules are sometimes extracted instead of the expected rules. The minimum rate of tautological true rules is also obtained using the first approach. Our method can have many practical applications, particularly in data analysis and in any area where we need to control what happens in the network, as we are able to extract logical dependencies in trained neural networks. We are now pursuing our research in this direction; the method is being applied to a real word problem. A method to extract numerical and logical dependencies is also under study.

REFERENCES

[1] G. E. Hinton, "Learning distributed representation of concept," in *Proceeding of the Eighth Annual Conference of the Cognitive Science society* 1986.

[2] Y. LeCun , J. Denker, S. Solla, R. Howard and L.D. Jackel, "Optimal brain damage," in *Advances in Neural Information Processing Systems, San Mateo* CA, Kaufmann 1990.

[3] S.J. Nowlan, G. Hinton, "Simplifying neural networks by soft weight-sharing," in *Advances in Neural Information Processing Systems, Denver* CO 1991.

[4] Y. Hayashi, "A neural expert system with automated extraction of fuzzy if-then rules," in *Advances in Neural Information Processing Systems* vol. 3, 578-584, 1990.

[5] R. Masuika, N. Watanabe, A. Kawamura , Y. Owada and K. Asakawa, "Neuro fuzzy system. Fuzzy inference using a structured neural network," in *Proceeding of the international Conference on Fuzzy Logic & Neural Networks* 173-177, 1990.

[6] L. Bochereau and P. Bourgine, "Extraction of semantic features from a multilayer neural network," in *Proceedings of IJCNN, Wash. DC* 1990.

[7] G. Towell and J. W. Shavlick, "Interpretation of artifial neural networks: mapping knowledge-based neural networks into rules," in *Advances in Neural Information Processing Systems, Denver* CO 1991.

[8] P. Burrascano, P. Fortini and G. Martinelli, "Perceptron with 3-valued connections," in *the 2nd Italian Workshop on Parallel Architectures and Neural Networks*.

Analysis, Modeling and Estimation through a Similarity Based Approach: An Economic Signal Case Study

Antonio Carlos Gay Thome
Manoel Fernando da Mota Tenorio

Parallel Processing Structures Lab
School of Electrical Engineering
Purdue University
W. Lafayette, In. 47907

Abstract - A key issue in a time varying signal estimation is the problem of identification and extraction of existing underlying patterns. Pattern consistency, however, is not a common rule in certain types of dynamics, particularly those related to economic processes in that case it is very difficult to provide an accurate estimation. This paper describes an approach to analyze, capture and model those more complex structured, possibly non-linear and nonstationary time series. Spectral analysis and digital filter theory are used to break the original series into more coherent and power compatible components. Each resulting component is then treated individually as a totally independent time series. Finally the individual results are combined to provide future estimations for the original signal. An example of a 4 week forecast of an oil price time series is presented, leading to a normalized root mean square error of 0.18.

I. Introduction

Estimation is a very important topic in system theory with application to many distinct areas such as Signal Processing, Control and Forecasting. Time series analysis is one of the existing approaches for forecasting that consists of the analysis of historical data in order to identify some underlying pattern that can be extrapolated into the future. This basic strategy rests on the assumption that the identified pattern will be repeated in the future. Pattern consistency however is uncommon in certain types of dynamics, particularly those related to economic processes in which it is difficult to provide an accurate estimation of future values.

The main characteristic of these economic processes is the structural changes that take place in the data as time passes. Under such conditions, the forecast is made with a high degree of instability in its accuracy, varying from excellent to very poor. The fact that all forecasting involves some degree of uncertainty is well recognized in the literature on this subject, by including an irregular component in the formal description of the time series. This component represents unexplained and hard to predict fluctuations found in the data. It is important, however, to recognize that the irregular component is not the only source of errors, and that the ability to accurately predict each of the other components also contributes to the overall performance.

To decompose the original series not based on the traditional elements, such as trend, seasonality and irregular fluctuations, but based on their coherence in terms of orthogonal elements and compatible power, generates a more homogeneous series to be treated and modeled individually. Based on this approach, a series can be decomposed in as many subseries as necessary to better separate and capture the distinct underlying patterns.

In section II a brief overview of different time series analysis approaches is presented, and the advantages and disadvantages of orthogonal decomposition is discussed. In section III the coherent power and the coherent behavior ideas are explained, which leads to the transformation of the prediction problem into a pattern recognition problem as stated in section IV. The fusion process of distinct predictors is presented in section V. And finally an example is discussed in section VI, followed by conclusion and future work in section VII.

II. Approaches to Time Series Analysis

The analysis of a time series is usually performed by assuming that there is an underlying function that represents the system which generated the series. A transformation scheme is used to represent such a function in a new space, in such a way as to enhance vital characteristics of the series, as well as to hide unimportant details. This process is known in the signal processing literature as filtering, or the increase of the ratio between the signal of interest and the background noise. Several schemes for function representation are available. They may involve different methodologies and basic assumptions. For example, in the classical time series analysis, the series is broken down into its main time behavioral components, namely, trend, seasonality, and irregular fluctuations. The first two are assumed to be deterministic, whereas the latter is assumed to be random in nature [1,2,3].

In other domains, such as signal and image processing for example, functions are normally represented by decompositions into sums of either orthogonal or nonorthogonal basis functions. For the nonorthogonal case, a function may be represented as a polynomial, a Taylor series, a sum of Gaussian functions, nonorthogonal wavelets transformations, or, of more recent interest, a sum of sigmoids, such as in Neural Networks. For the orthogonal case, functions may be represented as orthogonal polynomials, orthogonal projections, or by a sum of orthogonal basis functions as in the or the Fourier Transform [4,5].

In forecasting problems, it is generally agreed that if the original function can be well represented by a decomposition then each component can more readily be modeled due to a better signal-to-noise ratio. In the nonorthogonal case, the fusion of these components can be very complex and nonlinear due to the amount of redundant information. It may also be the case that the fusion, in practice, may lead to a worse prediction than the separate components. Such instability occurs mainly due to the high correlation between the components. In the orthogonal case, one may not end up with the most compact representation of the series, and may even lose the ability to make local judgements, since the representation gives global information on a transformed space. Nevertheless several key advantages are present in this class of representation scheme such as: the components are orthogonal and therefore have zero cross-correlation, the fusion is linear since each predictor adds independent information about the dynamics, the prediction process can be treated separately, and each component that is added increases the accuracy of the overall prediction. Thus one can trade the ability and effort to model for accuracy.

Economic time series are, in general, very complex, not being well described by any linear or even any conventional nonlinear parametric technique. The problem is that such series reflect complex environmental interactions thus generating interesting fractal characteristics. If the series is observed for a long interval, and then later observed for a short interval, trends, seasonalities, and irregular components may be observed. But the two series may have different characteristics. This makes it difficult to perform good prediction using classical models which are forced to chose a single interval of observation to model, and thus disregard either the macro or the micro characteristics of the system. Economic time series observed in different intervals often have differences that spawn several orders of magnitude. Thus no algorithm is capable of minimizing the overall error on both the macro and micro scale. Using an orthogonal decomposition based on the Fourier Transform, the power of each component can be observed independent of one another. Figure 1 shows the 0.3% Oil time series as traded in New York between 1979 and 1988. Figure 2 shows the power spectrum of the same series. The differences of power spectrum coefficients can be higher than 30 db over a bandwith of less than 4% of the Nyquist frequency. It is therefore impossible for most types of estimation algorithms, to estimate variations of signals under a signal-to-noise ratio in the order of -80 dB.

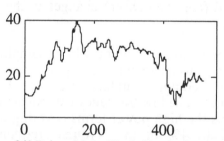

Fig. 1 - Oil Price, New York Trade from 1979/1988

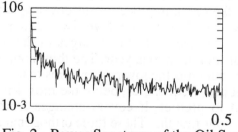

Fig. 2 - Power Spectrum of the Oil Series

III. Partitioning the Series

A. Subseries of Coherent Power

Using the power spectrum of the series, regions of compatible power are identified, i.e., regions with less than 30 dB variations between the highest and the lowest frequency terms. This is done because a good prediction algorithm is capable of prediction errors around 0.1 normalized root mean square error (nRMSE), which roughly corresponds to a variation of -20 to -30 dB. If components in the series produce variations in amplitude that are smaller than the resolution of the predictor, it is impossible for the predictor to capture them. Partitions are made into new subseries such that only the components within a reasonable resolution margin are placed together. This produces subseries that are easier to analyze as compared to the original series.

This fission process masks unwanted information and produces orthogonal series. Each resulting series is intrinsically an indicator of the trajectory of the original series. The degree of the contribution of each indicator is directly proportional to its energy. By using an orthogonal representation, orthogonal predictors can be created, each having access to an orthogonal information basis about the dynamics. This not only simplifies the design of each individual predictor, but also gives freedom to adopt different and better suited techniques to treat each individual component. The individual curves after fission are more homogeneous than the original series, and free from abrupt changes in the power spectrum.

The Oil series used in this study has a sampling rate equal to one week (5 trading days). The original series was decomposed in three subseries shown in figures 3 to 5. The low frequency component (figure 3) contains the high power terms covering a range from DC to 4% of the Nyquist frequency. It strongly correlates with the long term tendencies of the market. The second component (figure 4) contains the medium power terms covering a range from 4% to 12% of the Nyquist frequency. It strongly correlates with the changes in the market from four months to one year. The third component (figure 5) contains the low power terms that are also at the highest frequencies, being the most irregular and hard to predict. It covers changes from two weeks to four months. These three orthogonal series can be used not only for combined estimation, but also to realize estimations with different horizons based on one, two, or all individual components, e.g., the high power component alone permits long term tendency estimation that can be enriched with the second component contribution, for shorter horizons.

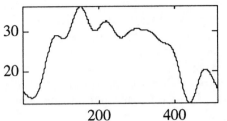

Fig. 3 - Low Frequency Component

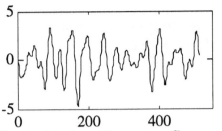

Fig. 4 - Medium Frequency Component

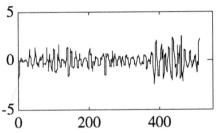

Fig. 5 - High Frequency Component

B. Subseries of Coherent Behavior

Among several different prediction techniques that could now be used over the orthogonal resulting series, one, based on a similarity approach is particularly interesting for economic time series. Through a similar process as used by human experts, the market can be decomposed into clusters of similar patterns whose outcomes, in the desired prediction horizon, are consistent among the elements in the same cluster. This property is here named *data consistency*. This transforms the prediction problem into a pattern recognition problem.

To use a similarity framework as discussed in [6], a feature vector (or state) needs to be designed in the series , and a similarity operator needs to be specified. The state dimension and composition might be defined as to capture time related information, or space related information (in the case of leading or co-occurring indicators). The state need not to be restricted to past observations of data, but it may also contain symbolic information which aids on the definition of uniqueness of states with similar outcomes on the predicted horizon. Ideally each state encodes the values for individual variables that uniquely define it, so that, when that state appears at the present time, its future outcome can be predicted to be the same as the outcome of a previous occurrence of that state in the reference data base. The series would then be stationary and fully deterministic, given the state definition. In practice, the states are not unique defined, and there exists an outcome variance within a cluster. The design process strives to minimize the sum of all the cluster variances. The individual cluster variance is proportional to the ability of the program to accurately predict a state which falls in that cluster.

IV. Prediction as a Pattern Recognition Problem

The most common way to represent a state, or to express a time series evolution, is through its representation as a function of "d" previous values of the time series itself [7]:

$$x(t+T) = f(x(t), \dots , x(t-d+1)) \qquad \mathcal{R}^d \rightarrow \mathcal{R}$$

This simple representation however, may not be sufficient to decompose a more complex structured series. As in the image processing literature [8], some extra features may be added to increase the contrast or difference between adjacent but inconsistent states. The state dimension and composition is, in fact, a keystone for the reference database construction. An extensive work on feature reduction and embedding selection has been recently developed by Hsu in his Doctoral dissertation [9]. In the Oil series under study, the state vector for each subseries also contains information about observed tendencies over some previous instants in time.

The reference database is built by defining clusters embodying the similar states selected according to the similarity operator. Such clusters divide the data hyperspace into hyperspheres represented by its centroid and a common radius. Ideally, outcomes within a hypersphere should have either no or a very small variation as compared to the standard deviation of the horizon outcome of the series. When data consistency is not present in a cluster, i.e., a large variation is present in the outcomes of historical patterns in that cluster, the state of the series needs to be redesigned by adding information to it. If that

is not possible, that cluster defines a state that is hard to accurately predict, and the variation of the outcomes are closely related to the certainty of that prediction. When very few elements are present in a cluster, estimation problems may occur and reliability on the prediction may be low. This requires more historical data to be present, or the similarity requirements of the state to be relaxed.

Once the cluster centers have been defined, they perform a number to symbol transformation, in which the trajectory of the original time series can be represented by a string of cluster names. Prediction is then accomplished by determining which cluster centers are close to the present state. Combining the selected cluster outcomes finally gives the predicted value.

An immediate implementation of this algorithm via a feedforward neural network is possible (figure 6). First, the hidden layer weights are assigned to be the cluster centers. Second, the hidden units, which represent the clusters, compute the similarity measure between the input vector and the cluster centers. This measure is multiplied by the output weights of the hidden nodes, which is the prototype value for the cluster outcome. The output unit then integrates all these estimates and normalizes them.

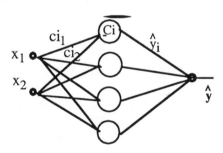

Fig. 6 The FeedForward Neural Network Interpretation of the Cluster Based Algorithm

V. Fusing Predictors for Accuracy

According to the literature [10], the most effective fusion processes are achieved when there is no positive cross-correlation between the individual model errors. When negative correlation occurs, which is quite rare, the gains can be spectacular. With high positive cross-correlation however, it is often difficult to achieve even a small improvement in accuracy, and if an unstable optimizing approach is used, the obtained result may be even worse than that of selecting the apparently best model. Actually fusing is theoretically no worse than any of the individual models [11,12], which can be intuitively shown as follows:

Let y_1^k and y_2^k be two distinct forecasts for the time instant t+k. The fused version gives:

$$\widehat{Y^k} = a_1 * \widehat{y_1^k} + a_2 * \widehat{y_2^k}$$

If y_1^k and y_2^k are based on the same information set, and if the optimum combination leads to an a_1 and a_2 different from zero, then it can be concluded that neither one nor the other is optimum. Now consider two different information sets $\{I_A, I_B\}$, and suppose that :

$$y_1^k = E\{x^k \mid I_A\}$$
$$y_2^k = E\{x^k \mid I_B\}$$

The optimum forecast based on all possible information is known to be:

$$Z^k = E\{x^k \mid I_T\} \text{ where } I_T = I_A \cup I_B$$

This complete estimation problem is normally very complex and expensive. But, if the sets I_A and I_B are uncorrelated then [13,14]:

$$Z^k = E\{x^k \mid I_T\} = E\{x^k \mid I_A\} + E\{x^k \mid I_B\}$$

which leads to the case where a_1 and a_2 are equal to 1.

VI. The Oil Series Example

In this example, an experiment in the prediction of the oil price traded in the New York market was conducted. The data is taken from the period of 1978 to 1988, and it is constituted of weekly price averages. The reference database was constructed with 450 points, from April 1978 to November 1986. The objective was to predict the average weekly price four weeks ahead. The series was broken into three coherent power components. A reference database was constructed for each series. The high power series was broken into 53 coherent behavior clusters, where the average of the cluster variances were 0.0005. For the medium and low power series, the averages were 0.1794 and 0.2928 for 119 and 174 clusters respectively.

The prediction period was from November 86 through January 1988: 63 weeks. During this period, the reference database was updated at every

time interval. The new point could be added to one of more of the existing clusters, or it could create a new one. The Root Mean Squared Error normalized by the standard deviation of the data for each series was: 0.0196, 0.3387, and 1.7571. The combined overall accuracy was 0.1882 (figures 7 and 8).

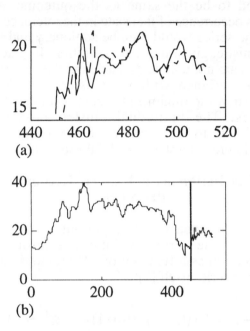

(a)

(b)

Fig. 7 - The 63 points, 4 steps ahead prediction - (a) scale of 14 to 18; (b) whole series

VII. Conclusions

This technique has shown to be promising for economic time series prediction. Our main conclusion from this study is that the prediction accuracy depends not only on power and data consistency, but it also depends on the sampling rate to prediction horizon ratio, as witnessed by the variances of the 3 components. For a better prediction of the third component, as well as improvements on the other 2, a daily signal would be necessary.

References

[1] Bowerman, B.L. and O'Connell, R.T., 1987, *Time Series Forecasting*, 2nd. Ed. PWS Publishers.
[2] Brockwell, P.J. and Davis, R.A., 1991, *Time Series: Theory and Methods*, 2nd. Ed. Springer Verlag.
[3] Box, G.E. and Jenkins, G.M., 1971, *Time Series Analysis: Forecasting and Control*, 1st. Ed. Holden-Day.

[4] Alexander, S.T., 1986, *Adaptive Signal Processing: Theory and Applications*, 1st. Ed. Springer Verlag.

[5] Press, W.H. and others, 1988, *Numerical Recipes, the Art of Scientific Computing*, 8th Ed. Cambridge.

[6] Hsu, W. and Tenorio, M.F., 1992, "A Similarity Based Approach to Forescating, "Worshop on Neural Networks, Proc. of, Auburn University, Auburn, Al.

[7] Takens, F., 1981, "Detecting Strage Attractors in Turbulance," Lecture Notes in Mathematics, Vol. 898, D. Rand, L. Young, Eds., Springer Verlag, Berlin, West Germany.

[8] Rao, A.R. and Jain, R.C., 1992, "Computerized Flow Field Analysis: Oriented Texture Fields", IEEE Transactions on Pattern Analysis and Machine Intelligence, vol 14,n° 7.

[9] Hsu, W., 1992, "Nonlinear Self-Adaptive Methods for Prediction", PhD Thesis, Purdue University, Lafayette, Indiana.

[10] Bunn, D., 1989, "Forecasting with more than one Model", Journal of Forecasting, vol. 8, pp. 161-166.

[11] Bates, J.M., and Granjer, C.W., 1969, "The Combination of Forecasts", Poer. Research Quartely, vol. 20, pp. 451-468.

[12] Granger, C.W. and Ramanathan, R., 1984, "Improved Methods of Combining Forecasts", Journal of Forecasting, vol. 3, pp. 197-204.

[13] Papoulis, A., 1984, *Probability, Random Variables, and Stochastic Processes*, 2nd Ed., McGraw-Hill, pp. 412-414.

[14] Baptista, E., 1980, "New Optimal Linear Filters for Multi-Sensors Applications", Phd Thesis, State University of New York at Buffalo.

Combined Mutually Connected Neural Network Model for Higher Order Association

Akira IWATA and Norihiko KOBAYASHI

Dept. of Electrical and Computer Eng., Nagoya Institute of Technology

Gokiso-cho, Showa-ku, Nagoya, 466, Japan

E-mail : iwata@mars.elcom.nitech.ac.jp

Abstract— A combined mutually connected neural network model for high order association are proposed. It contains plural functional modules each of which is mutually connected to neural network with hidden units in order to improve the performance of recall. The model comprises three different type of blocks ; Sub-Net, Intensive-Net and Intensive Sub-Net. Each module is mutually connected to each other and works dynamically in cooperation with other functional modules. The higher order association between three pieces of two-dimensional character dot patterns and a corresponding three character word patterns are well demonstrated by the model.

I. INTRODUCTION

In human brain, there are many functional modules which are connected to each other in hierarchical structure. These functional modules have not only bottom-up links from peripheral to nucleus (feed-forward connection), but also top-down links from nucleus to peripheral (feedback connection). Each functional module work dynamically in cooperation with other functional modules. Though each module has plural stable states and works dynamically when an initial input stimulus is received, the entire neural system becomes stabilized only if all the functional modules acquire one of the stable states. This function in human brain helps us associating or recalling images or words. Even from a blurred input stimulus, we can recall the complete images or words and recognize the input stimulus. For example, from an incomplete input stimulus, such as "sch_l" with two characters missed, human brain can recall that the two characters missed should be "oo", recognize that the input stimulus should be "school", and recall the image of the word "school".

Such operation is assumed as "Higher Order Association".

Several neural network models with mutual connections, such as Hopfield model [1], have been proposed for realizing associations. These mutually connected neural network models work dynamically, change their own neural activation from time to time, and finally become a stable state representing a memorized pattern, which is the nearest to the incomplete initial pattern. Therefore, the mutually connected neural network models have frequently been used for association. However, they can only associate a single character or a single pattern using a single network model. They have rarely been used as a model, in which plural networks operate in cooperation or competition with each other to associate a word or an image. Though Ohkuma [2] et al. propose an architecture combining plural Hopfield models, it has a problem that the number of patterns to be memorized is limited due to Hopfield model.

The authors propose a combined mutually connected neural network model for higher order association. It contains plural functional modules, each of which is a mutually connected neural network with hidden units in order to improve the performance of recall. This paper describes the mutually connected neural network module with hidden units, its learning rule to memorize arbitrary patterns, the combined model using plural modules, and the higher order associations.

II. MUTUALLY CONNECTED NEURAL NETWORK MODULE WITH HIDDEN UNITS

The structure of the mutually connected neural network module is shown in Figure 1. The module consists of two blocks of units: a block of input/output units which work as the input/output units of the network, and a block of hidden units which is invisible from the outside of the network.

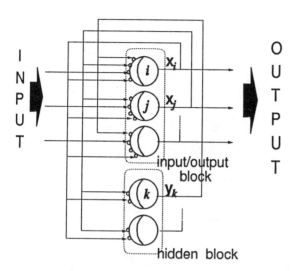

Figure 1: A mutually connected neural network module

All the units within the input/output block are completely mutually connected, while there is no such connection within the hidden block. On the other hand, the input/output units and the units within the hidden block consist of a fully feed-forward hierarchical neural network. That is, the input/output units are connected to the hidden units and then the input/output units are connected to the input/output again. According to this hierarchical structure, teaching signals are not needed for the hidden units in the learning phase of the network, while those are given to the input/output units. This network structure allows the module to be trained by the steepest decent method of error like Back-propagation.

The module has two different types of units: units which belong to the input/output block, and units which belong to the hidden block. Of the former units, the i th unit has the output value x_i and the internal state x_i', and of the latter units, the k th unit has the output value y_k and the internal state y_k'. x_i and y_k take real number values within the range $0 \leq x_i, y_k \leq 1$.

The connection w_{ij} is that from the j th unit to the i th unit in the input/output units, the connection w_{kj} is that from the j th unit of the input/output units to the k th unit of the hidden units, and the connection w_{ik} is from the k th unit of the hidden units to the i th unit of the input/output units. The operations of each unit are expressed by the following operational formulas:

$$x_i' = \sum_j^N w_{ij}x_j + \sum_k^M w_{ik}y_k + S_i \quad (1)$$

$$x_i = f(x_i'), \qquad f(x) = \frac{1}{1+e^{-x}} \quad (2)$$

$$y_k' = \sum_j^N w_{kj}x_j \quad (3)$$

$$y_k = f(y_k') \quad (4)$$

where S_i is an external stimulus to the i th input/output unit. The Sigmoid function is used for the function $f(x)$.

The input/output units update the states by receiving the outputs from the input/output and hidden units. On the other hand, the hidden units update the states by receiving outputs only from the input/output units.

The connection weights of the module are trained by the steepest decent method of error, in which the connection weights are updated according to the derivative of the error between the given teaching signals and the signal actually outputted from the network: It is supposed that the network has N input/output units and the M hidden units. Let a set of L learning patterns be $T = (T(1), T(2), \cdots, T(L))$, where $T(l) = (t_1(l), t_2(l), \cdots, t_N(l))$ $(0 \leq t_i(l) \leq 1)$. The error between the teaching signal $t_i(l)$ and the output x_i actually outputted from the i th input/output unit is defined as the error function E as follows:

$$E = \frac{1}{2}\sum_{i=1}^N (t_i(l) - x_i)^2 \quad (5)$$

the updated weight quantities, Δw_{ij}, Δw_{ik}, and Δw_{kj}, are obtained by decreasing the error according to the derivative of the error as follows:

$$\Delta w_{ij} = -\varepsilon \frac{\partial E}{\partial w_{ij}}$$
$$= \varepsilon_{ij}(t_i(l) - x_i)x_i(1 - x_i)t_j(l) \quad (6)$$
$$\Delta w_{ik} = -\varepsilon \frac{\partial E}{\partial w_{ik}}$$
$$= \varepsilon_{ik}(t_i(l) - x_i)x_i(1 - x_i)y_k \quad (7)$$
$$\Delta w_{kj} = -\varepsilon \frac{\partial E}{\partial w_{kj}}$$
$$= \varepsilon_{kj}\left(\sum_{i=1}^N (t_i(l) - x_i)x_i(1 - x_i)w_{ik}\right)$$
$$y_k(1 - y_k)t_j(l) \quad (8)$$

where $\varepsilon, \varepsilon_{ij}, \varepsilon_{ik}$, and ε_{kj} are positive coefficients. The learning rules is similar to the Back Propagation assuming the hidden units as intermediate units in a hierarchical feed-forward neural network. Therefore the output values of the hidden units are able to be train without receiving teaching signals directly. The iteration of the learning should be continued until the error E is decreased to nearly zero. It means that all the patterns contained in a set of the teaching pattern, T, are memorized in the module. That is, each learning pattern $T(l)$ has became one of stable states. If one of the learning patterns is given to the network, all input/output units keep their output values. Furthermore , it has been proved that the learning patterns are to be point attractors. The details of the provement will be described in the next article.

It has been investigated that the hidden block privides the effect to increase robustness of the network [3]. The hidden blocks also become bridges between network modules. So, the hidden units block of each module is combined to each other.

III. Combined Mutually Connected Neural Network Model

Plural mutually connected neural network modules have been combined to realize higher order association. The model, as shown in Figure 2, comprises three different type blocks; Sub-Net (hereinafter referred to as "S-Net"), Intensive-Net (hereinafter referred to as "I-Net") , and Intensive Sub-Net (hereinafter referred to as "IS-Net"). Each S-Net makes a mutually connected neural network modules together with several IS-Nets. S-Net corresponds to the input/output block, and IS-Net corresponds to the hidden block in a module. I-Net, which combines several IS-Nets, also forms a mutually connected neural network module. Since the states of the S-Net affects the IS-Net (hidden units), changes of the states of IS-Net (a part of I-Net) affect another IS-Nets, and then the states of all S-Net are affected. Each module of the model is mutually connected to each other. Not only all of the states of the units affect the others, but also these are reversely affected by the others. Each module works dynamically in cooperation with other functional modules.

When P pieces of S-Nets exist within the model, the output value of the units within p th S-Net can be expressed by using the vector formula as follows:

$$\mathbf{x}^p = (x_1^p, x_2^p, \cdots, x_{N^p}^p) \tag{9}$$

where N_p is the number of units within the p th S-Net. In the same way, when Q_p pieces of IS-Nets exist within the p th S-Net, the output value of the unit within the q th IS-Net can be expressed as

$$\mathbf{y}^{pq} = (y_1^{pq}, y_2^{pq}, \cdots, y_{M^{pq}}^{pq}) \tag{10}$$

where M_{pq} is the number of units within the q th IS-Net of the p th S-Net. When R pieces of units exist within the I-Net, the output value of the units within the r th I-Net which combines several IS-Nets can be expressed as

$$\mathbf{z}^r = (\mathbf{y}^{ab}, \mathbf{y}^{cd}, \cdots) \tag{11}$$

Here, it should be noted that an I-Net comprises several IS-Nets, and therefore a unit which belongs to an I-Net

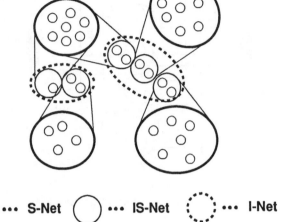

S-Net   IS-Net   I-Net

Figure 2: Combined mutually connected neural network model

also belongs to an IS-Net. That is, a unit has two different output values corresponding to Equations (10) and (11). Therefore, either output values are taken in the operation. Here, taking the other output value as a new one is referred to as "switching of the output value."

The followings are the output formulas of each Net.

$$\mathbf{x}^p = \mathbf{f}\left(\mathbf{W}_{ij}^p \mathbf{x}^p + \sum_q^{Q^p} \mathbf{W}_{ik}^{pq} \mathbf{y}^{pq}\right) \tag{12}$$

$$\mathbf{y}^{pq} = \mathbf{f}\left(\mathbf{W}_{kj}^{pq} \mathbf{x}^p\right) \tag{13}$$

$$\mathbf{z}^r = \mathbf{f}\left(\mathbf{V}^r \mathbf{z}^r\right) \tag{14}$$

where $\mathbf{W}_{ij}^p$ is the connection weight among the units within the p th S-Net, $\mathbf{W}_{ik}^{pq}$ is the connection weight from an IS-Net to an S-Net, and $\mathbf{W}_{kj}^{pq}$ is the connection weight from the S-Net to the IS-Net, and $\mathbf{V}^r$ is the connection weight among the units within the r th I-Net.

As before mensioned, a unit which belongs to an I-Net also belongs to an IS-Net. For this reason, depending on to which Net the unit belongs , which Equations, (13) or (14), should be used is determined.

This model operates in the following sequence:

1. The stimulus S enters each S-Net.

2. Updating the output values of the IS-Net.
In all the IS-Nets, their output values are updated by using Equation (13).

3. Updating the output values of the I-Net

In all the I-Nets, their output values are updated by using Equation(14).

4. Updating the output values of the S-Net
In all the S-Nets, their output values are updated by using Equation(12).

5. Steps 2 through 6 above are repeated until the output values of all the units come to stop varying.

The learning in which a teaching pattern is memorized in this model is performed in the following two stages.

.1. S-IS learning

In this stage, learning is performed in the S-Net and the IS-Net. The set of teaching patterns within the p th S-Net is supposed to be $T^p = (T^p(1), T^p(2), \cdots, T^p(L^p))(1 \leq p \leq P)$. Since S-Net and IS-Net correspond to the input/output block and hidden block of the mutually connected neural network as described in Section II, the same learning method is used for training.

The updating equations of each connection weight are obtained by using Equations (6),(7) and (8) as follows:

$$\Delta w_{ij}^p = \varepsilon_{ij}^p(t_i^p(l) - x_i^p)x_i^p(1 - x_i^p)t_j^p(l) \quad (15)$$

$$\Delta w_{ik}^{pq} = \varepsilon_{ik}^{pq}(t_i^p(l) - x_i^p)x_i^p(1 - x_i^p)y_k^{pq} \quad (16)$$

$$\Delta w_{kj}^{pq} = \varepsilon_{kj}^{pq}\left(\sum_{i=1}^{N}(t_i^p(l) - x_i^p)x_i^p(1 - x_i^p)w_{ik}^{pq}\right)$$
$$y_k^{pq}(1 - y_k^{pq})t_j^p(l) \quad (17)$$

In all the S-Nets and IS-Nets, the learning can be performed by adding the updated quantity obtained from the above equations to the connection weights. The learning is continued until the value of the error function for each S-Net becomes to nearly zero.

.2. I-Net learning

In the learning at this stage, the connection weight in the I-Net is updated. The teaching pattern can be obtained as the output values y^{pq} of IS-Nets as follows. The connection weights obtained by the above learning are used for the S-Net and IS-Net of the network.

1. The teaching patterns to be given to each S-Net, T^p are taken as a set of the teaching patterns to be given to the entire network, $U(n)$, where $U(n) = (T^1(l_1), T^2(l_2), \cdots, T^P(l_P))$. Several sets of teaching patterns are prepared, which are supposed to be $U = \{U(n), 1 \leq n \leq N\}$.

2. A teaching patterns, $U(n)$, is selected from the set U, and give to the S-Net as the stimuli.

$$\mathbf{x}^1 = T^1(l_1), \mathbf{x}^2 = T^2(l_2), \cdots, \mathbf{x}^P = T^P(l_P) \quad (18)$$

3. The output values of each IS-Net are updated from the output values of each S-Net by using Equation (13).

4. The output values y^{pq} of each IS-Net are switched to the output z of the corresponding I-Net.

5. The output z are taken as the r th teaching signal $T_y^r(i)$.

6. Steps 3 through 6 are repeated as many times as the number contained in the set U of the teaching patterns, $U(n)$, to obtain the set of the teaching patterns of the I-Net, $T_y^r = (T_y^r(1), T_y^r(2), \cdots, T_y^r(n))$.

The learning rule adopted here is also the steepest decent method of error. The I-Net is not the same as one used in Section II, but is the mutually fully connected neural network having no hidden units. Therefore, the learning rule described in Section II is applied.

The error function E from the teaching patterns $T_y^r(n) = (t_{y_1}^r(n), t_{y_2}^r(n), \cdots, t_{y_M}^r(n))$ can be defined as follows:

$$E = \frac{1}{2}\sum_i^{M}\left(t_{y_i}^r(n) - z_i^r\right)^2 \quad (19)$$

$$z_i^{'r} = \sum_j^{M} v_{ij}^r t_{y_j}^r(n) \quad (20)$$

$$z_i^r = f\left(z_i^{'r}\right) \quad (21)$$

where M is the number of units within the r th I-Net, and v_{ij}^r is the connection weight in the r th I-Net from the j th unit to the i th unit.

The updating equation Δv_{ij}^r is obtained by using the steepest error declining method as follows:

$$\Delta v_{ij}^r = -\varepsilon\frac{\partial E}{\partial z_i^r}\frac{\partial z_i^r}{\partial z_i^{'r}}\frac{\partial z_i^{'r}}{\partial v_{ij}^r}$$
$$= \varepsilon'(t_{y_i}^r(n) - z_i^r)z_i^r(1 - z_i^r)t_{y_j}^r(n) \quad (22)$$

In all I-Net, the learning can be performed by adding the updating quantities obtained from the above equation to the connection weights. The learning is continued until the value of the error function for each I-Net becomes to nearly zero.

IV. HIGHER ORDER ASSOCIATION BY COMBINED MUTUALLY CONNECTED NEURAL NETWORK MODEL

The higher order association is realized using this model. In the examination, the associations between three pieces of two-dimensional character dot patterns and a corresponding three-character word pattern are investigated.

The configuration of this model is illustrated in Figure 3. This model comprises plural S-Nets, which memorize each character pattern (each of which hereinafter referred to as "Character S-Net") and an S-Net which memorizes a three-character word pattern (hereinafter referred to as "Word S-Net"). Each S-Net has an IS-Net subordinated. These four IS-Nets are mutually connected in an I-Net. The sizes are set as follows: each Character S-Net contains 225 units (15 x 15 two-dimensional matrix); the Word S-Net,100 units; and the I-Net, 400 units (IS-Net 100 unit x 4).

The teaching patterns used for this model comprised 26 alphabets in capital, each 15x15 matrix, as illustrated in Figure 3. Ten three-character words are prepared for the Word S-Net: 'CAT', 'DOG', 'FOX', 'MAP', 'ANT', 'NET', 'CUP', 'BAT', 'PIG' and 'BOY'. Each word is expressed with a pattern which has the output value 1.0 for ten units out of 100 units of the S-Net and the output value 0.0 for the other 90 units as illustrated in Figure 4 . Association can be performed more easily when a word is expressed by using plural units, output of which is 1 due to the dispersion of the information of the word.

How the model operates when various stimuli are given to the S-Nets and word network is demonstrated as follows. Though various stimuli to be given to the model are conceivable, it is operated by giving the following stimuli in this experiment.

Character patterns with mixed noise as illustrated in Figure 5 (humming distance: 30) are given to each S-Net. The word pattern, which corresponds to the Word S-Net, is also given as a stimulus.

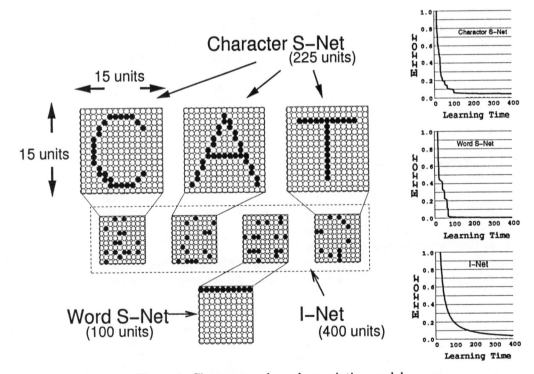

Figure 3: Character and word associative model

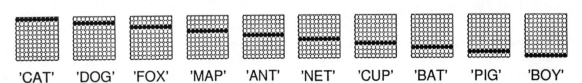

Figure 4: 10 word patterns

As illustrated in Figure 5, when the entire network is operated, the model works dynamically time by time, the character patterns in the Character S-Nets become clear gradually, and then the word pattern in the Word S-Net is also generated.

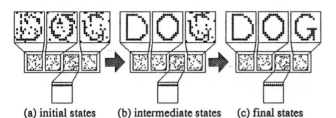

(a) initial states   (b) intermediate states   (c) final states

Figure 5: Association from 3 character patterns with mixed noise and a word pattern

In Figure 6, character patterns in the Character S-Nets are given, but no stimulus is given to the Word S-Net. This means that the intermediate value 0.5 of the values are assigned for the Word S-Net. The operation of the model is illustrated in Figure 6. As illustrated in this figure, when the model is operated, the pattern corresponding to the word indicated by three S-Nets appears in the Word S-Net gradually.

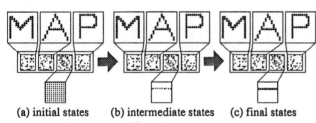

(a) initial states   (b) intermediate states   (c) final states

Figure 6: Association from 3 character patterns without a word pattern

In Figure 7, the two character patterns are given to two Charactor S-Nets, but no stimulus is given to the other Character S-Net. For example, when 'FOX' should be associated, the character patterns 'F' and 'O' are given as stimuli to the first and second Character S-Net respectively, and no stimulus is given to the third Character S-Net. An example of this operation is illustrated in Figure 7.

In Figure 8, any stimulus are not given to all of the Character S-Nets but only to the Word S-Net. In this experiment, a word pattern is continuously given as a stimulus to the Word S-Net. When the model operates, the character patterns of the Character S-Nets are also appeared. It is recognized that continuous giving of stimuli facilitates the association of the character pattern as expected. The information given by the stimuli is too little to have the information reflected on the entire network by giving the stimuli only at the start of operation. Therefore, the authors consider that the continuous giving of

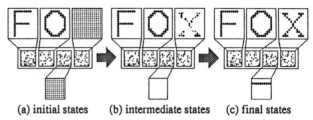

(a) initial states   (b) intermediate states   (c) final states

Figure 7: Association from 2 character patterns

stimuli enables the information given to diffuse over the entire model, and thereby the character pattern expected can be associated.

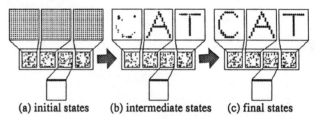

(a) initial states   (b) intermediate states   (c) final states

Figure 8: Association from a word pattern

V. CONCLUSION

An innovative neural network model for higher order associations by using mutually connected neural network modules is proposed. By using this method, plural mutually connected neural networks can be connected to each other via hidden units. Arbitrary number of network modules which have learned knowledge independently can be combined with each other by this model, and then each knowledge can be combined with other.

The higher order associations between three pieces of two-dimensional character dot patterns and a corresponding three-character word pattern have been well demonstrated.

REFERENCES

[1] Hopfield,J,J.: Neural networks and physical systems with emergent collective computational abilities. *Proc. Nat. Acad. Sic. USA 79*(1982),2554-2558.

[2] K.Ohkuma and T.Tanaka: A Multi-Layer Representation of the Hopfiled Network and Its Application as a Functional Module.Research and Technical Report of IEICEJ,NC91-157(1992-3,in japanese)

[3] N.Kobayashi,A.Iwata and N.Suzumura;Pattern Recollection Using Recrrent Neural Network By Steepest Decent Learning Procedure,Resarch and Technical Report of IEICEJ,NC91-133(1992-3,in japanese)

ON DECOMPOSING MLPS

S. Lucas, Z. Zhao* G. Cawley and P. Noakes
Department of Electronic Systems Engineering,
University of Essex,
Wivenhoe Park, Colchester CO4 3SQ, UK
email sml@uk.ac.essex

Abstract

This paper investigates the benefits of decomposing the MLP for pattern recognition tasks. Suppose we have N classes, then instead of employing 1 MLP with N outputs, we use N MLPs, each with a single output. In practice, this allows us to use fewer hidden units than would be employed in the single MLP. Furthermore, we find that decomposing the problem in this way allows convergence in fewer iterations. Not only do we save on the number of iterations as well as the time per iteration, but also it becomes straightforward to distribute the training over as many workstations as there are pattern classes. The speedup is then linear in the number of pattern classes, assuming we have as many processors as classes. If we have more classes than processors, then the speedup is linear in the number of processors.

We show that on a difficult hand-written OCR problem, the results obtained with the decomposed MLP are slightly superior than those for the conventional MLP, and obtained in a fraction of the time.

1 Introduction

This paper investigates the benefits of decomposing the MLP for pattern recognition tasks. Suppose we have n classes, then instead of employing 1 MLP with n outputs, we use n MLPs, each with a single output. This raises at least two interesting questions.

- Suppose we have a large network of workstations that lie mostly idle overnight. Can we *easily* exploit this power to learn our problem faster?

- Can we improve recognition rate on difficult problems by simplifying the learning task?

The answer to the first of these questions turns out to be *yes*, while initial results suggest a *maybe* in answer to the second.

The decomposing idea occurs naturally in personal verification tasks (e.g. speaker verification [1]), but seems to be seldom reported for recognition problems, and is certainly not the norm. The results presented below suggest that it should be.

2 The Decomposition

The decomposition is conceptually straightforward. Instead of having a single MLP with one output (Figure 1, we just have N decomposed MLPs (DMLP), each with a single output (Figure 2). But what about the hidden units? Naïvely, we might suppose that if we needed H units in the MLP, then perhaps we could get by with (H/N) units in the DMLP. Clearly, this simplistic reasoning fails for problems such as the *encoder*, where if we regard each output as a class, then we only require $log_2 N$ hidden units. However, for difficult pattern recognition tasks we find that such minimal hidden layers do not perform at all well.

2.1 Maximising information per pattern presentation

Assuming all N classes are equiprobable, then if we use a standard MLP with one out of N output coding, assuming we present patterns from the training set at random, the probability of any given output j being on

---

*Department of Physiscs, University of Keele, UK

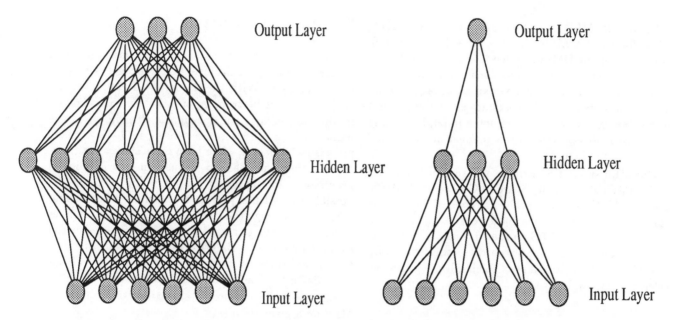

Figure 1: The standard MLP with one output for each of the N classes.

Figure 2: The Decomposed MLP with a single output and smaller hidden layer.

is $1/N$, and of being off is $(N-1)/N$. Hence, using $E = -\Sigma_i p_i log_2 p_i$, the entropy of each output j is:

$$E_j = -\frac{1}{N} log_2 \frac{1}{N} - \frac{(N-1)}{N} log_2 \frac{(N-1)}{N}$$

So, the information presented at each output per presentation for the MLP is $N \times E_j$, but only E_j for the DMLP, since in this case we have only one output. The important question is: can we improve training speed for the DMLP by maximising the output entropy?

We can easily make $E_j = 1$ for the DMLP using the following trick: we split the training set for each class into two sets: patterns of that class, and patterns of any other class. We then choose with equal likelihood to pick a pattern from its own class, or a pattern from the *all-other-classes set*. Hence, we now have $E_j = 2 \times -0.5 log_2 0.5 = 1$.

To put some figures on this, for 10 classes this equates to the information per-pattern presentation increasing from 0.46 to 1, (i.e. a factor of 2.2) and for 36 classes, we get an 0.18 to 1 (i.e. a factor of 5.6).

The disadvantage of course (this sentence was written with the benefit of hindsight! — see Section 4), is that we have deformed the probability distributions of the input vectors, so while we expect training to be faster (and this is indeed the case in practice), we may

just be learning the wrong things (but learning them quickly).

2.2 Connections per presentation

The time taken to process a pattern is (to a good approximation) proportional to the number of connections in the network. Given a fully-connected MLP with I input, H hidden and O output nodes the number of connections is:

$$C = (I \times H) + (H \times I)$$

Two useful measures of performance are (millions of) Conections Per Second (MCPS) and Connection Updates Per Second (MCUPS).

For most implementations, MCUPS will be a bit less than half the value of MCPS, but for many special architectures, such as some of those based on DSP chips, MCUPS may be only about one tenth of the MCPS figure, and the difference for dedicated neural chips is often even more pronounced.

For the DMLP let the number of hidden units be H_D. Assume $H_D = H/N$. In the Results Section below we have $I = 16$, $H = 100$, $O = 10$ and $N = 10$, so H_D is also 10.

So, for the MLP, $C = 16 \times 100 + 100 \times 10 = 2600$, while for the DMLP, $C = 16 \times 10 + 10 \times 1 = 170$. However, for the DMLP, we have to present each pattern to N nets, so the connections per pattern sums to 1700. Nonetheless, this gives an advantage even on a single processor. On N workstations, it can amount to an enormous advantage. As noted in [2], harnessing under-used workstations in this manner makes a good deal of economic sense.

Our MLP simulation written in C runs at 0.8 MCPS and 0.3MCUPS on a Sun Sparc ELC rated at 22 MIPS. For the 10 OCR class problem reported below this translates to 8 MCPS (distributed over 10 sparcs), and should achieve 29 MCPS on the 36 class alphanumeric problem (distributed over 36 sparcs) — this figure compares favourably with many of the hardware neural accelerators available [3].

2.3 Actual Speedup

For the OCR problem reported below we get a speedup in learning that is faster than would be expected from the increase in MCPS (by distributing the work over many workstations) and the reduction in the total number of weights, and results from the fact that convergence to the same error is achieved in fewer iterations.

This we suspect is due to the fact that each DMLP now has a simpler error surface to explore in weightspace, since each hidden unit now has a predefined function i.e. to set up hyperplanes to discriminate between the DMLPs assigned class and all other classes. This is not the case for the standard MLP, where the hidden units must contend for the pattern classes they will ultimately serve[1].

2.4 Recomposition

Given N DMLPs each with a single output, it is straightforward to reconstruct an MLP with N outputs and N times the number of hidden units, just by placing them side by side, looking at the same input vector.

---

[1] This reasoning is simplistic, since in a standard MLP a given hidden unit may be useful in the discrimination of many classes. Nonetheless, we believe there to be some truth in the idea.

3 Implementation

Many research institutions have many workstations of moderate power, which during off-peak hours may go largely unused. With the decomposed MLPs we can exploit this fact by training an MLP for each class on its own processor. The speedup is then linear in the number of pattern classes, assuming we have as many processors as classes. If we have more classes than processors, then the speedup is linear in the number of processors. In this latter case it would of course be possible to partition the dataset across different machines and average the weights after a certain number of iterations, but this kind of parallelism is less easily exploited by a network of workstations, since the iterations performed by each workstation in a given time depends on the loading on that machine.

Suppose we have an executable command to train an MLP on a given data set:

```
mlp   TrainingFile LearningRate ... etc
```

then we first need to modify this to take an additional parameter:

```
mlp   PatternClass
      TrainingFile LearningRate ... etc
```

Then, the following pseudo-code distributes the work over the given list of hosts:

```
Hosts :=
  MakeCircularList({Host1, Host2, ... HostM})
For i:=1 to PatternClasses
  on pop(Hosts)
      mlp i TrainingFile LearningRate ... etc
```

Here, *pop* returns the first element of the list and advances *Hosts* to point to the next element in the list, and *on* starts the mlp for class n running on that host. The only overhead is the reconstruction of an MLP from the N decomposed ones to gain results on the test data, but this may be done automatically upon completion of training of the slowest DMLP (some classes may be more difficult to learn than others), though we have not yet implemented the program to do this final part.

	Recognition Rate			
	DMLP	EDMLP	MLP-100	EUC
Training Set	91.2%	59.8%	87.3%	70.3
Test Set	77.7%	57.3%	75.5%	66.9

Table 1: Recognition rates for 10 class OCR problem, with approx 3,000 characters in the training set and 5,000 characters in the test set. DMLP = Decomposed MLP, EDMLP = decomposed MLP with maximum entropy pattern presentations, MLP-100 = conventional MLP with one hundred hidden units. EUC = euclidean classifier.

4 Results for OCR

We tested these ideas on a difficult hand-written post-code dataset. While in general these characters are alphanumeric, implying some 36 classes, we have so far only tested the approach on the numeric subset of this data. The data are supplied by the Royal Mail (formerly the British Post Office), and are scanned from real hand-written postcodes. This is an extremely difficult dataset, where the human performance is around 90% given no context.

4.1 Pre-processing

Each character consisted of a 42×48 bitmap extracted and segmented from the scanned and binary-quantised envelope. We considered it impractical to feed this directly into the net as this would mean 2016-dimension input vectors. Instead, we performed a radial transform of each character bitmap about its centre of gravity using 16 angular bins spaced evenly every 22.5 degrees. The mean distance of the points in each bin from the centre of gravity of the character was then computed and the values from all the bins used to compute a 16-dimensional radial-mean vector. Incidentally, this pre-processing method was inspired by the outermost point OCR method of Yamamoto [4].

Each net was trained using the on-line backpropagation as described by Fogelman-Soulie [5]. The results are shown in Table 1. We experimented with 10, 25, 50 and 100 hidden units in the MLP, with the 100 unit version giving the best performance.

It should be noted that MLP-100 took 15 hours to reach that performance level, wheras the DMLPS had achieved that level in about 45 minutes (i.e. one twenti-

eth of the time), and reached the superior performance quoted above after about 90 minutes. The EDMLPs (decomposed, trained with maximum entropy pattern presentations converged in about half the time of the DMLP, but only to offer an inferior result.

5 Conclusions

This work has shown that significant speedups can be obtained by decomposing an N class MLP recogniser into N single class *experts* for training purposes. The decomposed MLPs converge more quickly and tend to produce superior results to the conventional ones. For a 10 class OCR problem the speedup was by a factor of 20 over the conventional MLP. This translates to about 8 MCPS, but for an alphanumeric character recognition problem with 36 classes, we can achieve about 29 MCPS. This compares favourably with many of the neural accelerator boards currently available.

Maximising the rate of information presentation to the decomposed MLP produced disappointing results, albeit more quickly, and we are investigating this further. Most likely, it is due to the fact that the observed probability distribution of the input vectors is now deformed from the actual distribution.

Acknowledgements

The authors gratefully acknowledge financial support for some of the work from UK Royal Mail Research and Development.

References

[1] J. Oglesby and J. Mason, "Optimisation of neural models for speaker identification," in *Proceedings of IEEE International Conference on Acoustics, Speech and Signal Processing (ICASSP '90)*, pp. 393 – 396, Toronto, Canada: IEEE, (1990).

[2] G. Bell, "Ultracomputers: a teraflop before its time," *Communications of the Association for Computing Machinery*, vol. 35, no. 8, pp. 27 – 47, (1992).

[3] N. Mauduit, M. Duranton, J. Gobert, and J. Sirat, "Lneuro 1.0: A piece of hardware lego for build-

ing neural network systems," *IEEE Transactions on Neural Networks*, vol. 3, pp. 414 – 422, (1992).

[4] K. Yamamoto and S. Mori, "Recognition of hand-printed characters by an outermost point method," *Pattern Recognition*, vol. 12, pp. 229 – 236, (1980).

[5] F. Fogelman-Soulie, "Neural network architectures and algorithms: a perspective," in *Proceedings of the International Conference on Artificial Neural Networks (ICANN-91)*, pp. 605 – 615, Amsterdam: Elsevier, (1991).

STOCK RANKING: NEURAL NETWORKS Vs MULTIPLE LINEAR REGRESSION

A. N. REFENES, M. AZEMA-BARAC & A. D. ZAPRANIS
Department of Computer Science,
University College London,
Gower Street WC1 6BT,
London UK.

ABSTRACT

Modeling of the capital markets has traditionally been done in partial equilibrium. Such models have been very useful in expanding our understanding of the capital markets; nevertheless many empirical financial anomalies have remained unexplainable. Attempting to model financial markets in a general equilibrium framework still remains analytically intractable.

Because of their inductive nature, dynamical systems such as neural networks can bypass the step of theory formulation, and they can infer complex non-linear relationships between input and output variables. In this paper we examine the use of neural networks to replace classical statistical techniques for forecasting within the framework of the APT (Arbitrage Pricing Theory) model for stock ranking. We show that neural networks outperform these statistical techniques in forecasting accuracy terms by an average of 36 percentage points, and give better model fitness in-sample by one order of magnitude. We identify values for network parameters for which these figures are statistically stable.

1. INTRODUCTION

A great deal of effort has been devoted into developing systems for predicting stock returns in the capital markets. Limited success has been achieved. It is believed that the main reason for this is that the structural relationship between an asset price and its determinants changes over time. These changes can be abrupt. For example, one month a rise in interest rates will strengthen sterling, whilst the next month a rise will weaken sterling. This phenomenon of unstable structural parameters in asset price models is a special case of a general fundamental critique of econometric and statistical models. A relationship might be established, for example, between consumer spending and personal income. A tax cut could then be analysed

via its effect on personal income. Critics, however, assert that this cannot be done, because a change in policy (the tax cut) will not only change the level of income, but will change the relationship between spending and income. Neural networks could in principle deal with the problem of structural instability.

Neural network architectures have drawn considerable attention in recent years because of their interesting learning abilities. Several researchers have reported exceptional results with the use of neural networks [1, 3, 4, 5, 6]. Neural networks are generally believed to be an effective modeling procedure when the mapping from input to output vectors contains both regularities and exceptions and they are, in principle capable of solving any non-linear classification problem, provided that the network contains a sufficiently large number of free parameters (i.e. hidden unit and/or connections).

In this paper we investigate the performance of neural networks in the non-trivial application of stock ranking. The problem consists of a universe of stocks whose returns are linked to three factors. The idea is to predict the relative outperformance of each stock in the universe, six months in advance given the current values of these three factors. The whole process is part of the **APT** model (Arbitrage Pricing Theory). Currently the prediction is done by linear regression. Our target is to outperform linear regression with respect to three metrics:

- goodness of fit *in-sample* (convergence);

- goodness of fit *out-of-sample* (generalisation);

- stability of results with varying network parameters and different data sets.

We show that neural networks give better model fitness *in sample* by one order of magnitude and outperform linear regression in forecasting by 36 percentage points in terms of prediction accuracy in direction of change. We identify intervals of values for the parameters that influence network performance over which the results are stable, and show that the same performance figures persist across different training/test sets.

In section 2 of this paper we give a brief overview of the stock ranking application. In section 3 we discuss the neural network setup. We also define the metrics for evaluating the convergence and generalisation ability of different network configurations and comparing with multiple linear regression. In section 4 we discuss our results using as a benchmark the Multiple Linear Regression (**MLR**), and finally, in section 5 we give some brief concluding remarks.

2. STOCK VALUATION: THE APT MODEL

The Arbitrage Pricing Theory (APT) is widely used in portfolio management as an alternative to the the Capital Asset Pricing Model (CAPM). The APT has the benefit of being a more powerful theory; it requires less stringent assumptions than the CAPM, yet it produces similar results. The difficulty with the APT is that it shows that there is a way to forecast expected asset returns but it does not specify how to do it.

The key idea of the theory is that there exist a **set of factors** so that *expected returns* can be explained as a linear combination of each asset's exposure to these factors.

The APT is based on a *no-arbitrage* assumption that can be stated as requiring an upper limit on the ratio of the *expected-excess-return* so that any risk investment divided by the volatility of that same investment is bounded. If that ratio was not bounded then it would be possible to get positive expected-excess-returns for very low levels of risk. With the no-arbitrage assumption there always exist a portfolio that we call portfolio Q which is efficient and has the highest ratio of expected-excess-return to volatility. In this case any asset's (or portfolio's P) expected-excess-return will be proportional to their covariance with the portfolio Q. For portfolio P we have:

$$E(r(P)) = \gamma(n)\, E(r(Q)) \qquad (1)$$

where $\gamma(n)$ is the "beta" of the asset with respect to the portfolio Q, $E(r(P))$ is the expected excess return of the portfolio P, and $E(r(Q))$ is the expected excess return of the portfolio Q.

The advantage of this is that it does not require any special assumptions in order to arrive at the result. The disadvantage is that we do not know the portfolio Q. The effort to uncover the portfolio Q usually takes the form of searching for *attributes* of Q rather than the actual portfolio holdings. The idea is that the particular portfolio Q will depend on the universe of assets we are considering and the properties of those assets at that time.

Amongst the various techniques for putting the APT model to practical use DynIM is perhaps the most commonly used. According to the quantitative stock selection (DynIM) framework, three stages are necessary during the investment process:

- pre-processing of data to calculate relative values for the factors involved.

- ranking the stocks,

- constructing the portfolio.

The second stage of DynIM has so far been modeled by linear regression. However it is not always possible to estimate the exposure of an asset to the factors accurately using linear methods. In this paper we show that Neural Networks are an effective substitute for linear regression, and yield better accuracy both in fitting the model and predicting relative outperformance six months ahead.

3. EXPERIMENTAL SET-UP

3.1 The Stock Ranking Problem

The purpose of stock ranking is the construction of a portfolio. Stock ranking is defined as the task of assigning ratings to different stocks within a universe. This is actually a classification problem: *given a set of classes and a set of input data instances, each described by a suitable set of features, assign each input data instance to one of the classes.* In our case the different stocks form the set of input instances and the various ratings form the possible classes to which the input stocks can belong.

Table 3.1: Sample training data				
Y	A	B	C	STOCK CODE
-0.203553	+1.268286	-0.128681	+0.616215	6811.000000
-0.066618	-0.272814	-0.187851	-0.124382	6842.000000
+0.170599	+0.175118	+0.331097	+0.420197	6870.000000
-0.078946	-0.061965	-0.181817	+0.309313	6926.000000
+0.193520	-0.342653	+1.379686	+0.215267	8118.000000
+0.112259	+0.792553	-0.417726	+0.066999	8320.000000
-0.190763	+1.016654	+0.270754	+1.166889	8800.000000
-0.104398	-0.194282	+0.169641	-0.036239	8846.000000
-0.124752	-0.021836	+0.900211	+0.338135	9344.000000
-0.070049	-0.135540	-0.064680	+0.599856	9601.000000

Each stock instance can be described by a set of features which represent important financial information about the company which the stock represents.

More formally the problem statement is as follows : Let S represent the space of stocks, $S_1, S_2, S_3, ..., S_n$, and R be the set of possible (mutually exclusive) stock ratings, $R_1, R_2, R_3, ..., R_m$. Let F represent the k dimensional feature space, $F_1, F_2, F_3, ..., F_k$, describing each of the stocks. Each stock S_i can be considered as a k-tuple $(F_{1,S_i}, F_{2,S_i}, F_{3,S_i}, ..., F_{k,S_i})$ in the Cartesian space $F_1 x F_2 x F_3 x \cdots x F_k$. Rating the stocks involves finding the one-to-one mapping function f [1].

$$f : F_1 x F_2 x F_3 x \cdots x F_k \rightarrow R \qquad (2)$$

In this application we have 143 stocks updated on a monthly basis. Each stock is characterised by three factors (A, B, C) and the ranking is based on the predicted relative outperformance of each stock six months ahead.

3.2 Training and Test Sets

The training and test sets consist of data provided in a pre-processed form and presented as factor A, factor B, factor C and resultant outperformance Y. The factors A, B and C are parameters extracted from the balance sheets of the companies in the universe of the U.K. stocks. Details of these factors were not specified. **Table 3.1** gives an example of the training dataset we use in this application.

The rightmost column is a code for each stock in the universe. A, B, and C are the inputs to the network with Y being the target output (i.e. the outperformance of

the stock). The outperformance of the stock P in the tth month is the result of the application of an unknown function g on P_t / P_{t+6}, where P_t is the price of the stock P in the tth month, and P_{t+6} is the price of stock P after six months (in the $(t+6)^{th}$ month). More formally:

$$Y_t^P = g \left(\frac{P_t}{P_{t+6}} \right) \qquad (3)$$

where Y_t^P stands for the outperformance of the stock P in month t .

The dataset covers the period May 1985 to December 1991, and concerns 143 stocks. The overall size of the dataset therefore is given by: $143 \times m \times y = 143 \times 12 \times 6 - 36 = 10,260$ training vectors.

The networks are trained on 6 monthly batches of data and evaluated for the next six month period. Thus each training/test run consists of $143 \times 6 = 852$ training vectors. The intermediate size for each training run makes the problem non-trivial and allows for extensive tests on convergence and generalisation.

3.3 Performance Metrics

The main point of reference for evaluating the performance of the networks is by comparison to current "best practise" (i.e. multiple linear regression). The main measures of network performance that we are interested are the following:

- convergence: the *in-sample* performance of the network is important because it determines its convergence ability and sets a target of feasible *out-of-sample* performance which can be achieved by fine-tuning the network parameters and training discipline. The target here is to achieve good model fitness but without penalysing generalisation.

- generalisation: is the main property that should be sought. The aim here is to achieve generalisation performance (i.e. prediction of relative stock outperformance) which is better than that of linear regression. We use two metrics to quantify prediction accuracy (see below).

- stability: neural networks have been known to produce wide variations in their predictive properties. This is to say that small changes in network design, learning times, initial conditions, etc may produce large changes in network behaviour. Our target here is to identify intervals of values for these parameters which give statistically stable results, and to demonstrate that these results persist across different training and test sets.

To quantify the convergence and generalisation performance of the two methods (i.e. linear regression and neural networks) we use two metrics. The first metric is the common Mean RMS Error. The Mean RMS Error, clearly is a measure of the correctness of prediction in terms of absolute values and can sometimes be misleading because of its averaging properties. Another metric that could be used instead is Percentage of Change in Direction (POCID for short).

In terms of stock ranking, POCID is a measure of the relative outperformance of the stock universe. It provides an approximation to the "shape" of one's portfolio six months ahead. If our stock universe were a time-series, then POCID would give a metric of the direction of change. The Percentage of Change in Direction is calculated by finding the differences $(t_2 - t_1)$, $(t_3 - t_2)$, ..., $(t_m - t_{m-1})$ and $(o_2 - o_1)$, $(o_3 - o_2)$, ..., $(o_m - o_{m-1})$, where t_i are the desired values and o_i are the predicted values of the outperformance and m is the total number of patterns in the training set, and then by comparing the pairs of differencies $((t_i - t_{i-1}), (o_i - o_{i-1}))$ for each pair of adjacent training patterns one by one. The POCID metric is defined as the number of pairs $((t_i - t_{i-1}), (o_i - o_{i-1}))$ which have the same sign for both differences $(t_i - t_{i-1})$ and $(o_i - o_{i-1})$, expressed as a percentage of the total number of such pairs $(m - 1)$.

POCID to a certain extend, is sensitive to the order in which the training patterns are presented and therefore that order should be preserved. Furthermore, it cannot be regarded as a measure of correct prediction of the direction of change of the outperformance, but as an indication of how well the network predicts the shape of the universe of outperformances.

3.4 Network Set Up

The learning algorithm used is the standard backpropagation learning algorithm with a momentum term. All simulations run on SUN4 workstations; convergence is reached within 30,000 iterations typically requiring 3-4 days of CPU time.

The need for statistical stability in the results requires extensive experimentation with the parameters that influence network performance. Our target here is to identify intervals of values for these parameters which give statistically stable results, and to demonstrate that these results persist across different training and test sets. Below we give a list of these parameters and how they are varied in the performed simulations.

- Network Architecture: We examine layered, fully connected, feedforward networks. The number of neurons of the input and output layers are defined by the application and they are three for the input layer (one for each factor A, B and C) and one for the output layer (the representing the outperformance Y). The parameters in respect to network topology are the number of hidden layers and the number of neurons of each layer.

- Gradient Descent Terms: The parameters here are the learning rate and the momentum term. The epoch is kept always equal to one, so that the weights are updated after each presentation of a training pattern. This is the "on-line" or "stochastic" version of backpropagation, as opposed to the "batch" version. Also there is no offset added to the derivative of the transfer function. The objective is to find the ranges of momentum term and learning rate that yield stable performance for a given network architecture, as a function of the training time.

- Training Time: the number of presentations of the entire training set to the network (iterations).

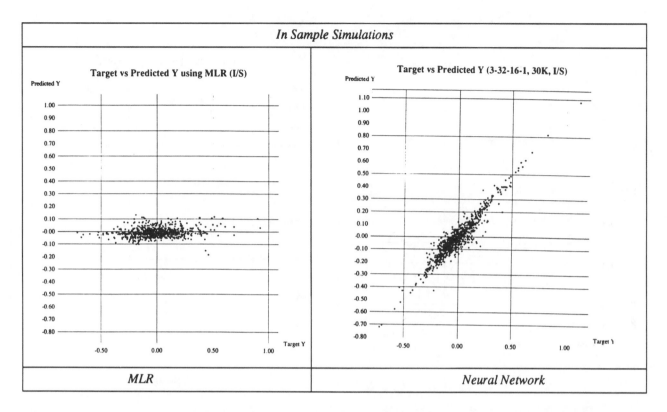

Figure 4.1: Target vs Predicted Outperformance, *in-sample* simulations (May '85 - Oct '85), with MLR and a 3-32-16-1 network with learning rate η = 0.3, momentum *m* = 0.7, trained for 30,000 iterations.

- This parameter is of great importance since the effect of any network configuration on network performance must be seen as a function of the training time. The aim is to identify the largest possible interval of network topologies for which the results show small standard deviation from the mean value.

- Transfer Function, Cost Function, and Initial conditions: these are not parameters; for all simulations we use the common asymmetric sigmoid, and the common quadratic error function. We test the stability of the results with varying initial conditions.

4. RESULTS

4.1 Overall Results: Comparison with MLR

The first performance target of this work is to show that the *in-sample* performance of the network gives a better fit than linear regression. The *in-sample* performance of the network is important because it determines its convergence ability and sets a target of feasible *out-of-*

sample performance which can be achieved by fine-tuning the network parameters and training discipline. Figure (4.1) shows two scattergrams depicting the target vs predicted outperformance for MLR and a neural network with topology 3-32-16-1, learning rate η = 0.3, momentum rate *m* = 0.3, trained for 30,000 iterations.

The ideal shape in both scattergrams in Figure (4.1) would be a straight line with a slope of 45 degrees, which crosses the origin. The reason is obvious; if the desired outperformance is, let's say 0.2 the ideal would be that the predicted is also 0.2; if the desired is -0.1 the predicted should be the same, and so on. The points (0.2, 0.2), (-0.1, -0.1) define the line we described above. We see in Fig. (4.1) that in the scattergram for MLR the dots are scattered all over the place; in contrast in the scattergram for the neural network they form a shape which resembles more of a line. The conclusion is evident: the neural network yields much better in-sample fitness than MLR.

The second network performance metric is generalisation. Our goal here was to achieve *out-of-sample* performance comparable to MLR.

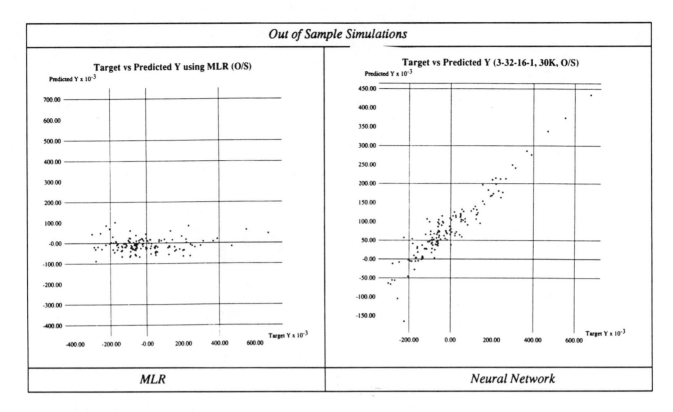

Figure 4.2: Target vs Predicted Outperformance; *out-of-sample* simulations (May '85 - Oct '85), with MLR and a 3-32-16-1 network with learning rate $\eta = 0.3$, momentum $m = 0.7$, trained for 30,000 iterations.

Figure (4.2) depicts again the target vs predicted outperformance for MLR and the same neural network as in Figure (4.1), but for *out-of-sample* testing. As we see in Figure (4.2) the results *out-of-sample* are much better than regression. The network clearly outperforms MLR in both cases.

Table 4.1 gives a summary of the values of the RMS and POCID metrics in and out of sample for both MLR and the neural network. It is interesting that out of sample the RMS for the neural network is marginally better than the RMS for MLR, while the POCID for the neural network is much better.

RMS is often a misleading metric of performance because of its averaging behaviour. The network performance *out-of-sample* in fact is far better than RMS implies. To illustrate this we depict in two graphs (see Figure (4.3)) the target and the predicted outperformance, for the stocks of the testing dataset (*out-of-sample*). We observe how much better the predicted line follows the shape of the target line in the case of the neural network. For this network configuration we have POCID of 85.2 against 51.4 for

the MLR, and RMS equal to 0.112 against 0.123 for the MLR. It is clear that both metrics, should be used in order to have a more exact indication of network performance.

METHOD	RMS(in-sample)	RMS(out-of-sample)
NN	0.044	0.112
MLR	0.138	0.123
	POCID(in-sample)	POCID(out-of-sample)
NN	85.5	85.2
MLR	54.9	51.4

Table 4.1

The results presented above far outperform MLR. However, for a real-life application such as the one described here it is important to examine how these results vary with network parameters. Our objective was to identify intervals of statistical stability for these parameters.

4.2 Stability with Network Architecture

We experimented with the architecture of the network, varying the number of hidden layers from one to three.

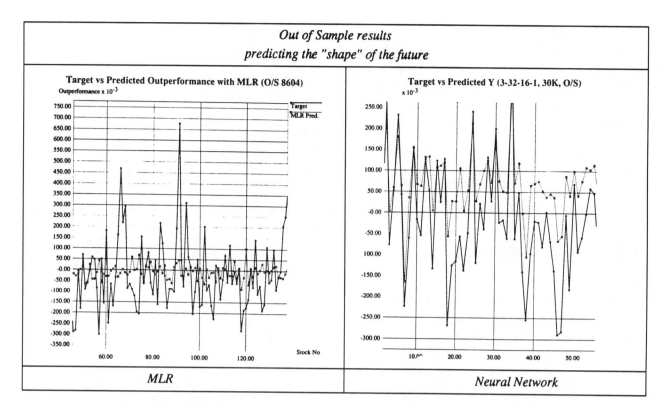

Figure 4.3: Target vs Predicted Outperformance for *out-of-sample* simulations (Nov '85 - Apr '86), with MLR and a 3-32-16-1 network with learning rate η = 0.3, momentum *m* = 0.7, trained for 30,000 iterations.

The number of neurons of each layer was also varied. For all these simulations the learning rate (η) and the momentum rate (*m*) were fixed (η = 0.3 and *m* = 0.7). The number of iterations varied from 500 to 30,000. At the high end of training times, the RMS error *in-sample* remains very stable varying from 0.044 to 0.072. Single layer networks give RMS outside this range. The *out-of-sample* performance also remains stable around 0.11 for networks with two hidden layers; the same is true for POCID which remains stable around 85% [7].

4.3 Stability with Gradient Descent Terms

In summary, learning rates in the range 0.2 to 0.4 when combined with a momentum term less than 0.7 yield better convergence ability. In general, one and two-layered networks with a learning rate η =0.2 and a momentum term $0.3 < m \leq 0.5$ yield the best combination of convergence and generalisation [7].

4.4 Stability with Training Time

For simple networks with one hidden layer, 5,000 iterations were sufficient to stabilise the RMS to a virtually unchanged (with the number of iterations)

value. For more complicated networks with more than one hidden layers, even 25,000 iterations are not sufficient to reach that limit. The POCID metric behaves like the RMS, tending asymptotically to a maximum which is generally found after the 25,000 iterations limit, although the shape of the curve is more noisy.

For *out-of-sample* performance, although we have the best results for large numbers of iterations, there are ranges with temporary performance drop-offs (both in terms of increased RMS or decreased POCID). We do not think however that these can be interpreted as signs of *overtraining*, because they appear rather early (mainly between 5,000 and 10,000 iterations). Probably their existence implies that the network is still *undertrained*, and the better solutions are yet to come for larger numbers of iterations. This behaviour persists across different datasets.

4.5 Stability with Different Training Sets

All the simulations we mentioned so far, were performed for the same training and testing datasets. The training dataset contained monthly data for the period May '85 to October '85, and the testing dataset contained data for April '86. In order to examine the effect of the dataset on the performance of the network, we performed simulations for the topology 3-32-16-1, using the mean values for the learning and network parameters.

The convergence and generalisation performance of the network did not alter significantly. It appears that the performance of the network is slightly worse than the mean performance in the previous dataset but well within the range of the standard deviation.

4.6 Stability with Initial Conditions

Backpropagation is known to be sensitive to the values of initial conditions i.e., random weights values. It is always desirable to observe the mean and standard deviation of the network performance measures for a large number of different initial conditions. We have so far performed only two simulation runs for the same network but with different initial conditions.

In-sample the curves for the RMS are very much the same but for all other comparisons in and *out-of-sample* the first set of initial weights marginally outperforms the second one. Some adjustment to the network configuration, while using the second set of initial weights, might help to bridge that gap in performance. It is clear that the starting point of the training phase can make a difference (maybe not a great one) and it should be one of our considerations when training the network.

5. CONCLUSIONS & CURRENT WORK

Classical statistical techniques for prediction reach their limitations in applications with non-linearities in the dataset. Most forecasting methods are only capable of picking up trends and have difficulty in modeling cycles that are by no means repetitive in amplitude, period or shape. Despite their inadequacies techniques such as multiple linear regression have proven a useful tool in the Capital Markets and are used routinely.

We showed that even simple neural learning procedures such as the backpropagation algorithm far outperform current "best practise" in a typical application for stock ranking within the framework of the Arbitrage Pricing Model. Their smooth interpolation properties allow neural models to fit better models to the data and to

generalise significantly better.

We believe that the performance measures obtained here, can be improved further with careful network design and pre-processing of the data. As far as the data is concerned there is at least one obvious area of improvement. It concerns the existence of malicious vectors in the training set. These are vectors which lie close to the boarders between classes (i.e. one-to-many mappings) and which the quadratic cost function used here finds difficult to learn (at best it averages). We have developed an algorithm for detecting such malicious vectors [7] and applied it to the training set. We found that up to 13% of the training data were classified as such vectors, and we currently experiment with various strategies for removing such vectors.

6. REFERENCES

[1] Dutta Sumitra, and Shashi Shekkar, "Bond rating: a non-conservative application", Computer Science Division, University of California.

[2] Hinton Geoffrey, "Connectionist Learning Procedures", Computer Science Department, Carnegie-Melon University, December 1987.

[3] Refenes A. N., "Constructive Learning and its Application to Currency Exchange Rate Prediction", in "Neural Network Applications in Investment and Finance Services", eds. Turban E., and Trippi R., Chapter 27, Probus Publishing, USA, 1992.

[4] Refenes A. N., et al "Currency Exchange rate prediction and Neural Network Design Strategies", Neural computing & Applications Journal, Vol 1, no. 1., (1992).

[5] Refenes A. N., & Zaidi A., "Managing Exchange Rate Prediction Strategies with Neural Networks", Proc. Workshop on Neural Networks: techniques & Applications, Liverpool (Sept. 1992).

[6] Schoenenburg E., "Stock price prediction using neural networks: a project report", Neurocomputing 2, pp. 17-27, 1990

[7] Zapranis A. D., "Stock Ranking Using Neural Networks", Project Report, Department of Computer Science, University College London, (Sept. 92).

Vectorized Backpropagation and Automatic Pruning for MLP Network Optimization

Suryan Stalin and T. V. Sreenivas

Department of Electrical Communication Engineering

Indian Institute of Science, Bangalore-560012, India

Abstract– In complicated tasks such as speech recognition, neural network architectures have to be improved for better learning and recognition performance. This paper presents an analysis of the backpropagation algorithm and reveals the significance of *vectorized backpropagation and automatic pruning* for better learning performance and MLP network optimization. During the learning phase, the network which uses vectorized backpropagation converges within 20% - 50% of the iterations required for the standard MLP to converge without affecting the test set performance. The network pruning algorithm reduces the number of hidden nodes and connection weights. The pruned network with only 40% connection weights of the unpruned network gives the same learning and recognition performance as the parent unpruned fully connected network.

I. Vectorized Backpropagation

The multilayer perceptron network (MLP) using standard backpropagation (BP) algorithm[1] minimizes output mean square error by modifying the weights and thresholds after each input pattern is introduced to the network. The learning procedure can be expressed as

$$w_{uv} \leftarrow w_{uv} - \eta \frac{\partial E_p}{\partial w_{uv}}, \tag{1}$$

$$RHS = w_{uv} - 2\eta \sum_{j=1}^{N} e_{jp} \frac{\partial e_{jp}}{\partial w_{uv}}, \tag{2}$$

where w_{uv} is the weight from node u to node v, η is the rate of learning, e_{jp} is the jth dimensional output error for the input pattern p and $E_p = \sum_{j=1}^{N} e_{jp}^2$ is the output mean square error for the pattern p.

Consider the pattern classification to be an N-class problem and let us choose the desired class identification vectors to be the N orthonormal vectors of the output space. In the N dimensional output space, $\mathbf{E}_p = [e_{1p}, ..., e_{Np}]^t$ is the output error vector for the pattern p. Let $\mathbf{E}_p^k$ and $\mathbf{E}_p^{k+1}$ be the error vectors before and after the weight updation for the input pattern p presented during the kth scan of the training set and let the jth component of the vector be e_{jp}^k and e_{jp}^{k+1} respectively. In the MLP network learning, the backpropagation algorithm uses the gradient descent approach which assures that

$$\mid \mathbf{E}_p^{k+1} \mid \leq \mid \mathbf{E}_p^k \mid \tag{3}$$

However, this condition does <u>not</u> assure reduction of the individual components of the error vector. i.e.,

$$\mid e_{jp}^{k+1} \mid \nleq \mid e_{jp}^k \mid \qquad for \ some \ j \ and \ k. \tag{4}$$

Thus, it is possible that the network may have unlearned for a particular class, while the average learning for all classes put together has improved with the training iterations. Fig. 1 shows the variation of $\mathbf{E}_p$ during the learning process. The output error vector after an update has the freedom of lying anywhere within the hyper-sphere of radius equal to the magnitude of error vector before the update. Thus, if we can formulate the learning rule such that all of the components e_{jp}^k are simultaneously reduced through each iteration, faster convergence of the neural network could be expected. This corresponds to a constrained minimization in which the updated error vector can lie only within the N-dimensional cuboid formed by the error vector before the updation as shown in Fig. 1.

This formulation of the learning rule in which each of the individual components of the error vector $\mathbf{E}_p$

are minimized through each iteration of learning is termed as "vectorized backpropagation(VBP)."

A. Multiplane MLP Network

The goal of minimizing the error components e_{jp} individually can be achieved if the network has a single output node. Thus, the multi-class pattern recognition problem has to be viewed as several two-class recognition problems. This can be achieved by modifying the learning rule (2) which results in the new multiplane MLP (MPMLP) architecture.

Consider the BP learning rule(2) where the connection weight w_{uv} is altered by the gradient of the error vector components. i.e.,

$$w_{uv}^j \Leftarrow w_{uv} - 2\eta \nabla_j \qquad (5)$$

Now, let us formulate a new network with one single out put node corresponding to the jth class and a stack of such networks for the N different classes. Each weight w_{uv} of the standard MLP network in learning rule (2) is extended as a vector $\mathbf{W}_{uv} = [w_{uv}^1, ..., w_{uv}^N]^t$, where w_{uv}^j is the weight in the jth stack. Each of the networks in the stack receive identical inputs and can be learnt independent of others in the stack. Thus, learning rule for the jth stack can be written as

$$w_{uv}^j \Leftarrow w_{uv}^j - 2\eta e_{jp} \frac{\partial e_{jp}}{\partial w_{uv}^j} \qquad (6)$$

The learning rule (6) provides a joint minimization of the individual error components e_{jp} than the minimization of the total error $|\mathbf{E}_p|$ as in the standard BP. i.e.,

$$|e_{jp}^{k+1}| \le |e_{jp}^k| \qquad \forall\ j, k. \qquad (7)$$

The new architecture of a stack of MLPs, referred to as multiplane MLP, is shown in Fig.2.

The choice of orthonormal target vectors to identify each class makes each plane of the MPMLP to solve a 2-class recognition problem with a single output node. Since each output space orthonormal vector of the MLP is representing a separate class, j^{th} plane of the MPMLP network learns to recognize j^{th} class independent of the learning in other planes. This is because the output error is propagated back only within each plane and there is no link across different planes.

II. NETWORK OPTIMIZATION

Vectorized backpropagation is useful for better convergence of the network. However, the realization through MPMLP increases the number of network weights. This can result in memorization effects and suboptimum local minima in learning due to the limited training data [3]. On the other hand, if the network size is too small, the network will fail to converge in learning. Since each plane of the MPMLP network is dealing with a different recognition task, the optimum size for each of the planes will be different. The Network pruning is a method in which a network of larger size is chosen and then iteratively reduced to an optimum size. Such Pruning accomplished during the learning process has been referred to as "dynamic pruning [4]." Pruning has also been performed after the learning process is complete [3]. However, in both methods, the pruning is limited to the reduction of network nodes only. Pruning of nodes leads to a drastic decision because many connections go through a node. Instead of such a fully connected MLP, wherein each node in a layer is connected to all nodes in the adjoining layers, reduced number of interconnections can be advantageous in some cases [6].

An automatic pruning algorithm [2] has been developed which is applicable to a general MLP network. In this method, pruning is incorporated into the learning algorithm and the network is iteratively reduced such that an optimum configuration is achieved along with the network convergence. Using an integrated measure of *forward and backward significance*, least effective connection weights are identified and removed.

A. Pruning Algorithm

Let C_m be the number of nodes in the mth layer of an MLP network where $m = 0$ is the input pattern layer and $m = 3$ is the final layer. Let the output at node i in the $(m-1)^{th}$ layer be x_i and the weight connecting node i to node j in the mth layer is w_{ij}^m. For each pattern $\mathbf{p}$ introduced to the network during learning, the backpropagation algorithm makes use of each connection weight in the network in two instances. In the forward direction, for final layer output calculations, each connection weight w_{ij}^m contributes $x_i w_{ij}^m$ to the total activation $\sum_i x_i w_{ij}^m$ of the node to which it is connected. In backward error propagation, each weight w_{jk}^m contributes $w_{jk}^m \delta_k^m$ to the total correction factor $\sum_k w_{jk}^m \delta_k^m$ for the weight w_{ij}^{m-1} in the previous layer as shown in (8).

$$w_{ij}^{m-1} \Leftarrow w_{ij}^{m-1} - \eta x_i \sum_k w_{jk}^m \delta_k^m \qquad (8)$$

where

$$\delta_k^m = -(d_k - y_k) y_k (1 - y_k) \; for \; the \; final \; layer \quad (9)$$
$$\delta_j^m = \sum_k w_{jk}^{m+1} \delta_k^{m+1} \; for \; other \; layers \qquad (10)$$

In (9), d_k and y_k represent the target output and the observed output at node k in the final layer. If both forward and backward contributions from a particular weight are not significant over the entire training set, it is clear that the weight is not playing a significant role in the learning process and such a link can be marked for pruning. However, changing the network structure too soon can affect the convergence of the learning process.

To determine the optimum degree of pruning, a parameter called *pruning factor* (f_p) is introduced ($0 < f_p < 1$). A connection weight w_{ij}^m is pruned if the following conditions are satisfied.

$$\mid x_i w_{ij}^m \mid \; < \; \mid \sum_i x_i w_{ij}^m \mid f_p \; for \; all \; \mathbf{p} \qquad (11)$$

$$\mid w_{ij}^m \delta_j \mid \; < \; \mid \sum_j w_{ij}^m \delta_j \mid f_p \; for \; all \; \mathbf{p} \qquad (12)$$

$f_p = 0$ implies learning without pruning and $f_p = 1$ means pruning to the maximum extent. Accordingly, by varying f_p the degree of pruning can be varied. If all weights attached to a node are pruned, it is equivalent to the removal of that node. Usually f_p is chosen close to 0. Elimination of the connection weights can cause convergence problems to the backpropagation algorithm, but care has been taken through (11) and (12) that the error caused by pruning is minimal.

B. Decision regions

Each perceptron in the standard MLP network with input vector X and weight vector W partitions its input space into 2 regions characterized by $XW^t > \theta$ and $XW^t < \theta$ with a hyperplane given by

$XW^t = \theta$ where, θ is the perceptron threshold [1]. Thus, C_1 perceptrons in layer-1 form in general C_1 hyper planes in the feature space [5]. These can partition the space into a maximum of 2^{C_1} decision regions (Fig. 3(b)). Input patterns occurring in different regions give rise to a different layer-1 output pattern with each node output being in the range of 0 to 1. The layer-1 outputs form an C_1 dimensional space where in the range is limited to an C_1 *dimensional hyper cube*. Thus, different decision regions in the input feature space are mapped to corresponding zones in the hyper cube (Fig. 3(c)). For perceptrons with hard limiting transfer functions (binary output), decision regions in the feature space are mapped to the corners of the cube. For sigmoidal perceptrons, the decision regions are mapped to the neighborhood of different corners. Removal of a node from layer-1 eliminates the corresponding hyper plane. This makes the decision region to loose one of its boundary and starts spreading in volume. These principles can be similarly extended to layer-2 and layer-3. Layer-2 forms decision regions by hyper planes in the space derived from layer-1. Node removal in layer-2 makes decision region to spread in layer-1. Thus, in general, pruning should be applied only until the decision region for a pattern class starts to overlap with another.

In Fig. 3(a), the decision boundary in the feature space corresponding to the first node in layer-1 is given by

$$XW_1^t = \theta_1 \qquad (13)$$
$$i.e., \qquad x_1 w_{11} + x_2 w_{21} = \theta_1 \qquad (14)$$

Pruning the link w_{21} modifies the boundary to

$$x_1 = \frac{\theta_1}{w_{11}} \qquad (15)$$

which represents a line parallel to the x_2-axis. This means that the perceptron decision is independent of the parameter x_2. Generalizing this fact for an N_m dimensional layer, *pruning the link w_{ij}^m modifies the hyper plane, in the space derived by $(m-1)^{th}$ layer, parallel to the axis along the ith dimension. Also, output of node j in the mth layer becomes independent of its ith dimensional input.*

III. Experimental results

MLP network's ability to tolerate distortion in the input patterns and yet classify them correctly depends on how well the network has learnt from the training set and this is referred to as network generality. The test set performance, defined as the proportion of the number of untrained patterns classified correctly by the network to the total number of all possible input patterns is used as a measure of network generalization. This is measure applicable to discrete pattern finite extent problems.

The learning as well as test set performance of the MPMLP is evaluated using a 3 class binary picture recognition problem and results are compared with that of an MLP. Binary pictures made of 3×3 and 5×5 grids (Fig.4) representing characters I, O and X are used for training. For the 5×5 grid experiment an 18-18-3 node fully connected architecture is used for the MLP network where as in MPMLP, the same number of nodes are distributed into 3 planes. For an n node output MLP network, the maximum possible mean square error per pattern is n. A value of 0.01% of the maximum possible error is taken as the threshold for convergence. The test set comprised of the $(2^9 - 3)$ untrained patterns for the 3×3 grid experiment and $(2^{25} - 3)$ for 5×5 grid experiment. The MPMLP, with the same number of total nodes as the MLP, converges within 20% - 50% of the iterations required for the MLP to converge (Fig.5(a) and 5(b)) without any deterioration in the testing performance. The test set performance of the MPMLP is found marginally better than that of the MLP network.

The addition of the pruning algorithm to the MPMLP network learning is evaluated in comparison with the parent unpruned MPMLP network which is trained with the *same random initialization* as the pruned network. Also the pruned MPMLP performance is compared with that of the pruned MLP network.

Weight reduction is measured using a reduction coefficient(ρ) given by

$$\rho = \frac{\sum_{m=1}^{m=3} \acute{C}_m}{\sum_{m=1}^{m=3} C_m C_{m-1}} \qquad (16)$$

where $\acute{C}_m$ is the number of weights remaining un-

pruned between the mth and $(m-1)^{th}$ layer. Thus the reduction coefficient for the mth layer is given by

$$\rho_m = \frac{\acute{C}_m}{C_m C_{m-1}} \qquad (17)$$

In all the experiments, for a fixed f_p, layer-1 weights have been subjected to maximum pruning followed by progressively less pruning for succeeding layers ($\rho_1 < \rho_2 < \rho_3$).

The reduction in the number of connection weights and the test set performance with respect to f_p is shown in Fig.6(a) and 6(b) for both MLP and MPMLP networks. Fig. 6(a) shows a greater reduction in connection weights of MPMLP than MLP. This justifies the effectiveness of pruning for MPMLP. As Fig. 6(b) shows, with the pruning factor in the range of 0-0.4, the network size is reduced with least deterioration, if not marginal improvement, in the testing performance. For f_p close to unity the network size becomes too small to maintain network generality.

Also, unless f_p is close to unity, pruning does not seem to affect the number of learning iterations for convergence. Thus, incorporating pruning while learning in an MPMLP architecture leads to an optimized architecture which can provide better performance.

References

[1] B. Widrow and M. A. Lehr, "30 Years of Adaptive Neural Networks: Perceptron, Madaline, and Backpropagation," IEEE Proceedings, Vol 78, No. 9, Sept. 1990.

[2] Suryan Stalin and T. V. Sreenivas, "Vectorised Backpropagation and Automatic Pruning for MLP Network optimization," Technical report , Dept. of ECE, Indian Institute of Science, Aug 1992.

[3] J. Sietsma and R.J.F. Dow, "Neural net pruning - Why and how," Proc. IEEE, Int.Joint Conf. Neural Networks, Vol 1, pp 325-333, 1988.

[4] B. E. Segee and M. J. Carter, "Fault tolerance of multilayer networks," Proc. IEEE, Int.Joint Conf. Neural Networks, Vol 2, pp 447-452, 1991.

[5] J. Makhoul, A. El-Jaroudi, and R. Schwartz, "Partitioning Capabilities of Two-Layer Neural Networks," IEEE Trans. on Signal Processing, Vol 1, No 6, pp 1435-440, June 1991.

[6] T. V. Sreenivas, Unnikrishnan, V. S. and D. N. Dutt, "Pruned Neural Network for Artifact Reduction in EEG Signal," IEEE, Int. Conf. Engineering and Medicine in Biology (EMBS), Florida, 1991.

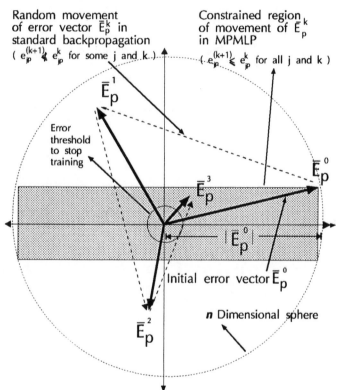

Fig. 1. Error vector variations in standard backpropagation and vectorized backpropagation.

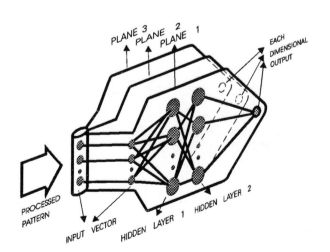

Fig. 2. Multiplane MLP network for N=3 class problem. The network in each plane provides recognition of a single class.

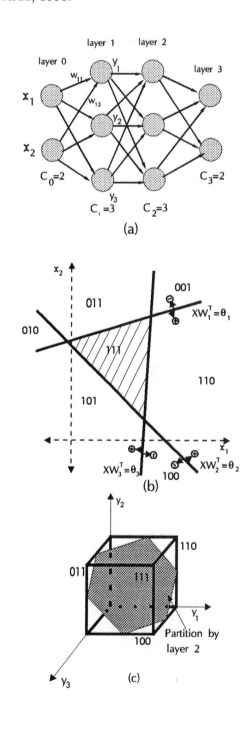

Fig. 3. (a) An MLP network with two dimensional input space. (b) Decision regions formed by layer 1. (c) N dimensional hyper cuboid in the layer 1 output space.

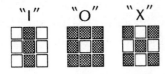

Fig. 4. 3x3 grid binary patterns representing characters I, O and X.

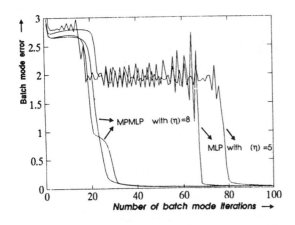

Fig. 5(a). Error convergence of MLP and MPMLP networks during the training phase of a 3 class 3x3 grid binary picture recognition problem. The best learning coefficients: η_{MLP}=5; η_{MPMLP}=8.

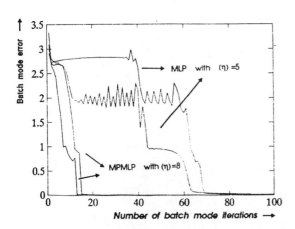

Fig. 5(b). Error convergence of MLP and MPMLP networks during the training phase of a 3 class 5x5 grid binary picture recognition problem. The best learning coefficients: η_{MLP}=5; η_{MPMLP}=8.

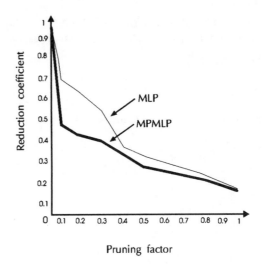

Fig. 6(a). Variation of reduction coefficient (ρ) with respect to pruning factor (f_p) for the MLP and MPMLP networks.

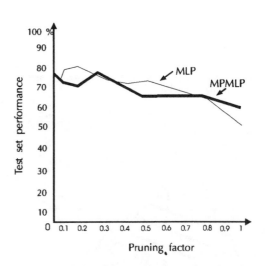

Fig. 6(b). Variation of reduction coefficient (ρ) with respect to pruning factor (f_p) for the MLP and MPMLP networks.

A Neural Network to Solve Discrete Dynamic Programming Problems

Roseli Ap. Francelin
USP - ICMSC - SCE
13560 - São Carlos - SP - Brasil

Fernando A. C. Gomide *
UNICAMP - FEE - DCA
13081 - Campinas - SP - Brasil

Abstract— Dynamic programming has provided a powerful approach to optimization problems, but its applicability has been somewhat limited because of the large computational requirements of the standard computational algorithm. In recent years a number of new procedures with reduced computational requirements have been developed. This paper proposes an artificial neural network to solve discrete dynamic programming problems. This approach presents some advantages with regard to alternative approaches because of the inheriting parallelism of the neural networks. Some important applications are addressed to illustrate the usefulness of the approach proposed.

I. INTRODUCTION

Recently, neural networks with a three-layer feedback topology for solving continuous optimization problems have been proposed [1]. A parallel implementation for this class of neural networks have also been developed using transputers to simulate the network with a configuration closer to a dedicated hardware implementation, and to verify the corretness of the proposed model [2].

One of the most powerful techniques developed for the solution of optimization problem is Bellman's dynamic programming [3]. This paper proposes an artificial neural network to solve discrete dynamic programming problems which is a static programmed network that designes his own interconnections and weights. It is organized as follows. First, the neural network's characteristics as well as a generalization of the network to optimization problems with more than one constraint are presented in Section II. Computational Requirements Analysis is performed in Section III to show the usefulness of the proposed approach. Finally conclusions and future work are addressed in Section IV.

*This work was partially supported by CNPq, the Brazilian National Research Council for grant 300729/86-3

II. A NEURAL NETWORK FOR DISCRETE DP

The procedure of solving a dynamic programming problem by *backward recursion* can be generalized to any number of variables. The decision functions of stages $N, N-1, \ldots, 2, 1$ are given by: $f_1 = r_N(y_{N-1}, x_N)$;

$$
\begin{aligned}
f_i &= r_{N-(i-1)}(y_{N-i}, x_{N-(i-1)}) + \\
&\quad F_{i-1}(y_{N-(i-1)}); \\
y_{N-(i-1)} &= t_{N-(i-1)}(y_{N-i}, x_{N-(i-1)})
\end{aligned}
\tag{1}
$$

$f_N = r_1(y_0, x_1) + F_{N-1}(y_1)$ where $y_1 = t_1(y_0, x_1)$ and F_j is the maximum of $f_j, j = 1, 2, \ldots, N$. Maximizing the decision function of each stage with respect to its decision variable, treating the input state as parameter, we get the parametric stage solutions $x_n = x_n(y_{n-1})$, $n = N, N-1, \ldots, 2, 1$.

Artificial neuron models are conventionally nonlinear units with a number of inputs and a single output response. These neurons possess a single nonlinear function to provide an output. The signum, threshold output and sigmoid functions can be used as the nonlinear function. The approach developed, as oposed to the usual nonlinear neuron, is based on a generalized neuron model, where the max and min neurons are particular instances. The max and min neurons are reviewed below, because they are essential in building the DPNN - Dynamic Programming Neural Network, proposed in this paper. Generalized neuron models are introduced in [4, 5, 6].

A. Max and Min Neural Processing

The artificial neuron is usually assumed to be a computational device which: power averages its n inputs a_i, $v = \sum_{i=1}^n w_i a_i$, according to the weights of the synapses linking the input (pre-synaptic) neurons n_i the post-synaptic neuron n_p, and recodes $v \in V$ into the axonic activation a_p of the post-synaptic neuron:

$$
a_p = \begin{cases} f(v) & \text{if } v \geq \alpha \\ 0 & \text{otherwise} \end{cases}
$$

where α is the axonic threshold and f is the encoding function or transfer function. If $f(v) = 1$ for all $v \geq \alpha$ the

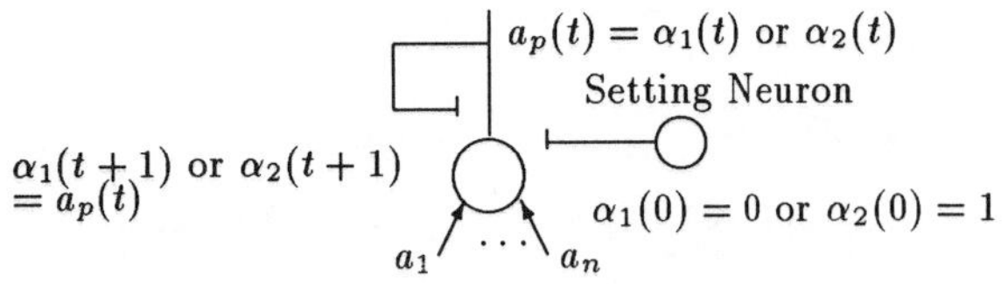

Figure 1: Recurrent Neuron

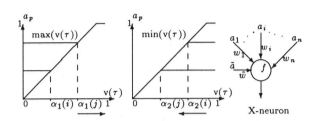

Figure 2: Max, Min Processing and X-neuron

neuron is a **binary neuron**, or a McCulloch and Pitts neuron. Otherwise, if $f : V \mapsto [0,1]$ two axonic thresholds α_1 and α_2 may also be defined such that:

$$a_p = \begin{cases} 1 & \text{if } v \geq \alpha_2 \\ f(v) & \text{if } \alpha_1 \leq v \leq \alpha_2 \\ 0 & \text{otherwise} \end{cases} . \qquad (2)$$

The values of α_1 and α_2 in many applications are furnished by a special type of neuron, called bias cell.

A modification of the McCulloch-Pitts neuron related with the axonic threshold control has been proposed by Gomide and Rocha [4, 5] to define a special type of neuron, called recurrent neuron. The recurrent synapsis is established if the axon of the neuron n_j makes contacts with dendrites or the cell body of n_j itself (Figure 1). If the recurrent synapsis is located near the axon, then it may control the axonic threshold as a function of the n_j's activity itself.

Max-Neuron (Figure 2): is defined if the axonic threshold $\alpha_1(\tau)$ at $\tau = 0$ in (2) is set as 0 by the setting neuron, and then at τ it is set equal to the firing level $a_p(\tau - 1)$ at $\tau - 1$:

$$\alpha_1(\tau) = a_p(\tau - 1); a_p(\tau) = \begin{cases} \alpha_1(\tau) & \text{if } v(\tau) \leq \alpha_1(\tau) \\ v(\tau) & \text{otherwise} \end{cases}$$
$$\qquad (3)$$

where $v(\tau)$ is the post-synaptic activation at τ. In this condition, the output $a_p(\tau)$ of the neuron at τ encodes (Figure 2): $a_p(\tau) = \bigvee_{i=1}^{\tau}(w_i a_i)$. If $w_i = 1$ for all i:

$$a_p(\tau) = \bigvee_{i=1}^{\tau} a_i \qquad (4)$$

where $\bigvee$ is the maximum operator.

Min-Neuron (Figure 2) can be defined analogously if an axonic threshold $\alpha_2(\tau)$ at $\tau = 0$ is set as equal to 1 by the setting neuron, and then at τ is set equal to the firing level $a_p(\tau - 1)$ at $\tau - 1$.

A **Y-neuron** is a Max-Neuron or Min-Neuron, depending if the optimization problem to be solved is either a maximization or minimization problem, respectively.

A **X-neuron** (Figure 2) is a neuron that receives input signals which are synchronized by the same mecanism adopted by Max-Neuron (or Min-Neuron) to provide an output s. The X-neuron's output s is given by:

$$s = f(\tilde{w}\tilde{a} + w_i a_i);$$
$$f(\alpha) = \begin{cases} \alpha & \text{if there is a connection with a} \\ & \text{Y-neuron, whose output is } \alpha, \quad (5) \\ 0 & \text{otherwise} \end{cases}$$

and $\tilde{a}$ is a fixed value for the X-neuron and a_i are values received from other neurons (in the DPNN these neurons are the Y-neurons).

In the DPNN to be derived in the next section, the X-neuron's inputs will have the following meaning. Considering n input pairs in the (t^{th}) X-neuron in a given layer k:

$$(\tilde{w}_k^t \tilde{a}_k^t, w_1 a_1), (\tilde{w}_k^t \tilde{a}_k^t, w_2 a_2), \ldots, (\tilde{w}_k^t \tilde{a}_k^t, w_n a_n)$$

we have that: $\tilde{w}_k^t$; corresponds to the coeficient of the variable x_{N-k} in the decision function r_{N-k} in (1), $\tilde{a}_k^t$; corresponds to the (t^{th}) value of the variable x_{N-k}, a_i: corresponds to the (i^{th}) input in the (t^{th}) X-neuron received from other neurons and w_i is the corresponding weight.

B. Connections of the DPNN Neurons

The DPNN is composed by two types of neurons: Y-neurons and X-neurons. The connections (weights) from layers of X-neurons to layers of Y-neurons, as well as connections from layers of Y-neurons to layers of X-neurons, are dynamically determined by the network itself. The layers of the DPNN alternate between Y-neurons layers and X-neurons layers, denoted here by Y-layers and X-layers, respectively. The first network layer is a X-layer denoted by X-layer-0. The (k^{th}) layer of the DPNN is either X-neurons layer, denoted by X-layer-k or a Y-neurons layer, denoted Y-layer-k.

The concepts of transmitters, receptors and controllers are fundamental to describe biological neurons learning

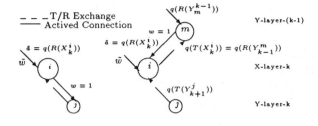

Figure 3: Connections between X-neuron to Y-neuron and Y-neuron to X-neuron

and dynamics. A detailed study of these concepts is provided in [6]. The DPNN is constructed based on those concepts, but in what follows the amounts of transmitters, receptors and controllers are interpreted as quantities defined by functions $q(\cdot)$ associated with the return functions components and the constraints of the optimization problem (see [8] for a detailed description). The algorithmic interpretation will, however, became clear later.

Assuming without loss of generality, a backward scheme, let: $X_k = \{x_k^1, x_k^2, \ldots, x_k^p\}$ be the set of the discrete values that the decision variable x_{N-k} can assume at stage $N-k$, $k = 0, 1, \ldots, N-1$; $Y_k = \{y_k^1, y_k^2, \ldots, y_k^r\}$ be the set of the discrete values that the state variable y_{N-k-1} can assume at stage $N-k$, $k = 0, \ldots, N-1$;

$$(XY)_k^j = \{(x_k^i, y_k^j), x_k^i \in X_k, y_k^j \in Y_k$$
$$/ \ t_{N-k}(x_k^i, y_k^j) \text{ is feasible}\}.$$

To establish the connections between X-layer-k and Y-layer-k neurons (Figure 3), consider the (i^{th})X-neuron in the X-layer-k, X_k^i and the amount of its receptor named $q(R(X_k^i))$. In the DPNN, this neuron receives a amount $q(T(Y_k^j))$ transmitted by the (j^{th})Y-neuron of the Y-layer-k, Y_k^j. The combination of these quantities activates the controller of this X-neuron. The controller function, in the DPNN proposed here, at the stage $N-k$, is defined to be the transformation equation t_{N-k} in (1), i.e.,

$$q(C(X_k^i)) = y_{N-k} = t_{N-k}(q(T(Y_k^j)), q(R(X_k^i)))$$

where the pair $(q(R(X_k^i)), q(T(Y_k^j)))$ corresponds to $(x_k^i, y_k^j) \in (XY)_{N-k}^j$. Being the value $q(C(X_k^i)) = y_{N-k}$ feasible , the connections (binding) between X-layer-(k) neurons and the Y-layer-k neurons, are established by:

$$W(X_k^i, Y_k^j) = \left\{ \begin{array}{ll} 1 & \text{if } q(C(X_k^i)) \geq 0 \\ 0 & \text{otherwise} \end{array} \right. \quad (6)$$

where $W(X_k^i, Y_k^j) = 1$ denotes the connection between the (i^{th}) X-neuron of the X-layer-k and the (j^{th})Y-neuron of the Y-layer-k.

To establish the connections between Y-layer-(k-1) and X-layer-k neurons (Figure 3), consider the (i^{th})X-neuron in the X-layer-k and the amount of its receptor named $q(R(X_k^i))$. In the DPNN, this neuron receives a amount $q(T(Y_k^j))$ transmitted by (j^{th})Y-neuron of the Y-layer-k. Consider the same controller function defined previously. Since the controller may participate in specification and regulation of the transmitter release at pre-synaptic terminal, it exerts an action in the X-neuron which transmits a amount $q(C(X_k^i))$ to all Y-neurons of the Y-layer-(k-1). This action will activate Y-neurons of the Y-layer-(k-1) (pre-synaptic cell), i.e., the (m^{th}) Y-neuron of the Y-layer-(k-1) for which

$$q(R(Y_{k-1}^m)) = q(T(X_k^i)) = q(C(X_k^i)).$$

Thus, the degree of matching $\mu(T(X_k^i), R(Y_{k-1}^m))$ between the transmitter $T(X_k^i)$ and its $R(Y_{k-1}^m)$ is a function of the amount of the controller. The connections (binding) between neurons of the Y-layer-(k-1) and the X-neurons of the X-layer-k, are established as follows:

$$W(Y_{k-1}^m, X_k^i) = \left\{ \begin{array}{ll} 1 & \text{if } q(T(X_k^i)) = q(C(X_k^i)) \\ & = q(R(Y_{k-1}^m)) \\ 0 & \text{otherwise} \end{array} \right. \quad (7)$$

where $W(Y_{k-1}^m, X_k^i) = 1$ denotes a connection between the (m^{th}) Y-neuron of the Y-layer-(k-1) and the (i^{th}) X-neuron of the X-layer-k, that is, it sets an unity weight for an input of X_k^i.

C. DPNN Construction and Processing Algorithm

Let X_k and Y_k be the sets as defined in the previous section; N be the number of stages; a_i's be the inputs to the (j^{th})Y-neuron of the Y-layer-k; $\tilde{a}_k^i$ be the input to the (i^{th})X-neuron of the X-layer-k; $s(.)$ be the output of a neuron in the network; $\tilde{w}_k$ be coeficients of the variable x_{N-k} in the return function r_{N-k} at stage k; $k = 0, 1, \ldots, N-1$; t_k be the transformation functions; $k = 1, \ldots, N$.

Initialization Pass
For each (i^{th}) Neuron in the layer-0 **do**
    read$(q(R(X^i))) = x_N^i \in X_0$
For each X-layer-k **do**
    For each (i^{th}) X-Neuron **do**
      Begin
        read$(q(R(X_k^i))) = x_{N-k}^i \in X_k$
        $\tilde{a}_k^i = q(R(X_k^i))$
      End
For each Y-layer-k **do**
    For each (i^{th}) Y-neuron **do**
      Begin
        read$(q(R(Y_k^i))) = y_{N-k-1}^i \in Y_k$
        $q(T(Y_k^i)) = q(R(Y_k^i))$
      End

W_{00} **Pass** *Creating connections layer-0 and Y-layer-0*
For each (j^{th}) Y-neuron in the Y-layer-0 **do**
    For each (i^{th}) X-neuron in the X-layer-0 **do**
        Compute $q(C(X_0^i)) = t_N(q(T(Y_0^j)), q(R(X_0^i)))$
        If $q(C(X_0^i)) \geq 0$ **then**
            $W(X_0^i, Y_0^j) = 1$
            $s(X_0^i) = \tilde{w}_0^i * \tilde{a}_0^i$
        else $W(X_0^i, Y_0^j) = 0$

Output Pass-0
For each (t^{th}) Y-neuron of Y-layer-0 **do**
    Begin
        p = 1
        For each (i^{th}) X-neuron of X-layer-0 **do**
            If $W(X_0^i, Y_0^t) = 1$ **then**
                Begin
                    $a_p(Y_0^t) = s(X_0^i)$
                    $p = p + 1$
                End
        compute $s(Y_0^t) = \max_p\{a_p(Y_0^t)\}$
End

Connections Pass *Creating connections between X-layer-k and Y-layer-k neurons*
For each (j^{th}) Y-neuron in the Y-layer-k **do**
    For each (i^{th})X-neuron in the X-layer-k **do**
        compute $q(C(X_k^i)) = t_{N-k}(q(T(Y_k^j)), q(R(X_k^i)))$
        If $q(C(X_k^i)) \geq 0$ **then**
            $q(T(X_k^i)) = q(C(X_k^i))$
            $W(X_k^i, Y_k^j) = 1$
        else $W(X_k^i, Y_k^j) = 0$
        Creating connections between Y-layer-(k-1)
        and X-layer-k neurons
        For (m^{th}) Y-neuron of the Y-layer-(k-1) **do**
            If $q(R(Y_{k-1}^m)) = q(T(X_k^i))$ **then**
                $W(Y_{k-1}^m, X_k^i) = 1$
        Receive the output s from the (m^{th}) Y-neuron,
            $s(Y_{k-1}^m)$
        Compute the output signal
            $s(X_k^i) = f(\tilde{w}_k^i * \tilde{a}_k^i + s(Y_{k-1}^m))$

Output Pass-k
For each (t^{th}) Y-neuron of Y-layer-k
    Begin
        p = 1
        For each (i^{th}) X-neuron of X-layer-(k-1) **do**
            If $W(X_{k-1}^i, Y_k^t) = 1$ **then**
                Begin
                    $a_p(Y_k^t) = s(X_{k-1}^i)$
                    $p = p + 1$
                End

Compute $s(Y_k^t) = \max_p\{a_p(Y_k^t)\}$
    End

Main Algorithm
Begin
    Perform Initialization Pass
    Perform W_{00} Pass
    Perform Output Pass-0
    For $k = 1, 2, 3, \ldots, N-1$ **do**
        Begin
            Perform Connections Pass
            Perform Output Pass-k
        End
End

Equivalence Theorem. The solution provided by DPNN is equivalent to that provided by the DP. (*The proof can be found in* [8]).

D. Generalization of the DPNN

So far we have only considered examples in which the stage problems were single-variable problems . However, the application of dynamic programming is not limited to this special case. Stage decomposition will in many cases lead to stage optimization problems involving several decision variables per stage so that x_n is not a single decision variable but a vector of such variables. The state variables y_n may also be vectors in a DP problem because, in principle, each side condition will require state variable. In the general case, the proposed DPNN the Y-neuron should have as many receptors as the number of state variables. This means that the DPNN will have as many Y-neurons in a Y-layer as the combinations of the state variables possible values. The same situation occurs for the controller functions. Therefore, the DPNN processing is exactly as described in the section, provided that the necessary modifications are made.

E. Illustrative Example

Consider the following optimization problem:

$$\max f = 0.8x_1 + 1.0x_2$$
$$\text{subject to } 4x_1 + 2x_2 \leq 1.2; \, x_1, x_2 \geq 0$$

In this example we have $N = 2$ stages and therefore the DPNN has four layers. We will follow the Main Algorithm step by step to illustrate how the DPNN works. Define:

- $X_0 = \{x_2^i\} = \{0.0, 0.1, 0.2, 0.3, 0.4, 0.5, 0.6\}$, $X_1 = \{x_1^i\} = \{0.0, 0.1, 0.2, 0.3\}$,

- $t_1 = y_0 - 4x_1$ and $t_2 = y_1 - 2x_2$, $Y_0 = \{y_1^i\} = \{0.0, 0.4, 0.8, 1.2\}$,

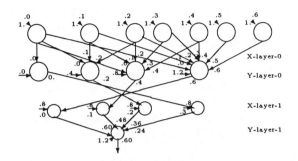

Figure 4: DPNN for Example 1

- $Y_1 = \{y_0^i\} = \{1.2\}$, $\tilde{w}_0^i = 1.0$; $i = 0, 1, \ldots, 6$,
  $\tilde{w}_1^j = 0.8$; $j = 0, 1, 2, 3$, $N = 2$;

During the Initialization Pass the following are set:
$q(R(X_0^i)) = x_2^i \in X_0$, $i = 0, 1, 2, \ldots, 6$; $q(R(X_1^i)) = x_1^i \in X_1$, $i = 0, 1, 2, 3$; $\tilde{a}_0^i = q(R(X_0^i))$, $i = 0, 1, \ldots, 6$; $\tilde{a}_1^i = q(R(X_1^i))$, $i = 0, 1, 2, 3$; $q(R(Y_0^i)) = y_1^i \in Y_0$, $i = 0, 1, 2, 3$; $q(R(Y_1^0)) = 1.2$.

Next, W_{00} Pass is performed. Here, the connections between the layers X-layer-0 and Y-layer-0 are created. For $j = 0, 1, 2, 3$ and for $i = 0, 1, 2, \ldots, 6$ the amount $q(C(X_0^i)) = t_2(q(T(Y_0^j)), q(R(X_0^i))) = q(T(Y_0^j)) - 2 * q(R(X_0^i))$ is calculated and the interconnections are established depending on its value. Furthermore the outputs of the X-layer-0 neurons, $s(X_0^i) = \tilde{w}_0^i * \tilde{a}_0^i = 1.0 * \tilde{a}_0^i$ are also computed.

For example, for $j = 1$ and $i = 0, 1, 2, \ldots, 6$ the following connections are created: $W(X_0^i, Y_0^1) = 1$, $i = 0, 1, 2$ because $q(C(X_0^i)) = 0.4 - 2 * x_2^i \geq 0$, $i = 0, 1, 2$ and $W(X_0^i, Y_0^1) = 0$, $i \geq 3$ because $q(C(X_0^i)) < 0$, $i \geq 3$. The outputs $s(X_0^i) = 1.0 * x_2^i$, $i = 0, 1, 2$ are also calculated.

The connections established after the W_{00} Pass is performed are showed in Figure 4.

Continuing with the Main Algorithm, the Output Pass-0 is executed where the Y-neuron's output, in the Y-layer-0, is computed. Consider the Y-neuron, Y_0^1 and his output $s(Y_0^1)$, $s(Y_0^1) = \max\{a_1, a_2, a_3\}$ where $a_1 = s(X_0^0) = 0.0$; $a_2 = s(X_0^1) = 0.1$; $a_3 = s(X_0^2) = 0.2$. Therefore, $s(Y_0^1) = max\{0.0, 0.1, 0.2\} = 0.2$. The outputs from the remaining Y-neurons, Y_0^0, Y_0^2, Y_0^3 are calculated, analogously. Next, we set $k = 1$ and the Connection Pass is performed. In this pass, the connections between the layers Y-layer-0 and X-layer-1 as well as X-layer-1 and Y-layer-1 are assigned. To establish these connections, the controller function:

$$
\begin{aligned}
q(C(X_1^i)) &= t_1(q(R(X_1^i)), q(T(Y_1^0))) \\
&= q(T(Y_1^0)) - 4 * q(R(X_1^i))
\end{aligned}
$$

is calculated for $i = 0, 1, 2, 3$.

To illustrate this, consider the Y-neuron, Y_1^0, in the Y-layer-1 and the X-neuron, X_1^1, in the X-layer-1. We have:

$$q(C(X_1^1)) = 1.2 - 4 * 0.1 = 0.8 > 0.$$

This imply that $W(X_1^1, Y_1^0) = 1$ and $W(Y_0^2, X_1^1) = 1$ because the neuron Y_0^2 is one that satisfy

$$q(R(Y_0^2)) = q(T(X_1^1)) = q(C(X_1^1)) = 0.8.$$

The neuron X_1^1 receives the output s from Y-neuron Y_0^2, $s(Y_0^2) = 0.4$, and its output is given by

$$s(X_1^1) = f(\tilde{w}_2^1 * \tilde{a}_2^1 + s(Y_0^2)) = 0.8 * 0.1 + 0.4 = 0.48.$$

Next the Output Pass-k is performed. In this Pass, the output of a single Y-neuron of the Y-layer-1 is calculated as follows:

$$s(Y_1^0) = \max\{a_1, a_2, a_3, a_4\}$$

where $a_1 = s(X_1^0)) = 0.8 * 0.0 + 0.60 = 0.60$; $a_2 = s(X_1^1) = 0.8 * 0.1 + 0.4 = 0.48$; $a_3 = s(X_1^2) = 0.8 * 0.2 + 0.2 = 0.36$; $a_4 = s(X_1^3) = 0.8 * 0.3 + 0.0 = 0.24$. Therefore, $s(Y_1^0) = \max\{0.60, 0.48, 0.36, 0.24\} = 0.60$ which corresponds to the optimal objective function value. The optimal solution can be recovered through connections providing

$$x_1^\star = 0.0; \ x_2^\star = 0.6; \ f = 0.6.$$

Applications examples such as knapsack and shortest path problems are addressed in [8].

III. Computational Requirements Analysis

Consider an optimization problem with N stages, k_i and j_i values for the state and decision variables respectively at stage i, $i = 1, 2, \ldots, N$. According [9], the dynamic programming solution requires an addition for each combination of (y_i, x_i) at stages $2, \ldots, N$ or $\sum_{i=2}^{N} k_i j_i$ additions. For each value of the state variable at all stages there are $j_i - 1$ comparisons, and at the last stage there are an additional $k_i - 1$ comparisons to determine the maximum of $f_N(x_N)$. A total of $\sum_{i=1}^{N} k_i(j_i - 1) + k_i - 1$ comparisons. Assume that the time spent for an addition and a comparison is t_A and t_C, respectively. Then the total time t_{DP} needed for the dynamic programming solution is $t_{DP} = (\sum_{i=2}^{N} k_i j_i) t_A + (\sum_{i=1}^{N} k_i(j_i - 1) + k_i - 1) t_C$.

For the DPNN, since the Y-neurons computations are performed in parallel, the corresponding comparisons are also processed in parallel and hence the total time t_{NN} needed for the DPNN solution is $t_{NN} = (\sum_{i=2}^{N} k_i j_i) t_A + N t_C$.

Clearly, $t_{NN} < t_{DP}$.

The total storage requirements for optimal decision and return functions, with reference to the backward recursion, according [9] is as follows. First, recall that $x_k(y_{k-1})$, $k =$

$N, N-1, \ldots, 2, 1$ is saved until the optimal is traced, but $F_K(y_{N-k})$ is saved only until $F_{k+1}(y_{N-(k+1)})$ has been computed. Thus storage space must be available for all N functions $x_k(y_{k-1})$, but for only two consecutive functions F_k. Recall also that, for an s-component decision variable there are $s + 1$ tabulations of optimal functions for each value variable $y_{N-(k+1)}$ consisting of a single tabulation of $F_k(y_{N-k})$ and s tabulations of $x_k(y_{k-1})$. Assume there are N stages, p state variables per stage, each having k feasible values and s decision variables per stage. Then, the total storage requirements for the dynamic programming solution is $N(s + 2)k^p$. Note the factor that has the most significant influence on the total storage requirements is the number of state variables per stage p.

In the case of the neural net model, since all information is saved in net topology, a $(2*N)$ layer DPNN with k^p Y-neurons per Y-layer and s X-neurons per X-layer is needed to obtain the optimal solution. For instante, assume that the right-hand side of the LP problem constraints in the previous section are 10 and 20. Each Y-layer would have require $11*21 = 231$ Y-neurons (in DP approach each table would have required 231 rows), and the number of X-neurons in each X-layer would increase with the number of feasible values for x_n.

IV. Conclusions and Future Work

This paper has proposed a neural network to solve discrete dynamic programming problems. It presents an algorithm for DPNN implementation and an equivalence between the DPNN and the dynamic programming procedure. This approach presents some advantages because of the inherited parallelism of the neural networks. The calculation of the controller function in each X-neuron, that corresponds to the calculation of the transformation functions in the DP approach, are done in parallel, whereas in the DP approach, the values are calculated sequentially and saved in a matrix. Most of the neural networks developed for optimization purposes, the interconnections are designed a priori and defined in the initialization phase. In the approach proposed here, the neurons establish his own interconnections and weights, provided the discrete variables values, transformation functions and return functions are given. The discrete variables values are represented by the amounts of receptors and transmitters of each neuron in the DPNN. It is believed that many large scale optimization problems, which requires a sequence of interrelated decisions, can be faster solved by this new approach as long as neural computers are available. Thus, our objective is to investigate the potential of this new approach in neurocomputers implementation in the future.

References

[1] Francelin, R.A., Gomide, F., and Loparo, K., " System optimization with artificial neural networks", *Proc. of the Int. Joint Conf. on Neural Neworks*, IJCNN'91, vol. 3, pp. 2639-2644, Nov. 1991.

[2] Francelin, R. A., Ricarte, I., and Gomide, F., " System optimization with artificial neural networks: parallel implementation using transputers", *Proc. of the Int. Joint Conf. on Neural Neworks*, IJCNN'92, vol. 4, pp. 630-635, June 1992.

[3] Bellman, R., *Dynamic programming* , Princeton N. J. : Princeton University Press, 1957.

[4] Gomide, F. and Rocha, A. F., " Neurofuzzy controllers", *Proc. of 2nd Int. Conf. on Fuzzy Logic and Neural Networks*, IIZUKA, JAPAN, July 1992.

[5] Gomide, F. A. and Rocha, A. F., " Neurofuzzy components based on threshold", *Proc. of IFAC Symposium on Intelligent Components and Instruments for Control Applications*, SICICA'92, Málaga, Spain, 20-22, May 1992.

[6] Rocha, A. F., *Neural Nets: a theory for brains and machines*, Lecture Notes in Artificial Intelligence, Springer-Verlag, 1993.

[7] Bruck, J. and Goodman, J. W., " On the power of neural networks for solving hard problems", *Neural Info. Processing Systems*, D. Z. Anderson (Ed.), AIP Conference Proc., pp. 137-143, 1988.

[8] Francelin, R. A. and Gomide, F. A. C. ,*A neural network to solve discrete dynamic programming problems*, DCA/FEE/UNICAMP Technical Report no. 016, ago, 1992.

[9] Nemhauser, G., *Introduction to dynamic programming*, John Wiley Sons, Inc., 1966.

CMAC Learning is Governed by a Single Parameter

Yiu-fai Wong*

Department of Electrical Engineering, 116-81

California Institute of Technology

Pasadena, CA 91125

wong@systems.caltech.edu

Abstract— This paper presents a Fourier analysis of the learning algorithm in the Cerebellar Model Articulation Controller (CMAC) proposed by Albus. We prove that CMAC is capable of learning any discrete input-output mapping by Fourier analysis. We obtain the convergence rates for the different frequencies, which are governed by a single parameter M—the size of the receptive fields of the neurons. This complements an earlier result that CMAC always learns with arbitrary accuracy. The approach here offers new insights into the nature of the learning mechanism in CMAC, which may not be obvious from the earlier approach. The analysis provides mathematical rigor and structure for a neural network learning model with simple and intuitive mechanisms.

I. INTRODUCTION

Albus's CMAC [1] is a three-layer feedforward network for learning input-output mappings. Its ideas and applications can be found in associative memory and learning schemes using locally tuned neurons [2, 3, 4, 5, 6, 7, 8, 9, 10]. There have been some investigations into the convergence properties of CMAC [11, 12, 13, 14]. Extensive analysis has been done by Parks and Militzer. In [12], the authors correctly recognized that CMAC learning is equivalent to iteratively solving a linear system and derived the solution the weights converge to. However, they had to assume that the system is invertible for convergence to occur. Wong and Sideris [13] independently showed that CMAC learning is equivalent to Gauss-Seidel iteration and that the linear system is invertible. Thus, CMAC always converges to give zero-error on any training set.

This work presented an even stronger result proved

in [15]: *CMAC learning is governed solely by the size of the receptive field of the neurons.* The key idea is to study the Gauss-Seidel iteration in the Fourier domain. Linear techniques can indeed give rigor to such a simple, yet nonlinear, neural network.

The paper is organized as follows: We will present a brief description of CMAC. We then summarize an earlier result that CMAC learning can be treated as Gauss-Seidel iteration of a linear system. A new proof is obtained by using Fourier analysis, leading to a complete characterization of the convergence in the frequency domain.

II. MECHANISMS OF CMAC

A schematic sketch of CMAC is shown in Figure 1. We will next describe briefly the building blocks of CMAC. Although we can cast the model in the framework of connectionist multi-layer feedforward networks, the description we adopt here is closer to the original version because conceptually both versions are similarly easy to visualize.

For simplicity, let us start with CMAC for one-dimensional mapping, say $R \mapsto R$. But both the description and analysis can be easily extended to the multi-dimensional case. The input interval $[a, b]$ is discretized into a fixed number of levels. Each input x can then be identified by its discretization level x_d. There is a mapping between the discretized input space and a set S of neurons which is also indexed by integers. For each input x, we first compute its discretization level x_d. Then M consecutive neurons are excited starting at x_d, i.e. the size of the receptive field of a neuron is M. The output of a neuron is 1 if excited, 0 otherwise. A weighted sum of the outputs of these neurons is taken to be the CMAC output.

If the discretization is very fine, there will be too many neurons so that it is physically impossible to implement them (this is especially true for multi-dimensional inputs). Albus solved this problem by hash coding the set of neurons into a smaller, manageable memory A_p with A_p mem-

*Work supported by Pacific Bell through a grant to Caltech and by NASA through the Caltech Jet Propulsion Laboratory, as well as a Charles Lee Powell Foundation Graduate Fellowship.

ory locations. Collision occurs when two different neurons are mapped to the same address. The question of collision due to hashing was addressed in [13] and it was argued there that its effect on CMAC learning is minimal. In fact, hashing does not cause a problem in simulations reported so far. From now on, we will assume that we have a big enough memory for the neurons so that there is no need for hashing.

Having described the mapping from input to output, we now describe the learning algorithm for CMAC. Let d_i be the desired output for the ith training sample. The network output is $g_i = \sum w_j$ where w_j is the weight for the excited neuron j. The error signal $\delta_i = d_i - g_i$. For each neuron excited by the input, $\delta w_j = \delta_i/M$. This rule can be derived from back-propagation [16] learning rule with learning rate $1/M$.

III. KEY RESULTS

Theorem 1 *Given a set of training samples composed of input-output pairs from $\mathcal{R}^n \mapsto \mathcal{R}^m$, CMAC always learns the training set with arbitrary accuracy if the input space is discretized such that no two distinct training input samples excite the same set of neurons. Furthermore, M completely specifies the learning convergence.*

Proof: We now transform CMAC learning to a linear system for the case of $m = n = 1$. We represent the neurons each input sample excites by a vector of characteristic function $\Theta_i(t)$ where

$$\Theta_i(t) = \begin{cases} 1 & \text{if } t^{th} \text{ neuron is excited by input sample } x_i \\ 0 & \text{otherwise.} \end{cases}$$

Let us call this vector the *indicator*. Form the matrix $A = [\Theta_1(t) \ \Theta_2(t) \cdots \Theta_P(t)]^t$ where P is the number of training samples. The goal of CMAC learning is to find a set of weights W such that

$$AW = D \tag{1}$$

where D is the vector of the desired outputs.

The key idea behind the proof in [13] is to identify the CMAC learning rule as Gauss-Seidel iteration of the linear system

$$C\Delta = D \tag{2}$$

where $C = AA^t$. An element c_{ij} of C is just the correlation between the indicators for i^{th} and j^{th} training sample. Thus, learning reduces to the convergence of the Δ. It turns out that C is symmetric and positive definite by noting that Θ_i's are linearly independent. Hence, the iterations always converges [17]. The weights W can be recovered from the accumulated output errors by the operation $W = A^t\Delta$. Putting all the equations together,

the weights are given by $W = A^t(AA^t)^{-1}D$. Note that $A^t(AA^t)^{-1}$ is the pseudo-inverse A^+ of A [18]. It is quite remarkable that Albus's intuitive scheme is actually a numerical implementation of this inversion procedure.

Having proved the learning convergence, we want to know how fast the learning converges. Write C as $C = L + R$ where L is the lower diagonal part of C and R is the upper offdiagonal part of C. From matrix theory [17], the convergence of Gauss-Seidel iteration is governed by the spectral radius of $(-L^{-1}R)$. However, the largest eigenvector is not clear analytically. The convergence can be very slow if the spectral radius is close to 1.

We can do better than this. The trick here is to use techniques from digital signal processing to analyze Gauss-Seidel iteration. Before we do that, we note that the linear system in equation (1) is underspecified. That is, it has more unknowns (weights) than equations (one equation for each training sample). Therefore, there are an infinite number of solutions. Any vector of weights which lies in the null space $\mathcal{N} = ker(A)$ of A will produce zero output. We will now try to characterize this null space.

IV. FOURIER ANALYSIS OF THE CONVERGENCE

To make the Fourier analysis approach more manageable, we restrict the input space to be one-dimensional. Let N be a number such that all the training samples have their discretization levels between 0 and N. Since we only present training samples x_i for some selected points on the interval, we have the known values of d_i and the unknown values of Δ_i^* for these i's. The rest of Δ_i^* and d_i are don't cares[1]. The number of neurons needed is therefore $N + M - 1$ and the dimension of matrix A is $N \times (N + M - 1)$. Since C is positive definite, we see that the dimension of the null space $\mathcal{N}$ is $M - 1$. It is not difficult to see that $\mathcal{N}$ consists of all sinusoids of frequency $2\pi k/M$ where $k = 1, \ldots, M - 1$. This is because a sum of M consecutive weights will produce a zero output. Note that these frequencies are also the zeros of the spectrum of a rectangular box of length M.

The Gauss-Seidel relaxation takes the form

$$\Delta_i^{(l+1)} = \Delta_i^{(l)} + \frac{1}{M}\left(d_i - \sum_{j<i} C_{ij}\Delta_j^{(l+1)} - \sum_{j\geq i} C_{ij}\Delta_j^{(l)}\right) \tag{3}$$

where

$$C_{ij} = \begin{cases} M - |i-j| & \text{if } |i-j| < M \\ 0 & \text{otherwise} \end{cases}$$

and l indexes iteration. Let $e_i^{(l)} = \Delta_i^{(l)} - \Delta_i^*$, where Δ_i^* is one of the desired values. (Note that because of the

---

[1]It matters when we consider the generalization of CMAC to untrained points, which we do not consider here.

don't-cares in Δ_i, Δ^* is not unique.) Let $e^{(l)}$ be the vector composed of $e_i^{(l)}$'s, At desired solution,

$$\Delta_i^* = \Delta_i^* + \frac{1}{M}(d_i - \sum_{j<i} C_{ij}\Delta_j^* - \sum_{j\geq i} C_{ij}\Delta_j^*) \quad (4)$$

Subtracting equation (4) from equation (3), one finds that the error evolve according to

$$e_i^{(l+1)} = e_i^{(l)} - \frac{1}{M}\left(\sum_{j<i} C_{ij}e_j^{(l+1)} + \sum_{j\geq i} C_{ij}e_j^{(l)}\right). \quad (5)$$

This system can be viewed as a linear shift-invariant system on an infinite grid. To take care of the boundary conditions when we replicate the interval over the infinite grid, the index i now runs from $-(M-1)$ to $N+M-2$. Thus, the period is $N_1 = N + 2M - 2$. It can therefore be analyzed in the Fourier domain. That is, techniques from digital signal processing can be used to analyze this numerical problem [19] provided that we present the inputs in a sequential order.

We now expand e in a Fourier series of the form

$$e_n = \sum_{k=0}^{N_1-1} \tilde{e}_k \exp(j\frac{2\pi}{N_1}kn). \quad (6)$$

Then in the Fourier domain, equation (5) becomes [19]

$$\tilde{e}_k^{(l+1)} = H(e^{j\frac{2\pi}{N_1}k})\tilde{e}_k^{(l)} \quad (7)$$

where

$$H(z) = \frac{-\sum_{n=1}^{M}(M-n)z^n}{M + \sum_{n=1}^{M}(M-n)z^{-n}}. \quad (8)$$

The weights are obtained by the operation $W^{(l)} = A^t\Delta^{(l)}$. Let W^* be one of the desired solutions. If we denote $W^{l+1} - W^*$ by $\delta W^{(l)}$, then $\delta W^l = A^t e^l$. It is clear that in the frequency domain, $\delta\tilde{W}^{(l+1)} = H(e^{j\omega})\delta\tilde{W}^{(l)}$. If CMAC is capable of learning any input-output mapping, we desire that $|H(e^{j\omega})| < 1$.

Note that $H(z)$ can be written as:

$$H(z) = \frac{-h(z)}{1 + h(-z)} \quad (9)$$

where $h(z) = \frac{(M-1)z - Mz^2 + z^{M+1}}{M(1-z)^2}$. With $h(z) = a(z) + jb(z)$, the magnitude of $H(z)$ is given by

$$|H(z)|^2 = \frac{1}{1 + \frac{1+2a(z)}{a(z)^2+b(z)^2}}. \quad (10)$$

It is obvious that $|H(z)| < 1$ if and only if

$$1 + 2a(z) > 0. \quad (11)$$

Equating the real and imaginary parts of $H(e^{j\omega})$, we find that $a(e^{j\omega}) = \frac{\sin^2\frac{M\omega}{2}}{2M\sin^2\frac{\omega}{2}} - \frac{1}{2}$ and $b(e^{j\omega}) = \frac{M\sin\omega - \sin M\omega}{4M\sin^2\frac{\omega}{2}}$. Thus,

$$1 + 2a(e^{j\omega}) = \frac{\sin^2(\frac{M\omega}{2})}{M\sin^2(\frac{\omega}{2})}. \quad (12)$$

It is seen that $1 + 2a(e^{j\omega}) > 0$ except at $\omega = 2\pi k/M, k = 1, \ldots, M-1$, where it vanishes. But these harmonics belong to the null space of A. They have no effect on the CMAC output. Thus W and Δ do converge, proving that the Gauss-Seidel iteration converges in the frequency domain. It should come as no surprise that these errors have the same dimension as the null space of the matrix A. The Fourier analysis obviously generalizes to the CMAC with n-dimensional inputs since the kernel $\exp(-jkx)$ separates. The case of m-dimensional output space is taken care by replicating the 1-dimensional output system m times.

Now, let us investigate the rate of convergence for the different frequencies by utilizing the properties of the filter $H(z)$. After considerable algebraic manipulations, we get

$$|H(e^{j\omega})|^2 = \left(1 + \frac{\frac{4}{M}\sin^2(\frac{M\omega}{2})}{(1-p(\omega))^2 + 2p(\omega)(1-\cos(\frac{M-1}{2})\omega)}\right)^{-1} \quad (13)$$

where $p(\omega) = \sin(\frac{M\omega}{2})/M\sin\frac{\omega}{2}$. In Figure 2, we plot the squared magnitude of $H(e^{j\omega})$ for two choices of M and we see that larger M means slower overall convergence, as observed in the last section. The magnitude is 1 at frequencies $2k\pi/M, k = 1, \ldots, M-1$. Hence, the convergence is slow for frequencies near the harmonics of $2\pi/M$. As M increases, there will be more of these harmonics. This in turn means that learning will be slower. Note that $H(e^{j\omega})$ is periodic with period$=2\pi/M$ and its minimum value is $\frac{M/2-1}{M/2+1}$. We also note that the d-c gain of the filter is at the minimum. Thus CMAC can learn smooth mappings quite effortlessly.

That e_i contains frequency components which cannot be reduced does not imply that CMAC cannot learn these frequencies. Remember that when we replicate d_i on an infinite grid, we introduce $M-1$ don't cares in d_i. It is these don't cares which give extra degrees of freedom enabling CMAC to represent any mapping. However, since learning is local, it takes a long time for CMAC to learn these particular frequency components.

To conclude, it is very satisfying that M, the size of the receptive fields of the neurons, governs the learning in CMAC. $H(e^{j\omega})$ gives the rate of convergence for the various frequencies components. Combining some of the conclusions in [13], we now summarize what we know about CMAC:

1. CMAC learning is essentially solving a linear system with known matrix algorithm which converges; this explains why

   - CMAC learning is highly accurate and;
   - CMAC converges exponentially fast.

2. CMAC is doing some kind of interpolation for inputs it has not been trained on; this gives it a certain generalization ability;

3. CMAC learning is slow for frequencies near harmonics of $2\pi/M$ and fast otherwise;

4. CMAC learning is very robust to the noise added in the learning process.

V. Summary

Using Fourier analysis to examine the learning algorithm in the original CMAC, we have presented a new proof that CMAC learning always converges. The approach gives additional insight to the learning process. It shows the convergence rates for the different frequency components of the desired solution. It also clearly shows the relationship between M, which is the size of the receptive field of the neurons, and the overall convergence rate. The results obtained give us a better understanding of CMAC. It is very satisfying that linear techniques can be utilized to rigorously analyze this simple neural network model. This is some encouragement for those who try to build mathematical models of simple neural networks. But it remains to be seen if similar rigor can be brought to bear on more complicated neural networks.

VI. Acknowledgements

I am deeply indebted to Edward C. Posner for his encouragement and advice.

References

[1] J. S. Albus, "A New Approach to Manipulator Control: The Cerebellar Model Articulation Controller (CMAC)," *Trans. ASME, J. Dynamic Syst. Meas. Contr.*, vol 97, 220-227, 1975.

[2] Pentti Kanerva, "Parallel Structures in Human and Computer Memory,", in *Neural Networks for Computing*, J.S. Denker, (Ed.), AIP Conf. Proc. *151*, Snowbird, 1986, 247-258.

[3] D.S. Broomhead and D. Lowe, "Multivariable Functional Interpolation and Adaptive Networks," *Complex Systems*, 2, 321-355, 1988.

[4] John Moody, "Fast Learning in Multi-Resolution Hierarchies," in *Advances in Neural Information Processing Systems 1*, D.S. Touretzky, (Ed.), Morgan Kaufmann Publishers, 1989, 29-39.

[5] W. Thomas Miller, "Real-Time Application of Neural Networks for Sensor-Based Control of Robots with Vision," *IEEE Trans. Syst. Man and Cyb.* vol SMC-19, 825-831, 1989.

[6] Tomaso Poggio and Federico Girosi, "Networks for Approximation and Learning," *Proceedings of the IEEE*, vol 78, 1481-1497, 1990.

[7] Michael Hormel, "A Self-organizing Associative Memory System for Control Applications," in *Advances in Neural Information Processing Systems 2*, D.S. Touretzky, (Ed.), Morgan Kaufmann Publishers, 1990, 332-339.

[8] M. J. Carter, F. J. Rudolph and A. J. Nucci, "Operational Fault Tolerance of CMAC Networks, " in *Advances in Neural Information Processing Systems 2*, D.S. Touretzky, (Ed.), Morgan Kaufmann Publishers, 1990, 340-347.

[9] L. G. Kraft and D. P. Campagna, "A Comparison between CMAC Neural Network Control and Two Traditional Adaptive Control Systems," *IEEE Contr. Syst. Mag.*, 36-43, April, 1990.

[10] C.-S. Lin and H. Kim, "CMAC-based adaptive critic self-learning control," *IEEE Trans. Neural Networks*, 2, 530-533, 1992.

[11] P.C. Parks and J. Militzer, "Convergence Properties of Associative Memory Storage For Learning Control Systems," in *IFAC Symposium on Adaptive Syst. in Control and Signal Processing*, Glasgow, UK, 1989.

[12] P.C. Parks and J. Militzer, "Convergence Properties of Associative Memory Storage For Learning Control Systems," in *Automation and Remote Control*, Plenum Press, New York, vol. 50, No. 2, 254-286, 1989.

[13] Yiu-fai Wong and A. Sideris, "Learning Convergence in the Cerebellar Model Articulation Controller," *IEEE Trans. Neural Networks* , 3, 115-121, 1992.

[14] N.E. Cotter and T.J. Guillerm, "The CMAC and a Theorem of Kolmogorov," *Neural Networks*, 5, 221-228, 1992.

[15] Yiu-fai Wong, *Towards a Simple and Fast Learning and Classification System*, Ph.D Thesis, Caltech, Electrical Engineering, January, 1992.

[16] D.E. Rumelhart, et al., *Parallel Distributed Processing*, vol 1, MIT Press, Cambridge, Mass., 1986.

[17] Joel Franklin, *Matrix Theory*, Prentice-Hall, 1968.

[18] D.E. Catlin, *Estimation, Control, and the Discrete Kalman Filter*, Springer-Verlag, New York, 1989.

[19] C.-C. Jay Kuo and B. C. Levy, "Discretization and Solution of Elliptic PDEs —A Digital Signal Processing Approach," *Proc. IEEE*, 78, 1808-18 42, 1990.

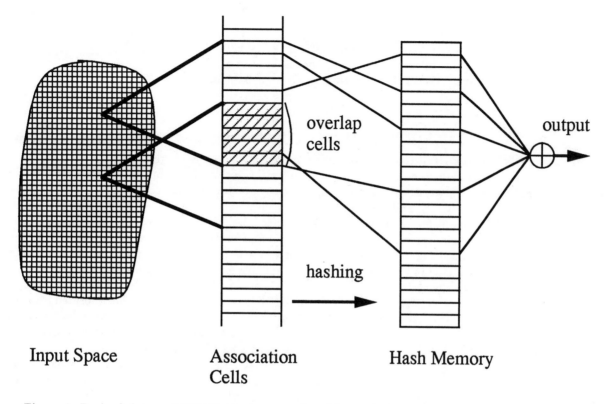

Input Space   Association   Hash Memory
Cells

Figure 1: Basic skeleton of CMAC: the input excites M association cells which are coded to produce the output.

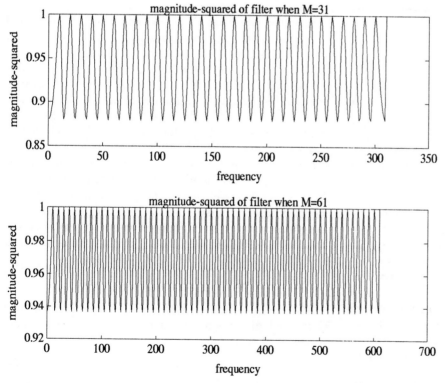

Figure 2: Comparison of the filters for two choices of M. It shows that the convergence is governed by M.

A Competitive & Selective Learning Method
for Designing Optimal Vector Quantizers

Naonori UEDA and Ryohei NAKANO
NTT Communication Science Laboratories
Hikaridai, Seika-cho, Soraku-gun, Kyoto 619-02 Japan

Abstract–A new competitive learning method with a "selection" mechanism is proposed for the design of optimal vector quantizers. A basic principle called the "equidistortioin principle" for designing the optimal quantizers is first derived theoretically, and then a new learning algorithm based on this principle is presented. Unlike conventional algorithms based on the "conscience" mechanism, the proposed algorithm can minimize distortion without a particular initialization procedure even when the input data cluster in a number of regions in the input vector space. The performance of this method is compared with that of the conscience learning method.

I. INTRODUCTION

According to Shannon's rate distortion theory, vector quantization (VQ) can always obtain better compression performance than any other coding method based on the encoding of scalars. This quantization has therefore been widely used to compress image and speech signals, and Gray [1] has published a complete review of VQ.

A vector quantizer maps each input vector in the k-dimensional Euclidean space R^k into one of the finite number of representative vectors in R^k. The performance of such a quantizer is measured by the distortion caused by reproducing an input vector with the corresponding representative vector. Thus, to obtain an optimal quantizer, the average distortion over all representative vectors should be minimized.

Variational techniques are not directly applicable to this kind of minimization problem because the underlying distribution of the input vector space is in general unknown. Even if this distribution is known or estimated, calculating the derivatives is difficult for higher dimensions except when the distribution has a particular form. Variational techniques are therefore inappropriate for the VQ design. Linde, Buzo, and Gray [2] proposed an algorithm with no differentiation for VQ design. This algorithm is well known as the LBG algorithm and has been widely utilized. Although their algorithm is not optimal, it at least assures local optimality.

Competitive learning (CL) algorithms [3]-[9], on the other hand, which have been developed in artificial neu-

ral networks, can also perform vector quantization. In CL, the representative vectors are referred to as neurons. That is, each weight vector of neurons in CL corresponds to a representative vector in VQ. According to a basic CL rule, only one neuron (the winner) can adjust its weight vector.

With this competitive learning rule, as pointed out in [5], it is possible to develop a situation in which some neurons never win the competition. Then, since all neurons are not available for VQ, the expected distortion becomes large. To overcome this problem, a "conscience" mechanism (CM) [7],[8] has recently been incorporated into the CL algorithm. The CM is a kind of "penalty" method that prevents some particular neurons from winning excessively. The goal of the CM is to bias the competition process so that each neuron has about the same probability of winning the competition. There are a few variants of CL algorithms based on the CM. The most recent, the frequency-sensitive CL algorithm (FSCL) [9], has performed best for VQ design.

From the viewpoint of the minimization of the expected distortion, however, all conventional CL algorithms are not optimal. That is, the conventional CL methods may minimize distortion only when the underlying probability distribution is uniform. We have recently found that for general distributions, they can not minimize the distortion.

In this paper, we prove that the minimum distortion cannot be established with the conventional CL algorithms and we simultaneously derive a new principle for obtaining the minimum distortion. Moreover, we present a new learning algorithm based on this new principle within a framework of competitive learning. Since no probabilistic model is assured in deriving the principle, the associated algorithm can minimize distortion without a particular initialization procedure even when the input data cluster in a number of regions in the input vector space.

II. VECTOR QUANTIZATION

A vector quantizer can be formally defined as a mapping Q of the k-dimensional Euclidean space R^k into a finite subset Y of R^k. Thus

$$Q : R^k \rightarrow Y, \qquad (1)$$

where $Y = \{y_i : i = 1, 2, \ldots, N\}$ is the set of N representative vectors. The quantizer, as shown in Fig. 1, is specified by the values of the representative vectors and by a partition of the space $\boldsymbol{R}^k$ into N disjoint and exhaustive regions $S_1, S_2, \ldots, S_N$, where $S_i = Q^{-1}(\boldsymbol{y}_i) \subset \boldsymbol{R}^k$. If we let $\boldsymbol{x} = (x_1, x_2, \ldots, x_k) \in \boldsymbol{R}^k$ be a k-dimensional random vector with joint probability density $p(\boldsymbol{x}) = p(x_1, x_2, \ldots, x_k)$, then

$$Q(\boldsymbol{x}) = \boldsymbol{y}_i \quad \text{if} \quad \boldsymbol{x} \in S_i, \quad \text{for} \quad i = 1, 2, \ldots, N. \quad (2)$$

The cost caused by reproducing $\boldsymbol{x}$ with $\boldsymbol{y}$ is given by a nonnegative distortion measure $d(\boldsymbol{x}, \boldsymbol{y})$. The most common distortion measure is the rth power of the Euclidean (or l_2) norm given by

$$d(\boldsymbol{x}, \boldsymbol{y}) = ||\boldsymbol{x} - \boldsymbol{y}||^r = \left(\sum_{j=1}^{k} |x_j - y_j|^2 \right)^{\frac{r}{2}} \quad (3)$$

which for $r = 2$ corresponds to the square error distortion measure. The goal in designing an optimal vector quantizer is to find a quantizer $Q(\boldsymbol{x})$ for fixed N and k such that the expected distortion

$$\begin{aligned} D &= \frac{1}{k} \int_{\boldsymbol{R}^k} d(\boldsymbol{x}, Q(\boldsymbol{x})) p(\boldsymbol{x}) d\boldsymbol{x} \\ &= \frac{1}{k} \sum_{i=1}^{N} \int_{S_i} d(\boldsymbol{x}, \boldsymbol{y}_i) p(\boldsymbol{x}) d\boldsymbol{x} = \frac{1}{k} \sum_{i=1}^{N} D_i(\boldsymbol{y}_i) \quad (4) \end{aligned}$$

is minimized. Here, D_i corresponds to a subdistortion in the subregion S_i. It is impossible to directly apply the variational technique because the underlying distribution $p(\boldsymbol{x})$ is in general unknown. Many algorithms based on a nonvariational approach have been proposed to solve this VQ design problem. In the next section, we briefly describe the competitive learning algorithms for VQ design.

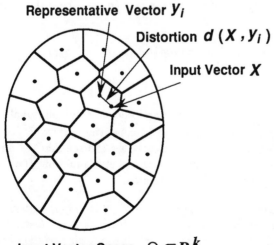

Representative Vector y_i

Distortion $d(X, y_i)$

Input Vector X

Input Vector Space $\Omega \subset \boldsymbol{R}^k$

Fig. 1. Vector quantization.

III. CONVENTIONAL LEARNING ALGORITHMS

A. Competitive Learning Rule

In CL algorithms, the input vector $\boldsymbol{x}$ is presented to all neural units (neurons). Each neuron i has a weight vector, and we let $\boldsymbol{y}_i = (y_{i1}, y_{i2}, \ldots, y_{ik}) \in \boldsymbol{R}^k$ denote the weight vector. Each neuron i computes the distortion $d(\boldsymbol{x}, \boldsymbol{y}_i)$ between its weight vector and the input vector. Then a winning neuron c with the minimum distortion is selected.

$$d(\boldsymbol{x}, \boldsymbol{y}_c) \le d(\boldsymbol{x}, \boldsymbol{y}_j) \quad \text{for all} \quad j \ne c. \quad (5)$$

To reduce the distortion of the winning neuron c, its new weight vector $\boldsymbol{y}_c(t+1)$ is then slightly adjusted towards the current input vector $\boldsymbol{x}(t)$.

$$\boldsymbol{y}_c(t+1) = \boldsymbol{y}_c(t) + \eta(t)(\boldsymbol{x}(t) - \boldsymbol{y}_c(t)) \quad (6)$$

The nonnegative parameter $\eta(t)$, which represents the learning rate for the weight adjustment, decreases monotonically to zero as learning progresses. The weight vectors of the other losing neurons are unchanged. In the above algorithm, the initial weight vectors are set to small random values.

B. Conscience Mechanism

The competitive learning algorithms are interesting because they perform vector quantization. Namely, in an ideal situation, they partition the input vector space into discrete and *equiprobable* regions. However, as pointed out by Rumelhart & Zipser [5], the use of the basic learning rule sometimes leads to a situation in which some neurons never win the competition.

To counter this defect, a *conscience* mechanism (CM) has recently been introduced [7]-[9]. With CM, the number of times each neuron has won is counted, and the count is incorporated into the distortion as a "penalty" so that all neurons have an equal chance of winning the competition. An algorithm into which the CM is incorporated was presented by DeSieno [8]. Another CM-based algorithm, called the frequency-sensitive competitive learning (FSCL) algorithm, has been reported, and claimed to be better for VQ design.

In the FSCL algorithm, to incorporate the count u_i, the number of times which neuron i has won the learning process, a modified distortion is defined as

$$d_i^*(\boldsymbol{x}, \boldsymbol{y}_i) = d_i(\boldsymbol{x}, \boldsymbol{y}_i) \cdot u_i. \quad (7)$$

At each step of the learning process, a neuron c with the minimum distortion $d_c^* = \min_i d_i^*$ is selected as a winner. Thus if a neuron i wins the competition frequently, its count u_i increases and d_i^* increases. This means that the likelihood of neuron i being the winner is reduced.

As one can see, the CM aims to establish an *equiprobable* partition of the input vector space. As shown in the next section, however, even though the equiprobable encoding is established, such an encoding can not minimize the expected distortion given by (4).

IV. EUIDISTORTION PRINCIPLE

A. Asymptotic Performance of Vector Quantizers

A number of theoretical VQ studies have pursued the problem of minimizing the distortion. Gersho [10] provides a unified and general development of many pre-existing results for the asymptotic performance of the vector quantization. According to his theory, for a smooth underlying probability density $p(\boldsymbol{x})$ and for a large number N of the representative vectors, the minimum distortion D^* is given by

$$D^* = C(k,r)N^{-\beta}\|p(\boldsymbol{x})\|_{\frac{1}{1+\beta}}, \qquad (8)$$

where $\beta = r/k$ and r is the power of the Euclidean norm denoted as in (3). The term $C(k,r)$ is a "quantization coefficient" depending only on the dimension k and the power r. Note that only a lower bound of the coefficient is known for general k. Since the coefficient is not essential for the following discussion, we will omit the details. The term $\|p(\boldsymbol{x})\|_\alpha$, the L_α norm of $p(\boldsymbol{x})$, is defined as

$$\|p(\boldsymbol{x})\|_\alpha = \left(\int p(\boldsymbol{x})^\alpha d\boldsymbol{x}\right)^{1/\alpha}. \qquad (9)$$

The above minimum value is attained only when an approximated *continuous* density function of the representative vectors is proportional to $p(\boldsymbol{x})^{\frac{1}{1+\beta}}$. From a simple consideration (omitted here), it can be seen that in such a case, all subdistortions $D_i, i = 1, 2, \ldots, N$ in an optimal partition have the same distortion. That is, $D_i = D^*/N, \quad i = 1, 2, \ldots, N$.

B. Generalization to Disjoint Multiple Clusters

So far we have assumed the underlying distribution to be continuous. Now, we generalize the above result to the general case where the distribution consists of multiple disjoint clusters.

Consider the case where the distribution consists of M disjoint clusters $(\Omega_1, \Omega_2, \ldots, \Omega_M)$, each cluster has a continuous density function $p_j(\boldsymbol{x}), j = 1, 2, \ldots, M$, and the ratio of the number of representative vectors for the jth cluster is n_j. Clearly, $\sum_{j=1}^M n_j = 1$. Let $D^{(j)}$ be the distortion in the jth cluster. Then, by utilizing the result in (8), we can obtain the minimum distortion $D^{(j)^*}$ for the jth cluster.

$$D^{(j)^*} = C(k,r)(n_j N)^{-\beta}\|p_j(\boldsymbol{x})\|_{\frac{1}{1+\beta}} \qquad (10)$$

Accordingly, by solving the following minimization problem, we can obtain an optimal ratio of the number of representative vectors in each cluster, where the ratio minimizes the total distortion over all clusters.

Minimize $\quad f(n_1, \ldots, n_M) = \sum_{j=1}^M n_j^{-\beta}\|p_j(\boldsymbol{x})\|_{\frac{1}{1+\beta}}$,

subject to $\quad \sum_{j=1}^M n_j = 1.$ $\qquad (11)$

This minimization problem can easily be solved by a method of Lagrange multipliers. That is, consider now finding the extrema of $F(n_1, n_2, \ldots, n_M, \lambda)$:

$$F(n_1, n_2, \ldots, n_M, \lambda) = \sum_{j=1}^M n_j^{-\beta}\|p_j(\boldsymbol{x})\|_{\frac{1}{1+\beta}} + \lambda(\sum_{j=1}^M n_j - 1). \qquad (12)$$

The conditions for the extrema are as follows:

$$\frac{\partial F}{\partial n_j} = 0 \quad (j = 1, 2, \ldots, M) \qquad \text{and} \qquad \frac{\partial F}{\partial \lambda} = 0. \quad (13)$$

From the former, we have

$$n_j = \left\{\frac{\beta}{\lambda}\|p_j(\boldsymbol{x})\|_{\frac{1}{1+\beta}}\right\}^{\frac{1}{1+\beta}}, \qquad \text{for} \quad j = 1, 2, \ldots, M. \qquad (14)$$

Eliminating λ, we obtain an optimal ratio n_j^* as

$$n_j^* = \frac{\displaystyle\int_{\Omega_j} p_j(\boldsymbol{x})^{\frac{1}{1+\beta}} d\boldsymbol{x}}{\displaystyle\sum_{j=1}^M \int_{\Omega_j} p_j(\boldsymbol{x})^{\frac{1}{1+\beta}} d\boldsymbol{x}}, \qquad \text{for} \quad j = 1, 2, \ldots, M. \qquad (15)$$

On the other hand, the Hessian matrix $(\nabla^2 f(\boldsymbol{n}))$ whose elements are the second derivatives of $f(\boldsymbol{n})$ with respect to the element of the vector $\boldsymbol{n} = (n_1, \ldots, n_M)^t$ becomes a diagonal matrix as

$$\nabla^2 f(\boldsymbol{n}) = diag\{h_1, \ldots, h_i, \ldots, h_M\}, \qquad (16)$$

where $\quad h_i = \beta(\beta+1)n_i^{-(\beta+2)}\|p_i(\boldsymbol{x})\|_{\frac{1}{1+\beta}}.$

Hence $f(\boldsymbol{n})$ is a convex function over M dimensional simplex $\sum_{j=1}^M n_j = 1, n_j > 0$ because the matrix $\nabla^2 f(\boldsymbol{n})$ is positive definite. Consequently, we can see that the above n_j^* gives the minimum of the vector function $f(\boldsymbol{n})$ and hence have the following lemma.

Lemma 1 *When the distribution of the input vectors consists of M disjoint multiple clusters and each cluster has a smooth density function $p_j(\boldsymbol{x})$, the following relation holds:*

$$n_j^* \propto \int_{\Omega_j} p_j(\boldsymbol{x})^{\frac{1}{1+\beta}} d\boldsymbol{x}. \qquad (17)$$

If the equiprobable principle leads optimality, β in (17) should be zero. However, $\beta = r/k \neq 0$. Consequently, the above lemma proves that the equiprobable principle dose not lead optimality from the standpoint of the minimization of the expected distortion.

Now, if $(n_j^* N)$ vectors exist in the jth cluster and all regions in the jth cluster have the same distortion, $D^{(j)^*}/(n_j^* N)$, then the total distortion over all clusters is minimized. On the other hand, calculating $D^{(j)^*}/(n_j^* N)$, we obtain

$$D^{(j)^*}/(n_j^* N) = C(k,r) N^{-(1+\beta)} \left(\sum_{j=1}^{M} \int_{\Omega_j} p_j(\boldsymbol{x})^{\frac{1}{1+\beta}} d\boldsymbol{x} \right)^{1+\beta} .$$

$$(18)$$

Looking at (18) carefully, we can see that $D^{(j)^*}/(n_j^* N)$ reduces to a constant independent of the index j. This means that when the expected distortion becomes minimum, not only all regions in one cluster have the same distortion, but also all regions in all clusters have the same distortion. In other words, we can give the following important theorem for designing an optimal vector quantizer.

Theorem 1 *For a large number of representative vectors, even though the underlying probability distribution of the input vectors consists of multiple disjoint clusters, the expected distortion becomes minimum if and only if every partitioned region S_i has the same subdistortion D_i, that is, $D_i = D^*/N$. Here D^* means the minimum distortion over all clusters.*

We can conclude therefore that to obtain the minimum distortion, *equidistortion* rather than *equiprobable* partition must be performed. This also means that the competitive learning algorithms based on the conscience mechanism does not lead optimality with respect to the optimal vector quantizers.

V. COMPETITIVE & SELECTIVE LEARNING (CSL) ALGORITHM BASED ON THE EQUIDISTORTION PRINCIPLE

A. Adding a Selection Mechanism to Competitive Learning

According to the equidistortion principle, the larger (smaller) number of representative vectors should be assigned to the subregions with larger (smaller) subdistortion. To perform such assignment, we add a *selection* mechanism to the competitive learning algorithm. This selection, like that utilized in the *genetic algorithms* [11], is based on a fitness measure. The fitness measure used here is defined as a function of the subdistortion. Hence, with the selection mechanism, we can adjust the number of representative vectors in regions according to the subdistortion there while the total number of vectors (neurons) is unchanged. As this learning with selection progresses, the

desired equivalent distortion is asymptotically established over all regions.

When T training data are practically available, they are repeatedly utilized to adjust the weight vectors of neurons until the algorithm converges. Then, in addition to the adjustment, the selection is performed every T learning times. Note that in order to practically guarantee the convergence of the selection itself, the number of neurons that are subject to the selection is forced to monotonically decrease every selection. Thus the selection always ends in a finite number of times. The details of the selection algorithm are given later.

CSL algorithm:

(1) Initialization: Given N (the number of neurons), a training set $\boldsymbol{X}$, convergence threshold ϵ, and initial weight vectors of neurons. Set $m = 1$ and $D(0) = \infty$.

(2) Training: For all $\boldsymbol{x} \in \boldsymbol{X}$, perform (I) and (II) like the conventional competitive learning algorithm described in III.A.

    (I) Find the closest neuron to $\boldsymbol{x}$.

    (II) Adjust weight vector of the winning neuron.

(3) Convergence test:

    (I) Compute the average distortion using

$$D(m) = \frac{1}{|\boldsymbol{X}|} \sum_{\boldsymbol{x} \in \boldsymbol{X}} \min_{\boldsymbol{y} \in \boldsymbol{Y}} d(\boldsymbol{x}, \boldsymbol{y}),$$

    where $\boldsymbol{Y}$ is the final weight vectors after step (2).

    (II) If $(D(m-1) - D(m))/D(m) \leq \epsilon$, halt with $\boldsymbol{Y}$ final representative vectors. Otherwise continue.

(4) Selection: If $s(m) > 2$, choose $s(m)$ neurons to be selected and perform selection algorithm for chosen neurons.

(5) Replace m by $m + 1$ and go to (2).

Note that in step (4), $s(m)$ denotes the number of neurons that are subject to the selection at the mth iteration. The number $s(m)$ is forced to decrease monotonically as m increases. These $s(m)$ neurons are determined by choosing alternately from both the first and the last rank of the subdistortion. For example, suppose that $D_1 = 30$, $D_2 = 10$, $D_3 = 40$, $D_4 = 50$, $D_5 = 45$, and $s(m) = 3$, then the fourth, the second, and the fifth neurons are chosen. Clearly, with this choosing rule, the variation in the subdistortion among the subregions is reduced more rapidly than with a random choice.

As one can see, the CSL algorithm is the same as the basic competitive learning algorithm (described in III.A.)

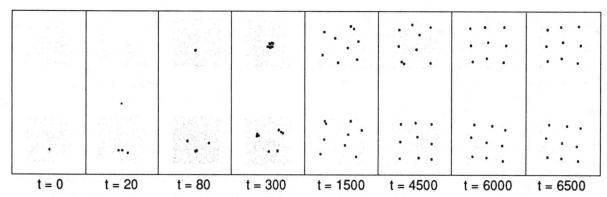

| t = 0 | t = 20 | t = 80 | t = 300 | t = 1500 | t = 4500 | t = 6000 | t = 6500 |

Fig. 2. Simulation result of the CSL algorithm for two-dimensional input vector space. The input space consists of two rectangular uniform probability density functions. Black dots represents the weight vectors of neurons. Initially, all weight vectors are set to the same value ($t = 0$). As the learning progresses, the weight vectors approach the optimal values.

except that the selection is performed at fixed time intervals. Namely, during the learning process, not only the total distortion is reduced by the basic competitive learning rule in step (2), but also the variation of the subdistortion among subregions divided by the weight vectors is reduced by the selection operation in step (4). In the next subsection, we will give a detailed description of the selection algorithm.

B. Selection Algorithm

The selection algorithm used here is different from the selection operation utilized in genetic algorithms, in that the proposed selection algorithm features a deterministic selection, while the latter features a stochastic one. With the conventional stochastic selection, we cannot obtain a reliable reproduction result reflecting the fitness measure for a small number of neurons because the *law of large numbers* is not satisfied. (This kind of problem would not occur in genetic algorithms, since they use a very large number of populations.) Let $s(m)$ be the number of neurons that are subject to the selection at the mth iteration in the CSL algorithm. Then, the selection algorithm for the $s(m)$ neurons is described as follows. (Note that in the algorithm, these neurons are referred to as $j = 1, 2, \ldots, s(m)$.)

Selection algorithm:

(1) Compute a normalized fitness measure using the subdistortion D_j.

$$g_j = D_j^\gamma / \sum_{j=1}^{s(m)} D_j^\gamma,$$

where $\gamma (< 1)$ is a nonnegative constant that prevents excessive selection.

(2) Determine the number of neurons to be reproduced:

(I) Compute $[g_j s(m)](\equiv u_j)$ for all j. ($[a]$ denotes the largest integer less than or equal to a.)

(II) For top $s(m) - \sum_{j=1}^{s(m)} u_j$ neurons with respect to the value of $g_j s(m) - u_j$, add one to each u_j.

(3) For every j, reproduce u_j neurons by adding random perturbation vectors δ_{jl} ($l = 1, 2, \ldots, u_j$) to y_j respectively, where $\|\delta_{jl}\| << \|y_j\|$. Halt.

The subdistortion in step (1) can be computed by

$$D_j = \sum_{x \in V_j} d(x, y_j),$$

where V_j denotes the *Voronoi region* belonging to y_j. That is,

$$V_j = \bigcap_{k, k \neq j} \{x \mid \|x - y_j\| < \|x - y_k\|\}.$$

In step (2), the final u_j denotes the number of neurons that should be reproduced from the jth neuron by the selection. Clearly, $u_j = 0$ means that the jth neuron should disappear. The meaning of step (2) is as follows. Since the reproduction ratios directly obtained by the normalized fitness measure in general take on real values, they must be converted to integers. First, in step (2-I), for each j an integer part of $g_j s(m)$ is assigned to u_j. In this step, $\sum_{j=1}^{s(m)} u_j (\leq s(m))$ neurons in total are determined. Therefore, in step (2-II), the rest ($s(m) - \sum_{j=1}^{s(m)} u_j$ neurons) are determined according to the values of the decimal parts of $g_j s(m) - u_j, j = 1, 2, \ldots, s(m)$. Table I presents a simple example ($s(m) = 5$) intended to demonstrate the basic operation in steps (1) and (2) of the selection algorithm.

The selection can be interpreted as multiplication and disappearance of neurons in the input vector space. Therefore, the selection operation is performed successfully even when the input data cluster in a number of regions in the input vector space as shown in Fig. 2.

TABLE I
A SIMPLE EXAMPLE ($s(m) = 5$)

Neuron No.(j)	step (1) D_j^γ	step (2-I) $g_j s(m)$	u_j	step (2-II) $g_j s(m) - u_j$		Final u_j
1	4.5	0.9	0	0.9	+1	1
2	16.0	3.2	3	0.2		3
3	3.4	0.68	0	0.68	+1	1
4	0.1	0.02	0	0.02		0
5	1.0	0.2	0	0.2		0

VI. VERIFICATION OF THE OPTIMALITY

To verify the optimality of the CSL algorithm based on the equidistortion principle, we have first applied it to a one-dimensional quantizer problem. Since if all training data are given, an optimal quantizer in only a one-dimensional distribution can be numerically obtained by Max's search method [12], we can verify the optimality of the proposed algorithm by comparing the learning result with the optimal values numerically obtained. For the lack of space, we omit the details of the numerical search technique. We also applied the CM-based learning method (FSCL algorithm) to the same problem.

Fig. 3(a) shows a one-dimensional density function with a gap. The density function, which is the same one utilized in [8][9], is generated from the product of two uniformly distributed random numbers between the values of 0.0 and 1.0 with all values between 0.2 and 0.4 removed. A total 5000 training data are included in the distribution. We used fifteen neurons (representative vectors) in total. In order to investigate the effect of the learning results on the different initializations, we utilized seven kinds of initial weight values of 0.0, 0.17, 0.34, 0.5, 0.67, 0.83, 1.0, which correspond to the values obtained by dividing equally the interval [0.0, 1.0]. These initial values are, for simplicity, referred to as "Init. #pt = 0,1,...,6", respectively. For example, Init. #pt. = 3 means that the weight values of fifteen neurons are equally initialized to 0.5. In these experiments, we adopted the second power of the Euclidean norm, that is, the mean square error (MSE).

For all Init.#pts, we performed the algorithms. For the lack of space, we show only the results of Init.#pt=0,2,5 in Figs. 3(b),(c). These figures show the time history of the learning process. To save space, a log-scale time axis is utilitzed in these figures. In Figs. 3(b),(c), the dotted lines denote the optimal weight values obtained by the numerical search method. In Fig. 3(c), bifurcations and disappearances of the time history of the weight values are due to the selection. With the proposed algorithm, we can see that the weight values asymptotically approach the optimal values as the learning progresses even when random initial weight values are chosen. On the other hand, the results of the FSCL algorithm are far from the optimal values and are strongly affected by the initialization of the weight values.

Table II shows the comparative distortion between the FSCL and the proposed algorithm. $N_1(N_2)$ denotes the number of neurons in region [0.0,0.2] ([0.4,1.0]) after the learning. The optimal pair obtained by the numerical search was $(N_1, N_2) = (6, 9)$. The minimum distortion obtained by the optimal values was 1.50×10^{-4}, and therefore the difference between the distortion by the proposed algorithm and the minimum one was less than 2% of the minimum distortion, which had never been obtain by conventional algorithms.

VII. CONCLUSION

In this paper, we proved that the equidistortion rather than the equiprobable principle is necessary and sufficient for designing optimal quantizers. As far as our literature survey, no one has pointed out this fact. In addition, we developed a new learning algorithm with a selection mechanism to ensure the equidistortion principle. From the experimental results, we could see that our principle is valid and that the associated algorithm is near globally optimal. Future work will focus on further experiments involving higher-dimensional quantizer problems.

ACKNOWLEDGEMENT

We thank Dr. Seishi Nishikawa for his encouragement. We also thank Mr. Takeshi Yamada for his valuable comments about "selection" and the other laboratory members for their useful discussions.

REFERENCES

[1] Gray R. M., "Vector quantization", *IEEE ASSP Magazine*, vol. 1, pp. 4–29, 1984.

[2] Linde Y., Buzo A., and Gray R. M., "An algorithm for vector quantizer design", *IEEE Trans. Communications*, vol. 28, 1980.

[3] Grossberg S., "Adaptive pattern classification and universal recoding.I: Parallel development and coding of neural feature detectors", *Biological Cybernetics*, vol. 23, pp. 121–134, 1976.

[4] Kohonen T., "Self-organization and associative memory", New York: Springer-Verlag, 1984.

[5] Rumelhart D. E. and Zipser D., "Feature discovery by competitive learning", Cambridge, MA: Bradford Books, 1986.

[6] Nasrabadi N. M. and Feng Y., "Vector quantization of images based upon the Kohonen self-organizing maps", in proc. *IEEE ICNN88*, pp. I:101–108, 1988.

[7] Hecht-Nielsen R., "Applications of counterpropagation networks", *Neural Networks*, vol. 1, pp. 131–141, 1988.

[8] DeSieno D., "Adding a conscience to competitive learning", in proc. *IEEE ICNN88*, pp. III:51-III:57, 1988.

[9] Ahalt S. C., Krishnamurthy A. K., Chen P., and Melton D. E., "Competitive learning algorithms for vector quantization", *Neural Networks*, vol. 3, pp. 277–290, 1990.

[10] Gersho A., "Asymptotically optimal block quantization", *IEEE Trans. Inform. Theory*, vol. 25, pp. 373–380, 1979.

[11] Goldberg D. E., "Genetic algorithms in search, optimization, and machine learning", MA: Addison Wesley, chap. 3, 1989.

[12] Max J., "Quantizing for minimum distortion", *IRE Trans. Inform. Theory*, vol. 6, pp. 7–12, 1960.

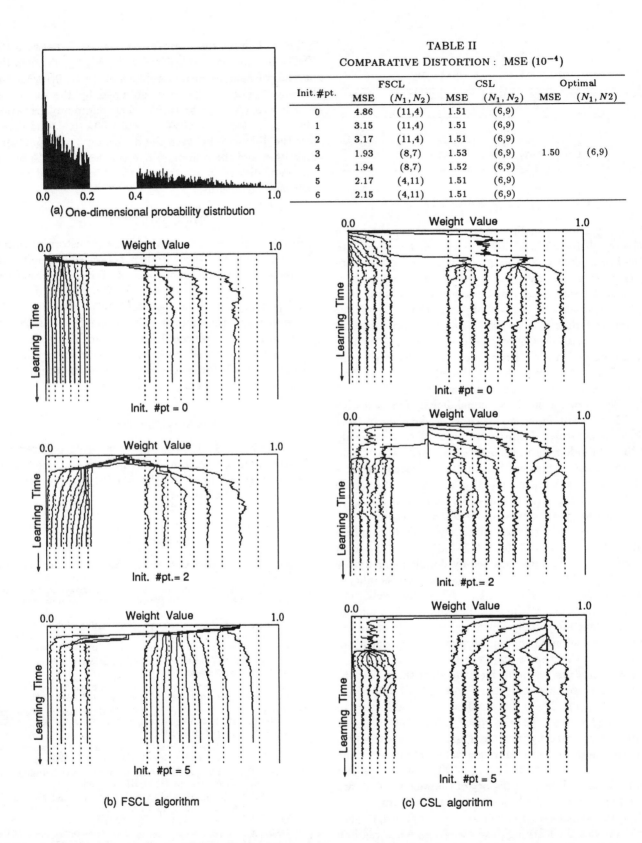

TABLE II
COMPARATIVE DISTORTION : MSE (10^{-4})

Init.#pt.	FSCL		CSL		Optimal	
	MSE	(N_1, N_2)	MSE	(N_1, N_2)	MSE	$(N_1, N2)$
0	4.86	(11,4)	1.51	(6,9)		
1	3.15	(11,4)	1.51	(6,9)		
2	3.17	(11,4)	1.51	(6,9)		
3	1.93	(8,7)	1.53	(6,9)	1.50	(6,9)
4	1.94	(8,7)	1.52	(6,9)		
5	2.17	(4,11)	1.51	(6,9)		
6	2.15	(4,11)	1.51	(6,9)		

(a) One-dimensional probability distribution

(b) FSCL algorithm

(c) CSL algorithm

Fig. 3. Comparison of the learning results on the different initializations. Dotted lines denote the optimal weight values obtained by Max's search method. (a) A one-dimensional probability distribution of a total 5000 training data. (b) Learning results by the FSCL algorithm. (c) Learning results by the proposed CSL algorithm.

1450

Bee-havior in a Mobile Robot:
The Construction of a Self-Organized Cognitive Map and its Use in Robot Navigation within a Complex, Natural Environment

Ashley Walker†, John Hallam†, David Willshaw‡
†Department of Artificial Intelligence, ‡Centre for Cognitive Science
†5 Forrest Hill , ‡2 Buccleuch Place
University of Edinburgh, Edinburgh †EH1 2QL ‡EH8 9LW, Scotland

Abstract--In this work, we model a mobile robotic control system on the spatial memory and navigatory behaviors attributed to foraging honey bees in an effort to exploit some of the robustness and efficiency these insects are known to enjoy. Our robot uses a self-organizing feature-mapping neural network to construct a topographically ordered map from ultra-sound range images collected while exploring the environment. This map is then annotated with metric positional information from a dead reckoning system. The resulting cognitive map can be used by the robot to localize in the world and to plan safe and efficient routes through the environment. This system has been thoroughly tested in simulation and is currently being implemented on the robot.

I. INTRODUCTION

A fundamental skill possessed by most animals is the ability to move around within their environments. Small insects, e.g., central place foraging honey bees (Apis mellifera), provide an excellent example of a robust navigational system which enables its user to travel along circuitous outbound journeys (e.g., covering distances up to 10 000 meters round trip [1]) in search of food and to return home along highly efficient routes--which are determined primarily by internal mechanisms, rather than by external sensory cues (e.g., chemical gradients). Furthermore, these insects have short range navigational abilities that allow them to pinpoint the small opening to their hive and to orient precisely toward the food bearing portion of a flower. Purposeful motion of this sort requires that the traveling agent have a system for representing spatial information which is integrated with its navigation, locomotive and motivational mechanisms [2].

The way in which insects (and "higher" animals) create, store, and use spatial memory is a subject of great interest and debate. In the particular case of the honey bee, nearly half a century of research has resulted in the development of coherent and structured models of this behavior. In the last two decades, it has been possible to use computer simulation to test the plausibility of these models and to compare different algorithms for achieving similar effects [3], [4], [5], [6]. In addition to increasing our understanding the operational principles involved in natural information processing, implementing models of animal behavior (in computer simulations and, moreover, in mobile robots) allows us to extract useful engineering knowledge which can be applied to the creation of more robust and efficient artificial systems designed to achieve similar functions.

This work has the latter goal in mind and addresses the task of (i) what sort of basic environmental spatial representation(s) may underlie robust, obstacle-free navigation and (ii) what sort of computational structure can provide an intelligent agent with a reliable and easily accessible memory for recording spatial information. In choosing spatial primitives, we do not employ a representation which requires formal recognition or reasoning about landmarks, obstacles and/or areas. Instead, we consider a simple, unprocessed representation of the patterns of environmental free space detected by the robot's sensors. As a spatial memory, we examine a distributed, decentralized neural network based structure which can easily be learnt by the robot using a self-organization process [7].

Our robotic map-building and navigation system was inspired by some elegant strategies utilized by foraging honey bees. These are modeled at a behavioral, rather than a neurophysiological, level of analysis. In the following subsections we provide an overview of these mechanisms.

A. Spatial Information utilized by Foraging Honey Bees
Honey bees navigate over long distances via dead reckoning (or path integration). The bee performs dead reckoning by monitoring the angles it steers (using an internal compass calibrated to the sun) and the distances it travels (using proprioceptive information) and then integrating this data into a vector pointing toward the hive. Due to the inaccuracies associated with dead reckoning, global localization--a visual image comparison process--is used to identify target locations once the bee has arrived in their vicinity [8]. Global localization requires that the bee record visual images, or "snapshots[1]" of important regions in its environment. As the bee approaches one of these sites, e.g., the hive, it recalls the relevant snapshots and compares them to its current retinal image in order to produce a set of motion vectors which will accurately align it with the entrance to the hive.

B. Spatial Memory mechanisms of Foraging Honey Bees
The way that these sensory inputs are organized in the honey bee's memory is not fully understood. Some researchers believe that snapshots are simply associated with the compass bearing along which the bee was traveling when the snapshots was taken. This implies snapshots may only be used serially to guide path specific navigation [8]. At the other

---

1 Snapshots are not completely unprocessed retinal images. Studies by [6] have shown that at least some amount of filtering is used to eliminate, for example, distant objects from snapshots used to give fine motion guidance near to a target.

extreme, it has been suggested that snapshots and the metric outputs of a dead reckoning process are combined within an internal cognitive map [9], [10]. In general, a cognitive map is an internal representation of the spatial relationships among observable points in an animal's environment which can be used to plan movements through that environment. In this scenario, goal locations have a map position which can be "looked up" and a route between the animal's current location and the goal location can be planned when some other internal motivational source encourages goal pursuit behavior.

In this work, we employ relevant features of the latter hypothesis--not in an effort to assess the validity of this invertebrate behavior theory--but because it yields insight into a more robust and efficient way to organize spatial information in a navigating robot. We suppose that bees may possess a cognitive map because it would endow the bee (and our robot) with the ability to (i) recover its positional information after displacement or a failure in the dead reckoning system, (ii) plan efficient, novel routes throughout the environment and (iii) make discriminating choices about routes based on known topography.

II SYSTEM DESIGN AND ARCHITECTURE

This research was conducted aboard a transputer based mobile robot called "Ben Hope." Earlier work [11] resulted in the creation of a parallel, distributed software control architecture (based upon that proposed by Brooks [12]) for the coordination of behaviors aboard the robot. Three basic behaviors exist to enable purposeful movement of the robot within its environment. The lowest layer of behavioral competence, WANDER, allows the robot to investigate the environment by pursuing motion in any (initially arbitrary) direction. Ben Hope is biased to seek out regions of free space in that if an AVOID module detects an obstacle(s) in the robot's direction of forward motion, an EXPLORE-FREE-SPACE behavior is triggered. The latter facilitates selection of the new direction of travel to be the one containing the most free space (as detected by acoustic range sensors).

A. Spatial Information utilized by Ben Hope

In implementing honey bee navigation mechanisms on this system, a DEAD-RECKONING module is created to monitor high resolution position encoders on the robot's wheels and to continually update a vector pointing towards its start-up position, or home. In order to facilitate global localization, Ben Hope is equipped with 12 ultra-sonic range sensors with a (combined) 360° field of view. Thus, the robot has an orientation independent view of the world, which allows it to recognize features therein regardless of its direction of travel.

Acoustic range data is chosen (instead of visual data) to underlie global localization in this real-time system due to the relative ease of interpretation of their returned signal. As with all sensors, sonar range data is subject to uncertainties which must be properly understood in order for the data to be used in a meaningful fashion. Due to specular reflection, a true range cannot be reliably obtained from these devices when measuring an acoustically smooth surface at an angle of incidence more than 1/2 of the beamwidth [13]. Two of the

most common ways to combat this sonar uncertainty include (i) engineering the environment so as to eliminate the problem (e.g., using acoustic retroreflectors as in [13]) or (ii) building a model of the uncertainty expected. The latter approach requires the robot to identify landmarks by matching their range signatures to stored templates [14]. Static model matching approaches require both a precise robot positioning system and a sophisticated matching algorithm to reason about uncertainty and error.

It is argued here (and elsewhere [15], [16]) that uncertainty may be dealt with more simply by relying on the dynamic, rather than the static, properties of these signals. Much uncertainty may be filtered out of a system which exploits the time averaged derivative of sensory signals--accumulated by an agent as it moves around in its world--in a way which forces larger changes in the sensor readings than those contributed by noise [15]. Mataric's [2] boundary tracing robot takes such a dynamic approach to sonar landmark detection by identifying semantic spatial primitives (e.g., "left-wall," "corridor," etc,) defined as combinations of its motion and sensory input averaged over time.

Our handling of sonar data intrinsically capitalizes on the dynamic character of the sensory information. We use an unsupervised neural network to extract the qualitative features of this data by statistically classifying sonar readings into general feature categories. Classifications are built up over training time and the final character of each feature category will represent an average of similar sonar images. This process enables the creation of a memory structure which, like the honey bee's spatial memory, supports a robust kind of pattern matching and does not require formal recognition of the contents of an image.

B. Spatial Memory mechanisms utilized by Ben Hope

In order to mimic the presupposed cognitive mapping capabilities of the honey bee, our robot must order the elements (or patterns) perceived in its environment into a topographically coherent and useful form. To this end, Ben Hope's MAP-BUILDING behavioral module utilizes a self-organizing feature-mapping (SOFM) neural network to map from external sensory space to an internal spatial representation. A modified version of Kohonen's Algorithm [17], [18] is used to perform the mapping because it seeks to produce an order reminiscent of the neurophysiology organization of the honey bee's memory, i.e., bees are thought to store their snapshots somewhere in the optic lobe or mushroom bodies--both of which contain topographical maps of the retina [19].

1. Organization of the Memory Map

The details of the mapping process are specified below.
- The cognitive map is represented in the robot's memory as a 2-dimensional output array of network nodes. Each individual node in this array contains a 12-dimensional weight vector (equivalent to the dimensionality of each sonar image) whose weight elements are randomly initialized. This corresponds to initially haphazard connections between the imaging surface and the map surface before learning.
- As prescribed by Kohonen [18], input vectors (i.e., 12-dimensional sonar readings) are presented to the network in a random order. In order to perform the mapping in real-time

(i.e., while the robot is exploring), initiation of the mapping procedure is delayed with respect to the commencement of exploration so as to allow a pool of sensory information to accumulate in memory from which to draw individual vector elements at random. Once this condition is met, mapping proceeds continuously for the duration of the exploration session.

• Kohonen's SOFM learning algorithm organizes this grid of map nodes into local neighborhoods which classify features in the input sensory data. The algorithm achieves this organization by determining which map node contains the weight vector most similar (in Euclidean distance) to a current input (i.e., the "winning node") and then selectively optimizing an area of the map surrounding that winning node such that it comes to represent an average of the training data for that class of feature

• We found it necessary to modify Kohonen's proposed weight update scheme by introducing inhibitory, as well as the standard excitatory, weight updating. In full, we enhance the weights of nodes within a rectangular optimization neighborhood surrounding the winning node and, at the same time, spread an equivalent amount of inhibition to nodes outside this region. Employing inhibition in this way serves to push the values of dissimilar weight vectors yet further away from the current input vector .

• This form of Hebbian learning is used to update weights by an amount proportional to the magnitude of the input. Kohonen decreases the proportionality term (i.e., the "learning rate") with training time to curtail learning. However, in this application, the learning rate remains constant so that the robot continues to learn about its environment for the duration of the exploration.

• Convergence of the map to a stable order is facilitated by decreasing the size of the optimization area (i.e., "neighborhood update zone") to the single node which is most excited upon stimulation by a particular input.

As training proceeds over several iterations, each map node learns to encode a particular pattern of free space visible from certain vantage points within the room. (See Figure 1.) Beginning from a grid of map nodes containing 12-dimensional randomly initialized weight vectors, an ordered map is created such that input vectors which are similar in 12-dimensional external sensory space are clustered to similar positions on the 2-dimensional internal array of map nodes.

2. Association of Position Metrics

In order for this map to underlie the sorts of useful navigatory behavior attributed to bees, metric information need be incorporated. The bee is thought to associate compass bearings [8], [10] with snapshots stored in memory. For our purposes, a more useful metric is positional information. The robot's dead reckoning system keeps a record of the (x,y) coordinate position from which each sonar sensor reading is taken. In the current implementation of the system, each of the unique acoustic image features classified by individual network nodes is associated with the coordinate position from which that feature can be seen within the natural environment. A Willshaw Net [20] is used to make these associations. Although the positions encoded by the system are specific coordinate values, the concept of a feature's associated

position is used loosely in this system. In actuality, each unique sonar feature is visible within a small area in the room which is, on average, 5% of the total room area.

This is an acceptable resolution for a sonar based navigation system operating in a cluttered laboratory environment. The topographically ordered map, with this metric annotation, need only facilitate navigation to a position within the sensing range of a goal location. An exact goal position can be reached by augmenting the robot with special purpose sensors (e.g., a simplified compound eye) and fine motion planning (e.g., based on visual information processing algorithms proposed for bees [3], [4]).

III. RESULTS

In this section, we examine the topographical order encoded within cognitive maps constructed as described in the previous section. Furthermore, the utility of this map to underlie obstacle-free navigation and efficient route planning is described. The results illustrated here were obtained from computer simulation using real data collected by the robot. Since the time of this writing, the MAP-BUILDING algorithm has been implemented on the robot's transputer control system and deployment of the NAVIGATION behavioral module will shortly follow.

A. The Cognitive Map Illustrated

In order to describe the character of the spatial memory map, we developed an original method for viewing the high dimensional weight vectors contained in each node of our completed cognitive map. In this representation, the 12x12 output array of cognitive map nodes is reduced to 36 node areas by averaging the contents of four adjacent nodes. The remaining 36 representative weight vectors are then thresholded such that individual weights above a thresholding parameter are turned ON--signifying a relatively long and unobstructed sonar view, or turned OFF--indicating that an obstacle was relatively close at hand. This new binary weight matrix representation is then examined, and, for each set of three bits (corresponding to a 90° field of view on the robot), the viewing area is deemed OPEN if two (or more) of the three bits were ON, otherwise it is labeled OBSTRUCTED. In Figure 1, a small circular robot symbol--with four viewing quadrants--is placed in each node area. A quadrant is shaded where visibility is OPEN and a blackened where the robot's encoded view is OBSTRUCTED. (For simplicity, no associated positional information is displayed.)

The cognitive map of Figure 1 is a guide to the types and locations of free space in Ben Hope's laboratory environment. The sonar readings vary smoothly across the map--which is evidence of the neighborhood preserving character of the mapping. The fidelity of the mapping can be further confirmed by examining the positions associated with each node. For example, it is the case that the cluster of totally obstructed views in the lower, left corner of the map are associated with coordinate positions which map to a highly cluttered area between two tables and a wall.[2]

---

[2] As a final confirmation, we employed Rank, or Nonparametric, Correlation to statistically determine whether nodes which are

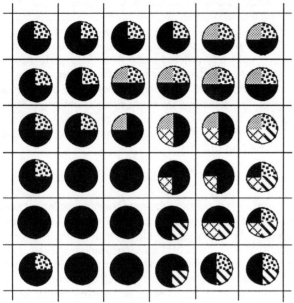

Figure 1: The Cognitive Map

The algorithm to produce these maps runs in real time. Exploration and mapping (in the laboratory environment tested) can be satisfactorily accomplished in approximately one hour. However, the quality of the map will, of course, increase with training time. Maps built up over a longer training period will be both more robust to the effects of sensor noise and will learn to ignore the positional changes of insignificant items (e.g., rubbish bins, empty boxes, etc.) and transient aspects of the environment (e.g., occasional students rushing through the laboratory). The latter will fade from memory because they receive no re-enforcement.

B. Map Based Route Planning:

Some model of the world (e.g., a map) is required by all agents who wish to navigate toward locations which cannot be sensed from their current position. Gould [9] and Gallistel [10] believe bees use a cognitive map to localize their position in the world and then may employ vector addition to perform route planning. This method of path finding seems to be very efficient navigation strategy for any animal whose physiology and environmental topography make obstacle avoidance along "bee-line" paths between targets possible. In the cluttered environment of our relatively large and less maneuverable robot, there are certain configurations of obstacles and objects which prevent straight line travel between two points. Noting this discrepancy between the artificial and

---

close together on the map do indeed correspond to world places that are close--*i.e.*, acoustically and geographically similar. Kendall's rank correlation coefficient yields a value, τ, between -1 (data is anti- correlated-- e.g., close map places are associated with widely separated world distances) and 1 (data is positively associated). In our cognitive map, the degree of correlation between map distances and high dimensional world distances is positive, $\tau=0.352$, and differs quite significantly (d=30.4) from the null hypothesis of $\tau=0$, or no correlation.

natural systems, we decided to pursue navigation along two parallel lines of research. The first aligns itself with the biological approach of performing relatively simple path planning (e.g., simple vector addition constrained by known topography) and using rather more enroute sensing to avoid obstacles. This method could not be simulated and therefore will not be considered further in this paper. The second approach is motivated by engineering concerns, and seeks to exploit the rich source of information about unobstructed world paths that the robot discovered in the exploration and mapping phase of learning. This information is incorporated into the cognitive map.

To this end, we employ a graphical representation of location connectivity relations discovered during exploration. Between all pairs of nodes in the map, an edge is defined if, during exploration, the robot discovered that these nodes encode the sonar features of adjacent world places. Since each node has an associated world position, the cost associated with each of these edges is simply the difference between the two coordinate points in the world. In the current implementation, we use an A* search algorithm to find the shortest path between the current node and the goal node. Such a path will necessarily be globally obstacle-free because it consists of path segments that were traveled during training.

It is safe to assume that local obstacle avoidance will be required to correct for the uncertainty in the positioning system and for the small scale drift of moveable objects (e.g., chairs). By tracking its corresponding map position as it moves through the world, the robot can use patterns of free space encoded in the map to make intelligent decisions about low cost local detours.

Figures 2 and 3 show two routes (embolded) planned by our navigation simulator. The faint projections emanating from the start node illustrate paths considered but eventually rejected as their cost built up. The coordinates of the room and all of the large-scale objects in the room were overlaid on the paths generated. (Objects depicted include: ▦ tables, ▦ shelves, ▦ desks, ▦ other.)

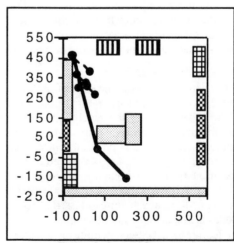

Figure 2: Sample Route 1

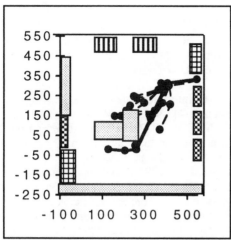

Figure 3: Sample Route 2

In the robot, the NAVIGATION module begins route planning by correlating the robot's current position with its encoded map position using an excitation based matching process. This involves comparing new sonar information with that stored in the map and computing an index of stimulation for each node. Nodes that respond most strongly encode sonar features that are most similar to those at the currently sensed world position. The robot localizes by selecting the single node which is most excited over several readings. (As each node encodes positional information, global localization may be used to re-calibrate the dead reckoning system using this procedure.) Once a correlation is made, the active node can spread expectation to nodes which encode neighboring world features and thereby decrease the pool of possible matches in subsequent localizations [2].

IV. DISCUSSION

These results suggest that a cognitive map created through self-organization can underlie robust and efficient navigation in a mobile robotic system employing dead reckoning and global localization. This map utilizes local sensory information to create a qualitative representation of the permanent features in the environment. The ability of this map to robustly and reliably encode spatial information lies in the qualitative nature of the representation. The map making algorithm does not depend on the accuracy of the sonar sensors or on precise positioning of the robot. Instead, sensor uncertainty is filtered through dynamic averaging. Similarly, small scale and transient environmental features are filtered from the final representation.

Formal recognition of objects and areas is not required by this system. Our review of honey bee information processing revealed that a lower level "primitive" such as patterns of free-space (or, alternatively, patterns of obstacle constellations) projected on a retina (or detected through a sonar ranging device) is a more simple and robust representation of spatial information.

Finally, by employing an unsupervised neural network to organize sensory information, we enable our robot to process only those aspects of the world that are relevant to it. In this way, we have constructed a theoretical tool which, as recom-

mended by Brooks [15], uses aspects that the creature is sensing as the primary formal notion.

V. FUTURE DIRECTIONS

The first step in the future development of this system is the implementation of a NAVIGATION module in the robot's transputer control architecture. We can then better assess the limitations of the navigation system described and compare it to the more biologically plausible method of weak planning and strong sensing. It has also been suggested [Harry Barrow, personal communication] that connectionist path finding strategies be investigated at this stage.

Furthermore, once the robot begins navigating, we may need to redefine our notion of localization. At present, the robot correlates its current world location with its map equivalent by comparing a series of images taken from that vantage point with the image features encoded in the map in order to calculate a single representative node. It may be the case that a more distributed approach will prove to be more robust. Such a scheme would employ some measure of the excitation across the entire map to localize. This may resemble the way that the hippocampus of a rat encodes places via a pattern of firing across many distinct CA neurons.

One of the most important differences between a biologically inspired system such as this and a real biological system is that the latter learns constantly. Our robotic system would be more robust if it continued to learn during navigation, or could be triggered to learn when its sensory readings perceived that the world had changed significantly since the last mapping session. Another element which could add to the biological plausibility and autonomousity of the system would be to add, to the control architecture, a motivational system which could encourage goal pursuit behavior.

When motivations are included, the robot should seek out meaningful places (e.g., a battery recharging outlet). Our objective thus far has been to design a coarse scale learning algorithm which allows the robot to create a robust spatial representation of its environment and then to perform map based navigation to within the sensing range of the goal location. In order to reach these more exact goal locations, we plan to employ a compound eye sensor which can perform pattern matching tasks more faithful to those that have been proposed for the honey bee.

ACKNOWLEDGMENT

We would like to thank Hugh Cameron, Sandy Colquhoun, Peter Forster, Douglas Howie and Martin Hughes for technical assistance and Beau Lotto for reviewing this manuscript.

REFERENCES

[1] Visscher, P.K., and T.D. Seeley. 1982. "Foraging strategy of honeybee colonies in a temperate deciduous forest". Ecology. 63 : 1790-1801.
[2] Mataric, M. J. 1991. "Navigating with a rat brain: a neurobiologically-inspired model for spatial representation".

International Conference on the Simulation of Adaptive Behaviour: from Animals to Animats. 169-175.

[3] Anderson, A. M. 1977. "A model for landmark learning in the honey-bee". Journal of Comparative Physiology. 114 : 335-355.

[4] Cartwright, B.A., and T.S. Collett. 1983. "Landmark learning in bees". Journal of Comparative Physiology. 151 : 521-543.

[5] Cartwright, B. A., and T. S. Collett. 1987. "Landmark maps for honey bees". Biological Cybernetics. 57 : 85-93.

[6] Cheng, K., T.S. Collett, A. Pickhard, and R. Wehner. 1987. "The use of visual landmarks by honeybees: bees weight landmarks according to their distance from the goal". Journal of Comparative Physiology. 161 : 469-475.

[7] Walker, V. A.. 1991. "Bee-haviour in a mobile robot". Unpublished M.Sc. Thesis, University of Edinburgh, Department of Artificial Intelligence.

[8] Wehner, R., and R. Menzel. 1990. "Do insects have cognitive maps?". Annual Review of Neuroscience. 13 : 403-414.

[9] Gould, J. L. 1986. "The locale map of honey bees: do insects have cognitive maps?". Science. 232 (16 May 1986) : 861-863.

[10] Gallistel, R.C. 1990. "The cognitive map". In The Organization of Learning. 102-172. Cambridge, MA: MIT Press.

[11] Forster, P. 1991. "A transputer-based autonomous mobile robot". Technical Paper #6, University of Edinburgh, Department of Artificial Intelligence.

[12] Brooks, R.A. 1986. "A robust layered control system for a mobile robot". IEEE Journal of Robotics and Automation. RA-2 (April) : 14-23.

[13] Steer, B. and T. Atherton. 1990. "Design for navigation". IEEE International Conference on Robotics and Automation. : 942-947.

[14] Kuipers, B. 1987. "A qualitative approach to robot exploration and map learning". AAAI Workshop on Spatial Reasoning and Multisensor Fusion.

[15] Brooks, R. A. 1991. "Challenges for complete creature architecture". International Conference on the Simulation of Adaptive Behaviour: from Animals to Animats. : 434-443.

[16] Malcolm, C., T. Smithers, and J. Hallam. 1989. "An emerging paradigm in robotic architecture". Invited paper at the Intelligent Autonomous Systems Conference.

[17] Willshaw, D.J., and C. von der Malsburg. 1976. "How patterned neural connections can be set up by self-organization". Proceedings of the Royal Society of London B. 194 : 431-445.

[18] Kohonen, T. 1988. "Self-Organization and Associative Memory". Springer, Berlin.

[19] Mobbs, P.G. 1982. "The brain of the honeybee Apis mellifera. I. The connections and spatial organization of the mushroom bodies". Philosophical Transactions of the Royal Society of London B. 198 : 309-354.

[20] Willshaw, D. J., O. P. Buneman, and H. C. Longuet-Higgins. 1969. "Non-holographic associative memory". Nature. 222 : 960-962.

Self-Architecture
Theory and Experiment of Biological Neural Networks*

Harold Szu, ^Jung Kim, and +Insook Kim,
Naval Surface Warfare Center, Code R44, Silver Spring MD 20903

^Center for Advanced Computer Studies, and +Department. of Biology
Univ. of SW Louisiana, Lafayette, LA 70504

ABSTRACT

Live neuron behavior on an electronic chip was recorded with a time-lapsed video under the microscope. By an image processing technique, we discovered the smallest size of intelligent biological neural networks (BNN). The dissociated chick embryonic brain neurons were experimentally placed on silicon glass plates deposited with metal oxide strips about 10 μm width for possible electronegativity neurite guidance. The neurite growth connecting other neurons was accomplished intentionally through selective paring in time rather than mechanically following the external electronegativity guidance.

We have theoretically mapped to artificial neural networks (ANN) to determine whether the connectivity patterns dictate the information processing efficiency, or vice versa. A dynamic interconnection model is based on the energy landscape $\mathbf{E}(v_i, W_{ij})$, which is a function of both the individual neuron output firing rates v_i and the pair synaptic weights W_{ij} of which a linear Hebbian rule becomes a special case, and general convergence theorem is proven. Consequently, a nonlinear backprop-like learning rule associated with slopes of the singlet sigmoidal function and the pair-correlation function is derived.

Keywords: Self-Architecture, Neurite Growth, Morphology, VLSI, Chip

*Supported NSWCDD Independent Research and Board of regents of Louisiana of Grant LEQSF-RD-A-28, and NSF Grant NSF-ADP-04

1. Biological Neural Network (BNN) Formations

The computational properties of BNN can be observed by in vitro systems that consist of the bottom up: electronic chips, the top-down: time-lapsed Video microscopic, and the middle: neurochemical control of synaptic growth (namely phosphoproteins: Synapsin IIb discovered by Han & Greengard in 1991 which promised to unlock the secret of memory). This paper describes how in real time dissociated chick embryonic brain neurons form live BNN on a silica glass plate revealing an intelligent behavior despite the external metal oxide guidance. A minimally intelligent BNN, called Peter-Paul-Mary, has been discovered with time-frozen frame analysis[Szu92].

The paper is organized as follows. A brief review of international research groups is given in Sect.1. Then, a time analysis of live dynamics follows in Sect.2, discussion about mathematical models in Sect.3, and further research perspectives in Sect.4.

Extracellular matrices have been known to guide the growth direction of nerve fibers. Kleinfeld et. al. have reported the hydrophilic guidance of live neural nets on pattern chip substrates [Klei88]. Gross has patterned live neural nets over weeks by trimming the dense interconnections with laser surgery [Gros91]. Kawana et. al.[Kawa90] have successfully applied the electronegativity of the metal (in the metal oxide pattern deposited on a silica glass) to guide live neurons into definite interconnection patterns. Neurons were then placed on substrates which had metal oxide patterns about 10 μm size. Metal oxide patterns were made by standard optical lithography with lift-off.

2. Time Analysis Dynamics

In the video imaging experiment [Szu92], three dissociated chick brain neurons were seeded on metal oxides on silicon glass plate At time t = 0:00, then the neuron connection patterns was video-recorded under the microscope at a fixed delay, say every 10 or 15 min. The play back rate is compressed at 30 video frames per second. Such a time-lapsed video-microscope-chip technique is proved to be powerful to analyze live neuron dynamics.

Step 1) Figure 1.A shows the culturing process at time t = 3:40. One neuron (named Peter denoted as a) of three dissociated neurons has been producing neurite outgrowth towards another neuron (named Paul denoted as b) located about twenty body lengths away below its own metal oxides strip about ten mm width.

Step 2) At time t = 6:49 (Figure 1.B), the neurite of Peter which has been growing along the axial direction of the metal oxides strip, starts crossing the non-metal oxides strip towards Paul's direction, instead of following the guided axial direction of the metal oxides strip.

Step 3) At time t = 8:10 (Figure 1.C), the neurite of Peter has just crossed the non-metal oxides strip.

Step 4) At time t = 8:22 (Figure 1.D), Peter-to-Paul contact has been made.

Step 5) At time t = 9:02 (Figure 1.E), the neurite of Mary has crossed the non-metal oxides strip. Interestingly, the initial neurite of Mary is not following the metal oxides strip.

Step 6) At time t = 9:46 (Figure 1.F), the neurite of Mary has been growing along the axial direction of the metal oxides strip.

Step 7) At time t = 11:38 (Figure 1.G), Paul started to produce its neurite outgrowth towards Mary. It took 3:16 time for Paul to initiate its neurite outgrowth, after the contact from Peter.

Step 8) At time t = 12:57 (Figure 1.H), Paul began the growing of neurites along the existed interconnection pathway built early by Peter-to-Paul and moving quickly toward Mary rather to Peter.

This preference becomes self-evident at later video frames. It is further supported by the detailed time analysis of the neurite outgrowth rate as shown in the sum up [Szu92], where Mary growth time from t = 11:38 to t = 14:03 is reduced about in half compared to that from t = 8:22 to t = 11:38,.

Step 9) At time t = 14:03 (Figure 1.I), the Paul-to-Mary interconnection is intentionally made because Paul has deliberately bypassed Peter and contacted Mary behind him.

Step 10) At time t = 14:42 (Figure 1.J), the neurite growth of Mary is almost stopped in the previous direction, and Mary starts to produce another neurite in the new direction (see the arrow in Figure 1.J).

Step 11) At time t = 22:10, Figure 1.K shows that the new nuerite of Mary grows very slowly while the old neurite of Mary is retracting.

Step 12) At time t = 23:50 (Figure 1.L), Mary is getting separated from Peter, while the old neurite of Mary is more retracted (see the arrow in Figure 1.L).

3. Theory of Self-Architectures

The minimal intelligence is the ability of comparisons and decision making ranging from the small perturbation of Hebbian learning to the drastic change of nonlinear dynamics of interconnections[Szu90]. We begins with the video observation that the smallest sizes of BNN that has exhibited a <u>self-architecture</u> are those associated with three live neurons [Szu92]. A single neuron alone has no choice in the connectivity pattern except to itself. Two neurons have only two choices, connected or not. Among three neurons, they can collectively have any one out of six possible interconnections as demonstrated in the above video frames.

Dynamic Interconnection Convergence Theorem.

From the BNN viewpoint, the probablity of ith neuron neurite outgrowth reaching at jth neuron (from Peter to Paul) defines the axonic pair correlation function T_{ij} which obviously requires a different notation than the dendritic synaptic junction weight W_{ij} before the formation of synapse. Given that distinction, we have generalized the linear Hebbian synaptic learning rule to the nonlinear dynamics learning rule as described below.

Convergence Theorem

Let the network energy $E(v_i, W_{ij})$ be both the output firing rates v_i and the synapatic weights W_{ij}. Then, without Hebbian rule, a local minimum of an N neurons architecture is given at

$$dE(v_i, W_{ij})/dt \leq \quad 0, \tag{1}$$

provided the condition that both the singlet sigmoidal function σ_1 and the synapse formation pair correlation function σ_2 are defined to have non-negative logic slopes as follows;

$$v_i = \sigma_1(u_i) = (1 + \exp(-u_i))^{-1}; \qquad \sigma'_1 = (dv_i/du_i) \approx G(u_i - \theta_i) \geq 0, \tag{2}$$

$$W_{ij} = \sigma_2(T_{ij}) \approx step(T_{ij} - \theta_{ij})/(1-\theta_{ij}); \sigma'_2 = (dW_{ij}/dT_{ij}) \approx \delta(T_{ij} - \theta_{ij})/(1-\theta_{ij}) \geq 0, \tag{3}$$

Although it is not necessary, but convenient to assume that all N neurons are initially connected together, and u_i is the net input (above the threshold value θ_i) collected initially from all N neuron outputs v_j passing through the synaptic weights W_{ij} which are subsequently pruned.

$$u_i = \sum_{j=1}^{N} W_{ij} v_j - \theta_i, \tag{4}$$

Furthermore, condition (ii) is the local energy descents:

Input firing rate dynamics: $\quad \partial u_i/\partial t \approx -\partial E/\partial v_i \tag{5},$

Output Axon dynamics: $\quad \partial T_{ij}/\partial t \approx -\partial E/\partial W_{ij} \tag{6},$

The mathematical proof is based on the universal truth of real positive quadratic expression obtained by chain rule of differentiations and substitution of gradient descents Eqs(5,6) as follows:

$$dE(v_i, W_{ij})/dt = \sum_{i=1}^{N} (\partial E/\partial v_i)(\partial v_i/\partial t) \quad + \sum_{i,j=1}^{N} (\partial E/\partial W_{ij})(\partial W_{ij}/\partial t)$$

$$= \sum_{i=1}^{N} (\partial E/\partial v_i)(\partial v_i/\partial u_i)(\partial u_i/\partial t) \quad + \sum_{i,j=1}^{N} (\partial E/\partial W_{ij})(\partial W_{ij}/\partial T_{ij})(\partial T_{ij}/\partial t)$$

$$\approx -\sum_{i=1}^{N} \sigma'_1 (\partial E/\partial v_i)^2 \quad - \sum_{i,j=1}^{N} \sigma'_2 (\partial E/\partial W_{ij})^2$$

$$\leq 0 \tag{7}$$

where the primes denote the nonnegative slopes of singlet and pair correlation functions Eqs(2,3). Thus, by definition of nonnegative logic Eqs(2,3) the energy landscape is always monotonously convergent for every quadratic term independent of the energy slope value and the size N. This independence is important as the network size changes through a dynamic interconnect.

The sigmoidal slope σ'_1 is known to be a radial base function or Gaussian-like window cnetered around θ_i. Since the pair correlation function T_{ij} has been approximately modeled as a "use-or-loss" probability function (properly normalized between 0 and 1). $\sigma_2(T_{ij})$ is a step function above the frequency threshold θ_{ij}.whose value can be statistically estimated about how often an existed pair of connection is ultilized from ith neuron to jth neuron when compared with other pairs. Note that the approximate Kronecker/Dirac delta function $\delta(T_{ij} - \theta_{ij})$ has a normalization constant appears in the denominator $(1-\theta_{ij})$ which could make the second window function σ'_2 a factor 10 bigger than the first Gaussian-like window if $\theta_{ij} = 0.9$ for an infrequently used pair of interconnect.

Now, we derive the synaptic weight chnage in a backprop-like algorithm as follows:

$$\Delta W_{ij} = (\partial W_{ij}/\partial t)\Delta t = (\partial W_{ij}/\partial T_{ij})(\partial T_{ij}/\partial t)\Delta t = -(\partial W_{ij}/\partial T_{ij})(\partial E/\partial W_{ij})\Delta t$$

$$= -(\partial W_{ij}/\partial T_{ij})(\partial E/\partial v_i)(dv_i/du_i)(\partial u_i/\partial W_{ij})\Delta t . \tag{8}$$

Substituting these results into Eq(8), one finds that the linear Hebbian learning rule

$$\Delta W_{ij} \approx v_i v_j$$

is a special case modified by means of both Gaussian and weighted Dirac windows:

$$\Delta W_{ij} = - G(u_i)(\partial E/\partial v_i)v_j \, \delta(T_{ij} - |\theta_{ij}|)/(1-|\theta_{ij}|)\Delta t \qquad (9)$$

Without the synaptic pruning window σ'_2 of Eq(3), the learnig rule Eq(8) is the traditional delta rule, which takes a long computational time to find itself within the Gaussian window of opportunity for a small weight change. Furthermore, the change is rarely large enough to nullify the interconnection weight in order to prune a specific interconnection weight. Thus, one expects that the modified delta formula, that has divided the backprop delta rule by a samll number $(1-|\theta_{ij}|)$ ≤ 1 and controlled by the second window, becomes efficient. The pair correlation probability function is also self-updated by

$$\Delta T_{ij} = (\partial T_{ij}/\partial t)\,\Delta t \quad = -(\partial E/\partial W_{ij})\Delta t$$
$$= -(\partial E/\partial v_i)(dv_i/du_i)(\partial u_i/\partial W_{ij})\Delta t = -G(u_i)(\partial E/\partial v_i)v_j\,\Delta t \qquad (10)$$

In a feedforward layer architecture, if a quadratic cost energy is chosen $\mathbf{E} = (d_i - v_i)^2/2$ is chosen for the supervised training in terms of the actual output v_i departed from the desired output d_i, then

$$(\partial \mathbf{E}/\partial v_i) = (v_i - d_i); \qquad i = 1,2,3, \text{ output layer neurons} \qquad (11)$$

$$(\partial \mathbf{E}/\partial v_i) = -\partial u_i/\partial t; \qquad i = 1,2,3, \text{ all other neurons} \qquad (12)$$

Eq(12) can be further feedbacked via the net input change Δu_i of Eq(4) and synaptic change ΔW_{ij} of Eq(9). Thus, the set of Eqs(8,12) may be useful for the self-organization in an architecture.

4. Conclusions

In this report, the synergism between electronics and neurosciences has been demonstrated. Much more work is needed. One shall investigate functional-specific neurons, such as those associated with hearing, seeing, sensing, moving, controlling, communicating, etc. and to observe the connectivity patterns on chips with real time measurements. As an interesting by-product of the architectural taxonomy study, one can quantitatively measure the single neuron sigmoidal function, that was done early by McCullouch and Pitts almost five decades ago, statistically in parallel via the chip technology. One can also generalize the Hebbian synaptic strength learning rule for new born networks by parallel and direct measurements of singlet and pair correlation function. These functions might reveal the major learning rule through the morphology change theorem, as opposed to the minor learning via linear Hebbian rule upon a fixed architecture.

We believe that the trend of modern neural network study will be centered around the learning with dynamic interconnections, which is capable of self-adapting from one architecture to another to accommodate both the hardware fault tolerance and the necessary software inference.

References

[Gros91]   Gross, G.W. & Kowalski, J.M. 1991 Experimental and Theoretical Analysis of Random Nerve Cell Network Dynamics, Neural Networks: Concepts, Applications, and Implementations, Prentice Hall

[Han91]   Han, H, Nichols, R.A, Rubin, M.R, Bahler,M, Greengard, P.1991.Induction of formation of presynaptic terminals in neuroblastoma cells by synapsin IIb, Nature 349:697-700.

[Kawa90]   Torimitsu, K. and Kawana A. 1990. Selective Growth of Sensory Nerve Fibers on Metal Oxide Pattern in Culture,Devel. Brain. Res. 51:128-131.

[Klei88]   Kleinfeld, D., Kahler, K.H., and Hockberger, P.E. 1988. Controlled Outgrowth of Dissociated Neurons on Patterned Substrates, J. Neuros. 8:4098-4120.

[Szu90]   Szu, H.H. 1990. Neural Networks Based on Peano Curves and Hairy Neurons, Telematics and Informatics, 7: 403-430, Pergamon Press.

[Szu92]   Szu, H.H.,Kim, J., Kim, I. 1992. Live Neural Network Formations on Electronic Chips, IJCNN-92 Beijing; Also appear INNS Appalanchian Conf.Radford VA

[Tana91]   Tanaka, E.M. and Kirschner, M. 1991. Microtubule Behavior in the Growth ones of Living Neurons During Axon Elongation, Jour. Cell Biol. 115:345-363.

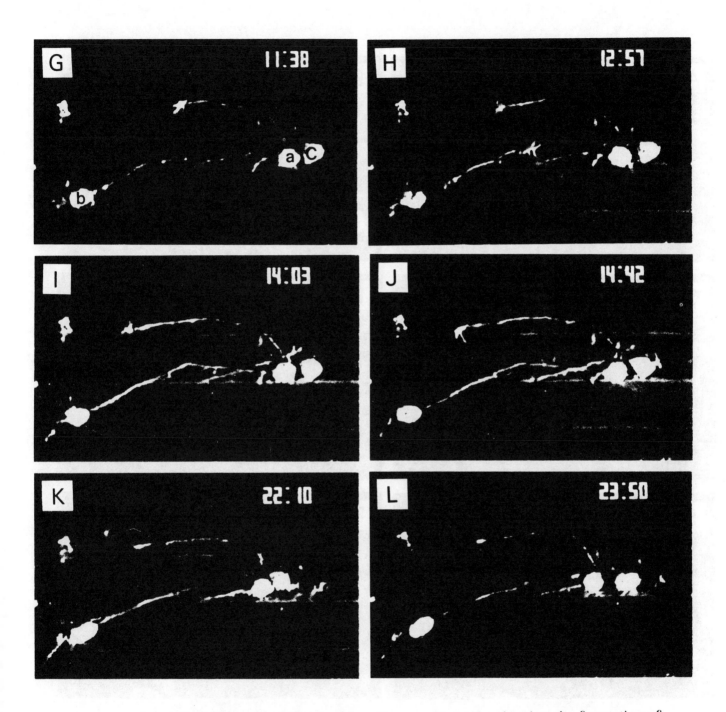

Figure 1.(Continued) Snapshot pictures taken from a video tape showing the formation of live neural networks from 3 dissociated chick embryonic neurons cultured on a VLSI chip. (Neuron a is named as Peter; Neuron b is named as Paul; Neuron c is named as Mary.)

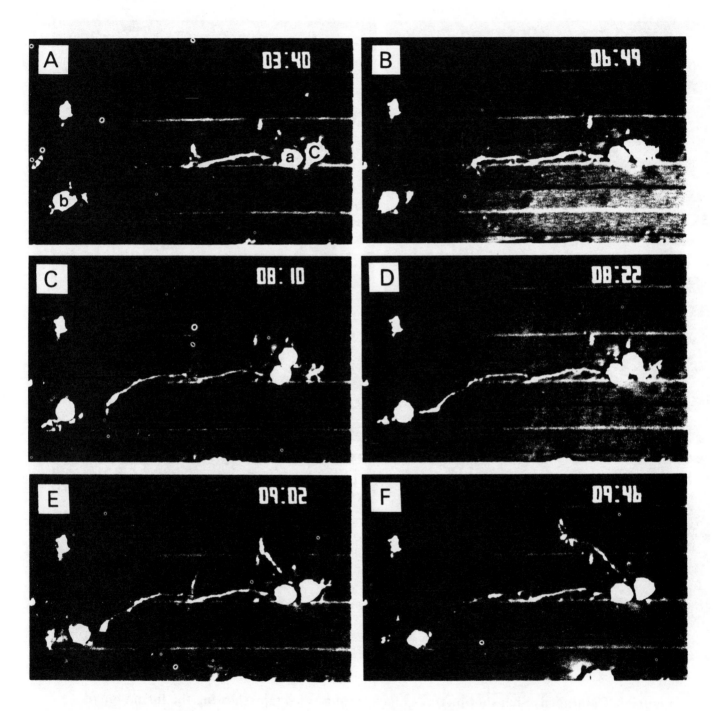

Figure 1. Snapshot pictures taken from a video tape showing the formation of live neural networks from 3 dissociated chick embryonic neurons cultured on a VLSI chip.
(Neuron a is named as Peter; Neuron b is named as Paul; Neuron c is named as Mary.)

Self Architecture--Theory and Experiment of Biological Neural Networks

Harold Szu[1], Jung Kim[2], and Insook Kim[3],

[1]Naval Surface Warfare Center Dahlgren Division, Code R44, Silver Spring MD 20903

[2]Ctr. Advanced Computer Studies, [3]Dept. of Biology, U. of SW Louisiana, Lafayette, LA 70504

Paper Code: NNWEP2OR-2-2

Abstract of the paper:

How to go beyond the classical Artificial Neural Networks (ANN) having endowed with a limited intelligence is addressed both theoretically and experimentally in this paper. Classical ANN are defined to have a fixed architecture (one layer, two layers, three layers, recurrent, etc.) and a small perturbation learning rule (Hebbian like bilinear product rule) among massively concurrent point processors of one internal degree of freedom (McCulloch-Pitts neuron models). A data-driven self architecture is mapped to a dynamic ANN with self organization in its architecture, in order to determine whether the connectivity patterns dictate the information processing efficiency, namely the functionality of the architectures versus the specificity of the architectures. Thus, lacking of fundamental theory, we turn to the inspiration of Biological Neural Networks (BNN). Live neuron behavior on an electronic chip was recorded with a time-lapsed video under the microscope. By an image processing technique, we have discovered the smallest size of intelligent biological neural networks (BNN) from Kawana's data. The dissociated chick embryonic brain neurons were experimentally placed on silicon glass plates deposited with metal oxide strips about 10 μm width for possible electronegativity neurite guidance. The neurite growth connecting other neurons was accomplished intentionally through selective paring in time rather than mechanically following the external electronegativity guidance. A dynamic interconnection model is based on a top-down energy landscape $\mathbf{E}(v_i, W_{ij})$, which is subsequently modifiable by input data, because it is a function of both the individual neuron output firing rates vi and a new pair correlation function of the synaptic weights Wij of which a linearized Hebbian rule: $W_{ij} = v_i v_j$ becomes a special case.

Given the standard M-P neuron model, the net input is $u_i = \sum_{j=1} W_{ij} v_j - \theta_i$, and the output is the sigmoidal function $v_i = \sigma_1(u_i)$. The pair-correlation function is approximated by a biologically plausible use-it-or-lose-it step function probability $W_{ij} = \sigma_2(T_{ij}) \approx \text{step}(T_{ij} - \theta_{ij})/(1 - \theta_{ij})$ normalized in terms of an adjustable average communication frequency θ_{ij}. Furthermore, the input dynamics: $\partial u_i / \partial t \approx - \partial E / \partial v_i$, and the output axon dynamics: $\partial T_{ij} / \partial t \approx - \partial E / \partial W_{ij}$. A general convergence theorem of self architect is proven for $dE/dt \leq 0$. Consequently, a nonlinear backward error propagation learning rule is derived which is associated with slopes of both the singlet sigmoidal function $v_i = \sigma_1(u_i)$ and the pair $W_{ij} = \sigma_2(T_{ij})$ for the first time. Simulation results seem so far to be inconclusive, indicating, for Minsky's example, different architectures, executed the exclusive or operation, could correspond to different local minimum energy landscapes. We hope to present that giving a cramped input and output mapping and an arbitrary connectivity pattern, the nonlinear Habbian dynamics can gradually switched on and off because theoretically it seems to be possible to add on wires on those red hot spots of traffic jams, and switch off some of those less useful interconnects. Preliminary efforts will be given.

Keywords: Nonlinear Hebbian, Dynamic Organization, Self Architecture, Neurite Growth, Morphology, VLSI, Chip, Data Driven Architecture, Backprop, Convergence Theorem

Adaptive Predictive Control of Nonlinear Time-Varying Systems using Neural Network

Yasundo Takahashi

Professor Emeritus of the University of California
Senior Technical Consultant, Mikuni Berkeley R&D Corp.

Abstract --- This paper presents predictive control of nonlinear dynamical systems in which the prediction is made using feedforward neural network as a plant model. Unlike control laws like LQ and pole-placement in modern control theory, the basic form of optimal predictive control is not tied with linear system's parameters, hence a viable candidate for control of nonlinear objects. The control is based on a minimization of the sum of predicted squarred errors over a prescribed range of prediction. A neural network, trained by back propagation to mimic the behavior of a plant, is used to compute the squarred error cost function for various candidates of controlling inputs. An optimal controlling input, by which the cost function will be minimized, is then numerically selected by, for instance, the Simplex method According to simulation tests on various nonlinear plants, the neural network adapts to time-varying plant dynamics as well as load upsets if the learning process is kept active through the control operation.

1. INTRODUCTION

Application of neural network(NN) for control of nonlinear dynamical systems has been attracting increasing interest in the recent years[4],[7]. While current linear control theory depends highly on mathematical systems theory, the techniques of NN is mostly experimental with emphasis on computer simulation. In Neuro-Control one intends to combine the two and challenge the field of nonlinear systems. The paper presents a predictive control in which NN is used, without theoretical rigor, as a highly adaptive model of nonlinear time-varying dynamical plant for response prediction.

H.Ziebolz's Two-Time Scale System was a predecessor of the predictive control. He and H.M.Paynter proposed in 1953 [1] to use Philbrick analog computer for prediction as a guide for making control decisions. The theory of optimal predictive control was consolidated by D.W.Clarke, C.Mohtadi and P.S Tuffs and joined the family of linear optimal control in 1987 [2]. They expressed the control law in terms of linear system's parameters for minimization of predicted quadratic cost function.

The same basic concept is applied on nonlinear plants in the following, computing predicted quadratic error using NN, and conducting minimization process numerically. According to the author's simulation studies, the NN for prediction is highly adaptive to plant parameter changes and disturbances. The adaptability of NN to plant responses is demonstrated on a first order linear discrete-time plant in the next Section. A numerical method [3] to minimize predicted cost function is introduced in Section 3. Sections 4 and 5 are examples of discrete-time and continuous-time nonlinear system control, respectively. The example of discrete-time nonlinear plant, taken from [4], is made time-varying in Section 4 to show a quick adaptation of the adaptive predictive control. While this example uses only input/output data of past and present, the continuous-time nonlinear plant control in Section 5 requires state vector feedback [6]. A structure oriented neural network is constructed for a nonlinear CR-system in this example. The last Section is a summary.

2. RESPONSE MATCHING BY NN

The quick adaptation of NN in time varying dynamical systems appears to stem from the way the weights in NN are adjusted by back propagation. To illustrate it, and to see the difference of NN (Fig.1) and ARMA for identification of a system, consider a linear discrete-time first-order plant;

$$y(t+1) = a\ y(t) + b\ u(t),$$
$$y(t+1) = \text{teacher signal, a=0.6, b=0.4}$$

where t is time point, $u(t)$ is input, $y(t+1)$ is output, and a,b are system parameters. The corresponding relation for NN with weights Wa, Wb is

$$yn(t+1) = Wa\ y(t) + Wb\ u(t).$$

If the NN is trained using the input-output signals taken from the left side of Fig.2, the pair (Wa,Wb) will move from its initial point (**Q**) as

$$\mathbf{Q} \rightarrow 0 \rightarrow 1 \rightarrow 2 \rightarrow \cdots$$

where **Q**-0 is orthogonal to a line $y(1)=ay(0)+bu(0)$ in the parameter plane in which $y(0),u(0),y(1)$ are fixed and a,b are variables. The line is indicated as L0-L0 in the right side of Fig.2. Likewise 0-1 is orthogonal to L1-L1 which is $y(2)=ay(1)+bu(1)$, and so on. Therefore the locus may eventually approach **P** that represents true values of a and b,

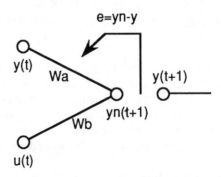

Fig.1 NN for y(t+1)=ay(t)+bu(t)

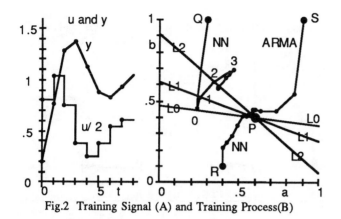

Fig.2 Training Signal (A) and Training Process(B)

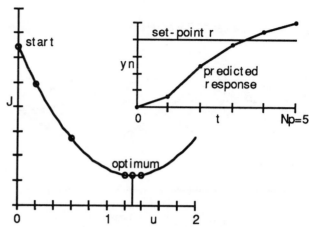

Fig.3 Cost-Function and Optimization

but the motion is primarily response matching ($yn(t+1)$ to $y(t+1)$) dictated by the steepest-descent algorithm. Parameter matching is indirect in NN. The state approaches the true set of parameters (**P**) more rapidly in the parameter identification using ARMA algorithm, as shown by a line starting on **S**. NN training with random input, a line from **R** in the figure, appears to take the state more directly to **P**, but it requires far more steps than ARMA to approach **P**.

Since NN is used in the following predictive control to generate future response of the plant, its capability to quickly match system's response contributes to adaptability of the control on parameter changes and disturbances of control object.

3 NN BASED PREDICTIVE CONTROL

The cost function to be minimized in discrete-time predictive control is

$$J = W_u \left[u(t) - u(t-1)\right]^2 + \sum_{i=1}^{N_p} \left[r(t+i) - y_n(t+i)\right]^2 \quad (1)$$

where $t = 0,1,2,\cdots$ is time point, $u(t)$ is plant input to be optimized, r is reference input, yn is predicted response determined by NN, Wu is a weight by which jump magnitude of u is suppressed, and Np is the range of prediction.

An example is illustrated in Fig.3. The optimal control, **u(t)**, that will minimize the cost function, is determined by "Simplex Method" [3]. The search, starting at $u=0$ in this example, proceeds as shown by small circles and reaches the minimum point very quickly. The J-curve is parabolic for linear systems if NN is an exact copy of the plant. If local minima is suspected when the system is nonlinear or NN is inexact, scanning a necessary range of u may be required. A predicted response is also shown in the Figure for $Np=5$. Set-point, r, is assumed to stay constant.

It is possible to consider more than one change of control u in the prediction. Clarke [2] named the number of control changes, Nu, as "control horizon". If $Nu=2$, the first term of Eq.(1) must include two-steps, while $yn(t+i)$ being computed for a control $u(t)$ followed by $u(t+1)$, although the second control is not really applied on the plant. Control horizon Nu

longer than 2 is seldom required. According to simulation studies on various linear and nonlinear systems, $Nu=1$ gives satisfactory performance in many cases.

If a plant is stationary and linear, and if the NN exactly mimics plant response, the result obtained by this method will completely agree with Clarke's optimal predictive control. Sustained load disturbance, however, will produce an offset error. In Clarke's method the offset is avoided by using signals of one-step difference for both input and output of the prediction. Although use of such differences is not allowed in nonlinear systems, offset is quickly eliminated by adaptation of NN if learning is kept active.

4 CONTROL OF DISCRETE-TIME SYSTEM

The example presented in this section is a discrete-time plant described by

$$y(t+1) = \frac{y(t)\, y(t-1)\, y(t-2)\, u(t-1)\, \big(y(t-2) - b(t)\big) + c(t)\, u(t)}{a(t) + y(t-1)^2 + y(t-2)^2} \quad (2)$$

where $u(t)$ is input, $y(t)$ is output, and
$$t = 0, 1, 2, \cdots$$
is time point. The plant is time-varying in the following simulation by specifying parameters $a(t)$, $b(t)$ and $c(t)$ as

$a(t_p) = 1.2 - 0.2 \cos (2\pi t_p/ T_{max})$,

$b(t_p) = 1 - 0.4 \sin (2\pi t_p/ T_{max})$,

$c(t_p) = 1 + 0.4 \sin (2\pi t_p/ T_{max})$

where tp is time for parameter change, and $Tmax=200$ (Fig.4) is time-span of control test. Narendra's Example 4 [4] is a special case of $a=1$, $b=1$ and $c=1$.

Fig.5 shows an ideal predictive control in which Eq.(2) is used not only for plant simulation but also as a model to compute response prediction, hence model=plant.

The test mode consists of stepwise changes [0.2, 0.4, 0.2, 0.1, 0.3] of set-point r over a period of 200 time steps. With controller parameters $Wu=0$ and $Np=1$ in Eq.(1), almost ideal performance is observed in Fig.5 as long as there is no disturbance. Controlling input, $u(t)$, creeps to keep plant output y on a desired set point, r. A step disturbance of

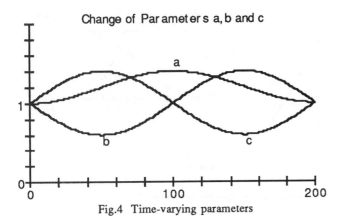

Fig.4 Time-varying parameters

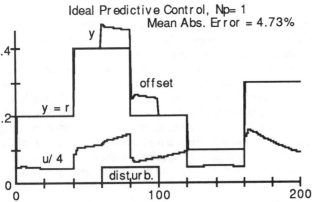

Fig.5 Control where prediction is made using plant dynamics

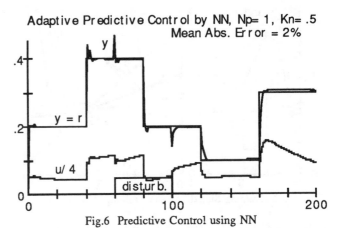

Fig.6 Predictive Control using NN

magnitude 0.8 from time step 60 through 100, however, produces an offset since disturbance input is not taken into account in the prediction.

Commonly used three layer NN is chosen as plant model for testing NN-based predictive control . The NN has 5 inputs, 5 nodes in each hidden layer, and one output. It was trained in series-parallel form [4] with input-vector $[u(t),u(t-1),y(t),y(t-1),y(t-2)]'$, using a random number in the interval $[-1.1, 1.1]$ as input $u(t)$, and $Kn=0.25$ as step size in the gradient method. The training was continued for 200,000 time steps.

The NN thus trained is then applied on the optimal predictive control. Keeping the learning process of NN active throughout the test with a step size (gain) $Kn=0.5$, offset by the disturbance on $60<=t<=100$ was eliminated, as shown in Fig.6. This is due to the quick adaptation of the NN. Fig.6 also demonstrates fast adaptation of the NN on time varying parameters of the plant. A slight steady-state error is seen in the last section ($t>160$) of the test in Fig.6, probably because parameter change was too fast to be followed by adaptation.

Model following of the same plant was also tested, replacing set point $r(t+i)$ in Eq.(1) by a prescribed signal, like,

$$r(t) = \frac{(\sin (2 \pi t / 20) + \sin (2 \pi t / 50))}{4},$$

using future values of the signal in the prediction. The results were satisfactory.

Since $u(t)$ and $u(t-1)$ are nonlinearly coupled with other variables in Eq.(2), indirect adaptive control is not feasible for this plant. General theoretical background currently available in nonlinear time varying systems is not sufficient to make a statement on the feasibility of the NN-based predictive control. However,various examples studied by computer simulation, indicate the predictive control by NN to be a viable approach for a broad class of adaptive control problems of nonlinear plants.

5 CONTROL OF CONTINUOUS-TIME SYSTEM

The example in this section is a C-R pressure-system shown in Fig.7. The system is nonlinear when flow through a resistor is proportional to square root of pressure difference across the orifice. Using informal expression for square root for brevity,

$$\text{SGN}(\Delta x) \sqrt{\text{ABS}(\Delta x)} \to \sqrt{\Delta x}$$

the state equations for pressures $x1,x2,x3$ are

$$C_1 \frac{d}{dt} x_1(t) = \frac{\sqrt{x_2(t) - x_1(t)}}{R_{12}} + \frac{\sqrt{x_0(t) - x_1(t)}}{R_1} + u(t) \quad (3a)$$

$$C_2 \frac{d}{dt} x_2(t) = \frac{\sqrt{x_1(t) - x_2(t)}}{R_{12}} + \frac{\sqrt{x_3(t) - x_2(t)}}{R_{23}} + \frac{\sqrt{x_0(t) - x_2(t)}}{R_2} \quad (3b)$$

$$C_3 \frac{d}{dt} x_3(t) = \frac{\sqrt{x_2(t) - x_3(t)}}{R_{23}} + \frac{\sqrt{x_0(t) - x_3(t)}}{R_3} + v(t) \quad (3c)$$

where C's are capacitance , R's are resistance as shown in Fig.7, $xo(t)$ is ambient pressure and $v(t)$ in Eq.(3c) is disturbance. A set of numerical values for system parameters,

C1=1, C2=1.2, C3=.5,

R1=1, R2=2, R3=1, R12=1, R23=1

is assumed in the following.

The network shown in Fig.8 will describe the state equations of this particular example. In Fig.8 the square roots in Eq.(3) are represented by the following $s1$ through $s5$;

$$s_1 = \sqrt{x_0(t) - x_1(t)}, \, s_2 = \sqrt{x_0(t) - x_2(t)} , \, s_3 = \sqrt{x_0(t) - x_3(t)}$$

$$s_4 = \sqrt{x_1(t) - x_2(t)} , \, s_5 = \sqrt{x_2(t) - x_3(t)}$$

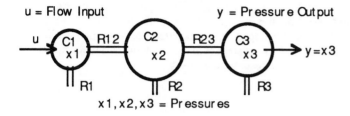

Fig.7 Continuous-time C-R plant

The pressure differences are taken by the elements of matrix *Wa*, while elements of sparse matrix *Wb* are for divisions by C's and R's. It has the form of NN with one hidden layer.

T.Muraji of Mikuni Corp. has proposed this form of NN, and to approximate the square roots by sigmoids. As shown in Fig.9, parameters *a* and *b* of a sigmoidal function $b*\tanh(ax/2)$ can be adjusted by back propagation to fit $\sqrt{x}$ over a specified range of *x*. Fig.8 then becomes a commonly used NN with one hidden layer. Using nominal values of C and R of the system and estimates of *a* and *b* of the sigmoid as initial values of elements in weight matrices $Wa(j,i)$ and $Wb(k,j)$, it was possible to get a reasonably accurate NN model for the plant within a short training period. A black-box approach using fully connected matrices with randomly assigned initial values for their elements takes far more training steps to reach a similar accuracy.

Fig.10 shows a simulation test of adaptive predictive control in which the prediction was made by the NN. Plant response was computed by Runge-Kutta method of degree 4 for a time-step size of $Ts=1$. Emulating a discrete-time control of sampling period $Ts=1$, input $u(t)$ was held constant in each "sampling interval". The same Runge-Kutta algorithm was applied on the outputs of NN to compute predicted values of state variables on sampling instants. Fig.10 is thus a simulation of discrete-time control in which NN is trained once every $Ts=1$ time span. With step size $Ka=.2$ and $Kb=.3$

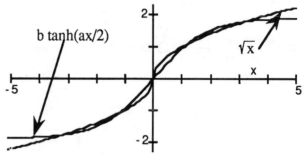

Fig.9 Sigmoidal approximation of square-root

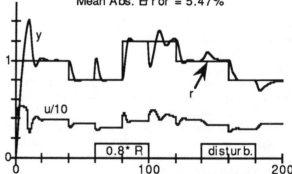

Fig.10 Predictive control using state-vector feedback

for adjusting sparse elements of weight matrices *Wa* and *Wb*, quick adaptation of the NN on both plant parameter change and disturbance upset was demonstrated.

In the test mode of Fig.10, the values of R12 and R23 was decreased from 1 to 0.8 in a time span $60<=t<100$. The resulting deviation in output *y* was almost as quickly eliminated as in the ideal case of using plant dynamics for prediction(model=plant). Offset caused by a step disturbance on $140<=t<180$ in the ideal case (like in Fig.5) is also eliminated by adaptation of the NN.

6 SUMMARY AND CONCLUSIONS

In this paper predictive control using NN as a model of a plant is suggested. Two examples are shown to demonstrate the control. The first example dealt with a discrete-time control based upon output feedback, while the continuous-time nonlinear plant in the second example required state variable feedback [6]. The NN based predictive control for both examples (Fig.11) consists of the following steps :

1. Train the NN as a model for the response characteristics of a plant,
2. Apply the NN for response prediction on various control candidates,
3. Select a best control numerically by an algorithm like Simplex Method,

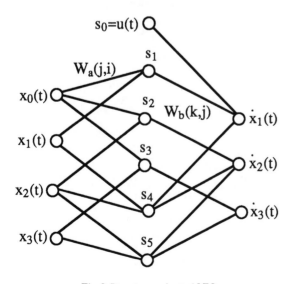

Fig.8 Structure oriented NN

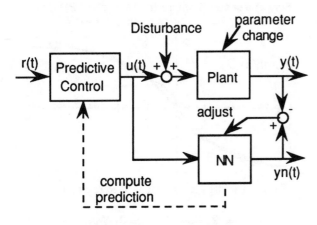

Fig.11 The Control System

4. Apply the optimal control on the plant,
5. Keep the learning process of NN active to adapt parameter change of the plant and disturbance input.

In view of the diversity and lack of general theory on nonlinear dynamics, there is no reason to claim general applicability of the control strategy. Stability of the control system has not been proven. However, computer simulations on a variety of systems seem to demonstrate high-quality performance. It gives the optimal predictive control if the system is linear and time invariant.

Rigorous mathematical basis has been central in the control theory of last three decades. The approach presented here is different. It may indicate a new paradigm associated with NN and nonlinear systems which still defy mathematical treatments. It is hoped the new paradigm will open a new field of complex system control when massively parallel neuro computer becomes available.

REFERENCES

[1] H.Ziebolz, H.M.Paynter, "Possibilities of a Two- Time Scale Computing System for Control and Simulation of Dynamic Systems", *Proc. of the National Electronic Conference,* Vol.9, 1953, pp.215-223
    H.Ziebolz, H.M.Paynter, *Regelungstechnik,* Heft 11, 2, 1954, pp.255-259
[2] D.W.Clarke, C.Mohtadi, P.S.Tuffs, "Generalized Predictive Control, Part I. The Basic Algorithm,"*Automatica,* Vol.23, 1987, pp.137-148. Ibid., "Part II. Extensions and Interpretations," *Ibid.,* 1987, pp.149-160.
[3] A.L.Nelder, R.Mead, "A Simplex Method for Function Minimization, "*Compt.J.,* 1964, p.308.
[4] K.S.Narendra, K.Parthasarathy, "Identification and Control of Dynamical Systems using Neural Networks," *IEEE Trans. on Neural Networks,* Vol.1, 1990,pp.4-27, .
[5] Y. Takahashi, *Adaptive Predictive Control of Nonlinear Time-Varying Systems using Neural Network,* Kagakugijutsu-Sha, Kanazawa, Japan, Sept. 1992.
[6] J.J.E.Slotine, W.Li, *Applied Nonlinear Control,* Prentice Hall, 1991
[7] K.J.Hunt, D.Sbarbao, R.Zbikowski, P.J.Gawthrop, "Neural Networks for Control Systems -- A Survey," *Automatica,* Vol.28, 1992, pp.1083- 1112.

Self-Generating vs. Self-Organizing, What's Different?

W.X. Wen, V. Pang, and A. Jennings
AISS/TSSS, Telecom Research Labs.
Clayton, Victoria 3168, Australia

Abstract

Comparisons between the Self-Generating Neural Network (SGNN) and the Self-Organizing Neural Network (SONN) are performed. Although the SGNN concept was developed from SONN, the results obtained show that it has quite a few significant advantages when compared with SONN. These include simplicity of design methodology, greater speed for both training and testing, higher accuracy of clustering/classification, and better generalization capability. An analysis is also conducted to investigate why SGNN is superior to SONN.

1 Introduction

The SGNN (Self-Generating Neural Network) method proposed in [13, 10] is based on both SONN (Self-Organizing Neural Network) [4] and traditional AI unsupervised learning methods, such as COBWEB and ARACHINE [2, 5]. It has been applied to different applications such as image coding, diagnostic expert systems and document/information retrieval systems [12, 6]. Two SGNN systems have been developed on SUN SPARC stations and IBM-PC/AT with X-window/MS-window 3 interfaces, respectively. Comparisons have been given in [11] to show the advantages of the SGNN method over COBWEB/CLASSWEB/ARACHINE.

The purpose of this paper is to give a comparative analysis between the performances of a type of SGNN, Self-Generating Neural Trees (SGNT), and SONN to show the difference between them and the reasons for this difference. The MONK problems [9] – a de facto standard benchmark set for testing supervised/unsupervised learning methods are used for comparison. The result of the comparison shows that SGNN/SGNT is superior to SONN in aspects such as the simplicity of design, speed of training and testing on conventional computer systems, better clustering/classification results, and better generalization capability.

2 The SGNT Algorithm

Neural networks are usually designed by human experts. It is quite tricky to choose the right structure of the neural network suitable for a particular application at hand. In this section, we briefly discuss the SGNT method proposed in [13] to generate a neural tree [1] automatically from training examples without any other human intervention.

For this kind of network, not only the weights of the network connections but also the structure of the whole network are all learned from the training examples directly. These include:

1. the number of the neurons in the network,

2. the interconnections among the neurons,

3. the weights on the connections.

A neural tree [1] generated in this way is called a Self-Generating Neural Tree (SGNT). The algorithm to generate an SGNT is basically a hierarchical clustering algorithm. Before we describe the SGNT algorithms, some related definitions are given below:

Definition 1: An *instance* e_i is a real vector of attributes: $e_i = < a_{i1}, ..., a_{in} >$.

Definition 2: A *neuron* n_j is a ordered pair $< W_j, C_j >$, where W_j is the real weight vector of the neuron: $W_j = < w_{j1}, ..., w_{jn} >$, and C_j is the child neuron set of n_j.

Definition 3: An *SGNT* is a tree $< \{n_j\}, \{l_k\} >$ of neurons generated automatically from a set of training instances by the algorithm given below, where $\{n_j\}$ is the neuron/node set and $\{l_k\}$ is the link set of the tree. There is a directed link from neuron n_i to n_j, if and only if $n_j \in C_i$.

Definition 4: A neuron n_k in a neuron set $\{n_j\}$ is called a *winner* for an instance e_i if $\forall j, d(n_k, e_i) \leq d(n_j, e_i)$ where $d(n_j, e_i)$ is the distance between neuron n_j and instance e_i.

Any distance measure can be used, but we use a modified Euclidean distance measure:

$$d(n_j, e_i) = \sqrt{\frac{\sum_{k=1}^{n}(a_{jk} - a_{ik})^2}{n}}.$$

The SGNT algorithm is a hierarchical clustering algorithm given in a pseudo-C language as follows:

Algorithm 1 (SGNT Generation/Training):

Input:

1. A set of training instances $E = \{e_i\}$, $i = 1, ..., N$.

2. A threshold $\xi \geq 0$.

3. A distance measure for each attribute/weight in instances/neurons.

Output: An SGNT generated from E.

```
Method:     copy(root,e_0);
    for(i=1,j=1;i<=N;i++) {
        minmumDistance = distance(ex,root);
        winner = oldWinner = root;
        minimumDistance = test(e_i,root);
        if(minimumDistance>ξ) {
            if(leaf(winner)) {
                copy(n_j,winner);
                connect(n_j,winner);
                j++;
            }
            copy(n_j,e_i);
            connect(n_j,winner);
            j++;
        }
        update(winner,e_i);
    }
```

where the routines are defined as follows:

1. copy(n,e): create a neuron n and copy the attributes/weights in the instance/neuron e to n.

2. distance(e,n): return the distance between instance e and neuron n.

3. test(e,subRoot): find a winner in the current SGNT/sub-SGNT rooted by subRoot for instance e and return the distance between the winner and e.

4. leaf(n): check a neuron n to see whether it is a leaf neuron in the current SGNT. A neuron in an SGNT is called a leaf neuron if it has no child neuron.

5. connect(n_0, n_1): connect neuron n_0 to n_1 making n_0 as a child neuron of n_1.

6. update(n_i, e_{k+1}): update the weight vector of neuron n_i by the attribute vector of e_{k+1} according to the updating rule (1) below.

$$w_{ij,k+1} = w_{ij,k} + \frac{1}{k+1} \cdot (a_{k+1,j} - w_{ij,k}). \qquad (1)$$

where $w_{ij,k}$ is the j-th weight of n_i after having seen the first k examples covered by n_i.

After an initial network has been built, some optimizations (called horizontal and vertical optimizations) are performed to improve the performance of the network. As the network is trained, the dead branches which stop growing are pruned away to reduce the size of the network. An SGNT branch is called dead if the number of examples covered by its root does not increase during repeated training. Finally, it is possible to simplify an SGNT by a method similar to Quinlan's method of decision tree simplification [7]. For more detailed information about the SGNT algorithm, optimization, pruning, and simplification, see [13].

3 SGNN/SGNT vs. SONN

Although the SGNN/SGNT bears much resemblance to SONN, it has many of its own features. To compare SGNT/SGNN with SONN, we conducted a systematic performance analysis for both methods. The benchmark that we chose was the MONK's problems [9]. The reasons for this choice are

1. MONK's tests have been performed for many (at least 20) well-known supervised/unsupervised learning methods at the 2nd European Summer School on Machine Learning during the summer of 1991. This makes an independent comparison of different methods possible.

2. The training and test data and the test results for other well-known methods are easily accessed.

3. The MONK's problems are not too complicated or time-consuming to test but are reasonably difficult to solve.

The MONK's problems [9] rely on an artificial robot domain, in which robots are described by six different attributes:

x_1:	head_shape	$\in$	round, square, octagon
x_2:	body_shape	$\in$	round, square, octagon;
x_3:	is_smiling	$\in$	yes, no
x_4:	holding	$\in$	sword, balloon, flag;
x_5:	jacket_color	$\in$	red, yellow, green, blue;
x_6:	has_tie	$\in$	yes, no.

The learning tasks of the three MONK's problems are binary classification tasks, each of them is given by the following logical description of a class.

- Problem M_1: (head_shape = body_shape) or (jacket_color = red). From 432 possible examples, 124 were randomly selected for the training set. No noise is present.

- Problem M_2: Exactly two of the six attributes have their first value. From 432 examples, 169 were selected randomly. No noise is present.

- Problem M_3: (Jacket_color is green and holding a sword) or (jacket_color is not blue and body_shape is no octagon). From 432 examples, 122 were selected randomly. and among them there were 5% misclassifications, ie. noise in the training set.

The results given in [11] show that SGNN/SGNT outperforms the most popular unsupervised learning methods, such as ECOBWEB and CLASSWEB, and is significantly faster than all those competitors. In this paper, we will use MONK's problems again to compare SGNN/SGNT and SONN. The comparison is conducted in three aspects: simplicity of network design, accuracy of classification/clustering and generalization capability, and the training/testing speed.

3.1 Design Efforts

As implied by the name Self-Generating, the design of an SGNT/SGNN requires much less effort from the designer. For the design of an SONN, such as LVQ [4], to handle a particular application, the designer has to decide

1. how many neurons the network needs,

2. how the neurons are arranged in the networks,

3. what is the neighbourhood size to use and how the neighbourhood should shrink during the training,

4. the usage count arrangement to make better use of the neurons, and

5. the appropriate learning rate for training the network and the strategy to reduce it.

Some of these system parameters affect the performance of the SONN significantly. This means that if they are selected improperly, the final system performance may not be as good as expected. Too many neurons or links will obviously waste the system resources and also cause unnecessary delay because of the exhaustive search strategy of SONN during both training and testing. Once the structure of the network has been determined, it remains fixed. Any change of the application requirement will lead

to a complete re-design and re-training of the network. The rest of the decisions that the network designer has to make are very tricky and there is no standard way to choose these parameters convincingly. The usual practice is to perform multiple experiments to choose them empirically. Therefore, this is often a tedious and fruitless design task.

For MONK's problems, we performed experiments with 6×6, 8×8, 12×12, and 14×14 LVQ grids. The 12×12 and 14×14 networks did not give significantly better performance than that of 8×8 network for MONK's problems, but 8×8 network was significantly better than 6×6 network. There was a severe penalty when increasing the network size because training time would become longer due to the number of nodes needed to be searched. In addition, the neighbourhood size for training must be initially large and this will further add to the length of the training schedule. Therefore, we decided to use the 8×8 network for our comparisons with SGNT/SGNN. Because there is no standard way of choosing the diameters of the neighborhoods and their shrinking strategy for LVQ network training, we chose them empirically according to experience accumulated in previous experiments (see Table 1). The learning rates used in the LVQ net-

learning rate	neighbourhood diameter	epochs
0.06	4	10
0.06	3	30
0.05	2	20
0.04	1	20
0.025	0	30

Table 1: The training schedule for LVQ nets

works is also given in Table 1. Neuron usage counters were not used because we were not concerned with making the best use of the neurons. We used two metrics, city block and Euclidean distance, for LVQ net training and testing. Our results seem to show that city-block is on average slightly better for the MONK's problems. This might be because an Euclidean metric requires the computation of a square of the sum followed by a square root, whereas a city block requires only the sum of the absolute differences. The networks were trained using 110 epochs in total.

In the case of SGNN/SGNT, all that needs to be done is to choose an appropriate parameter ξ and if we are lazy to do so, we can always choose $\xi = 0$. The SGNN/SGNT system will do everything else for the development of the neural network. According to our experiences, the system does this quite well. For the MONK's problems, SGNT generated three networks with 156, 168, and 82 neurons, respectively. These figures are greater than the 64 neurons used by an 8×8 LVQ network, but it should be noted that for MONK's problems there was no significant difference in performance between 8×8 and $14 \times 14 (= 196)$ LVQ networks except that the former was significantly faster to train/test than the latter. The generated SGNT networks had 5 levels and each of them was generated in only 5 epochs.

3.2 The accuracy of classification / clustering

The results of SGNT, SONN, and some other unsupervised methods for the MONK problems are given in Table 2. The results of LVQ nets show the averages of 10 runs

Learning method tested	Test results		
	M_1	M_2	M_3
SGNT	82.6%	78.2%	84.5%
8×8 LVQ (CB)	76.1%	63.0%	81.2%
8×8 LVQ (Eu)	72.5%	64.4%	75.7%
CLASSWEB 0.10	71.8%	64.8%	80.8%
CLASSWEB 0.15	65.7%	61.6%	85.4%
CLASSWEB 0.20	63.0%	57.2%	75.2%
ECOBWEB l.p.	71.8%	67.4%	69.1%

Table 2: Accuracy comparisons for unsupervised learning methods

with different initial weight sets. The results show that SGNT is better than SONN for the easier tasks such as M_1 and M_3. For the harder task M_2, the performance of SGNT is much better than SONN, as is the average performance of SGNT. This comparison shows that the fixed uniform structure (such as a grid structure) of SONN cannot be a perfect panacea for all applications. For different applications, ideally, different networks structures should be carefully designed. SGNN/SGNT gives a possible alternative to heavily handcrafted network methods, such as Neocognitron[3]. It automatically adjusts the neuron/link density in different parts of the network according to the training sample distribution for a particular application, whereas SONN treats all applications uniformly and consequently, wastes neurons/links in some parts of the network while has too few neurons/links to use in other parts even in a big network.

3.3 The training speed

For the MONK's problems, speed comparisons between the SGNT and SONN are given in Table 3. The results show that the SGNT is significantly faster than SONN. The problem here for SONN is that an exhaustive search of the whole network is performed to find a winner no matter how large the network is. Furthermore, as mentioned earlier, there are often redundant

Learning method tested	Training time (in sec)		
	M_1	M_2	M_3
SGNT	1.47	2.37	2.69
8×8 LVQ (CB)	62.74	85.72	62.04
8×8 LVQ (Eu)	86.12	117.01	84.56
CLASSWEB 0.10	1406.47	2013.78	1311.25
CLASSWEB 0.15	867.47	977.04	822.09
CLASSWEB 0.20	499.94	646.06	521.21
COBWEB's	Not available		

Table 3: Speed comparisons for unsupervised learning methods

neurons in SONN, thus extra delays are added to the search. SGNT/SGNN avoids the pitfalls of SONN by only searching a very small part of the network hierarchically. For SGNT, this becomes a very efficient tree search ($O(\log_b N)$). The SGNN/SGNT algorithm generates neurons/links only when they are really needed and the pruning and simplification of the network further reduce redundancy. Therefore, it is not surprising that SGNN/SGNT should be much faster to train/test than SONN.

4 Discussion

"The thought that my mind is really nothing but an empty sieve - often this, too, disconcerts me."

Logan Pearsall Smith,

"All Trivia"

There are a great many neural network researchers concerned with the issue of "scaling up" neural networks to tackle large problems, and more difficult problems than pattern recognition. A task such as target identification in the presence of noise and clutter is fairly well treated by current networks, but a more difficult task such as handwritten text is still fairly difficult. In all practical cases of network application to large problems, a strict network structure is constructed by the network designers. For example the AT&T zip code network has seven layers and a complex hierarchical structure [8]. More well known is the Neocognitron [3]. The success of the neocognitron derives very much from its structure and its careful training regime wherein the feature set is at a progressively higher level of abstraction towards the top of the network.

So it appears that to tackle large problems some structuring of the problem is necessary. The key question then becomes: how do such networks arise in nature? There is no designer present carefully feeding examples to the network in such a way that it has tractable and computationally feasible learning tasks at each layer. To resolve this question we can proceed in two ways: we can look in nature for how the networks develop, or attempt to construct models that emulate the biological capability. Our work on SGNT follows this second path, and the results on standard problems show that it is a powerful mechanism. SONN shows some promise in delivering a network solely on the basis of the sensory data. For example Kohonen's network [4] is quite successful at developing a network for pattern recognition. It gives the appearance of "principle free" learning: that the network structure arises solely on the basis of the training data.

However, Kohonen's network incorporates a neighbourhood measure that is reduced as the training of the network proceeds, which plays a major part in the network structure. Even though this is not a "principle based" method, it is still giving the network designer considerable control over the end result. So we argue that SONN's are developed with influence from the designer in selecting this schedule.

The SGNT approach is quite different: there are guiding principles and constraints that influence the formation of the network structure. These principles are derived from traditional AI concept formation/decision tree methods, so they have apparently little in common with biological mechanisms.

What are the biological equivalents of our pruning rules? Given that artificial neural networks are a greatly abstracted view of neural networks, we cannot say at this stage. But on the surface it does appear reasonable to limit the number of poorly formed hierarchies. Perhaps we can discover biological mechanisms that are similar. Even though speed of training is not of great importance in itself, it does show economy of computation which may imply evolutionary advantage for the corresponding biological network. There is considerable evidence that network development is not from a "blank sheet".

Acknowledgement

Discussions with Huan Liu and Maureen Molloy assisted in the preparation of the discussion. The permission of the Director of Telecom Australia Research Laboratories to publish this paper is acknowledged.

References

[1] L. Fang, A.Jennings, W.Wen, K.Li, and T.Li. Unsupervised learning in a self-organizing tree. In *Proc. IJCNN'91 (International Joint Conf. on Neural Networks)*, Singapore, Nov. 1991.

[2] D. Fisher. Knowledge acquisition via incremental conceptual slustering. *Machine Learning*, 2:139–172, 1987.

[3] K. Fukushima and N. Wake. Handwritten alphanumeric character recognition by the neocognition. *IEEE Trans. on Neural Networks*, 2, No. 3:355–365, 1991.

[4] T. Kohonen. *Self-Organization and Associative Memory*. Springer-Verlag, Berlin, 1984.

[5] K. McKusick and P. Langley. Constrains on tree structure in concept formation. In *Proc. IJCAI'91*, volume 2, pages 810–816, Sydney, Aug. 1991. Morgan Kaufmann.

[6] M. Moloy, W. Wen, V. Ciesielski, and A. Jennings. Neuopsychological diagnosis using a neural netowrk. In *preparation (submitted to Australian Cognitive Conference)*, Sept. 1992.

[7] J. Quinlan. Simplifying decision trees. *Int.J.Man-Machine Studies*, 27:221–234, 1987.

[8] E. Sackinger et al. Application of the ANNA neural network chip to high-speed character recognition. *IEEE Trans. on Neural Networks*, 3, No. 3:498–505, 1992.

[9] S. Thrun et al. The MONK's problems: A performance comparison of different learning algorithms. Tech Report CMU-CS-91-197, Carnegie Mellon University, Dec. 1991.

[10] W. X. Wen, A. Jennings, and H. Liu. Learning a neural tree. In *Proc. IJCNN'92 (International Joint Conf. on Neural Networks)*, Beijing, China, Nov. 1992.

[11] W. X. Wen, A. Jennings, and H. Liu. A performance analysis for self-generating neural networks. In *Proc. IJCNN'92 (International Joint Conf. on Neural Networks)*, Beijing, China, Nov. 1992.

[12] W. X. Wen, A. Jennings, and H. Liu. Self-generating neural networks and their applications to telecommunications. In *Proc. ICCT'92 (International Conference on Communication Technology)*, Beijing, China, 9 1992.

[13] W. X. Wen, H. Liu, and A. Jennings. Self-generating neural networks. In *Proc. IJCNN'92 (International Joint Conf. on Neural Networks)*, Baltimore, June 1992.

An Extended Self-Organizing Map with Gated Neurons

V. Chandrasekaran†, M. Palaniswami and Terry M. Caelli

School of Information Technology and Electrical Engineering

University of Melbourne, Parkville, Victoria-3052, Australia

†E-mail: vc@mullian.ee.mu.oz.au

Abstract— Kohonen's self-organizing maps have the capacity to create spatially organised maps of the input signals through the process of competition and cooperation among the neighbours. However these feature maps with winner-take-all philosophy have difficulty in achieving high performance in pattern classification problems. In addition, if the task is to recognise the individual patterns, it is almost impossible. In this paper the Kohonen's self-organizing map is extended by a novel technique of allowing the neurons in the feature map to compete in a selective manner. This is accomplished by introducing gated neurons prior to the winner-take-all layer and these gated neurons are activated by a cosine function with time-varying frequency. This results in a spatio-temporal signature at the output for each input pattern over a predetermined interval. This pattern is found to be unique in its characteristics and therefore lead to very high degree of recognition results. The simulations performed on a standard texture recognition problem indicate excellant performance.

I. INTRODUCTION

The fundamental phenomenon of biological neurons is the capability to adapt in direct response to received signals without the need for any external guidance. Artificial neural network architectures which have been developed to emulate the above phenomenon are able to *self-organise* in response to input stimuli. A self-organizing neural network incorporates an autonomous mechanism which allows the network to adapt without the need for an external supervisor. Such neural networks are sometimes referred to as *self-organizing maps*. A map is generated by establishing a correspondence between the N-dimensional input vectors and the nodes of the network such that the topological relationships between the input samples in N-dimensional space is reflected as faithfully as possible in the spatial arrangement of the network. Kohonen's self-organizing maps [1][2][3] fall under this category. In this map, the nodes of the networks are subject to effects known as competition and cooperation. The output computed for each neuron is based on *Learning Vector Quantiser* (LVQ) algorithm. The learning speed in these maps are many orders greater than that of many other neural networks especially when using computational shortcuts. Therefore use of these maps for the purpose of pattern detection and classification problems becomes very attractive. However, as noted by Kohonen in [1], if the maps are used for pattern recognition, their classification accuracy can be increased if the cells are fine-tuned using *supervised learning principles*. These supervised learning principles basically fine-tunes the decision regions. Many extensions of the original LVQ have been proposed to achieve this. With all these approaches one still finds that the accuracy of recognition is not all that impressive. Therefore there is a need to improve the performance of this kind of architecture without the loss of speed in training the networks.

The main drawback of the Kohonen's map for classification purposes is that the network uses the nearest codebook weight vector for deciding a class. When patterns of multiple classes are interwoven closely, then the recognition accuracy drops down to a low level. In order to achieve a high degree of satisfactory performance one should therfore devise means of obtaining unique characteristic information for each pattern from the topology already formed. This information can then be used for pattern recognition followed by its associated class identity. It is well known that spatio-temporal information can be used to enhance the quality of pattern recognition. In this paper, we propose novel gated neurons for the purpose of extracting suitable spatio-temporal information from spatially organised feature maps. These gated neurons introduces a selective competition among the neurons in the feature map.

II. Gated Neuronal Architecture

The general organisation of the proposed gated neuronal architecture of the self-organizing map is shown in Fig.1. It has four distinct functional levels. As in Kohonen's feature maps, similarity measures between the input vector and the weight vectors based on Minkowski's distance metric are computed by the neurons in the first level. These provide an indication of how close the input pattern is to a weight vector connecting the inputs to the neurons in the first layer.

The gated neuronal architecture is introduced at the second level which allows the input signal to pass through when the signal at the control input of the gate is positive. These gates are controlled by a cosine function with an adjustable frequency. The variable frequency nature of the gating function lets one to choose **a fine grating**. This allows the neurons in the first layer to compete in a selected manner. In addition the gates can be permanently closed through controllable logic gates at the time of forming the topological maps using standard LVQ techniques.

The winner-take-all approach is implemented in the third level. Here, in addition to the function of selecting the **winner**, the neurons have been provided with registers to store spatio-temporal information in respect of x-y coordinates, the time step and the neuronal output received from the first layer. The information is registered only when the associated neuron becomes the winner. The contents of these registers are reset just prior to the input pattern presentation.

The purpose of obtaining a *similarity measure* between the spatio-temporal patterns generated by the known input patterns and the unknown pattern being detected and classified is achieved in the fourth level. The measure of similarity is obtained by calulating linear correltion between spatial cooridinates recorded in the registers and the weights, between the neuronal activation received at the third layer during the time of "winning phase" and the information stored in weights over a definite period. These correlation factors are then combined to obtain an overall factor. The overall correlation values will range from -1 to 1. The neuron having the maximum correlation factor is selected and this neuron acts as a pointer to the specific pattern type and its associated class.

III. Training of Weights in First Level

A spatially organised feature map is essential to extract meaningful spatio-temporal information for efficient classification purposes. This organisation is achieved by training the weights at the input. Training of weights between the input and the first level is done using LVQ algorithm. At the time of training the weights, the neurons in the second level are kept closed permanently, thus letting the winner-take-all layer to select the winner among **all** the neurons in the first layer. This is no different from the known approach in Kohonen's feature maps, since the gated neural layer is transparent at this stage.

Vector Quantization is a classical method that produces an approximation to a continuous probability function $\rho(V)$ of the vectorial input variable V using a finite number of code book vectors W_i. Once the codebooks are chosen, then the approximation of V involves finding the reference vector W_c closest to V.

The weight update algorithm is given by :

$$w_{i,(x,y)}^{new} = \begin{cases} \{w_{i,(x,y)}^{old}+ \\ \quad \alpha(n,(x,y))[v_i - w_{i,(x,y)}^{old}]\} \\ \qquad\qquad \text{for } (x,y) \in N_w \\ \\ w_{i,(x,y)}^{old} \qquad\quad \text{otherwise} \end{cases} \quad (1)$$

where N_w represents all neurons in the neighbourhood of the winner and (x,y) provides the coordinates of the neuron in the feature map. Index i varies from 1 to input dimension m.

In order to select the winner, a distance metric is needed. This is chosen to be Minkowski's metric. The distance function is given as:

$$d(\mathbf{V}, \mathbf{W}_{(x,y)}) = \{\sum_i^n (v_i - w_{i,(x,y)})^\lambda\}^{\frac{1}{\lambda}} \text{for } x,y \in N_w \quad (2)$$

where for $\lambda = 2$, the metric is Euclidean. The learning rate α lies in the interval $[0,1]$ and is a function of discrete time index n and the spatial distance of (x,y) from the winning node (X,Y). The function for learning rate is of the form:

$$\alpha(n,(x,y)) = \alpha(0) \cdot f(n) \cdot g(d((x,y),(X,Y))) \quad (3)$$

where $f(n)$ is a monotically decreasing function of discrete time index n and a gaussian function is selected for $g(d((x,y),(X,Y)))$. $\alpha(0)$ is the initial learning rate at time 0. The introduction of a learning rate modifier based on the spatial distance is found to enhance the recognition with LVQ [4].

As in the case of learning rate, the size of neighbourhood is also a function of time and has the form:

$$N_w(n) = N_w(0) \cdot h(n) \quad (4)$$

where $N_w(0)$ is the size of neighbourhood at time 0 and $h(n)$ is a monotonically decreasing function of discrete time index n.

The winning node is selected based on the neuronal outputs obtained from a similarity measure defined by a gaussian function on the computed distance metric. The similarity measure is calculated using the following function.

$$O(x,y) = exp(\frac{-\mathbf{G} \cdot d(\mathbf{V}, \mathbf{W}_{(x,y)})^2}{\sigma^2}) \quad (5)$$

where G is the gain factor, σ is the variance and $O(x,y)$ is the output of neuron at (x,y)th location.

IV. SELECTIVE NEURAL COMPETITION AT SECOND LEVEL

This section explains the major deviation from the Kohonen's self-organizing approach by introducing a selection criteria for neurons to compete. The selection mechanism is similar to the "attentional approach" seen in biological systems. As stated previously, a cosine function with time-varying frequency term is chosen to achieve the task. It will also be possible to select other suitable functions from the family of wavelets. The basic concept is to choose the neurons on the basis of their activations falling in specfic regions of the function selected. In this paper regions of positive values of function are chosen for competition and the neurons with activations falling in negative regions of the function are excluded. The inclusion and the exclusion of a neuron will therefore depend on their activation levels and the fine grating of regions providing positive function values. For a fixed grating frequency, the selection of neurons will also be fixed and will not serve any useful purpose. A fixed grating is equivalent to a standard approach of self-organizing map. When the frequency term is a function of discrete time index n, the selection, competition, the associated winning node in the feature map and its activations all change with respect to time index n. The trace of the "winners" in the map over a predetermined period will be a distinct signature for each input pattern. The distinctiveness is due to the pattern's relative position to all codebook weight vectors in the topology created. In addition, the type of signature depends only on the spatial topology created in the feature map.

The following function is used for gate control.

$$gate(ctrl(\cdot)) = \begin{cases} ON & \text{when ctrl() is +ve} \\ OFF & \text{when ctrl() is -ve} \end{cases} \quad (6)$$

where the function $ctrl(\cdot)$ is given by:

$$ctrl(d(\cdot)) = cos(2\pi\xi(t)d(\cdot) + \theta) \quad \text{where} \quad (7)$$

$$\xi(t) = \begin{cases} \xi_{max}(1 - \frac{t}{T}) & \text{for } t \leq T \\ 0 & \text{otherwise} \end{cases} \quad (8)$$

In the above equation the distance $d(\cdot)$ is the value of the distance measure obtained at each neuronal input of first level. The value of θ provides a phase shift which could be adjusted if needed for generating unique spatio-temporal patterns. ξ_{max} defines the maximum frequency at which the fine grating is being performed. The variation in frequency is maintained over a fixed time interval T to accomplish the task of pattern identification in definite time. The selection process is explained in Fig.2. A typical spatio-temporal signature information is shown in Table.2b.

V. WINNER SELECTION IN THIRD LEVEL

The selection of winner is based on the maximum activation among (ie. least distance between) the neurons selected for competition. This procedure is the same as in Kohonen's feature map. However, the neurons must register the information in respect of their spatial coordinates (x,y), the maximum activation value at which the winner is selected, and the time step at which the specific node becomes a winner in the competition. This information is maintained until the data is collected over time interval T.

VI. PATTERN IDENTIFICATION AT FOURTH LEVEL

One of the immediate applications for this novel approach can be in pattern identification. The pattern identification process can be achieved by obtaining a linear correlation between the spatio-temporal information recorded at the third level and the information stored for each known pattern type earlier. This means that we need to have one neuron per pattern at the final layer to act as a pointer to that pattern. The neuron having maximum correlation is selected and the corresponding pattern identified. The correlation is calculated as under:

$$\rho(\mu, \nu) = \frac{\sum_{n=1}^{n=T}(\mu(n) - \bar{\mu})(\nu(n) - \bar{\nu})}{\sqrt{\sum_{n=1}^{n=T}(\mu(n) - \bar{\mu})^2}\sqrt{\sum_{n=1}^{n=T}(\nu(n) - \bar{\nu})^2}} \quad (9)$$

The pairs of variables $\mu(n), \nu(n)$ can be substituted with values of variables for which measures of association need to be found. In our case, three independant correlations are obtained for spatial co-ordinate x, spatial coordinate y and the winner activation level. The final measure is

obtained by:

$$\rho_{overall} = \rho(x_{uk}, x_k)\rho(y_{uk}, y_k)\rho(WO_{uk}, WO_k) \quad (10)$$

where subscripts uk and k represent unknown and known patterns and WO refers to winning neuron's activation.

VII. SIMULATIONS

A. Texture Data

The data used in the classification experiment was extracted from the images of eight textures. The size of each original texture image was 512 x 216 pixels. Each image was divided into 128 blocks of 32 x32 pixels. Subimages of 16 x 16 pixels were then extracted from the centre of each 32 x 32 block. Each subimage was then operated upon by 3 x 3 pixel masks. The type of texture images used in the experiment are:

(i) Raffia (ii) Grass (iii) Pigskin (iv) Wool

(v) Leather (vi) Sand (vii) Water (viii) Wood

The operation of the mask upon each subimage created a single real value which characterised the response of the image to the mask. Hence for each subimage, a vector of eight real-valued elements was obtained where each value correspond to a feature extracted from a convolution with each mask. The complete data set of 1024 vectors comprised eight sets, one for each texture type. For further details on feature extraction of images using masks and statistical classification techniques of feature vectors refer to [5].

B. Self-Organizing Neural Network Classifier

The neural network classifier with a neuronal array of 10 x 10 at first level is chosen for training and testing. The complete feature data set is used to obtain the topology. These vectors are uniformly interleaved so that no two vectors of the same category could be presented to the network consecutively while training.

Each of the 1024 vectors are scaled down by a factor of 200.0 and then presented repeatedly after initialising the weights in first level at random. The initial conditions are neighbourhood size 5, learning rate 0.05 and number of presentation epochs 50. In the second, third, fourth and fifth steps, these are modified to have $\{4, 0.005, 100\}, \{3, 0.0005, 200\}, \{2, 0.00005, 400\}$ and $\{1, 0.00005, 800\}$ respectively. The maximum frequency in the gate control function is set at a value of 100 with a fixed time period index T equal to 100. The Euclidean metric was chosen for simulations.

The texture patterns are then presented one at a time to the net and the identification task is performed through the correlation measure at the final level. It is found that the network is able to recognise **individual** patterns based on the their pre-recorded spatio-temporal signatures with an accuracy of 100%. The previous results for the same texture data classification (without individual pattern identification ability) were 72% for standard LVQ based feature map, 76% feedforward network, 82% for *single nearest neighbour classifier* and 87.6% using a *multivariate gaussian classifier* [6].

VIII. CONCLUSION

In this paper a new approach to the processing of information contained in the self-organizing feature maps is presented. This Gated Neuronal Architecture (GNA) has been able to extract the N-Dimensional spatial orientation of each pattern with respect to the codebook weight vectors, thereby enhancing the quality of recognition. It also facilitates the use of maps already trained without the need for any fine tuning process to improve the classifcation performance. The present results are based on the input patterns containing no perturbations to the ones used under training. We are in the process of carrying out simulations of pattern identification and classification under perturbed conditions, since in real-world applications features extracted do not exactly match the ones obtained during training phase due to problems such as nonlinearity of sensors, processing errors and degradation of instruments.

IX. REFERENCES

[1] Kohonen,T.(1990) "The Self-Organizing Map", Proceedings of the IEEE, Vol. 78, No. 9, pp 1464–1480, September 1990.

[2] Kohonen,T.(1990) "Some Practical Aspects of the Self-Organizing Maps", Proceedings of the International Joint Conference on Neural networks, Washington DC, Vol. II, pp 253–256, 1990.

[3] Kohonen,T.(1982) "Self-Organized Formation of Topologically Correct Feature Maps", Bilogical Cybernetics, Vol. 43, pp 59–69, 1982.

[4] Zheng-Ping Lo and Bavarian,B.(1991) "Improved Rate of Convergence in Kohonen Neural Network", Proceedings of the International Joint Conference on Neural networks, Seattle, Vol. II, pp 201–206, July 1991.

[5] Clarke,S.(1990) "Texture Characterization aand Classification using Statistical methods", M.S. thesis, Univ.of Melbourne, Dept. of Electrical and Electronic Engineering, 1990.

[6] Vincent Pang and Palaniswami,M.(1990) "Pattern Classification Using a Self-Organizing Neural Network", In proceedings of the IEEE Region 10 Conference on Computer and Communication Systems, Hong Kong, pp 562–566, September 1990.

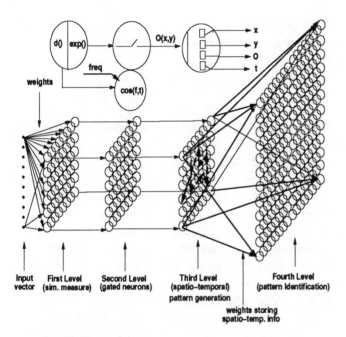

Note: When frequency is set to zero, the gate is closed permanently

Figure 1: Self-Organizing Map with Gated Neurons

**Typical Spatio–temporal Pattern
for feature no. 1**

| Co–ord. | | Activation | Winning at |
X	Y	O	Time Step
1	2	0.994888	0
2	2	0.991169	26
1	2	0.994888	27
2	1	0.989650	52
1	5	0.988917	54
2	2	0.991169	66
1	2	0.994888	69
2	2	0.991169	78
1	2	0.994888	83
2	2	0.991169	91
1	6	0.987361	93
2	6	0.984443	94
4	7	0.973125	95
5	8	0.965419	96
1	2	0.994888	97........

Table. 2b:

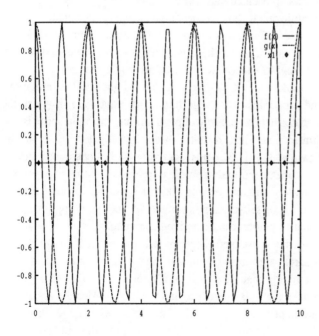

Figure 2: Cosine function Grating at two different frequencies. Selection of patterns with distance metrics falling on +ve region only

Recursive Least-Squares Approach to Self-Organizing Maps

Vesa T. Ruoppila, Timo Sorsa and Heikki N. Koivo
Tampere University of Technology, Department of Electrical Engineering
P.O. Box 692, SF - 33101 Tampere, Finland

Abstract—Self-organizing maps are a class of vector quantizers which have a special property of forming a low-dimensional representation of input data. The code vectors of the map organize during a recursive procedure according the statistical properties of the data trying to preserve the order defined by the lattice. In this paper, the code update of the self-organizing map is formulated as a parameter estimation problem, which is then solved by the recursive least-squares method. If the lattice or the size of the neighborhood is altered during the organization, the estimation problem becomes time variant. Therefore time weighting is used in the recursive least-squares algorithm. The proposed approach produces a simple code update formula which preserves the parallellism and computational simplicity of the original algorithm based on stochastic approximation. The computational burden of the code update is increased by $2n$ flops per iteration, where n is the number of the code vectors, compared to the original code update formula. Each code vector has a separate update equation with a scalar gain provided directly by the algorithm. The properties of the algorithm presented here are illustrated by simulation examples which demonstrate that the recursive least-squares method yields fast convergence of the code vectors.

I. INTRODUCTION

The self-organizing map, presented by Kohonen [6], [7], is a biologically-inspired algorithm to form a low-dimensional structured representation of input data. As a vector quantizer, the self-organizing map forms a mapping from input sequence to a finite set of code vectors. Each input vector is mapped to the nearest (according some measure) code vector associated to one element in a low-dimensional lattice.

The map organizes during a two-phase recursive procedure. First, the code vector which is nearest to the input vector is searched. Then the nearest code vector and its lattice neighbors are updated. As a result, the code vectors tend to organize into an ordered state according statistical properties of input data. In other words, the code vectors corresponding adjacent elements in the lattice are near each other also in the input space. Thus, the elements in the lattice describe order and relative distances between the corresponding code vectors in the input space. This is a very useful property when the map is used to visualize high-dimensional data.

The structured representation of data, provided by the self-organizing map, has been found useful in many technical applications. Self-organizing maps have been applied to pattern recognition tasks, such as detection of articulatory disturbances [10]. Texture classification by self-organizing maps have led to practical applications in quality control and cloud classification [16]. An equalizer structure employing a self-organizing map has been presented [8]. Process monitoring and fault detection are potential application areas and some preliminary results have already been published [17]. Also, methods based on a self-organizing map have been presented to form a piecewise linear approximation of the functional dependency between cartesian coordinates and joint angles of a robot [15].

Although self-organizing maps have been applied in various tasks there are several theoretical issues related to the algorithm that require more careful examination. Most of the results presented are valid only under very restrictive conditions. It has been demonstated experimentally that selection of parameters and the structure of the lattice is not very critical, when the organization of a map is considered. Although the theoretical results are mainly restricted to cover the scalar case, they give valuable insight into the limitations and properties of the algorithm. The scalar case in which the map consists of an array of elements and the input space is one dimensional, has recently been investigated in detail by Erwin *et al.* [2], [3]. The formulation of the code update task as a parameter estimation problem, presented in this paper, might provide a suitable framework, for example, for convergence analysis of self-organizing maps. Moreover, an optimal code update equation can be derived analytically.

In the subsequent sections we present a recursive least-squares algorithm to update the code vectors of a self-organizing map. But at first, a brief introduction to the basic concepts of self-organizing maps is given. Also the notation is introduced in Section II. Then we associate a quadratic objective function to the code update procedure in Section III. After that, the recursive least-squares algorithm is derived to minimize the objective function. Finally, in Section IV, the results of three simulation examples are presented in order to illustrate the properties of the algorithm.

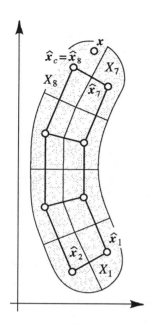
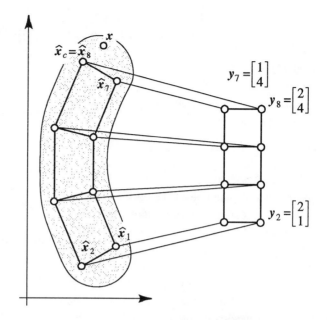

Fig. 1. The eight code vectors of self-organizing map $\hat{x}_1, \hat{x}_2, ..., \hat{x}_8$ fill the two-dimensional sausage-shaped input data distribution preserving the order defined by the rectangular lattice (on the right). The code vectors divide the input space into Voronoi regions $X_1, X_2, ..., X_8$ (on the left).

II. THE BASIC ALGORITHM

A self-organizing map consists of n elements which, in general case, are arranged in a low-dimensional lattice. Usually the lattice is a one-dimensional array or a two-dimensional lattice but also higher dimensional lattices can be used. The position of each indexed element $j = 1, 2, ..., n$ in the l-dimensional lattice is specified by the position vector y_j. Each element of the lattice is associated to an m-dimensional code vector $\hat{x}_j$, $j = 1, 2, ..., n$ (Fig. 1). An m-dimensional input vector x is mapped into the nearest code vector $\hat{x}_c$. This procedure divides the input space into Voronoi regions, denoted here by X_j, $j = 1, 2, ..., n$.

The connections and positions of the lattice elements could be described more formally by using notation familiar from graph theory, see e.g. [13]. In this paper, it suffices for notational convenience to use only position vectors y_j, $j = 1, 2, ..., n$, because only regular fixed-structure lattices are considered and Euclidean metric is used as a distance measure across the lattice.

The organization of a map follows an iterative procedure. Initially, at $t = 0$, the code vectors are randomly selected. At each successive time instant $t = 1, 2, ..., N$ the m-dimensional stochastic input vector $x(t)$ is compared with each code vector $\hat{x}_j(t-1)$, $j = 1, 2, ..., n$ to find the index of the nearest code vector $\hat{x}_c(t)$:

$$c(t) = \arg \min_j \| x(t) - \hat{x}_j(t-1) \|, \quad j = 1, 2, ..., n, \quad (1)$$

where $\| \cdot \|$ refers to Euclidean norm. After $c(t)$ has been found, the code vectors are updated according to the formula

$$\hat{x}_j(t) = \hat{x}_j(t-1) + \gamma(t) h_j(c(t), t) [x(t) - \hat{x}_j(t-1)], \quad (2)$$

$j = 1, 2, ..., n$, where $\gamma(t)$ is the step length. The neighborhood of the element $c(t)$ is defined by $h_j(c(t), t)$ which is a function of the distance between the elements j and $c(t)$. The stability and convergence of (2) requires the condition $0 \leq \gamma h_j \leq 1$.

If the parameters of the algorithm are suitably chosen, the algorithm will result in a vector quantization, where the order of the elements in the lattice reflects somehow the order of the corresponding code vectors. However, it must be pointed out that the concept of order is somewhat vague. The global order of the code vectors can not be defined uniquely unless the lattice and the input space have the same dimensions. Recently, Bauer and Pawelzik [1] introduced a numerical measure to indicate the violations of the ordering but it is too complex to be used in analytical studies.

The ordering of the map depends crucially on the parameters γ and h_j. The scalars h_j, $j = 1, 2, ..., n$, can be chosen so that they form Gaussian function, the center of which is placed at the element c in the lattice:

$$h_j(c(t), t) = \exp \{-d^2(j, c(t)) / \sigma^2(t)\}, \quad (3)$$

where $\sigma(t)$ is called to the radius of the neighborhood and

$$d(j, c(t)) = \| j - c(t) \|. \qquad (4)$$

It is essential for a successful global ordering of a map that initially the neighborhood has a large radius $\sigma_0 = \sigma(0)$ covering, for example, the whole map, whereas at the end of the organization it covers only the closest neighbors. The neighborhood radius is commonly contracted, for example, exponentially during the organization:

$$\sigma(t+1) = \sigma_p \sigma(t) + (1 - \sigma_p) \sigma_1, \qquad (5)$$

where σ_1 is the neighborhood size at the end of the organization and σ_p defines the rate of the decrease. These parameters have to be chosen experimentally since no analytical results are available. The effect of the neighborhood to the ordering of the map has been studied empirically in scalar case by Erwin et al. [2].

Now we write the code update equation (2) in a more compact form by introducing a new notation. This will lead straightforwardly to the quadratic objective function which serves as a basis of the recursive least-squares method.

Let us introduce two nm-dimensional vectors as follows:

$$\hat{x}(t) = \begin{bmatrix} \hat{x}_1(t) \\ \hat{x}_2(t) \\ \vdots \\ \hat{x}_n(t) \end{bmatrix}, \quad x^*(t) = \begin{bmatrix} x(t) \\ x(t) \\ \vdots \\ x(t) \end{bmatrix}. \qquad (6)$$

The vector $\hat{x}(t)$ is composed of all code vectors and $x^*(t)$ contains n input vectors $x(t)$ which are arranged into the nm-dimensional column vector. Further, the weighting factors h_j are collected to an $nm \times nm$ diagonal matrix

$$H = \begin{bmatrix} h_1 I_m & 0 & \cdots & 0 \\ 0 & h_2 I_m & \cdots & 0 \\ \vdots & \vdots & & \vdots \\ 0 & 0 & \cdots & h_n I_m \end{bmatrix}, \qquad (7)$$

where I_m is the $m \times m$ identity matrix and the arguments are omitted. By using this notation, (2) can be written in an equivalent form:

$$\hat{x}(t) = \hat{x}(t-1) \\ + \gamma(t) H(c(t), t) [x^*(t) - \hat{x}(t-1)]. \qquad (8)$$

This formalism can also be applied to more complex variants of self-organizing maps, for example, tree-structured time-varying lattices [5] and hierarchical self-organizing maps [9]. The form and connections of a lattice can be arbitrary, since this affects merely the numerical values of H.

III. RECURSIVE LEAST-SQUARES APPROACH

Let us consider the objective function

$$V_N(\hat{x}) = \frac{1}{N} \sum_{t=1}^{N} \beta(N, t) e^T(t) H(c(t), t) e(t), \qquad (9)$$

where

$$e(t) = x^*(t) - \hat{x}(t) \qquad (10)$$

and $\{\beta(N, t)\}$ is a sequence of positive real numbers. The introduction of the coefficients $\beta(N, t)$ in the objective function allows us to associate different weights with different observations $x(t)$. This is a common ad hoc method to handle time-varying problems in system identification [11].

In the context of self-organizing maps, the common practice of shrinking the neighborhood results in the time-varying characteristics by changing the stationary state of the algorithm, see e.g. [12]. Also the change of a lattice structure [5] alters the stationary state.

By assuming that

$$\partial h_j / \partial \hat{x} = 0_n^T, \quad \forall j = 1, 2, \ldots, n, \qquad (11)$$

where 0_n is an n-dimensional zero vector, the objective function (9) is quadratic in $\hat{x}$ and the minimizing value can be calculated simply. Now, the problem is in a very standard form. For example, the gradient descent method [11] results in the algorithm (8). However, we are seeking a more efficient algorithm so we proceed by deriving $V_N(\hat{x})$. This yields the equation

$$\hat{x}(N) = \left(\sum_{t=1}^{N} \beta(N, t) H(c(t), t) \right)^{-1} \\ \cdot \sum_{t=1}^{N} \beta(N, t) H(c(t), t) x^*(t). \qquad (12)$$

In principle $\hat{x}(N)$ could be calculated from this equation if the inverse exists. However, the minimizing value does not necessarily correspond to an ordered state of a map, since only a suitably chosen weighting sequence $H(c(t), t)$ produces organization. Thus (9) has to be minimized recursively. This leads us straightforwardly into the recursive least-squares algorithm which has been studied in detail, e.g. [11].

The expression (12) can be rewritten into a recursive form only if a convenient structure for $\beta(t, k)$ is introduced. Thus, it is assumed that

$$\beta(t, k) = \lambda(t) \beta(t-1, k), \quad k = 1, 2, \ldots, t-1, \qquad (13)$$

$$\beta(t, t) = 1. \qquad (14)$$

At time t, the latest observation $x(t)$ has the weight $\beta(t, t) = 1$. The old information $x(1), x(2), ..., x(t-1)$ is forgotten at the rate defined by the forgetting factor $0 \leq \lambda(t) \leq 1$.

By denoting

$$R(t) = \sum_{j=1}^{t} \beta(t, j) H(c(j), j), \tag{15}$$

$$f(t) = \sum_{j=1}^{t} \beta(t, j) H(c(j), j) x^*(j), \tag{16}$$

equation (12) gives

$$\hat{x}(t) = R^{-1}(t) f(t). \tag{17}$$

Using (13) and (14) it follows that

$$\begin{aligned} R(t) &= \lambda(t) \sum_{j=1}^{t-1} \beta(t-1, j) H(c(j), j) \\ &\quad + \beta(t, t) H(c(t), t) \\ &= \lambda(t) R(t-1) + H(c(t), t), \end{aligned} \tag{18}$$

and

$$f(t) = \lambda(t) f(t-1) + H(c(t), t) x^*(t). \tag{19}$$

Equations (17), (18) and (19) imply

$$\begin{aligned} R(t) &\hat{x}(t) \\ &= \lambda(t) f(t-1) + H(c(t), t) x^*(t) \\ &= \lambda(t) R(t-1) \hat{x}(t-1) + H(c(t), t) x^*(t) \\ &= [R(t) - H(c(t), t)] \hat{x}(t-1) + H(c(t), t) x^*(t). \end{aligned} \tag{20}$$

Solving for $\hat{x}(t)$ and observing (18) results in the recursive least-squares algorithm

$$\begin{aligned} \hat{x}(t) &= \hat{x}(t-1) \\ &\quad + R^{-1}(t) H(c(t), t) [x^*(t) - \hat{x}(t-1)], \end{aligned} \tag{21}$$

$$R(t) = \lambda(t) R(t-1) + H(c(t), t). \tag{22}$$

The algorithm (21)–(22) might seem computationally heavy since the matrix R has to be inverted at each iteration t. However, it is reasonable to choose $R(0) = aI_{nm}$, where a is a small positive scalar, for example 0.01. Therefore, due to the diagonality of H, only the inversion of n scalars is required to calculate R^{-1}. Thus, the algorithm (21)–(22) can be separated into n parallel code updates

$$\begin{aligned} \hat{x}_j(t) &= \hat{x}_j(t-1) \\ &\quad + r_j^{-1}(t) h_j(c(t), t) [x(t) - \hat{x}_j(t-1)], \end{aligned} \tag{23}$$

$$r_j(t) = \lambda(t) r_j(t-1) + h_j(c(t), t), \tag{24}$$

where each element $j = 1, 2, ..., n$ of the map has a scalar gain $r_j(t)$.

The algorithm (23)–(24) preserves the inherent parallellism and computational simplicity of the original code update formula (2). Equations (23)–(24) require $2n$ flops, consisting of n divisions, n additions and n multiplications, more computational work compared to the original formula. This additional computation has no practical importance since the computational load is usually dominated by the laborious task of finding the nearest code vector.

The algorithm requires the initial values $r_j(0)$ and $\hat{x}_j(0)$. Usually $r_j(0)$ can be chosen as $r_j(0) = a$, where a is the small positive scalar introduced earlier. It is of common practice to choose initial code vectors randomly. The objective function (9) suggests that if the correct initial values are unknown, the initial code vectors should be zero vectors. However, the nearest code vector cannot be uniquely determined using (1) if two or more code vectors are at the same distance from the current input vector. Therefore it is reasonable to use small random initial values unless some sensibly chosen ordered initial state is not used.

As can be seen from (24), the forgetting factor $\lambda(t)$ sets an upper bound to $r_j(t)$. This prevents the step length of (23) to go to zero. The forgetting factor can also be exploited to forget wrong, non-optimal, initial values. For example, by using the time-varying forgetting

$$\lambda(t+1) = \lambda_p \lambda(t) + (1 - \lambda_p) \lambda_1, \tag{25}$$

$\lambda(t)$ tends to λ_1 from the initial value $\lambda_0 = \lambda(0) < \lambda_1$ at the rate defined by λ_p. This is a practical trick to rapidly sweep away the effect of poor initial values [11].

IV. EXAMPLES

To illustrate the properties of the proposed algorithm, three simulation examples are discussed. The examples are chosen as simple as possible in order to visualize the lattice and the code vectors of the self-organizing map.

The initial values of the two-dimensional code vectors $\hat{x}_j(0)$, $j = 1, 2, ..., 64$, are selected randomly from the interval $[0.425, 0.575]$ and the initial gains $r_j(0) = 0.01$ are used in all examples.

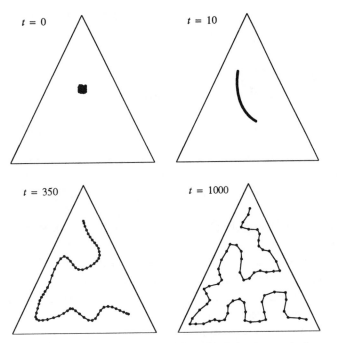

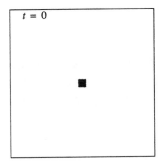

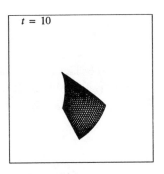

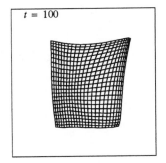

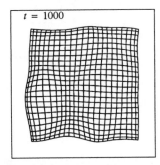

Fig. 2. The code vectors $\hat{x}_j(t)$, $j = 1, 2, \ldots, 64$, during the organization. The closest neighbors are connected by lines.

Fig. 4. The organization of the 24×24 square map. The four nearest lattice neighbors are connected by lines.

In the first and second examples, where one-dimensional maps in two-dimensional input space are studied, the value $\lambda = 0.95$ of the constant forgetting factor is employed. The parameters related to the neighborhood, see (5), are chosen as follows: $\sigma_0 = 1800$, $\sigma_p = 0.99$ and $\sigma_1 = 1$.

When the 2-D input space is mapped to the two-dimensional map, as presented in Example B, the constant forgetting is not sufficient and the map does not organize properly if the radius of the neighborhood is contracted too rapidly. Therefore the time-varying forgetting (25) is used with parameters $\lambda_0 = 0.92$, $\lambda_p = 0.99$ and $\lambda_1 = 0.99$. The neighborhood parameters are chosen as follows: $\sigma_0 = 250$, $\sigma_p = 0.99$ and $\sigma_1 = 10$.

In practical applications, the parameters have to be chosen usually in a more conservative way. It is advantageous to

decrease the radius of the neighborhood slower than in the simulations presented here. Then the map organizes more reliably. Unfortunately, these choises have to be made experimentally.

A. Example: One-Dimensional Map of 2-D Input Space

The first example, studied also in [7], considers the case where 1000 stochastic vectors $x(t) = [x_1(t)\ x_2(t)]^T$ are uniformly distributed in a triangle shaped region

$$P_1 = \{x \mid x_2 \geq 0 \wedge 2x_1 - x_2 \geq 0 \wedge 2 - 2x_1 - x_2 \geq 0\}. \quad (26)$$

The borders of the region P_1 are presented by lines in Fig. 2.

The code vectors are presented during the four different stages of the organization in Fig. 2. As the organization of the map progresses, the code vectors fill the triangle shaped area. As was expected, the recursive least-squares algorithm results in a remarkably faster convergence of the map than the original algorithm studied in [7]. However, it must be pointed out that the direct comparison between the results is not quite fair since the parameters related to the neighborhood affect crucially organization.

Let us next consider the case where 1000 stochastic two-dimensional vectors are uniformly distributed in two circles defined by

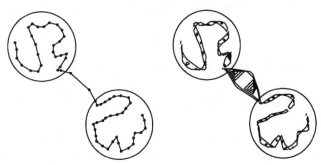

Fig. 3. The code vectors $\hat{x}_j(1000)$, $j = 1, 2, \ldots, 64$, (on the left) and the gains $r_j^{-1}(1000)$ presented by a contour in the input space (on the right).

$$P_2 = \{x \mid (x_1 - 0.75)^2 + (x_2 - 0.25)^2 \leq 0.22^2 \wedge \\ (x_1 - 0.25)^2 + (x_2 - 0.75)^2 \leq 0.22^2\}. \quad (27)$$

The borders of the region P_2 are presented by solid lines in Fig. 3. The map now tends to organize in such a manner that some code vectors are left outside of the input data set.

The organization of the map after 1000 iterations is presented in Fig. 3. The map has two totally unused elements $\hat{x}_{29} \approx [0.43 \; 0.58]^T$ and $\hat{x}_{30} \approx [0.55 \; 0.47]^T$. These outliers can be detected already during the code update sequence by examining the gains, see (24). At $t = 1000$, the gains of the two outliers are $r_{29}^{-1} \approx r_{30}^{-1} \approx 0.35$ when the average is 0.14. These indicators will become more obvious when the algorithm proceeds further. The inverses r_j^{-1} are presented in Fig. 3 by a contour in the input space. The belt composed of the contour curves is significantly wider at the elements $j = 29$ and $j = 30$ than at the other elements which fill the nonzero-density areas. The gain provided recursively by (24) could directly be used in approximating the probability function of $x(t)$ locally, near the particular code vector. This has been studied by Fritzke [4] who suggested a similar equation to (24) to count the hits occurred for each code vector.

B. Example: Two-Dimensional Maps of 2-D Input Space

In the third example, the organization of a two-dimensional map is examined, when 1000 stochastic input vectors are uniformly distributed in $P_3 = \{ x \mid 0 \le x_1 \le 1 \wedge 0 \le x_2 \le 1 \}$. This is a familiar example studied by numerous authors, e.g. [1], [7].

The organization of the map, composed of 576 code vectors associated to the 24×24 lattice, is presented after 1000 iterations in Fig. 4. Again, the code vectors fill rapidly the square P_3 presented by lines. In fact, after about ten iterations the map is already organized. When the organization goes on, the map fills the square more densely.

V. CONCLUSIONS

A recursive least-squares algorithm for updating the code vectors of the self-organizing map is derived by associating a quadratic cost function to the original code update formula. The least-squares approach yields a parallel code update formula where each code vector has a separate scalar gain. The gain is directly given by the recursive equation. The properties of the presented algorithm is illustrated by low-dimensional simulation examples. The results demonstrate that the algorithm results in fast convergence of the code vectors

without changing the basic properties of the self-organizing map.

REFERENCES

[1] H.-U. Bauer and K. R. Pawelzik, "Quantifying the neighborhood preservation of self-organizing feature maps," *IEEE Trans. on Neural Networks*, vol. 3, pp. 570–579, 1992.

[2] E. Erwin, K. Obermayer and K. Schulten, "Self-organizing maps: stationary states, metastability and convergence rate," *Biological Cybernetics*, vol. 67, pp. 35–45, 1992.

[3] E. Erwin, K. Obermayer and K. Schulten, "Self-organizing maps: ordering, convergence properties and energy functions," *Biological Cybernetics*, vol. 67, pp. 47–55, 1992.

[4] B. Fritzke, "Growing sell structures — a self-organizing network in k dimensions," I. Aleksander and J. Taylor (ed.), *Artificial Neural Networks 2*, Elsevier Science Publishers B. V., pp. 1051–1056, 1992.

[5] J. A. Kangas, T. K. Kohonen and J. T. Laaksonen, "Variants of self-organizing maps," *IEEE Trans. on Neural Networks*, vol. 1, pp. 93–99, 1990.

[6] T. Kohonen, "Self-organizing formulation of topologically correct feature maps," *Biological Cybernetics*, vol. 44, pp. 59–69, 1982.

[7] T. Kohonen, *Self-Organization and Associative Memory*. Springer-Verlag, Berlin, 1984.

[8] T. Kohonen, K. Raivio, O. Simula, O. Ventä and J. Henriksson, "Combining linear equalization and self-organizing adaptation in dynamic discrete-signal detection," in Proc. *IJCNN Int. Joint Conf. on Neural Networks*, San Diego, CA, USA, June 17–21, pp. 223–228, 1990.

[9] P. Koikkalainen and E. Oja, "Self-organizing hierarchical feature maps," in Proc. *IJCNN Int. Joint Conf. on Neural Networks*, San Diego, CA, USA, June 17–21, pp. 279–284, 1990.

[10] L. Leinonen, J. Kangas, K. Torkkola and A. Juvas, "Dysphonia detected by pattern recognition of spectral composition," *Journal of Speech and Hearing Research*, vol. 35, pp. 287–295, 1992.

[11] L. Ljung and T. Söderström, *Theory and Practice of Recursive Identification*, The MIT Press, 1983.

[12] S. P. Luttrell, "Code vector density in topographic mappings: scalar case," *IEEE Trans. on Neural Networks*, vol. 2, pp. 427–436, 1991.

[13] J. A. Mchugh, *Algorithmic Graph Theory*, Prentice-Hall, 1990.

[14] H. Ritter and K. Schulten, "Convergence properties of Kohonen's topology preserving map: fluctuations, stability, and dimension selection," *Biological Cybernetics*, vol. 60, pp. 59–71, 1988.

[15] H. J. Ritter, T. M. Martinetz and K. J. Schulten, "Topology-conserving maps for learning visuo-motor coordination," *Neural Networks*, vol. 2, pp. 159–168, 1989.

[16] O. Simula and A. Visa, "Self-organizing feature maps in texture classification and segmentation," I. Aleksander and J. Taylor (ed.), *Artificial Neural Networks 2*, Elsevier Science Publishers, pp. 1621–1628, 1992.

[17] T. Sorsa and H. N. Koivo, "Application of artificial neural networks in process fault diagnosis," *Automatica*, in press.

Unsupervised Learning for Multivariate Probability Density Estimation: Radial Basis Function and Exploratory Projection Pursuit

Jenq-Neng Hwang,   Shyh-Rong Lay,   Alan Lippman

Information Processing Laboratory
Department of Electrical Engineering, FT-10
University of Washington
Seattle, WA 98195

ABSTRACT

This paper discusses two types of "unsupervised learning" techniques for nonparametric multivariate density estimation, where no assumption is made about the data being drawn from any of known parametric families of distribution. The first type is based on a robust kernel method which uses locally tuned radial basis (Gaussian) functions; the second type is based on an exploratory projection pursuit technique which uses orthogonal polynomial approximation to 1-D density along several projections from multidimensional data. Performance evaluations using training data from mixture Gaussian and mixture Cauchy densities are presented.

I. INTRODUCTION

Although kernel methods and their (variable or adaptive) extensions are so far the most widely used methods for nonparametric density estimation, these rather ad-hoc methods normally suffer from two practical drawbacks [12]: one is the inability to deal satisfactorily with tails of distributions without oversmoothing the main part of the density, and the other is the curse of dimensionality (i.e., the exponentially increasing sample size required to estimate the multivariate density when the number of dimensions increases). A radial basis function (RBF) based kernel method is an improved alternative of a probabilistic neural network (PNN) [11] for density estimation. An RBF network is a two-layer feedforward network whose output nodes form a linear summation of the basis (or kernels) functions in the hidden layer.

Sequential and batch versions of K-mean clustering have been commonly used in training the weights associated with the hidden layer weights of an RBF network [8, 1, 3]. The clustering algorithm can determine the center locations of the Gaussian kernels, it can also provide the insights about the covariance structures of kernels via simple data analysis techniques on the clustered data. Unfortu-

nately, there is no guarantee that the resulting covariance structures can be simple enough (e.g., diagonal covariance matrices) to be implemented based on an RBF-like network. To overcome this problem and to further improve the approximation capability of kernel methods, Mahalanobis Gaussian kernels of nondiagonal covariance matrix structures have been proposed [9]. These methods resulted in laborious learning procedures and inconsistent performance due to the high sensitivity of control parameters.

To overcome the difficulties involved in constructing an RBF network, we propose to combine the statistical data sphering technique [5] with the centroid splitting generalized Lloyd clustering technique (also known as the LBG algorithm [7]). This robust construction method has been successfully applied by us to classification tasks [6]. Our intention is to decorrelate and normalize the data so that simplified (i.e., diagonal) covariance matrix structures can be obtained. Another additional benefit of this combined method is the capability of removing probabilistic outlier (especially for heavy tailed density), offered by the data sphering, that promotes the robustness of the center searching in the data clustering.

Although the robust construction kernel method can overcome some difficulties encountered in using RBF networks for density estimation, whose performance is still too sensitive to the settings of some control parameters, e.g., the number of kernels used, the size of training data, the excluding threshold radius for data sphering, the allowed smallest variance along each dimension, etc. We are thus motivated to study the statistical projection pursuit density estimation technique. In contrast to the locally tuned kernel methods, where data are analyzed directly in high dimensional space around the vicinity of the kernel centers, the projection pursuit methods globally and linearly project the data onto a one- or two-dimensional subspace, and analyze the projected data in these low dimensional subspaces with less efforts. More specifically, the projection pursuit defines some criterion of the interest of a projected configuration, instead of maximizing the variance adopted by the principal component analysis, and then uses a numerical optimization technique to find the projection of most interest [12, 5].

Donoho and Johnstone have done an intensive comparisons between projection pursuit and isotropic kernels methods for *regression approximation* of two-dimensional problems [2]. We believed that fitting a distribution from sample data is a much more difficult task due to the inherent constraint imposed by the probability density compared to that of regression approximations. In this paper, the robust RBF kernel method and projection pursuit method for multivariate density estimation are studied and compared. Data from different types of distributions are used for extensive simulations. In terms of estimation efficiency, the kernel method offers quite comparable training speed as that of projection pursuit estimators. On the other hand, projection pursuit is more parsimonious, i.e., in order to achieve comparable accuracy, the projection pursuit requires a fewer number of projections (vs. the number of kernel neurons) to approximate the true function. In terms of estimation accuracy, the projection pursuit is also more favored, especially no *a priori* information (e.g., number of kernels required) is needed.

II. ROBUST CONSTRUCTION OF RBF KERNELS

In the classification applications, some outlying training data are meaningful and can be carefully regularized to increase the generalization capability of the classifiers [10]. However, the outlying data in a density estimation application represent the small subset of data generated by heavy tailed deviations from the density. These data usually carry very little information about the density and does not represent any meaningful isolated class either (such as in classification applications).

If the RBF network construction is based on the PNN convention, where a symmetric kernel is placed on each training data site, then the outlying data won't play a significant role in approximating the true density since the amount of outlying data are relatively quite small. On the other hand, when the clustering techniques (e.g., K-mean or LBG) are adopted to reduce the number of kernels deployed, the outlying data play a more significant role. More specifically, most clustering algorithms are types of least squares estimators, which are all sensitive to outliers. Therefore, we are motivated to apply the data sphering technique before the data clustering [5, 6].

A. Data Sphering for Structure Decorrelation and Outlier Removing

Let $\mathbf{x}$ be a random variable in R^p. The goal of data sphering is to transform $\mathbf{x}$ into a sphered data $\mathbf{z}$ so that $E[\mathbf{z}] = \mathbf{0}$ and $E[\mathbf{z}\mathbf{z}^T] = \mathbf{I}$, the identity matrix. Sphering operation starts with an eigen-decomposition of the data covariance matrix $\Sigma = E[(\mathbf{x} - E[\mathbf{x}])(\mathbf{x} - E[\mathbf{x}])^T] = \mathbf{U}\mathbf{D}\mathbf{U}^T$, where $\mathbf{U}$ is an orthonormal and $\mathbf{D}$ is a diagonal $p \times p$ matrix. Each column of $\mathbf{U}$ is an eigenvector of Σ and the corresponding diagonal entry of $\mathbf{D}$ is its eigenvalue.

The data sphering procedure then transforms the original set of data $\{\mathbf{x}\}$ into $\{\mathbf{z}\}$, where $\mathbf{z} = \mathbf{D}^{-1/2}\mathbf{U}^T(\mathbf{x} - E[\mathbf{x}])$.

All sphered data with larger norm (e.g., $\|\mathbf{z}\| \geq \beta$), where β is a prespecified threshold, are treated as outlier and are excluded for clustering. This data sphering and outlier removing process can continue for several iterations (on the original data $\{\mathbf{x}\}$ until no outlying data can be removed. The sphered data $\{\mathbf{z}\}$ are then clustered using the LBG algorithm [7].

Another purpose of sphering the data is to remove location, scale, and correlational structure of the originally observed data so that the covariance matrices of the multivariate Gaussian kernels can be simplified to be diagonal matrices after the data clustering on the sphered data $\{\mathbf{z}\}$.

B. RBF Network Construction After Data Clustering

The bandwidths of the Gaussian kernel functions are simply designed to be proportional to (via a prespecified global scaling constant η) the data variances in each dimension of each cluster within each class. Through the choice of the scaling constant η, one can appropriately adjust the smoothness of the reconstruction surface. In case of very small variance, a minimum bandwidth is used to avoid abrupt cutoffs along some dimensions, i.e., to ensure some degree of smoothness. The height of each kernel is simply determined by the percentage of the subset of training data which are clustered to this center in the same class.

To verify our assumption of the reverse impact from outlying data to density estimation, simple 2-D density estimation experiments were conducted. Figure 1(a) shows a heavy tailed Cauchy mixture density function. The corresponding 12 cluster centers found by the LBG algorithm without data sphering are wide spreaded as shown in Figure 1(b). The approximated density based on these 12 RBF kernels, with the diagonal covariance matrices and kernel heights chosen as described above, is shown in Figure 1(c). Note that this estimated density is nothing near to the true density. On the other hand, when the data sphering is applied before the data clustering, the 12 cluster centers found by the LBG algorithm are much more representative to the true data distribution (see Figure 1(d)). Therefore, the approximated density, with the same diagonal covariance matrices and kernel heights selection procedure, is much closer to the true density (see Figure 1(e)).

III. Projection Pursuit Method via Exploratory Data Analysis

The spirit of projection pursuit density estimation is based on looking for interesting "lower dimensional" projection directions which reveal useful structures. In this paper, we implemented the projection pursuit density method proposed by Friedman [5]. There are five steps involved in this method:

1. Data Sphering: removing the location, scale, and correlation structures (as defined in last section).

2. Projection Index: indicating the degree of interestingness of different projection directions.

3. Optimization Strategy: searching the direction of maximal projection index efficiently.

4. Structure Removing: removing the effects caused by this projection direction.

5. Density Formation: combining all interesting directions to form the density function.

IV. Experimental Simulations

A. Simulated Data

Multidimensional data (2D-5D) of 4 Gaussian mixtures and 4 Cauchy mixtures are generated. The data are generated such that all elements in the same data vector are independent to each other. In Gaussian mixture data, the 4 Guassian distributions have different mean vectors and different diagonal covariance matrices. In Cauchy mixture data, the 4 Cauchy distributions have different center locations and width parameters.

Five randomly selected data sets of embedded densities with different sizes (400, 800, 1600, 3200, 6400) are used for training both of kernel and projection pursuit methods. Uniform grid multidimensional points are selected for evaluating the approximation performances of both methods.

B. Performance Evaluation Criterion

In all our simulations of the RBF kernel method for density estimation, we used various number of kernels (or LBG clusters), varying from 4, 5, 8, and 12. For the projection pursuit method, the iterations of finding more interesting projection directions terminated when the projection index fell below 0.05 times the largest index appeared so far. Instead of using mean squared error (MSE)

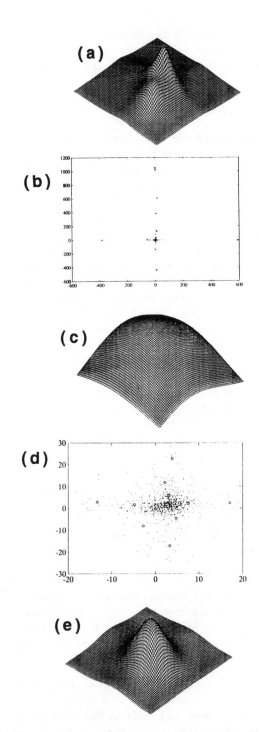

Figure 1: (a) A heavy tailed Cauchy mixture density function. (b) The corresponding 12 cluster centers found by the LBG algorithm without data sphering. (c) The estimated density based on the 12 cluster centers in (b). (d) The 12 cluster centers found by the LBG algorithm after data sphering. (e) The estimated density based on the 12 cluster centers in (d).

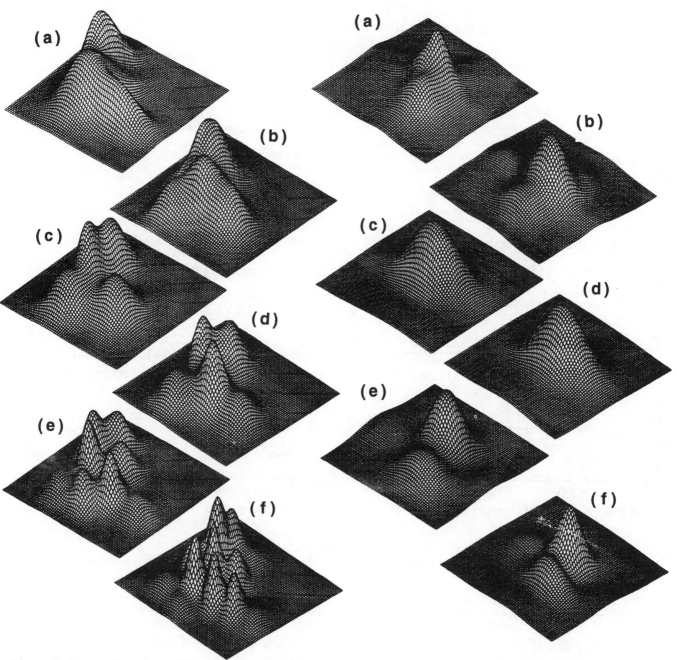

Figure 2: Perspective plots of Gaussian density. (a) True density. (b) Projection pursuit estimated density. (c) RBF estimated density with 4 kernels. (d) RBF estimated density with 5 kernels. (e) RBF estimated density with 8 kernels. (f) RBF estimated density with 12 kernels.

Figure 3: Perspective plots of Cauchy density. (a) True density. (b) Projection pursuit estimated density. (c) RBF estimated density with 4 kernels. (d) RBF estimated density with 5 kernels. (e) RBF estimated density with 8 kernels. (f) RBF estimated density with 12 kernels.

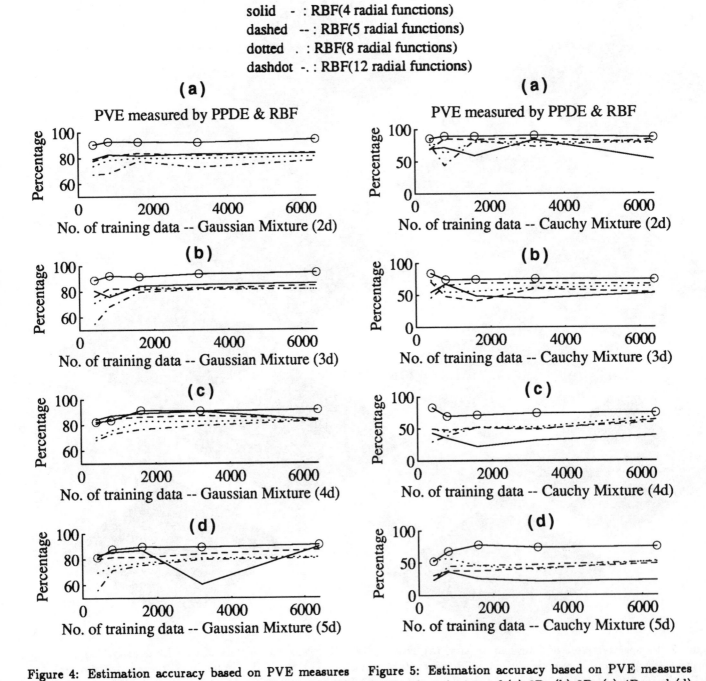

solid o -o : PPDE
solid   - : RBF(4 radial functions)
dashed -- : RBF(5 radial functions)
dotted . : RBF(8 radial functions)
dashdot -. : RBF(12 radial functions)

Figure 4: Estimation accuracy based on PVE measures for Gaussian mixtures of (a) 2D, (b) 3D, (c) 4D, and (d) 5D.

Figure 5: Estimation accuracy based on PVE measures for Cauchy mixtures of (a) 2D, (b) 3D, (c) 4D, and (d) 5D.

criterion to measure the similarity between the true density and the estimated density, we adopted the *percentage of variance explained* (PVE) criterion [4] for performance evaluation:

$$PVE = 100(1 - E/Var)\%$$

where $E = \frac{1}{N}\sum_n(\hat{P}_n - P_n)^2$ denotes the mean squared error between the estimated density $\hat{P}_n$ and the true density P_n over N testing data, and $Var = \frac{1}{N}\sum_n(P_n - \bar{P})^2$ denotes the training sample variance, where $\bar{P}$ denotes the sample average of the true density.

C. Simulation Results

It is our observation that the projection pursuit method consistently outperformed the kernel methods in approximation accuracy based on PVE measures in almost all the simulations. Especially, the RBF kernel method should be a natural fit for estimating the density of Guassian mixtures, while projection pursuit still performs better for this set of data. This result can be challenged by the fact that the data sphering technique, which globally orient (transform) the Gaussian mixture data from {x} to {z} before the data clustering, may destroy the original uncorrelated structure of {x} in each individual Gaussian mixture component and make it infeasible for the later diagonal covariance matrix construction of RBF kernels to approximate the oriented Gaussian mixtures. This challenge is valid and supported by some of our unreported simulations, which indicated that the RBF kernel methods can sometimes outperform the projection pursuit when a right number of kernels is chosen and the data sphering is only used to remove the outliers (very few for Gaussian distribution) without actual transforming the data from x to z before data clustering. Nevertheless, the projection pursuit method consistently outperforms both kernel methods (with/without the actual data orientation before data clustering) in estimating the Cauchy mixtures.

Furthermore, the projection pursuit method is more robust in that it is less sensitive to setting the values of some control parameters (e.g., the termination threshold for projection index). On the other hand, the performance of kernel methods is more sensitive to the selections of control parameters, e.g., the number of kernels used, the size of training data, the excluding threshold radius for data sphering, the allowed minimum bandwidth, etc. Figures 2(b) to 2(f) show the perspective plots of estimated densities that approximate the true Gaussian mixture density given in Figures 2(a). Figures 3(b) to 3(f) show the perspective plots of estimated densities that approximate the true Cauchy mixture density given in Figures 3(a). Figure 4 and Figure 5 show the accuracy of estimation to the Gaussian/Cauchy mixture densities evaluated over around 10,000 uniform grid testing points based on PVE measures. The performances are evaluated from 2 dimensions to 5 dimensions. The comparative results also include various numbers of Gaussian kernels used in constructing the RBF networks.

REFERENCES

[1] P. Burrascano. Learning vector quantization for the probabilistic neural network. IEEE Trans. on Neural Networks, 2(4):458-461, July 1991.

[2] D. L. Donoho and I. M. Johnstone. Regression approximation using projection and isotropic kernels. Contemporary Mathematics, Vol. 59, pp. 153-167, 1986.

[3] R. O. Duda, P. E. Hart. Pattern Classification and Scene Analysis. Wiley, New York, NY, 1973.

[4] J. H. Friedman, W. Stuetzle, and A. Schroeder. Projection pursuit density estimation. Journal of the American Statistical Association, Vol. 79, pp. 599-608, 1984.

[5] J. H. Friedman. Exploratory projection pursuit. Journal of the American Statistical Association, Vol. 82, pp. 249-266, 1987.

[6] S.R. Lay and J.N. Hwang. Robust construction of radial basis function neural networks for classification. To appear in Int'l Conf. on Neural Networks, San Francisco, 1993.

[7] Y. Linde, A Buzo, and R. M. Gray. An algorithm for vector quantizer design. IEEE Trans. on Communication, 28:84-95, Jan. 1980.

[8] J. Moody and C.J. Darken Fast learning in networks of locally tuned processing units. Neural Computation, 1(3):281-294, 1989.

[9] M. T. Musavi, W. Ahmed, K. H. Chan and K. B. Faris. On the training of radial basis function classifier. Neural Networks, 5:595-603, 1992.

[10] T. Poggio, F. Girosi. Networks for approximation and learning. Proceedings of IEEE, 78(9):1481-1497, September 1990.

[11] D.F. Specht. Probabilistic neural networks. Neural Networks, Vol. 3, pp. 109-118, 1990.

[12] B. W. Silverman. Density Estimation for Statistics and Data Analysis. Chapman and Hall Inc., London, 1986.

A Neural Network To Diagnose Liver Cancer

Philip S. Maclin and Jack Dempsey

University of Tennessee, Memphis, and Veteran's Administration Medical Center

Memphis, TN 38163

Abstract--Radiologists use abdominal ultrasonographic data and laboratory tests to perform differential diagnoses of hepatic (liver) masses, but interpretation is often difficult. A backpropagation neural network was designed to diagnose five classifications of hepatic masses: metastatic carcinoma, hepatoma (HCC), cavernous hemangioma, abscess, and cirrhosis. BrainMaker Professional version 2.5 software was used in this research. The input submitted to the network consisted of 35 numbers per patient case that represented ultrasonographic data and laboratory tests. The network architecture had 35 elements in the input layer, two hidden layers of 35 elements each, and 5 elements in the output layer. After being trained to a learning tolerance of 1%, the network classified hepatic masses correctly in 51 of 72 cases. That accuracy of 71% is higher than the 50% scored by the average radiology resident in training but lower than the 90% scored by the typical board-certified radiologist. Continued research should provide a computerized second opinion that will be especially helpful to clinicians.

1. INTRODUCTION

Abdominal ultrasonography and various laboratory tests are the primary tools used to diagnose hepatic cancers, but such diagnoses are difficult.[1] Our research deals with the specific problem of how to improve the diagnoses of hepatic (liver) masses using artificial neural networks trained on ultrasound data and laboratory test results.

Artificial neural networks are solving problems that previous technologies have been unable to resolve satisfactorily, especially in the diagnosis of disease and other applications involving pattern recognition.[2] An artificial neural network is an information-processing technique or a computer-based simulation of a living nervous system, with characteristics that come from a structure of many interconnected elements operating in parallel.

With increased curative surgical techniques for primary and secondary hepatic neoplasms, clinical imaging tasks have become more exacting.[3-4] Neural networks can help solve that problem in radiology. Among the most significant therapeutic advances in the management of primary and metastatic hepatic neoplasms is the continued evolution of aggressive surgical techniques.[5-6] Tumor detection, differential diagnosis of individual nodules, and mapping of the anatomic extensions of malignant disease are now routinely required. Related and unrelated hepatic substrate abnormalities such as cavernous hemangioma and focal fatty deposits are often discovered and must be differentiated from metastatic deposits. Also, modern imaging methods such as magnetic resonance imaging (MRI) frequently display tiny nodules (< 1 cm) that often prove difficult to adequately characterize (micrometastases versus other types of lesions).[7]

Although no results have been announced on the specific use of a neural network in the diagnosis of hepatic masses, they have been published on related projects. Although no application was attempted, Boone, Gross and Greco-Hunt discussed the possibility of using neural networks in radiologic diagnosis.[8] They concluded that "developments in this area may ultimately affect radiology."

Gross, Boone, Greco-Hunt, and Greenberg trained a neural network to choose 1 or more from 12 possible diagnoses based on 21 observations of neonatal chest radiographs.[9] They concluded that a trained neural network has the potential to diagnose neonatal cardiopulmonary disorders "with a consistency approximately equivalent to that of pediatric radiologists."

A prototype neural network was used to diagnose renal cancer in 52 kidney cases.[10] While the approach to the renal cancer diagnosis was similar to our hepatic mass research, diagnosing renal masses is considered less demanding than diagnosing hepatic masses. Furthermore, no laboratory test data was used in the renal research.

Mulsant[11] developed a backpropagation neural network that became increasingly proficient at clinical diagnosis of dementia, or irreversible deterioration of intellectual faculties from organic brain disorder. Mulsant concluded that neural computing can help diagnose difficult problems with its ability to learn from experience and to generalize.

Other successful neural networks include: emulation of biological system responses,[12-13] forms of memory and REM sleep,[14] nonlinear Bayesian estimation from sparse data,[15] speech recognition,[16-17] hypertension,[18] and pathologic diagnoses based on 110 radiographs of bone tumors.[19] In chemistry, various networks predict adverse drug reactions, physicochemical properties characteristic of a safe drug, product distributions from chemical reactions, and three-dimensional structures of proteins from amino acid sequences.[20]

In summary, biologically inspired neural networks learn from experience, generalize from previous examples to new ones, and abstract essential characteristics from inputs containing irrelevant data. Once trained, a network's response can be partially insensitive to minor variations in input. This ability to see through noise and distortion to the pattern that lies within is vital to pattern recognition in a real-world environment.

II. MATERIALS AND METHODS

Most artificial neural networks are developed in software since conventional computers can implement most ANNs using an appropriate programming language.[21] After success is proven, some networks are converted to hardware implementations (neurocomputers) to gain processing speed.[2] The majority of applications are either with neural network shells[22] or the C programming language for portability to various computers.[23] The most successful algorithm in solving clinical diagnosis programs so far has been backpropagation.[24-25]

BrainMaker Professional version 2.5, a software shell designed for neural network applications,[26] was used to diagnose hepatic masses in our research. BrainMaker uses standard backpropagation,[27-28] which is the most widespread learning algorithm for multilayered, straightforward connection. In considering what paradigm would be best for our hepatic mass application, standard backpropagation was chosen because of its successes in clinical diagnoses. Attributes of the hepatic mass application closely matched capabilities of the backpropagation paradigm.[21] Backpropagation has been applied to a wide variety of research applications, including medical diagnostics.[29]

Interpretation by a radiologist involves several steps. First, the ultrasound images from the patient's file are viewed and a list of any abnormalities present (referred to as the sonographic findings) is complied. Next, numeric data of laboratory tests from computer printouts are read. Then the radiologist uses a cognitive process in which conclusions are sought as to the possible diagnosis or diagnoses based on the radiographic findings.

Our research was based on unpublished raw data from hospital patients. At least two radiologists interpreted the characteristics found in the ultrasound images and agreed on their interpretations. The patient usually had only one ultrasound exam, but often had the same type of laboratory test repeated several times over a period of days. If a laboratory test was repeated several times, the radiologists relied more on the test with the date closest to that of the ultrasound reading. Consequently, our research used only the laboratory test with the closest date.

The network was trained 18 different times on 68 cases, 94.4% of the data, and tested on the remaining 4 cases, which were selected at random. Since the number of cases in the data set was limited to 72, the "leave out k" approach was used.[30] The "leave out k" method is a process that holds out a different group of facts each time the training is done and then tests with the holdout group. To verify that the network was properly tested on all facts, this procedure was replicated 18 times, and each time a different set of 4 was withheld for test purposes. This procedure resulted in 72 test cases, a number significant enough to find the robustness of generalization, or a global minimum. This approach was used because of the limited number in the data set. The limited data set was the result of having to use only patient histories in which autopsies or surgery had confirmed the diagnosis.

The neural network had 35 elements in the input layer. Some data attributes were represented as binary to the input processing elements. For example, ultrasound is reflected or transmitted from the hepatic mass so that the area appears white (hyperechoic), gray (hypoechoic), or very black (anechoic); if the mass appeared white, a binary 1 was submitted to the hyperechoic node and a binary 0 to the hypoechoic and anechoic nodes. Each laboratory test was represented as a numeric value to an input element and then normalized. If the laboratory test was not taken or unavailable, a binary 1 was submitted to an input element representing that test as missing. One problem was that laboratory data were often incomplete since few patients were given every possible laboratory test.

The output layer contained the five possible predominant classifications of the hepatic mass: metastatic carcinoma, hepatoma (HCC), cavernous hemangioma, abscess, and cirrhosis. Since the 72 patient cases used in this research had known histological or cytological results, the output classification was not arbitrary. Five output elements were used with a binary 1 or 0 for each possible predominant outcome.

For this hepatic mass application, the most successful network architecture had 35 input elements in the input layer, 35 elements in each of two hidden layers, and five elements in the output layer. Since the hidden layer architecture is a critical variable, four combinations commonly found in similar research were tested: a ratio of 1:1:1, two hidden layers of 35 elements each; a ratio of 1:2, one hidden layer of 70 elements; a ratio of 1:4, one hidden layer of 140 elements; and a ratio of 1:5, one hidden

layer of 175 elements.

The subjects were patients at Veterans Administration Medical Center in Memphis, Tennessee, who had been diagnosed as having hepatic lesions and later had the diagnosis verified by either surgical pathology or autopsy. Only cases in which the outcomes were certain were submitted to the neural network. Our research used only cases where the hepatic masses were abnormal, the outcome was confirmed by surgical pathology or an autopsy, and some supplemental laboratory test data were available. Since physicians seldom order every available laboratory test, a patient was commonly missing one or more possible tests.

Below are the 35 different fields of data that were input to separate elements on the neural net:

01 Size of the hepatic mass in millimeters. Values ranged from 0 to 150 mm and were normalized to range from 0 to 1.

02 Binary 1 if no hepatic mass was detected; otherwise 0.

03 Binary 1 if single mass was detected; otherwise 0.

04 Binary 1 if multiple mass was detected; otherwise 0.

05 Binary 1 if hyperechoic (sound was reflected, so the area appeared white); otherwise 0.

06 Binary 1 if hypoechoic (no sound was reflected, so the area appeared gray); otherwise 0.

07 Binary 1 if anechoic (sound was absorbed, so the area appeared very black); otherwise 0.

08 Binary 1 if internal echo was detected (the area appeared white); otherwise 0.

09 Binary 1 if no internal echo was detected (the area appeared black); otherwise 0.

10 Binary 1 if sound was transmitted; otherwise 0.

11 Binary 1 if no sound was transmitted; otherwise 0.

12 Binary 1 if air was detected (often indicating abscess); otherwise 0.

13 Binary 1 if no air was detected; otherwise 0.

14 Binary 1 if computed tomography (CT) enhancement was detected; otherwise 0.

15 Binary 1 if no CT enhancement was

detected; otherwise 0.

16 Binary 1 if CT fat was detected; otherwise 0.

17 Binary 1 if no CT fat was detected; otherwise 0.

18 Binary 1 if homogeneous (same texture) was detected; otherwise 0.

19 Binary 1 if not homogeneous (mixed texture); otherwise 0.

20 Amount of total bilirubin that was detected by test. Values ranged from 0.2 to 18.9 and were normalized to range from 0 to 1.

21 Binary 1 if no test was taken for total bilirubin.

22 Amount of direct bilirubin that was detected by test. Values ranged from 0.1 to 18.0 and were normalized to range from 0 to 1.

23 Binary 1 if no test was taken for direct bilirubin.

24 Amount of alkaline phosphatase that was detected by test. Values ranged from 66 to 1664 and were normalized to range from 0 to 1.

25 Binary 1 if no test was taken for alkaline phosphatase.

26 Amount of aspartate amino transferase (AST). Older terminology is glutamic-oxaloacetic transaminase. Values ranged from 10 to 903 and were normalized to range from 0 to 1.

27 Binary 1 if no test was taken for AST.

28 Amount of lactate dehydrogenase that was detected. Values ranged from 78 to 2035 and were normalized to range from 0 to 1.

29 Binary 1 if no test was taken for LDH.

30 Amount of gamma glutamyl transferase (gamma GT) detected. Values ranged from 29 to 9214 and were normalized to range from 0 to 1.

31 Binary 1 if no test was taken for gamma GT.

32 Amount of albumin that was detected. Values ranged from 1.0 to 4.7 and were normalized to range from 0 to 1.

33 Binary 1 if no test was taken for albumin.

34 Amount of white blood count that was detected. Values ranged from 2.5 to 21.0 and were normalized to range from 0 to 1.

35 Binary 1 if no test was taken for white blood count.

The column numbers for the output elements and the five possible diagnoses:

36 Binary 1 if hepatoma (HCC); otherwise 0.

37 Binary 1 if metastatic carcinoma; otherwise 0.

38 Binary 1 if abscess; otherwise 0.

39 Binary 1 if cavernous hemangioma; otherwise 0.

40 Binary 1 if cirrhosis; otherwise 0.

In the data, there were 32 cases of metastatic carcinoma, 9 cases of hepatoma (HCC), 17 cases of cavernous hemangioma, 4 cases of abscesses, and 10 cases of cirrhosis. See Table 1.

III. RESULTS

BrainMaker Professional version 2.5 software, a commercial neural network shell, was used to train the data on an 80486SX/25 microcomputer running MS-DOS 5.00. A spreadsheet was used to input and organize the raw data and print a text file to the disk for importing into the neural network software, which randomized the 72 facts and defined the maximum and minimum parameters for normalizing the inputs. The definition file and fact file in text (ASCII) were created. The software reads the definition file and fact files in the training phase. The neuron transfer function was sigmoid with a low value of 0, a high value of 1.0, a center of 0.5, and a gain of 1.0. Symmetry, blurring and noise were not used. Training tolerance was 0.01 (or 1%); testing tolerance was 0.2 (or 20%). Backpropagation learning rate was 1.0, and the backpropagation smoothing factor was 0.9.

To determine a suitable number of elements in the hidden layers, four different architectures were fully trained and tested. The best results (71% accuracy) were obtained with 2 hidden layers of 35 elements each. That network was trained on all 72 facts (cases) in 2651 iterations (1 hour and 11 minutes on a 80486SX/25), although to assure valid tests, 68 facts were trained separately 18 times. The time that the network took to learn the different sets of 68 facts ranged from 28 minutes to 1 hour and 29 minutes.

Table 1.
Diagnostic Accuracy by Category
Using 35:35:35:5 Architecture

Type mass	Correct	Wrong	Total	Percent
Carcinoma	22	10	32	68.75
HCC	4	5	9	44.44
Hemangioma	13	4	17	76.47
Abscess	4	0	4	100.00
Cirrhosis	8	2	10	80.00
	---	---	---	---.---
Totals:	51	21	72	70.83

Note: Correct diagnoses reflect the number of times the network correctly diagnosed the fact (patient case).

IV. DISCUSSION

Artificial neural networks are especially useful in diagnosing hepatic masses for several reasons. Since radiologists frequently use abdominal ultrasonagraphic data and laboratory tests to perform differential diagnoses of hepatic masses, enough data are available for computer-assisted diagnoses. Analysis of hepatic masses involves a number of health care personnel with varied training, experience, and skill in image interpretation. The ability to suggest a specific diagnosis from the hepatic mass varies considerably among physicians. Based on the results of our research, a properly trained neural network could provide a consistently high level of accuracy in suggesting appropriate differential diagnostic considerations. Classification tasks are a strong forte for artificial neural networks. Such a tool would help relieve the workloads of radiologists.

In this application, the artificial neural network was 71% accurate in correctly diagnosing disease in the hepatic mass. This accuracy is higher than the 50% scored by the typical radiology resident in training on these same cases at the Memphis hospital, but is lower than the 90% scored by a board-certified radiologist on the same cases. These results are similar to previous studies on neural network diagnosis.[19 & 31].

The result was a computer that thinks a lot like the radiologists. The same cases that gave Dr. Dempsey and other radiologists trouble when the cases were originally diagnosed gave the network trouble.

For future improvement, an obvious step is to add more cases to the knowledge base and retrain the neural network. For example, only nine HCC cases were in the training set because such cases are not common. The network was only 44% accurate in diagnosing those cases. The network needs more HCC cases to fully capture the range of readings on a typical HCC case. Likewise, if a radiologist who had seen the images and laboratory data for only nine HCC cases in his career would have difficulty in correctly diagnosing HCC cases.

Several technical techniques in programming neural networks merit further investigation to improve the performance of the neural network in diagnosing hepatic masses correctly. The standard backpropagation network is the only algorithm that has been attempted in our research. Other network algorithms might be investigated to see if they perform more accurate diagnoses than backpropagation did.

In addition, further research should be conducted to address the choice of training feature network elements, radiographic findings, different laboratory tests, and the possibility of eliminating bad examples from the training set.

If radiologists edit the training cases for a more balanced representation of possible diagnoses, the performance of the network probably would improve. Also more cases without missing lab tests should help.

Eventually the network is expected to match the accuracy of a top radiologist, which is now said to be about 90 percent accuracy. If that goal is achieved, the program could prove valuable to physicians in remote areas who need a second opinion. The system also could help hospitals cut costs by providing faster diagnoses with fewer costly specialists.

REFERENCES

[1] P.J. Bryan, W.M. Dinn, Z.D. Grossman, B.W. Wistow, J.G. McAfee, S.A. Kieffer, "Correlation of computed tomography, gray scale ultrasonography, and radionuclide imaging of the liver in detecting space-occupying processes." *Radiology*, vol. 124, 1977, pp. 387-393.

[2] M.M. Nelson and W.T. Illingworth, *A Practical Guide to Neural Nets*. Reading, MA: Addison-Wesley, 1991.

[3] P.H. Sugarbaker and N. Kemeny, N.,. "Management of metastatic liver cancer." *Adv. Surgery*, vol. 22, pp. 1-55, 1988.

[4] P.H. Sugarbaker, "Surgical decision making for large bowel cancer metastatic to the liver." *Radiology*, vol. 174, pp. 621-626, 1990.

[5] M.A. Adson, J.A. Van Heerden, M.H. Adson, J.S. Wayner, D.M. Ilstrup, "Resection of hepatic metastases from colorectal cancer." *Arch. Surgery*, vol. 119, pp. 647-651, 1984.

[6] R.A. Malt, "Current concepts: surgery for hepatic neoplasms." *New Eng. J. Medicine*, vol. 313, pp. 1591-1596, 1985.

[7] J.T. Ferrucci, "Liver tumor imaging: current concepts." *Amer. J.l of Radiol.* vol. 155, pp. 473-484, 1990.

[8] J.M. Boone, G.W. Gross, & V. Greco-Hunt, "Neural networks in radiologic diagnosis." *Invest. Radiol.*, vol. 25, pp. 1012-1016, 1990.

[9] G.W. Gross, J.M. Boone, V Greco-Hunt,, & B. Greenberg, "Neural networks in radiologic diagnosis. II. Interpretation of neonatal chest radiographs. *Invest. Radiol.*, vol. 25, pp. 1017-1023, 1990.

[10] P.S. Maclin, J. Dempsey, J. Brooks, & L. Rand, "Using neural networks to diagnose renal cancer." *J. Medical Systems* (U.S.), vol. 15 (1), pp. 11-19, 1991.

[11] B.H. Mulsant, "A neural network as an approach to clinical diagnosis." *MD Comp*, vol. 7(1), pp. 25-36, 1990.

[12] P. Frenger, "The silicon synapse or neural net computing." *Biomed. Sci. Instrum.*, vol. 25, pp. 267-73, 1989.

[13] R. Braham & J. Hamblen, "On the behavior of associative neural networks." *Biol. Cybernetics* (German), vol. 2, pp. 145-151, 1988.

[14] F. Crick, "Neural networks and REM sleep." *Biosci. Rep.* (England), vol. 8(6), pp. 531-535, 1988.

[15] R/ Shadmehr & D..Z. D'Argenio, "A neural network for nonlinear Bayesian estimation in drug therapy." *Neural Computation* vol. 2, pp. 216-225, 1990.

[16] R.P. Lippmann. "Review of neural networks for speech recognition. *Neural Computation* 1, 1-38, 1989.

[17] J.L. Elman & D. Zipser, "Learning the hidden structure of speech." J. *Acoustical Soc. Amer.* vol. 83(4), pp. 1615-26, 1988.

[18] R. Poli, S. Cagnoni, R. Livi, G. Coppini, G., Valli, "A neural network expert system for diagnosing and treating hypertension." *Computer*, vol. 24:3, pp. 64-71, 1991.

[19] D.W. Piraino, S.C. Amartur, B.J. Richmond, J.P. Schils, J.M. Thome, G.H. Belhobek & M.D. Schlucter, "Application of an artificial neural network in radiographic diagnosis. *J. Digital Imaging*, vol. 4(4), pp. 226-232, 1991.

[20] S. Borman, "Neural network applications in chemistry begin to appear." *Chem Engineering News*, Vol. 67, pp. 24-28, 1989.

[21] P.K. Simpson, *Artificial Neural Systems*. New York: Pergamon Press, 1990.

[22] R. Dyke, "NeuralWorks Professional II review." *Neural Network News*. Atlanta: AIWeek Inc., vol. 1(3), pp. 5, 1989.

[23] A. Blum, "Bidirectional Associative Memory Systems in C++." *Dr. Dobb's J*, vol. 15(4), pp. 16-26, 1990.

[24] D.G. Bounds, & P.J. Lloyd, "A multilayer perceptron network for the diagnosis of low back pain." *Proceedings of the IEEE International Conference on Neural Networks: Vol. II.* pp. 483-489, 1988.

[25] A. Guha, "Using small multilayer networks to search real hyperspaces." Neural Networks Supplement: *INNS Abstracts*, vol. 1, p.337, 1988.

[26] *BrainMaker Users Guide and Reference Manual, 4th edition.* Sierra Madre, CA: California Scientific Software, 1990.

[27] D.E. Rumelhart, J.L. McClelland, & PDP Research Group, *Parallel Distributed Processing: Explorations in the Microstructure of Cognition: Vols. 1 & 2*, Cambridge, MA; MIT Press, 1986.

[28] J.L. McClelland & D.E. Rumelhart, *Explorations in Parallel Distributed Processing*. Cambridge, MA: MIT Press, 1988.

[29] P.D. Wasserman, P.D., *Neural Computing: Theory & Practice*. New York: Van Nostrand Reinhold, 1989.

[30] *Neurocomputers* vol. 4(4), p. 5, 1990. Newsletter published monthly by Gallifrey Publishing, P.O. Box 155, Vicksburg, MI 49097.

[31] N. Asad, K. Doi, H. MacMahon, et al., "Potential usefulness of an artificial neural network for differential diagnosis of interstitial lung disease." *Radiology*, vol. 177, pp. 857-860, 1992.

Fully Parallel Summation in a New Stochastic Neural Network Architecture.

C.L. Janer, J.M. Quero and L.G. Franquelo,Member, IEEE

Escuela Superior de Ingenieros

Avda. Reina Mercedes s/n

Sevilla 41012 SPAIN

Abstract—A space efficient fully parallel stochastic architecture is described in this paper. This stochastic architecture circumvents the main drawback of stochastic implementations of neural networks — the concurrent processing of a high number of weighed input signals, leading to a simple realization of stochastic summation. An unlimited number of stochastically coded pulse sequences can be added in parallel using only very simple and space efficient digital circuitry. Any neural network, either recurrent or feedforward, can be implemented using this scheme provided that neurons take discrete values. Design criteria are deduced from the mathematical analsys of the involved stochastic operations. Simulation results are also given.

I. INTRODUCTION

Electronic realization of neural networks can be faced in different ways. On one hand analog approaches are very simple in terms of circuitry and have fast convergence times, specially when they are compared with digital implementations, but on the other hand their programming flexibility is very low. Digital implementations perform high flexibility and easy interface with general purpose computers but their efficiency in terms of consumed silicon area is very low, as a floating point multiplier is needed in every neuron to calculate the presynaptic activity. One way to circumvent this problem is to employ stochastic logic[1].

Stochastic logic systems realize pseudoanalog operations using stochastically coded pulse sequences. Multiplication of two stochastic pulse sequences should produce another stochastic stream of pulses whose firing probability is the product of the input firing probabilities. This can be achieved easily if the input sequences are stochastically independent. The circuit that implements this operation is a simple AND gate.

Stochastic summation is a much more difficult operation to perform, specially if the terms to be added are signed. Two types of circuits have been described in the bibliography. One is the OR gate [2] and the other is an up/down counter[3]. If two pulse sequences are feeded into an OR gate and the pulse sequences to be added do not overlap, the output firing probability is equal to the sum of both firing probabilities This OR-based add function is thus distorted by pulse overlap. In order to achieve a quasy linear behaviour pulse densities should stay very low, specially if many terms are to be added. This technique does not permit the integration of neurons with a very high number of synaptic connections as it would lead to extremely low maximum pulse density.

The up/down counters technique, although is widely used [4], has a very important drawback. The pulses coming from other neurons have to be multiplexed in time (i.e. *serialized*) leading to *high computation times* if the network has many neurons and many synapsys per neuron.

We propose a fully parallel stochastic architecture for neural networks whose neuron activity values take discrete values (either $-1, 1$ or $0, 1$). This architecture permits the integration of highly interconnected neural networks. It can be used either for recursive or feedforward nets and it is very efficient in terms of circuitry.

This paper is organized as follows. In section 2 the accuracy of stochastic multiplication is analyzed. The obtained results justify the scheme proposed in section 3, where design criteria are given. Section 4 is devoted to some applications of this novel architecture. Finally in section 5 conclusions are drawn.

II. STOCHASTIC MULTIPLICATION.

Fig.1 shows the generation and multiplication of a set of n independent stochastic signals. The out-

1498

put value obtained by accumulating the pulses N clock-cycles follows a binomial distribution having the expectation value E and the variance V.

$$E[\tilde{x}] = \mu = Nx \qquad (1)$$

$$V[\tilde{x}] = \sigma^2 = Nx(1-x) \qquad (2)$$

with

$$x = \frac{\prod_{i=1}^{i=n} a_i}{a_{max}^n} \qquad (3)$$

where a_i is the stored value and a_{max} is the maximum random number that can be generated. A natural way to evaluate the rate error of the

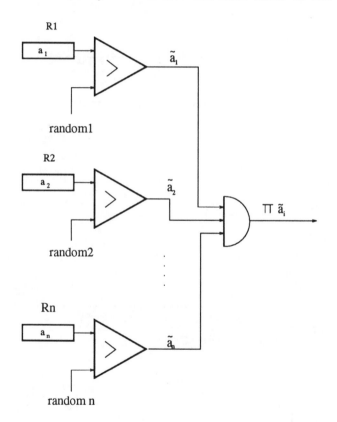

Figure 1: Stochastic multiplier.

stochastical multiplication result is to consider the following fraction

$$\frac{\sigma}{\mu} = \frac{\sqrt{N}\sqrt{x}\sqrt{1-x}}{Nx} \qquad (4)$$

The smaller this fraction is, the more accurate the aproximation will be. This expression is a

function of the ideal product x and the number of generated random values N. It has been plotted in Fig.2 and Fig. 3. Notice that if N is big enough $\frac{\sigma}{\mu}$ only depends slightly on x for x taking values not too close to zero. This fact is of most importance as it will become clear in next section.

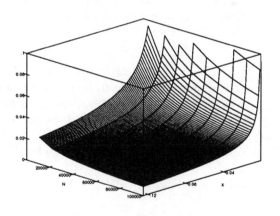

Figure 2: Product rate error.

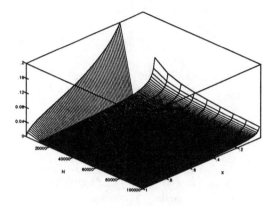

Figure 3: Product rate error (x closed to 0).

III. STOCHASTIC ARCHITECTURE

A. Basic Concepts.

The transfer function of a discrete neuron requires the application of the sign operator to the summation of weighed input signals. Consider the following identity

1499

$$sign(\sum_{i=1}^{i=n} x_i) = sign(\sum_{i=1}^{i=n} x_i^+ - \sum_{i=1}^{i=n} x_i^-) =$$

$$sign(e^{-\sum_{i=1}^{i=n} x_i^-} - e^{-\sum_{i=1}^{i=n} x_i^+}) =$$

$$sign(\prod_{i=1}^{i=n} e^{-x_i^-} - \prod_{i=1}^{i=n} e^{-x_i^+}) \qquad (5)$$

where

$$x_i^+ = \begin{cases} x_i & \text{for } x_i > 0 \\ 0 & \text{for } x_i < 0 \end{cases} \qquad (6)$$

and

$$x_i^- = \begin{cases} -x_i & \text{for } x_i < 0 \\ 0 & \text{for } x_i > 0 \end{cases} \qquad (7)$$

The last term in (5) can be regarded as the comparison of two pulse streams generated by two stochastic multipliers, therefore no adder is needed.

If the neural network has been adimentionalized in such a way that all terms to be aggregated take values ranging from zero to a small number close enough to zero, e^{x_i} can be aproximated by

$$e^{-x_i} \simeq 1 - x \qquad (8)$$

In Fig.4 rate error $((e^{-x} - (1 - x))/e^{-x})$ is plotted as a function of the number to be transformed x. This transformation is carried out because the accuracy of stochastic multiplication does not decrease strongly as x becomes closed to zero. If this did happen N would have to be large leading to slow dynamics.

B.Functional Description.

The fully parallel stochastic architecture is shown in Fig.5. In block M synapsys are compared with random numbers producing a set of uncorrelated streams of pulses whose densities are proportional to their values. The evaluation of (8) is performed by a simple NOT gate (block E). Block S is a logic block, where pulses are separated in either "positive" if weight and neuron values were equaly signed or "negative" if they were not. "Positive" and "negative" streams are multiplied separately, leading to two diferent stochastic signals. Two different implementations are suggested for neurons with either $\{-1, 1\}$ or $\{0, 1\}$ saturation states, as shown in Fig.6 and 7 respectively, where

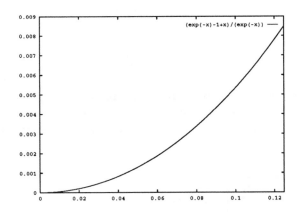

Figure 4: Multiplication rate error.

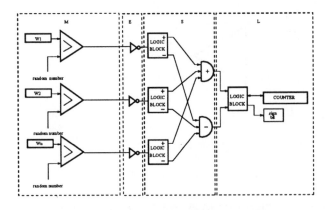

Figure 5: Architecture.

negative sign is coded by "1." In block L if the two signals are at high level at the same time the up/down counter remains unchanged. If only a "positive" pulse is at high level the counter is incremented by one and if the pulse is "negative" the counter is then decremented by one. Block L resets the sign bit if a zero crossing takes place.

Positive and negative terms are transformed and then are multiplied separately as it is shown in Fig.5. Due to the fact that these terms are close to unity many terms can be aggregated with a high degree of accuracy as it becomes clear from Fig.2 and Fig.3.

C. Maximun Error Boundary.

We shall denote the errors associated to the product term calculation x_i by ϵ_i, the errors associated to the exponential transformation by ξ_i and the error associated to aggregation by ζ

$$
\begin{array}{ccc}
x_1 + \epsilon_1 & & e^{x_1+\epsilon_1} + \xi_1 \\
x_2 + \epsilon_2 & & e^{x_2+\epsilon_2} + \xi_2 \\
\cdot & & \cdot \\
\cdot & \rightarrow & \cdot & \rightarrow \\
\cdot & & \cdot \\
x_n + \epsilon_n & & e^{x_n+\epsilon_n} + \xi_n \\
\end{array}
$$
$$\prod_{i=1}^{i=n}(e^{x_i+\epsilon_i} + \xi_i) + \zeta$$

Taking into account that errors are small and denoting rate errors by $\hat{\epsilon}_i, \hat{\xi}_i, \hat{\zeta}$ we obtain

$$\prod_{i=1}^{i=n}(e^{x_i+\epsilon_i} + \xi_i) + \zeta \simeq \prod_{i=1}^{i=n}e^{x_i+\epsilon_i} + \sum_{i=1}^{i=n}\xi_i\prod_{j\neq i}e^{x_j+\epsilon_j} + \zeta =$$

$$\prod_{i=1}^{i=n}e^{x_i(1+\hat{\epsilon}_i)}(1 + \sum_{j=1}^{j=n}\hat{\xi}_j + \hat{\zeta}) \qquad (9)$$

If we evaluate the logarithm of this expression and define $\widehat{\hat{\xi}_i} := \frac{\hat{\xi}_i}{x_i}$ we have

$$\sum_{i=1}^{i=n}x_i(1 + \hat{\epsilon}_i) + Log(1 + \sum_{j=1}^{j=n}x_j\widehat{\hat{\xi}_j} + \hat{\zeta}) \qquad (10)$$

Substracting $\sum_{i=1}^{i=n}x_i$ we obtain the total error

$$err \leq \sum_{i=1}^{i=n}x_i\hat{\epsilon}_m + Log(1 + \sum_{j=1}^{j=n}x_j\widehat{\hat{\xi}_m} + \hat{\zeta}) \leq$$

$$\sum_{i=1}^{i=n}x_i\hat{\epsilon}_m + \sum_{j=1}^{j=n}x_j\widehat{\hat{\xi}_m} + \hat{\zeta} \qquad (11)$$

the expression of the rate error is

$$\hat{err} = \frac{err}{\sum_{i=1}^{i=n}x_i} \leq \hat{\epsilon}_m + \widehat{\hat{\xi}_m} + \hat{\zeta} \qquad (12)$$

Errors $\hat{\epsilon}_m$ and $\hat{\zeta}$ tend to zero when N increases, and $\widehat{\hat{\xi}_m}$ can be done small enough if x is chosen within a proper range, as shown in Fig.8. For instance, if the pulse stream is considered to have a mean value of 0.12, its exponential transformation error will remain bellow **7%**.

IV. SIMULATION RESULTS

The dynamic behaviour of a discrete valued Hopfield neural network has been simulated. Three 25 neuron patterns, showed in Fig.9a,c were stored in this network.

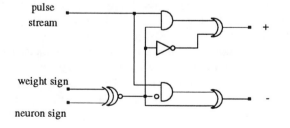

Figure 6: Logic block in S for neurons with saturated states $\{-1,1\}$.

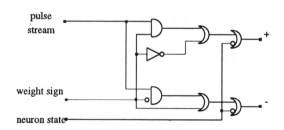

Figure 7: Logic block in S for neurons with saturated states $\{0,1\}$.

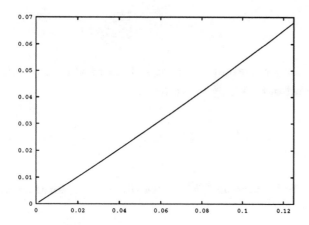

Figure 8: Transformation rate error.

```
1  1  1  -1  -1  -1  -1  -1  -1  -1
1  1  1  -1  -1  -1  -1  -1  -1  -1
1  1  1  -1  -1  -1  -1  -1  -1  -1
1  1  1  -1  -1  -1  -1  -1  -1  -1
1  1  1  -1  -1  -1  -1  -1  -1  -1
1  1  1  -1  -1  -1  -1  -1  -1  -1
1  1  1  -1  -1  -1  -1  -1  -1  -1
1  1  1   1   1   1   1   1   1  -1
1  1  1   1   1   1   1   1   1   1
1  1  1   1   1   1   1   1   1   1
```

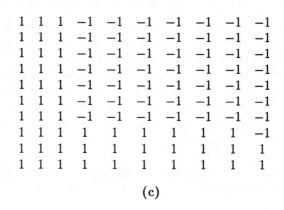

(c)

```
1  1  1  -1   1   1   1  -1   1  -1
1  1  1   1   1  -1   1  -1   1   1
1  1  1  -1  -1  -1   1   1   1  -1
1  1  1   1   1   1  -1  -1  -1  -1
1  1  1   1   1  -1  -1   1  -1   1
1  1  1  -1  -1   1  -1   1   1   1
1  1  1   1  -1  -1  -1  -1   1  -1
1  1  1   1  -1   1  -1   1  -1   1
1  1  1   1  -1   1  -1   1   1   1
1  1  1  -1   1  -1   1  -1  -1   1
```

(d)

Figure 9: Patterns stored in a hopfield net.

```
 1   1   1   1   1   1   1   1   1   1
 1   1   1   1   1   1   1   1   1   1
 1   1   1   1   1   1   1   1   1   1
-1  -1  -1   1   1   1   1  -1  -1  -1
-1  -1  -1   1   1   1   1  -1  -1  -1
-1  -1  -1   1   1   1   1  -1  -1  -1
-1  -1  -1   1   1   1   1  -1  -1  -1
-1  -1  -1   1   1   1   1  -1  -1  -1
-1  -1  -1   1   1   1   1  -1  -1  -1
-1  -1  -1   1   1   1   1  -1  -1  -1
```

(a)

```
-1  -1  -1  -1  -1  -1  -1   1   1   1
-1  -1  -1  -1  -1  -1  -1   1   1   1
-1  -1  -1  -1  -1  -1  -1   1   1   1
-1  -1  -1  -1  -1  -1  -1   1   1   1
-1  -1  -1  -1  -1  -1  -1   1   1   1
-1  -1  -1  -1  -1  -1  -1   1   1   1
-1  -1  -1  -1  -1  -1  -1   1   1   1
-1  -1  -1  -1  -1  -1  -1   1   1   1
-1  -1  -1  -1  -1  -1  -1   1   1   1
-1  -1  -1  -1  -1  -1  -1   1   1   1
```

(b)

Fig.10 shows the evolution of the Hamming distance between the neural state vector and the prototype vector (Fig.9a) for different a_{max}. They are also compared with the evolution of the architecture of Van den Bout [3]. The initial state was a corrupted vector of data (Fig.9d) resembling this stored pattern. For the suggested architecture, the number of clock cycles needed for full convergency is 25 when $a_{max} = 0.0625$, and 74 when $a_{max} = 0.125$. If a systolic array of parallel neuron processors [3] is used the evolution is slower, as showed in Fig.10, needing 100 clock cycles. The number of connections summed up in each clock cycle is N in every neuron while only one is possible in the systolic array. In order to test the behavior of this architecture in feedforward networks the two layer perceptron needed in [5] to carry out nondestructive evaluations has been implemented. The aim of this network is to classificate a set of input signals into four categories. Ten hidden units with eight input signals and two output units were configured using backpropagation

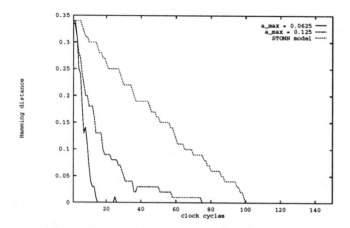

Figure 10: Dynamic behaviour of a hopfield net.

[6]. Fig.11 represents the dynamic behaviour of its two output neurons when applying one of the previously learnt patterns. In the steady state, the output counters reach limit counts of -128 and 128, corresponding to output neurons states -1 and 1 respectively, which are the associated target output values of the applied pattern. The pseudorandom evolution of the values of the output neurons are defined by the evolution of the neurons in the hidden layer. All patterns were applied, leading to their corresponding output vector.

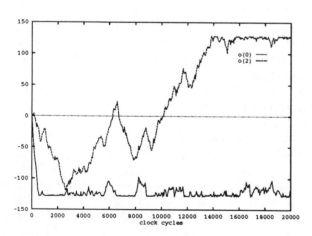

Figure 11: Dynamic behaviour of a two-output one-hidden layer perceptron.

V. Conclusions

A new approach to summation of stochastic weighed signals has been presented. The number of concurrent input signals is no longer a limit.

The evaluation of these signals is carried out in every cycle, leading to a full parallel implementation. Limiting the range the input signals allows for a very simple implementation. Simulation results validates this model for recurrent and feedforward networks.

References

[1] Y. Kondo and Y. Sawada. Functional Abilities of a Stochastic Logic Neural Networks *IEEE Trans. on Neural Networks*, vol.3, pp.434-443, 1992.

[2] Alan f. Murray, Dante Del Corso and Lionel Tarassenko. Pulse-Stream VLSI Neural Networks Mixing Analog and Digital Techniques *IEEE Trans. on Neural Networks*, vol.2,no.2, pp.193-204, 1991.

[3] D.E. Van den Bout and T.K. Miller III. A Digital Architecture Employing Stochaticism for the Simulation of Hopfield Neural Nets. *IEEE Trans. on Circuit and Systems*, vol.36, pp. 732-738. 1989

[4] W. Wike, D.E. Van den Bout and T.K. Miller III The VLSI Implementation of STONN. *IEEE Int. Joint Conf. on Neural Networks*, vol.2, pp.593-598, 1990.

[5] L. Udpa and S. S. Udpa. Application of Neural Networks to Nondestructive Evaluation. *First IEE Conference on Artificial Neural Networks*,pp. 143-147. 1989

[6] D. E. Rumelhart and J. L. McClelland. Parallel Distributed Processing. MIT Press. 1986.

Distributed Syntactic Representations with an Application to Part-of-Speech Tagging

Hinrich Schütze
Center for the Study of Language and Information
Ventura Hall
Stanford, CA 94305-4115
schuetze@csli.stanford.edu

Abstract— This paper proposes to represent the syntactic category of words in a distributed manner by deriving part-of-speech representations from a text corpus by means of a large scale singular value decomposition. The representations are input to an artificial neural network, which was trained on two days of the New York Times News Service attaining an accuracy of 92%–98% in tagging ambiguous lexical items.

I. Introduction

Work on syntax in the connectionist framework has taken one of two approaches. In the first approach, traditional syntactic categories are used as input to parsers and taggers (e.g. [1, 2]). This has the advantage that the input space is small and corpora of a realistic size can be used in training. However, there are many idiosyncratic words that don't fit well into any syntactic category. For example, *Thursday* is an adverbial in the sentences in (1), but it doesn't have the distribution of a prototypical adverb since it cannot be used as an adjectival modifier. Syntactically ambiguous words are another problem for a small set of categories. Words such as *care* can be used as nouns and verbs. The degree of salience of the two uses varies from word to word. Nominal and verbal use are equally salient for *care*, but the nominal use "the authority or jurisdiction of a bishop" is rare for *see*. Many English words, especially many high-frequency words, exhibit idiosyncrasies and ambiguity of this sort. A limited number of categories cannot do justice to such individual characteristics, but they are important for ranking possible parses and selecting the contextually preferred one.

(1) a. She arrived Thursday.

   b. The Senate Thursday passed landmark legislation ... (New York Times News Wire, 6 June 1990)

The second approach is to represent each word differently. This accounts for the fact that no two words behave exactly the same way syntactically, but it fails to represent the similarities that do exist. Attempts to induce such representations using neural nets (for instance in [3]) don't seem to be efficient enough for real-world applications. In this paper, a simple, but efficient method is proposed that induces a substantial part of the syntactic similarity between lexical items. A neural net can then be trained to use these representations in syntactic processing. The focus of the paper is on tagging although the purpose of the approach is to find a good representational basis for connectionist parsing.

II. Category Space

The first step in efficiently inducing representations that reflect syntactic similarity is to collect relevant distributional information about words. The 5,000 most frequent words in five months of the New York Times News Service (June through October 1990) were selected for the experiments. For each pair of these words $< w_i, w_j >$, the number of occurrences of w_i immediately to the left of w_j ($b_{i,j}$), the number of occurrences of w_i immediately to the right of w_j ($c_{i,j}$), the number of occurrences of w_i to the left of w_j with one word distance between them ($a_{i,j}$), and the number of occurrences of w_i to the right of w_j with one word distance between them ($d_{i,j}$) were counted. The four sets of 25,000,000 counts were collected in the 5,000-by-5,000 matrices B, C, A, and D, respectively. Finally these four matrices were composed into one large 5,000-by-20,000 matrix as shown in Figure 1. The figure also shows for two words where their four cooccurrence counts are located in the 5,000-by-20,000 matrix. In the experiments, w_{3000} was *resistance* and w_{4250} was *theaters*. The four marks in the figure show the position of the counts $a_{3000,4250}$, $b_{3000,4250}$, $c_{3000,4250}$, and $d_{3000,4250}$. They measure how often *resistance* occurred at positions -2, -1, 1, and 2 with respect to *theaters*.

A singular value decomposition was then performed on

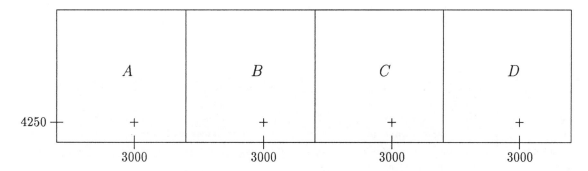

Figure 1: The setup for deriving distributed category representations.

this matrix and 15 eigenvectors extracted using a sparse matrix algorithm from SVDPACK [4]. As a result, each of the 5,000 words is represented by a vector of 15 real numbers. Since the original 20,000-component vectors of two words (corresponding to rows in the matrix in Figure 1) are similar if their distributional syntactic properties are similar, the same holds for the reduced vectors because the singular value decomposition finds the best least square approximation for the 5,000 original vectors in a 15-dimensional space that preserves distance between vectors.

Table 1 shows that the structure of the space is very intuitive. A sample of random and selected words and their nearest neighbors in category space is listed (ten or as many as would fit in the table). The words in the second column are ordered according to closeness to the head word. As can be seen from the table the regions of the space correspond well with traditional syntactic categories. There are regions for past tense/past participle forms (the neighborhood of *accompanied*), for adverbs (the neighborhood of *almost*), for plural nouns (the neighborhoods of *classes*, *directors* and *authors*), gerunds (the neighborhood of *causing*), singular nouns (the neighborhood of *goal*), adjectives (the neighborhoods of *Japanese* and *typical*), base forms of verbs (the neighborhoods of *represent* and *think*), and prepositions (the neighborhoods of *on*). (*york* is grouped with other second components of names and with nouns that always have prenominal modifiers.) So the main parts of speech all have a region in space. Note that different inflections occupy different locations due to their different distributional properties. Therefore, there are different regions for singular nouns and plural nouns. First names, last names and geographical terms are likewise separated in space from other syntactic classes.

Some words are misassigned because the cooccurrence counts that the vectors are based on are noisy, but there are also some linguistically interesting observations to be made. For example, *to* turns out to be close to the aux-

iliary verbs. Interestingly, Pollard and Sag argue in the tradition of GPSG that *to* is indeed an auxiliary [5].

The last two lines of the table show the neighbors of the two words discussed in the introduction: *Thursday* and *care*. The days of the week are between regions with nominal elements like *Ireland* and adverbs that have a distribution similar to the adverbial uses of weekdays. (*Ireland/Poland* and *yesterday/forth* are "on different sides" of *Thursday* as the following normalized correlation coefficients indicate: *Thursday/Ireland*: 0.918369, *Thursday/yesterday*: 0.925894, *Ireland/yesterday*: 0.802609.) A final point concerns ambiguous lexical items. Classes of words that can instantiate different syntactic categories have their own regions. For instance, the neighborhood of *care* contains words that can function as the base form of a verb as well as the singular form of a noun. These examples suggest that the derived representations represent idiosyncratic syntactic behavior and ambiguity.

Figure 2 reveals that the fine structure of the space is imperfect in some locations.[1] Whereas the upper right corner is fairly homogeneous in that it only contains adjectives (and forms ending in *-ing* that are mainly used as adjectives such as *continuing*), the rest of the plane has a mixture of adverbs, past participles and verbal forms ending in *-ing* that are mainly used to express the progressive. The reason that these forms ended up together is that they are all used with the auxiliary verb *to be*. In future experiments, a fifth matrix with counts of words at distance 3 will be added to the SVD matrix. This would presumably differentiate adverbs from participles and gerunds. One could also consider emphasizing the counts of *have*, *has* and *had* in the matrix that is used for the SVD, for instance by multiplying them with a small constant like 1.5 or 2. This would make participles and gerunds less similar since only the former can be used with the forms of *have*.

---

[1]The figure shows principal components 2 and 3 of the matrix of correlation coefficients of the 200 nearest neighbors of *frozen*. The following words were deleted to make the figure more legible: *financially, limited, picking, deeply, landing, closing, roughly.*

word	nearest neighbors
accompanied	submitted banned financed developed authorized headed canceled awarded barred
almost	virtually merely formally fully quite officially just nearly only less
causing	reflecting forcing providing creating producing becoming carrying particularly
classes	elections courses payments losses computers performances violations levels pictures
directors	professionals investigations materials competitors agreements papers transactions
goal	mood roof eye image tool song pool scene gap voice
japanese	chinese iraqi american western arab foreign european federal soviet indian
represent	reveal attend deliver reflect choose contain impose manage establish retain
think	believe wish know realize wonder assume feel say mean bet
york	angeles francisco sox rouge kong diego zone vegas inning layer
typical	famous bitter remarkable practical bigger weak constant larger troubled modest
authors	guerrillas actors courts pilots volunteers rebels marines communists arabs dancers
on	through in at over into with from for by across
fred	gary dan larry kevin brian tom charles jeff walter alan
to	will must would can could might cannot should may ll
care	rule work place vote act deal order track shape risk
thursday	wednesday tuesday monday friday sunday saturday yesterday ireland forth poland

Table 1: Ten random and seven selected words and their nearest neighbors in category space.

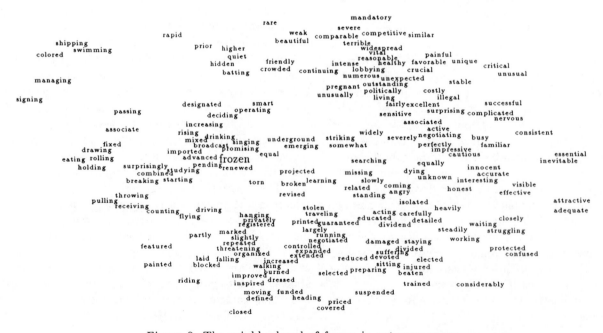

Figure 2: The neighborhood of *frozen* in category space.

Even if there are inconsistencies in the space, Table 1 shows that it represents most differences that are crucial for syntax and parsing. The next section uses the category representations for part-of-speech tagging.

III. PART-OF-SPEECH TAGGING WITH DISTRIBUTED SYNTACTIC REPRESENTATIONS

The architecture in Figure 3 was chosen in order to apply the distributed category representations to tagging. The vectors of the four words to the right and to the left of the word in the center that is to be tagged constitute the input (the words w_i in Figure 3). Each pair of adjacent words feeds into four units. (A line between two rectangles indicates that they are fully connected.) The sets of 4×30 weights on the connections between each pair of input words and its four hidden units in the second layer are linked, so there are only 120 distinct weights that connect input and hidden layer 1. The purpose of this setup is to reduce the number of parameters. The information that a pair of words contributes if it is to the right of the word to be tagged is also potentially useful if it occurs to the left etc. For this reason the six weight groups were linked. The first and second hidden layers are fully connected.

The resolution of VERB/NOUN ambiguities was chosen to evaluate the usefulness of the category representations. Therefore, the output layer consists of two units, one for verbs and one for nouns. In order to come up with a large sample of "good" verbs and nouns the vectors of the 5,000 words were clustered into twenty classes using the Buckshot clustering algorithm [6]. Nine of the clusters were discarded because they contained adjectives, prepositions or proper names. The remaining eleven clusters were categorized as verbal or nominal. About 5 to 10 percent of the members of each cluster were deleted as misassignments. The remaining 2300 words were used as targets in training. Of the output units, the target of the verb unit was set to one and the target of the noun unit to zero if the target word was in one of the verb clusters and vice versa. The training was done with standard backpropagation in batch mode, first on 2733 input-output pairs with learning rates of 0.02 and 0.005 (for 300 epochs), then on 6054 patterns with a learning rate of 0.0002, finally on all 12761 patterns in the first 200,000 words in the training corpus (June 1990, New York Times News Service) with a learning rate of 0.0001. (Momentum was set to 0.4)

The network was tested on occurrences of four ambiguous words in November 1990 (the first 50 or 100 occurrences with words surrounding them that were in the 5,000 covered by the original matrix). The results are comparable to those in [7, 8], although it is not clear how these results would generalize to a larger sample. However, the network solves the task without knowing the prior probability of the syntactic categories, in fact without any access to information on the word to be tagged. Since the target word is like an unknown word in the tagging framework adopted here, the numbers in Table 2 seem very promising.

IV. DISCUSSION

A possible problem with the approach taken here is that only the 5,000 most frequent words were considered. However, rare words tend to lack syntactic anomalies, so new syntactic problems are unlikely to be encountered among the less frequent words. The major restriction on the singular value decomposition is space (although time complexity becomes a problem for matrices with a rank greater than 50,000). The four matrices above had densities of less than 3%. Including less frequent words would make the matrices even more sparse, so that the overall space requirements would still be modest. It is therefore possible to apply the method to up to 50,000 words.

Note also that even if some cleaning up of the clusters is necessary, this can be done with a small investment of time. It took about two hours to go through the 5,000 words used here since a moderate error rate is unproblematic and most words are assigned correctly so that only misclassifications have to be detected.

The advantage of tagging with distributed representations is that only a small number of parameters has to be estimated. The tagger in Figure 3 has only $120+240+20 = 320$ parameters. This is possible because the syntactic representations contain a lot of information that is missing from the category labels used in other tagging algorithms (e.g. [7, 8]). Category labels have too much and too little information at the same time. They don't have enough information in that they do not respect the fine differences between individual words. It is well known (and unexplained) in linguistics that many words have properties that can't be inferred from their category labels, for instance the uses of *Thursday* as an adverb (cf. also [9]). Representing a word by its category label means making these differences, which are important for syntactic disambiguation, inaccessible to the neural net (or whatever the learning device is).

Category labels may also have too much information. For instance, in many approaches to tagging each of a few dozen high frequency words is assigned to a special category that only contains that word. So, *and* and *or* will have different categories. But that ignores the similarities there are between the two conjunctions. These similarities have to be painfully learnt although they are obvious from a simple analysis of the distributional patterns.

Examples for fine, but useful distinctions that are represented in category space are the closeness of *and* and *or* (they are nearest neighbors to each other with a correlation coefficient of 0.8) and also some syntactically im-

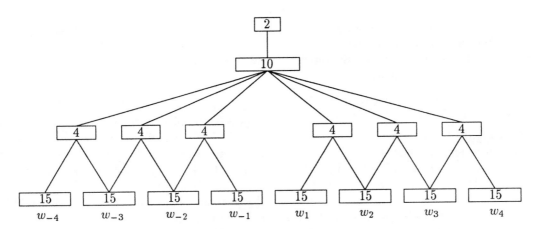

Figure 3: The architecture of the tagger

word		N	V	total
work	correct	61	34	95
	incorrect	1	4	5
lives	correct	73	19	92
	incorrect	0	8	8
returns	correct	39	10	49
	incorrect	0	1	1
sleep	correct	11	35	46
	incorrect	2	2	4

Table 2: Accuracy of the tagger.

portant semantic regularities that show up in the spatial structure: the neighbors of *authors* are predominantly agents (see Table 1). Agenthood is known to play an important role in syntax. A simple category NOUN doesn't respect the difference between agents and patients. Splitting the category NOUN up into agents and patients forces a decision upon words like *participants* that sometimes are active and sometimes aren't.

The approach presented here is an extension of work on word sense disambiguation and thesaurus induction that uses the same methodology [10, 11]: The main variations in the patterns of usage of lexical items are extracted by means of a singular value decomposition. The compactness of the induced representations makes it possible to do subsequent fine-grained processing in an efficient and flexible manner. This idea may be applicable to other domains in which neural networks haven't been used because surface measurements don't exhibit the similarity between semantically similar inputs without which connectionist networks learn very slowly if at all.

The use of a singular value decomposition is not a plausible model for the acquisition of syntactic categories by children. However, Maratsos and Chalkley propose that the absolute positions of words in sentences is important

evidence in children's learning of categories [12]. The results presented here show that *relative* position is sufficient for learning syntactic categories. There are cognitively more plausible implementations of principal component analyses (see [13]), so that the importance of relative position for learning syntactic categories could be of interest for research on language acquisition.

Future Directions. The arguments put forth for spatial representations of words as input to a connectionist net also apply to the output. If the architecture of the net in Figure 3 could be changed so that the 15-component vector of the word to be tagged is the target, arbitrary categorization would be avoided altogether. As a technical benefit, the incompatibility of different tag sets would no longer be a problem, since any discrete tag set could presumably be mapped onto the more fine-grained representations of category space.

The other major direction of future research is the incorporation of recurrent constraints [3, 14]. An analysis of the tagging errors for the words in Table 2 indicates that the absence of some form of recursiveness is a major problem for the tagger in its present form.

V. Conclusion

In applying artificial neural networks to parsing and tagging, one is faced with a dilemma. If traditional syntactic categories like VERB or NOUN are used as input in training and processing, one of the main advantages of connectionist architectures is lost: their ability to exploit even fine distinctions between individual words in finding the best way of satisfying the totality of constraints that are to be respected. On the other hand, if words are not lumped together into classes, but treated as separate entities, learning is so slow that large-scale applications don't seem feasible.

The application of a singular value decomposition to the patterns of syntactic distribution in a large text corpus overcomes this dilemma: A simple, but efficient regression makes the whole distributional pattern of a lexical item accessible in only a dozen or so real values. The simplifications done by the SVD can then be corrected by the non-linearity of the neural net. The hope is that this combination of fast regression and precise neural nets can be successfully extended to achieve robust parsing of general text.

Acknowledgment

I would like to thank Mike Berry for SVDPACK and Jan Pedersen, Martin Röscheisen, and two anonymous reviewers for very helpful comments.

References

[1] J. Benello, A. W. Mackie, and J. A. Anderson, "Syntactic category disambiguation with neural networks," *Computer Speech and Language*, vol. 3, pp. 203–217, 1989.

[2] M. Nakamura and K. Shikano, "A study of english word category prediction based on neural networks," in *Proceedings of ICASSP-89*, (Glasgow, Scotland), 1989.

[3] J. L. Elman, "Finding structure in time," *Cognitive Science*, vol. 14, pp. 179–211, 1990.

[4] M. W. Berry, "Large-scale sparse singular value computations," *The International Journal of Supercomputer Applications*, vol. 6, no. 1, pp. 13–49, 1992.

[5] C. Pollard and I. A. Sag, *Information-Based Syntax and Semantics, Volume 2*. Stanford CA: Center for the Study of Language and Information, in press.

[6] D. Cutting, D. Karger, J. Pedersen, and J. Tukey, "Scatter-gather: A cluster-based approach to browsing large document collections," in *Proceedings of SIGIR'92*, 1992.

[7] K. W. Church, "A stochastic parts program and noun phrase parser for unrestricted text," in *Proceedings of ICASSP-89*, (Glasgow, Scotland), 1989.

[8] J. Kupiec, "Robust part-of-speech tagging using a hidden markov model," *Computer Speech and Language*, vol. 6, pp. 225–242, 1992.

[9] J. R. Ross, "The category squish: Endstation Hauptwort," in *Papers from the Eighth Regional Meeting*, Chicago Linguistic Society, 1972.

[10] H. Schütze, "Dimensions of meaning," in *Proceedings of Supercomputing '92*, 1992.

[11] H. Schütze, "Word space," in *Advances in Neural Information Processing Systems 5* (S. J. Hanson, J. D. Cowan, and C. L. Giles, eds.), San Mateo CA: Morgan Kaufmann, in press.

[12] M. P. Maratsos and M. Chalkley, "The internal language of children's syntax: the ontogenesis and representation of syntactic categories," in *Children's language* (K. Nelson, ed.), vol. 2, New York: Gardner Press, 1981.

[13] J. A. Hertz, R. G. Palmer, and A. S. Krogh, *Introduction to the theory of neural computation*. Redwood City CA: Addison-Wesley, 1991.

[14] J. Schmidhuber, "Learning complex, extended sequences using the principle of history compression," *Neural Computation*, vol. 4, pp. 234–242, 1992.

Neural and Associative Modules in a Hybrid Dynamic System for Visual Industrial Quality Control*

A. König, H. Genther, M. Glesner
Darmstadt University of Technology
Institute for Microelectronic Systems
Karlstrasse 15, W-6100 Darmstadt, Germany

Abstract—This paper describes the development and application of neural and associative modules in the context of a hybrid and dynamic system concept for visual object inspection in industrial quality control. This system incorporates image processing techniques, knowledge base, and neural as well as non-neural classification methods. These modules are not hardwired in a processing chain, but can be flexibly configured under the control of a central unit that monitores the inspection process. The system assumes a configuration based on a priori knowledge and on the results of the self-monitoring process. In this work the first experiments and results utilizing an implemented subset of this concept will be presented, focusing on neural and associative modules and neural hierarchies. During our work we found an intriguing correspondence of neural associative memories and a well established conventional classification system. Data aquisition techniques and issues of dedicated hardware implementation will be covered in brevity.

I. INTRODUCTION

Quality maintenance in industrial production lines is a problem of ever increasing importance. The early detection and elimination of faulty parts during production avoids costs that the later exchange of these parts in systems would cause and increases reliability of assemblies and systems. Trained human operators bring the necessary skill and expertise for many con-trol tasks, especially in visual quality control, but due to constraints of costs and reliability Automated Quality Control (AQC) is of growing importance in the domain of industrial production.

Generally, AQC systems consist of an image aquisition and processing front end. Based on the computed features classification of the current object or object region is carried out. Rule-based systems can be applied for this task. A human expert formulates his expertise in a set of rules. Thus, object or region classification can be inferred by application of these rules. The definition of these rules will never comprise all situations that might arise during the real inspection progress. Especially small deviations from the specification cannot be covered in a fault tolerant way. Also, the definition of rules seems infeasible for many problems because no explicit knowledge is available. In addition, the production frame rates determined, e.g. by speed of conveyor, impose hard real time constraints on the quality control process.

Neural networks and Neural Associative Memories (NAMs) provide training and generalization properties that allow the recognition and classification of patterns that deviate to a certain degree from those presented during training. No explicit knowledge or rules has to be available. Statistics of training data determine the network configuration. The inherent massive parallelism of neural structures make them excellent candidate for real time constrained quality control applications.

The combination of rule-based systems with neural networks and NAMs provides systems for quality control that can exploit available explicit and can extract implicit knowledge of the underlying process. State-of-the-art systems [1] have a hard-wired topol-

*This work is under grant of the German Federal Ministry of Research and Development (BMFT) grant number 01 IN 110 B/6 (SIOB). Partners are danet GmbH Darmstadt GS KI and Fraunhofer-Institut für Informations- und Datenverarbeitung IITB Karlsruhe

ogy, i.e., after an initial development phase a set of features is selected and a classifier module is defined, featuring a certain network paradigm with a parameter setting found appropriate for the test data. Such an approach provides a possibly suboptimal solution which may show little robustness to deviations from the assumptions of the training phase.

In our research project SIOB the development of a generic and dynamic system for visual quality control is aspired. Objective of this research work is the specification and implementation of a hybrid and dynamic system with self-organizing properties and flexible topology incorporating image processing and feature extraction, knowledge base, neural network, and NAM modules. A subtask in this project is concerned with neural networks, NAM modules and related conventional techniques, as well as with feature extraction and data aquisition. We will report on this subtask and its achieved results. Introducing, a brief overview of the complete system concept and the implemented prototype system will be given.

II. GENERAL SYSTEM CONCEPT AND IMPLEMENTED PROTOTYPE SYSTEM

The concept of the aspired system features a Central Control Unit (CCU) that prescribes processing in the other functional blocks and monitors the results. By means of two-way connections the system is capable to detect failure and resort to alternative processing approaches. Change of parameters or modification of the entire topology may take place. In an initialization phase the system knowledge base (KB) is preset with knowledge gathered by experiments or by explicit knowledge of the production process and object, e.g., part lists, assembly, and geometry. After image aquisition object localisation and segmentation takes place. Features are extracted from object regions and are classified. The selection of feature extraction and classification techniques is carried out by the CCU. There is a pool of feature extraction techniques available in the Feature Extraction Unit (FEU) that proved useful during initial tests. The same holds for classification where neural network and NAM paradigms are available in the Classification Unit (CLU). The system concept targets not only on the use of individual networks or NAMs but also on the development of structures or hierarchies

with inherent invariance properties for classification. The modules that implement feature extraction and classification have to provide a high degree of flexibility and configurability to suit the needs of the system concept. Currently, a subset of the previously described system concept is implemented comprising image aquisition and object localisation, knowledge base, and feature extraction and neural network modules.

The work of Darmstadt University of Technology (THD) focuses on the implementation and application of neural network and NAM modules as well as on data aquisition for training and testing of these modules. Of course this involves also issues of feature extraction. The current implementation is a SUN workstation based simulation environment. Views of the objects are available as gray level images. A standard data format for information exchange has been defined. This Neural Interchange Format (NIF) is supported by all feature generation and classification modules and therefore the assembly of processing chains and hierarchies is feasible.

The FEU is implemented as a highly modular unit consisting of a core module that interfaces to an arbitrary number of independent feature extraction modules. These modules may also incorporate commercial or proprietary components. Fig.1 illustrates the structure of the FEU that provides two basic operating modes. The transparent mode is used for feature extraction during inspection under control of the CCU without operator interaction. In contrast the interactive mode displays the object and the generated features and allows the classification of selected regions by an operator. Thus, for supervised learning paradigms classification information is generated corresponding to the computed feature vectors. As multiple feature generators can be simultaneously active, vectors comprising several independent features can be computed and transferred along with their classification information to the CLU. Regions of interest can be rectangular or circular in shape. Polygon shapes or other shapes that might be of interest can be additionally implemented. Fig.2 displays the interactive version of the FEU with one feature extraction generator active. The NAG-feature [2] that is predominantly employed in the project provides ro-

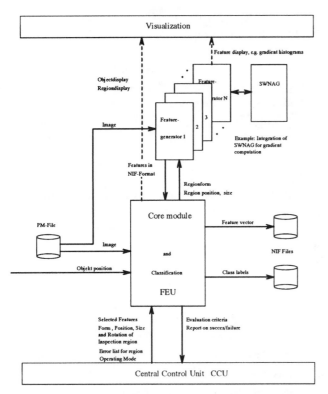

Figure 1: Block diagram of the FEU

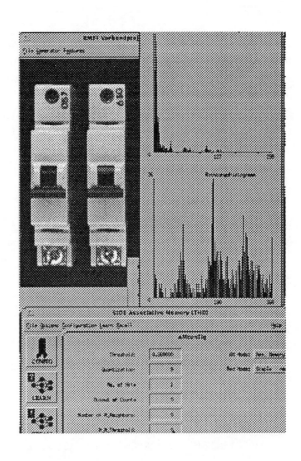

Figure 2: Object instance and NAG-feature

bustness towards scale and translation variance. This preprocessing technique computes the gradient of an image smoothed by a gaussian function. The gradient is stored separately in two image bands representing magnitude and direction. From the chosen region of interest histograms of gradient magnitude and direction are computed [3]. These histograms serve as feature vectors for ensuing classification approaches. The NAG-feature has one decisive parameter Θ that thresholds noise during histogram computation. All pixels in the gradient magnitude less than Θ will not contribute to the magnitude histogram nor to the direction histogram. This threshold was set to $\Theta = 12$ for our experiments. A module denoted as SWNAG[1] is incorporated in the FEU for the computation of these feature vectors. The FEU generates NIF files of feature vectors and corresponding class affiliation which are processed by the CLU. Classification results obtained from the CLU during recall can be assessed in the interactive mode of the FEU.

---

[1]SWNAG is proprietary software of Fraunhofer-Institut für Informations- und Datenverarbeitung IITB Karlsruhe

Several modules of the CLU have been implemented. This comprises MLP with BackPropagation (BP), Self Organizing feature Map (SOM), Learning Vector Quantization (LVQ) and NAM modules. These modules feature a large assortment of variants in addition to the basic algorithms. This enables the CCU to select the best fit variant for the current problem. All CLU modules can be dynamically configured for arbitrary network sizes at run time which is mandatory for the target system. CLU and FEU modules are developed using C++ programming language and OSF/Motif for interactive components. Furthermore, for visualisation purposes and tentative experiments during the development phase the khoros/cantata system and NeuralWorks Professionall II+ are additionally employed.

III. PROBLEM INSTANCE AND DATA AQUISITION

The target system is devised as a generic inspection tool for a wide field of objects. As a first problem instance a automatic cut-out[2] was selected and object samples were extracted from production lines. A front view of the part is displayed in Fig.2. Typical instances of errors are *missing part (, e.g. screw), omitted marking (, e.g. color bar), missing lacquer fixing, scratches, cracks,* and *fissures.* Based on the available samples (180 images) training and test databases were generated using the NAG feature. Prior to the generation of the actual database the available image data was analyzed respective to occuring defects or anomalies and their location of occurence. As an instance for database generation one region, the lower pole clamp, was chosen for inspection with regard to the presence or absence of the fixing screw and the screw type. This database was the baseline for the following classification experiments.

IV. CLASSIFICATION STRATEGIES

In the first tentative expirements individual networks were applied for the classification task (Fig.3.a). BP and NAM were trained and tested with the datasets and parameters of the paradigms were explored. For example, the NAM training procedure was investigated and improved (see section VI). This approach is feasible for the present small datasets, but not very sophisticated. Larger and more complex datasets will require a more elaborate approach. As this system targets on the use of multiple features that generally will be of very different size, value range and significance the direct processing of a concatenated feature vector by a single large classifier seems not be appropriate. This was also supported by results obtained from our simulations. Thus, the use of dedicated networks for each feature in a multilevel hierarchical classifier seems promising (Fig.3.b).

Such an approach allows the classification of each feature independent of its dimension and value range. Necessity arises, e.g., for the NAG-histograms which consist of 256 element magnitude vector and 180 element direction vector.

Individual neural nets or NAMs can be trained with corresponding single features in a first processing layer. Further, for particular regions where explicit

knowledge of region properties is available, algorithms can be formulated and incorporated in the hierarchie. This will straighten and simplify the structure. The classification or processing results of the primary layers will be evaluated by a following decision layer. This layer may consist of simple boolean functions, a neural network or NAM, or a fuzzy decision system. Neural networks provide weighting for

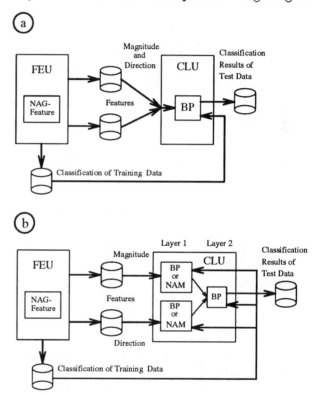

Figure 3: Classification strategies

each feature according to its significance. Furthermore, the certainty of the network or NAM decision can be output by the layer of individual networks. This supports an additional weighting of individual decisions by the decision layer. For this data fusion task BP networks are well suited. They provide by training an implicit weighting of the decision certainty. In contrast, fuzzy decision systems allow the explicit weighting of the decision certainty for the global classification by the formulation of rules.

V. CLASSIFICATION RESULTS

At this stage of the project, the available datasets are very small. We chose as classes *screw_in_place* (class1) and *screw_missing* (class2). For the single

---

[2]AEG Aktiengesellschaft, Geschäftsbereich Komponenten, Fachbereich Zähler und Elfa, Abteilung Fertigungstechnologie, Hameln

networks we used a training set of 55 vectors (46 class1 / 9 class2) and a test set of 12 vectors (10/2). Quickprop [4] proved to be the best BP training method. We applied a network of 436 input, 2 hidden, and 2 output neurons (Quickprop parameter settings: μ=2.5, batchsize=55). In 100 epochs the network was successfully trained and provided 100% recognition of the test set.

NAM is programmed by prototypes out of the training set. In plain mode all training patterns are used as prototypes. In this mode the test set was correctly classified. Applying the standard programming algorithm (see section VI) reduced the training set to three prototypes and caused misclassification. The improved algorithm generated four prototypes and provided correct classification results. The NAM simulator allows the definition of value quantization. This was set to 8 bit per feature value according to initial tests. Splitting in gradient magnitude and direction feature gave equivalent classification results for the individual networks.

For the hierarchical classifier we used three data sets comprising 45 (40/5, set 1), 10 (8/2, set 2), and 6 (4/2, set 3) vectors for training and testing. Classes were the same as above. Two BP networks (or NAMs) were used for gradient magnitude and direction in the first layer of the hierarchical classifier. In the second layer a BP network was employed as decision element. Network topology was 256/2/2 for magnitude, 180/2/2 for direction, and 4/2/2 for the decision network. The networks of the different layers were trained individually. After training of the first layer with data set 1, these networks were used with data set 2 in recall. The resulting output data was used for the second layer network as input training data. Data set 3 was used to test the completed structure. The hierarchical classifier provided 100% classification of the presented data. Instead of BP networks NAMs were used in this concept. In the decision layer application of a NAM proved not feasible due to quantization effects. BP networks are better suited because they can better tune to the patterns of the first layer and have superior generalization capability. In the first layer NAMs performed equivalently to the BP networks. Additionally, they offer the possibility of powerful hardware implementation.

Invariance for the NAG-feature with regard to rotation can be achieved by storing shifted copies of each gradient direction histogram vector in the NAM, as rotation of the pattern in the inspection region results in a cyclic shift of the histogram. This approach is more favourable than a standard cross correlation, as computation potentially can be carried out in parallel. Simulations have shown the feasibility of this idea which of course considerably enlarges the database (up to factor 180) and promotes the application of dedicated hardware. Regions with known properties often allow normalization by an algorithmic procedure, thus providing invariance towards rotation. Current work focuses on such an approach.

VI. NAM AND RCE-MODELL

During our work we found an interesting correspondence of the NAM to the well established RCE-modell [5] of Nestor Inc. The basic NAM training algorithms can be found in [6]. They were extended to the processing of integer and fixed point computation in our work.

Both approaches can be affiliated to the category of multireference classifiers. In recall an input vector is compared by a metric (Euclidean or manhattan distance) with all stored prototypes. The class of the prototype that fires determines the classification of the input vector. In training prototypes are selected by iterative algorithms from an initial large training set. The major differences of the models are that the RCE has individual thresholds for each prototype, determining regions of attraction, while the NAM conducts an unlimited competition, as in SOM or LVQ, and that the RCE targets in filling up class regions (hypervolumes), while the NAM algorithm identifies a subset of vectors that adequately approximate the class borders. Generally, the RCE approach will expend more prototypes than the NAM algorithm. The NAM algorithm may overspecialise to presented training set, and in recall give an erroneous classification by extrapolating in an untrained region. Both methods provide extremely short training times.

In our work we improved the NAM algorithm by introducing for training and recall a uniform distance threshold for all prototypes. If this threshold is exceeded in competition the NAM will store the input as a new prototype in training and indicate *untrained* as classification result in recall. This modification proved salient and superior to the basic form in our work. Future work will concern with an elaborate qualitative and quantitative comparison of NAM and RCE, also encompassing other network growing methods like *Dynamic Vector Quantization*, as a comparison with just standard LVQ seems unadequate.

VII. Hardware Implementation

Real time constraints for the inspection and classification task require the application of a powerful hardware background. Most of the computations can be carried out on fast workstations or by accelerators or dedicated processors.

For the implementation of NAMs we pursue a SIMD array approach. Scalable modular systems can be easily implemented by a simple and efficient VLSI design. Two simple NAM systems were completed already and a third system is under development [7], implementing the full scope of the simulator used in the experimental part of this work. For the direction histograms a processing speed of $\approx$ 0.6 MCPS per vector is expected. This amounts to $\approx$ 307 MCPS for a database of 512 vectors. A small FPGA prototype implementation of this NAM system is available since the end of 1992. A standard cell chip design is nearly completed. With regard to system size and speed a full-custom design and multichip module approach is currently investigated.

VIII. Conclusion and Future Work

This work has presented modules and concepts for a novel system in the field of visual object inspection in AQC. Our experiments validated the applicability of our modules for the requirements of the target system. Data sets available proved too small for more extensive experiments and training of structures or hierarchies has to be done in very cumbersome fashion. A learning support for these structures has to be embedded in further software design.

Future work will concentrate on the development and application of further feature extraction and classification modules and the exploration of salient neural structures for data fusion, significance evaluation, and certainty processing. A decisive issue will be the investigation of global learning schemes for these structures or hierarchies. The aquisition of large databases is the major task for statistical meaningful experiments. We will investigate the exploitation of fuzzy decision systems for a more lucid decision finding in the final layer of the hierarchical classifier.

Acknowledgment

We thank our partners Dr. Waleschkowski, Dr. Henrich, M. Schahn, and M. Decker of danet GmbH GS KI and Dr. Korn, F. Quint, and Prof. Winkler of IITB Karlsruhe for many valuable discussions. Especially, we would like to express our gratitude to Dr. Korn and F. Quint for their support concerning the NAG-feature and the Nestor RCE-model.

References

[1] I. F. Croall, J. P. Mason (Eds.), *Industrial Applications of Neural Networks*, ESPRIT Research Reports, Project 2092 ANNIE, Vol. 1, Springer Verlag, 1992

[2] A. Korn, "Toward a symbolic representation of intensity changes images", IEEE Transactions on Pattern Analysis and Machine Intelligence, Vol. PAMI-10, pp. 610-625, 1988

[3] A. Korn, "Zur Beschreibung und Erkennung von Bildstrukturen durch Auswertung von Richtungshistogrammen", Fortschrittsberichte, Band 114, Reihe 10, W. Schwerdtmann (editor), VDI-Verlag Düsseldorf, pp. 44-51, 1989

[4] S. E. Fahlman, "Faster-Learning Variations on Back-Propagation: An Empirical Study", in *Proceedings of The 1988 Connectionist Models Summer School*, pp. 38 - 51, San Mateo, Calif., Morgan Kaufmann, 1989

[5] D. L. Reilly, L. N. Cooper, C. Elbaum, "A Neural Model for Category Learning", Biological Cybernetics, 45, pp. 35 - 41, 1982

[6] W. Pöchmüller, A. König, M. Glesner, "Iterative Data Reduction Algorithms and their Application to Binary Associative Networks", in *Proceedings of the International Joint Conference on Neural Networks IJCNN'92*, Vol. II, pp. 3 - 9, Beijing, 1992

[7] A. König, M. Glesner, "VLSI-Implementation of Associative Memory Systems for Neural Information Processing", *3rd International Workshop on VLSI for Artificial Intelligence and Neural Networks*, Oxford, 1992

ANALYSIS OF LINSKER-TYPE HEBBIAN LEARNING: RIGOROUS RESULTS

Jianfeng FENG[†]   Hong PAN[*]
[†] Department of Probability and Statistics, Peking University, Beijing 100871
[*]Institute of Biophysics, Chinese Academy of Sciences, Beijing 100101
P.R. China

Abstract– In terms of a rigorous analysis of the nonlinear asymmetric dynamics of Linsker's unsupervised Hebbian learning network, we determine the whole set of fixed point attractors of the network and present the necessary and sufficient condition for the emergence of structured receptive fields. Thus the new rigorous criteria for the division of parameter regimes to ensure the development of various structured connection patterns can be obtained explicitly. The shape of a receptive field is totally governed by the feedforward synaptic density function between the present layer and the preceding one, while the existence of a parameter regime for its occurrence is determined by the covariance matrix of cell activities in the present layer, therefore by synaptic density functions of all preceding layers. We then reinterpret the generation of center-surround and other oriented structures with the aid of our general theorems and numerical examples, and refigure the distribution of a few types of principal parameter regimes for varying system parameters and the relationship between these types.

I. INTRODUCTION

With the purpose of understanding the self-organization mechanism of primary visual system, Linsker has proposed a multilayered unsupervised Hebbian learning network with random uncorrelated inputs and the spatially localized, topographically arranged arborization of synap-ses between source and target cell layers [1,2]. Linsker's simulations have found that for appropriate parameter regimes, several structured connection patterns occur progressively as the Hebbian evolution of weights goes layer by layer like in mammalian visual system. To apply the energy function or eigenvector stability analysis methods for the ordinary differential equation, formulating the mod-el without explicit expression about non-uniform connection distribution or introducing the linear approximation has been carried out in previous papers [1-4]. However, it was shown in Linsker's simulations that the non-uniform synaptic density function $r(\cdot)$ plays a crucial role in development of those feature-analyzing cells. So only with the synaptic density function $r(\cdot)$ fed explicitly into the

dynamics equation, we can explicitly analyze the effects of $r(\cdot)$ on behaviors of the network. On the other hand, the linear approximation may not adequately characterize the effects of the weight bounds on the dynamics, since the weight bounds represent a complex constraint for the dynamics development and the long-time behaviors of Linsker's network may be quite different from that of linearizing network in many respects. Therefore we believe that a rigorous analysis for the parameter space of the nonlinear asymmetric dynamics

$$\omega_{n+1}(i) = f\{\omega_n(i) + k_1 + \sum_{j=1}^{N_{\mathcal{L}}}[q(i,j) + k_2(j)]\omega_n(j)\} \quad (1)$$

should be helpful to understand its dynamical mechanisms deeper, here asymmetric means that $\{q(i,j), 1 \le i, j \le N_{\mathcal{L}}\}$ is not a symmetric matrix. In equation (1), $f(\cdot)$ is a nonlinear clipping function defined by

$$f(x) = \begin{cases} \omega_{max}, & \text{if } x > \omega_{max} \\ x, & \text{if } |x| \le \omega_{max} \\ -\omega_{max}, & \text{if } x < -\omega_{max} \end{cases}$$

for a constant $\omega_{max} > 0$. And the asymmetric matrix $q = \{q(i,j), 1 \le i, j \le N_{\mathcal{L}}\} = \{q_{ij}r(j), 1 \le i, j \le N_{\mathcal{L}}\}$ is obtained by the covariance matrix $\{q_{ij}\}$ of site activities at preceding layer $\mathcal{L}$ multiplied by a non-negative normalized synaptic density function $r(\cdot)$, $\sum_{i \in \mathcal{L}} r(i) = 1$, whereas we call q a covariance matrix for simplicity. In what follows, we confine ourselves to the dynamical system $\omega_n(i)$ defined by equation (1) with connection configuration space $[-\omega_{max}, \omega_{max}]^{N_{\mathcal{L}}}$ for constants k_1, k_2, and $k_2(j) = k_2r(j)$.

II. THE SET OF ATTRACTORS AND STABILITY

In fact, we are concerned mainly with the rigorous analysis of the set of all fixed point attractors of a first-order difference equation, taking the form

$$\omega_{n+1}(i) = f[\omega_n(i) + f_1(\omega_n, k_1, k_2)]. \quad (2)$$

where $\omega_n = (\omega_n(i), i = 1, ..., N_{\mathcal{L}})$. Since the nonlinear clipping function $f(\cdot)$ defines a hypercube in connection space within which the dynamics is dominated by the linear system $\omega_{n+1}(i) = \omega_n(i) + f_1(\omega_n, k_1, k_2)$, the short-time behaviors of connection patterns can be fully characterized in terms of the properties of eigenvectors and their eigenvalues. But this method of stability analysis will never be suitable for the long-time evolution of equation (1) or (2), provided the hypercube constraint is reached as the largest components of ω reach saturation. However, it is well-known that a fixed point or an equilibrium state of dynamics (2) satisfies

$$\omega_n(i) = f[\omega_n(i) + f_1(\omega_n, k_1, k_2)]. \tag{3}$$

and and $\omega_n(i) \in \{-\omega_{max}, \omega_{max}\}$. Because of the specific form of the nonlinear function $f(\cdot)$, the fixed point equation (3) implies that $\exists N$, as $n > N$,

$$\mid \omega_n(i) + f_1(\omega_n, k_1, k_2) \mid \geq \omega_{max},$$

So $\omega_n(i)$ must have the same sign as $f_1(\omega_n, k_1, k_2)$, i.e.

$$\omega_n(i) f_1(\omega_n(i), k_1, k_2)$$
$$= \omega_n(i)\{k_1 + \sum_{j=1}^{N_{\mathcal{L}}} [q(i,j) + k_2(j)]\omega_n(j)\} > 0.$$

THEOREM 1. *The whole set of fixed point attractors in Linsker's dynamics (1) is*

$$\Omega_0 = \{\omega, \omega(i)\{k_1 + \sum_{j=1}^{N_{\mathcal{L}}} [q(i,j) + k_2(j)]\omega(j)\} > 0,$$
$$1 \leq i \leq N_{\mathcal{L}}, \omega \in \{-\omega_{max}, \omega_{max}\}^{N_{\mathcal{L}}}\}.$$

Without loss of generality, we assume from now on that $\omega_{max} = 1$, namely thereafter we consider the dynamics (1) with connection space $\Omega = [-1, 1]^{N_{\mathcal{L}}}$. From the proof Theorem 1, we also conclude that

THEOREM 2. $\forall \omega \in \Omega_0$, *there exists a nonempty neighborhood* $o(\omega)$ *of* ω *satisfying* $o(\omega) \subset B(\omega)$, *where* $B(\omega)$ *is the attractive basin of attractor* ω *defined by* $B(\omega) = \{\varsigma : \varsigma \in [-1, 1]^{N_{\mathcal{L}}}, \omega_0 = \varsigma, \lim_{n \to \infty} \omega_n = \omega\}$.

III. DIVISION OF PARAMETER REGIMES

Now we are going to develop a more concrete sufficient and necessary condition to guarantee the emergence of various desired connection patterns. We define

$$\Omega^+(\omega) = \{i, \omega(i) = 1\}$$

as the set of sites at preceding layer $\mathcal{L}$ with excitatory weight for a connection pattern ω, and

$$\Omega^-(\omega) = \{i, \omega(i) = -1\}$$

the set of sites at layer $\mathcal{L}$ with inhibitory weight for ω. Note from Theorem 1 that a connection pattern ω is an attractor of the dynamics (1) if and only if for $i \in \Omega^+(\omega)$, we have

$$\omega(i)\{k_1 + \sum_j [k_2 r(j) + q(i,j)]\omega(j)\}$$
$$= \omega(i)\{k_1 + \sum_{j \in \Omega^+(\omega)} [k_2 r(j) + q(i,j)]\omega(j)$$
$$+ \sum_{j \in \Omega^-(\omega)} [k_2 r(j) + q(i,j)]\omega(j)\} > 0.$$

By the definition of $\Omega^+(\omega)$ and $\Omega^-(\omega)$, we deduce from inequality above that

$$k_1 + \sum_{j \in \Omega^+(\omega)} [k_2 r(j) + q(i,j)] - \sum_{j \in \Omega^-(\omega)} [k_2 r(j) + q(i,j)]$$

is greater than zero, namely

$$k_1 + k_2[\sum_{j \in \Omega^+(\omega)} r(j) - \sum_{j \in \Omega^-(\omega)} r(j)]$$
$$> \sum_{j \in \Omega^-(\omega)} q(i,j) - \sum_{j \in \Omega^+(\omega)} q(i,j).$$

Inequality above is satisfied for all i in $\Omega^+(\omega)$, and the left hand is independent of i. Taking maximum over the set $i \in \Omega^+(\omega)$ on both sides of this inequality, we thus obtain

$$k_1 + k_2[\sum_{j \in \Omega^+(\omega)} r(j) - \sum_{j \in \Omega^-(\omega)} r(j)]$$
$$> \max_{i \in \Omega^+(\omega)} [\sum_{j \in \Omega^-(\omega)} q(i,j) - \sum_{j \in \Omega^+(\omega)} q(i,j)].$$

On the other hand, for $i \in \Omega^-(\omega)$, we can similarly deduce that

$$k_1 + k_2[\sum_{j \in \Omega^+(\omega)} r(j) - \sum_{j \in \Omega^-(\omega)} r(j)]$$
$$< \min_{i \in \Omega^-(\omega)} [\sum_{j \in \Omega^-(\omega)} q(i,j) - \sum_{j \in \Omega^+(\omega)} q(i,j)].$$

So we newly introduce the slope function

$$c(\omega) = \sum_{j \in \Omega^+(\omega)} r(j) - \sum_{j \in \Omega^-(\omega)} r(j)$$

which is the difference of sums of the synaptic density function $r(\cdot)$ over $\Omega^+(\omega)$ and $\Omega^-(\omega)$, and two k_1- intercept functions

$$d_1(\omega) = \max_{i \in \Omega^+(\omega)} (\sum_{j \in \Omega^-(\omega)} q(i,j) - \sum_{j \in \Omega^+(\omega)} q(i,j)),$$

and

$$d_2(\omega) = \min_{i \in \Omega^-(\omega)} \left(\sum_{j \in \Omega^-(\omega)} q(i,j) - \sum_{j \in \Omega^+(\omega)} q(i,j) \right).$$

The definition of slope function $c(\omega)$ implies that it only depends on the synaptic density function $r(\cdot)$ between both successive layers under consideration and does not relate to density functions $r(\cdot)$ of other preceding layers. And two k_1- intercept functions $d_1(\omega)$ and $d_2(\omega)$ embody the dependence of dynamics (1) on $q(\cdot,\cdot)$, the covariance matrix with density function $r(\cdot)$, and so on density functions $r(\cdot)$ of all preceding layers.

THEOREM 3. *For every layer of Linsker's network, a connection pattern ω is a fixed point attractor of dynamics (1) if and only if*

$$d_2(\omega) > k_1 + c(\omega)k_2 > d_1(\omega). \qquad (4)$$

That is to say, for given synaptic density functions $r(\cdot)$, the parameter regime of (k_1, k_2) to ensure that ω is a stable attractor of dynamics (1) is a band which is determined by two parallel lines $k_1 + c(\omega)k_2 > d_1(\omega)$ and $k_1 + c(\omega)k_2 < d_2(\omega)$ (Fig. 1). It is noticed that as $d_1(\omega) > d_2(\omega)$, there is no regime of (k_1, k_2) for the occurrence of that ω as an attractor of dynamics (1). Thus the existence of such a structured receptive field ω as an attractor of dynamics (1) is determined by k_1-intercept functions $d_1(\cdot), d_2(\cdot)$, and therefore by the covariance matrix q or density functions $r(\cdot)$ of all preceding layers. On the other hand, the shape of a receptive field ω (or the spatial pattern of weight structure) is governed by k_1, k_2 and $c(\cdot)$, and so only by the synaptic density function $r(\cdot)$ between the present layer and the preceding one. Since the width of the band $[d_2(\omega) - d_1(\omega)]$ is narrow usually for an individual connection pattern ω as $r(i)$ is normalized, we have the following approximate relationship between two main system parameters k_1, k_2 and the average weight strength g of a stable connection pattern

$$\frac{-k_1}{k_2} \approx c(\omega) \approx \frac{\|\ \Omega^+(\omega)\ | - |\ \Omega^-(\omega)\ \|}{N_{\mathcal{L}}} \equiv g,$$

(if $r(i) \approx \frac{1}{N_{\mathcal{L}}}$), a relationship observed and assumed in Ref.1-4, where $|\cdot|$ represents the total number of elements in a set. Then it is readily seen that the difference between g and $\frac{-k_1}{k_2}$ originates from the synaptic density function $r(\cdot)$. Therefore, this just gives the reason why $\frac{-k_1}{k_2}$ is a good approximation of the mature g value.

IV. RECEPTIVE FIELDS BETWEEN LAYER B, C

Therefrom, we refigure and modify prior results about parameter regimes for varying k_1 and k_2 in Ref.4. We

We adopt the rigorous sufficient and necessary stability condition (4) to discuss various receptive fields between the second layer B and the third layer C observed in Linsker's simulations under the condition that synaptic connections between the first layer A and layer B are all-excitatory. Denote the synaptic density function between A and B as $p(\cdot,\cdot)$. Let $r(\cdot)$ be the synaptic density function between layer B and C. If it is assumed that the input activities at layer A obey the independent normal distribution with mean 0 and variance 1 as that used in Ref.1-4, then for layer C, $q(i,j) = \sum_{l=1}^{N_A} p(i,l)p(j,l)r(j)$. Our Theorem 4 tells that as

$$k_1 + k_2 > d_1(+) \equiv - \min_{1 \le i \le N_B} \sum_{j=1}^{N_B} \sum_{l=1}^{N_A} p(i,l)p(j,l)r(j),$$

the all-excitatory connection pattern is always an attractor of dynamics (1) (Regime A of Fig.1). Same conclusion holds as

$$k_1 - k_2 < d_2(-) \equiv \min_{1 \le i \le N_B} \sum_{j=1}^{N_B} \sum_{l=1}^{N_A} p(i,l)p(j,l)r(j)$$

for the all-inhibitory connection pattern (Regime B of Fig. 1). So the parameter plane of (k_1, k_2) is divided into the four regimes by these two conditions, in which the regime determined by $d_1(+) < k_1 + k_2$ and $k_1 - k_2 < d_2(-)$ is the coexistence regime of all-excitatory and all-inhibitory connection patterns (Regime C of Fig.1). Because of the requirement of the slow decrease of $r(\cdot)$ with respect to $p(\cdot,\cdot)$ which is imposed in Linsker's simulations, our Theorem 5 considers the extreme case, in which $r(\cdot)$ is a constant and $p(i,\cdot)$ almost concentrates on i, and indicates that any configuration in $\{-1,1\}^{N_B}$ satisfying $[|\Omega^+(\omega)| - |\Omega^-(\omega)|]/N_B = -k_1/k_2$ is an attractor of Linsker's network. In particular, if we put $|\frac{k_1}{k_2}|N_B$ be an integer less than N_B, then the center-surround cell is always an attractor of dynamics (1). And so is the bi-lobbed cell. In fact, in this case, each connection strength between layer B and C developed independently. So any pattern of connection strengths may emerge, and too many states coexist as attractors of Linsker's network. As the condition of Theorem 5 fails, the development of connections between layer B and C will depend on each other stronger and stronger in the sense that most of connections have the same sign as their neighbors in a receptive field. Thus in another extreme case, in which both $r(\cdot)$ and $p(\cdot,\cdot)$ are constants, Theorem 6 states that all attractors in $\{-1,1\}^{N_{\mathcal{L}}}$ are not stable except the all-excitatory and all-inhibitory connection patterns. In general case for $r(\cdot)$ and $p(\cdot,\cdot)$, there is a small regime around the origin in the parameter plane of (k_1, k_2), in which many attractors coexist (Regime F of Fig.1). As $k_2 = -3$ as taken

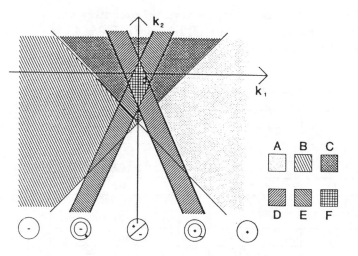

Fig. 1.

in Linsker's simulations, we conclude that now (k_1, k_2) is outside the parameter regime of coexistence of many attractors (Fig.1). It is just the reason that the emergence of a structured connection pattern is favored for k_2 large and negative.

Therefore, we can determine the following types of principal parameter regimes(Fig. 1):

PARAMETER REGIME	ATTRACTOR
$k_1 + k_2 > d_1(+)$,	All-excitatory connection pattern(A);
$k_1 - k_2 < d_2(-)$,	All-inhibitory connection pattern(B);
$k_1 + k_2 > d_1(+)$, $k_1 - k_2 < d_2(-)$,	All-excitatory and all-inhibitory connection patterns coexist($C = A\&B$);
$d_2(\omega) > k_1 + c(\omega)k_2 > d_1(\omega)$, where $c(\omega) > 0$	Any connection pattern in which the excitatory connections constitute the majority (e.g. the ON-center cell with large excitatory center radius r_{core} or the OFF-center cell with small inhibitory r_{core})(D);
$d_2(\omega) > k_1 + c(\omega)k_2 > d_1(\omega)$ where $c(\omega) < 0$,	Any connection pattern in which the inhibitory connections constitute the majority (e.g. the ON-center cell with small excitatory r_{core} or the OFF-center cell with large inhibitory r_{core})(E);
$d_2(\omega^1) > k_1 + c(\omega^1)k_2 > d_1(\omega^1)$ ...... $d_2(\omega^\mu) > k_1 + c(\omega^\mu)k_2 > d_1(\omega^\mu)$,	A small coexistence regime of many connection patterns around the origin of the parameter plane of (k_1, k_2) ($F = A\&B\&C\&D\&E$).

As an application of our above-mentioned analyses, we present some numerical results of the parameter regimes of (k_1, k_2, r_A, r_B) for ON-center cells, bi-lobbed cell, circularly symmetric cell with 3s-mode [4] and oriented cell, and refigure the condition of generating these structures between layer B and C. Let $p(i, j) \sim \exp(-\frac{\|i-j\|}{r_A^2})$, $i \in B$, $j \in A$, and $r(j) \sim \exp(-\frac{\|j\|}{r_B^2})$, $j \in B$. We consider layer B with 253 sites, that is the total number of sites inside the circle with grid radius 9(Fig. 2, Fig. 3). Denote the radius of the excitatory central region of an ON-center receptive field as r_{core} and denote an ON-center receptive field simply as $(r_{core}, 9)$(Fig. 3). We are going to give the parameter regime of (k_1, k_2, r_A, r_B), in which ON-center receptive field is developed. In our examples, we take $r_B = 10$.

Example: ON-center cells $(r_{core}, 9)$

a) $r_{core} = 1$. In this case, we have 5 excitatory sites and 248 inhibitory sites with $c((1, 9)) = -0.78$. In Table 1, the parameter regime of (k_1, k_2) is given for the occurrence of center-surround cell $(1, 9)$ with different r_A. Note that as $r_A \geq 1.0, (k_1, k_2) = \phi$, the empty set, namely, the connection pattern $(1,9)$ will never be an attractor of dynamics (1) in this parameter regime.

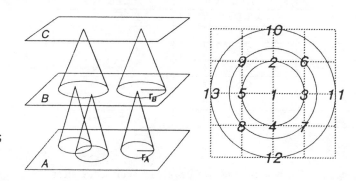

Fig. 2. An illustration of the Linsker's Network.

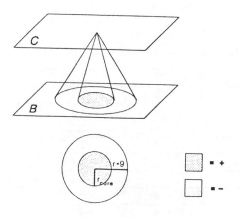

Fig. 3. On-center receptive field.

TABLE I
$$k_1 - 0.78k_2 > d_1((1,9)), \quad k_1 - 0.78k_2 < d_2((1,9))$$

r_A	$d_1((1,9))$	$d_2((1,9))$
0.1	$-4.7E-3,$	$2.1E-3$
0.5	$-2.1E-3,$	$1.5E-3$
1.0	$1.7E-3,$	$1.5E-3*$
1.1	$2.3E-3,$	$1.5E-3*$
1.2	$2.3E-3,$	$1.5E-3*$
5.0	$2.7E-3,$	$1.2E-3*$
6.0	$2.2E-3,$	$1.1E-3*$
10.	$1.7E-3,$	$1.5E-3*$

b) $r_{core} = 4$. In this case, we have 49 excitatory sites and 204 inhibitory sites with $c((4,9)) = -0.46$. Table 2 has the similar meaning as Table 1. Note that as $r_A \geq 5.0$, $(k_1, k_2) = \phi$, namely, $(4,9)$ will never be an attractor of dynamics (1) in this case.

TABLE II
$$k_1 - 0.78k_2 > d_1((4,9)), \quad k_1 - 0.78k_2 < d_2((4,9))$$

r_A	$d_1((4,9))$	$d_2((4,9))$
0.1	$-4.1E-3$	$2.1E-3$
0.5	$-1.9E-3$	$1.5E-3$
1.0	$2.3E-4$	$8.5E-4$
1.1	$2.8E-4$	$8.0E-4$
1.2	$3.2E-4$	$7.6E-4$
5.0	$6.8E-4$	$6.6E-4*$
6.0	$6.7E-4$	$5.5E-4*$
10.	$5.2E-4$	$3.7E-4*$

c) $r_{core} = 7$. In this case, we have 149 excitatory sites and 104 inhibitory sites with $c((7,9)) = 0.23$. Table 3 has the similar meaning as Table 1 again. The difference of this example from examples a) and b) is that (k_1, k_2) always exists and $c((7,9)) > 0$.

TABLE III
$$k_1 + 0.23k_2 > d_1((4,9)) \quad k_1 + 0.23k_2 < d_2((4,9))$$

r_A	$d_1((4,9))$	$d_2((4,9))$
0.1	$-2.9E-3$	$2.1E-3$
0.5	$-1.4E-3$	$1.4E-3$
1.0	$-2.0E-4$	$1.1E-4$
1.1	$-2.4E-4$	$1.8E-6$
1.2	$-2.9E-4$	$-9.6E-5$
5.0	$-8.2E-4$	$-8.1E-4$
6.0	$-7.4E-4$	$-7.3E-4$
10.	$-4.6E-4$	$-4.6E-4$

d) $r_{core} = 8$. In this case, we have 197 excitatory sites and 56 inhibitory sites with $c((8,9)) = 0.51$. Table 4 has the similar meaning as Table 1.

TABLE IV
$$k_1 + 0.51k_2 > d_1((8,9)), \quad k_1 + 0.51k_2 < d_2((8,9))$$

r_A	$d_1((8,9))$	$d_2((8,9))$
0.1	$-2.5E-3$	$2.1E-3$
0.5	$-1.20E-3$	$1.0E-3$
1.0	$-7.20E-4$	$-5.10E-4$
1.1	$-7.60E-4$	$-6.00E-4$
1.2	$-8.10E-4$	$-6.70E-4$
5.0	$-1.09E-3$	$-1.07E-3$
6.0	$-1.01E-3$	$-1.00E-3$
10.	$-7.00E-4$	$-7.00E-4$

Space constrains us to illustrate other numerical results in a schematic diagram(Fig. 4). For given r_A, $c(\omega)$ ranges from -1 to 1, when the number of excitatory connections in a receptive field $|\Omega^+(\omega)|$

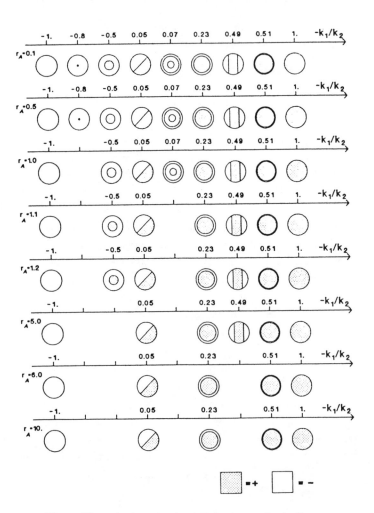

Fig. 4. Numerical results for different r_A and $-k_1/k_2$

changes from 0 to N_B and the number of its inhibitory connections $|\Omega^-(\omega)|$ changes from N_B to 0. From the definition of $c(\omega)$, $c(\omega) = \sum_{j \in \Omega^+(\omega)} r(j) - \sum_{j \in \Omega^-(\omega)} r(j)$, we observe that as ω is an ON-center cell with excitatory connections inside the circle with radius r_{core}, then $c(\omega')$ of the OFF-center cell ω' with inhibitory connections inside the circle with radius r_{core} and excitatory connections outside that circle is $c(\omega') = \sum_{j \in \Omega^+(\omega')} r(j) - \sum_{j \in \Omega^-(\omega')} r(j) = -c(\omega)$. Hence, we only need to consider ON-center cells because of the symmetry between $c(\omega)$ and $c(\omega')$. However, $d_1(\omega)$, $d_2(\omega)$ and $d_1(\omega')$, $d_2(\omega')$ are certainly different. It is recently clear from our numerical examples that as $c(\omega) > 0$ (i.e. an ON-center connection pattern has a large central excitatory region or an OFF-center one has a small inhibitory central region), the parameter regime (k_1, k_2, r_A, r_B) of the ON-center cell is broader than the OFF-center cell. It is same the other way round that as $c(\omega) < 0$, the OFF-center cell with large inhibitory r_{core} is less sensitive to parameters (r_A, r_B) than the ON-center cell with small excitatory r_{core}. This conclusion makes it clear why the parameter regime $(k_1 > 0, k_2 < 0)$ and $(k_1 < 0, k_2 > 0)$ favors the occurrence of the ON-center cell with large r_{core}, although there also exist the possibility of the emergence of the OFF-center cell with small r_{core}. In the meanwhile, the parameter regime $(k_1 < 0, k_2 < 0)$ and $(k_1 > 0, k_2 > 0)$ prefers the OFF-center receptive field with large r_{core} to the ON-center cell with small r_{core}.

V. CONCLUSIONS

From our rigorous results, we can point out that:

It is important to understand that circularly symmetric arbor functions set up the asymmetry of covariance matrix q. Then asymmetric q causes diversity of systematic behaviors in Linsker's network.

The nonlinear function $f(\cdot)$ in equation (1) which embodies boundary for synaptic strength gives rise to the coexistence of many attractors for the same family of parameters, as might be expected for a nonlinear dynamical system.

As was just mentioned, the covariance matrix q in the present layer is evolved from synaptic arbor density functions of all preceding layers. Our Theorem 6 indicates that in the case of fully feedforward connection the desired structured receptive fields will never arise at all, although there exist correlation in afferent activities.

Without localized synaptic arbor density function there would be no structured covariance matrix. And without structured covariance matrix which includes localized correlation in afferent activities, no structured receptive fields would exist.

The rigorous proof of our general theorems and the detailed discussion of analytic and numerical results will be reported elsewhere [5].

ACKNOWLEDGEMENT

We are grateful to Prof. M.-P. Qian and Prof. A.-K. Guo for their useful discussions and suggestions. H.P. is supported by the National Natural Science Foundation of China under Grant No. 9690013 to A.-K. Guo.

REFERENCES

[1] Linsker, R.(1986), From basic network principles to neural architecture, *Proc. Natl. Acad. Sci. USA* **83**: 7508-7512, 8390-8394, 8779-8783.

[2] Linsker, R.(1988), Self-organization in a perceptual network, *Computer* **21**(3): 105-117.

[3] Tang, D.S.(1989), Information-theoretic solutions to early visual information processing: Analytic results, *Phys. Rev. A* **40**: 6626-6635.

[4] MacKay, D.J.C., & Miller, K.D.(1990), Analysis of Linsker's application of Hebbian rules to linear networks, *Network* **1**: 257-297.

[5] Feng, J., & Pan, H.(1992), A rigorous analysis of Linsker's unsupervised Hebbian learning network, submitted.

Continuous Time Modeling of Nonlinear Systems: A Neural Network-Based Approach*

Ramiro Rico-Martínez and Ioannis G. Kevrekidis

Department of Chemical Engineering, Princeton University, Princeton NJ 08544.

Abstract— We present a neural network-based approach for continuous-time modeling of nonlinear systems. In a previous paper a similar goal was achieved by using feedforward networks and an explicit integrator scheme; the approach presented here is based on an implicit integrator and recurrent networks. The resulting continuous-time model (a set of ODEs) is capable of correctly capturing the long term attractors of the system.

I. INTRODUCTION.

Artificial Neural Networks (ANNs) have become a valuable tool for time series processing and nonlinear system identification tasks. The *ad hoc* models obtained by using experimental measurements to train ANNs can lead to qualitative understanding of the dynamic behavior and dependence on operating parameters of the processes studied. The application of the ANNs in this context is useful in cases where models based on first principles fail to quantitatively reproduce the dynamic picture observed experimentally or are simply not available.

For real time control applications ANN-based models should provide accurate short time predictions. Our work, however, focuses on the use of the long term predictions (attractors) towards the understanding and characterization of the dependence of the system behavior on parameters, and more specifically the instabilities and bifurcations it exhibits.

For a deterministic system, the geometrical concept of attractor reconstruction using time delays [1, 2] indicates that the future state of the system can be obtained as a function of measurements of a single state variable. This idea fits nicely in the context of "traditional" feedforward multilayer ANNs and has been successfully applied in the processing of nonlinear time-series (e.g. [3]). Typically, the ANN they use consists of a linear input layer, one or more (nonlinear) hidden layers and a linear output layer. The measurements of the state variable (current value as well as an appropriate number of delayed measurements) are the inputs to the ANN (additional input neurons can be used to incorporate the dependence on operating parameters); its output becomes the prediction of the state variable at a future measurement time.

Discrete mappings constructed using this methodology have been found capable of good short term prediction accuracy. They also may provide predictions of the attractors (long term behavior) close to the "correct" ones in phase space; however, their discrete nature prevents them from capturing the detailed structure of the bifurcation scenario of the continuous-time system they model. This shortcoming was illustrated in previous work [4] using experimental time series containing a sequence of period doubling bifurcations of periodic orbits. There we discussed the reasons for the failure of *any* discrete-time model (and not only discrete-time ANN-based models) in capturing the qualitative nature of continuous-time attractors and their bifurcations.

An alternative approach to the identification of continuous-time systems based on a feedforward ANN implementation of an explicit Runge-Kutta integrator was also described in the above reference. In this paper, an extension of that work is presented. An implicit integrator is now used, and we resort to recurrent network methodologies to devise the training algorithm. In the remaining sections the ideas behind the implementation of the explicit integrator-based approach are briefly reviewed, followed by a description of the implicit approach and some representative results.

II. CONTINUOUS-TIME MODELS.

Consider, as an example of a continuous-time model, an n-th order ODE, e.g.

$$y''' = f(y, y', y''; x), \qquad y' \equiv \frac{dy}{dt}$$

which can be easily transformed into a set of n coupled first order ODEs,

$$y_1' = y_2$$

$$y_2' = y_3$$

$$y_3' = f(y_1, y_2, y_3; x)$$

*This work was partially supported by DARPA/ONR and a NSF PYI award (CTS-8957213).

$$y_1 \equiv y, \quad y_2 \equiv y', \quad y_3 \equiv y''$$

with additional dependent variables including up to the (n-1) time derivative of the original dependent variable (x is an operating parameter). An obvious approach to fitting an ODE to continuous time data would be to evaluate time derivatives ($y_2 \equiv y'$, $y_3 \equiv y''$, and $y_3' \equiv y'''$ in our example) from the data by numerical differentiation. One would then train a traditional ANN of the type described above (with the inputs in our example being the measured y, and the numerically obtained y' and y'') to approximate the right hand side of the ODE ($f(y, y', y'')$ in our example, with target value the numerically obtained y'''). In the case of a single time series it will obviously be sufficient to train the network to predict only the right hand side of the n-th ODE. Upon successful completion of the training, the set of n first order ODEs can be numerically integrated to produce predictions at any desired time. The most obvious problem of this approach is the numerical sensitivity of the estimation of derivatives, especially high order ones, from time series, which can be further aggravated by the presence of noise.

We attempt here to construct a set of ODEs from the data using state measurements only, without direct numerical evaluation of time derivatives from the time series. Both the inputs and the outputs of the training algorithm of the network we want to construct will involve only state measurements. The target values (the state of the system at some future time $t + \tau$) are the result of integrating the (unknown) right hand side of the ODEs; this integration is "performed" by the physical system itself. We must therefore attempt to approximate the unknown right hand side of the ODEs from our experimental knowledge of the *results* of integrating these ODEs (for time τ, with known initial conditions, the state at time t). We will assume that the experimental data (the result of "physically" integrating the "true" underlying ODE) are practically indistinguishable from the result of numerically integrating this ODE using a simple numerical integration scheme.

A. The explicit integrator approach.

An ANN based procedure can be used to emulate a (numerical) integration scheme. Our first attempt made use of a fourth order Runge-Kutta (explicit) integrator.

Consider the autonomous ODE

$$\dot{\vec{Y}} = \mathbf{f}(\vec{Y}; \vec{X}) \tag{1}$$

$$\vec{Y} \epsilon \mathcal{R}^n, \qquad \vec{X} \epsilon \mathcal{R}^p, \qquad \mathbf{f} : \mathcal{R}^n \times \mathcal{R}^p \mapsto \mathcal{R}^n$$

The result $\vec{Y}_{n+1}$ of numerically integrating this equation for fixed values of the operating parameters $\vec{X}$ with initial conditions $\vec{Y}_n$ using a fourth order Runge-Kutta method and a time step of h is given by:

$$\vec{Y}_{n+1} = \vec{Y}_n + \frac{1}{6}(\vec{k}_1 + 2\vec{k}_2 + 2\vec{k}_3 + \vec{k}_4)$$

where:

$$\vec{k}_1 = h\mathbf{f}(\vec{Y}_n; \vec{X})$$

$$\vec{k}_2 = h\mathbf{f}(\vec{Y}_n + \frac{\vec{k}_1}{2}; \vec{X})$$

$$\vec{k}_3 = h\mathbf{f}(\vec{Y}_n + \frac{\vec{k}_2}{2}; \vec{X})$$

$$\vec{k}_4 = h\mathbf{f}(\vec{Y}_n + \vec{k}_3; \vec{X})$$

The basic element of this procedure is a traditional ANN that given $\vec{Y}_n$ evaluates $\mathbf{f}(\vec{Y}; \vec{X})$, the right hand side of our set of first order ODEs (Eq. 1). The training of this ANN that captures $\mathbf{f}(\vec{Y}; \vec{X})$ can be straightforwardly implemented using the above formulae. The inputs for the training vectors will be the state of the system at time t ($\vec{Y}_n$) and the target for training will be the state of the system at time $t + h$ ($\vec{Y}_{n+1}$). Note that the prediction of the target values, according to the Runge-Kutta formulae, is obtained only after processing the input values four times through the ANN that evaluates $\mathbf{f}(\vec{Y}; \vec{X})$. The training rules for the update of weights are derived using the chain rule and the Runge-Kutta formulae. Once the training has been successfully completed the ANN-fitted right hand side f can be used in conjunction with *any* numerical integrator and *any* time step.

The capabilities of the explicit integrator implementation are illustrated using data from the well-known Van der Pol oscillator (with $\alpha = 1.0$, $\delta = 4.0$ and $\omega = 1.0$):

$$\dot{y}_1 = -\alpha(y_2^2 - \delta)y_1 - \omega y_2$$
$$\dot{y}_2 = y_1$$

Fig. 1(a) shows points on the stable periodic trajectory used for training as well as the location of the unstable (with two positive eigenvalues) steady state exhibited by the system (marked +). A total of 240 vector pairs $(y_{1,n}, y_{2,n} : y_{1,n+1}, y_{2,n+1})$ were used during the training. These points were obtained using a backward difference "stiff" integrator with error control. A four layer ANN with two neurons in the input layer, two nonlinear hidden layers with sigmoidal activation functions and five neurons each, and a two neuron output layer was trained using a time step for the integrator of 0.1 time units. Fig. 1(b) shows the predictions of this ANN. The agreement is good, though the ANN predicts the eigenvalues of the unstable steady state to be complex with positive real part.

An example of the application of the methodology described here to the identification of bifurcations in experimental data can be found in [4].

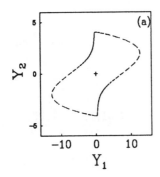 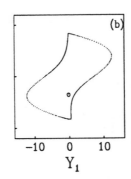 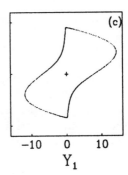

Figure 1: (a) Periodic attractor of the Van der Pol oscillator for $\alpha = 1.0$, $\delta = 4.0$ and $\omega = 1.0$. The unstable steady state in the interior of the curve is marked +.(b) Explicit integrator ANN-based predictions for the attractors of the Van der Pol oscillator shown in (a). The unstable steady state is marked o. (c) Implicit integrator ANN-based predictions for the attractors of the Van der Pol oscillator shown in (a).

An additional note should be made regarding the vector of states used in training for experimental data. We have found useful to preprocess the time series using a five-layered neural network that learns the identity mapping ("autoassociation", "self-supervised backpropagation") [5, 6] to obtain what has been called *NonLinear Principal Components* (NLPCs).

B. The implicit integrator approach.

The procedure outlined in the previous section, based on an explicit integrator, faces potentials drawbacks. We would expect it to fail when the underlying dynamics is "stiff", or when it contains widely disparate time scales (i.e. system with long quiescent periods followed by sharp bursts, such as intermittent or homoclinic phenomena).

One way to remedy this, is to base the training of the ODE network on an implicit integrator. If an implicit integrator is used to devise the training algorithm, the resulting network is recurrent, since now some of its inputs are equal to its outputs. This will require an on-line nonlinear solver, or else the training could be implemented using Pineda's algorithm for recurrent networks [7].

Consider one of the simplest implicit integrators; instead of the Runge-Kutta formulae we have:

$$\vec{Y}_{n+1} = \vec{Y}_n + \frac{h}{2}[\mathbf{f}(\vec{Y}_n; \vec{X}) + \mathbf{f}(\vec{Y}_{n+1}; \vec{X})] \qquad (2)$$

Note that now the prediction $\vec{Y}_{n+1}$ of the state of the system at time $t + h$ depends on itself; hence the recurrent connections in the network and the need for a nonlinear solver or Pineda's algorithm. We turn to the latter alternative.

We define, as usual, the error measure as:

$$E = \frac{1}{2}\sum_p \sum_k (T_k^p - Y_{n+1,k}^p)^2$$

where T_k^p is the target value for the k-th state on the p-th training vector and $Y_{n+1,k}^p$ is the corresponding prediction given by the implicit integrator-based network.

The dynamical evolution rule imposed to the network to evaluate its output during training takes the form of the following ODE:

$$\frac{dY_{n+1,j}^p}{d\tau} = -Y_{n+1,j}^p + [Y_{n,j}^p + \frac{h}{2}(f_j(\vec{Y}_n^p; \vec{X}) + f_j(\vec{Y}_{n+1}^p; \vec{X}))]$$

When this equation reaches its steady state, the "guess" $\vec{Y}_{n+1}$ of the value fed to the network that evaluates $\mathbf{f}$, used to evaluate errors and update weights, and the predicted $\vec{Y}_{n+1}$ (Eq. 2) are the same.

In addition, Pineda proposed the use of a second associated dynamical system to provide a "local" method for the updating of the weights (essentially to avoid the solution of a set of linear equations). Although the use of this approximation would be desirable for a parallel implementation of the algorithm (particularly in a SIMD environment), we have opted for the "non-local" matrix inversion required instead; the reduced number of recurrent units in the examples we have studied makes this alternative computationally easy.

The same data and network size used to test the Runge-Kutta algorithm was also used to test this new implementation. Convergence was reached after $O(10^3)$ sweeps. We used a conjugate gradient type algorithm for training; however, because of the approximation error introduced by the use of the dynamical evolution rule, very frequent restarts (after only 5-10 sweeps) of the conjugate gradient search were required. We found this alternative more efficient than the use of simple steepest descent.

Fig. 2 shows a schematic of the ANN embedded in the implicit integrator. There we have indicated the inputs and outputs of the embedded four-layered network. Fig.

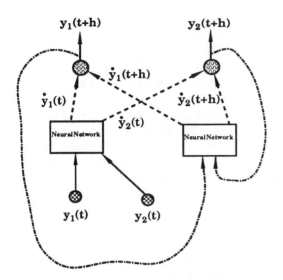

$y_1(t+h)$ $y_2(t+h)$

$\dot{y}_1(t+h)$

$\dot{y}_1(t)$ $\dot{y}_2(t+h)$

$\dot{y}_2(t)$

Neural Network   Neural Network

$y_1(t)$ $y_2(t)$

Figure 2: A schematic of the four-layered ANN embedded in the implicit integrator. The indicated inputs and outputs of the ANN pertain to the example discussed in the text.

1(c) shows the predictions given by the ANN after training was completed. These predictions are comparable to the ones obtained using the Runge-Kutta scheme described in the preceding section. This ANN, however, correctly predicts the nature of the eigenvalues of the unstable steady state inside the periodic trajectory (both eigenvalues are real and positive).

III. Conclusions.

We presented an ANN-based approach for the identification of continuous-time nonlinear systems. The resulting ANN-fitted right hand side constitutes an approximate continuous-time model of the continuous-time system; it is capable of correctly capturing the qualitative nature of the long term dynamics and bifurcations of the system. In addition, this approach can, in principle, be applied to the identification of stiff systems. The capabilities of neural networks to obtain continuous models and derivative information is an ongoing research topic (e.g., [8, 9, 10, 11]). In the direction of the research addressed here, important issues include, among others, the parallel implementation of the algorithms described (both in SIMD and MIMD architectures) and the role of the noninvertible dynamics introduced during the discretization of continuous models with explicit integrators.

Acknowledgment

We wish to thank Dr. Alan Lapedes for his insightful suggestions about the use of recurrent networks.

References

[1] N. H. Packard, J. P. Crutchfield, J. D. Farmer and R. S. Shaw. Geometry from a time series. *Phys. Rev. Letters*, 45:712–716, (1980).

[2] F. Takens. Detecting strange attractors in turbulence. In *Dynamical Systems and Turbulence*, (D. A. Rand and L. S. Young, eds.). *Lect. Notes in Math*, Springer, Heidelberg 366–381 (1981).

[3] A. S. Lapedes and R. M. Farber. Nonlinear signal processing using neural networks: prediction and system modeling. *Los Alamos Report LA-UR 87-2662* (1987).

[4] R. Rico-Martínez, K. Krischer, I. G. Kevrekidis, M. C. Kube and J. L. Hudson. Discrete- vs. Continuous-Time Nonlinear Signal Processing of Cu Electrodissolution Data. *Chem. Eng. Comm.*, 118:25–48 (1992).

[5] S. Usui, S. Nakauchi and M. Nakano. Reconstruction of munsell color space by a five-layered neural network. *Proceedings 1990 IEEE INNS International Joint Conference in Neural Networks*, San Diego, CA, II:515–520, (1990).

[6] M. A. Kramer. Nonlinear principal component analysis using autoassociative neural networks. *AIChE J.*, 37:233–243 (1991).

[7] F. J. Pineda. Generalization of back-propagation to recurrent neural networks. *Phys. Rev. Letters*, 59:2229–2232, (1987).

[8] A. R. Gallant and H. White. On learning the derivatives of an unknown mapping with multilayer feedforward networks. *Neural Networks*, 5:129–138, (1992).

[9] S. R. Chu and R. Shoureshi. A neural network approach for identification of continuous-time nonlinear dynamic systems. *Proceedings of the 1991 American Control Conference*, 1:1–5, (1991).

[10] B. A. Pearlmutter. Learning state space trajectories in recurrent neural networks. *Proceedings of the 1989 IEEE INNS International Joint Conference in Neural Networks*, II:365–372, (1989).

[11] M. Nikolau and V. Hanagandi. Recurrent neural networks in exact-linearization decoupling control of multivariable nonlinear systems. *1992 Annual AIChE Meeting*, Miami, Fl, Paper 125j (1992).

Optimization by Reduction to Maximum Clique

Arun Jagota

Department of Computer Science, SUNY/Buffalo   e-mail: jagota@cs.buffalo.edu

Abstract

We approximately solve, by reduction to MAX-CLIQUE, three NP-hard optimization problems in a binary weights Hopfield Net special case: *minimum vertex* and *set cover, constraint satisfaction problems* (*N*-queens), and *Boolean Satisfiability* (using a recent reduction). Approximation performance is experimentally determined on uniformly-at-random generated instances. Our optimizing dynamics are discrete and converge, independent of the problem, in O(number of units) unit-switches. Several earlier vertex cover neural net approaches exhibit poorer theoretical ratio bounds than ours (ours uses many more units). Our broad contribution is in optimizing several problems in a *single* binary weights (0/-1) network, which, for *all* problems in this paper, admits *no* invalid solutions. All reductions, except one, are goodness-preserving in a formal sense. We contrast this with the variety of handcrafted energy functions for the same individual problems in the literature, several of which admit invalid solutions also; several employ higher precision weights; and the goodness correspondence is not always clear, in a formal sense.

MAX-CLIQUE and Reductions to it

In a graph with undirected edges, a *clique* is a set of vertices such that every pair is connected by an edge. A clique is **maximal** if no strict superset of it is also a clique. A clique is **maximum** if it is the largest clique. A k-clique is a clique of size k. MAX-CLIQUE is the optimization problem of finding a largest clique in a given graph and is NP-hard [24] even to approximate [4].

In this paper, we approximately solve NP-hard problems by reduction to MAX-CLIQUE followed by approximate solution of MAX-CLIQUE in a Hopfield network special case (HcN) whose stable states are maximal cliques [21]. All the reductions described here have the following property: every maximal clique in a reduced instance corresponds to some feasible solution of the original problem. Since HcN admits only maximal cliques as stable states (see Lemma 1 later), no invalid solutions of a reduced problem are thus admitted as stable states. Define a reduction of optimization problem A to B as *goodness-preserving* if goodness(a_1) $\overset{A}{>}$ goodness(a_2) $\Leftrightarrow$ goodness($B(a_1)$) $\overset{B}{>}$ goodness($B(a_2)$) where a_1, a_2 are two feasible solutions of A; $B(a_1), B(a_2)$ are their corresponding solutions of B; and the goodness measures of A and B may be different. The reduction of MAX-

CLIQUE to HcN is goodness-preserving (larger maximal cliques $\Leftrightarrow$ deeper local minima; see later). All reductions to MAX-CLIQUE in this paper, except one, are goodness-preserving. Consequently, all these reductions are goodness-preserving in HcN: deeper minima formally correspond to better solutions; global minima are exactly the optimum solutions. Many of these reductions arise from the NP-hardness of MAX-CLIQUE. A neural network for graph matching such as the one described in [14] has less "computational power" in this sense (because maximum matching is in P; consequently no NP-hard problem is reducible to maximum matching unless $P = NP$).

In this section, we present the reductions. Subsequent sections describe HcN, the optimizing dynamics, the experimental results and some theoretical issues, and comparisons with earlier work.

SET AND VERTEX COVER. The *minimum vertex cover* (MVC) is an NP-hard optimization problem on graphs (see [10]); the *minimum set cover* (MSC) is its generalization to hypergraphs and thus NP-hard. Given a vertex-set $V = \{v_1, \ldots, v_n\}$ and an (hyper) edge-set $E = \{e_1, \ldots, e_m\}$ such that $e_i \subseteq V$, a subset $C \subseteq V$ such that for all $e_i \in E : e_i \cap C \neq \emptyset$ is called a set cover. That is, C is a set of vertices that cover all the edges. MSC is the problem of finding the smallest set cover in a given hypergraph instance. When, for all i, $|e_i|$ equals 2, the hypergraph is a graph and the set cover is a vertex cover. MSC then becomes MVC. MSC and MVC model many resource-selection problems.

C is a vertex cover in G iff $V \backslash C$ is a clique in G_c, the complement graph of G (edges in G_c are non-edges in G and vice-versa). This is one reduction of MVC to MAX-CLIQUE that we shall use on our Hopfield net special-case, mainly for empirical comparisons. Our main reduction is different, and is motivated by a well-known property of vertex covers attributed to F. Gavril (see [10]; page 134). This property also trivially generalizes to set covers. Therefore we describe it in the set cover setting and present the MSC-to-MAX-CLIQUE reduction that exploits it. We then specialize this reduction to the MVC case.

A *matching* M in a hypergraph is a set of edges such that no two share a vertex (i.e. $\forall e_i, e_j \in M : e_i \cap e_j = \emptyset$). Let $M_v = \cup_{e_i \in M} e_i$ denote the vertices in any *maximal* matching M. M_v is a set cover because for every edge e_i in E, $e_i \cap M_v \neq \emptyset$. Let $f(n) = \max_{e_i \in E} |e_i|$. A minimum set cover S^* must have at least one vertex from every edge in M. Hence $|M_v| \leq f(n)|S^*|$. That is, the vertices in *any* maximal matching are a set cover of size atmost $f(n)$ times that of the minimum set cover. Clearly, the approximation may be good only when $f(n) << n$. For a graph, $f(n) = 2$. Hence the vertices in *any* maximal matching in a graph are a vertex cover of size atmost twice that of the minimum vertex cover.

Our MSC-to-MAX-CLIQUE reduction exploits this property by representing maximal matchings of a hypergraph H as cliques of a new graph. The *linegraph* G_l of a hypergraph H has a vertex v_i for every edge e_i of H and two vertices v_i, v_j of G_l are adjacent iff the intersection of the corresponding edges e_i, e_j of H is nonempty. Given H, our reduction constructs the linegraph of H and then complements it. k-cliques in the resulting graph G_{l_c} are k-matchings in the hypergraph H. Thus every maximal clique of G_{l_c} represents a distinct set cover of H within factor $f(n)$ of optimum. Clearly, the size of G_{l_c} (number of vertices) may be upto $\Theta(n^{f(n)})$ which can be astronomical unless $f(n) << n$. When H is a graph G and we are interested in the minimum vertex cover, G_{l_c} is the complement of the linegraph of G and its size can be upto $\Theta(n^2)$ vertices.

Figure 1b shows the linegraph of the graph of Figure 1a. Figure 1c shows its complement. The 3-clique $\{ e_4, e_5, e_6 \}$ in Figure 1c is a 3-matching in Figure 1a.

CONSTRAINT SATISFACTION PROBLEMS.

The *constraint satisfaction problem* is a key AI problem, especially in computer vision and in natural language processing. For a good overview see [27].

Definition 1 *A Binary Constraint Satisfaction Problem (B-CSP) is a set of N variables $X_1, ..., X_N$ which take values from the sets $D_1, ..., D_N$ respectively, under given binary compatibility constraints. For all variable pairs X_i, X_j, $C(X_i, X_j) \subseteq D_i \times D_j$ is a binary constraint set and specifies the pairs (d_i, d_j) such that $X_i = d_i$ is compatible with $X_j = d_j$. A* **solution** *of a B-CSP is an N-tuple of values to the N variables so that all pairs of value assignments are compatible.*

Because graph k-coloring is a B-CSP, solving a B-CSP problem is in general NP-hard. The N-queens problem is one of placing N queens on an $N \times N$ chessboard so that no queen threatens another. The *standard* formulation of the N-queens problem as a B-CSP uses N variables: $X_i = j$ represents a queen on column i and row j.

Our reduction of a B-CSP to MAX-CLIQUE is as follows. For an N variable B-CSP, define an N-partite graph G, partition i representing variable X_i. Partition i contains $|D_i|$ vertices, one for each possible value of X_i and named by the value. We make $C(X_i, X_j)$ the set of edges between vertices in partition i and partition j. Every compatibility constraint of the B-CSP is represented as an edge of the graph. The fact that the vertex-set of a partition is an independent set (no edges) enforces the constraint that a variable may be assigned at most one value. It is clear that our reduction, in one sense, involves essentially only a language change and that there is a one-to-one correspondence between maximal sets of

mutually compatible assignments to k variables of a B-CSP and k-cliques of its clique-graph. Hence the set of N-cliques is exactly the set of the B-CSP's solutions. N-queens and graph k-coloring are two problems whose reduction to MAX-CLIQUE follows as a special case of that of B-CSPs. Figure 2 shows the reduction of 3-queens to MAX-CLIQUE.

BOOLEAN FORMULAE. Satisfiability of Boolean Formulae is in general *NP*-complete (see [10]). Finding the maximum number of simultaneously satisfiable clauses is NP-hard. We employ a recent reduction of Conjunctive Form (CF) boolean formulae to cliques in graphs [9]. We present it as a representation of any CF boolean formula as a B-CSP, followed by its representation as a B-CSP clique graph.

We illustrate it with an example. Consider the CF formula $(v_1 + v_2) (\bar{v}_1 + v_2) (v_1 + \bar{v}_2)$ consisting of a conjunction of 3 clauses c_1, c_2, c_3. We represent it as a B-CSP with variable X_i for clause c_i. The value-set of X_i is the set of literals in clause c_i. In this case, $D_1 = \{v_1, v_2\}$, $D_2 = \{\bar{v}_1, v_2\}$, and $D_3 = \{v_1, \bar{v}_2\}$. The constraint sets are: $C(X_i, X_j) = (D_i \times D_j) \setminus \{(u_i, u_j)\}$ where u_i and u_j represent *different* values to the *same* boolean variable (v_1 or v_2 in this case). That is, the only incompatible assignments are if two clauses assign different values to the same boolean variable. Figure 3 is the reduced graph for the above example. The reduced graph of a formula of m clauses is m-partite. k-cliques represent assignments that satisfy k clauses; m-cliques represent assignments that satisfy the formula. In this example, the 3-clique $\{c_1 v_1, c_2 v_2, c_3 v_1\}$ says that $v_1 = v_2 = T$ satisfies all clauses; hence the formula.

Hopfield-clique Network

The Hopfield Network [15, 16] is a recurrent N-unit network closely related to Ising spin models. $W = (w_{ij})$ is a real, symmetric with zero diagonal, matrix of weights, describing the interconnection weights of all unit pairs i, j. In the discrete version [15], unit states are: $S_i \in \{0, 1\}$. For $x \neq 0$, let $\theta(x) = 1$ if $x < 0$ and 0 otherwise. The network state $S = (S_i)$ is updated serially as follows: at time t exactly one unit i is picked and updated according to the rule $S_i(t) := \theta((WS(t-1))_i)$. This prescribes a family of serial-update rules, updates according to any of which monotonically decrease the energy function $E = -\frac{1}{2}S^T W S - I^T S$ [15], thus guaranteeing eventual convergence to a discrete local minimum of it. Here $I = (I_i)$ is the vector of external biases to units.

HOPFIELD-CLIQUE NETWORK. The Hopfield-clique Network (HcN) [18, 20] is a binary weights special case of the Hopfield Network. We describe the n-unit HcN in equivalent form [13] that has been implemented in optics [33]. $W = \{-1, 0\}^{n \times n}$ is the symmetric and zero diagonal weight matrix. $I = b^n$ is the vector of external unit biases; $0 < b < \frac{1}{2}$. $G_N = (V, E)$ is the graph underlying it whose vertices are the units and there is an (undirected) edge between vertices i and j if and only if $w_{ij} = 0$. V is the set of vertices. $I = b^n$ is the vector of external unit biases; $0 < b < \frac{1}{2}$. The discrete HcN has $S_i \in \{0, 1\}$. A set of vertices $V' \subseteq V$ is an alternative description of the network state $S = (S_i) \in \{0, 1\}^N$—the elements of V' are the units that are ON. We use these notations interchangably. S is a stable state if and only if $\theta(WS + I) = S$, that is, a local minimum state of the discrete energy function.

Lemma 1 ([18, 13]) *The HcN stable states are exactly the maximal cliques of its underlying graph G_N.*

Lemma 1 is straightforward and closely related versions may also be found in [11, 34].

Lemma 2 *The energy of a clique of size C is $-bC$.*

Lemma 2 may also be trivially verified by calculation of energy of a clique. From Lemma 2, the encoding of MAX-CLIQUE in HcN is goodness-preserving; maximum cliques are exactly the global minima follows as a corollary.

The associative memory storage rule of HcN may be used to store graphs (of reduced problems). Instances of all three problems in this paper are easier stored in HcN in terms of reductions to Maximum Independent Set (rather than MAX-CLIQUE). For this reason, we describe a version of the storage rule that complements the graph (to convert an MIS reduction to a MAX-CLIQUE one) before storage. The initial weight state is: For all $i \neq j$, $w_{ij}(0) = 0$. A set S of vertices is stored as follows. For all $i \neq j$, $w_{ij}(t + 1) := -1$ if units i and j are in the set S; $w_{ij}(t + 1) := w_{ij}(t)$ otherwise. A graph G may be stored by its edges. Since G is complemented, after storage, the stable states are maximal cliques of G_c (maximal independent sets of G).

Recall that in serial updates, exactly one unit i is picked and updated according to the rule $S_i(t) := \theta((WS(t-1))_i)$. Any serial-update (energy-descent) dynamics on discrete HcN converges in $\leq 2N$ unit-switches [21, 13]. An equivalent result is in [34].

STEEPEST DESCENT. Steepest descent (SD) is an instance of serial-update dynamics in which the unit i whose switch reduces the energy maximally is picked to switch. Specifically, i satisfies $\Delta E_i \leq \min_j \Delta E_j < 0$ for some choice of $S_i(t)$ and all choices of j and $S_j(t)$. Here, $\Delta E_k = -[S_k(t) - S_k(t-1)](WS(t-1))_k$ is the energy change caused by the particular switch of k. Let $SD(V_0)$ denote, starting with $V_0 \subseteq V$ as initial state, updating units via steepest descent until HcN converges to a stable state. $SD(V_0)$ is characterized as a graph algorithm [17] (also see [20, 13]). $SD(V)$ and $SD(\phi)$ emulate two greedy large-clique finding algorithms [17, 20] that are well known in the graph algorithms literature (see [12], [25]).

STOCHASTIC STEEPEST DESCENT. Stochastic Steepest Descent (SSD) is a stochastic variant of SD. In SSD, the deterministic moves of SD are replaced by *gradient descent* moves that are stochastic but favor the steepest direction. The unit to be updated is selected via a probability distribution P that has zero probability of "up-hill" moves and favors large (steepest-descent like) decreases in energy. Specifically, let $C(t) \equiv \{i | \Delta E_i(t) < 0\}$.

$P[S_i$ is switched at time $t] = 0$ if $\Delta E_i(t) \geq 0$; $\delta[\Delta E_i(t)]$ otherwise. $\sum_{i \in C(t)} \delta[\Delta E_i(t)] = 1$. P ensures that exactly one unit is switched. Our choice of δ (hence P) that approximates SD is the linear distribution, represented by $\delta[\Delta E_i(t)] = \frac{\Delta E_i}{\sum_{j \in C(t)} \Delta E_j}$. SSD performs only gradient descent moves because any serial-update gradient descent update scheme on HcN converges in $\leq 2N$ unit switches. Non gradient-descent heuristics like simulated annealing are *much* slower. The idea behind SSD is that multiple runs on the same input will produce different solutions. Let $SSD_{max}(V_0, i)$ denote i runs of SSD on the same graph, with V_0 as input for each run. The best clique found is chosen.

The experiments using SSD in this paper are on the original formulation of HcN (see [20]). Unfortunately, to understand SSD as empirically evaluated, the reader will need to apply the formulation of SSD presented here to the specific weights of the original HcN.

Earlier ANN Approaches

VERTEX COVER. A vertex cover algorithm A has *ratio bound* $f(n)$ if on any n-vertex graph, $\frac{C}{C^*} \leq f(n)$, where C is the vertex cover size obtained by A and C^* is the minimum vertex cover size.

The earliest Hopfield net encoding of the vertex cover problem that we are aware of is described in [11] (page 19) and attributed to M. Luby (1986). Given a graph $G = (V, E)$, a Hopfield net is constructed with weights $w_{ij} = -1$ for $(i, j) \in E$ and $w_{ij} = 0$ otherwise. Furthermore $w_i = deg(i) - \frac{1}{2}$ where w_i is a bias to each unit and $deg(i)$ is the degree of vertex i in G. We are unaware if this encoding has ever been used in practice. However, the ratio bound of this encoding is poor, as illustrated by the Figure 5 example (see [28]; page 48). L is a minimum vertex cover but it is easy to check that R is also a network stable state, which may thus be retrieved (even with steepest descent; depending on how ties break). By generalizing this example to $|L| = r$ and r groups $R_1, \ldots, R_r$ of vertices such that every vertex in R_i is connected to i different vertices in L, it is easy to check that the ratio bound is $\Omega(\frac{|R|}{|L|}) = \Omega(\log r)$, where $R = \cup_i R_i$ (see [28]; page 48).

At about the same time, [5] discuss solution of the vertex cover problem by reduction to Maximum Independent Set; they show an encoding of the latter which is essentially the same as in our current paper. No experiments on vertex cover are reported.

A second Hopfield net encoding of the vertex cover problem [32] is as follows. Given a graph $G = (V, E)$, a Hopfield net is constructed with weights $w_{ij} = -2A - Ba_{ij}$ and unit biases $w_i = B\sum_j a_{ij} = Bdeg(i)$ where

$deg(i)$ is the degree of vertex i in G. $a = (a_{ij})$ is the adjacency matrix of G. The underlying energy function is: $E = A\Sigma_{ij}V_iV_j - \frac{B}{2}\Sigma_{ij}[(1-V_i)(1-V_j)a_{ij}]$. The second term attempts to ensure that the network state is a vertex cover; the first term its minimality. A and B are positive constants that control the relative importance of these terms. Relative to other encodings, including ours, we see three possible disadvantages of this encoding. The potentially more serious one is that the constraint of legality of vertex cover is enforced only softly. This may lead to invalid solutions when A and B are chosen injudiciously (by analogy, see [2] for complications of Hopfield's TSP formulation and complicated analysis to attempt to correct them). In the encodings by all others (including both of ours), *only* vertex covers are stable states; no invalid solutions are admitted. One may enforce the legality constraint by setting $A = 0$. But then in fact V (all units ON) is also a stable state. One might think that other encodings, including ours, disallow invalid solutions at the cost of not enforcing minimality. This is not true. The two vertex cover via maximal independent set encodings described below (including one of ours) disallow invalid solutions while remaining biased towards minimal ones (formally, they are goodness-preserving). The situation with the encoding of [11] is not so clear but it appears to be biased towards minimality also. The second issue is that the ratio bound of this encoding is not clear. The third, lesser, disadvantage of the encoding of [32] is that the weights and biases are real-valued (though low-precision). In other encodings (including ours) the weights are binary-valued: $\{0, 1\}$ or $\{0, -1\}$. These encodings are easier to implement in hardware.

A third approach [34] was based on encoding maximal independent sets (MIS) (the authors use their own term: Irredundant Isolated Graphs) as stable states in the Hopfield model and using the well-known fact that if I is an independent set then $V\backslash C$—the set of OFF units in a stable state—is a vertex cover. Their encoding was earlier presented in [11] (page 17). *Our* second approach to vertex cover is essentially the same as above. A graph G is converted to its complement G_c on which MAX-CLIQUE is approximated using HcN. The obtained clique in G_c is an independent set in G; hence the set of OFF units is a vertex cover of G. Though this approach (hence the one in [34]) works well on uniformly-at-random instances (see Section: Experiments and Results), the same example of Figure 5 illustrates that the ratio bound is poor (again $\Omega(\log r)$). This time, L, which is a maximal independent set, may be retrieved as the stable state from which the vertex cover $R = V\backslash L$ is obtained. But L is the minimum vertex cover and $\frac{|R|}{|L|} = \Omega(\log r)$. Again, even steepest descent, with initial state V, may retrieve L, depending on how the ties break.

A fourth approach [30] uses a different type of neural network. Experimental results are reported only on small graphs (our results are comparable; see Section: Experiments and Results). It is not clear what the (worst-case) ratio bound of their approach is.

Thus, our *first* method based on maximal matchings is the only one amongst the above approaches that has a proven ratio bound of 2 (all stable states represent vertex covers within twice the optimum size). This holds regardless of the dynamics.

CONSTRAINT SATISFACTION PROBLEMS.

Two early neural net approaches to (a) graph coloring—a B-CSP—and (b) general B-CSPs are [5, 29] respectively. The 8-queens problem was solved in [3] and a solution of 1000-queens was alluded to in [23] but no details provided. An efficient discrete near-Hopfield network for CSPs was proposed in [1]. Some parts of the network use asymmetric connections; thus convergence is not guaranteed. However, in practice, it worked very well on N-queens (finding exact solution in empirically-observed $O(N)$ unit-switches). The 1024-queens problem was solved in minutes. Our reduction of CSPs to MAX-CLIQUE in the current paper was first presented in [19] though not published in the proceedings. A neural net approach to CSPs using hidden units was proposed in [6]. The number of hidden units required scales poorly with the CSP size; hence its use is limited to small CSPs. A continuous Hopfield net formulation of N-queens was presented in [35] but no empirical results were discussed. A more recent paper on neural approach to CSPs is [7]. The encoding is unclear and no empirical results are given. The (multiple term) energy functions in [3, 35] may admit invalid solutions if the constants (4 in [3]; 2 in [35]) are not chosen carefully. Our approach admits *only* maximally compatible sets of queens as local minima. The N-queens formulations in [3, 1, 19, 35] all use N^2 neurons; the one in [1] uses N additional "guard" neurons.

BOOLEAN SATISFIABILITY.

We are aware of three previous works on representing boolean formulae in Hopfield networks [8, 17, 31] such that satisfying assignments are represented as global minima. Unfortunately, only the abstract of [8] is published. The work in [17] uses the reduction of k-SAT to MAX-CLIQUE indirectly described in [10]. None of [17, 31] specifically discuss optimization issues (for e.g. empirical results). Our approach in the current paper is in some sense the simplest: the reduction we exploit is more compact than the one in [17]; the weights are binary (the weights in [31] though low-precision are integer-valued). The reduction used in [17] also does not allow approximation of maximum simultaneously satisfiable clauses; the reduction used in this paper does. This is an important consideration.

Experiments and Results

VERTEX COVER. A *p-random* n-vertex graph is one in which each of the $C(n, 2)$ pairs of vertices is connected by an edge with probability p. Table I reports vertex cover experiments using HcN on p-random 50- and 100-vertex graphs. The column labeled 'ISVC' is based on storing the given graph G directly in HcN (note that the storage rule actually stores G_c, its complement). A stable state (maximal independent set in G) is then found using $SD(V)$ on HcN; the vertex cover (of G) is read-out as the set of OFF units. The next three columns are dynamics applied to HcN constructed from storing G_l, the linegraph of G, in HcN (Note that its complement, G_{l_c} is actually stored; expected number $pC(n,2)$ of units are used). Each dynamics retrieves a stable state (maximal independent set in G_l; maximal matching in G). The vertices in G associated with the vertices (edges of G) in the stable state are a vertex cover. Smaller maximal cliques in G_{l_c} provide smaller vertex covers. Hence our optimization goal here is exactly the opposite—to find the smallest maximal clique (as opposed to the largest). Somewhat surprisingly, the problem of finding the smallest maximal clique is, in general, also NP-hard [22]. The dynamics that works best is $SSD_{min}(\Phi,n)$—n runs of SSD from initial state Φ; the smallest size output (worst in the traditional optimization sense) is picked.

From Table I, the independent set based approach (ISVC) performs the best; all the linegraph based approaches are significantly poorer. ISVC however has a poor (worst-case) ratio bound whereas the other three dynamics have ratio bound of 2. The variances in the results were small, justifying the small sample size.

Table I. Size of vertex cover found by various algorithms, averaged over 15 p-random n-vertex graphs in each row.

p	n	ISVC	SD(V)	SD(Φ)	$SSD_{min}(\Phi,n)$
0.5	50	42.86	48.0	48.6	46.2
0.1	100	72.3	95.2	93.46	86.0

N-QUEENS.
$SD(V)$ makes $\Theta(N^2)$ unit-switches; $SD(\Phi)$ makes N.

Table II. Number of mutually non-attacking queens placed efficiently via $SD(V)$ and $SD(\Phi)$

N	4	6	8	10	12	16	30	40	50
$SD(V)$	4	5	7	9	10	14	26	37	45
$SD(\phi)$	3	5	5	7	9	13	23	31	38

BOOLEAN SATISFIABILITY.
An n-variable 3-SAT boolean CNF formula has $8C(n,3)$ possible clauses. A p-random formula of the above kind independently selects each of these clauses for inclusion with probability p, generating an expected number $p\,8\,C(n,3)$ of clauses. Our network uses 3 units per clause.

Table III. Number of simultaneously satisfiable clauses found by various algorithms, averaged over 15 p-random n-variable 3-SAT boolean CNF formulae in each row.

p	n	SD(V)	SD(Φ)	$SSD_{max}(\Phi,N)$
0.5	5	35.5	35.6	37.06
0.02	20	166.33	162.13	168.93
0.001	50	161.4	160.4	162.06

Over all the runs, a satisfying assignment was found just *once*: by $SSD_{max}(V,N)$ with $n = 50; p = 0.001$. N is number of units.

CONCLUDING DISCUSSION.
From the empirical results reported above, it is obvious that are approaches are not the best ones for individual problems. Neural network methods designed for N-queens (for even large N) quickly find exact solutions (for example [1]). Conventional methods do even better. Recently, a simple local search algorithm has been proven to almost always find a satisfying assignment in 0.5-random 3-SAT formulae [26]. The main contribution of our work is a single binary-weights network for approximately solving several optimization problems without admitting invalid solutions and in one case (vertex cover) providing an asymptotically optimal ratio bound. Most of our mappings are goodness-preserving. The goal of this paper has not been to present a superior optimization technique but to exploit the simplicity and massive parallelism of neural networks for sufficiently good cost-effective optimization for real-world purposes.

References

[1] H. Adorf & M.D. Johnston. A discrete stochastic neural network for constraint satisfaction problems. In *Int. Joint Conf. on Neural Nets*, vol 3, pp 917–924. San Diego, June 1990, IEEE.

[2] S.V.B. Aiyer, M. Niranjan, & F. Fallside. A theoretical investigation into the performance of the Hopfield model. *IEEE Trans. on Neural Nets*, 1(2):204–215, 1990.

[3] Y. Akiyama, A. Yamashita, M. Kajiura, & H. Aiso. Combinatorial optimization with gaussian machines. In *Int. Joint Conf. on Neural Nets*, vol 1, pp 533–540. Washington D.C., June 1989, IEEE.

[4] S. Arora, C. Lund, R. Motwani, M. Sudan, & M. Szegedy. Proof verification and hardness of approximation problems. In *The Proc. of the 33rd Annual IEEE Symp. on Foundations of Comp. Sci.*, 1992.

[5] D.H. Ballard, P.C. Gardner, & M.A. Srinivas. Graph problems and connectionist architectures. TR 167, Dept of Comp Sci, University of Rochester, NY, 1987.

[6] Y. Baram & R. Dechter. Processing constraints by neural networks. TR, Dept of Comp & Info Sci, University of California, Irvine, CA, June 1991.

[7] P. Bourret & C. Gaspin. A neural based approach of constraints satisfaction problem. In *Int. Joint Conf. on Neural Nets*, vol 4, pp 588–593. Baltimore, June 1992, IEEE.

[8] W. Chen & K. Hsieh. A neural network for 3-satisfiability problems. In *Int. Joint Conf. on Neural Nets*, vol 2, page 587. Washington D.C., June 1989, IEEE. Abstract only in Proc..

[9] P. Crescenzi, C. Fiorini, & R. Silvestri. A note on the approximation of the maxclique problem. *Information Processing Letters*, 40(1):281–298, October 1991.

[10] M.R. Garey & D.S. Johnson. *Computers and Intractability: A Guide to the Theory of NP-Completeness.* Freeman, New York, 1979.

[11] G.H. Godbeer, J. Lipscomb, & M. Luby. On the computational complexity of finding stable state vectors in connectionist models (Hopfield nets). TR, Dept of Comp Sci, University of Toronto, Ontario, 1988.

[12] J.R. Griggs. Lower bounds on the independence number in terms of the degrees. *Journal of Combinatorial Theory, Series B*, 34:22–39, 1983.

[13] T. Grossman & A. Jagota. On the equivalence of two Hopfield-type networks. In *IEEE Int. Conf. on Neural Nets*, 1993. To Appear in.

[14] J. Hertz, A. Krogh, & R.G. Palmer. *Introduction to the Theory of Neural Computation*. Addison-Wesley, 1991.

[15] J.J. Hopfield. Neural networks and physical systems with emergent collective computational abilities. *Proc. of the Nat. Acad. of Sci., USA*, 79, 1982.

[16] J.J. Hopfield. Neurons with graded responses have collective computational properties like those of two-state neurons. *Proc. of the Nat. Acad. of Sci., USA*, 81, 1984.

[17] A. Jagota. A Hopfield-style network as a maximal clique graph machine. TR 90-25, Dept of Comp Sci, SUNY at Buffalo, NY, 1990.

[18] A. Jagota. A new Hopfield-style network for content-addressable memories. TR 90-02, Dept of Comp Sci, SUNY at Buffalo, NY, 1990.

[19] A. Jagota. Backtracking dynamics in a Hopfield-style network. In *Int. Joint Conf. on Neural Nets*. Seattle, July 1991, IEEE. Abstract only in Proc..

[20] A. Jagota. Efficiently approximating max-clique in a Hopfield-style network. In *Int. Joint Conf. on Neural Nets*, vol 2, pp 248–253. Baltimore, June 1992, IEEE.

[21] A. Jagota. A Hopfield-style network with a graph-theoretic characterization. *Journal of Artificial Neural Networks*, 1992. To Appear.

[22] A. Jagota. On the computational complexity of analyzing the Hopfield-clique network. Submitted to: Journal of Artificial Neural Networks.

[23] M. Kajiura, Y. Akiyama, & Y. Anzai. Neural networks vs. tree search in puzzle solving. In *Int. Joint Conf. on Neural Nets*, vol 2, pp 588. Washington D.C., June 1989, IEEE. Abstract only in Proc..

[24] R.M. Karp. Reducibility among combinatorial problems. In R.E. Miller & J.W. Thatcher, editors, *Complexity of Computer Computations*, pp 85–103. Plenum Press, New York, 1972.

[25] R.M. Karp. The probabilistic analysis of some combinatorial search algorithms. In J.F. Traub, editor, *Algorithms and Complexity: New Directions and Recent Results*, pp 1–19. Academic Press, New York, 1976.

[26] E. Koutsoupias & C.H. Papadimitriou. On the greedy algorithm for satisfiability. *Information Processing Letters*, 43(1):53–55, August 1992.

[27] A.K. Mackworth. Constraint satisfaction. In S.C. Shapiro, editor, *Encyclopedia of Artificial Intelligence, Second Edition*, pp 285–290, New York, 1992. John Wiley and Sons.

[28] R. Motwani. Lecture notes on approximation algorithms. TR, Dept of Comp Sci, Stanford University, 1992. Available from author.

[29] E. Page & G.A. Tagliarini. Solving constraint satisfaction problems with neural networks. In *IEEE Int. Conf. on Neural Nets*, vol ?, pp 741–747, New York, 1987. San Diego, IEEE.

[30] Y. Peng, J. Reggia, & T. Li. A connectionist model to vertex covering problems. *Int. Journal of Neural Systems*, 3(1):43–56, 1992.

[31] G. Pinkas. Symmetric neural nets and propositional logic satisfiability. *Neural Computation*, 3(2), 1990. To Appear ?

[32] J. Ramanujam & P. Sadayappan. Optimization by neural networks. In *IEEE Int. Conf. on Neural Nets*, vol 2, pp 325–332. (San Diego 1988), IEEE.

[33] I. Shariv, T. Grossman, E. Domany, & A.A. Friesem. All-optical implementation of the inverted neural network model. In *Optics in Complex Systems*, vol 1319. SPIE, 1990.

[34] Y. Shrivastava, S. Dasgupta, & S.M. Reddy. Neural network solutions to a graph theoretic problem. In *Proc. of IEEE Int. Symp. on Circuits and Systems*, pp 2528–2531, New York, 1990. IEEE.

[35] Y. Takefuji. Neural network models and n-queen problems. In Y. Takefuji, editor, *Neural Network Parallel Computing*, chapter 1, pp 1–26. Kluwer Academic Publishers, Boston, 1992.

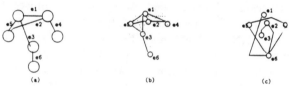

Figure 1. A graph, its line graph, and the complement of its line graph. k-cliques in (c) are k-matchings in (a).

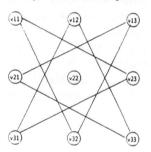

Figure 2. 3-queens B-CSP clique-graph
Edges represent compatible assignments

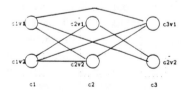

Figure 3 B-CSP clique-graph for the formula: $(v1 + v2)(\bar{v1} + v2)(v1 + \bar{v2})$
3-cliques represent assignments that satisfy all 3 clauses

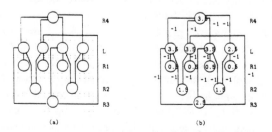

Figure 4. (b) is the vertex cover encoding of graph (a) in a Hopfield Network
The encoding has a large stable state, R, though the minimum vertex cover, L is small.

Feature Extraction of Event-Related Potential Waveforms
by Neural Networks

Fred Y. Wu

Department of Electrical & Computer Engineering, University of Miami,
P.O. Box 248294, Coral Gables, Florida 33124

Jeremy D. Slater, R. Eugene Ramsay
Department of Neurology, University of Miami,
Miami, Florida 33136

Lawrence S. Honig
Department of Neurology and Neurological Sciences,
Stanford University Medical Center, Stanford, CA 94305

Abstract -- Signal analysis by ANN requires only minimal assumptions about statistics of signals and noise. Thus, ANN methods may be useful in brain signal analysis, in which the signal characteristics are unknown and signal-to-noise ratios are well below one. Here, we describe the development of a neural network for classifying event-related potential data obtained from normal control subjects and from patients with multiple sclerosis. The classification strategy was then decoded by network analysis and compared with that obtained statistically. The network decision-making process is further illustrated by three examples, showing the variation of internal hidden units' responses to different input stimuli.

I. INTRODUCTION

A number of conventional classification schemes have been employed in brain electrical potential (BEP) analysis prior to 1980 [1], pertaining to whether distinct BEP patterns are associated with cognitive performance, sleep stages, metabolic and drug effects, or neurologic abnormalities. Since emergence of the backpropagation algorithm [2] in the mid-1980s, artificial neural network (ANN) technology has been increasingly used as a new approach in solving classification/prediction problems. Due to the fact that only minimal assumptions about statistics of signals and noise are required, ANN methods have been shown to be useful in multidimensional signal processing with signals of unknown characteristics and signal-to-noise ratios less than one [3]. Related signal processing applications using ANN have been developed, including automatic rejection of contaminants of neuroelectric signals [4], enhancement of averaged event-related potentials (ERP) waveforms by rejecting trials containing no event-related signal [5], prediction of brain state in anticipation of numeric stimulus [6], detection of electroencephalogram epileptiform spikes [7-9], and classification of brainstem auditory evoked potentials for hearing threshold detection [10]. We have demonstrated the feasibility of neural network methods in classifying ERP waveforms obtained from control subjects and patients with multiple sclerosis (MS) [11]. A network analysis methodology has also been proposed to reveal the classification strategy embedded in the network [12]. In this paper, we illustrate the network's decision-making process by three examples, showing the variation of internal hidden units' response to three specific input stimuli.

II. RESEARCH BACKGROUND

Event-related potentials (ERP) are brain-generated electrical signals recorded at the scalp, which are time registered to an experimental stimulus. Because the amplitude of these response-related neuroelectric signals is usually smaller than that of background stimulus-unrelated signals, an average of waveforms from a number of stimulus presentations is usually adopted to improve the signal-to-noise ratio. Statistical studies analyzing ERP waveforms have been conducted on control subjects and patients with neurological disorders [13-15], but clearly defined standards for the assessment of ERP abnormality are not presently available. Classical statistical techniques are handicapped by a requirement for a priori knowledge in selecting regression models, plus the limited representational power of available regression models. Artificial neural network (ANN) technology does not suffer from these limitations and has been employed to find unknown transformations in a variety of medical diagnostic situations [16-18].

In a study by Honig et al. [15], 31 patients diagnosed with multiple sclerosis (MS) and 32 control subjects underwent ERP P300 testing. ERPs, measured at 20 scalp positions, were digitized over a 512 millisecond epoch consisting of 256 data points. P300 was elicited with two different pitched tones.

Subjects were instructed to listen and silently count the high-pitched infrequent tones. P300 consists of two peaks, P3a, the first major positive central peak after 250 milliseconds, and P3b, the next positive potential. Midline peak latencies and amplitudes measured at Cz, as well as Pz for the more parietal P3b were published [15]. P300 latencies were significantly prolonged in MS patients compared with control subjects (P3a means, 294±5 vs 274±4 SEM milliseconds, P = 0.005; P3b means, 367±8 vs 335±4 milliseconds, P = 0.0005). Assessed by latency, waveform contour, and symmetry criteria, P300 abnormalities were found in a total of 65% (20/31) of MS patients versus 9% (3/32) of control subjects. This is equivalent to prediction accuracies of 65% and 91% respectively in the MS and control groups, if such criteria-based analysis is used in ERP pattern classification. The same data set was analyzed by both the conventional nearest neighbor (NN) classification scheme and ANN [11]. Classification accuracies of 82%(51/62) and 72%(43/60) for MS and control subjects were respectively achieved by NN classifiers. A neural network was constructed and trained by the backpropagation algorithm, using 25 input nodes in the input layer, 8 nodes in the hidden layer, and 2 nodes in the output layer. The output pairs of the network, (0, 1 or 1, 0 respectively), represent the group from which an input ERP waveform was obtained, (MS or control). The network was trained to classify the training set with an average accuracy of 98%. The network's prediction accuracies of ERP waveforms not contained in the training set, estimated by a cross-validation error method [19], were 75% and 87% for MS and control subjects respectively. Such a testing result suggests a better averaged prediction accuracy, than that obtained by NN classifiers and P300 statistical analysis.

Selection of training data is a crucial process in ANN research employing supervised learning algorithms. Relevant research includes the determination of the number of training samples [20,21] and the method of selecting boundary samples [21] to optimize the generalization capability of trained networks. A good training set should provide clear, correct, and sufficient instances, so that the network can generalize accordingly in the right direction. Unfortunately, such a premise is almost impossible for ANN applications in brain signal analysis, because it is usually hard, even for qualified clinical neurophysiologists, to definitively specify differences between normal and abnormal brain electrical waveforms. As a common solution to this problem, classification of training instances may be determined by several evaluators in a jury system. In an ANN approach to EEG spike detection [7], for example, spikes were defined as those events marked by four, five, or six evaluators as spikes. Notice that such a problem of determining the classification for training patterns does not exist in our application, in that a pattern's classification was defined by its source, rather than by expert opinion. However, it is useful to know the discrimination criteria discovered by the trained network in predicting the input pattern's source, as well as to develop networks that can be generalized to correctly identify the classification of new patterns.

III. NETWORK ANALYSIS

It is valuable to determine what the network has learned to achieve a better averaged classification accuracy than that obtained by conventional NN classifiers and P300 statistical analysis. To reveal the classification strategy developed by a trained network, a general approach is conducted through the analysis of both the weight matrix and the activation patterns of hidden units [22]. In order to guide the network to develop a general criterion in ERP classification rather than memorizing training patterns, a network with three hidden units was used for analysis [12]. A test data set was formed by eight patterns, five selected from the patient group and three selected from the control group. Six of these eight patterns were those illustrated in the paper of Honig et al. [15] and the other two were patterns "misclassified" by the latency-criteria based analysis introduced in that paper. The rest of the 114 patterns were used to form the training set. The network was trained to correctly classify 98% (112/114) of the training patterns. In the trained network, the thresholds of three hidden units are respectively 0.705, 0.272, and -0.149, and their output weights to output nodes are (-2.25, 2.25), (3.88, -3.88), and (-2.69, 2.69). The test data set was then applied, resulting in a prediction accuracy of 87% (7/8).

A network analysis method derived from that introduced in [23,24] was used. For each input ERP pattern, p, the activation vector in the hidden layer, $H^{(p)}$, is recorded.

$$H^{(p)} = [h_i]^{(p)}$$

where h_i is the activation level (output) of the ith hidden unit responding to an input pattern p. The Euclidean distance between each pair of activation vectors was calculated. Neighbors of each pattern were sorted by the calculated distance to form a neighborhood table, to which a k-NN clustering strategy [25] was then applied. 17 clusters were obtained, with patterns in each group having similar activation vectors in the hidden layer and sharing the same network's classification result.

A weight-state vector, V, of a hidden unit i corresponding to an input pattern P is defined by:

$$V_i(P) = [W_{ij}P_j]$$

where W_{ij} is the weight of the link between the ith hidden node and the jth input node, and P_j is the jth feature of input pattern P. The vector sum S, which determines the activation of the hidden unit is defined by:

$$S_i(P) = \sum_j W_{ij} P_j$$

17 cluster centroids of ERP waveforms were computed and used as characterized inputs. The weight-state vector of each cluster was then computed and analyzed. Network's classification criteria so discovered are summarized as follows:

1. *"If a positive wave occurs in the range between 262 and 322 msec followed by a significant negative potential drop at 442 msec, hidden unit #2 will be activated (h2 > 0.8). Unless hidden units #1 and #3 are both activated, the network will generate a "Normal ERP" classification response."*

2. *"If a positive wave delays to the range between 302 and 382 msec, and the potential at 442 msec is not significantly negative, hidden unit #2 will be deactivated (h2 < 0.2). The network will generate a "MS ERP" classification if either hidden unit #1 or #2 is activated."*

3. *"If there exists no strongly negative signal at 202 and 462 msec, hidden unit #1 will be activated (h1 > 0.8)."*

4. *"If a positive wave occurs early (202 - 302 msec) and no significant positive potentials exist at 322 and 342 msec, or peaks exist at 202 and 382 msec, hidden unit #3 will be activated (h3> 0.8)."*

The results of network analysis indicate that hidden unit #2 provides a basic screening for ERP waveform abnormalities, while the other two hidden units provide supplemental tests to optimize the overall diagnostic performance. Moreover, an interesting match was identified between the network's classification strategy and the P300 latency criteria obtained statistically. Of the total 122 patterns, 63% (39/62) from MS patients but only 5% (3/60) from control subjects, showed low h2 activation (h2 < 0.2). This indicates that classification accuracies of 63% and 95% in respective groups can be achieved by hidden unit #2 alone. This result is close to that obtained by criteria-based analysis employing P300 latency, waveform contour, and symmetry criteria (65% vs 91%). Hidden unit #2 of the network utilizes the variations of ERP peaks in the range between 262 and 442 msec in making classification decisions; this is similar to the P300 latency criterion (defined as major peaks after 250 msec) used by human analysts in ERP classification. Therefore the ANN has

by itself isolated specific ERP regions which are significant in determining the pattern classification. Similar facts can be discovered by statistical analysis, although by means of a more difficult and time-consuming process.

IV. EXAMPLES

Three examples (Figures 1, 2 and 3) are used to show the internal responses of network's hidden units to different input stimuli. In each figure, the input ERP waveform is represented by a dotted line; the weight vector of links that go into the hidden unit is represented by a long-dashed line; the resulting weight-state vector is represented by a solid line. An ERP waveform obtained from a MS patient is used in the first example. Its hidden units' analysis is shown in Figure 1. The delayed peak results in the deactivation of hidden unit #2, and therefore the waveform is identified as a MS pattern by this first screening test. Since there is no significant potential drop at 202 and 462 msec neither is there early peak before 302 msec, hidden unit #1 is activated and #3 is deactivated. Hidden unit #2's activation status dominantly determines the network's outputs (output weights of hidden unit #2 are the largest); consequently, the network's final decision is correctly made by classifying the pattern into the MS group. In the second example, an ERP waveform obtained from a control subject is used. Its hidden units' analysis is shown in Figure 2. The waveform's peak falls in the range (262-232 msec), and therefore hidden unit #2 is activated. Since it is not an early peak, hidden unit #3 is deactivated. Hidden unit #2's decision is still dominant in this case, and its activation results in the pattern being correctly classified into the control subjects' group. In the third example, the waveform obtained from a MS patient is used. Its hidden units' analysis is shown in Figure 3. Hidden unit #2 is activated due to the normal latency of the waveform's peak. The pattern thus passes the first screening test and is identified as a control pattern. However, both hidden units #1 and #3 are also activated. (There is no significant potential drop at 202 and 462 msec, and the peak occurs early in the range, 202-302 msec). The decision made by hidden unit #2 is therefore reversed by the supplemental tests provided by the other two hidden units. The pattern is still correctly classified as a MS pattern.

V. CONCLUSIONS

The significance of using ANN together with network analysis resides in the feature extraction capability of networks: factors significantly determining the classification are automatically extracted. This significantly reduces the work of statistical analysis, especially in the preliminary stage, when a priori knowledge of the investigated domain is limited. Instead of using a conventional black box ANN approach, in which networks do not explain their reasoning, network analysis can be used to explain the network's response to any specific input pattern. A neural network was developed for classifying ERP waveforms obtained from control subjects and patients with multiple sclerosis. Its averaged prediction accuracy appears better than that obtained by nearest neighbor classifiers and criterion-based statistical analysis. Of even greater value, it is possible to analyze what the network has learned to improve the classification accuracy: a network analysis technique was applied to decode the classification strategy from the trained neural network. An interesting match was identified between the network's classification strategy and the P300 latency criteria obtained statistically. The network's decision-making process was finally illustrated by three examples, showing the variation of internal hidden units' responses to different input stimuli.

ACKNOWLEDGMENT

This work was supported by the Epilepsy Center of University of Miami, and by the general research award (1991) of University of Miami.

REFERENCES

[1] A.S. Gevins, "Pattern recognition of human brain electrical potentials", *IEEE Trans. Patt. Analy. & Mach. Intell.* vol. PAMI-2, pp. 383-404, 1980.

[2] D. Rumelhart et al., "Learning internal representations by error propagation", in *Parallel Distributed Processing*, Massachusetts: MIT Press, 1986, pp. 319-362.

[3] A.S. Gevins and N.H. Morgan, "Application of neural-network (NN) signal processing in brain research", *IEEE Trans. ASSP*, vol. 36, pp. 1152-1161, 1988.

[4] A.S. Gevins and N.H. Morgan, "Classifier-directed signal processing in brain research", *IEEE Trans. Biomed. Eng.*, vol. BME-33, pp. 1054-1068, 1986.

[5] A.S. Gevins et al., "Improved ERP estimation via statistical pattern recognition", *EEG Clin. Neurophysiol.*, vol. 64, pp. 177-186, 1986.

[6] A.S. Gevins et al., "Human neuroelectric patterns predict performance accuracy", *Science*, vol. 235, pp. 580-585, 1987.

[7] R.C. Eberhart and R.W. Dobbins, "Case study I: The detection of electroencephalogram spikes", in *Neural Network PC Tools*, R.C. Eberhart and R.W. Dobbins, Eds. San Diego: Academic Press, 1990, pp. 215-234.

[8]. K. Wilson et al., "Detection of epileptiform spikes in the EEG using a patient-independent neural network", *IEEE proc.Computer-based Medical Systems*, pp. 264-271, Baltimore, May 1991.

[9] O. Ozdamar et al., "Multilevel neural network system for EEG spike detection", *IEEE Proc.Computer-based Medical Systems*, pp. 272-279, Baltimore, May 1991.

[10] D. Alpsan and O. Ozdamar, "Brainstem auditory evoked potential classification by backpropagation networks", *IJCNN*, pp. 1266-1271, Singapore, November 1991.

[11] F.Y. Wu, J. Slater, R.E. Ramsay, and L.S. Honig, "Neural networks for EEG diagnosis", in *Intelligent Engineering Systems Through Artificial Neural Networks*, vol. II, C. Dagli, L. Burke and Y. Shin, Eds. New York: ASME Press, 1992, pp. 559-564.

[12] F.Y. Wu, J. Slater, L.S. Honig, and R.E. Ramsay, "A neural network design for event-related potential diagnosis", *Computers in Biology and Medicine*, in press.

[13] J. Patterson et al., "Latency variability of the components of auditory event-related potentials to infrequent stimuli in aging: Alzheimer-type dementia, and depression", *Electroencephalogr. Clin. Neurophysiol.* vol. 71, pp. 450-460, 1988.

[14] D. Goodin and M. Aminoff, "Electrophysiological differences between demented and nondemented patients with Parkinson's disease", *Ann. Neurol.* vol. 21, pp. 90-94 1987.

[15] L.S. Honig et al., "Event-related potential P300 in multiple sclerosis", *Arch. Neurol.* vol. 49, pp. 44-50, 1992.

[16] F.Y. Wu and K. Yen, "A PC-based neural network for on-line measurement of regional cerebral blood flow", *Comput. in Biology and Medicine*, vol. 22, pp. 23-32, 1992.

[17] R. Poli et al., "A neural network expert system for diagnosing and treating hypertension", *Computer*, vol. 24, pp. 64-71, March 1991.

[18] G. Gindi et al, "Neural network and conventional classifiers for fluorescence-guided laser angioplasty", *IEEE Trans. Biomed. Eng.*, vol. 38, pp. 246-252, 1991.

[19] S. Weiss and C. Kulikowski, *Computer Systems That Learn*, San Mateo: Morgan Kaufmann Publishers, 1991, pp. 31-33.

[20] E.B. Baum and D. Haussler, "What size gives valid generalization?", *Neural Computation*, vol. 1, pp. 151-160, 1989.

[21] K.G. Mehrotra, "Bounds on the number of samples needed for neural learning", *IEEE Trans. Neural Networks*, vol. 2, pp. 548-558, 1991.

[22] D. Touretzky and D. Pomerleau, "What's hidden in the hidden layers", *Byte*, pp. 227-233, August, 1989.

[23] T.J. Sejnowski and C.R. Rosenberg, "Parallel networks that learn to pronounce english text", *Complex Systems*, vol. 1, pp. 145-168, 1987.

[24] R.P. Gorman and T.J. Sejnowski, "Analysis of hidden units in a layered network trained to classify sonar targets", *Neural Networks*, vol. 1, pp. 75-89, 1988.

[25] R. Jarvis and El Patrick, "Clustering using a similarity measure based on shared near neighbors", *IEEE Trans. Computers*, vol. C-22, pp. 1025-1034, 1973.

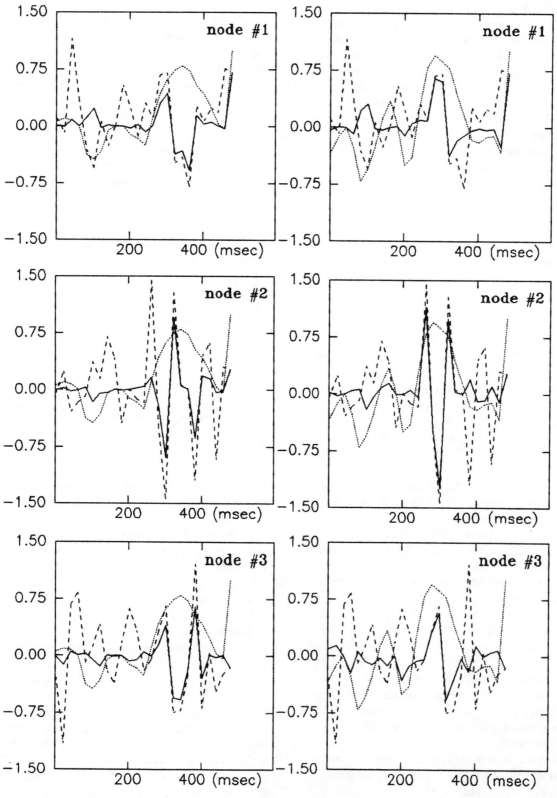

Figure 1. MS pattern (cza52)   **Figure 2. Normal pattern (czn7)**

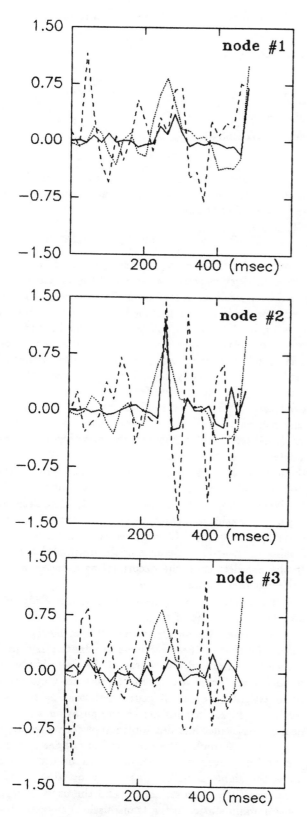

······· input ERP waveform

– – – – weight vector

———— weight-state vector

Figure 3. MS pattern (cza49)

Neural Network Techniques for Multi-user Demodulation*

U. Mitra and H.V. Poor

Dept. of Electrical Engineering
Princeton University
Princeton, New Jersey, USA 08544

Abstract—

Adaptive methods for demodulating multi-user communication in a Direct-Sequence Spread-Spectrum Multiple-Access (DS/SSMA) environment are investigated. In this setting the noise is characterized as being the sum of the interfering users' signals and additive Gaussian noise. The optimal receiver for DS/SSMA systems has a complexity that is exponential in the number of users.

Adaptive Radial Basis Function (RBF) networks that operate with knowledge of only a subset of the system parameters are studied. This approach is further bolstered by the fact that the optimal detector in the synchronous case can be implemented by a RBF network when all of the system parameters are known.

The RBF network's performance is compared with other multi-user detectors. The centers of the RBF neurons, when the system parameters are not fully known, are determined using clustering techniques. This work shows that the adaptive RBF network obtains near optimal performance and is robust in realistic communication environments.

I. INTRODUCTION

There is a need for multi-user communication for computer networks, radio transmission, telephony, and satellite broadcast channels. In this work, we propose a Radial Basis Function (RBF) neural network as an alternative to the optimal multi-user detector. In Code Division Multiple-Access (CDMA) communication, each user is distinguished by a unique code (called a *spreading code*) which is used to modulate their binary antipodal data. The signal sent over the shared channel is the sum of the individual users' signals. Ambient channel noise is characterized as an additive, white Gaussian process.

CDMA communication, which is a form of spread spectrum communication, allows simultaneous and asynchronous communication; thus many more subscribers can share a frequency band which leads to more efficient use of that band. In other channel division modes, resources are commonly left unused.

II. PREVIOUS MULTI-USER RECEIVERS

In order to grasp the need for simple, robust and adaptive multi-user receivers, a review of the previously used multi-user receivers is presented. The conventional single user receiver is a filter matched to the code of the user. It is optimal, with respect to the probability of detection error, in the presence of additive Gaussian noise only. The matched filter suffers from the *near-far problem*, *i.e.* performance is severely degraded by the effects of a large received power for the interferers with respect to the desired user. The optimal receiver for multi-user detection uses maximum likelihood sequence detection [11] which is implemented by a dynamic programming algorithm. Such a detection scheme has a complexity that is exponential in the number of users. Due to this complexity, much attention is being devoted to the development of sub-optimal receivers with more moderate complexity. The *decorrelating detector* achieves near-optimum performance when the users' spreading codes form a linearly independent set and retains the near-far resistance of the optimal detector [5]. In the noiseless case, the decorrelating detector achieves perfect demodulation.

Whereas the optimal detector requires knowledge of the distinguishing codes of each of the users as well as their received power, the decorrelating detector needs only the codes. Neither of these receivers is adaptive and performance is diminished if a subset of the users is not communicating. There are several factors that motivate us to investigate the use of neural networks as multi-user receivers. First, in addition to computational efficiency, near-far resistance and near-optimal performance, we seek adaptivity. Secondly, the decision boundaries formed by the optimal receiver are non-linear in nature. And finally, the highly structured nature of multiple-access interference (it is cyclo-stationary and the users' spreading codes remain static during transmission) suggests that a neural network should be able to learn how to combat

*This research was supported by the National Science Foundation under Grant NCR 90-02767.

the multiple-access interference (MAI) with great facility. Aazhang, Paris, and Orsak [1] showed empirically that multi-layered perceptrons can perform as multi-user receivers. The authors have supplied further, theoretical evidence of the merit of these neural network receivers [7]. Here, we investigate an alternative neural network structure, the Radial Basis Function network, as a potential multi-user receiver.

III. RADIAL BASIS FUNCTIONS

Whereas a single layer perceptron network performs a non-linear operation on a linear combination of the components of the vector input data, Radial Basis Function (RBF) networks output a linear combination of non-linear functions, each of which is applied to the vector input data. Originally RBFs were used in the multi-dimensional data fitting arena where each data pair $(\underline{x}_{input}, y_{output})$ had a corresponding RBF neuron associated with it and the output weights were found by solving for the optimal weights to minimize an error criterion. Researchers noted that this interpolation activity was akin to the process of finding a function to meet pre-defined input and output associations which were described in the form of the data pairs previously mentioned.

The RBF network structure is defined by the equations given below:

$$y = \sum_{i=1}^{N} W_i \Phi_i(\underline{x} - \underline{c_i})/\sigma_i{}^2. \quad (1)$$

$\Phi_i(\cdot)$ is a continuous, non-linear function from $R^+ \to R$. Other conditions which stem from regularization and approximation theory can be found in [8]. $\underline{x}$ is the input data vector, $\underline{c_i}$ is called the *center* of the RBF neuron, σ_i is the *spread* of the neuron and the W_i are the weights which optimize some error criterion. The methods by which the $\Phi_i(\cdot), c_i, \sigma_i$, and W_i are selected, constitute much of the current research on RBF networks. Traditionally, the centers were randomly chosen from the given data set, the spreads were then calculated by determining the minimum distance between centers using the appropriate distance metric and the weights could be solved for given a simple error criterion (e.g. minimum mean squared error) [4]. Particular applications of the RBF network can effectively circumscribe the gamut of practical methods used to find these network parameters.

Our investigation of RBF networks as multi-user receivers is inspired by the work of Chen, Mulgrew and McLaughlin [2] who used these networks and modifications thereof to perform equalization. Before we consider the RBF network as a multi-user receiver, we describe the communication model and discuss maximum likelihood detection for synchronous communication.

IV. COMMUNICATION MODEL

This paper addresses the analysis of an adaptive multi-user receiver for single user demodulation with moder-ate complexity. We consider this problem in the context of coherent, synchronous Direct-Sequence Spread-Spectrum Multiple-Access (DS/SSMA) signaling. After chip matched-filtering and chip-rate sampling, such a signal can be modeled in discrete time as,

$$\underline{r}_i = \sum_{j=1}^{K} \underline{s}_j^i + \underline{n}_i \quad where \ \underline{s}_j^i = A_j b_j^i \underline{m}_j, \quad (2)$$

and $\underline{r}_i$ is the received signal at time i, K is the number of active users, $\underline{s}_j^i$ is j'th user's signal at time i, $\underline{m}_j$ is the j'th user's spreading code, A_j the amplitude and b_j^i the bit value of the j'th user at time i. Note that the time index i is with respect to the symbols and not the chips. The additive Gaussian noise process is $\underline{n}_i$. It is assumed that all relevant timing and phase information is available. In addition, the receiver is assumed to have access to the desired user's spreading code, but not those of the interfering users.

V. HYPOTHESIS TESTING AND MAXIMUM LIKELIHOOD DETECTION

Our detection problem can easily be cast into one of *hypothesis testing* [9]. Effectively there exist two possibilities of interest: our desired user transmits a +1 or a −1. This desired bit is embedded in noise which consists of additive Gaussian noise and the MAI. When all of the system parameters are known (the number of users, all users' spreading codes, delays, transmitting powers), we can characterize the statistics of this noise. We shall be considering Bayesian hypothesis testing, which minimizes the average cost incurred by the decision rule. Let $\underline{r}$ be the observation of the desired signal in noise, $\underline{r} = \Theta + \underline{n}$, where $\underline{\Theta}$ is the desired signal vector, i.e. $\underline{\Theta} = A_1 \underline{m_1}$ or $\underline{\Theta} = -A_1 \underline{m_1}$; n is the noise component. We denote the probability density of the observation r under the null hypothesis (H_0) by p_0, and similarly p_1 is the density under the alternative hypothesis, H_1. The likelihood ratio is then $L(\underline{r}) = \frac{p_1(\underline{r})}{p_0(\underline{r})}$. The Bayesian decision rule (δ_b) compares the likelihood ratio to a threshold, τ, which is determined by the cost function and the prior probabilities of Θ. For zero cost for a correct decision and a unit cost for an incorrect decision, and equal priors, $\tau = 1$. We assume that each user's data bit is independent of the other users' bits and each data bit is equally likely to be +1 or −1. This leads to the following distributions for our scenario,

$$p_l(\underline{r}) = \frac{1}{2^{K-1}} \sum_{i=1}^{2^{K-1}} \frac{1}{(2\pi)^{2^{K-2}} |\sigma^2 I|^2}$$

$$\exp -\{\frac{1}{2\sigma^2} \|\underline{r} - \Theta_l - \underline{\mu_i}\|^2\}, \quad (3)$$

where K is the number of users, σ is the Gaussian noise variance, Θ_l is the desired signal vector given H_j and $\underline{\mu_i}$ is the i'th permutation of the sum of the interferer's signals. This results in the likelihood ratio,

$$L(\underline{r}) = \frac{\sum_{i=1}^{2^{K-1}} \exp -\{\frac{1}{2\sigma^2}\|\underline{r} - \underline{\Theta}_1 - \underline{\mu}_i\|^2\}}{\sum_{i=1}^{2^{K-1}} \exp -\{\frac{1}{2\sigma^2}\|\underline{r} - \underline{\Theta}_0 - \underline{\mu}_i\|^2\}}. \quad (4)$$

The resulting decision rule is,

$$\begin{aligned} \delta_b(\underline{r}) = \; & sgn(\sum_{i=1}^{2^{K-1}} \exp -\{\frac{1}{2\sigma^2}\|\underline{r} - \underline{\Theta}_1 - \underline{\mu}_i\|^2\} \\ & - \sum_{i=1}^{2^{K-1}} \exp -\{\frac{1}{2\sigma^2}\|\underline{r} - \underline{\Theta}_0 - \underline{\mu}_i\|^2\}), \quad (5) \end{aligned}$$

where the sgn function returns the sign of its operand.

Recalling (1), it is clear that the Bayesian decision rule can be implemented with a RBF network under the following conditions:

$$\Phi(\underline{x}) = \exp -\{\frac{1}{2}\|\underline{x} - \underline{c}_i\|^2\} \quad (6)$$

$$W_i = \begin{cases} 1 & \text{if } i \in I_1 \\ -1 & \text{if } i \in I_0 \end{cases} \quad (7)$$

where σ_i is the Gaussian noise variance, σ^2, $\underline{c}_i$ is equal to $\underline{\mu}_i$ from above, and I_j is the set of indices corresponding to hypothesis H_j.

It has been shown that the above maximum-likelihood detector is in fact the optimal one-shot detector for decentralized detection of a single user in the multi-user communication scenario [10]. So, if all the system parameters are known we can implement the optimum single user detector above. In practical communication systems, all system parameters are not known; in this investigation we focus on communication when only a subset of the parameters are known to the receiver.

VI. DETECTION WITH KNOWN SYSTEM PARAMETERS

Once the exact centers for the RBF neurons are known, one can determine exactly what the weights for the linear combiner should be [8]. In order investigate the dynamics of the system, however; we chose to use Least Mean Squares (LMS) adaptation techniques to see whether the optimal weights for the network could be learned given that the centers were known.

The LMS update equation for the weights is:

$$\underline{W}_{k+1} = \underline{W}_k + \eta(y_k - d_k)\underline{\Phi}(\underline{r}_k), \quad (8)$$

where η is the adaptation gain which controls the rate of change, $y_k(= W_k^T \underline{\Phi}(\underline{r}_k))$ is the output of the RBF network at time k, $\underline{\Phi}(\cdot)$ is the vector RBF non-linear functions applied to the input, d_k is the desired user's bit value at time k and $\underline{r}_k$ is the received multi-user signal. The LMS adaptive algorithm converges in the mean to the set of weights that minimize the mean squared error between the desired signal and the algorithm output. It can be shown that the mean weight values are numerically indistinguishable from those required for the optimal synchronous detector, i.e.

the two optimality criteria (minimum mean squared error and minimum probability of error) result in the same set of weights. This implies that even in the presence of additive Gaussian noise, our RBF network will yield the minimum probability of error demodulator in the mean.

Adaptation with the additive noise present still yields close to optimal performance (with nearly optimal weights) as is shown in Figs. 1 and 2 where the probability of error with respect to changing SNR (with respect to the desired user) or Near Far Ratio (NFR = E_2/E_1, where E_i is the received power of user i) is plotted. N is the length of the spreading codes used. The performance of the RBF network is compared to several other known detectors: the optimal detector described in (6) - (7), the decorrelating detector, the conventional matched filter, a linear filter that minimizes the mean squared error, and the single layer perceptron network studied in [7]. Convergence of the RBF network was effectively attained within 20 to 50 bit intervals when the weights were initialized with small random values.

Practically, one does not always have access to the exact centers for this network. We next investigate methods for determining the centers given a subset of parameter information.

VII. CLUSTERING TECHNIQUES FOR CENTER ESTIMATION

As was seen in Section V, the distribution of our observations, $\underline{r}$, is a Gaussian mixture. The goal of any clustering

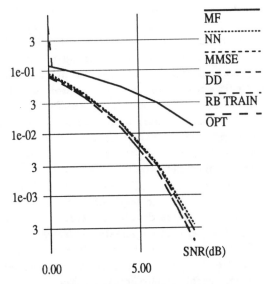

Figure 1: Probability of Error as a function of SNR1 for several detectors in a 2-user synchronous Gaussian channel (N=31) with NFR = 4.0.

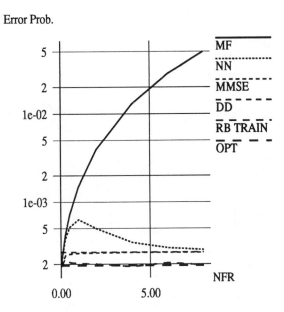

Figure 2: Probability of Error as a function of NFR for several detectors in a 2-user synchronous Gaussian channel (N=31) with SNR1 = 8.0dB.

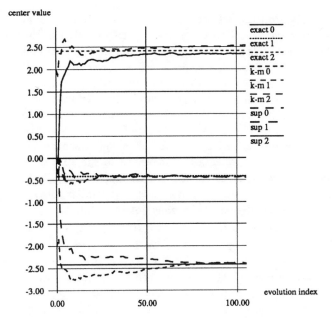

Figure 3: Comparison of the Supervised and K-Means Clustering Algorithms. The evolution of the three components of the first center is shown (N=3).

technique we use is to determine the modes of the distribution; these are the desired centers of the RBF network. Traditional clustering techniques are computationally intensive [3]. Most techniques operate on a *proximity map* which describes the distances between all the points in a data set, given an appropriate distance metric. Clustering involves iterating an algorithm over the map until the final set of clusters is achieved. Rather than using traditional clustering techniques which make no assumptions about the data to be clustered, we will exploit our knowledge of the system parameters and modify conventional methods.

A. Supervised Clustering

In the RBF network application to equalization [2], the authors suggest, among other techniques, supervised clustering for finding the centers. Supervised clustering for our application requires the knowledge of all of the users' bits. Note that the number of centers is exponential in the number of users. All the observations that stem from a particular combination of the K users' bits are averaged to yield the desired center. The distribution of the observation conditioned on a particular combination of the bits is simply a Gaussian distribution with the variance of the noise and a mean which is the sum of each of the user's signals given that bit combination. The Law of Large Numbers guarantees that averaging in this manner will yield the mean of the distribution, which is our desired center.

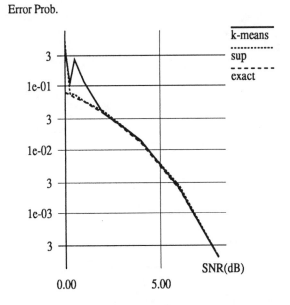

Figure 4: Probability of Error as a function of SNR1 for the RBF network with the centers known exactly, and estimated by the Supervised and by the K-Means Clustering algorithms in a 2-user synchronous Gaussian channel (N=31) with NFR = 4.0.

B. Derivative of K-Means Clustering

In the previous clustering example, we assumed knowledge of each users' bit sequence only. In a communications system, this is an unlikely scenario. It is more conventional that we have access to the spreading codes, but not the bit sequence. We use the k-means clustering algorithm [6] which is initialized with centers which correspond to all possible bit combinations, but we assume that each user is transmitting with unit received power. The distance metric used was Euclidean. The convergence of this algorithm to the modes of the Gaussian mixture from which the observations are derived can be found in [6]. Each center has as many components as the length of the spreading code. The evolution of the first center is shown in Fig. 3. Notice that both clustering methods have similar convergence rates, though the rates may not be practical.

We next examine how well the RBF network performs with these centers estimated by the two different clustering methods. In moderate NFR (NFR=4.0), the clustering algorithms work adequately when the SNR1 is varied. This is shown in Fig. 4. We expect that the supervised method will better estimate the centers than the k-means method when the NFR is large or very small (i.e. less than unity). This is somewhat borne out by the performance simulations. When the NFR is extremely large, the k-means algorithm is initialized with values that are far away from the desired values. The supervised algorithm makes no assumptions about the initial values. Fig. 4 shows the performance of the two clustering methods' RBF networks. However, by increasing the amount of

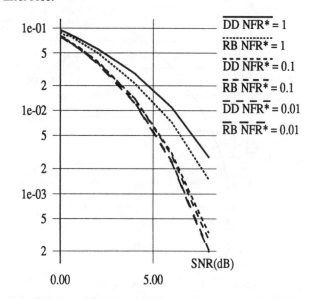

Figure 6: Probability of Error as a function of SNR1 for the decorrelating detector and the RBF network in a 3-user synchronous Gaussian channel (N=31) with NFR = 4.0, where the third user is spurious.

training time for the centers, we can improve the performance of the k-means algorithm, this is reflected in the plots in Fig. 4.

The two clustering techniques employed require knowledge of the number of users in the system. Since all users are transmitting with differing amounts of received power, it is the strong interferers that pose the largest problem to our detection system. Focusing only on mitigating the effects of the powerful interferers, would reduce the size of our RBF network. We next consider the robustness of the RBF network when we consider a subset of the interferers which are relatively more powerful than the rest of the interferers.

VIII. SMALL SPURIOUS USER IN KNOWN SYSTEM

A robust multi-user demodulator will be able to withstand the presence of small, unknown users. Generally in a multi-user environment, the MAI due to powerful users presents the most degrading noise factor. The next set of experiments determines how robust the RBF network is to the insertion of a relatively small, but unknown third user into a two user system. The RBF neuron centers are those for the two user system with total parameter knowledge and the linear weights are trained in the presence of the third user as well as the existing MAI and ambient channel noise. The performance of the RBF network was

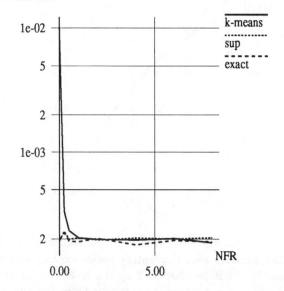

Figure 5: Probability of Error as a function of NFR for the RBF network with the centers known exactly, and estimated by the Supervised and by the K-Means Clustering algorithms in a 2-user synchronous Gaussian channel (N=31) with SNR1 = 8.0dB.

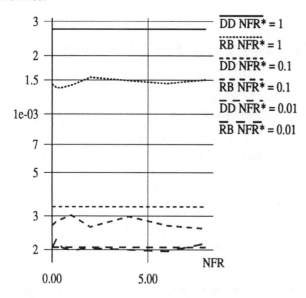

Error Prob.

$\overline{\text{DD NFR*}} = 1$
$\overline{\text{RB NFR*}} = 1$
$\overline{\text{DD NFR*}} = 0.1$
$\overline{\text{RB NFR*}} = 0.1$
$\overline{\text{DD NFR*}} = 0.01$
$\overline{\text{RB NFR*}} = 0.01$

NFR

Figure 7: Probability of Error as a function of NFR for the decorrelating detector and the RBF network in a 3-user synchronous Gaussian channel (N=31) with SNR1 = 8.0dB, where the third user is spurious.

compared to the decorrelating detector for the two user system.

Figures 6 and 7 show the results of these simulations. Once again the RBF network outperforms the decorrelating detector. NFR* is the near far ratio between the spurious third user's received power and that of the desired user's. These findings imply that even in situations where we may know all of the system parameters, we can choose to ignore the smaller users and thus reduce the complexity of the RBF network detector. The knowledge of the number of strong interferers would allow us to also reduce the complexity of the clustering algorithms used to determine the centers of the RBF neurons.

IX. CONCLUSIONS

In this paper we have shown that the optimal multi-user receiver for synchronous detection of DS/SSMA signals can be implemented with a Radial Basis Function network. We have investigated several aspects of making this network adaptive: how to find the optimal weights, and the use of clustering methods to determine the centers of the RBF neurons. Simulations were performed to compare the performance of the RBF network and several previously derived multi-user receivers. These simulations show that the RBF network has the desirable properties of fast convergence and near-optimal performance in realistic communication environments.

Further areas of study will concentrate on faster methods for clustering the data and better exploitation of the known system parameters. In addition, the issue of RBF network size must be addressed. The current implementation has 2^K neurons when there are K users. A realistic communication system should be able to handle a few hundred users.

REFERENCES

[1] B. Aazhang, B.-P. Paris, and G. Orsak, "Neural networks for multi-user detection in CDMA communication," *IEEE Trans. on Comm.*, August 1991.

[2] S. Chen, B. Mulgrew, and S. McLaughlin, "Adaptive bayesian equaliser with decision feedback," to appear in *IEEE Signal Processing Magazine*, August 1991.

[3] A. K. Jain and R. C. Dubes, *Algorithms for Clustering Data.* Advanced Reference Series, New Jersey: Prentice Hall, 1988.

[4] D. Lowe, "Adaptive radial basis function nonlinearities, and the problem of generalisation," in *Proceedings of the 1st IEE International Conference on Artificial Neural Networks*, pp. 171 – 175, IEE, October 1989.

[5] R. Lupas and S. Verdu, "Linear multiuser detectors for synchronous code-division multiple-access channels," *IEEE Trans. on Info. Theory*, vol. 35, no. 1, pp. 123–136, January 1989.

[6] J. B. MacQueen, "Some methods of classification and analysis of multivariate observations," in *Proceedings of the Fifth Berkeley Symposium on Mathemtical Statistics and Probability*, pp. 281–297, 1967.

[7] U. Mitra and H. V. Poor, "Adaptive receiver algorithms for near-far resistant CDMA," in *Proceedings of the 3rd Symposium on Personal, Indoor and Mobile Radio Communications*, IEEE, October 1992.

[8] T. Poggio and F. Girosi, "Networks for approximation and learning," *Proceedings of the IEEE*, vol. 78, no. 9, pp. 1481 –1497, 1990.

[9] H. V. Poor, *An Introduction to Signal Detection and Estimation.* New York: Springer-Verlag, 1988.

[10] H. V. Poor and S. Verdu, "Single-user detectors for multi-user channels," *IEEE Trans. on Comm.*, vol. 36, no. 1, pp. 50–60, January 1988.

[11] S. Verdu, "Minimum probability of error for asynchronous gaussian multiple-access channels," *IEEE Trans. on Info. Theory*, vol. 32, no. 1, pp. 85–96, January 1986.

Wavelet Neural Networks and Receptive Field Partitioning*

Toufic I. Boubez

Department of Biomedical Engineering, and
CAIP Parallel Computing Laboratory, Rutgers University
Piscataway, New Jersey 08855-1390
(e-mail: boubez@caip.rutgers.edu)

Richard L. Peskin

Department of Mechanical and Aerospace Engineering, and
CAIP Parallel Computing Laboratory, Rutgers University
Piscataway, New Jersey 08855-1390

Abstract— Basis function neural networks have been used for many years, with a variety of basis functions: radial, splines, polynomials. We propose the use of wavelet functions as basis functions. Wavelets have many advantages over other basis functions: orthonormal sets of wavelets can easily be constructed, thus network weights can be computed directly and independently. Wavelets can be used to provide a multiresolution approximation of the discriminant functions and offer localization in space and frequency. These properties are put to good advantage by the proposed method, which constructs a sparse wavelet network by including and positioning wavelets from increasing levels of resolution to maximize the classification score.

I. INTRODUCTION

The problem of learning a mapping from a given set of examples is encountered in several disciplines under different names, such as function approximation, pattern recognition, nonparametric regression and statistical learning. Feed-forward multi-layer neural networks have recently emerged as a popular tool both for classification purposes and for approximating continuous functions [1–8]. In a recent paper [10], neural networks learning is associated with long standing methods in classical function approximation, particularly the use of basis functions. The idea of using networks of basis functions is by no means a new one, with splines [11, 12], polynomial [13, 14] and radial basis functions [9, 10], being the most popular. Recent work with wavelets, however, has shown their power in modeling functions, especially those with sharp transitions and localized behavior [15, 16, 17, 18]. A logical consequence is the combination of those theories into the formation of wavelet networks, where the neurons in the network have wavelet-like response functions, and the connection weights are the corresponding wavelet coefficients. Additional support for this concept comes from sensory physiology and the behavior of afferent neurons in the sensory pathways [19]. Center-surround retinal ganglion cells, for example, possess receptive fields of different scales and locations throughout the visual field, with the well-known "Mexican-hat" activation function (Fig. 1). These cells are connected to simple and complex cortical cells in a hierarchy of overlapping receptive fields that is very reminiscent of the hierarchical nature of local support in wavelet basis functions. In this paper we describe basis function neural networks and wavelet-based multiresolution analysis. We then develop the wavelet neural network model and introduce a hybrid constructive-destructive network creation algorithm. Finally, we present a preliminary implementation of the model and compare its results with some well-known neural network models.

II. BASIS FUNCTION NETWORKS

Basis function networks can be considered a particular case of the general feed-forward neural network model. The premise of these networks is that the function to be approximated can be written as the expansion:

$$f(\mathbf{x}) = \sum_i \alpha_i B_i(\mathbf{x}) \qquad (1)$$

*This research was supported in part by the National Science Foundation under NSF grants IRI-9116558 and ECS-9110424, and by the Comuptational Engineering Laboratory of the Center for Computer Aids for Industrial Productivity (CAIP). CAIP is supported by the New Jersey Commission on Science and Technology, Rutgers–the State University of New Jersey, and the CAIP Industrial members.

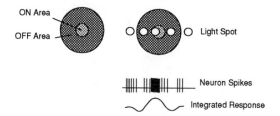

Figure 1: On-center receptive field of retinal ganglion cell. Neuron firing and integrated activation function are shown as a light spot is moved across the receptive field.

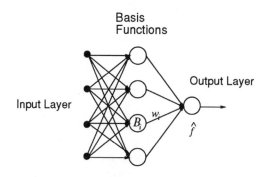

Figure 2: Basis Function Network

where the B_i are basis functions and the α_i are the corresponding coefficients. The network structure is such that there is only one hidden layer, containing neurons whose activation functions are not sigmoid, but correspond to the chosen basis functions. The connection weights are taken to represent the associated coefficients. The weights and other basis parameters are computed by any one of the popular learning methods such as back-propagation [20]. The output layer performs the summation of the weighted outputs from the hidden layer, to generate the function approximation (Fig. 2). Several types of basis functions can be used, the most common being radial basis functions (RBF) [9, 10], splines [11, 12] and polynomial functions [13, 14]. The main problem in this approach is that of selecting an appropriate set of basis functions and their optimization parameters. In addition, as in classical function approximation, the problem of scaling the number of input dimensions, the so-called "curse of dimensionality", is not properly dealt with.

III. THE WAVELET TRANSFORM

A. The Continuous Wavelet Transform

The name "wavelets" [16] refers to a family of functions that, in the continuous case, take the form:

$$\psi^{(a,b)}(x) = |a|^{-1/2}\psi(\frac{x-b}{a}) \tag{2}$$

where a is a dilation factor and b a translation factor of the original function $\psi(x)$, which has to be square integrable and satisfy:

$$C_\psi = \int |\xi|^{-1}|\hat{\psi}(\xi)|^2 d\xi < \infty \tag{3}$$

By varying these factors, the location and frequency content of the wavelet function can be controlled. The continuous wavelet transform is defined as:

$$(Wf)(a,b) = \langle f, \psi^{(a,b)}\rangle \tag{4}$$

allowing us to decompose $f(x)$ into its components at different scales of frequency and space (location) by varying a and b. The function $f(x)$ can then be reconstructed by performing the inverse operation and integrating over the transform space of a and b [17] so that:

$$f(x) = \frac{1}{C_\psi} \int \int (Wf)(a,b)\psi^{(a,b)}\frac{dadb}{a^2} \tag{5}$$

B. Multiresolution Analysis

Let us now define a linear operator A_{2^j} such that $f_{2^j} = A_{2^j}f(x)$ approximates $f(x)$ to a resolution of 2^j samples per unit length, and that f_{2^j} is the best approximation of f in the corresponding vector space denoted by $\mathbf{V}_{2^j} \subset \mathbf{L}^2(\Re)$. A_{2^j} is then an orthogonal projection on $\mathbf{V}_{2^j}$. The ladder of subspaces in $\mathbf{L}^2(\Re)$:

$$\forall j \in \mathbf{Z}, \quad \mathbf{V}_{2^j} \subset \mathbf{V}_{2^{j+1}} \quad \dots \tag{6}$$

is called a multiresolution approximation of $\mathbf{L}^2(\Re)$. Clearly then a higher resolution space $\mathbf{V}_{2^{j+1}}$ will generally contain more information than $\mathbf{V}_{2^j}$. This difference in content is spanned by the orthogonal complement of $\mathbf{V}_{2^j}$ in $\mathbf{V}_{2^{j+1}}$, $\mathbf{O}_{2^j}$.

To properly characterize a signal $f(x)$, we now need to compute its representation at a certain resolution 2^j, called the "smooth signal" and the difference of information between the resolutions 2^j and 2^{j+1}, called the "detail signal". It can be shown that in a multiresolution approximation there exists a unique function $\phi(x)$, called a scaling function, such that if we set $\phi_{2^j}(x) = 2^j\phi(2^j x)$, then $(\sqrt{2^{-j}}\phi_{2^j}(x-2^{-j}n))_{n\in\mathbf{Z}}$ forms an orthonormal basis of $\mathbf{V}_{2^j}$. The discrete approximation of $f(x)$ at a resolution 2^j can then be represented by a set of inner products:

$$A_{2^j}^d f = ((\langle f(x), \phi_{2^j}(x - 2^{-j}n)\rangle))_{n\in\mathbf{Z}} \tag{7}$$

Furthermore, if H is a discrete filter with impulse response:

$$h(n) = \langle \phi_{2^{-1}}(u), \phi(u-n)\rangle \qquad \forall n \in \mathbf{Z} \tag{8}$$

then this scaling function $\phi(x)$ can be computed by:

$$\hat{\phi}(\omega) = \prod_{p=1}^{+\infty} H(2^{-p}\omega) \qquad (9)$$

It can also be shown that, given the conjugate filter G such that

$$G(\omega) = e^{-i\omega}\overline{H(\omega + \pi)} \qquad (10)$$

then the function whose Fourier transform is given by:

$$\hat{\psi}(\omega) = G(\frac{\omega}{2})\hat{\phi}(\frac{\omega}{2}) \qquad (11)$$

is and orthogonal wavelet whose dilations and translations

$$(\sqrt{2^{-j}}\psi_{2^j}(x - 2^{-j}n))_{n \in \mathbf{Z}} \qquad (12)$$

form an orthogonal basis spanning the space $\mathbf{O}_{2^j}$ of the detail signal at resolution 2^j. By successively applying the two filters H and G, $f(x)$ can be characterized to any resolution.

In practice, the multiresolution decomposition of a signal f of length N is performed through a pyramid scheme. In the first step, at level $L = 0$, the filters H and G are applied to obtain the smooth and detail signals, respectively, of length N each. These two signals are then decimated by two to length $N/2$ to reduce them to the proper resolution. The filtering and decimation procedure is the applied to the smooth signal to obtain a second level of smooth and detail signals. This recursion is repeated until the desired resolution is achieved.

These constructions are valid for one-dimensional wavelets. In higher dimensions, it is usually considered computationally more efficient to use outer products of one-dimensional basis functions [12], even if the functions are not separable in dimensions [13]. This will be the method used in the examples presented later.

IV. Wavelet Networks

A. A General Model

We can now construct a network of neurons whose activation functions possess wavelet-like properties of translation, dilation and local support. These neurons can be combined as a set of basis functions that can be used for clustering and continuous function approximation. Again, the weights can be thought of as the wavelet coefficients (Fig. 3) and a back-propagation scheme can be derived to compute them through training. Following the neural networks convention, if we denote by s_i and y_i the internal state and output of neuron i, respectively, the network equations can be written for this new model:

$$\begin{aligned}
s_i &= \mathbf{A}_i\mathbf{x} \\
y_i &= \phi(s_i, b_i) \quad \text{for scaling function neurons} \\
y_i &= \psi(s_i, b_i) \quad \text{for wavelet neurons} \qquad (13)
\end{aligned}$$

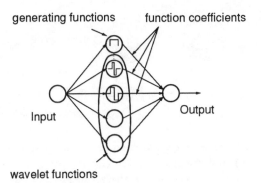

Figure 3: Wavelet Basis Network

where $\mathbf{A}_i$ is a diagonal matrix whose elements are the dilation parameters in each dimension, and $\mathbf{b}_i$ is the translation vector. The objective of training is then to optimize the values of $\mathbf{A}_i$ and $\mathbf{b}_i$. A simpler model would have one global dilation parameter a_i for each unit, so that $s_i = a_i\mathbf{x}$. This general model, however, has some of the same drawbacks as the original neural networks model of sigmoidal activation functions. The number of units is still hard to determine, and the training time can be extensive, due to the large parameter space to be explored. By taking advantage of the localized representation of sets of orthonormal wavelets and the recursive nature of their construction, several improvements can be obtained. For this, we shall make use of the recursive partitioning method to subdivide the feature space into subregions corresponding to the receptive fields of the neurons in the network. By having the activation function of a neuron correspond to a wavelet function over its receptive field, a multiresolution approximation of the input function is obtained.

B. The Receptive Field Partitioning Model

If $\hat{f}(\mathbf{x})$ is the approximation of $f(\mathbf{x})$ over the domain of interest, traditional recursive partitioning regression can be written as:

$$\text{if } \mathbf{x} \in R_m, \text{ then } \hat{f}(\mathbf{x}) = g_m(\mathbf{x}) \qquad (14)$$

where R_m are disjoint regions that partition the domain, and g_m are different approximating functions defined on each subregion. This partitioning is achieved through training by recursively splitting each subregion at every step into two other subregions according to some fitting criterion. In the Multivariate Adaptive Regression Splines (MARS) algorithm [11] for example, multivariate spline

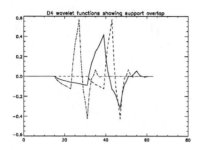

Figure 4: Overlapping Support for some D4 wavelet functions

basis functions $B_m^{(q)}(\mathbf{x})$ are used to approximate $f(\mathbf{x})$

$$\hat{f}(\mathbf{x}) = \sum_{m=1}^{M} a_m B_m^{(q)}(\mathbf{x}) \qquad (15)$$

and a lack-of-fit criterion $LOF(g(\mathbf{x}))$ is computed to select the new term to be added at every step.

The most important distinction to make is that different wavelet basis functions have overlapping support. In particular, for a given function at level L_i, several functions can be generated at level L_{i+1} over the same support interval (Fig. 4). In the proposed *Receptive Field Partitioning (RFP)* model, this provides a way to refine the wavelet decomposition in areas of greatest error computed by a LOF function. Another advantage is that the wavelet set can be grown as a tree, where the support of each parent node spans the support of all its children nodes. Neural Tree Networks (NTN) [8] offer several implementation advantages over general feedforward networks.

In addition, a useful constructive algorithm can take advantage of the following:

- A set of discrete one dimensional wavelet basis functions over each dimension of the training domain can be constructed in advance to any resolution desired and stored. The appropriate resolution can be determined by preconditioning the data set. Precomputing the wavelet functions allows for measurable speedups in training time, since a look-up table method can be used for determining the output of each hidden unit.

- Since an orthonormal set of bases can be constructed, each wavelet coefficient is in effect the projection $\langle f, \psi \rangle$ of the approximated function onto the corresponding basis function. This leads to two major gains: the wavelet coefficients can be computed without resorting to gradient descent or other optimization methods, and there is no need to retrain units whose weights have already been computed

as the refining proceeds and additional wavelets are required.

- Because of the local support property, only a small set of elements need be active at one time. This is especially important during training. For each training example, only wavelets whose support interval, or receptive field, includes that particular point are affected by the weight changes. We shall call this the *receptive field activation principle*. In this manner, the number of operations can be greatly reduced at every step, since typically, in a recursion of level L, only $O(L)$ elements will be active at any point.

C. The Receptive Field Partitioning (RFP) Algorithm

We can now proceed with a general algorithm to construct a wavelet neural network (WNN). To avoid the geometric explosion of the number of basis functions with the input space dimension, it is extremely important that a sparse set of basis functions be used. This sparse set is best determined by a constructive method. The object, then, is to start with the bases at the lowest level in each dimension (coarse resolution) and refine the approximation by adding units from higher resolutions as the error warrants. These units are added to partition the receptive field of the basis with the highest error. This objective is highly facilitated by the localized properties of the wavelet functions used.

The algorithm starts by generating an initial set of bases, the *seed bases*, consisting of the generating functions and the bases at the lowest (coarse) resolution, and maintains two pools of bases throughout the training. The first pool, the *main pool*, contains all the bases that are being used in the current computation and constitutes the actual neural network. The second pool, the *development pool*, contains all the bases that have not been refined yet, and is a subset of the first. Any basis that is selected for refinement get removed from this pool and its children are added to both pools. After the score target has been reached, the network is pruned by removing nodes whose effect on the total score is minimal.

The algorithm is summarized below:

Input: Feature vectors, wavelet type (ie Haar, D4, etc.), score target.

Initialize:

1. Compute the seed bases.
2. Create the main and development pools.
3. Compute the coefficients for the seed bases.
4. Compute the classification score.

Main Loop:

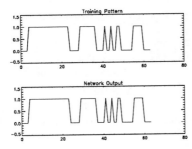

Figure 5: One-dimensional Training Pattern and Results

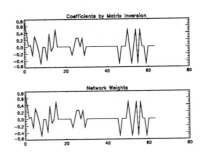

Figure 6: Coefficients obtained by matrix inversion compared to the ones obtained by the network

While (score < target_score)

1. Compute LOF for development pool.

2. Select basis ϕ with largest LOF and generate its sub-bases ϕ_i.

3. Remove ϕ from development pool but keep it in the main pool.

4. Add ϕ_i to the development and main pools.

5. Compute the coefficients for ϕ_i.

6. **if** (size(main_pool) is large) **then** prune.

7. Compute the classification score.

End While

Prune Network

Output: Wavelet Network structure and weights (coefficients).

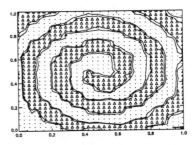

Figure 7: Two-dimensional Spiral Training Pattern and Results

V. RESULTS

Preliminary versions of the methods described in this paper were implemented and tested on one-dimensional and two-dimensional test patterns. For comparison purposes, we also trained networks using the Cascade-Correlation algorithm [21] on the same test patterns. In the first test, a one-dimensional pattern, in the form of a set of input-output pairs was used to train a network of Haar wavelets as basis functions, with $LOF(\psi_i) = \langle \psi_i(\mathbf{x}), Error(\mathbf{x}) \rangle$. The training was performed in 17 epochs, and the resulting network has 36 nodes. The results are shown in Fig. 5. In this case, as the input samples are evenly distributed, we can compute the exact wavelet coefficients by matrix inversion, and compare them to the network. We find that there are 36 non-zero coefficients and that the network has obtained the correct coefficients (Fig. 6). The cascade-correlation program took an average of 1556 epochs and 16 cascaded hidden units with 170 weights to achieve the same results.

The next test consisted of a two-dimensional spiral pattern of 1024 evenly-spaced data points. In this instance outer products of the one-dimensional D4 wavelet were used as two-dimensional basis functions (Fig. 4). The network was trained using the RFP algorithm to a target score of 0.9 (90% successful classification) and achieved it in 83 epochs using 170 weights for 170 units. Again, results and network weights compared very well with the results and non-zero coefficients obtained by matrix inversion methods (Figure 7). It should be noted at this point that matrix inversion methods involve the computation of every coefficient for the whole set of bases (1024 coefficients in this case), whereas the given algorithm will construct the set of bases with non-zero coefficients that will approximate the training pattern to a given competence level. The cascade-correlation program failed in several attempts to learn the pattern. This could be due, however, to a bad choice of initial parameters, although several different ones were tried.

The final test was the well-known double spiral pattern benchmark [21], which involves classifying points that fall on two interlocked spirals (Figure 8). Fahlman [21] reports that a modified version of back-propagation in use at MITRE required 150,000 to 200,000 epochs to solve the problem and that no solutions could be found using standard back-propagation. The Cascade-Correlation algorithm required an average of 1700 epochs to learn the pattern, with a median of 15 sigmoid units [21]. The RFP

21 epochs; score=95.4%

Figure 8: Two-Spiral benchmark pattern and results

algorithm, given a target score of 95%, achieved a score of 95.4% in 21 epochs for an unpruned total of 202 units and weights.

ACKNOWLEDGMENT

We wish to thank Prof. R. Mammone for his help and advice.

REFERENCES

[1] W.Y. Huang & R.P. Lippmann, "Comparisons between neural network and conventional classifiers", *Proc. IEEE First Conference on Neural Networks*, **4**, pp. 485–493, 1987.

[2] D.E. Rumelhart, J.L. McClelland & the PDP Research Group, *Parallel Distributed Processing*, The MIT Press, 1986.

[3] E.B. Baum, "On the capabilities of multilayer perceptrons", *J. of Complexity*, **4**:3, pp. 193–215, September 1988.

[4] G. Cybenko, "Approximation by superpositions of a sigmoidal function", *Math. Control, Signals and Systems*, **2**, pp. 303–314, 1989.

[5] K.M. Hornik, M. Sinchcombe & H. White, "Multilayer feedforward networks are universal approximators", *Neural Networks*, **2**, pp. 359–366, 1989.

[6] E.D. Sontag, "Feedforward nets for interpolation and classification", Department of Mathematics, Rutgers University.

[7] R.P. Lippmann, "Pattern classification using neural networks", *IEEE Comm. Magazine*, November 1989.

[8] A. Sankar & R.J. Mammone, "Neural Tree Networks", *Neural Networks: Theory and Applications"*, Ed. R. Mammone & Y Zeevi, Academic Press, 1991.

[9] J. Moody & C. Darken, "Fast learning in networks of locally-tuned processing units", *Neural Computation*, **1**, pp. 281–294, 1989.

[10] T. Poggio & F. Girosi, "Regularization algorithms for learning that are equivalent to multilayer networks", *Science*, **247**, pp. 978–982, February 1990.

[11] J.H. Friedman, "Multivariate Adaptive Regression Splines", *The Annals of Statistics*, **19**:1, pp. 1–141, 1991.

[12] S.H. Lane, M.G. Flax, D.A. Handelman & J.J. Gelfand, "Multi-layer perceptrons with B-spline receptive field functions", *Advances in Neural Information Processing Systems -3*, 1991.

[13] T.D. Sanger, "Basis-function trees for approximation in high-dimensional spaces", *Proc. 1990 Connectionist Models Summer School*, Morgan Kaufmann, 1990.

[14] T.D. Sanger, R.S. Sutton & C.J. Matheus, "Iterative construction of sparse polynomial approximations", *1991 NIPS Conference*, December 1991.

[15] G. Strang, "Wavelets and dilation equations: a brief introduction", SIAM Review, **31**:4, pp. 614–627, 1989.

[16] I. Daubechies, "Orthonormal bases of compactly supported wavelets", *Comm. on Pure and Applied Math.*, **XLI**, pp. 909–996, 1988.

[17] I. Daubechies, *Ten lectures on wavelets*, lecture notes, 1992.

[18] S.G. Mallat, "A theory for multiresolution signal decomposition: the wavelet representation", *IEEE Trans. PAMI*, **11**:7, July 1989.

[19] E.R. Kandel & J.H. Schwartz, editors, *Principles of Neural Science*, 2nd edition, Elsevier, 1985.

[20] D.E. Rumelhart, G.E. Hinton, R.J. Williams, "Learning representations by back-propagating errors", *Nature*, **323**, pp. 533–536, October 1986.

[21] S.E. Fahlman & C. Lebiere, "The cascade-correlation learning architecture", *Advances in Neural Information Processing Systems II*, Ed. D.S. Touretzky, pp. 524–532, 1989.

Generation of Traveling Wave Mode in A Chained Neural Oscillator Network Model

Hirofumi Nagashino, Koji Kakuyama and Yohsuke Kinouchi

Department of Electrical and Electronic Engineering, Faculty of Engineering,
The University of Tokushima, Tokushima 770 JAPAN

Abstract We analyzed a chained neural oscillator network model for a possible mechanism of generation of biological rhythm such as locomotion and peristaltic movement. Each oscillator unit is inhibited by its nearest neighbors. Numerical analysis emplying Poincaré map and computer simulation of the model have clarified characteristics of oscillation. It has been found out that among multi-stable oscillatory solutions traveling wave mode is generated by the chained networks of ring and linear structures and it can occur not only by setting proper initial conditions but also by transition from other mode with change of a parameter.

1. INTRODUCTION

The central nervous system of vertebrates and invertebrates generates and controls various rhythmic activities such as locomotion and peristaltic movement. It has been found out in a number of species that such behaviors are produced by central pattern generators (CPGs) which are believed to involve collections of oscillators [1,2]. It is considered that CPGs generate fundamental rhythmic patterns without any periodic inputs or feedback from peripheral systems.

The time scale of period of the rhythms is seconds, which is much longer than the firing interval of a single neuron. Most of the models for the mechanism of the rhythm generation incorporate the time scale with intrinsic property of a neuron [3-6]. Nagashino et al. [7,8] proposed a possible alternative mechanism. It produces the long period by the coupling of a number of elements in the model network. The network is composed of neurons that have impulse generation characteristics and inhibit reciprocally nearest neighbors. The mechanism is based on the phase difference of firing between neurons. Under the considerable fluctuations of biological states, however, it is more appropriate to develop a model that generates such rhythmic activities by collective variables.

We have analyzed a neural network model whose element is a neural oscillator coupled in chained structures. In this paper, we show multi-phase mode and traveling wave mode as multi-stable oscillatory solutions in the present model. The multi-phase mode is the same kind of oscillation as have been reported in some networks of coupled oscillators [9,10]. On the other hand, oscillatory behaviors such as the traveling wave mode have not been reported before. The traveling wave mode gives much longer period of oscillation than that of a single oscillator approximately proportional to the number of oscillators. It occurs in the linear structure as well

as in the ring structure. These results are similar to the firing modes in reciprocal inhibition neural networks composed of a number of pulse generating neurons. We show a) the existence regions and b) the transitions of the oscillatory solutions with respect to coupling coefficient of oscillators in the ring networks and c) initial conditions for generation of the traveling wave mode.

2. A CHAINED NEURAL OSCILLATOR NETWORK MODEL

Fig. 1 shows the neural oscillator model that is the unit of a chained neural oscillator network model in the present work. Each oscillator unit is composed of an excitatory and an inhibitory neuron. Each "neuron" is assumed to represent the average behavior of a number of neurons. These two neurons are coupled to each other forming a negative feedback loop. The excitatory neuron has a self-excitatory connection forming a positive feedback loop. Without both of the loops, there is no oscillation. This self-excitatory connection does not mean the recurrent connection of a neuron to itself, which has not been observed in general, but rather simplifies the interconnection of a number of excitatory neurons. Existence of bi-directional connections of excitatory neurons has been reported [11,12]. For suitable ranges of coupling coefficients, the unit generates a rhythmic output without any tonic external input. The oscillators are assumed to be identical.

Fig. 2 shows a chained neural oscillator network model with reciprocal inhibition to nearest neighbors. The excitatory neuron in an oscillator unit receives inhibition from the inhibitory neuron of two adjacent oscillators. The coupling coefficient is denoted by c_O and uniform in the network for simplicity of analysis. Let u_{ek} and u_{ik} denote the membrane potential of the excitatory neuron E_k and the inhibitory neuron I_k respectively in k-th unit. Their dynamics is expressed as

$$\tau_e \dot{u}_{ek} + u_{ek} = c_{ee}z_{ek} - c_{ei}z_{ik} - c_O(z_{ik-1} + z_{ik+1}) \tag{1a}$$

and

$$\tau_i \dot{u}_{ik} + u_{ik} = c_{ie}z_{ek}, \tag{1b}$$

where $k=1, 2, \ldots\ldots, N$ and z_{rk} ($r=e$ or i) is the output of the neuron expressed as

$$z_{rk} = \frac{2}{\pi} \tan^{-1} u_{rk}, \tag{2}$$

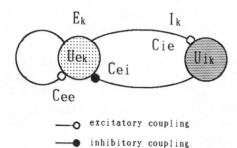

Fig. 1 A neural oscillator model.

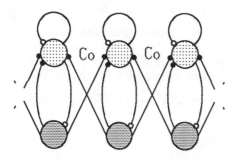

Fig. 2 A chained neural oscillator network model with reciprocal inhibition.

where $|z_{rk}| < 1$. These outputs are assumed to be the average values of the impulse frequencies of the neurons over a certain period of time. They increase monotonically and are saturated at ± 1. For ring structure, when $k=1$, N takes the place of $k-1$ and when $k=N$, 1 replaces $k+1$. For linear structure, when $k=1$, $z_{k-1}=0$ and when $k=N$, $z_{k+1}=0$. Symbol $\cdot$ denotes the derivative with respect to time. The time constants of the membranes of the excitatory and inhibitory neurons are denoted by τ_e and τ_i respectively. In the following for simplicity of analysis, they are assumed to be equal and set to one. The coupling coefficients of the coupling from neuron r' to neuron r within each oscillator are denoted by $c_{rr'}$, where $r, r'=e$ or i.

3. ANALYSIS OF A SINGLE NEURAL OSCILLATOR

In this section, we show the stable solutions of the single neural oscillator with different coupling coefficients by linear approximation analysis. The dynamics of the single oscillator is described as

$$\dot{u}_e + u_e = c_{ee}z_e - c_{ei}z_i \tag{3a}$$

and

$$\dot{u}_i + u_i = c_{ie}z_e, \tag{3b}$$

where u_e and u_i are the membrane potential of the excitatory and the inhibitory neuron respectively. The linearized system of (3a) and (3b) at the origin has a single equilibrium, the origin. The analysis of the stability of the equilibrium

gives eigenvalues λ as

$$\lambda = \frac{c_{ee}}{\pi} - 1 \pm \frac{1}{\pi}\sqrt{c_{ee}^2 - 4c_{ei}c_{ie}}. \tag{4}$$

The equilibrium is stable when

$$c_{ee} < \pi \tag{5a}$$

and

$$c_{ee} < \frac{\pi^2 + 4c_{ei}c_{ie}}{2\pi}. \tag{5b}$$

Eigenvalues are real and at least one of them is positive when

$$c_{ee} > \frac{\pi^2 + 4c_{ei}c_{ie}}{2\pi}, \tag{6}$$

or

$$c_{ee} > \pi \tag{7a}$$

and

$$c_{ee} > 2\sqrt{c_{ei}c_{ie}}. \tag{7b}$$

In this case, (3) has two stable equilibria, one of which is positive, the other negative. Their absolute values are equal. When

$$\pi < c_{ee} < 2\sqrt{c_{ei}c_{ie}}, \tag{8}$$

the egenvalues are conjugate comlex numbers and have positive real part and an oscillatory solution exists in (3). Fig. 3 shows these three regions of coupling coefficients c_{ee} and c_{ei} when $c_{ie}=1$. From (4), angular frequency ω of the oscillation is given as

$$\omega = \frac{1}{\pi}\sqrt{4c_{ei}c_{ie} - c_{ee}^2}. \tag{9}$$

In the following, the coupling coefficients inside each oscillator are fixed as $c_{ee}=4$, $c_{ei}=5$ and $c_{ie}=1$, which gives the oscillatory solution. We analyzed the chained network with different values of mutual inhibitory coupling coefficient c_o of the oscillators, which is uniform throughout the network.

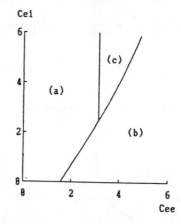

Fig. 3 Relationship between coupling coefficients and the stable solutions of the neural oscillator unit. (a) monostable equilibrium at the origin, (b) bistable equilibria, (c) oscillatory solution.

4. MULTI-PHASE MODE

In the chained neural oscillator network of the ring structure, for relatively weak mutual coupling, there exist rhythmic patterns in which the waveform is nearly sinusoidal (The stronger the mutual coupling is, the greater the distortion of the waveform is.) and the phase difference between adjacent oscillators is uniform. We call this type of oscillatory solutions multi-phase mode. The number of patterns depends on the number of oscillators in the network.

4. 1 Classification of multi-phase mode

The number of solutions of the multi-phase mode is equal to the number of oscillators in the network, as is shown below. The number of phases is confined to the divisors of the number of oscillators. In the individual solution of the multi-phase mode, the adjacent oscillators have the same phase difference. Solutions with different phase differences may exist which have the same number of phases. For example, when the number of oscillators N is 5, there are synchronized mode and 5 phase mode. In the synchronized mode, all the oscillators are synchronized in oscillation and the membrane potentials of excitatory and inhibitory neurons are equal respectively;

$$u_{e1}=u_{e2}=u_{e3}=u_{e4}=u_{e5}$$

and

$$u_{i1}=u_{i2}=u_{i3}=u_{i4}=u_{i5} .$$

The synchronized mode exists in networks of any number of oscillators. One example of 5 phase mode is illustrated in

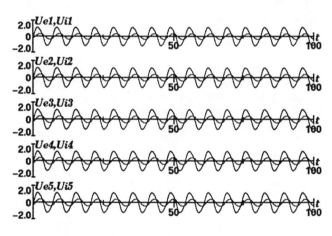

Fig. 4 Multi-phase mode in the ring structure. N=5.

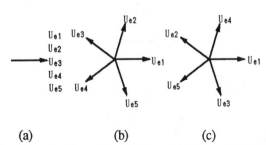

(a)   (b)   (c)

Fig. 5 The phase of each oscillator in the multi-phase mode, N=5.
(a) Synchronized mode, (b) 5 phase mode I, (c) 5 phase mode II.

Fig. 4. In this solution, the phase difference between the adjacent oscillators is $-2\pi/5$. There are symmetric pairs of 5 phase mode; in one solution, the phase shift rotates clockwise and in the other counter-clockwise in the ring structure. In one pair, the order of the phase shift is oscillator 1, 2, 3, 4, 5 or oscillator 1, 5, 4, 3, 2. Phase difference is $\pm 2\pi/5$. We call this pair 5 phase mode I. In the other pair, the order of the phase shift is oscillator 1, 3, 5, 2, 4 or oscillator 1, 4, 2, 5, 3. Phase difference is $\pm 4\pi/5$. We call this pair 5 phase mode II. As is shown below, for arbitrary N, the phase difference of the adjacent oscillators are $2j\pi/N$ ($j = 0, \pm 1, \ldots\ldots, \pm N'$), where

$$N' = \left\{ \begin{array}{l} N/2 \ (N: \text{even}) \\ (N\text{-}1)/2 \ (N: \text{odd}) \end{array} \right\} .$$ (10)

4. 2 Analysis of oscillation phase by linear approximation

We analyze the relationship between the angular frequency of the oscillation and the oscillation phase of each oscillator by linear approximation of (2) at the origin. The dynamics of the linearized network model in case N>2 is expressed as

$$\dot{u}_{ek} + u_{ek} = \frac{2}{\pi}c_{ee}u_{ek} - \frac{2}{\pi}c_{ei}u_{ik} - \frac{2}{\pi}c_o(u_{ik\text{-}1} + u_{ik+1})$$ (11a)

and

$$\dot{u}_{ik} + u_{ik} = \frac{2}{\pi}c_{ie}u_{ek} .$$ (11b)

The eigenvalues of (11) are

$$\lambda = \frac{c_{ee}}{\pi} - 1 \pm \frac{1}{\pi}\sqrt{c_{ee}^2 - 4c_{ie}(c_{ei} + 2c_o \cos\frac{2\pi}{N}j)} ,$$ (12)

where $j=0, 1, \ldots\ldots, N\text{-}1$. For $N=2$, $2c_o$ is replaced by c_o, as is also the case below. Therefore, the condition for oscillation is given as

$$c_{ee} > \pi$$ (13)

and

$$c_{ee}^2 - 4c_{ie}(c_{ei} + 2c_o \cos\frac{2\pi}{N}j) < 0 .$$ (14)

The angular frequencies ω are obtained as

$$\omega = \frac{1}{\pi}\sqrt{4c_{ie}(c_{ei} + 2c_o \cos\frac{2\pi}{N}j) - c_{ee}^2} .$$ (15)

The number of these angular frequencies is $N/2+1$ when N is even and $(N+1)/2$ when N is odd.

We calculate the angular frequencies of oscillation by an alternative method which employs the phase relation of the periodic solution obtained from computer simulation. The waveform is assumed to be sinusoidal. Denote the phases of k-1-th, k-th and k+1-th oscillators by $\phi_{k\text{-}1}$, ϕ_k and ϕ_{k+1} respectively. The membrane potential u_{ek} of the excitatory neuron in k-th oscillator is expressed as

$$u_{ek} = a \cos(\omega t + \phi_k) ,$$ (16)

where $k=1, 2, \ldots\ldots, N$. Amplitude a and angular frequency ω are unknown. From (11b), the membrane potential u_{ik} of the inhibitory neuron is expressed as

$$u_{ik} = b \cos(\omega t + \phi_k - \theta) ,$$ (17)

where

$$b = \frac{2ac_{ie}}{\pi\sqrt{1+\omega^2}} \quad (18)$$

and

$$\theta = \tan^{-1}\omega . \quad (19)$$

Substituting (16) and (17) into (11a), rearranging it in terms of $\cos\omega t$ and $\sin\omega t$ and setting the coefficients zero, we obtain that the amplitude a is arbitrary and the angular frequency ω is expressed as

$$\omega = \frac{1}{\pi}\sqrt{4c_{ie}(c_{ei} \pm 2c_o\cos\frac{\phi_{k+1}-\phi_{k-1}}{2}) - c_{ee}^2} , \quad (20)$$

where

$$(\phi_{k+1}-\phi_{k-1})/2 = \phi_k \text{ or } \phi_k + \pi \quad (21)$$

from computer simulation. By comparing (20) with (15), from the compound signs, positive sign is selected when

$$(\phi_{k+1}-\phi_{k-1})/2 = \phi_k$$

and negative sign is selected when

$$(\phi_{k+1}-\phi_{k-1})/2 = \phi_k + \pi .$$

The phase ϕ_k is expressed as

$$\phi_k = \frac{2\pi}{N}j(k-1) , \quad (22)$$

where $j = 0, \pm 1, \ldots\ldots, \pm N'$ and N' is expressed in (10). The greater the absolute value of j is, the greater are the phase difference of the adjacent oscillators and the period of oscillation. The relationship between the value of j and $x = \cos 2\pi j/N$ is illustrated in Fig. 6. For example, when $N=5$, $j=0$ corresponds to the sinchronized mode, $j=\pm 1$ to 5 phase mode I and $j=\pm 2$ to 5 phase mode II. Taking the nonlinearity of (2) into account, whether the angular frequency is larger or smaller than the value obtained from (15) depends on the value of j.

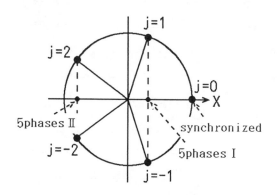

Fig. 6 Multi-phase mode and x, j

5. TRAVELING WAVE MODE

While the multi-phase mode occurs for relatively weak mutual coupling of oscillators in the ring structure, another type of oscillatory behaviors is seen for certain regions of stronger mutual coupling. This kind of oscillatory solutions exists in the linear structure as well as in the ring structure. Since these patterns can be regarded as traveling wave as is shown below, we call this mode traveling wave mode. Traveling wave mode exits in the network in which the number of oscillators is large enough.

The traveling wave mode occurs by the following mechanism. Suppose that infinite number of oscillators are arranged in a chained line with inhibitory coupling as is shown in Fig.7. The coupling coefficient is assumed to be suitable for the generation of the traveling wave mode. For this region of the coupling coefficient, there also exists a stable equilibrium in which membrane potentials are ......, $+\overline{U_r}$ $-\overline{U_r}$, $+\overline{U_r}$, $-\overline{U_r}$, ... in order, where $\overline{U_r}$ is positive and $r=e$, or i. Suppose that the initial conditions of the potentials are given as ......, $+\overline{U_r}$, $-\overline{U_r}$, U_r, $+\overline{U_r}$, $-\overline{U_r}$, ... Let k denote the oscillator number whose initial values of potentials are given U_r, that is $u_{ek}(0)=U_e$ and $u_{ik}(0)=U_i$ [Fig. 7(a)].

Roughly speaking, if U_e is larger than U_i [Fig. 7(b)], positive feedback has more effect than negative feedback on the excitatory neuron, so that u_{ek}, then as a result u_{ik}, goes to a positive value, then u_{ek-1} and u_{ik-1} go to negative values

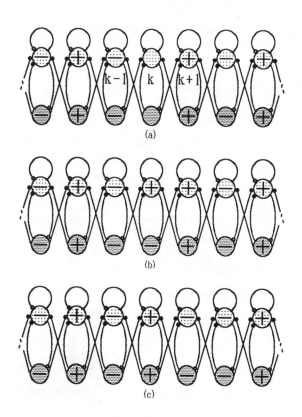

(a)

(b)

(c)

Fig. 7 Outline of switching of local euilibria in the traveling wave mode. Time proceeds in order of (a), (b) and (c).

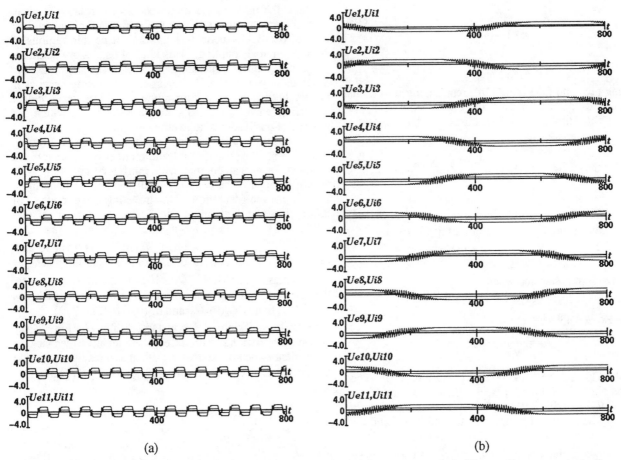

(a) (b)

Fig. 8 Traveling wave mode in the ring structure. *N*=11. (a) traveling wave mode I, (b) traveling wave mode II.

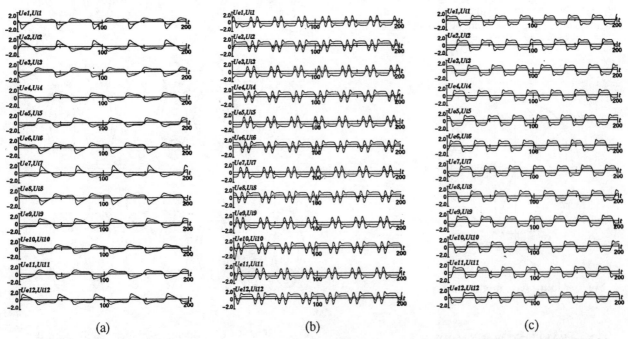

(a) (b) (c)

Fig. 9 Traveling wave mode in the ring structure. *N*=12. (a) traveling wave mode I-a, (b) traveling wave mode I-b, (c) traveling wave mode I-c.

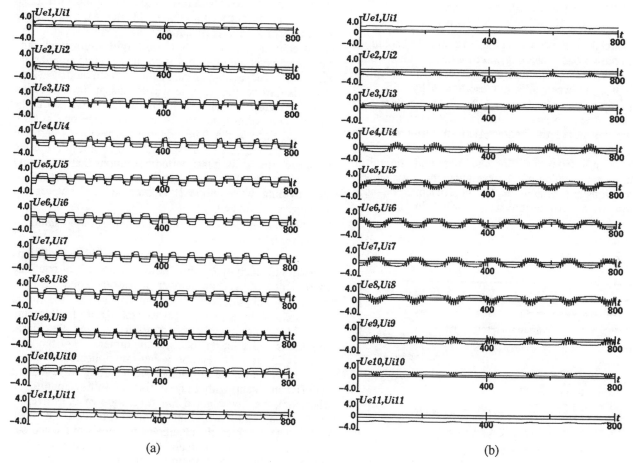

(a)   (b)

Fig. 10 Traveling wave mode in the linear structure, N=11. (a) traveling wave mode I, (b) traveling wave mode II.

[Fig. 7(c)]. In this way, switching from positive to negative or from negative to positive local equilibrium occurs in succession along the network. If U_e is smaller than U_i, opposite switching occurs; that is u_{ek} , then as a result u_{ik}, goes to a negative value, then u_{ek-1} and u_{ik-1} go to positive values and so on. The period of the traveling wave mode is much longer than that of the oscillation of the oscillator unit. It is approximately proportional to the number of oscillators.

5.1 Ring structure

For the ring structure composed of odd (even) number of oscillators, the switching described above at odd (even) number of locations gives a periodic solution. The switching rotates through the network. In other words, it is considered that traveling waves are propagated along the oscillators. Fig. 8 shows the examples of the oscillatory solutions of the traveling wave mode in the network containing 11 oscillators. There are two patterns of the traveling mode; one is the pattern in which the switching is completed in a short period [Fig. 8(a)] and the other is the pattern in which the switching occurs with a number of cycles of transient oscillation [Fig. 8(b)]. We call the former one traveling wave mode I and the latter traveling wave mode II. Fig. 9 shows three solutions of

traveling wave mode I in the network composed of 12 oscillators.

5.2 Linear structure

In the linear structure, the waveforms of the potentials of the neurons in the oscillators are not the same since the oscillators at the both ends receive inhibition only from one side, so that the multi-phase mode does not exist. However, you can generate the traveling wave mode in which the switching goes back and forth repeatedly from one end to the other. The traveling wave mode can occur with suitable tonic inputs to the oscillators at the both ends and proper initial conditions to the membrane potentials for the switching. Fig. 10 shows the traveling wave mode I and II in the network of the linear structure. The number of oscillators N is 11 and constant input -1.36 is given to u_{e1} and 1.36 to u_{e11}.

In this way, the traveling wave mode can occur not only in the ring structure but also in the linear structure. It is reasonable to consider that the traveling wave mode is characteristic to the chained structure of oscillators. These results are similar to the firing modes in reciprocal inhibition neural networks composed of a number of neurons [7,8].

6. EXISTENCE REGIONS AND TRANSITIONS OF OSCILLATORY SOLUTIONS

We obtained the existence regions of oscillatory solutions of multi-phase mode, traveling wave mode and other modes in a network of ring structure with respect to the coupling coefficient c_O between adjacent oscillators by numerical analysis employing Poincaré map [13]. First, we obtained a fixed point of each periodic solution by Newton's method. Then, we calculated the characteristic multipliers of the solution with different values of c_O and examined its stability and bifurcation from it. We also obtained the initial conditions for generation of the traveling mode among multistable solutions at a certain coupling coefficient. The mode transition with bifurcation was studied by computer simulation.

6.1 Existence regions

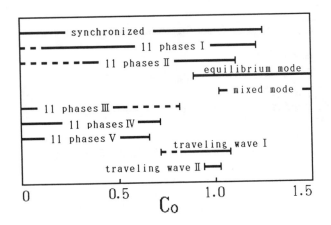

Fig. 11 Existing regions of oscillatory modes in the ring strcture. N=11.

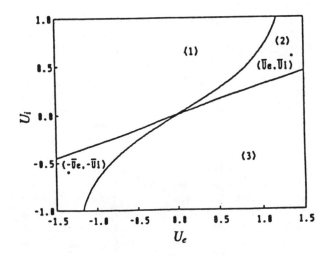

Fig. 12 Initial conditions and generation of traveling wave mode in the ring structure. N=11.

Fig. 11 shows the existence regions of oscillatory modes and equilibrium mode with respect to the coupling coefficient c_O in the ring network composed of 11 oscillators. There are a number of solutions of equilibrium mode with different initial conditions. In a solution of equilibrium mode, the membrane potential of each neurons has a stable equilibrium which differs depending on oscillators. Mixed mode is a kind of oscillatory solutions. The waveforms of the oscillation differ in different oscillators. The number attached to 11 phase mode corresponds to the absolute value of j in (22). The solid lines in the figure denote the regions where the stable periodic solutions exist. The dashed lines denote the existence regions for quasi-periodic solutions that emerge by Hoph bifurcation from the periodic solutions. The region for the traveling wave mode II is included by that for the traveling wave mode I.

6.2 Initial conditions and generation of oscillatory solutions of traveling wave mode

As shown in Fig. 11, the regions of oscillatory solutions overlap with each other. For an identical value of coupling coefficient c_O, a certain number of periodic solutions exist stably. Which solution comes out depends on the initial conditions of the network. It is extraordinarily troublesome to elucidate completely the relation between the initial conditions and solutions because the dimension of the state space is $2N$ and the relation is very complicated. We are particularly interested in whether the traveling wave mode I and II can occur with easy setting of initial conditions. Therefore, we investigated the generation of the traveling wave mode I and II with limited initial conditions, in which only 2 state variables, the membrane potentials of the neurons in oscillator 1, were varied and the rest of the state variables are set to the local equilibrium in which every other oscillator keeps the same values of membrane potentials, positive for one group and negative for the other.

Fig. 12 shows the result of computer simulation when N=11. The initial values of membrane potentials except those in oscillator 1 are given as

$$u_{r3} = u_{r5} = u_{r7} = u_{r9} = u_{r11} = \overline{U}_r,$$
$$u_{r2} = u_{r4} = u_{r6} = u_{r8} = u_{r10} = -\overline{U}_r$$
$$(r = e \text{ or } i),$$

where

$$\overline{U}_e = 1.356 \text{ and } \overline{U}_i = 0.5956.$$

Initial values $u_{e1}(0) = U_e$ and $u_{i1}(0) = U_i$ are varied. For the initial conditions in region (1), the traveling wave mode I occurs in which the wave is propagated in order of oscillator 1, 3, 5, ... For region (3), also traveling wave mode I occurs, but the order of wave propagation is opposite, oscillator 1,10,8, ... For region (2), traveling wave mode II occurs. In this way, the traveling wave mode can occur with easy setting of initial conditions among multi-stable solutions.

6.3 Transitions of oscillatory solutions

It is also our great concern whether the traveling wave mode can occur by transitions from other modes when the coupling coefficient of oscillators are varied beyond the

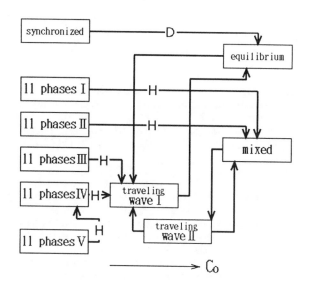

Fig. 13 Mode transitions in the ring structure. $N=11$.

existing regions of those modes. Fig. 13 shows the mode transition obtained by computer simulation when $N=11$. Transition with Hoph bifurcation is denoted by simbol H and transition with D-type of branching by symbol D. D-type of branching occurs in degenerated systems. It occurs in the present model because the oscillators are identical and their coupling is uniform. Traveling wave mode I occurs by transition from 11 phases IV when the coupling coefficient c_o increases and from equilibrium mode when c_o decreases. Traveling wave mode II occurs by transition from mixed mode when c_o decreases.

7. CONCLUSIONS

In this paper, we proposed a chained neural oscillator network model for a mechanism of rhythm generation in biological neural networks and showed generation of not only well-known multi-phase mode but also traveling wave mode as multi-stable oscillatory solutions by numerical analysis employing Poincare map. The period of the traveling wave mode is much longer than that of the oscillation of the oscillator unit. It is approximately proportional to the number of oscillators. The traveling wave mode is classified in two categories. One of them has a long transient period with a number of cycles of oscillation in switching from one local equilibrium to the other. These results are similar to the firing modes in reciprocal inhibition neural networks composed of a number of neurons. The traveling wave mode might exist in various chained oscillator networks. It has been found out that the traveling wave mode occurs by transitions from other modes. The initial conditions which bring the generation of the traveling wave mode have also been obtained. The traveling wave mode in the ring networks composed of even number of oscillators and in the linear networks is open to future analysis.

In the present work, the mutual coupling of oscillators is confined to be uniform and only for nearest neighbors. The oscillators are identical. The traveling wave mode will occur also in more complicated networks since the solutions have a certain measure of existence regions for the coupling coefficient and the traveling wave mode occurs due to the local coupling properties. More detailed analysis of such cases is necessary in the future.

ACKNOWLEDGMENTS

We are grateful to Prof. H. Kawakami and Dr. T. Yoshinaga for their helpful advice.

This work is partly supported by Grant-in-Aid for Science Research of Ministry of Education, Japan, No. 03805028.

REFERENCES

[1] A. H. Cohen, S. Rossignol and S. Grillner, Eds. *Neural control of rhythmic movements in vertebrates*, John Wiley & Sons, New York, 1988.

[2] J. W. Jacklet, Ed., *Neuronal and cellular oscillators*, Marcel Dekker, New York, 1989.

[3] R. F. Reiss, "A theory and simulation of rhythmic behavior due to reciprocal inhibition in small nerve nets," *Proc. 1962 AFIPS Spring Joint Computer Conference*, pp. 171-193, 1962.

[4] R. Suzuki, I. Katsuno and K. Matano, "Dynamics of 'Neuron Ring', Computer simulation of central nervous system of starfish," *Kybernetik*, vol. 8, pp. 39-45, 1971.

[5] A. I. Selverston, "A consideration of invertebrate central pattern generators as computational data bases," *Neural Networks*, vol. 1, pp. 109-117, 1988.

[6] P. A. Getting, "Reconstruction of small neural networks," in *Methods in Neuronal Modeling*, C. Koch and I. Segev Eds., The MIT Press, Cambridge, 1989, pp. 171-194.

[7] H. Nagashino, H. Tamura and T. Ushita, "Firing modes in reciprocal inhibitory neural networks and their analysis," *Electronics and Communications in Japan*, vol. 61, pp. 27-35, 1978.

[8] H. Nagashino, H. Tamura and T. Ushita, "Existence and control of rhythmic activities in reciprocal inhibition neural networks," *Trans. IECE Japan*, vol. E62, pp. 768-774, 1979.

[9] D. A. Linkens, "Analytical solution of a large number of mutually coupled nearly sinusoidal oscillators," *IEEE Trans. Circuits and Systems*, vol. CAS-21, pp. 294-300, 1974.

[10] T. Endo and S. Mori, "Mode analysis of a ring of a large number of mutually coupled van der Pol oscillators," *IEEE Trans. Circuits and Systems*, vol. CAS-25, pp. 7-18, 1978.

[11] S. M. Ahn,. and W. J. Freeman, "Steady -state and limit cycle activity of mass of mass of neurons forming simple feedback loops (I): Lumped circuit model," *Kybernetik*, Vol. 16, pp. 87-91, 1974.

[12] P. A. Getting, "Emerging principles govering the operation of neural networks", in *Annual Review of Neuroscience*, vol. 12, W. M. Cowan, et al. eds., Annual Reviews Inc., Palo Alto, 1989, pp. 185-204.

[13] H. Kawakami and K. Kobayashi, "A computation of periodic solutions of nonlinear autonomous systems," *Proc. 1979 Int. Sym. Circuits and Systems*, pp. 44-45, 1979.

IMAGE COMPRESSION USING STOCHASTIC NEURAL NETWORKS

Ying Liu
Dept. of Math. and Computer Science
Savannah State College
Savannah, Georgia 31404

ABSTRACT

In this paper, we study image compression using stochastic artificial neural networks (SANN). The idea is to store an image in a stable distribution of a stochastic neural network. Given an input image $f \in F$, one can find a SANN $t \in T$ such that the equilibrium distribution this SANN is the given image f. Therefore, the input image, f, is encoded into a specification of a SANN, t. This mapping from F (image space) to T (parameter space of SANN) defines SANN transformation. We show that the compression ratio R of SANN transformation is

$$ R = O(\frac{n}{K(\log n)^2}) $$

where n is the number of pixels. To complete a SANN transformation, we have to solve an SANN equations. We will present two SANN equations. The solution of SANN is briefly discussed.

1. INTRODUCTION

In this paper, we study image compression using stochastic artificial neural network (SANN). Image compression has drawn intensive attention recently. There are two basic approach, transform coding and predictive coding [1]. In the predictive coding, redundancy in the image is exploited and used to compress data. One of the recent development is Fractal theory[2], which uses the idea of storing data in stable configuration of dynamical systems. Storing information in stable configuration of dynamical systems is a profound idea which has a lot of applications. The idea was introduced by Hopfield in the Hopfield model [3] and Barnsley in the fractal theory [2].

There are many generalizations of image compression using stable configuration of dynamical systems. Examples includes dynamical systems with internal controls [4], dynamical systems other than Barnsley's IFS[5]. Pattern recognition is another field where the idea of using stable configurations of dynamical systems are used [1,6,7]. There are many applications of the idea of using stable configurations of dynamical systems[9].

The idea of storing images in stable configurations of deterministic dynamical systems can be generalized to storing images in stable distributions of stochastic dynamical systems. Boltzmann machine is an example of using the stable distributions of stochastic dynamical systems [10]. In reference [2], the idea of storing images in stable distributions of probabilistic IFS is used, but not mentioned. It is also worthwhile to mention that the statistical physics (already 100 year old) deals with the problems of finding the invariant distributions from the specification of a dynamical systems, which are inverse of our problems. In this paper, we will use the idea of storing images in stable distributions of dynamical systems.

Let an image have $n = 2^N$ pixels. Then we will use a SANN with N neurons. Each configuration of the SANN corresponds one pixel in the images. The SANN defines a Markov chain. Each configuration of the SANN is a state of the Markov chain. Because each Markov chain possesses an invariant distribution, a SANN has a stable distribution.

An image can be decomposed into a norm and a unit vector. The unit vector can be considered as a stable distribution of a SANN. Let F be the set of all images. Let T be the parameter space of a family of SANN. Given an input image $f \in F$, one can find a SANN such that the equilibrium distribution this SANN is the given image f. Therefore, the input image, f, is encoded into a specification of a SANN. We call the mapping from F to T the SANN transformation, standing for transformation of stochastic artificial neural network.

In this paper, we will introduce the idea of storing information in stable distributions of stochastic dynamical systems. Specially, we will use SANN to encode images. This defines SANN transformation. We will show that the data compression ratios of the SANN transformation is

$$R = O(\frac{n}{K(\log n)^2})$$

To complete a SANN transformation, we have to solve an SANN equations. We will derive two SANN equations and briefly discuss the solutions.

Section 2 introduces SANN. Section 3 briefly discusses the limiting behavior of SANN. Section 4 presents the basic idea of image encoding: to store an image in an stable distribution of a SANN. In section 5, we derive the SANN equations and several related theorems. In section 6, we will discuss how to solve the SANN equation. An example will be given in section 7.

2. STOCHASTIC NEURAL NETWORKS

An example of stochastic neural network is the Boltzmann machine[10]. In this paper, we will use a different type stochastic neural networks. For the purpose of introducing our notations, we will first introduce the definition of artificial neural network(ANN). Then we will define SANN.

Definition: A binary artificial neural network (ANN) is

$$C = \{X, \Sigma\},$$

where X is a set of N neurons and the ith neuron can be in one of two states 1 or 0. The mapping rule is

$$\Sigma = w_1 = \{ M, T, g \}$$

Here, (1) M is an NxN real valued, zero-diagonal matrix, and M_{ij} is the strength of the synaptic connection from neuron j to neuron i; (2) T is an Nx1 matrix and t_i is the threshold voltage of the ith neuron; and (3) g defines the action of each neuron. For example, let g = sgn, then

$$u_i = sgn \left(\sum M_{ij}u_j - t_i \right).$$

SANN have a set of synaptic connection matrices. At each time step, only one of the connection matrix is choosing. The probability of choosing the mapping w_i is p_i.

Definition The stochastic Artificial Neural Network (SANN) is

$$C = \{X, \Sigma\},$$

where X is a set of N neurons and the ith neuron can be in one of two states 1 or 0. The mapping rule is

$$\Sigma = \{ (w_i, p_i), i=1,2,3 \ldots K \}$$

$$\sum p_i = 1.$$

Here, w_i are normal neural network mappings and p_i is the probability to choose the mapping w_i. Each time only one mapping is chosen.

3. INVARIANT DISTRIBUTION OF STOCHASTIC NEURAL NETWORKS

Let $P = \{ p_{ij} \}$ be a stochastic matrix. In an irreducible finite Markov chain, the limits[8]

$$u_k = \lim p_{jk}^{(n)} \qquad n \longrightarrow \infty$$

exist and are independent of the initial state j. In other words, one can start with any initial state j, after infinite steps, the probability of being in state k is always the same. Furthermore

$$\sum u_k = 1$$

$$u_j = \sum_i u_i p_{ij} \quad or \quad U = P^T U$$

where P^T stands for transpose of P.

Whatever the initial distribution, the probability of the state k is u_k. The initial distribution will be converted to a stationary distribution, the invariant distribution.

Example Let the initial distribution of a markov chain be

$$a_k^{(0)} = a_k.$$

After one step, the distribution is

$$a_k^{(1)} = \sum_j a_j p_{jk}.$$

After n steps

1559

$$a_K^{(n)} = \sum_j a_j p_{jk}^{(n)}.$$

After infinite steps, the distribution is the invariant distribution.

The significance of the stationary distribution becomes apparent if we image a large number of processors simulate a Markov chain simultaneously. To be specific, consider N processors simulating independently. At the nth step, the expected number of processors in state k equals $N a_k^{(n)}$ which tends to $N u_k$. After a sufficient long time, the distribution will be approximately invariant and the number of processors in each state reaches equilibrium.

Note that if k is a transient state, $u_k = 0$. In other words, $u_k > 0$ implies that k is persistent state for a finite Markov chain.

Let x_i, i = 1, 2, ..., N be neuron states. The vector

$$X = \{x_1, x_2, \ldots, x_n\}$$

is called the configuration of the SANN. The configuration transition is mathematically described by a Markov chain with 2^n configurations $x \in X$. When all the configurations are connected, it forms a Markov chain, having a invariant distribution. Whatever initial configuration of SANN starts from, the probability distribution converge to the invariant distribution $u(x)$. The state x appears with relative frequency $u(x)$ over long period of time.

The SANN defines a Markov chain. Each configuration of the SANN is a state of the Markov chain. The state of a Finite Markov chain is divided into Persistent and transient. Because each Markov chain possesses an invariant distribution, the SANN has a stable distribution.

4. IMAGE ENCODING USING STOCHASTIC NEURAL NETWORKS

In this section, we introduce the basic idea of image encoding: storing an image in a stable distribution of a stochastic dynamical systems.

An irreducible finite chain possesses a stationary distribution. This invariant distribution can be considered as an image. Image digitization refers to the process of converting a function f(x,y) into a set of integers:

$$x = 0, 1, 2, \ldots, M;$$

$$y = 0, 1, 2, \ldots, N;$$

$$f(x,y) \in \{0, 1, 2, \ldots, G, \quad , G > 1)\}$$

For simplicity, in the following discussion we use one dimensional image. For two dimensional case, we can simply add one more index.

For an image f(x), we can construct the L^p (p=1) norm and a unit vector:

$$||f(x)|| = \sum_x f(x)$$

$$f(x) = ||f(x)|| \, u(x)$$

$$u(x) = \frac{f(x)}{||f(x)||}$$

The unit vector u(x) can be considered as an invariant distribution of a chain.

Let an image have NxM pixels. Each pixel is a state in a Markov chain. Those pixel having zero intensities, f(x) = 0, are transient states. An irreducible image can be decomposed into norm and unit vector. The unit vector can be considered as an invariant distribution of a Markov chain.

Definition: Let each of NxM pixels be a state of a Markov chain. Then the invariant distributions of irreducible subchains, multiplied by proper norms, define an image. In particular, if the set of all NxM states form a irreducible chain, an image is the invariant distribution of the chain multiplied by a constant.

Example Let a stochastic matrix be

$$\begin{pmatrix} p_{00} & p_{01} & 0 & 0 \\ p_{10} & P_{11} & p_{12} & 0 \\ 0 & p_{21} & p_{22} & p_{23} \\ 0 & 0 & p_{32} & P_{33} \end{pmatrix}$$

Then the stationary distribution is [8]

$$u_0 = (1 + \frac{p_{01}}{p_{10}} + \frac{p_{01}p_{12}}{p_{10}p_{21}} + \frac{p_{01}p_{12}p_{23}}{p_{10}p_{21}p_{32}})^{-1}$$

$$u_1 = \frac{p_{01}}{p_{10}}u_0 \qquad u_2 = \frac{p_{01}p_{12}}{p_{10}p_{21}}u_0$$

$$u_3 = \frac{p_{01}p_{12}p_{23}}{p_{10}p_{21}p_{32}}u_0$$

Let f be a norm, according to above definition,

$$f(u_0 \quad u_1 \quad u_2 \quad u_3)$$

is an image with four pixels.

Example Let an image have 10 pixels. Let a stochastic matrix be

state j	state k	p_{jk}
1	2	1/2
1	4	1/2
2	3	1
3	7	1
4	3	1
5	6	1
6	5	1
7	1	1
8	7	1
9	1	1/2
9	2	1/2
10	3	1

Apparently, { 5, 6 } forms a closed set, { 1, 2, 3, 4, 7 } forms a closed set. State 8, 9, 10 are transient. The distribution for {5,6} is uniform. The distribution for {1,2,3,4,7} can be determined as follows: There are two closed loops: {1->2->3->7->1} and {1->4->3->7->1} with equal probabilities. Therefore, the probabilities for state 1, 3, 7 are the same. The probabilities for 2, 4 are one half of that for state 1. This gives $u_1 = 1/4$ and $u_2 = 1/8$. Finally, the image defined by the above chain is

$$(\frac{a}{4}, \frac{a}{8}, \frac{a}{4}, \frac{a}{8}, \frac{b}{2}, \frac{b}{2}, \frac{a}{4}, 0, 0, 0)$$

where a and b are the two norms.

Let an image have $n = 2^N$ pixels. Then the SANN which encode the image has N neurons. Each configuration of the SANN corresponds one pixel in the images. A configuration vector $x \in X$ is a position of a pixel.

The unit vector can be considered as a stable distribution of a SANN. Let F be the set of all images. Let T be the parameter space of a family of SANN. Given an input image $f \in F$, one can find a SANN such that the equilibrium distribution this SANN is the given image f. Therefore, the input image, f, is encoded into a specification of a SANN. We call the mapping from F to T as SANN transformation, standing for transformation of stochastic artificial neural network.

The data compression ratios can be estimated as follows., There are $n = 2^N$ bytes for specifying an image, assuming each pixel has 256 intensities. There are $O(N^2)$ parameters for each synaptic transition matrix and there are K of them. Therefore,

Theorem The compression ratio R for SANN transformation is

$$R = O(\frac{n}{K(\log n)^2})$$

Example Let
(1) an image has 1K by 1K pixels;
(2) each pixels have 256 intensities;
(3) each elements of connection matrix be specified by two bytes;
(4) K = 10,
the data compression ratio is above 200.

5. SANN EQUATIONS

A SANN defines a SANN transformation. To encode an image by the transformation, we have to solve an SANN equations. In this section, we will present the SANN equations. Let T be the parameter space of a family of SANN. Then $t \in T$ is a SANN. Let F be the image space. Then $f \in F$ is an image. Let the distance between the image f and f' be d(f,f').

Given an input image $f \in F$, one can find a SANN such that the equilibrium distribution of this SANN is the given image f, that is, the distance between the given image f and the invariant distribution of t is zero:

$$d(f, u(t)) = 0.$$

Therefore, the input image, f, is encoded into a specification of a SANN, t. The above equation is call the first SANN equation.

Let P be the stochastic transition matrix for a Markov chain. Let f_j be the invariant distribution. Then

$$f_j = f_i P_{ij}$$

Let $t \in T$ be an SANN, then t defines a stochastic matrix P(t). When the SANN reaches its invariant distribution, it will remain there forever. This generate the second SANN equation

$$d(f, P^T(t)f) = 0.$$

The above equation can be rewritten as

$$f(j) = f(i) P(i,j),$$

where f(i) is the array of pixel intensities of the given image f and P is a matrix defined as follows:

$$P(i,j) = p_k , \text{ if } w_k(i) = j,$$
$$k = 1,2,3 \ldots K;$$

$$P(i,j) = 0, \text{ otherwise}$$

Here p_k is the probability defined in a SANN, w_k is the mapping of the neural network using rule w_k, and i, j are positions of pixels. In the above equation, each of the w_k is specified by a set of free parameters. P is a sparse matrix with only K elements in each row:

$$P(i,j) = \sum_k p_k \, \delta_{i,w_k(i)}$$

From which,

$$f(j) = \sum_{k=1}^{K} f(i) p_k \, \delta_{i,w_k(i)}$$

Here w_k are functions of a set of free parameters $t \in T$. This is another form of the second SANN equation.

In the image encoding problem, f(i) are given and $t \in T$ is the unknown point. In the image decoding problem, $t \in T$ is given and $f \in F$ is the unknown image. In either case, the above equation need to be solved. Note that in the decoding case, the equation is linear for f(i).

6. SOLVING SANN EQUATIONS

There are two SANN equations. The first equation requires to generate the invariant distribution u(x) from SANN and then compare it with the given image f(x). The second equation requires f(x) be transformed by neural network mapping once. Therefore, it is much fast to solve the second SANN equation than the first one.

Local search algorithm can be used for solving SANN equation. The local search approach is based on trial and error. It starts at an initial point in T and searches for a better solution within its neighborhoods. The algorithm halts when no further improvement can be made and a local optimum is reached. The success of the local search is dependent upon the initial point or points since it determines the neighborhood that will be searched.

Another way to search a better point in the parameter space is given as follows. First of all, the gradient of D(t) = d(f, f P(t)) is evaluated. The negative of the gradient gives the direction of the steepest descent. The scale of progress can be either fixed or decreased as approaching local minima.

7. AN EXAMPLE

Because of limited space, we will present a text book example. Assume that an image has 8 pixels, therefore, the SANN have three neurons. For simplicity, we assume the thresholds of all neurons are 0. Let two connection matrices be:

$$M_1 = \begin{pmatrix} 0 & -1 & 2 \\ -1 & 0 & -1 \\ 2 & -1 & 0 \end{pmatrix}$$

$$M_2 = \begin{pmatrix} 0 & 1 & -2 \\ 1 & 0 & 1 \\ -2 & 1 & 0 \end{pmatrix}$$

with probabilities p_1 and p_2. The configurations of the network is 000 = 0, 001 = 1, ..., 111 = 7. The stochastic connection matrix defined by the SANN

$$P(i,j) = \sum_k p_k \, \delta_{i,w_k(i)}$$

is

i	j	P(i,j)
0	0	1
1	3	p1
1	5	p2
2	2	p2
2	7	p1
3	3	p1
3	4	p2
4	5	p2
4	6	p1
5	2	p1
5	5	p2
6	1	p2
6	6	p1
7	2	p1
7	5	p2

This stochastic transition matrix will define an image. State set { 0 } is a closed set, which will be ignored here. The image defined can be obtained as follows. There are two loops in the configuration space of the SANN: 2->7->5->2 and 1->3->4->6->1. However, the second loop can transit to the first one while the first can not transit to the second. Therefore, state 1, 3, 4, and 6 are transient and the set {2,5,7} is a closed set. The distribution among states 2, 5, and 7 can be determined by the following stochastic transition matrix:

$$(x_2 \ x_5 \ x_7) =$$

$$(x_2 \ x_5 \ x_7) \begin{pmatrix} p_2 & 0 & p_2 \\ p_1 & p_2 & 0 \\ p_1 & p_2 & 0 \end{pmatrix}$$

This generate the distribution of $(1/2, p_2/2, p_1/2)$. Therefore, this SANN defines the image

f $(0,0, \ 1/2,0, \ 0, p_2/2, \ 0, \ p_1/2 \ )$

where f is the norm of the image.

The inverse problem (image encoding) is that given an image, find the SANN specification. For example, let an image with 8 pixels and 256 intensities be

$(0,0, \ 50,0, \ 0,20, \ 0,30)$

then the SANN specification is two transition matrix M_1, M_2 with p1 = 3/5, p2 = 2/5, and the norm is f = 100.

As stated by the theorem, we expect this scheme to have very high data compression ratio.

8. CONCLUSION

In this paper, we have introduced stochastic artificial neural network (SANN) and presented an image encoding idea: storing an image in an stable distribution of a SANN. We have derived the SANN equations and briefly discussed how to solve the SANN equation. SANN transformation are expected to give very high data compression ratio, as stated in the theorem.

[1] Bart Kosko, Neural Networks and Fuzzy Systems, Prentice hall, 1991.

[2] M.F. Barnsley, Fractals Everywhere, Academic Press, 1988.

[3] J.J. Hopfield, "Neurons with graded response have collective computation properties like those of two-state neurons," Proc. Nal. Academy of science, 81, May 1984, pp. 3088-92.

[4] Ying Liu and Hede Ma, " ω-Orbit Finite Automata for Data compression," Proceeding of Data Compression Conference '91, IEEE Computer Press, Snowbird, Utah, 166 - 175, April, 1991.

[5] Ying Liu and Hede Ma, "Comparison between image analysis using class 2 and class 3 dynamical systems," Proc SPIE 1657, San Jose, CA., pp. 461 - 475, February, 1992.

[6] Ying Liu and Hede Ma, "Pattern recognition using ω-Orbit Finite Automata," Visual communication and image processing '91: Image processing, K. H. Tzao, T. Koga, Editor, Proc SPIE 1606, Boston, pp. 226 - 240, November, 1991.

[7] Ying Liu, "Two pattern recognition algorithm using dynamical systems," Proc. of IROS and IEEE Fifth Int'l Conf. on Intelligent Robots and Systems, pp. 1363 - 1271, July, 1992.

[8] W. Feller, An introduction to probability theory and its application, John Wiley and Sons, 1968.

[9] Ying Liu, " Fractal, neural networks, cellular automata, formal languages and coding theory," To appear Proc. of IEEE SMC '92.

[10] See for example, S. Amary, K. Kurata, and H. Nagaoka, "Information Geometry of Boltzmann machines," IEEE Trans., Neural Network, Vol. 3, No.2, pp. 260 - 271, 1992.

Employing Shape to Aid Magnetic Resonance Brain Segmentation

Andrew J. Worth and David N. Kennedy

Center for Morphometric Analysis, Neuroscience Center, Massachusetts
General Hospital-East, Building 149, 13th St., Charlestown, MA 02129.

Abstract— As part of an ongoing project for automatic segmentation of magnetic resonance (MR) brain images, the use of a psychophysically and neuropsychologically motivated representation of shape is explored. Shapes are recognized and learned in a translation and scale invariant manner and then used to aid segmentation. Object recognition is achieved after training the system to associate observed shapes and their relative locations with an object defined by a human expert. This paper describes the inspiration and current implementation of a Shape Recognition Module and some preliminary results.

I. INTRODUCTION

Magnetic Resonance Imaging (MRI) is a non-invasive technique that provides an unequaled view of the anatomic configuration of the living human brain. For Magnetic Resonance (MR) brain slice images, segmentation refers to the pixel by pixel labeling of regions as grey matter, white matter, and other types of tissues or fluids. At a higher level these regions can be labeled as anatomical structures and then grouped across slices to give three-dimensional descriptions of these structures. An examination of the current literature on segmentation and our own initial research shows that the segmentation problem cannot be completely automated using standard segmentation techniques[1, 2].

Since segmentation is an important basic step in image processing, a great deal of research is done in this area. There are, however, a number of problems that have yet to be fully addressed. Any system that relies on the stability or constancy of the intensity will have problems because intensity is not an absolute measure (with MRI and most other imaging techniques as well). Also, due to partial volume blurring, not all intensity based borders are sharp edges. In fact, as pointed out by Neumann and Ottenberg [3], step edges are very rare in real image data. A problem that is beyond all low-level segmentation schemes is that not all anatomic borders are intensity based borders. For example, in a brain image there is no intensity edge dividing the left and right cerebral hemispheres at the corpus callosum. A similar problem arises when portions of an edge are lost due to low resolution, e.g. between the caudate and the putamen. An additional unfortunate fact about many segmentation systems is that in order to achieve success, the method must often be overly domain specific. Specialized tricks are necessary to obtain the proper segmentation for a given task and this lack of generalizability forces each new task to be dealt with separately.

The conclusion that many researchers reach is that there is a need for higher-level or a-priori information to help with segmentation and image analysis tasks [1, 4, 5, 6, 7, 8, 9]. Our approach is to represent and use shape as a general method of incorporating application specific knowledge to aid segmentation. The exact shapes of objects have to be learned for each particular application, but the general use of shape is the same.

The purpose of this work is to investigate how the notion of "shape" can be used to aid MR brain image segmentation. Providing expectations of the shapes of objects to be recognized is a general way to include high-level domain specific knowledge in the segmentation task. We follow the neural network approach (the consideration of psychophysical and neuroanatomical constraints) because inspiration for computational mechanisms can be obtained by examining how people solve the problem. The human expert knows the topology of the brain and has expectations regarding the topography of the brain. That is to say, the expert knows the various parts of the brain, what they look like and where they are in relation to one another.

This paper presents initial work on the use of shape to aid MR brain segmentation. The following section presents the motivation and major properties of the Shape Recognition Module. It also describes the operation of this module and of the whole segmentation system. Finally, initial results of the system and its most difficult problems are discussed.

II. Shape Recognition Module

A. Motivation

It appears that people are not sensitive to continuous metric variations in shape [10, 11]. Therefore, the emphasis in the Shape Recognition Module (SRM) is not an exact representation of shape, but a representation of the relations of features that make up a shape. This constraint should enable flexible matching between inputs and stored shapes.

The SRM was originally inspired by consideration of the visual attention literature (e.g. [12, 13, 14], for a somewhat dated review, see [15]). This lead to the notion that an object could be represented by local collections of features linked together using attention across spatial scales. The features (both locally and across scales) could be learned and processed using attentional gating. The resulting model turned out to be surprisingly similar to that described by Nakayama [16].

The Shape Recognition Module is derived from the outline of a Shape Recognition Model given in [17]. The motivation for the use of shape as domain specific knowledge to aid the MR brain segmentation process comes from the fact that human experts know what the shape of the brain is and use it when performing the segmentation [18, 19]. Shape can be used to aid MR brain segmentation because structures of the brain the have characteristic shapes and because shapes that make up the brain are found at characteristic locations relative to each other. The location of one region of the brain provides information as to the location of other brain regions. For example, one ventricle is usually located at a certain place with respect to the other ventricle. Once one ventricle is found, the other can be expected to be found accordingly. Also, large regions are made up of smaller regions: the right cerebral hemisphere is usually found at a given location inside the head.

B. Operational Overview

The method used in the SRM is based on the following principles, 1) shapes are composed of features which are generated by patterns of gray-scale intensities in the original image, 2) characteristic shapes and their relative locations can be detected and these shapes can be grouped into objects, 3) objects can be recognized as specific anatomical brain regions by comparing their constituent features with the features of known objects, and 4) Features can be localized so that for a given anatomical brain region, the corresponding location in the original brain image can be segmented and labeled. These principles lead to the four basic tasks of the SRM: 1) Detect features at all spatial scales and at all locations, 2) Recognize collections of these features as salient shapes at various scales and locations, 3) Recognize that a subset of this collection of shapes be-

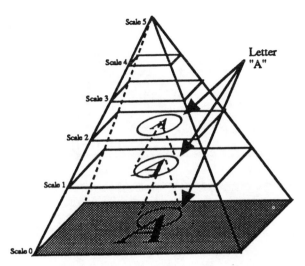

Figure 1: The structure of the Shape Recognition Module. An object (e.g. the letter "A") is a collection of shapes at various scales and their relative locations to each other. Shapes are groups of particular instances of features.

longs to a known object, and 4) Provide an expectation of the location of that object.

C. The Complete Segmentation System

In the complete segmentation system, the purpose of the SRM is to aid the Grey-White Decision Network (GWDN) in segmenting and labeling previously learned objects. The GWDN is described in [2, 17, 20]. Briefly, the GWDN segments the brain slice image by making pixel-by-pixel decisions considering MR signal intensity, neighboring decisions, and edge information. Grossberg and Mingolla's [21] Boundary Contour System (BCS) is used to extract edges from the original image. In short, in the BCS an edge is a relatively large change in intensity at any orientation that has both short and long-range support in the image. The details of operation of the BCS as an edge detector for MR Brain images is described in [22].

The SRM aids the GWDN by pointing out the locations of recognized shapes in the original image. The SRM sends "expectation" signals to the GWDN that indicate where the object is expected to be found. This expectation image is used as an additional constraint in the GWDN segmentation process: segmentation is performed on only the part of the original image which is expected to be part of the given anatomical region.

D. SRM Definitions

We define an anatomical region of interest in an MR brain image (such as a section of the cerebral cortex, the thalamus, or a ventricle) as an *object*. Objects are then defined in terms of *shapes* which are defined as collections of *features*. Features such as edges and bright or dark colored

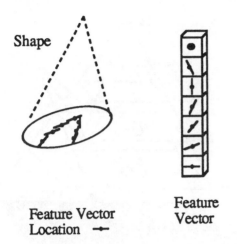

Figure 2: Features are grouped into vectors that are detected at each location. Currently, features consist of intensity and oriented edges.

blobs are obtained more or less directly from the raw MR image at multiple spatial scales. These definitions are illustrated in Fig. 1 and Fig. 2. Note that each level of the multi-resolution pyramid is a multi-valued image representing the response of feature detectors at every location.

A multi-resolution pyramid scheme is used to provide both adequate recognition and also adequate localization [23]. The largest scale features are not precisely located on the original image, but they provide the general shape of the image that is likely to be similar across different brain images. This allows some generalization in matching input shapes to stored shapes. The smallest scale features can be precisely located on the original image, but are likely to vary considerably across images. Therefore, the SRM uses the general (large scale) shapes to recognize the image and the precise (small scale) shapes to localize the anatomical region of interest.

A shape is defined as a collection of *salient* features such as blobs and edges in a small area at a given spatial scale. Salient means that these features are significant in some way: high-contrast, high-curvature, or any stimulus that "pops out" preattentively as in Treisman and Gelade's [12] parallel feature detection stage. A certain number of the most salient pixels at one spatial scale are used to determine the location of the attended area for a shape at the next smaller spatial scale. The shape at the smaller spatial scale is then represented by a small array of feature vectors (Nakayama's "icon") coinciding in location with the salient pixel at the next larger spatial scales.

An object is defined as the collection of learned shapes at the relative locations and scales where they were detected. The top-most shape in an object may be detected

or recognized at any level of the feature pyramid. Each feature of this highest level shape can be learned as its own shape at the next lower level. Thus, each shape can be composed of lower-level shapes and can also be a part of a higher-level shape. The largest spatial scale image at the top of the pyramid is the size of a single shape.

E. How it works

First, the original image is downsampled (shrunken) and features are extracted at multiple spatial scales. After this, attention is focused on various scales and locations in the pyramid to recognize and learn objects. A segmentation of an object that was done by a human expert is used to teach the SRM which collections of features should be grouped into shapes and which of these shapes should be grouped into an object. When the entire pyramid has been examined, the object of interest is localized and the low-level pixel classification into grey, white, and other matter is performed at only the locations of the features that belong to the object. Each of these steps in described in more detail in the paragraphs that follow.

Feature Extraction The Boundary Contour System (BCS) is responsible for extracting features at multiple spatial scales. The type of low-level features extracted at this stage of the model can include: edges, line terminations, line junctions, etc. Higher-level features such as good continuations, closure, pragnanz, symmetry (i.e. the Gestalt grouping laws) should also be considered here.

Attention The SRM looks for salient features at all spatial locations and scales in parallel. The subsequent serial matching process is then guided by attention in two ways; top-down, and bottom-up. In the bottom-up search for salient shapes, the SRM attempts to match each shape at potentially every scale and location. However, this search is driven and limited by the salience of the features. Attention is only focused on a given location and scale if there is the possibility of a salient shape at that location. For example, if there is no large change in contrast in the image at a given location (i.e. nothing salient at that location), there is no attempt to match any shape at that location.

The second kind of attention is invoked if a partially detected object requires that a given shape be present at a given location. Top-down attention is focused on the expected location to search for the expected shape. For example, to be sure that the object being viewed is the letter "A", after detecting the general shape of the letter at a high level, expectations may be generated to look for the cross-bar in the middle of the "A" at a lower level. For a MR brain image, the recognition of the shape of the left ventricle can indicate that the object is the left cerebral hemisphere. This leads to expectations of gyri and sulci with certain shapes.

Recognition Since there are two types of attention, there must be some way of deciding which one will drive the search and recognition process. Objects in memory become activated as their constituent shapes are recognized by attending to bottom-up salience. If there is no object with a large activation, then there is no need to generate top- down shape match expectations and the bottom-up shape matching can continue. Bottom-up shape matching continues until some object becomes sufficiently active (when it looks like this object must actually be present in the input). Switching to a top-down search saves time because each bottom-up match must be made with all of the possible shapes in memory. The active object node provides context from which expectations can be generated.

For completely bottom-up recognition, salient features draw attention to a location. The group of features in that location are then learned or recognized as a shape. The group of features is recognized if it matches with a previously learned shape. This continues until there are no more features that are salient enough to draw attention. At this time, the active shapes are learned as an object. After each shape match is made, any object that contains a matched shape should have an increase in activation so that at some point the most likely object can induce a top-down search.

In the case of top-down recognition, an object must have become active because many of its shapes have already been recognized. This leads to the expectation of shapes in their expected locations. When a shape is expected, it is searched for in the general area of the expected location and scale. The matching of expected shapes continues until there are no more expected shapes or else the system switches back to a bottom-up search. The two reasons a bottom-up search can be re-started are the detection of an extremely salient shape, and a sever mismatch between the expected shapes and the shapes that are actually present.

Matching and Vigilance The matching process is a critical aspect of the system. Fuzzy or partial matches should be allowed in some cases. This is controlled by vigilance parameters as prescribed by Adaptive Resonance Theory (ART) [24]. This parameter determines how close an input must be to a stored pattern to be considered a match. How well a stored shape matches different instances of the same input shape determines how well the system works. Most of the burden of this match is placed on preprocessing and the choice and representation of the

features that are to be compared. This aspect of the system is a main focus of ongoing research.

Learning Shapes and Objects When shapes are encountered for the first time, they are learned completely. But an exact copy of the features (a template) would not allow generalized recognition of this shape in the future. Therefore, shapes are blurred before they are stored. This has the effect of allowing sloppy or distorted shapes to match. Also, each time a shape does match a stored shape, the stored shape is adjusted to be more similar to the input shape. This allows the stored shape to adapt to the central tendencies of the distribution of matching shapes. This technique is used in ART2-A [25]. Objects are learned in a similar way. One main difference is that the locations of shapes are learned relative to each other (in object centered coordinates). Flexibility is added in that an object will be recognized when the majority of its shapes match and there can be some substitution of individual shapes if the rest of the shapes match exactly. But if an object has too many different shapes, it can be learned as a new object.

Learning an Expert's Segmentation In order to learn that an object corresponds to a particular anatomical region in the brain, the SRM is provided with a mask (the result of a human expert's segmentation) which delineates the portion of the image that corresponds to a given region. Then, only the features that correspond to the masked section of the image are grouped into shapes and then into an object.

Localization of a Recognized Object Once an object has been learned and then recognized in the input, the SRM needs to locate the features in the input that caused the object to be recognized. This is a correspondence problem; which input feature corresponds with which stored feature. Once this is solved, labels attached to the stored features can be applied to the input features. When this is done at the scale of the original image, it is effectively segments the original image. This problem can be solved by optimization techniques, but the large number of possible feature matches can lead to combinatorial explosion. Another solution is to have small enough shapes and a tight enough match criteria (vigilance) that the labeling error is negligible.

III. RESULTS

The Shape Recognition Model and Module have not been implemented in their entirety, but have evolved as a result of various implementations. Each implementation focuses on a subset of the operations of the whole model and

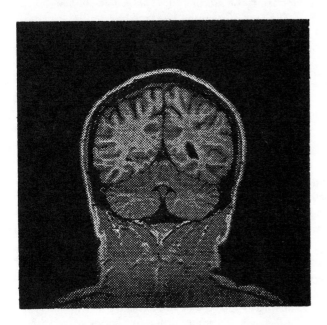

Figure 3: Input image of the segmentation system.

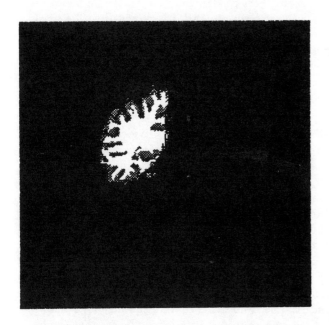

Figure 4: Output image of the segmentation system. Using the "expectation" signals from the SRM, the GWDN produces a segmentation of only the right cerebral hemisphere. White matter is white, grey matter is grey, and all else is colored black.

results in its confirmation and/or re-definition and also underscores the more difficult problem areas of the system.

Fig. 3 is the original input and Fig. 4 shows the result when the SRM is used along with the GWDN. The SRM was trained to recognize the shape of only the right cerebral hemisphere for this image. These results are presented only for the next-to smallest scale features. Using the smallest scale features would provide an even more precise location of the brain region of interest.

IV. CONCLUSION

Fig. 4 demonstrates that even though the current implementation is very crude and makes many simplifying assumptions, it can effectively represent shapes and objects and can use this to label the output of the GWDN. This initial implementation of the system points out that the most difficult problems involve matching and generalization. Generalization here refers to the ability to recognize features, shapes, and objects across different brains. This difficulty lies in the transformation of an array of pixel intensities to an appropriate recognition event. If there is hope for patterns to be recognized correctly, they must be distinguishable from each other in the feature space that is presented to the pattern recognizer. Then, the main problem of visual object recognition becomes one of pre-processing. A system that starts with extracted lines or deals with a "blocks world" ignores much of this problem. As advocated by the school of ecological psychology, the invariances in the world must be extracted [26]. Elementary features must be transformed into higher level features. The highest level features can then be matched with previously stored representations.

Acknowledgment   This work was supported in part by grant NS 20489 and NS 24279 from the National Institute of Neurologic Disorders and Stroke.

REFERENCES

[1] H.S. Stiehl. 3D Image Understanding in Radiology. *IEEE Engr. in Medicine and Biology*, 9(4):24–28, 1990.

[2] AJ Worth, S Lehar, and DN Kennedy. A recurrent cooperative/competitive field for segmentation of magnetic resonance brain images. *IEEE Trans Knowledge Data Eng*, 4(2):156–161, 1992.

[3] H Neumann and K Ottenberg. Estimating Attributes of Smooth Signal Transitions from Scale-Space. *Proceedings of the Inter. Conf. on Pattern Recognition*, ICPR-92, The Hague (Netherlands), August, in press, 1992.

[4] B. Bhanu. Automatic target recognition: State of the art sruvey. *IEEE Aerospace Elect Sys*, AES-22(4):364–379, 1983.

[5] RM Haralick and LG Shapiro. Survey: Image segmentation techniques. *Computer Vision, Graphics and Image Processing*, 29:100–132, 1985.

[6] DJ Michael. Handx: a model-based system for automatic segmentation of bones from digital hand radiographs. *IEEE TMI*, 8(1):64–69, 1989.

[7] M. Bowmans. 3-d segmentation of mr images of the head for 3-d display. *IEEE Transactions on Medical Imaging*, 9(2):177–183, 1990.

[8] W. Snyder, A. Logenthiran, P. Santago, K. Link, G. Bilbro, and S. Rajala. Segmentation of magnetic resonance images using mean field annealing. *Proc Information Processing in Medical Imaging*, 12:218–226, 1991.

[9] CG Perrott and LGC Hamey. Object Recognition, A Survey of the Literature, Macquarie Computing Report No. 91-0065C, School of MPCE, Macquarie University, NSW 2109, Australia, 1991.

[10] I Biederman. Recognition-by-Components: A Theory of Human Image Understanding. *Psych. Review*, 94(2):115–147, 1987.

[11] JT Todd and FD Reichel. Ordinal Structure in the Visual Perception and Cognition of Smoothly Curved Surfaces. *Psych. Review*, 96(4):643–657, 1989.

[12] AM Treisman and G Gelade. A Feature Integration Theory of Attention. *Cognitive Psychology*, 12:97–136, 1980.

[13] C.W. Eriksen and J.D. St. James. Visual Attention Within and Around the Field of Focal Attention: A Zoom Lens Model. *Perception & Psychophysics*, 40(4):225–240, 1986.

[14] J.M. Wolfe, K.R. Cave and S.L. Franzel. Guided Search: An Alternative to the Feature Integration Model for Visual search. *Journal of Experimental Psychology: Human Perception and Performance*, 15(3):419–433, 1989.

[15] WA Johnston and VJ Dark. Selective Attention. *Ann. Rev. Psychol.*, 37:43–75, 1986.

[16] K Nakayama. The iconic bottleneck and the tenuous link between early visual Processing and perception. In C Blakemore (Ed.) *Vision: Coding and Efficiency*, Cambridge University Press, 411–422, 1990.

[17] AJ Worth. Neural networks for automatic segmentation of magnetic resonance brain images. unpublished doctoral dissertation, Boston University, 1993.

[18] DN Kennedy, PA Filipek and VS Caviness Jr.. Anatomic Segmentation and Volumetric Calculations in Nuclear Magnetic Resonance Imaging. *IEEE Trans. on Medical Imaging*, 8(1), March, 1989.

[19] P.A. Filipek, D.N. Kennedy, V.S. Caviness Jr., and et al. Magnetic resonance imaging-based brain morphometry: Development and application to normal controls. *Ann Neurol*, 25:61–67, 1989.

[20] AJ Worth, S Lehar and DN Kennedy. A recurrent cooperative/competitive field for segmentation of magnetic resonance brain imagery. *Proceedings of the Inter. Joint Conf. on Neural Networks*, November (Singapore), 2:1403–1408, 1991.

[21] S. Grossberg and E. Mingolla. Neural dynamics of surface perception: Boundary webs, illuminants, and shape-from-shading. *Computer Vision, Graphics and Image Processing*, 37:116–165, 1987.

[22] S. Lehar, A.J. Worth, and D.N. Kennedy. Application of the boundary contour/feature contour system to magnetic resonance brain scan imagery. *Proceedings of the International Joint Conference on Neural Networks*, June (San Diego), 1:435–440, 1990.

[23] D Marr and HK Nishihara. Representation and Recognition of Three Dimensional Shapes. *Proceedings of the Royal Society of London*, Series B, 200:269–294, 1978.

[24] GA Carpenter and S Grossberg. The ART of adaptive pattern recognition by a self-organizing neural network. *Computer*, 21:77–88, 1988.

[25] G.A. Carpenter, S Grossberg, and D.B. Rosen. ART 2-A: An adaptive resonance algorithm for rapid category learning and recognition. *Neural Networks*, 4:493–504, 1991.

[26] JJ Gibson. *The Ecological Approach to Visual Perception*. Boston: Houghton Mifflin, 1979.

A New Analytical Method for AM Neural Networks and Its Application to Pattern Recognition

Miao Zhenjiang,   Yuan Baozong
(Ph.D candidate)   (IEEE Senior Member)
Institute of Information Science
Northern Jiaotong University
Beijing 100044, China, Tel.3240616

Abstract--In this paper, the problems of asymptotical stability and associative memory for Hopfield type neural networks are analyzed. First, we introduce a new kind of energy function which is different from Hopfield's definition. Then, the networks' asymptotical stability is analyzed by means of the new energy function. Two theorems are obtained. By comparing these two theorems with the existing conclusions, it can be found that in some cases they are consistent and in other cases they are not equivalent but complement each other. Finally, by using these theorems, we design one associative memory neural network and demonstrate their applications to pattern recognition.

1. Introduction

Neural networks are widely used in pattern recognition and artificial intelligence, etc. Associative memory (AM) is a very important function for these applications. But how to design a AM neural network? i.e., what conditions must be satisfied by the networks? In this paper, we introduce a new kind of energy function and analyze the networks' asymptotical stability by means of the energy function. Two theorems are obtained. By comparing these two theorems with the existing results [1], it can be found that, in some cases, they are consistent, and in other cases,they are not equivalent but complement each other. Using these theorems, we design one associative memory neural network and demonstrate their applications to pattern recognition with one example.

2. Theoretical background

In this section, we give some mathematical concepts and lemmas which will be used in the following part.

Lemma 1(Krasovskii Theorem) [2] : Consider the system defined by

$$\dot{X} = f(X)$$

where X is an n−dimensional vector. Assume that f(0) = 0 and that f(X) is differentiable with respect to $x_i, i = 1,2,...,n$. The Jacobian matrix J(X) for the system is

$$J_{ij}(x) = \frac{\partial f_i(x_i)}{\partial x_j}$$

Define

$$\hat{J}(X) = J^H(X) + J(X)$$

where $J^H(X)$ is the conjugate of J(X). If the Hermitian matrix $\hat{J}(X)$ is negative definite, then the equilibrium state X = 0 is asymptotically stable. A Liapunov function for this system is

$$V(X) = f^H(X)f(X)$$

Definition 1: For matrix A, if there is a positive diagonal matrix D which satisfies,

$$|c_{ii}| > \sum_{\substack{j=1 \\ j \neq i}}^{n} |c_{ij}|, \quad C = AD$$

we call A a generalized diagonal dominant matrix.

Lemma 2 [3] : If $A = (a_{ij})_{n \times n}$ is a generalized diagonal dominant matrix and all a_{ii} ($i = 1,2,...,n$) are real numbers, the number of a_{ii} ($a_{ii} > 0$) or a_{ii} ($a_{ii} < 0$) ($i = 1,2,...,n$) is equal to the number of c_{ii} ($c_{ii} > 0$) or c_{ii} ($c_{ii} < 0$) ($i = 1,2,...,n$), c_{ii} is the real part of ith eigenvalue of matrix A.

Lemma 3 [4] : Hermitian matrix is negative (positive) definite if and only if all its eigenvalues are negative (positive).

Definition 2 [5] : For Hermitian matrix A, if A satisfies

$$[tr(A)]^2 > (n-1)tr(A^2)$$

we call A trance dominant matrix.

Lemma 4 [5] : Matrix A is positive–definite if A is a trance dominate matrix and all its diagonal elements are positive. Equivalently, we get that matrix A is negative–definite if A is a trance dominate matrix and all its diagonal elements are negative.

3. The existing conclusions about asymptotical stability

The neural network which we will discuss is described by the following differential equation,

$$\dot{X} = -AX + Tf(X) + I \qquad (1)$$

where $X = (x_1, x_2, ..., x_n)^T \in R^n$; A = diag $(a_{11}, a_{22}, ..., a_{nn})$ is an n × n constant matrix with each $a_{ii} > 0$; $T = [T_{ij}]_{n \times n}$ is an n × n constant matrix; $f(X) = (f_1(x_1), f_2(x_2), ..., f_n(x_n))^T$, $f_i(x_i)$ is a differentiable function. $I = (I_1, I_2, ..., I_n)^T$ is a constant vector.

For convenience, let

$$d0_i(x_i) = \frac{\partial f_i(x_i)}{\partial x_i}$$

Theorem 1 [1] : $X^s \in R^n$ is an asymptotically stable equilibrium of the network

(1) if $a_{ii}, T_{ij}, I_i, i, j = 1,2,...,n$ satisfy the following at $X = X^s$,

$$AX = Tf(X) + I \qquad (2)$$

$$\sum_{\substack{i=1 \\ i \neq i}}^{n} |T_{ii} d0_i(x_i)| + T_{ii} d0_i(x_i) - a_{ii}$$

$$< 0 \qquad i = 1,2,...,n \qquad (3)$$

This theorem implies that, by selecting T_{ij}, a_{ii} and I_i which satisfy conditions (2) and (3), the vector X^s is guaranteed to be a locally asymptotically stable equilibrium of the network. Only this kind of equilibrium can be used in associative memory because AM neural network must at least guarantee that:

(c1) each prototype pattern is an equilibrium of the network;

(c2) each prototype pattern is attractive.

If we design a neural network and each of their prototype patterns satisfies (2) and (3), the network is an AM network.

4. The new analytical method and conclusions

In this part, we introduce a new kind of energy function by Krasovskii method and analyze the networks' asymptotical stability by means of this energy function.

(1) can also be written as follows

$$\dot{x}_i = -a_{ii}x_i + \sum_{j=1}^{n} T_{ij}f_j(x_j) + I_i \qquad i = 1,2,...,n \qquad (4)$$

$X^s = (x_1^s, x_2^s, ..., x_n^s)^T$ is the network's equilibrium, so we have

$$-a_{ii}x_i^s + \sum_{j=1}^{n} T_{ij}f_j(x_j^s) + I_i = 0$$

Let

$$u_i = x_i - x_i^s, \quad h_i(x_i) = f_i(x_i) - f_i(x_i^s)$$

We have

$$\dot{u}_i = \dot{x}_i - \dot{x}_i^s = \dot{x}_i = -a_{ii}(u_i + x_i^s)$$

1571

$$+ \sum_{j=1}^{n} T_{ij}(h_j(x_j) + f_j(x_j')) + I_i$$

$$= -a_{ii}u_i + \sum_{j=1}^{n} T_{ij}h_j(x_j)$$

$$= -a_{ii}u_i + \sum_{j=1}^{n} T_{ij}h_j(u_j + x_j')$$

Its equivalent form is

$$\begin{cases} \dot{u}_i = -a_{ii}u_i + \sum_{j=1}^{n} T_{ij}\left[f_j(u_j + x_j') - f_j(x_j') \right] \\ \quad = g_i(u_i) \\ g_i(0) = 0 \end{cases}$$

We can use lemma 1 to define Liapunov function as follows

$$V(U) = g^H(U)g(U)$$

From lemma1 we know that, if the Hermitian matrix $\hat{J}(U)$ is negative definite, then the equilibrium state $X = 0$ is asymptotically stable. $\hat{J}(U)$ is as follows,

$$j^H(U) + \hat{J}(U) = \begin{cases} -2a_{ii} \\ \quad + 2T_{ii}\dfrac{\partial f_i(u_i + x_i')}{\partial u_i} \\ \qquad\qquad i = j \\ T_{ij}\dfrac{\partial f_j(u_j + x_i')}{\partial u_j} \\ \quad + T_{ji}\dfrac{\partial f_i(u_i + x_i')}{\partial u_i} \\ \qquad\qquad i \neq j \end{cases}$$

$$i, j = 1, 2, \ldots, n$$

For convenience, let,

$$d_i(u_i) = \frac{\partial f_i(u_i + x_i')}{\partial u_i}$$

Theorem 2: $X' \in R^n$ is an asymptotically stable equilibrium of network (1) if $a_{ii}, T_{ij}, I_i, i, j = 1, 2, \ldots, n$ satisfy the following at $X = X'$, i.e., $U = 0$,

$$AX = Tf(X) + I \qquad (5)$$

$$T_{ii}d_i(u_i) - a_{ii} < 0 \qquad i = 1, 2, \ldots, n \qquad (6)$$

$$\sum_{\substack{j=1 \\ j \neq i}}^{n} \left| T_{ij}d_j(u_j) + T_{ji}d_i(u_i) \right|$$

$$- 2\left| T_{ii}d_i(u_i) - a_{ii} \right|$$

$$< 0 \qquad i = 1, 2, \ldots, n \qquad (7)$$

Proof: (5) ensures that X' is the equilibrium of network (1).

From lemma 1, we need prove (6) and (7) guarantee that $\hat{J}(U)$ is a negative–definite matrix.

According to lemma 3, we know that, in order to ensure $\hat{J}(U)$ negative–definite, we must ensure that all of its eigenvalues are negative.

Lemma 2 tells us that, in order to ensure all eigenvalues of $\hat{J}(U)$ are negative, we must guarantee that $\hat{J}(U)$ is a generalized diagonal matrix and all of its diagonal elements are negative. (6) ensures all diagonal elements of $\hat{J}(U)$ are negative. (7) ensures $\hat{J}(U)$ is a generalized diagonal matrix according to Definition 1 (where D is an Unit Matrix). < end >

The equivalent form of theorem 2 is as follows.

$X' \in R^n$ is an asymptotically stable equilibrium of network (1) if $a_{ii}, T_{ij}, I_i, i, j = 1, 2, \ldots, n$ satisfy the following at $X = X'$, i.e., $U = 0$,

$$AX = Tf(X) + I$$

$$\sum_{\substack{j=1 \\ j \neq i}}^{n} \left| T_{ij}d_j(u_j) + T_{ji}d_i(u_i) \right|$$

$$+ 2(T_{ii}d_i(u_i) - a_{ii}) < 0 \qquad i$$

$$= 1, 2, \ldots, n$$

Theorem 3: $X' \in R^n$ is an asymptotically stable equilibrium of network (1) if $a_{ii}, T_{ij}, I_i, i, j = 1, 2, \ldots, n$ satisfy the following at $X = X'$, i.e., $U = 0$,

$$AX = Tf(X) + I \qquad (8)$$

$$T_{ii}d_i(u_i) - a_{ii} < 0 \qquad i = 1, 2, \ldots, n \qquad (9)$$

$$\{\sum_{i=1}^{n}[-2a_{ii}+2T_{ii}d_i(u_i)]\}^2 > (n-1)\sum_{i=1}^{n}\{[-2a_{ii}$$

$$+2T_{ii}d_i(u_i)]^2 + \sum_{\substack{j=1\\j\neq i}}^{n}[T_{ji}d_i(u_i)$$

$$+T_{ij}d_j(u_j)]^2\} \tag{10}$$

The proof of theorem 3 is almost the same as that of theorem 2. The only difference is to use lemma 4, not lemma 3, to prove this theorem.

For Hopfield neural network, $T_{ij} = T_{ji}$, $f_i(x_i) = f_j(x_j)$. In this case, theorem 2 is the same as theorem 1. In other words, they are consistent. But in more generalized case, they are not equivalent but complement to each other.

6. Applications

Example 1: The network consists of 10 processing units. The set of vectors to be stored is :
$$V^1 = (-1,1,1,1,-1,1,1,-1,-1,1)^T, \quad V^2$$
$$= (1,1,-1,1,-1,1,-1,1,-1,1)^T,$$
$$V^3 = (-1,1,-1,-1,1,1,-1,1,1,1,)^T, \quad V^4$$
$$= (-1,1,1,1,-1,1,1,-1,1,-1,1)^T,$$
$$V^5 = (-1,1,-1,1,-1,1,1,-1,-1,1)^T,$$

We choose $f_i(x_i) = (2/pi)\arctan(x_i)$, ($pi = 3.1416$), and use theorem 2 (the equivalent form) as constraints to design this neural net. Let

$$eq_i = -a_{ii}x_i + \sum_{j=1}^{n}T_{ij}f_j(x_j) + I_i$$

$$ieq_i = \sum_{\substack{j=1\\j\neq i}}^{n}\left|T_{ij}d_j(u_j) + T_{ji}d_i(u_i)\right|$$

$$+ 2(T_{ii}d_i(u_i) - a_{ii})$$

For V^1, the network that we design has the following parameters(seeTABLE 1).

We can see V^1 basically satisfy theorem 2. For V^2, V^3, V^4 and V^5, the results are almost the same.

We take vector V^1 as an example to see the AM result in detail. The initial inputs are the following cases:

(s1) The initial input has one element which is deferent from V^1 (+1 $\longrightarrow$ 0., $-1 \longrightarrow$ 0.), for example, the initial input $(-1,0.,1,1,-1,1,1,-1,-1,1)^T$, the second element is different from that of V^1.

(s2) The initial input has two, three or four elements which are deferent from V^1 (+1 $\longrightarrow$ 0., $-1 \longrightarrow$ 0.), for example, the initial input $(-1,0.,1,1,0,1,1,-1,-1,1)^T$, the second and fifth elements are different from those of V^1.

(s3) The initial input has more than four elements which are deferent from V^1 (+1 $\longrightarrow$ 0., $-1 \longrightarrow$ 0.), for example, the initial input $(-1,0.,1,1,0,0,1,0,-1,0)^T$ which has five elements deferent from V^1, and $(0,0.,0,0,0,0,0,0,0,0)^T$ which has ten elements deferent from V^1.

In the above cases, there are
$$C_{10}^1 + C_{10}^2 + C_{10}^3 + C_{10}^4 + C_{10}^5 + C_{10}^6 + C_{10}^7$$
$$+ C_{10}^8 + C_{10}^9 + C_{10}^{10} = 1023$$

inputs in all. By associative memory of the designed network, the initial input can be restored to the correct form of V^1 if the initial input is in the attractive domain of V^1, in other words, it can be recognized as V^1. In our experiment, the recognizing results are as follows(see TABLE 2).

Where j represents the number of different elements between V^1 and initial input, sum_j the total initial inputs, cn_j the number of correct recognition.

In the case of (s1) and (s2), all recognizing results are correct. But in the third case, there are 16 incorrect results. If we change initial inputs as (+1 $\longrightarrow$ 0.1, $-1 \longrightarrow$ -0.1) for V^1, for example, $(-1,0.1,1,0.1,-0.1,0.1,1,-1,-0.1,1)^T$, all recognizing results are correct in the 1023 input cases.

We also can take V^2, V^3, V^4 and V^5 as an example to simulate AM. This experiment is carried out in the following two cases.

(a) The initial input has one element which is deferent from V^2, V^3, V^4 or V^5 ($+1 \longrightarrow 0., -1 \longrightarrow 0.$). In this case, there are 10 initial inputs for each.

(b) The initial input has two elements which are deferent from V^2, V^3, V^4 or V^5 ($+1 \longrightarrow 0., -1 \longrightarrow 0.$). There are 45 initial inputs for each.

In case (a), the recognizing results are, all incorrect for V^2, one incorrect for V^3, all incorrect for V^4 (The system restores all initial inputs to V^1.), one incorrect for V^5. In case (b), the recognizing results are, all incorrect for V^2, nine incorrect for V^3, forty three incorrect for V^4 (The system restores the initial inputs to V^1.), nine incorrect for V^5. If we change initial inputs as ($+1 \longrightarrow 0.1, -1 \longrightarrow -0.1$) for V^3 and V^5, ($+1 \longrightarrow 0.7, -1 \longrightarrow -0.7$) for V^2 and V^4, for example, $(-1,0.1,-1,-1,1,1,-0.1,1,1,1)^T$ for V^3 and $(-1,1,1,0.7,-1,1,-0.7,1,-1,1)^T$ for V^4, all recognizing results are correct in case (a) and (b).

From our experiment, we can find that V^1 has the largest attractive domain, V^3 and V^5 the second place, and V^2 and V^4 the smallest.

Overall, we get several conclusions about network's asymptotic stability. Using these conclusions, we can design associative memory neural networks. We proposed an optimal design method in [6].

Reference

(1) Z.Miao, B.Yuan, Analysis and Optimal Design of Hopfield Type Associative Memory Neural Networks, unpublished

(2) K. Ogata, Modern Control Engineering, Prentice-Hall, 1970, pp.735-736

(3) Z.You, L.Li, Distribution of the eigenvalues for conjugate generalizeddiagonally dominant matrixes, Journal of Mathematical Research and Exposition, Vol.9, No.2, 1989, pp.309-310

(4)J. N. Franklin, Matrix Theory, Prentice-Hall, 1968, pp.105

(5)B. Tu, J. Li, Distribution of the Characteristic Roots of Matrice and Their Applications to the Stability Thoery, Chinese Annals of Mathematics, Vol.8(A), No.6, 1987, pp.659-663

(6) Z.Miao, B.Yuan, Optimal design of Hopfield type neural networks with application to associative memory , Proc. of 1992 IEEE INNS Joint Intel. Conf. on Neural Networks, Beijing, China, Vol.II, pp.131-136

TABLE 1

i	1	2	3	4	5	6	7	8	9	10
eq_i	−0.12	0.001	0.013	−0.01	0.030	0.000	0.000	0.030	−0.04	0.000
ieq_i	−23.1	−144.	−22.8	−30.2	−35.5	−140.	−28.5	−35.5	−29.9	−138.

TABLE 2

j	1	2	3	4	5	6	7	8	9	10
sum_j	10	45	120	210	252	210	120	45	10	1
cn_j	10	45	120	210	251	206	114	41	9	1

Design of an Elliptical Neural Network
with Application to
Degraded Character Classification

Michael C. Moed   Chih-Ping Lee*
Research Scientist   Research Scientist

United Parcel Service
Research and Development
51–53 Kenosia Ave
Danbury, CT 06810

Abstract—

This paper describes a novel neural network architecture that is used to classify a set of patterns into one of a set of known classes. The network is comprised of a set of trainable neural processing units (neurons) that have an elliptical activation function and a set of adaptable connections. A fast training algorithm is provided for the network that guarantees that all elements of an arbitrary training set can be correctly learned by the network in finite time. To demonstrate the network's ability to train, and its ability to quickly generalize and classify noisy test data, a network is developed to classify degraded omnifont alphanumeric machine printed characters. Using a training set of over 69,000 characters and a separate test set of over 36,000 characters, classification accuracy of 97.5 percent with average network throughput of 211 characters per second is achieved.

I. Introduction

Artificial neural networks (ANNs) have been widely applied to the task of pattern classification. They function as a powerful computational tool whose benefits include adaptability, parallel computation, and robustness to noise. For the task of pattern classification, ANNs are able to form non-linear decision boundaries that can accurately represent training data and can generalize this data to classify novel, noisy patterns.

One of the most popular ANNs used for pattern classification is a feedforward network employing the Backpropagation training algorithm [1]. Using a set of non-linear processing neurons with sigmoid activation functions, the Backpropagation network can form arbitrarily-shaped decision regions in a hyperspace [2]. Using each neuron to compute a hyperplane decision boundary, decision regions are formed by training the weighted connections between neurons, thereby altering the hyperplane locations in the decision space.

Though extremely powerful and useful, from a pattern classification viewpoint the Backpropagation network suffers in two areas. First, the training technique is slow, and has difficulty in globally minimizing the difference between desired and actual classification outputs. This implies that there is no guarantee that a Backpropagation network can learn to correctly classify the training set in a reasonable amount of time. Second, if a trained network misclassifies a test patten, it is very difficult to determine which neuron, or set of neurons, led to the misclassification, and how to retrain and correct the error.

Another ANN that has been used for pattern classification is named the Restricted Coulumb Energy network (RCE) [3, 4]. The neuron activation function for the RCE is a hypersphere. Each neuron maintains a set of weights that represents the center of the hypersphere in the decision space, and a threshold value that represents the radius. In certain implementations, each hypersphere is associated with a particular pattern class. For these implementations, if a test pattern falls within the boundary of a hypersphere, the pattern is classified as the class associated with the hypersphere. Through training, the neurons of the RCE network adapt to determine the location and size of the hypersphere decision boundaries. By clustering hypersphere of different sizes, it is possible to represent arbitrarily complex classification regions in the decision space.

The RCE network eliminates the two Backpropagation problems mentioned above. First, the training technique forces the network to converge to a set of neurons that cor-

---

*Current address: Emhart Glass, 123 Day Hill Rd., Windsor, CT 06095

rectly classify all training sets. Second, if a test pattern is misclassified, one can determine exactly which neuron(s) were activated incorrectly, and modifications can be made to correct this problem. The RCE network, however, may require large computational resources or a large storage space to represent arbitrariliy shaped decision regions.

Refer to Figure 1 for an illustrative example. In this figure, we see a two dimensional decision space, so a pattern to be classified is represented by the vector (f_0, f_1). As shown in the figure, we have two possible decision classes, A and B, with corresponding decision regions. The decision region for $\mathbf{A}$ can be represented by just a few circular neurons (a 2D hypersphere is a circle) without much error. However, the decision region for $\mathbf{B}$ requires many hypersphere neurons due to its oblong shape. Using a reduced number of neurons for $\mathbf{B}$ would lead to large error regions. The large number of neurons needed for $\mathbf{B}$ leads to a large processing time and storage requirement, compared to the amount required for $\mathbf{A}$. The argument easily can be extended for a decision space of any dimension greater than 2.

To eliminate the problems that the RCE network has with decision regions shaped similar to $\mathbf{B}$, one may employ a network with neurons that can form more adaptable decision boundaries. The focus of this paper is on the design one such ANN, with neurons that have hyperellipsoidal decision boundaries [5, 6, 7]. This ANN is called an *Elliptical* neural network. As demonstrated in Figure 2, hyperellipsoids can represent arbitrary shapes (such as a narrow band or plane) much more easily than hyperspheres, and are guaranteed to be at least as efficient. This is guaranteed because a hyperellipsoid can default to a hypersphere if required. The ease of shape adaptation should reduce the amount of processing time and storage required by a network, when compared to the RCE model.

The paper proceeds as follows. Section II presents the architecture of the Elliptical neural network and governing equations. Section III presents a training algorithm that is guaranteed to converge in a finite number of iterations, and to correctly classify all training set data. Section IV describes the application of this network to the task of degraded alphanumeric machine printed character classification. Section V presents conclusions and describes plans for future work.

II. Architecture of an Elliptical Neural Network

The Elliptical neural network is comprised of several layers of neurons. As described below, each layer performs a specialized function. For reference, a diagram is presented in Figure 3. Without loss of generality, we assume that the network is classifying an input pattern vector $\mathbf{F}$ of k real values into one of s possible output classes.

The first layer of neurons $\mathbf{I}$ is called the *Input Layer* and functions as a set of broadcast elements. Each neuron $i_j \in \mathbf{I}$ receives as input one component of the pattern vector $\mathbf{F}$ to be classified, and broadcasts this value to all neurons in the *Processing Layer* $\mathbf{E}$.

The neurons in $\mathbf{E}$ form the hyperellipsoidal decision boundaries in the input space. Each neuron $e_x \in \mathbf{E}$ receives input from every neuron in $\mathbf{I}$, and maintains two sets of trainable parameter vectors $\mathbf{C_X}$ and $\mathbf{B_X}$. The first vector, $\mathbf{C_X} = (c_x^0, c_x^1, \ldots, c_x^{k-1})$, represents the center of the hyperellipsoid e_x in a k dimensional decision space. The second vector, $\mathbf{B_X} = (b_x^0, b_x^1, \ldots, b_x^{k-1})$, represents the axes of e_x. The number of neurons in $\mathbf{E}$, labeled *Enum*, is also determined through the training technique. An example of a neuron with $k = 2$ is presented in Figure 3.

Each neuron e_x computes a preliminary value e_x^{pre} according to the equation:

$$e_x^{pre} = \sum_{j=0}^{k-1} \frac{(c_x^j - f^j)^2}{(b_x^j)^2} \tag{1}$$

where f^j is the jth element of the input pattern vector $\mathbf{F}$. From this equation one can see that if a feature vector $\mathbf{F}$ falls within or on a hyperellipsoid decision boundary for a neuron e_x, then $e_x^{pre} \leq 1$; else, $e_x^{pre} > 1$. For computational convenience, each neuron then inverse thresholds this value to generate is final output e_x^{out} according to the equation:

$$e_x^{out} = \begin{cases} 0 & \text{if } e_x^{pre} > 1 \\ 1 & \text{if } e_x^{pre} \leq 1 \end{cases} \tag{2}$$

The neuron now outputs a 1 (state = *asserted*) if the feature vector lies within or on its decision boundaries, else it outputs a 0 (state = *non-asserted*).

Neurons in the next level, called the *Output Layer*, determine the amount of support provided to each of s output classes by the Processing Layer neurons. To determine the support, the Output Layer $\mathbf{O}$ contains a set of s neurons $(o_0, o_1, \ldots, o_{s-1})$, each of which corresponds to one of the s output classes. Each neuron o_i receives as input a set of weighted final output values from the Processing Layer neurons. The set of weights, developed through training, is called $\mathbf{W}$ and is of dimension $(s \times Enum)$.

Each neuron o_i in $\mathbf{O}$ computes its output value according to the equation:

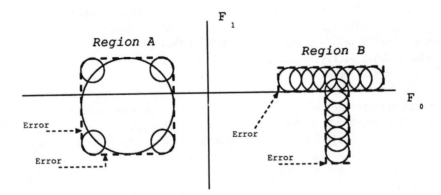

Figure 1: Decision space coverage using hyperspheres.

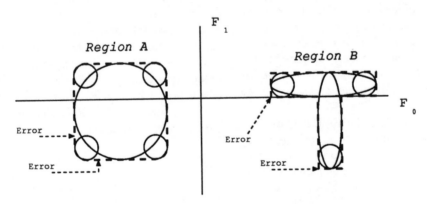

Figure 2: Decision space coverage using hyperellipsoids.

$$o_i = \sum_{j=0}^{Enum-1} \mathbf{W}_{ij} e_j^{out} \qquad (3)$$

Final classification is performed by determining the Output Layer neuron o_i that outputs the largest value. The input pattern $\mathbf{F}$ is then classified as the output class corresponding to this output layer neuron. If no output class has a value greater than 0, the input pattern is rejected.

There are several natural extensions to this architecture. For a given input pattern, one can use the values of the Output Layer neurons to compute a confidence value for the selected output class. This would allow a user to reject a classification if the class' support did not exceed a user-defined threshold. This is important when pattern misclassification is more costly then pattern rejection. Using the support values, the network can also provide alternative classifications and their relative ranks. This is helpful when combined with a postprocessing context database, which provides a secondary aid in classification. Also, when combining this network with other classification techniques, several output class alternatives is important to implement a voting strategy between the classifiers.

One may also extend this architecture to reduce input pattern rejection. If an input pattern vector is rejected on the first pass, one can alter the inverse thresholding setpoint of the Processing Neurons to allow each neuron to become asserted if the pattern vector is "just outside" the boundary of a decision region. The setpoint can be adjusted to maintain a user-defined acceptable misclassification rate, and will in turn reduce the rejection rate.

III. A Training Technique for an Elliptical Neural Network

Training the Elliptical network involves specializing the network architecture and parameters for a particular pattern classification task. There are four items that are modified during this training procedure. These items are:

1. The number of Processing Layer neurons.

2. The value of $\mathbf{C_X}$ for each Processing Layer neuron e_x. This value represents the center of the hyperellipsoidal decision boundary for that neuron.

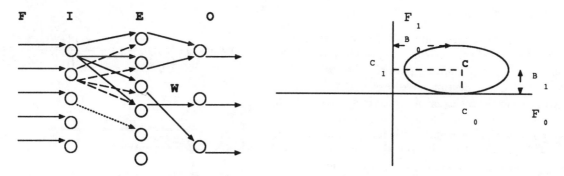

Figure 3: Left: Network Diagram. Right: Neuron Example

3. The value of $\mathbf{B_x}$ for each Processing Layer neuron e_x. This value represents the axes of the hyperellipsoidal decision boundary for that neuron.

4. The matrix $\mathbf{W}$ which contains weighted connection values between the Processing Layer and the Output Layer.

The training procedure presented below specializes the four above items using a technique that guarantees the following:

- All training patterns will be correctly classified.

- The training time is finite and of order $\mathbf{O}(n^3)$ where n is the size of the training set.

The nature of the training technique is an iterative growth and shrink process of Processing Layer neurons. The general idea is to create new Processing Layer neurons whose hyperellipsoids cover training set patterns of a particular output class, and shrink them so they don't overlap training set patterns of a different class (which will be covered by other hyperellipsoids). The algorithm is presented below.

Training Algorithm

Given a set $\Omega = (\omega_0, \omega_2, \ldots, \omega_{s-1})$ of s output classes. and a training set $\mathbf{T} = (t_0, t_1, \ldots, t_{n-1})$ of size n, where each element t_i has a pattern vector t_i^F and an output class t_i^ω ($\omega \in \Omega$), perform the following.

1. Set $Enum = 0$, $\mathbf{E} = $ NULL, $\mathbf{W} = [0]$. There are no Processing Layer neurons currently in the network.

2. Repeat until all training set patterns are correctly classified (max = n iterations):

   (a) Repeat for all j: $0 \leq j \leq n - 1$:

      i. Let $\mathbf{F}'$ equal the training pattern $t_j^F \in \mathbf{T}$. Let $\omega' = t_j^\omega$.

      ii. Provide $\mathbf{F}'$ to the Input Layer neurons as input to the network. Observe the set of asserted Output Layer neurons.

      iii. For every asserted Output Layer neuron o_h that corresponds to a different output class than ω' determine the set of asserted, supporting Processing Layer neurons for o_h.

      iv. For each asserted, supporting Processing Layer neuron in this set, SHRINK the (incorrectly) asserted neuron so that $\mathbf{F}'$ falls outside its decision boundary. The maximum number of SHRINK operations is n for this step.

      v. If no asserted Output Layer neuron o_h corresponds to output class ω' then perform the following:

         A. Let $Enum = Enum + 1$. Create a new Processing Layer neuron e_{Enum}. Add e_{Enum} to the set $\mathbf{E}$.

         B. Set $\mathbf{C_j} = \mathbf{F}'$. The new neuron is centered at the training pattern location.

         C. Set $\mathbf{B_j} = \mathbf{\Lambda}$, a vector of constant values. The initial axes are all the same size, so the decision surface for e_{Enum} is initially a hypersphere.

         D. For each training set element t_m: $0 \leq m \leq j$, SHRINK e_{Enum} so it does not misclassify these training set elements.

         E. Set $\mathbf{W}_{\omega', Enum} = 1$

3. Now, update support matrix $\mathbf{W}$. Repeat for all j: $0 \leq j \leq n - 1$:

   (a) Let $\mathbf{F}'$ equal the training pattern $t_j^F \in \mathbf{T}$. Let $\omega' = t_j^\omega$.

   (b) Provide $\mathbf{F}'$ to the Input Layer neurons as input to the network. Let $\mathbf{E}'$ equal the set of asserted Processing Layer neurons.

(c) For each $e_x \in \mathbf{E}'$, let $\mathbf{W}_{\omega'x} = \mathbf{W}_{\omega'x} + 1$.

One can see from the above algorithm that the support that a Processing Layer neuron provides to an Output Layer neuron is the number of training patterns that fall within the Processing Layer neuron. We reason that a decision region that contains a cluster of same-class training patterns is more likely to be able to classify a same-class noisy test pattern than a region with few training patterns. Thus, a Processing Layer neuron that contains multiple training patterns may be considered to have "better" classification capabilities than one that contains fewer training patterns, and should provide a larger degree of support for an output class.

It is also evident that if a misclassification occurs when testing the network, one can readily determine which processing neuron(s) provided support to the incorrectly asserted Output Layer neuron. If desired, one can alter the size of the Processing Layer neuron to exclude this test vector using the SHRINK algorithm below. As noted earlier, this ability is one of the strengths of this architecture.

The SHRINK algorithm reduces the size of a hyperellipsoidal decision region for a neuron e_x when a training pattern vector $\mathbf{F}$ lies inside e_x and is incorrectly classified by e_x. The goal of SHRINK is to find a new hyperellipsoidal boundary (maintaining the same center $\mathbf{C_X}$) within the old boundary such that the new hyperellipsoid has the largest possible volume, yet $\mathbf{F}$ is outside the boundary. The proposition is given by the following:

Given a hyperellipsoidal decision region computed by e_x, with center $\mathbf{C_X}$, axes $\mathbf{B_X}$, and Volume V_x, determine a new set of axes $\mathbf{\Gamma_X} = (\gamma_x^0, \gamma_x^1, \ldots, \gamma_x^{k-1})$ to maximize $V_x(\mathbf{\Gamma_X})$, where:

$$V_x(\mathbf{\Gamma_X}) = \rho \prod_{j=0}^{k-1} \gamma_x^j \qquad (4)$$

subject to:

$$\gamma_x^j \leq b_x^j, \text{ for all } j: 0 \leq j \leq k-1$$

and

$$\sum_{j=0}^{k-1} \frac{(c_x^j - f^j)^2}{(\gamma_x^j)^2} \geq 1$$

where ρ is a volumetric constant.

Using the method of Lagrange multipliers, one can determine that the Γ_x that satisfies this proposition can be found by using the following method:

SHRINK Algorithm

1. For any j ($0 \leq j \leq k-1$) such that $f^j = c_x^j$, set $\gamma_x^j = b_x^j$.

2. For the all other j,

$$\eta = argmax(j) \left[\frac{(\prod_{h=0, h \neq j}^{k-1} b_x^h)|c_x^j - f^j|}{\sqrt{1 - \sum_{h=0, h \neq j}^{k-1} \{(c_x^h - f^h)^2/(b_x^h)^2\}}} \right] \qquad (5)$$

3. Set:

$$\begin{cases} \gamma_x^\eta = \dfrac{|c_x^\eta - f^\eta|}{\sqrt{1 - \sum_{h=0, h \neq \eta}^{k-1} \{(c_x^h - f^h)^2/(b_x^h)^2\}}} - \epsilon \\[2ex] \gamma_x^j = b_x^j \text{ for all other } j, 0 \leq j \leq k-1 \end{cases} \qquad (6)$$

In equation (6), ϵ is a small positive constant. From the description of the SHRINK algorithm it is evident that only one axis need be reduced to maximize the size of the reduced hyperellipsoid volume.

The training algorithm provides the following guarantees:

1. Each Processing Layer neuron corresponds to only one output class.

2. Several training patterns may lie within the decision boundary of the same Processing Layer neuron if each pattern has the same output class.

3. Several Processing Layer neurons can have the same output class.

4. Training patterns with different output classes will be covered by different Processing Layer neurons.

5. All training set patterns will lie within the boundary of at least one Processing Layer Neuron.

Other training methods for elliptical networks do not provide such guarantees. In [5], the proposed training method requires the placement of hyperellipsoidal neurons at preclustered data centers. Given this fixed number of neurons, the method then adjusts the size of each neurons hyperellipsoidal "bounding box" based on assumed information about the distribution of data in the region. This method does not provide above guarantees 4 and 5. In [6], an LVQ algorithm based on the Mahalanobis distance metric is used to alter the shape and center of a fixed number of hyperellipsoidal decision boundaries. Unfortunately, this method may violate guarantees 4 and 5 as well.

IV. Application of an Elliptical Neural Network to Character Classification

Character recognition is a classic pattern classification problem to which ANNs have been applied. In most character recognition applications, a feature vector is derived from the bitmap of an imaged alphanumeric character, and this vector is provided to the network as input. The network then processes the vector and outputs a value representing the "closest" character class, according to some metric.

At UPS Research and Development, we have assembled a database of over 105,000 machine printed characters from package labels that have been shipped by UPS. The labels have been optically scanned using a CCD-based scanner with a resolution of 250 dots-per-inch (dpi). A segmented bitmap image of every character on each of these labels and associated key-entered truth value have been stored in the database.

Due to the nature of the package labels, machine printed characters vary greatly from label to label. Almost any printing technique, including laser print, typewriter, dot-matrix, and carbon copy may appear on the label. Also, any machine printed font may be present. The size of the characters is also variable, although for this experiment, we limited the allowed font sizes to be between 8 and 18pt. Finally, many of the machine printed characters tend to be degraded due to printing technique, tape, poor contrast or marks and blurs introduced through shipping. It is sufficient to say that a large proportion of these characters cannot be recognized using simple template matching techniques.

A system consisting of seven Elliptical neural networks was constructed to classify the degraded machine print characters. The combined system was evaluated using four criteria:

- Accuracy rate (percent correct classification).

- Substitution rate (percent misclassification).

- Rejection rate (percent no classification).

- Speed.

There were 64 characters that our system was designed to classify. These were the upper case alphas (A-Z), the lower case alphas (a-z) the ten digits (0-9), "&", and "#". The 64 characters were divided into seven sets based on similarity of shape. The sets are: S1: OD0oCcQadge; S2: 1lIi7; S3: WwVvUuYyTtr; S4: EBFPp2Zz; S5: 35Ss8f9qg&Jj; S6: 4#ARKkXx; and S7: 6LbMNHhmn. In total, there were over 69,000 characters in the training set and over 36,000 characters in a separate test set. Unfortunately, we did not have an even distribution of character instances, e.g. there were many more "s" than "j" in the database.

If a single network was used for all 64 characters, the number of Processing Layer neurons would be large, resulting in a large execution time. Instead, we trained seven networks each on a separate character set. A preprocessing nearest mean classifier is employed as a rough classifier. It determines to which set a particular input bitmap belongs, and routes the input to the appropriate network.

Two sets of features vectors are extracted from each bitmap. The first feature vector is obtained through a Hadamard Transform, and yields a feature vector of 66 elements. The second feature vector is obtained through a *Grid Transform*. The Grid Transform divides the input bitmap into 64 separate square regions and sums the number of black pixels in each region. This yields a feature vector of 64 elements. A Discriminant Transformation is applied to both feature vectors to increase feature discrimination and reduce vector size.

Table 1: Results of Machine Print Experiments

Set	Num	Acc.	Sub.	Rej.	Speed
S1	8237	98.3	1.4	0.3	77.7
S2	3246	88.5	11.2	0.3	180.4
S3	4531	98.0	1.7	0.3	167.8
S4	5299	99.2	0.6	0.2	441.6
S5	4958	97.4	1.7	0.9	115.3
S6	4888	99.2	0.6	0.2	444.4
S7	5658	98.1	1.2	0.7	176.8

The results are presented in Table 1. The number column is the number of characters in the test set. Accuracy, substitution, and reject are all percentage values. Speed is in characters per second on a SPARC II running Unix. The speed value only reflects the Elliptical network processing time, and does not reflect feature extraction time, or the time for rough classification. The average speed for all networks was 211 cps with an accuracy of 97.5%. One can see from the results that the network performed with high accuracy and with very high speed. Given the nature of the data set, this justifies the claim that the Elliptical network can efficiently generalize training information to correctly classify noisy data.

V. Conclusions and Discussion

This paper discussed the design of an artificial neural network architecture based on a neuron that has a hyper-ellipsoidal activation function. A training algorithm was provided that guarantees correct classification of training data. Experimental evidence demonstrated the classification abilities and speed that this architecture can provide.

We are currently improving upon the design of the pre-processing classifier, in order to increase the reliability of feature vector routing. Experiments have shown that by allowing a few characters to be members of more than one set, we can get preprocessing accuracy of over 99%.

We are also developing machine print databases for training that we believe will lead to better classification results. The proposed database will have more uniform representation of each of the 64 character classes. The database will combine live package images of characters with computer generated characters. The computer generated characters will represent over 40 font types and 8-18 point sizes. We will also develop a set of distortion filters similar to [8] that can be applied to the font sets to generate characters with defects representative of our package labels.

Finally, we are looking at ways to further improve the efficiency of the network, including methods to segment the decision space. This would restrict the number of Processing Layer neurons that need to process input, and reduce processing time.

References

[1] D. E. Rumelhart, G. E. Hinton, and R. J. Williams, "Learning internal representations by error propagation," in *Parallel Distributed Processing Volume I* (D. E. Rumelhart and J. L. McClelland, eds.), pp. 318–362, Cambridge, MA: The MIT Press, 1986.

[2] R. P. Lippmann, "An introduction to computing with neural nets," *IEEE ASSP Magazine*, pp. 4–22, April 1987.

[3] D. L. Reilly, C. Scofield, C. Elbaum, and L. N. Cooper, "Learning system architectures composed of multiple learning modules," in *IEEE First International Conference on Neural Networks*, vol. II, pp. 495–503, 1987.

[4] L. N. Cooper, C. Elbaum, and D. L. Reilly, "Self organizing general pattern class separator and identifier," *US Patent Number 4326259*, 1982.

[5] S. N. Kavuri and V. Venkatasubramanian, "Solving the hidden node problem in networks with ellipsoidal units and related issues," in *International Joint Conference on Neural Networks*, vol. I, (Baltimore), pp. 775–780, 1992.

[6] P. M. Kelly, D. R. Hush, and J. M. White, "An adaptive algorithm for modifying hyperellipsoidal decision surfaces," in *International Joint Conference on Neural Networks*, vol. IV, (Baltimore), pp. 196–201, 1992.

[7] M. C. Moed, "An elliptical neuron-based network for character classification," tech. rep., United Parcel Service, Research and Development, Danbury, CT, January 1992.

[8] H. S. Baird, "Document image defect models," in *Proceedings IAPR Workshop on Syntactic and Structural Pattern Recognition*, (Murray Hill, NJ), pp. 38–46, 1990.

Parallel Implementation of Time Delay Neural Networks for Phoneme Recognition

D.M. Weber*

Department of Electrical and Electronic Engineering

University of Stellenbosch, Stellenbosch 7600, South Africa.

Email: weber@firga.sun.ac.za

Abstract— **Large training problems using the back propagation (BP) as a training algorithm are very computationally demanding when used for multi layer perceptrons (MLP). In speech recognition applications, this is especially true. In order to overcome these problems, implementation issues were addressed. The algorithm was parallelized by splitting the training database across many processors and updating the network weights using an arithmetic average of the weight updates for each transputer microprocessor. The parallel implementation achieves a speedup factor of 8.8 over a VAX 3600 and scales well up to 16 transputers in a hypercube configuration. Phoneme recognition accuracy for Afrikaans fricatives, nasals, stop consonants and glides are given.**

I. INTRODUCTION

Neural networks are currently being used as pattern classifiers in the speech recognition projects currently being undertaken at the University of Stellenbosch. In this specific case, Time Delay Neural Networks (TDNN) [1] were used to perform phoneme recognition using short time bark scale spectra as features. The neural network is presented with a 210ms "window" of speech for contextual information. What this means is that there are 440 units in the input layer of the neural network. For the average phoneme recognition application, there are 25000-45000 weights in the TDNN. Given further that for a given phoneme class such as stops, there are about 2000 phonemes in the training database and it takes the TDNN trained with a modified BP algorithm about 800 iterations through the entire training data corpus to converge. This is a massive computational problem. A VAX 3600 can take an unreasonable amount of cpu time to accomplish this task.

The software implementing the TDNN was originally written for the VAX under VMS in C. Due to the compu-

tational demand and excessive training times, a parallel solution was considered. Any parallel solution had to consider the speedup potential and the fact that rewriting the code in another language was considered undesirable. The idea was to re-use as much of the original code as possible. This immediately eliminated fine grained parallelism as a possible means of parallelizing the algorithm. Fortunately, BP lends itself well to coarse grained parallelism if the training data is split across the available processors, a technique known as domain decomposition. The algorithm must keep the network weights consistent across all the processors so that the algorithm functions correctly. It is this sharing of information that restricts the speedup factor as the number of processors is increased.

The final speedups obtained were in the order of a factor 10 faster than a VAX 3600 for 16 transputer processors on the 64 transputer machine at the University of Stellenbosch. For typical network training parameters and a processor network configured as a hypercube, the speedups scale well up to 16 processors. The recognition results are presented in the last section.

II. BACK PROPAGATION OVERVIEW

In order to see how the BP could be parallelized, we must take a brief look at how the algorithm works. Details can be found in [2] and [3]. The actual network architecture used was a TDNN [1]. There are a few topological differences but the training algorithm is essentially identical to algorithms for ordinary Multi-Layer Perceptrons (MLP). The following notation will be used in the discussions that follow:

- ω_{ij} represents a weight in the weight matrix.

- $U = \{u_1, \ldots, u_N\}$ is the set of N input/training tokens.

- E^u is the error with respect to input token u. This is computed by feeding an input token forward through the network and comparing the network output against the input token.

*The author would like to thank Datafusion Systems for their support of this research.

- The subscript p represents a variable computed on the pth processor in the network.

The algorithm can be summarized to a series of steps:

1. Set $\partial E / \partial w_{ij} = 0$.

2. Present an input token, $u \in U$, to the network and compute E^u.

3. Compute the partial derivative, $\partial E^u / \partial w_{ij}$ using the back-propagation algorithm.

4. $\partial E / \partial w_{ij} \mathrel{+}= \partial E^u / \partial w_{ij}$ (Accumulate average weight update).

5. Repeat from step 2 until $Nupdate$ input tokens in the set U have been presented.

6. Use the accumulated gradient $\partial E / \partial w_{ij}$ to update the weights ω_{ij} using some update rule.

7. Repeat from step one until some convergence criterion has been reached.

The back-propagation algorithm and update rule referred to above can be any means of computing the weight update for an MLP. In this case an algorithm implementing a momentum rule and bounded weight updates was used. This algorithm had good convergence properties and is described by [2].

From this algorithm, a few obvious routes to parallelism are apparent. Each computation of $\partial E^u / \partial w_{ij}$ can be performed independently of all the other training tokens. This can be performed in parallel and the resulting processor specific accumulated error vector for processor p, $\partial E_p / \partial w_{ij}$, is passed to some central node for computation of the final accumulated error vector $\partial E / \partial w_{ij}$. Further parallelization can be obtained by decomposing the problem into individual MLP layers or even individual neurons. The primary tradeoffs are discussed in the following section.

III. Parallel Implementation

When choosing a scheme for parallelization, there are a number of factors to be taken into account. The most important of these is the degree of parallelism (see Davidson [4] for a tutorial). A list of some of these considerations is given here.

1. **Fine vs. Course Grained Parallelism**: Fine grained parallelism means that the computational load is spread at a very low level on small jobs such as the computation of the output of a single neuron. Course grained parallelism implies that each processor be allocated a substantially larger task such as

the computation of an entire iteration of the back-propagation algorithm.

2. **Topology Independence**: Any parallel environment that offers parallel programming constructs that are independent of the way that the processors are connected holds a considerable advantage in that the programmer is relieved of all message routing problems.

3. **Communication Overheads**: A naive approach here can result in paralysis, not parallelism. The idea is to minimize the communication requirements between processors so as to maximize the time each processor actually performs computations.

The original program was implemented in ANSI C on a VAX. This made a C implementation much more attractive than Occam. The algorithm is briefly described now. Note that there are P processors available and that the steps in italics (steps 3 to 6) are executed in parallel.

1. Divide the N input and training tokens U into P sets $U_1 \ldots U_P$ of approximately equal sizes. Distribute a set U_p to each processor p.

2. *Set $\partial E_p / \partial w_{ij} = 0$.*

3. *Present an input token, $u \in U_p$, to the network and compute E_p^u.*

4. *Compute the partial derivatives, $\partial E_p^u / \partial w_{ij}$ using the back-propagation algorithm.*

5. *$\partial E_p / \partial w_{ij} \mathrel{+}= \partial E_p^u / \partial w_{ij}$ (Accumulate average weight update).*

6. *Repeat from step 3 until* Nupdate *input tokens from the set U_p have been presented.*

7. Accumulate $\partial E_p / \partial w_{ij}$ to obtain $\partial E / \partial w_{ij}$

8. Distribute $\partial E / \partial w_{ij}$ to all processors.

9. Use the accumulated gradient $\partial E / \partial w_{ij}$ to update the weights ω_{ij} using some update rule on a per processor basis.

10. Repeat from step 2 until some convergence criterion has been reached.

This algorithm requires a local copy of the weight matrix to be maintained on each processor. These were updated locally using identical update rules so the weights, in spite of being locally updated, remain the same across all processors. The only communication involved then becomes the accumulation and distribution of $\partial E / \partial w_{ij}$. The weight update calculation for each processor is identical so this step in the algorithm cannot be considered to be parallel. The bulk of the computational load is the feed forward and back-propagation portion of the training algorithm and this is successfully parallelized in this implementation.

The efficiency of this implementation is limited by how often the weighs must be updated. For a typical phoneme recognition application, the weights can be updated after 150 input tokens have been processed per processor.

This algorithm was successfully implemented and, using conditional compilation, is portable as a single source to most platforms that support ANSI C. The parallel constructs were implemented using the EXPRESS environment.

IV. Performance Benchmarks

In this section, the performance improvements of the parallel version over sequential versions will be investigated. The performance of the parallel version is very dependent on how the configuration is set up. In particular, the performance is very dependent on the *Nupdate* parameter. This parameter controls how frequently the network weights are updated as described in the previous section. If the weights are updated very frequently, a high communication overhead is incurred. This results in poor performance on large Transputer networks. For this reason, the *Nupdate* parameter was chosen to be typical of a phoneme recognizer training problem.

The final benchmarks were tested on a small but typical stop consonant recognizer training problem. All relevant TDNN parameters were chosen to be the same as for stop consonant recognition. This TDNN was then trained for 30 epochs, an epoch being one pass through the training data. Actual convergence was not used as a criterion because the actual number of epochs before convergence can vary considerably between serial and parallel versions with no bias in favor of either implementation. This occurs because of the random numbers added to each input token to help generalization are, well, random. It was, however, possible to ensure that all versions received the same initial weight matrix.

The time taken for each training session was then measured. The tests performed on the Transputers were performed on binary hypercube topologies [4]. Binary hypercubes of order m have 2^m processors. The transputers cannot support a hypercube of orders greater than 4 because only 4 interprocessor links are available on the device. For this reason, benchmark results show 1,2,4,8 and 16 processor configurations. The 16 processor configuration had one link in the hypercube interconnection structure removed to allow for a link to the host computer. Some experiments with larger mesh configurations

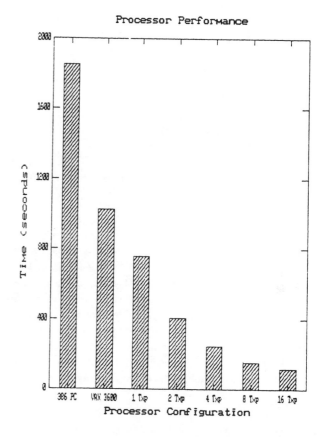

Figure 1: Processor performance for a 20Mhz 386/387 PC, VAX 3600 and various Transputer hypercube configurations

resulted in poor performance.

The benchmark results show a speedup factor of 8.8 over a VAX 3600 and a factor of 15.5 over a 20MHz 386 PC with a 387 numeric co-processors. This is a great improvement and illustrates that parallel solutions can be very successful if they are carefully designed.

V. Recognition Experiments

This section briefly discusses the results of four consonant recognition experiments performed with the parallel TDNN. First, a short description of the speech database, from which the phonemes were extracted, will be given. The next section will describe the pre-processing that was performed on the speech signal before it was presented to the TDNN and the remaining sections will describe the recognition experiments and the results obtained.

A. The Speech Database

For performance evaluation, a large vocabulary database of Afrikaans words, containing about 35000 phonemes, was used. The database consists of phonetically balanced sentences uttered by 20 different speakers. All utterances

Nasals Confusion Matrix			
	m	n	η
m	319	74	52
n	117	840	116
η	5	42	213
Npairs : 1778			
Ncorrect : 1372			
% Correct : 77.2%			

Table 1: Confusion matrix for nasal recognition.

Glides Confusion Matrix		
	j	w
j	168	26
w	4	89
Npairs : 287		
Ncorrect : 257		
% Correct : 89.5%		

Table 2: Confusion matrix for glide recognition.

were recorded in a sound-proof booth and digitized at a 16kHz sampling rate. The 39 male and female speakers making up the database were divided into a training group of 20 speakers and a test group of 19 speakers. Care was taken to ensure that the sexes were evenly distributed across the two groups. The acoustic waveforms of each phoneme used in the experiments were then extracted from the database and processed as described in the following section. The total number of phonemes from the appropriate classes in the database was over 15000.

B. Pre-processing

Input speech was sampled at 16kHz, preemphasized by $H(z) = 1 - 0.9z^{-1}$ and a 512 point FFT computed every 10 ms. Bark-scale coefficients were computed from the power spectrum by computing log energies in each Bark-scale critical band [5]. Each Bark spectrum is called a frame. An input token to the TDNN consists of 21 frames of speech with a 10ms frame rate, thus effectively framing the phoneme with a time frame of 210ms. All Bark-scale coefficients for a given input token were normalized. This was accomplished by subtracting from every coefficient the average coefficient energy computed over all 21 frames of an input token and then normalizing each coefficient to lie between +1 and −1.

C. Recognition Results

A total of four different experiments were performed, corresponding to the recognition of stops, nasals, fricatives and glides. As was motivated in the introduction, a separate TDNN was trained for each of these broad phoneme classes. The TDNN configuration in terms of layers, delays etc. was adjusted to reflect the requirements of each phoneme class. It should be noted that the TDNN algorithm's convergence criterion was the maximum recognition accuracy on the test data because the test set recognition rates often decrease to a level below the maximum recognition rate if the network is over trained. Tables 2, 1, 3 and 4 show these results.

C.1. Nasal Recognition

There are a total of three different nasals used in Afrikaans in the database. The TDNN recognition results are given in table 1. Nasal phonemes are usually recognizable by the formant transitions either side of the phoneme and not by the formant structure of the nasal itself. The input token spans a 210ms segment of speech making contextual information or the formant transitions either side of the nasal available to the network. The result obtained was good.

C.2. Glides

The glides are a small class of consonant found with a relatively low frequency in Afrikaans. The recognition results are good because the two phonemes are quite different and also because there are only two of them in the set. The recognition results are given in table 2.

C.3. Stops Recognition

The Afrikaans language uses a total of six stops, all of which were used in the recognition experiment. The list and recognition results are given in table 3.

Stops are phonemes that are very short in duration, usually around 10-20ms which is very close to the 10ms time resolution of the Bark spectra used to make up the input token. Their spectral characteristics are also fine and difficult to distinguish. In this case, the neural network relies heavily on contextual information. The results are not surprising given the coarse features used.

C.4. Fricative Recognition

A total of seven fricatives were used for this experiment. Table 4 gives the results for the experiment. Fricatives are fairly easily recognizable phonemes on the spectrogram. They have long durations and clear spectral characteristics, making them easier to recognize than the nasals and stops of the previous two experiments.

This section presented and discussed the results of four recognition experiments. The 79.9% accuracy achieved for fricative recognition is very satisfactory. The recognition results for nasals was surprisingly good and showed

Stops Confusion Matrix						
	b	d	*g*	k	p	t
b	208	13	53	31	15	113
d	66	230	62	48	12	346
g	3	15	67	34	3	15
k	23	0	40	385	3	160
p	45	0	7	45	28	204
t	3	4	22	51	0	828

Npairs : 3182
Ncorrect : 1746
% Correct : 54.87%

Table 3: Confusion matrix for stops recognition

Fricatives Confusion Matrix							
	f	h	s	v	x	z	ʃ
f	274	6	12	14	40	0	2
h	0	62	2	21	2	2	0
s	11	6	594	2	60	6	8
v	10	30	2	144	10	0	0
x	24	10	4	8	223	0	8
z	0	6	6	3	6	32	0
ʃ	0	0	12	0	5	0	20

Npairs : 1687
Ncorrect : 1349
% Correct : 79.96%

Table 4: Confusion matrix for fricative recognition

that the TDNN architecture is capable of using context in the recognition process. The results for the recognition of stops were disappointingly low when compared to results obtained using classical techniques. It is expected that these results will improve as the TDNN's are refined and the Bark scale spectra used as input tokens are improved.

It is important to note that these results were obtained using the same type of recognition machine. It was not necessary to make a detailed study of each class of phoneme and then develop complex algorithms for the recognition of individual phonemes in each class. This is a considerable advantage of this method. The parallel implementation of the TDNN algorithm proved to be a major asset. The TDNN algorithm converged after 800-1500 epochs for all the phoneme classes tested. Reference [1] reported training times of between 20000 and 50000 using a TDNN on similar problems with the momentum method and a staged learning strategy. Thus, the convergence rate has been increased by a factor of between 20 and 50.

VI. Conclusion

The parallel version of the TDNN has proved to be a fast implementation of a computationally very demanding algorithm. It is functionally identical to the sequential version and is therefore highly portable. Communications overheads do play a limiting factor in the performance speedups as the number of processors in the network increases but the solution provides a far superior (in terms of speed) solution to the VAX/VMS and MS-DOS versions. This implementation makes back-propagation neural networks useful for very large problems as has been demonstrated in the speech recognition experiments.

Two acknowledgments are in order. First, Jako van der Merwe who wrote the original sequential version of the program and developed the sequential training algorithm and second, Neels Krüger who helped run the recognition experiments. Thanks to both.

References

[1] Alex Waibel, Toshiyuki Hanazawa, Geoffrey Hinton, Kiyoro Shikano, and Kevin J. Lang. Phoneme recognition using time-delay neural networks. *IEEE Transactions on Acoustics, Speech, and Signal Processing*, 37(3):328–339, Mar 1989.

[2] J.J.N. van der Merwe. Connectionist networks for phoneme recognition. Master's thesis, University of Stellenbosch, 1990.

[3] Richard P. Lippmann. An introduction to computing with neural networks. *IEEE Transactions on Acoustics, Speech, and Signal Processing*, pages 4–22, Apr 1987.

[4] David B. Davidson. A parallel processing tutorial. *IEEE Antennas and Propagation Society Magazine*, pages 6–19, April 1990.

[5] E. Zwicker. Subdivision of the audible frequency range into critical bands (frequenzgruppen). *The Journal of the Acoustical Society of America*, 33(2):248, Feb 1961.

Multiresolution Neural Networks for Omnifont Character Recognition

Jin Wang   Jack Jean

Department of Computer Science and Engineering

Wright State University

Dayton, Ohio 45435, U.S.A.

Abstract— A multiresolution OCR using neural networks is proposed in this paper for omnifont character recognition. It is motivated by human reading process in which a low resolution is used to effectively process the majority of clean and unambiguous text, while a more complicated recognition scheme is invoked only when a high resolution is needed. Compared with the method that utilizes single resolution, the multiresolution system not only speeds up recognition by up to 20 times, but also improves accuracy of isolated character recognition from 99.8% to 99.9%. The multiresolution approach captures the essence of better reading, and provides the building blocks for the next-generation OCR systems.

I. Introduction

The applications of neural network technology to the problem of optical character recognition (OCR) have been mostly concentrated on handwritten digit or Kanji character classification [1, 2, 3, 4, 10], only a few are concerned with printed character recognition [11, 12, 13, 14]. Although commercial omnifont OCR systems have been available in recent years, the overall word recognition accuracies of the best products are only about 95% in 1990 [8] and 97% in 1991 [9] due to diverse document formats, noise/distortion in character images, and degradation in print quality. As concluded in a recent survey [5], omnifont OCR performance should be greatly improved to meet the needs of document image processing and office automation.

One way to improve classification accuracy is to apply techniques developed for handwritten character recognition to their machine print counterparts. Though theoretically sound, this approach has serious performance problems due to high computational requirements. Using the Neocognitron model, for instance, a system trained on 35 alphanumeric characters takes 3.3 seconds on a SUN SPARC workstation to recognize one character [3]. As another example, the neural network developed at AT&T for ZIP code recognition can process up to 10 digits per second using a digital signal processor [1], and about 1000

digits when a specially-designed VLSI chip is employed [2]. Without special hardware support, those throughput numbers will go even lower for the task of classifying 62 alphanumeric characters; as a result they can hardly be useful in practice since commercial omnifont OCR systems can deliver an average software speed of 400 words per minute [9], or about 35 to 40 characters per second.

The solution proposed in this paper is *multiresolution* processing, a technique commonly used in image processing and vision understanding but not yet in neural network-based OCR. While reading document text, humans seem to switch between a fast reading mode and a slow one. When the text is reasonably clean and unambiguous, no special attention is needed for recognition and the reading goes smoothly and quickly. When noisy or confusing characters are encountered (e.g., is it "w" or 'w', 'g' or '9'), however, a closer look is given to relevant details and the reading slows down. In other words, multiresolution processing is employed in reading text: A low resolution is used to effectively process the majority of clean and non-confusing characters, while a more complicated recognition scheme is invoked only when a high resolution is needed.

Multiresolution processing is not new in pattern recognition. In speech recognition, for example, Lang and Waibel discussed the idea of multiresolution training to speed up the learning process of their time-delayed neural network (TDNN) [17], but the network itself was not multiresolution.

In the next section, an omnifont multiresolution OCR using neural networks is described. Experiments and results are detailed in Section 3. Concluding remarks are given in the last section.

II. Multiresolution OCR and Network Generalization

The multiresolution OCR, shown in Figure 1, has two different neural networks: Net_1, a simple and fast network, and Net_2, a sophisticated and powerful one. Net_1 uses a low resolution to effectively process most of the characters that are clean and unambiguous. Net_2 is invoked only when either discriminating details need to be examined in

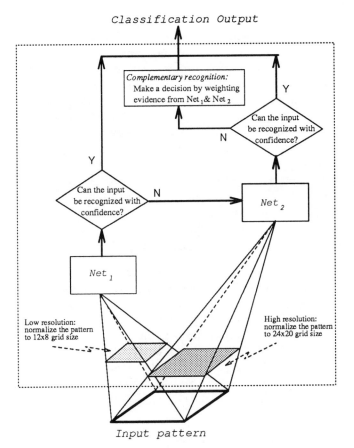

Classification Output

Complementary recognition:
Make a decision by weighting
evidence from Net_1 & Net_2

Can the input
be recognized with
confidence?

Can the input
be recognized with
confidence?

Net_2

Net_1

Low resolution:
normalize the pattern
to 12x8 grid size

High resolution:
normalize the pattern
to 24x20 grid size

Input pattern

Figure 1: A multiresolution OCR using Net_1, a simple and fast neural network, and Net_2, a sophisticated and powerful one. Here redundancy of complementary recognition is exploited at a high level.

high resolution or character patterns with noise/distortion cannot be reliably recognized by the simple net. A high rejection threshold is adopted to insure that Net_1 makes almost no errors. Since Net_1 and Net_2 differ in their architectures, they are likely to make different kinds of mistakes and complement each other. Thus even when Net_2 cannot recognize the input pattern *alone* due to excessive noise/distortion, a final decision can be made by properly weighting evidence available from Net_1 and Net_2.

A. Net_1 and Net_2 Architectures

The key to multiresolution processing is to keep the reading burden, say, 85% of characters, on Net_1. This not only improves the overall throughput of the system, but also allows powerful but computationally expensive neural network architectures to be considered for Net_2. Therefore Net_1 should be simple, fast, with very few substitution errors and a relatively low rejection rate. Note that at a low resolution noise/distortion in characters is less severe, and the degree of freedom is reduced. Both helps Net_1 achieve a relatively robust performance. A fully-connected feed-

forward network with one hidden layer was thus selected for Net_1.

Character patterns can be rejected by Net_1 for many reasons such as severe noise/distortion, or increased shape resemblance in low resolution. A robust recognition of those patterns calls for sophisticated neural network techniques for Net_2. While some works employ conventional methods to extract features explicitly in a preprocessing stage [10, 13], the state-of-the-art neural networks rely on their problem-tailored architectures to perform feature extraction directly from the raw image [1, 2, 3, 17]. This architecture-based neural network approach not only avoids the problem of losing vital information due to imperfect feature extraction, but also offers a solution to integrate statistical methods with syntactic ones in a single framework. For this reason, eight variants of the locally-connected neural network architecture developed by Le-Cun *et al.* at AT&T [1, 2] were considered for Net_2.

Among the eight network candidates, the one illustrated in Figure 2 was selected as the best choice through experiments. In this network, the four hidden layers are denoted H_1 through H_4. Local features are extracted by 15 *feature maps* via a 5×5 moving window at H_1, and then averaged over a 2×2 non-overlapping area at H_2. Here a feature map consists of many hidden neurons and each neuron, acting as a feature detector, has the same set of weights, including the bias (*weight sharing*). Similar operations are applied at H_3 and H_4. The output neurons are then fully connected to H_4 to perform alphanumeric character recognition. The great reduction of adjustable weights, achieved through heavy constraints imposed on the architecture and weights, effectively avoids overfitting and consequently improves the network's generalization.

Two modifications were made in the architecture to further reduce the number of adjustable weights and to speed up network training which was in the order of days. First, the operations performed at H_2 and H_4 were simplified as a weight averaging over a 2×2 area with bias set to zero, and no sigmoid function was applied after the averaging. Thus there were no adjustable weights between H_2/H_1 and between H_4/H_3. The effectiveness of this simplification was confirmed by our experiments. Second, the normal 0-1 representation rather than bipolar representation was used for binary input patterns. This is because the input character area of 24×20 is enlarged to 36×32 in order for the 5×5 window to be placed at any position of the image boundary. Since at the 24×20 resolution black pixels count about 43% out of the 480 pixels, the percentage of black pixels in the *enlarged* area is only 18% (43% * (24x20)/(36x32)). More than 30% speedup in training time was obtained after routines for the signal forward passing and weight updating at H_1 were specially coded for binary inputs.

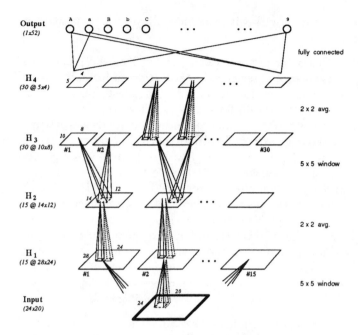

Figure 2: The locally-connected architecture of Net_2, modified from the one developed by LeCun *et al.* at AT&T. Fifteen feature maps are used at H_1, and 2-to-1 feature map connections are used between H_3 and H_2.

B. Complementary Recognition

For a given training data set, its samples are used to train both Net_1 and Net_2. The information contained in the training set is extracted *twice*, once by Net_1 and once by Net_2, but each with a different architecture and under a different resolution. The two sets of features so extracted are thus quite different, resulting in complementary recognition of Net_1 and Net_2. This *redundancy of recognition*, a principle suggested in [5, 6] and shown to be quite successful in [6, 7], can be exploited at a high level by properly weighting evidence from Net_1 and Net_2 when neither of them can make a decision alone. Note that this complementary recognition differs from traditional approaches where two or more conventional feature extraction algorithms are invoked all the time [6, 7].

C. Further Speedup

The difference in classification speed between Net_1 and Net_2 is about 50 times as shown in the next section. Thus even if Net_1 can process, say, 85% of the characters, Net_2 will still be invoked at a 15% rate which limits the overall speedup of the proposed multiresolution approach. A careful observation of the rejected characters from Net_1 indicates that i) at a high resolution most of the rejects are clean and unambiguous, and can be recognized by a simple net; and ii) the rest of data usually contain severe noise/distortion, calling for a sophisticated net such as Net_2.

Thus a *simple* high-resolution network, Net_{12}, can be added as a filter in front of Net_2 to reduce its invocation rate. In other words, Net_2 would be invoked only when neither Net_1 nor Net_{12} can recognize the input. Like Net_1, Net_{12} should be simple and fast, yet at the high resolution a simple net tends to give unsatisfactory generalization when the training data set is not large enough. The solution adopted here is to apply the weight smoothing technique [18] which imposes constraints on neighboring weights in each hidden neuron to capture the spatial correlations present in input patterns. In our experiments, Net_{12} was able to process about 80% of the rejects from Net_1, effectively reducing Net_2 invocation rate to 2.2-4.0% from 13.4-17.6% and achieving a speedup of 14-20 compared with that of using Net_2 alone.

III. Experiments

A low resolution grid size of 12×8 (12 rows by 8 columns) was chosen for Net_1 and a normal (high) resolution of 24×20 for Net_{12} and Net_2. Patterns of size 12×8 were obtained by a shrinking process at run-time using linear normalization and some proper thresholding. Both 12×8 and 24×20 bitmaps are black-and-white.

In the following, we describe four issues: training/testing data sets, pairwise reject thresholding for Net_1, individual network training/testing, and multiresolution neural networks.

A. Training and Testing Data Sets

A total of 22,644 alphanumeric data samples were collected from multiple optical scans of 21 LaTeX fonts, 13 Macintosh fonts, and some typewriter fonts using a 300 dpi scanner. Eight of the 21 LaTeX fonts are of size 12 and the remaining ones are of size 10. All characters were segmented and normalized into 24×20 bitmaps.

Among the 22,644 characters, 15,080 were partitioned into a training set of 8508 samples, and a testing set of 6572, denoted TEST1. The remaining 7564 characters were noisy data obtained from xerox copies of the test data images (first generation and second generation). These data plus those of TEST1 form a larger testing set, TEST2, of 14,136 (=6572+7564) characters.

Although there are 62 classes (A-Z, a-z, 0-9) in each font, some of them cannot be distinguished from each other after normalization and they are considered equivalent for recognition purposes. This shortens the list to the following 52 classes where equivalent classes are indicated by square brackets:

AB[Cc]DEFGHIJKLM[Oo0]PQR[Ss]T[Uu][Vv][Ww][Xx]Y[Zz]
abdefghijk[l1]mnpqrty
23456789

B. Pairwise Thresholding

An input pattern is rejected by Net_1 if the difference between the maximum output and the second maximum output is less than a threshold. While a high threshold ensures a low substitution error rate of Net_1, it severely reduces the overall throughput of the system since the computation burden is shifted to Net_2. On the other hand, using a low threshold may speed things up, but it is likely to increase Net_1's errors and the system is doomed to give poor recognition. A *universal* thresholding simply does not work well because a high threshold is needed to reject confusing characters such as 'i'/'j' and 'O'/'Q' which look even more similar to each other at a low resolution, while a low threshold would suffice for the rest of the cases.

The solution adopted here is *pairwise* thresholding: A different rejection threshold is used for a different pair of characters, the top two choices of Net_1 for a given input. For instance, a high threshold is used for 'O' and 'Q', and a low threshold for 'O' and 'j'. Thus 52×52 pairs would require 2704 thresholds. Each threshold was determined by the training set from which Net_1 would produce, for each input, the top two choices and two corresponding confidence levels. In our experiments, the use of pairwise thresholding reduced Net_2's invocation rate by 4.5% compared with that of single thresholding.

C. Network Training and Testing

In the following we describe training and testing of Net_1, the low resolution net, Net_{12}, the "filter" before applying Net_2, and Net_2, the high resolution net. All training as well as testing was conducted on DEC 5000/200 workstations (rated at 27 MIPS) using single precision floating-point arithmetics.

C.1. Net_1

In the training data set, some character images of one font are exactly the same as, or only a few pixels different from, some other characters of another font. For example, 'I' of one font and 'l' of another. This becomes more of the case at 12×8 resolution. The normal "one-high-only" training scheme, in which only one of the output neurons is set to high and the rest are set to low, was modified to "one-or-two-high" training. For instance, if two training patterns 'I' and 'l' are detected to be of less than 5 pixels in difference, the output neurons corresponding to 'I' and 'l' are set to high when those two patterns are presented.

Net_1 was trained on the 8508 training samples with 92 neurons in the hidden layer for 80 passes, and it took 5.5 hours. The performances were no error and 5.36% rejects on the training set, 0.02% errors and 13.39% rejects on TEST1, and 0.08% errors and 17.58% rejects on TEST2. The throughput was 235 characters per second.

C.2. Net_{12}

Net_{12} is similar to Net_1 except that the input resolution is 24×20. It was trained on the training set with the smoothing operation [18] for 80 passes, and it took about 29 hours. The performance was 99.59% on TEST1 and 99.00% on TEST2 (with no rejection). The throughput was 80 characters per second.

C.3. Net_2

The training of Net_2 was much more time-consuming. One way to train Net_2 is to present only those training samples rejected by Net_1 or Net_{12}. Though fast, this approach resulted in poor generalization because too few samples could be presented and a strong internet dependency was established. Thus Net_2 was trained from scratch.

To find an appropriate architecture for Net_2, a total of eight nets, denoted A through H and shown in Table 1, were trained and tested. In this table, the number of features maps in H_i is denoted as $|H_i|$. The connections between H_3 and H_2 are represented as $\{r_1, \ldots, r_N\}$, where $N = |H_1|$, and r_k $(k = 1, \ldots, N)$ is the number of H_3 feature maps whose neurons take inputs from k feature maps at H_2. For instance, net C has five feature maps at H_1 (and thus at H_2); "$r_2=10$" means neurons at 10 feature maps of H_3 take their inputs from two feature maps at H_2 ($\binom{5}{2} = 10$). Note that "$r_5=5$" means there are five H_3 feature maps each taking inputs from all the feature maps at H_2.

Table 1: ARCHITECTURES FOR Net_2 AND TRAINING TIME

Net	$|H_1|$	$H_3 - H_2$ Connections	CPU hrs /Pass	# of Passes	CPU Days
A	4	{0,6,0,10}	1.09	140	6.4
B	4	{0,6,0,15}	1.49	140	8.7
C	5	{0,10,10,5,5}	1.93	140	11.3
D	6	{0,15,0,15,0,0}	1.83	140	10.7
E	8	{8,28,0, ..., 0}	1.21	140	7.1
F	15	{30,0, ..., 0}	0.93	180	6.9
G	20	{40,0, ..., 0}	1.26	180	9.4
H	30	{60,0, ..., 0}	1.88	180	14.1

The eight nets were trained for up to 180 passes and the training was stopped if no recognition improvement could be achieved when tested on TEST1. The training time, measured on a DECstation 5000/200, is also given in Table 1. The long training time was within expectation as it took 3 days to train the ZIP code classifier with 4 feature maps on a SPARC workstation [1]. Network recognition rate on TEST1 and TEST2 vs. classification speed is shown in Figure 3-(a). The next step is to select one of the eight nets and construct a high-performance multiresolution OCR using the available building blocks.

D. Multiresolution Neural Networks

When combining nets, will the selection of net E or net H, the best two among the eight, yield a better overall recognition than the other choices? To see which of the Net_2 candidates should be chosen for the final combination, six nets, B, C, D, E, F, and H, were tested. To separate the speedup effect of adding Net_{12} in front to Net_2, we first discuss combining Net_1 and Net_2.

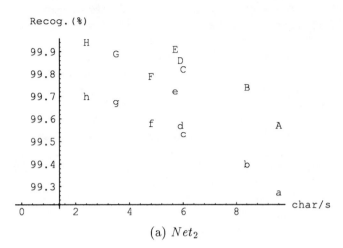

(a) Net_2

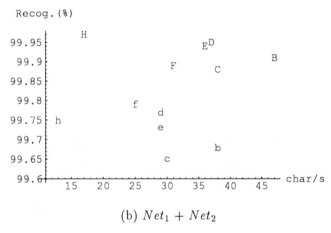

(b) $Net_1 + Net_2$

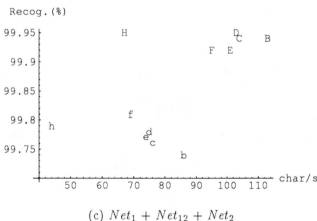

(c) $Net_1 + Net_{12} + Net_2$

Figure 3: Recognition accuracy vs. classification speed. For each net, the recognition rate on TEST1 is represented by the upper-case letter corresponding to the net in Net_2, while the rate on TEST2 is by the lower-case letter.

D.1. $Net_1 + Net_2$

Each of the six Net_2 candidates was further trained for 5 passes with those training samples that were rejected by Net_1. This "customization" process slightly adjusted its weights in favor of the rejected samples. The resulting net was thus better equipped to handle noisy and confusing patterns it targets while not losing its overall ability to recognize ordinary characters.

For Net_1 and Net_2, the activation value of an output neuron is used as the confidence score. When Net_2 is invoked and the input cannot be confidently recognized, the top two choices and their corresponding confidence scores from both Net_1 and Net_2 are weighted in favor of Net_2 to make a final decision. As an example, let {(O, 0.7), (G, 0.6)} be the output from Net_1 and {(G, 0.6), (C, 0.4)} from Net_2. First, the scores from Net_1 are weighted by 1 and the scores from Net_2 are weighted by 2; the two lists are then combined and sorted to produce {(G, 1.8), (C, 0.8), (O, 0.7)}; finally the scores in the candidate list are renormalized to the range of 0.1 to 0.9. In this example, 'G' is selected as the recognition result.

The resulting six multiresolution OCRs were then tested on TEST1 and TEST2, and their performances are summarized in Table 3-(b). Net_2 invocation rates were 13.39% on TEST1 and 17.58% on TEST2. Although net F was an average achiever when used alone, the OCR with F as Net_2 delivered the highest recognition of 99.79% on TEST2. This rate is even higher than that of net E, the best candidate of Net_2, and represents 200% in the reduction of error rate compared with that of using net F alone (0.21 vs. 0.42). Note that net F was also the *least* expensive among the eight candidates in terms of CPU hour per training pass (see Table 1). Although it has 368,212 connections, 262,080 are at H_1. Our implementation that targeted to binary inputs drastically reduced the computation time spent at H_1 and shortened the training time.

D.2. Adding Net_{12}

Net_{12} was further trained with the rejects from Net_1 for five passes and then added in front of Net_2 for more speedup. Net_2's invocation rates were reduced to 2.18% on TEST1 and 3.95% on TEST2. The testing results are summarized in Figure 3-(c). Again the OCR with F as Net_2 did best on TEST2 (99.81%), probably due to a better complementary recognition. The speedup was 14-20 compared with that of using net F alone. The improvement in accuracy over using any of the eight Net_2 candidates alone is statistically significant (by using the criteria listed in the appendix in [4]). Thus this three-net system was chosen as the finalist and it was tested on a faster machine with results shown in the last column of Table 2. From Figure 3 we see that the importance of selecting the optimal architecture for Net_2 is greatly reduced thanks to the net's low invocation rate achieved by multiresolution and filtering.

It is interesting to note that when characters in TEST1 were randomly selected and read by one of the authors at the 24×20 resolution, the rates were 99.83% correct, 0.091% rejected, and 0.076% in error.

In summary, the use of multiresolution OCR not only increases recognition throughput by 14 to 20 times compared with that of using Net_2 alone, but also improves recognition accuracy. In Table 2, a brief comparison of different kinds of OCRs is given.

IV. Conclusions

A neural network-based multiresolution OCR for omnifont character recognition was described in this paper. Motivated by human reading process, this approach used low resolution processing to effectively filter out the majority of clean and unambiguous text, invoking high resolution processing only when needed. It not only drastically speeded up text reading, but also improved recognition accuracy significantly due to the complementing nature of the networks used. In a sense, the multiresolution OCR using multiple nets resembles the "society of mind" approach suggested by Minsky and Papert [19] in answering the scaling-up dilemma facing connectionist models.

The multiresolution OCR has been used as a primary classifier to segment merged characters in document text [12]. By combining deferred and immediate segmentation techniques in a single framework, the high-accuracy of isolated character recognition has been successfully translated into high recognition rates on documents.

As neural network technology is maturing, more neural network solutions will be integrated into future OCR systems. The multiresolution approach captures the essence of better reading, and provides the building blocks for the next-generation OCR systems.

References

[1] Y. LeCun, B. Boser, J. S. Denker, D. Henderson, R. E. Howard, W. Hubbard, and L. D. Jackel, "Handwritten zip code recognition with multilayer networks," *International Conference on Pattern Recognition*, 1990, pp. 35-44.

[2] B. E. Boser, E. Sackinger, J. Bromley, Y. LeCun, and L. D. Jackel, "Hardware requirements for neural network pattern classifiers," *IEEE Mirco*, February, 1992, pp. 32-40.

[3] K. Fukushima and N. Wake, "Handwritten alphanumeric character recognition by the neocognitron," *IEEE Trans. on Neural Networks*, Vol. 2, No. 3, May 1991, pp. 355-365.

[4] Leon Bottou and Vladimir Vapnik, "Local learning algorithms," *Neural Computation*, Vol. 4, 1992, pp. 888-900.

[5] Q. Tian, P. Zhang, T. Alexander, and Y. Kim, "Survey: omnifont printed character recognition," *Proceedings of Visual Communications and Image Processing '91: Image Processing*, SPIE, Vol. 1606, 1991, pp. 260-268.

[6] M. T. Y. Lai and C. Y. Suen, "Automatic recognition of characters by Fourier descriptors and boundary line encodings," *Pattern Recognition*, Vol. 14, 1981, pp. 383-393.

[7] S. N. Srihari, "High-performance reading machines," *Proceedings of the IEEE*, July 1992, pp. 1120-1132.

[8] B. Meng, "Text without typing," *MacWorld*, October 1990, pp. 177-183.

[9] S. Diehl and H. Eglowstein, "Tame the paper tiger," *Byte*, April 1991, pp. 220-238.

[10] M. D. Garris, R. A. Wikinson, and C. L. Wilson, "Methods for enhancing neural network handwritten character recognition," *1991 International Joint Conference on Neural Networks* (I), pp. 695-700.

[11] J. Wang and J. S. N. Jean, "Resolving multifont character confusion with neural networks," *Pattern Recognition*, in press.

[12] J. Wang and J. S. N. Jean, "Segmentation of merged characters by neural networks and shortest-path," *1993 Symposium on Applied Computing*, in press.

[13] A. Rajavelu, M. T. Musavi, and M. V. Shirvaikar, "A neural network approach to character recognition," *Neural Networks*, Vol. 2, No. 5, 1989, pp. 387-389

[14] Y. Hayashi, M. Sakata, T. Nakao, T. Ohno, and S. Ohhashi, "Alphanumeric character recognition using a connectionist model with the pocket algorithm," *1989 International Joint Conference on Neural Networks* (II), pp. 606.

[15] S. Kahan, T. Pavlidis, and H. S. Baird, "On the recognition of printed characters of any font and size," *IEEE Trans. on Pattern Analysis and Machine Intelligence*, Vol. PAMI-9, No. 2, March 1987, pp. 274-288.

[16] S. Harmalkar and R. M. K. Sinha, "Integrating word level knowledge in text recognition," *1990 International Conference on Pattern Recognition*, pp. 758-760.

[17] K. J. Lang and A. H. Waibel, "A time-delayed neural network architecture for isolated word recognition," *Neural Networks*, Vol. 3, No. 1, 1990, pp. 23-43.

[18] J. S. N. Jean and J. Wang, "Weight smoothing to improve network generalization," *IEEE Trans. on Neural Networks*, in press

[19] M. L. Minsky and S. A. Papert, *Perceptrons: An Introduction to Computational Geometry* (expanded edition), The MIT Press, Cambridge, 1988.

Table 2: Performance Comparison of Machine-Printed OCRs

		Conventional OCRs		Neural Networks		
		Literature	Commercial	Others	Net F	Multiresolution
Accuracy (%)	Omnifont	97	97^b, 99.9^c		99.6-99.8	99.8-99.9
	Similar Fonts	99.6		97-99		
Software Speed (char/sec)		5^a	35-40	n/a	7.5	107-148
Hardware Platform		VAX 11/759^a	PC-386^d	n/a	DEC 5000/240^e	
References		[15, 16]	[8, 9]	[13, 14]		

^{a} From [15]. ^{b} Measured on words with spelling check. ^{c} Claimed by vendors. ^{d} About 5 MIPS at 25 MHz. ^{e} Rated at 42 MIPS which is about 50% faster than DEC 5000/200, the machine mentioned in the text.

A PATTERN RECOGNITION ANN THAT ACTS AS

ITS OWN IN-BAND AND/OR BANDPASS FILTER

M. E. Ulug

Intelligent Neurons Inc.,
Deerfield Beach, Florida 33441

ABSTRACT

This paper describes an Orthonormal Neural Network, or for short
ONN. The ONN is a single layer neural network that mimics the
quadratic phase relationship between the adjacent "simple" cells in
the visual cortex. It can perform as a pattern recognition network
that can act as its own in-band filter and/or bandpass filter. The
system design of a single stage electro-optical ONN that classifies
in the forward and filters in the reverse direction is described.

1. INTRODUCTION

An ONN [9],[10,[11],[12]
consists of n input
signals, [n.N] sibling
nodes, and m output nodes.
As shown in Figure 1 each
input signal is connected
to N sibling nodes where
the Fourier series
processing is done. As
will be shown in Section 2
an ONN can map any L_2
mapping function [7]
between input and output
vectors within a mean
square error accuracy
without using hidden
layers or the backpropagation rule. Because the
ONN is a single layer network with no
nonlinearities at its output nodes, it

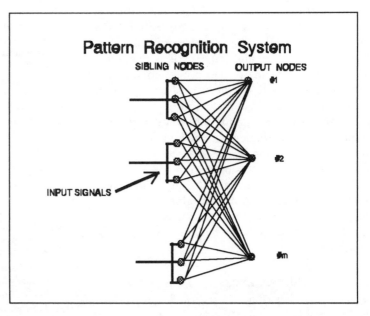

Figure 1

has a bowl shaped error surface. The sharp slopes of this surface
makes the ONN tolerant to loss of computational accuracy and,
therefore, suitable for analog and/or electro-optical implementation. There are two advantages to Fourier processing. First, it
is possible to reduce the training time by initializing the network
using the constant terms of the series. Second, when an ONN is
used as an auto-associative network, the values of the synaptic
links between the sibling and output nodes represent the frequency
spectrum of the signals at the output nodes [10]. This property
makes it easy to design nonlinear bandpass filters. In this
particular signal processing area Kohonen described the noise
filtering properties of linear orthogonal projections [5].
Klimasauskas discussed the use of backpropagation neural networks

for noise filtering [4]. A non-linear filter is also described by Hecht-Nielson [3].

2. ONN AS PATTERN RECOGNITION SYSTEM

We built several pattern recognition systems [11] using the ONN architecture given in Figure 1. The ONN can map any L_2 mapping function between input and output vectors within a mean square error accuracy. We will prove this by referring to the following result [1]: "Given a function $f:[0,1]^n \rightarrow \mathbf{R}^m$, we say that f belongs to L_2 [7] if each of f's coordinate functions is square-integrable on the unit cube (it is easy to relax the $[0,1]^n$ condition). If a vector function of a vector variable is in L_2, then each of its components can be approximated by its Fourier series to any degree of accuracy in the mean squared error sense." For $1 <= k <= [(N-1)/2]$, where N is the number of sibling nodes per input signal (an odd number), the following functions are used in the sibling nodes:

$$\varphi_1(x_i) = \frac{1}{\sqrt{2}} \tag{EQ 1}$$

$$\varphi_{2k}(x_i) = \sin(k\pi x_i) \tag{EQ 2}$$

$$\varphi_{2k+1}(x_i) = \cos(k\pi x_i) \tag{EQ 3}$$

It can be shown that the functions given above are orthonormal for $-1 <= x <= 1$ [8]. In training we are using a modified version of the Widrow and Hoff rule [13]. The modification consists of using the following algorithm, called **Coefficient Initialization,** which reduces the errors to less that 10^{-6} in fewer than 10 cycles:

(i)   Calculate the coefficient of the constant term, c_1, assuming an activation of $f(x) = [(ea)/n]$ as follows:

$$c_1 = [e.a.(2)^{0.5}]/n \tag{EQ 4}$$

where a = the actual target value assigned to the output nodes,
       e = percentage of activation achieved before training,
       n = number of input signals,
(ii) Set the coefficients of the other nodes to zero.

3. ONN AS A BANDPASS FILTER

In the bandpass filter application we used an autoassociative architecture [10],[12]. This is shown in Figure 2. We had seven input signals, n=7, one output node, and eleven sibling nodes per input signal, N=11. This gave us a constant term and five sin and five cos terms per input signal. The arguments of these sin and cos terms varied from (πx_i) to $(5\pi x_i)$. We referred to these as harmonics. The number of sibling nodes per input signal, N, and hence the harmonics, $[(N-1)/2]$, that were deployed depended on the type of application. We took seven consecutive samples from the noise corrupted signal and applied them in the form of a time series to seven sets of sibling nodes. The sampling equations are shown below:

$c(t)$ = corrupted signal
Δt = sampling interval

$[c(t_0), c(t_0 + \Delta t), \ldots, c(t_0 + (n-1)\Delta t)]$

$[c(t_0 + \Delta t), c(t_0 + 2\Delta t), \ldots, c(t_0 + n\Delta t)]$

$[c(t_0 + 2\Delta t), c(t_0 + 3\Delta t), \ldots, c(t_0 + (n+1)\Delta t)]$

. . . . .

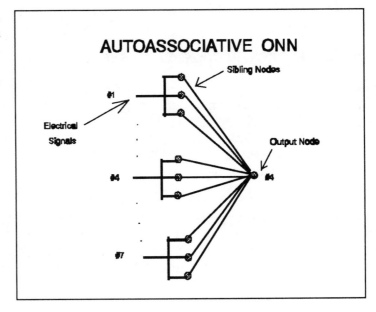

AUTOASSOCIATIVE ONN

Figure 2

The target values of the output node were the signals that were applied to the middle tap (4th input signal). Because the transfer functions of the sibling nodes were the different terms of Fourier series, the synaptic link values represented the frequency spectrum of the signal of the output node which was the same as the signal that was applied to the middle tap. Using this unique property we trained the system using all five harmonics. Then by using only some of the harmonics in testing we created a low pass or a high pass filter. Of course a band pass filter could also be constructed using this technique. In training seven sets of noise corrupted signals were applied to the seven sets of sibling nodes. The corrupted signal was generated by blending the following uncorrupted signal [0.0, 0.05, 0.1, 0.15 ,0.2, 0.25, 0.3, 0.25, 0.2, 0.15, 0.1, 0.05, 0.0] with a noise signal having the consecutive values of 0.1 and -0.1.

The training was terminated after the 13th cycle when the mean squared error became $0.434 \cdot 10^{-6}$. To recover the original signal we used only the first and second harmonics, i.e., in the test program the constant terms and the 3rd, 4th and 5th harmonics were set to zero. Note that the recovered signals were multiplied by 26.04 in order to compare them with the original signals. The following results were obtained in testing (recall):

Corrupted Signal	Recovered Signal	Original Signal
0.05	0.152572	0.15
0.3	0.218342	0.2
0.15	0.239664	0.25
0.4	0.300000	0.3
0.15	0.239664	0.25
0.3	0.218342	0.2
0.05	0.152572	0.15

In a similar way by only using the 5th harmonic and setting all other terms to zero we recovered the noise signal from the corrupted signal. Also note that the recovered signals were multiplied by 59.386 in order to compare them with the original noise signals. The following results were obtained in testing:

Corrupted Signal	Recovered Noise	Original Noise
0.05	0.119425	0.1
0.3	-0.101972	-0.1
0.15	0.087625	0.1
0.4	-0.100000	-0.1
0.15	0.087625	0.1
0.3	-0.101972	-0.1
0.05	0.119425	0.1

4. ONN AS AN IN-BAND FILTER:

To perform in-band noise filtering it was necessary to know the waveform, but not the amplitude, of the noise signal. In this application we used the same architecture given in Figure 2. In training six sets of noise samples consisting of consecutive values of 0.2 and -0.2 were used as 7 input signals. The target values of the output node were the noise corrupted signals. In this system the error did not become zero but tended towards the values of the original signal. For this reason the program recovered the original signal from the noise corrupted signal by running continuously in training mode. The training was terminated after the 9th cycle when the mean squared error became 0.006667. We used 5 sibling nodes per input signal. It was observed that the network error, i.e., the recovered signal, was a very close approximation of the original uncorrupted signal [11].

5. ELECTRO-OPTICAL IMPLEMENTATION OF THE CLASSIFYING ONN:

In some pattern applications connectivity requirements may be prohibitive even for a VLSI chip where the "on chip communications" is limited in terms of delays, chip area, and power dissipation, and "interchip communications" are limited by the number of output pins. We use a VLSI chip for computational work, and optical links between sibling and output nodes. In Figure 3 we show the block diagram of an electro-optical ONN. In both the training and testing modes the system uses [n.N] input nodes/light emitters and m output nodes. Each output node contains [n.N] light detectors. With this arrangement all m classes can be trained in parallel. Our electro-optical ONN is a single layer system [10]. The synaptic link values obtained in training are stored in a RAM. The subsystems shown in Figure 3 will now be described.

STDM Multiplixer: The facilities of the "Math Unit" are synchronous time division multiplexed (STDM) to the input signals, x_i's.

Math Unit: The Fourier terms are generated using a gated oscillator for each input signal x_i and the results stored in a RAM.

Optical Unit: We are using a system similar to the optical but not the electronic part of the D-Stop architecture proposed by A. Krishnamoorthy at al [6]. At the input node we have [n.N] light emitters which are pulse width modulated. At each of the m output nodes we have [n.N] light detectors. Each output node receives [n.N] light beams from the input node and passes the light intensities to their "Activation unit." To

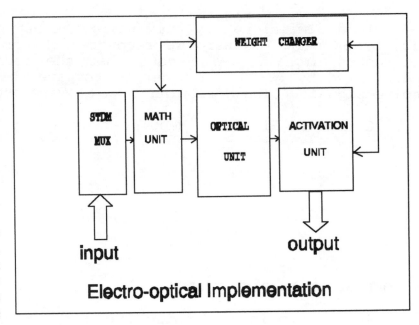

Figure 3

achieve this the optical system of the D-Stop [6] uses three lenses and a holographic beam splitter. The [n.N] light images of the input node are demagnified by the first two lenses. The third lens and a holographic beam splitter replicates [n.N] images into m sets of [n.N] images creating m output nodes. Another alternative is to replicate the [n.N] light images using a refractive microlens array [2]. Note that in our design the output nodes do not contain any electronic parts. All the computational work is carried out in a VLSI chip that has the following four subsystems:

Activation Unit (m units are used) : Each unit receives the pulse width modulated light beam intensities from its output node. These are multiplied with the synaptic link values supplied by the "Weight Changer" unit. The negative and positive values of these multiplicative products are summed and supplied to the Weight Changer unit as the activation generated at this output node.

Weight Changer Unit (m units are used): The activation received from the output node is compared with the target values assigned to this particular output node. As a result of this comparison a set of squared errors are formed. Using this set a new set of weights are generated and passed back to the Activation unit. In training this feedback process continues until the error becomes very small.

6. ELECTRO-OPTICAL IMPLEMENTATION OF THE FILTERING ONN:

In signal processing one output signal at a time is obtained from a frame of n input signals or [n.N] light emitters/sibling nodes. Hence we need to process many frames either one after another, or in parallel to obtain a filtered signature. We achieve parallel processing by using the optical unit in reverse. In the case of the Classifying ONN the input node contained [n.N] light emitters and each of the m output nodes had [n.N] light detectors. We completely reverse the locations of the light emitters and detectors so that the m output nodes emit and input node detects. We then connect each of the [n.N] sibling signals of the first input frame multiplied by the appropriate weights to the first light emitters of the m output nodes. These light intensities will be received by the first light detector of the input node and summed in an analog fashion. We would then connect each of the [n.N] sibling signals of the second input frame multiplied by the appropriate weights to the second light emitters of the m output nodes. These light intensities will be received by the second light detector of the input node and summed in an analog fashion. The rest of the connections will proceed in an identical way. The optical unit operating in reverse direction with reverse emission/detection capabilities will allow us to process m input signal frames in parallel and obtain a filtered signature in a minimum time. The sharp slopes of the bowl shaped error surface of the ONN will permit the use of analog summation. The full duplex operation of the classifier/filter system is also possible. However, this requires the use of more expensive optical equipment.

7. CONCLUSIONS

The architecture and computer simulation of a new neural network called ONN is described. It is shown that a pattern recognition ONN can act as its own in-band and/or bandpass filter. The system design of a single layer, electro-optical ONN that classifies in the forward and filters in the reverse direction is described.

REFERENCES

[1] Dunford, N., and Schwartz, J. T. (1966); "**Linear Operators**," Part 1, Third Printing, Wiley, NY.
[2] Farhat, N. and Psaltis, D., "**Optical Signal Processing**", J. Horner Ed., New York, Academic Press, 1987.
[3] Hecht-Nielsen, N. (1991); "**Neurocomputing**," Addison Wesley, Readings, Mass..
[4] Klimasauskas, C. (1989); "Neural Nets and Noise Filtering," Dr. Dodd's Journal, Jan., p.32.
[5] Kohonen, T. (1984); "Self Organization and Associative Memory," Springer-Verlag, pp 442-456.
[6] Krishnamoorthy, A. V., Yayla, G, Esener, S. C.. "A Scalable Optoelectronic Neural System Using Free-Space Optical Interconnectecs", IEEE Transactions on Neural Networks, Vol. 3, No. 3, May 1992.
[7] Royden, H.L. (1971); "**Real Analysis**," p. 111, The Macmillan Company, NY.
[8] Spiegel, M.R. (1962); "**Theory and Problems of Advanced Calculus**," pp. 301-320, McGraw-Hill Book Company, New York, NY.
[9] Ulug, M.E.,"A Rapid Learning Orthonormal Neural Network for Signal Processing", Proceedings of IJCNN-92, Baltimore, Maryland.
[10] Ulug, M.E.,"ANN Bandpass Filters for Electro-Optical Implementation", Proceedings of IJCNN-92, Baltimore, Maryland.
[11] Ulug, M.E.,"A Rapid Learning Orthogonal Neural Network for Pattern Recognition", Proceedings of 1992 IEEE/RNNS Symposium on Neoro-informatics and Neurocomputing, Rostov-on-Don.
[12] Ulug, M.E.,"A Signal Processing Neural Network Resembling the Simple Cells of the Visual Cortex", Proceedings of 1992 IEEE/RNNS Symposium on Neoro-informatics and Neurocomputing, Rostov-on-Don.
[13] Widrow, B., and M.E. Hoff (1960); "Adaptive Switching Circuits," 1960 IRE WESCON Convention Rec., NY.: IRE, 96-104.

An ARTMAP based Hybrid Neural Network for Shift Invariant Chinese Character Recognition

Cheng-An Hung and Sheng-Fuu Lin*

Department of Control Engineering

National Chiao Tung University.

1001 Ta Hsueh Rd, Hsinchu, Taiwan 30050, R.O.C.

Abstract—In this paper, we propose an ARTMAP based hybrid neural network to recognize position-shifted Chinese characters. Faster learning speed of a hybrid architecture makes practical the use of neural network in large scale neural computation. Four translation-invariant transformations were used to extract features of two-dimensional patterns. Results of experimentation with three different hybrid neural networks are also presented.

I. Introduction

Supervised learning neural network classifiers with high accuracy and robust performance provide a new direction for adaptive pattern recognition. But a large set of output codes require increasing amounts of training time and patterns, the computational complexity of the learning process quickly reaches unmanageable proportions [1]. Hecht-Nielsen [2] used a counterpropagation network to improve learning speed. The counterpropagation is a hybrid neural network which combines supervised and unsupervised learning in the same network. Since the hybrid neural network architecture is fixed; that is, the number of nodes and its interconnectivity are specified before learning begins. Hence it is necessary to retrain the network after adding a new pattern. This problem can be solved by using a self-growing neural network [3]. One feature of a self-growing architecture is that the nodes and connections may be added during learning. Model families of Adaptive Resonance Theory (ART) and its variations [3,4,5,6] are self-growing neural networks.

In this paper, we intend to combine a unsupervised self-growing neural network and an inter-ART module for position-shifted Chinese characters. The hybrid neural network uses fast initial learning with a slower rate of forgetting to classify unnormalized input patterns. If the memory capacity could be chosen arbitrarily large, the network would achieve 100% recognition for a fixed training set.

II. An ARTMAP Based Hybrid Neural Network (AHNN)

The principal elements of an ARTMAP based hybrid neural network are shown in Fig. 1. This supervised learning system includes a self-growing module, a inter-ART module, and a target field module. The self-growing network can rapidly learn to cluster input patterns without supervision. Any ART module can be used to replace this network for different applications. The inter-ART module consists of a map field, a map field gain control, and a map field orienting subsystem. It links the F_2 field of a self-growing neural network and the target field module. In classification problems, the target field requires all target values to be set to 0 except for the node that is marked to correspond to the class the input is from. That target value is 1. As described above, the system can be applied to identify the corresponding category for an input pattern.

In this remainder of this section, we will describe the main computations of the hybrid network. The algorithm is given below:

1. Input

   Given a M-dimensional input vector $I \equiv [I_0, ..., I_M]$ to F_1.

2. F_2 activation

   The initial choice at F_2 field is one node with index J satisfying

   $$J = Arg \min_{j \in N_c} \|I - Z_j\|, \qquad (1)$$

   where N_c is a set of committed nodes, $Z_j \equiv [z_{1j}, ..., z_{Mj}]$, and $\|I - Z_j\| \equiv \sqrt{\sum_{i=1}^{M}(I_i - z_{ij})^2}$. When F_2 makes a choice, the F_2 may be characterized as $y_J = 1$ and $y_j = 0$ if $j \neq J$.

---

*Please address all correspondence to the second author.

1600

3. Map field activation

The activity of the map field is defined as

$$b_k = \begin{cases} 1 & \text{if } d_k + G + \sum_j y_j u_{jk} > 1 + \bar{u} \\ 0 & \text{otherwise,} \end{cases} \quad (2)$$

where d_k is the target value, $k = 1, ..., P$; u_{jk} is an adaptive weight in the pathway from the jth F_2 node to the kth map field node, and $\bar{u}$ is a critical weight strength such that $0 < \bar{u} < 1$. The map field gain control signal G obeys the equation

$$G = \begin{cases} 0 & \text{if } F_2 \text{ and } F_3 \text{ are both active} \\ 1 & \text{otherwise.} \end{cases} \quad (3)$$

This rule for map field activation is called the 2/3 *Rule* [3].

4. Reset or resonance

Two mismatch events can trigger a reset signal r to the orienting subsystem of a self-growing neural network. One is determined by R_1, and the other is determined by R_2. As illustrated in Fig. 1, the matching signal R_1 is defined by

$$R_1 = \begin{cases} 1 & \text{if } \|I - \hat{Z}_J\| > \rho \\ 0 & \text{otherwise,} \end{cases} \quad (4)$$

where ρ is a distance threshold. If the effective radius ρ is chosen large enough, the network can carry out learning with the minimum necessary number of F_2 nodes. The map field matching signal R_2 is determined by

$$R_2 = \begin{cases} 1 & \text{if } |d| - |b| > 0 \\ 0 & \text{otherwise,} \end{cases} \quad (5)$$

where $|d| \equiv \sum_{k=1}^{P} d_k$ and $|b| \equiv \sum_{k=1}^{P} b_k$.

The binary reset signal r satisfies the equation

$$r = \begin{cases} 1 & \text{if } R_1 + R_2 > 0 \\ 0 & \text{otherwise.} \end{cases} \quad (6)$$

When the signal is one, J is reset to the index of an arbitrary uncommitted node. Otherwise, node J remains active until an input pattern I shuts off. This state is called *resonance*.

5. Learning

When resonance occurs, the hybrid neural network either refines its weights or learns a new category. Here, we consider two learning processes, called *map field learning* and *long-term memory* (LTM) *learning*.

- Map field learning

  The adaptive weights u_{jk} initially satisfy

$$u_{jk}(0) = 1. \quad (7)$$

When an input I activates an F_2 category node J and resonance is established,

$$u_{Jk} = b_k. \quad (8)$$

It implies that node J can learn to predict the corresponding class for an input pattern I.

If the target field receives no input vector $d \equiv (d_1, ..., d_P)$, then all u_{jk} remain equal to 1 by (2).

- LTM learning During resonance with the F_2 category J is active, the LTM traces is set to be

$$\hat{z}_{Ji}^{new} = z_{iJ}^{new}$$
$$= \begin{cases} z_{iJ}^{old} + \beta y_J [\min(I_i, z_{iJ}) - z_{iJ}^{old}] & \text{if } J \in N_c \\ I & \text{if } J \in N_u, \end{cases} \quad (9)$$

where N_u is a set of uncommitted F_2 nodes. The learning rate $\beta \in [0, 1]$.

The learning rule (9) is the same as the Cluster Unidirectional algorithm used by [7].

6. Retrieving

When the target values are absent, the input pattern I could retrieve a recognition code based on previous learning or make no prediction. If the F_2 node J is active and it only activates one node k in the map field, then we say that I retrieves a class k. If all map field nodes are inactive, then we say that I makes no prediction.

□

III. TRANSLATION-INVARIANT FEATURE EXTRACTION

Most of pattern recognition techniques, especially template matching methods, are sensitive to shifts in position. The position-shifting problem can be overcome by using translation-invariant features. Some well-known techniques such as the Fourier transform, Rapid transform [8], M-transform [9], and two-dimensional moments [10,11] are used to extract features of one- or two-dimensional patterns which are invariant under translation. These transformations may be applied to the problem of recognizing position-shifted Chinese characters.

A two-dimensional image $f(n_1, n_2)$ of $N_1 \times N_2$ pixels with each pixel represented by 1 or 0 is dependent on whether it is black or white. The methods used to extract features of a character image are described as follows.

A. Fourier Transform

The Fourier transform representation of signals plays a important role in both one-dimensional (1-D) and two-dimensional (2-D) signal processing. We discuss the idea of invariant transforms by starting with the discrete Fourier transform (DFT) for a 2-D image $f(n_1, n_2)$:

$$F(k_1, k_2) = \sum_{n_1=0}^{N_1-1} \sum_{n_2=0}^{N_2-1} f(n_1, n_2) W_{N_1}^{-k_1 n_1} W_{N_2}^{-k_2 n_2}, \quad (10)$$

where $W_N \equiv e^{2\pi j/N}$, $j = \sqrt{-1}$, $k_1 = 0, 1, ..., N_1 - 1$, and $k_2 = 0, 1, ..., N_2 - 1$.

Translation of a character is reflected as a phase change in frequency domain. The magnitude component of the DFT is relatively stable. In general, the magnitude features are translation invariant.

B. Rapid Transform

The rapid transform (R-transform) is a class of fast translation-invariant transforms for position independent pattern recognition problems. It is faster than the fast Fourier transform (FFT) since the arithmetic computation involves only summation and absolute difference.

The R-transform is similar to Walsh-Hadamard transform (WHT) except for the absolute difference operation. If the input pixels are binary, the summation and absolute difference operations can be replaced with the operations logical AND and OR. The generalization of R-transform is called the M-transform.

C. Moment-Invariant Features

Two-dimensional moments are a set of nonlinear functions which are invariant to translation, sacle, and rotation and are defined on geometrical moments of the image. A set of feature vectors called *moment invariants* which are useful for recognizing rotated, shifted, and scaled patterns can be found in [10,11].

IV. EXPERIMENTS

A database consisting of 100 printed Chinese characters is used in our experiments. Each character in the data set has 50 samples with different positions and different levels of noise. In most experiments, we use one clean smaple to train the classifiers and the remaining noisy samples to test them. Fig. 2 (a) shows a set of noiseless patterns and Fig. 2 (b) shows a set of 15% noise patterns. The noisy pattern is done by randomly selecting some of the pixels of a noiseless binary image and reversing their values from 0 to 1 or vice versa.

A. ARTMAP: Binary Pattern Recognition

There are two training schemes for ARTMAP, which are described as fast learning and slow learning. The ARTMAP simulations in the section were all carried out in fast learning conditions. Using fast learning the weight values are modified to update the category to a perfect match in just one presentation of the input. Any subsequent learning will refine these categories by incorportating more features found in the training patterns.

Since a binary pattern match can be computed by counting the number of matching bits, the most critical parameter of ARTMAP is the baseline vigilance threshold. It controls the resolution of the classification process. Lower vigilance parameters ($\rho < 0.5$) will produce coarser categories. Conversely, higher vigilance parameters (tending to 1) will produce finer categories.

The ARTMAP network can learn to classify printed Chinese characters rapidly and accurately. In our simulations, recognition is achieved by finding a category whose match function meets the vigilance criterion. The resonant state is nonadaptive since the LTM traces are fixed. If the match function is below the vigilance parameter, the character is classified as unknown.

For recognizing noisy patterns, the network is trained with noiseless patterns and tested with the noisy ones. The experimental results obtained from our simulations show that the better choice of vigilance parameter is 0.8. If the vigilance parameter is set too large, the rejection rate will increase.

First-order similarity measure of ARTMAP leads to a loss of higher-order information about the input pattern. Therefore it is not invariant under translation, rotation, or scaling. These invariances can be achieved by incorporating additional processing stages. In our simulations, the M-transform is applied to extract features of printed Chinese characters which are invariant under translation.

The recognition results of shifted patterns via M-transform are shown in Fig. 3. A recognition rate of 100 percent can be achieved for noiseless patterns, while the recognition rates are very low for noisy patterns. As the above results indicate, the performance of M-transform is sensitive to noise.

B. Hybrid Neural Networks: Analog Pattern Recognition

After describing the binary pattern recognition, we will apply two hybrid neural networks which are designed for continuous-valued inputs to recognize the position-shifted and noisy Chinese characters. One is our proposed hybrid neural network and the other is a hybrid neural network whose self-growing neural network is replaced by ART 2-A. The major difference of two hybrid neural networks is that the former codes unnormalized inputs and the latter codes normalized inputs. Three sets of experiments are carried out. The 2-D Fouier transform, the R-transform, and the 2-D moments are utilized in our experiments.

(1). 2-D Fourier transform:

In the first set of experiments, 2-D Fourier transform was used in our character recognition task. Fig. 4 graphically display the performance of ART 2-A classifier using the first 35 magnitude features. As the above results indicate, the performance significantly worsened when the threshold θ is made larger than zero. It implies that the noise suppression/contrast enhancement may be inappropriate for the feature space.

In order to reduce the number of features efficiently, we choose features according to the larger ordering of their standard deviations. Fig. 5 shows the recognition results of AHNN and a linear STM feedback ART 2-A. The classifier with a small size of features can perform as well as the previous experiment with larger number of features.

(2). R-transform:

In the second set of experiments, the R-transform was used to extract features of printed Chinese characters which are invariant under translation. One of the most attractive properties of R-transform is its simple computation. As the technique used in 2-D FFT features, we can also choose features according to the standard deviations scheme. The performance of two classifiers using fifteen features is plotted in Fig. 6.

(3). 2-D moments:

Finally, eight central moments and six moment-invariant features were chosen to train our classifiers to recognize noisy and shifted Chinese characters. Because the numerical values of moment-invariant features are very small, we use the logarithms of the absolute values of these six functions to train the AHNN classifier. The moment-invariant features are all negative, they are not appropriate for ART 2-A. The experimental results are shown in Fig. 7. We find that the moment features are very sensitive to noise.

To summarize the results of the previous three sets of experiments, we can find that the performance of AHNN using fifteen critical FFT features is the best. In our experiments, the learning phase of the hybrid neural network runs approximately several minutes on an 80386-based computer.

V. Conclusions

In this paper, we propose a hybrid neural network to recognize printed Chinese characters. Shorter learning time is obtained in our experiments. Because we use a self-growing architecture and an inter-ART module to classify patterns, the problem of distance vigilance selection can be overcome. If the vigilance parameter is set large, the network can carry out learning with the minimum necessary number of category representation nodes.

We also compare the performance of four transformations for recognizing position-shifted Chinese characters. As the above experiments indicate, the performance of classifiers using fifteen critical FFT features is better than that using other features. Future works include the modification of the feature extractor and the classifier for recognizing the rotated, scaled, and multi-font printed Chinese characters. Further work also includes the recognition of handwritten Chinese characters.

References

[1] S.B. Cho and J.H. Kim, "Hierarchically structured neural networks for printed Hangul character recognition," *IEEE IJCNN*, Vol.1, pp.265-270, 1990.

[2] R. Hecht-Nielsen, "Counterpropagation networks," *Applied Optics*, Vol. 26, No.23, pp.4979-4985, 1987.

[3] G.A. Carpenter and S. Grossberg, "A massively parallel architecture for a self-organizing neural pattern recognition machine," *Computer Vision , Graphics, and Image Processing*, Vol.37, pp.54-115, 1987.

[4] G.A. Carpenter and S. Grossberg, "ART2: stable self-organization of category recognition codes for analog input patterns," *Applied Optics*, Vol.26, No.23, pp.4919-4930, 1987.

[5] G.A. Carpenter, S. Grossberg and D. Brosen, "ART 2-A: an adaptive resonance algorithm for rapid category learning and recognition," *Neural Networks*, Vol.4, pp.493-504, 1991.

[6] G.A. Carpenter, S. Grossberg and J.H. Reynolds, "ARTMAP: supervied real-time learning and classification of nonstationary data by a self-organizing neural network," *Neural Networks*, Vol.4, pp.565-588, 1991.

[7] B. Morre, "ART 1 and pattern clustering," in *Proceedings of the 1988 Connectionist Models Summer School*, D. Touretzky, G. Hinton, and T. Sejnowski, Eds. San Mateo, CA:Morgan Kaufmann Publishers, pp.174-185, 1989.

[8] P.P. Wang and R.C. Shiau, "Machine recognition of printed Chinese character via transformation algorithms," *Pattern Recognition*, Vol.5, pp.303-321, 1973.

[9] H. Burkhardt and X. Müller, "On invariant sets of a certain class of fast translation-invariant transforms," *IEEE Trans. ASSP*, Vol.28, No.5, pp.517-523, October 1980.

[10] G.L. Cash and M. Hatamian, "Optical character recognition by the method of moments," *Computer Vision , Graphics, and Image Processing*, Vol.39, pp.291-310, 1987.

[11] A. Khotanzad and J.H. Lu, "Classification of invariant image representations using a neural network",*IEEE Trans. ASSP*, Vol.38, No.6, pp.1028-1038, June 1990.

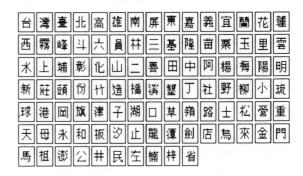

(a)

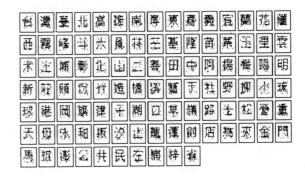

(b)

Fig 2: (a) A set of noiseless Chinese characters. (b) A set of 15 % noise Chinese characters.

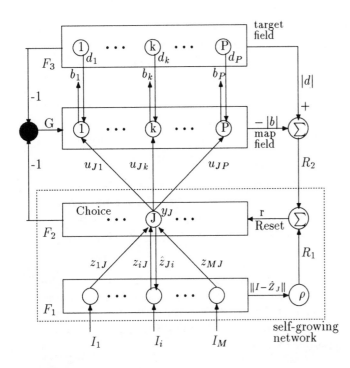

Fig 1: An ARTMAP based hybrid neural network architecture.

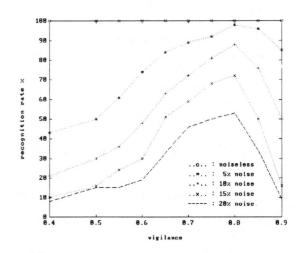

Fig 3: Performance of the ARTMAP via M-transform.

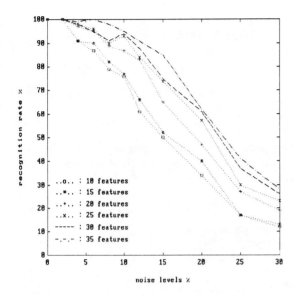

Fig 4: Classification results of ART 2-A using the first 35 FFT features.

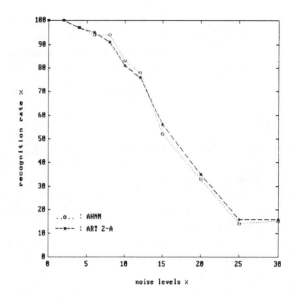

Fig 6: Recognition results of the linear STM feedback ART 2-A and the AHNN classifiers using 15 critical R-transform features.

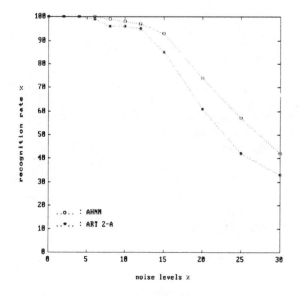

Fig 5: Classification results of the linear STM feedback ART 2-A and the AHNN classifiers using 15 critical FFT features.

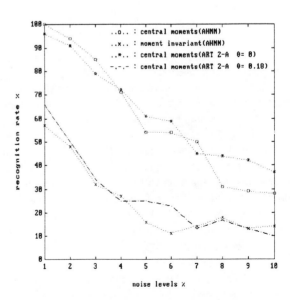

Fig 7: Recognition results using eight central moments and six moment invariants.

Connectionist Network for Feature Extraction and Classification of English Alphabetic Characters

Shyam W. Khobragade† and Ajoy K. Ray‡

Email : shyam@gmrt.ernet.in   Email : akray@sys320.iitkgp.ernet.in

†Tata Institute of Fundamental Research, Ganeshkhind, Pune - 411 007, India.

‡Electronics & ECE Department, Indian Institute of Technology, Kharagpur - 721 302, India.

Abstract— **A new non-adaptive Connectionist Architecture based Feature Extractor (CAFE) for English alphabetic patterns is presented here. Two different adaptive connectionist networks, viz. Multi-layer back propagation network (MBPN) and Counter propagation network (CPN) have been implemented for classification of the patterns and their performance analysis has been reported. The system is tolerant to translation and deformation and has been observed to classify noisy and distorted patterns correctly.**

Keywords: Connectionist network, pattern scanner, CAFE, adaptive connectionist classifiers, MBPN, CPN, supervised learning, fault tolerant system, performance analysis.

I. INTRODUCTION

The problem of *pattern classification* may be viewed as (a) the problem of *characterization* and (b) the problem of *abstraction* and *generalization*. During the phase of characterization, a set of attributes or features are associated with each pattern, while the space of these feature values is partitioned in a set of meaningful regions during the process of abstraction.

The recent advances in the area of *artificial neural networks* have opened new directions of research towards the development of fault-tolerant and flexible pattern classifiers. A number of connectionist architecture based character recognizer units have been reported in literature [2][3][4][5].

We present a *system* [Fig. 1] employing a *pattern scanner* (PATSCAN) [1] which takes a visual pattern as an input and yields a binary frame corresponding to that pattern, a *new* non-adaptive connectionist strategy for feature extraction and adaptive neural networks for classification of English alphabetic characters. Two schemes, viz. the *back-error propagation network* and a *counter propagation network* have been implemented

and their performances have been reported. The system has been found to classify noisy and distorted patterns correctly.

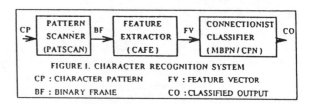

FIGURE I. CHARACTER RECOGNITION SYSTEM
CP : CHARACTER PATTERN   FV : FEATURE VECTOR
BF : BINARY FRAME   CO : CLASSIFIED OUTPUT

II. PATTERN SCANNER

The PATSCAN is a microprocessor based hardware system for digitization of optical patterns, built around an integrated array of Reticon solid-state two-dimensional photo sensors of size 64x64. The character patterns were scanned by this scanner which yields sufficiently high resolution, low noise digitized patterns which could be subsequently classified. The pixel gray levels were translated to a binary matrix using an adaptive threshold scheme [1].

III. FEATURE EXTRACTION

The CAFE uses an input pattern enclosed in a minimal binary frame of (m x n) pixels, which is an output of PATSCAN and extracts a set of 12-dimensional analog feature vector using a non-adaptive network. To obtain position sensitivity, the frame is divided into twelve non-disjoint parts [**Fig. 2**]. The 12-dimensional vector is used as an *encoded* version of the description of the edges on different parts of the frame.

A. Frame Division

The frame has been divided in three parts each — along the vertical and horizontal directions and along 45^0 and 135^0 [**Fig. 2**]. The ratio of the maximum width of the division along a particular direction measured perpendicular to that direction of division has been kept variable.

B. Edge Element Extraction

Corresponding to each pixel in a frame, four outputs indicating the existence of 0^0, 45^0, 90^0 and 135^0 edge elements are available. Considering the directly connected pixels as neighborhood, a particular type of edge element is detected if there is a difference in neighboring binary pixel values [**Fig. 3**]. There may be more than one type of edge element at a pixel location. The same procedure is repeated for all pixels in the frame.

C. Edge Length Extraction

The *connectionist network* for edge length extraction is shown in **Fig. 4**. The number of pixels per row per region of a binary frame having value **1** decide the length of an edge which may be termed as (a) long, (b) medium or (c) short. Further **Fig. 5** shows that bigger size edge dominates the smaller ones.

D. Feature Vector Computation

The *connectionist model* shown in **Fig. 6** reveals the computation of analog feature value in a particular region R_i which can be expressed as

$$V_{R_i} = \alpha * sR_i + \beta * mR_i + \gamma * lR_i$$

where sR_i, mR_i and lR_i are the total number of *short*, *medium* and *long* edges respectively in the region R_i. α, β and γ are coefficients of expression (or *weight* values) where $\alpha < \beta < \gamma$. The computation of the individual analog feature values in a proper sequence (as in frame division) yields an *m-dimensional* feature vector

$$V = (V_{R_1}, V_{R_2}, \ldots, V_{R_m})$$

where m is 12 in this case. This m-dimensional analog feature vector is the input to the adaptive pattern classifiers.

This is a *generalized* feature extractor which works well for any size of binary frame greater than or equal to (16 x 16) pixels frame and for any kind of visual image as well. The performance can be improved by optimizing the sizes of different regions in frame division stage and proper setting of the coefficient values α, β and γ .

IV. MULTILAYER BACK PROPAGATION CLASSIFIER

This is a *supervised* multi-layer network which works on *gradient-decent* training technique and minimizes squared error between actual output and desired output

of the network. The *learning algorithm* of this network is given in [9] [10] [15]. This network has been extensively used for various applications. This has been implemented here as a *classifier* to test its performance for various cases using a set of training and testing patterns extracted by our *feature extractor* (CAFE).

A. Practical Issues

The input to this classifier is a *preprocessed 12-dimensional analog feature vector* which is an output of CAFE described above, while the output is a one-dimensional array of twenty six processing elements (nodes) each representing a class of input English alphabetic patterns.

The *performance* and the *convergence rate* of this classifier have been tested for various cases, specifically, the number of hidden layers, number of nodes in each hidden layer, the values of gain factor (η) and momentum constant (ξ), slope of sigmoidal transfer function, number of training patterns in a batch slab and iteration counter number.

The performance of network for the topology of three hidden layers has been tested with other parameters such as $\eta = 0.1$, $\xi = 0.8$, iteration counter=100, batch slab=1 and the slope of transfer function=1.0.

V. COUNTER PROPAGATION CLASSIFIER

The counter propagation classifier architecture consists of three slabs — an input layer of transparent nodes equal to the size of feature vector, a middle layer of self-organizing feature map with neighborhood concept and a final Grossberg layer with the nodes equal to the number of classes. Although self-organizing map is *unsupervised* , the CPN as a whole is trained by *supervision*. This network learns the mapping from feature vector to class number. The accuracy to which the desired outputs are achieved is dependent upon the number of winner nodes and the total nodes used at middle layer. The CPN is more simpler and takes less time for training.

A. CPN Learning Algorithm

Define a classifier network by specifying the size of input feature vector and the number of nodes at Kohonen and Grossberg layers [11][12]. Then initialize the reference vectors W_{ji} and U_{kj} for all links and neighborhood radius (NR) at Kohonen layer. Take maximum NR at the beginning [13][14][15]. Present a *pair of* input training sample (x) and its desired response (y). Find the *shortest* sample–to–reference *distance* node at Kohonen layer using $d_j(k) = \|x_i(k) - W_{ji}(k)\|$ where d_j is the *distance function* of node j for the k-*th* sample x and the corresponding reference vector W_{ji}. Then activate the response (z_j) of winner node and its neighborhood nodes N_c only, at middle layer. That means, $z_j = 1$ if $j \in N_c$, otherwise *0*. Update the *reference vectors* at Kohonen layer using

$$W_{ji}(k+1) = W_{ji}(k) + \alpha_c(k) \cdot (x_i(k) - W_{ji}(k)) \cdot z_j$$

where $W_{ji}(k)$ is the *j-th* reference vector after *k-th* training sample $x\ (k)$ has been presented. $\alpha_c(k)$ is a learning parameter $[0 < \alpha_c(k) < 1]$ that decreases with training sample number k.

Compute an actual response at Grossberg layer using an expression

$$y'_k = \sum_{j=0}^{N-1} U_{kj}^{old} \cdot z_j$$

where y'_k is the actual output and U_{kj} is a reference vector of *k-th* node at Grossberg layer. Then update the reference vector using

$$U_{kj}^{new} = U_{kj}^{old} + \beta_c \cdot (y_k - U_{kj}^{old}) \cdot z_j$$

where β_c is another learning parameter $[0 < \beta_c(k) < 1]$ which decreases linearly with training sample number. Repeat this procedure by presenting next input sample. The presentation of all these labeled input training samples is considered as the first iteration. Continue this process for some specified number of iterations with same set of training samples and same neighborhood radius (NR). Then decrease the radius linearly by 1 [13] [14] [15] and repeat again the above procedure. Keep that radius (NR) constant for next set of iterations and further reduce it linearly. Continue this till the convergence of output at Grossberg outstar layer. Now the *classifier* is ready for testing.

B. Practical Issues

In earlier versions of CPN, *only winner* node was activated in *middle layer* in training and testing phases. In this algorithm, we have incorporated the concept of *neighborhood* at middle layer (as in Kohonen's *Self-organizing feature map*) and neighborhood nodes are also activated with winner node. Thus the original *CPN learning algorithm* [11][12] has been updated. Grossberg layer weights are also adapted during training. The *performance* of this classifier is tested using same set of training and testing samples which were used in case of *back propagation classifier*. Absolute error at output was the criteria to decide the convergence process.

The performance has been tested for various cases specifically, the *network topology* and number of *passes* of a set of input training samples for *same radius* of neighborhood, as shown in **graph 3** and **graph 4**.

VI. RESULTS

A set of 18 labeled training patterns from each of the 26 classes of English alphabet were used for training the classifier networks and total 100 patterns for testing. The *performance of back propagation classifier was* tested for 1, 2 and 3 layers and a total of hidden nodes ranging from 40 to 100. The performance found to be better for more number of hidden layers, each containing more number of nodes. The rate of *convergence* was better when the number of nodes in each hidden layer were increased. **Graph 1** shows the convergence of MBPN for three different topologies. *Topology 1* contains *one* hidden layer with 60 nodes, *topology 2* contains *two* hidden layers with total of 60 hidden nodes and *topology 3* contains *three* hidden layers with total of 60 hidden nodes. **Graph 1** shows that the convergence is faster for more number of hidden layers, although the total number of hidden nodes are same in all the three topologies. **Graph 1** is *actual output* **vs.** *pattern number*. In this case, a set of 18 training patterns were fed serially to the classifier and each time the actual output at that particular class node was noted. Then another set of 18 patterns from another class was given to the classifier and the actual output at previous class node was noted down. It is clear from the graph that the actual output tends to **1** (desired output) for first 18 patterns (same class patterns) and **0** for next set of 18 patterns from another class. **Graph 2** reveals that the *convergence* is faster for larger value of *acceleration constant* (η). The increase in *momentum factor* (ξ) within the range from 0.1 to 0.9 doesn't affect the convergence rate significantly. The rate of convergence increases with the slope value of *sigmoidal transfer function*. The *batch–slab size* is the number of training patterns taking part in *adaptation of weights* at a time. During training phase, three procedures were tested for adaptation of weights. One, adapt the weights after presentation of each pattern. Two, accumulate the error at output for all the patterns from a class and update the weights once. Then present the patterns from next class. Three, accumulate the output error for all the patterns from all classes and adapt the weights once. Then present all the patterns again for next iteration and so on. It was observed that the convergence is faster for smaller value of *batch–slab*, while the performance was better for the second case of adaptation.

Iteration counter value is a number for which times each training pattern has to adapt the weights before presenting another pattern (as in first case of adaptation). It is noted that the increase in iteration counter value increases the convergence rate to a great extent.

The *performance* of *counter propagation classifier* is shown in **graph 3a** and **graph 3b**. It is clear that the performance is **100%** for *unity* radius of neighborhood, **ie.** , considering the directly connected nodes as neighborhood. The classifier was tested for three different sizes of middle layer, specifically, 8x8, 10x10 and 12x12 nodes and three different number of *passes*, by value 10, 20 and 30.

The number of *passes* is a number for which all the training patterns were presented these many iterations for same radius of neighborhood (NR) before decreasing it. It has been noted from the **graph 4** that the convergence rate decreases with increase in number of passes per radius.

The training and testing patterns were synthesized by computer which were of different natures such as *normal, distorted, containing background noise* and *with space shifting* in frame as shown in **Fig. 7**.

The *character recognition system* as a whole has been found to be tolerant to translation and deformation and was observed to classify the noisy and distorted patterns correctly. There is no need of separate *preprocessing* for noisy and distorted patterns.

The PATSCAN is a PC-based unit. The *scanning process* of input patterns and *feature extraction part* was computed on PC-AT and *training* of classifiers was done on Cyber-180 mainframe computer. The *frozen weights* of trained classifiers were then transferred and stored in PC-AT where PATSCAN was plugged in. The system was tested *online* with different types of test patterns [**Fig. 7**] which found to be fully successful.

ACKNOWLEDGMENT

The help of Mr. Debashish Ghosh in data generation and feature extraction part is greatfully acknowledged.

REFERENCES

[1] A.K.Ray, A.K.Ghosh and A.K.Majumdar, *PATSCAN — a microprocessor-based pattern scanner system*, Journal of Microcomputer Applications, Communication, 10, pp. 71-82, 1987.

[2] K.T.Blackwell, T.P.Vogl, S.D.Hyman, G.S.Barbour and D.L.Alkon, *A New Approach To Hand-written Character Recognition*, Pattern Recognition, Vol.25, No.6, pp. 655-666, 1992.

[3] F.Y.Shis, Moh, F.C. Chag, *A New ART-Based Neural Architecture for Pattern Classification and Image Enhancement without prior knowledge*, Pattern recognition, Vol.25, No.5, pp. 533-542, 1992.

[4] H.J.Lee and B.Chen, *Recognition of Hand-written Chinese Characters via short-line segments*, Pattern Recognition, Vol.25, No.5, pp. 543-552, 1992.

[5] D.J.Burr, *A Neural Network Digit recognizer*, IEEE Int. Conf. on Systems, Man and Cybernetics, Oct 1986.

[6] K.Fukushima, *A Neural Network for Visual Pattern Recognition*, IEEE Computer Magazine, pp. 65-75, March 1988.

[7] K.Fukushima and S.Miyake, *A New Algorithm : For Pattern Recognition, Tolerant of Deformation and shift in position*, Pattern Recognition, Vol.15, No.6, pp. 455-469, 1982.

[8] D.Marr and E.Hildreth, *Theory of Edge Detection*, Proc. R. Soc. London, B-207, pp. 187-217, 1980.

[9] D.E.Rumelhart, J.L.McClelland and the PDP Research Group, *Parallel Distributed Processing : Explorations in the Microstructure of Cognition*, Vol.1, MIT Press, Cambridge. pp. 318-362, 1986.

[10] D.E.Rumelhart, G.E.Hinton and R.J.William, *Learning representations by back-propagation errors*, Nature, Vol.323, pp. 533-536, Oct 1986.

[11] R.Hetch-Nielsen, *Counter Propagation Networks*, Applied Optics, pp. 4979-4984, 1987.

[12] R.Hetch-Nielsen, *Applications of Counter Propagation Networks*, Neural Networks, Vol.1, pp. 131-139, 1988.

[13] T.Kohonen, *Self-organization and Associative Memory*, 2nd Edition, Berlin, Heidelberg, Germany : Springer-Verlag, 1984.

[14] J.A.Kangas, T.Kohonen and J.T.Laaksonen, *Varients of Self-organizing Maps*, IEEE Trans. on Neural Networks, Vol.1, No.1.

[15] R.P.Lippmann, *An Introduction to Computing with Neural Nets*, IEEE ASSP Magazine, pp. 4-22, April 1987.

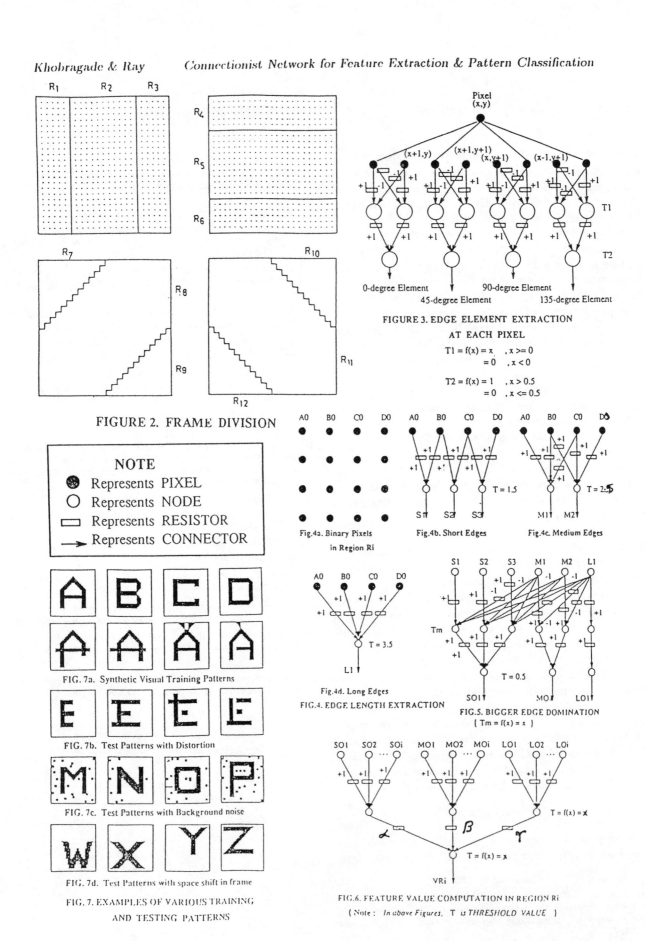

FIGURE 2. FRAME DIVISION

FIGURE 3. EDGE ELEMENT EXTRACTION
AT EACH PIXEL

$T1 = f(x) = x$, $x >= 0$
$= 0$, $x < 0$

$T2 = f(x) = 1$, $x > 0.5$
$= 0$, $x <= 0.5$

NOTE

◉ Represents PIXEL
○ Represents NODE
▭ Represents RESISTOR
→ Represents CONNECTOR

FIG. 7a. Synthetic Visual Training Patterns

FIG. 7b. Test Patterns with Distortion

FIG. 7c. Test Patterns with Background noise

FIG. 7d. Test Patterns with space shift in frame

FIG. 7. EXAMPLES OF VARIOUS TRAINING
AND TESTING PATTERNS

Fig.4a. Binary Pixels in Region Ri

Fig.4b. Short Edges

Fig.4c. Medium Edges

Fig.4d. Long Edges

FIG.4. EDGE LENGTH EXTRACTION

FIG.5. BIGGER EDGE DOMINATION
($Tm = f(x) = x$)

FIG.6. FEATURE VALUE COMPUTATION IN REGION Ri
(Note : *In above Figures,* T *is THRESHOLD VALUE*)

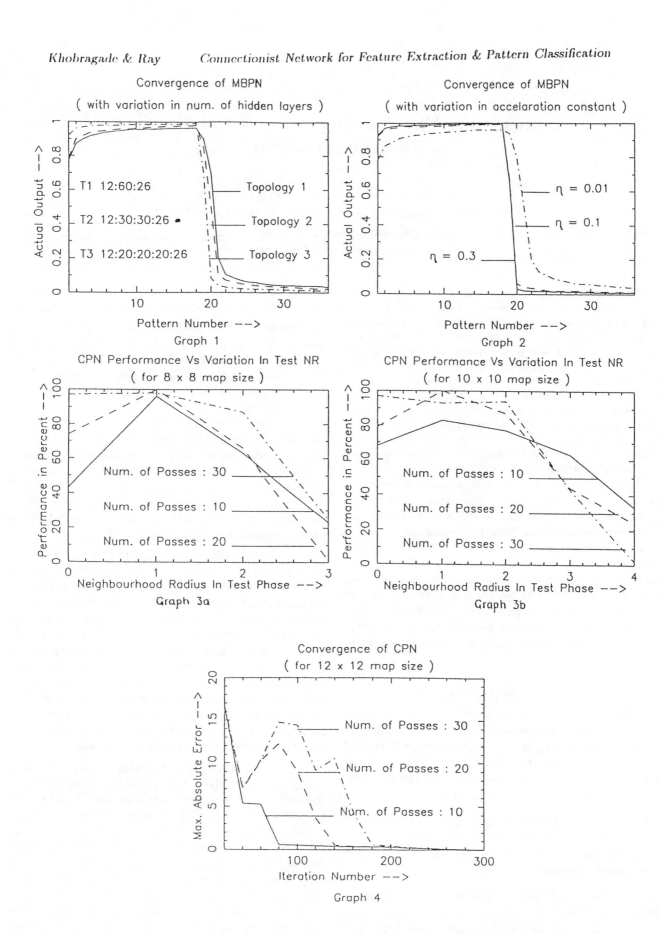

Convergence of MBPN
(with variation in num. of hidden layers)

T1 12:60:26 — Topology 1
T2 12:30:30:26 — Topology 2
T3 12:20:20:20:26 — Topology 3

Graph 1

Convergence of MBPN
(with variation in accelaration constant)

$\eta = 0.01$
$\eta = 0.1$
$\eta = 0.3$

Graph 2

CPN Performance Vs Variation In Test NR
(for 8 x 8 map size)

Num. of Passes : 30
Num. of Passes : 10
Num. of Passes : 20

Graph 3a

CPN Performance Vs Variation In Test NR
(for 10 x 10 map size)

Num. of Passes : 10
Num. of Passes : 20
Num. of Passes : 30

Graph 3b

Convergence of CPN
(for 12 x 12 map size)

Num. of Passes : 30
Num. of Passes : 20
Num. of Passes : 10

Graph 4

Representing Visual Schemas in Neural Networks for Scene Analysis

Wee Kheng Leow and Risto Miikkulainen

Department of Computer Sciences, University of Texas at Austin,

Austin, Texas 78712, USA

leow@cs.utexas.edu, risto@cs.utexas.edu

Abstract— Using object recognition in simple scenes as the task, this research focuses on two fundamental problems in neural network systems: (1) processing large amounts of input with limited resources, and (2) the representation and use of structured knowledge. The first problem arises because no practical neural network can process all the visual input simultaneously and efficiently. The solution is to process a small amount of the input in parallel, and successively focus on other parts of the input. This strategy requires that the system maintains structured knowledge for describing and interpreting successively gathered information.

The proposed system, VISOR, consists of two main modules. The Low-Level Visual Module (simulated using procedural programs) extracts featural and positional information from the visual input. The Schema Module (implemented with neural networks) encodes structured knowledge about possible objects, and provides top-down information for the Low-Level Visual Module to focus attention at different parts of the scene. Working cooperatively with the Low-Level Visual Module, it builds a globally consistent interpretation of successively gathered visual information.

I. INTRODUCTION

Consider the task of recognizing objects in simple scenes. A scene analysis system has to identify the objects in the scene (e.g., an arch and two trees, Fig. 1a) and determine what the scene depicts (e.g., a park). In designing a neural network system that performs this task, we encounter two fundamental problems:

1. How can a fixed, finite neural network process indefinitely large amounts of information?
2. How can a neural network represent and use structured knowledge?

In fact, these problems are also encountered in many other neural network application areas, such as speech understanding and natural language processing. The goal of this research is to develop general solutions to these problems, using scene analysis as a concrete task.

Consider the first problem: limited processing resources. In practice, it is only possible to construct a neural network with a fixed number of input units and internal processing units. The weights and activities have finite precision and are bounded within certain ranges of values. The number of input units may be smaller than the size of the scene (in pixels). Even if the network can capture a large part of the scene at once, it may not be able to process all the information in parallel unless it has an exponential amount of units and connections [1]. The only viable option is to process a small amount of visual input in parallel, and successively focus on different parts of the scene. This strategy also seems to be in use in biological vision systems [2].

Since the network is fixed and finite, it may not have enough storage space for the indefinitely large amounts of input information. It will have to build and maintain a *partial interpretation* of the information gathered so far. Based on gathered information, it estimates the likelihood that the input features belong to some known objects. As more information is received, it strengthens or weakens the tentative estimates. It continues processing other parts of the scene until it has gathered sufficient information to build a consistent interpretation. Each partial interpretation corresponds to an intermediate stable state of the network, and the globally consistent interpretation corresponds to the final stable state.

A system that adopts this strategy requires an internal model, generally known as *schema* in psychological research, for making the interpretations [2]. Thus, the solution to the first problem requires that neural networks encode schemas, or in general, structured knowledge; that is, it requires addressing the second problem. One approach is to represent such knowledge symbolically in neural networks [3, 4, 5]. The approach works in simple cases but does not generalize well to more complex tasks. Neural networks are not very good at manipulating symbols explicitly. However, they are good at feature extraction, association, constraint satisfaction, pattern classification, and making other fuzzy decisions. These tasks are performed through "neural" processes such as cooperation and competition among units and networks.

The VISOR system (VIsual Schemas for Object Representation) is designed to address the two fundamental problems in the domain of object recognition and scene analysis. Simplifications have been made to help focus the research effort on the main issues—the representation and learning of schemas. The scenes considered in this project consist of objects made up of straight lines and simple shapes such as rectangles and triangles. The knowledge that describes objects and scenes involves four positional relationships (left, right, above and below) and one hierarchical relationship (is-part-of). Such knowledge can be conveniently encoded in terms of maps and connections among units. Despite the simplified task, this research aims at deriving general solutions that are applicable to more complex scenes and other tasks.

II. Related Work

Rumelhart et al. [6] suggested a general method for encoding conceptual schemas in a PDP model. Individual components of schemas, such as sofa, bed, bathtub, and toilet are represented as units in a network. The weight of the connection between two units represents how likely the two components are to be present in a schema, and the activity pattern of the network encodes a schema instantiation. The network does not encode hierarchical relationships among the schemas.

Hinton [7] described three methods for representing hierarchical knowledge. The second method is similar to the one used in VISOR. The units in the network are organized into different levels. The higher the level, the more complex is the object that the unit represents. Lower-level units representing components of objects are connected to one or more higher-level units representing the objects themselves.

The cognitive model of Norman and Shallice focuses on the activation and control of schemas [8, 9]. In this model, domain-specific action schemas and thought schemas can be activated independently of each other. A small subset of schemas to be "run" are selected by two distinct processes known as Contention Scheduling and Supervisory Attentional System. Contention Scheduling is a domain-specific process analogous to conflict resolution in traditional AI systems. It selects schemas according to simple criteria that are domain-specific. Supervisory Attentional System is a general planning system that operates on schemas in every domain. It controls the activation of schemas by biasing the operations of Contention Scheduling. The activation and control of schemas in VISOR are analogous to the Contention Scheduling process.

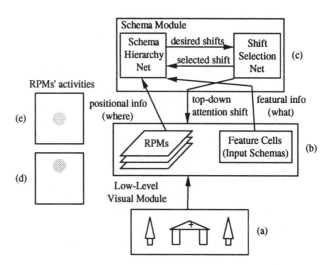

Figure 1: VISOR consists of the Low-Level Visual Module (LLVM, b) and the Schema Module (c). LLVM extracts "what" and "where" information from the scene (a). Figures (d) and (e) indicate the activities of fine-scaled and coarse-scaled Relative Position Maps (RPMs) when attention is focused at the position marked with "+".

III. The Architecture of VISOR

VISOR is based on the separation of the "what" and "where" pathways in low-level vision ([10]; Fig. 1). It consists of the Low-Level Visual Module (simulated using procedural programs) and the Schema Module (implemented with neural networks). The Low-Level Visual Module (LLVM, Fig. 1b) focuses its attention at one position in the scene at a time, and extracts the feature (line, rectangle or triangle) at that location. As its output, the Feature Cells indicate how strongly the LLVM believes a particular feature is present (Fig. 2). The Relative Position Maps (RPMs) encode the relative positions of the features at several scales. For example, suppose that part of the scene contains an arch and two trees (Fig. 1a). Also suppose that attention is currently focused on the triangular roof of the arch. At a fine scale, the RPM identifies the triangle as located above the two rectangles, and gives a peak response at the top part of the map (Fig. 1d). At a coarser scale, the RPM identifies the blob of features constituting the arch as located in the middle of the blobs corresponding to the two trees, and forms a peak response at the center of the map (Fig. 1e). At scales that are larger than that of the retina, the positions of the eyes are taken into account.

The Schema Module (Fig. 1a) maintains the hierarchy of schemas, integrates successive input information, and determines the next position of attention. It consists of two main neural networks: the Schema Hierarchy Net (SHN) and the Shift Selection Net (SSN). The SHN is a multi-layer network of schema representation nets, or schema-nets for short (Fig. 2). A schema-net consists of

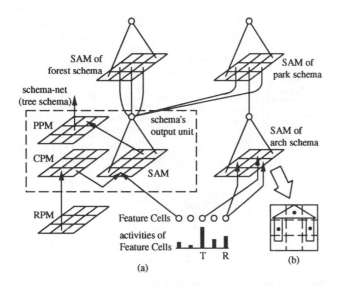

Figure 2: (a) The Schema Hierarchy Net encodes part-whole relationships among the schemas. Arrows represent one-way connections, and solid lines represent both the bottom-up and top-down connections (which are different). For simplicity, the schema-net components are shown only for the tree schema. The Feature Cell marked "T" is sensitive to triangles, and the one marked "R" to rectangles. (b) The arch image encoded by the arch schema. The grid represents the SAM and the black dots denote the positions of the components in the SAM.

four main components: the output unit, the Sub-schema Activity Map (SAM), the Current Position Map (CPM), and the Potential Position Map (PPM). Before describing these components in detail, let us first look at how the schema hierarchy is represented in the SHN.

Each layer of schema-nets corresponds to a level in the schema hierarchy. A schema-net can simultaneously be a sub-schema of higher-level schemas and a super-schema of lower-level schemas. The sub-schemas of the first-level schemas consists of the Feature Cells. The connectivity of the SHN encodes the part-whole relationships among the schemas. Consider, for example, the representation of an arch. Fig. 2(b) shows an arch that is made up of three components: a triangular roof and two rectangular pillars. The grid superimposed on the arch represents a map called the Sub-schema Activity Map (SAM) in the arch schema-net. The black dots indicate the positions of the components in the map. For example, the triangle is located at the top-center of the arch map. Corresponding to each black dot, there is a connection from a Feature Cell to a SAM unit. The connection indicates that the feature is a component of the arch schema at the position of the SAM unit.

The SAM units' activities indicate how strongly the sub-schemas are believed to be present in the scene. These activities may change as more information is extracted from the scene. In effect, SAM encodes a sum-

mary of current evidence for a schema.

In addition to the dynamic information encoded in SAM, it is necessary to keep information about the static structure of the schema, so that the system can decide where to focus its attention next. Such information is stored in the Potential Position Map (PPM). A high activity in a PPM unit indicates that a sub-schema is expected at the corresponding position.

The current position of attention is stored in the Current Position Map (CPM), coded by the location of a single active unit in the map. Each CPM unit connects multiplicatively to the SAM unit at the corresponding location. If a CPM unit is on, the corresponding SAM unit's activity can be updated. Otherwise, the SAM unit's activity remains unchanged. In other words, only the activities of the sub-schemas that match the current position are propagated upwards.

The certainty, or confidence, that a schema matches the input is summarized in the activity of the schema's output unit (or schema's activity for short). In addition to bottom-up connections from the schema's own SAM units, the output unit receives top-down connections from the super-schemas' SAM units (Fig. 2). If a higher-level schema matches an input object with high confidence, then its sub-schemas are expected to match the object's components as well; hence the top-down feedback. There are also mutually inhibitory connections among the schemas' output units to allow the schemas to compete in interpreting the input. (The detailed schema activation equations are given in the appendix.)

After processing the information at a particular position in the scene, VISOR will shift its attention to a new position. The Shift Selection Net (SSN) determines this position (Fig. 1c). As will be described in more detail in Section IV, it makes its decision based on the schemas' activities and their desired shift vectors.

IV. VISOR OPERATION

At the beginning of the scene analysis process, all the schemas are reset to their initial states. That is, none of their CPM units is on (no current position of attention), and the activities of their SAM units are 0 (nothing has been found).[1] After each focusing of attention, the Schema Module processes the featural and positional information received from the LLVM in four main stages: (1) setting current positions of attention within schemas, (2) updating schemas' activities, (3) selecting schemas' desired next position of attention, and (4) selecting one of the next positions for actual attention shift. Let us

---

[1] The initial activities could be set to any values between 0 and 1. In effect, schemas with higher initial activities would then be expected to match the objects and the scene better than those with lower initial activities; in other words, expectation and bias could be modeled.

briefly go through the events of one processing cycle:

1. Setting Current Positions. After the LLVM has shifted its attention to the selected location in the scene, the schemas update their current positions of attention. If a schema is not attending to anything, that is, none of its CPM units is on, its current position is set at the peak position in the RPM (Fig. 2). If one of the CPM units is on, the current position is shifted in the direction and by the amount encoded in the shift vector received from the SSN. If the amount of shift goes beyond the spatial extent of the CPM, then the schema is first reset to its initial state, and then its current position is set at the peak position in the RPM.

2. Schema Activation. At this stage, one of the CPM units is active, and its position indicates the current position of attention. The activity of the SAM unit at the corresponding map position is updated (Appendix). Other SAM units' activities remain unchanged. The activity of the schema's output unit is also updated according to how well the schema matches the input (See the appendix for details). If it matches well, its activity increases as a result of increased SAM activity; otherwise, its activity decreases as a result of mutual inhibition among the schemas. The activity of a schema in turn feeds back to its sub-schemas and boosts their activities. This feedback signal corresponds to top-down expectation: if a schema matches an object well, then its sub-schemas are expected to match the object's components. The activities are updated asynchronously for several cycles until they stabilize.

3. Selection of Desired Next Positions. After the activities have stabilized, each schema chooses a position at which it would like the system to focus its attention. These are the positions where a schema expects to discover features that will contribute to increasing its activity. The schema's selection is based on the following criteria:

1. Select a position where a sub-schema is expected, that is, a position where there is high activity in the PPM unit.
2. Prefer a position that has low SAM activity. For practical (and biological) networks, the activities of the units are finite and bounded within certain ranges of values. Focusing attention at positions with already high SAM activities is not effective in increasing the activity of the schema.
3. Prefer a position close to the current position so that attention shift is minimized.

The selected position is encoded as a shift vector (x-shift, y-shift) and is sent to the SSN.

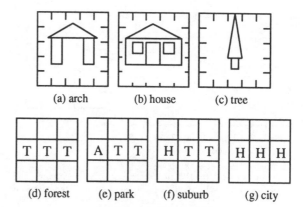

Figure 3: Handcoded schemas used in the experiments. Figures (a)-(c) depict first-level schemas (map size = 5×5), (d)-(g) second-level schemas (map size = 3×3). A = arch, H = house, T = tree.

4. Selection of The Actual Next Position. The SSN receives the desired shift vectors from all schemanets as its input, and selects one of them to be adopted. It prefers a small shift desired by a highly active schema. This criteria favors the interpretation of the visual input in terms of the best-matched schema while minimizing the amount of attention shift. Finally, the selected shift vector is propagated to all the schemas and to the LLVM.

V. Experimental Results With VISOR

Three experiments on object recognition and scene analysis were performed. The first experiment illustrates the recognition of a perfect instance of an object, the second that of distorted instances, and the third that of a complete scene. All the schemas were handcoded in the SHN. The first level of the SHN consisted of the arch, the house, and the tree schemas (Fig. 3a-c). Of these, the arch and the house schemas are very similar. Both have flat triangular roofs, and the rectangular pillars of the arch may be confused with the square windows of the house. The second-level schemas (used in the third experiment) were forest, park, suburb and city (Fig. 3d-g). These schemas are very similar as well. For example, if the scene is either a forest, park or suburb, and VISOR scans from right to left, it will be unable to disambiguate until the object on the far left is identified. Note that these second-level schemas are not intended to be general representations of these scenes. They were conjured up to test the performance of VISOR in highly ambiguous situations.

In the first experiment, a house image was input to VI-SOR. Fig. 4(a) is a plot of the activities of the first-level schemas as VISOR processes the scene. The positions of attention at each time step are shown in Fig. 4(b). The system was purposely set to start in an ambiguous state—it focused on the triangular roof of the house.

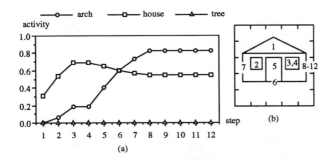

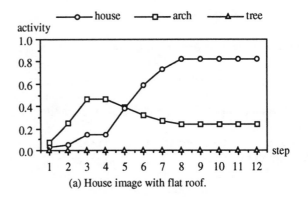

(a) House image with flat roof.

Figure 4: Experimental results of processing a house image. (a) Activities of first-level schemas. (b) The sequence of positions of attention.

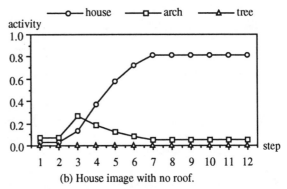

(b) House image with no roof.

Figure 5: Activity patterns of schemas with two different house images.

Initially, VISOR thought that the object was most likely an arch. After the fifth step, the activity of the house schema increased and surpassed that of the arch schema. After the eighth step, VISOR reached the final stable state and concluded that the image was (most likely) a house.

The second experiment illustrates the processing of distorted images. Two variations of the house image were shown to VISOR. The first had a flat roof, and the second had no roof. In both cases, VISOR started by attending to the left window. Fig. 5 illustrates the schemas' activities for the two cases. The effect of featural distortion is most apparent at the second time step when VISOR was attending to the roof. The more the image differs from that represented in the schema, the lower the activities of the arch and the house schemas. That is, VISOR is less certain about the identity of the object. However, in both cases, VISOR was finally able to conclude that the input object was most likely a house.

In the third experiment, VISOR received a suburb image that exactly matched the suburb schema. VISOR was set to initially attend to the triangle of the rightmost tree (Fig. 3). Note that this state is ambiguous because the forest, park and suburb schemas all have a tree as the rightmost component. At step 2, the rightmost tree was identified (Fig. 6). At step 5, the middle tree was identified. At this time, detailed information of the middle tree was stored in the SAM of the tree schema, but detailed information of the rightmost tree was lost. The previous activity of the tree schema (corresponding to the rightmost tree) was stored only in the SAMs of the second-level schemas. Throughout the first 6 time steps, VISOR was unable to determine whether the input scene was a suburb, a park or a forest. At step 7, VISOR focused attention at the triangular roof of the house. It thought that the object on the far left was most likely an arch, and that the whole image was most likely a park. Final disambiguation occurred at step 13 after attending to the left wall of the house. After this time, the house

schema became most active at the first level indicating that the last attended object was a house. Consequently, the suburb schema became the most active second-level schema. Once the activities have stabilized, there is no need to focus attention at other parts of the scene, and the process terminates.

VI. Conclusions

The goal of this research is to develop representation and learning schemes for visual schemas in neural networks. The representation scheme supports integration of successive information so that scene analysis can be accomplished with limited processing resources. The system is implemented simply in terms of maps and cooperative and competitive networks. We are currently working on a method for VISOR to learn schema representations from examples of visual scenes. In a real environment, there can be more than two trees in a park scene, and the arch can be anywhere among the trees. Methods for representing such variations are also currently being investigated.

References

[1] J. K. Tsotsos. How does human vision beat the computational complexity of visual perception? In Z. W. Pylyshyn, editor, *Computational Processes in Human Vision*. Ablex, Norwood, New Jersey, 1988.

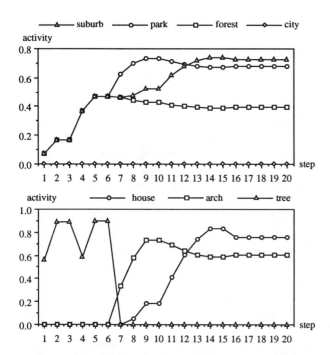

activity

0.8
0.6
0.4
0.2
0.0

1 2 3 4 5 6 7 8 9 10 11 12 13 14 15 16 17 18 19 20 step

activity

1.0
0.8
0.6
0.4
0.2
0.0

1 2 3 4 5 6 7 8 9 10 11 12 13 14 15 16 17 18 19 20 step

Figure 6: Experimental results of processing a suburb image. The bottom graph shows the activities of the first-level schemas, the top graph those of the second-level schemas.

[2] J. E. Hochberg. *Perception, 2nd Ed.* Prentice-Hall, Englewood Cliffs, New Jersey, 1978.

[3] D. S. Touretzky. BoltzCONS: Reconciling connectionism with the recursive nature of stacks and trees. In *Proceedings of 8th Annual Conference of Cognitive Science Society*, pages 522–530, 1986.

[4] J. Pollack. Recursive auto-associative memory: Devising compositional distributed representation. In *Proceedings of 10th Annual Conference of Cognitive Science Society*, pages 33–39, 1988.

[5] D. S. Touretzky and G. E. Hinton. A distributed connectionist production system. *Cognitive Science*, 12:423–466, 1988.

[6] D. E. Rumelhart, P. Smolensky, J. L. McClelland, and G. E. Hinton. Schemata and sequential thought processings in PDP models. In J. L. McClelland and D. E. Rumelhart, editors, *Parallel Distributed Processings*. MIT Press, Cambridge, Massachusetts, 1986.

[7] Geoffrey E. Hinton. Representing part-whole hierarchies in connectionist networks. In *Proceedings of 10th Annual Conference of Cognitive Science Society*, pages 48–54, 1988.

[8] D. A. Norman and T. Shallice. Attention to action: Willed and automatic control of behavior. Technical Report 99, Center for Human Information Processing, Univ. of California, San Diego, La Jolla, California, 1980.

[9] T. Shallice. Specific impairments of planning. *Philosophical Transactions of the Royal Society of London B*, 298:199–209, 1982.

[10] David C. Van Essen and C. H. Anderson. Information processing strategies and pathways in the primate retina and visual cortex. In S. F. Zornetzer, J. L. Davis, and C. Lau, editors, *Introduction to Neural and Electronic Networks*. Academic Press, Orlando, Florida, 1991.

APPENDIX: SCHEMA ACTIVATION EQUATIONS

Below, the equations governing the activation of units in a schema's Sub-schema Activity Map (SAM), and the activation of the schema's output unit are presented (see also Fig. 2). The following notation is used:

U_i: output unit of schema i
A_i: activity of U_i
u_{ix}: SAM unit of schema i at position x
a_{ix}: activity of u_{ix}
c_{ix}: activity of CPM unit of schema i at position x
W_{ixj}: bottom-up connection weight from U_j to u_{ix}
M_{ixj}: top-down connection weight from u_{ix} to U_j
w_{ix}: feedforward connection weight from u_{ix} to U_i
m_{ix}: feedback connection weight from U_i to u_{ix}
e_{ij}: inhibitory connection weight from U_i to U_j
$\alpha, \beta, \gamma, \delta$: parameters, $0 < \alpha, \beta, \gamma, \delta < 1$

When $c_{ix} = 1$, the SAM units' activities are updated according to

$$a_{ix} = \sum_j W_{ixj} A_j + \alpha m_{ix} A_i \qquad (1)$$

When $c_{ix} = 0$, a_{ix} remains unchanged. The first term $\sum_j W_{ixj} A_j$ sums over all the sub-schemas j of schema i and represents the total bottom-up contribution from the sub-schemas. The second term $m_{ix} A_i$ is the feedback from schema i's output unit to its SAM unit.

The schemas' output activities are updated according to

$$A_i = f(\beta \sum_x w_{ix} a_{ix} + \gamma \sum_{j,y} M_{jyi} a_{jy} - \delta \sum_j e_{ji} A_j) \quad (2)$$

The activation function $f(z)$ is a sigmoidal function of the form

$$f(z) = \begin{cases} 0 & \text{if } z < 0 \\ z & \text{if } 0 <= z <= 0.9 \\ 1/(1 - e^{-s(z-b)}) & \text{if } z > 0.9 \end{cases} \quad (3)$$

where $s = -5.493$ and $b = 0.500$. The first term $\sum_x w_{ix} a_{ix}$ sums over all the SAM units u_{ix} of schema i. It is the total feedforward contribution from the SAM. The second term $\sum_{j,y} M_{jyi} a_{jy}$ sums over all the SAM units u_{jy} of all the super-schemas j of schema i. It gives the total top-down contribution from all the super-schemas. The last term $\sum_j e_{ji} A_j$ sums over all the schemas j at the same level as schema i giving the total inhibition from those schemas.

A Comparison of Neural Network and Nearest-Neighbor Classifiers Of Handwritten Lower-Case Letters

Thomas M. English, Maria del Pilar Gomez-Gil, and William J. B. Oldham
Computer Science Department
Texas Tech University
Lubbock, Texas 79409-3104 USA

Abstract—We have applied *k*-nearest-neighbor classifiers, fully-connected networks, and networks of an architecture devised by LeCun to the problem of recognizing handwritten (cursive) lower-case letters. Results reported here differ from those of studies involving hand-printed characters: LeCun networks have given higher accuracy (77%) than fully-connected networks (74%), which in turn have given higher accuracy than *k*-nearest-neighbor classifiers (71%). We have also observed that training with an error criterion based on the L^{10} norm allows LeCun networks to avoid some local minima encountered when the squared error (L^2) criterion is used.

I. INTRODUCTION

Artificial neural networks trained by error back-propagation have achieved relatively high accuracy in classification of hand-printed digits and capital letters [1]-[3]. Here we address the similar, but more difficult, problem of classifying handwritten (*i.e.*, cursive) lower-case letters. Several classifiers that have given equal accuracy in experiments with hand-printed characters [2], [3] have given distinctly different accuracies in our experiments. In particular, variants of LeCun's highly constrained architecture [4] have achieved higher accuracy than have *k*-nearest-neighbor classifiers and fully-connected networks of several sizes. These results were obtained with a training set of about the same size as that used in the Martin and Pittman [2] study of letter recognition.

In preliminary experiments we observed that a LeCun network gave very low outputs in response to "difficult" exemplars in the training set, even after extended training. More emphasis was given to atypical exemplars by generalizing the back-propagation procedure to reduce the L^p norm (defined in Section III) of the vector of deviations from desired outputs, and by choosing $p > 2$ [5]. We have found that use of a super-squared error criterion ($p > 2$) allows the back-propagation procedure to avoid some local minima that are encountered when the conventional squared error criterion ($p = 2$) is used.

In the following sections, we describe the database of handwritten letters used in our experiments. Then details of the training procedure are given, including the generaliza-

M. Gomez-Gil is currently with Depto. de Ingenieria y Sistemas Computacionales, Universidad de las Americas, 72820 Puebla, Mexico.

This research was supported by an equipment grant through the Data-Parallel Research Initiative of Digital Equipment Corporation and MasPar Computer Corporation.

tion of back-propagation to L^p error criteria. After describing our extension of the LeCun architecture, we present experiments comparing that architecture to other classifiers, and comparing error criteria. We discuss the results and draw several conclusions.

II. DATABASE OF HANDWRITTEN LETTERS

A total of 300 complete alphabets (7800 lower-case cursive letters) was generated by 61 writers (10 of whom were left-handed). A random selection of 225 alphabets (5850 letters) was used in training all classifiers described in this paper, with the remaining 75 alphabets reserved for testing. Since most writers were represented in both the training and testing sets, the problem we address is better described as *multiple-writer* than as *writer-independent* letter recognition.

Subjects generated alphabets by writing isolated letters in delineated cells of a transparent sheet. Although writers were instructed to produce cursive letters, the database includes many printed letters. Printed instances of *b*, *s*, and *z* are particularly common. Each cell of the data collection sheet yielded a 56 × 66 pixel grayscale image. Preprocessing reduced each of these higher-resolution images to a 16 × 16 pixel binary picture.

Preprocessing entailed thresholding, several "cleaning" operations, and size normalization. The threshold was chosen to be slightly darker than the mean of the minimum and maximum grayscale values in the picture. The cleaning operations removed disconnected components from picture borders, removed irregular "bumps" from the edges of letters, and opened closed loops in letters. Size normalization was accomplished using an algorithm due to Gudesen [6]. Further details of the database preparation may be found in [7].

III. DETAILS OF THE TRAINING PROCEDURE

Back-propagation can be used improve performance according to any criterion which is a differentiable function of network outputs [8]. We generalize the procedure to reduce the L^p norm of the error vector,

$$\left(\sum_n \sum_i |o_{ni} - d_{ni}|^p \right)^{1/p}$$

1618

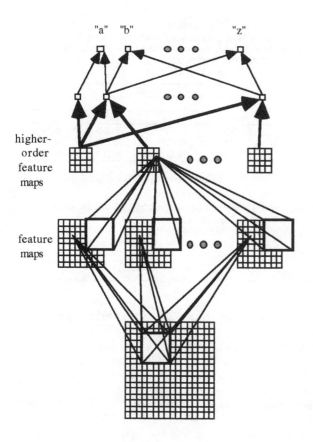

Fig. 1. The LeCun architecture.

TABLE I
CONNECTIONS FROM FEATURE MAPS TO HIGHER-ORDER FEATURE
MAPS IN THE ENLARGED LECUN NETWORK

Map	Higher-Order Map																	
	1	2	3	4	5	6	7	8	9	10	11	12	13	14	15	16	17	18
1	×	×	×													×	×	×
2	×	×	×													×	×	×
3	×	×	×	×	×	×												
4	×	×	×	×	×	×												
5				×	×	×	×	×	×									
6				×	×	×	×	×	×									
7							×	×	×	×	×	×	×					
8							×	×	×	×	×	×						
9										×	×	×	×	×	×			
10										×	×	×	×	×	×			
11													×	×	×	×	×	×
12													×	×	×	×	×	×

where o_{ni} is the activation of the i-th output unit in response to the n-th exemplar, d_{ni} is the corresponding desired output, and $p > 0$. A simpler, but equivalent, error criterion is

$$E = 1/p \sum_n \sum_i |o_{ni} - d_{ni}|^p$$

The required partial derivatives, which the "teacher" presents as error signals to the output units, are

$$\partial E / \partial o_{ni} = \text{signum}(o_{ni} - d_n) \, |o_{ni} - d_{ni}|^{p-1}$$

where signum(x) is -1 for $x < 0$ and is 1 otherwise.

To speed learning, each hidden unit amplified incoming error signals by a factor of 6 [9]. To avoid overfitting the training set, we adjoined the sum of squared weights to the error criterion [10]. In practical terms, this means that each weight decayed in magnitude immediately prior to the addition of adjustments computed by back-propagation. Following [11], we chose 0.001 as the decay factor. Relatively mild overfitting was observed in all training runs.

Training was accomplished on a MasPar MP-1 data-parallel computer. Our simulator achieves its best utilization of the MP-1 by computing weight adjustments for a batch of 2048 training inputs, summing the adjustments, and then updating the weights [12]. In the present study, the training set was split into three batches of 1950 images.

All non-input units applied hyperbolic tangent activation functions, and desired outputs were specified as -1 or $+1$. Initial network weights (including biases) were uniformly distributed on the interval $[-0.01, 0.01]$. Output unit biases were set initially to -1, however, to reduce the initial "lurch" in weight space. For each combination of network architecture and error criterion, the learning rate was set to the greatest power of 10 (*e.g.*, 0.0001) that gave consistent reduction of error. There was no momentum in the first five epochs, after which the momentum factor was set to 0.9. Momentum increased to as much as 0.99 in epochs following the apparent peak in generalization.

IV. EXTENSION OF THE LECUN ARCHITECTURE

Here we describe our extension of LeCun's architecture (see Figure 1) to letter recognition. We refer to the 8×8 grids of units in the first hidden layer as *feature maps*, and to the 4×4 grids in the second hidden layer as *higher-order feature maps*. Apart from having 26 (rather than 10) output units, the network described here differs from that originally applied to hand-printed digit recognition [1] by having 50% more units in each hidden layer.

Specifically, there are 18 higher-order feature maps, each of which receives information from 10 of the 18 feature maps. The connections from feature maps 1-12 to higher-order feature maps are given in Table I. Feature maps 13-18 are connected to all higher-order feature maps. All units in the higher-order feature maps are connected to the 45 units in the third hidden layer, which are all connected to the 26 output units. The number of non-input units (and biases) is 1511, and the number of connections is 90 792.

V. EXPERIMENTS

We consider first the performance of k-nearest-neighbor classifiers, with training and trial images as described in

TABLE II

CLASSIFICATION ACCURACIES ACHIEVED BY THE SMALLER LECUN
NETWORK FOR TRAINING AND TRIAL IMAGES, EXPRESSED AS A
FUNCTION OF ERROR CRITERION USED IN TRAINING.

| Norm | Accuracy | |
	Train	Trial
2	95.90%	68.62%
10	97.42%	74.26%
14	99.93%	73.90%

TABLE III

CLASSIFICATION ACCURACIES ACHIEVED BY THE LARGER LECUN
NETWORK FOR TRAINING AND TRIAL IMAGES, EXPRESSED
AS A FUNCTION OF ERROR CRITERION AND INITIAL
CONDITIONS IN TRAINING.

| | Norm | | | |
| | 2 | | 10 | |
Condition	Trial	Train	Trial	Train
1	73.49%	99.18%	77.08%	99.91%
2	73.90%	98.92%	76.97%	99.97%
3	76.15%	99.42%	76.15%	99.57%

TABLE IV

COMPARISON OF TRIAL-SET CLASSIFICATION ACCURACIES ACHIEVED
BY THE 5-NEAREST-NEIGHBOR CLASSIFIER, FULLY-CONNECTED
NETWORK WITH 370 HIDDEN UNITS, LOCALLY-CONNECTED
NETWORK, AND THE LARGER LECUN NETWORK.

5-NN	Full	Local	LeCun
70.82%	73.85%	74.21%	76.15%

Section II. The nearest-neighbor classifier ($k = 1$) achieved only 68.72% accuracy. For all choices of k in $\{3, 5, ..., 13\}$, accuracy of 69.90% or better was achieved, with peak accuracy of 70.82% at $k = 5$. The optimal choice of k agrees well with Lee's observation of peak accuracy at $k = 9$ for a training set about five times as large as ours [3].

In preliminary experiments with the LeCun architecture, we used the original digit recognizer [1], simply increasing the number of output units from 10 to 26. As can be seen in Table II, using the back-propagation procedure to improve performance according to L^{10} and L^{14} error criteria resulted in substantially higher accuracy than was achieved with the conventional L^2 error criterion. (Experiments with L^4 and L^6 criteria, conducted under slightly different conditions, gave peak trial-set accuracies in the range of 71–72%.)

The trial-set accuracies cited in Table II are the best that were observed in the course of training. The training-set accuracies, however, were recorded at the time of peak generalization. Further training with the L^{10} and L^{14} error criteria resulted in perfect classification of the training set. Extended training with the squared error criterion gave training-set accuracy of only 97%. Since all L^P errors can be driven arbitrarily small after achieving perfect classification of the training set, we conclude that a local minimum encountered with the squared error criterion was avoided with the super-squared error criteria.

Subsequent experiments involved the larger LeCun network described in Section IV. Table III gives a comparison of the L^2 and L^{10} error criteria for three sets of initial weights. In all three cases, the L^{10} criterion gave peak generalization at least as good as that given by the L^2 criterion. Note, however, that the L^2 and L^{10} criteria produced equal trial-set accuracy in one case. With the L^{10} criterion, the training set was eventually classified perfectly in all three runs. With the L^2 criterion, training for about one thousand epochs beyond peak generalization gave at best 99.68% training-set accuracy.

Several other back-propagation networks were trained with the L^{10} criterion. To gauge the effect of weight-tying, a LeCun network was trained with independent updates of all weights and biases (92 303 free parameters). Peak trial-set accuracy was only 74.21%. Fully-connected networks with single hidden layers of 185, 370, and 555 units gave peak trial-set accuracies of 68.36%, 73.85%, and 73.69%, respectively. Table IV summarizes results obtained for the various classifiers reported upon in this paper. Since the fully-connected and locally-connected ("untied" LeCun) networks were trained with only one initial condition, the

lowest accuracy achieved by LeCun networks is presented for comparison.

In the case of the best LeCun network, no letter was classified with better than 93.3% accuracy (observed for *b* and *d*), or with worse than 62.7% accuracy (observed for *y* and *z*). The number of errors was only three times as large as the number of distinct confusions. The most frequent confusions, accounting collectively for 18% of all errors, were *e-l*, *h-k*, *m-n*, and *g-q*. All *m-n* confusions were classifications of *n* tokens as *m*. This is due to the fact that some writers produce *n* with two humps, while no writer produces *m* with one hump.

VI. DISCUSSION

In principle, the LeCun architecture is no more accurate than the fully-connected architecture when the training set is "large." Networks with minimal squared error for the training set approach Bayes-optimality as the training set grows [13]. Further, there exists a network of our fully-connected architecture with squared error arbitrarily close to the minimum [14]. (There is no practical way to obtain this network, however.)

We are left with the question of whether the advantage of the LeCun architecture disappears for *practical* training set sizes. At present, training sets an order of magnitude larger than the one we have used are practical, and may be sufficient to erase the advantage of LeCun nets in the particular problem we have addressed. But our results underscore the fact that similar classification problems may differ considerably in difficulty, and that the success of "brute force" techniques in one of those problems does not obviate the need for careful classifier design in the others.

At present we do not have a satisfying explanation for the observed advantage of the super-squared error criterion. Qualitative observations of the training process suggest, however, that class modes are accommodated very rapidly with the squared error criterion, and that it is subsequently difficult to reduce the error for patterns in low-density regions of the input space. That is, the error for these "unusual" patterns cannot be decreased without temporarily increasing the error for a large number of other patterns. With super-squared error criteria, the atypical patterns contribute significantly to the error gradient before the network comes to process them very poorly, and it is subsequently possible to obtain a good response for those patterns without disrupting the network's response in modal regions of the input space. In effect, increasing p seems to reduce the "greediness" of the back-propagation procedure's reduction of error.

For some applications, error criteria based upon L^p norms with $p < 2$ may give better results than the squared error criterion. In a picture coding application where less emphasis upon exceptional regions of the image is desirable, the L^1 norm has been found advantageous [15]. For pattern recognition, the previously-mentioned relationship of minimal squared error and Bayes-optimality should be taken into account. It may prove advantageous to begin training with a super-squared error criterion, and to end training with a transition to the squared error criterion.

It should be observed, however, that the advantage of the super-squared error criterion was not as pronounced in the larger LeCun network as it was in the smaller. We cannot discount the possibility that the larger network is too small for the problem, and that the advantage of the super-squared error criterion would disappear for the optimal choice of network dimensions. We have yet to address this question, since the larger of the LeCun networks requires all memory available in our simulation environment.

Finally, we note that our preprocessing of letter images may have contributed to the relatively low recognition accuracies obtained. Previous studies suggest that our binarization and "cleaning" of images may have had a deleterious effect [1], [2]. In fact, inspection of incorrectly classified images suggests that occasional poor performance of the preprocessor accounts for some errors. Most errors are attributable to the inherent difficulty of the problem, however. It seems unlikely that the preprocessing biased the experiments in favor of any recognizer or error criterion.

VII. CONCLUSIONS

We have presented evidence corroborating LeCun's claim that a highly-constrained network, with prior conceptions of appropriate processing represented in the constraints, should generalize better than a network incorporating no problem-specific information [4]. We have also shown that, for our database, various back-propagation networks give considerably higher accuracy than does the best k-nearest-neighbor classifier. The question of how much more data must be collected to erase the differences between these classifiers remains open.

We have also shown that use of super-squared error criteria allows the back-propagation procedure to avoid some local minima encountered when the conventional squared error criterion is used. Unfortunately, we do not know how to choose an appropriate error criterion, apart from trial and error. It is possible that super-squared error criteria are useful for avoiding local minima in the earlier stages of training, but that completion of training with the squared error criterion is desirable.

REFERENCES

[1] LeCun, Y., Boser, B., Denker, J. S., Henderson, D., Howard, R. E., Hubbard, W., and Jackel, L. D. 1989. Backpropagation applied to handwritten zip code recognition. *Neural Comput.* 1 (4), pp. 541-51.

[2] Martin, G. L., and Pittman, J. A. 1991. Recognizing hand-printed letters and digits using backpropagation learning. *Neural Comput.* 3 (2), pp. 258-67.

[3] Lee, Y. 1991. Handwritten digit recognition using k nearest-neighbor, radial-basis function, and backpropagation neural networks. *Neural Comput.* 3 (3), pp. 440-49.

[4] LeCun, Y. 1989. Generalization and network design strategies. In *Connectionism in Perspective*, R. Pfeifer, Z. Schreter, F. Fogelman, and L. Steels, eds. North-Holland, Amsterdam.

[5] English, T. M., and Boggess, L. C. 1992. Back-propagation training of a neural network for word spotting, in *Proceedings ICASSP-92*, vol. 2, pp. 357-60.

[6] Gudesen, A. 1976. Quantitative analysis of preprocessing techniques for the recognition of hand-printed characters. *Pattern Recognition* 8 (4), pp. 219-27.

[7] Gomez-Gil, M. del P. 1991. Recognition of handwritten letters using a locally connected back-propagation neural network. M.S. thesis, Dept. of Computer Science, Texas Tech University.

[8] Rumelhart, D. E., Hinton, G. E., and Williams, R. J. 1986. Learning internal representations by error propagation. In *Parallel Distributed Processing*, D. E. Rumelhart, J. L. McClelland, and the PDP Research Group, eds., Chap. 8. MIT Press, Cambridge, MA.

[9] Rigler, A. K., Irvine, J. M., and Vogl, T. P. 1991. Rescaling of variables in back propagation learning. *Neural Networks* 4 (2), pp. 225-29.

[10] Chauvin, Y. 1990. Dynamic behavior of constrained back-propagation networks. In *Advances in Neural Information Processing Systems 2*, D. S. Touretzky, ed., pp. 642-49. Morgan Kaufmann, San Mateo, CA.

[11] Lang, K., Waibel, A., and Hinton, G. E. 1990. A time-delay neural network for isolated word recognition. *Neural Networks* 3 (1), pp. 23-43.

[12] Grajski, K. 1992. Neurocomputing using the MasPar MP-1. In *Digital Parallel Implementations of Neural Networks*, Przytula and Prasanna, eds. Prentice-Hall, Englewood Cliffs, NJ.

[13] Shigeki, M., and Kanaya, F. 1991. A neural network approach to a Bayesian statistical decision problem. *IEEE Trans. Neural Networks* 2 (5), pp. 538-40.

[14] Hornik, K., Stinchcombe, M., and White, H. 1989. Multilayer feedforward nets are universal approximators. *Neural Networks* 2, pp. 359-66.

[15] Mougeot, M., Azencott, R., and Angeniol, B. 1991. Image compression with back propagation: Improvement of the visual restoration using different cost functions. *Neural Networks* 4 (4), pp. 467-76.

Self-Organized Color Image Quantization
for Color Image Data Compression

Keith R. L. Godfrey

Yiannis Attikiouzel

Centre for Intelligent Information Processing Systems
Department of Electrical and Electronic Engineering
The University of Western Australia
Nedlands 6009 Australia

Abstract - This paper presents a neural network approach to image color quantization and hence image data compression. Self-organizing feature maps form a basis for general vector quantization and this is applied to the tristimulus color values of image pixels. For image telecommunication systems such as videoconferencing, it is desirable to constrain the encoder to a single pass of the image using the normal raster scan but this conflicts with the training requirements of a self-organized network. By appropriate choice of codebook size, this limitation can be turned into an advantage. The network performs a mix of vector quantization and run length coding, thus compressing the image data in two ways.

I. Introduction

With the advent of videoconferencing and color medical imaging there is an emerging need for fast data compression algorithms for color images. Color image compression can be considered in two parts: pixel quantization and image spatial coding. Quantization concerns the coding of individual pixels in the image. Image spatial coding refers to the use of neighbourhood relationships and image geometry to compactly describe the contents of an image. For monochrome images, the benefit from pixel quantization is small when compared with that of spatial coding. In color images the compression possibilities from pixel quantization are significant. With 256 levels of red, green and blue in a typical color image, there are 16,777,216 possible values for each pixel. It is very unlikely that all pixel colors will occur simultaneously in any image and it is physically impossible in any image smaller than 4096x4096 pixels, so the entropy of the color values will typically be much smaller than their raw size. The pixel colors can be compressed losslessly down to the entropy level and further if loss is permitted. Color quantization is the process of coding the pixel colors below the pixel entropy but with minimal visual degradation.

There have been many different approaches to color quantization. Classical approaches such as Yamaguchi [1] use mathematical transforms. Celenk [2] applied clustering methods to the color space. Braudaway's algorithm [3] works by iteratively refining an initial color palette. Orchard and Bouman [4] developed a hierarchical tree structured color palette with local error diffusion.

The approach in this paper is to use a self-organising neural network for color quantization, with an adaptive codebook for faster training. A neural network has the advantage that it learns adaptively from the data presented and it works best with a large amount of data, which exists in a digital image. A neural network architecture is also well suited to high speed processing because it is massively parallel. As color quantization involves an analysis of the pixels in an image to determine a codebook and this codebook is not previously known, a self-organising network is required. Supervised and reinforced paradigms are not appropriate for this task due to the amount of corrective data that they require for training.

In the following sections, Kohonen's self-organizing feature maps are applied to color pixel quantization. A neural network model is developed to generate an adaptive codebook from sequential scanning. The resulting network is shown to be an effective color pixel quantizer and the choice of codebook size is discussed.

II. Self-Organization and Vector Quantization

Self-organising networks have been applied to vector quantisation of monochrome images. Nasrabadi and Feng [5] used Kohonen's self-organising feature maps [6,7,8,9] to code two-dimensional image vectors. Lu and Shin [10] followed their work one year later with emphasis on edge preservation, as this is typically a problem of spatial vector quantization. Fang et al [11] developed a self-orgnizing vector quantizer VLSI chip and built it. These approaches have been successful in their spatial task but none mentions the use of color.

III. Applying Self-Organization to Color Quantization

Color pixels are quantized by assigning each pixel to one color from a codebook. A self-organizing neural network can achieve this by matching each pixel's color to the closest color in a self-organized array. Prior to matching each pixel, the network must first be trained to develop its codebook of colors from the image.

A self-organizing architecture for color quantization is developed as follows. The network uses the type of processing element introduced by Teuvo Kohonen [6] and comprises three slabs: an input slab, a self-organizing slab and an output slab. If the inputs are the red, green and blue tristimulus values of a single pixel then, after training with random presentations of colors from an image, each element in the self-organizing slab will correspond to a single time-averaged color. The set of colors thus formed becomes the codebook for pixel classification. The size of the codebook is determined by the size of the self-organizing slab, so an image can be quantized to any desired extent by *a priori* specification of the dimensions of the neural network. To code the quantized output, the winning self-organized node is mapped to a binary output vector by means of a set of binary weights leading from the self-organizing slab to the output slab.

The network is shown in Figure 1. During classification, the input tristimulus color is compared to each color in the codebook by measuring the Euclidean distance in red-green-blue space. The distance between the input and the i-th codebook vector is:

$$distance_i^2 = (r - R_i)^2 + (g - G_i)^2 + (b - B_i)^2$$

where $[R_i, G_i, B_i]$ is the vector of tristimulus values for the i-th codebook color and $[r, g, b]$ is the input tristimulus vector. The winning codebook color is the one with the smallest distance measure. There is no pre-processing required for the tristimulus values in this case, in the sense of transformations to other color representations. Spherical coordinates are inappropriate for the distance measure because colors close to black would be sparsely separated.

Self-organization is achieved by shifting every codebook vector towards each target vector pattern by a small amount. The winner is normally shifted by a larger amount than the other codebook vectors. The learning rule is:

$$[R_i, G_i, B_i]_{new} = [R_i, G_i, B_i]_{old} + D_i$$

where $D_i = \alpha [r-R_i, g-G_i, b-B_i]$ for i=winner

and $D_i = \beta [r-R_i, g-G_i, b-B_i]$ for i<>winner

with $\alpha > \beta$, since α is the learning rate for winning vectors and β is the learning rate for the other vectors.

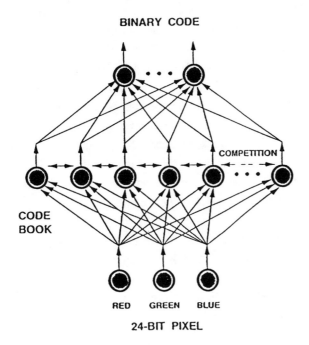

BINARY CODE

COMPETITION

CODE
BOOK

RED   GREEN   BLUE

24-BIT PIXEL

Figure 1.   Self-Organising Neural Network
for Color Quantization

IV. Sequential Scanning

The standard self-organizing architecture is an effective quantizer but its codebook must be determined prior to quantization. This typically requires a training run through random selections of pixel colors from the image until the codebook converges to an average color representation of the whole image. This training phase adds a considerable overhead to the quantization process. It implies that each complete video frame would have to be received and stored before training could commence and the training must finish before the coded sequence can be generated.

Images are normally transmitted in a raster scan sequence, from top to bottom and left to right. It is desirable for a color quantizer to code the image sequentially in the scanned order, so that the complete image is not required beforehand for training. By feeding the pixels sequentially to the self-organizing feature maps, the training and quantization is performed simultanously so the codebook

will develop adaptively through the image. To build a communication system with this kind of quantizer as the coder, the coding algorithm must be invertible so that it can be decoded at the receiver. It is necessary to send each new codebook vector when it is entered, as well as the binary codebook indices of all recognised quantized vectors, but it is undesirable to send any additional training information as this requires extra information transfer. The learning algorithm must therefore be modified because the actual R,G,B values of each pixel will not be transmitted and hence will not be available to the decoder.

Instead of moving each vector towards the input vector, each non-winning vector can be moved towards any newly entered codebook vector and also towards any existing winning codebook vector, since these are always present at both the encoder and decoder. It is no longer possible to update the winner so the learning parameters α and β are replaced by a single parameter γ. The weight update algorithm is therefore becomes:

$$D_k = \gamma [R_i - R_k , G_i - G_k , B_i - B_k] \qquad k <> i$$

where $[R_i, G_i, B_i]$ is the winning vector, transmitted simply as its index i if in the codebook, or $[R_i, G_i, B_i]$ if not.

The adaptive codebook algorithm works as follows. Each pixel is transmitted first as a codebook index and then as a R,G,B triplet if new to the codebook. An input pixel will be new to the codebook if the winning distance $distance_i$ is greater than a predetermined threshold T. If the codebook is indexed by N bits, so that there are 2^N possible vectors in the codebook, one vector is dedicated to highlight new entries, leaving $2^N - 1$ ordinary vectors. When a new entry is required, it initially is placed in the first unused position, but after the codebook is full it replaces the entry with the greatest Euclidean distance from the input pixel.

V. Compression Results

It can be shown that the total number of bits for an image compressed by the above algorithm is:

$$\text{total bits} = N \times (\text{number of pixels}) +$$
$$24 \times (\text{number of codebook entries})$$

where a codebook entry could be either a new entry or a replacement and 24 represents the number of extra bits which must be transmitted for a codebook entry's R,G,B tristimulus values.

Information theory [12] predicts the minimum number of bits required to represent a particular sequence. If C represents the set of colors in an image, the information content of each color $C_i = [\ R_i,\ G_i,\ B_i\ ]$ is given by $log_2(\ 1\ /\ P(C_i)\ )$ and the average entropy of each pixel is:

$$entropy\ =\ \Sigma_i\ \ P(C_i)\ \ log_2(\ 1\ /\ P(C_i)\ )$$

where $P(C_i)$ is the probability of meeting that color in the image. The entropy is the minimum number of bits for lossless representation of each pixel and hence the maximum number of bits required if loss is permitted.

Figure 2 shows an image of yachts moored on the Swan River in Perth, Western Australia, digitised to 256x256 pixels. The image uses 24-bit color but has an entropy of only 10.325 bits per pixel. In Figure 3, the image has been compressed by a self-organizing adaptive codebook network with a learning parameter $\gamma = 0.0001$, distance threshold $T = 30$ and codebook size of $N=6$ giving 31 entries. The resulting image has been compressed to 6.05 bits per pixel, with minimal visual degredation.

Both images are displayed on an IRIS-4D workstation in full 24-bit color. As color cannot be reproduced in this publication, only the green components of the images are shown. The images have been half-toned through a 8x8 dithering grid.

VI. Choice of Codebook Size

If the codebook size is small and/or if the threshold distance is small, there will be fewer entries in the codebook than can accurately represent the image. A significant portion of the image pixels will therefore miss the codebook and require insertion at both the coder and decoder. In the extreme case, a codebook of size 1 would require almost every pixel to be transmitted, consuming 24 bits each.

If the codebook size is too large and/or if the threshold distance is large, there will be sufficient entries to describe the image and some may remain unused.

By scanning the image horizontally, the codebook is storing the most useful recent colors that it has encountered, which is a general form of run length coding. A run length coder is equivalent to a vector quantiser with a codebook size of 1, capable only of detecting each change of code. With increasing codebook size, there is a greater number of colors that are stored, up to the maximum number required for an image. Thus, it is possible to constrain the self-organising network to perform a mixture of quantization and run length coding by adjusting the codebook size. If the codebook size is sufficiently large that its vectors do not need replacement, the network performs quantization only. If the codebook is smaller, some vectors will be replaced during the horizontal scans.

VII. Conclusions

A self-organizing network has been developed to quantize the pixels in 24-bit full color images. The network incorporates Kohonen's self-organizing feature map with binary output mapping and the learning algorithm is modified so that it can be trained on a single sequential pass through each image. By appropriate choice of codebook size, the network can perform a combination of pixel quantization and run length coding. A demonstration 24-bit color image was compressed to 6.05 bits per pixel with minimal visual degredation and the images have been reproduced here in monocrome.

Acknowledgments

This work has been supported in part by the Australian Telecommunications and Electronics Research Board and OTC Limited.

References

[1]   H. Yamaguchi, "Efficient Encoding of Colored Pictures in R, G, B Components", IEEE Transactions on Communications, Vol. COM-32, No. 11, November 1984, pp 1201-9.

[2]   M. Celenk, "Colour image segmentation by clustering", IEE Proceedings - Part E, Vol. 138, No. 5, September 1991, pp 368-76.

[3]   G. Braudaway, "A procedure for optimum choice of a small number of colors from a large color palette for color imaging", Electronic Imaging '87, San Francisco CA, 1987.

[4]   M. T. Orchard and C. A. Bouman, "Color Quantization of Images", IEEE Transactions on Signal Processing, Vol. 39, No. 12, December 1991, pp 2677-90.

[5]   N. M. Nasrabadi and Y. Feng, "Vector Quantization of Images Based Upon the Kohonen Self-Organizing Feature Maps", Proc. Int. Conf. on Neural Networks (ICNN'88), Vol. I, pp 101-8, San Diego, 1988.

[6]   T. Kohonen, "Self-organized formation of topologically correct feature maps", Biological Cybernetics, vol. 43, pp 59-69, 1982.

[7]   T. Kohonen, "Self-Organization and Associative Memory", Springer-Verlag, 1984.

[8]   T. Kohonen, "An Introduction to Neural Computing", Neural Networks, Vol. 1, No. 1, pp 3-16, 1988.

[9]   R. Hecht-Nielsen, "Neurocomputing", Addison Wesley, 1990.

[10] C. C. Lu and Y. H. Shin, "A Neural Network Based Image Compression System", IEEE Transactions on Consumer Electronics, Vol. 38, No. 1, February 1992, pp 25-9.

[11] W. C. Fang, B. J. Sheu, O. T. C. Chen and J. Choi, "A VLSI Neural Processor for Image Data Compression Using Self-Organization Networks", IEEE Transactions on Neural Networks, Vol. 3, No. 3, May 1992, pp 506-18.

[12] S. Haykin, "Communication Systems", Wiley, 1983.

Figure 2:   Original yachts image (green component)
image: 24 bits per pixel,
entropy: 10.325 bits per pixel.

Figure 3:   Compressed yachts image (green component)
quantised: 6.05 bits per pixel

Application Oriented Automatic Structuring of Time-Delay Neural Networks for High Performance Character and Speech Recognition

Ulrich Bodenhausen and Alex Waibel

Computer Science Department, University of Karlsruhe, Postfach 6980, 7500 Karlsruhe 1, FRG,

and

School of Computer Science, Carnegie Mellon University, Pittsburgh, PA 15213

Abstract-Highly structured artificial neural networks have been shown to be superior to fully connected networks for real-world applications like speech recognition and handwritten character recognition. These structured networks can be optimized in many ways, and have to be optimized for optimal performance. This makes the manual optimization very time-consuming. A highly structured approach is the Multi State Time Delay Neural Network (MSTDNN) which uses shifted input windows and allows the recognition of sequences of ordered events that have to be observed jointly. In this paper we propose an Automatic Structure Optimization (ASO) algorithm and apply it to MSTDNN type networks. The ASO algorithm optimizes all relevant parameters of MSTDNNs automatically and was successfully tested with three different tasks and varying amounts of training data.

I. INTRODUCTION

Highly structured artificial neural networks have been shown to be superior to fully connected networks for real-world applications like speech recognition [1, 2] and handwritten character recognition [3]. The importance of the network structure has also recently been examined by Geman et al. [4]. They come to the conclusion that "dedicated machines are harder to build but easier to train" and suggest that important properties of the task have to be built into the architecture of the network. Similar conclusions have been made by Minsky and Papert [5]. But manual design of intermediate representations and the network structure can be very time-consuming for real-world applications. It may not even be possible to optimize the structure before the exact application of the user is known. For example, the user might try to train a speech recognizer on a language and/or an amount of training data that the structure was not optimized for[1].

One reason for the introduction of structure to the network is the relationship between the number of trainable parameters, amount of training data and generalization (see [6, 7, 8] and others). Networks with too many trainable parameters for the given amount of training data learn well, but do not generalize well. This phenomenon is usually called overfitting. With too few trainable parameters, the network fails to learn the training data and performs very poorly on the testing data. Imposing structure into the network can increase the generalization performance by reducing the number of trainable parameters [1, 2].

Unfortunately, highly structured networks can be optimized in many more ways than fully connected networks. In order to achieve optimal performance without time-consuming manual optimization, we propose an AUTOMATIC STRUCTURE OPTIMIZATION (ASO) algorithm that automatically optimizes the structure and the total number of parameters synergetically and also considers the current amount of training data. Rather than starting with a distributed internal representation, the structure of the network is constructed by adding units and connections in order to selectively improve certain parts of the network. At the beginning of the training run the internal representation is completely local and gets more and more distributed in the following optimization process. Only a concept for structuring the network has to be specified before training. The concept for structuring the network is derived from (simple) knowledge about the task, such as invariances. The algorithm combines a constructive and a pruning method. The constructive approach is used to find a network structure that is specifically tailored for the task and the current amount of training data. Weight decay and/or Optimal Brain Damage (see next paragraph) can be used to further refine this architecture to achieve optimal performance.

II. PREVIOUS WORK

Two types of approaches have been proposed for the automatic optimization of network architectures: Constructive algorithms that start with a minimal architecture and increase the resources of the network; and algorithms that

---

1. See Table 3 for an example: A network that was well optimized for a training set of 1170 patterns also generalized reasonably for a training set of 1560 patterns, but failed to learn a reduced training set of 520 patterns with various learning rates and momentums.

avoid overfitting by limiting the computational power of fixed architectures.

Regularization techniques like weight-decay or weight elimination [9, 10, 11] belong to the second group. They add some complexity measure to the cost function that is optimized by the learning rule. This can reduce the risk of overfitting the data with too many trainable parameters in the network, but the decay or elimination parameter has to be well adjusted for optimal results. Optimal Brain Damage (OBD) [12] is an algorithm that selectively removes unimportant weights from a network. The basic idea is to use second-derivative information to make a trade-off between network complexity and training set error. Although these algorithms can improve existing (reasonable architecures) considerably, it is not clear whether a foolish network can be optimized to state-of-the art performance.

Constructive algorithms like Cascade Correlation [13] start with a small network and increase the resources during the training phase. For example, Cascade Correlation starts with no hidden units and tries to solve the classification problem without them. If this fails, hidden units are added one after the other.

III. CONCEPT OF THE AUTOMATIC STRUCTURE OPTIMIZATION ALGORITHM

The proposed algorithm is based on four principles:

- built-in invariances
- task decomposition
- confusion matrix dependant construction of the network
- early constructive changes of the network architecture

A. Built-in Invariances:

If there is any knowledge about the task, it should be built into the structure of the network. For speech and handwritten character recognition, a classifier that is robust against temporal distortions is highly desirable. This can be achieved by using shifted input windows over time as in the Time-Delay Neural Network (TDNN) [1, 2]. Shifting the window reduces the number of weights and ensures that the hidden abstractions that are learned are invariant under translations in time.

B. Task Decomposition:

Instead of learning very complex decision surfaces for the classification of events, it may be better to decompose the classification into the recognition of subevents that have to be observed jointly. In many cases the decision surfaces for the recognition of these subevents are much easier to learn. This method is used in many speech recognition systems. For example, the recognition of words can be decomposed into the recognition of sequences of phonemes or phoneme like units. TDNN's have recently been extended to

Multi State Time-Delay Neural Networks (MSTDNNs) [14, 15] that allow the recognition of sequences of ordered events that have to be observed jointly. Unfortunately, this also means another architectural parameter has to be optimized.

C. Confusion Matrix Dependant Construction of the Network Architecture:

It was frequently observed that application-oriented researchers using neural networks use the confusion matrix of the training data for manual optimization of the network architectures. A certain architecture is trainied until the stopping criterium is reached and then the confusion matrix is evaluated. If a structured approach is used (as in many speech recognition systems), the modelling can be refined if too many errors in a certain class are observed. This kind of approach could be very useful for an automatic optimization procedure.

D. Early Constructive Changes of the Network Architecture:

Waiting for a whole training run and then making decisions on the further optimization of the network is computationally very expensive. Our experience shows that it is possible to detect the most important mistakes very early in the training run and change the architecture early in the training run. Starting the training run again is not necessary.

IV. APPLICATION OF THE ASO ALGORITHM TO THE MSTDNN

As can be seen, MSTDNN type networks conform with the first two principles of paragraph 2 and are also very powerful classifiers [14, 15]. The architecture of these highly structured networks can be optimized in many ways. For best performance, the size of the input windows, the number of hidden units and the (word specific) state sequence topologies are of critical importance for optimal performance. This makes MSTDNNs a suitable candidate for the demonstration of the ASO algorithm.

The ASO algorithm optimizes all relevant parameters of MSTDNN structures for a given amount of training data. The minimal configuration of a MSTDNN consists of an input layer, a state layer and an output layer (see Fig. 1). Let us consider a word recognition task where each output unit represents a word. Each state unit represents a small piece of the utterance like phonemes or sub-phonemes. The network is initialized with a window size of one (one connection between an input unit and a unit of the following layer) and one state unit per output unit. The net input of the output units is computed by integrating the weighted activity of the single or multiple state unit(s) over time. The activation of the output units is given by the sigmoid of the net input. The state units can be regarded as a special type of hidden units because of their very constrained connectivity to the output units.

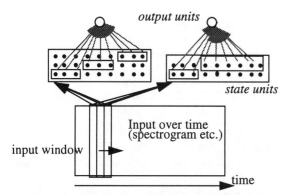

Fig. 1: An example of a simple MSTDNN with an input layer, a state layer and an output layer (consisting of two ouput units). In this example the first output unit is connected with three state units and the second output unit is connected with two state units.

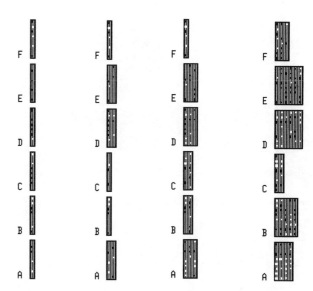

Fig. 2: The weights from the input units to the state units for the recognition of the capital letters A .. F. Negative weights are displayed by white blobs, positive weights by black blobs. Eight input units are used to represent the features recorded from the touch sensitive tablet (see [3]).

Left: The weights after initialization. All windows have a size of one.

Middle left: The weights after the first epoch. The input window for the characters "A", "D" and "E" were increased to a size of two. The input windows for the characters "B", "C" and "F" were not increased.

Middle right: The input window for the characters "A", "D" and "E" were increased again. The windows for the characters "B" and "C" were increased to a size of two.

Right: The weights after the fifth epoch.

During training, the size of the input window of the state units as well as the number of state units increases depending on the performance of the corresponding output units. The criterium for the allocation of further resources is derived from the confusion matrix on the training set. At each epoch the mistakes of each output unit are counted. If the counter for output unit j is higher than the mean of all counters, then resources for this particular unit are added. At first, the size of the input window from the input layer to the corresponding state unit is increased by adding one set of random connections (see Fig. 2). In the next epoch, these new connections are trained together with the already existing connections and the above procedure is applied again.

If the size of the input window of a state unit converges and the corresponding output unit still makes more mistakes than the average unit, then a new state unit is added (see Fig. 3). The size of the input window of the 'old' state unit is halved to avoid a dramatic increase of the number of trainable parameters. The 'new' state unit receives input from an input window of the same size as the 'old' state unit, but with random connections. From now on, the output unit receives input from both state units.

The allocation of resources is controlled by a simple scheme:

- Adding more resources is easy if the number of connections is small compared to the number of training patterns and gets harder with an increasing number of connections. This avoids hard upper bounds for the network resources.

- All resources that are added to the network are initialized randomly. This reduces the risk that the new resources disturb the learning process. A side-effect is that noise is added which prevents the network from getting stuck in local minima. This noise is reduced afterwards because

the new connections are trained together with the already existing connections.

- The maximal size of the input windows also depends on the number of states that model a word. If a word is modeled by many states the state units don't need such a large input window as a state unit that models a whole word.

In case of more than one state unit per output unit the inputs of the output units can be computed in three different ways: The simplest way is to give each state unit an equal share of the time slice that the output unit represents. The second possibility is to use Dynamic Time Warping (DTW) to find the best path through the activation matrix of the state units [16]. The third possibility is to smooth the DTW path by Gaussian functions positioned according to the DTW segmentation (see Fig. 4). Smoothing of the DTW path allows the states to model the transitions between two states more accurately. If each state specializes on different parts of the spectrogram, then the transition between these parts may not be modeled by any of them. Smoothing allows both states to partially represent the transition.

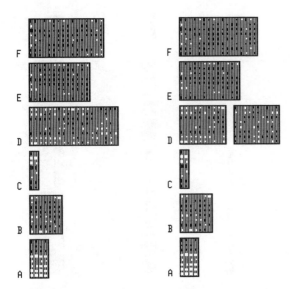

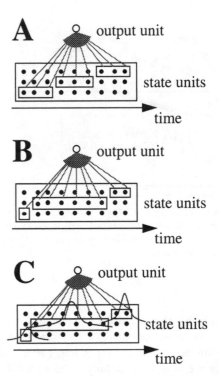

Fig. 3: The splitting of a state in the same training run as in Fig. 2. The modeling of the character "D" with one state and a big window is still insufficient (left side). A new state is added and the size of the old window is halfed (right side). The weights for the old (first) state remain the same and the weights for the new (second) state are initialized randomly.

Fig. 4: Three choices for the connectivity between the state units and the output units. A: Each state gets an equal share of the time slice. B: Using DTW to find the best path through the activation matrix. C: Smoothing the DTW path by gaussian functions positioned according to the DTW segmentation.

V. SIMULATIONS

The ASO algorithm was tested with a speech recognition task and two handwritten character recognition tasks.The chosen tasks are small enough to allow a reasonable number of experiments with the algorithm and are large enough to be relevant for an application oriented algorithm. The tasks are:

- Recognition of the English alphabet (aprox. 3000 words spoken by a single male speaker (DBS) taken from the same database that was used in [14]). The letters of the english alphabet were recorded in a sound-proof booth with a sampling rate of 12kHz. The speech was Hamming windowed and a 256-point FFT computed every 5 ms. 16 normalized melscale coefficients were computed as described in [1]. [1]

- Recognition of the digits 0, 1, 2, ..., 9 written on a touch sensitive tablet (aprox. 1000 digits written by aprox. 70 writers, recorded as described in [3][2])

- Recognition of the capital letters A, B, ..., Z written on a touch sensitive tablet (aprox. 2500 capital letters written by aprox. 50 writers, recorded as described in [3])

The databases were cut into training data, validation data and testing data. The validation data is used to determine the stopping criterium for the training phase. For the current simulations the hidden layer of the original MSTDNN was left out. Methods that add hidden units between the input units and the state units are currently tested. The results for both manually optimized architectures and automatically optimized architectures are summarized below (see Tables 1-3). Results with different manually optimized architectures (single state TDNNs with hidden layer) are added for the handwritten character recognition task for comparison.

Fig.5 shows the connections from the input layer to the state layer after constructing the network with the ASO algorithm for the alphabet recognition task. 13 characters are modeled by three states, 8 characters are modeled by two states and 5 characters are modeled by one state only. Fig.5 also shows that the ASO algorithm constructs a rather inhomogenous architecture that would be hard to find manually. It should also be noted that the ASO algorithm constructs different architectures for the same data depending on the initialization of the network [17]. Fig.5 also shows that the

---

1. Melscale coefficients were computed from the power spectrogram by computing log energies in each melscale energy band, where adjacent coefficients in frequency overlap by one spectral sample and are smoothed by reducing the shared sample by 50%. Adjacent coefficients in time were collapsed for further data reduction resulting in an overall 10 ms frame rate. All coefficients were then normailzed.

2. During writing, the position and the pressure of the pen are recorded from the tablett. Resampling is used to reduce the temporal variations of the digits. From these data points, the directions and the curvatures of the pen strokes are computed and are added to the data.

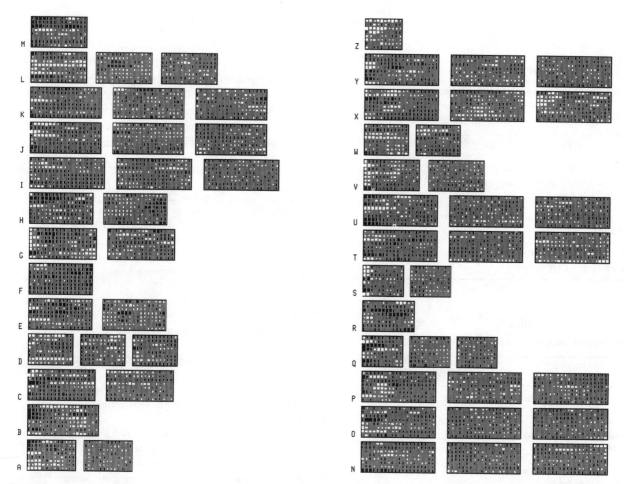

Fig. 5: The weights from the input units to the state units for the recognition of the capital letters after constructing the architecture (see Fig. Fig. 2 for further explanations). The character "A" is modeled by two state units. Each of these state units gets input from input windows with size 13. The character "B" is modeled by one state etc.. 13 characters are modeled by three states, 8 characters are modeled by two states and 5 characters are modeled by one state only. It can be seen that the new states generally have smaller weights (displayed by smaller blobs) than the older states.

new states generally have smaller weights than the older states. This can be explained by the amount of training that the weights get. Weights that are installed early in the training run are trained when the output error is still very high. Weights that are installed later when the output error is already lower do not get the same amount of training. This explains the good generalization abilities of some architectures with an unusual high number of trainable parameters that we sometimes observed.

Table 3 shows that the MSTDNN network optimized by ASO can adapt to different amounts of training data. The handtuned architecture performed equally well for the amount of data that it was optimized for, but did not generalize as well for more data and failed to learn a small subset completely for various learning rates and momentums.

VI. CONCLUSIONS

The results on three different tasks show that the ASO algorithm can achieve equal or better results than handtuned architectures without any tuning to the particular task. The results suggest that the ASO algorithm is able to optimize MSTDNN type networks for real world applications with varying amounts of training data effectively. Preliminary experiments with weight decay, weight elimination and OBD together with the ASO algorithm have been encouraging. In future, the algorithm will be applied to continous speech recognition and continous (cursive) handwritten character recognition tasks.

The design principles of the ASO algorithm (as described in paragraph III) should also allow the design of automatic structuring algorithms for other tasks.

TABLE 1.

Speech Recognition Performances (Alphabet Recognition)

	training	testing
manually optimized MSTDNN architecture with DTW	94.3%	85.0%
manually optimized MSTDNN with gaussian smoothing of the DTW path	98.9%	88.0%
automatically optimized MSTDNN architecture with standard DTW	97.1%	85.0%
automatically optimized MSTDNN with gaussian smoothing of the DTW path	99.5%	91.7%

TABLE 2.

Handwritten Character Recognition Performances (Digit Recognition)

	training	testing
manually optimized MSTDNN architecture without hidden units	98.3%	96.5%
automatic optimization of the window size, 1 state unit per output unit	97.2%	97.0%
automatic optimization of the window size and the number of state units	99.6%	98.0%
automatically optimized architecture with gaussian smoothing of the DTW path	100%	99.5%
TDNN architecture proposed by [Guyon, 1991] on the same data	100%	95.5%
TDNN architecture manually optimized for the same data	100%	98.5%

TABLE 3.

Handwritten Character Recognition Performances on Test Data (Capital Letters) depending on training set size

number of training patterns	TDNN architecture manually optimized for 1170 training patterns	automatically optimized MSTDNN architecture
520	no convergence	81.5%
1170	88.5%	88.5%
1560	90.5%	91.3%

ACKNOWLEDGEMENT

The authors gratefully acknowledge the support of the McDonnel-Pew Foundation (Cognitive Neuroscience Program) and would like to thank Patrick Haffner and Joe Tebelskis for lots of helpful discussions. Thanks to Stefan Manke for providing results from manually tuned networks.

REFERENCES

[1] Waibel, A., Hanazawa, T., Hinton, G., Shiano, K., and Lang, K. Phoneme Recognition using Time-Delay Neural Networks. *IEEE Transactions on Acoustics, Speech and Signal Processing*, March 1989

[2] Lang, K. PhD Thesis, Carnegie Mellon University, PA, 15213

[3] Guyon, I., Albrecht, P., Le Cun, Y., Denker, W., Hubbard, W. Design of a Neural Network Character Recognizer for a Touch Terminal, *Pattern Recognition,* 24(2), 1991

[4] Geman, S., Bienenstock, E., and Doursat, R., "Neural Networks and the Bias/Variance Dilemma," Neural Computation, vol. 4, pp. 1 - 58, 1992

[5] Minsky, M.L., Papert, S.A. Perceptron-Expamded Edition MIT Press,, 1988

[6] Baum, E.B., and Haussler, D., "What Size Net Gives Valid Generalization", *Neural Computation*, 1: 151-160, 1989

[7] Solla, S. , Schwartz, D.B., Tishby, N., and Levin, E., "Supervised Learning: a Theoretical Framework". in: *Advances in Neural Information Processing Systems 2*, 1989

[8] Moody, J. ,"The Effective Number of Parameters: An Analysis of Generalization and Regularization in Nonlinear Learning Systems". in: *Advances in Neural Information Processing Systems* 4, 1991.

[9] Rumelhart, D.E. Learning and Generalization Plenary Address, IEEE International Conference on Neural Networks,San Diego, 1988

[10] Weigend, A.S., Hubermann, B.A., and Rumelhart, D.E., Predicting the Future: A Connectionist Approach, *TR SSL-90, Xerox Science Laboratory, Palo Alto, CA, 1990*

[11] Chauvin, Y. A Back-Propagation Algorithm with Optimal Use of Hidden Units In; Touretzky, D. editor, Neural Information Processing Systems 1, Denver, 1988, Morgan Kaufmann, 1989

[12] Le Cun, Y., Denker, J.S., Solla, S.A. Optimal Brain Damage In; Touretzky, D. editor, Neural Information Processing Systems 2, Denver, 1989, Morgan Kaufmann, 1990

[13] Fahlmann, S.E. The Cascade-Correlation Learning Architecture In; Touretzky, D. editor, Neural Information Processing Systems 2, Denver, 1989, Morgan Kaufmann, 1990

[14] Haffner, P., Franzini, M., and Waibel, A. Integrating Time Alignment and Neural Networks for High Performance Continuous Speech Recognition, *ICASSP* 91

[15] Haffner, P., and Waibel, A. Time-Delay Neural Networks Embedding Time Alignment: A Performance Analysis, *Eurospeech* 91

[16] Sakoe,H., and Chiba, S., Dynamic Programming Algorithm Optimization for Spoken Word Recognition, *IEEE Transactions on Acoustics, Speech and Signal Processing*, (26): 43-49, 1978

[17] Bodenhausen, U., and Manke, S., Connectionist Architectural Learning for High Performance Character and Speech Recognition, *ICASSP Proceedings, Minneapolis ,* April 1993

A Display Oriented Technique for Interactive Pattern Recognition by Multilayer Neural Network

Mohamed Daoudi, Denis Hamad and Jack-Gérard Postaire
Centre d'automatique de Lille
Université des Sciences et Technologies de Lille
59655 Villeneuve d'Asq Cedex, France.

Abstract- In this paper, we describe an on-line interactive graphics system which has been designed to separate a set of multidimensional multivariate observations into groups or clusters. Neural network allows us to map into a two dimensional display. A set of analysis cluster procedures and graphical routines has been developed to take advantage of two dimensional display.

I. THE ROLE OF THE HUMAN OPERATOR IN PATTERN CLASSIFICATION.

The aim of pattern classification is to discover, in a population of multidimensional data, the presence of clusters which regroup similar data. In general, the data are characterised by a set of attributes which constitute the multidimensional observations. For convenience, the data are usually represented as points in a multidimensional space and the distance between those points is a classical measure of similarity between the data they represent.

When no a priori information about the data is available, i.e. when working in an unsupervised context, the analyst usually calls for clustering algorithms to separate the set of multidimensional observations into groups or clusters which share some property of similarity. Some clustering schemes are based on the optimisation of a criterion which takes into account the distances between and within the clusters [1]. Others are based on the analysis of the underlying probability density function of the available observations in order to extract its modes [2]. In most cases, when using such algorithms, the operator's part is reduced to adjusting the parameters which condition the performance of the procedures [3][4].

An approach where the analyst gets much more involved consists in representing the multidimensional data in a space of lower dimension than that of the original data space. Numerous methods are available to map multidimensional data as points in a plane while preserving similarity relationships between data elements. The most common among them is certainly the principal components analysis technique [5].

If it can be assumed that clusters on the plane are images of multidimensional clusters in the original data space, the interest of such a plane representation is to involve the outstanding visual perception capacities of human beings in the clustering process. Hence, provided the procedure used to map the N-dimensional observations X_q, q=1, 2, ..., Q, onto a two dimensional space do not change too much their relative positions, a human observer can usefully analyse graphic displays without conscious use of any analytical model of clusters, or any mathematical decision rule. It is hoped that any information lost in the dimensionality reduction process is fully compensated by the benefits associated with the integration of the human operator for organising the data [6][7].

The superiority of humans over automatic clustering procedures comes from their ability in recognising cluster structures in a two dimensional space, even in the presence of outliers between the clusters, of bridging clusters and of all kinds of irrelevant details in the data points distribution.

The aim of this paper is to present a simple and fast way to provide the operator a plane representation of multidimensional data through neural networks for interactive classification. After a quick presentation of the architecture of neural networks and training algorithms in section 2, it's shown how this technique of parallel processing of information provides a two dimensional representation of data in section 3.

When giving the operator the interactive means which will help him to isolate clusters of two dimensional points, this visualisation becomes base of a clustering procedure where the operator doesn't loose his grip on the data he is analysing (Section 4). The results we have obtained with artificially generated data show the quality discrimination between classes within same multidimensional samples which have been submitted to analysis (Section 5).

II. ARCHITECTURE OF THE MULTILAYER NEURAL NETWORK.

The network architecture considered here is of the type described in Rumelhart, Hinton, and Williams [8], [9], [10], [11]. Multilayer networks are made of an input layer which receives available information, one layer of output units, and one or several hidden layers.

In classical structures, the only connections allowed in this type of network go from layer to layer and from the input to the output, loops and connections within layer are not allowed.

Each unit output is computed as follows. First a weighted sum of the activation levels O_h, $h = 1, 2, \dots H$, of the H units connected to unit number i is computed as :

$$S_i = \sum_{h=1}^{H} w_{h,i} \cdot o_h$$

where $w_{h,i}$ is the weight of the connection from unit h to unit i. The output of unit number i is finally a function of $f(S_i)$, where f is generally a sigmoid function defined by :

$$f\left(S_i\right) = \frac{1}{1 + e^{-S_i}}$$

In order to take advantage of such networks to represent multidimensional data on a plane, it is necessary to specify more clearly their architecture.

The input layer receives the information carried by the observations to be classified. Let $X = \left[X_1, X_2, \cdots, X_q, \cdots, X_Q\right]^T$ be the Q available N dimensional observations where :

$$X_q = \left[x_{1,q}, \cdots, x_{n,q}, \cdots, x_{N,q}\right]^T$$

The input layer of the network is made of N units I_n, n=1, ..., N, such that unit I_n is solicited by attribute $x_{n,q}$, of observations

X_q when this one is presented to the network. Because of homogeneity constraints which will appear in the training phase, the output layer is also composed of N units, denoted O_n, n=1, 2, ..., N. Finally, a hidden layer made of only two units, brings all the information necessary for a plane representation of the data (see Fig. 1).

The training phase during which the network learns the structure of the data is of upmost importance. As any prototype with known classification is available, the network is trained in an unsupervised mode, using a back propagation technique in an auto associative mode. The Q available observations are successively presented to the network input. The weights of the connections are iteratively modified in order to obtain, at the output of the network, responses as close as possible to its inputs, for all the available observations, in order to minimise E.

To be more specific, the problem consists in minimising the mean square error E such as :

$$E = \sum_{q=1}^{Q} \left\| Y_q - X_q \right\|^2 \quad \text{where } Y_q = \left[y_{1,q}, \cdots, y_{n,q}, \cdots y_{N,q}\right]^T$$

is the output vector of the network.

During the training phase, the connection weight adjustment is performed by means of the generalised delta rule [10].

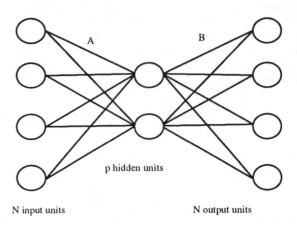

Fig. 1. The network in auto-associative mode.

III. THE MAPPING PROCESS.

Cottrell et al. have used linear units in conjunction with the technique of auto-association to perform image compression [12]. In the auto-association mode, which is called also auto-encoding or identity mapping [10], the network is modified iteratively until its output become close to its inputs. If the network uses hidden units, it will provide an efficient ways of compressing the information contained in the input patterns. An analysis of linear auto-association has been provided by Bourlard and Kamp [13] based on singular value decomposition of matrices (SVD). Another analysis of the behaviour of E has been published by Baldi and Hornik [14], [15]. The main result is that E has a unique local and global minimum corresponding to an orthogonal projection onto the subspace spanned by the first principal eigenvectors of a covariance matrix associated to the training patterns. The weights connecting the inputs to the hidden layer are described by an p*N real matrix B and those from the hidden layer to the output by an N*p real matrix A.

In the linear case, the auto-associative approach gives :

$$A = U C$$
$$B = C^{-1} U^T$$

1634

where $U = [u_1, u_2, \cdots, u_P]$ denote the matrix formed by the orthonormal eigenvectors of the covariance matrix associated with the eigenvalues $\lambda_1 > \lambda_2 > \cdots > \lambda_p$ and where C is a p*p invertible matrix. If C is the identity matrix, the outputs of the hidden layer are given by $u_1^T X_q, u_2^T X_q, \cdots, u_p^T X_q$ and this approach leads to the same results as the so-called principal components analysis (PCA). The weight vector corresponding to the first hidden unit is exactly equal to the dominant eigenvector of the input correlation matrix associated to the training patterns.

However, for most solutions found by running a gradient descent algorithm on the function E, the sub-space found by gradient descent algorithm is different from the sub-space found by the Principal Component Analysis. This is due to the fact that the backward errors used in the learning process are distributed over all the units of the hidden layer.

The back-propagation approach is simple. It can be applied to non-linear networks and to a variety of problems without having any detailed a priori knowledge about their structure or mathematical properties of the optimal solution. We have used neural network with three layers : an input layer composed of N inputs units, and output layer composed of N outputs units, and a hidden layer composed of two units.

In the training phase, all the Q available observations are sequentially presented at the input of the network. Its weight connections are iteratively modified until the difference in mean square sense between the input and the output becomes smaller than a given threshold.

After this learning phase, the Q observations are presented one by one to the network. The two outputs of the hidden layer are considered as the two coordinates of the image in plane of the multidimensional input data. The data can be easily displayed so that this procedure can be used for interactive classification.

IV. INTERACTIVE CLASSIFICATION.

Although the idea of using the outputs of the hidden layer is not new, it provides a useful interface for computer interactive classification of multidimensional data.

When called by the user, pop-up menus for data manipulation are displayed into utility boxes. The work space which is dominant in term of screen area, is a two dimensional space in which the user does the work of clustering the data. It is a large window used to display the image data points as dark spots on a bright background. All the available data points are mapped onto this two dimensional window.

All the items of the main menu are somewhat associated to relatively standard commands in computer interactive system, since the software has been developed under the X-Window environment. However, the "Classification Menu", which takes full advantage of the proposed two-dimensional mapping technique, deserves a particular attention.

A classical solution for identifying two dimensional clusters is to enclose them by boundaries, which can be drawn on the screen by means of the mouse. In order to release the operator from this tedious task, we propose another clustering strategy which uses the well known ISODATA procedure to cluster the data [16]. Although, the performance of this algorithm is highly dependant upon a set

of control parameters which can easily be adjusted by the on line user.. This algorithm can be used in two different ways : if the clusters are not overlapping, the analyst selects the apparent centres by means of the mouse. Once the centres are clicked on the display, the ISODATA procedure is used to cluster data. But if the clusters are overlapping, the analyst are choose interactively the various parameters which control the procedures and he can apply the ISODATA procedure directly within the multidimensional space of the observations.

Thanks to a zooming procedure, each cluster can appear full screen. A more thorough observation of each cluster displayed individually on the whole screen can reveal subclusters which could not be as obvious when the whole set is displayed. The user, by means of a coarse to fine strategy, can discover substructures which are not discernible in the display of the whole data set.

Once classification is achieved, each cluster is displayed in a different colour in order to allow the analyst to evaluate visually the quality of the results.

The statistical characteristics of each cluster as well as the assignation of the observations to each of them are available on request.

V. EXPERIMENTAL RESULTS AND DISCUSSION.

To provide some insight into the behaviour of the interactive system, and to present the main facilities of it, some results are reported, using an artificially generated data set.

The data are computer generated 4-dimensional gaussian random vectors. They consist of 1700 observations drawn from each of the three distributions with the statistical parameters given in Table I.

The results of classification obtained are compared with the Bayes theoretical minimum error rate achievable when the true statistics of the data are known. They demonstrate the ability of the procedure to cluster data of high dimensionality, even in a non trivial situation with overlapping clusters (see Fig. 2).

These results show that even someone who does not have any software system background can use the interactive system to classify multidimensional observations in an unsupervised context (see Fig. 3).

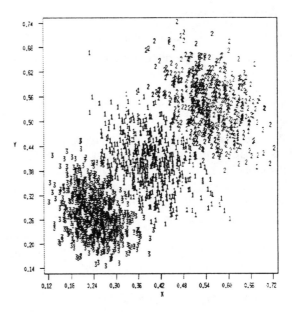

Fig. 3. Clustering by ISODATA algorithm.

TABLE I
Cluster statistics.

	Mean vector	Covariance matrix	Number of data points
Cluster 1	0 0 0 0	1 0 0 0 0 1 0 0 0 0 1 0 0 0 0 1	500
Cluster 2	2 2 2 2	1 0 0 0 0 1 0 0 0 0 1 0 0 0 0 1	500
Cluster 3	4 4 4 4	1 0 0 0 0 1 0 0 0 0 1 0 0 0 0 1	700

Theoretic Bayes error rate : 2.9 %

TABLE II
Estimation of cluster statistics

	Mean vector	Covariance matrix			
Cluster 1	-0.05 0.07 0.00 0.02	1.04 0.03 -0.03 -0.04 0.04 0.984 0.00 0.02 -0.04 0.001 0.99 0.08 -0.05 -0.02 0.09 1.00			
Cluster 2	1.99 1.97 1.95 1.90	1.01 0.09 0.11 0.05 0.09 1.16 0.03 0.05 0.11 0.02 0.97 0.07 0.05 0.05 0.07 1.06			
Cluster 3	3.89 3.97 3.95 4.00	1.21 0.25 0.30 0.25 0.25 1.21 0.28 0.18 0.31 0.28 1.29 0.23 0.25 0.18 0.23 1.32			

TABLE III
Confusion matrix

	Cluster 1	Cluster 2	Cluster 3
Cluster 1	473	8	19
Cluster 2	25	475	0
Cluster 3	8	0	692

Actual error rate : 3.53 %

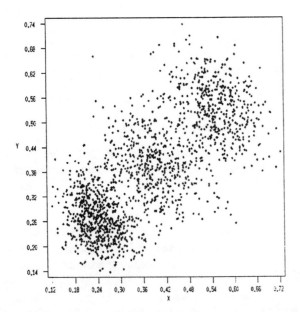

Fig. 2. Outputs of hidden layer units.

REFERENCES.

[1] K. Fukunaga, W. L. G. Koontz, "A criterion and an algorithm for grouping data, " IEEE Trans. Comput., Vol. 21, pp. 171-178, 1970.

[2] J. -G. Postaire, A. Touzani,. "Mode boundary detection by relaxation for cluster analysis, " Pattern recognition, Vol. 22, pp. 477-490, 1989.

[3] P. A. Devijver, J. Kittler, *Pattern recognition : A statistical approach,* Prentice Hall, Englewood Cliffs, N.J, 1982.

[4] R. O. Duda, P. E. Hart, *Pattern classification and scene analysis,* Wiley, New York., 1973

[5] Y Chien, *Interactive pattern recognition,* New York : Marcel Dekker, 1978.

[6] J. W. Sammon,. "Interactive pattern analysis and classification, " IEEE Trans. Comput. Vol. C-19, pp 594-616, 1970.

[7] K. Fukunaga, J. M. Mantock, "A non parametric two-dimensional display for classification, " IEEE Trans. Pattern Anal. Machine Intell., Vol. PAMI-4, pp. 427-436, 1982.

[8] Y. Le Cun, "Learning process in asymmetric threshold network, " Disorder systems and biological Organisation, E. Bienenstock, F. Fogelman Soulie, and G. Weibush (Eds), Berlin : Springer, 1986.

[9] R. P. Lippman, "An introduction to computing with neural nets, " IEEE ASSP Magazine, pp 4-22, 1987.

[10] D. E. Rumelhart, G. E. Hinton, and R. J. Williams, "Learning internal representation by error propagation, " Parallel Distributed Processing : Explorations in the micro structures of cognition, Vol. 1, pp. 318-362, MIT Press, Cambridge, Mass, 1986.

[11] P. W. Wasserman, *Neural computing Theory and Practise,* VNR, New York, 1989.

[12] G. W. Cottrel, P. W. Munro, and D. Zipser, "Image compression by back propagation : a demonstration of extensional programming. " In : Advances in cognitive Science, Vol. 2, Sharkey, N. E. ed. Norwood, NJ Abbex, 1988.

[13] H. Boulard, Y. Kamp, "Auto-association by the multilayer perceptrons and singular value decomposition, " Biological cybernetics, Vol. 59, pp 291-294, 1988.

[14] P. Baldi, K. Hornik, "Neural networks and principal component analysis : learning from examples without local minima, " Neural Networks, Vol. 2, N° 1, pp 53-58, 1989.

[15] P. Baldi, K. Hornik, "Back-propagation and unsupervised Learning in Linear Networks, " Technical report, Jet Propulsion Laboratory and Division of Biologie, California Institute of Technology, 1991.

[16] G. H. Ball, J. D. Hall, "A clustering technique for summarising data. Behaviour, " Sci, Vol. 12, pp 153-155, 1967.

Parallel Computation of Neural Networks in a Processor Pipeline with Partially Shared Memory

Yoshikuni Okawa

Osaka University

Yamadaoka, Suita

Osaka 565, Japan

Takayuki Suyama

NTT Communication Science Laboratories

2-chome, Hikaridai, Seika-cho

Soraku-gun, Kyoto 619-02 Japan

Abstract—A new parallel architecture of a processor pipeline is proposed. It is a linearly connected processors via dual bank switchable memory blocks. A layered neural network with the back propagating error algorithm is adopted as a bench mark test. The essential part of the algorithm is multiplication of a matrix with a vector. A few additional data transfer operations are necessary. We have build an experimental system and done several measurements, which prove the feasibility of the proposed architecture in some fields of practical applications.

I. INTRODUCTION

When a neural network is implemented in an actual system, many learning processes have to be repeated so as to determine the connecting weights between network nodes. Its computing time raises rapidly, as the number of units increases. When a neural network is used in ,such as ,a feedback loop of a real-time control system, the case is more critical in the sense that the computing time must be shorter than a given time interval.

Generally, human requires a rapid response when he is developing an entirely new system. If responses in a trial error process are slow, his thinking procedures suffer serious interruptions which cause re-initiation processes. To use a neural network in a real situation, we have to at least have one of the fastest computing systems.

We propose a parallel computing system for the computation of neural networks to accelerate the computing speed. Only some of the simple layered networks are considered, and for the learning process the back propagating error of Rumelhart et al.(1988) is adopted. Under these conditions the essential part of the necessary computation reduces to simple multiplications between a matrix and a vector.

Many papers have already been published on parallel processing of the neural network calculation. Pomerleau et al.(1988) proposed an algorithm for Warp, which indicates that the ring, or the pipelined parallel architecture is suitable to this computation. Sato et al.(1988) reported their works in a ring multi-processor system.

We design a unique architecture of pipelined processors connected by dual partially shared memory blocks. By a partially shared memory block we mean a bank switchable memory which is occupied by only one processor during a specified time period, but can be switched to another processor in other time quanta. The design of bank switchable memory blocks is easy, since there is no access control circuitry as is usually the case in a fully shared memory. The cost of a bank switchable memory is therefor the lowest. Instead the control complexity becomes the more complicated because of the inclusion of the bank switching mechanism in softwares. The overall performance of a bank switchable memory clearly falls behind a fully shared memory.

On parallel computers with partially shared memory blocks, there are at least two existing systems: Buehrer et al.(1982) of Swiss ETH's EMPRESS, and SM3 of Florida University (Chaitanya and Su, 1986) and (Su and Thakahore,1987). But by the characteristics of partially shared memory blocks their applications are limited in a special fields such as scientific computations, sorting, etc. whose algorithms are clearly defined and control timings are entirely known beforehand.

Recently, Hwang, Tseng and Kim (1989) and Scherson and Ma (1989) almost at the same time proposed an architecture in which partially shared memory blocks are allocated on a square matrix. Every memory block is connected to either a row or a column bus, and the entire memory matrix is switched to the row or the column. They call this architecture an orthogonal multiprocessor or OM. The communication delay is short by the via memory characteristics. But this system suffers an implementing problem. If we write the number of used processors p, then the system requires p^2 memory blocks, which is exactly the same situation as we have already experienced in the case of a crossbar switch.

Generally speaking, to shorten the computing time of a scientific computation we have to put as many processors as possible, which has been proved from the case of a systolic array processor. The condition of OM's requirement of p^2 memory blocks prevents it from applying an OM in its most suitable application field. This is a contradiction.

In this paper we propose a multiprocessor architecture with partially shared memory blocks. It is a subset of OM, but requires only $2p$ memory banks. We call this a processor pipeline (PP) with dual partially shared memory banks, and make a neural network program run on it as a bench mark test.

We have proved that at least in the problem of computing neural network a PP has a comparable performance as an OM, despite the necessary number of memory blocks is $2p$, not p^2. The algorithm consists of multiplications of a matrix and a vector with a few data circulating operations. To do a broadcasting function all memory banks are connected by a bus which is extended from a host (or control) computer. Beside we adopt an auxiliary communicating method of the relaying information between pipelined processors. We have implemented an experimental multiprocessor system using commercially available LSI chips. We have experimented various programs on it, and measured the resulted performances.

II. BASIC CONFIGURATION OF A PROCESSOR PIPELINE

The basic configuration of the proposed processor pipeline architecture is shown in Fig. 1, where four processors and ten connecting memory modules are indicated. Every processor has two forward and two backward memory blocks. In a computing interval each processor selects two memory blocks, one of which is from forward, and one from backward. A processor takes data from a forward memory and stores the results to a backward memory. Thus, a pipelined processing proceeds. After a time quantum expires, all processors exchange the holding memory blocks.

A pipeline architecture is appropriate in the domains where different procedures of almost same size apply successively, and the communications are restricted in the direct neighbors. The efficiency decreases greatly when it is used out of this problem domain.

III. ALGORITHM FOR A NEURAL NETWORK

We focus our attention only to the layered networks. Write the number of layers as L. A pattern X is an input to a network, and a pattern O is its output, which depends on a weight matrix W in a network. A process to compute an output vector O, given X and W, is called the forward computation.

A neural network is trained to every situation by changing its weight W, which is called a learning process. Y is a reinforcing vector.

3.1 The forward computation

Consider the ith unit of the kth layer. Every unit in the $(k-1)$th layer sends its signal to this unit. The signal from the jth unit in the $(k-1)$th layer is written as $o^{k-1}{}_j$. Its weight is written as w^{k-1,k_i}. An input to the ith unit in the kth layer is

$$i^{k_i} = \sum_j w^{k-1,k_i} o^{k-1}{}_j - \theta^{k_i} \tag{1}$$

where θ^{k_i} is a threshold value at this unit. Write an output of this unit as o^{k_i}. Then we have

$$o^{k_i} = f(i^{k_i}). \tag{2}$$

We will use the following equation as f

$$f(x) = \frac{1}{1 + \exp(-x)}. \tag{3}$$

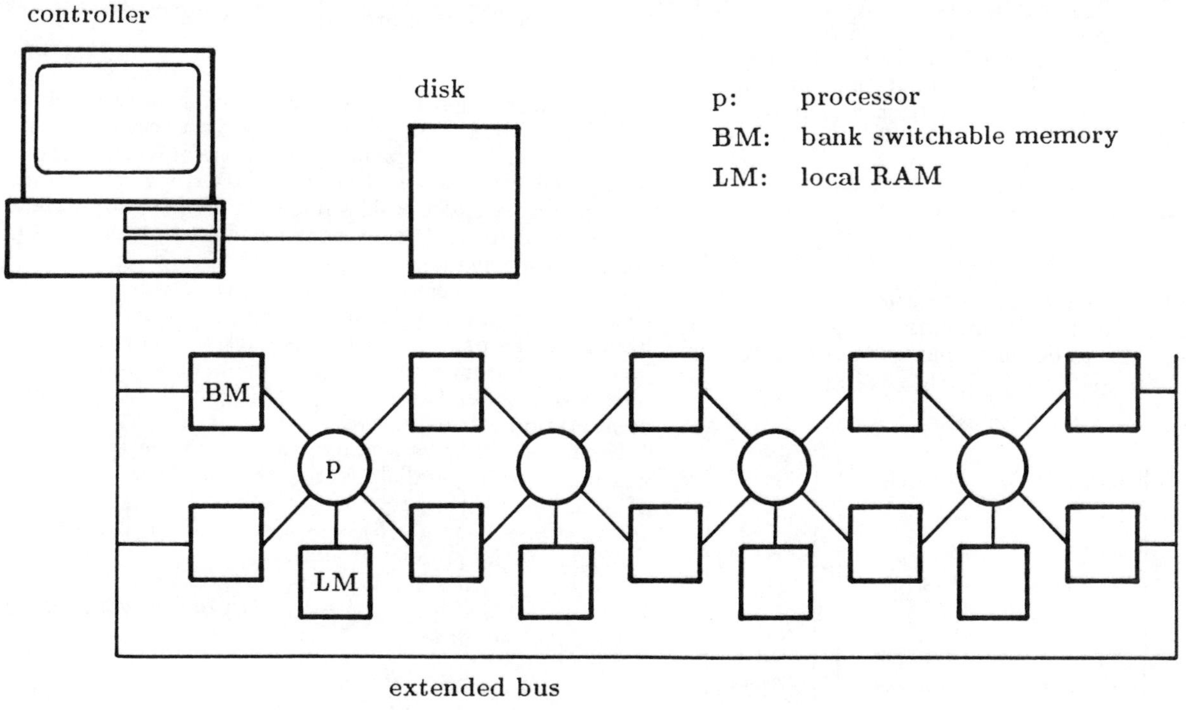

controller

disk

p: processor
BM: bank switchable memory
LM: local RAM

Fig. 1   The basic configuration of the processor pipeline.

3.2 The backward computation

For a modifying process to W we adopt the back propagating error method. Write the correcting amount of w^{k-1,k_j} as $\Delta w^{k-1,k_j}$, then we have

$$\Delta w^{k-1,k_j} = -\varepsilon d^{k_j} o^{k-1_i} \qquad (4)$$

$$d^{L_j} = (o^{L_j} - y^j)f'(i^{L_j}) \qquad (5)$$

$$d^{k_j} = (\sum_i w^{k_j,k+1_i} d^{k+1_i})f'(i^{k_j}) \qquad (6)$$

where y_j is an element of Y, and o^{L_j} is an element of O. Using eq.(3) to compute f', we have

$$f'(i^{k_j}) = o^{k_j}(1 - o^{k_j}). \qquad (7)$$

In the actual situation we make the following correction

$$\Delta w^{k-1,k_j}(t+1) = -\varepsilon d^{k_j} o^{k-1_i} + \alpha \Delta w^{k-1,k_j}(t) \qquad (8)$$

which is a low-pass filter frequently used in usual numerical computations. The criterion function is

$$r = \sum_j (o^{L_j} - y^j)^2. \qquad (9)$$

The computation ends when r becomes smaller than the specified value.

3.3 The parallel algorithm

The number of available processors is denoted as p. First we will show the algorithm for the forward computation. The parallel processor proceeds from the first layer to the next. Now we concentrate to the computation of one single layer. Rewrite eqs.(1) and (2), deleting the number of a layer k, we have

$$i_i = \sum_j w_{ji} o_j \qquad (10)$$

$$o_i = f(i_i). \qquad (11)$$

where in eq.(10) a subtracting operation is scaler, so is omitted. The number of input units to the considered layer is M and the number of output units in this layer is N. Let $m = \lceil \frac{M}{p} \rceil$, and $n = \lceil \frac{N}{p} \rceil$. Using m and n, we can write eq.(10) in a matrix form as

$$\begin{bmatrix} i_1 \\ \vdots \\ i_n \\ i_{n+1} \\ \vdots \\ i_{2n} \\ i_{2n+1} \\ \vdots \\ i_{pn} \end{bmatrix} = \begin{bmatrix} w_{1,1} & \cdots & w_{pm,1} \\ \vdots & \vdots & \vdots \\ w_{1,n} & \cdots & w_{pm,n} \\ w_{1,n+1} & \cdots & w_{pm,n+1} \\ \vdots & \vdots & \vdots \\ w_{1,2n} & \cdots & w_{pm,2n} \\ w_{1,2n+1} & \cdots & w_{pm,2n+1} \\ \vdots & \vdots & \vdots \\ w_{1,pn} & \cdots & w_{pm,pn} \end{bmatrix} \begin{bmatrix} o_1 \\ \vdots \\ o_m \\ o_{m+1} \\ \vdots \\ o_{2m} \\ o_{2m+1} \\ \vdots \\ o_{pm} \end{bmatrix} \qquad (12)$$

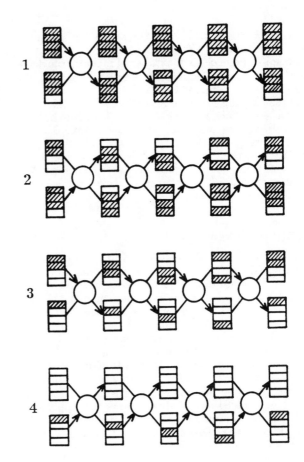

Fig. 2   The learning process in the pipeline.

which indicates that the essential part of the forward computation is a matrix multiplication with a vector. We divide the matrix W horizontally, each one of which is given to a pipeline processor. Every processor is given a complete vector o, and $n \times M$ submatrix of W to compute a part of a vector i. It then subtract θ from i, and finally computes f using eq.(11).

After each processor finishes its part of the computation, it gives data to the succeeding processor, and takes data from the predecessor (like a bucket relay.) These relayed data becomes the input to the computation of the next layer. After L repetitions of this cycle the forward computation will be finished.

Next, we will show an algorithm to do the back propagating error in parallel. Notice that we have two forms of equations for this: eq. (5) to the final layer and eq. (6) to the others. As eq. (5) is in a scaler form, it raises no problem for the parallel processing.

We have to consider the parallel execution of eq. (6). Like eq. (10), if we rewrite èq. (6) omitting the layer subscript k, we have

$$g_j = \sum_i w_{ji} d_i. \qquad (13)$$

Comparing this equation with eq. (4), we will see that the

weight matrix W is transposed. The situation is shown graphically in the following matrix form.

$$
\begin{bmatrix} g_1 \\ \vdots \\ \vdots \\ g_{pm} \end{bmatrix} = \begin{bmatrix} w_{1,1} & \cdots & w_{1,pn} \\ \vdots & \vdots & \vdots \\ \vdots & \vdots & \vdots \\ w_{pm,1} & \cdots & w_{pm,pn} \end{bmatrix} \begin{bmatrix} d_1 \\ \vdots \\ \vdots \\ o_{pn} \end{bmatrix} \quad (14)
$$

The policy to rearrange the weight matrix W in a processor pipeline is out of consideration, since it requires data transmission time. We contrive an algorithm to do a partial sum in each processor, which is relayed to the following processors where the sum of partial sums will be gathered. The situation will be understood by the following equation.

$$
\begin{bmatrix} g_1 \\ \vdots \\ \vdots \\ g_{pm} \end{bmatrix} = \begin{bmatrix} proc \\ 1 \end{bmatrix} + \begin{bmatrix} proc \\ 2 \end{bmatrix} + \ldots + \begin{bmatrix} proc \\ p \end{bmatrix} \quad (15)
$$

Fig. 2 shows the successive state changes of the pipeline in the case of four processors. Each partial sum is passed to the succeeding processors and the total is accumulated in the control computer, which is again broadcast to the memory blocks for the next computation.

IV. Experiments

We have designed and built an experimental parallel processing system from commercially available ICs and LSIs. The specifications of the processor and the memory board are listed in Table 1. The master (or control) computer is a personal computer (PC-9801 VX).

CPU	80286+80287 (10MHz)
Memory	128KB SRAM+64KB ROM

(a) Parallel processor

Memory	64KB SRAM (no wait)
Port	1 bus port+4 cable ports

(b) Memory block

CPU	80286+80287 (10MHz)
PC	PC-9801 VX21 (NEC)

(c) Master computer

Table 1   The specifications of the parallel system.

First, we have measured the processing time for the forward computation. An initial W is chosen from random numbers. All elements of an input vector is set to 1. The results are shown in Fig. 3 and 4. In Fig. 3 the number of units in a network is on the horizontal axis and the measured computing time on the vertical axis. The processing times are measured on three different cases: (1) one CPU (+) , (2) 8 CPU(⊔) and (3) on a personal computer(◇).

The CPU of the master computer is same as that of parallel processors, but in a personal computer we use the C language while in parallel processors the programs are written in the assembler language. By this difference of the adopted languages the processing speed of the master computer is slower than a parallel processor. The speed up ratio of the parallel processor is shown in Fig. 4. It increases as the number of units becomes larger, but it tends to reach some saturating point. For example, the speed up ratio is near 6.2, when 40 units are active. That means about 75% of the CPU resource is utilized in the necessary calculations, but in other words 25% is wasted in the overheads, synchronizations, data exchanges, etc.

time (sec)

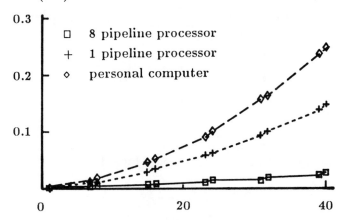

the number of units

Fig. 3   Processing time of the foward computation.

speed up ratio

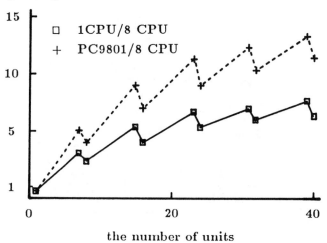

the number of units

Fig. 4   Speedup ratio of the forward computation.

Next, the measurements of the learning (or backward) process are executed. The learning processes are not so deterministic as the forward process, since the number of cycles needed in the computation is not known a priori. We plan three bench mark tests for this process.

Test 1

When an input data is (0,1), then a desired output is (1,0), and vice versa. Two pairs are given to a neural network, alternately. The process is finished when r of eq.(9) becomes equal to or less than 0.05. Both the number of the repeated cycles and the computing time are recorded. The weight matrix W is given by random number. Since a learning process is affected by the initial value of W, the measurements are repeated ten times with different initial W, which are averaged. The results are listed in the following table. This test is the case of a smallest network.

Table 2   NOT (6 units).

	computing time(msec)	the number of cycles	time per one cycle(msec)
1CPU	1,524.4	146	10.44
8CPU	2,461.7	200	12.31
speed up	0.62		0.85
utl.ratio	7.8%		10.6%

Test 2

A numeric character is given by a 7 × 5 dot pattern. There are 35 units in the entry layer, and 10 units in the output layer. The middle layer consists of 30 units. The results are indicated in the following Table 3.

Table 3   Numerical Fonts (75 units)

	computing time(msec)	the number of cycles	time per one cycle(msec)
1CPU	404,771	174	2,324.9
8CPU	67,884	174	390.4
speed up	5.96		5.955
utl.ratio	74.5%		74.4%

Test 3

This is the case of discriminating alphabetic characters. The test conditions are almost same as Test 2. The structure of the network is 35 × 25 × 26, which is the largest of three tests. To shorten the computing time the stop condition is changed to $r < 0.1$. The results are shown in Table 4.

Table 4   Alphabetic Fonts (86 units)

	computing time(msec)	the number of cycles	time per one cycle(msec)
1CPU	2,762,490	320.2	8,627.4
8CPU	437,946	327.4	1,337.6
speed up	6.31		6.45
utl.ratio	78.9%		80.6%

In Test 1 (the NOT problem), the processing time of 8 CPU is larger than that of 1 CPU. This indicates that the small scale problem is not suitable for parallel computation. The number of units is 6 in this case, which is smaller than the number of the used processors. At least two of the processes are working with not existing units. These and other overheads causes the parallel processing inefficient. Anyway, it is clear that parallel processing must not be applied to such a small scale problem as this.

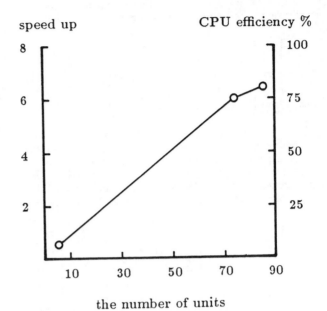

Fig. 5   The backward error propagating computation.

In the numeric font problem, the speed up of about 6 is reached, which states that 75% of the available CPU resources of parallel processing is utilized. The number of the used units is 75. Comparing with the forward computation, the efficiency of the backward computation almost equals to or a little less than that of the forward process.

In the alphabetic font problem, the better results are obtained. The speed up ratio reaches to near 6.5, and the CPU efficiency is slightly over 80%, which is the best results throughout the experiments. The computing time is 46 seconds in the case of 1 CPU, while 7.3 seconds in 8 CPU. We conclude that parallel processing is reasonable in this type of computation. These results are shown graphically in Fig. 5.

V. Conclusion

We propose a parallel architecture of a linear multiprocessor combined by partially shared memory blocks, and an algorithm to compute a neural network in it. We actually have built an experimental system (8 processors, and 16 memory blocks), and done several performance measurements.

When the number of units is small (e.g., < 10), the parallel processor falls behind a single CPU. This is reasonable when we consider the existence of the overheads in parallel processing. It is commonly acknowledged that parallel processing is not suitable for extremely small scale problems.

But when the number of units reaches the practical range, the performance of 8 CPU increases to 6 to 7 speed up. The processor efficiency is 75 to 80%. In other word, $\frac{1}{4}$ or $\frac{1}{5}$ of the CPU time is wasted, mainly, in the data exchange operation (distribution of the computed results to the processors for the next computing cycle.)

The proposed parallel processing system may be suitable for a medium or a large grain problem. When we put the more processors to the pipeline in order to speed up the calculation, the number of units in one processor becomes the less, which deteriorates the efficiency of parallel processing. There exists the optimum number of processors ,given the number of units for a neural network.

Our parallel processing system is, clearly, a system of moderate speed, and of low cost. Its cost to performance ratio is excellent. For commercial applications the proposed system will be strongly recommended. When the fastest speed is demanded, Warp or other VLSI-oriented architecture must be considered.

Future research works will be (1) speed up of switching time of memory blocks, (2) extension of algorithms to other types of neural networks than the simple one described in this paper, (3) providing a software support system, etc.

VI. Reference

Annaratone, M. et al., 1987, The Warp Computer: Architecture, Implementation, and Performance, IEEE Trans. on Computers, Vol.C-36 No.12, pp.1523-1537.

Buehrer, R. E. et al., 1982, The ETH-Multiprocessor EMPRESS: A Dynamically Configurable MIMD System, IEEE Trans. on Computers, Vol.C-31 No.11, pp.1035-1044.

Chaitanya, K. B. and Su, S. Y. W., 1986, The Architecture of SM3: A Dynamically Partitionable Multi-computer System, IEEE Trans. on Computers, Vol.C-35 No.9, pp.790-802.

Hwang, K., Tseng, P. S. and Kim, D., 1989, An Orthogonal Multiprosessor for Parallel Scientific Computation, IEEE Trans. on Computers, Vol.38 No.1, pp.47-61.

Pomerleau, D. A., et al., 1988, Neural Network Simulation at Warp Speed, International Conference on Neural Network, Vol.2, pp.143-150.

Rumelhart, D. E., Hinton, G. E. and Williams, R. J., 1986, Learning representations by back-propagating errors, Nature, Vol.323 No.9, pp.533-536.

Sato, Y. et al., 1988, A Neural Network Accelerator Using General Purpose Floating Point Digital Signal Processors (in Japanese), Mytech MBE88-134.

Scherson, I. D. and Ma, Y., 1989, Analysis and Application of Orthogonal Access Multiprosessor, J. of Parallel and Distributed Computing, Vol.7 No.2, pp.232-255.

Su, S. Y. W. and Thakore, A. K., 1987, Matrix Operation on a Multicomputer System with Switchable Main Memory Modules and Dynamic Control, IEEE Trans. on Computers, Vol.C-36 No.12, pp.1467-1484.

A SCALY ARTIFICIAL NEURAL NETWORK ARCHITECTURE FOR ISOLATED WORD RECOGNITION USING THE BRITISH TELECOMMUNICATIONS ENGLISH ALPHABET DATABASE

M. J. Creaney and R. N. Gorgui–Naguib

Department of Electrical and Electronic Engineering
University of Newcastle Upon Tyne
Newcastle–Upon–Tyne NE1 7RU
U.K.

ABSTRACT

The use of neural networks for the recognition of isolated letters from the English Alphabet is investigated. A scaly architecture neural network model is used and is trained using the error back propagation algorithm. Two different methods of non–linear time alignment are used and the performance of the neural network when used with each compared. The use of different transfer functions within the processing units of the neural network is looked at and several versions of the sigmoid function compared. Variance of the learning rate in the error back propagation algorithm is investigated by comparing the performance of the neural network when three different values of learning rate are used.

I. INTRODUCTION

Two of the major problems in speech recognition systems have been due to fluctuations in the speech pattern time axis and spectral pattern variation [1]. Neural networks have proved to be useful tools for pattern recognition so are therefore suitable for the task of discriminating between different categories of spectral patterns such as those obtained for speech signals. A network with a scaly architecture [2] is investigated in this paper and its ability as a speech recognition tool assessed.

Various algorithms are available for dealing with speech pattern time axis variation, among these are, dynamic time warping [3] and time segmentation [4]. Both of these methods are looked at in this paper and used in conjunction with a neural network to produce models which have features to deal with both the aforementioned problems. The performance of the two models and their relative merits are compared.

II. THE SCALY NEURAL ARCHITECTURE

The neural network under consideration is a feed forward multi–layer neural network [5] with a scaly type architecture [2].

The software used (see section IV) offers the choice of three different non–linear activation, $f(x)$ functions, these are as follows

standard : $f(x) = 1.71 * \tanh(0.666x)$
sigmoid01 : $f(x) = 1 / (1 + \exp(-x))$
sigmoid11 : $f(x) = (1 - \exp(-x)) / (1 + \exp(-x))$

The network is trained using all the functions and the results compared for small sets of letters and then the best function is used to train a network to recognise all 26 letters of the alphabet.

In its most general form a feed forward back propagation neural network usually has, for a three layer network, every node in the input layer connected to every node in the hidden layer and every node in the hidden layer connected to every node in the output layer. This is a fully connected network. Signals flow in the forward direction from the input layer through the hidden layers to the output layer except during training. In the training phase error signals are sent in the reverse direction.

It has been shown that the performance of a neural network does not necessarily improve as the number of connections between the neurons is increased. Krause and Hackbarth [2] showed that using a scaly type architecture to reduce the total number of connections in a network supported high recognition rates for isolated word recognition. Here the scaly architecture is applied between the input layer and the hidden layer as shown in Fig. 1. The input data is preprocessed and presented to the network such that successive feature vectors or frames are presented to the network inputs, each coefficient of the feature vectors being presented to one input neuron. The hidden neurons are also grouped into frames of the same size as those in the input layer. The input frames are further grouped into input zones with each frame of hidden neurons being assigned to a zone of input neurons. Each hidden neuron is connected to its equivalent neuron in the input frames of the zone associated with that hidden frame. The input zones overlap such that some of the input frames connected to one hidden frame will also be connected to the adjacent hidden frame.

For example, when using the dynamic time warping algorithm (see section III A), all input patterns are warped to 35 feature vectors each of 8 coefficients. To accommodate this, an architecture with 280 input neurons is required. The scaly neural network therefore consists of an input layer with 35 frames each of 8 neurons. The number of frames in a zone is taken as 10 frames with an overlap of 5 frames so the number of frames

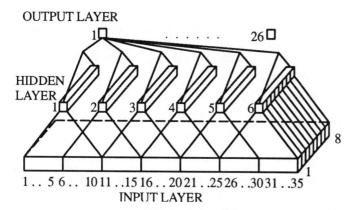

Fig. 1. Scaly Neural Network Architecture.

required in the hidden layer is 6. The hidden layer therefore consists of 6 frames each of 8 neurons equalling 48 neurons in all. The number of output classes is 26 so 26 neurons are required in the output layer. This netwrok is illustrated in Fig. 1.

The neural network weights are initialised to values between –0.5 and +0.5 using a random number generator. The back propagation algorithm [5] is then used to train the network.

The weights are changed according to the following rule

$$\Delta pW_{ji} = \varepsilon * \delta_{pj} * O_{pi}$$

where,
ΔpW_{ji} is the change for the weight joining the jth node to its incoming connection.
δ_{pj} is the error for this jth unit.
O_{pi} is the value of the ith incoming connection.
ε is a constant which determines the rate of learning.

The network is trained using three different values of ε (0.005, 0.008 and 0.01) for the recognition of small sets of letters and then the value of ε which gives the best results is used when the network is trained to recognise all 26 letters of the alphabet.

III. TIME ALIGNMENT

Time alignment of the input pattern vectors is required since speaking rate variation results in non–linear fluctuations in the speech pattern time axis. The length of the input pattern vector is also constrained by the number of input neurons to the neural network since the structure of the type of network in question cannot vary. The input pattern vectors have to be modified to fit the neural network while still retaining all their discriminating features. The performance of a neural network is dependent upon the performance of the time alignment algorithm [4].

The simplest time alignment algorithms are linear. However, they take no account of the importance of the feature vectors within the pattern vector when removing or duplicating them. Important features, therefore, may be lost in the process.

On the other hand, non–linear time alignment algorithms are more complicated and involve higher computational expenditure. Their advantage lies in the fact that they recognise important features and attempt to retain these features in the time aligned pattern vector. Two non–linear time alignment algorithms are implemented as described in the following sections.

A. Dynamic Time Warping

Dynamic time warping for time alignment was introduced by Sakoe and Chiba in 1978 [3] when it was used in conjunction with dynamic programming techniques for the recognition of isolated words. The method has been used in conjunction with a neural network by Sakoe et al in 1989 [1] for the recognition of isolated digit words.

This algorithm removes timing differences between speech patterns by warping the time axis of one speech pattern until it maximally coincides with the other. All pattern vectors are warped against a reference pattern vector of the same category which has the same number of feature vectors as there are frames in the input layer of the neural network.

The reference speech pattern can be expressed as a sequence of feature vectors

$$A = a_1, a_2, ..., a_i, ..., a_K$$

Let B be the pattern vector to be time aligned against A where

$$B = b_1, b_2, ..., b_j, ..., b_M$$

Fig. 2 shows A and B developed against the i and j axes.

Consider a warping function

$$j = j(i)$$

between the input pattern time j and the reference pattern time i. A measure of the difference between the two feature vectors a_i and b_j is the distance

$$d(i,j) = \|a_i - b_j\|$$

The weighted summation of these distances on the warping function is

$$E = d(i,j(i)) * w(k)$$

where w(k) is a weighting coefficient. E reaches a minimal value when the warping function is determined to optimally time align the two pattern vectors.

Certain restrictions are applied to the warping function to ensure that it approximates the properties of actual time axis fluctuations. Such properties are monotonicity and continuity [3]. Boundary conditions are imposed as follows

$$j(1) = 1$$
$$j(K) = M$$

An adjustment window is implemented such that :–

$$|i - j(i)| <= r$$

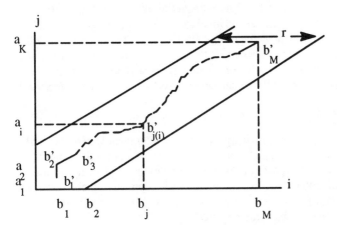

Fig. 2. Warping Function And Adjustment Window

where r is a positive integer. The adjustment window condition is imposed since time axis fluctuation does not yield excessive timing difference. Therefore the algorithm must do likewise.

The final constraint imposed is the slope constraint condition. The result of this condition is that if $b'_{j(i)}$ moves forward in one direction, either for the i or j axis direction, m times consecutively, then it must step n times in the diagonal direction before it can step further in that direction. This ensures a realistic relation between A and B by ensuring that relatively short segments of one are not mapped to relatively long segments of the other. The intensity of slope constraint is measured as follows :—

$$P = n/m$$

The warping function slope is more rigidly restricted by increasing P but if it is too severe then time normalisation is not effective.

Minimisation of E can be achieved by applying dynamic programming principles. The corresponding equation is as follows

$$g(i,j) = \min \begin{cases} g(i-2,j-3) + 2*(d(i-1,j-2) + d(i,j-1) + d(i,j))/3 \\ g(i-1,j-1) + d(i,j) \\ g(i-3,j-2) + d(i-2,j-1) + d(i-1,j) + d(i,j) \end{cases}$$

with, initially , $g(1,1) = d(a_1,b_1)$.

The entailing result is that, for the initial condition, the first feature vector of B is taken as the first feature vector of the warped pattern vector, b'_1. Subsequent feature vectors for the warped pattern vector are chosen such that the nth feature vector is that feature vector from the input pattern vector closest to the nth feature vector of the reference pattern vector. This means that the total euclidean distance between A and B , (g(K,M)), is minimised and is known as the residual distance value.

B. Time Segmentation

Time Segmentation was introduced by Kuhn et al in 1981 [4]. It is based on the assumption that despite any timing differences, for speech signals of the same category, fluctuations in

frequency with time will occur in the same sequence but over different lengths of time. It was used in conjunction with a neural network by Demichelis et al [6] for the recognition of isolated digits and by Smith [7] for the recognition of letters of the English alphabet.

A and B are used as in the previous section and it is also assumed that each feature vector has N features

$$a_i = (a_{i1}, a_{i2}, ..., a_{il}, ..., a_{iN})$$

which can be represented as a point in N–dimensional space.

Where there is no change in frequency there will be a high density of points and where the frequency changes are rapid the frequency points will be widely spaced. The number of feature vectors can be reduced by removing those that occur during the stationary portions of the speech. Kuhn et al [4] achieved this by summing the Euclidean distances between successive feature vectors of a pattern vector to give the total length D of the pattern vector. If F feature vectors are required in the time aligned pattern vector then D is divided into F segments of length L where, L = D/F

The most suitable vectors from the pattern vector are selected as follows. The first feature vector of the input pattern vector is taken as the first feature vector of the time aligned pattern vector. Successive feature vectors of the time aligned pattern vector are then chosen such that the euclidean distance between each of them is as close to L as possible. The final time aligned pattern vector should therefore consist of F feature vectors with euclidean distances between them of approximately L.

This algorithm can only be used for the compression of pattern vectors which implies that using it on its own entails warping all pattern vectors to the size of the smallest pattern vector. This can result in a very large pattern vector being warped to a very small length.This, obviously, is a restrictive consequence if all the discriminating features are to be retained in the time aligned pattern vectors. The size to which all the pattern vectors are warped is chosen as, roughly, the mean of all the speech data pattern sizes. This requires compression in some cases and expansion in others. Therefore, a linear time alignment algorithm is used for the expansion of pattern vectors. This algorithm duplicates vectors at regular intervals throughout the pattern vector until it is of the correct length. This version of the time segmentation algorithm is the one used here.

IV. EXPERIMENTAL PROCEDURE AND SIMULATION RESULTS

The source of the data for training and testing the neural network is a database from the British Telecommunications Research Laboratories. It consists of each of the letters of the English alphabet being repeated three times by 104 individual speakers. The data is used in multiple speaker training and test form which involves using the first two utterances for training and the third utterance for testing. There are 53 male speakers and 51 female speakers of various ages.The speech signals are recorded in a low noise environment with high quality recording equipment. They are sampled at 20KHz using a 16–bit A/D converter and the exact start and finish of each utterance have been labelled. Once endpointed Mel Frequency Cepstral Coefficients are calculated resulting in each feature vector being characterised by 8 coefficients.

The neural network simulator used obtaining these experiments is called Galatea and is produced as part of a joint EEC project called PYGMALION. The software consists of a set of C libraries which build, train and run different types of neural networks. The Gain Back Propagation algorithm is used to train and test the neural network on a *SUN ipc Spark* station.

A. Experimental Outline

1) Training on 'A' and 'B': In using both methods of time alignment the mean length of an utterance is calculated and all utterances warped to that length. For the dynamic time warping algorithm an utterance from each category is obtained to act as the reference pattern vector against which all other utterances of that category are warped. The desired outputs are generated such that a +1 is at the output of the neuron of the correct category and a –1 on all the other output neurons. For example , the desired outputs for A are

$$+1 -1 -1 -1 -1 -1 -1 -1 -1 -1 -1 -1 -1 -1 -1 -1 -1 -1 -1$$
$$-1 -1 -1 -1 -1 -1 -1$$

The network is trained using each of the three values of ε (0.005, 0.008 and 0.01) for the function sigmoid01 over 40 sweeps. The same procedure is followed for the functions sigmoid11 and standard. Training is then extended to 300 sweeps for sigmoid01 and sigmoid11 and 1000 sweeps for standard so that the performance of the network on the training data is attaining a reasonably high level for either of the time alignment algorithms with one of the values of ε.

2) Training on 'A', 'B' and 'C': The same procedure is followed as for the 'A' and 'B' trial with training being extended to the same number of sweeps.

3) Training on the complete alphabet: From the previous experiments the function which is achieving the best performance overall and the value of ε which is achieving the best performance in this function are selected. The neural network is then trained over 1000 sweeps using these parameters, first using the dynamic time warping data and then the time segmentation data. The trained networks are then presented with the test data to gauge their performance on newly applied data.

B. Simulation Results

1)Training on 'A' and 'B': Performance and error against number of sweeps is looked at. Table I shows the performance and error after 300 training sweeps. For performance the sigmoid11 function is clearly the best performer achieving 100% performance on the training data for both time alignment methods and all values of ε within 255 sweeps.

TABLE I

ERROR AND PERFORMANCE OF NETWORK IN RECOGNISING THE LETTERS 'A' AND 'B' AFTER 300 TRAINING SWEEPS

Sigmoid Function	ε		Time Alignment Algorithm	
			Dynamic Time Warping	Time segmentation
Sigmoid01	0.005	Error	0.19249	0.19257
		Perf.	99.51%	98.32%
	0.008	Error	0.19242	0.19246
		Perf.	99.76%	99.04%
	0.01	Error	0.19239	0.19245
		Perf.	100.00%	99.04%
Sigmoid11	0.005	Error	0.00254	0.00239
		Perf.	100.00%	100.00%
	0.008	Error	0.00170	0.00177
		Perf.	100.00%	100.00%
	0.01	Error	0.00153	0.00154
		Perf.	100.00%	100.00%
Standard	0.005	Error	0.04112	0.03869
		Perf.	59.95%	68.51%
	0.008	Error	0.04196	0.04404
		Perf.	58.25%	61.54%
	0.01	Error	0.03649	0.04665
		Perf.	63.83%	63.22%

There is little difference in the rate of learning for the sigmoid01 and the sigmoid11 functions when either of the time alignment algorithms is used or the different values of ε are used. The time segmentation algorithm results in a slightly faster learning rate especially in the early stages i.e. the first 20 training sweeps. For the standard sigmoid function the time segmentation algorithm results in much faster learning than the dynamic time warping algorithm. In most cases a value of $\varepsilon=0.01$ gives a slightly faster learning rate.

Error indicates the difference between the desired outputs and the actual outputs. Again the sigmoid11 function is superior achieving error values of less than 0.01 after 50 training sweeps.

The rate at which error decreases with the number of training sweeps does not vary much with different time alignment algorithms and values of ε. The time segmentation results in a slightly faster decrease in error especially in the early stages of learning and this is optimum when $\varepsilon=0.01$.

2)Training on 'A','B' and 'C': Similar results to those shown in the previous section are achieved with the best performing function being sigmoid11. Table II shows the performance and error after 300 training sweeps.

Table II

ERROR AND PERFORMANCE OF NETWORK IN RECOGNISING THE LETTERS
'A','B' AND 'C' AFTER 300 SWEEPS

Sigmoid Function	ε		Time Alignment Algorithm	
			Dynamic Time Warping	Time segmentation
Sigmoid01	0.005	Error Perf.	0.19271 95.95%	0.19274 95.99%
	0.008	Error Perf.	0.19260 97.09%	0.19258 97.28%
	0.01	Error Perf.	0.19258 97.25%	0.19255 97.28%
Sigmoid11	0.005	Error Perf.	0.00385 99.68%	0.00369 99.20%
	0.008	Error Perf.	0.00288 99.51%	0.00264 99.52%
	0.01	Error Perf.	0.00243 99.84%	0.00232 99.52%
Standard	0.005	Error Perf.	0.04949 47.25%	0.07462 18.27%
	0.008	Error Perf.	0.05505 38.03%	0.07826 18.11%
	0.01	Error Perf.	0.05791 34.79%	0.08490 4.49%

After 300 training sweeps using the sigmoid11 function a performance greater than 99% is achieved by both time alignment algorithms and all values of ε. The faster learning rate for the time segmentation algorithm is slightly more pronounced especially in the early stages of training.

For the standard sigmoid function the dynamic time warping algorithm performs much better than the time segmentation algorithm.

The speed of learning and the final values of performance and error are not as good as for 'A' and 'B' only which would be expected due to the extra learning incurred with the addition of the letter 'C'.

3) Training on the whole alphabet: When the network is trained to recognise the whole English alphabet the time segmentation (TS) algorithm gives the better results. The final performance when time segmentation is used is 70.92% as opposed to 51.96% when the dynamic time warping (DTW) algorithm is used. The final error for time segmentation is 0.03915

whereas for dynamic time warping it is 0.04715. These results are obtained with the training data. The learning curves for performance and error with both time alignment algorithms over the whole alphabet are shown in Fig. 3.

When the network is presented with the test data it achieves a performance of 62.0% with the time segmentation algorithm and 48.65% with the dynamic time warping algorithm. Both values are slightly less than those obtained with the training data. A slightly higher error than for the training data is achieved in both cases, 0.04715 for time segmentation and 0.05721 for dynamic time warping. The test data has never-been seen by the network before so higher error values and lower performance rates are to be expected.

V. DISCUSSION AND CONCLUSIONS

A. Effect of the Architecture on Performance Rates

For small sets of letters high performance rates and low error levels are achieved by the scaly architecture. Performance does fall significantly for the task of recognising all 26 letters of the alphabet. The network's ability to learn decreases with the addition of one extra letter between learning to recognise 'A' and 'B' and learning to recognise 'A', 'B' and 'C'. The decrease in ability to learn for the whole alphabet is therefore to be expected. As the number of training sweeps is increased further, the performance for this task should improve but the

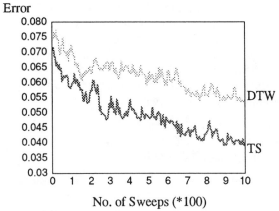

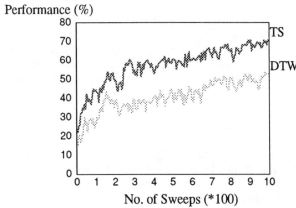

Fig. 3. Results Of Training Neural Network to Recognise Full Alphabet

cost in learning time will be greatly increased. Other possibilities could be investigated for increasing the performance of the network. Only one possible scaly type architecture has been implemented but many possible variations can be realised by

changing the number of neurons in a zone and the overlap between zones. The change in performance achieved by introducing scaly type architecture between the hidden layer and the output layer can also be investigated.

B. Effect of the Activation Function

One activation function clearly outperforms the others for this recognition task and network. This is the sigmoid function over the range –1 to +1 which performs much better than the standard sigmoid function and slightly better than the sigmoid function over the range 0 to +1.

For both the sigmoid11 and sigmoid01 functions, with small sets of letters, the learning curves are fairly smooth with rapid early learning and little fluctuation up and down. The standard sigmoid learning curves fluctuate up and down which results in slow early learning, lower performance rates and higher error levels compared with the other two functions. When trained to recognise the whole alphabet with the sigmoid11 function, it can be seen that the learning curves (see figure 3) for the network are no longer smooth but fluctuate up and down. It would appear therefore that the increased amount of categories to be recognised leads to greater fluctuations.

C. Effect of the Learning rate

Overall $\varepsilon = 0.01$ gives the highest performance rates coupled with low error levels. There are cases in which one of the other values achieves better results but usually this is only in reaching the maximum performance more rapidly than $\varepsilon = 0.01$. The difference between the two curves achieving this value is approximately 20 sweeps.

The exception is for the standard sigmoid function. With the task of learning 'A', 'B' and 'C $\varepsilon = 0.005$ achieves the best results overall and with the task of learning 'A' and 'B' there is only a small difference between the performance of $\varepsilon = 0.01$ and $\varepsilon = 0.005$ but $\varepsilon = 0.01$ is best.

A more detailed study of how performance varies with ε is required before any real conclusions about the effect of ε can be drawn.

D. The Time Alignment Method

In training the network to recognise the letters 'A' and 'B' the dynamic time warping algorithm and the time segmentation algorithm achieve similar esults for the functions sigmoid11 and sigmoid01. The time segmentation algorithm achieves a faster rate of learning in the early stages of training.

For the standard sigmoid function the time segmentation algorithm achieves the best results.

For the letters 'A', 'B' and 'C' time alignment methods again achieve similar results for the sigmoid01 and sigmoid11 functions. The time segmentation algorithm again achieves a faster rate of learning in the early stages of training. For the standard sigmoid function the dynamic time warping algorithm gives better results than the time segmentation algorithm.

For the task of recognising all 26 letters of the alphabet with $\varepsilon = 0.01$ and using the activation function sigmoid11 the time segmentation function achieves the best performance and the lowest error. This suggests that the time segmentation algorithm is more suitable when there is a greater number of letters to be recognised.

The dynamic time warping algorithm is used here with a slope constraint of P=2 and window size of r=10. Better performance using this algorithm for large recognition tasks could be investigated by looking at the variation of these parameters.

In conclusion the scaly type architecture neural network has been shown to be suitable for the recognition of isolated words in the form of letters of the English alphabet achieving high recognition rates for small vocabularies. Using the value $\varepsilon = 0.01$ and the sigmoid activation function over the interval –1 to +1 field the most suitable options for the recognition task in question. The time alignment algorithms investigated both prove to be supportive of high recognition rates when used with a scaly architecture neural network.

REFERENCES

[1] H. Sakoe, R. Isotani, K. Yoshida, k. Iso and T. Watanabe. "Speaker–Independent Word Recognition Using Dynamic Programming Neural Networks" in *IEEE ICASSP*, pp.29–32, 1989.

[2] A. Krause and H. Hackbarth. "Scaly Artificial Neural Networks for Speaker–Independent Recognition of Isolated Words" in *IEEE ICASSP*, pp.21–24, 1989.

[3] H. Sakoe and S. Chiba. "Dynamic Programming Algorithm Optimization for Spoken Word Recognition" in *IEEE trans. on Acoustics, Speech and Signal Processing*, vol.26, no.1, pp.43–49, 1978.

[4] M. H. Kuhn, H. Tomaschewski and H. Ney. "Fast Nonlinear Time Alignment For Isolated Word Recognition" in *IEEE ICASSP*, pp.736–740, 1981.

[5] D. E. Rumelhart, G. E. Hinton and R. J. Williams. "Learning Internal Representations by Error Propagation" in D. E. Rumelhart and J. L. McLelland, editors, *Parallel Distributed Processing: Explorations in the Microstructure of Cognition. Vol 1. Foundations*, pp. 318–362, MIT Press, 1986.

[6] P. Demichelis, L. Fissore, P. Laface, G. Micca and E. Piccolo. "On the Use of Neural Networks for Speaker Independent Isolated Word Recognition" in *IEEE ICASSP*, pp.314–317, 1989.

[7] A. D. Smith. "Isolated Word Recognition using gradient backed–propagation neural networks", MEng. Thesis, University Of Newcastle–Upon–Tyne, 1990.

Fuzzy Neural Networks with Fuzzy Weights and Fuzzy Biases

Hisao Ishibuchi, Hideo Tanaka

Department of Industrial Engineering, University of Osaka Prefecture

Gakuencho 1-1, Sakai, Osaka 593, JAPAN

Hidehiko Okada

Kansai C&C Research Laboratory, NEC Corporation

Shiromi 1-4-24, Chuo-ku, Osaka 540, JAPAN

Abstract— In this paper, we propose an architecture of multi-layer feedforward neural networks whose weights and biases are given as fuzzy numbers. The fuzzy neural network with the proposed architecture maps an input vector of real numbers to a fuzzy output. The input-output relation of each unit is defined by the extension principle. We derive a learning algorithm of the fuzzy neural network for real input vectors and fuzzy target outputs. Moreover, the derived learning algorithm is extended to the case of fuzzy input vectors and fuzzy target outputs.

I. INTRODUCTION

From the viewpoint of the principle of incompatibility[1], which asserts that high precision is incompatible with high complexity in dealing with humanistic systems by computers, several methods have been proposed for deriving inexact models from input-output data. For example, Tanaka et al.[2] proposed the concept of fuzzy regression analysis where the following fuzzy model with fuzzy parameters was employed:

$$Y(\boldsymbol{x}) = A_0 + A_1 x_1 + \cdots + A_n x_n, \qquad (1)$$

where $\boldsymbol{x} = (x_1, \cdots, x_n)$ is an n-dimensional real input vector and A_i is a fuzzy parameter given as a symmetric fuzzy number. Thus the output $Y(\boldsymbol{x})$ from the fuzzy model (1) is also a symmetric fuzzy number. The fuzzy parameters in (1) can be easily obtained using a linear programming technique. We show an example of fuzzy model with a single input in Fig.1 where fuzzy outputs corresponding to eight input values are depicted.

Several methods for deriving non-linear fuzzy models from input-output data were also proposed. For example,

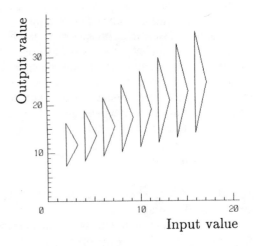

Fig.1. Example of fuzzy model

Ishibuchi & Tanaka[3,4] proposed a method for obtaining a non-linear interval model using two standard BP networks[5].

This paper proposes an architecture of fuzzy neural networks with fuzzy weights and fuzzy biases, and derives its learning algorithm for the modelling of non-linear fuzzy systems which map a real input vector to a fuzzy output. First we define the input-output relation of each unit of the fuzzy neural network by the extension principle[1]. Next we derive a learning algorithm from a cost function defined by the level sets of a fuzzy actual output and a fuzzy target output. Last we show that the derived learning algorithm can be applied to the case of fuzzy input vectors and fuzzy target outputs by slightly modifying it.

Hayashi et al.[6] also proposed a similar architecture of neural networks with fuzzy weights but the learning

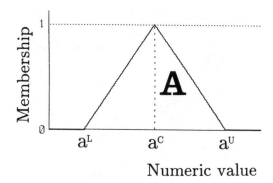

Fig.2. Triangular fuzzy number A

algorithm in [6] was totally different from our approach. In Hayashi et al., the BP algorithm[5] is directly fuzzified based on a fuzzy-valued cost function (i.e., the rule for changing fuzzy weights is also defined by fuzzy numbers), while a learning algorithm is derived from a non-fuzzy cost function in this paper.

II. ARCHITECTURE OF FUZZY NEURAL NETWORKS

A. Fuzzy Weights and Fuzzy Biases

We extend the standard BP networks in Rumelhart et al.[5] to fuzzy neural networks with fuzzy weights and fuzzy biases. We use symmetric triangular fuzzy numbers for fuzzy weights and fuzzy biases.

Let us denote a triangular fuzzy number A as $A = (a^L, a^C, a^U)$ where a^L, a^C and a^U are the lower limit, the center and the upper limit of A (see Fig.2). The membership function of A is defined as

$$\mu_A(x) = \begin{cases} 0, & for\ x \leq a^L \\ (x - a^L)/(a^C - a^L), & for\ a^L < x \leq a^C \\ (a^U - x)/(a^U - a^C), & for\ a^C < x \leq a^U \\ 0, & for\ a^U < x \end{cases}$$

(2)

The membership function of A is 1 at the center a^C and positive in the open interval (a^L, a^U), that is, (a^L, a^U) is the support of the fuzzy number A.

We propose an architecture of fuzzy neural networks that have fuzzy weights and fuzzy biases. The proposed architecture is shown in Fig.3 where the fuzzy weights and the fuzzy biases are as follows (in Fig.3, biases are omitted).

$$W_j = (w_j^L, w_j^C, w_j^U), \quad W_{ji} = (w_{ji}^L, w_{ji}^C, w_{ji}^U), \quad (3)$$

$$\Theta = (\theta^L, \theta^C, \theta^U), \quad \Theta_j = (\theta_j^L, \theta_j^C, \theta_j^U). \quad (4)$$

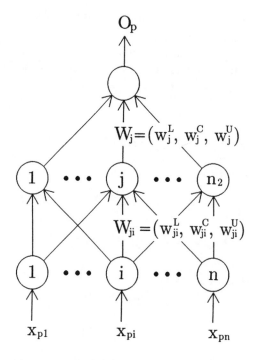

Fig.3. The proposed architecture of neural networks with fuzzy weights and fuzzy biases

Since we use symmetric triangular fuzzy numbers for the fuzzy weights and the fuzzy biases, the following relations hold:

$$w_j^C = (w_j^L + w_j^U)/2, \quad w_{ji}^C = (w_{ji}^L + w_{ji}^U)/2, \quad (5)$$

$$\theta^C = (\theta^L + \theta^U)/2, \quad \theta_j^C = (\theta_j^L + \theta_j^U)/2. \quad (6)$$

The level sets of fuzzy numbers are defined as

$$[A]_h = \{x : \mu_A(x) \geq h\}, \quad (7)$$

where $[A]_h$ is the h-level set of the fuzzy number A. Since the level sets of fuzzy numbers are closed intervals, we denote $[A]_h$ by its lower limit $[A]_h^L$ and its upper limit $[A]_h^U$ as

$$[A]_h = [[A]_h^L, \ [A]_h^U]. \quad (8)$$

Since the fuzzy weights W_j and W_{ji} are symmetric fuzzy numbers, the h-level sets can be calculated as

$$[W_j]_h^L = w_j^L(1 - h/2) + w_j^U h/2, \quad (9)$$

$$[W_j]_h^U = w_j^L h/2 + w_j^U(1 - h/2), \quad (10)$$

$$[W_{ji}]_h^L = w_{ji}^L(1 - h/2) + w_{ji}^U h/2, \quad (11)$$

$$[W_{ji}]_h^U = w_{ji}^L h/2 + w_{ji}^U(1 - h/2). \quad (12)$$

The h-level sets of the biases Θ and Θ_j can be calculated in the same manner.

B. Definition of Input-Output Relation of Each Unit

When an n-dimensional real input vector $\boldsymbol{x}_p = (x_{p1}, x_{p2}, \cdots, x_{pn})$ is presented to the input units of the fuzzy neural network in Fig.3, the input-output relation of each unit can be written as follows.

Input units :

$$o_{pi} = x_{pi}, \ i = 1, 2, ..., n. \tag{13}$$

Hidden units :

$$O_{pj} = f(Net_{pj}), \ j = 1, 2, ..., n_2, \tag{14}$$

$$Net_{pj} = \sum_{i=1}^{n} W_{ji} o_{pi} + \Theta_j, \ j = 1, 2, \cdots, n_2. \tag{15}$$

Output unit :

$$O_p = f(Net_p), \tag{16}$$

$$Net_p = \sum_{j=1}^{n_2} W_j O_{pj} + \Theta. \tag{17}$$

This definition is the same as the standard BP network[5] except that the weights W_{ji}, W_j and the biases Θ_j, Θ are fuzzy numbers. In (13)-(17), uppercase letters and lowercase letters denote fuzzy numbers and real numbers, respectively. The activation function in the hidden units and the output unit is the sigmoid function: $f(x) = 1/\{1 + \exp(-x)\}$.

The fuzzy input-output relation in (13)-(17) is defined by the extension principle[1]. For example, the fuzzy input-output relation by the activation function $f(\cdot)$ is defined as follows (see Fig.4).

$$\mu_{f(Net)}(y) = \max_{x}\{\mu_{Net}(x) : y = f(x)\}, \tag{18}$$

where Net is a fuzzy input and $f(Net)$ is the corresponding fuzzy output.

While the input-output relation of each unit is defined by the extension principle, the calculation of actual fuzzy outputs are performed using interval arithmetic[7] for level sets. For example, the fuzzy output $f(Net)$ in Fig.4 is calculated by interval arithmetic for 50 level sets ($h = 0.02, 0.04, \cdots, 1.00$). This approach was applied to the calculation of fuzzy outputs corresponding to fuzzy input vectors to the standard BP network in Ishibuchi et al.[8-10].

The input-output relation of each unit for the h-level sets can be derived from (13)-(17) as follows.

Input units :

$$o_{pi} = x_{pi}, \ i = 1, 2, \cdots, n. \tag{19}$$

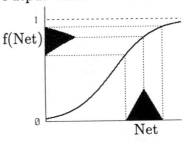

Fig.4. Fuzzy input-output relation

Hidden units :

$$[O_{pj}]_h = [f(Net_{pj})]_h = f([Net_{pj}]_h), \ j = 1, 2, \cdots, n_2, \tag{20}$$

$$[Net_{pj}]_h = \sum_{i=1}^{n} [W_{ji}]_h o_{pi} + [\Theta_j]_h, \ j = 1, 2, \cdots, n_2. \tag{21}$$

Output unit :

$$[O_p]_h = [f(Net_p)]_h = f([Net_p]_h), \tag{22}$$

$$[Net_p]_h = \sum_{j=1}^{n_2} [W_j]_h [O_{pj}]_h + [\Theta]_h. \tag{23}$$

These input-output relations for h-level sets are similar to those of the neural network with interval weights and interval biases in Ishibuchi et al.[11].

III. LEARNING ALGORITHM OF FUZZY NEURAL NETWORKS

A. Training Data

Let us assume that m input-output pairs $(\boldsymbol{x}_p, T_p)$, $p = 1, 2, ..., m$, of the real input vector $\boldsymbol{x}_p$ and the corresponding fuzzy target output T_p are given. We also assume that the target output T_p is a triangular fuzzy number:

$$T_p = (t_p^L, t_p^C, t_p^U). \tag{24}$$

It should be noted that the fuzzy target output T_p may be non-symmetric while the fuzzy weights and the fuzzy biases are symmetric triangular fuzzy numbers.

1652

B. Definition of Cost Function

Let us denote the h-level sets of the fuzzy actual output O_p and the corresponding fuzzy target output T_p as

$$[O_p]_h = [[O_p]_h^L, \ [O_p]_h^U], \quad [T_p]_h = [[T_p]_h^L, \ [T_p]_h^U], \quad (25)$$

where $[\cdot]_h^L$ and $[\cdot]_h^U$ denote the lower limit and the upper limit of the h-level set. For the h-level sets, we define the following cost function (i.e., error measure) to be minimized in the learning of the proposed fuzzy neural network.

$$e_{ph} = ([T_p]_h^L - [O_p]_h^L)^2/2 + ([T_p]_h^U - [O_p]_h^U)^2/2. \quad (26)$$

This cost function satisfies the relation:

$$e_{ph} = 0 \ \ if \ \ [O_p]_h = [T_p]_h. \quad (27)$$

In the learning for the p-th input-output pair $(\boldsymbol{x}_p, T_p)$, we can use several values of h. Therefore the cost function for $(\boldsymbol{x}_p, T_p)$ is defined as

$$e_p = \sum_h h \cdot e_{ph}, \quad (28)$$

where the cost function e_{ph} for the h-level sets is weighted by the value of h in order to attach the greater importance to the higher level. This cost function satisfies the relation:

$$e_p = 0 \ \ if \ \ O_p = T_p. \quad (29)$$

Moreover, if we use an infinite number of values of h in (28), the cost function defined by (28) satisfies the relation:

$$e_p = 0 \ \ if \ and \ only \ if \ \ O_p = T_p. \quad (30)$$

Therefore the actual fuzzy output O_p approaches the fuzzy target output T_p as the cost function e_p approaches zero. In computer simulations, we use five values of h, i.e., $h = 0.2, 0.4, 0.6, 0.8, 1.0$.

C. Derivation of Learning Algorithm

In the learning of the fuzzy neural network, we adjust the lower limits and the upper limits of the fuzzy weights W_j, W_{ji} and the fuzzy biases Θ, Θ_j. In a similar manner to the BP algorithm[5], the learning rules for the fuzzy weights W_j, W_{ji} can be written as

$$\triangle w_j^L(t+1) = -\eta \cdot h(\partial e_{ph}/\partial w_j^L) + \alpha \triangle w_j^L(t), \quad (31)$$

$$\triangle w_j^U(t+1) = -\eta \cdot h(\partial e_{ph}/\partial w_j^U) + \alpha \triangle w_j^U(t), \quad (32)$$

$$\triangle w_{ji}^L(t+1) = -\eta \cdot h(\partial e_{ph}/\partial w_{ji}^L) + \alpha \triangle w_{ji}^L(t), \quad (33)$$

$$\triangle w_{ji}^U(t+1) = -\eta \cdot h(\partial e_{ph}/\partial w_{ji}^U) + \alpha \triangle w_{ji}^U(t), \quad (34)$$

where η is a learning constant and α is a momentum constant. In computer simulations of this paper, we specify η and α as $\eta = 0.5$ and $\alpha = 0.9$. The derivatives $\partial e_{ph}/\partial w_j^L$, $\partial e_{ph}/\partial w_j^U$, $\partial e_{ph}/\partial w_{ji}^L$ and $\partial e_{ph}/\partial w_{ji}^U$ in (31)-(34) can be derived from the cost function (26) using (9)-(12) and (19)-(23). For example, $\partial e_{ph}/\partial w_j^L$ is derived as follows.

i) If $0 \le [W_j]_h^L \le [W_j]_h^U$ then

$$
\begin{aligned}
\frac{\partial e_{ph}}{\partial w_j^L} &= \frac{\partial e_{ph}^L}{\partial w_j^L} + \frac{\partial e_{ph}^U}{\partial w_j^L} \\
&= \frac{\partial}{\partial [O_p]_h^L}\{([T_p]_h^L - [O_p]_h^L)^2/2\} \\
&\quad \cdot \frac{\partial [O_p]_h^L}{\partial [Net_p]_h^L} \frac{\partial [Net_p]_h^L}{\partial [W_j]_h^L} \frac{\partial [W_j]_h^L}{\partial w_j^L} \\
&\quad + \frac{\partial}{\partial [O_p]_h^U}\{([T_p]_h^U - [O_p]_h^U)^2/2\} \\
&\quad \cdot \frac{\partial [O_p]_h^U}{\partial [Net_p]_h^U} \frac{\partial [Net_p]_h^U}{\partial [W_j]_h^U} \frac{\partial [W_j]_h^U}{\partial w_j^L} \\
&= -([T_p]_h^L - [O_p]_h^L)[O_p]_h^L \\
&\quad \cdot (1 - [O_p]_h^L)[O_{pj}]_h^L(1 - h/2) \\
&\quad - ([T_p]_h^U - [O_p]_h^U)[O_p]_h^U \\
&\quad \cdot (1 - [O_p]_h^U)[O_{pj}]_h^U h/2 \\
&= -\delta_{ph}^L[O_{pj}]_h^L(1 - h/2) \\
&\quad - \delta_{ph}^U[O_{pj}]_h^U h/2, \quad (35)
\end{aligned}
$$

where

$$\delta_{ph}^L = ([T_p]_h^L - [O_p]_h^L)[O_p]_h^L(1 - [O_p]_h^L), \quad (36)$$

$$\delta_{ph}^U = ([T_p]_h^U - [O_p]_h^U)[O_p]_h^U(1 - [O_p]_h^U). \quad (37)$$

ii) If $[W_j]_h^L \le [W_j]_h^U < 0$ then

$$\partial e_{ph}/\partial w_j^L = -\delta_{ph}^L[O_{pj}]_h^U(1 - h/2) - \delta_{ph}^U[O_{pj}]_h^L h/2. \quad (38)$$

iii) If $[W_j]_h^L < 0 \le [W_j]_h^U$ then

$$\partial e_{ph}/\partial w_j^L = -\delta_{ph}^L[O_{pj}]_h^U(1 - h/2) - \delta_{ph}^U[O_{pj}]_h^U h/2. \quad (39)$$

After the adjustments of the fuzzy weights by (31)-(34), it is undesirable but may happen that the lower limits of the fuzzy weights exceed the upper limits. In order to cope with this undesirable situation, we define new fuzzy weights after the adjustments as

$$w_j^L = \min\{w_j^L(t+1), w_j^U(t+1)\}, \quad (40)$$

$$w_{ji}^L = \min\{w_{ji}^L(t+1), w_{ji}^U(t+1)\}, \quad (41)$$

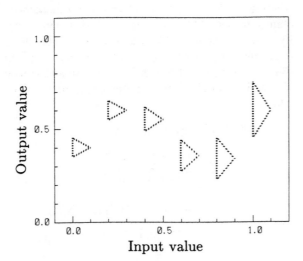

Fig.5. Training data for the learning of the neural network

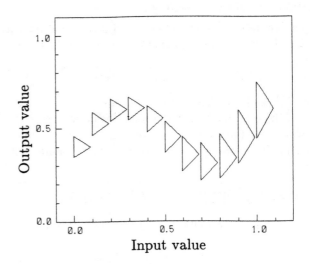

Fig.6. Fuzzy actual outputs from the trained neural network

$$w_j^U = \max\{w_j^L(t+1), w_j^U(t+1)\}, \qquad (42)$$

$$w_{ji}^U = \max\{w_{ji}^L(t+1), w_{ji}^U(t+1)\}. \qquad (43)$$

The centers w_j^C and w_{ji}^C are determined from w_j^L, w_j^U, w_{ji}^L and w_{ji}^U by (5). The fuzzy biases are changed in the same manner as the fuzzy weights.

D. Numerical Example

We show a simulation result of the learning of the proposed fuzzy neural network. The training data is shown in Fig.5. In Fig.5, fuzzy target outputs corresponding to six input values: $x = 0.0, 0.2, \cdots, 1.0$, are given as triangular fuzzy numbers. Using the proposed learning algorithm, we trained the fuzzy neural network with a single input unit, five hidden units and a single output unit. The learning algorithm was iterated 10,000 times, i.e., 10,000 epochs. The sum of the cost function e_p over the given six training patterns was 0.0082 after 10,000 iterations. In Fig.6, we show the actual fuzzy outputs from the trained neural network corresponding to 11 input values: $x = 0.0, 0.1, ..., 1.0$. From this figure, we can see that good fitting to the six fuzzy target outputs and good interpolation for the five new inputs were accomplished.

IV. EXTENSION TO FUZZY INPUT VECTORS AND FUZZY TARGET OUTPUTS

The proposed approach can be extended to the case of fuzzy input vectors and fuzzy target outputs. Let $(\boldsymbol{X}_p, T_p)$ be the p-th input-output pair where $\boldsymbol{X}_p$ is an n-dimensional fuzzy input vector and T_p is a fuzzy target output. In this case, the input-output relation in (13)-(17) is modified as follows.

Input units :

$$O_{pi} = X_{pi}, \ i = 1, 2, \cdots, n. \qquad (44)$$

Hidden units :

$$O_{pj} = f(Net_{pj}), \ j = 1, 2, \cdots, n_2, \qquad (45)$$

$$Net_{pj} = \sum_{i=1}^{n} W_{ji} O_{pi} + \Theta_j, \ j = 1, 2, \cdots, n_2. \qquad (46)$$

Output unit :

$$O_p = f(Net_p), \qquad (47)$$

$$Net_p = \sum_{j=1}^{n_2} W_j O_{pj} + \Theta. \qquad (48)$$

The input-output relation of the output unit is the same as the case of a real input vector in Section II.

Using the fuzzy input vector $\boldsymbol{X}_p$ and the fuzzy target output T_p, the fuzzy neural network can be trained by the learning algorithm defined by (31)-(34) and (40)-(43). That is, we can also use the cost function e_{ph} in (26) for this case. The derivatives $\partial e_{ph}/\partial w_j^L$, $\partial e_{ph}/\partial w_j^U$, $\partial e_{ph}/\partial w_{ji}^L$ and $\partial e_{ph}/\partial w_{ji}^U$ can be derived from the cost function e_{ph} in (26) using the input-output relation for h-level sets in a similar manner as the case of the real input vector $\boldsymbol{x}_p$ ($\partial e_{ph}/\partial w_j^L$, $\partial e_{ph}/\partial w_j^U$ are the same and $\partial e_{ph}/\partial w_{ji}^L$, $\partial e_{ph}/\partial w_{ji}^U$ are more complicated.)

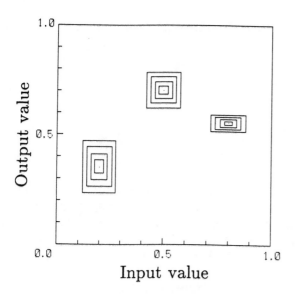

Fig.7. Training data

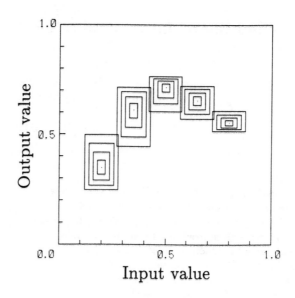

Fig.8. Fuzzy actual outputs

In Fig.7 and Fig.8, we show a simulation result. Fig.7 is the training data and Fig.8 is the fuzzy actual outputs from the trained fuzzy neural network after 10,000 iterations. In these figures, five level sets corresponding to $h = 0.2, 0.4, 0.6, 0.8, 1.0$, are depicted.

V. CONCLUSION

In this paper, we proposed an architecture of fuzzy neural networks with fuzzy weights and fuzzy biases. For the input-output pairs of real input vectors and fuzzy target outputs, a learning algorithm is derived from a cost function defined by the level sets of a fuzzy actual output and the corresponding fuzzy target output. The derived learning algorithm was extended to the case of fuzzy input vectors and fuzzy target outputs.

REFERENCES

[1] L.A.Zadeh, "The concept of a linguistic variable and its application to approximate reasoning - I, II and III," Information Sciences, vol.8, pp.199-249, pp.301-357 and vol.9, pp.43-80, 1975.

[2] H.Tanaka, S.Uejima and K.Asai, "Linear regression analysis with fuzzy model," IEEE Trans. on System, Man and Cybernetics, vol.12, pp.903-907, 1982.

[3] H.Ishibuchi and H.Tanaka, "Regression analysis with interval model by neural networks," Proc. of IJCNN'91 (November 18-21, 1991, Singapore) pp.1594-1599.

[4] H.Ishibuchi and H.Tanaka, "Fuzzy regression analysis using neural networks," Fuzzy Sets and Systems, vol.49, pp.257-265, 1992.

[5] D.E.Rumelhart, J.L.McClelland and the PDP Research Group, Parallel Distributed Processing, vol.1. MIT Press, Cambridge, 1986.

[6] Y.Hayashi, J.J.Buckley and E.Czogala, "Direct fuzzification of neural network and fuzzified delta rule," Proc. of the 2nd International Conference on Fuzzy Logic & Neural Networks (July 17-22, 1992, Iizuka, Japan) pp.73-76.

[7] G.Alefeld and J.Herzberger, Introduction to Interval Computations. Academic Press, New York, 1983.

[8] H.Ishibuchi, R.Fujioka and H.Tanaka, "An architecture of neural networks for input vectors of fuzzy numbers," Proc. of FUZZ-IEEE'92 (March 8-12, 1992, San Diego) pp.1293-1300.

[9] H.Ishibuchi, R.Fujioka and H.Tanaka, "Neural networks that learn from fuzzy if-then rules," IEEE Trans. on Fuzzy Systems, in press, 1993.

[10] H.Ishibuchi, H.Okada and H.Tanaka, "Learning of neural networks from fuzzy inputs and fuzzy targets," Proc. of IJCNN'92 (November 3-6, 1992, Beijing, China) vol.III, pp.507-511 and pp.481.

[11] H.Ishibuchi, H.Okada and H.Tanaka, "A neural network with interval weights and its learning algorithm," Proc. of IJCNN'92 (November 3-6, 1992, Beijing, China) vol.III, pp.447-452.

Blind Bilevel Image Restoration Using Hopfield Neural Networks

Hui-Juan Liu and Yi Sun

Institute of Image Processing and Pattern Recognition

Shanghai Jiao Tong University

Shanghai 200030, P.R. China

Abstract — In the paper we present a Hopfield neural network approach to blind bilevel image restoration. In the approach two kinds of Hopfield neural networks are used. One is the analog Hopfield neural network utilized to estimate the parameters of the finite point spread function (PSF) of a blurring system. The other one is the modified Hopfield neural network [1][2][3][4] used to restore bilevel image. The entire model is based on alternative operation of the two networks. In the modified Hopfield neural network the EHE criterion [5][6] is applied for the purpose of obtaining a more precise solution. Simulation results show that after a few iterations the model always obtains a bilevel image whose quality is almost the same as or even better than what is obtained by the modified Hopfield network when the precise parameters of PSF are used. The results are amazing good. However, if the EHE criterion is not used, the model can hardly get a good bilevel image.

I. INTRODUCTION

It is an interesting and applicable issue to find the precise positions of edges of a bilevel image from blurred image with knowing neither the blurring function nor the original bilevel image. In mathematics, this blind restoration problem is unsolvable if no other constraints are given. It is fortunate that we generally have some acceptable assumptions on the issue such as, the original image is bilevel or bipolar and the blurring function is shift-invariant and spatially finite. Meanwhile, we find that the blind restoration problem can be considered containing two estimation problems. One is estimation of the parameters of the blurring function according to an estimated bilevel image and the given blurring one. The other is estimation of the original bilevel image using estimated parameters of blurring function and the given blurred image. Clearly, the first one can be solved by the analog Hopfield neural network and the second one can be solved by using the modified Hopfield neural network. Naturally, we establish a model composing of the two kinds of Hopfield neural networks for blind bilevel image restoration. Firstly, the finite point spread function (PSF) without degradation is assumed. A bilevel image is obtained by means of the modified Hopfield network using the assumed PSF function and the blurred image. Alternatively, the analog Hopfield network is used to estimate a new PSF function by taking use of the obtained bilevel image and the blurred one. The procedure continues until the difference of two bilevel images or the difference of parameters of two PSF functions in two successive iterations does not decrease or achieves an acceptable small value.

II. MODEL DESCRIPTION

An image collection system is a linear one and can be modeled by the convolution summation,

$$y(k,l)=a(k,l)*x(k,l)+n_s(k,l), \ 0\le k,l\le N-1 \qquad (1)$$

here * denotes convolution. $x(k,l)$, $y(k,l)$, $n_s(k,l)$ and $a(k,l)$ represent the original bilevel image, blurred image, observing noise and PSF function, respectively. By using the lexicographic notation, (1) can be written as below

$$\mathbf{y}=\mathbf{A}\mathbf{x}+\mathbf{n_s} \qquad (2)$$

here $\mathbf{x}\in\{0,1\}^n$, $\mathbf{y},\mathbf{n_s}\in\mathbf{R}^n$, $\mathbf{A}\in\mathbf{R}^{n\times n}$ and $n=N^2$. $\mathbf{x}$, $\mathbf{y}$, $\mathbf{n_s}$ and $\mathbf{A}$ represent, respectively, the original bilevel image, blurred image, observing noise and degradation. In blind bilevel image restoration problem $\mathbf{y}$ is given but $\mathbf{x}$ and $\mathbf{A}$ are unknown. We should use some assumptions to estimate $\mathbf{x}$. In the paper three important and acceptable conditions are assumed: 1)original image is bilevel; 2)the degradation is spatially shift-invariant; 3)the nonzero range of burring function is limited in a small square. Additional assumptions are also made in final simulations for the purpose of computation simplification: 1)the degree of noise is sufficient small; 2)the original image can be periodically extended.

A. Modified Hopfield neural network

The modified Hopfield network model was proposed by Paik *et al.* [1] to be used for multi-level image restoration. The same model was also proposed in [2], [3] and [4] to solve bilevel image restoration and reconstruction problems. The modified Hopfield neural network is superior to its original one in that the modified one can stably converge to a fixed point without checking the change in energy function.

As is discussed in [2], [3] and [4], the network can operate in not only simultaneous and sequential updating modes but also partially simultaneous and mixed updating modes. Because the upper bound of the residual for a fixed point reaches smallest value when the network operates in sequential updating mode, in the paper we focus our discussion on the sequential updating mode in order to obtain a high quality image.

We define the energy function of the modified Hopfield neural network as

$$E(\mathbf{x}) = \frac{1}{2}(\|\mathbf{Ax} - \mathbf{y}\|^2 + \mu\|\mathbf{Dx}\|^2) \qquad (3)$$

The second term of (3) is used for the purpose of obtaining a smoother image. $\mathbf{D}$ is a finite difference operator. μ is a positive constant depending on the degree of noise. In the paper we assume the degree of noise is small enough to allow $\mu \approx 0$. The input vector of the network at time k is defined as

$$\mathbf{h}(k) = \mathbf{Wx}(k) - \theta \qquad (4)$$

here $\mathbf{W} = -\mathbf{A}^\mathsf{T}\mathbf{A} - \mu\mathbf{D}^\mathsf{T}\mathbf{D}$ and $\theta = -\mathbf{A}^\mathsf{T}\mathbf{y}$. The ith element of $\mathbf{h}(k)$ is the input of the ith neuron. When the network operates in sequential updating mode, the operation has following form:

Algorithm 1
0) Let $t_i = \frac{1}{2}|w_{i,i}|$, $i = 1, \cdots, n$. Give $\mathbf{x}(0)$. Let $k = 0$ and $i = 1$.
1) Check termination.
2) If $x_i(k) = 0$ and $h_i(k) > t_i$ then $x_i(k+1) = 1$; otherwise, if $x_i(k) = 1$ and $h_i(k) < -t_i$ then $x_i(k+1) = 0$.
3) $k = k + 1$. $i = i + 1$, If $i > n$ then $i = i - n$. Go to step 1).

In Algorithm 1, $w_{i,i}$ denotes the iith element of $\mathbf{W}$, and $x_i(k)$ and $h_i(k)$ denote, respectively, the ith elements of $\mathbf{x}(k)$ and $\mathbf{h}(k)$.

It was proved in [1] that after a finite number of iterations Algorithm 1 stably converges to a fixed point which is a local minimum of $E(\mathbf{x})$.

In image restoration the matrix $\mathbf{A}^\mathsf{T}\mathbf{A}$ corresponds to the autocorrelation function of the shift-invariant function of a blurring system. The autocorrelation function has a larger value at origin than at any other points. Therefore we have

$$|w_{i,i}| > |w_{j,i}|, \quad i = 1, \cdots, n; j \neq i, j = 1, \cdots, n \qquad (5)$$

This characteristic of the network can be utilized for choice of neuron to be updated at each step and make the network operate more efficiently. This is the basic idea of the EHE criterion [5][6]. With the EHE criterion Algorithm 1 is modified as following form:

Algorithm 2
0) Let $t_i = \frac{1}{2}|w_{i,i}|$, $i = 1, \cdots, n$. Give $\mathbf{x}(0)$. Let $k = 0$.

1) Find a subset $\mathbf{J}$ so that $\mathbf{J} = \{i \mid i \in \{1, \cdots, n\}, h_i(k) > t_i$ when $x_i(k) = 0$ or $h_i(k) < -t_i$ when $x_i(k) = 1\}$. If $\mathbf{J} = \phi$ then terminate.
2) Find a number i in $\mathbf{J}$ so that $|h_i(k)| \geq |h_j(k)|$, $\forall j \in \mathbf{J}$.
3) Let $x_i(k+1) = 1$ if $x_i(k) = 0$; otherwise, $x_i(k+1) = 0$.
4) $k = k + 1$, go to step 1).

Clearly, Algorithm 2 also converges to a fixed point which is a local minimum of $E(\mathbf{x})$ after a finite number of iterations. It was verified in [5] that in the same conditions Algorithm 2 can obtain an image with higher quality in a much smaller number of iterations than Algorithm 1.

B. Least-square estimator of analog Hopfield neural network

Because the degradation is spatially shift-invariant, $\mathbf{A}$ can be described by n variables. Then equations (2) can be rewritten as follows,

$$\mathbf{y} = \mathbf{Xa} + \mathbf{n}_s \qquad (6)$$

here $\mathbf{X} \in \{0,1\}^{n \times n}$ is constructed from $\mathbf{x}$ and $\mathbf{a} \in \mathbf{R}^n$ is from $\mathbf{A}$. The relationship between (6) and (2) is easily derived by noticing that both (2) and (6) are obtained from (1). Clearly, (2) and (6) are identical except that they have different forms of expression.

Since the nonzero range of the blurring function is limited in a small square, a smaller number of elements of $\mathbf{a}$, e.g. m, is sufficient to express (6) after eliminating the zero elements of $\mathbf{a}$. In other words it is reasonable to assume $\mathbf{X} \in \{0,1\}^{n \times m}$ and $\mathbf{a} \in \mathbf{R}^m$ in (6) and $m < n$. When $\mathbf{y}$ and $\mathbf{X}$ are given, $\mathbf{a}$ can be estimated in least squares sense.

We define an energy function for the analog Hopfield neural network as

$$E(\mathbf{a}) = \frac{1}{2}\|\mathbf{Xa} - \mathbf{y}\|^2 \qquad (7)$$

Then the network operates in the following form

$$\frac{d\mathbf{u}}{dt} = -(\mathbf{X}^\mathsf{T}\mathbf{X})\mathbf{a} + \mathbf{X}^\mathsf{T}\mathbf{y} \qquad (8)$$

$$a_i = g(u_i), \qquad i = 1, \cdots, m \qquad (9)$$

here $g(u_i) = b\tanh(\lambda u_i)$, $b > 0$ and $\lambda > 0$. u_i is the summation of all the inputs to the ith neuron in the network, a_i is the state of the ith neuron and g is the neuron's activation function. Since $g'(u_i) > 0$ and $\mathbf{X}^\mathsf{T}\mathbf{X}$ is a non-negative definite matrix, it is guaranteed that the network always converges to the global minimum of $E(\mathbf{a})$. However, the uniqueness of the global minimum depends on the property of connection matrix $\mathbf{X}^\mathsf{T}\mathbf{X}$. For example, if $\mathbf{X}^\mathsf{T}\mathbf{X}$ is singular, there may exist infinite minima. A simple case is that the original image is uniform (all-one or all-zero image), then it is impossible to correctly estimate the degradation model.

Another problem is that the solution may be beyond the range of $(-b,b)^m$, but the state of the network is always in $(-b,b)^m$ in above network. Gao et al. [7] proposed a method to solve this problem. The main idea is that when the network converges to a fixed point c_1, its position is checked. If c_1 is near the bound of $(-b,b)^m$, then a in (8) is replaced by $a-c_1$ and the network operates continually. The procedure repeats until the state of the network converges to a fixed point c_K which is not near the bound of $(-b,b)^m$. Then the final solution is $a=c_1+c_2+\cdots+c_K$.

C. Mixed model of two kinds of Hopfield networks

In the approach to the blind bilevel image restoration the two kinds of Hopfield neural networks discussed previously operate in alternative manner. One is used to estimate the degradation model and the other is to obtain the estimation of original bilevel image. The algorithm is described as follows:

Algorithm A
1) Let $l=0$;
2) If $l=0$ let $a_1(0)=1$, $a_i(0)=0$ for $i=2,\cdots,m$; otherwise construct X according to $x(l)$, and then estimate an $a(l)$ by means of the analog Hopfield neural network (8) and (9) using X and y.
3) Construct A from $a(l)$ and estimate a $x(l)$ using Algorithm 2 on the basis of A and y.
4) If $l\geq 2$ and $|\Delta x(l)|>|\Delta x(l-1)|$, then terminate with restored bilevel image $x(l-1)$ and estimated degradation model $a(l-1)$.
5) $l=l+1$; Go to 2)

where $|\Delta x(l)|$ is the number of different pixels between $x(l)$ and $x(l-1)$ and is defined as

$$|\Delta x(l)| = \|x(l)-x(l-1)\|_1 \qquad (10)$$

When we do not know the degradation model, a rational assumption about it is that no degradation is made by the model. That is, the PSF is a unit impulse response function. In this case we have $a_1(0)=1$, $a_i(0)=0$ for $i=2,\cdots,m$ and the corresponding matrix A in (2) is a unit matrix.

Naturally, Algorithm A can terminate in other reasonable ways. For example, the step 4) can be replaced by one of following operations.

• If $l\geq 2$ and $|\Delta a(l)|>|\Delta a(l-1)|$, then terminate with restored bilevel image $x(l-1)$ and estimated degradation model $a(l-1)$.
• If $l\geq 1$ and $|\Delta x(l)|\leq\epsilon_x$, then terminate with restored bilevel image $x(l)$ and estimated degradation model $a(l)$.

• If $l\geq 1$ and $|\Delta a(l)|\leq\epsilon_a$, then terminate with restored bilevel image $x(l)$ and estimated degradation model $a(l)$.

here $|\Delta a(l)|$ is defined as

$$|\Delta a(l)| = \|a(l)-a(l-1)\|/\|a(l-1)\| \qquad (11)$$

ϵ_x and ϵ_a are small positive values.

III. SIMULATION RESULTS

We take use of Algorithm A to restore original bilevel image from the image degraded by defocusing function without knowing the degradation model. The size of the original bilevel image and the blurred one is 16×16 and n is equal to 256. The shift-invariant function is written as a convolution over a small window taking the form $f(l,k)=(\alpha\beta/\pi)\exp(-\alpha^2 l^2-\beta^2 k^2)$ for $|l|$, $|k|=0,1,\cdots,7$. Little noise is added by quantifying y to 32-bit representation. Many blurred images degraded with different parameters α and β are used to test the Algorithm A. The results are much better than expected. In the paper we present a typical one of the tests.

In the typical test $\alpha=0.95$ and $\beta=1.00$ are chosen. We chose $m=49$, that is to assume the nonzero range of original degradation function is a 7×7 square. Fig.5 and Fig.6 show the original bilevel image and the blurred multi-level image, respectively.

The performance of Algorithm A with respect to the iteration number is described in Fig.1 and Fig.2. In Fig.1 $|\Delta a'(l)|$ is defined as

$$|\Delta a'(l)| = \|a(l)-a\|/\|a\| \qquad (12)$$

here a is the precise (original) degradation model.

In Fig.2 $|\Delta x'(l)|$ is the number of different pixels between $x(l)$ and the original bilevel image defined as

$$|\Delta x'(l)| = \|x(l)-x\| \qquad (13)$$

here x denotes the original bilevel image. To measure the quality of restored image the signal to noise ratio (SNR) is computed using

$$SNR=20\log_{10}[(n-|\Delta x'(l)|)/|\Delta x'(l)|] \qquad (14)$$

The dashed line in Fig.2 denotes the quality of restored bilevel image using precise degradation parameters. Any point below it represents a higher quality of restored image.

According to the step 4) in Algorithm A, the networks stop at the 4th iteration with the restored image $x(3)$ and degradation model $a(3)$. The blindly restored bilevel image $x(3)$ is shown in Fig.8 and the restored bilevel image using precise degradation parameters is shown in Fig.7 (which is restored by Algorithm 2 alone). Due to Fig.2 the SNR of the both restored images is 27.82 db. The precise and estimated degradation parameters are shown in Fig.3 and Fig.4, respectively. The relative difference between them are $|\Delta a'(3)| = 0.162077$. The result is amazing good.

Both Fig.1 and Fig.2 show that some regularities exist in the operation of Algorithm A. In the first few iterations $|\Delta a'(l)|$ monotonously decreases, then increases a little and finally reaches small values forever. The quality of the restored image reaches a high level in the first few iterations, then becomes little worse with corresponding to the slightly worse estimated degradation model and finally achieves high levels which are almost the same as that of restored image using precise degradation model. These regularities are verified by a lot of experiments with different α and β.

We should emphasize that if we substitute Algorithm 1 for Algorithm 2 in Algorithm A, the results become very bad and it is difficult to find any useful regularities in the operation of Algorithm A. The only difference between Algorithm 1 and Algorithm 2 is that the EHE criterion is used in Algorithm 2 for choice of neuron to be updated at each step. This fact shows once more that with the EHE criterion the modified Hopfield neural network can update more efficiently and rationally.

IV. CONCLUSIONS

The blind bilevel image restoration using two kinds of Hopfield neural networks are proposed in the paper. The two Hopfield neural networks operate alternatively. One is used to estimate the degradation model and the other is used to restore bilevel image. Simulation experiments show amazing good results. The quality of blindly restored image is almost the same as that restored by precisely given degradation model. The results also show the efficiency of the EHE criterion.

REFERENCES

[1] J. K. Paik and A. K. Katsaggelos, "Image restoration using a modified Hopfield network", *IEEE Trans. on Image Processing*, Vol.1, No.1, pp.49-63, Jan. 1992.

[2] Y. Sun and S.-Y. Yu, "A modified Hopfield neural network used in bilevel image restoration and reconstruction", *International Symposium on Information Theory and its Application*, ISITA'92 Singapore.

[3] Y. Sun, "A Hopfield-like neural network used in bilevel image restoration and reconstruction", technical research report of Institute of Image Processing and Pattern Recognition of Shanghai Jiao Tong University in August 1991 (in Chinese).

[4] S.-Y. Yu and Y. Sun, "A new algorithm for bilevel section reconstruction and its neural network implementation", *Journal of Automation* (in Chinese), in press.

[5] Y. Sun and S.-Y. Yu, "An eliminating highest error criterion in Hopfield neural network for bilevel image restoration", *International Symposium on Information Theory and its Application*, ISITA'92 Singapore.

[6] Y. Sun and S.-Y. Yu, "An eliminating highest error (EHE) criterion in Hopfield neural networks for bilevel image restoration", *Pattern Recognition Letters*, in press.

[7] K.-Q. Gao, M. O. Ahmad and M. N. S. Swamy, "A Neural network least-square estimator", *IEEE Int. Joint Conf. on Neural Networks*, San Diego, 1990, Vol.3, pp.805-810.

[8] J.J. Hopfield, "Neural networks and physical systems with emergent collective computational abilities", in *Proc. Nat. Acad. Sci. USA*, Vol.79, Apr. 1982, pp.2554-2558.

[9] G. Demoment, "Image reconstruction and restoration: overview of common estimation structures and problems", *IEEE Trans. Acoust., Speech, Signal Processing*, Vol. 3, No.12, pp.2024-2036, Dec. 1989.

[10] T. Pavlidis, J. Swartz and Y. P. Wang, "Fundamentals of bar information theory", *IEEE Computer*, pp.74-86,1990.

[11] J. S. Chen and G. Medioni, "Detection, localization and estimation of edges", *IEEE Trans. on PAMI*, vol.11, pp.191-198, 1989.

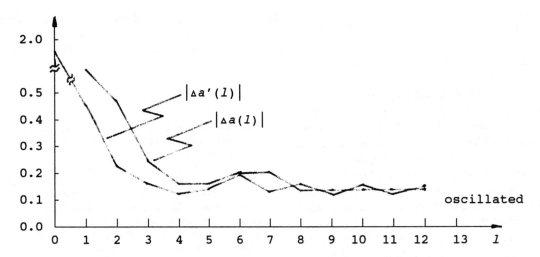

Fig.1. Difference between degradation parameters estimated in successive iterations
and between original image and the estimated one at each iteration.

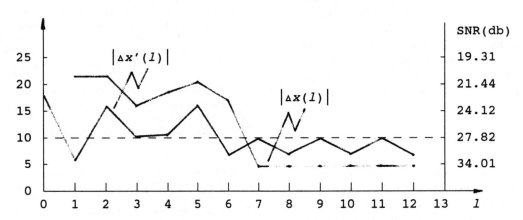

Fig.2. Difference of images restored in two successive iterations and
signal to noise ratio of the image restored at each iteration.

```
0.0000    0.0000    0.0000    0.0000    0.0000    0.0000    0.0000
0.0000    0.0001    0.0030    0.0081    0.0030    0.0001    0.0000
0.0000    0.0022    0.0451    0.1226    0.0451    0.0022    0.0000
0.0000    0.0055    0.1112    0.3023    0.1112    0.0055    0.0000
0.0000    0.0022    0.0451    0.1226    0.0451    0.0022    0.0000
0.0000    0.0001    0.0030    0.0081    0.0030    0.0001    0.0000
0.0000    0.0000    0.0000    0.0000    0.0000    0.0000    0.0000
```

Fig.3. Parameters of original degradation.

```
 0.0072   -0.0024    0.0071    0.0160    0.0038    0.0084    0.0132
 0.0172   -0.0002    0.0014    0.0073    0.0008    0.0022   -0.0061
 0.0101    0.0028    0.0498    0.1267    0.0448    0.0024   -0.0040
-0.0021   -0.0084    0.0976    0.2668    0.1152   -0.0038   -0.0153
-0.0004    0.0019    0.0602    0.1350    0.0583    0.0009    0.0021
-0.0031   -0.0049   -0.0004    0.0088    0.0103    0.0008   -0.0013
 0.0027   -0.0003    0.0015    0.0030   -0.0162   -0.0025    0.0016
```

Fig.4. Parameters of estimated degradation in iteration 3.

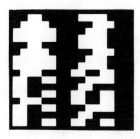

Fig.5. Original bilevel image.

Fig.6. Blurred image.

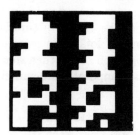

Fig.7. Restored image using precise degradation
parameters, SNR=27.82 db.

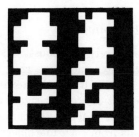

Fig.8. Blindly restored image, SNR=27.82 db
which is the same as that in Fig.7.

Detection of Tonals in Lofargrams Using Connectionist Methods

D.M. Weber and C.C. Krüger *
Department of Electrical and Electronic Engineering
University of Stellenbosch, Stellenbosch 7600, South Africa
Email: weber@firga.sun.ac.za

Abstract— **A method for enhancing and detecting tonals detected by passive sonar systems is presented. The detection process is performed in the frequency domain using contour enhancing neural networks for preprocessing and multi-layer perceptrons for the actual detection. This method enables reliable detection of tonals at a signal to noise ratio of -17dB with an accuracy of 95%. The accurate detection of tonals results in a reduction of information to be processed by higher level classification procedures.**

I. Introduction

Passive sonar applications rely on acoustic signals radiated from a particular source such as a ship to extract information about the source. It has the advantage that all vessels radiate some sort of acoustic signal as a result of any engines, turbines etc. that may be running on the vessel [1],[4]. The signals from such machinery are characterized by a number of fundamental frequencies and a related harmonics in the spectrum of the signal. These harmonics are known as tonals. These are usually unique to the type of vessel and can be used to extract information about the vessel. Traditionally, the sonar signal is represented as a lofargram (**LO**w **F**requency **A**nalysis and **R**ecording) which is a time/frequency representation similar to a traditional speech spectrogram (Fig. 1). In this representation, the tonals appear as vertical lines. The human eye is able to see very faint lines in a lofargram in spite of any noise present. The eye is capable of resolving a tonal that is 20dB smaller than the noise floor in the sonar signal by "integrating" the tonal over time by using the lofargram representation. The methods presented here are designed to reduce the information present in the lofargram to a binary indication of the presence of a tonal or not. This information is then passed on to a higher level for further analysis and preprocessing.

*The authors wish to thank the Institute for Maritime Technology for their support for this research

Traditional sinusoid detection algorithms such as MU-SIC are in general not suited to this application for a number of reasons. These techniques have high computational complexity and require reasonable signal to noise ratios to function effectively. The method presented here can easily be carried out in real time using modest computing equipment. The very high frequency resolution offered by these methods is not required for this application. Linear filtering could be used instead. This would be implemented by averaging a suitably weighted history of power spectra and a binary decision could then be implemented using simple thresholds. There are some drawbacks to such approaches, particularly in the choice of thresholds. The detection of tonals from the lofargram representation an exercise in pattern recognition rather than sinusoid detection due to the dynamic temporal characteristics of these signals.

II. Preprocessing

In order to generate a lofargram, the sonar signal is sampled at 1024Hz and broken up into segments of 1024 samples. This data is used to compute the short term power spectrum using the FFT. The resulting information is then plotted horizontally on the lofargram using grey scales or binary dithering. Successive power spectra are plotted in a waterfall so that a history of spectra over time is build up and displayed, the most recent power spectrum being represented at the bottom of the lofargram. A block diagram of the process is shown in Fig 2.

III. Tonal Detection

In this section, four methods to detect the tonal lines that appear in lofargrams using connectionist techniques, is presented. These methods all exploit the temporal information available from the lofargram representation, so as to emulate the integration and detection capabilities of the eye in detecting tonals.

1. **Graph Theory**: This method was investigated so that comparisons could be made between exist-

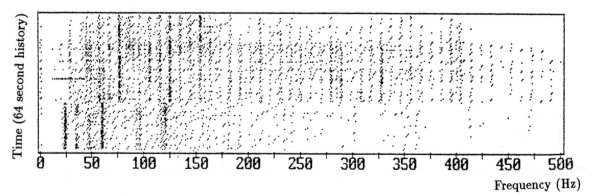

Figure 1: Lofargram display for a typical passive sonar signal.

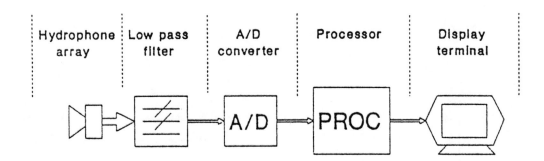

Figure 2: Block diagram of a typical passive sonar setup.

ing approaches and the connectionist approach described here. The implementation is based on [3] and [6]. Only the results of this will be shown here.

2. **Multi-layer Perceptrons**: In this approach, an MLP [5] was trained to detect tonals or lines in a small window. This window was then scanned over the lofargram, allowing the MLP to tonals. This is discussed in section A.

3. **Contour Enhancement**: Contour enhancing neural networks as described in [2] and [7] were employed to enhance and integrate tonals while simultaneously suppressing the noise between tonals. This method is presented in section B.

4. **Hybrid**: Here, contour enhancement is used to preprocess the tonal data and MLP's are used to do the actual detection. This proved to be the most successful method.

A. MLP Tonal Detection

This application made use of a standard 3 layer MLP trained using the back propagation algorithm. The input layers were arranged in a 9×5 window, which was

scanned along the frequency axis of the lofargram, pixel for pixel. The MLP had two neurons in the output layer to indicate the presence or non presence of a tonal and was then trained to recognize vertical lines in a noise background. This configuration allowed the MLP to "see" the previous 5 power spectra at a particular frequency as well as the spectral information in adjacent frequency bins.

Fig. 3 shows tonal detection using an MLP.

B. Contour Enhancing Networks

Contour enhancing neural networks as described in [2] have many useful properties. The basic network structure is given in (1) and illustrated in Fig. 4.

$$\dot{x}_i = -x_i \left[A + \sum_{k \neq i} f(x_k) \right] + (B - x_i) \left[f(x_i) + I_i^+ \right] \quad (1)$$

Here, x_i is the activation of the ith neuron. I_i^+ is the input to the ith neuron in the network. $f(x_k)$ is an activation function which plays a critical part in the dynamics of the network. In this case, a sigmoid function was used because it provides simultaneous contour enhance-

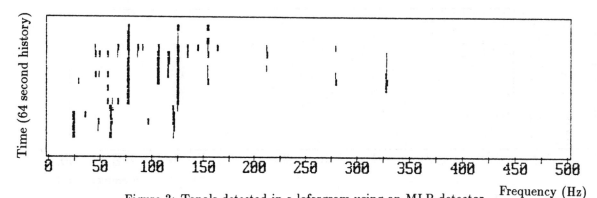

Figure 3: Tonals detected in a lofargram using an MLP detector.

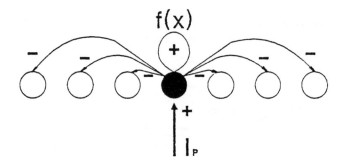

Figure 4: Topology of a contour enhancing network.

Figure 5: Contour enhancement and noise quenching properties [2].

ment, limiting and noise quenching or suppression. The parameters A and B tune the response of the network. Details of the exact network dynamics and the effect of the parameters can be located in [2]. This structure is a competitive, recursive, on-center off-surround, contour enhancing neural network.

In [2], a pattern (power spectrum in this application) is applied to the input of the network and the network is then allowed to converge to some criterion (usually at time infinity) for the same input. In this application however, successive power spectra are applied to the input neurons of the network so that the network is never allowed to converge for a single input as described in [2]. Each input neuron corresponds to a unique frequency bin in the power spectrum. This configuration has the following properties:

- **Contrast Enhancement**: These networks can enhance structures such as tonals in a lofargram while simultaneously suppressing smaller, random structures such as those cause by noise. A tonal appearing at a given frequency/neuron will be enhanced over noise appearing at adjacent frequen-

cies/neurons due to the competition between neurons.

- **Short Term Memory**: STM allows the network to remember previous events. In the case of lofargrams, this STM effectively integrates over the previous power spectra outputs for a given frequency. This effectively smooths the tonal while integrating the effect of the noise away. This is very similar to linear filtering in that the basic neurons are leaky integrators.

- **Adaptation**: Passive sonar signals are time variant. The contour enhancing network is a non-linear structure that allows fast adaptation to the appearance of new tonals as well as adaptation to tonals that change in frequency. The network handles multiple tonals with no difficulty.

- **Signal Strength Independence**: The effective threshold implemented by this network is independent of the strength of the signal.

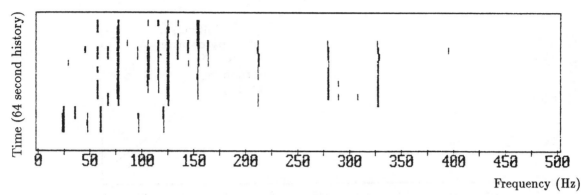

Figure 6: Detection of tonals using a hybrid detection scheme.

Experiments with this network have shown that it can enhance a sinusoid 20dB below the noise floor within a very short space of time. This scheme requires some sort of integration to solve the differential equation. In this application, the trapesium rule was found to be effective.

C. Hybrid Scheme

Here, the contour enhancement network was applied to the lofargram data to improve the visibility of the tonals and was then presented to the MLP for detection. This resulted in an improved performance of the system, particularly at high signal to noise ratios. Fig. 6 shows the result.

IV. RESULTS AND CONCLUSION

In order to test the effectiveness of the detection methods proposed, each method was tested for probability of detection as well as the false alarm rate as a function of signal to noise ratio. Passive sonar data are hard to come by and the signal strengths are impossible to determine so these results were obtained using simulated data. The graphs in fig. 7 and 8 show these results.

The hybrid scheme has been found to be an effective means of enhancing lofargrams, particularly if the lofargram serves as input data to some higher level of pattern recognition such as ship recognition. The method has modest computational requirements and could be implemented in real time using a DSP microprocessor. The properties of the contour enhancing network enable the algorithm to function in a variety of conditions, enabling effective binary decisions to be made without resorting to hard thresholds.

REFERENCES

[1] V. M. Albers. *Underwater Acoustics handbook.* University Press, Pennsylvania, 1978.

[2] Stephen Grossberg. Contour enhancement, short-term memory, and constancies in reverberating networks. *Studies in Applied Mathematics*, 52:217–257, 1973.

[3] O. J. Morris, M. J. Lee, and A. G. Constantinides. A unified method for segmentation and edge detection using graph theory. In *Proceedings ICASSP*, pages 2051–2054, Tokyo, 1986.

[4] R. W. B. Stephens. *Underwater Acoustics.* Wiley-Interscience, London, 1970.

[5] J. J. N. van der Merwe. Connectionist networks for phoneme recognition. Master's thesis, University of Stellenbosch, October 1990.

[6] C. R. Walters. An improved passive sonar display technique. In *Undersea Defence Technology: Conference and Exhibition*, pages 337–341, April 1991.

[7] D. M. Weber. Contour enhancing neural networks. *Proceedings of the First South African Workshop on Pattern Recognition*, pages 94–103, 1990.

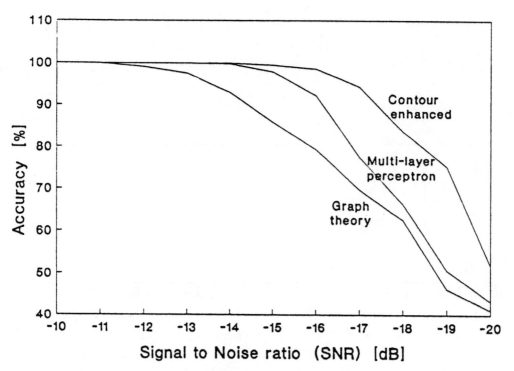

Figure 7: Accuracy of detection vs. signal to noise ratio for the tonal detection schemes. Note that the graph marked "Contour enhanced" is the result for the hybrid scheme.

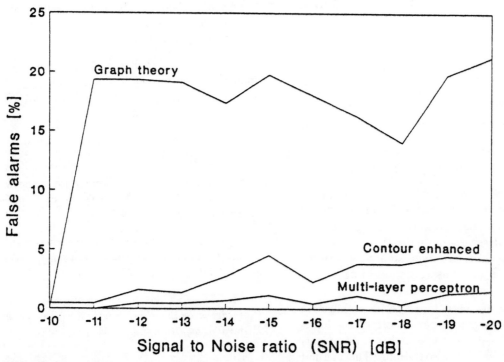

Figure 8: False alarm performance vs. signal to noise ratio for the tonal detection schemes. Note that the graph marked "Contour enhanced" is the result for the hybrid scheme.

An Application of Neural Networks in Adaptive Information Retrieval

S.K.M. Wong   **Y.J. Cai**

Department of Computer Science, University of Regina
Regina, Saskatchewan, Canada S4S 0A2

Y.Y. Yao

Department of Mathematical Sciences, Lakehead University
Thunder Bay, Ontario, Canada P7B 5E1

Abstract

This paper shows how a neural network can be used in the design of an adaptive information retrieval system. In particular, a two-layer neural network is used to implement a linear retrieval system; a three-layer neural network is used to implement a bilinear retrieval system. The results of this preliminary investigation strongly suggest that neural networks are useful tools for developing adaptive information retrieval systems.

I. INTRODUCTION

In a typical information retrieval environment, there exist a group of users and a set of *documents*. An information retrieval system is designed with the objective of providing, in response to a user query, documents that will contain the information desired by the user. More specifically, the system ranks the document representatives (surrogates) so that the user will obtain the required information by reading those documents being ranked at the top.

In information retrieval, one can represent documents and queries by vectors in a vector space [8].

This requires the application of an automatic or manual indexing procedure to identify from the individual text the keywords (index terms) and their occurrence frequencies, from which the document vector is constructed. Similarly, we can construct a vector to represent the query. In addition to the difficult task of indexing, one has to introduce an appropriate function to rank the document vectors according to the user's preference.

It is important to design a retrieval system with a learning capability in order to take advantage of the user's feedback. There are two kinds of adaptive models. In the single-query feedback method, the query vector is constructed by inductive learning [6, 10]. The multi-query feedback method, on the other hand, is designed to learn the term-association matrix [4, 5]. Although these methods have produced encouraging results [8], it remains necessary to develop a systematic method for estimating the required parameters.

In our preliminary work [10], we analyzed only the single-query feedback. In this study, we want to establish a common framework for both the single-query and multi-query feedback processes. First, we will show that the single-query feedback can be understood in term of a two-layer neural network, whereas the multi-query feedback can be implemented by a three-layer neural network with a linear threshold function [9]. We will demonstrate that the learning algorithms in neural networks provide effective methods for constructing suitable ranking functions.

II. ADAPTIVE INFORMATION RETRIEVAL SYSTEMS

Given a set of documents D, a user *preference* can be defined by a binary relation $\succ$ on D [10] as:

$$d \succ d' \text{ if the user prefers } d \text{ to } d'. \tag{1}$$

The preference relation $\succ$ describes the user's judgments on the usefulness of the documents. Suppose each document $d \in D$ is represented by a vector $\mathbf{d} = (d_1, d_2, ..., d_n)$ in a n-dimensional vector space V^n, namely:

$$\mathbf{d} = \sum_{i=1}^{n} d_i \mathbf{t}_i \tag{2}$$

where $\mathbf{t}_i$ is a *document term* vector. The set of vectors $\{\mathbf{t}_1, \mathbf{t}_2, ..., \mathbf{t}_n\}$ is assumed to be a basis of the vector space V^n. The relation $\succ$ on D can be mapped to a relation on the set $\mathbf{D}$ of document vectors. For convenience, we will denote the relation on $\mathbf{D}$ by the same symbol $\succ$.

It is clear that if documents are to be ranked in a manner beneficial to the user, the ranking should faithfully reflect the user's preference relation. Therefore, the primary objective of an information retrieval system is to find an *order-preserving* function f on $\mathbf{D}$, satisfying the following condition: for $\mathbf{d}, \mathbf{d}' \in \mathbf{D}$,

$$\mathbf{d} \succ \mathbf{d}' \implies f(\mathbf{d}) > f(\mathbf{d}'). \tag{3}$$

This condition is equivalent to:

$$f(\mathbf{d}') \geq f(\mathbf{d}) \implies \neg(\mathbf{d} \succ \mathbf{d}'). \tag{4}$$

That is, a function obeying condition (3) ensures that the less preferred documents will not be ranked ahead of the preferred. Such a function f is called an *acceptable* ranking function.

Let $\mathbf{q} = (q_1, q_2, ..., q_n)$ denote a query vector in V^n, namely:

$$\mathbf{q} = \sum_{j=1}^{n} q_j \mathbf{s}_j, \tag{5}$$

where $\mathbf{s}_j$ is a *query term* vector. Likewise, the set $\{\mathbf{s}_1, \mathbf{s}_2, ..., \mathbf{s}_n\}$ is assumed to be a basis of the vector space V^n. In the adaptive linear model for single-query feedback [10], the ranking function f is chosen to be: for all $\mathbf{d} \in \mathbf{D}$,

$$
\begin{aligned}
f(\mathbf{d}) &= \mathbf{d} \cdot \mathbf{q} = \sum_{i,j} d_i q_j \mathbf{t}_i \cdot \mathbf{s}_j \\
&= \sum_{i=1}^{n} d_i \left(\sum_{j=1}^{n} q_j \mathbf{t}_i \cdot \mathbf{s}_j \right) = \sum_{i=1}^{n} d_i w_i, \quad (6)
\end{aligned}
$$

where $w_i = \sum_{j=1}^{n} q_j \mathbf{t}_i \cdot \mathbf{s}_j$ and $\mathbf{t}_i \cdot \mathbf{s}_j$ denotes a scalar product. According to the acceptable ranking criterion (3), the task is to construct a *solution* row matrix $\mathbf{w} = (w_1, w_2, ..., w_n)$ such that for any $\mathbf{d}, \mathbf{d}' \in \mathbf{D}$,

$$\mathbf{d} \succ \mathbf{d}' \implies \mathbf{d}\mathbf{w}^{\mathrm{T}} > \mathbf{d}'\mathbf{w}^{\mathrm{T}}, \tag{7}$$

where $\mathbf{w}^{\mathrm{T}}$ denotes the transpose of $\mathbf{w}$. Of course, the *complete* preference relation is not known *a priori* unless the user has read all the documents. In practice, we may assume that the user is able to express his preference judgments on some document pairs. The problem is then reduced to constructing the matrix $\mathbf{w}$ from the preference information on a sample set of documents.

Let $\mathbf{Q}$ denote a set of query vectors. For multiple queries, the user preference can be defined by a binary relation $\succ$ on $\mathbf{D} \times \mathbf{Q}$ as follows:

$$
\begin{aligned}
(\mathbf{d}, \mathbf{q}) \succ (\mathbf{d}', \mathbf{q}) \iff \quad &\text{the user prefers } \mathbf{d} \text{ to } \mathbf{d}' \\
&\text{with respect to query } \mathbf{q}. \quad (8)
\end{aligned}
$$

We may use the following ranking function:

$$
\begin{aligned}
g(\mathbf{d}, \mathbf{q}) &= \mathbf{d} \cdot \mathbf{q} = \sum_{i,j} d_i q_j \mathbf{t}_i \cdot \mathbf{s}_j \\
&= \sum_{i=1}^{n} \sum_{j=1}^{m} d_i a_{ij} q_j = \mathbf{d}\mathbf{A}\mathbf{q}^{\mathrm{T}} \quad (9)
\end{aligned}
$$

where $a_{ij} = \mathbf{t}_i \cdot \mathbf{s}_j$ measures the strength of association between document term t_i and query term s_j, and $\mathbf{A} = (a_{ij})$ is therefore called the *term-association matrix*. Then, the task in multi-query feedback is to construct a term-association matrix $\mathbf{A}$ such that for any two document-query pairs $(\mathbf{d}, \mathbf{q}), (\mathbf{d}', \mathbf{q}) \in \mathbf{D} \times \mathbf{Q}$,

$$(\mathbf{d}, \mathbf{q}) \succ (\mathbf{d}', \mathbf{q}) \implies g(\mathbf{d}, \mathbf{q}) > g(\mathbf{d}', \mathbf{q})$$
$$\iff \mathbf{d}\mathbf{A}\mathbf{q}^{\mathrm{T}} > \mathbf{d}'\mathbf{A}\mathbf{q}^{\mathrm{T}}. \quad (10)$$

This term-association matrix can be learned from the user's preference judgments on a sample set of document-query pairs.

In the next section, we will show how the feedback problems can be solved by the neural network learning algorithms.

III. NEURAL NETWORKS FOR RELEVANCE FEEDBACK

In information retrieval, the primary objective is to rank the documents according to the user's preference rather than to classify them. We therefore have to modify the standard neural network learning algorithms for the purpose of ranking [1, 2, 7].

A. The single-query feedback

The single-query feedback can be modeled by a two-layer neural network. Each document term forms one node in the input layer. Given a document vector $\mathbf{d} = (d_1, d_2, \ldots, d_n)$ as input, the network produces a weighted sum, $\sum_i d_i w_i$, as its output. We call $\mathbf{w} = (w_1, w_2, \ldots, w_n)$ a *solution* matrix. This means that the two-layer network generates an ordered list of documents by a linear ranking function.

Consider two document vectors $\mathbf{d}$ and $\mathbf{d}'$ with $\mathbf{d} \succ \mathbf{d}'$. We say that the neural network correctly ranks the two documents if $\mathbf{d}\mathbf{w}^{\mathrm{T}} > \mathbf{d}'\mathbf{w}^{\mathrm{T}}$; otherwise, an error occurs. This error can be corrected by adding $\mathbf{d}$ to $\mathbf{q}$ and subtracting $\mathbf{d}'$ from $\mathbf{q}$. The following modified learning algorithm can be used to construct a solution matrix [10]:

Algorithm FIND-SOLUTION-MATRIX

(i)   Choose an initial $\mathbf{w}_0$ and let $k = 0$;

(ii)   Let $\mathbf{w}_k$ be the row matrix in the $(k+1)$th iteration; identify the set of incorrectly

ranked document vectors:

$$\Gamma(\mathbf{w}_k) = \{(\mathbf{d}, \mathbf{d}') \mid \mathbf{d}\mathbf{w}_k^{\mathrm{T}} \le \mathbf{d}'\mathbf{w}_k^{\mathrm{T}}\}; \quad (11)$$

If $\Gamma(\mathbf{w}_k) = \emptyset$, terminate the procedure;

(iii) Let

$$\mathbf{w}_{k+1} = \mathbf{w}_k + \sum_{(\mathbf{d}, \mathbf{d}') \in \Gamma(\mathbf{w}_k)} (\mathbf{d} - \mathbf{d}'); \quad (12)$$

(iv)   Let $k = k + 1$; go back to step (ii);

It can be proved that this procedure converges to a solution matrix satisfying equation (7) in a finite number of steps, provided that such a solution exists. Thus, this learning algorithm provides a systematic method for finding a solution to the single-query feedback problem.

B. The multi-query feedback

Here we suggest to use a three-layer neural network to implement the multi-query feedback. We use a linear threshold function $f = \alpha x$ in all layers [9], where α is a scaling factor that regulates the magnification of the processing element's activity x. Figure 1 shows the configuration of such a network. Document vectors are the input to the network. The nodes in the input layer represent the document terms. The nodes in the hidden layer are query terms. The weight a_{ij} between document term t_i and query term s_j represents the degree of their association. Since the value q_j represents the importance of term s_j in a query, it is used as the scaling factor. The output layer consists of only one node, which pools the input from all the query terms. For this neural network, we set the weights of all its input to 1. More precisely, we have:

Input layer: Given the input vector $(d_1, d_2, \ldots, d_n)$ with the scaling factor $\alpha^{(1)}$ and all connection weights $\beta_i^{(1)}$ being equal to 1, the activation of node t_i is:

$$g_i^{(1)} = \alpha^{(1)} d_i \beta_i^{(1)} = d_i.$$

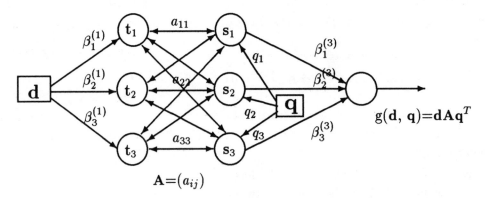

Figure 1: A Multi-Query Feedback Network Configuration

Hidden layer: With $g_i^{(1)}$ $(i = 1, 2, ..., n)$ as input, the activation of the node associated with query term s_j is:

$$g_j^{(2)} = \alpha_j^{(2)} \sum_i g_i^{(1)} a_{ij}$$
$$= q_j \sum_i d_i a_{ij} = \sum_i d_i a_{ij} q_j,$$

where a_{ij} is the strength of association between document term t_i and query term s_j, and $\alpha_j^{(2)} = q_j$.

Output layer: With $g_j^{(2)}$ $(j = 1, 2, ..., n)$ as input, the output is:

$$g = \alpha^{(3)} \sum_j g_j^{(2)} \beta_j^{(3)}$$
$$= \sum_j \sum_i d_i a_{ij} q_j = \mathbf{d}\mathbf{A}\mathbf{q}^{\mathrm{T}},$$

where all the input weights $\beta_j^{(3)}$ and scaling factor $\alpha^{(3)}$ are equal to 1.

The network configuration as shown in Figure 1 is similar to the Gamba perceptron [3] except that a) we use a linear threshold function instead of a step threshold function, and b) the weights of the input and output layers in this neural network are fixed. This makes the task of training the network much easier, because only the weights of the neural network in the hidden layer are adjustable. We suggest the following algorithm to construct a term-association matrix.

Algorithm FIND-ASSOCIATION-MATRIX

(i) Choose an initial matrix $\mathbf{A}_0$ and let $k = 0$;

(ii) Let $\mathbf{A}_k$ be the matrix in the $(k + 1)$th; iterationidentify the set of incorrectly ranked pairs :
$$\Gamma(\mathbf{A}_k) = \{[(\mathbf{d}, \mathbf{q}), (\mathbf{d}', \mathbf{q})] \mid \mathbf{d}\mathbf{A}_k\mathbf{q}^{\mathrm{T}} \le \mathbf{d}'\mathbf{A}_k\mathbf{q}^{\mathrm{T}}\};$$
If $\Gamma(\mathbf{A}_k) = \emptyset$, terminate the procedure;

(iii) Let
$$\mathbf{A}_{k+1} = \mathbf{A}_k + \left[\sum_{[(\mathbf{d},\mathbf{q}),(\mathbf{d}',\mathbf{q})] \in \Gamma(\mathbf{A}_k)} (\mathbf{d} - \mathbf{d}') \right]^{\mathrm{T}} \mathbf{q} ;$$

(iv) Let $k = k + 1$; go back to step (ii);

One can show that this procedure converges to a term-association matrix satisfying equation (10) in a finite number of steps, provided that such a matrix exists.

We performed experiments on a number of document collections to test the effectiveness of the learning algorithms. The experimental results indicate that our approach compares favorably with the other feedback methods [4, 5].

IV. CONCLUSION

In this paper, we have shown how the problem of adaptive information retrieval can be transformed into a problem of learning in a neural network. In particular, we have demonstrated that a two-layer neural network is an effective tool to implement a linear adaptive retrieval system. Likewise, we can use a three-layer neural network to implement a bilinear adaptive retrieval system. More importantly, this preliminary investigation suggests that a neural network provides a sound basis for designing an adaptive information retrieval system.

Although our discussion here focuses on information retrieval, the proposed approach can be used to design other decision support systems in which the primary objective is to rank decision alternatives.

REFERENCES

[1] M. A. Arbib, Brains, *Machines, and Mathematics*, New York: Springer-Verley, 1988.

[2] R. O. Duda and P. E. Hart, *Pattern Classification And Scene Analysis*, New York: Wiley, 1973.

[3] M. Minsky and S. Papert, *Perceptrons – An Introduction to Computational Geometry*, extended edition, Massachusetts: MIT Press, 1988.

[4] V. V. Raghavan and G. S. Jung, A machine learning approach to automatic pseudo-thesaurus construction. *Proceeding of the 4th International Symposium on Methodologies for Intelligent Systems: Poster Session Program*, 111-121, 1989.

[5] V. V. Raghavan and C. T. Yu, Experiments on the determination of the relationships between terms. *ACM Transactions on Database Systems, 4*, 240-260, 1979.

[6] J. J. Jr. Rocchio, Relevance Feedback in Information Retrieval. In Salton, G. (ed.), *The SMART Retrieval System — Experiments in Automatic Document Processing*, Englewood Cliffs, NJ: Prentice-Hall, 313-323, 1971.

[7] Rumelhart, McClelland and the PDP Research Group, *Parallel Distributed Processing*, Volume 1: Foundations, The MIT Press, 1986.

[8] G. Salton and M. H. McGill, *Introduction to Modern Information Retrieval*. New York: McGraw-Hill, 1983.

[9] P. K. Simpson, *Artificial Neural Systems - Foundations, Paradigms, Applications, and Implementations*. New York: Pergamon Press, 1990.

[10] S. K. M. Wong and Y. Y. Yao, Query formulation in linear retrieval models, *Journal of the American Society for Information Science, 41*, 334-341, 1990.

SCRIPT - A Prototype
for the Recognition of continuous, cursive, handwritten Input
by means of a Neural Network Simulator

Dr.Bettina Harriehausen-Mühlbauer
Andreas Koop
IBM Germany, Science Center
P.O. Box 10 30 68
6900 Heidelberg, Germany

Abstract--This paper describes SCRIPT, a prototype for the recognition of continuous handwriting, where the recognition is independent from the size and resolution of the handwritten input. The system has presently stored (learned) different handwritings, but individual customization, i.e. learning of a new handwriting, is possible anytime. SCRIPT is a modular system, which uses several neural nets as well as a fuzzy logic component. The system is designed so that different types of input, e.g. scanned handwriting as well as input via a pen-computer, is possible. For reasons of testing, input via scanned images have been chosen.

INTRODUCTION

Most systems developed for the recognition of handwritten input use additional data, like the speed of writing, positions and number of strokes which build up the handwriting, and the sequential order of those lines, on top of the information about the image, which is provided in form of a pixel-graphic in this case. Nevertheless, such additional information is not given to the big ideal of all systems designed for the recognition of handwritten input - the human eye and brain. For this reason, we omit such information as well and rather substitute it partly by linguistic knowledge, which enables the recognition of unclear handwriting, just as it is done in many "human" cases.

Rather simple algorithms are implemented in this system in order to guarantee a high processing speed. SCRIPT is implemented on an IBM RS6000 workstation, running under AIX 3.2. The neural netwok simulator SNNS (=Stuttgart Neural Network Simulator) [1] used in this System shortened the time of development for the entire system tremendously.

This paper will describe the individual modules of this system in the order of processing; from the input data to the ASCII-code. A survey can be found in Fig. 3.

A. Inputting the Image

For technical reasons, an IBM 3119 scanner with a resolution of 75-300 dpi has been used as the interface to the input. In order to avoid difficulties with unsatisfactorily scanned images, the scanning is done in black/white, and a pen with an unchanging width of the stroke has been used.

Furthermore, the lines of the handwritten input have to be at least 1 pixel + X apart, where X is the maximum distance of two clusters that can be put together, e.g. to build an "i". The images with the handwriting are stored in the commonly used TIFF-format on the harddisc of a RS6000 workstation and can individually be loaded into the workspace, where they are present as a NxM matrix (where N=width and M=height of the image) with the maximal size of the DIN A4 format (8 1/2" x 11"). The matrix is built-up dynamically and one element, i.e. one pixel, equals 1 byte - and not 1 bit. Using storage this way is done to gain speed, as all results of the computation of the next module, Image Processing I, can directly be stored in the matrix in form of indexes like: 0= no pixel, 1= "initial pixel", 2-255= pixel with special features, e.g. belongs to a special word, is active. By our definition, we understand an "initial pixel" to be the black pixel from the scanned image, i.e. which represent the writing. Moreover, the choice to follow the individual steps of processing on the screen by using different coloring for the active step is provided this way.

B. Image Processing I

The tasks of this module are:
(a) the clustering of the individual pixel to words and single letters as well as punctuation and special characters,
(b) the ordering of the words in every line, and
(c) the calculation of the distance between the individual words.

(a) The clustering is composed of three steps, the result of which is the exact clusteridentification consisting of 'line' and 'cluster-number':

Step 1: The actual clustering: The algorithm used for the actual clustering can well be described by Fig. 1.

The image is scanned from left to right and top to bottom until the first "initial" pixel is found. This pixel receives a clusternumber between 2 and 255 and the linenumber 1. (We presume that less or equal than 254 clusters are needed per line.) All direct and indirect neighbors receive the same number. For an explanation see Fig. 2. In case no additional neighbors with the initial- pixel-value of 1 are found, the scanning continues until the next pixel with the value 1 is found. The clusternumbers will now be incremented accordingly. When the gap between the lines is reached, e.g.

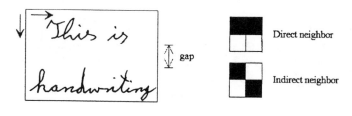

Fig. 1. The algorithm for the actual clustering.   Fig. 2. Neighbors

Direct neighbor

Indirect neighbor

gap

30 pixel wide with a resolution of 75 dpi and a line spacing of 1 cm, the linenumber will be incremented by 1 and the clusternumber will be set back to 2.

Step 2: "Special" symbols, like punctuation and single

strokes This step deals with the identification of dots and single lines, e.g. the dot on top of the 'i', which have so far been considered being separate clusters belonging to a larger cluster (word). Again, the algorithm works from left to right and top to bottom. A cluster A is assigned to another cluster B, i.e. receives the ID of B, when this other cluster B has a different ID from A and is located less than the minimal distance between lines below.

(b) *Step 3:* So far, the clusternumbering, i.e. which letter receives the clusternumber 2, was rather randomly done. Meaning: which word of the line had the smallest y-value, the left upper corner being (0,0). In this step, all the numbers are sorted and the first word of the first line will receive the ID (1,1).

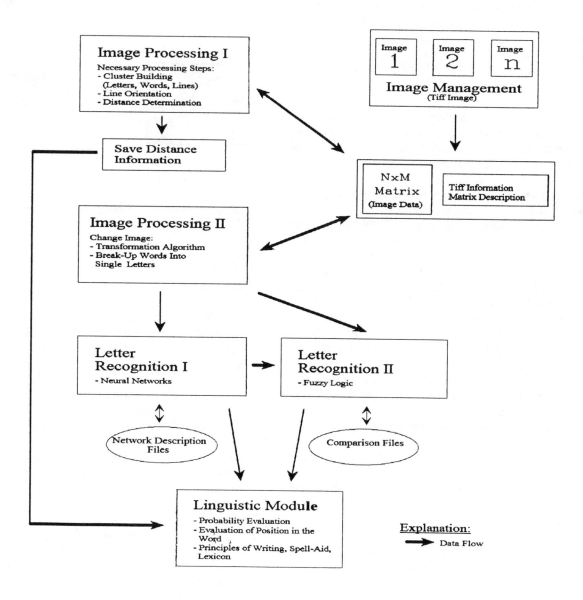

Fig. 3. The modules of SCRIPT with the important datastructures

1673

(c) Computation of the distances:

The distances between the single clusters are the euclidian distances measured in pixel. This information is stored in a special file which is later used by the Linguistic Module in order to determine which single letters should be put together to form words.

C: Image processing II

This module processes the cluster so that it can be sent to the Letter-Recognition-Modules as input for recognition. For this system can recognize size-independent writing, the clusters have to be transformed to a standard size first. Furthermore, this reduction to standard size is important, as the neural nets in this system have a fixed number of input units and the pixel of the transformed area are directly used as input, i.e. 1 pixel equals one input unit. This standard size has been set to 50 units vertically and $z = 50 * (x/y) * s$ horizontally. 's' is an distortion factor. The area from the NxM matrix marked by the smallest/largest x- and y-positions of pixel of one cluster is being processed, shown in Fig. 4.

A side-effect of this transformation is a reduction of information, which will later be important for the processing by the neural net, as this reduction reduces the number of input-units tremendously. For example, an image containing one word, which is 1 cm high and 4 cm long, and which is scanned by 300 dpi, contains approximately 55,800 pixel on this area of 4 cm^2. After the transformation, this same area will only be presented by about 10,000 units. The transformation-algorithm will now be illustrated by means of an extreme example in Fig. 5.

These transformations can be used to reduce or enlarge an area by having a different distortion-factor for the reference-lines horizontally or vertically. A reference-matrix is built-up, where one element has a value between 0 (=blank) and 1 (=black). A threshold has to be defined to decide when a pixel should be painted black in the transformed matrix. As the bordering area only involves 1 pixel (in this case 'marked' or 'left blank'), the difference between (a) and (b) is not of great importance - considering we regard an area of 50 pixel in total length.

As the next step, a cluster has to be segmented into single letters. As no clear criteria exist to determine the end of one letter and the beginning of the next, and, moreover, the system does not know the number of characters the cluster is composed of, we do not follow the approach of 'segmentation AND recognition' at this point, but rather chose 'segmentation BY recognition'.

Three different alternatives for the segmentation of words are possible, but only the first two are implemented in our system:

(a) strictly sequential, from the beginning (left) to the end

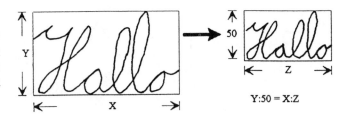

Fig.4: Size of the matrix-area that is processed

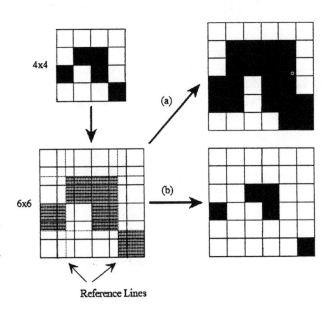

Fig. 5. Enlargement/Reduction of a pixelgraphic to a standard size

(right)

(b) Prominent letters are chosen as the starting point

(c) backwards, from the end to the beginning

For the following reason, we omit option (c): when we look at examples of real handwriting, a lot of times the words get "fuzzier", i.e. the writing gets unclearer, towards the end of the word.

(a) Strictly sequential segmentation: The idea to process a text sequentially resembles the way humans read a text. First, one tries to recognize the first letter, i.e. the first character of a cluster. In case it is recognized, it will be "cut off" and the next letter will be processed. As the input-units of the neural net are of fixed size (present experiments use a 50x50 input-layer), the size of the cluster has to be altered according to the input-layer, which is shown in Fig. 6.

The recognition of the letter 'c' in Fig. 6 is rather difficult, as parts of the letter 'a' appear in the input-area. Now the cluster will be reduced/enlarged with a distortion-factor (here: s > 1) until one letter will be significantly better recognized than another. 'Significant' meaning, that the value of the output-activation of the letter is > 0.5 and the distance between the value of the output-unit from the next

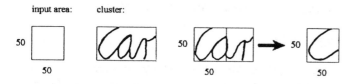

Fig. 6: Adaptation of a cluster to the input layer

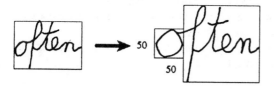

Fig. 7. Transformation on the vertical axis

candidate, i.e. letter, is > 0.2. Once the word 'car'is enlarged, only the letter 'c' appears in the input-area. This method can also be used on the vertical axis: As it is better for the letter 'o' to appear bigger in the input-area in Fig. 7, it will be enlarged to 50x50.

(b) Selection of prominent letters: To segment a word into single letters by means of its prominent features corresponds to the way a trained reader reads a text; he will not only read through the text from left to right, but will recognize words by their overall shape. In case some letters cannot be read easily, they will be added associatively by the brain. In other cases, for instance when reading through a text rather quickly, typos will only be recognized when the eye has moved way past that word, as the shape of the word has been recognized correctly, the rest was associatively added, and it was only realized later, that the addition didn't match reality.

The algorithm works as follows: All large deviations from the vertical centre of the cluster, e.g. a 't' and a 'g' are remarkable among other small letters, will be recognized and the input-unit of the neural net will be put onto their position in the cluster. Again, distortions might be necessary in order to reach the effects described in the previous chapter.

These two processes for the segmentation, (a) and (b), complement one another and their information will be put together in the Linguistic Module.

As we have seen, a very close cooperation between the modules 'Image Processing II' and 'Letter Recognition I' is necessary.

Letter Recognition I

The tasks of this module are the segmentation of the content of the cluster in cooperation with 'Image processing II' and the evaluation of that part of the cluster, which has to be recognized. In case of a recognized character, the Linguistic Module receives the following information:
- cluster ID

- position in the cluster (relative to the total length of the cluster)
- the first 10 possible characters in form of a tripel (ASCII-character, evaluation, type of writing)

The evaluation is directly derived from the output-activations. The type of writing can contain additional information, like 'font', 'name of the user', etc. This will be explained in greater detail in a later chapter about 'learning'.

The "philosophy" behind this module is not geared towards the storage of a lot of information in one single neural net, but rather to have different nets for the most important elements of each type of writing, e.g. a single net for each of the following elements: numbers, capital letters, small letters, and special characters. The advantage of this "philosophy" is that none of the nets will be overloaded, i.e. has learned by heart, but has thereby lost the power to generalize. It is always the same type of net, only with different tasks: numbers in one case, special characters in the other, etc. At this point, we operate with a feed-forward-net with standard-backpropagation, 50 x 50 units as input layer, 2 x 50 units in a hidden-layer, and a number of output-units, the number of which is individually set, i.e. 10 for the number-net, 26 for the capital-letter-net, etc. The different nets are loaded from the hard-disc one after the other and are processed one by one.

At this point in time, the final structure of the net is still undergoing minor alternations, as the use of "sites", Zell in [1], p.12, is still under debate in order to reduce the number of units and links and thereby reaching a gain of processing speed.

Already at this point, not every single input-unit is connected with every hidden layer, as the number of links (2500 x 100 = 250,000) would reach an unacceptable time for processing. A connection-number of 2 x 50 x 50 = 5000 was chosen, so that every line and every column is connected with one hidden-unit:

Regarding this example, the total number of units are 2500 (input) + 100 (hidden) + 10 (output) = 2610, which are connected with 5000 (between input and hidden) + 500 +

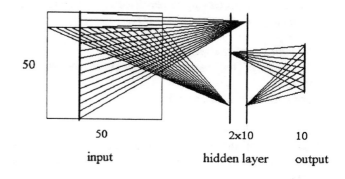

Fig. 8. The structure of the neural net.

1675

500 (both figures: from hidden to output) = 6000 links. Experimenting with nets of such a large size would not be possible without the help of a simulator. The SNNS proved to be an excellent tool for quickly testing the ideas regarding the topology of nets and their relevance for the solution of our problems.

The SNNS is a simulator for neural nets which has been developed at the Institute for Parallel and Distributed High Performance Systems at the University of Stuttgart since 1989. The goal of the efforts of the developers was and still is to create an efficient and flexible simulation environment for research on and application of neural nets.

Once the segmentation of a character is finished, it will be passed on to the Letter Recognition Module II in form of a pixel-graphic in the transformed format, as previously described, for further processing and additional evaluation.

The learning of characters: When dealing with nets of such a large size, learning is still a time-consuming process, even when the system is running on fast computers.

Learning is done the following way: A complete set of characters (numbers, capital letters, small letters, special characters) of a new handwriting will be scanned on one page, with the restriction that the order of the clusters are determined by the system, and thereby no user-input will be necessary anymore. The user only will be requested to provide the information about the new handwriting via the keyboard, e.g. Mr. Miller`s handwriting. The characters are already segmented, will be standardized by the described mechanisms, and will be passed on to the two Letter Recognition Modules as input samples.

Letter Recognition II

This module follows a different approach to store the knowledge about the handwriting. In this module, a comparison-file is built-up by means of parameters, which describe functions on the pixel-graphic. Such functions are, for instance, different forms of regression. It will be shown in the near future, whether this will provide clear features for the distinction of different characters.

Fuzzy logic will be used at that point in the system, when parameter of characters to be classified are compared with the data stored in the comparison-files.

The learning of new characters:
- calculation of the parameter-values from the provided characters
- storing the values/data in a file

The recognition:
- calculation of the parameter-values from the characters that have been segmented by the Letter Recognition Module
- comparison with the present parameter-constellations
- as a result, a tripel (ASCII-character, evaluation, type of writing) is passed on to the Linguistic Module.

Linguistic Module

The Linguistic Module is basically designed to enhance the rate of recognition. It is based on three different components:

(a) it calculates certain positions in the word
(b) principles of writing (vowels - consonants) are used to rank alternative characters
(c) a spell aid algorithm is used to match recogized words with a lexicon

The input provided by the system:
- Data about distances (from Image Processing I) of the form:

Cluster ID 1	Cluster ID 2	Distance
(1,1)	(1,2)	5
(1,2)	(1,3)	7
...	...	...

- The Letter Recognition I module provides different kinds of information (see: chapter on Letter Recognition I module):
  * the cluster ID
  * the position in the cluster (relative to the total length of the cluster)
  * the first 10 alternative characters in forms of tripel (ASCII-character, evaluation/probability-ranking, type of writing)
- 20 tripel of the form: ASCII-character, evaluation, type of writing (from Letter Recognition II module - "Fuzzy Logic", to compare the calculated and stored parameters)

Once certain positions in the word have been calculated and alternative sequences of letters have been recognized and proposed, linguistic information is used to rank the alternatives. First, general principles of writing are used, mostly to rule out certain letter-sequences.

Principles of writing include the following rules (for German):

(1) When 2 "Umlaut"-dots are recognized, the letter beneath these dots has to be 'a', 'o', or 'u'.

(2) When a diminiutive is formed of a double vowel, like in 'Boot-Bötchen' (boat - small boat), the second vowel is omitted, i.e. sequences of "Umlaut-vowel" are unacceptable.

(3) The same consonant never appears 3 times in a row. This is also a rule for the border of compounds, e.g. Schiff (boat) + Fahrt (cruise) forms the compound 'Schiffahrt' and not 'Schifffahrt'.

(4) The sequence 'chs' is rather rare (only about 25 occurences). A more likely sequence for that sound is 'ks'.

(5) In case a 'c' is recognized, it is very likely to be followed by a 'k' or 'h'.

(6) In case the sequence 'sc' is recognized, it is very likely to be followed by a 'h' to form 'sch'.

(7) 'l', 'm', 'n', and 'r' are often preceded by 'h' (so-called "stretching - h").

(8) In word-final position, voiceless consonants ('t', 'k', 'p') follow the letter 's' to form '-st#', '-sk#', and '-sp#'. The voiced counterparts ('d', 'g', 'b') are not accepted in this position. After these general writing rules ruled-out certain alternatives, the proposed words are matched against a full-form lexicon. For reasons of better results, this lexicon is split into a high-frequency part, marking words that appear very often in the language, such as the closed classes of conjunctions, articles, and prepositions, and the rest.

When the proposed word matches a lexical entry, no further processing by the linguistic module will be done, and the proposal will be regarded as correct. In case no match is found in the lexicon for the proposed word, that sequence of letters is passed-on to a so-called "spell-aid" algorithm, which computes 5 alternatives for the input-string. This algorithm works the following way:

(a) It works from low to high priority. This means that letters will be substituted first, which were ranked with a rather low priority by the previous modules; i.e. letters, which could not be recognized or determined very well:

80%	70%	90%	50%
W	a	n	l

In the case of this example, no match was found for the string 'Wanl'. As the previous modules computed the lowest probability rate of 50% for the 'l', that letter will be the first one to be substituted, followed by the 'a', 'W', and 'n'.

(b) It is based on a search for and substitution of similar-looking letters. The alternatives are provided by the Letter Recognition modules, which have previously ranked possible alternatives according to their probability. In case no alternative was provided by the Letter Recognition modules, which might happen when the modules suggest the same letter just with different types of writing, the Linguistic Module call "fall back" on a list of stored similarities, such as 'k-h', 'u-n', 'a-o', etc.

(c) After each substitution of a letter, a new search for a match in the lexicon is started.

Different correct alternatives will be the output. The first 5 are given to the user, ranking them according to their frequence (i.e. whether or not they are marked as being high-frequency words) and their closeness to the original input, i.e. how many letters had to be substituted to find a valid match.

For example, the system recognizes the string "LAndes", for which no match could be found in the lexicon. According to the above principles, the linguistic module will offer the following choices (the first of which is the correct choice): LAndes - Landes, Landest, Ländest, Landser, Langes.

Again, as we are still in the phase of testing, we hesitate to give exact numbers for the rate of correct regognition pre and post the linguistic module. We expect to have clear results by the end of spring 1993.

SUMMARY

This paper gave a detailed description of the different modules of SCRIPT, a prototype for the recognition of cursive, continuous handwriting, which is completely based on pure image-information. We do not attempt to operate without a general linguistic knowledge, as we believe especially this component to be important for reaching acceptable results regarding the rate of recognition. As SCRIPT is still under development, some figures (exact results) are still pending at this point in time.

ACKNOWLEDGMENT

We would like to thank Dr. Andreas Zell and his group at the IPVR for providing the SNNS as a research tool.

BIBLIOGRAPHY

[1] A. Zell et al. SNNS. Stuttgart Neural Network Simulator. User Manual, Version 2.1. Universität Stuttgart, Institute for Parallel and Distributed High Performance Systems. Report No. 8/92.

A Local Neural Implementation of Histogram Equalization

Thomas H. Hildebrandt

Electrical Engineering and Computer Science Department
Room 304 Packard Laboratory   Lehigh University
19 Memorial Drive West   Bethlehem, PA 18015
thildebr@athos.csee.lehigh.edu

Abstract — **Histogram equalization is a technique for optimizing the utilization of quantization levels — typically in connection with the processing of visual images. By modifying the quantization levels in a signal processing system, the output can be conformed to an ideal histogram. If the statistics gathered on the input are limited spatially or temporally, then this modification is governed by the input's context. Here, we advance a generalized version of histogram equalization as a model for contextual processing in neural networks.**

We first review the concept of histogram equalization as applied to image grey scales. We extend this idea to more general types of quantization, including domains in which the statistics are gathered temporally as well as spatially. We then present and analyze an artificial neural circuit which implements generalized histogram equalization. Finally, by noting that the feedback paths in this implementation are local, we relate the elements of our formal circuit to components of a biological neural model. We conclude that histogram equalization is a useful model for short-term adaptation, that it is easily implemented in artificial neural circuitry, and that it is biologically plausible as well.

I. INTRODUCTION

A. Background

As applied to images, histogram equalization involves counting the number of pixels in an image which occupy each possible grey level, and then creating a mapping between these input grey levels and the grey levels actually displayed so that each displayed grey level is used approximately equally[1]. The effect of this mapping is to enhance the contrast of the image by better utilizing the range of grey levels available. Modifications to the target histogram have been proposed to handle the case in which there are large variations in the average grey level across the input image but the variation within a local region is small[2, 3, 4, 5]. A fairly comprehensive review of earlier methods is given in [6].

B. Extension to Temporal Statistics

Similar methods can be applied to sequences of images whose statistics change temporally. In fact, it is an implicit assumption in the above papers that they do so — the equalization mapping is recomputed for each input image. In a neural implementation of histogram equalization, it is unreasonable to expect external information (in the form of a weight set) to be supplied for each image to be processed. It is also reasonable to assume that all the images to be processed will possess similar statistics. We therefore make temporal variations in the histogram explicit, and endow the model with the ability to adapt to them. Specifically, we first consider histogram equalization in which the statistics are gathered in time alone, and then extend this model to gather statistics in spatial dimensions as well.

Most systems which perform histogram equalization do so as an offline, batch process. If we consider a system in which the quantization levels are modified online according to the error between the measured and ideal histograms, then we have described a system which can track changes in the statistics of its input. A block diagram for the system thus described appears in Figure 1(a).

When histogram equalization is thus regarded as a modification of the quantization levels, rather than as a mapping from one quantization of the image to a different one, the method becomes at once more powerful and easier to implement. These improvements come from the fact that by using feedback, one of the quantizers can be eliminated. In addition to reducing the amount of hardware required, removal of the initial quantization allows the final quantization to act directly on the unquantized input. This improves the accuracy of the quantized output. The merging of the initial and final quantizations entails temporal feedback of the difference between the estimated and ideal histograms. The feedback amounts to an adaptive adjustment of the quantization levels, based on the input's context (temporal, spatial, or both). A block diagram of the resulting system model is given in Figure 1(b).

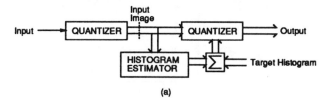

(a)

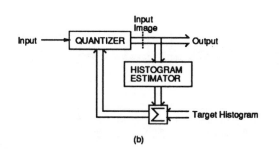

(b)

Figure 1: System models for online histogram equalization: (a) Feedforward, (b) feedback.

C. Extension to Other Features

There is no reason to restrict the scope of histogram equalization to the allocation of grey levels in images. More generally, we may view histogram equalization as a method for modifying the quantization levels applied to an input so that a histogram of the resulting quantization agrees with some pre-specified "ideal" histogram. The level to be quantized can be a feature which has been extracted from less abstract input data, and the fed-back signal can affect the histogram of the output by acting directly on the threshold or sensitivity of the corresponding feature-selecting cell.

D. Organization of this Paper

In the following section, we give a more precise definition of temporal histogram equalization and develop an algorithm to perform it. In Section 3, we give a neural implementation, and justify this by relating

its components to neurochemical processes. In Section 4, we extend our neural model to handle spatial equalization as well.

II. TEMPORAL EQUALIZATION

In this section, we define histogram equalization, and analyze it with the purpose of implementing it within the standard neural model[7]. For the purpose of simplifying the analysis, we assume that the statistics are gathered temporally, i.e. the histogram to be equalized is the frequency of occurrence of each encoding symbol (grey level) with respect to a single input.

A. Definition

Consider a system which produces mutually exclusive symbols $X_1, X_2, \ldots, X_N$, corresponding to the quantization levels in the input image. These symbols occur with instantaneous probabilities $P^t(X_1)$, $P^t(X_2)$, ..., $P^t(X_N)$, respectively, meaning the probability of X_1 at time t, etc. We abbreviate these probabilities as p_1^t, p_2^t, etc., where $p_i^t \in [0,1]$ and $\sum_i p_i^t = 1$. Suppose we are given expected or ideal probabilities $\alpha_1, \alpha_2, \ldots, \alpha_N$, where $\alpha_i \in [0,1]$ and $\sum_i \alpha_i = 1$. Assume that we can control the probability of occurrence of each symbol through the signal γ_i such that

$$p_i^t = \beta_i^t + f_i(\gamma_i^{t-1}) \,, \qquad (1)$$

where $f_i(\cdot)$ is some unknown but monotonically increasing function (i.e. $f_i'(\cdot) > 0$) and β_i^t is the part of the occurrence probability of symbol X_i^t over which we have no control. This β_i^t is assumed to vary slowly, i.e. is for our purposes constant[1]. The goal of histogram equalization is to control the γ_i such that the measured probability estimate $\tilde{p}_i^t$ of each symbol approaches its ideal probability α_i, i.e. $\tilde{p}_i^t \to \alpha_i$.

B. Analysis

In this model, we do not have direct access to the probability p_i^t, so it is necessary to estimate it based on the average frequency of occurrence of the symbol X_i. An estimate for p_i^t can be computed by counting the number of occurrences of the symbol X_i in a set of M samples, and dividing this by M. Immediately, we are faced with a dilemma: If the sample size is large, then accuracy will be high, but the rate at which changes in the statistics of the input are accommodated will be slow; if the sample size is

---

[1]This distinction also gives rise to our notion of context. Samples which are within the current context have similar statistics and may be averaged without losing information. However, the number of samples included in the estimate should be small enough to exclude from the average the systematic variations represented by β_i^t.

small, then the rate at which the estimate adjusts to changes in the input statistics will be high but accuracy will be low. An appropriate sample size can be chosen using standard adaptive quadrature techniques by relating observed trends in the estimate to an approximation of the error. For simplicity, we will assume that an appropriate fixed sample size has been chosen a priori.

A problem with this method is that it requires explicit storage of the $M - 1$ preceding samples. A cheaper method, in terms of storage, is to compute the current estimate as the sum of δ times the current estimate and $1 - \delta$ times the previous estimate. Hence

$$\tilde{p}_i^t = (1 - \delta)\tilde{p}_i^{t-1} + \delta X_i^t \; , \qquad (2)$$

where X_i^t is a Boolean value which represents that event X_i occurred at time t. Here, δ is a parameter which determines how fast the influence of past samples decays, and therefore effectively controls the size of the temporal context. The error in the estimate $\tilde{p}_i^t$ is also determined by the choice of δ, and is given by

$$\epsilon \approx \delta \mathrm{E}\{X_i\}. \qquad (3)$$

Now, assuming that the estimate $\tilde{p}_i^t$ is sufficiently close to p_i^t, we can force the p_i and α_i to converge by changing the γ_i as follows:

$$\Delta \gamma_i^t = \eta_i(\alpha_i - \beta_i^t) \; . \qquad (4)$$

Since $f(\gamma)$ is monotonically increasing, this choice of $\Delta\gamma$ always changes so as to reduce the error between p_i and α_i. To guarantee convergence, the constant of proportionality η_i must be chosen such that the loop gain is less than 2 (again assuming that the p_i and hence the β_i vary sufficiently slowly): $\eta_i f'_{i\max} < 2$ where $f'_{i\max} = \max_\gamma f'_i(\gamma)$. This inequality assumes that $\tilde{p}_i^t$ tracks p_i^t exactly, which is not the case. In fact,

$$\frac{\partial \, \tilde{p}_i^t}{\partial p_i^t} = \delta \qquad (5)$$

on the average, which allows us to choose η to be somewhat larger: $\eta_i < \frac{2}{\delta f'_{i\max}}$.

Based on this analysis, we can construct the signal processing model shown in Figure 2. In the figure, the portion enclosed in the dashed box is inaccessible, meaning that we do not know the values of β_i^t or p_i^t, nor the exact form of $f_i(\cdot)$ or the symbol generator. The complete figure represents the circuitry required for one encoding symbol (grey level), i.e. it corresponds to one bin in the histogram. In the following section, we relate this system to the components of an artificial neural model.

III. NEURAL IMPLEMENTATION

A. The ANN Model

Given the above formulation, the implementation of histogram equalization in artificial neural hardware is a direct mapping from the signal processing system shown above. Refer to Figure 3, which represents a system involving four mutually exclusive encodings for a particular input.

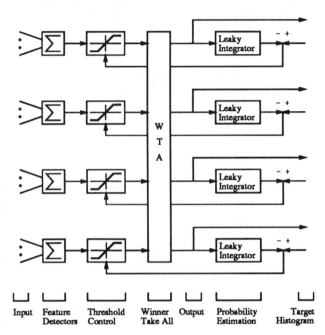

Figure 3: Neural system overview.

The input stage consists of a feedforward neural network which detects a number of features from the input. Each feature corresponds to one of the possible input symbols X_i. The output of this stage passes through a set of threshold circuits which are controlled by feedback signals. Lateral inhibition or a winner-take-all network is applied to the output of this layer, so that a unique output symbol is chosen at the end of each clock interval. This output of this winner-take-all (WTA) network is also the output of the circuit; the remaining components are involved with the generation of the signal fed back to each threshold unit.

The probability of occurrence of each symbol is estimated using a running sum or "leaky integrator" as given by equation (2). This function is easily implemented in neural hardware using a single input weighted by δ and an input weighted by $(1 - \delta)$ fed back from its output. We assume a synchronous ANN model, so that the feedback delay Δ has a precise definition, namely one complete update.

Feedback signals used to adjust the frequency of

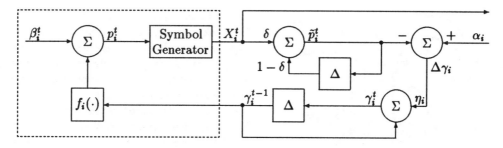

Figure 2: Signal processing model (per symbol).

occurrence of each symbol are generated by comparison of the probability estimates $\tilde{p}_i^t$ with the fixed reference levels α_i. The difference is fed back in order to adjust the threshold of the corresponding feature extracting cell prior to the application of lateral inhibition or WTA.

In the neural system, the function $f_i(\cdot)$ and signal generator have been replaced by a feature detecting cell and a threshold unit, respectively. In Figure 2, the generation of the true symbol probability p_i^t is only hypothetical. However, by controlling the threshold level of the corresponding neuron, we can raise or lower the likelihood that a randomly selected input will cause a particular neuron's output to reach the far side of the WTA network. Thus, we can model the boxed portion of that figure with these two components. In the neural implementation, the restriction that the symbols X_i be mutually exclusive is handled by the WTA network.

B. Biological Interpretation

In this subsection, we relate the components of the above ANN model for histogram equalization to a biological neuron model in order to establish its plausibility as a signal processing technique employed by the brain. It is already clear that it can be used practically in artificial neural systems. However, it is interesting to consider histogram equalization as a model for short-term memory which is used for contextual processing, and is therefore not directly involved in the transfer of information to long-term memory.

The relative strength of the signal favoring symbol X_i is encoded as the frequency of action potentials occurring within the neuron being examined. Inhibitory connections of sufficiently high gain between this neuron and others implement the winner-take-all function. This function may also be implemented by interneurons[8, pp.132–136].

The arrival of each action potential at the synaptic bulb releases a quantum of neurotransmitter into the synapse. Assuming that the rate of re-uptake of the neurotransmitter is essentially constant, the synapse itself implements the leaky integrator function which in turn estimates this synapse's average firing rate: The initial concentration of neurotransmitter in the synapse is proportional to the estimated probability $\tilde{p}_i^t$.

The level α_i is established by the density of neurotransmitter receptors present at the surface of the postsynaptic membrane. This reduces the concentration of free neurotransmitter in the synapse in proportion to the degree to which postsynaptic response is facilitated. In other words, the target histogram level is proportional to the postsynaptic weight.

Inhibitory receptors on the synaptic bulb[8, p.241] can be invoked to explain the negative feedback relation between the neurotransmitter density in the synapse and the firing rate of the presynaptic cell. The temporal sampling interval Δ is determined by the fundamental resonant frequency of this chemical feedback circuit. Since neurotransmitter-mediated depolarization also depends on the diffusion of neurotransmitter across the synapse, the time constant of this feedback circuit is expected to be on the order of the observed maximum rate of change of the firing rate. Thus, we have described a mechanism by which information regarding the magnitude of postsynaptic weights can be propagated backwards across synapses on a time scale which is in line with the behavior being described.

Finally, since the neurotransmitter density in the synapse is related to the difference between the expected and measured probabilities for symbol X_i, sufficient information reaches the postsynaptic cell to enable it to reconstruct the signal entering the synapse. Due to the reversible nature of binding between neurotransmitter and its receptors, the density of activated receptors on the postsynaptic membrane will track the concentration of free neurotransmitter in the synapse. A schematic representation of the neurotransmitter pathways described above is given in Figure 4.

In this model, it remains to be established that

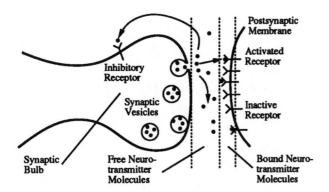

Figure 4: Schematic representation of neurotransmitter pathways required to implement the histogram equalization model.

postsynaptic receptor density exerts a significant effect upon the concentration of neurotransmitter in the synapse. However, evidence from recent studies suggest that habituation leads to presynaptic as well as postsynaptic changes[9]. Among these is an increase in the size of neurotransmitter vesicles in the presynaptic bulb. In this case, mere exhaustion of the available reserves of neurotransmitter in the presynaptic bulb can be invoked to explain the negative feedback effect on which our model depends.

C. Extension to Fuzzy Probability

The restriction that the symbols X_i be mutually exclusive is not necessary, and was adopted merely for clarity of presentation. If we drop this assumption, then the interpretation of the p_i^t as probabilities changes to that of fuzzy probabilities, or merely the frequency of occurrence of the corresponding symbol X_i. The interpretation of the parameters α_i changes to the ideal or expected frequency of occurrence of the corresponding symbol X_i. Noting that in this case $\sum_i p_i^t \neq 1$ and $\sum_i \alpha_i \neq 1$, the remaining equations are unchanged.

IV. SPATIAL EQUALIZATION

In the preceding section, we made the assumption that a separate network, such as the one shown in Figure 3, is applied to each pixel in the input image. In other words, we performed only temporal and not spatial histogram equalization. Yet in most references on the subject, it is spatial equalization which is stressed.

As rendered, the model is already interesting, particularly if the symbols produced by the network are interpreted more generally than as simple grey levels. To be useful for spatial histogram equalization, however, we must dispense with the local nature of

the feedback signal, which allowed us to describe the feedback mechanism in terms of a single synapse: If there are any layers intervening between the symbol generation (e.g. the determination of a particular grey level) and the target histogram information, then active feedback is necessary. Fortunately, the crucial component of the model remains intact. The target histogram is still realized by propagating weight information backward across the synapses.

It is a simple matter to generate and modify a histogram over any given area as follows. The outputs of neurons with like outputs are simply summed; each histogram-forming neuron corresponds to one grey level in the input image. To these outputs are applied the temporal estimation (if necessary) and the target histogram data. The resulting difference signals are fanned back out to the feature detecting cells on the previous layer, thereby effecting the desired histogram modification. A block diagram for this system is shown in Figure 5.

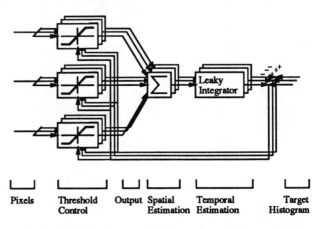

Pixels   Threshold   Output Spatial   Temporal   Target
          Control   Estimation Estimation   Histogram

Figure 5: Block diagram for spatial histogram equalization. Each plane represents a different grey level.

In terms of a biological model, we can relate the elements performing summation (spatial histogram) to interneurons. These interneurons have an excitatory effect upon the feature selecting neurons in the preceding layer (corresponding to one bin in the histogram). The firing rates of these interneurons are controlled in turn by the target histogram (the weights present at their outputs) through the feedback mechanism described in the preceding section.

V. DISCUSSION

Two interesting points are raised by the above analysis. The first is that to implement a threshold modification mechanism like histogram equalization, a system must possess learning mechanisms with different learning rates and retentions[2]. Though not mentioned explicitly above, we assume that the ideal histogram is established by a learning process which is slower than that represented by our histogram estimation process. In this long-term learning process, variations in β_i would be averaged out. In other words, long-term learning cannot respond to the short-term, systematic changes represented by β_i. As we have described it, our model is able to track these short-term changes, thus implementing the contextual adaptation we initially sought.

The second point of interest is that this model for short-term adaptation in biological systems relies explicitly upon the propagation of information backward across synapses. Based on known neurochemical processes, we suggest mechanisms by which this transfer can be effected. However, it remains to be established that these signal pathways are actually being exploited for the purpose of threshold or sensitivity control as suggested here.

VI. CONCLUSION

We have presented an implementation for temporal and spatial histogram equalization in neural hardware. Since the temporal version relies on feedback local to a synapse, it is a plausible model for histogram equalization in biological neural systems. It also raises the interesting idea that the weights on the succeeding layer of a network can be used to supply target histogram information to the current layer. The spatial version is less plausible biologically, but is easily implemented within the standard connectionist paradigm.

The neural circuits we have described should be of practical use. Note in particular, that our model enables the implementation of feedback mechanisms which depend on feedforward weight sets (as in Fukushima's neocognitron[10]) without requiring duplicate weight sets for the feedback path. In future work, we will investigate these models experimentally, and describe their application to more general normalization functions within a neural framework.

A. Acknowledgement

I am grateful to the reviewers and proofreader for their helpful comments.

REFERENCES

[1] E.H. Hall. Almost uniform distributions for computer image enhancement. *IEEE Transactions on Computers*, C-23(2):207–208, 1974.

[2] P.A. Chochia. Image enhancement using sliding histograms. *Computer Vision, Graphics, and Image Processing*, 44:211–229, 1988.

[3] Albert M. Vossepoel, Berend C. Stoel, and A. Peter Meershoek. Adaptive histogram equalization using variable regions. In *Proceedings of the 9th International Conference on Pattern Recognition*, pages 351–353. IEEE, 1988.

[4] Konrad W. Leszczynski and Shlomo Shalev. Robust algorithm for contrast enhancement by local histogram modification. *Image and Vision Computing*, 7(3):205–209, 1989.

[5] John M. Gauch. Image contrast enhancement via blurred weighted adaptive histogram equalization. In *Proceedings of SPIE - The International Society for Optical Engineering*, volume 1606, pages 386–399. SPIE, Int Soc for Optical Engineering, Bellingham, WA, USA., 1991.

[6] S.M. Pizer, E.P. Amburn, J.D. Austin, R. Cromartie, A. Geselowitz, T. Greer, B. ter Haar Romeny, J.B. Zimmerman, and K. Zuiderveld. Adaptive histrogram equalization and its variations. *Computer Vision, Graphics and Image Processing*, 39:355–368, 1987.

[7] D.E. Rumelhart and J.L. McClelland. *Parallel Distributed Processing*. MIT Press, Cambridge, MA, 1986.

[8] Patrick L. McGeer, Sir John C. Eccles, and Edith G. McGeer. *Molecular Neurobiology of the Mammalian Brain*. Plenum Press, New York, second edition, 1987.

[9] Bruce L. McNaughton. The mechanisms of expression of long-term synaptic enhancement: Thesis, antithesis, synthesis. In Michel Baudry and Joel L. Davis, editors, *Long-Term Potentiation: A Debate of Current Issues*, pages 77–91, Cambridge, MA, 1991. MIT Press.

[10] Kunihiko Fukushima. A hierarchical neural network model for associative memory. *Biological Cybern.*, 50(2):105–113, April 1984.

---

[2]This phrase is a bit redundant, since a fast learning rate implies short retention, and slow learning a long period of retention.

Performance of Multilayer Neural Networks in Binary-to-Binary Mappings Under Weight Errors

Najwa Sara Orzechowski   Soundar R. T. Kumara   Chita R. Das

The Pennsylvania State University Department of Industrial Engineering

University Park, PA 16802

Abstract: In this research, the probability of misclassification error of a multilayer neural network used in binary-to-binary mappings is derived. The connection weights, determined through training, are assumed to be subject to an additive, random, normally distributed error. The probability of misclassification is also derived through simulation of example application. The simulation results and the theoretical results are shown to match very closely. Our results give predictability to NN performance and allow for changing NN design parameters, such as weight vectors and number of nodes, in order to obtain a certain tolerance to weight errors.

I. INTRODUCTION

In this research, we study the performance under faulty conditions, of a multilayer neural network model used in binary-to-binary mappings. The neural network is assumed to be successfully trained using a training algorithm such as the backpropagation algorithm [1]. A set of optimal weights is therefore determined to insure the desired mappings of a given training set.

Most studies of NN misclassification rate used simulation techniques (for example [2]-[5]). A theoretical approach to this problem is included in [6]. This approach uses assumptions that do not always apply. For example, in real problems, the number of nodes in a network layer is not necessarily very large (order of 100 or more) as assumed in that paper. In addition, it is not always the case that all possible input patterns (that can be formed using n bits) are equally likely to be presented. Rather, in real problems, it is the patterns used in training as well as variations of them that are more likely to be presented. Furthermore, the weight errors introduced are more likely to be random variables, rather than a certain known small ratio.

We derive the probability of misclassification as a function of the network parameters (number of nodes, connection weights,) for a certain input pattern. We assume that the weights are subject to a random additive gaussian noise of mean 0 and standard deviation σ, due to hardware implementation limits. This would be the case, for example, when the weights are physically implemented as resistors[8]. In our NN model, a classification error is equivalent to an output inversion from binary 0 to binary 1 or vice-versa, at a certain output node.

Notation: When there is more than one-layer in a neural network, the layer number is a superscript. The input layer is layer 0, since there is no neural processing at that layer. The number of nodes in layer l is n(l). A neural network is characterized by its weight vectors W_i^l connecting nodes in layer l-1 to nodes in layer l. W^l is an n(l-1) X n(l) vector. A scalar component of W^l is w_{ij}^l. It is the weight of the connection from node i to node j. Since we are interested in the probability of output inversion at a certain node j in layer l, we are also interested in the weight vector coming onto that particular node. This vector is noted as $W^l = (w_1^l, w_2^l ..., w_{n(l-1)}^l)$ where the subscript j is dropped for simplicity. An input pattern is an n-bit long vector $X = (x_1, x_2 ... x_n)$. Since many values are relative to a certain input pattern p, for simplicity of notation, we drop the subscript p. $N(0, \sigma)$ denotes the normal distribution with mean 0 and standard deviation σ. $Prob(\overline{S} > S)$ denotes the probability that the random number $\overline{S}$ is greater than S.

II. BRIEF REVIEW OF NEURAL NODE OPERATION

A neural node is shown in Fig 1a. In operation mode, a node receives an input pattern p represented by a binary vector $X = (x_1, x_2 .. x_n)$ and uses the weight vector $W = (w_1, w_2 .. w_n)$ determined through training, to classify the input into one of two classes. The output of the node is either 0 or 1. For a given input pattern p represented by $X = (x_1, x_2 .. x_n)$, the node calculates

$$S = \sum_{i=1}^{n} x_i w_i \tag{1}$$

and makes the classification decision by calculating the output

$$x^1 = f(S) \tag{2}$$

where f is a non-linear activation function such that $f(S) = 1$ if $S > 0$ and $f(S) = 0$ if $S \leq 0$. A feedforward multilayer network is made of layers of nodes, arranged as in Fig. 1b. The output of one layer is input to the following layer. In other words, a node j in layer l calculates S_j^l given by:

$$S_j^l = \sum_{i=1}^{n(l-1)} W_{ij}^l X_i^{l-1} \tag{3}$$

and outputs x_j^l given by

$$x_j^l = f(S_j^l) \tag{4}$$

Note that, for simplicity, (1) and (3) do not include a threshold . If a non-zero threshold is used, and it is not subject to error, our results do not change at all. If it is subject to error, it can be treated as an additional weight with a constant "1" input. This would simply increment the value of k (defined later) by 1, for all patterns.

III. FUNDAMENTAL CONDITION FOR OUTPUT INVERSION AT ANY NODE

An output inversion at any node in the NN is the result of error in the value of S at that node, since the output is a function f of S. Due to the non-linearity of the activation functions f, an error in S does not always result in an output inversion. For an output inversion to occur, the value of ΔS, the change in S due to faulty conditions in the NN, has to exceed a certain threshold dependent on the pattern p being classified :

1. If, under normal, non-faulty conditions, pattern p is classified in class 0, this implies that the value of S is negative. In this case, for an error to occur, S has to increase by at least its absolute value, in order to reach a positive value and therefore result in output inversion from 0 to 1. Thus, letting P be the probability of output inversion for pattern p at a given node, we state:

$$P=Prob(\Delta S>|S|)\qquad(5)$$

2. If, on the other hand, pattern p is a class 1 pattern, S is positive and a classification error occurs if and only if S decreases by at least its value. Thus

$$P=Prob(\Delta S<-S)\qquad(6)$$

Hence if we determine the distribution and/or the nature of ΔS, we can calculate P using either equation (5) or (6), depending on the expected classification of the pattern, which is the target output in the training set.

IV. SINGLE NODE SUBJECT TO WEIGHT ERRORS

In this section, we derive the probability of misclassification error of a single trained neural node, for a given pattern p, when the values of all the components of W have an additive error, assuming that the error is normally distributed $N(0, \sigma)$.

Let Δw_i be the error introduced to w_i Using the erroneous values of the weights, an erroneous S value, say $\overline{S}$, is calculated:

$$\overline{S}=\sum_{i=1}^{n} x_i(w_i+\Delta w_i)=\sum_{i=1}^{n} x_i w_i+\sum_{i=1}^{n} x_i \Delta w_i$$

$$\overline{S}=S+\sum_{i=1}^{n} x_i\Delta w_i$$

therefore, the error introduced to S, ΔS is given by

$$\Delta S=\overline{S}-S=\sum_{i=1}^{n} x_i\Delta w_i\qquad(7)$$

Note that when the input value $x_i= 0$, an error introduced to the weight value w_i will have no effect on ΔS, and therefore no effect on the network's performance. Let us define, for each pattern p, a value k equal to the number of 1's in the pattern. This value has also been referred to as activity of the pattern[7]. In other words,

$$k=\sum_{i=1}^{n} x_i\qquad(8)$$

ΔS is then the sum of k normally distributed errors, and since these are all independent, ΔS is also normally distributed, with mean 0 and standard deviation $\sqrt{k}\ \sigma$. Since Prob($\Delta S < -S$) = Prob($\Delta S > S$) when ΔS is normally distributed, and since $|S|=S$ for S>0, equations (5) and (6) can be combined and the probability of output inversion is then:

$$P=prob(\Delta S>|S|)\qquad(9)$$

for all S, which can be mathematically computed given that $\Delta S \sim N(0, \sqrt{k}\ \sigma)$.

An extension of this result can be made for the one-layer network. Since each node in a one-layer network receives the input pattern through its own independent weight vector, the probability of output inversion, due to weight errors, at each node is independent of the other nodes and can be calculated using (9). Letting P_1 through P_n be these probabilities for nodes 1 through n, determined by (9) and assuming that a classification error occurs whenever at least one of the output nodes presents an inverted output then the overall probability of misclassification of the network would be:

$$P=1-\prod_{i=1}^{n} (1-P_i)\qquad(10)$$

V. SINGLE NODE SUBJECT TO INPUT ERRORS

Consider again the single node network of Fig. 1a. Let

us suppose this time that the weight values are fixed and deterministic, and that the binary input values $x_1..x_n$ are subject to error: With each input x_i, there is a probability P_i of inversion from 1 to 0 or vice-versa. We wish to calculate P, the probability of output inversion of the network under these conditions. Letting Δx_i be the error introduced to input i, the erroneous S value is then given by

$$\overline{S} = \sum_{i=1}^{n} w_i (x_i + \Delta x_i) = \sum_{i=1}^{n} w_i x_i + \sum_{i=1}^{n} w_i \Delta x_i$$

and therefore,

$$\Delta S = \overline{S} - S = \sum_{i=1}^{n} w_i \Delta x_i \qquad (11)$$

P then depends on the values of Δx_i, i.e. on *which* and *how many* inputs actually get inverted. There are 2^n possible subsets to a set of n nodes. Let D_m be a subset of nodes in the input layer. Let B_m be the event that the D_m subset of inputs are inverted. Let A be the event that the output of the network is inverted. Then, from conditional probability law:

$$P = P(A) = \sum_{m=1}^{2^n} P(A/B_m) P(B_m) \qquad (12)$$

We know that

$$P(B_m) = (\prod_{i \in D_m} P_i) (\prod_{i \notin D_m} (1 - P_i)) \qquad (13)$$

To find $P(A/B_m)$, we find an expression of ΔS given that B_m occurred (i.e. the subset D_m of inputs are inverted) For that purpose, we define D_{m1} and D_{m3} exhaustive and mutually exclusive subsets of D_m such that:

$D_{m1} = \{ i \in D_m , x_i = 0 \}$ and $D_{m2} = \{ i \in D_m , x_i = 1 \}$.

then define $y_i = \Delta x_i = \begin{cases} 1 \text{ if } i \in D_{m1} \\ -1 \text{ if } i \in D_{m2} \\ 0 \text{ if } i \notin D_m \end{cases}$

Then the value of ΔS given that the set D_m of inputs are inverted is, using (11),

$$\Delta S_m = \sum_{i=1}^{n} w_i y_i \qquad (14)$$

Since ΔS_m is deterministic, equation (5) reduces to
$$P(A/B_m) = 1 \quad \text{if } \Delta S_m > -S$$
$$P(A/B_m) = 0 \quad \text{otherwise.}$$
A similar result can be derived using (6) (for S positive). Substituting (13) in (12) yields:

$$P = \sum_{m=1}^{2^{n(0)}} \prod_{i \in D_m} P_i \prod_{i \notin D_m} (1 - P_i) P(A/B_m) \qquad (15)$$

which can be computed as shown above and using (14).

VI. SINGLE NODE SUBJECT TO INPUT *AND* WEIGHT ERRORS: MULTPLE-LAYER NETWORKS

When a node is subject to both input and weight errors, the erroneous S value calculated is

$$\overline{S} = \sum_{i=1}^{n} (w_i + \Delta w_i) (x_i + \Delta x_i)$$

$$\overline{S} = \sum_{i=1}^{n} w_i x_i + \sum_{i=1}^{n} w_i \Delta x_i + \sum_{i=1}^{n} \Delta w_i (x_i + \Delta x_i)$$

Therefore,

$$\Delta S = \sum_{i=1}^{n} w_i \Delta x_i + \sum_{i=1}^{n} \Delta w_i (x_i + \Delta x_i) \qquad (16)$$

To find P, we need to condition, as in the previous section, on *which* and *how many* inputs actually get inverted. Again, there are 2^n possible subsets to a set of n elements. We define D_m, D_{m1}, D_{m2} and y_i's as in the previous section. Similarly, we define events A and B_m. $P(B_m)$ is given, as in the previous section by (13). We proceed to derive $P(A/B_m)$.

Using the definition of y_i's for a given set of nodes D_m, the change due to *input errors* only, $\Delta_1 S_m$ is given by the first term in (16):

$$\Delta_1 S_m = \sum_{i=1}^{n} y_i w_i \qquad (17)$$

The change in S due to *weight errors* given that a set D_m of inputs are inverted, is given by the second term in (16). Using a similar reasoning as in section 3, this value, $\Delta_2 S_m$

1686

is the sum of a certain number $\overline{k}$ of normally distributed errors. This number $\overline{k}$ is the new k-value of the input pattern when event B_m occurs, and is given by:

$$\overline{k} = k + \sum_{i=1}^{n} y_i \qquad (18)$$

where k is the number of ones in the input pattern if no input errors occurred. Therefore,

$$\Delta_2 S_m \sim N(0, \sqrt{k}\sigma) \qquad (19)$$

and the total error introduced to S due to both normally distributed weight errors and a set D_m of input errors is

$$\Delta S_m = \sum_{i=1}^{n} y_i w_i + \Delta_2 S_m \qquad (20)$$

Using the fundamental condition of output inversion given in (5) (a similar reasoning can be applied using (6)), substituting (20) for ΔS:

$$P(A/B_m) = Prob\left(\sum_{i=1}^{n} y_i w_i + \Delta_2 S_m > -S\right) \qquad (21)$$

which implies that

$$P(A/B_m) = Prob\left(\Delta_2 S_m > -S - \sum_{i=1}^{n} y_i w_i\right) \qquad (22)$$

Finally, summing (23) over all possible values of B_m (all 2^n possible subsets), we get the result:

$$P = \sum_{m=1} \left(\prod_{i \in D_m} P_i\right) \left(\prod_{i \notin D_m} (1-P_i)\right) Prob\left(\Delta_2 S_m > -S - \sum y_i w_i\right)$$

$$(23)$$

where $\Delta_2 S_m$ is given by (19).

Claim : The above also solves the multiple layer network problem. Nodes in layer l beyond the first layer receive their inputs from the outputs of the previous layer, l-1. These previous layer outputs carry a probability of being inverted due to weight errors at previous layers. Hence, a node in a layer l beyond the first layer is subject to two sources of errors: errors in the input to that node, which are outputs of layer l-1, and errors in the weight vector at

layer l. Let us consider a typical node in layer l>1. The input pattern to layer l is the output pattern from layer l-1, $x_1{}^{l-1}, x_2{}^{l-1}, \dots x_{n(l-1)}{}^{l-1}$, where n(l-1) is the number of nodes in layer l-1. Let $P = P_j{}^{l}$ be the probability of output inversion of a node j in layer l, which is the value to be determined in this section.

We derive the following results by induction: Equation (9) gives the formula for $P_i{}^1$ for layer l=1. In the following, we assume we have $P_i{}^{l-1}$ for all nodes i in a given layer l-1 (l>1) and we derive the probability of output inversion of node j in layer l, $P = P_j{}^l$. This value is simply given by (23), using the $y_i{}^{l-1}$ values instead of the y_i values and $P_i{}^{l-1}$ values instead of P_i values. The number of nodes n becomes n(l-1), the number of nodes in layer l-1. Using these values, equation (23) becomes

$$P_j^l = \sum_{m=1}^{2^{n(l-1)}} \left(\prod_{i \in D_m} P_i^{l-1}\right) \left(\prod_{i \notin D_m} (1-P_i^{l-1})\right) Prob\left(\Delta_2 S_m > -S_j^l - \sum_{i=1}^{n(l-1)} y_i^{l-1} w_i^l\right)$$

where $\Delta_2 S_m$ is given by (19) which becomes

$$\Delta_2 S_m \sim N(0, \sqrt{k^{l-1}}\sigma)$$

and $\overline{k^{l-1}}$ is given by (18) which becomes

$$\overline{k^{l-1}} = k^{l-1} + \sum_{i=1}^{n(l-1)} y_i^{l-1}$$

Finally, when there are more than one node at the output layer, the overall probability of error of the network can be calculated as in (10).

Complexity Considerations:

As n gets large, equation (23) would require the use of a computer to perform the calculation. The complexity of this calculation is in the order of 2^n. This can be prohibitive for large problems. However, this can be dramatically improved by making the following assumption: The event that 3 or more nodes in a hidden layer result in inverted outputs is unlikely. Therefore, we would only need to generate subsets of less than 3 elements. The complexity of the calculation would then be of the order of n^2. This assumption will be referred to as the complexity reducing assumption.

Example : Theoretical and simulation results:

Consider the (54:6:1) network trained to classify mechanical parts into two classes. The training set, shown in Fig. 2, consists of 4 binary input patterns and their target classification output. Each pattern is a digitized black and white pixel representation of a mechanical part, translated into a 54-bit binary pattern. The input layer therefore consisted of 54 input nodes. After successful training, using the backpropagation algorithm, with z=0.01, we simulated the operation of the neural network in classifying pattern 1. In each iteration, normally distributed errors are generated and added to the values of W. The complexity reducing assumption was used in the theoretical calculations. The results of the theoretical computations as well as those of simulation are shown in Table 1. Note that the two results are in good agreement.

VII. SUMMARY AND CONCLUSIONS

In this paper, we developed a theoretical model of the probability of classification error of a multilayer NN used in binary-to-binary mappings. This probability is for a certain input pattern and it is a function of the network parameters: number of nodes and weight vectors. We also showed that simulation results match the theoretical ones very closely for different values of the standard deviation of the weight errors. The results show that if the standard deviation of the weight errors is below a certain value, the misclassification rate remains zero. Since the value of S for a certain pattern is a function of the weight vectors, and since there exists a number of weight vectors that assure the desired input-output mapping of an application, choosing a set of weight vectors that yield greater S absolute values would result in tolerance of higher weight error standard deviations.

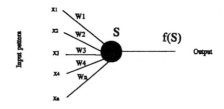

Figure 1a: A Neural Node

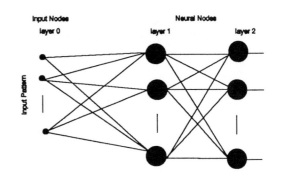

Figure 1b: A Multilayer Neural Network

REFERENCES

[1] Rumelhart, D. E., McClelland, J. L., and the PDP research group, *Parallel Distributed Processing, Explorations in the Microstructure of Cognition*, Vol.1: Foundations, MIT Press, Cambridge, MA, 1986.

[2] Baranowski, S. and Pimmel, R. , "Performance studies of learning vector quantization neural network classifiers", *Intelligent Engineering Systems through Artificial Neural Networks*, Dagli, C. H. ; Kumara, S. R. T. ; and Shin, Y. C. (eds), ASME Publishers, 1991, pp.149-153,

[3] Char, J. M. ; Cherkassky, V. ; Wechsler, H. and Zimmerman, G. L., " Distributed and fault tolerant computation for retrieval tasks using distributed associative memories", *IEEE Transactions on Computers*, vol. 37, pp. 484-490, April 1988.

[4] Cherkassky, V. and Vassilas, N. , "Performance of the back-propagation networks for associative database retrieval", IJCNN, vol. 1, pp 77-84, June 1989.

[5] Nijhuis, J. A. G. and Spaanengurg, L, " Fault tolerance of neural associative memories", *IEE Proceedings*, vol. 136, Pt. E, pp. 389-394, September 1989,

[6] Stevenson, M. ;Winter, R. and Widrow, B. , "Sensitivity of feedforward neural networks to weight errors", *IEEE Transactions on Neural Networks*, vol. 1, pp 71-80, March 1990.

[7] Gutierrez, M.; Wang, J.; and Brondin, R.;"Estimating hidden unit number for two-layer perceptrons", *IJCNN*, v.1, pp.I-677-681, San Diego 1989.

[8] Bolt, G.;"Fault models for artificial neural networks", *IJCNN*, v.2, pp.1373-1378, Singapore 1991.

Table 1: Probability of Misclassification for Two-Layer
(54:6:1) Problem under Weight Errors

Std. Dev	Simulation	Theoretical
0.1	0	0
0.2	0	0
0.3	0.000053	0.000093
0.4	0.002457	0.002532
0.5	0.01216	0.01255
0.6	0.03159	0.3168
0.7	0.0579	0.058
0.8	0.0636	0.0688
0.9	0.1213	0.1217

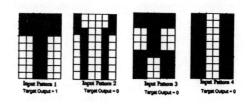

Figure 2: Training set for 54:6:1 Neural
Network

Maximum Likelihood Sequence Estimation of Minimum Shift Keying Modulated Signals using a Hopfield Neural Network

Gerd Pfeiffer

Department of Communications Engineering

University of Paderborn

Pohlweg 47–49

D–4790 Paderborn

Abstract—For the detection of minimum shift keying modulated signals in the presence of intersymbol interference and additive white Gaussian noise the feasibility to use artificial neural networks due to Hopfield is investigated. The well known principle of maximum likelihood sequence estimation is mapped onto the neural network and an appropriate receiver structure to detect the transmitted signals is described. Simulation results give insight into the equalizer performance which is approximately as good as the performance of a Viterbi equalizer.

I. INTRODUCTION

Digital signal transmission over mobile radio channels is often influenced by time-varying intersymbol interference (ISI) caused by the fading-multipath propagation channel and additive white Gaussian noise (AWGN). Viterbi equalizers based on the principle of maximum likelihood sequence estimation (MLSE) are well suited to detect a transmitted sequence in presence of the distortions mentioned above. Nevertheless, the high computation intensity and the hardware complexity for setting up the MLSE on the basis of the Viterbi algorithm limit its use for high speed data transmission.

As shown by Provence for binary [1] and quadrature phase shift keying (QPSK) [2] modulated signals the MLSE algorithm mapped onto a neural network due to Hopfield and Tank [3] can offer an alternative to the Viterbi algorithm. The results presented in [1, 2] were not based on enough data to draw definitive conclusions. Further results not illustrated here show that MLSE for QPSK communications systems is not as well suited as for minimum shift keying (MSK) or offset QPSK modulation schemes because of the independence of consecutive symbols [4]. The purpose of this paper is to present new investigations and simulation results with respect to the detection of minimum shift keying (MSK) modulated signals. For that, a receiver structure is introduced and some results concerning the network complexity and the bit error rate performance for stationary channels are presented.

II. MAXIMUM LIKELIHOOD SEQUENCE ESTIMATION

The structure of the baseband digital communications system considered in this paper is shown in Fig. 1. A transmitted data sequence is assumed to take on MSK-type symbols [5]

$$s_k = s_{I,k} + js_{Q,k} = e^{-j\Phi_k}, \tag{1}$$

where

$$\Phi_k = \pi/4 + \pi/2 \sum_{n=0}^{k} q_n . \tag{2}$$

The unmodulated information sequence is represented by $\{q_k\}$ and has statistically independent values $\in \{-1, 1\}$.

In a linear system with coherent carrier demodulation the received signal in an equivalent lowpass notation can be described as

$$r(t) = \sum_k s_k h(t - kT_S) + n(t) , \tag{3}$$

where $h(t)$ is the complex-valued impulse response of the transmission channel including the effects of transmitter filter $p(t)$ and multipath fading channel $g(t)$. The channel is assumed to be bandlimited such that the time duration of $h(t)$ is greater than the symbol interval T_S. Additionally, the received signal is corrupted by complex Gaussian noise $n(t)$ with zero mean and variance N_0.

The best known method to estimate $\{q_k\}$ out of the received signal $r(t)$ is named maximum likelihood sequence estimation (MLSE). An MLSE based equalizer observes the received signal $r(t)$ for a specified time T_B and determines as the best estimate the data sequence $\{\tilde{s}_M\}$ which results in the maximum of the likelihood function $p(r(t), 0 < t < T_B | \{\tilde{s}_M\})$.

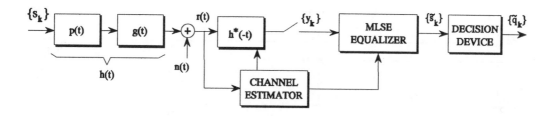

Fig. 1: Baseband data transmission system

For TDMA (time division multiple access) in mobile radio systems the observation time is given by the period of one time slot (see Fig. 2). The determination of $p(r(t), 0 \leq t < T_B | \{\tilde{s}_M\})$ can be realized by finding the sequence $\tilde{s}_1, \tilde{s}_2, \ldots \tilde{s}_M$ for which the MLSE cost function (metric)

$$J(\{\tilde{s}_M\}) = \sum_{k=1}^{M} 2 \operatorname{Re}\{\tilde{s}_k^* \, y_k\} - \sum_{k=1}^{M} \sum_{i=1}^{M} \tilde{s}_k^* \, x_{k-i} \, \tilde{s}_i \qquad (4)$$

is maximum [5]. $\operatorname{Re}\{(\cdot)\}$ denotes the real part of $(\cdot)$. The variables y_k can be generated by passing $r(t)$ through a filter matched to $h(t)$ and sampling the output at the symbol rate $1/T_S$ (see Fig. 1). x_k describes the sampled response of the matched filter to $h(t)$ or in other words x_k represents the sampled values of the autocorrelation function of $h(t)$.

Due to the unknown channel and to the nature of the TDMA signalling in Fig. 2, it is necessary to get an estimate for the channel impulse response within each time slot to enable matched filtering of $r(t)$ and to determine x_k. A well suited method for channel estimation is the correlative channel sounding technique presented in [6]. This method uses a training sequence, which is transmitted within each burst to calculate the channel impulse response via crosscorrelation of the known and the received

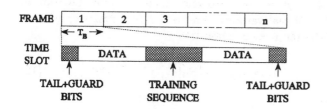

Fig. 2: Typical signalling format in digital TDMA mobile radio systems

training sequence. A description of the algorithm is given in [6]. For simulation purposes (see section V.) the channel impulse response is assumed to be optimal estimated in the receiver.

Generally, direct evaluation of (4) to determine the most likely sequence $\{\tilde{s}_M\}$ is impractical due to the computation intensity. A more efficient method for implementing MLSE is the Viterbi algorithm, which reduces the number of required computations. The complexity of the algorithm depends on the channel memory L. Therefore, for higher transmission rates the exponential increasing computational and hardware complexity limits its use in practice.

III. Hopfield Network

The artificial neural network used in this work is due to Hopfield and Tank [3, 7]. It consists of a set of simple processing elements (neurons) and interconnections (synapses). The general structure is illustrated in Fig. 3. Each processing element k can be modelled as an amplifier with nonlinear input/output relation $v(t) = g(u(t))$ (e.g. $g(\cdot) = \tanh(\cdot)$), a normal (+) and an inverted (-) output. A synapse between two neurons is defined by a conductance $T_{ik} = 1/R_{ik}$ which connects one of the two outputs of amplifier k to the input of amplifier i. Additionally, each amplifier has an input resistor ρ_k and a capacitor C_k leading to a reference ground. These components partially define the time constant of the network and are provided for integrative analog summation of the synaptic input currents of the other neurons.

The set of differential equations describing the dynamics of the network with N neurons (see Fig. 3), can be shown to be

$$C \frac{du_i(t)}{dt} = -\frac{u_i(t)}{R} + \sum_{k=1}^{N} T_{i,k} v_k(t) + I_i \quad i = 1, \ldots N, \quad (5)$$

where $C = C_i$, $R = R_i$, and $g(\cdot) = g_i(\cdot)$ are assumed to be independent of i. R_i is the parallel combination of ρ_i and the weights T_{ik}. Redefining $T_{i,k} := T_{i,k}/C$ and $I_i := I_i/C$,

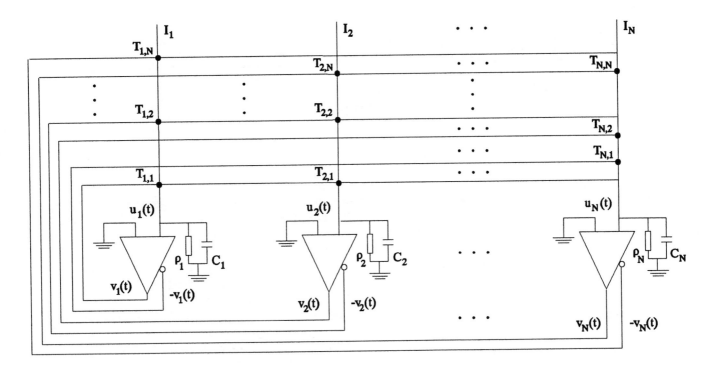

Fig. 3: Neural network due to Hopfield and Tank

(5) can be written as

$$\frac{du_i(t)}{dt} = -\frac{u_i(t)}{\tau} + \sum_{k=1}^{N} T_{i,k} v_k(t) + I_i \qquad i = 1, \ldots N. \quad (6)$$

$\tau = RC$ is the time constant of the network. Hopfield [7] showed that the equations of motion for a network with symmetric connections ($T_{i,k} = T_{k,i}$) lead to a convergence to stable states. If the slope of the amplifier gain curve given by $g(\cdot)$ is sufficient, the stable states of a network of N neurons are the local minima of the quantity

$$E = -1/2 \sum_{k=1}^{N} \sum_{i=1}^{N} v_k(t) T_{k,i} v_i(t) - \sum_{k=1}^{N} v_k(t) I_k . \quad (7)$$

Rewriting (7) in vector notation the energy function is given to

$$E = -1/2\, \mathbf{v}^T \mathbf{T} \mathbf{v} - \mathbf{v}^T \mathbf{i} \quad (8)$$

where

$$\mathbf{v}^T = [v_1(t) \quad v_2(t) \quad \ldots \quad v_N(t)], \quad (9)$$
$$\mathbf{i}^T = [I_1 \quad I_2 \quad \ldots \quad I_N], \quad (10)$$

and

$$\mathbf{T} = \begin{bmatrix} T_{1,1} & T_{1,2} & \cdots & T_{1,N} \\ T_{2,1} & T_{2,2} & \cdots & T_{2,N} \\ \vdots & \vdots & \ddots & \vdots \\ T_{N,1} & T_{N,2} & \cdots & T_{N,N} \end{bmatrix} . \quad (11)$$

IV. Reformulation of the MLSE Cost Function

The primary difference between the MLSE cost function (4) and the neural network energy function (7) is that the variables of the MLSE cost function can take on four complex values whereas those for the energy function only can take on values of ± 1 for stable states.

To map the MLSE cost function onto the neural network, it is necessary to reformulate the cost function in terms of real variables due to [2]. In a first step (4) can be written in vector notation

$$\hat{J}(\{\tilde{s}_M\}) = -2\mathrm{Re}\{\tilde{\mathbf{s}}_M^{*T} \mathbf{y}\} + \tilde{\mathbf{s}}^{*T} \mathbf{X} \tilde{\mathbf{s}} , \quad (12)$$

where

$$\tilde{\mathbf{s}}^T = [\tilde{s}_1 \quad \tilde{s}_2 \quad \ldots \quad \tilde{s}_M] , \quad (13)$$
$$\mathbf{y}^T = [y_1 \quad y_2 \quad \ldots \quad y_M] , \quad (14)$$

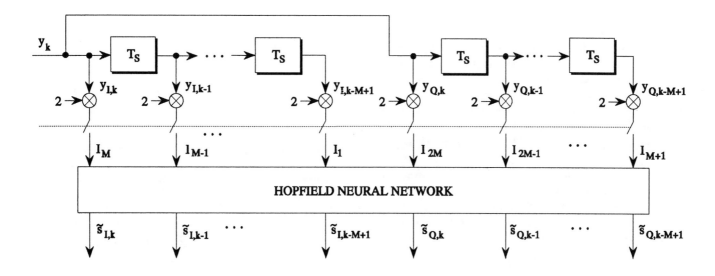

Fig. 4: Structure of the neural network based MLSE equalizer

and

$$\mathbf{X} = \begin{bmatrix} x_0 & x_1^* & x_2^* & \cdots & x_{M-1}^* \\ x_1 & x_0 & x_1^* & \cdots & x_{M-2}^* \\ \vdots & \vdots & \vdots & \ddots & \vdots \\ x_{M-1} & x_{M-2} & x_{M-3} & \cdots & x_0 \end{bmatrix}. \quad (15)$$

Additionally, the maximization problem of (4) has been changed to a minimization problem by multiplying (4) with -1.

The vectors $\tilde{\mathbf{s}}$, $\mathbf{y}$ and the matrix $\mathbf{X}$ are complex-valued. Therefore, we can write

$$\tilde{\mathbf{s}} = \tilde{\mathbf{s}}_I + j\tilde{\mathbf{s}}_Q , \quad (16)$$

and

$$\mathbf{y} = \mathbf{y}_I + j\mathbf{y}_Q , \quad (17)$$

where

$$\tilde{\mathbf{s}}_I^T = [\tilde{s}_{I,1} \quad \tilde{s}_{I,2} \quad \ldots \quad \tilde{s}_{I,M}], \quad (18)$$
$$\tilde{\mathbf{s}}_Q^T = [\tilde{s}_{Q,1} \quad \tilde{s}_{Q,2} \quad \ldots \quad \tilde{s}_{Q,M}], \quad (19)$$
$$\mathbf{y}_I^T = [y_{I,1} \quad y_{I,2} \quad \ldots \quad y_{I,M}], \quad (20)$$
$$\mathbf{y}_Q^T = [y_{Q,1} \quad y_{Q,2} \quad \ldots \quad y_{Q,M}], \quad (21)$$

and define the two matrices

$$\mathbf{X}_I = \begin{bmatrix} x_{I,0} & x_{I,1} & x_{I,2} & \cdots & x_{I,M-1} \\ x_{I,1} & x_{I,0} & x_{I,1} & \cdots & x_{I,M-2} \\ \vdots & \vdots & \vdots & \ddots & \vdots \\ x_{I,M-1} & x_{I,M-2} & x_{I,M-3} & \cdots & x_{I,0} \end{bmatrix} \quad (22)$$

and

$$\mathbf{X}_Q = \begin{bmatrix} x_{Q,0} & -x_{Q,1} & -x_{Q,2} & \cdots & -x_{Q,M-1} \\ x_{Q,1} & x_{Q,0} & -x_{Q,1} & \cdots & -x_{Q,M-2} \\ \vdots & \vdots & \vdots & \ddots & \vdots \\ x_{Q,M-1} & x_{Q,M-2} & x_{Q,M-3} & \cdots & x_{Q,0} \end{bmatrix}. \quad (23)$$

From the relations found in (22) and (23) it can be noticed that $\mathbf{X}_I = \mathbf{X}_I^T$ is symmetric and $\mathbf{X}_Q = -\mathbf{X}_Q^T$ is skew symmetric with $x_{Q,0} = 0$. As a result the cost function can be rewritten in terms of the vectors and matrices defined above. We yield

$$\begin{aligned} \hat{J}(\{\tilde{s}_M\}) &= -2(\tilde{\mathbf{s}}_I^T \mathbf{y}_I + \tilde{\mathbf{s}}_Q^T \mathbf{y}_Q) \quad (24) \\ &+ \tilde{\mathbf{s}}_I^T \mathbf{X}_I \tilde{\mathbf{s}}_I + \tilde{\mathbf{s}}_Q^T \mathbf{X}_Q \tilde{\mathbf{s}}_Q + 2\tilde{\mathbf{s}}_Q^T \mathbf{X}_Q \tilde{\mathbf{s}}_I . \end{aligned}$$

Defining the matrix

$$\hat{\mathbf{X}} = -2 \begin{bmatrix} X_I & X_Q^T \\ X_Q & X_I \end{bmatrix} \quad (25)$$

and the two vectors

$$\hat{\mathbf{s}}^T = [\tilde{\mathbf{s}}_I^T \mid \tilde{\mathbf{s}}_Q^T], \quad \hat{\mathbf{y}}^T = 2[\mathbf{y}_I^T \mid \mathbf{y}_Q^T] \quad (26)$$

(25) can be written in a compact form as

$$\hat{J}(\{\tilde{s}_M\}) = -\hat{\mathbf{s}}^T \hat{\mathbf{y}} - 1/2\,\hat{\mathbf{s}}^T \hat{\mathbf{X}}\,\hat{\mathbf{s}} . \quad (27)$$

Since $\mathbf{X}_I$ is symmetric and $\mathbf{X}_Q$ is skew symmetric, $\mathbf{X}$ is symmetric, which satisfies the symmetry condition for the stability of the Hopfield neural network. Comparing (27) with (8) it can be seen that (8) is a reformulation of the MLSE cost function. Substituting $N = 2M$, $\mathbf{T} = \hat{\mathbf{X}}$, $\mathbf{i} = \hat{\mathbf{y}}$, and $\mathbf{v} = \hat{\mathbf{s}}$ shows that both functions are identical under these conditions.

Fig. 4 illustrates a part of the neural network based MLSE equalizer. Inphase- and quadrature component of the received signal y_k were shifted into a tapped delay line. After shifting one burst of M symbols and closing all switches simultaneously, the output values of the register are equal to the input of the neural network. The amplifier inputs were initialized to $u_k(t = 0) = 0$. After a transient period, the output of each amplifier is given to a decision device, where an estimate $\{\tilde{q}_k\}$ of the transmitted binary sequence is made.

V. Simulation Results

The transmission system including the neural network based MLSE equalizer due to Fig. 1 has been simulated on a digital computer. Therefore, the set of N differential equations given by (6) has been numerically solved using Heun's method of order 2 [4]. The nonlinear input/output function of all amplifiers was implemented as $g(u(t)) = \tanh(Gu(t))$, where G is the gain constant of the amplifiers and is set to 1000 for all simulations. The channel impulse response is given by $h(t) = 0.707\delta(t) + 0.707\delta(t - LT_S)$, where L describes the channel memory.

Fig. 5 depicts the bit error rate performance of the neural network based equalizer. A TDMA structure (see Fig. 2) with bursts containing 156 bits is simulated. The number of tail and guard bits is chosen to $D = 7$ bit due to [8]. To evaluate the performance of the neural network based MLSE equalizer a comparison is made between the conventional MLSE equalizer and the neural network. The simulated Viterbi algorithm can take into account channels with memory up to $L = 4$. It can be seen that the performance of the neural network based MLSE is approximately the same as the one for the Viterbi equalizer if the channel memory is $L \leq 4$. Simulating the transmission channel for $L = 5$ the Viterbi equalizer can not detect the distorted signal in contrast to the Hopfield net, which can equalize the channel.

The performance of the Hopfield network is dependent on the number D of tail and guard bits. To illustrate the influence on the bit error rate, Fig. 6 shows the performance for a channel with memory $L = 5$ in dependence on the bit position in the time slot at an average signal-to-noise ratio of $\gamma_b = 11$ dB. The simulation results indicate that the bit error rate increases at the edges of the burst. Further investigations (see Fig. 7) show the influence of D on the bit error rate for different burst lengths, $\gamma_b = 10$ dB, and $L = 1$. M denotes the number of

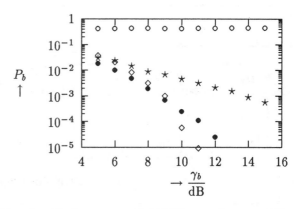

Fig. 5: Performance of MLSE equalizers, • Hopfield ($L = 3$), ⋆ Hopfield ($L = 5$), ⋄ Viterbi ($L = 3$), ∘ Viterbi ($L = 5$)

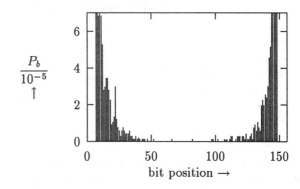

Fig. 6: Bit error rate versus information bit position ($\gamma_b = 11$ dB, $N = 156$, $D = 7$)

bits per burst. For increasing M the influence of D is decreasing.

VI. Summary and Conclusions

A neural network implementation of an MLSE equalizer has been presented. For MLSE equalizers based on the Viterbi algorithm simulation results show that the receiver fails if the channel memory is more than the constraint length of the equalizer. Increasing the constraint length leads to exponential increase in hardware and software complexity. Here, the Hopfield net offers an attractive alternative because the neural network is able to detect the transmitted sequence without increasing the network complexity. The dependence of the bit error rate performance on the number of tail and guard bits has been demonstrated. In future, further investigations considering time-variant channels and quantization effects are planned.

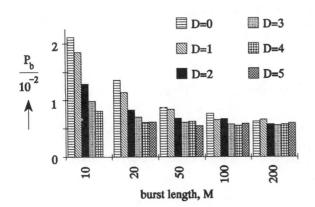

Fig. 7: Bit error rate versus burst length M for different D ($\gamma_b = 8$ dB, $L = 1$)

ACKNOWLEDGMENTS

The author thanks T. Dumrauf for valuable comments and extended programming work.

REFERENCES

[1] J.D. Provence, "Neural network implementation for maximum-likelihood sequence estimation of binary signals in gaussian noise," In *Proceedings IEEE First International Conference on Neural Networks*, vol. 3, pp. 703–714, San Diego, USA, June 1987.

[2] J.D. Provence, "Neural network implementation for an adaptive maximum-likelihood receiver," In *IEEE International Symposium on Circuits and Systems*, vol. 3, pp. 2381-2385, Espoo, Finnland, June 1988.

[3] J.J. Hopfield, D.W. Tank. " 'Neural' computation of decisions in optimization problems," *Biological Cybernetics*, no. 52, pp. 141-152, 1985.

[4] T. Dumrauf, *Leistungsfähigkeit neuronaler Netzwerke nach Hopfield zur Entzerrung und Demodulation intersymbolinterferenzbehafteter Signale,* Diplomarbeit Nr. 5/92, Universität Paderborn, 1992.

[5] J.G. Proakis, *Digital Communications.* vol. 1, McGraw-Hill, 2nd ed., 1989.

[6] G.L. Turin, "Introduction to spread-spectrum anti-multipath techniques and their application to urban digital radio," *Proceedings of the IEEE*, vol. 68, no. 3, pp. 328-353, March 1980.

[7] J.J. Hopfield, "Neurons with graded response have collective computational properties like those of two-state neurons," *Proc. Nat. Acad. Sci.*, vol. 81, pp. 3088-3092, May 1984.

[8] *GSM Recommendation 05.02*, "Multiplexing and multiple access on the radio path," version 3.3.0, April 1989.

3D Motion Estimation Using Single Perspective Sparse Range Data via Surface Reconstruction Neural Networks

Jenq-Neng Hwang,   Yen-Hao Tseng

Information Processing Laboratory
Department of Electrical Engineering, FT-10
University of Washington
Seattle, WA 98195

ABSTRACT

3D motion estimations under detection/occlusion noise and/or partial object viewing are difficult invariant pattern recognition tasks. On the other hand, the biological neural networks of human are extremely adept in these tasks. It has been suggested by the studies of experimental psychology that the task of matching rotated and scaled shapes by human is done by mentally rotating and scaling gradually one of the shapes into the orientation and size of the other and then testing for a match. Motivated by these studies, we present a novel and robust neural network solution for these tasks. The method operates in two stages: The object is first parametrically represented by a surface reconstruction neural network (SRNN) trained by the boundary points sampled from the exemplar object. When later presented with boundary points sampled from the distorted object without point correspondence, this parametric representation allows the mismatch information back-propagate through the SRNN to gradually determine (align) the best similarity transform of the distorted object. Application to 3D motion estimation using sparse range data collected from a single perspective view is presented.

I. INTRODUCTION

In 3D motion estimation (or invariant pattern recognition in general), one important issue is partial viewing of the object due to limited number of perspective view angles. More specifically, only the visible surface (or surfaces) is available and it is generally assumed that no information available beyond that. This issue further complicates the research for 3D motion estimation.

This paper proposes a novel surface reconstruction neural network (SRNN) approach to overcome the shortcomings encountered in the existing methods discussed above. Our method can be supported by the experimental human psychology studies which show that *the task of matching rotated and scaled shapes is done by mentally rotating and scaling one of the shapes into the orientation and size of the other and then tested for a match*. Furthermore, it was also reported that the mental transformations of size and orientation appeared to be carried out by gradually alternating small steps of sizes and orientations [3].

Our proposed SRNN approach consists of two stages of efforts. The object shape (as well as the whole 2D/3D image space) is first represented by a surface reconstruction neural network (SRNN) trained by the boundary points sampled from the exemplar object. The SRNN parametrically reconstructs (interpolates), in a least squares sense, the surface of the exemplar object as well as the profile of the whole space based on the available sparse boundary data. More specifically, every point (in continuous domain) in the 2D/3D space will be assigned a value. If the point falls on the reconstructed boundary, it is assigned a value "0". If a point is outside (or inside) of the reconstructed object, it has positive (or negative) value with the magnitude linearly proportional to the perpendicular distance of this point to the object boundary (constant slope profile). When later presented with those boundary points of the distorted object, this parametric SRNN representation allows easy accumulation of the mismatch information from all the distorted testing data. More importantly, the mismatch information can back-propagate through the SRNN to iteratively determine the best similarity transform of the distorted object (similar to the gradual mental transformation). The distance measure can then be computed in the reconstructed representation domain between the exemplar object and the aligned distorted object.

One point worthy of mentioning is that most conventional shape description using parametric functions (e.g., polynomials, splines, deformable functions [8]) which specifically describe the shape of the objects without modeling the whole image space. Our proposed SRNN representation, on the other hand, gives a continuous description of the whole image space and the shape is implicitly defined as the subspace that gives $\phi(\mathbf{x}) = 0$.

The organization of this paper is as follows: In Section II, we discuss the learning procedures involved in training an SRNN. Section III proposes our mechanism of estimating the similarity transform parameters by incorporating the trained SRNN through a mental image transform-like approach. Section IV presents the the application of the SRNN to 3D motion estimation when the testing object is described by a set of sparse range data collected from one single perspective view angle. Concluding remarks are given in Section V.

II. A Surface Reconstruction Neural Network

Given a set of data points $\{\mathbf{x}\}$ (in $\mathcal{R}^2$ or $\mathcal{R}^3$) that lie on or close to the 2D curve or 3D surface of an object, the goal of surface reconstruction is to reconstruct the 2D curve or 3D surface of the object, expressed by a smooth and continuous function $\phi(\mathbf{x})$ such that the training data set is given as sample root points ($\mathbf{B} = \{\mathbf{x}^{(i)}, i = 1, \ldots, n\}$) of $\phi(\mathbf{x})$, i.e., $\phi(\mathbf{x}) = 0$, $\mathbf{x} \in \mathbf{B}$

A. A Cost Function Without Regularization

We have adopted a standard 2-layer (one hidden layer) perceptron (MLP) for our SRNN with different cost function. In this SRNN, the activation values of the kth neuron of the lth layer is denoted as $a_k(l)$, $l = 0, 1, 2$, where $l = 0$ specifies the input layer (consists of 2 or 3 input neurons with values equal to $\mathbf{x}$); $l = 1$ specifies the hidden layer (consists of H hidden neurons with commonly used sigmoid nonlinearity, $\frac{1}{1+e^{-\bullet}}$); and $l = 2$ specifies the output layer (consists of a single output neuron with slightly modified sigmoid nonlinearity, $\frac{2}{1+e^{-\bullet}} - 1$).

Instead of using the mean-square-error cost function criterion for training the SRNN, we have proposed a more effective cost function [6]:

$$E \equiv \frac{1}{2} \sum_{\mathbf{x} \in \mathbf{B}} \frac{\phi^2(\mathbf{x})}{\|\nabla_{\mathbf{x}}\phi(\mathbf{x})\|^2} \tag{1}$$

Mathematically, minimizing this new cost function is equivalent to minimizing the *mean-square distance DIST* between the data and the reconstructed surface [1].

Unfortunately, simulations have indicated the presence of fake boundary curves (or surfaces) in the exterior part of the object due to the difficulty of approximating abrupt changes of some boundary curves. These additional fake curves sometimes degrade the matching accuracy when used in invariant pattern recognition applications [6]. In addition to the fake boundary curves/surfaces, another problem was also observed about using this new cost function in Eq. (1). The magnitude of the positive and negative values created by SRNN for nonboundary regions

are very small (e.g., 0.01) and quite flat (i.e., very small gradient values). Therefore, it is inappropriate to use this reconstructed representation for the measure of degree of matching between a similarly shaped object $\mathbf{B}'$ and the reconstructed object $\mathbf{B}$ regardless the similarity measure is based on $\sum_{\mathbf{x} \in \mathbf{B}'} \phi^2(\mathbf{x})$ or $\sum_{\mathbf{x} \in \mathbf{B}'} \frac{\phi^2(\mathbf{x})}{\|\nabla_{\mathbf{x}}\phi(\mathbf{x})\|^2}$.

B. A Regularized Cost Function to be Minimized

To attack the encountered problems of fake boundaries and the small valued flat nonboundary region, regularizing terms are effectively added into the new cost function in Eq. (1):

$$E \equiv c_1 \sum_{\mathbf{x} \in \mathbf{B}} \frac{\phi^2(\mathbf{x})}{\|\nabla_{\mathbf{x}}\phi(\mathbf{x})\|^2} + c_2 \sum_{\mathbf{x} \in \mathbf{O}} \left(\frac{1 - \phi(\mathbf{x})}{1 + \phi(\mathbf{x})} \right)^2$$
$$+ c_3 \sum_{\mathbf{x} \in \mathbf{G}} (\|\nabla_{\mathbf{x}}\phi(\mathbf{x})\| - 1)^2 \tag{2}$$

where $\mathbf{O}$ is the set of data points uniformly sampled from a large enough sphere to enclose the whole exemplar object. $\mathbf{G}$ is the set of data points sampled along the direction of gradient in a constant step starting from each boundary point "after" the SRNN is trained by the data of $\mathbf{B}$ and $\mathbf{O}$ sets. c_i are the weighting constants. In our simulations, we set $c_1 = 1$, $c_2 = 0.01$, and $c_3 = 0.001$.

Fake Boundary Removal Regularization: Note that all the fake boundary curves/surfaces are created due to the inability of SRNN to form a closed object description to some sharp corners. These fake curves/surfaces always extend to infinity at some point in the space. The first regularizing term ($\mathbf{x} \in \mathbf{O}$) is thus added to force the $\phi(\mathbf{x})$ value of the points outside the object to be one consistently so that a no-zero-crossing zone outside the object is ensured. This is done by uniformly sampling additional points from a large enough sphere which encloses the exemplar object. In our simulations, the large enough sphere has a radius which is twice of the maximum Euclidean distance of all points in $\mathbf{B}$ to their centroid. We also found that the convergence rate of training the SRNN using the regularized cost function (using $\mathbf{B}$ and $\mathbf{O}$) is much faster than that of no regularization (using $\mathbf{B}$ only).

Note that after this regularizing training, the set of boundary points $\mathbf{B}$ is converted into a whole 2D/3D image space description, which is somewhat like a binary image. More specifically, value "1"for exterior region of the exemplar object and negative value of very small magnitude for interior region of the object.

Constant Slope Profile Regularization: The second regularizing term ($\mathbf{x} \in \mathbf{G}$) is imposed *after* the training

Figure 1: The SRNN reconstructed curves and constant slope profile of the 2-D airplane based on the proposed regularized cost function.

of the SRNN using data sets of **B** and **O**. This regularizing term further converts the somewhat binary image description to a constant slope profile image description with respect to the reconstructed boundary. This kind of profile construction is normally achieved by a (chamfer) distance transform in a discrete and nonparametric manner that approximates the Euclidean distance of each discrete image pixel from its nearest boundary pixel [2]. More specifically, this regularization creates a reconstructed image representation which has a constant slope (e.g., $\|\nabla_{\mathbf{x}}\phi\| = 1$) along the radial direction of the object boundary instead of using very sharp cutoff in representation. In our simulations, the sample points in **G** is generated as follows: 1) compute the gradient vector $\nabla_{\mathbf{x}}\phi$ of each boundary point in **B** after the SRNN is trained using **B** and **O** data sets; 2) starting from each boundary point, sample along the direction of gradient in a constant step until the other boundary point is met or exceeding a pre-specified limiting coordinate value; 3) repeat Step 2 by sampling along the opposite gradient direction.

Figure 1 shows the reconstructed shape of a 2-D airplane based on the proposed regularized cost function using the 500 uniformly sampled boundary points. It also shows the reconstructed constant slope profile of the whole 2-D image given by the trained SRNN.

III. ALIGNMENT OF DISTORTED OBJECTS

After trained by the (reference) exemplar object with regularizations, the SRNN establishes an implicit parametric representation of the curves or surfaces (and the whole image space). We are now ready to perform the matching between the represented exemplar objects and any distorted testing object $\{\mathbf{y}^{(i)}\}$ without point correspondence if the latter one can be pre-aligned (i.e., appropriately

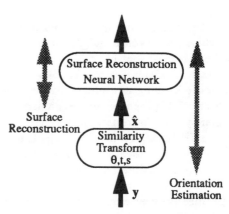

Figure 2: A trained SRNN for representing the exemplar object is coordinated with the similarity transform module for gradual (mental) object alignment.

translated, rotated, and scaled). Our design of alignment of the distorted object is based on the studies by experimental psychology that the task of matching rotated and scaled shapes is done by mentally rotating and scaling gradually one of the shapes into the orientation and size of the other one and then tested for a match [3].

Figure 2 shows the gradual (iterative) similarity transform module in coordination with the SRNN. The basic idea is to allow the *similarity transform module* gradually update the similarity transform parameters $(\theta, \mathbf{t}, s)$ through the guidance of the trained SRNN for exemplar object (by keeping constant the weights of the SRNN). The testing boundary points $\{\mathbf{y}\}$ can thus be best transformed (via rotation $\mathbf{R}(\theta)$ of angle vector θ, scaling constant s, and translation vector $\mathbf{t}$) to the same orientation of the exemplar boundary points $\{\mathbf{x}\}$. Note that, $\hat{\mathbf{x}} = s\mathbf{R}(\theta)\mathbf{y} - \mathbf{t}$. Therefore, the goal of the similarity transform module is to have the transformed (aligned) data $\{\hat{\mathbf{x}}\}$ best match that of the surface reconstructed representation $\phi(\mathbf{x})$ of the exemplar object.

Only by using this kind of cascading configuration, we can efficiently provide the necessary mismatch information in the representation domain from the master SRNN to the slave similarity transform module in the training of the latter one. This idea is similar in concept to several neural network controller designs [7]. The updating of the similarity transform parameters can be implemented by an iterative optimization search. We again used the Gauss Newton search in our implementation.

$$\theta_k \Longleftarrow \theta_k - \eta \frac{\partial E}{\partial \theta_k} = \theta_k - \eta \sum_j^m \frac{\partial E}{\partial \hat{x}_j} \frac{\partial \hat{x}_j}{\partial \theta_k} \qquad (3)$$

where $\frac{\partial E}{\partial \hat{x}_j}$ is calculated in a network inversion procedure [5], which is similar to the derivative calculation of weights

$\frac{\partial E}{\partial w}$ in the back-propagation learning. The mathematical expression of the partial derivatives $\frac{\partial \hat{x}_j}{\partial \theta_k}$ can be pre-calculated since the function (similarity transform equation) is well defined.

The determination of the best similarity transform alignment goes through a couple of iterative sweeps. In each sweep, two steps of updating are consecutively performed. First, only the rotation and the translation parameters are updated (keeping the scaling parameter fixed). Second, after the rotation and the translation parameters converge, the scaling parameter is updated (keeping rotation and translation parameters fixed). This completed the updating of one sweep. The updating process continues until no more changes through all the three steps in one sweep.

IV. 3D Motion Estimation from A Single Perspective

The proposed SRNN can be naturally applied to 3D invariant pattern recognition applications where the testing data might represent partial portion of the complete object due to a limited number of viewing perspective angles. The is demonstrated by the following 3D motion estimation example.

Given a known 3D moving object already represented by an SRNN, we are to estimate its motion based on a sequence of sets of 3D sparse range data $\mathbf{B}'_k = y$, $k = 0, 1, \ldots$, taken from one (varying) perspective of the object. Any similarity transformed data $y = (y_1, y_2, y_3)^T$ on the moving object is obtained by randomly sampling the surface points from the rotated and translated version of the exemplar object. To minimize the complexity involved, the size scaling effect is ignored in this application (i.e., $s = 1$). By using the similarity transform module cascaded between the input and the trained SRNN (see Figure 2), the motion estimation can be done in a similar manner as invariant pattern recognition. Note that we are aligning the distorted object through the similarity transform module to the orientation of the exemplar object. Therefore, the motion parameters estimated are defined with respect to the distorted object, which is different from the usual definition of motion parameters with respect to the exemplar object, this concern can be easily answered. As given in Figure 2 (assume $s = 1$)

$$\hat{x} = \mathbf{R}(\theta)y - t \qquad (4)$$

where $\theta = (\alpha, \beta, \gamma)$, and $t = (t_1, t_2, t_3)^T$ represent roll, pitch, yaw rotation angles and translation vector respectively with respect to the distorted object. Note that, Eq. (4) can be rewritten as

$$y = \mathbf{R}^T \hat{x} + \mathbf{R}^T t \qquad (5)$$

Therefore, after the similarity transform module estimates the $\mathbf{R}$ and t motion parameters with respect to the distorted object, the desired rotation matrix with respect to the exemplar object can be easily obtained as $\mathbf{R}^T$ and the desired translation vector with respect to the exemplar object is $\mathbf{R}^T t$.

By taking advantage of the continuity assumption in tracking the motion, the initial guess of angles (or locations) at each time instance is set to be the estimated angles (or locations) at previous time instance except the initial guesses in the very beginning, i.e., the 0th time instance.

Without loss of generality, let's assume the exemplar object is centered at origin. Due to large portion of missing data resulted from a single perspective range data collection, the initial guess of t in the similarity transform module at the 0th time instance cannot be solely relied on the centroid information of the partial data $\mathbf{B}'_0$. The centroid $\bar{y} = (\bar{y}_1, \bar{y}_2, \bar{y}_3)^T$ is defined from sample average of the single perspective range data in $\mathbf{B}'_0$. If the range finder is assumed to point to y_3 direction, then the initial guesses of t_1 and t_2 at the 0th time instance can still be set to be $\bar{y}_1$ and $\bar{y}_2$, while the initial guess of t_3, the depth of the data, at the 0th time instance should be compensated to be

$$t_3 = \bar{y}_3 + \sqrt{V_x^2 - V_y^2}, \qquad (6)$$

where $V_x = \frac{1}{|\mathbf{B}|} \sum_{x \in \mathbf{B}} \|x - \bar{x}\|$ and $V_y = \frac{1}{|\mathbf{B}'|} \sum_{y \in \mathbf{B}'} \|y - \bar{y}\|$ are the effective volumes of exemplar object and the single perspective range finding object, separately. $\bar{x}$ and $\bar{y}$ denotes the sample average of data sets $\mathbf{B}$ and $\mathbf{B}'$ respectively.

The initial guess of the rotation angles at the 0th time instance is obtained by starting with 32 different possible rotation combinations: $\alpha = \{-135°, -45°, 45°, 135°\}$, $\beta = \{-45°, 45°\}$, and $\gamma = \{-135°, -45°, 45°, 135°\}$. After the presentation of 1st single perspective range data set $\mathbf{B}'_1$, the one produces smallest matching error L_2 is chosen as the initial guess for future motion tracking.

To demonstrate that our motion estimation can work in a wide range of motion parameters, a simulation with trajectory of 101 time instances was conducted. First, a synthetic exemplar object (3D wagon) was generated and one view of the object is shown in Figure 3(a). There are 600 range data uniformly sampled from six views (front, end, left, right, top, and bottom) used for training the SRNN, which consists of one hidden layer of 16 hidden neurons. One single cross section of the constant slope profile of the 3D image space representing the 3D wagon is shown in Figure 3(b).

This SRNN is then cascaded with the similarity trans-

(a)

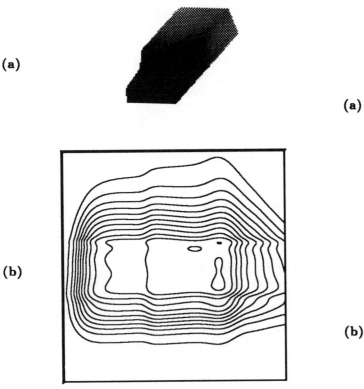

(b)

Figure 3: (a) One perspective view of a synthetic exemplar object (3D wagon). (b) One cross section of the reconstructed SRNN constant slope representation of the whole 3D image.

form module for motion estimation of the 3D wagon. We fixed the camera viewing angle and moved (translate and rotate) the wagon. Images with noise-free and Gaussian noise $N(0, 0.2V_y)$ were used to test the performance of our method. There were only 100 range data randomly sampled from a single perspective The estimation results of 3 rotation angles parameters during the motion tracking in the 101 time instances are shown in Figure 4. The estimation results of 6 motion parameters (3 rotation angles and 3 translation coordinates) during the motion tracking in the 101 time instances are shown in Figures 4 and 5.

V. CONCLUSION

This paper presents a regularized surface reconstruction neural network approach to perform robust invariant 2D/3D object recognition and motion estimation. By efficiently embedding the whole 2D/3D image space into a neural network parametric representation, we are able to elegantly duplicate the human's mental image transform and matching capability in performing the rotating and

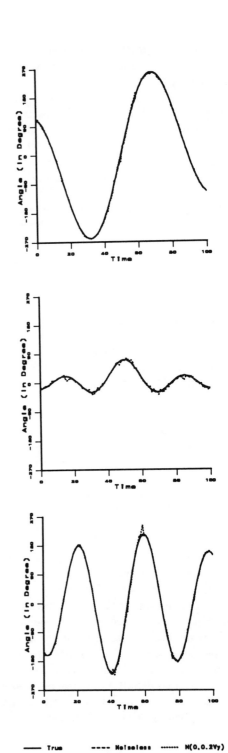

Figure 4: Motion estimation results of 3 rotation angles based on noiseless and noisy sparse range data collected from a single perspective view. (a) Estimation of α. (b) Estimation of β. (c) Estimation of γ.

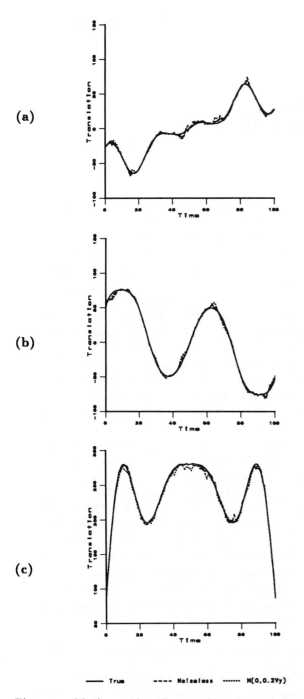

(a)

(b)

(c)

——— True   ---- Noiseless   ······· N(0,0.2Vy)

Figure 5: Motion estimation results of 3 translation co-ordinates based on noiseless and noisy sparse range data collected from a single perspective view. (a) Estimation of t_1. (b) Estimation of t_2. (c) Estimation of t_3.

scaling of objects as suggested by the studies of experimental psychology. The preliminary simulations of applying this technique to invariant 2D target classification and 3D object motion estimation using sparse range data collected from a single perspective view are encouraging. Further research in using this technique for standard 2D images (instead of range data) is explored.

REFERENCES

[1] R. J. Bolle and B. C. Vermuri. On three-dimensional surface reconstruction methods. *IEEE Trans. on PAMI*, 13(1):1-13, January 1991.

[2] G. Borgefors. Hierarchical chamfer matching: a parametric edge matching algorithm. IEEE Trans. on PAMI, 10(6):849-865, Nov. 1988.

[3] C. Bundesen and A. Larsen. Visual Transformation of Size. Journal of Experimental Psychology: Human Perception and Performance, 1(3):214-220, 1975.

[4] J. N. Hwang and P. S. Lewis. From nonlinear optimization to neural network learning. In Proc. *24th Asilomar Conf. on Signals, Systems, & Computers*, pp. 985-989, Pacific Grove, CA, November 1990.

[5] J. N. Hwang, J. J. Choi, S. Oh, and R. J. Marks II. Query based learning applied to partially trained multilayer perceptrons. IEEE Trans. on Neural Networks, Vol. 2, No. 1, pp. 131-136, January 1991.

[6] J.N. Hwang and H. Li. Invariant object recognition via surface reconstruction neural networks. Int'l Joint Conf. on Neural Networks, Vol. 3, pp. 184-189, 1992.

[7] D. Nguyen and B. Widrow. The truck backer-upper: an example of self-learning in neural networks. In *Int'l Joint Conf. on Neural Networks (IJCNN), Washington D.C.*, pages II357–II363, June 1989.

[8] L. H. Staib and J. S. Duncan. Boundary finding with parametrically deformable models. IEEE Trans. on PAMI, 14(11):1061-1075, November 1992.

Textured Image Segmentation via Neural Network Probabilistic Modeling

Jenq-Neng Hwang,   Eric Tsung-Yen Chen

Information Processing Laboratory
Department of Electrical Engineering, FT-10
University of Washington
Seattle, WA 98195

ABSTRACT

It has been shown that a trained back-propagation neural network (BPNN) classifier produces outputs which can be interpreted as estimates of Bayesian *a posteriori* probabilities. Based on this interpretation, we propose a back-propagation neural network (BPNN) approach for the estimation of the local conditional distributions of textured images, which are commonly represented by a Markov random field (MRF) formulation. The proposed BPNN approach overcomes many of the difficulties encountered when using MRF formulation. In particular our approach does not require the trial-and-error choice of clique functions or the subsequent unreliable estimation of clique parameters. Simulations show that the images synthesized using BPNN modeling produced desired textures more consistently than MRF based methods. Application of the proposed BPNN approach to synthesis and segmentation of real world textures is also presented.

I. INTRODUCTION

In statistical image analysis we usually try to estimate the true scene (in image restoration) or texture labels (in image segmentation) based on the observed image. Markov random field (MRF) modeling has been widely used in both tasks [2, 4]. The MRF is a parametric representation of images and requires a careful choice of models (clique functions). In addition, the clique parameters which generate the local conditional probabilities require tedious and laborious estimation. Different estimation techniques have been proposed, e.g., coding method, maximum pseudo likelihood [1], and linear least square methods using histogramming [2]. These methods require the solution of a set of nonlinear equations that are difficult and cumbersome to solve or least square solutions to a big set of linear equations [2]. Moreover, most real world textured images may possess approximately local neighborhood pixel interactions but not necessarily follow the

assumptions of MRF, where the global distribution of the image is constituted from the neighborhood local distribution in an exponential form based on the linearly weighted *clique* potentials (i.e., Gibbs distributed). The method proposed here is a much relaxed probabilistic model based on the nonparametric representation of the local interactions using feedforward back-propagation neural networks (BPNNs). We believe our BPNN model is a parsimonious representation whose local interactions are consistent with a much higher order MRF. More specifically, the simple linear weighting interaction of cliques in the Gibbs distribution for a very large order neighborhood may well result in local nonlinear interactions that can be approximated by a BPNN model using only the pixel values in a smaller order neighborhood.

In the next section, we will investigate the Bayes probability approximation capability of a BPNN network. Section III will cover the MRF model approach and our proposed BPNN based probabilistic model. In Section IV we compare the performance of the proposed BPNN method with existing MRF method in synthesizing artificial textures, and show examples of using the proposed BPNN method for synthesizing real world textures, which can hardly be done using MRF methods. Application of the proposed model to segmentation of real world textures is illustrated in Section V and followed by concluding remarks in Section VI.

II. BAYES PROBABILITY ESTIMATION OF BPNNs

In a classification application, it is normally assumed that the input vector, $\mathbf{x} \in \mathbb{R}^n$, belongs to one of M classes, g_m, $1 \leq m \leq M$ (note that, the definition of class can be different grey levels in a restoration application, or can be different texture labels in a segmentation application). The main objective of a classification task is to decide to which of the M classes the vector $\mathbf{x}$ belongs. The decision can be made based on some forms of deterministic discriminant function, e.g., the Euclidean distance measure. A more general decision rule is based on the probabilistic decision, such as maximum *a posteriori* (MAP) approaches which guarantees the minimum classification error. In an MAP approach, for each of the classes one requires to estimate the posterior probability, $P(g_m|\mathbf{x})$, which is usually computed via the Bayes' rule:

$$P(g_m|\mathbf{x}) = \frac{P(\mathbf{x}|g_m)P(g_m)}{P(\mathbf{x})} \propto P(\mathbf{x}|g_m)P(g_m) \quad (1)$$

where $P(\mathbf{x}|g_m)$ is the conditional density (also known as likelihood) and $P(g_m)$ is the *a priori* probability of the class g_m.

Since $P(g_m)$ is easy to compute, most conventional pattern classification literatures have been focusing on the research of estimating the likelihood $P(\mathbf{x}|g_m)$. On the other hand, when a BPNN is used for this classification task, there is usually an input layer of n neurons corresponding to the n-dimensional input vector $\mathbf{x}$, one or two layers of "well chosen" hidden neurons, and one output layer of M neurons with each one representative of one of the M different classes. It has been shown that the output activations $\mathbf{y}$ of a BPNN trained by the standard back-propagation learning, which minimizes the mean squared error (MSE) between the actual output $\mathbf{y}$ and the desired target binary vector $\mathbf{t}$, indeed provide a least squares estimate of the posterior probability [5]. Therefore neural network classifiers bypass the stage of estimating the likelihood and directly estimate the posterior probability.

A. Kullback-Leibler Training Criterion

Unfortunately, the MSE criterion tends to give better estimates at large values than at small values [5]. In case of noisy input vector, $\mathbf{x}$, there is no clear winner by simply judging from the output activation values of the neural networks, it then becomes very important to consider all the posterior probabilities generated by the neural network to make the final decision. The performance is usually severely degraded by the deficiency created by the MSE criterion. One criterion called Kullback-Leibler (KL) criterion which overcomes this deficiency and provide a better probability estimate can thus be adopted. The KL criterion, derived from information theory, suggests the *relative entropy*, E_{KL}, to be a better measure of the difference between the desired probability $\{t_m = P(g_m|\mathbf{x})\}$ and the actual estimated probability $\{y_m\}$ determined by the activation value output neuron [6]. More specifically, given K finite training vectors $\{\mathbf{x}^{(k)}, \; k = 1, \ldots, K\}$, E_{KL} can be approximated by:

$$\begin{aligned} E_{KL} &= \sum_{m=1}^{M} \sum_{k=1}^{K} \frac{1}{2} \left[(1 + t_m^{(k)}) \log(\frac{1 + t_m^{(k)}}{1 + y_m^{(k)}}) \right. \\ &\quad + \left. (1 - t_m^{(k)}) \log(\frac{1 - t_m^{(k)}}{1 - y_m^{(k)}}) \right] \quad (2) \end{aligned}$$

where $y_m^{(k)} = y_m^{(k)}(\mathbf{x}^{(k)}, \mathbf{w})$ is a function of inputs $\mathbf{x}^{(k)}$ and all the BPNN weights $\mathbf{w}$. The targets $\{t_m^{(k)}\}$ and the actual outputs $\{y_m^{(k)}\}$ are confined within the interval $[-1, 1]$. In this setting, the desired posterior probability is denoted as $\frac{1}{2}(1 + t_m^{(k)})$, and similarly the actual estimated posterior probability is denoted as $\frac{1}{2}(1 + y_m^{(k)})$.

B. Posterior Probability Approximation Capabilities

To verify the posterior probability approximation capabilities of a 2-layer (one hidden layer) BPNN trained with Kullback-Leibler criterion, we conducted a simple binary classification task with data generated from two sets of mixture Gaussians (class 1 has two Gaussian-mixtures and class 2 has three):

$$\begin{aligned} P(x_1, x_2|g_1) &= \frac{1}{2} [N_{x_1}(-0.2, 0.2)N_{x_2}(-0.2, 0.1) \\ &\quad + N_{x_1}(-0.6, 0.01)N_{x_2}(-0.6, 0.6)] \\ P(x_1, x_2|g_2) &= \frac{1}{3} [N_{x_1}(0.5, 0.2)N_{x_2}(0.6, 0.2) \\ &\quad + N_{x_1}(0.0, 0.1)N_{x_2}(0.0, 0.6) \\ &\quad + N_{x_1}(0.9, 0.2)N_{x_2}(0.5, 0.2)] \end{aligned}$$

where $N_{x_i}(m, \sigma)$ denotes a Gaussian (normal) distribution in i-th dimension with mean m and standard deviation σ.

A subset of simulated data is shown in Figure 1, where '*' denotes the class 1 and 'o' denotes the class 2. There are 6,000 random samples generated for each class for BPNN training using the Kullback-Leibler criteria. Another 10,000 uniform grid samples are used for testing classification accuracy. Table 1 shows the classification accuracy of the 10,000 testing data and the *percentage of variance explained* (PVE) [3] between the true Bayesian density and the estimated density:

$$PVE = 100(1 - E/Var)\%$$

where $E = \frac{1}{N} \sum_n (\hat{P}_n - P_n)^2$ denotes the mean squared error over N testing data, and $Var = \frac{1}{N} \sum_n (P_n - \bar{P}_n)^2$ denotes the sample variance.

It can thus be concluded that a BPNN trained with Kullback-Leibler criterion can give quite satisfactory approximation of posterior probability in a classification task.

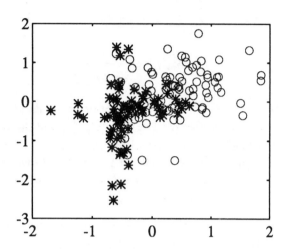

Figure 1: A subset of randomly generated training data of Gaussian mixtures from two different classes.

No. of Hidden Neurons	Classification Accuracy	PVE Measure
10 Neurons	86.12%	75.39%
20 Neurons	85.81%	68.25%
30 Neurons	85.83%	74.82%

Table 1: Classification accuracy of the 10,000 testing data and the PVE measures between the true Bayesian density and the estimated density.

III. MARKOV RANDOM FIELD AND BPNN MODELING

An MRF model, which specifies the *a priori* joint distribution $P(\mathbf{x})$ of an image $\mathbf{x} = \{x_{ij}\}$, induces the posterior distribution for the restoration or segmentation purposes and is determined by the local conditional distributions $\{P(x_{ij}|x_{\eta_{ij}})\}$ of all pixels $\{x_{ij}\}$ (where $x_{\eta_{ij}}$ is the set of neighboring pixels of x_{ij}). The Gibbs sampler, introduced by Geman and Geman [4], is a simple but powerful technique. By successively updating a univariate component according to its local characteristics $\{P(x_{ij}|x_{\eta_{ij}})\}$, the convergence towards a maximum configurdation of the joint distribution $P(\mathbf{x})$ is guaranteed under rather general conditions where Brooks expansion [1] is valid.

A. Markov Random Field and Gibbs Distribution

In an MRF setting, an image is treated as a discrete 2-D random field defined over $N_1 \times N_2$ rectangular lattice of points, $\mathbf{L} = \{(i,j)|1 \le i \le N_1,\ 1 \le j \le N_2\}$. A neighborhood system η defined on $\mathbf{L}$ is a collection of subsets of $\mathbf{L}$,

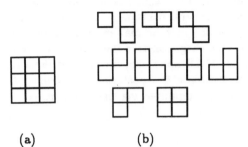

Figure 2: (a) The 2nd order neighborhood system $\eta^{(2)}$. (b) The associated cliques for $\eta^{(2)}$.

$\eta = \{\eta_{ij}|(i,j) \in \mathbf{L},\ \eta_{ij} \subseteq \mathbf{L}\}$, which satisfies the following two conditions: 1) $(i,j) \notin \eta_{ij}$, and 2) if $(k,l) \in \eta_{ij}$, then $(i,j) \in \eta_{kl}$ for any $(i,j) \in \mathbf{L}$.

A neighborhood system can be extended to any order hierarchically, e.g., 1st order neighborhood system $\eta_{ij}^{(1)}$ contains the nearest four pixels surrounding (i,j), and 2nd order neighborhood system $\eta_{i,j}^{(2)}$ contains the nearest eight pixels surrounding (i,j), and so on.

A *clique*, $\mathbf{c}$, associated with a specific neighborhood η_{ij} is a subset of $\mathbf{L}$ such that 1) $\mathbf{c}$ contains the single pixel (i,j), or 2) for $(i,j) \ne (k,l)$, $(i,j) \in \mathbf{c}$ and $(k,l) \in \mathbf{c}$ implies that $(i,j) \in \eta_{kl}$. The collection of all cliques of $(\mathbf{L},\eta)$ is denoted by $\mathbf{C}$. Figures 2(a) and 2(b) show a 2nd order neighborhood system $\eta^{(2)}$ and its associated 10 cliques.

A random field $\mathbf{x} = \{x_{ij}\}$ defined over the lattice $\mathbf{L}$ is *Gibbs distributed* with respect to η if its joint distribution is of the form

$$P(\mathbf{x}) = \frac{1}{Z} exp(-U(\mathbf{x})) \qquad (3)$$

where $U(\mathbf{x}) = \sum_{\mathbf{c} \in \mathbf{C}} V_{\mathbf{c}}(\mathbf{x})$ is the *energy function*, $V_{\mathbf{c}}(\mathbf{x})$ is the *potential* associated with each individual clique $\mathbf{c}$, and Z is a normalization factor.

Note that the Gibbs distribution is a kind of exponential distribution which states that the joint distribution of $\mathbf{x}$ can be decomposed into local potential functions

$$P(x_{ij}|x_{\eta_{i,j}}) = \frac{1}{Z} exp(\sum_{\mathbf{c} \in \mathbf{C}_{ij}} V_{\mathbf{c}}(x_{ij}, x_{\eta_{i,j}})). \qquad (4)$$

The potential functions $\{V_{\mathbf{c}}(\mathbf{x})\}$ (also called as clique functions) defined over cliques of neighborhood system η are usually based on an *ad hoc* parametric form with each (weighting) parameter controlling each type of clique [2], e.g., the most widely used one is

$$V_{\mathbf{c}}(\mathbf{x}) = \begin{cases} -a\beta_k, & all\ x_{ij}\ in\ \mathbf{c}\ of\ k^{th}\ type\ are\ equal \\ a\beta_k, & otherwise \end{cases}$$

$$(5)$$

where a is an arbitrarily chosen scaling constant, and $\{\beta_k\}$ are the clique parameters. Note that, although this class of clique functions have been successfully used in modeling artificial textures of small number of grey levels or small order of neighborhood, they cannot be easily extended and applied to most real world textures.

One commonly used estimation method for determining the clique parameters $\{\beta_k\}$ of a MRF is the coding method [1], which is basically a maximum likelihood method under conditional independence assumption, i.e., the Markov assumption. In this method, each pixel in image is "coded" based on the assumed neighborhood system, specifically, pixels that are not neighbors are assigned the same label. Nevertheless, the coding method requires solution to a set of nonlinear equations that are difficult and cumbersome to solve and can not be used reliably.

B. Unreliable Estimates of Clique Parameters

A computationally more feasible method was proposed based on a least square framework [2], which estimates parameter values by solving linear equations using histogramming. Due to the requirement of counting local configuration based on single realization and solving the pseudo inverse of a large size matrix, this method also results in an unreliable estimate.

To illustrate the unreliablity of the parameter estimation, comparative simulations were performed. Figure 3 shows two different types of artificial textures of 4 grey levels with parameters specified in Table 2 [2]. We start with two original artificial textures of 2nd order MRF with size 128×128 (see row A of Figure 3). These two textured images were generated by Gibbs sampling technique [4] based on 4 nonzero clique parameters given in column A of Table 2. In fact, there should be 9 clique parameters for 9 different cliques excluding the single pixel clique (see Figure 2(b)). Based on the original textured images, the clique parameters were then estimated using linear least square method [2]. Note that the estimation results are quite inconsistent when the number of parameters to be estimated and the forms of clique functions vary. For example, Column E4 in Table 2 denotes the estimates for the first four parameters (with the knowledge of the rest parameters being zero in advance) based on the a choice of scaling constant $a = 0.5$. The resynthesized textured image based on this estimate is shown in row E4 of Figure 3. Column E9 in Table 2 denotes the estimates for all the 9 parameters (without the knowledge of the rest parameters being zero in advance) based on the same scaling constant. The resynthesized textured image based on this estimate is also shown in row E9 of Figure 3.

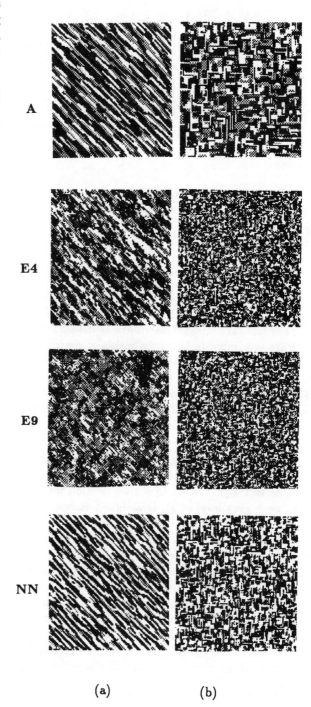

(a)   (b)

Figure 3: (a) The original and the estimated & resynthesized images of artificial texture type 1. (b) The original and the estimated & resynthesized images of artificial texture type 2.

	A	E4	E9		A	E4	E9
β_1	1.0	0.64	0.71	β_1	2.0	1.31	0.98
β_2	1.0	0.80	0.87	β_2	2.0	1.29	0.93
β_3	-1.0	-0.47	1.58	β_3	-1.0	-0.57	-0.70
β_4	1.0	1.27	1.01	β_4	-1.0	-0.67	-0.68
β_5	0.0		-1.41	β_5	0.0		0.00
β_6	0.0		0.17	β_6	0.0		-0.16
β_7	0.0		0.43	β_7	0.0		0.00
β_8	0.0		-1.62	β_8	0.0		0.06
β_9	0.0		0.58	β_9	0.0		0.61
	(a)				(b)		

Table 2: (a) True and estimated clique parameters for texture type 1. (b) True and estimated clique parameters for texture type 2.

C. The BPNN Probabilistic Modeling

In an MRF setting, each clique type associated with the assumed neighborhood system should be well defined. Since all the local conditional distributions determine the joint, we are interested in the distribution of center pixel x_{ij} conditioned on its neighbors $x_{\eta_{ij}}$, i.e., $P(x_{ij}|x_{\eta_{ij}})$. Notice that instead of using the complicated parametric form of MRF clique functions in specifying $P(x_{ij}|x_{\eta_{ij}})$, we can formulate this local conditional probability easily in a BPNN setting for classification problems.

In our BPNN probabilistic modeling, the training is constructed by simply feeding each BPNN with neighborhood configuration $x_{\eta_{ij}}$ of each pixel x_{ij} and assigning center value as target $t = g_m$ in a classification formulation (i.e., each grey level of x_{ij} is assigned as one class). For example, in our training of the two artificial textures (see row A of Figure 3), each BPNN contains 8 inputs to represent 8 (2nd order) neighboring pixels, 10 hidden neurons, and 4 output neurons to represent 4 grey levels. All the 128×128 pixels are used as training data (a wrap around image configuration is assumed). 1000 iterations of training is used. After training, the BPNN responds to the neighborhood configuration inputs by providing the posterior probabilities as outputs for the center cite being assigned to all grey levels, i.e., the BPNN represents a model of underlying field which is conventionally modeled by Gibbs distribution of parametric form in $P(x_{ij}|x_{\eta_{ij}})$.

The resynthesized images using BPNN modeling and the Gibbs sampling procedure is shown in row NN of Figure 3. Two BPNNs are trained (one for each texture) and the training accuracies are 90% and 89% for texture type 1 and 2, respectively. Compared with those resynthesized images (in rows E4 and E9) using MRF modeling shown

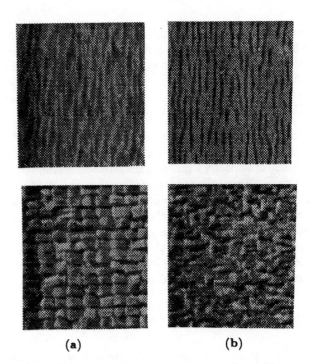

Figure 4: (a) The original images of real world texture type 1 and 2. (b) The BPNN estimated & resynthesized images of real world texture type 1 and 2.

in Figure 3, we found our BPNN approach gives desired textures more consistently.

To further illustrate the consistency of the proposed BPNN for modeling textures, simulations were conducted for synthesizing real world textures. We trained two BPNNs of 24-30-16 configuration on two different types of real world textures of 16 grey levels as shown in Figure 4(a). Note that, a larger 5×5 neighborhood system is used. We were not able to perform this task using MRF method because no meaningful formulation of clique functions can be defined for this large number of grey levels and high order of neighborhood (i.e., exponentially increasing number of clique types). On the other hand, the BPNN method could be applied in a straightforward manner as we did for the artificial textures. The estimated and resynthesized textures by BPNN modeling and Gibbs sampling were able to give quite desirable results (see Figure 4(b)).

IV. APPLICATION TO TEXTURE SEGMENTATION

We are to segment a textured image (see Figure 5), that consists of two real world textures of 16 grey levels (see Figure 4), using the proposed BPNN modeling. This image has the mask shape artificially created by hand drawing (see Figure 5(a)). The corresponding textured image is shown in Figure 5(b). The segmentation procedure based

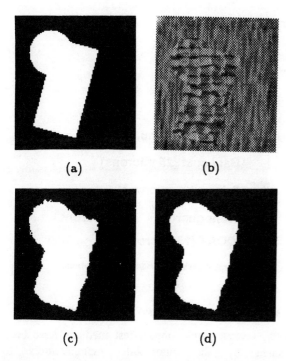

(a)   (b)

(c)   (d)

Figure 5: (a) The segmentation mask with shapes artificially created by hand drawing. (b) The corresponding
textured image for (a). (c) The segmentation result after
50 iterations of Gibbs sampling based on BPNN model.
(d) The segmentation result after median filtering.

on MAP strategy and Gibbs sampling are then applied [1].
The *a priori* probability $P(g_m)$ required in segmentation
(see Eq. (1)) is based on a simple 3×3 MRF model with
all clique parameters equal to one. Figures 5(c) shows
the segmentation results after 50 iterations of Gibbs sampling. The segmentation results can be further improved
by smoothing with a simple 3×3 median filtering to remove those sporadic mistakes in the segmentation process
(see Figure 5(d)).

V. Concluding Remarks

We have proposed a BPNN approach for modeling Markov
random field. Our simulation results shows that a BPNN
trained with Kullback-Leibler criterion can provide a
fairly good estimate of Bayesian a posteriori probability for probabilistic image modeling. While conventional
MRF modeling relies on difficult parameter estimation
techniques, our method gives a simpler and more reliable solution which provides conditional probabilities required by Gibbs sampler. The proposed technique is verified by successful application to textured image syntheses
and segmentation to both artificial textures and real world
textures.

References

[1] J. Besag. On the statistical analysis of dirty pictures
J. R. Statist. Soc. B. 48:259-302, 1986

[2] H. Derin and H. Elliott. Modeling and segmentation
of noisy and textured images using Gibbs random
fields. IEEE Trans. on PAMI, 9(1):39-55, January
1987.

[3] J. H. Friedman, W. Stuetzle, A. Schroeder Projection
Pursuit Density Estimation. Journal of the American
Statistical Association, Vol 79, pp. 599-608, 1984.

[4] S. Geman, D. Geman. Stochastic relaxation, Gibbs
distribution, and the Bayesian restoration of images.
IEEE Trans. on PAMI, 6(6):721-741, November 1984.

[5] J. Makhoul. Pattern recognition properties of neural networks. IEEE-SP Workshop on Neural Networks for Signal Processing, pp. 173-186, Princeton
NJ, 1991.

[6] B. S. Wittner, J. S. Denker Strategies for teaching
layered networks classification tasks. In Neural Information Processing Systems. ed. D. Z. Anderson, ppi.
850-859, New York: American Institute of Physics.
1988

STONE IMPACT DAMAGE TO AUTOMOTIVE PAINT FINISHES - A NEURAL NET ANALYSIS OF ELECTROCHEMICAL IMPEDANCE DATA

A. C. Ramamurthy* and Mirana Uriquidi-Macdonald**

BASF Corporation, 26701, Telegraph Road, Southfield, MI 48086
** Department of Engineering Science and Mechanics
The Pennsylvania State University, University Park, PA, 16802

ABSTRACT- Automotive car bodies are subject to impact by stones either lofted from tires or launched by other passing vehicles. Impact can result either in physical loss of paint and the possibility of failure at the metal/phosphate - Polymer interface. Corrosion brought about as a result of impact is referred to as Impact Induced Corrosion or IIC. Electrochemical Impedance is very sensitive to delamination at the metal - polymer interface and is able to discern the influence of velocity, angle of impact, the type of coating and ambient temperature. Neural Network analysis of electrochemical impedance data are presented.

I . INTRODUCTION

A common source of damage to automotive paint finishes is due to impact of small stones either lofted by tires or from other passing vehicles. Stone impact damage can result in either physical loss of paint or delamination at the metal-polymer interface [1,2]. Physical loss of paint is a "cosmetic" issue while delamination leads to corrosion beneath the coating which can ultimately lead to perforation. We refer to corrosion due to impact as Impact Induced corrosion or IIC. Figure 1 shows a typical multilayer automotive paint system. The ECOAT layer serves as barrier for corrosion protection, Stoneguard™ as an "anti" stone chip layer, the Basecoat contains all the color pigments and the Clearcoat serves as glossy scratch and UV resistance layer.

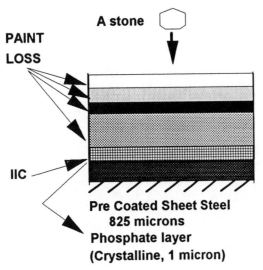

A stone

PAINT LOSS

IIC

Pre Coated Sheet Steel
825 microns
Phosphate layer
(Crystalline, 1 micron)

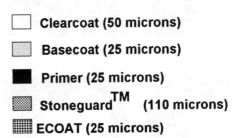

☐ Clearcoat (50 microns)

▨ Basecoat (25 microns)

■ Primer (25 microns)

▨ Stoneguard™ (110 microns)

▦ ECOAT (25 microns)

Fig 1. Paint layers for Modern Automobiles

II. ADVANCED EXPERIMENTAL AND ANALYSIS TECHNIQUES

Recently, several single impact test methods have been implemented by the automobile manufacturers to systematically evaluate paint systems. These techniques have the ability to precisely control velocity, angle of incidence of the projectile and operate over a wide temperature range.

Single impact methods have also led to the use of advanced post impact damage techniques such as digital image analysis, thermal imaging, ultrasonic microscopy and EIS [3] to estimate percent paint loss and impact induced corrosion. The ultimate goal of this analysis is to discern the effects of impact variables and be able to construct an "impact response surface" for any given substrate/coating system.

Impact phenomenon of which IIC is a part of, is a complex non-linear threshold phenomenon and Table I shows a partial list of variables that are known to affect impact response. Given a complex phenomenon such as impact damage, a coatings formulator typically resorts to a well planned statistical design to, A) design new impact resistant coating systems and B) efficiently carry out impact experiments. These procedures takes into account all the chemical and experimental variables necessary to design new coating systems based on the impact response. Analysis of the data [4,5] can provide insight into main effects, two and three factor interactions between the variables that may influence the phenomenon. This insight offers suggestions to the coatings designer to make the required polymer/pigment modifications (in one or more layers) which would "weaken" the effect on the variables, e.g., temperature or type of pigments, which adversely affect impact response.

Table I : Complexity of impact damage phenomenon

VARIABLES	ATTRIBUTES
Projectile	Size Density Shape Modulus Poisson's ratio
Impact	Velocity Angle of incidence
Environment	Temperature Humidity Corrosion cycle
Coating	Viscoelsatic properties Adhesion Fracture toughness
Fixture	Stiffness
Substrate	Type Thickness High strain rate- properties

Besides this capability, it is also desirable to be able to predict damage response outside the range of conditions chosen for the laboratory simulation. Predictions outside the range, if found reliable via independent experiments, can help set confidence & tolerance limits for a given substrate/coating system. Since there exists no deterministic approach to account for our observations on impact induced corrosion, we suggest the application of Neural Networks (NN) as a predictive tool. It is our intention to show in the present work , the feasibility of using NN to account for the intrinsic complex relation between the input variables and the observed impact response.

Neural networks are relatively new mathematical techniques for solving complex non linear problems frequently encountered in science and engineering [6]. A typical NN may contain from few to several hundred simulated neurons. Each connection is associated with a number or weight, and each neuron associated with a transfer function. NN's can be trained to operate either in the supervised or unsupervised mode. In the supervised mode as used in the present work, NN "learns" adjusting its weights when given the input and target values.

In this work we introduce Electrochemical Impedance Spectroscopy as a sensitive tool to detect and quantify impact induced corrosion. Also, in this work, we present our first attempt to rationalize impact response (for IIC) using Neural Network methods. To the best of our knowledge, this work is the first investigation reported on the application of EIS for detecting IIC and to present a preliminary approach for data analysis.

III. EIS BODE PLOTS AS AN IIC DIAGNOSTIC [11]

It is well known that electrochemical impedance is a very sensitive technique for detecting delamination at the metal-polymer interface [7]. Since the objective of this work is not to discern the mechanistic aspects of IIC, EIS merely serves as a quantitative diagnostic tool. Figure 2 shows a typical Bode magnitude plot for a coated metal in contact with an electrolyte solution. Under impact loading, if the Metal-Polymer interface remains intact, one typically observes a straight line with a slope -1 and the low frequency impedance magnitude (typically at 0.1 Hz) would exceed 10^9 ohms . cm^2. If impact causes delamination at the metal/phosphate - ECOAT (refer to Figure 1) interface, one expects impedance magnitude at low frequencies, to be in the range 10^3 to 10^5 ohms. cm^2 .

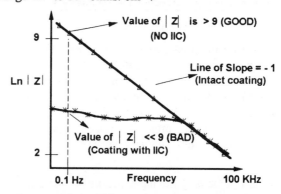

Figure 2: Typical Bode plots for an intact coating and for a system exhibiting impact induced corrosion

This work exploits the measurement of impedance, $|Z|$ at low frequencies as measure of IIC. The lower the $|Z|$ value at 0.1 Hz, the greater the degree of IIC. Visualization of interaction effects of impact variables (velocity and angle of incidence) and ambient temperature is not straightforward by examining raw impedance data. Our preliminary approach which involved viewing superimposed Bode plots obtained under various experimental conditions failed to provide any insight on the influence of variables which effect IIC. In the present work we propose to use $|Z|$ measured at 0. 1 Hz for Neural Net analysis.

III. EXPERIMENTAL

The test matrix consisted of only variations in the ECOAT layer and phosphate pre treatment. TABLE II shows the test matrix and impact conditions chosen in the present study. TYPE A and TYPE B ECOAT's were model systems in which significant changes in polymer structure were implemented while TYPE C was a commercial system currently used in the industry.

The impact device used in this work was developed and is marketed by VIANOVA resins in GRAZ, Austria and is described in the literature [8].

Table II : Impact matrix and parameters

ECOAT	PHOSPHATE	PIGMENT	IMPACT VARIABLES
TYPE A	+	P	Velocity: 60, 80 and 120 km/hr.
	-	C	Angle of Incidence: 45, 60 and 90 degree.
TYPE B	+	P	
	-	C	Temperature: -20, 0 and + 20 Celsius.
TYPE C (Commercial)	+	P	

+ : Phosphated Cold Rolled Steel.
- : Bare Cold Rolled Steel
P : Pigmented ECOAT.
C : Clear ECOAT.
Cold Rolled Steel supplied by ACT, Hillsdale, MI.
Phosphate : Gardobond 24 by CHEMETALL, Frankfurt, Germany.

IV. DATA ANALYSIS

A Forward-Backward propagation Neural Network with two hidden layer of neurons was used in the analysis. Neural Works Professional II/PLUS (Neural Ware, Pittsburgh, PA) running on a Macintosh II ci computer was used in this work. During training, the artificial neural net learns from input vectors (temperature, projectile velocity, projectile angle of incidence), and output vectors (measured impedance).

During the test mode only the input vectors are used, and the net predicted the results (impedance). The total data set had nine metal-polymer interfaces for which the magnitude of the impedance at 0.1 Hz was measured at three temperatures, three projectile velocities and three angles of incidence. The data set was divided into two sections. The first section consisted of approximately 66 % of the total data while second one with 34 %. The selection process was random. The former section went into the "training" mode the latter section serving as the "test" mode.

The analysis was carried out on the entire data set (for all the nine systems), averaging the measured impedance for all the tests at given temperature, angle and velocity. Figure 3 shows the NN predictions trend for TYPE a (+) coating. |Z| decreases with increase in velocity (Figure 3 A) and temperature (Figure 3 B) while exhibiting a minimum at 60 degree angle of impact (Figure 3 C) These trends observed however are not the same for each one of the nine individual systems investigated in this study.

V. RESULTS AND DISCUSSION

Figures 4 to 6 show typical Bode plots illustrating the influence of velocity, angle of incidence, ambient temperature. It is clear from these representative plots, EIS is able to clearly discern the influence of the variables at the levels chosen in this study.

NN analysis indicate the best correlation between predicted and measured data are obtained for Type A (+)

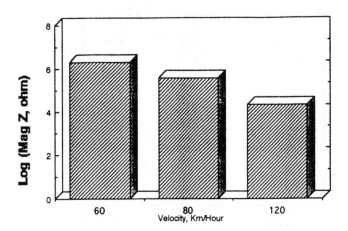

Fig. 3 A

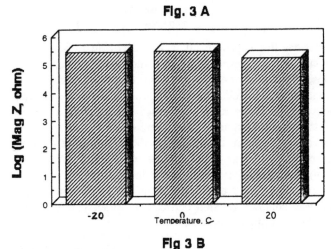

Fig 3 B

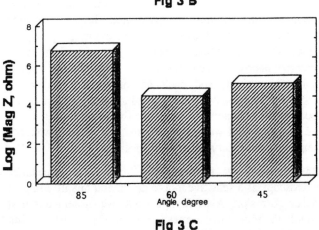

Fig 3 C

system (Figure 7). For the other eight systems NN predictions are very good for higher |Z| values but at the lower end predicted values are higher than measured values. This discrepancy is due to the quality of data. Since the various coating systems behave differently with velocity, angle and temperature, it is not clear at this stage of research

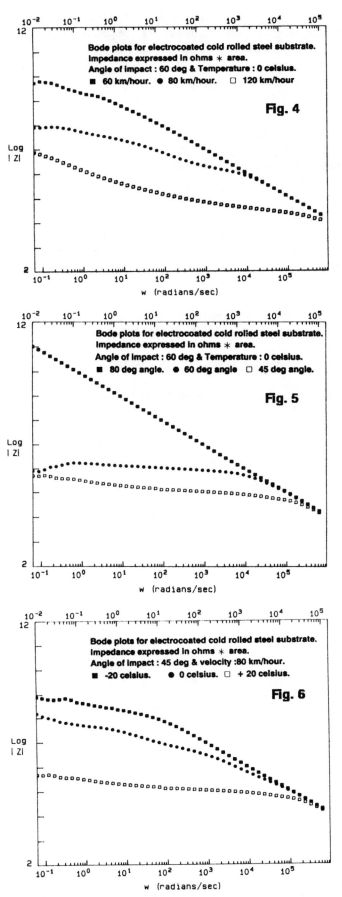

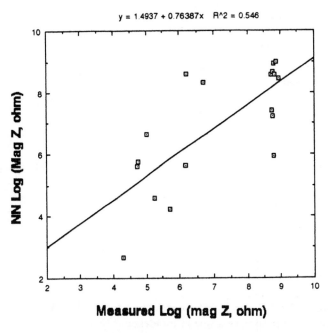

$y = 1.4937 + 0.76387x$ $R^2 = 0.546$

Fig 7. Correlation between NN predicted impedance and measured impedance for TYPE A (+) system.

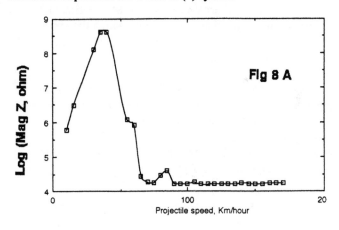

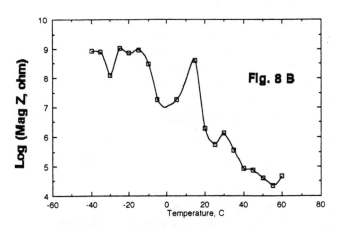

Fig 8 A & B : NN predicted impedance's for TYPE A (+) system as a function of velocity and temperature.

1711

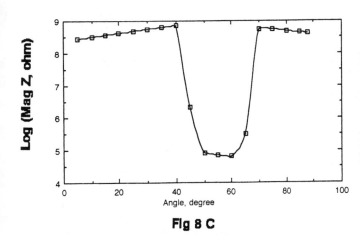

Fig 8 C

Figure 8 C : NN predicted impedance's for TYPE A(+) system as a function of angle of incidence.

if the trends in the observed impedance are real and within experimental error. Furthermore, the value of experimental error is unknown and the data set is small. Due to the above considerations, data for Type A + was used to train the NN and to explore its predictions.

Figure 8 shows NN predictions of impedance as function of temperature, velocity and angle for TYPE A (+) system. The oscillations observed in the temperature plot are due to poor quality of data as pointed out above. NN predictions follow a trend indicated by the dashed line, which is in agreement with experimental observations.

For velocities above 35 km/hr, NN predictions with experimental observations are good. NN also predicts a constant impedance reached at higher velocities which is supported by experimental observations. The discrepancy at low velocities may be due to the fact that impact damage is a threshold phenomenon and the data set is not trained in this regime. NN predictions with the variable, angle of incidence, are good and are supported by our experimental observations.

VI. CONCLUSIONS

This study has been able to show that EIS is a very sensitive post impact diagnostic probe to detect delamination at the metal-polymer boundary. Considering the noisy quality of data, the learning of the NN was good. We have been able to show that NN is able to make predictions that are in agreement with independent experimental observations. Based on this preliminary work, future use of NN as predictive tools will rely on a comprehensive data set

obtained under rigorous experimental conditions using stone projectiles, alternate treatments of impedance data and also taking into account parameters such as stone shape, mass, and density.

VII. REFERENCES

1. A. C. Ramamurthy, W. I. Lorenzen, S. Bless and N. S. Brar, Proceedings of the American Chemical Society, Division of PMSE. 67, 114 (1992).

2. U. Zroll, Farbe und Lack. 91, 1123 (1985).

3. A. C. Ramamurthy, T. Ahmed, L. D. Favro, R. L. Thomas, D. K. Hohnke and R. P. Cooper, SAE paper # 930051, Presented at the 1993 Annual Congress, Detroit, MI.

4. G. E. P. Box, W. G. Hunter and J. S. Hunter, Statistics for experimenters, Part III, John Wiley (1978).

5. R. V. Lenth, Technometrics, 31, 469 (1989).

6. J. M. Zurada, Introduction to Artificial Neural Systems, West (1992).

7. F. Mansfeld and M. W. Kendig, Werkstoffe und Korrosion. 36, 473, (1985)

8. E. Ladstadter, Farbe und Lack. 90, 577 (1984).

An Approximation Network for Measurement Systems

M.B. Zaremba, E. Porada, W.J. Bock

Département d'informatique
Université du Québec
Hull, Québec J8X 3X7 Canada

Abstract– The problem of extraction of the measurand value in optical measurement systems is addressed. It is required that the values the calibration points be recreated exactly, while maintaining precise approximation between the points. A neural processing method is provided to solve the problem. A two-layer feed-forward network that offers a possibility of on-going insight into the approximation precision, the optimal selection of the successive training inputs, and the linear separability of the training inputs is constructed. Examples are given to illustrate the proposed method.

I. INTODUCTION

In a growing number of modern measurement systems, the relationships of the measurand with the sensor output, in addition to the form of the sensor signal itself, are becoming increasingly complex. In particular, two-dimensional, distributed signals generated by some optical systems are a challenge for the design of optimal signal processing and pattern recognition methods. The paper addresses the problem of the extraction of the measurand value from a modulated sensor signal. In our case, the measurand is detected by a fibre-optic strain sensor that produces a planar pattern. The intensity values of selected sampling points of the planar image are then processed by a connectionist network in order to provide a precise output from the measurement system. In mathematical terms, the network interpolates a desired function (the parameter values) defined in the domain of sensor output.

It has been proved [2,3,4] that any continuous function can be approximated by multilayer feedforward neural networks with at least one hidden layer of neurons whose transfer functions are monotone and bounded. The above results are very important from a theoretical point of view. Their practical applications require constructive methods of efficient weight modulation when it is assumed that a limited number of hidden neurons are available.

In this paper we present a constructive method for building an approximation network. The network consists of two layers of connections: indexing (orthogonalization) and interpolating ones. The connection weights responsible for indexing are obtained by a self-programming procedure. The weights of the interpolating layer connections are determined by the measurement system calibration process. The problem of linear separation of training inputs is handled by introducing bias values at the input layer. The method presented here allows for fast learning and accurate determination of the measurand. The size of the network is determined by the degree of precision required.

The first part of the paper deals with network architecture. Section 3 describes the inductive learning procedure used during network building. Remarks regarding an optimal approximation procedure are given in Section 4. This is followed by two examples. They emphasize, successively, the precision of self-programmability and and the linear separability problem.

II. NEURAL NETWORK ARCHITECTURE FOR SENSOR SIGNAL PROCESSING

In the measurement system under consideration, the sensor output signal is sampled at a number of points before being fed to a neural processor. The input to the processor consists therefore of n-dimensional vectors $\mathbf{x} = \mathbf{x}(v)$, where v represents the measurand. Our aim is to build a network that will recover v from $\mathbf{x}$. The architecture of the neural processor solving that inverse problem is shown in Fig. 1.

The input layer I performs a non-linear operation

$$\mathbf{x} = [x_1, x_2, ..., x_n] \rightarrow \mathbf{y} = [y_1, y_2, ..., y_n],$$

where $y_i = \psi(x_i - \beta_i)$, ψ being an increasing, continuous function (the transfer function of input neurons). β_i represents the bias coefficient of input neuron i. The biased input $\mathbf{y}$ is sent to the first layer $I \times J$ of connections, where the connection weights form an $n{\times}n$ matrix $\mathbf{W}$. An internal representation of $\mathbf{y}$ is formed in the hidden layer J. Thus, the input-to-internal representation processing is the operator

$$\mathbf{x} \rightarrow \mathbf{y}\mathbf{W}.$$

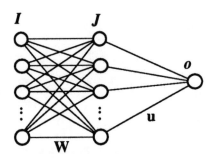

Fig. 1. Architecture of the neural network

The layer of connections beween the hidden neurons and the single output neuron o will be called the *interpolation layer*.

Denoting the numerical value produced by the network from input $\mathbf{x}$ as $f(\mathbf{x})$, we have

$$f(\mathbf{x}) = \mathbf{yWu},$$

where $\mathbf{u} = [u_1, u_2, ..., u_n]^T$ is a column vector of optional weights in the interpolation layer.

III. THE INDUCTIVE LEARNING PROCEDURE

The learning procedure discussed in this section refers to modulation of the biast coefficients β_j and to the calculation of the weight matrix $\mathbf{W}$. Using the interpolation method for approximation, the procedure also indicates the successive training inputs that ensure the best performance of the network.

Thus, modulation of the bias coefficients will allow for selection of measurand values $v_1, v_2, ..., v_n$ (called *calibration values*) such that the inputs $\mathbf{x}(v_1)$, $\mathbf{x}(v_2)$, ..., $\mathbf{x}(v_n)$ have linearly independent biased representations

$$\mathbf{y}(v_1), \ \mathbf{y}(v_2), \ ..., \ \mathbf{y}(v_n).$$

As for the weight matrix, the procedure will install on the network the matrix $\mathbf{W} = \mathbf{Y}^{-1}$, where

$$\mathbf{Y} = \begin{bmatrix} \mathbf{y}(v_1) \\ \vdots \\ \mathbf{y}(v_n) \end{bmatrix}.$$

By definition, the inverse matrix satisfies

$$\mathbf{y}(v_j)\mathbf{Y}^{-1} = \mathbf{e}_j, \ j = 1, 2, ..., n, \tag{1}$$

where $\{\mathbf{e}_j\}$ is the standard basis in $\mathbb{R}^n$, so that the internal representation of training input j will be a unitary impulse signal in the hidden neuron j. This will result in the following interpolation capability of the network:

$$f(\mathbf{x}(v_j)) = \mathbf{y}(v_j)\mathbf{Wu} = \mathbf{e}_j\mathbf{u} = u_j, \ j = 1, 2, ..., n;$$

that is, the connection weights u_j in the interpolation layer determine the values of the network function at the selected (training) inputs. In this way, the network can interpolate an arbitrary function of $\mathbf{x}$. In particular, when u_j is set to v_j, then f interpolates the measurand.

The linear separability of training inputs is an essential condition for existance of the inverse matric. The separation of one training input from another has usually taken advantage of non-linear transfer functions in the hidden layer (e.g. [3]). By assigning that task to the bias coefficients in the input layer, we are able to simplify and make it constructive the the learning procedure. It consists of an iterative application in step $k = 1, 2, ..., n$ of the two following operations:

1. Testing and modulation of the coefficient β_k in order to generate $\mathbf{y}(v_k)$ linearly independent from $\mathbf{y}(v_1)$, ..., $\mathbf{y}(v_{k-1})$.

2. Adjustment of the weight matrix $\mathbf{W}$ with regard to the requirement

$$\mathbf{y}(v_j)\mathbf{W} = \mathbf{e}_j, \ j = 1, 2, ..., k. \tag{2}$$

Initially, all weights and bias coefficients are set to 0. Before execution of step k, the bias coefficients $\beta_1, \beta_2, ..., \beta_{k-1}$ are already installed in the input neurons 1, 2, ..., $k-1$, a weight matrix $\mathbf{W} = \mathbf{W}^{(k-1)}$ is formed, and we have

$$\mathbf{y}(v_j)\mathbf{W}^{(k-1)} = \mathbf{e}_j, \ j = 1, 2, ..., k-1.$$

(In particular,

$$f^{(k-1)}(\mathbf{x}(v_j)) = u_j, \ j = 1, 2, ..., k-1, \tag{3}$$

that is, the network interpolates an arbitrary function at the training inputs used in the previous steps.)

The modulation of weights in step k aims at obtaining the weight matrix that satisfies (2) and, consequently, ensures extention of the interpolation formula (3) to $j = k$.

A. Bias coefficient in input neuron k and calibration value in step k.

Consider an arbitrary bias coefficient β_k in input neuron k. The biased representation of an input $\mathbf{x}(v)$ in neuron k is

$$y_k(v) = \psi(x_k(v) - \beta_k).$$

Consider an arbitrary calibration value $v_k = v$. We proved [5] that $\mathbf{y}(v)$ is linearly independent of $\mathbf{y}(v_j)$, $j < k$, if, and only if,

$$\mathbf{y}(v)\mathbf{W}^{(k-1)}\mathbf{u} - y_k(v) \neq 0, \tag{4}$$

where

$$
\begin{aligned}
u_j &= y_k(v_j) \quad \text{for } j = 1, ..., k-1, \\
u_j &= 0 \qquad \text{for } j = k, ..., n.
\end{aligned}
\tag{5}
$$

The function of the parameter v defined in (4) is called α-*function*; we denote it by $\alpha_k(v)$, so

$$\alpha_k(v) = f^{(k-1)}(\mathbf{x}(v)) - y_k(v).$$

The α-function is the difference between two terms which can be computed by the means of the present network. For the purpose of computing the first term, the weights in the interpolation layer are set to the values (5). The second term is the output from neuron k. In this way, the present network can be used for testing β_k and v_k in step k. By displaying the α-function for different levels of β_k, we can chose the proper bias coefficient in neuron k together with the best current calibration value. A criterion for the best selection is discussed in Sec. IV (see concluding paragraph). Here, let us note that

$$\alpha_k(v_j) = 0, \quad j = 1, 2, ..., k-1 \tag{6}$$

by the interpolation property (3).

B. Step k of weight modulation

Upon the selection of β_k and v_k we can proceed with the modulation of connection weights. The installation of the weight matrix $\mathbf{W}^{(k)}$ can be fully automated and managed by the network itself, which means that a connection changes its weight in the learning phase according to a *self-programming law*. The law expresses the new weight w^{new} in terms of the current weight w and the *training signals* a and b introduced into both ends of the connection. We then applied the following simple self-programming law

$$w^{\text{new}} = w + cab,$$

where c is a constant. Thus, if the input neuron i receives a training signal a_i and the hidden neuron j receives b_j, then

$$w_{ij}^{\text{new}} = w_{ij} + ca_i b_j. \tag{7}$$

Training data can be introduced into all input and hidden neurons simultaneously: vectors $\mathbf{a}$ and $\mathbf{b}$ are sent to the input layer I and the hidden layer J, respectively, and all connections change their weights according to law (7). In step k, the new weights form the matrix

$$\mathbf{W}^{(k)} = \mathbf{W}^{(k-1)} + c\,\mathbf{a} \times \mathbf{b}, \tag{8}$$

where $\times$ denotes the outer vector product. Thus, in one self-programming step the previous weight matrix is incremented by a matrix proportional to the correlation matrix of training data applied in that step.

The main problem we must solve in step k consists in finding the training data $\mathbf{a}, \mathbf{b}$ and the constant $c = c_k$, such that the new matrix $\mathbf{W} = \mathbf{W}^{(k)}$ (defined in (8)) satisfies (2). We have proved in [5] that the following vectors

$$\mathbf{a} = \mathbf{W}^{(k-1)}\mathbf{u} - \mathbf{e}_k, \quad \mathbf{b} = \mathbf{x}(v_k)\mathbf{W}^{(k-1)} - \mathbf{e}_k \tag{9}$$

and $c_k = -1/\alpha_k(v_k)$ are the desired training data ($\mathbf{u}$ is defined in (5)).

Note that the backpropagation learning method applies cycles of similar matrix incrementations untill the process converges. The training data are derived from the current training input array and output errors. The process restarts every time a successive training input is presented.

Our method requires n self-programming steps; in each step the corresponding training data (9) are applied once. After step n, the weight matrix $\mathbf{W}$ becomes $\mathbf{W}^{(n)} = \mathbf{Y}^{-1}$. If now the weights u_j are set to v_j, the network output is v_j for inputs $\mathbf{x} = \mathbf{x}(v_j)$.

IV. UNIFORM APPROXIMATION

The measurement precision depends on the uniform approximation of the measurand by the network function. Recall that after $k-1$ steps of modulation, the network performs a function

$$\mathbf{x} \to f^{(k-1)}(\mathbf{x}) = \mathbf{y}\mathbf{W}^{(k-1)}\mathbf{u},$$

where $\mathbf{y}$ is the biased representation of $\mathbf{x}$ and $u_j = v_j$ for $j < k$. The current deviation of the network output from v is the following function

where $\mathbf{y}$ is the biased representation of $\mathbf{x}$ and $u_j = v_j$ for $j < k$. The current deviation of the network output from v is the following function

$$E_{k-1}(v) = f^{(k-1)}(\mathbf{x}(v)) - v,$$

which expresses the present approximation errors of the system. By the interpolation property (3), we have

$$E_{k-1}(v_j) = 0, \quad j = 1, 2, ..., k-1.$$

An estimate of the uniform convergence of the deviation function to 0 *after* step k is given by the following transition formula:

$$E_k(v) = E_{k-1}(v) - [\alpha_k(v)/\alpha_k(v_k)]E_{k-1}(v_k) \qquad (10)$$

as proved in [5]. Let us show the scheme of the convergence demonstration.

First, the formula (10) proves that the step k of the self-programming affects the deviation function only in the domain where $\alpha_k(v) \neq 0$. Moreover, if for a value v we have $\alpha_k(v) \neq 0$ but $E_{k-1}(v) = 0$, then that v can be used as calibration value without affecting the deviation function, however the α-function becomes zero at $v_k = v$ (see (6)). In this way, the two function can be made to share the same set of roots, or, equivalently, they can be made to change sign simultaneously. This, in turn, signifies that the function $E_{k-1}(v)/\alpha_k(v)$ does not change its sign in the measurement range, so the two components of $E_k(v)$ in (10) are both positive or both negative. Consequently,

$$|E_k(v)| \leq \max\{|E_{k-1}(v)|, |[\alpha_k(v)/\alpha_k(v_k)]| \cdot |E_{k-1}(v_k)|\}.$$

This inequality is crutial for the uniform convergence of the deviation function to zero: If

$$v_k = \text{maximum point of } |\alpha_{k-1}(v)|$$

then $|[\alpha_k(v)/\alpha_k(v_k)]| \leq 1$ and the uniform norm of $E_k(v)$ does not exceed the uniform norm of $E_{k-1}(v)$.

Second, the deviation function diminishes in the neighbourhood of the present calibration value, taking the value 0 at v_k. Its uniform norm decreases in the most significant way when the maximal deviation drops to 0, i.e., when v_k is also the maximum point of $|E_{k-1}(v)|$. This indicates a criterion for selection of β_k in step k. The selection aims at the α-function maximally correlated with the deviation function. The calibration value in calibration step k is selected next as the maximum point of α-function.

V. EXAMPLES

First, we will illustrate the self-programming method with an example of simulated extraction of v from the Gaussian distributions

$$X(v,r) = 5\sin(v/4)\exp(-v^2 r^2).$$

The accuracy of the processing versus the network size is evaluated in the range $0 \leq v \leq 10$. The sample of $X(v,r)$ is an array $\mathbf{x}(v)$, where $x_i(v) = X(v, r_i)$. In this example $r_i = i/40$, $i = 1, 2, ..., n$. Any set of n such samples forms a linearly independent system, so all bias coefficients are set to 0 and will not be modulated.

As few as six calibration steps make the relative errors of the network decrease below 0.1%. The calibration is illustrated in Fig. 2, where steps 7 and 9 are shown. Although the deviation and α-functions are represented on a logarithmic scale, it can easily be seen that they are proportional to a great degree. The small triangles indicate the previous calibration values; the two functions are zero at those points, according to the interpolation performance of the network. The vertical arrow points to the successive calibration value. We tested the self-programming up to step 12, where the maximum output deviation dropped to 10^{-4}. Beyond step 12, computation errors contribute significantly to the approximation errors, so any continuation of the modulation is pointless. Finally, the network uses only 12 input neurons and 12 samples of the input distribution.

The second example illustrates the calibration process in the case of strong linear dependences in the set of sensor output distributions. The measurement device [1] includes a fiber-optic sensor and a neural processor of the sensor signals. The optical signal from the sensor is converted into an array of analog signals that are fed to the neural network. Conversion of the sensor output to the network input requires the use of photoelectric systems which generally introduce bias effects and non-linearities in the transformation of light intensity to analog (voltage) signals. In the experiment described here, the input layer of the neural processor is formed of 20 non-linear converters with individual bias coefficients.

The sensor light output consisting of a planar light intensity distribution was affected by the longitudinal strain put upon the sensing fiber. The network was calibrated with regard to the measurement task of recovering the strain value from the light intensity distribution. In each calibration step k, the processor is exposed to sensor output, the strain upon the sensing fiber covering the range of 0-720 [microstrains]. A display of the α-function and the deviation function enables the control of calibration process. Eventually, the bias coefficient of the

a)

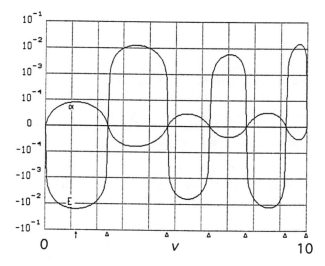

b)

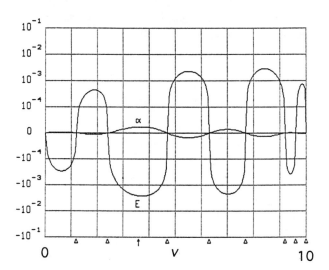

Fig. 2. Plots of the α-function and the deviation function.
   a) calibration step 7
   b) calibration step 9

$E_k(v)/720[\mu strain]$, and the α-function in calibration steps 2 and 11. As in the first example, the small triangles indicate the previous calibration values (v_1 was set to 720 [μstrain]), while the vertical arrow points to the actual calibration value. Thus $v_2 = 108$ [μstrain] and $v_{11} = 360$ [μstrain].

a)

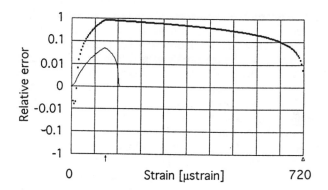

b)

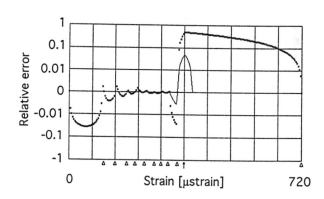

Fig. 3. Examples of the α-function and the network error.
   a) calibration step 2
   b) calibration step 11

converter k must be adjusted to produce a non-zero α-function correlated with the deviation function. Thus, in each step, the strain value where the α-function was maximal coincided with the point of maximal error; this value determined the successive calibration point.

Figure 3 shows the relative error of the network on a logarithmic scale, i.e., the function $e_k(v) =$

Twenty calibration steps produced a network computing the strain value with an error smaller than 0.1% in the measurement range 100-620 [μstrain]. The poor approximation, observed in the lowermost measurement range, is due firstly to poor sensor sensitivity in that range and to a comparatively small neural network size.

5. CONCLUSIONS

An efficient solution of the function approximation problem oriented toward the requirements of measurement systems was presented. In such systems it is often necessary that the value of the measurand at the calibration points be extracted very precisely, while maintaining precise interpolation between the points. We showed that modulation of the connection weights with regard to more and more refined interpolation does not require more than the resolution of linear problems and that the solution can be generated by a self-programming procedure. Thus, we constructed universal approximators of the measurand, using only two-layer feedforward linear networks. The network construction method provides the possibility of on-going insight into the approximation precision and also the means to determine the optimal selection of the successive training inputs. The linear separation of the training inputs can be obtained by the variation of the bias levels at the input layer. The method presented was illustrated by examples related to a birefringent-type fiber-optic strain sensor.

REFERENCES

[1]   Bock, W.J., Porada, E, and Zaremba,M.B., "Neural processing-type fiber-optic strain sensor", *Proc. IEEE Instrumentation and Measurement Technology Conference,* May 1992, New York, pp. 635-639.

[2]   Funahashi, K., "On the approximate realization of continuous mappings by neural networks". *Neural Networks*, Vol. 2, No. 3, 1989, pp. 183-192.

[3]   Hornik, K., Stinchcombe, M. and White, H. "Multilayer feedforward networks are universal approximators". *Neural Networks*, Vol. 2, No. 4, 1989, pp. 359-366.

[4]   Stinchcombe, M. and White, H., "Universal approximation using feedforward networks with non-sigmoidal hidden layer activation functions". *Proc. Int. Joint Conf. on Neural Networks,* Washington, DC, 1989, Vol. 1, pp. 613-617.

[5]   Zaremba, M.B. and Porada, E., "Self-programming of neural networks for indexing and function approximation tasks". *Appl. Math. and Comp. Sci.,* Vol.2, No.2, 1992, pp. 251-276.

EVALUATION OF THE PERFORMANCE OF VARIOUS ARTIFICIAL NEURAL NETWORKS TO THE SIGNAL FAULT DIAGNOSIS IN NUCLEAR REACTOR SYSTEMS

Shahla Keyvan and Ajaya Durg
Nuclear Engineering Department
University of Missouri-Rolla
Rolla, MO 65401

Luis Carlos Rabelo
Department of Industrial
and Systems Engineering
Ohio University
Athens, OH 45701

Abstract--This is a study on the evaluation of the performance and comparison between various paradigms of artificial neural networks in nuclear reactor signal analysis for the purpose of developing a diagnostic monitoring system. Reactor signals from Experimental Breeder Reactor (EBR-II) are analyzed. The signals are both measured signals collected by Data Acquisition System (DAS) as well as simulated signals. ART2, ART2-A, Fuzzy Adaptive Resonance Theory (Fuzzy ART), and Fuzzy ARTMAP paradigms of the Adaptive Resonance Theory (ART) family, Standard Backpropagation, Cascade Correlation, and RCE networks are examined and compared in this study.

I. INTRODUCTION

The goal of this study is to develop a diagnostic monitoring system based on artificial neural networks and ARMA models for pattern recognition of faulty signals, identification of the faults, and prediction of the reactor condition. The system utilizes a hierarchy which combines unsupervised/supervised learning(See Figure 1). The first level of this hierarchy should have real time learning, degradation detection capabilities, and ability in qualitative classification. The second level of hierarchy is composed of several specialized supervised elements yielding a quantitative measure. Finally, third level based on an established database will forecast the progress of the wear. A comprehensive semi-benchmark tests have been performed, aimed at evaluating the performance of various paradigms to the application in the first level of hierarchy. ART2[3], ART2-A[5], Fuzzy Adaptive Resonance Theory (Fuzzy ART)[6], and Fuzzy ARTMAP[4,7,8] paradigms of the ART family, Standard Backpropagation[13], Cascade Correlation[9], and RCE networks[1,14] are examined and compared in this study.

This work is supported by National Science Foundation under reference number: ECS-9111145.

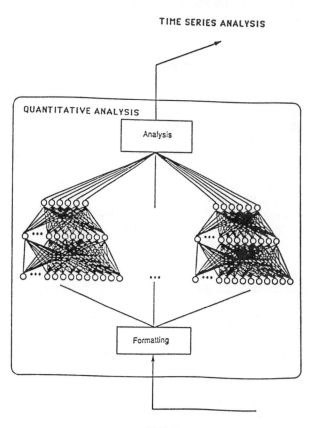

TIME SERIES ANALYSIS

QUANTITATIVE ANALYSIS

Analysis

Formatting

QUALITATIVE ANALYSIS

FIGURE 1. HIERARCHICAL SYSTEM SCHEME

ART2 is selected due to its powerful basic design characteristics. Fuzzy ART is selected because of its algorithm is developed based upon traditional neural network models such as ART 1, while incorporating fuzzy logic operators, hence enhancing the capabilities of ART 1 for analog input. Also, fuzzy ART includes two optional features (complement coding and slow recoding) which enables the network to overcome limitations associated with sequential data presentation. In addition, fuzzy ART is capable of retaining previously learned concepts in response to stochastic input fluctuations, while rapidly learning infrequent events. ART2-A is selected due to its speed and simplicity of the design. Fuzzy ARTMAP (based on hyper-rectangles) is selected because it has the capability to handle nonstationary stochastic signal and because of its supervised learning traits. RCE (based on hyper-sphere) is selected due to its unique design and speed. Standard Backpropagation is selected because of its popular utilization, hence a good reference for comparison with other selected paradigms. Cascade Correlation is selected because it represents a powerful network and contrary to Backpropagation, hidden units/layers are not pre-set in advance, rather each hidden unit/layer is added as needed. These selected schemes are are powerful paradigms which exhibit some desired properties for the quantitative level of hierarchical system.

II. SIGNAL DESCRIPTION

The signals utilized in this study are divided in two groups, the actual measured signals and the simulated signals. The measured signals are the pump power signals from pump number 1 of the EBR-II nuclear reactor. These samples are collected from sensors by plant data acquisition system(See Figure 2). Four sets of simulated signals were generated from the original signal representing the pump power simulated for four levels of degradation due to deposition of sodium oxide on the pump shaft using the system dynamics The system is based on noise analysis and utilizes Dynamic Data System (DDS) approach of Autoregressive Moving Average (ARMA) regression modeling. The mathematical representation of the model for a univariate system is:

$$(1 - a_1 Z^{-1} - a_2 Z^{-2} ..... - a_n Z^{-n}) Y(k) =$$
$$(b_1 Z^{-1} - b_2 Z^{-2} .... - b_{n-1} Z^{-(n-1)}) R(k)$$

where,

$Y(k)$ = discrete signal data,
k = index of time interval,
$R(k)$ = white noise residual,
$Z^{-1} Y(k) = Y(k-1)$,
a,b = autoregressive, moving average parameters.

The autoregressive and moving average parameters are then decomposed into pairs of complex discrete roots (eigenvalues), i.e. for a second order dynamic :

$$r_{1,2} = a \pm b i$$

where,

$$a_1 = r_1 + r_2 \qquad a_2 = - r_1 r_2$$

similarly,

$$r^*_{1,2} = a^* \pm b^* i$$

where,

$$b_1 = r^*_1 + r^*_2 \qquad b_2 = - r^*_1 r^*_2$$

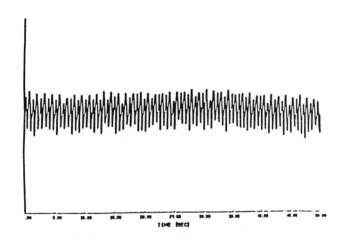

FIGURE 2.MEASURED PUMP POWER SIGNAL

The measure of wear progress in the system is achieved by introducing new parameters (representing an index of wear progress) which are based on the increase of the impact of the wear related dynamic on the signal fluctuation as degradation progresses [17,10]. The measured signals are referred to as category N. The four sets are classified as categories A, B, C, and D respectively. For the evaluation of the ART family, a specific time window from the measured signals (category N) is used to provide two sets of patterns, of 500 data points dimensionality representing first level of degradation. Similarly the two sets of simulated data for second level degradation are obtained from pattern B. In addition, to show the capability of Fuzzy Art in pattern recognition with less input dimensionality than is required for ART2 and ART2-A, twelve sets of data samples with a 250 input dimensionality were utilized.

For evaluation of the Fuzzy ARTMAP, RCE, Standard Backpropagation, and Cascade Correlation data of the five categories are used. This data is divided into various training and testing sets.

III. CASCADE CORRELATION PARADIGM

A major disadvantage with the Backpropagation algorithm is that it learns slowly. One of the reasons for this slowness is what is known as moving target problem [4]. Briefly stated, the problem is that all the units are trying to evolve into feature detectors simultaneously, complicating the problem faced by each individual unit. Cascade correlation scheme tries to overcome this moving target problem by adding just one hidden unit each time to the network. The hidden units are cascaded one after another until the network yields the desired performance. This architecture is termed as cascade architecture. For each new hidden unit, the correlation between the new unit's output and the residual error signal is maximized as defined below by:.

$$S = S_j |S_p (b - b_{ave}) (Ep,j - E_{ave})|$$

Where j is the network output at which the error is measured, p is the training pattern, b is the output of the candidate unit, Ej is the residual error at the output unit j. b_{ave} and E_{ave} are the values of b and Ej averaged over all the patterns. Hence the paradigm is termed as cascade correlation [4].

IV. FUZZY ARTMAP

Fuzzy ARTMAP [7,8] is a supervised learning paradigm. It incorporates two Fuzzy ART modules that are interlinked through a mapping field. The inputs to the Fuzzy ART modules are presented in complement form (i.e., A= (a,1,-a)). The symmetry achieved leads to the generation of hyper rectangles in multidimensional spaces. The process of learning increases the category resolution as a result of the growth of the rectangles and the decreasing value of weights. This increases the stability of the category formation process.

During training, at the start of each input presentation the vigilance factor of the first Fuzzy ART module equals the baseline vigilance of Fa, and the map field vigilance factor is set to 1. When a prediction by the first Fuzzy ART module is disconfirmed at the second Fuzzy ART module, match tracking is induced. The match tracking rule raises the vigilance factor of the first Fuzzy ART module enough to lead to activations of other categories. If the prediction of the first Fuzzy ART module is confirmed at second Fuzzy ART module, Map field learning takes place. This process implements a Maximum Learning Rule which maximizes code compression and enhances generalization

The neurodynamics of Fuzzy ARTMAP allows "incremental supervised learning of recognition categories and multidimensional maps in response to arbitrary sequences of analog or binary input vectors"[8]. In addition, architecture of the Fuzzy ARTMAP self organizes its internal structure as opposed to Standard Backpropagation.

V. ANALYSIS OF RESULTS

To evaluate and compare the learning and differentiation of patterns (N, A, and B) of the ART2, ART2-A, and Fuzzy ART networks several tests are performed. The result of this test is given in table I. The ART2 and ART2A networks are capable of distinguishing these patterns properly without any pre-processing of data. As shown in table I, the first two sets belonging to category N are assigned to category 0, the two sets of category A are in category 1, and category 2 is assigned to the two sets of category B. However, the Fuzzy ART network is not capable of proper classification of the 6 sets of raw (no pre-processing) data unless the normalization option is used. With the normalization pre-

processing, the fuzzy network is performs very well and classifies patterns properly as shown in table I[11,12].

TABLE I
Results of testing pattern classification for unsupervised paradigms of ART family

FILE	SIZE	NETWORK	PRE-PROCESSING	CATEGORY
NAB	500	ART2	NONE	001122
NAB	500	ART2A	NONE	001122
NAB	500	Fuzzy ART	L 1 NORMALIZATION	001122
NAB	250	Fuzzy ART	COMPLEMENT CODING	010123234545
NAB	250	ART2	NONE	010123214525
NAB	250	ART2A	NONE	010123214525

Next, another test is run to verify the fact that the Fuzzy ART networks is capable of proper classification when using its complement coding feature with much less input data than ART2 and ART2-A networks. Results of this test is shown in table I, with 250 input dimensionality in each set. Fuzzy ART is the only network among the ART networks tested here that is capable of properly distinguishing each pattern.

To evaluate and compare the performance of the selected supervised paradigms (RCE, Cascade, Backprop, and FUZZY ARTMAP) two separate Tests are performed. First only three categories(N,A, and B)are applied. Results are shown in table II.

TABLE II
Results of Fuzzy ARTMAP, RCE, Backprop, and Cascade for N, A, B based on three trials for testing

Trained on data	Tested on data	set size	number of patterns train	number of patterns test	RCE	Cascade	Backprop	Fuzzy ARTMAP
File 1a	1b	55	7*	7	100	90	90	100
File 2a	2b	55	7	7	90	90	90	100
File 3a	3b	55	7	7	95	81	95	95

* This represents 7 sets of size 55 data for each pattern N, A, and B, hence 21 patterns in total.

Next, all supervised networks were trained and tested on five categories N, A, B, C and D. Results for each signal is listed in Table 3. Fuzzy ARTMAP gives the Best performance.

A. Order of Data Presentation

To observe the effect of data presentation,order was randomly changed to observe the effect on the performance. The networks were trained using data from different time windows, for the N,A,and B categories. Result show that performance does not seem to change with new order of presentation.

1721

TABLE III
Network performance on signals N, A, B, and C D

NETWORK	N	A	B	C	D	TOTAL
RCE	6/7	6/7	5/7	7/7	5/7	83%
CASCADE	5/7	4/7	7/7	4/7	6/7	74%
BACKPROP	4/7	5/7	7/7	1/7	5/7	63%
FUZZY ARTMAP	5/7	6/7	7/7	6/7	6/7	86%

B. Fragmented/Noisy Data

To observe the effect of noisy data on the network pattern recognition performance, the above explained window corrected data sets were modified, and 1perturbations were introduced in each dataset. Even at low noise level of 10%, the performance of the networks are drastically reduced to 33% for RCE and Backprop, and to 0% for Cascade. However, Fuzzy ARTMAP was able to score 95%.

Training and recall speed are an important criteria for the development of real-time systems. For the purpose of network comparison, each paradigm was trained with same data set several times to get an average. For the supervised paradigms examined RCE and Fuzzy ARTMAP are the fastest networks. Cascade Correlation takes on the average, considerable less time than Backpropagation.

In the case of unsupervised paradigms, the ART family, all the tests were performed using fast learning trials. For ART2 the duration (on average) of one of these fast learning trials was two minutes using a simulator built in the C programming language for a Macintosh IIfx running under A/UX. The fast learning sessions required only one presentation of the input data set to provide stable results. Under the same condition a fast learning trial takes less than one second for both ART2A and Fuzzy ART, baring in mind that both have the same stabilization performance behavior.

V. CONCLUSIONS

RCE, Fuzzy ARTMAP, and Cascade Correlation networks determine their own network topology based on the input patterns. RCE performs better compared to Cascade Correlation network in the cases studied. Backpropagation gives performance close to Cascade Correlation but the latter seems to do better as number of patterns are increased.. RCE, Cascade, and Fuzzy ARTMAP are independent of presentation order in data patterns for the cases studied. In the case of Backprop input data are fed at random.

Noise as low as 10% of the data drastically affects the performance in all the three networks RCE, Cascade and backpropagation. Fuzzy ARTMAP was more robust in the presence of noise.

Several experiments are in progress to compare the plasticity and incremental learning capabilities of different artificial neural network paradigms. Nuclear reactor operations require systems capable of broadening their horizon, and evolving to cope with new information/situations. This is very important because the number of possible categories and new situations are unknown in several thousand hours of reactor operational time. Artificial neural networks might support the development of these systems.

REFERENCES

[1] Bachmann,C., Cooper, L., Dembo, A.,and Zeitiuni, O., "A relaxation model for memory with high storage density", Proceedings of the National Academy of Sciences, USA, 221, pp. 2088-3092.

[2] Carpenter, G. and Grossberg, S.,"A massively Parallel Architecture for a Self-Organizing Neural Pattern Recognition Machine", Computer Vision, Graphics, and Image Processing, 1987, vol. 37, pp. 54-117.

[3] Carpenter, G. and Grossberg, S.,"ART 2: Self-Organization of Stable Category Recognition Codes for Analog Input Patterns", Applied Optics, 1987, vol. 26, pp. 4919-4930.

[4] Carpenter, G. and Grossberg, S. and Reynolds, J.,"ARTMAP: Supervised Real-Time Learning and Classification of Nonstationary Data by a Self-Organizing Neural Network", PATTERN RECOGNITION By SELF-ORGANIZING NEURAL NETWORKS, G. Carpenter and S. Grossberg (EDs.), MIT Press, 1991, pp. 503-544.

[5] Carpenter, G. and Grossberg, S. and Rosen, D., "ART2-A: An adapdtive resonance algorithm for rapid category learning and recognition", CAS/CNS Technical Report, Boston University, CAS/CNS-91-011, 1991.

[6] Carpenter, G. and Grossberg, S. and Rosen, D., "Fuzzy ART", Poster paper presented at the Neural Networks for Vision and Image Processing Conference, Wang Institute of Boston University, May 10-12,1991.

[7] Carpenter, G. and Grossberg, S., Reynolds, J., and Rosen, D.,"Fuzzy ARTMAP: A Neural Network architecture for supervised Learning of Analog Multidimensional Maps",CAS/CNS Technical Report, CAS/CNS-91-016,1991.

[8] Carpenter, G. and Grossberg, S., Markuzon, N., Reynolds, J., and Rosen, D.,"Fuzzy ARTMAP: An Adaptive Resonance Architecture for incremental of Analog Multidimensional Maps", Proceedings of the International Joint Conference on Neural Networks, Baltimore, pp. III309-III314, 1992.

[9] Fahlman,S. and Lebiere,C.,"The Cascade Correlation learning Architecture", Technical Report CMU-CS-90-100, February 14,1990.

[10] Keyvan, S. , "Degradation Monitoring of Pump Components in a Nuclear Power Plant", American Neclear Society/ European Nuclear Society, Topical Meeting, July 31- August 3,1988 Snowbird, Utah.

[11] Keyvan, S. and Rabelo, L. C., "Sensor Signal Analysis by Neural Networks for Surveillance in Nuclear Reactors", IEEE Transactions on Nuclear Science, pp. 292-298, 1992.

[12] Keyvan, S., Rabelo, L. C. and Malkani, A., "Nuclear Reactor Condition Monitoring by Adaptive Resonance Theory", Proceedings of the International Joint Conference on Neural Networks, Baltimore, pp. III321-III328, 1992.

[13] Rumelhart, D., McClelland, J. and the PDP Research Group, PARALLEL DISTRIBUTED PROCESSING: Explorations in the Microstructure of Cognition, vol. 1:Foundations, Cambridge, Massachusetts: MIT Press, 1986.

[14] Scofield, C., Reilly, D., Elbaum, C. and Cooper, L., "Pattern Class Degeneracy in an unrestricted storage density memory", Nestor Inc., 1988.

Neural Networks As Massively Parallel Automatic Test Pattern Generators

A. Majumder

Motorola Inc.

6501 William Cannon Dr. W.

Austin, Texas 78735

(512) 891-2409

R. Dandapani

Department of ECE

University of Colorado at Colorado Springs

Colorado Springs, Colorado 80933-7150

(719) 593-3572

Abstract—Neural networks are characterized by small-grain parallelism where a large number of inexpensive neurons (processors) can act simultaneously toward solving a given optimization problem. Remarkable computational power in neural networks of simple neurons has been demonstrated in solving the Traveling-Salesman Problem. Therefore, neural networks present a promising paradigm for computationally intensive CAD applications like Automatic Test Pattern Generation for digital circuits. In this paper we compare the performances of 2-Valued and 3-Valued neural networks as Automatic Test Pattern Generators (ATPGs). The performance data were obtained by implementing the neural network-based ATPGs on the Myrias Scalable Parallel Supercomputer.

I. INTRODUCTION

Neural networks are characterized by small-grain parallelism where a large number of inexpensive neurons (processors) can act simultaneously toward solving a given optimization problem. Remarkable computational power in neural networks of simple neurons has been demonstrated in solving the Traveling-Salesman Problem[1]. Therefore, neural networks present a promising paradigm for computationally intensive CAD applications like Automatic Test Pattern Generation for digital circuits.

Chakradhar et al.[2] proposed an Automatic Test Pattern Generator based on 2-Valued neural networks. The test generation problem was formulated as an optimization problem and was solved by Hopfield's[3] binary neural networks where neurons take on values from the set $\{0, 1\}$. A 3-Valued version was proposed by Fujiwara[4] where neurons take on values from the set $\{0, 1, 1/2\}$.

The purpose of this paper is to compare the performances of both models. The performance data were obtained by implementing the neural network-based ATPGs on the Myrias Scalable Parallel Supercomputer[5].

II. NEURAL NETWORKS

2.1 Background on Neural Networks

A neural network is a collection of neurons interacting with each other. A neuron (processing element) can be modeled as a simple threshold unit[6] as in Fig. 2-1. A neuron receives weighted inputs signals from other neurons, which are summed together. After the summation, the signal is processed through a threshold function f, which produces the output signal.

The state of a neuron is its activation value. Various logic operations are realized by specifying the thresholds for the neurons and the weights associated with the links. Fig. 2-1 shows a typical neuron. The weight T_{ij} characterizes the link connecting neurons i and j. I_i and V_i are the threshold and the activation value, respectively, of neuron i. A neuron determines its state by calculating the weighted sum of the states of all the connected neighboring neurons and comparing this sum with its threshold.

2.2 Logic Circuit Modeling by Neural Networks

Hopfield nets are utilized in modeling logic circuits using neural networks. Hopfield nets are a subclass of neural networks with the link weights having the same strength (sign and magnitude) in both directions. In the following, the terms Hopfield net and neural net are used interchangeably.

It has been shown that an arbitrary logic circuit can be represented by a neural network[1]. Every net (signal) in the logic circuit is represented by a neuron and the value of the net is the activation value of the neuron. Neural networks for 2-input AND, OR, NAND, NOR as well as NOT/BUFFER gates can constitute a convenient basis set. Networks containing other gate types can be constructed from this basis set. The neural network for a digital circuit is characterized by an energy function E that has global minima only at the neuron states consistent with the function of all gates in the circuit. All other neuron states have higher energy. E assumes an arbitrary value of Z, for all consistent states and $E>Z$ for all inconsistent states. Also, the value of Z is known a priori. We chose Z=0.

Even though a net in a digital logic circuit may only have values from the set $\{0, 1\}$, it has been shown[1, 3] that neurons in the neural network representing the digital logic circuit may have activation values either from the set $\{0, 1\}$ or the set $\{0, 1, X\}$ where X denotes don't care. Hence, we can have 2-Valued model and 3-Valued model of the same logic circuit.

In the 2-Valued model, the energy function is of the form[2]:

$$E = -\frac{1}{2} \sum_{i=1}^{N} \sum_{j=1}^{N} T_{ij} V_i V_j - \sum_{i=1}^{N} I_i V_i + K \qquad (2\text{-}1)$$

where N is the number of neurons in the neural network, T_{ij} is the weight of the link between neurons i and j, V_i is the activation value of neuron i, I_i is the threshold of neuron i, and K is a constant. For a digital circuit, $T_{ij}=T_{ji}$ and $T_{ii}=0$.

In the 3-Valued model, the energy function is of the form[2]:

$$E = -\frac{1}{2} \sum_{i=1}^{N} \sum_{j=1}^{N} T_{ij} V_i V_j - \sum_{i=1}^{N} I_i V_i \text{ j}$$

$$- \sum_{i=1}^{N} \sum_{j=1}^{N} W_{ij} V_i (1 - V_i) V_j (1 - V_j) \qquad (2\text{-}2)$$

where N is the number of neurons in the neural network, T_{ij} is

1724

the weight of the link between neurons i and j, V_i is the activation value of neuron i, I_i is the threshold of neuron i, W_{in} is the weight associated with the link between neurons i and j which is effective only when V_i and V_j are both 1/2, and K is a constant. $T_{ij}=T_{ji}$, $W_{ij}=W_{ji}$ and $T_{ii}=T_{jj}=0$[2]. The third term in (2-2) is introduced to stabilize neurons under the value 1/2.

2.3 Purposes of Introducing the 3-Valued Model

The problem of test generation is to find out a consistent labeling of the neurons in the ATPG neural network (to be explained in Section 2.4) with values from the set $\{0, 1\}$ or $\{0, 1, X\}$ where X denotes don't care. The sets $\{0, 1\}$ and $\{0, 1, X\}$ correspond to the 2-Valued and 3-Valued models, respectively. Fujiwara gave the following arguments in favor of the 3-Valued model:

1. Avoids unnecessary assignment of values 0 and 1 (pruning the search space).
2. Obtains necessary and sufficient values to detect a given fault (minimal test vectors).
3. Speeds up convergence to the global minima.

2.4 Test Generation Using Neural Networks

Fig. 2-2 illustrates a network which specifies constraints for test generation. The circuit-under-test, its faulty image (a fault-injected neural network representing the circuit-under-test), and the output interface constitute the ATPG neural network. This network is constructed by joining the good circuit and the faulty image in such a manner that the primary inputs of the two circuits are connected directly and that at least one of the primary outputs of the faulty circuit will differ from the corresponding good circuit output. Therefore, if a test exists for a fault, there exists a consistent labeling of the neurons in the neural network that does not violate the functionality of any gate. To find a test pattern for a given fault, minimum value of E is first obtained using a gradient descent technique augmented by probabilistic relaxation. The activation values of the primary input neurons in the consistent labeling of the ATPG neural network form the test pattern for the given fault.

III. Implementation And Results

3.1 Test Generation System

Fig. 3-1 shows the implemented test generation system. First, from a gate level description of the circuit the original fault-free neural network is created. Then for each targeted fault, the ATPG neural network is created and iterative relaxation (Section 3.2) is commenced. An efficient neural pruning scheme[7] is implemented in the ATPG neural network creation stage. It is to be noted that the vast majority of the CPU time is spent in the iterative relaxation stage. The Myrias Scalable Supercomputer[4] was used in simulating this neural test generation system taking advantage of the large-grain parallelism of the system. This was accomplished by simulating N ATPG neural networks at the same time, where N represents the number of processors available.

3.2 Iterative Relaxation Algorithm

Relaxation is the stage where a neural network randomly updates the states of its neurons and converges toward a sta-

ble, minimum energy global state. If the gradient descent (a greedy algorithm) is used to simulate the relaxation process, it is possible that the algorithm can terminate at a local minimum. To escape from local minima, higher energy moves are occasionally accepted in a probabilistic hill climbing algorithm. Since the final objective still is to minimize energy, the higher energy moves are allowed but lower energy moves are statistically favored. Probabilistic search algorithms are also referred to as simulated annealing methods[8]. The following neuron update rules were used in the implemented simulated annealing algorithm.

2-Valued model: The probability that neuron i takes state value 1 is given as

$$P_i = P(V_i = 1) = \frac{1}{1 + e^{-\Delta E_i / T}}$$

where $\Delta E_i = E(V_i = 0) - E(V_i = 1)$
and T is a parameter which acts like the temperature of a physical system.

3-Valued model: The probability that neuron i takes state value 0, 1 or 1/2, is given as

In case of $\theta_i > 0$

$$P_{i1} = P(V_i = 1) = \frac{1}{1 + e^{-(U_i - \theta_i)/2T}}$$

$$P_{i0} = P(V_i = 0) = 1 - \frac{1}{1 + e^{-(U_i + \theta_i)/2T}}$$

$$P_{i\frac{1}{2}} = P(V_i = \frac{1}{2}) = 1 - (P_{i1} + P_{i0})$$

$$= \frac{1}{1 + e^{(-(U_i + \theta_i))/(2T)}} - \frac{1}{1 + e^{-(U_i - \theta_i)/2T}}$$

where

$$U_i = \sum_{j=1}^{N} T_{ij}V_j + I_i$$

$$\theta_i = \sum_{j=1}^{N} W_{ij}V_j(1 - V_j)$$

and N is the number of neurons in the network.

In case of $\theta_i \leq 0$

$$P_{i1} = P(V_i = 1) = \frac{1}{1 + e^{-U_i/T}}$$

$$P_{i0} = P(V_i = 0) = 1 - P_{i1} = 1 - \frac{1}{1 + e^{-U_i/T}}.$$

It has been shown that the simulated annealing algorithm behaves as an optimization algorithm only if it is allowed an infinite number of transitions[8]. However, a polynomial-time approximation of the simulated annealing algorithm is available that leads to near-optimal solutions[8, 9]. The cooling schedule for this polynomial-time simulated annealing algorithm is briefly discussed below:

(i) Length of Markov Chains: It has been argued[8] that for this polynomial-time cooling schedule only a "small" number of transitions is required to approach the stationary distribution for a given next value of the control parameter. Therefore, the length of Markov chains can be taken as equal to the size of the neighborhood, for neighborhoods larger than 100 in size. The neighborhood of a state i is a set of states that are 'close' to i in some sense. In this implementation, the neighborhood of a state i has been taken as the set of all states that are reachable by changing the state of only one neuron. Therefore, for the 2-Valued model the length of Markov chain is the same as the number of neurons in the ATPG neural network, while for the 3-Valued model it is twice the number of neurons in the ATPG neural network. This ensures a finite probability of reaching any state from any given state within one Markov chain length.

(ii) Initial Value of the Control Parameter: This value should be large enough to allow virtually all transitions to be accepted.

(iii) Decrement of the Control Parameter: Next value of the control parameter, c_{k+1}, is calculated from the present value, c_k, using the following equation

$$c_{k+1} = \frac{c_k}{1 + \frac{c_k \ln(1+\delta)}{3\sigma_{c_k}}} \qquad (3\text{-}1)$$

where δ is the distance parameter, and

$$\sigma_{c_k} = \left(\frac{1}{L} \sum_{i=1}^{L} (f_i(c_k) - \bar{f}(c_k))^2 \right)^{\frac{1}{2}}$$

where L is the Markov chain length, $f_i(c_k)$ is the cost function,

and $\bar{f}(c_k) = \frac{1}{L} \sum_{i=1}^{L} f_i(c_k)$

(iv) Stop Criterion: Global minima of ATPG neural network is known *a priori* ($E=0$). This serves as the stop criterion for the simulated annealing algorithm.

Utilizing the above polynomial cooling schedule, test generation was performed on several circuits. Performance related results that were obtained relative to several cooling schedule parameters are given in the following section.

3.3 Results

In the previous section a polynomial-time cooling schedule was briefly introduced. In this section we discuss the finite-time behavior of the simulated annealing algorithm, as it is applied to the test generation problem, by means of an empirical performance analysis.

Traditionally, the performance of an approximation algorithm is related to the following two quantities[8].

— the *quality* of the final solution obtained by the algorithm, and

— the *running time* required by the algorithm.

The quality of a final solution with energy E_f can be quantified by the *error* $\in$ which can be defined as

$\in = E_f - E_{optimal} = E_f - Z = E_f$, since $E_f = Z = 0$.

Hence, $\in$ is the difference between the final energy E_f and the

optimal energy $E_{optimal}$. The running time can be quantified by the CPU time required by the algorithm.

The performance of the simulated annealing algorithm has been investigated by carrying out an average-case analysis. Average case relates here to the average value of the error and the running time computed from the probability distribution over the set of final solutions that can be obtained by the algorithm for a given problem instance. This probability distribution results from the probabilistic nature of the simulated annealing algorithm. In contrast, in the analysis of deterministic algorithms, average case relates to a probability distribution over a set of problem instances.

We applied the simulated annealing algorithm to several ISCAS '85 benchmark circuits[10] of differing sizes, a 4-bit binary full adder with fast carry and an arithmetic logic unit[11] (see Table 3-1). For a given set of detectable faults, average values of the error and the running time were obtained by running the simulated annealing algorithm 5 times, for the same fault set using different initial random number seeds. In order to keep the performance evaluation general, a set of ten randomly selected detectable faults were utilized for each circuit. Initial state for the 2-Valued model was $V_i=0$ for all i except the fault site. Initial state for the 3-Valued model was $V_i=1/2$ for all i except the fault site.

Fig. 3-2(a) shows (a) the average running time ($\bar{t}$), (b) the average error ($\bar{\in}$), and (c) the average number of Markov chains in the simulated annealing process ($\overline{MC}$) as a function of the initial acceptance ratio[1] (χ_0) for a fixed value of the distance parameter (δ). Fig. 3-2(a) shows that starting off at smaller values of the initial acceptance ratio, i.e., using lower values of the control parameter, leads to faster execution of the algorithm. This can be understood by realizing that the algorithm starts off at smaller values of the control parameter, while it terminates at approximately the same value of the control parameter. For a particular value of χ_0, the simulated annealing algorithm utilizing the 3-Valued model requires more execution time than that utilizing the 2-Valued model. This is due to the fact that the 3-Valued model has a more complex, i.e., more computationally expensive, update rule than its 2-Valued counterpart.

Fig. 3-2(b) shows that the average error remains virtually constant as χ_0 increases. This behavior will be discussed later in conjunction with Fig. 3-3(b).

Fig. 3-2(c) shows that the average number of Markov chains in the simulated annealing process increases as χ_0 increases. this is expected since the algorithm terminates at approximately the same value of the control parameter. Simulated annealing algorithms utilizing both the 3-Valued and the 2-Valued model behave identically. The algorithm utilizing the 3-Valued model requires larger number of Markov chains as compared to its 2-Valued counterpart. In other words, the algorithm utilizing the 3-Valued model requires a larger number of neuron transitions as compared to its 2-Valued counterpart. This is an interesting result since it is in direct contradiction with claims made by Fujiwara[3]; claims (1) and (3) given in Section 2.3 are not supported by results in Fig. 3-2(c) and 3-3(c), respectively.

Fig. 3-3 shows (a) the average running time ($\bar{t}$), (b) the average error ($\bar{\in}$), and (c) the average number of Markov chains in the simulated annealing process ($\overline{MC}$) as a function of the distance parameter (δ) for a fixed value of χ_0. Fig. 3-3(a) shows that the running time decreases as δ increases. This is a direct consequence of the nature of the decrement function (3-1), i.e., smaller values of δ lead to more decrement steps, and therefore larger running times.

Fig. 3-3(b) shows that $\in$ decreases as δ decreases. From (3-1), it's obvious that δ controls the decrement step of the temperature-like control parameter in the simulated annealing algorithm. Hence, by analogy with the thermal annealing process it is expected that larger values of δ will provide lower quality final solution. For a given value of δ, the algorithm utilizing the 3-Valued model provided lower quality final solutions as compared to its 2-Valued counterpart. From Fig. 3-3(b), $\overline{\in}$ = 15.3 for the 2-Valued model and $\overline{\in}$ = 29.3 for the 3-Valued model. In Fig. 3-2(b), we found $\overline{\in}$ to remain virtually constant near these values despite changes to χ_0. Hence, we can conclude that $\overline{\in}$ is more strongly dependent on δ than χ_0.

Fig. 3-3(c) shows that smaller values of δ lead to a larger number of Markov chains. From (3-1), it is seen that smaller values of δ lowers the decrement step of the control parameter. Since the algorithm terminates at approximately the same value of the control parameter, we can justify the observed behavior.

Fig. 3-4 shows (a) the average running time ($\overline{t}$), (b) the average error ($\overline{\in}$), and (c) the average number of Markov chains in the simulated annealing process ($\overline{MC}$) as a function of the problem size in the test generation problem for fixed values of the initial acceptance ratio (χ_0) and the distance parameter (δ). The problem size is quantified by the number of signal lines (except fanout branches) in the fault-free neural network where all XOR/XNOR gates have been replaced by their AND, NOT, OR/NOR equivalents and all gates with more than two inputs have been replaced by their 2-input equivalents. Fig. 3-4(a) shows how the average running time increases with the problem size.

Fig. 3-4(b) shows that average error increases with increasing problem size. This denotes that for larger problem sizes smaller values of δ will be required in order to obtain same quality final solution. This observation in conjunction with Fig 3-3(a) indicate that the simulated annealing algorithm may be computationally very expensive for large problem instances.

Fig 3-4(c) shows an increase in the average number of Markov chains in the simulated annealing algorithm as problem size increases. This seems to indicate that simulated annealing algorithms with larger problem instances terminate at increasingly lower values of the control parameter. This behavior can be understood by realizing the process by which the simulated annealing algorithm was terminated in this experiment. From (3-1), it is seen that the decrement function for the control parameter depends on the deviation σ_{c_k} obtained at the end of the last Markov chain. If no neuron is updated during a Markov chain, i.e., if σ_{c_k} = 0, then c_{k+1} = 0 denoting the termination of the simulated annealing process. For larger problem sizes, and therefore larger Markov chains, increasingly larger probabilities exist that some neurons may be updated even at very low values of the control parameter. This increased probability of obtaining a nonzero σ_{c_k} delays the termination point and contributes to increased number of Markov chains.

In the following chapter, we draw some conclusions.

IV. CONCLUSIONS

In this study we have implemented two neural network based ATPGs for combinational circuits. One uses a 2-Valued neural network model while the other uses a 3-Valued neural network model for the logic gates. Some key findings were made as to the applicability of neural nets as ATPGs if simulated annealing is used to simulate the relaxation process. It was found that the average running time, the average error and the average number of Markov chains increase with increasing problem size. In order to maintain a fixed level of quality in the final solution, the distance parameter has to be lowered (since the average error decreases with decreasing values of the distance parameter for fixed value of the problem size). But this further increases the average running time. Thus for larger problem instances, the average running time increases due to two main reasons: (i) Larger problem size itself and (ii) lower value of the distance parameter needed in order to obtain a fixed level of quality in the final solution. These can lead to very expensive computational behavior of the simulated annealing algorithm for large problem instances.

Also, the 2-Valued and the 3-Valued models were compared with each other. It was claimed by Fujiwara that the purposes of introducing the 3-Valued model were to avoid unnecessary assignment of values 0 and 1, and to speed up the convergence to the global minima. In this paper it has been shown empirically that the 3-Valued model requires a larger number of Markov chains than the 2-Valued model, and that the 3-Valued model does not speed up the convergence to the global minima. It is to be noted that test vectors with don't cares present were obtained in simulations for the 3-Valued model.

Another significant finding was that a valid test vector was obtained for the injected fault even when global convergence was not achieved. A reason for this behavior may be due to the achievement of a neural network state where most neurons possess consistent activation values with the exception of a few neurons. If the neural network terminates in this state and if those neurons possessing inconsistent activation values do not include any primary input neurons, then we may have a valid test vector for the injected fault even though a global minimum has not been achieved. At the termination of the simulated annealing process in a local minima, we can perform a fault-free and a faulty simulation (for the particular fault at hand) in order to determine if the primary output values constitute a valid test vector for the injected fault. Since this simulation cost is much lower than the cost of the simulated annealing algorithm, this does not increase the overall computational cost significantly, but carries potential for great cost savings in case it finds a valid test vector for the injected fault.

V. FIGURES AND TABLES

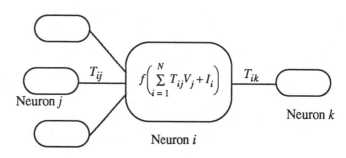

Fig. 2-1. A typical neuron.

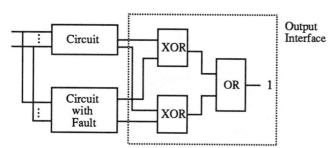

Fig. 2-2. ATPG network for a circuit with two outputs.

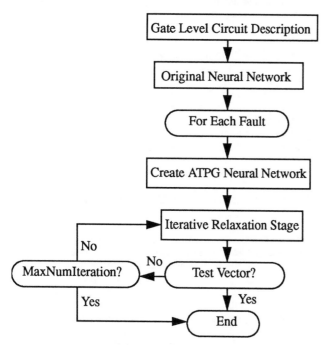

Fig. 3-1. The test generation system.

TABLE 3-1. CHARACTERISTICS OF CIRCUITS USED

Circuit Name	Circuit Function	Total Gates	Input Lines	Output Lines	Problem Size
SN5483A	4-Bit Binary Full Adder With Fast Carry	40 (4 XOR)	9	5	106
SN54181	ALU	63 (8 XOR)	14	8	199
C432	Priority Decoder	160 (18 XOR)	36	7	324
C499[a]	ECAT	202 (104 XOR)	41	32	703
C880	ALU and Control	383	60	26	495
C1355[a]	ECAT	546	41	32	631
C1908	ECAT	880	33	25	1094

[a] Circuits C499 and C1355 are functionally equivalent. All XOR gates of C499 has been expanded into their 4-NAND gate equivalents in C1355.

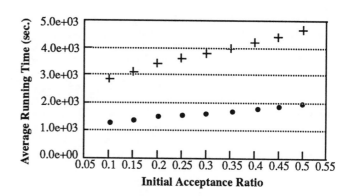

Fig. 3-2(a). Average running time $\bar{t}$ as a function of the initial acceptance ratio χ_0 for fixed value of the distance parameter δ (problem instance: C432, $\delta = 0.05$).

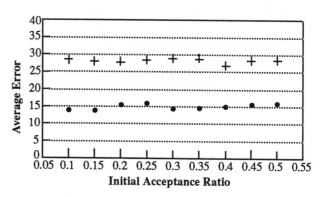

Fig. 3-2(b). Average error $\bar{\epsilon}$ as a function of the initial acceptance ratio χ_0 for fixed value of the distance parameter δ (problem instance: C432, $\delta = 0.05$).

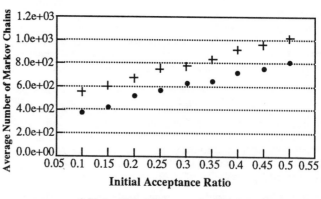

Fig. 3-2(c). Average number of Markov chains in the simulated annealing process $\overline{MC}$ as a function of the initial acceptance ratio χ_0 for fixed value of the distance parameter δ (problem instance: C432, $\delta = 0.05$).

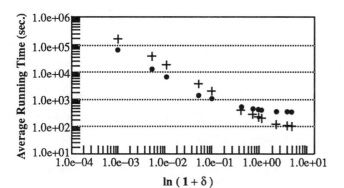

● 2-Valued Model   + 3-Valued Model

Fig. 3-3(a).   Average running time $\bar{t}$ as a function of the distance parameter δ for fixed value of the initial acceptance ratio χ_0 (problem instance: C432, $\chi_0 = 0.48$).

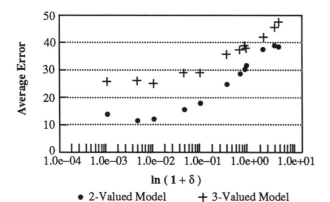

● 2-Valued Model   + 3-Valued Model

Fig. 3-3(b).   Average error $\bar{\epsilon}$ as a function of the distance parameter δ for fixed value of the initial acceptance ratio χ_0 (problem instance: C432, $\chi_0 = 0.48$).

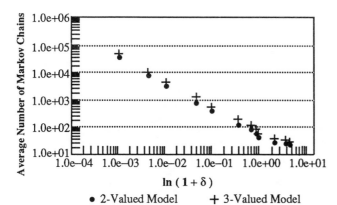

● 2-Valued Model   + 3-Valued Model

Fig. 3-3(c).   Average number of Markov chains in the simulated annealing process $\overline{MC}$ as a function of the distance parameter δ for fixed value of the initial acceptance ratio χ_0 (problem instance: C432, $\chi_0 = 0.48$).

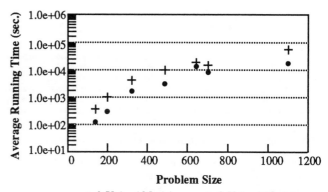

● 2-Valued Model   + 3-Valued Model

Fig. 3-4(a).   Average running time $\bar{t}$ as a function of the problem size for fixed values of the initial acceptance ratio χ_0 and the distance parameter δ ($\chi_0 = 0.48$, $\delta = 0.05$).

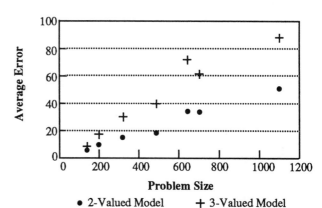

● 2-Valued Model   + 3-Valued Model

Fig. 3-4(b).   Average error $\bar{\epsilon}$ as a function of the problem size for fixed values of the initial acceptance ratio χ_0 and the distance parameter δ ($\chi_0 = 0.48$, $\delta = 0.05$).

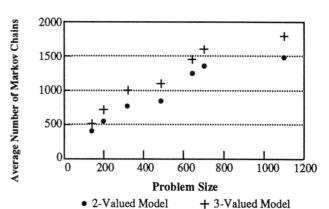

● 2-Valued Model   + 3-Valued Model

Fig. 3-4(c).   Average number of Markov chains in the simulated annealing process $\overline{MC}$ as a function of the problem size for fixed values of the initial acceptance ratio χ_0 and the distance parameter δ ($\chi_0 = 0.48$, $\delta = 0.05$).

REFERENCES

[1] J.J. Hopfield and D.W. Tank, ""Neural" computation of decisions in optimization problems," *Biological Cybernetics,* vol. 52, no. 3, July 1985, pp. 141-152.

[2] S.T. Chakradhar, M.L. Bushnell and V.D. Agrawal, "Toward massively parallel automatic test generation," *IEEE Trans. Computer-Aided Design,* vol. 9, no. 9, September 1990, pp. 982-994.

[3] J.J. Hopfield, "Neurons with graded response have collective computational properties like those of two state neurons," *Proc. Nat. Academy of Sciences,* vol. 81, no. 10, May 1984, pp. 3088-3092.

[4] H. Fujiwara, "Three-valued neural networks for test generation," *20th Int'l Symp. on Fault-Tolerant Computing,* pp. 64-71.

[5] *Parallel Programmer's Guide,* Myrias Research Corporation, Edmonton, Alberta, Canada, 1990.

[6] P.K. Simpson, *Artificial Neural Systems.* Pergamon Press, Inc. 1990.

[7] A.K. Majumder, "Toward massively parallel automatic test generation for digital circuits," Master thesis, Univ. of Colorado at Colorado Springs, 1992.

[8] E. Aarts and J. Korst, *Simulated Annealing and Boltzmann Machines.* John Wiley & Sons, 1990.

[9] E.H.L. Aarts and P.J.M. Van Laarhoven, "Statistical cooling: a general approach to combinatorial optimization problems," *Philips J. Res.,* vol. 40, no. 4, pp. 193-226, September 1985.

[10] F. Brglez and H. Fujiwara, "A neutral netlist of 10 combinational benchmark circuits and a target translator in FORTRAN," distriibuted on a tape to participants of the Special Session of ATPG and Fault Simulation, *Int'l Symposium on Circuits and Systems,* June 1985; partially characterized in F. Brglez, P. Pownall, R. Hum, "Accelerated ATPG and Fault Grading via Testability Analysis," *Proc. IEEE Int'l Symposium on Circuits and Systems,* June 1985, pp. 695-698.

[11] *The TTL Data Book for Design Engineers,* Texas Instruments Incorporated, 2nd ed., Dallas, 1981.

Detection of Type-Specific Herpesvirus Antibodies by Neural Network Classification of Western Blot Densitometer Scans

James M. Lamiell, John A. Ward, Julia K. Hilliard
Brooke Army Medical Center and Southwest Foundation for Biomedical Research, San Antonio, Texas USA

Abstract—We developed a fully connected, feedforward, 3 layer (350-3-3) neural network (NN) for Western blot densitometer scan (WBDS) pattern classification for diagnosing B virus infections in humans. NN supervised training employed backpropagation. The training set consisted of average WBDSs for 3 classification groups. We determined optimum NN parameters for this NN topology and application. The NN achieved a correct classification rate of 85 and an incorrect classification rate of 2 percent, compared to rates of 65 and 25 percent, respectively, achieved by humans as assessed with a real-world WBDS test set. The average NN true positive rate was 0.87 and false positive rate was 0.02, compared to rates of 0.65 and 0.09, respectively, for humans. Receiver operating characteristic curve analysis of NN classification performance demonstrated excellent results. A NN can be successfully trained to classify WBDSs with performance superior to that of humans.

INTRODUCTION

Herpesvirus simiae (B virus) is 1 of at least 35 herpesviruses that infect primates. A B virus infection in Old World monkeys (natural hosts) causes minimal or no symptoms. The B virus may be transmitted to humans by exposure to contaminated body fluids, across mucous membranes, or through skin disruption. A B virus infection in humans is frequently fatal. The prevalence of B virus infection in captive primate colonies ranges from 30 to 60 percent. Probably every year at least 1 US research worker dies from a B virus infection acquired by exposure to an infected primate or human [1].

The earliest possible diagnosis of a B virus infection in humans and treatment with antiviral medication provides the best chance for survival. B virus and herpes simplex virus type 1 (HSV1, which causes human cold sores) and type 2 (HSV2, which causes human genital herpes) are similar. This similarity makes it difficult to identify B virus infections in humans and distinguish them from ubiquitous human HSV infections.

Viral proteins (antigens) against which an infected host forms antibodies can be identified by Western blot (WB) analysis [2]. Viral antibodies vary with the host and the stage of virus infection. Viral proteins are labelled with ^{35}S-methionine 4-24 hours after infection of cell cultures to identify antigens. Labeled polypeptides are separated by molecular weight with a 1 dimensional density gradient sodium dodecyl sulfate-polyacrylamide gel, then the gel is electro-blotted onto a nitrocellulose membrane. Special film is exposed to the electroblotted membrane to produce an autoradiograph which reveals a banding pattern of viral and cellular proteins present in infected cultured cells. This banding pattern is compared with molecular weight protein standards similarly separated so molecular weights of the infected cell polypeptides can be determined.

The electroblotted membrane is reacted with serum from control pools and from an individual with unknown antibody status to reveal antibodies. Antigen-antibody binding can be detected through a series of "reporter" reactions if antibodies are present in the unknown serum. A second antibody conjugated with biotin (biotinylated) that is specific for human or nonhuman primate immunoglobulin G is reacted with the antibodies bound to viral antigens. The biotinylated second antibody is reacted with avidin-linked alkaline phosphatase which can be detected with an alkaline phosphatase specific dye. The dye pattern is scanned with a densitometer. The position of each peak on this WBDS can be matched with the molecular weight of the polypeptide to which the serum antibody has bound. The area under each WBDS peak is proportional to the concentration of the antibody.

Signal processing techniques [3] and correlation analysis [4] have been used to classify WBDSs. A connectionist approach to this difficult WBDS pattern classification problem provides flexibility and good results.

METHODS

WBDS pattern complexity is illustrated by Fig. 1 (WBDSs were made available by the Southwest Foundation for Biomedical Research and were preprocessed with a 21 point moving average high pass filter and a low peak detector). Each WBDS was mapped to a common horizontal molecular weight axis since WB migration distance is proportional to the logarithm of molecular weight. Molecular weights range from 200 kd on the left to 10 kd on the right of the horizontal axis after mapping. The WBDS ordinate axis is proportional to molecule concentration.

There were 120 WBDSs available from 4 serum types: B virus negative rhesus monkeys (NGR), B virus positive rhesus monkeys (BVR), HSV1 positive humans (H1H), and HSV2 positive humans (H2H). There are 30 WBDSs from each group (arranged by column in Fig. 1), all WBDSs are unique, the diagnosis is known for each WBDS, and there are no WBDSs from individuals with mixed infections. The

The opinions and assertions contained herein are the private views of the authors and are not to be construed as official or as reflecting the views of the Department of Defense or the United States Army.

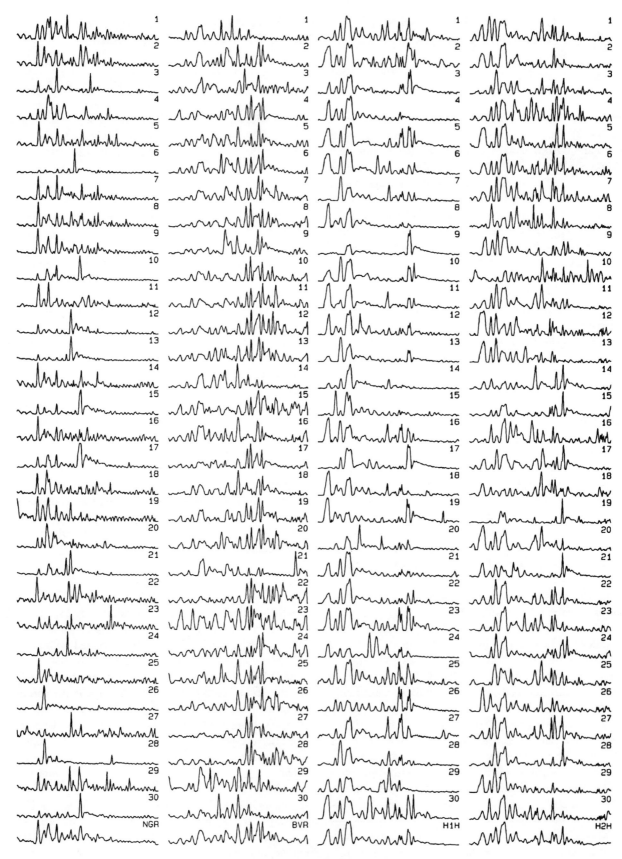

Fig. 1. Western blot densitometer scans.

bottom row of Fig. 1 includes the column averages of the upper 30 WBDSs in each column.

The problem is to reliably classify an unknown WBDS into 1 of the groups (NGR, BVR, H1H, or H2H). We used a fully connected, multilayered, feedforward NN for this pattern classification problem. We reasoned that a single layer perceptron would be inadequate for this problem since the WBDS patterns are probably never linearly separable [5].

Our NN topology consists of 3 layers (input, hidden, and output) of processing elements (PEs, also called neurodes, neurons, nodes, units, or elements). Such a 3 layer NN is capable of solving any classification problem that can be solved by a NN [6]. Each PE output is a function of its inputs. All PE interconnections are unidirectional, NN layers are fully connected to adjacent layers, and each connection has an associated weight. All input layer PEs have unique weighted connections to all hidden layer PEs, and all hidden layer PEs have unique weighted connections to all output PEs. The output (activation) value of each PE is related to its i inputs (x_i) and their associated connection weights (w_i). We used a sigmoid activation function. Since net PE input is the sum of the product of each input and its associated connection weight, the sigmoid activation function relates the PE activation value (output) and its inputs by:

$$\text{output} = 1/(1 + \exp(-\Sigma w_i x_i)) \qquad (1)$$

We employed a supervised learning scheme (backpropagation) to train the NN, i.e. adjust connection weights to optimize output PE outputs [7]. There are faster algorithms that are important for some applications [8], but backpropagation learning speed was adequate for this application.

Backpropagation involves NN pattern input, NN output computation, then comparison of computed and desired NN outputs. The difference between computed and desired outputs is used to adjust NN connection weights. The presentation of all the test set patterns to the NN is called a training epoch. Connection weights can be adjusted after each pattern or each epoch. We adjusted connection weights after presentation of each WBDS pattern to the NN.

NN input is the WBDS. The preprocessed WBDSs were normalized to have (ordinate) values ranging from 0 to 1. There are 350 input values for the NN since there are 350 samples along the WBDS molecular weight axis. Therefore our NN has 350 input PEs. The NN was configured to have 3 output PEs. Each output PE output varies from 0 to 1, and each unique output PE was designated as only 1 of BVR, H1H, or H2H. The NN was trained to output 1 at the BVR output PE when a BVR pattern was input to the NN, otherwise the BVR output PE was trained to output 0. The NN was trained similarly for H1H, H2H, and NGR (all output PE output values 0).

The training set consisted of the average patterns of the BVR, H1H, and H2H groups (bottom row, Fig. 1) since the NN trained to the average WBDS. This was determined after training the NN with randomly selected sets of 25 from each

of the BVR, H1H, and H2H groups followed by testing with the remaining 5 WBDSs from each group. There was never a significant classification performance difference between this training and testing scheme and the scheme using the average of all 30 group WBDSs followed by testing with all WBDSs. This training strategy provides for easy incorporation of experience into training since the WBDS group averages can be updated whenever new known WBDSs are obtained. This strategy limits the training set to a reasonable size as experience accumulates.

A performance metric is essential for NN training. We used the maximum epoch node error as the performance metric, i.e. the maximum absolute difference between desired and computed PE outputs for all PEs and all patterns in a training epoch had to be less than 0.1 in order to terminate NN training. Fig. 2 illustrates the relation between average node error, test set performance, and training epochs to converge. Our NN usually required 50 to 150 training epochs to converge.

The number of hidden layer PEs (h) determines the number of NN trainable connection weights (353h in our NN configuration). If the number of trainable connection weights is excessive compared to training set size, then the NN may not generalize [9,10]. On the other hand, if the number of trainable connection weights is too small relative to training set size, then convergence to appropriate NN connection weights may be impossible. Fig. 3 shows the relationships between the number of hidden layer PEs, training epochs to converge, and test set performance. We opted for improved classification performance at the expense of speed, and selected 3 hidden layer PEs as optimum for this application.

NN connection weights are initialized randomly in the range from -W to +W. The initial weight range (2W) is an important NN performance parameter. We evaluated a

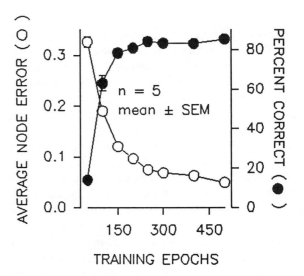

Fig. 2. NN performance as a function of number of training epochs.

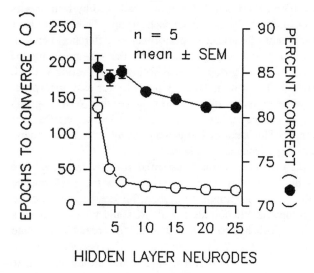

Fig. 3. NN performance as a function of the number of hidden layer PEs.

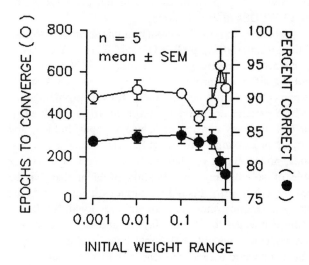

Fig. 4. NN performance as a function of the initial neural network weight range.

variety of W values by assessing the number of training epochs to converge and test set performance (Fig. 4). The optimum initial weight range was 0.5.

There were other design considerations. We utilized an input and hidden layer bias of 1.0. The NN learning coefficient was optimized at 1.0 for this application. A momentum term added nothing to NN performance. We attempted to improve ability to generalize by adding low amplitude noise and phase shift to the WBDSs, but there was no improvement. The NN was implemented on a personal computer with a custom developed C program. The textbook by Eberhart and Dobbins [11] provided excellent program development guidelines.

RESULTS

We assessed NN classification of a 120 WBDS test set (Fig. 1). The NN was trained in 10 distinct training sessions using NN parameters and the training set outlined above. Each training session generated unique NN connection weights since initial NN connection weights were randomly assigned. The 10 NN connection weight sets were assessed in the NN with the test set.

We used less stringent classification thresholds since ideal output PE output values (0 or 1) are unusual: if the output value of an output PE exceeded a high threshold (0.6) then it was considered to be 1, and if it was less than a low threshold (0.4) then it was considered to be 0. Output PE outputs from 0.4 to 0.6 were indeterminate (nondiagnostic). If more than 1 output PE output value exceed 0.6, then the result was indeterminate since each test WBDS is a member of 1 and only 1 of the 4 groups. The aggregate NN performance (considering all output PE output values) with the WBDS test set is shown in Table I.

NN aggregate performance was consistent. There were 26 improperly classified (incorrect or indeterminate) WBDSs in the 10 sessions. Nine WBDSs were improperly classified in all 10 sessions (NGR04, NGR06, BVR01, BVR14, BVR21, BVR29, H2H01, H2H08, and H2H19). There was a tendency for the NN to incorrectly classify NGR04 as H2H, BVR01 as NGR, H2H01 as H1H, and H2H08 as NGR.

There are 4 alternatives concerning an output PE output value. If an output PE output correctly classifies a WBDS into a group in which it belongs, then this is a true positive decision (TP). If an output PE output incorrectly classifies a WBDS into a group in which it does not belong, then this is a false positive decision (FP). If an output PE output incorrectly classifies a WBDS as not in a group in which it belongs, then this is a false negative decision (FN). If an output PE output correctly classifies a WBDS as not in a group in which it does not belong, then this is a true negative decision (TN).

Enumeration of these decisions (TP, FP, FN, and TN) for several cases provides a means to evaluate a diagnostic test (classification system). Derived performance measures include the true positive rate (TPR) which is TP/(TP+FN), and the false positive rate (FPR) which is FP/(FP+TN). The

TABLE I
WBS CLASSIFICATION PERFORMANCE (MEAN±SEM)

Aggregate Performance (n=120)	Neural Network (n=10)	Humans (n=8)
Correct (percent)	85.1±0.8	64.5±3.3
Incorrect (percent)	2.0±0.4	25.2±3.7
Indeterminate (percent)	12.9±0.9	10.3±3.0

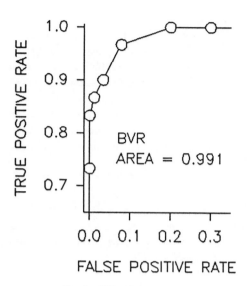

Fig. 5. BVR PE ROC curve.

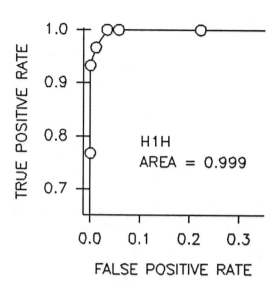

Fig. 6. H1H PE ROC curve.

TPR is the sensitivity, or probability of the test being positive given that the disease is present. (1 - FPR) is the specificity, or probability of the test being negative given that the disease is not present. TPR and FPR were computed with the WBDS test set for each output PE (Table II). The average TPR was about 0.87 and the average FPR was about 0.02, considering all output PEs.

Receiver operating characteristic (ROC) curves were used to evaluate NN classification of the WBDS test set [12,13]. One set of NN connection weights was selected from the 10 sessions described above. Instead of using high and low thresholds, a single threshold value was used to classify each output PE output as classifying the WBDS as belonging or not belonging to the group for that output PE, i.e. there were no indeterminate classifications. The threshold value was varied from 0 to 1, while TP, FP, FN, and TN were enumerated for the WBDS test set with each threshold value. TPR and FPR were computed, and curves of TPR versus FPR (ROC curves) were constructed for each of the 3 output PEs (Figs. 5-7).

A perfect diagnostic test has FPR=0 and TPR=1. The area under the ROC curve assesses NN discriminative power [14]. This ROC curve area is the probability that given 2

WBDSs (1 belonging to a group classified by an output PE and 1 not belonging to that group), the output PE output will be greater for the WBDS that belongs to the group. The ROC curve area for a perfect diagnostic test is 1.0. The ROC curve area is 0.5 for a diagnostic test that does not discriminate between groups (FPR=TPR), and such a nondiagnostic test is no better than a coin toss in discriminating groups. The ROC curve areas for all NN output PEs are greater than 0.99 (Figs. 5-7).

NN performance was compared to human performance. Eight humans were shown the WBDS test set along with average WBDSs for each of the 4 groups, and asked to classify each WBDS into the group which it most resembled based on classification criteria of their choice. If there was no resemblance to any of the 4 groups, then the humans

TABLE II
WBDS PERFORMANCE ANALYSIS (MEAN±SEM)

Group (n=30)	Neural Network (n=10)		Humans (n=8)	
	TPR	FPR	TPR	FPR
BVR	0.833±0.005	0.014±0.003	0.739±0.019	0.064±0.013
H1H	0.937±0.012	0.011±0.002	0.638±0.062	0.078±0.013
H2H	0.840±0.007	0.025±0.002	0.583±0.062	0.121±0.023

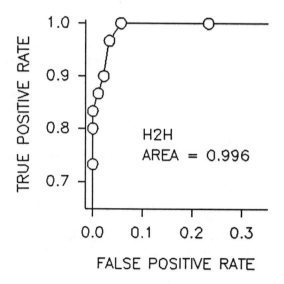

Fig. 7. H2H PE ROC curve.

classified the WBDSs into an indeterminate group. The aggregate human results are shown in Tables I and II for comparison with NN performance. The average human TPR was 0.65 and the average FPR was 0.09.

There was agreement between the WBDSs misclassified by the NN and those misclassified by the humans. There were 15 WBDSs that were misclassified in at least 8 of 10 NN sessions. Twelve of these 15 WBDSs were also misclassified by at least 6 of 8 humans.

DISCUSSION

NN performance was excellent in this difficult pattern classification application. The NN performed significantly better than humans given the same pattern classification problem. We do not consider human pattern classification to be the optimum solution for WBDS pattern classification, but human performance was worse and NN performance was better than anticipated.

There was substantial agreement between the NN and the humans on WBDS patterns that were indeterminate or misclassified. There will probably always be 5 to 10 percent of WBDS patterns that are difficult to distinguish and classify regardless of classification scheme.

Since the NN WBDS pattern classification error rate was low and most misclassifications were indeterminate results, this NN could be an initial stage of pattern classification. Thus, if the NN classified a WBDS then that result would be used, but if the NN provided an indeterminate classification result then that result would be submitted to another processing stage, perhaps even another NN, for more refined classification.

NN parameters had to be customized for this application. Customization is empiric, requiring experimentation to optimize NN parameters. In this application, such a development time investment is worthwhile because accurate solution of the B virus identification problem is so important for those who might have a B virus infection.

As we worked with the NN, its noise immunity and ability to classify incomplete WBDSs became apparent. The NN was capable of correctly classifying a WBDS with as much as 20 percent of the WBDS pattern missing. However, the NN was very sensitive to any horizontal shift in WBDS patterns, i.e. pattern shifts as small as 2 points right or left along the molecular weight axis frequently had a significant effect on NN performance. Horizontal alignment of all patterns on a common molecular weight (horizontal) axis is essential. Even though molecular weight standards are run with the WBDS, error is possible. For example, if all H2H scans were consistently and erroneously shifted relative to BVR scans, then it is possible the NN would distinguish the patterns based on this artifactual shift rather than intrinsic differences in WBDS pattern shapes. We will develop a reliable and consistent mechanism for horizontal alignment of all WBDSs to a common molecular weight axis.

Since the diagnosis of B virus infections in humans is so difficult, it is almost never based on the results of a single test. Therefore, we see the NN WBDS analysis as just 1 input into an expert system diagnostic assistant for diagnosing B virus infections in humans. For example, other inputs into this expert system could be the results of restriction endonuclease analysis, preliminary viral culture, biopsy specimen histology, patient symptoms, exposure history, and the results of competition enzyme immunoassay.

REFERENCES

[1] G.P. Holmes, J.K. Hilliard, K.C. Klontz, A.H. Rupert, C.M. Schindler, E. Parrish, et al, "B virus (Herpesvirus simiae) infection in humans: epidemiologic investigation of a cluster," Ann Intern Med, vol. 112, pp. 833-839, 1990.

[2] R.M. Muñoz, J.K. Hilliard, S.L. Lipper, "Early antibody responses(s) to Herpes B virus specific polypeptides in sera and cerebrospinal fluid (CSF) from infected humans: case studies," VIIth International Congress of Virology, vol. 203, pp. 12-23, 1990.

[3] S. Millership and K. Ragoonaden, "Automated lanes detection and comparison of bacterial electrophoretic protein fingerprints using fast Fourier transformation," Comput Biomed Res, vol. 25, pp. 392-406, 1992.

[4] J.A. Ward and J.K. Hilliard, "Automated screening of Western blot densitometer scans for the detection of type-specific herpes virus antibodies," Proc 95th Ann Meeting of the Texas Academy of Science, 1992.

[5] M.L. Minskey and S.A. Papert, Perceptrons: An Introduction to Computational Geometry, expanded edition. MIT Press, 1990.

[6] R.P. Lippmann, "An introduction to computing with neural nets," IEEE ASSP Magazine, pp. 4-22, April 1987.

[7] D.E. Rumelhart and J.L. McClelland, Parallel Distributed Processing. MIT Press, 1986.

[8] S.E. Fahlman, "Faster-learning variations on back-propagation: an empirical study," Proc 1988 Connectionist Models Summer School, pp. 38-51, 1988.

[9] E. Rich and K. Knight, Artificial Intelligence. McGraw-Hill, Inc., 1991.

[10] P.H. Winston, Artificial Intelligence. Addison-Wesley Publishing Co., 1992.

[11] R.C. Eberhart and R.W. Dobbins, Neural Network PC Tools. Academic Press, Inc., 1990.

[12] J.R. Beck and E.K. Shultz, "The use of relative operating characteristic (ROC) curves in test performance evaluation," Arch Pathol Lab Med, vol. 110, pp. 13-20, 1986.

[13] M.L. Meistrell, "Evaluation of neural network performance by receiver operating characteristic analysis: examples from the biotechnology domain," Proc 13th Ann Symp on Computer Applications in Medical Care, pp. 295-301, 1989.

[14] J.A. Hanley and B.J. McNeil, "The meaning and use of the area under a receiver operating characteristic (ROC) curve," Radiology, vol. 143, pp. 29-36, 1982.

Neural Net Simulation with MUSIC

Urs A. Müller, Anton Gunzinger and Walter Guggenbühl
Electronics Laboratory, Swiss Federal Institute of Technology
CH-8092 Zürich, Switzerland

Abstract—Experimental research on neural networks often demands huge computing power as well as high flexibility in the design of learning algorithms and network structures. High performance can be provided by parallel computers but the difficulty usually lies in the programming of these systems. This paper describes a neural net simulation platform, implemented on the MUSIC parallel distributed memory computer (Multiprocessor System with Intelligent Communication), which is able to run simulations at supercomputer speed and yet is very flexible and easy to use. The low price power consumption and size allow to use the system as a desktop supercomputer which does not have to be shared among a large community of users.

I. Introduction

Since neural networks usually have a great potential for parallelism, many parallel simulators have been reported in the past [1, 2, 3, 4, 5, 6]. The programming of parallel systems often is very complicated and therefore most of these simulators are restricted to specific network structures and learning algorithms. Furthermore, the application of learning algorithms sometimes is limited due to the use of neural net inherent parallelism. Partitioning of the training set, for instance, restricts the back-propagation algorithm to batch learning (continuous weight update is not possible).

The MUSIC system supports data collection and distribution by hardware what allows the efficient implementation of data-parallel algorithms. An implementation of the back-propagation algorithm confirms the enormous computing power and efficient programming environment: A 60-processor system is able to simulate 247 million connection updates per second (including the forward path) using 32 bit floating-point precision and continuous weight update. A new simulation environment frees the programmer from implementing a user shell and allows less experienced persons to use MUSIC's performance.

Beside the simulation of neural nets MUSIC is currently also being used for the simulation of molecular dynamics in chemistry. Further applications in numerical mathematics and in signal processing are in development.

II. The MUSIC System

The key idea of the MUSIC architecture (see Figure 1) is to support the collection and distribution of data sets among all processing elements by autonomously working hardware implemented communication controllers. The communication network itself is a pipelined ring bus, operated at a 5-MHz clock rate. Its width is 40 bit: 32 bit data and 8 bit token. A programmer must only determine the data partitioning, the actual data communication is then carried out by the communication controllers.

The processing elements (DSP 96002 from Motorola) run at a 40-MHz clock rate (independent of the communication clock rate) with a peak performance of 60 Mflops each. A MUSIC board contains three processing elements and a board manager (transputer T805) which has access to the host interface of the DSPs. The managers of different boards interconnect by their transputer links, forming a standard transputer network. One of the transputers is connected to the host computer (UNIX workstation, PC or Macintosh). To provide the fast data throughput required by many applications, special I/O modules (for instance for realtime video input/output) can be added. An SCSI interface module is currently being developed. It will allow direct access to fast mass storage via the MUSIC ring bus and is planned to be used for fast throughput of learning patterns if MUSICs memory (126 Mbyte) is not large enough to hold the complete pattern set.

Up to 21 boards or 63 processing elements fit into a standard 19-inch rack which results in a 3.8 Gflops system with computing costs of about $111 per Mflops and a power consumption of not more than 800 W (including forced air cooling). Table I summarizes the technical data of the MUSIC prototype system. More MUSIC computers are currently under constructions and will be used by different research groups for various applications. A more detailed description of the MUSIC architecture is found in [7].

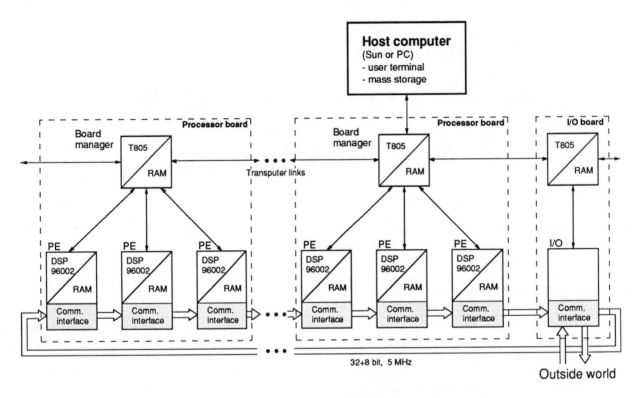

Fig. 1. Overview of the MUSIC hardware.

TABLE I
MUSIC SYSTEM TECHNICAL DATA

Number of Processors:	63
Peak Performance:	3.8 Gflops
Floating Point Format:	IEEE 32 and 44 bit
Static RAM:	15.8 Mbyte
Dynamic RAM:	126 Mbyte
Programming Language:	C, Assembler
Cabinet:	Standard 19-inch rack
Cooling:	Forced air cooling
Total Power Consumption:	< 800 W
Price/Performance:	8'500 flops/$
Host Computer:	PC, Sun or Macintosh

III. BACK-PROPAGATION IMPLEMENTATION

The first implemented learning algorithm on MUSIC was the well-known back-propagation applied to fully connected multilayer perceptrons [8]. The motivation was to gain experience in programming the system and to demonstrate its performance on a real-world application. The back-propagation algorithm has been implemented on many computers, allowing a comparison of MUSICs performance with that of other systems (see Table II).

Different levels of parallelism are inherent in a multilayer perceptron. Probably the simplest way is to distribute complete different learning experiments (e.g. with different parameters) to different computers (*parallelization in experimental space*). This method does neither require special programming of the algorithms nor does it need intensive communication between the processing elements. However, it is not applicable if the results of one experiment are needed to setup the next one.

A next deeper level is *parallelization in pattern space*. All processors run the same program on an individual subset of the learning patterns. This method is highly efficient if the training set is large in relation to the number of processing elements and is therefore reported frequently in the literature [1, 2, 4]. However, it does not allow the updating of the weights immediately after each pattern presentation and is therefore restricted to batch learning. Batch learning, on one hand, forms the basis of most theoretical studies of the back-propagation but on the other hand it is empirically known that continuous weight update converges much faster if the training sets contain redundancy. Additionally, batch learning usually cannot be applied to adaptive systems. We therefore think that this method should not be applied in systems which are intended to be used for research in learning behaviour of neural nets where maximum freedom in the choice of the algorithms is required.

The next level of parallelism is *parallelization in layer space*. This means computing different layers on different processing elements. To keep all processors busy the pat-

TABLE II

COMPARISON OF BACK-PROPAGATION IMPLEMENTATIONS

| System | No. of PEs | Performance | | | Cont. weight update |
		Forward [MCPS]	Learning [MCUPS]	Peak (%)	
PC (80486, 50 MHz)*	1	1.1	0.47	38.0	Yes
Sun (Sparcstation 10)*	1	3.0	1.1	43.0	Yes
Transputer T800 [5]	64	27.0	9.9	—	—
Warp [1]	10	—	17.0	—	No
CM-2** [4]	64K	180.0	40.0	—	No
RAP [9]	40	574.0	106.0	50.0	Yes
NEC SX-3***	1	—	130.0	9.6	Yes
MUSIC-10*	30	360.0	151.0	34.0	Yes
MUSIC-20*	60	504.0	247.0	28.0	Yes
GF11 [2]	356	—	901.0	54.0	No

*Own measurements

**Estimated numbers

***By N. Koike of NEC (no published reference available).

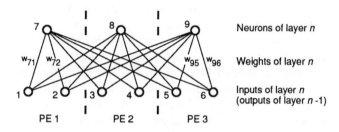

Fig. 2. Partitioning of weights and layers.

terns have to be propagated and back-propagated through the neural net in a pipelined manner (see for instance [10]). This still restricts the implementation to batch learning because for continuous weight update a propagate/back-propagate cycle has to be completed before the next pattern may be presented.

To allow continuous weight update the parallelization level has to go one step further, as realized in the MUSIC implementation: *partitioning in neuron space* (another implementation is reported in [3]). In each iteration step the output of a specific layer is computed. All processing elements have a local copy of the complete input vector of the layer and compute a subset of its output. In the subsequent communication cycle the partial vectors are collected and a copy of the assembled vector is distributed to each processing element to serve as input for the next layer. The backward path is similar, except, that in addition to back-propagating the errors also the weights are updated. The partitioning is illustrated in Figure 2.

One difficulty, however, is the fact that the processors need different subsets of the weights for the forward-propagation than for the back-propagation (compare Fig-

ure 2). The communication of the updated weights after each propagate/back-propagate cycle is normally not feasible because the number of weights increases almost with the square of the number of neurons. To avoid the communication saturation the updated weights are not communicated. Instead each processor holds a copy of both weight subsets needed (for propagate and back-propagate) and updates both of them (we found this method proposed in [11]).

As shown in Table II, MUSIC demonstrates impressive speed on back-propagation simulation. One day of simulation time on MUSIC corresponds to about one year on a modern computer workstation. It can even outperform modern supercomputers. The availability of this high computing power allows experimental research to be much more profound than it was thinkable before.

However, for experimental research not only large computing power but also an almost unlimited flexibility in designing learning algorithms and network structures is required. An important focus of the project therefore is the implementation of a flexible neural net simulation environment on MUSIC.

IV. A NEURAL NET SIMULATION PLATFORM

It seems hard to capture the present variety of neural net models into one program (with many parameters and options) and it's even much harder to give such a program the necessary flexibility for experimental research. The goal of our neural net simulation environment therefore is to provide a platform which allows the development and implementation of new neural models in minimum time.

The basic elements, common to most neural nets, are data objects such as layers or patterns, parameter objects such as weights and a set of (neural) functions to interconnect the data objects. A specific neural net structure is then determined by the size and number of the allocated data and parameter objects and by the order in which they are updated. This determination of the network structure must also be "programmed" by the user but is quite different from defining data objects and programming neural functions. The latter means defining a new or modifying an existing learning algorithm; compiler turnaround time is usually not critical. In contrast, programming the neural net structure often means online experimenting, for instance determining the optimal network dimensions or trying out different learning strategies. In contrast to other work (for instance [3]) which uses the same programming language for the two tasks, we decided to provide different environments.

The *neural functions* run on the MUSIC parallel environment. The main difference to a single-processor environment is that the data-parallel code must be able to produce only a subset of the resulting data block. Just three functions are needed to control the communication: `Init_comm()` initializes the communication network for the redistribution of a particular data block. The user program gets all the parameters it needs to run a SPMD (single program multiple data) program (array sizes, dimensions and buffer pointers); `Send_data()` informs the communication network that a new data subset is ready to be transported to other processing elements and `Synchronize()` waits until all expected data values have arrived and are ready to be used for the following computation steps.

For the *definition of the neural net structure* a simpler command language is sufficient. The advantage is that it can also be used by less computer experienced users. Furthermore, a simple command language can be interpreted at runtime what dramatically reduces turnaround times and allows all kinds of gradations in experimental research: from the interactive programming of smaller experiments till large off-line learning jobs.

The capability of the command language must include variables, loop control, if/then conditions, data input and output and, of course, the possibility of calling neural functions. Instead of creating a new language definition we decided to consider an existing one. The choice was BASIC which shows all of the above mentioned capabilities and is very easy to learn and to use. It additionally has the advantage of being widely spread. A software interface allows to call neural (or other) parallel functions from the BASIC interpreter. To allocate a new layer with 300 neurons for instance you would have to type:

```
a = new_layer(300)
```

The variable *a* afterwards holds an index to the created layer which later can be used in other function calls to reference that layer. To propagate from layer *a* to layer *b* with the weights *w* you would type:

```
propagate(a, b, w)
```

Other functions allow the randomization of weights, the loading of pattern and weight sets, the computation of mean squared errors and so on. Each instruction can be assigned to a program line and can then be run as a program. The sequence

```
10 a = new_layer(300)
20 b = new_layer(10)
30 w = new_weights(a, b)
```

for instance defines a two layer perceptron with 300 input and 10 output neurons being connected with the weights *w*.

Extending the simulator with a new learning algorithm means that the programmer has to write just the data-parallel code of the algorithm. For the back-propagation algorithm this took less than a day. It is also conceivable to run a C++ precompiler on the MUSIC system.

A MUSIC simulator for single processing environments (like a PC or workstation) is also available. This allows to run the neural simulation platform on single processor systems, at least those algorithms which are not implemented in assembly language. We often use this possibility as a convenient way of software development.

V. PERFORMANCE

Running an interpreter on a parallel machine can be problematic because interpreting the commands increases the sequential part of the application which is known to be a fundamental limit in speedup (Amdahls law [12]). Therefore the BASIC code is not directly interpreted on the processing elements but first is compiled to a simple stack oriented meta-code which afterwards can be run at optimum speed. The compilation phase is not really noticeable to the user since compiling 1000 source lines takes less than a second on a Sun Sparcstation 2.

The fully optimized assembler version (Table II) has been compared to a BASIC controlled C version as well as to the BASIC controlled assembler version with respect to speed and implementation costs. In the latter version the BASIC interpreter was used to call the optimized assembler kernels of the back-propagation. The results are summarized in Table III. In the implementation costs of the optimal version the implementation of the control program and user shell are considered. This work is omitted when using the BASIC interpreter.

The use of C reduced the simulation speed by a factor of 3.6 but the saving of a factor 10 in development time

TABLE III

COMPARISON OF DIFFERENT IMPLEMENTATIONS

Version	Rel. speed	Implementation costs
BASIC and C	100 %	0.5 Weeks
BASIC and assembler	330 %	2 Weeks
Optimal version	360 %	6 Weeks

is probably more important in research than the loss in speed. Anyway, if a specific algorithm proofs to work well, the way to an optimized implementation is still open.

VI. CONCLUSIONS

The implementation of a parallel neural net simulation environment makes MUSIC a useful tool for neural net training, especially for large networks and training sets. The performance measured in practical experiments is 300 times higher than the one of a modern computer workstation. It reaches the level of supercomputers but with the price, space and electrical power consumption of several orders of magnitude lower and a turnaround time which is not reduced by a large community of users. The parallelism is not completely hidden but is kept to a minimum. The programming environment is powerful enough to make the implementation of data parallel algorithms not essentially more difficult than on a single-processing environment and certainly not more complicated than on a modern vector-processor based supercomputer as has ben confirmed by practical examples.[1]

ACKNOWLEDGMENT

The authors would like to express their gratitude to all members of the MUSIC team: Peter Kohler, Hansruedi vonder Mühll, Bernhard Bäumle, Walter Scott and Alexander Eichenberger. They further thank the students U. M. Franz, H. Walther, M. Zehnder, F. Bühlmann, P. Guggenbach and P. Haag for the help in building and testing the MUSIC system during their graduate work.

REFERENCES

[1] Dean A. Pomerleau, George L. Gusciora, David S. Touretzky, and H. T. Kung. Neural network simulation at Warp speed: How we got 17 million connections per second. In *IEEE International Conference on Neural Networks*, pages II.143–150, July 24–27, San Diego, California 1988.

[2] Michael Witbrock and Marco Zagha. An implementation of backpropagation learning on GF11, a large SIMD parallel computer. *Parallel Computing*, 14(3):329–346, 1990.

[3] Nelson Morgan, James Beck, Phil Kohn, Jeff Bilmes, Eric Allman, and Joachim Beer. The ring array processor: A multiprocessing peripheral for connectionist applications. *Journal of Parallel and Distributed Computing*, 14(3):248–259, March 1992.

[4] Xiru Zhang, Michael Mckenna, Jill P. Mesirov, and David L. Waltz. An efficient implementation of the back-propagation algorithm on the connection machine CM-2. In David S. Touretzky, editor, *Advances in Neural Information Processing Systems (NIPS-89)*, pages 801–809, 2929 Campus Drive, Suite 260, San Mateo, CA 94403, 1990. Morgan Kaufmann Publishers.

[5] Heinz Mühlbein and Klaus Wolf. Neural network simulation on parallel computers. In David J. Evans, Gerhard R. Joubert, and Frans J. Peters, editors, *Parallel Computing-89*, pages 365–374, Amsterdam, 1990. North Holland.

[6] R. Männer, H. Horner, R. Hauser, and A. Genthner. Multiprocessor simulation of neural networks with NERV. In *3rd International Conference on Supercomputing*, New York, June 1989. The Association for Computing Machinery (ACM).

[7] Urs A. Müller, Bernhard Bäumle, Peter Kohler, Anton Gunzinger, and Walter Guggenbühl. Achieving supercomputer performance for neural net simulation with an array of digital signal processors. *IEEE Micro*, 12(5):55–65, October 1992.

[8] D. E. Rumelhart, G. E. Hinton, and R. J. Williams. Learning internal representation by error propagation. In David E. Rumelhart and James L. McClelland, editors, *Parallel Distributet Processing: Explorations in the Microstructure of Cognition*, volume 1, pages 318–362. Bradford Books, Cambridge MA, 1986.

[9] Phil Kohn, Jeff Bilmes, Nelson Morgan, and James Beck. Software for ANN training on a ring array processor. In John E. Moody, Steven J. Hanson, and Richard P. Lippmann, editors, *Advances in Neural Information Processing Systems 4 (NIPS-91)*, 2929 Campus Drive, Suite 260, San Mateo, California 94403, 1992. Morgan kaufmann.

[10] Soheil Shams and K. Wojtek Przytula. Implementation of multilayer neural networks on parallel programmable digital computers. In Magdy A. Bayoumi, editor, *Parallel Algorithms and Architectures for DSP Applications*, pages 225–253, Boston/Dordrecht/London, 1991. Kluwer Academic Publishers.

[11] Hyunsoo Yoon and Jong H. Nang. Multilayer neural networks on distributed-memory multiprocessors. In *International Nueral Network Conference (INNC-90) Paris*, pages 669–672, Dordrecht/Boston/London, July 9–13 1990. INNS and IEEE, Kluwer Academic Publishers.

[12] Gene M. Amdahl. Validity of the single processor approach to achieving large scale computing capabilities. In *AFIPS Spring Computer Conference Atlantic City, NJ*, pages 483–485, April 1967.

---

[1] According to NEC it took two month to optimally implement back-propagation on the vector supercomputer SX-3 (Table II). This is about the same amount of time as one of the authors needed for the optimized MUSIC implementation (Table III).

NEURAL NETWORK APPROACH TO IDENTIFY
BATCH CELL GROWTH

M. J. Syu
Department of Chemical Engineering
National Cheng-Kung University
Tainan, Taiwan, R.O.C.

George T. Tsao
Laboratory of Renewable Resources Engineering
A. A. Potter Engineering Center, Purdue University
West Lafayette, Indiana 47907

ABSTRACT

A saturation-type transfer function with a back-propagation neural network (BPNN) was proposed for solving the modeling problem of batch cell growth system. Batch chemical processes are usually influenced by their initial conditions. For batch cell cultures, the initial state strongly governs the growth pattern during the time course. In modeling a chemical system, we are always interested in how to model the outcome of the system related to some affecting factors. In a batch system, some of the initial conditions are certainly important affecting factors. Trying to model the cell growth with information concerning only the initial conditions is not yet possible from a kinetic approach. The difficulty comes from numerical analysis and insufficient knowledge regarding certain growth parameters as they vary with time. Accordingly, neural network methodology with the concept developed earlier was proposed to solve this problem. The feasibility and capability of the neural network to model the pattern of batch cell growth by providing initial conditions only is tested in this study. A 2-3-8 BPNN with initial glucose and cell concentrations as the two inputs, cell densities measured at eight each hours as the eight outputs was thus constructed. The simulation and prediction results of this BPNN are presented to demonstrate the performance and applicability of this newly discovered transfer function. Sensitivity analysis of the initial factors from this neural network model (NNM) is also discussed. The optimization of the initial conditions for this system is also performed.

1. Introduction

Neural network was first proposed by McCulloch and Pitts in 1943 [1]. This methodology tries to simulate the structure and function of human neuron system while in a much simpler manner. As a result, artificial neural network (ANN) implements networking and computation to identify the behavior of different systems. Back-propagation neural network (BPN) being one of the ANN paradigms is very powerful in functional mapping. It was introduced by Werbos in 1974 [2] and has been brought a lot of attentions since 1985

[3,4]. During the passed few years, the structure, learning, and convergence of BPN have been widely investigated [5,6]. Furthermore, BPN has also been successfully implemented to a different varieties of systems including simulation and prediction of multicomponent adsorption [7], fault diagnosis of chemical process [8], dynamic identification and adaptive control of chemical systems [9], chaotic signal prediction [10].

Neural network can be an alternative to the classical approach which is guided by kinetics, material and energy conservation principles in the modeling of microbial cell growth. In a neural net, the "transfer function" usually plays a central role. This article is to introduce a novel transfer function which is different from sigmoid function. This function of the saturation form has been found very useful in constructing neural networks to describe batch cell growth and other bioprocesses [11].

There has been a well-defined method to model the behavior of batch cell growth. Two differential equations on the cell growth and glucose consumption rates are derived from material balances. Once given the initial conditions of both glucose and cell concentrations, the time sequence of cell concentration can be obtained by solving the two equations simultaneously.

The specific rates can be expressed in general forms as:

$$\frac{dX}{dt} = r_x \equiv f(X,G) \tag{1}$$

$$\frac{dG}{dt} = r_G \equiv g(X,G) \tag{2}$$

Where G is the glucose concentration, X is the cell density. Usually, the effects due to the cells and glucose concentration are more significant, the rates are thus expressed in terms of both. Also, assume that the effects from the other factors are incorporated in both forms of f(·) and g(·).

Equations (1) and (2) can be easily solved if initial conditions for cell and glucose concentrations are known, provided that the values of the parameters are all known. To solve the above equations, we will need the data for cell mass and glucose concentration at different time (i.e., X(t) and G(t)).

In the case of insufficient measurements, state estimation may be helpful but not always reliable in supporting the simulation. How can we simulate the patterns of batch cell growth from the initial conditions without any additional information regarding the above mentioned parameters? In the traditional approach, the simulation can be performed to obtain the outcome of a system stepwise. For example, to model the batch cell culture, it is the cell density at each individual time, X(t), t=1, ..., being modeled.

In the approach of neural network, we can model X at different t as a group, in a parallel manner. For each given initial condition (e.g. X(0) and G(0)), there should be only one set of $\{X(t) \mid t=1, 2, ..., n\}$ mapped. If we consider each set, $\{X(t)\}$, as a pattern corresponding to a set of initial conditions, a successful NNM will potentially predict the batch growth pattern from solely the given initial conditions. This approach of pattern recognition based on NNM is different from the conventional approach in two important aspects: one is to reduce the amount of necessary information in modeling. For example, in this case, the information on G(t) would not be needed. The other is to model the behavior of the system (e.g. the batch cell growth) in parallel (as a whole set) but not in time sequence.

3. Back-Propagation Neural Network (BPNN)

In general, the neural networks with learning capability are categorized as supervised learning and unsupervised learning. The BPNN achieves its minimum state through supervised learning and its architecture. The major features of the back-propagation neural network are the connecting weights between neighboring layers, the transfer function(s), and the learning rule(s) governing the update of weights. The inputs, x_i^{s-1} from the previous layer are combined together by a linear summation, i.e.,

$$I_j^s = \sum_i \omega_{ji}^s x_i^{s-1} + \theta_j \tag{3}$$

where ω_{ji}^s are the values of weights connecting the ith element in the previous layer and the jth element in the current layer, and θ_j is the bias term which acts as an auxiliary buffer to distribute the errors throughout the structure of the network.

The outputs which form the processing elements in the next layer are obtained from a nonlinear (or linear) transformation of the above summation as shown in the equation below:

$$x_j^s = f(I_j^s) \tag{4}$$

in which f(·) is the transfer function. The transfer function is one of the central components in creating a neural network. We have discovered that a transfer function of a saturation form very useful in modeling batch cell growth and other bioprocesses.

$$f(z) = \frac{bz}{1 + |z|} \qquad \text{(Saturation–type function)} \tag{5}$$

in which b can be an adjustable parameter.

Neural networks permit the use of many different types of transfer functions such as the thresholding function, the linear function, the squashing function, etc [4]. In BPNN, various kinds of transfer functions are also employed; the sigmoid function, $\frac{1}{1 + e^{-z}}$, is the one most frequently applied to different types of systems. However, the saturation-type function is implemented in this study instead.

The BPNN has the capability of self-learning which is the main difference as compared to conventional models and certain other neural network algorithms. BPNN uses a learning algorithm to adjust each weight in the network so that the resulting output is closely adapted to the desired output. On the other hand, conventional computation algorithms do not learn from the data sets. In building the NNM for batch cell growth, the delta-learning rule has been used. This learning process essentially implements the gradient descent searching algorithm in minimizing the generated error. The generated error, E, was expressed as the sum-squared error,

$$E = \frac{1}{2} \sum_k (d_k - o_k)^2 \tag{6}$$

The changing of weights is expressed as $\Delta\omega_{ji}^s$:

$$\Delta\omega_{ji}^s = -\eta \frac{\partial E}{\partial \omega_{ji}^s} \tag{7}$$

Or,

$$\Delta\omega_{ji}^s = \eta e_j^s x_i^{s-1} \tag{8}$$

where η is the learning rate (coefficient).

$$e_j^s = f'(I_j^s) \sum_k e_k^{s+1} \omega_{kj}^{s+1} \qquad \text{(For hidden layer)} \tag{9}$$

$$e_k^s = (d_k - o_k) f'(I_k^s) \qquad \text{(For output layer)} \qquad (10)$$

in which e_j^s is the error generated from j^{th} element in s^{th} layer, ω_{kj}^{s+1} is the connecting weights between j^{th} element in s^{th} layer and k^{th} element in $s+1^{th}$ layer, d_k is the desired k^{th} output, o_k is the kth real output, and $f'(I_j^s)$ is the first derivative of the transfer function.

We may consider the learning process as an optimization problem with the objective function being defined as the generated error. The function of this neural network is mainly to couple networking and optimization strategy in order to reach a minimum state in the error space.

The first derivative of this saturation-type transfer function is:

$$f'(z) = \frac{b}{(1 + |z|)^2} \qquad (11)$$

The supervised learning is thus governed by the adaptation of the weights to achieve an optimal state. The above algorithm is applied to the data from batch cell cultures.

4. Material and Methods

4.1 Microorganism, inoculum, and growth medium

The bacterial culture used in this work is *Klebsiella oxytoca* ATCC 13882. The medium for preparing the inoculation of *K. oxytoca* contained 20 g/L glucose. The inoculum began by aseptically transferred to 100 ml of sterilized medium. The culture was incubated at 37°C with agitation at 220 rpm in a floor shaker (Model G24, New Brunswick Scientific, Edison, NJ). The organism was precultured twice before each experiment in order to adapt to the culture environment. *K. oxytoca* was cultured on PA medium with trace metals [12]. Glucose was the limiting substrate.

4.2 Shaker Flask Experiment

The batch cell culture experiments were carried out in flasks by a floor shaker. The temperature and agitation speed are the same as those for inoculum. The cells for the experiments were aseptically transferred from the preculture to the flasks. Each flask contained 120 ml of sterilized medium with varied glucose concentrations. The amounts of inoculum were varied to obtain different initial cell concentration for each flask. All experimental conditions were kept identical, with the initial glucose and cell concentrations as the only varied parameters. From the batch cell cultures, samples were taken every hour. Each culture lasted 8 hours. A spectrophotometer (Coleman model 55, Perkin-Elmer, Maywood, IL) was used to measure the absorbance of the samples at a wavelength of 540 nm. Cell dry weight is directly proportional to absorbance in the absorbance range of 0.3. The relationship was found to be 0.32 g dry weight per unit absorbance. Samples were analyzed for glucose by a glucose analyzer (model 27, YSI Company, Inc., Yellow Springs, OH). The instrument was calibrated with a solution of known glucose concentration.

5. Results and Discussion

The experiments were carried out at different initial conditions. Fourteen sets of experimental data were collected. Equal number of data sets (i.e., 7 each sets), were used for learning and prediction in neural network modeling. A 2-3-8 BPNN (Fig.1) was thus created from this effort.

5.1 Transfer Function

The transfer function used in this work is a saturation-type function, $\frac{bz}{1 + |z|}$, modified from the Michaelis-Menten (or Monod) equation which is derived for bioreaction systems. The absolute term occurred in the denominator of this saturation function is to avoid the singularity. This saturation-type transfer function has been successfully implemented to the modeling of multicomponent adsorption systems. In this work, we will again demonstrate the capability of this saturation-type function in identifying the growth patterns of cells.

To avoid divergence, the transfer functions are essentially bounded. Bounded nonlinear functions are always required to be asymptotic, as a result, the "tailing" always occurs near both ends of the curves. The "tailing" might lead to an adverse effect on the convergence. Once the system falls into a bad local minimum, the "tailing" might prevent the system from getting out of this local minimum. Under such a circumstance, the convergence may not be improved even spending a lot of computation time. In the sigmoid function, there is an exponetial term in its denominator while there is no such a term in this saturation function. It is the existence of the exponential term in sigmoid function that makes the "tailing" effect more severe than the saturation function. Moreover, the adjustable parameter, b, in this saturation function could be adjusted to make the slope "steeper". this adjustable parameter has the function of improving the convergence within different range. This might explain why the saturation function performs better than the sigmoid function.

5.2 Simulation and Prediction Results

According to Kolmogorov's theorem [13], if there exists a three-layer feedforward neural network with n inputs, the number of processing elements can be (2n+1). For instance, five hidden neurons should be required for two inputs in this case. Indeed, we found that a single hidden layer is enough for this work. Meanwhile, the above theorem illustrates only existence, not uniqueness, though it does provide the knowledge for the number of PEs in the hidden layer. A BPNN with the dimension of n-(2n+1)-m might be redundant. Actually, the BPNN being obtained has demonstrated a reduced dimension for hidden neurons in this case. With two inputs, three neurons in the hidden layer has been found sufficient for the modeling of this batch cell growth. The 2-3-8 BPNN being created has two inputs, 3 PEs in the hidden layer, and 8 outputs. The inputs are initial glucose and cell concentrations, the 8 outputs are the cell concentrations measured at eight each hours from the first hour to the eighth hour, i.e., $\{X(t)|\ t=1, ..., 8\}$. The data for input:output can be notated as $(G_o, X_o) : \{X(t)|\ t=1, 2, ..., 8\}$. The structure of a BPNN was searched by learning from these seven data sets. Part of the simulation results by these seven data sets are given in Figs.2(a) and 2(b). Therefore, the parallel modeling of the different growth patterns in different batches of cell cultures has been successfully performed.

A second seven data sets were provided for testing the capability of prediction by this 2-3-8 BPNN model. Part of the prediction results are shown in Figs.3(a) and 3(b). The results in Fig.3(a) are the interpolated predictions. This neural network approach has demonstrated the capability in such kind of prediction. Furthermore, the results in Fig.3(b) are the extrapolated predictions. As observed from Fig.3(b), the initial glucose concentration is beyond the upper bounds of the training data. The initial cell density in this figure is also beyond the lower bound of the training sets. This 2-3-8 BPNN still gives excellent results for such extrapolated prediction. We may conclude that this 2-3-8 BPNN has the ability to predict some of the patterns which have never been seen during the training process. We should notice that only 7 data sets were used in training the NNM, and the model being created can predict an equal number of data sets very well.

5.3 Sensitivity Analysis

The effects of initial cell density and initial glucose concentration on the growth of cells are plotted in Figs.4 and 5, respectively. In Fig.4, the initial glucose concentration shows similar effect on cell growth at different initial cell density. It is observed that there is an optimal initial glucose concentration for each experi-

ment. At low initial glucose levels, the bacteria may not have enough substrate to grow. At high glucose levels, the growth of bacteria would be inhibited. If dividing the range of initial glucose concentration into two phases at the optimal point, in the range of lower glucose level, a more sensitive but positive effect is inspected, while at a higher (than optimal point) glucose level, a less sensitive but negative effect exists. Therefore, higher initial glucose concentration elongates the doubling time and causes lower productivity but higher final cell density. As a result, the initial glucose level could be determined according to different demands.

In Fig.5, the initial cell density shows a positive effect on the growth of cells. However, the sensitivity of this effect is significantly influenced by the initial glucose level. As the initial glucose level is increased, the system is less sensitive to the increase of initial cell density. It is realized that the negative (inhibition) effect of high glucose concentration on the growth of cells will reduce the positive effect of initial cell density. As shown in Fig.5, the curve at lower G_o is steeper and the negative effect has not yet appeared. As G_o is increased, a flatter curve is observed and the vertical distance between curves are closer. The negative effect of G_o is beginning to influence the positive effect of X_o. While the negative effect takes over the positive effect, the curve turns to go down.

It is obvious from these two plots that the batch growth of cells are rather sensitive to both initial conditions. It is also observed that these two initial conditions mutually influence the effect of the other on the growth pattern.

5.4 Optimization of Cell Growth

It is clear from the above analysis that the cell density shows a monotonic increasing behavior with respect to the initial cell density. Therefore, if the maximum cell density at 8th hour is defined as an objective function, then, to start the batch culture from a higher initial cell density would be beneficial.

We can conclude from the previous section that there is an optimal initial glucose concentration for each culture. According to the above objective function, the optimal glucose concentration was searched from the 2-3-8 BPNN. In Fig.6, the optimal glucose concentration was found to occur at 54.5 g/L for the batch cell culture with the initial cell density of 0.12 g/L. The maximum cell density is 4.96 g/L. This optimal point will shift with different initial cell density. Table 1 lists the optimal initial glucose concentration for different initial cell density and also the maximum cell density being reached. It is shown that as the initial cell density is increased from 0.08 g/L to 0.16 g/L, the optimal initial glucose concentration shifts from 53.8 g/L to 55.1 g/L. The maximum cell density varies from 3.49 g/L to 6.14 g/L accordingly.

6. Conclusion

A novel transfer function of the saturation form has been discovered and found very useful in building neural network models for bioprocesses. Given only the information of initial conditions on cell density and glucose concentration, a 2-3-8 BPNN was thus designed with the capability of both simulation and prediction. The BPNN also shows the capability in modeling the higher-dimension outputs (8-dimension) with lower-dimension inputs (two-dimension). From this approach, the disadvantage of conventional modeling has been overcome. Furthermore, the achievement which is impossible from kinetic approach has now become possible from neural network approach. Also, the pattern (the whole time sequence) of cell concentration, instead of the cell concentration at each individual time, has been successfully predicted. The model is robust enough to efficiently learn from the provided data sets, and meanwhile, perform prediction well. From the sensitivity analysis done by this 2-3-8 BPNN, we learn that higher initial cell density and medium initial glucose concentration will benefit the batch cell cultures. The optimal initial concentrations at different inoculums were also found.

7. Acknowledgements

This work was supported by the National Science Foundation under the Grant 8912150-BCS.

8. References

[1] W. S. McCulloch and W. Pitts, "A Logical Calculus of the Ideas Immanent in nervous activity," *Bulletin of Math. Bio.*, 5, pp. 115-133, 1943.

[2] P. J. Werbos, "Beyond Regression: New Tools for Prediction and Analysis in the Behavioral Sciences," PhD Dissertation, Appl. Math., Harvard University, November, 1974.

[3] D. B. Parker, "Learning-Logic," Technical Report TR-47, Center for Computational Research in Economics and Management Science, MA Massachusetts Institute of Technology, April, 1985.

[4] D. E. Rumelhart and J.L. McClelland, Parallel Distributed Processing: Explorations in the Microstructure of Cognition, I & II, MIT Press, Cambridge, MA, 1986.

[5] R. A. Jacobs, "Increased Rates of Convergence Through Learning Rate Adaptation," *Neural Networks*, 1, pp. 295-307, 1988.

[6] Y. Hirose, K. Yamashita, and S. Hijiya, "Back-Propagation Algorithm Which Varies the Number of Hidden Units," *Neural Networks*, 4, pp. 61-66, 1991.

[7] M.-J. Syu, G.-J. Tsai, and G. T. Tsao, "Artificial Neural Network Modeling of Multicomponent Adsorptive Separation", *Advanced in Biochemical Engineering/Biotechnology*, Vol. 49, Springer-Verlag, in press, June, 1993.

[8] S. N. Kavuri and V. Venkatasubramanian, "Combining Pattern Classification and Assumption-Based Techniques for Process Fault Diagnosis:, *Computers Chem. Engng.*, 16, 4, pp. 299-312, 1992.

[9] N. Bhat and T. J. McAvoy, "Use of Neural Nets for Dynamic Modeling and Control of Chemical Process Systems," *Computers Chem. Engng.*, 14, pp. 573-583, 1990.

[10] A. Lapedes and R. Farber, "Non-Linear Signal Processing Using Neural Networks: Prediction and System Modeling," Los Alamos National Laboratory Report LA-UR-87-2662, 1987.

[11] M.-J. Syu,"Neural Network Modeling and Control of Bioprocesses", PhD Dissertation, Purdue University, Aug., 1992.

[12] N. B. Jansen, M. C. Flickinger, and G. T. Tsao, *Biotechnol. Bioeng.*, 26, p. 362, 1984.

[13] A. N. Kolmogorov, "On the Representation of Continuous Functions of Many Variables by Superposition of Continuous Functions of One Variable and Addition," *Dokl. Akad. Nauk. SSSR*, 114, pp. 369-373, 1957.

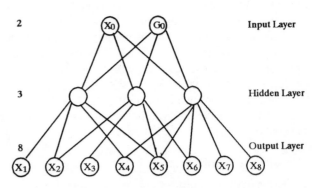

Go Initial glucose concentration
Xi: Cell mass concentration at i^{th} hour

Fig. 1 2-3-8 BPNN for cell growth

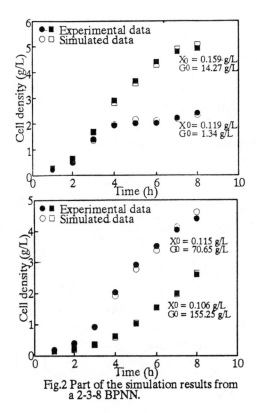

Fig.2 Part of the simulation results from a 2-3-8 BPNN.

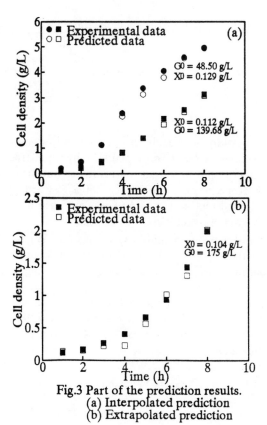

Fig.3 Part of the prediction results.
(a) Interpolated prediction
(b) Extrapolated prediction

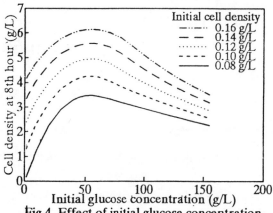

Fig.4 Effect of initial glucose concentration on cell growth

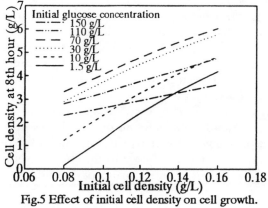

Fig.5 Effect of initial cell density on cell growth.

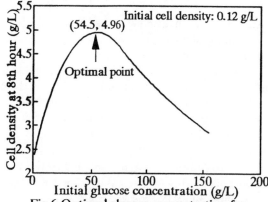

Fig.6 Optimal glucose concentration for maximum cell density at 8th hour

Initial Cell (g/L)	Optimal Initial Glucose (g/L)	Max. Cell at 8th h (g/L)
0.08	53.8	3.49
0.10	54.1	4.26
0.12	54.5	4.96
0.14	54.8	5.58
0.16	55.1	6.14

Table 1. Optimal initial glucose concentration at different initial cell density

Optimal Parallel Back-Propagation Schemes for Mesh-connected and Bus-connected Multiprocessors

Takashi YUKAWA and Tsutomu ISHIKAWA
NTT Network Information Systems Labs.
Musashino-shi, Tokyo, Japan.
e-mail: yukawa@nttaip.ntt.jp

Abstract— This paper proposes optimal parallel schemes that minimize communication overhead for the back-propagation algorithm on neural networks (NNs). First, a parallel computation framework of the back-propagation algorithm is discussed and the lower-bound of communication overhead is provided. Then, optimal schemes for mesh-connected and bus-connected architectures based on this framework are proposed. The scheme for the mesh-connected architecture achieves the lower-bound of communication overhead. The scheme for the bus-connected architecture reduces it to the square-root order of the number of processors, while the conventional scheme requires a linear order overhead.

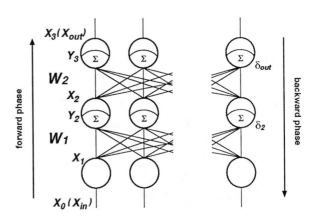

Figure 1: A multi-layer neural network

I. INTRODUCTION

Recently, multi-layer neural networks (NNs) have been extensively employed in various engineering fields such as pattern classification, image processing and voice recognition. However, the large computation requirements of the back-propagation(BP) algorithm[1], which is the most commonly used training scheme for multi-layer NNs, limits their usefulness. To reduce training time, various parallel schemes have been proposed[2, 3, 4, 5, 6].

The most efficient parallel computation is achieved when the computation is distributed uniformly over processors without redundant computation and there is minimum communication between processors. This paper proves that a parallel computation based on mesh-partitioning of NN weight matrices provides the lower-bound communication overhead and well-balanced loads for the BP Algorithm. The paper also proposes optimal parallel schemes for mesh-connected and bus-connected multiprocessors. The scheme for the mesh-connected architecture attains the lower-bound of communication overhead with no redundant computation. The scheme for the bus-connected architecture reduces communication overhead to the square-root order of the number of processors,

while the conventional scheme requires linear-order overhead.

II. BACKGROUND

Back-propagation is the algorithm most often used to train multi-layer NNs. It trains the NNs by repetitive adjustment of connection weights according to output error. One back-propagation cycle consists of a forward phase and a backward phase. The two phases are formulated as consecutive matrix-vector multiplications.

Figure 1 illustrates a multi-layer NN. Let $\mathbf{W}_l$ be the weight matrix for the l-th layer, where the element of row i and column j, $W_l[i,j]$, is the weight for a connection between unit i in layer l and unit j in layer $(l+1)$. Let $\mathbf{X}_l$ be an output vector for the layer l, where the i-th element $X_l[i]$ is the output of unit i in layer l. In the forward phase, the output vector from layer l is first multiplied by the weight matrix:

$$\mathbf{Y}_{l+1} = \mathbf{W}_l \times \mathbf{X}_l. \tag{1}$$

By passing through a nonlinear function F, the output of

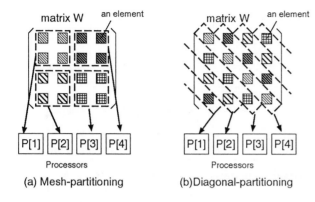

Figure 2: Examples of Mapping

unit i in layer $(l+1)$ is obtained by

$$X_{l+1}[i] = F(Y_{l+1}[i]), \qquad (2)$$

where $Y_{l+1}[i]$ is the i-th element of $\mathbf{Y}_{l+1}$. We describe the input signal $\mathbf{X}_0$ and the output of the NN $\mathbf{X}_3$ for the three-layer NN as $\mathbf{X}_{in}$ and $\mathbf{X}_{out}$ for convenience. The backward phase consists of the error calculation for each unit and the adaptation of weights. The error for the output layer, δ_{out}, is calculated by

$$\delta_{out}[i] = (d[i] - X_{out}[i]) \times F'(Y_{out}[i]), \qquad (3)$$

where F' is the derivative of the nonlinear function F. The error for the layer l, δ_l, is calculated by

$$\delta_l[i] = \theta_l[i] \times F'(Y_l[i]), \qquad (4)$$

where

$$\boldsymbol{\theta}_l = \mathbf{W}_l^T \times \boldsymbol{\delta}_{l+1}, \qquad (5)$$

and $\mathbf{W}^T$ is the transposed matrix of $\mathbf{W}$. An adapted new weight $W_l[i,j]'$ is calculated by

$$W_l[i,j]' = W_l[i,j] + \eta \delta_{l+1}[i] X_l[j], \qquad (6)$$

where η is the learning rate, which regulates the rate of adjustment of the weights.

III. The Lower-bound of Communication Overhead for The Parallel BP Algorithm

This section presents a parallel computation framework for the BP algorithm and provides the lower-bound of communication overhead. First, what is needed to achieve good performance in parallel matrix-vector multiplication, which is frequently used in the BP algorithm, is discussed and a parallel computation framework is presented. Then, analyzing data transfer requirements on an ideal multiprocessor system, it is proved that mesh-based partitioning of the matrix achieves the minimum communication overhead for matrix-vector multiplication. Finally, differences between the BP algorithm and simple matrix-vector multiplication is discussed and the lower-bound of communication overhead for the BP algorithm is provided.

A. Parallel Matrix-Vector Multiplication

Efficient parallel computation of matrix-vector multiplication requires that the following be satisfied.

1. The weight matrices are mapped statically throughout computation. It is obvious that migration of the weight matrix leads to a large data transfer requirement because the weight matrices have enormous numbers of elements.

2. The amount of calculation and data transfer requirements on processors must be uniform. Redundant calculations have to be avoided, as they obviously lead to speed loss.

The above requirements are satisfied by the three-phase operation described below.

Assume that the weight matrix $\mathbf{W}$ has N rows and M columns, the input vector $\mathbf{X}$ has M elements and the result vector $\mathbf{Y}$ has N elements. The element of the i-th column and j-th row in the matrix is expressed as $W[j,i]$, the i-th element of the input vector is expressed as $X[i]$, and an j-th element of the result vector is expressed as $Y[j]$.

- **distribution:** An element $X[i]$ is distributed to all processors onto which elements $W[*,i]$ (* means any number) are mapped.

- **partial result calculation:** The multiplication $W[j,i] \cdot X[i]$ is calculated in each processor without interaction between processors. A partial result for $Y[j]$ is distributively obtained on the processors onto which elements $W[j,*]$ are mapped.

- **accumulation:** The partial results involved with an element $Y[j]$ are transferred and accumulated on any processor onto which an element $W[j,*]$ is mapped. Thus, any element of the result vector is obtained on some single processor.

B. Optimal Partitioning and Calculation for Matrix-Vector Multiplication

This subsection describes the lower-bound of communication overhead for the parallel matrix-vector multiplication. To obtain the lower-bound of communication overhead, we define an ideal multiprocessor system. Then the number of communication steps for the ideal system is estimated and optimized.

B.1. Ideal Multiprocessor System

The ideal multiprocessor system has the communication abilities described below.

- Processors can receive one datum at one time.

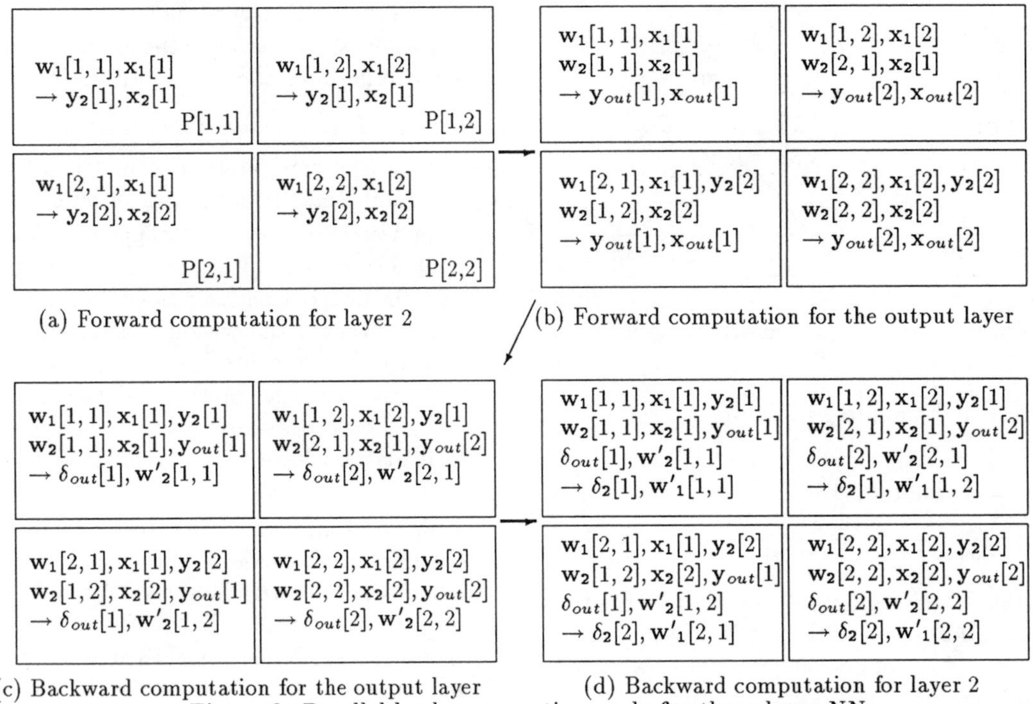

$w_1[1,1], x_1[1]$ $\rightarrow y_2[1], x_2[1]$ $P[1,1]$	$w_1[1,2], x_1[2]$ $\rightarrow y_2[1], x_2[1]$ $P[1,2]$
$w_1[2,1], x_1[1]$ $\rightarrow y_2[2], x_2[2]$ $P[2,1]$	$w_1[2,2], x_1[2]$ $\rightarrow y_2[2], x_2[2]$ $P[2,2]$

(a) Forward computation for layer 2

$w_1[1,1], x_1[1]$ $w_2[1,1], x_2[1]$ $\rightarrow y_{out}[1], x_{out}[1]$	$w_1[1,2], x_1[2]$ $w_2[2,1], x_2[1]$ $\rightarrow y_{out}[2], x_{out}[2]$
$w_1[2,1], x_1[1], y_2[2]$ $w_2[1,2], x_2[2]$ $\rightarrow y_{out}[1], x_{out}[1]$	$w_1[2,2], x_1[2], y_2[2]$ $w_2[2,2], x_2[2]$ $\rightarrow y_{out}[2], x_{out}[2]$

(b) Forward computation for the output layer

$w_1[1,1], x_1[1], y_2[1]$ $w_2[1,1], x_2[1], y_{out}[1]$ $\rightarrow \delta_{out}[1], w'_2[1,1]$	$w_1[1,2], x_1[2], y_2[1]$ $w_2[2,1], x_2[1], y_{out}[2]$ $\rightarrow \delta_{out}[2], w'_2[2,1]$
$w_1[2,1], x_1[1], y_2[2]$ $w_2[1,2], x_2[2], y_{out}[1]$ $\rightarrow \delta_{out}[1], w'_2[1,2]$	$w_1[2,2], x_1[2], y_2[2]$ $w_2[2,2], x_2[2], y_{out}[2]$ $\rightarrow \delta_{out}[2], w'_2[2,2]$

(c) Backward computation for the output layer

$w_1[1,1], x_1[1], y_2[1]$ $w_2[1,1], x_2[1], y_{out}[1]$ $\delta_{out}[1], w'_2[1,1]$ $\rightarrow \delta_2[1], w'_1[1,1]$	$w_1[1,2], x_1[2], y_2[1]$ $w_2[2,1], x_2[1], y_{out}[2]$ $\delta_{out}[2], w'_2[2,1]$ $\rightarrow \delta_2[1], w'_1[1,2]$
$w_1[2,1], x_1[1], y_2[2]$ $w_2[1,2], x_2[2], y_{out}[1]$ $\delta_{out}[1], w'_2[1,2]$ $\rightarrow \delta_2[2], w'_1[2,1]$	$w_1[2,2], x_1[2], y_2[2]$ $w_2[2,2], x_2[2], y_{out}[2]$ $\delta_{out}[2], w'_2[2,2]$ $\rightarrow \delta_2[2], w'_1[2,2]$

(d) Backward computation for layer 2

Figure 3: Parallel back-propagation cycle for three-layer NN

- The inter-processor network can transfer any data required by the processors at one time.

The lower-bound of communication overhead is obtained by optimal partitioning and mapping on the ideal system, because the inter-processor network can transfer more data than any other architecture.

B.2. Communication Step Estimation

For uniform amount of computation over the processors, MN/P matrix elements, M/P input vector elements and N/P result vector elements have to be mapped onto each processor, where P is the number of processors. There are several mapping methods that satisfy this requirement. Now, assume that the number of rows involved with one processor is K_r and the number of columns involved with one processor is K_c. Figure 2(a) and (b) show examples of mapping a 4×4 matrix onto 4 processors. In Fig. 2(a), $K_r = K_c = 2$, and in Fig. 2(b), $K_r = K_c = 4$. All elements in the matrix must be mapped over processors, thus

$$K_r K_c \geq MN/P. \qquad (7)$$

In the distribution phase, the processor which involves K_c columns must collect $K_c - M/P$ input vector elements to compute partial results. After the partial result calculation phase, K_r partial results are obtained on each processor, and $K_r P$ partial results over the system, thus, $K_r P/N$ partial results involves on result vector element.

In the accumulation phase, each processor computes N/P result vector elements, thus $(K_r P/N) \times N/P - N/P = K_r - N/P$ partial results have to be collected for each processor.

Since the processor can receive one datum in one communication step, the number of communication steps C is estimated as

$$C = K_c - M/P + K_r - N/P = K_c + K_r - (M+N)/P. \qquad (8)$$

B.3. Optimization

The minimum communication steps are obtained by minimizing Eq. 8 under the constraint of Eq.7. It is obvious that the number of communication steps C is minimized when

$$K_r K_c = MN/P. \qquad (9)$$

Therefore,

$$C = K_c + 1/K_c \cdot MN/P - (M+N)/P. \qquad (10)$$

Optimizing C by K_c,

$$\frac{dC}{dK_c} = 1 - \frac{1}{K_c^2} \cdot \frac{MN}{P} = 0, \qquad (11)$$

$$K_c = K_r = \sqrt{MN/P}. \qquad (12)$$

Therefore, the lower-bound of communication steps $C_{\min}$ is

$$C_{\min} = 2\sqrt{MN/P} - (M+N)/P. \qquad (13)$$

Equations 9 and 12 are satisfied only when the matrix is divided into square submatrices. Thus, the lower-bound of communication steps for the ideal multiprocessor system is obtained by mesh-partitioning of the matrix.

C. Differences between BP Algorithm and Simple Matrix-Vector Multiplication

Parallel computation of the BP algorithm differs from simple iteration of matrix-vector multiplication in the following points.

1. The weight matrix multiplied by the input vector in the forward phase has to be transposed for calculation of the error vector in the backward phase. Therefore, the number of communication steps in the backward phase is expressed as the equation in which the expressions for rows and columns of the forward phase equation are exchanged.

2. Equations 4 and 6 show that the input vector element $X[i]$ and the result vector element $Y[j]$ are required to adapt the weight $W[i,j]$. Therefore, these values must be mapped onto the same processor to avoid redundant data transfer.

D. Minimum Communication Overhead for BP Algorithm

Figure 3 illustrates one parallel BP cycle for a three-layer NN which satisfies the requirements discussed above. The boxes in the figure represent processors labeled $P[i,j]$. The matrix is divided into $P = p \times q$ submatrices. Thus, each submatrix has $K_r = N/p$ rows by $K_c = M/q$ columns and is expressed as $\mathbf{w}[1,1], \mathbf{w}[1,2], \ldots$. The vector $\mathbf{X}$ is divided into q subvectors and the vector $\mathbf{Y}$ is divided into p subvectors. These subvectors are respectively expressed as $\mathbf{x}[1], \mathbf{x}[2], \ldots$ and $\mathbf{y}[1], \mathbf{y}[2], \ldots$. The submatrices and subvectors in the processor are described in the boxes. Note that if a weight matrix of layer l, $\mathbf{W}_l$, is divided into $p \times q$ submatrices and submatrix $\mathbf{w}_l[i,j]$ is mapped onto processor $P[i,j]$, the weight matrix of layer $(l+1)$, $\mathbf{W}_{l+1}$, is divided into $q \times p$ submatrices and submatrix $\mathbf{w}_{l+1}[i,j]$ is mapped onto processor $P[j,i]$.

According to the previous discussion, the number of communication steps for one layer for one BP cycle is

$$C = \underbrace{K_r + K_c - (M+N)/P}_{\text{forward phase}} + \underbrace{K_c + K_r - (N+M)/P}_{\text{backward phase}}$$
$$= 2(N/p + M/q) - 2(M+N)/P, \qquad (14)$$

and the minimum number of communication steps is obtained when

$$N/p = M/q = \sqrt{MN/P}, \qquad (15)$$

and given as

$$C_{\min} = 4\sqrt{MN/P} - 2MN/P. \qquad (16)$$

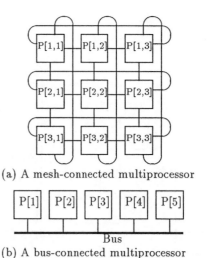

(a) A mesh-connected multiprocessor

(b) A bus-connected multiprocessor

Figure 4: Mesh-connected and Bus-connected Multiprocessors

This is the lower-bound of the number of communication steps for parallel back-propagation computation.

IV. OPTIMAL PARALLEL SCHEMES

In this section, we construct and optimize parallel schemes, which are based on the parallel computation framework described above, for some existing (not ideal) architectures. The communication ability depends on processor architecture, so optimization of mapping and computation is needed for each architecture to achieve the lower-bound of the communication overhead.

A. A Parallel Scheme for a Mesh-connected Multiprocessor

Each processor of a mesh-connected architecture has four communication links to communicate with neighbor processors as shown in Figure 4(a).

The weight matrix is mapped in an obvious and simple way such that submatrix $\mathbf{w}[i,j]$ is mapped onto processor $P[i,j]$ for even layers and onto $P[j,i]$ for odd layers. To make full use of the links, the elements of a result subvector are distributed over the processors. Figure 5 demonstrates an example of matrix-vector computation, in which the matrix $\mathbf{W}$ has 9×9 elements and is mapped onto 3×3 processors, thus, each submatrix $\mathbf{w}[i,j]$ has 3×3 elements. It is obvious that the vectors $\mathbf{X}$ and $\mathbf{Y}$ have nine elements and the subvectors $\mathbf{x}[i]$ and $\mathbf{y}[j]$ have three elements. We describe the k-th element in the subvector $\mathbf{x}[i]$ as $x[i](k)$.

At first, element $x[i](k)$ is located on a processor $P[k,i]$. It is transferred to the processor $P[k+1,i]$ in the subvector distribution phase, in which all the elements can be transferred to a downward processor at one time as shown in Fig. 5(b). This means that P elements are transferred

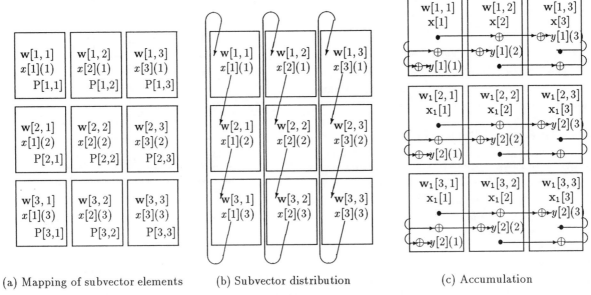

(a) Mapping of subvector elements   (b) Subvector distribution   (c) Accumulation

Figure 5: Parallel scheme for a torus topology

at one time in the subvector distribution phase. Iterating this operation, the elements of the subvector $\mathbf{x}[i]$ are distributed over processors $P[*, i]$. For a matrix having $M \times N$ elements and $p \times q$ processors, $(p-1) \times M$ elements have to be transferred in the subvector distribution phase; thus, this phase requires $M(p-1)/P$ communication steps.

The submatrix-subvector multiplication phase requires no communication, and the partial results are obtained. In the accumulation phase, the processors accumulate the partial results in pipe-lined fashion as shown in Fig. 5(c). In the first step, the partial result for $y[j](k)$ on processor $P[j, k+1]$ is transferred to processor $P[j, k+2]$. The processor receiving the partial result adds it to the processor's own partial result. The added result is transferred to $P[j, k+3]$ in the next step and also added to its own partial result. Iterating the above step, the elements of result vector $y[j](k)$ are obtained on processor $P[j, k]$ in the end. The accumulation steps for all j and k are processed in parallel. This parallelization of the accumulation phase is accomplished with uniform load on processors and no redundant data transfer. This procedure can transfer P elements in parallel and $(q-1) \times N$ elements are transferred, thus, $N(q-1)/P$ communication steps are required in this phase. Therefore, $\{M(p-1) + N(q-1)\}/P$ communication steps are required for the forward phase for each layer.

The backward phase differs from the forward phase only in that the matrix is transposed; thus, $\{N(q-1) + M(p-1)\}/P$ communication steps are required. The total number of communication steps for one layer is

$$C = \frac{2}{P}\{M(p-1) + N(q-1)\} = 2\left(\frac{N}{p} + \frac{M}{q}\right) - 2\frac{M+N}{P}. \tag{17}$$

This is the same equation as that for the ideal system, Eq.14. Thus, the minimum number of communication steps is obtained when

$$N/p = M/q = \sqrt{MN/P}, \tag{18}$$

and given as

$$C_{opt} = 4\sqrt{NM/P} - 2(M+N)/P. \tag{19}$$

This is the lower-bound of communication steps.

Our scheme differs from Kung's scheme[2], which maps each layer of a NN onto each row of the mesh-connected processors, in that all processors and links can work for every layer. The scheme also differs form Suzuki's[3] in that elements of subvectors are distributed over all of the processors. Suzuki's scheme maps the elements of the subvectors onto the top or left-edge processors and propagates the elements to the lower or right-side neighbor processors step by step for subvector distribution. This creates a load imbalance and decreases the parallelism of communication links, because the starting calculation is delayed on the downward or leftward processors and transfer of partial results is concentrated on downward or leftward links. In contrast to this, our scheme can start the calculation at the same time on all processors and it uses all links uniformly.

This scheme can apply to a hypercube architecture because the hypercube has a mesh connection as its subgraph. The scheme is also optimal for the hypercube because the scheme achieves the lower-bound communication overhead.

B. A Parallel Scheme for a Bus-connected Multiprocessor

A bus-connected architecture shown in Figure 4(b) has a broadcast mode, that can transfer one unit of data to all processors in one communication step.

The scheme for the bus-connected architecture maps submatrices $\mathbf{w}[i, j]$ onto processor $P[(i - 1) \times q + j]$ for even layers and onto processor $P[(j - 1) \times q + i]$ for odd layers. In the subvector distribution phase, each element in the subvectors can be distributed to all processors in one step using broadcast mode. Each partial result transfer consumes one communication step in the accumulation phase.

In the subvector distribution phase, each element is broadcast to all processors but only the processors involved with the element acquire it. There are M elements, so M communication steps are required in this phase. In the accumulation phase, since all data transfers are point-to-point, $M(p-1)$ communication steps are required. Therefore, the number of communication steps required in forward phases is $M + M(p-1) = Mp$. The backward phase differs from the forward phase only in that the matrix is transposed, thus, $N + N(q-1) = Nq$ communication steps are required. Therefore, total count of communication steps for one layer is given as:

$$C = Mp + Nq. \tag{20}$$

In the same way as the previous section, the minimum number of communication steps is obtained when

$$N/p = M/q = \sqrt{MN/P}, \tag{21}$$

and given as

$$C_{opt} = 2\sqrt{MNP}. \tag{22}$$

Suzuki's scheme[3] divides the weight matrix on the basis of row. It can accumulate the partial results without communication in the forward phase, but it requires a large amount of communication in the backward phase. In our scheme, the mesh partitioning of a weight matrix distributes communication requirements between the forward and backward phases, reducing the number of communication steps.

Since the bus-connected architecture consumes one communication step for a point-to-point communication, data transfer in the accumulation phase cannot be parallelized. Therefore, the communication overhead for the bus-connected architecture increases P-fold compared with that for the mesh-connected architecture.

V. Conclusion

A mapping and computation framework for parallelizing the back-propagation algorithm for NNs has been presented and optimal schemes for mesh-connected and bus-connected multiprocessors based on the framework have been proposed. The framework provides a parallel computation method that reduces communication overhead by dividing NN weight matrices into meshes and dividing parallel calculation of matrix-vector multiplication into three phases. The framework also estimates data transfer requirements and provides the lower-bound of communication overhead. Parallel schemes for mesh-connected and bus-connected architectures are based on the framework and the optimal aspect ratio of divided weight matrices are provided. The scheme for the mesh-connected architecture attains the lower-bound of communication overhead with no redundant computation. The scheme for the bus-connected architecture reduces it to the square-root order of the number of processors, while the conventional scheme requires a linear order overhead. The framework can optimize parallel schemes not only for mesh-connected and bus-connected architectures, but also other architectures.

References

[1] D. E. Rumelhart, G. E. Hinton and R. J. Williams, "Learning Internal Representation by Error Propagation," in *Parallel Distributed Processing, Vol. 1*, pp. 318–362, MIT press, 1986.

[2] S. Y. Kung and J. N. Hwang, "Parallel Architectures for Artificial Neural Nets," in *Proc. IEEE International Conference on Neural Networks*, pp. II-165–II-172, 1988.

[3] Y. Suzuki and L. E. Atlas, "A Study of Regular Architectures for Digital Implementation of Neural Networks," in *Proc. IEEE International Symposium on Circuits and Systems*, pp. 82–85, 1989.

[4] Y. Fujimoto, "An Enhanced Parallel Planar Lattice Architecture for Large Scale Neural Network Simulations," in *Proc. International Joint Conference on Neural Networks*, pp. II-581–II-586, 1990.

[5] S. W. Aiken, M. W. Koch and M. W. Roberts, "A Parallel Neural Network Simulator," in *Proc. International Joint Conference on Neural Networks*, pp. II-611–II-616, 1990.

[6] D. Jackson and D.Hammerstrom, "Distributing Back Propagation Networks Over the Intel iPSC/860 Hypercube," in *Proc. International Joint Conference on Neural Networks*, pp. I-569–I-574, 1991.

USING NEURAL NETWORKS FOR UNDERWATER TARGET RANGING

Robert J. F. Dow and Jocelyn Sietsma
DSTO Materials Research Laboratory
PO Box 50
Ascot Vale
Melbourne 3032
AUSTRALIA

Abstract - Underwater weapons often have to range their targets from complex and highly variable signals, referred to as signatures. If artificial neural networks are applied to this task, the complexity of the ranging problem demands the use of networks with relatively large internal structures. This paper discusses the application of layered, feed-forward networks learning by back-propagation (Rumelhart networks) to this problem. The work discussed demonstrates that these networks may have improved generalisation by using noise added to the training set.

Introduction

This paper describes the application of a back-propagation network to the task of detecting and ranging a moving object underwater. A complex multi-dimensional time signal is used as input, and the network is required to indicate whether the relevant type of object is present within a certain distance. Artificial neural networks were chosen for this task because of their known strengths in signal processing and pattern classification applications. Complex signal processing or statistical techniques have not been widely used in this field as space for processors is limited, response times are required to be very fast, and the properties of signatures are very poorly categorised or understood. The success of a neural network approach is, however, not guaranteed, as many researchers have had problems in scaling-up networks to large, complex tasks.

In previous work [1] it has been shown that small networks can be made to generalise better by the addition of noise to the training set and that this generalisation changes the internal representation of the network by using more of the units in a unique manner i.e. only a reduced number of hidden units can be "pruned" from the generalised network and have no effect on network performance. The complexity and variability of the time dependent signals, known as signatures, used for target identification and ranging in underwater sensors implied that large networks would be needed just to solve the problem, before any attempt was made at pruning.

We began by using networks of the following size: input layer 180, first hidden layer 70, second hidden layer 30 and output layer 1, expressed as (180)-70-30-1. Although it has been shown [2,3] that networks with a single hidden layer can, given sufficient units, approximate functions to arbitrary accuracy, complex functions can sometimes be modelled with fewer total units by including more hidden layers (eg. the 2 spirals problem in [4]). As this task was expected to be complex a three-layer (two-hidden-layer) network was used.

These networks failed to learn the training set of 630 patterns successfully so any attempt at pruning was meaningless. The network size was increased until the training set could be learnt. This required a network of (180)-150-50-1. An attempt was made to prune this network but it was found that no units could be pruned from the first hidden layer and only two from the second hidden layer. This may indicate from previous work [1] that the network would be unable to learn any further patterns as all of its units were already used uniquely.

It was decided to test whether the large network ((180)-150-50-1) could learn a "universal" test defined as containing all patterns relevant to the ranging problem. The universal set contained 9360 patterns and the performance on this set would be the measure of performance of all trained networks. Four training regimes were used: (a) training on the training set of 630 patterns, (b) further training of this network with noise added to the training set, (c) further training on the network of (a) using the universal set, and (d) training on the universal set using the same initial weights as for (a). The performance of all four networks was then tested on the universal set and compared.

Description of the Experiment

The patterns for the neural net training set were generated by using the signatures of ten targets seen by a sensor during nine different encounter geometries and at seven points in time during each encounter. The pattern presented to the network was formed by time sampling three different aspects of the signature and presenting 60 of these three-valued samples to the network, giving 180 values in the input vector. The output value of the network was either zero or one and was determined by whether the sensor was within a certain region centred on the target (within region of interest, desired output = 1; outside region of interest,

desired output = 0). The training set therefore consisted of 630 patterns. The "universal" set was formed by using 39 encounter geometries, the same ten targets' signatures and 24 points in time during each encounter to produce a total of 9360 patterns.

All training was continued until either there were no errors in the case of the training set or, in the case of the training on the universal set, until the number of errors oscillated about a constant value. Four neural networks were produced, called ANN1 to ANN4 (ANN being Artificial Neural Network). The training regimes used were as follows;
ANN1 - 300 iterations on the training set.
ANN2 - Used ANN1 and performed further training using noise added to the training set for a further 350 iterations.
ANN3 - Used ANN1 and performed a further 500 training iterations using the universal set.
ANN4 - Used the same initial random weights as ANN1 and performed 500 training iterations using the universal set.
The noise used was independent samples from a gaussian distribution of mean zero and standard deviation 20.0. The standard deviation of the training set data was 47.3.

All testing was performed on the universal set of 9360 patterns. The output was taken as a one if the output was greater than 0.5 and zero if less than 0.5. This was then compared with the required output of the neural network for that pattern, which would be either a one for the sensor within the region of interest or a zero outside this region. A mismatch was logged as an error. Depending upon where during the encounter the error occurred, it would be recorded in one of 19 categories or "bins", determined by how far away from the boundary of the region the error occurred. The zero and negative bin numbers (0 to -9) represent increasing distance inside the area of interest, with bin 0 representing events close to the boundary, and bin -9 representing events close to the target. The positive bin numbers (1 to 9) represent increasing distance outside the area of interest. The rationale for this sorting of the results was that an error near the boundary between the two modes of the sensor was less critical than an error well inside one of the modes; in geometric terms an error which would cause the sensor to signal that a target was close when actually displaced a large distance from the target would waste the sensor, as would an error when the sensor was very close to the target, whereas it may be easier to recover from an error near the boundary.

The number of patterns tested corresponding to each bin varied from 56 to 1240, due to the peculiarities of the encounter geometries. The number of tests per bin were as follows:-

Bin No.	-9	-8	-7	-6	-5	-4	-3	-2
No. of Tests	1264	96	320	480	278	600	616	310

Bin No.	-1	0	1	2	3	4	5	6	7	8	9
No. of Tests	620	620	482	948	892	606	574	296	210	116	56

Results

The results in terms of total number of errors for ANN1 was 2753 errors out of the 9360 tests, and for ANN2 2352 errors. The results for ANN1 and ANN2 indicate that noise added to the training set can improve generalisation, as the training of ANN2 consisted of starting from the weights of ANN1 and training with the 630 patterns in the initial training set which ANN1 could already classify correctly, but with noise added to the patterns. The improvement from ANN1 to ANN2 is an interesting result, although some caution should be exercised in this assessment, as discussed later. It is also a interesting result in terms of pruning. ANN1 was effectively unable to be pruned

and yet ANN2 demonstrated improved generalisation. This result indicates that generalisation for large networks is still achievable using a noise distorted training set even though to learn a training set without noise added uses all units uniquely.

Our earlier work had indicated that training a network with excess hidden units with noisy data caused a reduction in the number of redundant units in the trained network, accompanied by an improvement in generalisation to previously unseen inputs. This work shows that using more of the available units independently is not the only way in which noise added to the training can improve generalisation. ANN2 shows a small improvement even though there are no excess units available.

The results in terms of total number of errors for ANN3 was 311 errors out of the 9360 tests (error rate of 3.3%), and for ANN4 386 errors (4%). This is a significant achievement for the network to accurately learn 96 per cent of such a large and complex set of patterns particularly as all units of other networks of the same size appeared to be uniquely used by the very much smaller training set.

The detailed results for ANN1 and ANN2 are shown in Figure 1. The display is designed to measure how well the network has performed on the universal set relative to each bin. Clearly training on the initial set of 630 patterns has not allowed the network to generalise particularly well to the universal set. However, as with the total results there is an improvement for ANN2 over ANN1 in most bins. Another feature is of the results is the very low percentage of errors in all bins in the 1 to 9 area, so that the sensor would give a false alarm on very few occasions. Equally encouraging is the decline in percentage error as the bin numbers become more negative, so that at the closest point to the target (bin -9) the error for ANN2 is three percent. The -9 bin also has the largest number of tests, 1240, so that the reliability of this result is good. There is cause for caution, however, in the increase in errors for ANN2 in bins 1 - 5. Although the general performance of this noise-trained network is better than that of ANN1, the rate of some types of error has increased. This may be a reason for not favouring ANN2 over ANN1, in cases where one type of error carries a much higher penalty than other types.

The detailed results for ANN3 and ANN4 are shown in Figure 2. The network has shown very good ability to learn the universal set in spite of the fact that learning the training set used all network units uniquely. A feature of Figure 2 is that the errors occur almost entirely at the boundary between the two areas. This result is not unexpected given that the network is being required to learn a precise but arbitrary boundary between sets of complex and similar patterns.

It should be noted that these displays do not indicate sensor performance as there are only 39 encounter geometries and 10 targets spread over the 9360 tests. The sensor is quite effective for all ANN's as it only has to signal that the target is in the region of interest at any one of the correct times and the neural network ranging has been successful for that encounter geometry.

Conclusions

The most important result of this work is that noise added to the training set has assisted generalisation in a complex and real world problem. This has been observed before (for example in [5]), but it had been our hypothesis that the

mechanism by which noisy training improved generalization was by causing the network to use previously unused or under-used units on the hidden layers. This hypothesis is not adequate in this case, as the networks trained without noise added to the data showed no unused units under our tests. A second result is that a large network has successfully learnt to distinguish between two subsets of a large set of complex and similar patterns even though in learning the very much smaller training set of patterns the network had uniquely used all units. This again indicates that a network can be capable of improved performance, and so might be considered to have "unused capacity", when it does not have unused units.

Bibliography

1. Sietsma, J, and Dow, R.J.F. Creating Artificial Neural Networks That Generalize. *Neural Networks*, Vol 4, pp 67-79, 1991.
2. Funahashi, K. On the Approximate Realization of Continuous Mappings by Neural Networks. *Neural Networks*, Vol 2, pp 183-192, 1989.
3. Hornik, Stinchcombe and White. Multilayer Feedforward Networks are Universal Approximators. *Neural Networks*, Vol 2, pp 359-366, 1989.
4. Lang and Witbrock. Learning to Tell Two Spirals Apart. *Connectionist Models Summer School 1988*, pp 52-59. Morgan Kaufman, San Mateo, CA.
5. Elman and Zipser. Learning the Hidden Structure of Speech. *Journal of the Acoustical Society of America*, Vol 83, No. 4, pp. 1615-1626. April 1988.

Figure 1. ANN1 & ANN2 Results

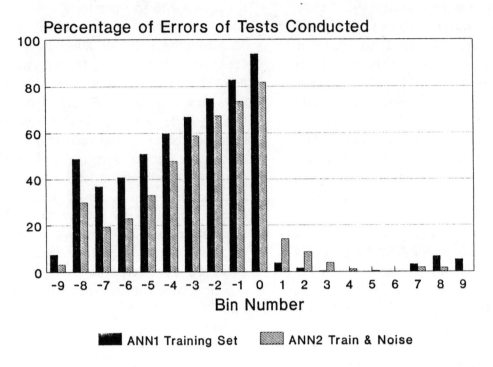

ANN3 & ANN4

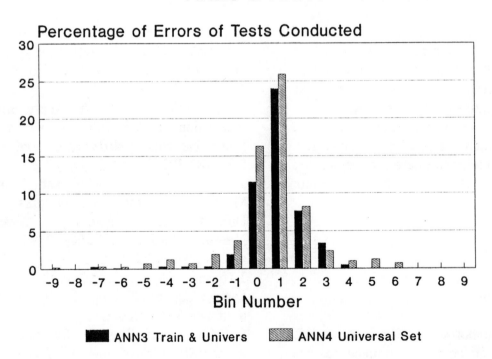

An Application of Neural Networks in the Control of Chemical Reactors

F. Panetsos, A.G. García

Escuela Politécnica Superior, Universidad Carlos III de Madrid,
Av. del Mediterraneo 20, 28913 Leganés Madrid, Spain

J.M. Zaldívar

J.R.C. of the C.E.C., Institute for Safety Technology, Process Engineering Division,
21020-Ispra (VA), Italy

Abstract - In this paper the use of neural networks for control of temperature in a jacketed vessel in which exothermic reactions take place, is discussed. Different neural network architectures and combinat imulation. The results indicate that the neural network approach can be used to deal with the control of the highly non-linear discontinous chemical processes.

I. INTRODUCTION

The rapid development of the Chemical Industry in recent years has increased the complexity of chemical plants, the diversity of products and the number of processes. This changing environment has made batch and semibatch operations more popular due to their versatility, which allows the production of special chemicals in small amounts (when compared to those of continuous processes), and permits a rapid change from one process to another with minor modifications.

Batch and semibatch chemical processes are small and not expensive procedures in the chemical production but are very complex, with strongly non-linear dynamics and time varying parameters. In a batch cycle is no steady-state and therefore no "normal" conditions. However, the study of accident case histories [1] shows that batch units are usually more frequently involved in accidents (57% of cases) than continuous process plants (about 11%). This situation implies continuous corrections and decisions to be made by the operator.

Consequently, more intelligence in the process control computers which will aid the operator in controlling the operation and in diagnosing problems or process abnormalities is of great importance in the operation of these plants. In particular, systems for identification and control based on artificial neural networks represent one of the most

promising approaches in this area. Conventional adaptive controllers and neural network-based controllers have been compared [2] with closed-loop system stability, speed of adaptation, noise rejection, the number of required calculations, etc. The results shown that the neural network approach works well in the presence of noise, works for linear and non-linear systems, can be implemented very efficiently and can be used to deal with the control of the highly non-linear batch and semibatch chemical processes.

We have used supevised and unsupervised neural networks in order to control a typical batch reactor. In this paper the performances of the combination of feed-forward neural networks are reported. The first results of the unsupervised networks are very positive but the simulations are not still completed.

II. THE TEMPERATURE CONTROL PROBLEM

Normally, the temperature development of a reactor in which exothermic reactions take place is controlled by means of removing the heat generated through a cooled heat transfer fluid that circulates in the jacket. The heat flow is proportional to the driving force (temperature difference between the reactor, T_m and the jacket, T_e):

$$q_{removed} = U \cdot S \cdot (T_m - T_e) \qquad (1)$$

where the proportionality factor $U \cdot S$, called the effective heat transfer coefficient, depends on the fluids properties, operating conditions and the geometry of the system. As opposite, the heat generated by chemical reaction assuming a well mixed tank reactor can be defined as

$$q_{generated} = V_m \Delta H_R r \qquad (2)$$

where "r" is the rate of reaction that follows an experimental

This work has been partially supported by the Spanish Government (CICYT) project TAP92-1036-C02-01 and a grant from the CEC to F. Panetsos.

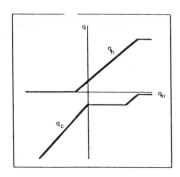

Fig. 1   Heating/Cooling split

dependence on temperature. If for some reason (e.g. loss of cooling, loss of mixing, etc.) the rate of heat generation exceeds the rate of heat removal, the temperature of the reacting mass will begin to rise. This will cause an increase in the rate of heat generation due to the exponential dependence of the reaction rate on the temperature and the process will continue to accelerate producing a large amount of heat in a very short time with the consequent dangers for people, installations and environment. Therefore, it is of great importance from the view points of safety and performance to accurately control the temperature of these reactors.

In the present work the Mettler reaction calorimeter RC1 [3,4], as an example of a typical batch reactor, has been used. It is a computer-controlled batch reactor able to carry out isothermal, adiabatic, isoperibolic, and temperature programmed experiments. The controller distributes the needed power by acting either on the electrical resistance or on the control valve according to an empirical criterion [5], which decomposes the needed power (q_N) into two different componets: heating power, q_h, and cooling power, q_c (fig.1). The cooling flow (q_c) and the electrical heating power (q_h) are manipulated by the controller according to a cascade control scheme described in fig. 2. The controller of the outer loop (C1) corrects deviations of the reactor temperature

from the set value T_s, following a P (Proportional) criterion defined by the user, providing the set value of the heat transfer fluid temperature which is adjusted by the inner loop controller (C2) by means of a PI (Proportional-Integral) criterion. Controller C2 uses a model based algorithm which carries out an energy balance in the heated loop every sampling time, calculating the power necessary to reach or maintain the required temperature [5].

A numerical simulator of the reaction calorimeter described previously was developed [6,7]. The mathematical model was divided into three parts: the fundamental equations obtained from mass and energy balances, and equilibrium relations; the thermo-kinetic models introduced in these equations; and the model of the heating/cooling circuits [7]. According to the cascade control scheme described in fig. 2, the model of the temperature controller calculates the needed power and then splits it. The outer loop (C1) follows a proportional criterion, using a K_{P1} value defined by the user to calculate the set-point of jacket temperature:

$$T_{e_s} = T_s + K_{P_1} (T_s - T_m)$$

(3)

This value is limited in order to protect the glass reactor against breakage by avoiding a difference between T_m and T_e grater than 50 °C. The set value of the temperature of the heat transfer fluid, T_{es}, is used as the set-point of the inner loop controller (C2) which follows a self-adaptive, proportional-integral criterium based on an energy balance:

$$q_n = K_{P_2} (T_{e_s} - T_e) +$$

$$K_i \int (T_{e_s} - T_e) \, dt - q_{pumps} - q_{loses}$$

(4)

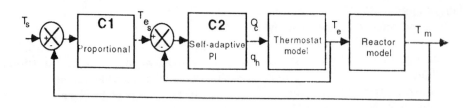

Fig. 2   RC1 temperature control scheme

where respectively q_{pumps} and q_{losses} take into account the power introduced due to friction caused by the recirculating pumps, and the heat losses of the thermostat to the surroundings. This q_N is then split into two different values q_h and q_c according to fig. 1 which are introduced into the set of algebraic-differential equations that solve the dynamic behaviour of the heating/cooling loop.

III. CONTROL USING NEURAL NETWORKS

A. Objectives and Approach

The objective was the control of the reactor by neural networks using as less as possible explicit knowledge about the processes and the reactions. In a first attempt neural networks have been used to substitute the part of the controller in which the global needed power q_N is calculated. In that case, the prediction of the needed values of electrical heating power (q_h) and cooling flow (q_c) were done using classical methods, splitting q_N into two parts. The second attempt has been the substitution of the whole controller by a neural network. The approach followed, consists in the use of the simulator of the Reaction Calorimeter RC1 in order to generate the data that feed into the network during the learning procedure. Networks with sigmoidal activation functions taking on values between 1 and -1 have been trained using the back-propagation learning algorithm [8]. The variables of the reactor and the needed values are trated as a time-series and the adaptive control as time series forecasting. For every time t, the measured variables that characterize the state of the plant are:

T_m Reactor Temperature

T_e Jacket Temperature

T_c Cold Fluid Temperature

and the needed values for the control are:

q_N Global Power.

q_c Cooling power

q_h Electrical Heating power

Pure autoregressive models using only these three variables plus the temperature set-point, T_{sp}, have been implemented and trained without success. So the input values have been substituted by $T_m - T_{sp}$, $T_e - T_{sp}$ and $T_c - T_{sp}$. The criteria

$$\frac{d^2 T_m}{dt^2} > 0 \quad \text{and} \quad \frac{d(T_m - T_e)}{dt} > 0 \qquad (5)$$

generally used for early warning detection of hazardous

states [9] have been added, implicitly involving the notion of time.

Networks to predict the values of needed power (q_N) using an input layer with five neurons and one neuron in the output layer have been used with very good results (table 1), (fig.3).

Direct prediction (without calculation of q_N) of the values of q_c and q_h using the same five neurons as input, and two neurons in the output layer representing the needed q_c and q_h have been carried out. For these networks the mean and mean square errors calculated in the training and test set are small, but the neural network resulting is not abler to control the temperature properly.

For this reason, the networks have been decomposed in two parts. The first (denoted as FN network) predicts q_N. The second (denoted as QN network) calculates q_c and q_h using six input neurons, five of them representing the same previous variables and the sixth representing q_N. Several architectures have been tested for the two networks which have been trained separately using values derived directly from the simulator of the reactor. q_N values, used both, as desired output for FN networks and input values for QN networks, was calculated by the simulator.

All neural networks have been trained using the same procedure: a set of different time simulation profiles corresponding to different operating conditions (initial concentrations and temperatures, reagent introduction rate, and set-point) for normal and abnormal but controlled situations (partial agitator and cooling circuit break-down failures) have been used to create a data set. The failures have been produced at different simulation times during the process. Simulation data have been sampled with an interval of 30 s and with two different sample periods, one of 5 s and one of 2 s and 5200 samples have been extracted randomly from thirtyfive runs in order to generate the training set. All data were normalized in [-1,1].

The trained networks have been tested using unseen patterns consisting of three 150-sample complete runs (test set) and performances have been monitored. As a final step, the networks have been inserted in the simulator substituting its control algorithms in order to evaluate the performances of the networks in real-time conditions.

B. Performances

Performances in the training and test set are expressed in terms of mean and mean square error throughout the set. Once a particular neural network has been trained, the control algorithm of the simulator has been substituted by it and the dynamic behaviour on the system tested. (For performances in the use of the network as controller see fig. 3, 4). Different architectures have been used in order to verify the complexity of the task and to compare the results.

Good performances were obtained from a large number of networks and the differences, as can be observed in Tables 1-6 are not very important. After one hundred presentations (learning rate = 0.1 and momentum = 0.9), all networks were close to a good minimum and after another 100 or 200 presentations (decrasing progressively the learning rate to 0.01) the simulations were stopped. Results obtained by FN4, QN4 and QCQH4 networks are presented because representative of the whole set of architectures.

In the following tables the network architectures represented are: FN1 a (5,5,5,1), FN2 a (5,5,1), FN3 a (5,10,5,1) and FN4 a (5,10,10,1) Network. QN1 is (6,5,5,2), QN2 a (6,5,2), QN3 a (6,10,5,2) and QN4 a (6,10,10,2) Network.

The chemical system used in the study of all the cases was a simple neutralization reaction between hydrochloric acid and sodium hydroxide. In order to check the possibilities of generalisation to other chemical systems, a different reaction (esterification of 2-butanol by propionic anhydride [10]) was chosen.

IV. CONCLUSIONS

The general scope of this work was to evaluate the possibility of employing neural networks in chemical reactor control in batch and semibatch processes. The question to answer was if these networks can learn to imitate nonlinear dynamic systems behaviour, and if yes, with what degree of generalization, that means, if the behaviour learned for one chemical system can be extrapolated for completely different

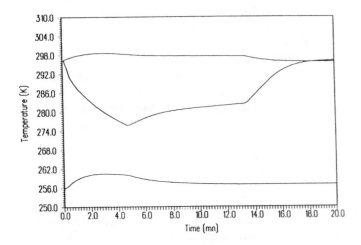

Fig. 3   Simulated temperature-time profiles for an isothermal neutralization reaction. The part of the temperature control algorithm calculating q_N has been replaced by a trained FN4 neural network. The curves represent T_m, T_e and T_c from top

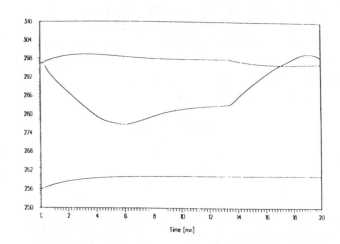

Fig. 4   Simulated temperature-time profiles for the isothermal neutralization reaction presented in fig.3. The temperature control algorithm has been replaced by a an FN (5,10,10,1) and a QN (6,10,10,2) Network. The curves represent T_m, T_e and T_c from top.

TABLE I

q_N PREDICTION

	M.E.	M.S.E
FN1	0.01528	0.03842
FN2	0.01704	0.03873
FN3	0.01644	0.03856
FN4	0.01365	0.03646

TABLE II

q_c AND q_h PREDICTION USING q_N CALCULATED FROM Fl.SIM

	M.E.	M.S.E
QN1	0.01589	0.02491
QN2	0.01050	0.02163
QN3	0.00596	0.01319
QN4	0.00997	0.01600

TABLE III

q_c AND q_h PREDICTION USING q_N CALCULATED FROM FN1

	M.E.	M.S.E
QN1	0.04126	0.11548
QN2	0.03655	0.11273
QN3	0.03443	0.11308
QN4	0.03699	0.11362

TABLE IV

q_c AND q_h PREDICTION USING q_N CALCULATED FROM FN2

	M.E.	M.S.E.
QN1	0.04487	0.11504
QN2	0.04183	0.11247
QN3	0.03922	0.11332
QN4	0.04128	0.11390

TABLE V

q_c AND q_h PREDICTION USING q_N CALCULATED FROM FN3

	M.E.	M.S.E.
QN1	0.04324	0.11573
QN2	0.03967	0.11317
QN3	0.03758	0.11341
QN4	0.03983	0.11414

TABLE VI

q_c AND q_h PREDICTION USING q_N CALCULATED FROM FN4

	M.E.	M.S.E.
QN1	0.03938	0.11089
QN2	0.03483	0.10951
QN3	0.03210	0.10955
QN4	0.03444	0.10984

systems. The answer is positive, the results are very encouraging and indicate that neural networks can be trained in order to predict the behaviour of complex systems in limitate regions. However, further studies and experiments are needed in order to determine if a generalization of these results is possible using more complex networks and different architectures.

An analysis of the behaviour of processes in which neural network controllers are compared against a traditional scheme indicates two main differences. The differences in the behaviour of the two processes are in the duration of the heating phase (the neural netwok controller heats slowly) and in the shape of the jacket temperature profile that in some cases is irregular. The former difference is due to the training, since the set of examples taken was oriented to the creation of safe cooling procedures for safety reasons. The origine of the later difference seems to be related to the magnitude of the maximum absolute error over all the training set.

REFERENCES

[1] B. Rasmussen, "Occurrence and Impact of Unwanted Chemical Reactions", J. Loss Prev. Process Ind.,1,92 (1989).

[2] L. G.Kraft and D. P. Campagna, "A Comparison between CMAC Neural Network Control and two Traditional Adaptive Control Systems", IEEE Contr. Syst. Mag., 9 (1990) 36 - 43.

[3] R. Riesen and B. Grob, "Reaction Calorimetry in Chemical Process Development", Swiss Chem., 7, 39-43, (1985).

[4] RC1 user's manual.

[5] W. Regenass et al., United States patent 4, 456, 386; Jun.26, (1984).

[6] H. Hernández and J.M. Zaldívar, "The JRC FIRES Project for Investigations on Runaway Reactions": "Heat Transfer and Major Technological Hazards", Eurotherm Seminar n° 14, 15-17 May (1990).

[7] J.M. Zaldívar, H. Hernández and C. Barcons, "Development of a Mathematical Model and Numerical Simulator for a Reaction Calorimeter: FISIM, RC1 Version", Technical Note N° I.90.109, Commission of the European Communities, Joint Research Centre, Ispra (Italy), 1990.

[8] D. Rumelhart, G. Hinton and R. Williams, "Learning Internal Representations by Error Propagation", in "Parallel Distributed Processing", Rumelhart, D. and McClelland, J. MIT Press (1986).

[9] L. Hub and J.D. Jones, "Early On-Line Detection of Exothermic Reactions", Plant/Operation Progress (1986) 221.

[10] T.J. Snee, "Runaway Reactions: A Case Study' Safety of Batch Chemical Reactors and Storage Tanks", Ed. by A. Benuzzi and J.M. Zaldívar, Kluwer Academic Publishers (1991).

Speech Synthesis with Artificial Neural Networks

Ton Weijters and Johan Thole
Department of Computer Science, University of Limburg,
P.O. Box 616, 6200 MD, Maastricht, The Netherlands
weijters@cs.rulimburg.nl

Abstract—Speech synthesis and speech recognition are well-known applications of Artificial Neural Networks. In this contribution we focus on speech synthesis. So far the main efforts have been to master the grapheme-to-phoneme conversion. In this process symbols (graphemes) are converted into other symbols (phonemes). Neural networks however are especially competitive for tasks where complex nonlinear transformations are needed, as well for tasks where insufficient domain-specific knowledge is available. The conversion of phonetic transcription of a text into a number of speech parameters seems such a task. We show some significant results of our approach to train a neural network to perform this conversion.

I. INTRODUCTION

Artificial Neural Networks (ANNs) are successfully trained for grapheme-phoneme conversion [1, 2, 3, 4]. The quality of ANN transcriptions is in general not better, and at most comparable with the quality of transcriptions carried out by traditional systems. This is not surprising because neural networks are especially competitive for tasks where complex nonlinear transformations are needed or insufficient domain-specific knowledge is available [5]. In the grapheme-phoneme domain none of the two conditions is satisfied: in principle the transformation is pure symbolic (converting a text into a phonetic transcription may be considered as a discrete mapping task) and the success of traditional systems is an indication that sufficient domain-specific knowledge is available.

The conversion of text into a number of speech parameters which form an appropriate input for a speech generator is not symbolic: complex non-linear transformations are involved. For this reason grapheme-to-speech conversion seems a suitable task to be modelled with the use of neural networks. But there are additional arguments to consider the use of a neural network for this conversion.

Traditionally, a grapheme-to-phoneme conversion system consists of a syllabification module, a morphological parser, a lexical database, a phonological knowledge base, transliteration rules and phonological rules [6]. Obviously grapheme-to-phoneme conversion is only the first step in a text-to-speech system. In a conventional symbolic system, some form of syntactic and semantic analysis must be performed in order to provide the phonetic representation of a text with information about rhythm and intonation.[1] This representation is thereafter converted into time-varying acoustic parameters from which the speech waveforms can be computed. Until now, a complete rule system for an adequate regulation of rhythm and intonation has not come through.

By dividing a complex system into different independent modules the complexity can be reduced. However, the use of independent modules has also disadvantages. One such a disadvantages is exactly the independence. Many problems with natural-language processing have to do with cross-over phenomena, in which different levels affect one another. Such phenomena are often difficult to capture within the more traditional framework in which the modularity of different types of linguistic information, such as phonology, morphology, syntax and semantics, is hypothesized. In an ANN it is not necessary to distinguish the different levels.

In spite of the potential power of ANNs to handle cross-over phenomena we must point out that the performance of ANNs on tasks such as syntactic and semantic analysis is not impressive. The types of neural networks for which learning algorithms have been developed lack the essential property of being able to represent and manipulate complex hierarchical structures [7]. Recently, new methods have been defined [8, 9, 10, 11, 12]. The practical properties of these methods are not clear. The text-to-speech domain seems a challenging test domain for the methods referred to above.

---

[1] One of the important reasons for the artificial sound of the spoken language of a speech generator is the absence of the appropriate intonation.

Notwithstanding the difficulties to represent and manipulate complex hierarchical structured data within ANNs they seem to offer a useful supplementary modelling technique for speech synthesis. But is this really the case? Here we present the results of our experiments in which we have attempted to train an ANN for the transformation of phonemes into speech parameters.

This contribution has the following structure. In Section 2 we describe the data used for training and testing the ANNs. In Section 3 we give a description of the chosen network architectures. In Section 4 we examine the results at various stages of the learning process and the performance of the networks on the test data. In the last Section we evaluate the results of our experiments.

II. THE LEARNING AND TEST MATERIAL

To investigate the ability of a network for reaching significant generalizations, it is necessary to distinguish between learning and test material. Below, a description is given of the learning and test material used in our experiments.

The desired output of our network is a sequence of speech parameters adequate to function as input for a speech generator. For practical reasons we have chosen the LVS-package parameter format. The LVS-package (named after its developer Leo Vogten Speech-analysis system) is a traditional speech-analysis system that can be used for the conversion of text into speech. It is developed at the Institute for Perception Research (IPO) in Eindhoven. The learning and test material for our experiments are generated with the LVS-package. The package is also used for speech generation based on the output of the neural network.

The choice of the LVS-package for the generation of the learning and test material is dictated by practical grounds. The quality of the data generated by a speech synthesizer is by definition lower than the quality of real speech. But the output of the LVS-package can easily be adapted for use into an ANN. The preparation of learning and test material on the basis of real human speech is preferable, but the preparation of this material takes up a large amount of time.

Because an ANN-phonetic transcription was already available [4] we choose the first 300 sentences of *De Avonden*, a Dutch novel by Gerard Reve as learning and test material. With the LVS-package, this text is converted into a phonetic transcription and the corresponding speech-

parameters. About 90% of this material serve as learning material, the remainder as test material.

In the LVS-package two simplifications are used for the representation of speech. First, speech is not represented by its continuously varying waveform, but by a sequence of so-called speech frames: short intervals of time in which it is assumed that the waveform is constant. Second, the partitioning of the original complex waveform in terms of fundamental waveforms (so-called formants). In practice the use of 5 formants has been found to be adequate. In the LVS-package each speech frame codes for 10 ms of sound and is defined with the following 13 parameters:

1:	voiced or unvoiced,
2:	for voiced sounds, the fundamental frequency,
3:	the total amplitude of the sound,
4 to 13:	the frequency and bandwidth of the first 5 formants.

The LVS-parameters are integers between an upper and lower limit. The output of a backpropagation network consists of real values in the interval [0,1]. For this reason it is conventional to scale the LVS-parameters to this interval.

The number of frames necessary for the specification of a phoneme is not constant but depends on the kind of phoneme and the word-and-sentence context. For example, the duration of the first /e/ in the Dutch word *eten* is shorter than the first /e/ in *eden*. The speech parameters generated by the LVS-package provide the right information making it possible to determine which frames realize a phoneme.

III. THE NETWORK ARCHITECTURE

Grapheme-to-phoneme conversion networks generally employ a seven character window sliding over the text. We use a similar window for the conversion of phonetic transcriptions into speech parameters. The speech frames for the fourth phoneme in the window are calculated; the first three and last three phonemes offer contextual information.

The use of the window technique has two important drawbacks. The first one has to do with the contextual information which may not be sufficient for a syntactic or semantic analysis and therefor insufficient for an adequate regulation of sentence intonation and rhythm.

The second drawback deals with the strong dependency of successive frames. As stated before, the number of speech frames necessary for the realization of one phoneme is variable (between 5 and 35). The differences between these frames are minimal. Of course it is possible to generate all these frames in one pass of a large network (with 35 * 12 = 420 output units), but this method does not take into account the strong dependency of successive frames.

In our experiments a different network architecture is chosen. Two sub-networks LastNET and FrameNET are constructed. With LastNET the duration of a phoneme is determined. FrameNET is used for the generation of the speech frames. The output of LastNET is passed on to FrameNET and is used by FrameNET as a control parameter.

LastNET is a standard backpropagation network with one hidden layer and 10 hidden units. The input is the local representation of a seven-phoneme window, the output is a real value between 0.15 and 0.85. The value indicates the duration of the phoneme in the middle of the window: an output of 0.15 indicates an duration of 0 frames, 0.17 of 1 frame, 0.19 of 2 frames, and so on.

FrameNET is a Jordan backpropagation network with one hidden layer [13]. In Fig. 1 an outline of the architecture of FrameNET is given. The input of this network is composed of three components.

The first component is equal to the input of LastNET: the local representation of a seven phoneme window. The speech frames for the fourth phoneme in the window must be determined.

The second component is the output of LastNET: this output is used in FrameNET in two ways. In the first place the output serves as a control parameter indicating when to move the window one position forward. In the second place the output of LastNET is used to indicate in which stage of the speech frame generation the network is. For this information one input unit is used. The value of this unit is the result of the following division: #done/#duration. In this division #duration is the total duration of the current phoneme, #done is the number of frames already generated. During the generation of the first speech frames this value will be near to zero, during the generation of the last frames near to one.

The third component of the input of FrameNET is a copy of the preceding output of the network (the technical term *Jordan network* is used for this type of network). The intuition guiding us in back-coupling the output is that successive frames are very similar to each other. The feedback gives information about the previously realized speech frame. This information, in combination with the phoneme window and the information about the position into the phoneme (first frames, last frames, etc.) must give the network the opportunity to generate the correct speech frames.

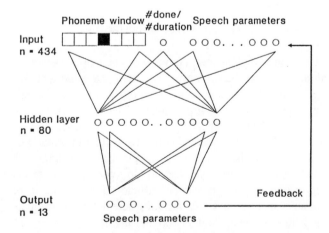

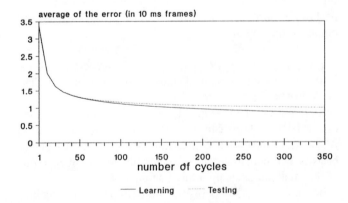

Fig. 1. An outline of the network architecture of FrameNET.

Fig. 2. The performance of LastNET during training.

IV. THE PERFORMANCE OF THE NETWORKS

A. *The performance of LastNET*

Fig. 2 shows the learning graph of LastNET for 350 cycles. On the vertical axis the average of the error (expressed in 10 ms speech frames) is given. The horizontal axis contains the number of learning and testing cycles. We see a rapid descent of the error during the first fifty cycles. Later on the improvement on both learning and test material is minimal. The difference in performance on learning and test material is small. After 350 cycles no decrease in the performance on the test material was registered.

The error deviation during processing the test material is important. Fig. 3 shows a histogram of the error deviation after 100, 250 and 350 cycles: the improvement during cycles 251 to 350 is minimal.

B. *The performance of FrameNET*

Fig. 4 contains the learning graph of FrameNET. On the vertical axis the average of the error (expressed in the euclidian distance) is given and on the horizontal axis the number of learning and testing cycles.

Fig. 5 shows the formants of a piece of test material. Solid lines belongs to target formants as generated by the LVS-package, dotted lines belongs to the formants as generated by FrameNET.

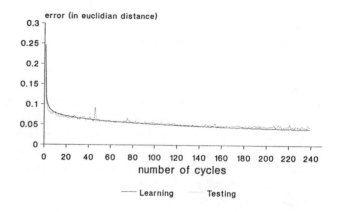

Fig. 4. The average error of FrameNET expressed in the euclidian distance between the network output and the target output.

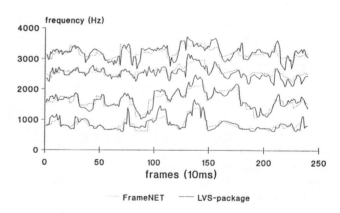

Fig. 5. Formants as generated by FrameNET and the target formants.

C. *The audibility of the generated speech frames*

On the basis of the data as given in Fig. 4 en 5 we can only draw the tentative conclusion that speech frames generated by FrameNET are rather similar to the speech frames generated by the LVS-package. But even more important is the audibility of the speech generated with the FrameNet output. Reliable research into this aspect is not carried out. Some sentences of the test material are offered to the LVS-package and recorded on a normal audio tape (the LVS-sentences).

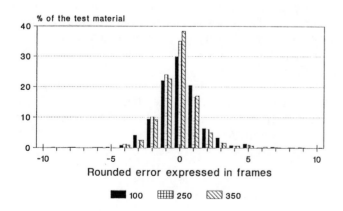

Fig. 3. The error derivation of LastNET after 100, 250 and 350 cycles.

The phonetic transcriptions of the same sentences are presented to LastNET and FrameNET; the resulting speech frames are offered to the speech synthesizer of the LVS-package. Also the pronunciation of these sentences is recorded on tape (the ANN-sentences).

Listening to the resulting records suggest the following subjective conclusions. The characteristics of the speech generated with the ANNs are very similar to that generated by the LVS-package: it seems that the same person is speaking. The audibility of the LVS-speech is better than the audibility of the ANN-speech. If the pronunciation of a LVS-sentence is clear, the pronunciation of the ANN-version is also acceptable. The following goes for both: the pronunciation is better when sentences have a shorter average word length. The LVS-intonation of a sentence is comparable with the ANN-intonation of the same sentence.

V. EVALUATION

In Section 1 arguments have been given why ANNs provide a promising modelling technique for text-to-speech systems. We have tried to find out whether this is indeed the case. In summarize we can claim that the results are promising, but a number of problems remain to be solved. Below we will explain this claim.

In this contribution no attention is paid to problems related to the preparation of the learning and test material, the choice of a network architecture and parameter tuning (learning rate, momentum, etc.). To illustrate this, we describe one of the problems with the training and test material.

The performance of an earlier FrameNET version was clearly lower than that of the FrameNET version discussed above. The performance of the network was especially bad after a silence. Inspection of the LVS-parameters made clear that during a silence all 13 parameters were equal to zero. For a silence it is technically sufficient that the amplitude of the fundamental frequency is zero. Theoretically it is more natural not to change the frequency parameters: during a short silence the position of the different speech organs will not change or they will move into the position for the pronunciation of the next phoneme. For this reason it seems not natural that during a silence all 13 parameters are equal to zero. Updating the learning and test material in accordance with the discussion above improved the performance of LastNET considerably. This demonstrates that the contextual information (the preceding output of the network) is used by the network.

The use of the LVS-package to generate learning and test material has practical advantages, but also disadvantages. The quality of the output of the LVS-package is by definition inferior to real speech parameters of human speech. At first sight this will have a negative effect on the performance of the networks. But we have to be very careful with optimistic predictions: the use of the LVS-package can have a positive effect too: the training material generated by the LVS package is possibly much more homogeneous. The results of training and testing a network with this material would as a consequence be positively influenced.

In Section 1 we remarked that one of the advantages of ANNs is that it is not necessary to use different modules. For that reason there is the hope that they will be better at dealing with interactions between (linguistic) levels. However, in our experiments we distinguish three different modules: LastNET, FrameNET and a network for the transcription of text into a phonetic representation. Is it possible to integrate these three networks into one real parallel network? Only in that case it is possible to deal adequately with interactions between levels. As far as the grapheme-to-phoneme network is concerned there seems to be no problem: both LastNET and FrameNET can be adapted for training with textual input. The combination of LastNET and FrameNET seems less easy: the output of LastNET is used as control parameter in FrameNET. For this reason the result of LastNET must be available before FrameNET can start: a parallel combination of LastNET and FrameNET appears not to be straightforward. At the moment we are not able to provide a solution for this problem.

Also the use of the window technique in combination with a copy of the proceeding output has drawbacks: this combination gives some contextual information but is inadequate for a real syntactic or semantic analysis. This analysis seems necessary to get on with intonation and rhythm. In our experiments we have ignored this deficiency. Elsewhere we will investigate the effectiveness of the new methods, referred to in Section 1, to deal better with intonation and rhythm.

ACKNOWLEDGMENTS

We would like to thank IBM Nederland for providing us with the necessary computing facilities under the DAEDALOS Joint Study Agreement, Hugo van Leeuwen and Leo Vogten of the Institute for Perception Research (IPO) at

Eindhoven are gratefully recognized for their support during the preparation of training and test material and the validation of the network output. Finally, we would like to thank Richard van Nieuwenhoven for his practical contribution to the experiments, and Jaap van den Herik and Patrick Hudson for their valuable comments.

References

[1]   T.J. Sejnowski, and C.R. Rosenberg, "Parallel networks that learn to pronounce english text". *Complex Systems*, Vol. 1, 1987, pp. 145-168.

[2]   C.R. Rosenberg, "Analysis of NETtalks internal structure," in *Proceedings of the Ninth Annual Cognitive Science Conference*. Seattle, WA, August 1987.

[3]   G. Dorffner, "Replacing symbolic rule systems with PDP networks. Netzsprech: a German example," *Applied Artificial Intelligence*, Vol. 3, 1989, pp. 45-67.

[4]   A.J.M.M. Weijters, "NetSpraak: a graphene-to-phoneme conversion network for Dutch," in *Proceedings IEEE Symposium on Neural Networks,* H. Koppelaar, M.G. Voorzanger, G.R. den Heijer, F.J. Bernard and P.T. ter Wee, Eds. IEEE Student Branch Delft, Department of Technical Mathematics and Computer Science, Delft University of Technology, 1990, pp. 59-68.

[5]   A.J.M.M. Weijters, "A simple look-up procedure superior to NETtalk?", in *Proceedings of the International Conference on Artificial Neural Networks - ICANN-91*, Espoo, Finland, 1991, pp. 1645-1648.

[6]   W. Daelemans, "GRAFON-D: a grapheme-to-phoneme conversion system for Dutch," in *Proceedings Twelfth International Conference on Computational Linguistics* (COLING-88). Boedapest, 1988, pp. 133-138.

[7]   J.A. Fodor, and Z.W. Pylyshyn, "Connectionism and cognitive architecture: A critical analysis," *Cognition*, Vol. 28, 1988, pp. 3-71.

[8]   J.L. Elman, *Finding structure in time. TR 8801*, Center for Research in Language, University of California, San Diego, 1988.

[9]   J.L. Elman, *Incremental learning, or the importance of starting small*. Technical Report 9101, Center for Research in Language, University of California, San Diego, 1991.

[10]   S.M. Lucas, and R.I. Damper, "Syntactic neural networks," *Connection Science*, Vol 2, No. 3, 1999, pp. 195-221.

[11]   J.B. Pollack, "Recursive distributed representations," *Artificial Intelligence*, Vol. 46, No. 1-2, 1990, pp. 77-105.

[12]   P. Smolensky, "Tensor product variable binding and the representation of symbol structures in connectionist systems," *Artificial Intelligence*, Vol. 46, No. 1-2, 1990, pp. 159-216.

[13]   M.I. Jordan, "Attractor dynamics and parallelism in a connectionist sequential machine," in *Proceedings of the Eighth Annual Meeting of the Cognitive Science Society*. Hilsdale, NJ, 1986.

Automatic Speech Recognition Using

Hidden Markov Models and Artificial Neural Networks

Nazeih M. Botros, Ph.D., M. Siddiqi, and M. Z. Deiri

Department of Electrical Engineering
Southern Illinois University
Carbondale, IL 62901.
Tel: 618-536-2364 Fax: 618-453-7455

Abstract: In this study, we present an algorithm for isolated-word recognition taking into consideration the duration variability of the different utterances of the same word. The algorithm is based on extracting acoustical features from the speech signal and using them as the input to Multi-Layer Perceptrons Neural Networks. Each word in the vocabulary is associated with a network. The networks are implemented as predictors for the speech samples for a certain duration of time. The back-propagation algorithm is used to train the networks. The Hidden Markov Model (HMM) is implemented to extract temporal features (states) from the speech signal. The input vector to the network consists of sixteen cepstral coefficients, two delta cepstral coefficients, and five elements to represent the state. The networks are trained to recognize the correct words and to reject the wrong words. The training set consists of ten words (digit 0 to digit 9), each uttered seven times, by three different speakers. The test set consists of three utterances of each of the ten words. Our results show that we are able to recognize all of these words.

I. INTRODUCTION

Automatic speech recognition is carried out mostly by extracting features from the speech signal and storing them in reference templates in the computer. These features carry the signature of the speech signal. If a voice interaction with the computer takes place, the computer extracts features from this voice signal and compares it with the reference templates. If a match is found, the computer executes a programmable task.

The matching process is considered the most difficult task in speech recognition. This is due to the duration and acoustic variability of the utterances of the same word even if it is spoken by the same speaker. Several pattern recognition techniques have been implemented in the matching process. Several researchers [3], [5], and [7] have implemented Hidden Markov Model (HMM) for the matching process. Although the model can take into consideration the duration variability, its classifying power is not very powerful. On the other hand, artificial neural networks have a high classification power but can not handle non-stationary signal such as speech. In recent years researchers have attempted to combine HMM and neural networks to carry out the

matching process. This current study investigates such combination.

II. DIGITAL PROCESSING OF THE SPEECH SIGNAL

Filtering and Sampling

This step is performed using a commercially available device made by Scott Instruments. The device accepts speech input through either a head-set or a noise canceling microphone. The raw data is filtered using a band-pass filter with 300-3500 HZ bandwidth, sampled using a 12 bit A/D at a rate of 7.78 KHz and then stored in a Sparc workstation. A linearization algorithm is used to convert the data from its compressed form to a linear form. An End-Point Detection algorithm is applied to determine the begin and end of the word [1].

Features extraction

The digitized data is normalized and a high frequency pre emphasis with a transfer function $H(z) = (1 - az^{-1})$ is performed. The preemphasized data is blocked into overlapping frames. Each frame is 45 ms duration, with 15 ms frame spacing and 30 ms overlapping. Each frame is multiplexed by a 45 ms Hamming window. The window is used to minimize the effect of chopping a finite samples from the original continuous speech signal. For each frame, a vector of 10-order Linear Prediction Coding (LPC) coefficients (α_i) is computed from the auto correlation vector using a Levinson-Durbin recursion method, [6]. A cepstral analysis is applied on the LPC coefficients and fourteen cepstral coefficients (c_n) are obtained as follows:

$$C_n = -\alpha_n - \sum_{i=1}^{n-1} \frac{n-i}{n} \alpha_i C_{n-i} \quad n \geq 1$$

The above coefficients are weighted by a window of the form:

$$W_c(m) = 1 + \frac{Q}{2} \sin\left(\frac{\pi m}{Q}\right), \quad 1 \le m \le Q$$

Also, two delta cepstral coefficient are obtained by taking the derivative of the weighted coefficients [3]. The sixteen coefficients (fourteen cepstral and two delta) constitute the extracted features for this study.

III. HIDDEN MARKOV MODEL ANALYSIS

In Hidden Markov Model (HMM) algorithm, each word is modeled by a state-transition network with a small number of states, N. Each state corresponds to a set of temporal events or stochastic processes in the spoken word. The number of states corresponds roughly to the number of sounds or phonemes of the word. In the following we summarize the analysis of the algorithm. Details of the algorithm can be found in [2-7]. The algorithm models each word using the following elements:

N, the number of states.

M, the number of mixtures (clusters) per state.

D, the dimension of the observation vector. This is equal to the order of LPC cepstral analysis.

$O = \{ O_1, O_2, \ldots, O_t, \ldots O_T \}$, the observation sequence. In this study, the cepstral and delta cepstral coefficients are the observation sequence.

T, the length or duration of observation sequence. This is equal to the total number of frames.

$\delta = [\delta_i]$, the initial state probability for state i.

$A = [a_{ij}]$, the state transition probability matrix that describes how the new state j may be reach from the old state i. $a_{ij} = Pr(j$ at $t+1 \mid i$ at $t)$ is defined as the probability of going to state j at time $t+1$, given that the model is in state i at time t.

$B = [b_j(x)]$, the state output observation probability distribution function matrix, which corresponds to the output of each state, where $b_j(x) = Pr(x$ at $t \mid j$ at $t)$.

Details of estimating the above elements can be found in [3] and [7]. The HMM can be represented using the compact notation $\lambda = (A, B, \delta)$. Figure 1 shows a left-right HMM implemented in this study. The model can handle duration variability due to the possibility of looping around the same state.

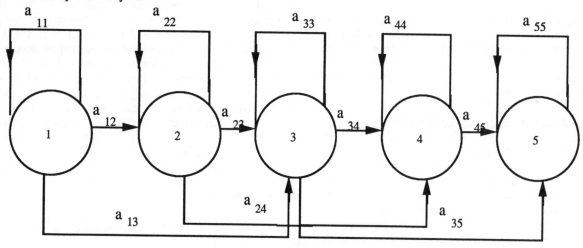

Figure 1. Left-right HMM with 5 states

The Viterbi Algorithm

The Viterbi algorithm is used to find the optimal state sequence for a given observation sequence, [4] and [7]. Results of the Viterbi algorithm are the optimal state sequence, S^* and the maximum likelihood estimation P^*. This maximum likelihood estimation is used in the recognition procedure to find the model that best matches the observation sequence of the unknown word.

HMM training Procedure

This procedure is a variation of the well-known k-means clustering algorithm. The procedure is fast and efficient but its performance depends on the good choice of initial conditions. After initialization, each set of training observation sequences is segmented into states, based on the current model λ. The segmentation is done by finding the optimum state sequence via the Viterbi algorithm, then backtracking along the optimal path.

After state segmentation, a segmental k-means algorithm is used to cluster the observation vectors within each state into a set of M clusters. Each cluster represents one of the M mixtures of the state observation densities, $b_j(O)$. The clustering is done using an Euclidean distance measure. The state transition coefficients, a_{ij}, are updated using the Baum-Welch re-estimation procedure, [4] and [7]. After the A and B parameters are updated, a new HMM model, λ^* is obtained. The resulting model is then compared to the previous model by computing the probability distances measure:

$$\text{Distance} = \frac{\log P(O\backslash\lambda) - \log P(O\backslash\lambda^*)}{P(O\backslash\lambda)} \times 100\%$$

If this distance exceeds a threshold, the old model λ is replaced by the new model λ^*, and the training continues. If the distances falls below the threshold, then the model is assumed converge and the final model parameter is saved as the reference HMM template for the recognition procedure.

HMM recognition

After the training procedure is completed, the recognition process is carried out. The model of the unknown word is matched against all the models in the HMM reference templates using the Viterbi algorithm. A decision rule, based on the maximum log likelihood estimation, is applied to determine the model that best matches the observation sequence of the unknown word. If the estimation falls bellow a preset threshold, then the unknown word is declared "unrecognizable".

IV. HMM -NEURAL NETWORKS ALGORITHM

In this algorithm, the neural network is implemented as a predictor. It predicts the observation vector (cepstral and delta cepstral coefficients) of the next frame given the observation vector of the current frame and the HMM state to which this current frame belongs to. The Viterbi algorithm is used to determine this state.

The neural network implemented in this study is a multi-layer perceptron with twenty-one input nodes; sixteen nodes to represent the observation vector and five nodes to represent the five states. The state is indicated by entering a value of "1" at the corresponding node and entering zeros at other nodes. For example, state 2 is represented as 00010 while state 3 is represented as 00100. The network has eight hidden nodes and sixteen output nodes. The back-propagation training procedure is implemented to train the network. For each trained word there is a network. To recognize a word, its observation vector and the state of each frame are introduced to every networks. A prediction error is calculated for each frame using the Euclidean distance. This error represents the difference between the predicted values of the observation vector of the frame and the actual ones. This error is summed over all frames of the word to obtain the total error for each network. The word is recognized as that of the network that gives the lowest error. However, the word is declared unrecognizable if this lowest error is higher than a pre-determined threshold. This recognition threshold is determined experimentally by observing the values of the lowest errors for each word.

V. RESULTS AND DISCUSSION

Table 1 shows a partial results of HMM for the digit "five". The table shows seven training and three testing utterances for each word. The model is able to recognize the words of this small vocabulary with 100% accuracy . For additional tests of the model, we have tried to recognize words which are phonetically close to some of the words in the vocabulary. For example, the words ("OR" and "FOUR"), ("A" and "EIGHT"), and ("TREE" and "THREE"). The model generates scores for the words "OR", "A", and "TREE" which are very close to the scores generated by the words "FOUR", "EIGHT", and "THREE" respectively. This closeness make it impossible to accurately recognize the above words. Also, as shown in the Table, some of the scores for different words are close to each others which could lower the recognition accuracy especially when the size of the vocabulary increases.

Table 2 shows a partial results of HMM-Neural Network Algorithm for the digit "five". As shown in this Table, the recognition accuracy has improved significantly over that of HMM. Also, We are able to differentiate between the words ("OR" and "FOUR"), ("A" and "EIGHT"), and ("TREE" and "THREE").

In the above HMM-Neural Network Algorithm each network is trained to recognize a single word. So adding a new word to the vocabulary does not require re-training all other networks of the vocabulary. This makes addition of new words as well as training of the individual networks an easy task. However, since each network is taught to recognize a single word without learning to reject all other words, the recognition accuracy deteriorates with the addition of words that are acoustically close to that of the vocabulary. Examples of such words are ("OR" and "FOUR"), and ("A" and "EIGHT"). To avoid this deterioration, we train the network of each of these words to minimize the error for that word and maximize the error for all other words that acoustically close to that word. The results of this training are shown below.

Before Maximizing Error		After Maximizing Error	
FOUR	400(average)	FOUR	400(average)
OR	572	OR	3500

SCORES FOR NETWORK "FOUR"

Before Maximizing Error		After Maximizing Error	
EIGHT	380(average)	EIGHT	380(average)
A	790	A	3300

SCORES FOR NETWORK "EIGHT"

VI. CONCLUSION

This study is done with an isolated word, speaker independent, limited vocabulary speech recognition system using HMM and neural networks. Artificial neural networks are implemented as pattern predictors instead of pattern discriminator. The results are satisfactory.

The highlights of the technique applied in this study are as follows:

1. Temporal distortion of speech is normalized by determining the states.

2. The size of the vocabulary can be increased without the need for extensive retraining. This is due to the partial independence of the network of each word.

3. The technique can be applied to continuous speech recognition.

4. The networks are trained to recognize the correct words and to reject the wrong words. This rejection training is very crucial in improving the recognition accuracy especially when the vocabulary size increases dramatically.

VII. REFERENCES

1. L.R. Rabiner, M.R. Sambur, "An Algorithm for Determining the Endpoints of Isolated Utterances," The Bell Systems Technical Journal, Vol. 54, No. 26, pp. 297-314, Feb. 1975.

2. John Makhoul, "Linear Prediction: A Tutorial Review," Proceedings of the IEEE, Vol. 63, No. 4, pp. 561-580, April 1975.

3. L.R. Rabiner, "A Tutorial on Hidden Markov Models and Selected Applications in Speech Recognition," Proceedings of the IEEE, Vol. 77, No. 2, pp. 257-285, Feb. 1989.

4. G.D. Forney, JR., "The Viterbi Algorithm,", Proceedings of the IEEE, Vol. 61, No. 3, pp. 268-277, March 1973.

5. E. Levin, "Connected Word Recognition using Hidden Control Neural Architecture," Speech Technology, pp. 102-107, Feb./March 1991.

6. N. Botros and Z. Deiri, "Isolated-Word Recognition Using Traditional and Neural Network Approaches," International Journal of Microcomputer Applications , vol. 9, no. 2, pp. 48-51, 1990.

7. C. Teh, "Implementation of Hidden Markov Models for Speech Recognition", Master thesis, Southern Illinois University at Carbondale, 1991.

THE WROD is FIVE	ZERO	ONE	TWO	THREE	FOUR	FIVE	SIX	SEVEN	EIGHT	NINE	TEN
TRAINING SETS											
PATTERN 1	-568	-736	-994	-974	-603	-408	-820	-606	-1167	-765	-901
PATTERN 2	-632	-746	-968	-1117	-755	-362	-886	-623	-1147	-749	-1023
PATTERN 3	-673	-803	-1033	-1264	-805	-427	-941	-685	-1174	-825	-1106
PATTERN 4	-634	-749	-970	-1196	-662	-390	-872	-662	-1082	-755	-1056
PATTERN 5	-585	-663	-932	-1146	-718	-351	-807	-570	-1108	-669	-1003
PATTERN 6	-671	-777	-1086	-1223	-794	-377	-940	-700	-1234	-773	-1152
PATTERN 7	-674	-775	-1116	-1186	-819	-407	-906	-699	-1353	-750	-1217
TESTING SETS											
PATTERN 8	-686	-785	-1110	-1222	-891	-420	-902	-665	-1270	-773	-1148
PATTERN 9	-642	-769	-1055	-1081	-724	-498	-852	-638	-1219	-790	-922
PATTERN 10	-666	-735	-1021	-1183	-845	-421	-915	-631	-1203	-735	-1095

Table 1. IIM Results

THE WORD is FIVE		ZERO	ONE	TWO	THREE	FOUR	FIVE	SIX	SEVEN	EIGHT	NINE	TEN
TRAINING SETS	PATTERN 1	1903	1306	1555	1323	1349	230	1176	1539	1619	802	1686
	PATTERN 2	2131	1322	1949	1686	1608	361	1548	2036	1785	954	1663
	PATTERN 3	2263	1247	2040	2030	1700	374	1627	2219	2000	1024	1739
	PATTERN 4	1384	1364	1783	1880	1519	332	1568	1728	1797	1016	1605
	PATTERN 5	1942	1111	1618	1555	1204	255	1522	1683	1923	915	1323
	PATTERN 6	2275	1389	1740	1936	1307	303	1718	2062	2094	1014	1705
	PATTERN 7	2331	1450	1819	2014	1557	269	1782	2121	2062	1080	1757
TESTING SETS	PATTERN 8	1705	1456	2212	2135	1517	692	1955	1979	2225	1129	1776
	PATTERN 9	2060	1520	2021	1884	1600	878	1694	1819	2279	1141	2133
	PATTERN 10	2152	1217	1957	1861	1272	426	1812	2119	2157	889	1554

Table 2.   HMM-Neural Network Results

ON THE COMPARISON RESULTS OF THE NEURAL NETWORKS TRAINED USING WELL-LOGS FROM ONE SERVICE COMPANY AND TESTED ON ANOTHER SERVICE COMPANY'S DATA

Heidar A. Malki
University of Houston
Electrical-Electronics Technology
Houston, Texas 77204-4083

Jeffrey L. Baldwin
Mind & Vision Computer Systems
18627 North Lyford
Katy, Texas 77449

Abstract--This paper demonstrates the ability of neural networks to recognize facies logged by two different service companies on the same well. Two main tests were conducted: 1) Train the network with one service company and test it with another service company's data and 2) Train the network with both service company's data and test on each service company's data.

I. INTRODUCTION

The main goal of this paper is to compare the result of facies classification obtained from processing two different service company's data on the same well using neural networks. Specifically, if a neural network is trained on a set of training patterns extracted from one service company's well-log suite, then how well the network will perform on the log data obtained from another service company is of primary concern. This is a very important task which depends on several parameters such as resolution of the logging devices, noise, and human operator technique. It is a very difficult problem to address if conventional software packages are used for this comparison.

A geologist can classify facies from visual inspection of log data curves in combination with past experience. A geologist relies on experience and memory of what facies exist, and the appearance of log curves in various depositional environments when classifying facies from well logs. Neural networks can perform repetitious, mundane tasks involving pattern recognition faster and more efficiently than humans due to the parallel architecture of neural networks. It is worth mentioning that neural networks do not replace geologists. They will, however, allow more efficient utilization of the geologist's time and experience by performing repetitious facies identification from log profiles [1].

Neural networks have been successfully used to identify facies from well-log data. Lovenzetti [2] used neural networks to predict lithology from Vp and Vs acoustic data. Peck et. al. [3] applied neural networks for lithological interpretations. In [4] synthetic spontaneous potential (sp) and resistivity logs are used to train neural networks for lithology classification. All of this work has shown promising results in this field. To the best of our knowledge, no one has applied neural networks to train one service company's data and test it with another service company's well-log data. This has been a challenging task and an important problem for many geologists and log analysts using the conventional methods. In this paper, we have conducted this task with reasonable success.

II. GEOLOGY AND WELL LOG DATA

The geology of rocks used in this research is complex and multifaceted. This is a good test case because the complexity of these rocks matches that of most difficult-to-solve, real-world problems and because there is excellent control in this research well.

Most of the rocks in this well are comprised of silicon and aluminum-silicon crystalline structures called silicates and aluminosilicates. The rocks were formed by sedimentation in lagoons and near shore fronts, so these rocks are described geologically as siliciclastic. While a few limestone, dolomite, and coal formations are present, the overwhelming majority of rocks are of remarkably similar physical properties such as density, amount of void space (porosity), etc. This is due to the fact that most rocks are aluminosilicates and created by similar sedimentation mechanisms.

Subsurface formations are measured by various downhole devices lowered into wellbores after a hole has been drilled to a prespecified depth. The measurements are of three basic classes: electrical, nuclear, and acoustic. Each of these measurement classes has several different types of measurements (called logs because the recordings used to be written in log books) that can be made. For example, measuring the resistivity of formations with radio waves and recording the naturally occurring electrical potentials that exist downhole are both electrical measurements. Also, determining the rock density with gamma radiation, the rock void space space with neutron radiation, and recording naturally occurring levels of radiation in rocks are all three nuclear measurements. The physics of these measurements is well known but the interpretation of exactly what they mean is anything but clear.

The types of logs used in this research are short-spaced conductivity, natural gamma ray activity, bulk density, photoelectric effect, and neutron porosity recorded on a sandstone scale. Two service companies provided their versions of these measurements: Schlumberger (SWS) provided CLLS, GR, LDT RHOB, PEF, and CNL NPHI, while Welex - now Haliburton Logging Services (HLS) - provided SGRD, GR, SDL RHOB, PES (short-spaced), and DSN NPHI.

Even though the same well is logged by both service companies, there are differences between the two determinations of intrinsic formation characteristics. These differences are 1) Naturally-occurring borehole enlargement after the SWS logs and before the HLS were run has caused uncompensated environmental effects in the HLS logs, 2) Different fabrication and design of the two companies' measurement tools, and 3) Slightly different recording practices between the two companies (SWS has recorded one set of data at 1/2-foot increment and another set at 1/10-foot increment while HLS has recorded all data at 1/4-foot increments). These types of differences occur often and must routinely be dealt with in some manner by the petrophysicists who interpret log measurements. Since SWS and HLS logs in this well exhibit differences that are as similar as those observed in normal petrophysical data processing environments, then the data set used in this research will be representative of real-world requirements for neural network versatility if a successful interpretation is to be achieved.

Log measurements are utilized for a variety of tasks both quantitative and qualitative. Quantifying amount and type of hydrocarbons-in-place has obvious economic interests. Geologists often use log measurements to discover information about the geology and depositional environments of formations so as to predict location and size of reservoirs from data taken in a single well. The quantitative and qualitative relationships between log measurements and desired results are often highly non-linear, perturbed in varying degrees by white and non-white noise, only partially parameterized, and often overly simplistic. This is thus a field of science in need of technologies such as are afforded by neural networks.

III. RESULTS AND DISCUSSION

Several neural network training sets and structures were constructed for this segment of the research. The training set for the first segment performed and published [5] earlier this year was taken from a human's sequence stratigraphic interpretation. The training sets for the work reported here were obtained from a visual lithofacies description performed by a petrophysicist skilled in the art. In this work we have used multilayer neural networks based on the back-propagation training algorithm [6].

The practice of this research was to train on SWS and test on HLS data, and then train on the same HLS data and test on SWS data. Results were then contrasted for comparable network and data set configurations. The configuration alterations were of three types: 1) Changes to input log normalization ranges, 2) Increased curve filtering

by block average of the high resolution SWS data, and 3) Increased number of neurons in the hidden layer.

Results of training and testing the neural networks upon the two service companies' data sets are abstracted in this paper. A set of training procedures and parameter values established in the first segment of this research [5] was decided upon and this set of procedures and values was not significantly altered during this research work (e.g., number of training cycles=100000 always, Boltzmann Machine connection updates were always used, temperature annealing was always used). Thus, we were able to look separately at the effects of the three network and data set configuration alterations listed above.

Table I presents comparisons related to normalization effects. Column 1 lists the lithofacies number and column two shows the number of occurrences of each type in the test interval. Not every depth was assigned a lithofacies description and the total number of points in the test interval was about 10 times as large as this validation set. The remainder of the columns in this table present Percent-Correct-Classification (PCC) results for each of the neural network and data set configurations used. The bottom row in each table list totals of each column (the PCCs of individual lithofacies must be adjusted by the frequency of occurrence before computing the total PCC for each column). The top row of each table lists which network was used (numbered in arbitrary order), followed by which company's data was used for training (S=SWS, H=HLS) and then by which data was used for testing.

SWS input log data was normalized to some range before training and testing. When the HLS data utilized these same normalization ranges then the notation "H(U)" appears in the table to indicate that the HLS was data un-normalized to HLS ranges. When the HLS data utilized normalizations ranges that were derived for HLS data then the notation "H(N)" appears. If the SWS data utilized normalizations ranges derived from HLS data, then the notation "S(U)" is used. The notation "S" indicates that SWS data has been normalized to ranges derived for SWS data.

Table I clearly indicates that the best neural network performance is obtained by normalizing each data set to its own compatible range. Such ranges are discovered by crossplot of each input log datum from one company against the same log datum type from the other company. Effects of calibration error and to a lesser extent tool design and fabrication are thus normalized-out. The different neural networks appearing in Table I are for different degrees of block averaging on the SWS input data. In every case, using compatible normalization ranges produces the best results.

Notice, however, that training on SWS and testing on HLS data does not produce quite as good results as training on HLS and testing on SWS data. This is due to the uncorrected environmental effects in the HLS data. When a network trains on HLS data, it is able to produce correct results from erroneous and correct data (environmental effects are not present in every HLS log at every depth).

However, when a network trains on SWS data where the data is completely correct then it has no ability to compensate for incorrect data. This has implications for persons in the petroleum industry wishing to make use of this technology: be sure to train using both "perfect" data and some representations of problem data.

Table II presents comparisons of networks trained with differing degrees of averaging on the SWS data. The amounts of averaging correspond roughly to 14 levels, 22 levels, 32 levels, and 44 levels. Averaging of 32 levels produced input SWS curves of roughly equivalent resolution compared to the HLS curves. The 44 level average was included to test the hypothesis that training on HLS and testing on SWS data produced better results than vice versa because the higher frequency content of the SWS data appears to the network as "noise". This hypothesis is invalidated by over-averaging the SWS logs and repeating the tests (the last two columns in Table II). This table again has implications for persons in the petroleum industry wishing to make use of this technology: be certain that the resolution of the training set is either the lowest of all sets to be tested in the future, or include representations of low resolution data in the training sets.

Table III presents comparisons of networks with different hidden layer sizes (24, 30, and 35 neurons). The three sets of neural network structure sizes encompass changes in the amount of filtering on the SWS input log curves and change training sets to simultaneously include both SWS and HLS log data. Table 3 demonstrates that for all cases, 30 neurons in the hidden layer produces better results than 24 neurons, but not as good as for 35 neurons. Optimal network size for this problem is thus about 30 neurons. Also, it is apparent that better results are obtained when both service companies' data are used to produce training sets. The implications are clear: 1) test several neural network configurations to determine optimal network size, and 2) be certain to include in a training set representations of as many service company data sets as you plan to process in the future.

IV. CONCLUSIONS

Perusal of Table I clearly reveals that the best neural network performance is obtained by normalizing each data set to its own internally compatible range. Table 2 indicates that including low resolution data in the training sets increases the correct classification in the testing phase. Table 3 demonstrates that optimal network size for this problem is about 30 neurons. Finally, better results are obtained when both service companies' data are used to produce training sets.

ACKNOWLEDGMENT

The authors wish to thank Exxon Production Research Company for providing the data which this research is based on.

REFERENCES

[1] J. L. Baldwin, "Using a Simulated Bi-directional Associative Neural Network Memory with Incomplete Prototype Memories to Identify Facies from Intermittent Logging Data Acquired in a Siliciclastic Depositional Sequence: A Case Study," SPE #22843 presented at the 1991 Annual Technical Conference and Exhibition, Dallas, TX, October 6-9, 1991.

[2] Elizabeth A. Lovenzetti, "Predicting Lithology from Vp and Vs using Neural Networks," submitted to Society of Exploration Geophysicists Annual Meeting, October 24-27, 1992.

[3] M. D. Pollitt, J. Peck, and J. J. Scoble, "Lithological Interpretation Based on Monitored Drilling Performance Parameters," The Metal Mining Division of CIML, 1991.

[4] M. D. McCormack, "Neural Computing in Geophysics," Geophysics, January, 1991.

[5] Heidar A. Malki and Jeffrey L. Baldwin, "Well-Log Analysis using Multilayer Neural Networks to Classify Facies," IEEE International Conference on System Engineering, Kobe, Japan, September 17-19, 1992.

[6] D. E. Rumelhart, G. E. Hinton, and R. J. William, "Learning Internal Representation by Error Propagation," in D. E. Rumelhart and J. L. McClelland (eds.), Parallel Distributed Processing: Explorations in the Microstructure of Cognition. Vol. 1: Foundations, MIT Press, 1986.

TABLE I. EFFECTS OF NORMALIZATION RANGE CHANGES

FACIES #	FREQ	23 S H(U)	23 S H(N)	25 S H(U)	25 S H(N)	29 S H(U)	29 S H(N)	24 H(U) S(U)	24 H(U) S(N)	26 H(N) S(U)	26 H(N) S(N)
1	103	0	3	0	0	0	11	0	14	31	44
2	11	27	73	0	73	100	100	0	0	0	0
3	47	43	94	32	83	0	49	0	0	0	0
4	446	11	56	10	67	7	29	100	93	100	84
5	31	100	74	100	100	100	100	100	100	100	100
6	105	0	8	0	17	0	35	73	70	72	72
7	41	0	0	0	0	0	20	100	100	100	100
8	375	96	92	99	95	91	77	35	23	22	29
9	47	89	96	55	89	83	96	26	53	55	38
10	82	100	96	100	100	100	100	96	100	94	100
11	21	0	0	100	100	100	100	0	0	0	0
12	26	100	100	100	100	100	100	0	12	0	0
TOTAL	1,335	46	62	46	69	44	54	61	58	61	58

TABLE II. EFFECT OF AVERAGING SWS LOGS
(TRAINING AND TESTING)

FACIES #	FREQ	23 14 LEV S S	25 22 LEV S S	28 32 LEV S S	29 44 LEV S S	23 14 LEV S H(N)	25 22 LEV S H(N)	29 32 LEV S H(N)
1	103	24	36	28	40	3	0	11
2	11	100	100	100	100	73	73	100
3	47	81	100	100	70	94	83	100
4	446	92	92	94	93	56	67	29
5	31	100	100	90	100	74	100	100
6	105	62	67	69	89	8	17	35
7	41	100	85	100	100	0	0	20
8	375	83	87	88	86	92	95	77
9	47	94	83	96	100	96	89	96
10	82	100	100	100	99	96	100	100
11	21	100	100	100	100	0	100	100
12	26	65	92	100	100	100	100	100
TOTAL	1,335	82	85	86	87	62	69	54

TABLE III. EFFECT OF CHANGING NETWORK SIZE

FACIES #	FREQ	31A-1 S+H S 24N	32A-1 S+H S 30N	35A-1 S+H S 35N	29A-1 S S 24N	34A-1 S S 35N	29A-3 S H(N) 24N	34A-3 S H(.5) 35N	31A-3 S+H H(.5) 24N	32A-3 S+H H(.5) 30N
1	103	0	30	0	40	43	11	13	0	35
2	11	0	91	0	100	100	100	100	0	100
3	47	0	72	0	70	51	49	27	0	73
4	446	100	97	0	93	73	29	30	97	95
5	31	100	100	0	100	100	100	86	100	100
6	105	74	77	0	89	52	35	20	64	76
7	41	93	100	0	100	93	20	0	100	100
8	375	82	83	0	86	88	77	87	94	94
9	47	96	96	0	100	91	96	100	100	100
10	82	100	98	0	99	100	100	100	100	100
11	21	100	100	0	100	86	100	0	100	100
12	26	0	100	0	100	100	100	100	0	100
TOTAL	1,335	79	86	2	87	77	54	52	79	88

Identification of High Noise Time Series Signals
Using Hybrid ARMA Modeling and Neural Network Approach

Xin Feng and Jessica Y. Schulteis
Department of Electrical and Computer Engineering
Marquette University
1515 W. Wisconsin Avenue
Milwaukee, Wisconsin 53233 USA

Abstract - A new approach for time series signal identification with high noise background is proposed. The new approach takes advantage of both ARMA spectrum estimator and artificial neural networks (ANNs). The Dynamic Data System (DDS) modeling strategy and ARMA spectrum estimator are used to provide high resolution spectrum estimate, and the back-propagation ANN is used as the feature pattern classifier. Simulation experiments based on vibration signal diagnosis are also presented. The new approach demonstrated a better performance than the conventional FFT-ANN approach in high noise environments.

I. INTRODUCTION

Identification of high noise time series signals has always been a challenging work to signal processing engineers and researchers. Traditional methods include spectral estimation using both parametric and non-parametric methods such as ARMA modeling and FFT algorithms. In recent years, the applications of Artificial Neural Network (ANN) in signal processing has gained popularity [1-3]. The commonly used FFT-ANN approach [2] utilizes FFT as a preprocessor to obtain spectral estimate of the time series signal, and employs back-propagation ANN as the pattern classifier. However, this approach suffered from the so-called "noise situation" dilemma [4][5]. Consequently the performance of FFT-ANN approach is not satisfactory when dealing with signals with high noise back-ground, i.e. those with low Signal-to-Noise Ratios (SNRs).

In this paper, we propose a new approach that is effective for high noise time series signal identification. The new approach takes advantage of both ARMA modeling and back-propagation ANN techniques. The ARMA spectral estimator provides the spectral estimates with much better quality, which can be used as the input to the ANN. As a result, the ANN performs better on classification. The new approach demonstrated a much better performance over the FFT-ANN method in vibration time series

signal identification with low SNRs in the laboratory experiments.

II. ARMA MODEL AND DDS MODELING STRATEGY

A. ARMA Dynamic System

From dynamic systems point of view, an observed time-series signal , $\{X_t,\ t=1,2,..., N\}$, can be treated as the response of a stochastic dynamic system stimulated by white noise input, as shown in Fig. 1, and represented by the ARMA(n,m) model:

$$X_t - \sum_{i=1}^{n} \phi_i X_{t-i} = a_t - \sum_{j=1}^{m} \theta_j a_{t-j} \qquad (1)$$

$$a_t \sim NID(0,\sigma_a^2) \qquad (2)$$

where n and m are model order parameters, ϕ_1, ϕ_2, ... , ϕ_n are auto-regressive parameters, θ_1, θ_2, ... , θ_m are moving average parameters, and $\{a_t\}$ satisfies the white noise assumption. It has been discussed thoroughly in [6] that the ARMA system output $\{X_t\}$ can be represented by:

$$X_t = \sum_{j=0}^{\infty} G_j a_{t-j} \qquad (3)$$

where G_j's are called Green's function with $G_0 = 1$.

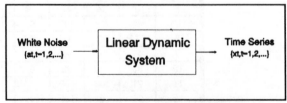

Fig. 1. Block diagram of ARMA dynamic system

Actually, G_js are the impulse response of the system. For ARMA(n,n-1) model, the Green's function can be represented as

$$G_j = g_1 \lambda_1^j + g_2 \lambda_2^j + \dots + g_n \lambda_n^j, \quad j = 1, 2, \dots \quad (4)$$

where $\lambda_1, \lambda_2, \dots, \lambda_n$ are roots of the characteristic equation

$$\lambda^n - \phi_1 \lambda^{n-1} - \dots - \phi_n = 0 \quad (5)$$

and

$$g_i = \frac{\lambda^{n-1} - \theta_1 \lambda_i^{n-2} - \dots - \theta_{n-1}}{(\lambda_i - \lambda_1) \dots (\lambda_i - \lambda_{i-1})(\lambda_i - \lambda_{i+1}) \dots (\lambda_i - \lambda_n)}, \quad i = 1, 2, \dots, n$$

$$(6)$$

B. DDS Modeling Strategy

The *Dynamic Data System (DDS)* method, proposed by S.M. Wu and Pandit [6], is a practical and efficient ARMA modeling strategy that employs ARMA(n,n-1) models to approximate general ARMA (n,m) model. The search effort for an adequate ARMA model is greatly reduced since only one model parameter, *n*, is involved. In implementing the DDS, the ARMA(2n,n-1) model is used instead of ARMA(n,n-1), starting from n=1, i.e. the low order model ARMA(2,1). The adequate ARMA model is approached by gradually increasing n. The reason for this strategy is that the characteristic roots of a natural dynamic system occur conjugately, and this strategy can further reduce the search time for finding an adequate model order. The search stops at certain *n* where further increase of *n* does not significantly reduce the Residual Sum of Squares (RSS). The final ARMA(n,m) model can be determined by inspecting estimated parameters and their confidence intervals. If the value of a parameter is small and its confidence interval includes zero, this parameter may be removed from the model and a lower order model will be obtained. Both the F-test [6] and the AIC criterion [7] are employed in the DDS modeling strategy to determine the appropriate ARMA model.

C. ARMA Spectral Estimate

Fourier spectral analysis, with the use of FFT algorithms, has been the major tool for digital signal processing. This "non-parametric" approach does not assume a specific parametric model for the observed time series signals. On the other hand, the resolution and unbaisedness of ARMA spectral estimators, which is known as the "parametric" spectral estimate method, generally exceeds those obtained by other conventional non-parametric methods such as FFT algorithm [8]. The spectral estimate of the ARMA(n,m) process is given by,

$$f(k) = \frac{\sigma_a^2 \left| 1 - \sum_{l=1}^{m} \theta_l e^{-j2\pi lk/n} \right|^2}{\left| 1 - \sum_{i=1}^{n} \phi_i e^{-j2\pi ik/n} \right|^2} \quad (7)$$

where k = 0,1,..., (N-1)/2, and the estimate of $f(k)$ is obtained by substituting parameter estimates $\phi_1, \phi_2, \dots, \phi_n$, $\theta_1, \theta_2, \dots, \theta_m$ into (7).

III. BACK-PROPAGATION ANN

Consider a feed-forward ANN consisting of M layers, of which the first denotes the input layer, the last (Mth) is the output layer and others are hidden layers. A three-layer ANN is shown in Fig.2. It is assumed that the ($k-1$)th layer has N_k processing elements (PEs). The ANN model considered here is based on the following equations:

$$i_j^* = \sum_{i=1}^{N_{k-1}} W_{ij}^{k-1,k} O_i^{k-1} + \theta_j^k \quad (8)$$

$$O_j^k = f(i_j^k) \quad (9)$$

where O_i^k represents the output of the ith PE at the kth layer, $w_{ij}^{k-1,k}$ denotes the connection weight from the ith PE at the ($k-1$)th layer to the jth neuron at the kth

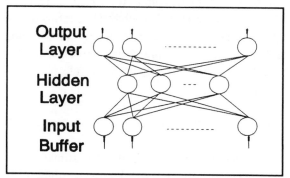

Fig. 2. A typical three-layer feed-forward ANN

layer, θ_j^k is a threshold of the jth PE at the kth layer. The output $w_{ij}^{k-1,k}$ is generated through a nonlinear activation function given by

$$f(x) = \frac{1}{1 + \exp(-x)} \qquad (10)$$

Back-propagation is the most popular supervised training algorithm for multi-layer feed-forward ANNs. Typically, the train employs the gradient descent optimization to minimize the total error, J:

$$J = \frac{1}{2} \sum_p \sum_{j=1}^{N_M} (O_{jp}^M - y_{jp})^2 \qquad (11)$$

where p is an index over cases (input-output pairs) and y is the desired state of an output PE. The back-propagation algorithm can be summarized in equations below:

$$w_{ij}^{k-1,k} = w_{ij}^{k-1,k} - \varepsilon \delta_j^k O_i^{k-1} \qquad (12)$$

$$\delta_j^M = (O_j^M - y_j) \, f'(i_j^M) \qquad (13)$$

$$\delta_j^k = f'(i_j^k) \sum_{l=1}^{N_k+1} w_{jl}^{k,k+1} \, \delta_l^{k+1}, \quad k = M-1,...,2 \qquad (14)$$

where (12) is the iteration function of weights, in which ε is the learning rate. Equations (13) and (14) specify the error signal. If a PE is an output PE, its error signal is given by (13) as the standard delta rule, in which f'(*) is the derivative of the activation function which is given by

$$f'(i_j^k) = o_j^k(l - o_j^k) \qquad (15)$$

The error signal for hidden units for which there is no specified target is determined recursively in terms of the error signals of the units to which it directly connects and the weights of those connections. For comprehensive discussions of ANN architecture, the reader is referred to [4], [9], and [10].

IV. THE PROPOSED ARMA-ANN APPROACH

Because the parametric ARMA spectral estimator provides better spectral estimates with high magnitude of sig

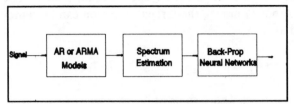

Fig. 3. Process of the ARMA-ANN approach

nificant frequencies and eliminate noise frequency, it can be used, as an ideal preprocessor, to provide quality spectral data of time series signals to the ANN for pattern classification. Fig. 3 illustrates such an approach.

The first step of the proposed ARMA-ANN approach is to establish the appropriate ARMA model by using DDS modeling strategy described in Section II. After the ARMA model is established, the autospectrum can be obtained using (7). The resolution and unbaisedness of ARMA spectral estimators, which is known as the parametric spectral estimate method, generally exceeds those obtained by conventional non-parametric FFT algorithms [8].

The standard back-propagation ANN can be used as the spectral pattern classifier because of its popularity and effectiveness. Specifically the three-layer ANN with standard back-propagation is chosen in our experiment.

V. EXPERIMENTS ON VIBRATION SIGNAL IDENTIFICATION

We have experienced the new ARMA-ANN based approach on vibration analysis application and obtained some significant results. Following are discussions of the experimental process.

A. Vibration Signal identification

The goal of vibration signal analysis [12] is to diagnose the mechanical failure of rotating parts in a machine and identify the cause of failure. Each machine defect produces a unique set of vibration signals. For example, rolling element bearings are the most common cause of small machinery failure. Typically, the overall vibration level changes are virtually undetectable in the early stage of deterioration. Figs. 4 and 5 illustrate two typical mechanical components that may cause vibration. The vibration in the motor fan assembly is often caused by the misalignment of two shafts, while the vibration in Fig. 5 may be caused by the internal bearing wear out.

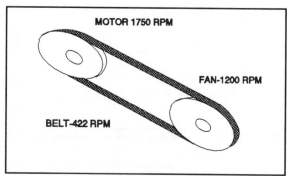

Fig. 4. A typical motor fan assembly

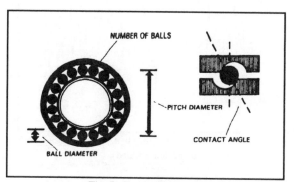

Fig. 5. Bearing geometry

B. Simulation of Vibration Signals

According to the study of bearing vibration behavior [12], vibration signals of a specific device with ball defect, defect on outer race, and defect on inner race have the spectra with peak frequencies at 94Hz, 263Hz and 437Hz respectively. Synthetic simulated signals representing the above three defects were then generated with sampling rate of 1000 Hz and 0.25 second sample duration (250 points). Figs. 6 and 7 show a sample signal set and its Fourier transform. Clearly it contains three significant vibration frequency "peaks". For experimental purpose, the white noise sequences were obtained by using pseudo random number generator and were added to each set of signals to obtain various SNR levels. Fig. 8 shows a sample of noise-added time series signals. Altogether 30 samples of such signals were generated for each SNR level at 10dB, 0dB, and -10dB respectively.

C. ARMA modeling and spectral estimation

The ARMA(7,6) models were obtained by using DDS modeling strategy for simulated signals. For comparison purpose, both FFT algorithm and parametric ARMA spectral estimator were used to estimate the spectra. Figs. 9 and 10 illustrate the results of spectral estimates by both FFT and ARMA models. Obviously the ARMA model obtained a spectral estimate with sharp resolution and much better quality.

D. ANN Training

A three-layer, fully connected feedforward ANN was used as the pattern classifier with 64 input neurons corresponding to the 64 sample points of the spectral data. The number of hidden neurons varied from 10 to 30 with

standard sigmoidal functions. The three output neurons, labeled O_1, O_2, and O_3, represented the corresponding three category of vibrations. The weights connected between neurons were initialized with small random values.

V. COMPARISON OF RESULTS

Following are the comparison results using FFT-ANN and ARMA-ANN approaches. In addition, we have experienced the AR-ANN approach, which is a simplified ARMA-ANN approach. We applied 10 sample time series signals to train the ANN and other 20 samples for ANN testing, for each SNR levels at 10dB, 0dB, and -10dB. The number of hidden neurons were 10, 15 and 30 respectively.

A. FFT-ANN Approach

With the FFT estimated spectra as the input to the ANNs, the back-propagation training algorithm converged right after 10,000 iterations. Table I listed the percentage of successful identifications of sample time series signal sets with various SNR levels. Obviously the FFT-ANN method worked well for signals with 10dB SNR level. The

TABLE I
TEST AND COMPARISON RESULTS FROM FFT-ANN APPROACH

	10 hidden elements	15 hidden elements	30 hidden elements
10 dB	100%	100%	100%
0 dB	93.4%	96.7%	93.4%
-10 dB	76.9%	76.9%	76.9%

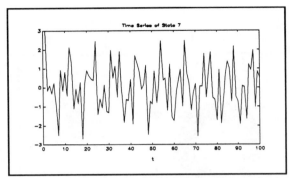

Fig. 6. Sample vibration signals with ball, inner race, and outer race defections (no noise added).

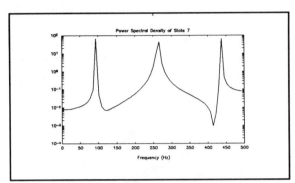

Fig. 7. Frequency distribution of sampled vibration signals (no noise added).

performance downgraded slightly at 0dB level. However, with SNR at -10dB level, the error representing mis-classified signals jumped to 20% so the overall performance is not satisfactory.

B. ARMA-ANN Approach

In this experiment we used the spectra obtained from ARMA(7,6) models to train and test the ANNs. The same as before, the back-propagation training algorithm converged right after 10,000 iterations, and the results are listed in Table II. As we expected, the ARMA-ANN approach performed much better than FFT-ANN approach at 0dB and -10dB level.

TABLE II

TEST AND COMPARISON RESULTS FROM ARMA-ANN APPROACH

	10 hidden elements	15 hidden elements	30 hidden elements
10 dB	100%	100%	100%
0 dB	100%	100%	100%
-10 dB	90.1%	93.4%	90.1%

C. AR-ANN Approach

Auto-regressive (AR) model is a simplified ARMA model that does not contain moving average parameters. The benefits of using AR model are that the model is simple and the parameter estimation algorithm is linear and thus is computational efficient. In this experiment the adequate model was determined as AR(6). The spectral estimates were obtained by using similar formula as expression (7). Surprisingly, the ANN converged with 6000

iterations, and test results are listed in Table III.

TABLE III

TEST AND COMPARISON RESULTS FROM AR-ANN APPROACH

	10 hidden elements	15 hidden elements	30 hidden elements
10 dB	100%	100%	100%
0 dB	100%	100%	100%
-10 dB	96.7%	96.7%	96.7%

D. Summary

It can be seen clearly from the above discussions that the new hybrid ARMA modeling and ANN approach demonstrates a superior performance over the conventional FFT-ANN approach for vibration signal identification application with low SNRs. The simplified AR-ANN approach provides a simple but effective

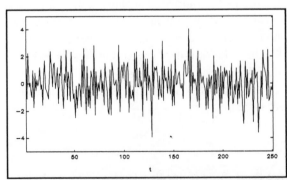

Fig. 8. Noise-Added sample vibration signals with ball, inner race, and outer race defections.

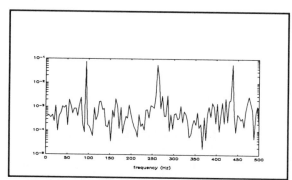

Fig. 9. Spectral estimate of sampled signals of Fig. 8. obtained from FFT.

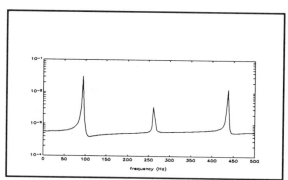

Fig. 10. Spectral estimate obtained from ARMA(7,6) spectral estimator.

approach as an alternate to the ARMA-ANN approach. Also it appeared that there is no significant improvement in ANN's performance as the number of hidden neurons increases. Table IV summarizes the percentage of successful identifications for three spectral estimation methods using ANNs with 15 hidden neurons:

TABLE IV

COMPARISON OF RESULTS WITH 15 HIDDEN NEURONS ANN

SNR Level	Fourier Spectrum	ARMA model	AR model
10 dB	100%	100%	100%
0 dB	96.7%	100%	100%
-10 dB	76.9%	93.4%	96.7%

VI. CONCLUSIONS

In this paper, we propose a new approach that uses ARMA model as the high quality spectral estimation method and ANN as the pattern classifier for application of high noise time series signal identification. The new approach indeed show a better performance over the FFT-ANN method with low SNR signals. The new method is practical to use so it can be applied to a variety of industrial applications.

One remaining problem of using ARMA modeling technology is that the parameter estimation method is nonlinear, which is time consuming and may cause instability during modeling process. So the AR modeling method is more preferred because of its simplicity, stability, and easy of use.

REFERENCES

[1] J. M. Mendel, "Use of high-order statistics in signal processing and system theory: an update," *Proceedings, SPIE Conference on Advanced Algorithms and Architectures for Signal Processing*, Vol. 3, pp. 126-144, San Diego, 1988.

[2] S. Chakrabarti and N. Bindal, "*Radar target discrimination using artificial neural networks*," *Proceedings, The Artificial Neural Networks in Engineering (ANNIE'91) Conference*, St.Louis, Missouri, Nov. 1991.

[3] B. Kosko, *Neural Networks for Signal Processing*, Prentice-Hall, 1991.

[4] B. Kosko, *Neural Networks and Fuzzy Systems*, Prentice-Hall, 1991.

[5] S. Grossburg, *Studies of Mind and Brain*, Riedel, Boston, 1982.

[6] S. M. Pandit and S. M. Wu, *Time Series and System Analysis with Applications*, John Wiley, New York, 1983.

[7] M.B. Priestly, *Spectral Analysis and Time Series*, Vols. 1 and 2, Academic Press, New York, 1981.

[8] R. G. Gan, K. F. Eman, and S. M. Wu, "An extended FFT algorithm for arma spectral estimation," *IEEE Transactions on Acoustics, Speech, and Signal Processing*, Vol. ASSP-32, No. 1, pp. 168-170, Feb. 1984.

[9] R. P.Gorman and T. J. Sejnowski, "Analysis of hidden units in a layered network trained to classify sonar targets," *Neural Networks*, Vol. 1, pp. 75-89, 1989.

[10] X. Feng and T. P. Moerke, "A new combined and data visualization method for computer system performance and capacity planning," *Proceedings, IEEE SouthCon/92*, March, 1992.

[11] X. Feng and R. A. Clinkenbeard, "An Unsupervised Learning and Fuzzy Logic Approach for Software Category Identification and Capacity Planning," *Proceedings, International Joint Conference on Neural Networks (IJCNN)*, Vol. 2, pp. 272-277, June, 1992.

[12] W. T. Thomson, *Theory of Vibration with Applications*, Prentice-Hall, New Jersey, 1984.

[13] G. E. P. Box and G. M. Jenkins, *Time Series Analysis: Forecasting and Control*, Holden-Day, San Francisco, 1970.

Accepted by '1993 IEEE International Conference on Neural Networks, San Francisco, CA'

Results of the Time Series Prediction Competition
at the Santa Fe Institute

Andreas S. Weigend

Xerox PARC

3333 Coyote Hill Road

Palo Alto, CA 94304

phone: (415) 812–4765

fax: (415) 812–4241

weigend@cs.colorado.edu

Neil A. Gershenfeld

Media Lab and Department of Physics

MIT / E15-425

Cambridge, MA 02139

phone: (617) 253–7680

fax: (617) 258–6264

neilg@media.mit.edu

Abstract. From August 1991 onward, a set of time series was made generally available at the Santa Fe Institute. Several prediction tasks were specified and advertised. We here analyze the the submissions that we received before the deadline when the true continuations were revealed. One result is that connectionist networks, trained with error back-propagation, outperformed the other methods on all series. Among the architectures that performed best was a time delay neural network (also called finite impulse response network) and a recurrent network, designed to capture the multiple time scales present in currency exchange rates.

1 Motivation

Most observational disciplines, including physics, biology and finance, try to infer properties of an unfamiliar system from the analysis of a measured time record of its behavior. There are mature techniques associated with traditional time series analysis. During the last decade, new approaches such as neural networks have emerged, promising insights not available with these standard methods. However, the evaluation of this promise has been difficult. Adequate benchmarks were lacking, and most of the literature has been fragmentary and anecdotal.

Global computer networks enabled these disjoint communities to attack these problems through the widespread exchange of data and information. In order to foster this process, we organized the *Time Series Prediction and Analysis Competition* under the auspices of the Santa Fe Institute during the fall of 1991. With the assistance of an advisory board from the relevant disciplines, we selected a group of data sets that cover a broad range of interesting attributes. The data was made generally available at **ftp.santafe.edu** (and will remain publicly accessible there).

The participants in the competition were asked to submit:

- Forecasts of the continuation of the data sets (that were withheld).
- Analyses of the number of degrees of freedom, the noise characteristics, and the nonlinearity of the system.
- Models of the governing equations.
- Descriptions of the algorithms employed.

In order to explore the results of the contest, we organized a *NATO Advanced Research Workshop* in the spring of 1992. Workshop participants included members of the advisory board, representatives of the groups that had collected the data, participants in the contest, and some interested observers. Although the participants came from a broad range of disciplines, the discussions were framed by the analysis of common data sets and hence it was usually possible to find a meaningful common ground. In this paper, we focus on the first two data sets; more details can be found in the book edited by Weigend and Gershenfeld [WG93].

2   Datasets and Tasks

We selected the following data sets for the competition and workshop:

- A clean physics laboratory experiment (NH_3 laser).
- A computer generated series designed for this competition.
- Tick-by-tick currency exchange rate data (Swiss Franc – US Dollar).
- Astrophysical data from a variable white dwarf star.
- Physiological data from a patient with sleep apnea.
- J. S. Bach's last (unfinished) fugue from *Die Kunst der Fuge.*

Figure 1 shows 1,000 points of the first three series each as a function of time. Some of the characteristics of the four sets with prediction tasks are summarized in *Table 1*. The remaining sets were only used in the analysis category, not in the prediction category.

	laser	synthetic	exchange rates	music
origin	physics laboratory	computer	a Swiss bank	human
characterization	low-dim det chaos	high-dim det chaos	stochastic (?)	fugue
noise	clean	some	noisy	
stationarity	stationary	small drift	several time scales	
length	1,000	100,000	30,000	3,808
predict:	100 values & errors	500 values	60 values (total)	*ad lib*

Table 1: Attributes of the sets with prediction tasks.

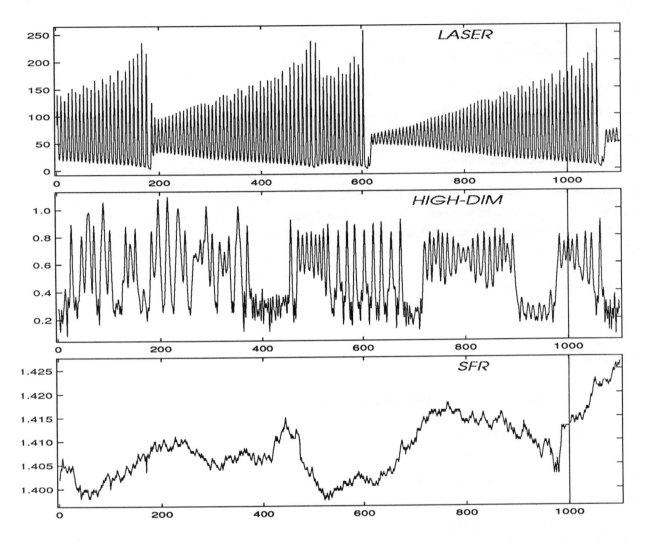

Figure 1: *Graphs of the laser series, the high-dimensional synthetic series and the tickwise exchange rate data, plotted on the same time scale. The 1000 points for the Swiss Franc data correspond to March 21 to March 25, 1991.*

2.1 Error measures

A standard measure to evaluate the quality of predictions is the **normalized mean squared error**,[1]

$$\text{NMSE}(N) = \frac{\sum_{k \in \mathcal{T}} \left(\text{observation}_k - \text{prediction}_k\right)^2}{\sum_{k \in \mathcal{T}} \left(\text{observation}_k - \text{mean}_{\mathcal{T}}\right)^2} \approx \frac{1}{\widehat{\sigma}_{\mathcal{T}}^2} \frac{1}{N} \sum_{k \in \mathcal{T}} (x_k - \widehat{x}_k)^2 \tag{1}$$

$k = 1 \cdots N$ enumerates the patterns in the held-back test set $\mathcal{T}$. $\text{mean}_{\mathcal{T}}$ and $\widehat{\sigma}_{\mathcal{T}}^2$ denote average and variance of the target values in $\mathcal{T}$. A value of $\text{NMSE} = 1$ thus corresponds to the value obtained by simply predicting the average.

For the laser data, we also asked to submit an estimate of the uncertainty of the predictions. The contributions were evaluated according to a likelihood criterion: Assuming a Gaussian error distribution for the observed data, and given

---

[1]We use **NMSE** as abbreviation rather than an abbreviation for relative mean squared error in order to avoid confusion with its square root, the rms or root-mean-squared error.

that the experimental resolution was one count, [2] the probability that an observation $x_k \pm 0.5$ was generated by a Gaussian with center $\widehat{x}_k$ and width $\widehat{\sigma}_k$ is given by the likelihood

$$p(x_k|\widehat{x}_k, \widehat{\sigma}_k) = \frac{1}{\sqrt{2\pi\widehat{\sigma}_k^2}} \int_{x_k-0.5}^{x_k+0.5} \exp{-\frac{(\xi - \widehat{x}_k)^2}{2\widehat{\sigma}_k^2}} \, \mathrm{d}\xi \quad . \tag{2}$$

In other words, k's contribution to the overall likelihood is given by the area between $x_k - 0.5$ and $x_k + 0.5$ under a Gaussian of the estimated width, centered at the prediction value. If the uncertainty is underestimated and the predicted value is not very close to the observed value, the value is very small. If the width is overestimated, the normalization (the factor in front of the integral) suppresses the contribution with $1/\widehat{\sigma}_k$. Hence, both too small and too large estimates of the uncertainty reduce the likelihood that the observation was "generated" by the prediction, or the "model".

To obtain the likelihood of the entire test set, we assume independence of each test point. The individual likelihoods can then be multiplied to obtain the probability of the data given the model,

$$p(\mathrm{D}|\mathrm{M}) = \prod_{k=1}^{N} p(x_k|\widehat{x}_k, \widehat{\sigma}_k) \quad . \tag{3}$$

To avoid too small numbers, we take the negative logarithm. In order to get a quantity that is independent of the size of the test set, we normalize by the number of points N in set $\mathcal{T}$, and thus finally obtain the **negative average log-Likelihood, nalL**

$$-\frac{1}{N} \sum_{k=1}^{N} \log p(x_k|\widehat{x}_k, \widehat{\sigma}_k) = \frac{1}{N} \sum_{k=1}^{N} -\log \left[\mathrm{pnorm}(x_k + 0.5; \widehat{x}_k, \widehat{\sigma}_k) - \mathrm{pnorm}(x_k - 0.5; \widehat{x}_k, \widehat{\sigma}_k) \right] \tag{4}$$

where $\mathrm{pnorm}(\xi; x, \sigma)$ denotes the cumulative probability of a Gaussian centered at x with standard deviation σ,

$$\mathrm{pnorm}(\xi; x, \sigma) = \frac{1}{\sqrt{2\pi\sigma^2}} \int_{-\infty}^{\xi} \exp{-\frac{(\xi - x)^2}{2\sigma^2}} \, \mathrm{d}\xi \quad . \tag{5}$$

Having defined the error criteria, we now turn to the submissions we received.

3 Entries and Evaluation

3.1 Laser data

Table 2 lists the methods applied to the laser data, the computers and CPU time required, as well as the relative mean square error the negative average log-likelihood. The submitted continuations of the laser are shown in *Figure 2*.

In *Figure 2* and *Table 2*, the letter *W* refers to the entry by Eric Wan. This architecture was presented at the 1990 Connectionist Models Summer School [Wan90] and is also desribed in [WG93]. The key idea is that each weight gets replaced by a tapped delay line. This architecture is equivalent to a time delay neural network.

---

[2]The signal to noise ratio is 300:1, and the data was quantized to 8 bits and given as integers.

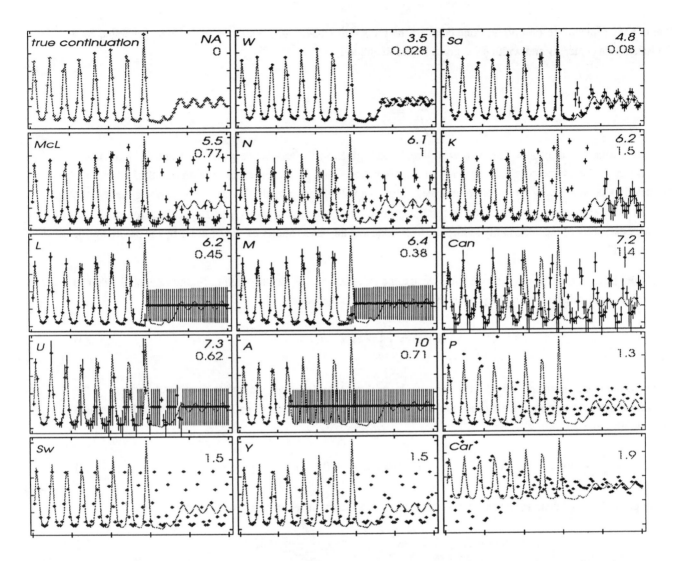

Figure 2: *Predicted continuations of the laser data. The letters correspond to the code of the entrant, the upper figure measures (the averaged negative logarithm of) the likelihood that the data were generated by the model, the lower number is the averaged normalized sum squared error.*

3.2 Synthetic data

We now turn to the second data set, the high-dimensional data that we generated for the competition. *Table 3* lists the entries received. Since all of the contributions deteriorate fairly quickly, we give the normalized sum squared error only averaged over the first 15 and the first 30 predictions. The first 30 points of the submitted predictions are shown with the true continuation in *Figure 3*.

In *Figure 3* and *Table 3*, the code *ZH* refers to the entry by Zhang and Hutchinson (in [WG93]), who trained a total of 108 different networks, each of which estimated predictions for different numbers of steps ahead. Two distinct network architectures were used, one type for the first 10 predictions, and the second for the remaining 490 predictions; all networks had 100 hidden units. The first type of network predicted some number of temporal positions using the last 20 data points from the data set, plus the predictions from "earlier" networks. The second type of network predicted five temporal positions, using the last 20 data points from the data set, plus 10 more sparsely sampled data

	method		computer	time	NMSE(100)	nalL
W	conn	1-12-12-1; lag 25,5,5	SPARC 2	12 hrs	0.028	3.5
Sa	loc lin	low-pass embd, 8 dim, 4nn	DEC 3100	20 min	0.080	4.8
McL	conn	feedforward, 200-100-1	CRAY Y-MP	3 hrs	0.77	5.5
N	conn	feedforward, 50-20-1	SPARC 1	3 weeks	1.0	6.1
K	visual	look for similar stretches	SG Iris	10 sec	1.5	6.2
L	visual				0.45	6.2
M	conn	feedforward, 50-350-50-50	386 PC	5 days	0.38	6.4
Can	conn	recurrent, 4-4c-1	VAX 8530	1 hr	1.4	7.2
U	tree	k-d tree; AIC	VAX 6420	20 min	0.62	7.3
A	loc lin	21 dim, 30 nearest neighb's	SPARC 2	1 min	0.71	10.
P	loc lin	3 dim time delay	Sun	10 min	1.3	-
Sw	conn	feedforward	SPARC 2	20 hrs	1.5	-
Y	conn	feedforward, weight-decay	SPARC 1	30 min	1.5	-
Car	linear	Wiener filter, width 100	MIPS 3230	30 min	1.9	-

Table 2: Entries received before the deadline for the prediction of the laser. NMSE gives the normalized sum squared error (or relative mean square error), nalL gives the negative logarithm of the likelihod of the data given the predicted values and predicted errors, averaged over the prediction set.

points extending further back in history. They found that direct predictions (a different network for each position) worked better than iterated predictions.

3.3 Money, Music, the Stars and the Heart

In this paper, space limited us to focus on only two out of the six data sets. The remaining results are discussed in the book edited by Weigend and Gershenfeld [WG93]. It consists of of three parts:

1. **Overview.** In the first part, we present the results of the competition and the workshop and analyze the advantages and disadvantages of the various techniques both in time series prediction and in characterization. In the area of prediction, recurring themes include the importance for careful assessments of the statistical reliability of the results, and the need to match the level of description of the model to the system being studied (from deterministic low-dimensional dynamics to stochastic processes). In the area of characterization, several techniques are presented that try to estimate the number of degrees of freedom of the system or the rate at which the system loses memory of its state. A common feature here is the desire to reduce the sensitivity to geometrical artifacts abundant in standard methods (such as correlation dimensions and Lyapunov exponents). The methods discussed include information-based measures as well as estimators based on evaluating the reliability of the embedding.

2. **Details.** In the central part, fifteen scientists who applied their methods to the data, motivate and describe their ideas in individual chapters. Although from a wide variety of different disciplines (statistics, experimental and

	method		computer	time	NMSE(15)	NMSE(30)
ZH	conn	...-30-30-1 and 30-100-5	CM-2 (16k)	8 days	0.086	0.57
U	tree	k-d tree; AIC	VAX 6420	30 min	1.3	1.4
C	conn	recurrent, 4-4c-1	VAX 8530	n/a	6.4	3.2
W	conn	1-30-30-1; lags 20,5,5	SPARC 2	1 day	7.1	3.4
Z	linear	36 AR(8), last 4k points	SPARC	10 min	4.8	5.0
S	conn	feedforward	SPARC 2	20 hrs	17.	9.5

Table 3: *Entries received before the deadline for the prediction of the high-dimensional, synthetic data.*

computational physics, electrical and mechanical engineering, economics and finance, biology and medicine, musicology and others), all contributors focus on the same sets of data. Their strictly refereed contributions are as self-contained as possible.

3. **Data.** In the third part, the scientists who contributed the time series describe the scientific questions behind their data and the kinds of models typical in their home disciplines. They then analyze their data with the current methods in their respective fields, and finally gauge what they have learned from the new techniques that were applied to their data in the competition and at the workshop.

4 Discussion

In this competition and subsequent workshop, we brought together scientists from different disciplines predicting and analyzing temporal sequences: statistics, experimental and computational physics, electrical and mechanical engineering, economics and finance, music, etc. Quite to our surprise, it turned out that connectionist networks consistently outperformed all other methods received, ranging from visual predictions to sophisticated noise reduction techniques.

Although all the networks that did well used some form of error back-propagation, its blind application did clearly not guarantee success. The successful architectures all tried to capture some of the specific temporal issues for temporal sequences. In particular, among the architectures that performed best was a time delay neural network (also called finite impulse response network), a large set of feed-forward network for each sub-task, and a recurrent network designed to capture multiple time scales.

Acknowledgements. We thank Udo Hübner from the *Physikalisch-Technische Bundesanstalt* in Braunschweig, Ary Goldberger and David Rigney from *Beth Israel Hospital and Harvard Medical School* in Boston, Don Winget, James Dixon and Chris Clemens from the *Department of Astronomy and McDonald Observatory, University of Texas at Austin*, a member of a Swiss bank, and Johann Sebastian Bach from the *Thomaskirche zu Leipzig* for the data. We also thank all competition entrants for their submissions.

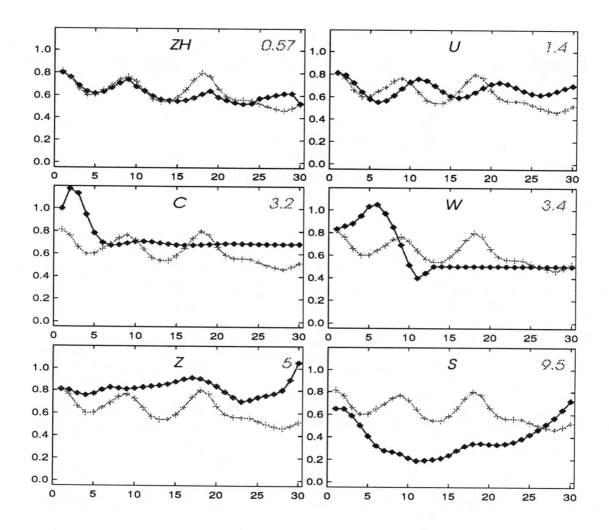

Figure 3: Predicted continuations of the synthetic data. The numbers are the normalized sum squared errors, averaged over 30 steps.

References

[Wan90] Wan, Eric A. *Temporal backpropagation: An efficient algorithm for finite impulse response neural networks*. In Touretzky, D. S., Elman, J. L., Sejnowski, T. J., and Hinton, G. E., editors, *Proceedings of the 1990 Connectionist Models Summer School*, pages 131–137. Morgan Kaufmann, 1990.

[WG93] Weigend, Andreas S. and Gershenfeld, Neil A., editors. **Predicting the Future and Understanding the Past: a Comparison of Approaches.** *(Proceedings of the NATO Advanced Research Workshop on Time Series Analysis and Forecasting held in Santa Fe, New Mexico, May 1992)*, Santa Fe Institute Studies in the Sciences of Complexity. Addison-Wesley, 1993.

Simultaneous Discovery of Detectors and a Way of Using the Detectors via Genetic Programming

John R. Koza
Computer Science Department
Margaret Jacks Hall
Stanford University
Stanford, California 94305
Koza@cs.stanford.edu
415-941-0336

Abstract—Conventional approaches to problems of pattern recognition and machine learning usually require that the user hand-craft detectors for key features in the problem environment. Conventional approaches often additionally require the user to specify in advance the size and shape of the eventual way of combining the detectors into a compete solution. This paper describes a general approach for simultaneously discovering detectors and a way of combining the detectors to solve a problem via genetic programming with automatic function definition. Genetic programming provides a way to genetically breed a computer program to solve a wide variety of problems. Automatic function definition automatically and dynamically enables genetic programming to define potentially useful functions dynamically during a run and to facilitate a solution of a problem by automatically and dynamically decomposing the problem into simpler subproblems. This approach is illustrated with a problem of letter recognition.

I   Introduction and Overview

Conventional approaches to pattern recognition and machine learning usually require that the user hand-craft detectors for key features in the problem environment. Conventional approaches often additionally require the user to specify in advance the size and shape of the eventual way of combining the detectors into a compete solution. However, in many instances, finding the detectors and a way of combining the detectors in order to solve the problem really is *the problem*. Indeed, the necessity for pre-identification of the particular components of solutions and the necessity for pre-determination of a way of combining these components has been recognized as a bane of machine learning starting with Samuel's ground-breaking work in machine learning involving learning to play the game of checkers [Samuel [1959].

In Samuel's checker player, learning consisted of progressively adjusting numerical coefficients in an algebraic expression of a predetermined functional form (specifically, a polynomial of specified order). Each component term of the polynomial represented a hand-crafted detector reflecting some aspect of the current state of the board (e.g., number of pieces, center control, etc.). The polynomial weighted each detector with a numerical coefficient and thereby assigned a single numerical value of a board to the player. If a polynomial were good at assigning values to boards, the polynomial could be used to compare the boards that would arise if the player were to make various alternative moves – thus permitting the best move to be selected from among the alternatives on the basis of the polynomial. In Samuel's learning system, the numerical coefficients of the polynomial were adjusted with experience, so that the predictive quality of the polynomial progressively improved. Samuel predetermined the way the detectors would be combined to solve the problem by selecting the functional form of the polynomial. Samuel recognized, from the beginning, the importance of enabling learning to occur without predetermining the size and shape of the solution and of "[getting] the program to generate its own parameters [detectors] for the evaluation polynomial."

This paper describes a general approach for simultaneously discovering detectors and a way of combining the detectors to solve a problem. The approach involves using genetic programming with automatic function definition to evolve a solution to the problem.

Genetic programming provides a way to search the space of all possible programs composed of certain terminals and primitive functions to find a function which solves, or approximately solves, a problem.

Automatic function definition enables genetic programming to define potentially useful functions automatically and dynamically during a run and also to combine these defined functions dynamically during a run in order to solve a problem.

Since the metaphor of a detector is especially apt in the field of pattern recognition, our general approach will be illustrated by means of a problem from the field of pattern recognition.

Sections I, III, and VI of the article by Koza, Keane, and Rice [1993] in these ICNN-93 proceedings provide necessary background on genetic programming and automatic function definition for this article.

Section II of this article states the illustrative pattern recognition problem. Section III details the preparatory steps for applying genetic programming with automatic function definition to the problem. Section IV describes a solution to the problem.

II   Letter Recognition Problem

Since the metaphor of a detector is especially apt in the field of pattern recongition, we will illustrate our approach to the problem of finding detectors and finding a way to combine them with a problem of letter recognition from the field of pattern recognition.

Fig. 1 shows the letters I and L, each presented in a 6 by 4 pixel grid of binary (ON or OFF) values.

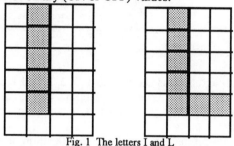

Fig. 1 The letters I and L

The goal of pattern recognition is to discover a computer program that can take any of the 2^{24} possible patterns of bits as its input and produce a correct identification I, L, or NIL (i.e., not the letter I or the letter L) for the pattern as its output.

Note that the correct identification of a pattern of pixels requires not only establishing that all the specific pixels that must be ON are indeed ON, but also inspecting other pixels on the grid to exclude the possiblity of an imperfect letter or another letter.

Fig. 2 shows two patterns that are neither the letter I nor the letter L. The pattern on the left has a misplaced ON pixel in the lower right hand corner of the grid instead of as the rightmost pixel of the bottom of the L. The second pattern has a missing ON pixel in an otherwise correct letter L.

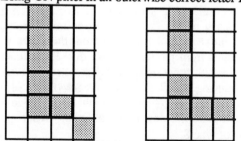

Fig. 2 Two patterns that should not be recognized as the letter L

There are, of course, many different ways to structure a computer program to perform the task of letter recognition. The particular approach presented in this paper was chosen to illustrate and emphasize the discovery of *local* detectors and *hierarchical* combinations of the detectors to solve a problem.

If one were trying to verbally describe the letter L to someone who was not familiar with the Roman alphabet, one might give a dynamic description involving drawing a vertical line of five pixels downwards (south) from some specified starting location in the 6 by 4 grid and then drawing a horizontal line of two pixels to the right (east). This dynamic description of the pattern contains both locally-acting and hierarchical aspects. This can be implemented using a slow-moving turtle with limited vision. The turtle

starts at a designated starting location on the grid and can move one step at a time to the north (up), south (down), east (right), or west (left). The turtle's vision is limited to its immediate neighborhood consisting of the nine pixels centered at its current location. The one pixel where the turtle is currently located is called "X" (center) and the eight neighboring pixels at distance one are called N, NE, E, SE, S, SW, W, and NW.

One way to structure a computer program to recognize letters is for the "main" result-producing branch to be a decision tree that produces a return value consisting of an identification of the pattern (I, L, or NIL). The use of a decision tree structure in the result-producing branch permits easy handling of arbitrary numbers of possible outcomes. The result-producing branch will activate various alternative actions and, ultimately, return an identification of the pattern. The desired bias toward local inspection and hierarchical combination can be attained by specifying that the result-producing branch of the program will be capable of moving the turtle but only capable of sensing the single pixel where the turtle is currently located. The result-producing branch will not have direct access to the any other pixel sensors; however, it may call on the detectors. The result-producing branch will contain logical predicates consisting of compositions of Boolean conjunctions, disjunctions, and negations operating on the values returned by the detectors.

The function-defining branches define detectors that examine the entire nine-pixel local neighborhood of the turtle and evaluate logical predicates involving what the turtle sees. Thus, the function definitions will be compositions of the Boolean conjunctions, disjunctions, and negations and the nine pixel sensors (X, N, NE, E, SE, S, SW, W, and NW). For example, the function definition

```
(defun vertical-line ()
  (values (AND N X S (NOT SW) (NOT W) (NOT NW)
              (NOT SE) (NOT E) (NOT NE))))
```

is a detector that returns T only if the turtle is currently located at the midpoint of a vertical line segment consisting of three ON pixels surrounded on both sides by three OFF pixels. Note that there are no dummy variables in this defun since the nine pixel sensors are global variables established by virtue of the turtle's current location on the grid.

III   Preparatory Steps for Using Genetic Programming

In what follows, we apply genetic programming with automatic function definition to the problem of letter recognition described above.

We decided that each individual overall S-expression in the population will consist of five function-defining branches (defining detectors called ADF0 through ADF4) and a final (rightmost) result-producing branch.

Genetic programming will evolve function definitions in the five function-defining branches of each overall S-expression and then, at its discretion, it will call some, all, or none of the defined functions (detectors) in the result-producing branch. The structures of both the function-defining branches and the result-producing branch are determined by the combined effect, over many generations, of the selective pressure exerted by the convolution-based fitness measure and by the effects of the operations of Darwinian fitness proportionate reproduction and crossover.

There are five major steps in preparing to use genetic programming, namely determining

(1) the set of terminals,
(2) the set of primitive functions,
(3) the fitness measure,
(4) the parameters for controlling the run, and
(5) the method for designating a result and the criterion for terminating a run.

The terminal sets and function sets are different for the function-defining branches and the result-producing branch of each individual S-expression in the population.

We first consider the five function-defining branches (i.e., the detectors).

Since the function-defining branches are to define detectors which are capable of analyzing what the turtle sees at its current location on the grid, the terminal set T_{fd} for each function-defining branch consists of the nine pixel sensors, so that

$$T_{fd} = \{X, N, NE, E, SE, S, SW, W, NW\}.$$

The function set F_{fd} for the function-defining branch is

$$F_{fd} = \{AND, OR, NOT\},$$

taking 2, 2, and 1 argument, respectively. Note that there are no side-effecting functions in the function-defining branches.

Each function-defining branch is a composition of primitive functions from the function set F_{fd} and terminals from the terminal set T_{fd}.

We now consider the result-producing branch.

We envision that the result-producing branch of each program will be a decision tree which consists of compositions of decision-making functions to return the identification I, L, or NIL. Thus, the terminal set T_{rp} for the result-producing branch is

$$T_{rp} = \{I, L, NIL\}.$$

Since the result-producing branch is to be a decision tree, its function set will include the three-argument conditional decision-making "IF-THEN-ELSE" operator. This operator is implemented as a macro as described in Koza [1992a].

The function set of the result-producing branch will also contain eight operators that can move the turtle one step in any one of the eight possible directions from its current location. For example, the side-effecting operator (GO-N) would move the turtle north (up) one step in the 6 by 4 grid. As the turtle moves, the values of the nine pixel sensors (X, N, NE, E, SE, S, SW, W, and NW) are dynamically redefined. For simplicity, the grid is toroidal. These eight operators take no arguments. Each operator returns the value (T or NIL) of the pixel to which the turtle moves (i.e., it returns the new X).

The one-argument HOMING operator evaluates its argument and, in addition, has the side effect of rubber-banding the turtle to its position at the start of the evaluation of the HOMING. HOMING is equivalent to the brackets in a Lindenmayer system.

The Boolean functions AND, OR, and NOT are included in the function set to enable the result-producing branch to define logical predicates.

Finally, the five automatically defined functions (ADF0 through ADF0) that constitute the detectors are included in the function set of the result-producing branch. These five defined functions take no arguments.

Thus, the function set F_{rp} for the result-producing branch is

$$F_{rp} = \{IF, AND, OR, NOT, HOMING, ADF0, \\ ADF1, ADF2, ADF3, ADF4, GO-N, \\ GO-NE, GO-E, GO-SE, GO-S, \\ GO-SW, GO-W, GO-NE\},$$

The first five functions above take 3, 2, 2, 1, and 1 argument, respectively, and the remaining functions take no arguments (and could, optionally, if desired, have been treated as terminals).

The result-producing branch is a composition of primitive functions from the function set F_{rp} and terminals from the terminal set T_{rp}.

Note that the above terminal sets and function sets satisfy the closure property in that each primitive function in the function set is well defined for any combination of arguments from the range of values returned by every primitive function that it may encounter and the value of every terminal that it may encounter.

Since each individual S-expression in the population consists of five function-defining branches and one result-producing branch, we must create the initial random generation so that every individual S-expression in the population has this particular constrained syntactic structure. Specifically, every individual S-expression must have the invariant structure represented by the six points of types 1 through 6 described in Section VI of Koza, Keane and Rice [1993]. Each of the five function-defining branches is a random composition of functions from the function set F_{fd} and terminals from the terminal set T_{fd}. Each function and terminal in each function-defining branch is of type 7. The result-producing branch is a random composition of functions from the function set F_{rp} and terminals from the terminal set T_{rp}. Each function and terminal in the result-producing branch is of type 8.

Moreover, since a constrained syntactic structure is involved, we must perform crossover so as to preserve the syntactic validity of all offspring as the run proceeds from generation to generation. Since each S-expression must have the invariant structure represented by the six points of types 1 through 6, crossover is limited to points of types 7 and 8. Structure-preserving crossover is implemented by allowing any point of type 7 or 8 in any branch of the overall S-expression to be the crossover point in the first parent. However, once the crossover point in the first parent has been selected, the crossover point of the second parent must be of the same type. In practice, this means that crossover will only exchange a sub-tree from a function-defining branch with a sub-tree from another function-defining branch or that crossover will exchange a sub-tree from a result-producing branch with a sub-tree from another result-producing branch. This restriction on the selection of the crossover point of the second parent ensures the syntactic validity of the offspring.

Because of the complexity of the solutions evolved by genetic programming for this problem, we discovered, after initially solving this problem, that imposing an additional constrained syntactic structure on the result-producing branch would greatly enhance our ability to understand the solution. Specifically, we constrained the first (antecedent) argument of each IF operator to be a composition of the three Boolean functions (AND, OR, NOT), the five automatically defined functions (ADF0 through ADF4), the eight turtle-moving operators (e.g., GO-N), and the HOMING function. In addition, we constrained the two consequent arguments of each IF operator to be compositions of the IF operator and the terminals (I, L, and NIL). These additional syntactic contraints had the helpful effect of clearly isolating and highlighting the structure of the decision tree within the result-producing branch. Thus, the original type 8 was subdivided into types 8a and 8b. As before, the initial random population was randomly generated in comformity with these new constraints and structure-preserving crossover was performed to preserve the new syntactic structure (now involving types 7, 8a, or 8b).

The third major step in preparing to use genetic programming is the identification of the fitness measure for evaluating the goodness of each pattern-recognizing individual in the population. The fitness cases for genetic programming are chosen to represent a sufficient variety of situations so that the program is likely to generalize to handle all possible combinations of inputs. In this regard, the fitness cases are similar to the necessarily small, finite number of combinations of inputs used to test and debug computer programs.

Each individual in the population is tested against an environment consisting of N_{fc} = 78 fitness cases, each consisting of a 6 by 4 pixel pattern and the correct identification (I, L, or NIL) for that pattern. The set of fitness cases included the two letters (i.e., the positive cases) and 76 different negative fitness cases. The negative cases included every version of the letters I and L with one ON pixel deleted; every version of the letters I and L with one extraneous ON pixel added adjacent to the correct pixels; checkerboard patterns; the all-ON and all-OFF pattern; various patterns bearing some resemblance to I, L, or other letters; and various random patterns bearing no resemblance to I, L, or other letters.

When an individual S-expression in the population is tested against a particular fitness case, the result can be a true-positive (i.e., the individual correctly identifies an I as an I or an L as an L), a true-negative (i.e., a pattern that is not an I or L is correctly identified as NIL), a false-positive (i.e., a non-letter is identified as a letter), a false-negative (i.e., a letter is identified as a non-letter), or a wrong-positive (i.e., an I is identified as an L or an L is identified as an I).

For this problem, fitness is the sum, over the fitness cases, of the weighted errors produced by the S-expression. The smaller the sum of weighted errors, the better. A 100%

correct pattern-recognizer would have a fitness of zero. True-postives and true-negatives contribute zero to this sum. False-positives contribute 38 (in order to give the two positive cases equal weight with the 76 negative cases). Wrong-positives contribute one. False-negatives contribute 23 (i.e., the number of pixels minus one) to maintain consistency with work not described herein involving translation-invariant pattern recognition and cellular automata.

The fourth major step in preparing to use genetic programming is the selection of values for certain parameters. Our choice of 8,000 as the population size and our choice of 101 as the maximum number of generations to be run reflect an estimate on our part as to the likely difficulty of this problem and the practical limitations on available computer time and memory. Our choice of values for the various secondary parameters that control a run of genetic programming are the same default values as we have consistently used on numerous other problems [Koza 1992a], except that we continue our recently adopted practice of using tournament selection (with a group size of seven) as the selection method.

Finally, the fifth major step in preparing to use genetic programming is the selection of the criterion for terminating a run and the selection of the method for designating a result. We will terminate a given run if we encounter a 100% correct individual or after 101 generations. We designate the best individual obtained during the run (the best-so-far individual) as the result of the run.

IV   Results for One Run

A review of one particular successful run will serve to illustrate how genetic programming simultaneously evolves the detectors and a way of combining the detectors for the problem of letter recognition.

A Discovery of Solution for One Run

The 8,000 randomly generated individuals found in the initial generation of the population (generation 0) are, as one would expect, not very good. The fitness of the worst individual pattern-recognizer in the population for generation 0 has 44 points (i.e., functions and terminals in the body of its five function-defining branches and its result-returning branch) and has the enormous unfavorable fitness (error) of 3,535. However, even in a randomly created population of programs, some individuals are better than others. For example, an individual at the 33rd percentile of generation 0 has fitness of 1,771.

The best individual from generation 0 has 186 points, has a fitness of 53, and is shown below:

```
(PROGN (DEFUN ADF0 ()
        (VALUES (OR (OR (AND (OR S X) (OR N SW))
        (OR (OR N E) (AND S NW))) (AND (OR (NOT
        S) (AND S SE)) (OR (AND W SE) (NOT
        N))))))))
       (DEFUN ADF1 ()
        (VALUES (AND (AND (NOT (NOT X)) (NOT (OR
        S X))) (OR (AND (AND SW NW) (NOT SW))
        (NOT (AND N SW))))))))
```

```
(DEFUN ADF2 ()
  (VALUES (OR (AND (NOT (AND W E)) (OR
  (AND NW W) (NOT NW))) (OR (OR (AND N E)
  (AND S SE)) (OR (AND W SE) (OR SE
  NE))))))
(DEFUN ADF3 ()
  (VALUES (AND (NOT (AND (NOT SE) (OR W
  SW))) (OR (NOT (OR NW NE)) (AND (NOT S)
  (NOT NW))))))
(DEFUN ADF4 ()
  (VALUES (AND (NOT (OR (OR W SW) (OR NW
  NW))) (AND (AND (AND X N) (NOT NE)) (OR
  (OR N SE) (OR X E))))))
(VALUES
  (IF (OR (NOT (AND (GO-S) (GO-S))) (AND
  (NOT (ADF0)) (HOMING (GO-N)))) (IF
  (HOMING (AND (GO-S) (ADF0))) (IF (OR
  (GO-N) (ADF2)) (IF (ADF1) L I) (IF
  (ADF1) I NIL)) (IF (HOMING (GO-S)) (IF
  (ADF1) L I) (IF (GO-W) L NIL))) (IF (OR
  (OR (GO-E) (ADF3)) (AND (ADF3) (ADF3)))
  (IF (HOMING (GO-N)) (IF (ADF3) L NIL)
  (IF (GO-S) NIL L)) (IF (NOT (ADF1)) (IF
  (GO-E) NIL I) (IF (ADF1) L L)))))).
```

The result-producing branch of this best-of-generation individual makes multiple references to four of its five detectors, contains numerous movements in various directions of the turtle, contains numerous Boolean functions, contains numerous IF operators, and is capable of arriving at all three possible conclusions for a given pattern. The detectors (defined functions) each look at numerous pixels and performs various logical functions on what is seen.

Fig. 3 shows, by generation, the fitness of the best-of-generation individual. As can be seen, the average fitness of the population as a whole tends to improve (i.e., drop) from generation to generation. Specifically, the fitness of the best-of-generation individual drops to 42, 31, 22, 14, 10, 7, 6, 5, and 3 for generations 5, 10, 15, 20, 25, 30, 35, 40, and 45, respectively. The fitness of the best-of-generation individual drops to 2 for generations 47, 48, and 49.

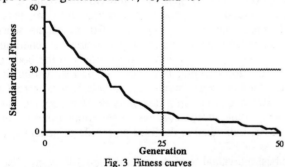

Fig. 3 Fitness curves

The hits histogram is a useful monitoring tool for visualizing the progressive learning of the population as a whole during a run. The horizontal axis of the hits histogram represents the number of hits (0 to 78) while the vertical axis represents the number of individuals in the population (0 to 8,000) scoring that number of hits.

Fig. 4 shows the hits histograms for generations 0, 15, 30, and 50 of this run. Notice the left-to-right undulating movement of both the high point and the center of mass of

these three histograms. This "slinky" movement reflects the improvement of the population as a whole. Four solutions to the problem emerge at generation 50.

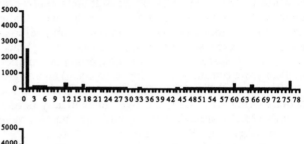

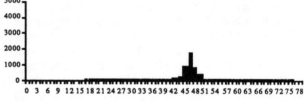

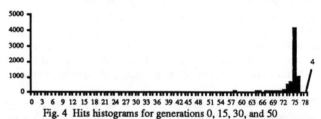

Fig. 4 Hits histograms for generations 0, 15, 30, and 50

By generation 50, the best-of-generation individual has 312 points (of which 149 are in the result-producing branch) and has the perfect fitness value of zero. This best-of-run individual is shown below:

```
(PROGN (DEFUN ADF0 ()
        (VALUES (OR (OR (AND W SE) (OR (AND (NOT
        (OR SW SW)) (NOT (AND X SW))) (NOT (OR
        (NOT S) (AND X NW))))) (AND (OR (NOT S)
        (AND W SE)) (OR (OR S X) (NOT N))))))
       (DEFUN ADF1 ()
        (VALUES (AND (AND (NOT (NOT X)) (NOT (OR
        S X))) (NOT (OR S X)))))
       (DEFUN ADF2 ()
        (VALUES (OR (AND (NOT (AND W E)) (OR
        (AND NW W) (NOT NW))) (OR (OR (AND N E)
        (AND S SE)) (OR (AND W (NOT NW)) (OR SE
        NE))))))
       (DEFUN ADF3 ()
        (VALUES (AND (NOT (AND (NOT SE) (OR W
        SW))) (OR (NOT (OR NW (NOT NW))) (AND
        (NOT S) (AND (NOT (AND (NOT SE) (OR W
        SW))) (OR (NOT (OR NW (NOT (AND (NOT SE)
        (OR W SW)))) (AND (NOT S) (OR (NOT (NOT
        NW)) (NOT SE))))))))))))
```

1798

```
(DEFUN ADF4 ()
  (VALUES (AND (NOT (OR (OR W SW) (OR NW
NW))) (AND (AND (AND X N) (NOT NE)) (AND
(NOT (OR (OR E SW) (OR NW NW))) (AND
(AND (AND (AND X N) (NOT NE)) (NOT NE))
(OR (OR N SE) (OR X E)))))))))
(VALUES
  (IF (OR (NOT (ADF4)) (AND (OR (NOT (AND
(GO-S) (GO-S))) (AND (OR (NOT (AND (GO-
S) (GO-S))) (AND (NOT (AND (ADF3)
(ADF3))) (HOMING (GO-S)))) (OR (NOT (AND
(GO-S) (GO-S))) (AND (HOMING (GO-N))
(HOMING (GO-N)))))) (OR (NOT (ADF4))
(AND (OR (NOT (AND (GO-S) (GO-S))) (AND
(OR (NOT (AND (GO-S) (GO-S))) (AND (NOT
(AND (ADF3) (ADF3))) (HOMING (GO-N))))
(OR (NOT (AND (GO-S) (GO-S))) (AND
(HOMING (GO-N)) (HOMING (GO-N)))))) (OR
(NOT (AND (GO-S) (GO-S))) (AND (NOT (AND
(GO-S) (ADF3))) (HOMING (GO-N)))))))) ;
antecedent of outermost IF
      (IF (HOMING (AND (GO-S) (ADF0))) (IF
(GO-S) NIL L) (IF (HOMING (GO-S)) (IF
(ADF1) L I) (IF (ADF1) L NIL))) ; then-
part of outermost IF
      (IF (OR (OR (GO-E) (ADF3)) (AND (OR
(NOT (ADF4)) (AND (NOT (ADF3)) (OR (NOT
(AND (GO-S) (GO-S))) (AND (NOT (GO-S))
(AND (ADF3) (ADF3))))))) (HOMING (GO-
N)))) (IF (ADF2) (IF (GO-S) L NIL) (IF
(GO-S) (IF (ADF3) L NIL) (IF (GO-S) NIL
L))) (IF (NOT (ADF1)) (IF (GO-E) NIL I)
(IF (ADF1) L L))) ; else-part of
outwemost IF
  ))).
```

B.   *Analysis of the Solution for One Run*

The performance of the 100% correct best-of-run individual from generation 50 from the run described above can be understood by first considering how this program successfully recognizes the pixel pattern for the letter L. To aid in this process, Fig. 5 identifies the seven pixels that must be ON for the pattern to be the letter L with the Roman numerals I through VII and identifies the 14 adjacent pixels that must be OFF for the letter L with the lower-case letters a through n.

a	I	n	
b	II	m	
c	III	l	
d	IV	k	j
e	V	VI	VII
f	g	h	i

Fig. 5 The seven ON and 14 OFF pixels constituting the letter L

When the best-of-run individual from generation 50 encounters an L, it moves the turtle 25 times. The turtle always starts at pixel III for any pattern. Fig. 6 shows the 25 steps in this trajectory, with the turtle starting at pixel III and

ending at pixel n. The figure omits certain numbers where the turtle repetitively moves back and forth over the same two adjacent pixels.

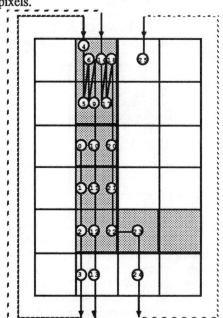

Fig. 6 Trajectory of the turtle for identifying an L for best-of-run individual from generation 50

Since the result-producing branch begins with (IF (OR (NOT (ADF4)) ..., the defined function ADF4 is evaluated with the turtle being at its starting location (pixel III) at turtle step 0. Detector ADF4 examines seven of the nine pixels within view.

Fig. 7 shows the seven pixels values required to cause the function definition for ADF4 to return a value of T. ADF4 depends on seven pixels, lacks any reference to pixel S, and effectively ignores pixel SE.

Off	On	Off
Off	On	Off
Off		

Fig. 7 Arrangement of pixels required to cause ADF4 to return T

When the turtle is located at pixel III, pixels II and III are ON, and pixels b, c, d, m, and l are OFF, so ADF4 returns T. (see Fig. 8) These latter five pixels all lie adjacent to the vertical segment of the L. Thus, when the turtle is at pixel III, ADF4 acts as a detector for two of the three vertically stacked pixels of a potential L being ON and as a detector for five of the six pixels adjacent to the potential L being OFF. ADF4 is an incomplete detector for a vertical line segment.

Since ADF4 returns T when the turtle is located at pixel III, (NOT (ADF4)) is NIL, so the second clause of the first OR must be evaluated. This second clause begins with (AND (OR (NOT (AND (GO-S) (GO-S)))).... When the first argument of the inner AND, namely (GO-S), is evaluated, the turtle moves south (down the vertical segment of the L) from pixel III to pixel IV. Since pixel IV is ON after this turtle step 1, the (GO-S) operator returns T, thus necessitating evaluation of the second argument of this inner

AND. This second argument, which consists of another (GO-S) operator, moves the turtle south again from pixel IV to pixel V. Since pixel V is also ON after turtle step 2, the inner AND returns T. However, the NOT necessitates evaluation of the second argument of the OR, namely

```
(AND (OR (NOT (AND (GO-S) ... )) ... ))
```

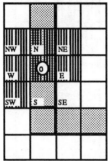

Fig. 8 Detector ADF4 applied at pixel III at turtle step 0

The (GO-S) operator (the first argument to the inner AND above) now moves the turtle south to pixel g. Pixel g is OFF at turtle step 3, since it is below the vertical segment of the L. Note that when LISP evaluates the two-argument Boolean AND function, it skips evaluation of the second argument if the first argument evaluates to NIL. (Similarly, evaluation of the second argument of the OR function is skipped if the first argument evaluates to T). The second (GO-S) argument to the AND is replaced with an ellipsis, since it will not be evaluated. This illustrates that when side-effecting operators are contained in arguments to Booolean functions, the operators are conditionally executed in LISP depending on the context. Since the NOT negates the NIL returned by the AND, the second argument to the OR containing seven points is also skipped and replaced with a second ellipsis.

Now two (GO-S) operators move the turtle to pixels I and II (since the grid is toroidal) at turtle steps 4 and 5. The (GO-N) moves the turtle back to pixel I at turtle step 6, but the HOMING rubber bands the turtle back to pixel II at turtle step 7. This sequence is repeated at turtle steps 8 and 9, leaving the turtle at pixel II.

Detector ADF4 is now applied at pixel II. Fig. 9 shows that when the turtle is located at pixel II, ADF4 returns T when pixels I and II are ON and when pixels a, b, c, n, and m are OFF.

Detector ADF4 returns T and thereby provides the new information that pixels a and n are OFF. Thus, by turtle step 9, seven pixels (a, b, c, d, n, m, and l) have been verified as being OFF via two applications of detector ADF4 and one additional pixel (g) has been verified as being OFF via the (GO-S) operator. In addition, five pixels (I, II, III, IV, and V) have been verified (often repetitively) as being ON. Several pixels have been verfied by more than one action by turtle step 9.

Between turtle steps 10 and 21, the turtle repetitively moves up and down (via several HOMINGs) along the vertical segment of the L, but provides no information that is not already known.

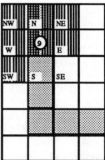

Fig. 9 Detector ADF4 applied at pixel II at turtle step 9

The turtle arrives at pixel IV at turtle step 21 and begins evaluation of the last six points of the antecedent clause of the outermost IF of the value-returning branch, namely

```
(AND (NOT (AND (GO-S) (ADF3)))
     (HOMING (GO-N)))))))).
```

The (GO-S) operator moves the turtle to pixel V (the junction of the L, which is ON) and executes detector ADF3.

Fig. 10 shows the pixels values required to cause ADF3 to return a value of T. As can be seen, ADF3 examines five pixels (NW, W, SW, S, and SE) to see if they are all OFF.

off		
off		
off	off	off

Fig. 10 Arrangement of pixels required to cause ADF3 to return a value of T

Fig. 11 shows that when the turtle is located at pixel V (the junction of the L), ADF3 returns T when pixels d, e, f, g, and h are OFF. These five pixels all lie adjacent to the junction of the L, so ADF3 acts as a detector for emptiness adjacent to the junction of an L.

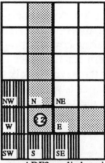

Fig. 11 Detector ADF3 applied at pixel V at turtle step 22

Since the NOT negates the return value of the AND, the (HOMING (GO-N)) is not executed.

For the letter L, the antecedent part of the outermost IF of the value-returning branch of the best-of-run individual of generation 50 evaluates to NIL, so that the second (then) argument of the IF is skipped and the third (else) argument is executed. The (GO-E) operator moves the turtle east to pixel VI (which is ON) and causes detector ADF2 to be evaluated for turtle step 23.

Fig. 12 shows that ADF2 examines six pixels. ADF2 returns a value of NIL when NW, W, and E are ON and when N, NE, and SE are OFF.

Fig. 12 Arrangement of pixels required to cause ADF2 to return a value of `NIL`

Fig. 13 shows that when the turtle is located at pixel VI at turtle step 23, `ADF2` returns a value of `NIL` when pixels IV, V, and VII are ON and when pixels i, j, and k are OFF.

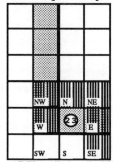

Fig. 13 Detector ADF2 applied at pixel VI at turtle step 23

The result now depends on the expression below involving detector `ADF2`:

```
1    (IF (ADF2)
2        (IF (GO-S) L NIL)
3        (IF (GO-S)
4            (IF (ADF3) L NIL)
5            (IF (GO-S) NIL L)) ... ).
```

For the letter L, `ADF2` evaluates to `NIL` on line 1. As a result, line 2 is skipped and the `(GO-S)` operator on line 3 moves the turtle south to pixel h at turtle step 24. Since pixel h is OFF, line 4 is skipped and the `(GO-S)` operator on line 5 moves the turtle toroidally to pixel n for turtle step 25. Since pixel n is OFF for the L, the result-producing branch and the S-expression as a whole therefore returns L, which is indeed the correct identification of the pattern.

Notice that if detector `ADF2` returns `T` on line 1 above, this would mean that either pixel i, j or k was ON or that pixel VII was OFF (since pixels IV and V have been previously established as being ON). Any of these four possibilities would mean that the pattern is a flawed pattern for which `NIL` (rather than L or I) should be returned. For example, if pixel VII were OFF and pixel i were ON (as shown in the left half of Fig. 2) or if pixel VII were ON and pixel i were ON, the pattern would be a flawed L. In these situations, the `(GO-S)` operator on line 2 would be executed, thereby moving the turtle to pixel h. Since pixel h is already known to be OFF, the result-producing branch and the S-expression as a whole would return `NIL`, which, under the circumstances, would be correct identification of the pattern. Similarly, the result-producing branch and the S-expression as a whole returns the value `NIL` for the 14 fitness cases for which there is an extraneous ON pixel adjacent to an L (in locations a through n) and the seven fitness cases for which there is a missing pixel within an L (in locations I through VII).

In summary, the best-of-run individual from generation 50 applies detectors at turtle steps 0, 9, 22, and 23 and considers direct input from the turtle over 25 steps in order to determine that all seven pixels (I through IV) that should be ON for an

L are indeed ON and that all 14 pixels that should be OFF for an L are indeed OFF, as shown in Fig. 14.

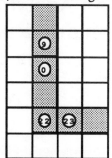

Fig. 14 Turtle steps 0, 9, 22, and 23 where detectors ADF2, ADF3, and ADF3 are applied

In identifying the letter I, the turtle moves up and down the vertical column consisting of pixels I through V and pixel g for the first 22 turtle steps much as in the identification of the L. However, when the turtle moves east on turtle step 23, pixel VI is OFF for the I.

Notice that detector `ADF0` is used for determining that certain patterns should be classified as `NIL`, although it not used in classifying the positive cases. Also, notice that although `ADF1` is merely the constant function `NIL`, it does appear, and is used, in the result-producing branch.

V   Conclusions

We have demonstrated the use of genetic programming with automatic function definition to simultaneously discover the detectors and a way of ssing the detectors to perform a letter recognition task.

ACKNOWLEDGEMENTS

James P. Rice of the Knowledge Systems Laboratory at Stanford University programmed the above on a Texas Instrument Explorer II[+] computer. Martin Keane and Simon Handley made helpful comments on this paper.

REFERENCES

Koza, John R. *Genetic Programming: On the Programming of Computers by Means of Natural Selection*. Cambridge, MA: The MIT Press 1992. 1992a.

Koza, John R. Hierarchical automatic function definition in genetic programming. In Whitley, Darrell (editor). *Proceedings of Workshop on the Foundations of Genetic Algorithms and Classifier Systems, Vail, Colorado 1992*. San Mateo, CA: Morgan Kaufmann Publishers Inc. 1992. 1992b.

Koza, John R. and Rice, James P. *Genetic Programming: The Movie*. Cambridge, MA: The MIT Press 1992.

Koza, John R., Martin A. Keane, and Rice, James P. Performance improvement of machine learning via automatic discovery of facilitating functions as applied to a problem of symbolic system identification. In these ICNN-93 Conference Proceedings. 1993.

Samuel, Arthur L. Some studies in machine learning using the game of checkers. *IBM Journal of Research and Development*, 3(3): 210–229. July 1959.

An Analytical Learning Algorithm for the Dendro-dendritic Artificial Neural Network via Linear Programming

Bo Ling *and* **Fathi M.A. Salam**
Circuits and Systems & Artificial Neural Nets Laboratories
Department of Electrical Engineering
Michigan State University
East Lansing, MI 48824

Abstract - We present an analytical learning algorithm to find the weight matrix of the dendro-dendritic neural network. This learning algorithm utilizes linear programming to find all (necessarily) *non-negative* and small weights. A sufficient stability criterion is given which guarantees all stored patterns to be asymptotically stable.

I. INTRODUCTION

In [1] and [2], the Dendro-dendritic Artificial Neural Network (DANN) was introduced which has been shown to exhibit qualitatively the same dynamic properties as gradient continuous-time feedback neural nets. Compared to the Hopfield neural network [6], the dendro-dendritic neural network has several advantages: reduced number of weights, natural symmetry, direct implementation in MOS VLSI, etc. [2].

A 50-neuron CMOS silicon VLSI chip [3] has been fabricated. An on-chip hardware learning scheme is implemented. This chip has been successfully used in pattern/character recognition applications ([3], [4]). A microcomputer learning algorithm using Runge-Kutta integration routine was also proposed in [5]. In the dendro-dendritic neural network, each synaptic weight is implemented via an nMOS transistor acting as a nonlinear synapse. The logical high and logical low in the chip can be globally set at any analog value ([3], [4]). The gate voltages of the feedback nMOS transistors can also be adjusted globally. Given any specific patterns, all synaptic weights are updated in real time.

In this paper, we show a sufficient stability criterion for the dendro-dendritic neural network. We formulate the problem of finding all the *non-negative* weights as standard linear programming problem. Thus, for given patterns, weights can be directly determined, and most elements in the optimal basic feasible solution are zero. Moreover, all stored patterns are bound to be asymptotically stable. Based on our optimization approach, all weights are relatively small. Thus, the weights are implementable as large resistive elements and hence power dissipation in the network is minimized.

Our paper is organized as follows: in section II, the dendro-dendritic neural network and some of its important properties are described briefly; our stability criterion is shown in section III; in section IV, our learning algorithm combined with linear programming is introduced; and finally, in section V, a numerical example is given as an illustration.

II. THE DENDRO-DENDRITIC NEURAL NETWORK

In this section, we describe briefly the dendro-dendritic neural network [2] and some of its interesting properties. The mathematical model of the dendro-dendritic neural network is given as:

This work is supported in part by ONR Grant N00014-92-J-1441
and the Michigan Research Excellent Fund (REF).

$$c_i \frac{du_i}{dt} = \sum_{j=1, j \neq i}^{n} T_{ij}(u_j - u_i) + T_{ii}(v_i - u_i) + I_i - \frac{1}{r_i}u_i$$

$$v_i = s_i(u_i) \tag{2.1}$$

for $i = 1, ..., n$, where n denotes the number of neurons in the network; u_i is the input of the ith neuron, v_i is the output of the ith neuron; c_i is the capacitor and r_i is the resistor connected to the ith neuron; $s_i(.)$ the activation function which is a bounded monotone C^1-function. One type of circuit configurations of the dendro-dendritic neural network for 3-neuron is shown in Figure 1.

It is reasonable to assume $c_i = c_0$, $r_i = r_0$ and $s_i = s_0$ for $i = 1, ..., n$. Thus, (2.1) can be rewritten as follows:

$$c_0 \frac{du_i}{dt} = \sum_{j=1, j \neq i}^{n} T_{ij}(u_j - u_i) + T_{ii}(v_i - u_i) + I_i - \frac{1}{r_0}u_i$$

$$v_i = s_0(u_i) \tag{2.2}$$

In compact matrix form, (2.2) reads

$$c_0 du/dt = -Wu + Tv + I$$

$$v = S(u) \tag{2.3}$$

where $W = [w_{ij}]$, $w_{ij} = -T_{ij}$ for $i \neq j$ and $w_{ii} = \sum_{j=1}^{n} T_{ij} + r_0^{-1}$, $T = \text{diag}(T_{11}, ... T_{nn})$, $I = [I_1, ..., I_n]^T$,

$u = [u_1, ..., u_n]^T$, $v = [v_1, ..., v_n]^T$, and $S(u) = [s_0(u_1), ..., s_0(u_n)]^T$.

The energy function is defined as [2]:

$$E = -\frac{1}{2}\sum_{i=1}^{n}\sum_{j=1, j\neq i}^{n} T_{ij}u_i u_j - \sum_{i=1}^{n} T_{ii}\int_0^{u_i} s_0(x)\,dx - \sum_{i=1}^{n} I_i u_i + \frac{1}{2}\sum_{i=1}^{n}\left(r_0^{-1} + \sum_{j=1}^{n} T_{ij}\right)u_i^2 \tag{2.4}$$

or in vector form:

$$E(u) = \frac{1}{2}u^T W u - I^T u - \sum_{i=1}^{n} T_{ii}\int_0^{u_i} s_0(x)\,dx \tag{2.5}$$

which is continuously decreasing with respect to time t and vanishes only at an equilibrium of the network (2.3). This also implies that no limit cycle (or chaos) of (2.3) exists. Now define the Hessian matrix at a point u as $J_{\nabla E}(u) = W - TD_u S(u)$.

Since the activation function s_0, of each neuron, is a bounded C^1-function, (2.3) has a unique solution for $t \geq 0$ starting from each initial condition $u(0)$. As shown in [2], system (2.3) is a gradient-like system where isolated local minima of (2.4) are asymptotically stable. And, by the *Inverse Function Theorem*, u is isolated if u is an equilibrium of (2.3) such that $\det(J_{\nabla E}(u)) = \det(W - TD_u S(u)) \neq 0$. Moreover, u is a local minimum of (2.4) if $J_{\nabla E}(u) > 0$. It is also shown in [2] that all trajectories of (2.3) converge to a bounded and closed (compact) region. Hence, there is only finite number of isolated equilibria of (2.3). In summery, the dendro-dendritic neural network has the following important properties:

(1) For the energy function defined in (2.4), $dE(u)/dt \leq 0$, and $dE(u)/dt = 0$ if and only if u is an equilibrium point of (2.3).

(2) There exists a unique solution of (2.3) for $t \geq 0$ for each initial condition $u(0)$.

(3) Isolated local minimum of $E(u)$ is an asymptotically stable equilibrium of (2.3).

(4) There are only finite number of equilibria of (2.3).

(5) Let u^0 be an equilibrium point of (2.3). u^0 is isolated if $\det(J_{\nabla E}(u^0)) \neq 0$.

(6) Let u^0 be an equilibrium point of (2.3). u^0 is a local minimum of function $E(v)$ if and only if the Jacobian matrix $J_{\nabla E}(u^0) > 0$.

(7) All solutions are bounded.

(8) No limit cycles nor other forms of recurrent solutions exit.

Thus, the dendro-dendritic neural network has all the desired properties of the Hopfield-type neural network. But, compared with the Hopfield-type neural network, the dendro-dendritic neural network has the following advantages:

(1) Less number of weights. For an n-neuron network, the Hopfield network uses a maximum of n^2-n weights, the dendro-dendritic network uses a maximum of $n(n+1)/2$ weights.

(2) Natural symmetric weights. In the dendro-dendritic neural network circuit, $w_{ij} = w_{ji}$ naturally. In the Hopfield neural network, this property can never be true due to circuit hardware mismatch.

III. STABILITY CRITERION

In the following analysis, we assume s_0: $(-\infty, +\infty) \rightarrow (\Delta_1, \Delta_2)$ for $\Delta_2 \geq \Delta_1 > 0$, $s_0(0) = 0$, and the desired patterns are binary, e.g., $v = [v_1, ..., v_n]^T$ with $v_i = v_-$ or v_+. Corresponding to $v = [v_1, ..., v_n]^T$, we have $u = [u_1, ..., u_n]^T$ with $u_i = u_-$ or u_+, where $s_0(u_-) = v_-$ and $s_0(u_+) = v_+$.

For the energy function defined in (2.5), it is easy to verify that

$$\nabla E(u) = Wu - I - TS(u) \tag{3.1}$$

$$J_{\nabla E}(u) = W - TD_u S(u) \tag{3.2}$$

where $\nabla E(u)$ is the gradient and $J_{\nabla E}(u)$ is the Hessian of $E(u)$. A stability theorem is stated as follows:

Stability Theorem: Let u^0 be an equilibrium of (2.3) where $T_{ij} \geq 0$ $i \neq j$ and $T_{ii} > 0$. Then u^0 is asymptotically stable if $s_0'(u_i^0) < 1 / (r_0 T_{ii})$ for all i.

Proof: Suppose $T_{ij} \geq 0$ for $i \neq j$, $T_{ii} > 0$. Define $B = W - TD_u S(u^0)$. Then, $b_{ii} = w_{ii} + T_{ii} s_0'(u_i^0)$

$$= \sum_{j=1}^{n} T_{ij} + r_0^{-1} - T_{ii} s'_0(u_i^0), b_{ij} = w_{ij} = -T_{ij} \text{ for } i \neq j. \text{ Suppose } s_0'(u_i^0) < 1 / (r_0 T_{ii}) \text{ for all } i. \text{ Then, } b_{ii} > 0. \text{ It is}$$

easy to see that $|b_{ii}| > \sum_{j=1, i \neq j}^{n} |b_{ij}|$. By *Gershgorin Circle Theorem* [10], B has only positive eigenvalues.

Therefore, $J_{\nabla E}(u^0) > 0$, which implies u^0 is a local minimum of $E(u)$. Thus, u^0 is asymptotically stable. This completes the proof.

Remark 1: This stability theorem supports the implementation of all the weights in the dendro-dendritic neural network as conductances. The real-time experiments [3] have shown that the dendro-dendritic neural network with positive weights can store any desired (binary) patterns.

Remark 2: The analysis above does not consider the time-delays of signals. See [11] for the time delay analysis of similar models. It should be mentioned, however, that the 50-neuron DANN chip [3] does not exhibit any time-delay behavior.

IV. FINDING THE WEIGHT MATRIX VIA LINEAR PROGRAMMING

First, consider the single pattern case. Let $u = [u_1, ..., u_n]^T$ be an image pattern, where $u_i = u_-$ or u_+. In order to be an equilibrium of the dendro-dendritic neural network (2.3), u must satisfy:

$$- Wu + TS(u) + I = 0 \tag{4.1}$$

which is equivalent to

$$W' u + TS(u) = R^{-1}u - I \tag{4.2}$$

where $w_{ij}' = - w_{ij} = T_{ij}$ for $i \neq j$, $w_{ii}' = - w_{ii} + r_0^{-1}$, $T = \text{diag}(T_{11}, ..., T_{nn})$, $R^{-1} = r_0^{-1}E_n$, where E_n is the identity matrix, $I = [I_1, ..., I_n]^T$. For simplicity, one may set $I_i = 0$ for $i = 1, ..., n$. Thus, (4.2) results in:

$$W' u + TS(u) = R^{-1}u = r_0^{-1}E_n u \tag{4.3}$$

By proper algebraic operations, (4.3) can be transformed into

$$Ax = b \tag{4.4}$$

where $x = [x_1, ..., x_N]^T$, $N = n(n+1)/2$ (the number of unknowns in (4.3)), and $b = r_0^{-1} u$,

$$A = \begin{bmatrix} s_0(u_1) - u_1 & & & \vdots & u_2 - u_1 & u_n - u_1 & \vdots & \\ & s_0(u_2) - u_2 & \mathbf{O} & \vdots & u_1 - u_2 & \mathbf{O} & \vdots & \mathbf{O} \\ \mathbf{O} & & \ddots & \vdots & \mathbf{O} & \ddots & \vdots & u_n - u_{n-1} \\ & & s_0(u_n) - u_n & \vdots & u_1 - u_n & & \vdots & u_{n-1} - u_n \end{bmatrix}$$

$$x_i = \begin{cases} T_{i,i} & 1 \leq i \leq n \\ \\ T_{1,i+1-n} & n+1 \leq i \leq 2n-1 \\ \vdots & \vdots \\ T_{n-1,n} & i = N \end{cases} \tag{4.5}$$

Without loss of generality, assume $s_0(u_i) \neq u_i$ for $i = 1, ..., n$. From the structure of A in (4.4), it is easy to show the following proposition:

Proposition 4.1: Let $u = [u_1, ..., u_n]^T$ be an image pattern with $u_i = u_-$ or u_+, A as defined in (4.4). Then, rank$(A) = n$.

The minimum-norm solution of (4.4) is given by $x = A^+ b$ where $A^+ = A^T(AA^T)^{-1}$. Once x is solved, all weights, T_{ij} for $i, j = 1, ..., n$, can easily be reconstructed via (4.5). Those weights will make u stored exactly as an equilibrium of (2.3).

Now, consider the case of multiple patterns. Suppose we are given m binary patterns, $u^1, ..., u^m$. For each vector u^i, we have

$$- W u^i + T S(u^i) + I = 0$$

which can be transferred to the equivalent matrix equation: $A^i x = b^i$. Thus, in order to find weights, T_{ij} for $i, j = 1, ..., n$, for storing those m patterns, $A^i x = b^i$, $i = 1, ..., m$, must have common solutions. In other words,

$$\begin{bmatrix} A^1 \\ A^2 \\ ... \\ A^m \end{bmatrix} x = \begin{bmatrix} b^1 \\ b^2 \\ ... \\ b^m \end{bmatrix} \tag{4.6}$$

must have solutions. In [7], we show how to apply the *Morris-Odell's Theorem* to check the existence of solutions and find common solutions of (4.6). Thus, we may assume common solutions of (4.6) exist. Define $A = [(A^1)^T, ..., (A^m)^T]^T$, $b = [(b^1)^T, ..., (b^m)^T]^T$. Then, the common solutions of (4.6) is given by $x = A^+ b + N(A)$, where $N(A)$ is the null space of A. Based on the *Stability Theorem* in section III, we wish to find non-negative solutions of (4.6). In other words, we need to find solutions of:

$$Ax = b$$
$$x \geq 0 \tag{4.7}$$

It is observed that the solution of (4.7) is not unique. The elements of the solution x are the weights in our neural network. It is desired to have small values of those weights so that they can be implementable as large resistive elements to achieve minimized power dissipation in the network. In other words, our problem can be stated as:

$$\text{Minimize} \sum_{i=1}^{N} x_i \qquad \qquad (4.8a)$$

$$\text{s.t.} \qquad Ax = b \qquad \qquad (4.8b)$$

$$x \geq 0 \qquad \qquad (4.8c)$$

which is a standard linear programming problem.

The solutions of (4.8b) and (4.8c) are called feasible solutions. An optimal feasible solution is one which satisfies (4.8). An optimal basic feasible solution is an optimal feasible solution which has exactly p non-zero elements, other elements are all zero, where $p = \text{rank}(A)$. It can be shown [9] that

(1) The feasible solution set K is convex.

(2) If K is non-empty, there exists at least one extreme point of K.

(3) The convex set K possesses at most a finite number of extreme points.

(4) Optimal values of the objective function occurs only at extreme points of K.

Without loss of generality, assume $s_0(u_+) > u_+$ and $s_0(u_-) < u_-$. This assumption can be always satisfied since we are free to set the values of u_+ and u_-. Moreover, $s_0(.)$ can also be chosen as such. With this assumption, we have the following theorem:

Theorem 4.2: Let $u = [u_1, ..., u_n]^T$ be a binary pattern with $u_i = u_-$ or u_+. Then, there exists an optimal basic feasible solution of (4.8).

Proof : Let A be defined as in (4.4). Partition $A = [A_1, A_2]$, where $A_1 = \text{diag}(s_0(u_1)-u_1, ..., s_0(u_n)-u_n)$. Define $x_1 = A_1^{-1} r_0^{-1} u = \text{diag}(1/(s_0(u_1)-u_1), ..., 1/(s_0(u_n)-u_n)) r_0^{-1} u$. Then, $x = [x_1, 0]^T$ is a basic feasible solution of the linear programming problem (4.8) with A and b defined as in (4.4). Thus, the feasible solution set K is non-empty, which implies that an optimal basic feasible solution of (4.8) exists. This proves our result.

Remark: Theorem 4.2 guarantees the existence of optimal basic feasible solution of (4.8) for single input pattern. In the multiple-pattern case, the situation is quite different. How to find conditions which guarantee the existence of the feasible solution of (4.8) for multiple-patterns case is currently under investigation. The real-time experiments [3] have shown multiple binary patterns can be stored and retrieved.

Among all numerical algorithms about linear programming, the simplex method is the most significant algorithm. It proceeds from one basic feasible solution to another in such a way as to continuously decrease the value of the objective function until a minimum is reached [9]. Standard packages of the simplex method are available. Therefore, it is easy to find weights for the dendro-dendritic neural network once multiple patterns are provided.

V. NUMERICAL EXAMPLE

Consider a 3-neuron dendro-dendritic neural network. The binary input pattern takes two values: 5 volts and -5 volts. And define $u_+ = 2$ volts, $u_- = -2$ volts, which implies $s_0(u_+) = 5 > u_+$ and $s_0(u_-) = -5 < u_-$. Suppose a binary pattern $v = [5, 5, -5]^T$ is given. Corresponding to this pattern, $u = [2, 2, -2]^T$. Since the number of neurons is 3, the maximum number of weights $N = 6$. The matrix A in (4.4) is constructed as:

$$A = \begin{bmatrix} 3 & 0 & 0 & 0 & -4 & 0 \\ 0 & 3 & 0 & 0 & 0 & -4 \\ 0 & 0 & -3 & 0 & 0 & 4 \end{bmatrix}$$

Let $r_0 = 1$ KΩ Then $b = r_0^{-1} u = [0.002, 0.002, -0.002]^T$. Our linear programming problem is formulated as follows: *Minimize* $x_1 + x_2 + x_3 + x_4 + x_5 + x_6$, *s.t.* $Ax = b$, $x_1 \geq 0$, $x_2 \geq 0$, $x_3 \geq 0$, $x_4 \geq 0$, $x_5 \geq 0$, $x_6 \geq 0$. The solution $[x_1, x_2, x_3, x_4, x_5, x_6]^T = [0.00067, 0.00067, 0.00067, 0, 0, 0]^T$ is an optimal basic feasible solution. Thus, the weights are: $T_{11} = 0.00067$, $T_{22} = 0.00067$, $T_{33} = 0.00067$, $T_{12} = 0$, $T_{13} = 0$, $T_{23} = 0$. The resistors of 1.5 KΩ are needed to implement those weights. From the dendro-dendritic neural network (2.1), we know there are no connections among the three neurons. In other word, for this example, the network is decoupled. From a mathematical point of view, $[x_1, x_2, x_3, x_4, x_5, x_6]^T = [0.00067, 0.00067, 0.00067, 0, 0,$

$0]^T$ is an optimal basic feasible solution which minimizes the quantity $x_1 + x_2 + x_3 + x_4 + x_5 + x_6$. But from an implementation point of view, this optimal basic feasible solution may not yield good robust performance, e.g. fault tolerance, since the network with those weights are basically decoupled. There is a trade-off between small values of weights and good system performance. If we focus on a better system performance, we may only want to find feasible solutions, instead of optimal basic feasible solutions. In this example, we can find a solution $[x_1, x_2, x_3, x_4, x_5, x_6]^T = [0.002, 0.002, 0.002, 0.001, 0.001, 0.001]^T$ which is only a feasible solution. The corresponding weights are: $T_{11} = T_{22} = T_{33} = 0.002$, $T_{12} = T_{13} = T_{23} = 0.001$. In this case, the network is not decoupled. We can also define the objective function (4.8a) as to *minimize* $\{x_1^2 + ... + x_N^2\}$ and apply nonlinear programming algorithms. This will result in optimal solutions which will not make the network decoupled.

VI. CONCLUSION

We have shown a sufficient stability criterion, and we have formulated the problem of finding *non-negative* weights as a standard linear programming problem. Thus, all the weights can be directly implemented as inductances. Based on this approach, all stored patterns are bound to be asymptotically stable. The algorithm also yields small values for the weights which is attractive from a circuit implementation point of view.

REFERENCES

[1] Fathi M.A. Salam, "A model of neural circuits for programmable VLSI implementation of the synaptic weights for feedback neural nets", *1989 IEEE International Symposium on Circuits and Systems*, Portland, Oregon, May 1989, pp. 849-851.

[2] Fathi M.A. Salam, "New artificial neural models: basic theory and characteristics", *1990 IEEE International Symposium on Circuits and Systems*, New Orleans, Louisiana, May 1990, pp. 200-203.

[3] Fathi M.A., Yiwen Wang, "A real-time experiment using a 50-neuron CMOS analog silicon chip with on-chip digital learning", *IEEE Trans. on Neural Networks*, Vol. 2, No. 4, July 1991.

[4] Yiwen Wang, Fathi M.A. Salam, "Experiment using CMOS neural network chips as pattern/character recognizers", *1991 IEEE International Symposium on Circuits and Systems*, pp. 1196-1199.

[5] Fathi M.A. Salam, Yiwen Wang, "Learning scheme for analog CMOS neural chips", *Memorandum* No. MUS/EE/A90/07, Department of Electrical Engineering, Michigan State University, East Lansing, MI 48824, 1990.

[6] J.J. Hopfield, "Neurons with graded response have collective computational properties like those of two-state neurons", in *Proc. Natl. Acad. Sci. U.S.A.*, Vol. 81, pp. 3088-3092, 1984.

[7] Bo Ling, Fathi M.A. Salam, "A cellular network formed of Hopfield networks", in *Proc. of the 35th Midwest Symposium on Circuits and Systems*, Washington, D.C., Aug. 9-12, 1992.

[8] Phillip E. Allen, Douglas R. Holberg, *CMOS Analog Circuit Design*, Holt, Rinehart and Winston, Inc., 1987.

[9] David G. Luenberger, *Introduction to Linear and Nonlinear Programming*, Addison-Wesley Publishing Company, 1965.

[10] D.K. Faddeev, V.N. Faddeeva, *Computational Methods of Linear Algebra*, W.H. Freeman and Company, 1963.

[11] C.M. Marcus, R.M. Westervelt, "Stability of analog neural networks with delay", *Phys. Rev.* A39 (1989).

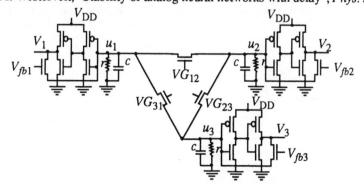

Figure 1: One type of circuit configurations of DANN with 3 neurons.

LAMBDA LEARNING RULE FOR
FEEDFORWARD NEURAL NETWORKS

Jacek M. Zurada

Department of Electrical Engineering

University of Louisville, Louisville, KY 40292

email: jmzura02@ulkyvx.louisville.edu

Abstract: Feedforward layered networks of continuous perceptrons are traditionally trained using the delta and generalized delta training rules. These learning concepts are formalized in well-known error back-propagation training (EBPT) concept. Although the EBPT algorithm has been widely used and hundreds of technical reports illustrate its successful applications, the lambda learning rule often offers a considerable improvement of learning. The paper outlines both the rule and the complete generalized lambda learning algorithm for layered networks. It also focuses on visualization of learning and draws comparisons between the two learning approaches.

I. SINGLE CONTINUOUS PRECEPTRON LEARNING

Let us revise the delta learning rule for a single continuous perceptron (neuron) as shown in Fig. 1, where the activation function is typically assumed

$$f(\lambda, \text{net}) = \frac{1}{1 + e^{-\lambda net}} \qquad (1)$$

and the activation value and augmented input vector are, respectively

$$\text{net} = \omega^t \mathbf{y}$$
$$\mathbf{y} = [x_1 \ x_2 \ ... \ x_{n-1} \ \ -1]^t$$

Assuming that the neuron learns with $(n-1)$ dimensional non-augmented weight space, n of its weights are adjustable in the classical delta rule [1].

The lambda learning rule involves expansion of the learning space to $(n+1)$ dimensions. In this rule in addition to weight learning, the steepness λ of the activation function undergoes adjustment in the negative gradient direction. The first observations of this useful property has been made in [2] and, independently, in [3]. More recent papers also show the benefits of the "gain parameter" learning as compared to EBPT. A number of simulations have confirmed that the method has not only accelerated learning, but also has improved generalizations and has introduced a better participation of nodes in representing the input [4].

In this paper, we further evaluate the "gain parameter"

learning in addition to the conventional weight learning under the name of so called *lambda learning rule*. The focus is on outlining a closed-form generalized lambda learning algorithm, and on the visualization of learning itself for the two selected benchmark cases. Using the customary expression for error between the desired output value, d, and the actual one, o,

$$E(\omega, \lambda) = \frac{1}{2}\left[d - o(\omega, \lambda)\right]^2 \qquad (2)$$

we obtain the following weight adjustments for a single neuron learning

$$\triangle \omega_i = \eta_1 \frac{\partial E}{\partial \omega_i} = -\eta_1(d - o) \ f'(\lambda net)\lambda x_i \qquad (3a)$$

$$\triangle \lambda = \eta_2 \frac{\partial E}{\partial \lambda} = -\eta_2(d - o) \ f'(\lambda net)\text{net} \qquad (3b)$$

where $f'(\text{net}) = o(1 - o)$

and η_1, and η_2, are positive learning constants usually selected of arbitrary small values. Noticeably, expression (3a) coincides exactly with the delta learning rule. Additional weight adjustment as in (3b) is the essence of the lambda rule. It expresses such block changes of the value λnet that although the individual weights remain invariant, the overall impact of learning typically increases, since the adaptive gain factor in the exponent of (1) is suitably adjusted. This feature may be of particular importance when all weights are considerably too small or too large, and/or the neuron learning progresses slowly. Intuitively, (3b) corresponds to separate and independent weight scaling step, when all the multiplicative weights are adjusted up or down in a block-wise fashion in a direction which minimizes the current training error.

II. SINGLE LAYER LEARNING

The lambda learning rule can now be easily formulated for a single or double layer learning. Assume that the output layer of a two-layer network undergoes the training. Here, K steepness coefficients, λ_i, $i = 1, 2, ... , K$, undergo adjustments in addition to the individual weights ω_{kj}. With reference to Fig. 2, the adjusted learning variables for a single learning step can be obtained from (3) as below (primes denote updated values)

$$\omega'_{kj} = \omega_{kj} + \eta_1(d_k - o_k) \ f'(\text{net}_k)\lambda_k y_j \qquad (4a)$$

$$\lambda'_k = \lambda_k + \eta_2(d_k - o_k) \ f'(\text{net}_k)\text{net}_k \qquad (4b)$$

where $j = 1, 2, ... , J$, and k is the neuron number, weights and λ of which undergo adjustments. Understandably, k must be incremented from 1 through K in order for the entire layer to update its weights and λ values for a single input pattern.

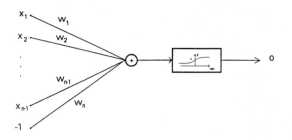

Fig. 1:   Illustration to lambda learning rule of a single neuron

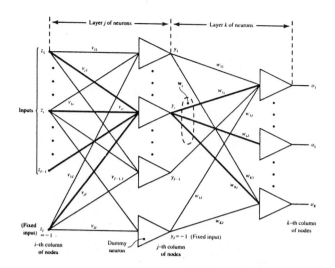

Fig. 2: Layered feedforward network for illustration of lambda/generalized lambda learning

III. HIDDEN LAYER LEARNING

This section presents the generalized lambda rule which extends the use of the lambda learning rule defined in (3) and introduced in (4). The generalization below refers to the hidden layer learning, specifically, to learning of weights v_{ji} using the notation of Fig. 2. Obviously, the learning of j-th neuron is performed such that v_{ji} and λ_j, $i = 1, 2, \dots, I$, and $j = 1, 2, \dots, J$, are adapted.

Using the overall output error definition

$$E = \frac{1}{2} \sum_{k=1}^{K} (d_k - o_k)^2 \qquad (5)$$

we obtain for weights and steepness coefficients adjustments

$$\frac{\partial E}{\partial v_{ji}} = \frac{\partial E}{\partial net_j} \cdot \frac{\partial net_j}{\partial v_{ji}} \qquad (6a)$$

$$\frac{\partial E}{\partial \lambda_j} = \frac{\partial E}{\partial y_j} \cdot \frac{\partial y_j}{\partial \lambda_j} \qquad (6b)$$

Introducing the commonly used error term values δ_{yj} for the j-th hidden neuron such that

$$\delta_{yj} = \frac{\partial E}{\partial net_j} \qquad (7)$$

and noticing from (5) that

$$\frac{\partial E}{\partial y_j} = - \sum_{k=1}^{K} (d_k - o_k) \, f'(net_k) net_k \qquad (8)$$

expressions (6) can be rearranged to the form

$$\frac{\partial E}{\partial v_{ji}} = \delta_{yj} \, z_i \lambda_j \qquad (9a)$$

$$\frac{\partial E}{\partial \lambda_j} = f'(\lambda_j net_j) net_j \sum_{k=1}^{K} (d_k - o_k) f'(net_k) net_k,$$

$$\text{for } j = 1, 2, \dots, J. \qquad (9b)$$

Therefore, the generalized lambda rule results in the following adjustments

$$\Delta v_{ji} = \eta_1 f'_j(net_j) z_i \lambda_j \sum_{k=1}^{K} \delta_{ok} \omega_{kj} \qquad (10a)$$

$$\Delta \lambda_j = \eta_2 f'_j(net_j) net_j \sum_{k=1}^{K} \delta_{ok} net_k \qquad (10b)$$

where

$$\delta_{ok} = (d_k - o_k) \, f'(net_k)$$

is the error signal term of the k-th neuron of an output layer.

IV. COMPLETE TRAINING ALGORITHM

The modified algorithm of error back-propagation training based on the lambda and generalized lambda rule is outlined below. Inspection of the algorithm flowchart indicates that only steps 5 and 6 of the algorithm are modified as compared with the regular EBPT algorithm [5]. These steps correspond to output- and hidden layer-weights and lambda coefficients adjustments.

BEGIN: Given are P training pairs of vectors of inputs and desired outputs

$$\{z_1, d_1, z_2, d_2, \dots, z_p, d_p\},$$

where z_i is $(I \times 1)$, d_i is $(K \times 1)$ and $i = 1, 2, \dots, P$. Note that the Ith component of each z_i is of value -1 since input vectors are augmented. Size $J - 1$ of the hidden layer having outputs y is selected. Note the the Jth component of y is of value -1, since hidden layer outputs are also augmented; y is $(J \times 1)$ and o is $(K \times 1)$.

Step 1: $\eta_1, \eta_2 > 0$, acceptable training error E_{max} chosen.

Weights W and V are initialized at small random values; W is $(K \times J)$, V is $(J \times I)$.

$$q \leftarrow 1, \, p \leftarrow 1, \, E \leftarrow 0$$

Step 2: Training step starts here. Input is presented and the layers' outputs computed $[f(net)$ as in (1) is used]:

$$z \leftarrow z_p, \, d \leftarrow d_p$$

$$y_j \leftarrow f(v^t_j z), \text{ for } j = 1, 2, \dots, J$$

where v_j, a column vector, is the j'th row of V, and

$$o_k \leftarrow f(w^t_k y), \text{ for } k = 1, 2, \dots, K$$

where w_k, a column vector, is the k'th row of W.

Step 3: Error value is computed:

$$E \leftarrow \frac{1}{2}(d_k - o_k)^2 + E, \text{ for } k = 1, 2, \dots, K$$

Step 4: Error signal vectors δ_o and δ_y of both layers are computed. Vector δ_o is $(K \times 1)$, δ_y is $(J \times 1)$.

The error signal terms of the output and hidden layers in this step are, respectively

$$\delta_{ok} = (d_k - o_k)(1 - o_k)o_k, \text{ for } k = 1, 2, \dots, K$$

$$\delta_{yj} = y_j(1 - y_j) \sum_{k=1}^{K} \delta_{ok} w_{kj}, \quad \text{for } j = 1, 2, \dots, J$$

Step 5: Output layer weights and gains are adjusted:

$$w_{kj} \leftarrow w_{kj} + \eta_1 \delta_{ok} \, \lambda_k \, y_j,$$

$$\lambda_k \leftarrow \lambda_k + \eta_2 \, \delta_{ok} net_k, \text{ for k} = 1, 2, \dots, K \text{ and } j = 1, 2, \dots, J$$

Step 6:   Hidden layer weights and gains are adjusted:

$$v_{ji} \leftarrow v_{ji} + \eta_1 \delta_{yj} \lambda_j z_i,$$

$$\lambda_j \leftarrow \lambda_j + \eta_2 \delta_{yj} \, net_j, \text{ for } j = 1, 2, \ldots, J \text{ and } i = 1, 2, \ldots, I$$

Step 7:   If $p < P$ then $p \leftarrow p + 1$, $q \leftarrow q + 1$, and go to Step 2: otherwise go to Step 8.

Step 8:   The training cycle is completed.
For $E < E_{max}$ terminate the training session. Output weights $\mathbf{W}$, $\mathbf{V}$, and the cycle counter q, and error E. If $E > E_{max}$, then $E \leftarrow 0$, $p \leftarrow 1$, and initiate the new training cycle by going to Step 2. END.

V. EXPERIMENTAL RESULTS AND CONCLUSIONS

Simulation of learning efficiency using the lambda learning rule has been tested on a number of cases, including a bit-map classifier. Although the lambda learning rule-based algorithm is numerically about as complex as the classical EBPT, it can offer an improvement in the efficiency of training. Since the improvement comes at about no additional cost, the algorithm seems to be a promising one and likely to become important. Below are selected results of learning simulations. The same learning constants and initial weights have been used for comparison of both algorithms (simulations are made for bipolar neurons' characteristics).

Learning using the EBPT and the lambda learning rule has been simulated and compared for the XOR problem. Fig. 3 shows two typical learning profiles for EBPT and lambda learning rule and it indicates faster learning for the method employing adaptive gain. Two hidden-layer neurons have been used in this experiment. Fig. 4 illustrates gain variations during training and corresponds to the bottom error curve of Fig. 3. It can be seen that the output neuron's gain changes sign during learning and its gain variations are substantially correlated with an associated error curve of Fig. 3.

Fig. 5 displays output neuron's weight variations during learning using both methods and having profiles on Fig. 3. It can be seen that the slopes of weight curves are generally higher for the lambda learning. Also, weights stabilize faster for lambda learning than for the EBPT case. Interestingly, weights are varying in the same directions in both cases, with the EBPT leading to larger absolute final weight values.

Somewhat similar observations can be drawn from Fig. 6 displaying hidden neurons' weight learning for both methods. Weight change similarly but slower, and settle at lower absolute values for lambda learning. This is due to the fact that lambda values become larger than 1 for the two hidden neurons (see Fig. 4).

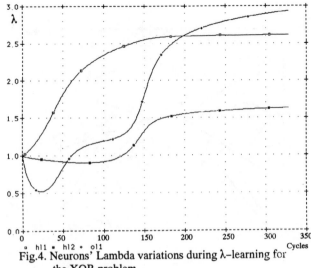

Fig.4. Neurons' Lambda variations during λ–learning for the XOR problem

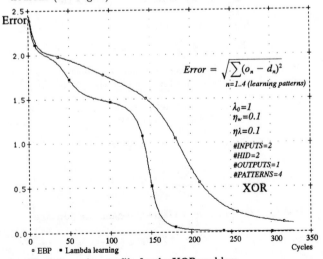

$$Error = \sqrt{\sum_{n=1..4 \, (learning \, patterns)} (o_n - d_n)^2}$$

$\lambda_0 = 1$
$\eta_w = 0.1$
$\eta\lambda = 0.1$

#INPUTS=2
#HID=2
#OUTPUTS=1
#PATTERNS=4

XOR

Fig.3. Learning profile for the XOR problem

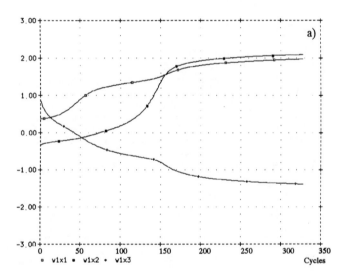

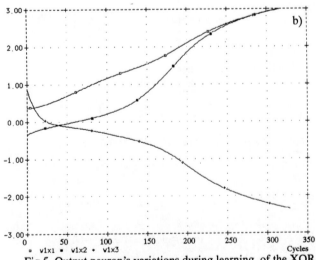

Fig.5. Output neuron's variations during learning of the XOR problem: a) λ–learning b) EBPT

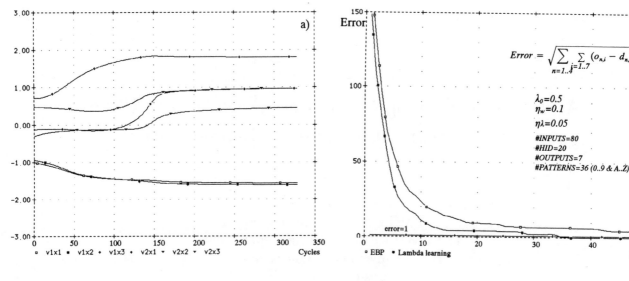

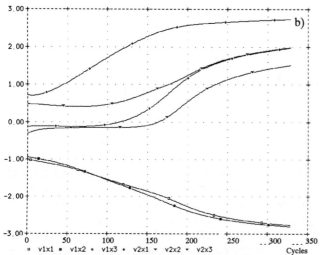

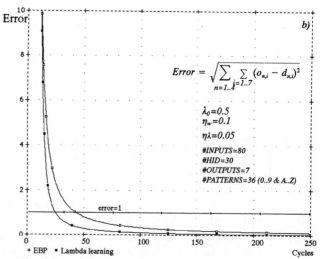

Fig.6. Hidden neurons' weight variaitions during learning of the XOR problem: a) λ–learning b)EBPT

Fig.7. Learning profiles for character clasifier

Efficiency of both algorithms has also been compared for training of a 36-class classifier of digits 0-9 and 26 letter characters with 8 x 10 binary input pixel field. The desired output vector has been the 7-bit ASCII code of each character. The architecture with 30 hidden nodes have been used. Fig. 7 depicts two typical learning profiles produced for this application and indicates that the lambda learning method yields several times faster learning for the same final level of classifier's performance. Noticeably, Fig. 7a illustrates the case in which the EBPT method has not been successful and the lambda learning algorithm was.

In addition to the typical simulation results discussed in this section, some additional observations are in place. The lambda learning algorithm seems to be more sensitive to initial weights and λ values. For small networks, such as XOR, $\lambda=1$ and $\eta=0.1$ yield seemingly best results. Initial weights uniformly spread within $\pm 1/\sqrt{\text{fan-in}}$ yield satisfactory results for initial value of $\lambda=1$. It has also been found experimentally that both methods with weights initialized improperly result in persistent saturation of weights. In such case no further learning occurs despite large output error value. Many simulations also indicated that lambda learning has lead to quick and excellent solutions in cases when the standard EBPT has failed to produce acceptable results in reasonable time.

Most recent paper [6] discusses the equivalency conditions which entail learning constants, and initial weights

and gain values. Under certain initial learning conditions the lambda learning rule and the EBPT should yield identical results. This will allow unifying further comparative discussions on different variations of gradient-descent learning algorithms.

VI. LITERATURE

[1] D. E. Rumelhart and J. L. McClelland, editors. *Parallel Distributed Processing: Explorations in the Microstructure of Cognition: Foundations.* Volume 1, MIT Press, Cambridge, Mass., 1986.

[2] R. Tawel, Does the neural 'learn' like the synapse? in Advances in Neural Information Processing Systems, D. S. Touretzky, Ed., San Mateo, Calif., Morgan Kaufmann, 1989, pp. 169-176.

[3] J. R. Movellean, Self-regulated temperature in back -propagation networks, paper presented at the Ninth Annual Berkeley-Stanford Conf., 1987, Berkeley, Calif.

[4] J. K. Kruschke, J. R. Movellean, Benefits of Gain: Speeded Learning and Minimal Hidden Layers in Back -Propagation Networks, IEEE Trans. on Syst., Man, and Cybern., vol. 21, No. 1, Jan-Feb. 1991, pp. 273-279.

[5] J. M. Zurada, *Introduction to Artificial Neural Systems*, West Publishing Company, St. Paul, Minn., 1992.

[6] Q. Jia, S. Usui, An Equivalent Relation Concerning the Gain in Back-Propagation Algorithms, Proc. of the IJCNN, Bejing, China, Nov. 3-6, 1992, pp. II 387-392.

A Method of Training Multi-layer Networks with Heaviside Characteristics using Internal Representations.

R J Gaynier
T Downs
Intelligent Machines Laboratory
Electrical Engineering Department
University of Queensland
St. Lucia, Qld. 4072
Australia

Tel: 7 365 3564
Fax: 7 365 4999
Email: gaynier@s1.elec.uq.oz.au

Abstract— Two algorithms have recently been reported for training multi-layer networks of neurons with Heaviside characteristics. In these the weights are treated as continuous random variables and the output of a neuron is probabilistic with a distribution that is a differentiable function of the weight parameters. A limitation of these methods is that they are restricted to networks with two layers of variable weights. Other algorithms have been developed for this problem which use internal representations to train networks with Heaviside characteristics. However these suffer from the need to perform "bit flipping" on the internal representations in an effort to reduce the output error and as a result these methods do not guarantee that the network will converge to a solution. We present a learning algorithm that employs internal representations, which are continuous random variables, for the training of multi-layer networks whose neurons have Heaviside characteristics. This algorithm is an improvement over the others in that it is applicable to networks with any number of layers of variable weights and does not require "bit flipping" on the internal representations to reduce output error. The algorithm is extended to apply to recurrent networks. Some illustrative results are given.

I. Introduction

Two algorithms have recently been reported for training multi-layer networks of neurons with Heaviside characteristics [1], [2]. In these the weights are treated as continuous random variables. The network error is decreased by adjusting the mean and variance of the weight parameters to increase the probability of the desired output. A limitation of these methods is that they are restricted to networks with two layers of variable weights. Other algorithms have been developed (CHIR for example [3]) which use internal representations to train networks with Heaviside characteristics. However these suffer from the need to perform "bit flipping" on the internal representations in an effort to reduce the output error and as a result do not guarantee that the network will converge to a solution.

The algorithm presented here is similar to the approach of Krogh et al. [4], where a cost function is introduced which is an explicit function of the internal representations as well as the weights. Our cost function differs in that 1) it is solely a function of the internal representations and 2) the internal representations are considered as activations, rather than outputs, of the hidden units (as suggested by Rohwer in [5]). The internal representations are also treated as continuous random variables, so that the ouputs of the hidden units, resulting from the internal representations, can then be expressed as a probability. This provides us with a cost function which is a differentiable function of the mean and variance of the internal representations. The mean and variance of the internal representations can then be adjusted to reduce the cost function and therefore improve the internal representations.

The algorithm begins with randomly selected weight values and also randomly selected values for the mean and variance of the internal representations. Learning is carried out in two steps. In the first step delta rule learning is applied separately to the weights using the internal representations as target values to the input layer, and as inputs to the output layer. For this purpose the internal representations are treated as deterministic and are considered equal to their mean values. In the second step the mean and variance are adjusted as previously described. The algorithm alternates between adjustments to the weights and adjustments to the internal representations.

We have also adapted this algorithm to recurrent networks whose neurons have Heaviside characteristics. This modified algorithm has been developed for problems of the trajectory dynamics type; application to problems of the stable end point type [6] is currently under investigation. The networks we consider are fully recurrent and identical in structure to those described by Williams and Zipser in [7] (except for the Heaviside characteristic). As in the feed forward case the cost function is solely a function of the internal representations but now contains several additional terms (explained later). Delta rule learning is applied to the weights as in the feed forward case.

II. THE ALGORITHM

A. The Feed Forward Learning Algorithm

The algorithm reduces the overall network error by attempting to find good internal representations and then adapting the weights to implement them. Our cost function allows us to adjust the internal representations toward better values. Once suitable internal representations have been found, the search for suitable weights reduces to a set of single layer problems. Training is a two step process, the first step being the adjustment of the weights while holding the internal representations constant, and the second step being the adjustment of the internal representations while holding the weights constant. Training alternates between these two steps making small adjustments in the weights and internal representations until the network converges to a solution.

For clarity, let us initially consider a network with a single layer of hidden units. The algorithm begins with randomly chosen values of mean and variance for the internal representations (recall that these are considered the activations of the hidden units) and randomly chosen values for the network weights. The first step is to adapt the weights in an effort to find mappings from input to internal representation and from internal representation to output. This is a single layer learning problem and

delta rule learning [14] is applied. During this step the the activations of the hidden units are set equal to the current mean values of the internal representations. Each layer is treated independently during training. The internal representations are used as inputs during training of the output layer and as targets during the training of the input layer. The changes made to the weights at this step are as follows:

$$\triangle w_{ji} = \{T_{jt} - \mathcal{H}[w_{ji}\mathcal{H}(\mathcal{M}_{it})]\}\mathcal{H}(\mathcal{M}_{it}) \qquad (1)$$

$$\triangle w_{ik} = (\mathcal{H}(\mathcal{M}_{it}) - y_{it})\mathcal{I}_{kt} \qquad (2)$$

where w_{ji} is the weight connecting output unit j to hidden unit i and w_{ik} is the weight connecting hidden unit i to input k. T_{jt} and y_{jt} are the target and actual outputs of unit j for input pattern t. $\mathcal{I}_{kt}$ is the value of input k for pattern t. $\mathcal{M}_{it}$ is the mean of the internal representation for unit i and input pattern t and $\mathcal{H}$ is the Heaviside transfer function.

In the second step the mean and variance of the internal representations are adjusted using ideas similar to those described in [2]. First note that we can calculate the probabilities of the hidden units attaining particular values (given the mean and variance of the internal representations) as follows:

$$Pr\{y_{it} = 1\} = \Phi\left(\frac{\mathcal{M}_{it}}{\mathcal{S}_{it}}\right) \simeq G\left(\frac{\mathcal{M}_{it}}{\mathcal{S}_{it}}\right) \qquad (3)$$

where Φ is the cdf of the standard normal distribution given mean $\mathcal{M}_{it}$ and variance $\mathcal{S}_{it}$ of the internal representation. The function G is an analytic approximation to the standard normal[1] used so that we can differentiate the probabilities with respect to $\mathcal{M}_{it}$ and $\mathcal{S}_{it}$. Figure 1 illustrates this point. We now define the cost function

$$E = \frac{1}{2}\sum_t \sum_j \sum_i [(w_{ji}(Pr\{y_{it} = 1\} - Pr\{y_{it} = -1\}) - T_{jt}]^2$$

$$(4)$$

This cost function describes the mean square error between the target outputs and the outputs that would be produced if the activations of the hidden units were equal to the internal representations.[2] The mean square error cost function is the most commonly used but other cost functions are possible. Later we discuss results for an entropic [10] cost function as well. Using the analytic

---

[1] The approximation we employed was $G(x) = \frac{1}{2}\left(1 + tanh(y)\right)$ where $y = 0.7988x\left(1 + 0.04417x^2\right)$. According to [8], the maximum absolute error incurred in using this approximation is 0.000140.

[2] This cost function makes use of the unbounded weighted sum of the probabilities and is employed here in order to simplify the presentation. In actual implementation we apply a squashing function in order to speed up convergence.

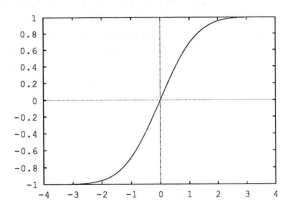

Figure 1: $Pr\{y_{it} = 1\} - Pr\{y_{it} = -1\}$ versus $\frac{\mathcal{M}_{it}}{\mathcal{S}_{it}}$

approximation of equation (3), equation (4) can now be written

$$E = \frac{1}{2}\sum_t\sum_j\sum_i [w_{ji}(2G\left(\frac{\mathcal{M}_{it}}{\mathcal{S}_{it}}\right) - 1) - T_t]^2 \quad (5)$$

Note that the internal representations have to be capable of implementation by the input layer of weights. Internal representations which present a nonlinearly separable problem to the input layer are obviously not suitable. To help avoid this a second term is added to equation (5) which provides a measure of the difference between the hidden unit activations due to the input layer of weights and the internal representations. By minimising this new cost function we not only attempt to minimise the output error (first term) but also encourage internal representations which are nearer the actual activations (second term) and which are therefore less likely to be nonlinearly separable. The new cost function is

$$E = \frac{1}{2}\sum_t\sum_j\sum_i\sum_k\{[w_{ji}(2G\left(\frac{\mathcal{M}_{it}}{\mathcal{S}_{it}}\right) - 1) - T_{it}]^2$$
$$+[\mathcal{M}_{it} - w_{ik}\mathcal{I}_{kt}]^2\} \quad (6)$$

Following arguments similar to those used in deriving the back-propagation algorithm, the change required in $\mathcal{M}_{it}$ and $\mathcal{S}_{it}$ to reduce the error can be shown to be:

$$\triangle \mathcal{M}_{it} = -\eta\frac{\partial E}{\partial \mathcal{M}_{it}} \quad (7)$$

$$\triangle \mathcal{S}_{it} = -\eta\frac{\partial E}{\partial \mathcal{S}_{it}} \quad (8)$$

In this way we can increase the probability of having desireable internal representations. Steps one and two are repeated until the internal representations converge to a solution.

A network consisting of more than a single layer of hidden units can be trained similarly, with each layer of hidden units having its own set of internal representations. The first step of the algorithm, the adaptation of the weights, remains unchanged except that the internal representations at each layer are used as target vectors to train the previous layer of weights and as input vectors to train the next. Delta rule learning is still applied. In an implementation on a parallel computer all layers can be updated at the same time since the information required for training is local to the weights. In the second step the internal representations are adjusted as previously described but now the targets (T_t) of equations (4) and (5) are the internal representations from the next higher layer. This applies for all layers excluding the highest layer which uses the desired output exactly as before.

B. Pruning and Construction Algorithm for the Feed Forward Case

Since the outputs of the hidden units are binary, it is trivial to determine when hidden units are performing exactly the same function within the network and hence when pruning can be applied. Any pair of hidden units whose outputs are the same for every pattern in the input set can obviously be merged; this is done by replacing the two units with a single unit whose output weight is the sum of the output weights of the inital two units. Similarly, any pair of hidden units whose outputs have opposite sign for every input pattern can also be merged. This pruning procedure is quite easily implemented for networks with Heaviside units. This is not true in the case of sigmoidal units.

The internal representations can provide a simple measure of network performance during training. If the output error is greater than zero but the internal representations have converged to a solution this may indicate that the network is too small to find a solution. A construction algorithm similar to Hanson's meiosis [9] can be implemented to increase network size in order to accommodate a given problem. The construction algorithm we have implemented differs from Hanson's in that he uses the coefficients of variation (ie. the variance/mean ratios) of the weights as his growth criterion. We only concern ourselves with the gradient of the means of the internal representations. A hidden unit is created if the gradients of the means of the internal representations for the existing hidden units are below a predetermined "gradient threshold" when the output error is still greater than zero. The decision to add an additional unit is solely dependent on the internal representations.

By combining the pruning and construction techniques

during training it is assured that hidden units will be added to improve network performance but that there will be no duplication of function among them.

C. The Recurrent Learning Algorithm

For recurrent, as well as feedforward networks, the training of network weights becomes a set of single layer problems once a suitable set of internal representations is known. So to adapt the learning algorithm to recurrent networks the weight adaptation procedure remains unchanged and only the cost function needs to be modified. This modification is required to include terms which describe additional constraints placed on the internal representations. For recurrent networks, Equation (6) becomes

$$
\begin{aligned}
E = & \frac{1}{2} \sum_t \sum_j \sum_i \{[(2G\left(\frac{\mathcal{M}_{it}}{\mathcal{S}_{it}}\right) - 1) - T_{it}]^2 \\
& + [\mathcal{H}\{w_{ji}(2G\left(\frac{\mathcal{M}_{it}}{\mathcal{S}_{it}}\right) - 1)\} - T_{j(t+1)}]^2 \\
& + [w_{ji}(2G\left(\frac{\mathcal{M}_{it}}{\mathcal{S}_{it}}\right) - 1) - \mathcal{M}_{j(t+1)}]^2\} \qquad (9)
\end{aligned}
$$

with equations (7) and (8) remaining unchanged. The first term of equation (9) describes the error contributed by the difference between the output at time t and the desired output (for each neuron which has an output value specified) given the internal representation at t. The second term describes the error contributed by the difference between the output at time $t + 1$ and the desired output at $t + 1$ given the internal representations at t. The last term describes the error contributed by the difference between the actual activation at $t + 1$ and the internal representation at $t + 1$ given the internal representation at t. Each weight is adapted using the Delta rule and either the desired output or the internal representation is used as the target depending on whether the connection is to an output unit or to a hidden unit.

III. Results

A. Feed Forward Networks

Simulations were run of the 3 bit parity problem on a 2 layer network with 6 hidden units. The algorithm succeeded in finding a solution in 77% of the 100 trials. Simulations were also run of an 8 to 8 encoder problem with 6 hidden units and the success rate was 97%. Both quadratic and entropic cost functions [10] were tried and there was no significant difference in the results. 3 layer networks were also successfully trained to perform the same problems.

Figure 2 shows how different parameters vary as the network is successfully trained on 100 data presentations of the 3 bit parity problem. Figure 2(a) shows how the

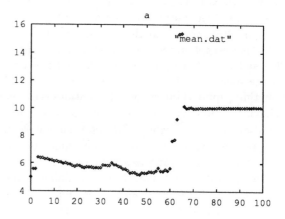

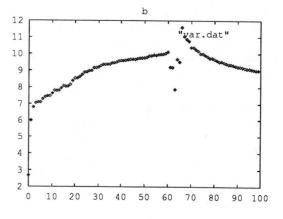

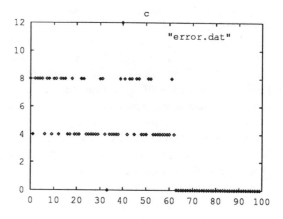

Figure 2: a) Sum of Means, b) Sum of Variances and c) Network Error for 100 training iterations

sum of the mean values of the internal representations varies, figure 2(b) shows how the sum of the variances of the internal representations varies, and figure 2(c) shows the variations in the network error, where network error is the sum of the output errors over the 8 input vectors.

Figure 2(c) shows that the output error has a tendency to flip between 4 and 8 before a solution is found. Figures 2(a) and 2(b) show quite unremarkable behaviors except for the short period just before a solution is found, when something appoaching chaotic fluctuations is evident. The behavior of these two curves can be explained as follows.

Initially the mean values of the internal representations[3] are provided with randomly chosen values between -0.5 and +0.5 and the variances with randomly chosen values between 0.0 and +0.5. During training, some of the mean values change sign and others maintain the same sign. The fact that some mean values change sign (or go close to changing sign) accounts for most of the behavior depicted in figure 2(a) and 2(b). If a particular internal representation in the final solution has a mean value whose sign differs from its initial value then, in the stages of training, the learning algorithm will make the following adjustments to the internal representation:

(i) the mean values will be shifted towards zero (inorder, ultimately, to change sign).

(ii) the variance will be increased in order to increase the probability of a value with opposite sign.

Eventually, since all internal representations that are to change sign (or go close to changing sign) will recieve similar sized increments (or decrements) a stage will be reached where all such internal representations have mean values close to zero and relatively large variances. Some slightly chaotic behavior then takes place, as the internal representations compete with one another to achieve a sign change (and hold on to it). Once a suitable set of sign changes has been established, their mean values settle quickly to their final values and, if training is continued beyond the acquisition of a solution, the variances of the internal representations continue to decrease. They do not decrease to zero, however, because a continuum of solutions exists around that given by the mean values.

In general, we found that rather more hidden units were required for high success rates than are required in the case of sigmoidal units. This is possibly a reflection of the comparative weakness of Heaviside units pointed out by Sontag [11]. It has been our experience that the "on off" nature of the Heaviside units leads to a more significant role being played by the bias connections. We have observed that learning is more efficient when the starting points of the bias connections are randomised over a

larger range of values than the other weights (as suggested in [12]).

Simulations of the construction algorithm were also conducted and the entropic cost function was used. The exclusive OR was attempted beginning with a single hidden unit and the algorithm successfully found a solution in 99% of the trials with an average of 2.8 hidden units. Simulations of the 3 bit parity problem had a success rate of 96% with an average of 5.69 hidden units. These success rates compare favorably with those for the meiosis algorithm in [9] and performs much better than our original algorithm with a fixed number of hidden units. Slightly larger networks were produced than by meiosis which used an average of 2.13 hidden units for the exclusive OR and 4.1 for the 3 bit parity. This is to be expected as Hanson's meiosis employs sigmoidal rather than Heaviside characteristics and the comparisions are made for illustrative purposes only. Lower gradient thresholds produced smaller networks but with lower success rates for all problems attempted. Smaller networks and lower success rates were also obtained when the quadratic, rather than the entropic, cost function was employed. This seems to support the conclusions of Solla et al. in [10] concerning the steepness of the error surfaces of the two cost functions.

A 3 layer implementation of the construction algorithm found solutions to the 3 bit parity problem with a 96% success rate and to the 4 bit parity problem with a 100% success rate. The decision to add a hidden unit at a particular layer was based solely on the gradients of the internal representations at that layer. This is unlikely to be the most efficient method of construction for networks of more than 2 layers and further work will be carried out in this area.

B. Recurrent Networks

We have initially tested the recurrent version on some of the tasks described by Williams and Zipser [7]. The algorithm is capable of performing the "Pipelined XOR", "Simple Sequence Recognition" and "Learning to Oscillate". The most interesting result so far is that while Williams and Zipser found their algorithm was only able to learn to oscillate when teacher-forcing was used, our algorithm was able to learn to oscillate without teacher-forcing. We believe this is because the internal representations of the neuron which forms the output quickly take on the appropriate values to produce the correct output. This then implements a quasi teacher-forcing.

More extensive trials of the algorithm including pruning and construction features are being conducted. Future plans include developing a version for problems with stable end points with modification of the minimal trajectory algorithm [13] being one possible approach.

---

[3] Recall that in our formulation, the internal representations are activations of neural units

REFERENCES

[1] P L Bartlett, T Downs, "Using Random Weights to Train Multi-layer Networks of Hardlimiting Units" IEEE Transactions on Neural Networks, 3, pp202-210, March 1992.

[2] T Downs, P L Bartlett, J Shaw, "A Backpropagation Algorithm for Networks of Neurons with Step Function Charactistics" Submitted to IEEE Transactions on Neural Networks.

[3] T Grossman, "The CHIR Algorithm for Feed Forward Networks With Binary Weights" Advances in Neural Information Processing Systems 2, pp 516-523, Morgan Kaufmann 1990.

[4] A Krogh, G I Thorbergsson, J A Hertz, " A Cost Function for Internal Representations" Advances in Neural Information Processing Systems 2, pp 733-740, Morgan Kaufmann 1990.

[5] R Rohwer, "The 'Moving Targets' Training Algorithm" Advances in Neural Information Processing Systems 2, pp 558-565 Morgan Kaufmann 1990.

[6] F J Pineda, "Generalization of Back-Propagation to Recurrent Neural Networks", Physical Review Letters, Vol. 59, pp 2229-2232, 1987.

[7] R J Williams, D Zipser "A Learning Algorithm for Continually Running Fully Recurrent Neural Networks", Neural Computation 1, pp 270-280, 1989.

[8] S Kotz, N L Johnson,(eds.) Encyclopaedia of Statistical Sciences, Wiley, New York, 1985.

[9] S J Hanson "Meiosis Networks", Advances in Neural Information Processing Systems 2, pp 553-541, Morgan Kaufmann 1990.

[10] S A Solla, E Levin, M Fleisher "Accelerated Learning in Layered Neural Networks", Complex Systems 2, pp 625-640, 1988.

[11] E D Sontag "Sigmoids Distinguish More Efficiently Than Heavisides" Neural Computation 1, pp 470-472 1989.

[12] D Nguyen, B Widrow "Improving the Learning Speed of 2-Layer Neural Networks by Choosing Initial Values of the Adaptive Weights", IEEE International Conference on Neural Networks, Vol 3, pp 21-26.

[13] D Saad "Training Recurrent Neural Networks-The Minimal Trajectory Algorithm", International Journal of Neural Systems, Vol. 3, No 1 pp 83-101, 1992.

[14] D Rumelhart, J McClelland "Parallel Distributed Processing" MIT Press, p 53, 1986.

Backpropagation for Linearly-Separable Patterns: a Detailed Analysis *

Paolo Frasconi   Marco Gori   Alberto Tesi

Dipartimento di Sistemi e Informatica

Via di Santa Marta 3 - 50139 Firenze - Italy

e-mail : marco@ingfi1.cineca.it

Abstract— In this paper we propose a sufficient condition for learning without local minima in multilayered networks. In particular we remove a fundamental assumption on the network architecture. We prove that the conclusions drawn in [10] also hold provided that the weight matrix associated with the hidden and output layer is pyramidal and has full rank. Moreover, the analysis is carried out by using LMS-threshold cost functions, which allow us to identify *spurious* and *structural* local minima. Index Terms - Backpropagation, local minima, multilayered networks, linearly separable patterns.

I. INTRODUCTION

Backpropagation is probably the most widely applied neural network learning algorithm. Backprop's popularity is related with its ability of dealing with complex multidimensional mappings. During the last few years, some research efforts have been devolved in explaining, from a theoretical point of view, the success of multilayered networks (MLN) in solving practical problems. One important aspect concerns the multilayered networks' capability to learn arbitrary input/output mappings. This problem has been tackled in a number of ways, and steps have been done towards the definition of design criteria to be applied in order to meet the specifications. In particular, in [4, 5, 6] the universal interpolation capability of a "large enough" MLN has been proven with just one hidden layer of sigmoidal units. Moreover, in [7], some bounds on the required number of hidden neurons are given, depending on the type of mapping to be realized. Another important research topic is that of investigating on the generalization to new examples (e.g. see [1]). In order to understand the effectiveness of learning algorithms in finding optimal solutions, the analysis of local minima of the cost function is also very important, no matter what kind of nu-

merical method is used. A wide variety of cases exists in which Backprop is known to fail because of local minima ([3, 9, 10, 8, 15, 12]). The difficulty with Backprop is that, once the architecture is chosen, no general method exists that guarantees gradient descent to converge to the global minimum. Therefore, the investigation of the shape of the cost function is a very important issue for understanding the effectiveness of multilayered networks in solving practical problems. Some novel results have been proposed in [10]. In particular, sufficient conditions were given which guarantee Backprop to discover the optimal solution. These conditions concern both the training set and the network architecture. The former requires a linearly separable training set. The latter assumes a two-layered network, in which each output unit receives inputs only from a subset of hidden units, being such subsets disjoint.

In this paper we focus the analysis on stationary points of gradient (i.e. on the values of weights for which the gradient is null). We prove that, if the matrix of weights connecting hidden to output neurons is pyramidal and full rank, the result given in [10] can be extended to arbitrarily connected two-layer networks. Moreover, the analysis of the cost function is based on LMS-Threshold cost functions [16] instead of the ordinary quadratic index. This study makes it possible to understand better the joint role of squashing and cost functions for stationary points. In [10], the assumption of asymptotic targets avoids the kind of local minima shown in [3]. The use of LMS-Threshold functions represents a more general way to circumvent these kind of stationary points, referred to as *spurious local minima* in this paper.

The paper is organized as follows: in section 2 we propose a vectorial formulation of Backprop equations which turns out to be very useful for investigating the problem of local minima. In section 3 we prove that, under the hypothesis that the patterns are linearly-separable, no local minima exist in the cost surface.

---

*This research was partially supported by MURST 40% and CNR Grant 90.01530.CT01.

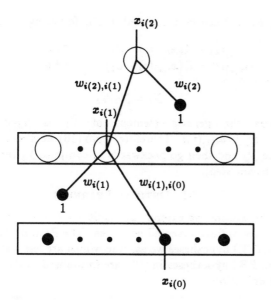

Figure 1: Network architecture and symbol definitions.

II. NOTATION AND VECTORIAL PROBLEM FORMULATION

Basically, the problem of learning in $MLNs$ is to find a set of weights which minimizes the mismatching between network outputs and target values. This strategy is referred to as supervised learning. More formally, there is a network $\mathcal{N}$, a learning environment $\mathcal{L}_e$ (set of data used for learning), and a cost index E_T ([14]).

- **Network $\mathcal{N}$.**
  It has a multilayered architecture (see Fig. 1). With reference to index l, we distinguish among the input layer ($l = 0$), the hidden layer ($l = 1$), and the output layer ($l = 2$). The number of neurons per layer is denoted with $n(l)$. Each neuron of layer l is referred to by its index $i(l)$, $i(l) = 1, \ldots, n(l)$.

When pattern t is presented at the input, for each neuron, we consider

$$
\begin{aligned}
a_{i(l)}(t) &: \quad \text{neuron } i(l)\text{'s activation} \\
x_{i(l)}(t) &: \quad \text{neuron } i(l)\text{'s output.}
\end{aligned} \tag{1}
$$

The activation is computed by propagating forward the outputs of the neurons of the previous level as follows

$$
a_{i(l)}(t) = w_{i(l)} + \sum_{i(l-1)=1}^{n(l-1)} w_{i(l),i(l-1)} x_{i(l-1)}(t), \tag{2}
$$

where $w_{i(l),i(l-1)}$ is the weight of the link between the neurons $i(l), i(l-1)$ and $w_{i(l)}$ is the threshold (see Fig. 1).

The output of neuron $i(l)$ is related to the activation by a "squash-like" function

$$
x_{i(l)} = f(a_{i(l)}), \tag{3}
$$

where $f(\cdot) : R \to [\underline{d}, \overline{d}]$ is a C^2 function with a positive first derivative.

- **Learning Environment $\mathcal{L}_e$.**
  We use a set of supervised data for learning. It is convenient to think of it as a collection of T input/output couples for network $\mathcal{N}$

$$
\mathcal{L}_e \doteq \{(X_o(t), D(t)), X_o(t) \in R^{n(o)}, \\ D(t) \in R^{n(2)}, t = 1, \ldots, T\}. \tag{4}
$$

$X_o(t)$ is the input pattern and $D(t)$ is its corresponding target. We denote with $S_c, c = 1..C$ the c-th class, and with T_c the number of patterns belonging to S_c, $\sum_{c=1}^{C} T_c = T$. If pattern t belongs [not belongs] to class S_c, then

$$
d_c(t) = d_2, \qquad [d_c(t) = d_1],
$$

where $[d_1, d_2] \subset [\underline{d}, \overline{d}]$. All the targets are collected in the vector

$$
\mathcal{D} \doteq [D(1), \cdots, D(T)]' \in R^{T,n(2)}.
$$

We consider linerly separable patterns, that means a vector $A \in R^{n(0)+1}$ exists such that

$$
\begin{aligned}
A' X_o^e(t) &> 0 \qquad \text{if pattern } t \in S_c \\
A' X_o^e(t) &< 0 \qquad \text{if pattern } t \notin S_c
\end{aligned} \tag{5}
$$

where $X_o^e(t) \doteq [X_o'(t)\ 1]'$.

- **Cost index.**
  For a given $\mathcal{L}_e$, the input-output data fitting is measured by means of the cost function

$$
E_T = \sum_{c=1}^{C} \sum_{t \in S_c} [l_2(x_c(t) - d_2) + \\ \sum_{i(2)=1, i(2) \neq c}^{n(2)} l_1(x_{i(2)}(t) - d_1)] \tag{6}
$$

where $l_k(\cdot) : R \to R$, $k = 1, 2$ are C^2 functions (except $\alpha = 0$), such that

$$
\begin{aligned}
l_1(\alpha) &= 0 & \text{if } \alpha &\leq 0 \\
l_1(\alpha) &> 0, \quad l_1'(\alpha) > 0 & \text{if } \alpha &> 0 \\
l_2(\alpha) &= 0 & \text{if } \alpha &\geq 0 \\
l_2(\alpha) &> 0, \quad l_2'(\alpha) < 0 & \text{if } \alpha &< 0
\end{aligned} \tag{7}
$$

where $'$ stands for differentiation with respect to α. In Fig. 2 an example of functions $l_1(\cdot)$ and $l_2(\cdot)$ is reported.

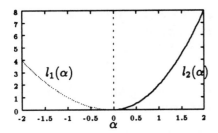

Figure 2: An example of functions $l_1(\cdot)$ and $l_2(\cdot)$.

In order to develop a BP vectorial formulation (see also [10]), we need some additional definitions.

1. $X_{i(l)} \doteq [x_{i(l)}(1), \cdots, x_{i(l)}(T)]' \in R^T$ is called *output trace* of neuron $i(l)$. This vector stores the output of neuron $i(l)$ for all the T patterns of the learning environment.

2. The output trace for all the neurons of a given layer l is called *output layer trace*. It is kept in the matrix

$$\mathcal{X}_l \doteq [X_{1(l)} \cdots X_{n(l)} \; \Pi] \in R^{T,n(l)+1} \quad 0 \le l \le 2 \tag{8}$$

where $\Pi \doteq [1 \cdots 1]' \in R^T$ is used to deal with biases.

3. $w_{i(l),i(l-1)}$ is the weight which connects neuron $i(l-1)$ to neuron $i(l)$ (see Fig. 1). The associated matrix $\mathcal{W}_{l-1} \in R^{n(l),n(l-1)}$ is referred to as *weight layer matrix*, $l = 1, 2$. We say $\mathcal{W}_{l-1}$ is pyramidal if $n(2) \le n(1)$.

4. We assume $y_{i(l)}(t) \doteq \partial E_t / \partial a_{i(l)}(t)$ and we call *delta trace* the vector

$$Y_{i(l)} \doteq [y_{i(l)}(1) \cdots y_{i(l)}(T)]'$$

and *delta layer trace* the matrix

$$\mathcal{Y}_l \doteq [Y_{1(l)} \cdots Y_{n(l)}] \in R^{T,n(l)} \quad (l = 1, 2).$$

5. For weights connecting layers l and $l-1$ the gradient can be represented by a matrix $\mathcal{G}_{l-1} \in R^{n(l-1)+1,n(l)}$, whose generic element $g(i(l-1), i(l))$ is given by $\partial E_T / \partial w_{i(l),i(l-1)}$ if $i(l-1) \le n(l-1)$ and $\partial E_T / \partial w_{i(l)}$ if $i(l-1) = n(l-1)+1$ (bias term gradient contribution).

With these definitions the gradient matrix can be computed as follows

$$\mathcal{G}_{l-1} = \mathcal{X}'_{l-1} \mathcal{Y}_l. \tag{9}$$

Each row t of matrix $\mathcal{X}_{l-1}$ can be computed by feeding the network with pattern t and by propagating forward activations and outputs (eqs. (2), (3), *forward step*). Matrix

$\mathcal{Y}_l$, $l = 1, 2$ can be computed by the following equations

$$\begin{aligned} \tilde{y}_{i(2)}(t) &= l'_2(x_{i(2)}(t) - d_2), &\text{if } t \in S_c \\ \tilde{y}_{i(2)}(t) &= l'_1(x_{i(2)}(t) - d_1), &\text{if } t \notin S_c \end{aligned} \tag{10}$$

$$\tilde{\mathcal{y}}_1 = \mathcal{y}_2 \mathcal{W}_1, \tag{11}$$

where the generic element of $\tilde{\mathcal{y}}_1$ is $\tilde{y}_{i(1)}(t) \doteq y_{i(1)}(t)/f'(a_{i(1)}(t))$. Therefore, from (10) we directly compute $\mathcal{y}_2$ and then go backwards to compute $\mathcal{y}_1$ (eq. (11), *backward step*).

III. Optimal Learning

In this section we extend the result establibed in [10] to the case of full connected networks. The Pattern Recognition (PR) hypotheses we assume, which are less restrictive than PR2 hypotheses in [10], are formalized in the following definition:

Definition 1 *We say that the learning environment and the neural network satisfy the PR3 hypotheses if the following facts hold:*

- *Network.*

  1. *The network has a feedforward architecture with one input layer, one hidden layer and C outputs;*

  2. *Full connections are assumed from each layer $l-1$ towards layer l, $l = 1, 2$; no shortcuts connections are admitted, i.e. connections from layer 0 to layer 2;*

  3. *Weight matrix $\mathcal{W}_1$ has full rank*

  4. *The network is pyramidal, i.e. $n(2) \ge n(1)$;*

- *Output coding.*

  - *Exclusive coding is used for the output, i.e. if pattern t belongs to class S_c, $c = 1..C$, then*

  $$D(t) = [\underline{d}, \cdots, \overline{d}, \cdots, \underline{d}]'$$

- *Learning environment.*

  - *$\mathcal{L}_e$ is a linearly separable set;*

Lemma 1 *The column $Y_{i(2)} \in R^T$ of matrix $\mathcal{y}_1 \in R^{T,n(1)}$ gets the following "sign" structure*

$$sign(Y_{i(2)}) = [-e_1^1 | \cdots | -e_1^{c-1} | e_1^c | -e_1^{c+1} | \cdots | -e_1^C]' \tag{12}$$

where $e_1^c \doteq [1 \; 1 \; \cdots \; 1] \in R^{T_c}$, $c = 1..C$. T_c is the number of patterns per class.

Proof

For the output layer the following relationship holds

$$y_{i(2)}(t) = f'(a_{i(2)}(t))l'_2(x_{i(2)}(t) - d_1), \quad \text{if } t \in S_c$$
$$y_{i(2)}(t) = f'(a_{i(2)}(t))l'_1(x_{i(2)}(t) - d_2), \quad \text{if } t \notin S_c$$
$$(13)$$

From assumptions (7) it readily follows that

$$y_{i(2)}(t) \leq 0 \quad \text{if } t \in S_c$$
$$y_{i(2)}(t) \geq 0 \quad \text{if } t \notin S_c. \quad (14)$$

$\nabla\nabla$

Before proving the main result, we need the following Lemma concerning a particular structure of stationary points.

Lemma 2 *If the PR3 hypotheses hold then*

$$\mathcal{X}'_0 \mathcal{Y}_1 = 0 \quad \text{iff} \quad \mathcal{Y}_1 = 0 \quad (15)$$

Proof

The inverse implication is trivial. Let us consider the direct one. Suppose, by contradiction, $\mathcal{X}'_0 \mathcal{Y}_1 = 0$ and $\mathcal{Y}_1 \neq 0$. From PR3 hypotheses it follows that there exist C vectors $A_c, c = 1..C$ which separates the training set, i.e.:

$$\text{sign}(A'_c \mathcal{X}'_0) = [-e_1^1| \cdots | - e_1^{c-1}|e_1^c| - e_1^{c+1}| \cdots | - e_1^C] \quad (16)$$

Now, for $i(1) = 1..n(1)$ consider the matrices

$$P_{i(1)} \doteq \text{diag}\{f'(a_{i(1)}(1)), \cdots, f'(a_{i(1)}(T))\} \in R^{T,T} \quad (17)$$

Since the prime derivatives of squash are positive, it follows that $\mathcal{Y}_2$ and $P_{i(1)}\mathcal{Y}_2$ have the same sign structure. In particular, the generic column $P_{i(1)}Y_c$ takes the sign structure of eq. (12), for all $i(1)$. Therefore:

$$A'\mathcal{X}'_0 P_{i(1)}\mathcal{Y}_2 \neq 0 \quad \forall i(1) = 1..n(1). \quad (18)$$

Eq. 18 can be right-multiplied by the weights matrix towards the output layer $\mathcal{W}_1$. Since we assumed this matrix is pyramidal and full rank, the following inequality also holds:

$$0 \neq A'\mathcal{X}'_0 P_{i(1)}\mathcal{Y}_L \mathcal{W}_1 = A'\mathcal{X}'_0 P_{i(1)}\tilde{y}_1 \quad (19)$$

Then it follows that for some column $k(1)$

$$A'\mathcal{X}'_0 P_{i(1)}\tilde{Y}_{k(1)} \neq 0. \quad (20)$$

Hence, choosing $i(1) = k(1)$,

$$0 \neq A'\mathcal{X}'_0 P_{k(1)}\tilde{Y}_{k(1)} = A'\mathcal{X}'_0 Y_{k(1)} \Rightarrow A'\mathcal{X}'_0 \mathcal{Y}_1 \neq 0 \Rightarrow \mathcal{X}'_0 \mathcal{Y}_1 \neq 0 \quad (21)$$

which is in contradiction with the hypothesis.

$\nabla\nabla$

Theorem 1 *The gradient descent method leads to the absolute minimum* $(E_T \to 0)$ *if the MLN and the learning environment satisfy PR3 hypotheses.*

Proof

Consider a stationary point:

$$\mathcal{X}'_0 \mathcal{Y}_1 = 0$$
$$\mathcal{X}'_1 \mathcal{Y}_2 = 0 \quad (22)$$

Under PR3 hypotheses, Lemma 2 holds and then $\mathcal{Y}_1 = 0$. We have:

$$0 = \mathcal{Y}_1 \Rightarrow 0 = \tilde{y}_1 = \mathcal{Y}_2 \mathcal{W}_1 \quad (23)$$

where the last equality comes from back-propagation step. For the hypotheses on $\mathcal{W}_1$ we obtain

$$\mathcal{Y}_2 = 0 \quad (24)$$

which in turn implies $E_T = 0$.

$\nabla\nabla$

IV. Conclusions

We have analyzed the problem of cost surface analysis in Backpropagation neural networks. In particular we have extended the result given in [10], which claims that no local minima exist assuming linearly separable patterns and some constraints on the network architecture. In this paper we limit the analysis to stationary points of gradient, and we show that they cannot be local minima if patterns are linearly separable and weight matrix towards output neuron is pyramidal and full rank. The result holds for arbitrarily connected two-layers networks.

The analysis is proposed for LMS-threshold functions and allows us to identify the concept of *spurious local minima*. This kind of functions have been suggested by Sontag and Sussman [16] for the case of networks without hidden neurons. As shown in the paper, we can get rid of this kind of local minima also assuming finite weights, which is not guaranteed with $PR2$ hypotheses given in [10]. Finally, this study makes it more explicit how the presence of local minima can be related to the structure of the problem. These *structural local minima* depend on the joint relationship between network and learning environment. Finding conditions for guaranteeing optimal convergence in these cases is an open research problem.

Acknowledgment

We wish to thank Monica Bianchini for her help in discussing and correcting the content of this paper.

References

[1] E.B. Baum, D. Haussler, "What Size Net Gives Valid Generalization", Neural Computation, vo. 1, no. 1, pp. 151-160.

[2] R. Bellman, *Introduction to Matrix Analysis*, McGraw-Hill, Second Edition, New York, 1974.

[3] M. L. Brady, R. Raghavan, and J. Slawny, "Back-Propagation fails to Separate Where Perceptrons Succeed," *IEEE Transactions on Circuits and Systems*, vol. 36, pp. 665-674, 1989.

[4] G. Cybenko, "Approximation by superpositions of a single sigmoidal function", *Mathematics of Control, Signal and Systems*, vol. 3, pp. 303-314, 1989.

[5] R. Hecht-Nielsen, "Theory of Backpropagation Neural Network", *Proceedings of the IEEE-IJCNN89*, vol. I, pp. 593-605, Washinghton D.C., 1989.

[6] K. Hornik, M. Stinchcombe, and H. White, "Multilayer Feedforward Networks are Universal Approximators", *Neural Networks*, vol. 2, pp. 359-366, 1989.

[7] Huang, and Huang, "Bounds on the Number of Hidden Neurons", IEEE Trans. on Neural Networks, vol. 2, no. 1, pp. 47-55, January 1991

[8] D. R. Hush, J.M. Sales, and B. Horne, "Error Surfaces for Multi-layer Perceptrons", IEEE-IJCNN91, Seattle 8-12 July, 1991, I-759,764.

[9] M. Gori, "Apprendimento con supervisione in reti neuronali,", *Ph.D. Thesis*, Universita' di Bologna, February 1990.

[10] M. Gori and A. Tesi, "On the problem of local minima in Backpropagation," *IEEE Trans. on Patt. Anal. Machine Intell.*, vol. 14, no. 1, pp. 76-86, January 1992

[11] M. Gori and A. Tesi, "Some examples of local minima during learning with Backpropagation," *Parallel Architectures and Neural Networks*, Vietri sul Mare (IT), May 1990.

[12] J. M. McInerney, K.G. Haines, S. Biafore, R. Hecht-Nielsen, "Can Backpropagation error surfaces have non-global minima?," *Proc. of the IEEE-IJCNN89*, II-627

[13] T. Poston, C. Lee, Y. Choie, Y. Kwon, "Local Minima and Back Propagation", *Proc. of the IEEE-IJCNN91*, Seattle 8-12 July 1991, II-173,176.

[14] D. E. Rumelhart, G. E. Hinton, and R. J. Williams, "Learning Internal Representations by Error Propagation," in *Parallel Distributed Processing. Exploration in the microstructure of Cognition. Vol. 1: Foundations.*, MIT Press, 1986.

[15] E. D. Sontag and H. J. Sussman, "Backpropagation Can Give to Spurious Local Minima Even for Networks without Hidden Layers", *Complex Systems*, vol. 3, pp. 91-106, 1989.

[16] E. D. Sontag and H. J. Sussman, "Backpropagation separates when perceptrons do," Washington DC, 1989, *Proc. of the IEEE-IJCNN89*, pp. 91-106.

The Use of Fuzzy Membership in Network Training for Isolated Word Recognition

Yingyong Qi and Bobby R. Hunt
Department of Electrical and Computer Engineering

Ning Bi
Department of Speech and Hearing Sciences

University of Arizona
Tucson, AZ 85721

Abstract—We present a modification to the use of fuzzy membership in the training of an artificial neural network. The modified membership function can be applied to patterns that have a multi-center data structure in the feature space, and is used in network training for isolated word recognition. Results indicate that the network trained using this fuzzy membership function has better overall recognition rate than either the network trained by the conventional error back-propagation method or the classifier derived from vector quantization.

I. INTRODUCTION

The use of an artificial neural network for pattern classification involves a training phase and a classification phase. Here, training refers to the adaptive modification of the weight of each network link so that a known pattern of input will produce a pre-defined pattern of output. The process of network training is rather complicated, and an effective method was not available until the error back-propagation algorithm was developed. Through the use of this training method, a neural network can delineate an arbitrarily complicated pattern space that conventional methods of pattern classification may fail to partition. Once training is completed, pattern classification using neural network is a straightforward mapping from the input to the output pattern space, and only requires algebraic computations that can be implemented using simple circuit elements.

There are occasions when the ability to construct substantial complexity in the decision surface is a disadvantage. Consider the circumstance when the patterns to be classified occupy overlapping regions in the pattern space. It is possible to build a neural network which constructs a decision surface that completely "threads" through the *implied* boundary represented by the training patterns. However, this "tightly-tuned" fitting to the training patterns may not be an optimal choice for later pattern classification because some training patterns may represent outliers of the pattern ensemble.

One way of dealing with non-representative training patterns is to consider the collection of patterns as a fuzzy set where each pattern identifies itself with a continuous membership value. With these membership values, it is possible to modify the back-propagation algorithm so that training patterns with large membership values play a more crucial role than those with small membership values in modifying the weights of the network. As a result, the network will unlikely be degraded by a few possible outliers in the training set.

Hunt, Qi, and DeKruger [1] made a simple modification to the error back-propagation algorithm to allow the use of fuzzy membership in network training. The membership function was constructed based on geometric properties of the pattern space, and the membership value for each training pattern was computed as a non-linear function of the normalized distance from each pattern to the centroid of a pattern class. These membership values were used in network training for the spatial classification of synthetic data clusters and for the voiced-unvoiced classification of speech signals [2]. Results indicated that the use of fuzzy membership exhibited a number of desired properties for network training and classification [1].

The Hunt et al.'s method for computing fuzzy membership, however, is appropriate when each class of pattern constitutes a convex set, i.e, each class of pattern occupies a continuous area in the feature space. The method is not directly applicable when each class of pattern has a multi-center data structure, in which patterns of the same class may cluster around several centers and the space between these clusters may be occupied by patterns of a different class. A multi-center data structure is typical in many practical applications of pattern classification and the problem of isolated word recognition exemplifies the situation.

In this work, we modified the method for computing fuzzy membership so that it is equally applicable to simple convex and multi-center data sets. The modified method was applied to network training for isolated word recognition. Section I presents the modification of the fuzzy membership function. Section II describes the procedures and results of experiments using this membership function. Section III includes the discussions and conclusions.

II. THE MODIFIED FUZZY MEMBERSHIP FUNCTION

The original fuzzy membership function is defined as a nonlinear, monotonic-decreasing function of the normalized L_2 norm between each training vector and the cluster center. The function has the form

$$\phi_r(x_k) = \frac{2}{1 + exp(f_r(x_k)^p)} \tag{1}$$

where x_k is the kth feature vector, $f_r(\cdot)$ is a function described below, p is a parameter that controls the rate of the exponential function, and $\phi_r(\cdot)$ is the membership for the rth class. The function f_r is the normalized distance from the centroid of the rth class, i.e.,

$$f_r(x_k) = (\bar{x}_r - x_k)^T C_r^{-1} (\bar{x}_r - x_k) \tag{2}$$

where $\bar{x}_r$ and C_r are the centroid vector and covariance matrix of the rth class.

As mentioned earlier, this membership function is defined mainly for data sets that have a single center for each class of pattern. An extension of this definition for a multi-center data set could be made through replacing the $\bar{x}_r$ in equation 2 by the centroid of cluster i in class r, $\bar{x}_r^i$, and use the same equation 1 for computing the membership. This simple modification, however, is not appropriate when the number of vectors in each cluster is significantly unbalanced. For example, when a group of training vectors of the same class forms two clusters and one cluster has a large number of vectors and the other one has a few, the vectors in the small cluster will have membership values that are comparable to those in the large cluster based on equation 1. These membership values, however, contradict the fact that vectors in the small cluster should not be as representative as those in the large cluster for the particular pattern class.

In our modification of the membership function, we add a multiplicative factor to equation 1 so that the membership function not only depends on the normalized L_2 norm between the training vector and the centroid; but also depends on the relative number of vectors in each cluster. The modified membership function is

$$\phi_r(x_k) = (n/N)^\alpha \frac{2}{1 + exp(f_r(x_k)^p)} \tag{3}$$

where n is the number of vector in cluster i, and N is the total number of vectors in class r. α controls the relative weight of this factor. $f_r(\cdot)$ now can be replaced by

$$f_r(x_k) = (\bar{x}_r^i - x_k)^T C_r^{-1} (\bar{x}_r^i - x_k) \tag{4}$$

where $\bar{x}_r^i$ is the centroid of cluster i of class r. Equation 3 will be the same as equation 1 for a simple convex data set.

We note that the membership function so defined has the requisite property to be a membership function, i.e., it maps any vector in the pattern space into the interval $[0, +1]$. It also satisfies our geometric intuition since a vector near the centroid and within a large cluster should have a membership value that approaches one, and a vector either far away from the centroid or within a relatively small cluster should have a membership value that approaches zero.

We recognize that this membership function is data-defined. Information for constructing the membership function such as the number of vector in each cluster, the number of cluster in each class, and the centroid vector and covariance matrix of each cluster will be determined using statistical methods. Thus, parameters for constructing the membership function may not be available from a *priori* theoretical prescription. A more instructive discussion on data-defined, rather than linguistically defined, membership can be found in the article of Hunt et al. [1].

III. ISOLATED WORD RECOGNITION

In the following experiments, this modified membership function was applied to the problem of isolated word recognition. A few remarks about isolated word recognition are in order.

It is well-known that the vector quantization (VQ) method is extremely effective for the classification of patterns that have a multi-center data structure [3]. In the VQ method, the training of a classifier is accomplished by successively reorganizing the training data into a given number of clusters until each cluster possesses certain desired statistical properties [4]. A codebook is then generated from the training patterns based on the data clusters, and used as a dictionary for pattern recognition. Using the method of vector quantization, together with other techniques such as dynamic time warping and Hidden Markov Chain modeling, isolated word recognition can achieve an accuracy greater than 90% [5, 6]. It is not our intention here to compete with such a comprehensive word recognition system. Our focus is to see if the use of fuzzy membership in training could improve the performance of an artificial neural network in a limited word recognition problem. We used the straightforward vector quantization method here mainly for the following reasons:

1. The results obtained using VQ establishes a baseline where a comparison of performances between this classical pattern classification method and the neural network can be made.

2. The clustering process in vector quantization provides information on the structure of the data set and can be used for fuzzy membership computations.

A. Vocabulary

The database of this work consisted of isolated words produced by twenty female graduate students in the Department of Speech and Hearing Sciences of University of Arizona. Each subject read a word list consisting of eight repetitions of 10 digits, 26 alphabet letters, and 16 words (see appendix A). These words were recorded using a microphone and an audio tape recorder. The microphone was placed at about 10 cm from the lips of the speaker during recording and all recordings were made in a quiet room.

These recordings were digitized into the computer using a 10 kHz sampling rate and a 16 bit quantization level. The signal was passed through a lowpass filter with a cut-off frequency of 4.5 kHz prior to digitization. A waveform editor was used visually to label the silence space between words.

Two subsets of words from the labeled speech files were used in the experiments. One subset was the 10 numerical digits and the other was all the alphabet letters that contain the vowel /i/, i.e., the letter B, C, D, E, G, P, T, V, and Z. The first subset is a easy vocabulary set and the second subset is a difficult one for recognition [7]. For example, B and D only differ by one phoneme at the beginning of the word and there is little information to compensate for the small acoustical differences between them.

We assert that the use of vocabulary sets that have different degrees of possible pattern overlapping in the pattern space allows us to have a more complete examination of the advantages and limitations of using fuzzy membership in network training [1]. The similarity in size of these two data sets also allows for easy comparison of results.

B. Feature Vector

The feature vector for each word has sixty elements which include the normalized gain constant and cepstral coefficients of perceptual, linear predictive spectra [8]. The process of computing the feature vector is summarized as follows:

1. FFT short-term power spectra were computed for each word. A 25.6 ms Hamming window and a 12.8 ms window step size were used in the computation.

2. The short-term power spectra were warped in frequency based on the psychoacoustical bark scale and smoothed in amplitude by 16 weighting functions that simulate the critical bands of human auditory system.

3. This power spectra were time-normalized into a fixed (10) number of frames. The time normalization was made based on the relative spectral variation rate within each word. Only those spectral frames that produced a relatively large rate of spectral variation were kept.

4. Each frame of the time-normalized power spectra was approximated by a 5th order linear predictive (LP) model. The normalized

gain constant of the LP model and 5 cepstral coefficients, which were converted from the 5 LP coefficients, produced 6 elements for each frame.

5. The final feature vector for each word was a sequential concatenation of the 10 frames of feature elements.

In all the following experiments, the feature vectors were organized into 3 groups: the training set, the closed set, and the open set. Words in the training set were used for training exclusively. A word in the closed set means that other words from the speaker had been used for training before the recognition; whereas a word in the open set means that words from the speaker had never been used for training. There were 400 training vectors for digits and 360 training vectors for letters (4 repetitions of each word from 10 speakers). The number of vectors in the closed set was the same as the number of vectors in the training set (the other 4 repetitions of each word from the same 10 speakers). The number of vectors in the open set was 800 for digits and 720 for letters (8 repetitions of each word from the other 10 speakers). The division of feature vectors into these 3 sets was made randomly.

C. Word Recognition using Vector Quantization

The method of vector quantization was used first for the isolated word recognition. Training was accomplished using a modified LBG algorithm, in which only one cluster was split for each clustering cycle [4]. The number of clusters was a controlled parameter for the vector quantization algorithm and varied from 1 to 14 (at which the error rate for digit training set reached zero). Recognition was made based on the L_2 norm between the input and the cluster centers. Recognition error rates as a function of number of cluster can be summarized as the following.

1. The error rate is a decreasing function of the number of clusters for the training set.

2. The error rate for the closed set has a shallow minimum as the number of cluster increases.

3. The error rate for the open set behaves similarly to that for the closed set. The magnitude of error for the open set, however, is much larger than that for the closed set.

4. The error rate for letter recognition is much larger than that for digit recognition.

We noted that the best recognition rate do not result from minimizing the error rate for the training set, which is supportive to our claim that the decision surface should not fit all training patterns tightly in order to achieve an optimal recognition rate in pattern recognition.

D. Recognition Using Neural Network

The word recognition here was made by a neural network. The network was trained using the method of Hunt et al. for including fuzzy membership in the error back-propagation algorithm or the fuzzy back-propagation (FBP) algorithm [1]. For comparison, the network also was trained using the conventional back-propagation (BP) algorithm.

Fuzzy membership values were computed using the modified fuzzy membership function (equation 3) with $p = 1.5$ and $\alpha = 0.2$. All other necessary information for computing fuzzy membership, i.e., the centroid and covariance of each cluster, the number of vector in each cluster, and the number of cluster in each pattern class, was obtained from results of vector quantization.

The network architecture was a high-order, flat-net, due to the consideration that substantial reduction of acoustic information was made in the feature extraction process, and the final feature vector was approximately an uncorrelated or orthogonal representation of each word. In this network, the input nodes were inter-connected fully and directly with the output nodes. The number of nodes in the input layer was equal to the length of the feature vector (60), and the number of node in the output layer was equal to the number of output category which was 10 for digits and 9 for letters.

Network recognition was made by identifying the node that had the maximum output. If the maximum was not unique, one of the maxima was chosen randomly. A classification error was counted whenever the maximum of the output was located at a node other than the predesignated node for the particular word during training. Recognition error rates were computed for each training scheme (BP and FBP) in every 20 training iterations until a total of 4000 training iterations were exhausted. The classification error rates as a function of number of training iterations can be summarized as the following.

1. The error rate for the training set is a monotonic, decreasing function of the number of

training iterations.

2. The error rate for the closed set has a minimum as the number of training iteration increases.

3. The error rate for the open set also has a minimum. This minimum, however, does not occur simultaneously with the minimum for the closed set.

4. The magnitude of error for the open set is larger than that for the closed set. The error rate for letter recognition is much larger than that for digit recognition.

Here, we noted again that the best classification rates for the closed and open sets do not result from minimizing the error rate for the training set.

The classification error rate for network trained by the FBP algorithm was a function of the number of clusters used in the fuzzy membership computation. The best network performance was obtained when the number of clusters was around 5 and the worst network performance was obtained when the number of clusters was 1 for both digit and letter recognitions.

The classification error rates as a function of training iterations for digit and letter recognition indicate that the network trained by the FBP algorithm achieved a higher overall performance than that trained by the BP algorithm when the number of clusters was chosen properly for computing the fuzzy membership. To make a specific comparison, let us use the minimum error rate for the closed set recognition to determine weights for the network and compare the error rates for open set recognition, which are plotted in Fig. 1 together with error rates for vector quantization. As can be seen, the network trained by the FBP has the lowest error rates for both digit and letter recognitions. The difference in error rate between networks trained by BP and FBP algorithm is particularly significant for letters than for digits, which is consistent with our early findings that the use of fuzzy membership in network training increases the performance of the network more significantly for patterns that occupy partial overlapping regions in the feature space than for patterns that rarely overlap [1].

IV. Discussions and Conclusions

The relatively high error rates for the vector quantization method can be attributed, in part, to

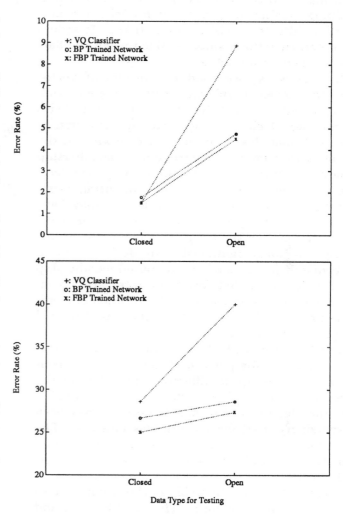

Figure 1: Error rates for digit recognition (top) and alphabet recognition (bottom)

the limited size of the training set. Typically, hundreds or thousands of training samples are needed in building a reliable VQ-classifier because of the statistical nature of the vector quantization method. When the size of training set is limited, as occurs in certain practical situations, the neural network could be a superior alternative, as has been demonstrated before [2].

The use of a flat-net seems to be an oversimplified approach for the word recognition task defined here. However, we have tried many network architectures with different degree of complexities; but none of them produces a recognition rate higher than that of the flat-net. Because the purpose of this work is to examine the effect of using of fuzzy membership function in network training, further extensive search of the best network architecture was not undertaken. It should be noted that the results obtained using the flat-net are quite reasonable.

In this work, we used the results of vector quantization to provide information for computing fuzzy membership. Interestingly, the best choice of number of clusters for vector quantization in terms of final classification error rate was not the same as that for the construction of membership function. Thus, before an optimal way for selecting the number of clusters for computing membership can be derived, this selection may have to be made on a *posteriori* basis. It is clear, however, that neither too few nor too many clusters for computing fuzzy membership are desirable. From informal inspections of the computed membership values, it seems that low error rates are associated with a skewed-Gaussian distribution of membership with the center of gravity biased toward larger membership.

Finally, we would like to point out that statistical methods for pattern classification and neural network use quite different approaches for the training of a classifier. Because of its simplicity and flexibility, the neural network has been increasingly used for pattern classification. The use of fuzzy membership in network training could function as a bridge between these two approaches.

In conclusion, we presented a modification to the use of fuzzy membership in the training of an artificial neural network. This modified method enables the computation of fuzzy membership for data that have a multi-center structure in the feature space. The method was applied to network training for isolated word recognition and an overall reduction of error rate was obtained.

REFERENCES

[1] B. Hunt, Y. Qi, and D. Dekruger, "Fuzzy classification using set membership functions in the back propagation algorithm," *Heuristics, Journal of Knowledge Engineering*, vol. 5, pp. 62–74, 1992.

[2] Y. Qi and B. Hunt, "Voiced-Unvoiced-Silence classifications of speech using hybrid features and a network classifier," *IEEE Trans. Acoust., Speech, Signal Processing*, vol. In Press, 1992.

[3] J. Makhoul, S. Roucos, and H. Gish, "Vector quantization in speech coding," *Proc. IEEE*, vol. 73, pp. 1551–1589, 1985.

[4] Y. Linde, A. Buzo, and R. Gray, "An algorithm for vector quantizer design," *IEEE Trans. Commun.*, vol. COM-28, pp. 84–95, Jan. 1980.

[5] B. Juang, "On the hidden markov model and dynamic-time warping for speech recognition – a unified view," *AT&T B.L.T.J.*, vol. 63, pp. 1213–1243, 1984.

[6] L. Morgan and S. Scofiled, *Neural Network and Speech Processing*. Englewood Cliffs, New Jersey: Prentice-Hall, 1991.

[7] R. Cole, K. Fanty, Y. Muthusamy, and M. Gopalakrishnan, "Speaker-independent rcognition of spoken english letters," in *IJCNN*, vol. 2, (San Diego, CA), pp. 45–51, 1990.

[8] Y. Qi and R. Fox, "Analysis of nasal consonants using perceptual linear prediction," *J. Acoust. Soc. Amer.*, vol. 91, pp. 1718–1726, 1992.

Evolving Fuzzy Clusters

David B. Fogel
Patrick K. Simpson

ORINCON Corporation
9363 Towne Centre Drive
San Diego, CA 92121

Abstract - An alternate training technique for the fuzzy min-max clustering neural network is introduced. The original fuzzy min-max clustering neural network utilized an algorithm similar to leader clustering and adaptive resonance theory to place hyperboxes in the pattern space. This paper introduces an alternative clustering technique that utilizes evolutionary programming and information criteria to produce a set of hyperboxes.

I. INTRODUCTION

Fuzzy min-max neural networks represent a synergism of fuzzy sets and neural networks in a unified framework. The use of fuzzy sets as classes (Zadeh, 1965), as clusters (Ruspini, 1969), and as basis functions for function approximation (Wang & Mendel, 1992) is well known. Fuzzy min-max neural networks create fuzzy set classes, clusters, and basis functions in a similar fashion using a membership function based on a hyperbox core. Fuzzy min-max neural network classification (Simpson, 1992a) creates classes from the union of fuzzy sets. Fuzzy min-max neural network clustering (Simpson, 1990a & 1992b) creates clusters from individual fuzzy sets. Fuzzy min-max neural network function approximation uses fuzzy clusters as basis functions (Simpson & Jahns, 1992). This paper presents a superior approach to finding the hyperbox cores used for fuzzy clusters. The previous approach was based upon leader clustering (Hartigan, 1975) and adaptive resonance theory (Carpenter & Grossberg, 1987). In this paper we introduce the use of evolutionary programming (Fogel, et al., 1966; Fogel, 1992) to determine the placement of the hyperbox cores that are used for the fuzzy min-max clustering neural network.

This paper is organized as follows. In section II is a review of fuzzy sets and the hyperbox membership functions used by fuzzy min-max neural networks. Section III reviews fuzzy min-max clustering neural network. Section IV introduces the evolutionary programming approach to determining hyperbox placement. Section V provides results from a two-dimensional data set that illustrates the utility of the evolutionary approach to hyperbox placement. Section VI offers some conclusions and describes future work.

II. FUZZY SETS AND FUZZY MIN-MAX CLUSTERS

A. Fuzzy Set Definition

A fuzzy set α is defined as an ordered pair

$$\alpha = \{x, m_\alpha(x)\} \ \forall \, x \in X \tag{1}$$

where X is the entire space of objects, x is an object from X, and $0 \le m_\alpha(x) \le 1$ is a membership function that describes that degree to which x belongs to the set α.

B. Fuzzy Sets as Clusters

Fuzzy sets bring a new dimension to traditional clustering systems by allowing a pattern to belong to multiple clusters to different degrees. Each fuzzy set is a separate cluster. In the fuzzy min-max clustering neural network, a fuzzy set is defined as a membership function that uses a hyperbox core. If the patterns being clustered have only one dimension, the hyperbox membership function collapses to the common trapezoid membership function.

To make the computations simpler, the pattern space is rescaled to the unit hypercube. As such, hyperboxes lie within the unit hypercube. A hyperbox is completely defined by a min-point and a max-point. The hyperbox membership function for the j'th hyperbox, b_j, is defined as

$$\begin{aligned}
b_j &= f(A_h, V_j, W_j) \\
&= \frac{1}{n} \sum_{i=1}^{n} \big[1 - g(v_{ji} - a_{hi}, \gamma) \\
&\qquad\qquad - g(a_{hi} - w_{ji}, \gamma) \big]
\end{aligned} \tag{2}$$

where g is the common ramp transfer function defined as

$$g(x, \gamma) = \begin{cases} 1 & \text{if} \quad x\gamma > 1 \\ x & \text{if} \quad 0 \le x\gamma \le 1 \\ 0 & \text{if} \quad x < 0 \end{cases} \tag{3}$$

and where the remaining parameters are defined as follows:

$A_h \in [0,1]^n$ h'th input pattern $A_h = (a_{h1}, a_{h2}, ..., a_{hn})$,

h	index for the patterns. The number of patterns is not specified here. It is not necessary for the algorithm to have this information because it is an on-line learning clusterer,
n	number of dimensions for the input patterns and the input layer,
p	number of fuzzy set hyperboxes (i.e. number of clusters),
γ	*the slope of the membership function.* A value of $\gamma = 1.0$ will guarantee that the membership function will cover the entire space. Values greater than *1* will sharpen the sides of the trapezoidal membership function,
$V_j \in [0,1]^n$	min vector for the j'th hyperbox fuzzy set, $V_j = (v_{j1}, v_{j2}, ..., v_{jn}), j = 1, 2, ..., p$, and
$W_j \in [0,1]^n$	max vector for the *j*'th hyperbox fuzzy set $W_j = (w_{j1}, w_{j2}, ..., w_{jn}), j = 1, 2, ..., p$.

III. EVOLUTIONARY PROGRAMMING OVERVIEW

Simulating evolution provides a stochastic optimization algorithm. There are three main lines of investigation in this field: evolutionary programming (Fogel, 1962, 1964; Fogel et al., 1966; Conrad, 1974; Atmar, 1976; Fogel, 1991a, 1992), evolution strategies (Schwefel, 1965; Rechenberg, 1973; Schwefel, 1981; Bäck et al., 1991) and genetic algorithms (Fraser, 1957; Bremermann, 1958; Reed et al., 1967; Holland, 1975; Goldberg, 1989; Davis, 1991). Space limitations preclude a detailed description of the similarities and differences between these approaches. Broadly, both evolutionary programming and evolution strategies simulate evolution at the phenotypic level (the adaptation and diversity of behavior) whereas genetic algorithms simulate evolution at the genotypic level (the manner in which genetic mechanisms transform DNA). For more information regarding philosophical and mathematical justification for these approaches, see Holland (1992), Atmar (1992), Fogel (1992).

IV. EVOLVING FUZZY CLUSTERS

The present clustering experiments focus on the use of evolutionary programming to optimize the position of a variable number of boxes given a set of two-dimensional data. The use of two-dimensional data allows visual analysis of the clustering performance. Extensions beyond two dimensions is the subject of future work. An initial population of 250 solutions was chosen by first determining a random number of boxes for the selected solution, ranging uniformly between one and five. Two defining points for each box (min,max) were then selected at random from a uniform

distribution ranging between [0,100]. The data was assumed to be in the range [0,100] in both dimensions. One offspring was created from each parent. The position of all boxes in the selected parent was varied by adding a Gaussian random variable with a mean of zero and variance of one to both dimensions of each defining minimum and maximum point. Further, there was a 50 percent chance of varying the number of boxes for each solution. If a change was indicated, there was an equal chance for adding or deleting a box up to the maximum of five and down to the minimum of one. Boxes to be added to placed randomly (uniform) in the range [0,100] in each dimension. Boxes to be deleted were selected at random with equal probability.

Scoring all parents and offspring with respect to the quality of clustering is analogous to choosing and weighting an optimal subset of regressor variables in statistical modeling. In optimal subset selection, it is desired to include those independent variables that are relevant in explaining a significant percentage of the variation of the dependent variable, but it is recognized that the inclusion of a sufficient number of extraneous variables can completely "explain" the available data while yielding no insight into the underlying process. It is desired that the model include as many regressors as possible so that the "information content" in these factors can influence the predicted value of the dependent variable; yet it is also desired that the model include as few regressors as possible because the variance of the model's predictions increases as the number of regressors increases (Montgomery and Peck, 1982).

Fogel (1991b) indicated a relationship between selecting and weighting regressor variables and determining optimal neural structures (nodes and connection strengths) in pattern classification problems. He proposed the use of an information statistic based on *Akaike's information criterion (AIC)* (Akaike, 1974). This measure provides a justifiable trade-off between the residual error associated with a network and the number of free weights and bias terms. A similar procedure can be used to assess the appropriateness of any clustering of data provided by a fuzzy min-max neural network.

In the present research, scoring was accomplished using a *minimum description length principle (MDL)* (Risannen, 1984). This procedure is similar to the *AIC*. The *MDL* was derived such that a minimum coding for a given set of data would be obtained. The specific criterion is:

$$MDL(\theta) = -log_2 (f(x/\theta)) + 0.5p \, log_2 n \qquad (4)$$

where x is the observed data, $f(x/\theta)$ is the conditional likelihood function given a parameter vector θ, p is the number of independently adjusted parameters in θ, and n is the data size. The first term indicates the goodness-of-fit of the clustering while the second term provides a penalty function for having to use a given number of clusters. The optimum θ minimizes the *MDL*. The application of the *MDL* requires the assumption of a parametric distribution of points in a cluster defined as the interior of a positioned box. This was assumed to be uniform over the area of the box. The *MDL* for any box was then determined simply by counting the number of data points contained in that box (*p = 4* for any box). After all assigned boxes were assessed, consideration was given to points that were not contained in any box. These points were treated as outliers drawn from a uniform distribution over the entire available range of the data [0,100] in both dimensions. The total *MDL* for a given solution was determined by summing each of the individual MDL scores for each box in that solution including the box containing any outliers.

There are specific considerations in the use of the *MDL* that deserve greater attention:

(1) Under the assumed uniform distribution, the likelihood for any point in a box is:

$$l = 1/((b-a)(d-c)), \qquad (5)$$

where *(a,b)* and *(c,d)* are the ranges in the first and second dimension, respectively. Thus, the *MDL* will be minimized at negative infinity should any box converge to bound even a single data point and have zero width or height. The penalty term associated with boxes that contain only one datum (*n = 1*) vanishes. To relieve this problem, the *MDL* of a box was only scored when it contained two or more data points. This is intuitively reasonable as it makes little sense to speak of a "cluster" of one point.

(2) If a box contains no data (*n = 0*), the penalty term becomes negative infinity and again the *MDL* score is minimized inappropriately. Requiring a box to contain at least two points before it will be scored removes this problem but then extraneous boxes that contain no data incur no penalty. This can be handled in two ways. A small penalty term can be applied to the overall MDL of a solution for each box regardless of the number of data points each contains, or boxes that contain no data can be pruned at the completion of a clustering run. The latter method was used in the current experiments.

(3) The *MDL* for any outliers can be assessed even if there is only one such datum. As the size of the outlier box is constrained to be the entire available range of the data, there is no possibility of driving the *MDL* score to negative infinity by perfectly fitting a box to the outlier. The choice of the value of *p* for the outlier box may at first appear problematic as it is constrained to always be the range of the data. Its location is not free to vary. Yet, just like any other box, it is defined by four parameters. As the *MDL* is used to assess a fixed clustering, it is reasonable to impose a penalty term for the outlier box just as for any other box.

Probabilistic survival was incorporated by imposing a round-robin competition based on each solution's *MDL* score as described in Fogel (1991a). In broad terms, the

lower a solution's *MDL* score the greater the chance that it would be retained. A *generation* consisted of one complete iteration of mutation, evaluation and selection. Evolution was halted after 250 generations.

V. EXPERIMENTAL RESULTS

Three specific clustering problems were considered. The first involved two nonoverlapping clusters of data. The first had data uniformly distributed between 20 and 40 in the first dimension (denoted *U(20,40)*) and distributed *U(40,60)* in the second dimension. The second cluster had data distributed *U(60,80)* and *U(40,60)* in the first and second dimensions, respectively. The final best clustering appears in **Figure 1**. There were no outliers and the boxes tightly fit the data. **Figure 2** indicates the optimization of the best and mean *MDL* scores as a function of the number of generations. These curves are typical of the rate of optimization achieved in other evolutionary programming applications (Fogel and Atmar, 1992).

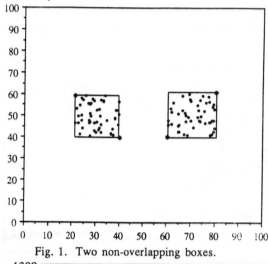

Fig. 1. Two non-overlapping boxes.

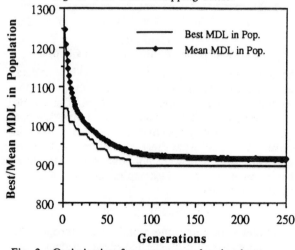

Fig. 2. Optimization for two nonoverlapping boxes.

The second case involved a simple modification of the first in which a narrow bridge of data between the two boxes was included. These data were distributed

$U(40,60)$ and $U(49,51)$ in the first and second dimension, respectively. The process rapidly converges on an optimal solution, indicated in **Figure 3**. Four data were not included in any cluster. **Figure 4** indicates the optimization of the best and mean *MDL* scores as a function of the number of generations.

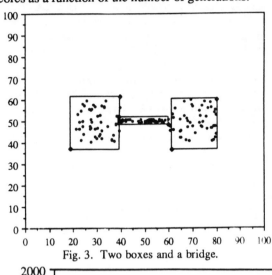

Fig. 3. Two boxes and a bridge.

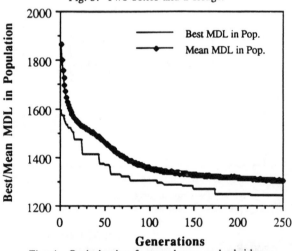

Generations

Fig. 4. Optimization for two boxes and a bridge.

The third case involved two overlapping regions of data. The first was distributed $U(40,60)$ and $U(30,50)$ in the first and second dimensions, respectively. The second was distributed $U(55,75)$ and $U(45,65)$ in the first and second dimensions, respectively. The data appears in **Figure 5**. The final best clustering appears in **Figure 6**. Five data were not contained in any box. The optimization of the best and mean *MDL* scores is indicated in **Figure 7**.

VI. CONCLUSIONS

Evolutionary programming rapidly and appropriately placed hyperboxes to cluster the observed data. The specific algorithm used was very rudimentary. It did not incorporate the standard methods of scaling the variance of perturbation terms as a function of the overall error (Fogel, 1991) or more sophisticated methods of self-

optimizing the mutation terms (Bäck et al., 1991; Fogel et al., 1992). These methods provide the potential to refine the placement and assignment of hyperboxes beyond that which was observed in the current experiments. The evolution of the hyperboxes was relatively quick, requiring only four minutes of CPU time per trial on a 15 MIPS Sun IPC Workstation. However, execution time will increase with dimensionality and the number of boxes assigned.

Evolutionary programming provides an innovative approach to placing hyperboxes in pattern space that serve as the core for fuzzy clusters. This is an important example of how evolutionary algorithms can be utilized to determine the parameters for the cluster membership function. In addition, evolutionary programming can also be used to determine the fuzzy membership functions for problems in control, forecasting, and information processing. The combination of evolutionary and fuzzy systems has significant engineering and scientific potential.

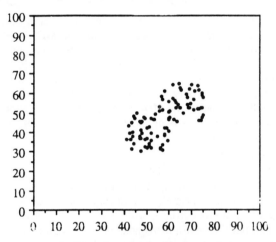

Fig. 5. Data for two overlapping boxes.

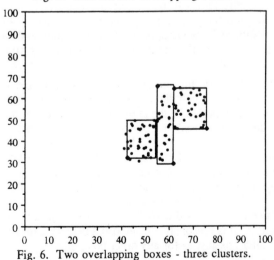

Fig. 6. Two overlapping boxes - three clusters.

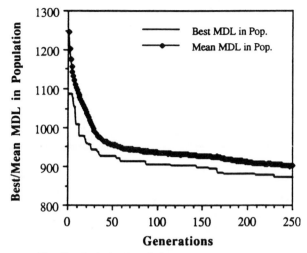

Fig. 7. Optimization for two overlapping boxes.

REFERENCES

Akaike, H. (1974). A New Look at the Statistical Model Identification, *IEEE Trans. Auto. Cont.*, Vol., 19, No. 6, pp. 716-723, 1974.

Atmar, J.W. (1976). Speculation on the Evolution of Intelligence and Its Possible Realization in Machine Form, Doctoral dissertation, New Mexico State University, Las Cruces, NM.

Atmar, J.W. (1992). The Philosophical Errors that Plague both Evolutionary Theory and Simulated Evolutionary Programming, *Proc. of the First Ann. Conf. on Evolutionary Programming*, D.B. Fogel and W. Atmar (Eds.), Evolutionary Programming Society, La Jolla, CA, pp. 27-34.

Bäck, T., Hoffmeister, F. and Schwefel, H.-P. (1992). A Survey of Evolution Strategies, *Proc. of the Fourth Int. Conf. on Genetic Algorithms*, R.K. Belew and L.B. Booker (Eds.), Morgan Kaufmann Publishers, San Mateo, pp. 2-9.

Bezdek, J. (1981). *Pattern Recognition with Fuzzy Objective Function Algorithms*, Plenum Press, New York.

Bezdek, J. (1987). Some non-standard clustering algorithms, *NATO ASI Series, vol. G14: Developments in Numerical Ecology*, P; Legendre & L. Legendre, Eds., Springer-Verlag, Berlin.

Bremermann, H.J. (1958). The Evolution of Intelligence. The Nervous System as a Model of Its Environment, Tech. Report No. 1, Contract No. 477(17), Dept. of Mathematics, Univ. of Washington, Seattle.

Carpenter, G. & Grossberg, S. (1987). A massively parallel architecture for a self-organizing neural pattern recognition machine, *Computer Vision, Graphics & Image Understanding*, Vol. 37, pp. 54-115.

Conrad, M. (1974). Evolutionary Learning Circuits, *J. Theo. Biol.*, Vol. 46, pp. 167-188.

Davis, L., Ed. (1991). *Handbook of Genetic Algorithms*, Van Nostrand Reinhold, NY.

Fogel, D.B.(1991a). *System Identification through Simulated Evolution: A Machine Learning Approach to Modeling*, Ginn Press, Needham, MA.

Fogel, D.B. (1991b). An information criterion for optimal neural network selection, *IEEE Trans. Neural Networks*, Vol. 3, No. 5, pp. 490-497.

Fogel, D.B. (1992). Evolving Artificial Intelligence," Doctoral dissertation, UCSD, 1992.

Fogel D.B. and Atmar W.. Eds. (1992). *Proc. of the First Ann. Conf. on Evolutionary Programming*, Evolutionary Programming Society, La Jolla, CA.

Fogel, D.B., Fogel, L.J., Atmar, W., Fogel, G.B. (1992). Hierarchic methods of evolutionary programming, *Proc. of the First Ann. Conf. on Evolutionary Programming*, D.B. Fogel and W. Atmar (Eds.), Evolutionary Programming Society, La Jolla, CA, pp. 175-182.

Fogel, L.J. (1962). Autonomous automata, *Industrial Research*, Vol. 4, pp. 14-19.

Fogel, L.J. (1964). On the Organization of Intellect, Doctoral dissertation, UCLA.

Fogel, L.J., Owens, A.J., and Walsh, M.J. (1966). *Artificial Intelligence through Simulated Evolution*, John Wiley, NY.

Fraser, A. (1957). Simulation of Genetic Systems by Automatic Digital Computers. I. Introduction, *Australian J. of Biol. Sci.*, Vol. 10, pp. 484-491, 1957.

Goldberg, D.E. (1989). *Genetic Algorithms in Search, Optimization and Machine Learning*, Addison-Wesley, Reading, MA.

Hartigan, J. (1975). *Clustering Algorithms*, John Wiley & Sons, New York.

Holland, J.H. (1975). *Adaptation in Natural and Artificial Systems*, Univ. of Mich. Press, Ann Arbor, MI.

Holland, J.H. (1992). *Adaptation in Natural and Artificial Systems*, 2nd ed., MIT Press.

Kohonen, T. (1990). *Self-Organization and Associative Memory: Third Edition*, Springer-Verlag, Berlin.

Montgomery, D.C. & Peck, E.A. (1982). *Introduction to Linear Regression Analysis*, John Wiley, NY.

Rechenberg, I. (1973). *Evolutionsstrategie: Optimierung Technischer Systeme nach Prinzipien der Biologischen Evolution*, Frommann-Holzboog Verlag, Stuttgart.

Reed, J., Toombs R., and Barricelli, N.A. (1967). Simulation of Biological Evolution and Machine Learning," *J. Theo. Biol.*, Vol. 17, pp. 319-342.

Rissanen, J. (1984). Universal Coding, Information, Prediction and Estimation, *IEEE Trans. Info. Theory*, Vol. 30, pp. 629-636.

Poggio, T. & Girosi, F. (1990). Networks for approximation and learning, *Proceedings of the IEEE*, Vol. 78, pp. 1481-1497.

Ruspini, E. (1969). A new approach to clustering, *Information and Control*, Vol. 15, pp. 22-32.

Schwefel, H.-P. (1965). Kybernetische Evolution als Strategie der Experimentellen Forschung in der Strömungstechnik, Diploma thesis, Technical Univ. of Berlin, 1965.

Schwefel, H.-P. (1981). *Numerical Optimization of Computer Models*, John Wiley, Chinchester, 1981.

Simpson, P. (1990a). Fuzzy adaptive resonance theory, *SIUC Neuroengineering Workshop*, Sept. 6-7, Carbondale, IL. Also, General Dynamics Electronics Division, Technical Report, GDE-ISG-PKS-11.

Simpson, P. (1990b). *Artificial Neural Systems: Foundations, Paradigms, Applications, and Implementations*, Pergamon Press: Elmsford, NY.

Simpson, P. (1991). Fuzzy min-max classification with neural networks, *Heuristics*, Vol. 4, No. 1, pp. pp. 1-9.

Simpson, P. (1992a). Fuzzy min-max neural networks: 1. classification, *IEEE Trans. on Neural Networks*, Vol. 3, pp. 776-786.

Simpson, P. (1992b). Fuzzy min-max neural networks: 2. clustering, *IEEE Trans. on Fuzzy Systems*, Vol. 1, No. 1, in press.

Simpson, P.& Jahns, G (1992). Fuzzy min-max neural networks for function approximation, *Twenty-Sixth Annual Asilomar Conference on Signals, Systems, and Computers*, Pacific Grove, CA, October 26-28.

Wang, L & Mendel, J. (1992). Universal approximation with fuzzy sets, *Proceedings of the First IEEE International Conference on Fuzzy Systems*, San Diego, CA, March 8-12.

Zadeh, L. (1965). Fuzzy sets, *Information and Control*, Vol. 8, pp. 338-353.

Neurofuzzy Interpolation: II - Reducing Complexity of Description

M. Regattieri   F. J. V. Zuben
UNICAMP/FEE/DCA - C.P. 6101 - Campinas - SP - 13081 - Brasil
e-mail: myriam@dca.fee.unicamp.br
vonzuben@dca.fee.unicamp.br

A. F. Rocha
RANI - Research on Natural and Artificial Intelligence
R. Tenente Ary Aps, 172 - 13200 - Jundiaí - SP - Brasil
e-mail: eina@bruc.bitnet

Abstract – This paper describes a neurofuzzy method of information compression. A neural-like structure is developed to operate on a set of sequential data in order to extract the minimal amount of data that can still accurately represent the entire original set. Fuzzy interpolation is used to regenerate the whole original set of data whenever necessary.

I. INTRODUCTION

Storage is a fundamental step in information processing. In many practical applications, however, memory restrictions impose serious constraints on data storage. A way to avoid the problem is to compress data. Redundancy and dependence cannot occur in a compressed data set. Each piece of stored compressed information shall not only represent a novelty but also allow the regeneration of the original data set as faithfully as possible. The information compression and the regeneration capability can both be considered complementary activities in the field of information processing. Systems with powerful information processing capabilities can, in the recall phase, restore all the information disregarded in the compression phase. It seems that human memory, to a great extent, operates in this way [1]. Biological systems almost without exception tend to optimize their resources, and this principle must also be reflected in the utilization of memory.

The purpose of the presented paper is to introduce a neural system for data compression (NSDC) which takes advantage of recent knowledge disclosed by biology about brains [2]. In this approach, neurons are assumed to be agents exchanging messages to compute the solution of a problem. The proof that NSDC selects the most representative data to store in a compressed way is provided by showing that nonlinear fuzzy interpolation [3] adequately restores the original data set.

Section II presents the general algorithm applied to extract the representative information from a given data set, as well as the neural structure that encodes this algorithm. Section III briefly describes how to reconstruct the original data set from the compressed one. Finally, in section IV, the power of the method is demonstrated in a typical application.

II. A NEURAL SYSTEM FOR DATA COMPRESSION (NSDC)

A. Neural Structure Description

The structure of NSDC (Fig. 1) is described here for the case of two-dimensional data sets. The net is supposed to sequentially receive each point (x_i, y_i), $i = 1,...,n$, from the original data set as its input, and to generate the compressed data set as its output. It performs this job in four sequential layers:

Layer I: Given two sequential points (x_i, y_i) and (x_{i+1}, y_{i+1}), it determines the direction d_j between them.

Layer II: Given two directions d_j and d_{j+1}, it calculates the variation of direction vd_k as clockwise, counter-clockwise or null.

Layer III: Given three sequential variations of direction vd_k, vd_{k+1} and vd_{k+2}, stored in Layer II, it determines whether this sequence contains a representative point (x_r, y_r). A representative point is defined whenever this sequence assumes one of a set of specific configurations (see Fig. 3). In other words a representative point corresponds to maximum, minimum or return point submitted to some constraints as explained in section 2B.

Layer IV: Given a memory storing the last five points in the sequence, (x_j, y_j) $(j=i-3,i-2,...,i+1)$, the representative point (x_r, y_r) is given by the second or third point in this sequence ($r=i-2$ or $i-1$), according to the decision process discussed in section 2B.

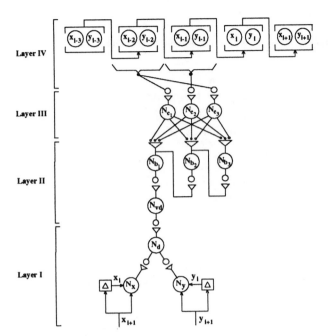

Fig. 1. The Neural System for Data Compression (NSDC)

B. Neural Processing Description

In the NSDC, the basic neuron computation is based on a transmitter-receptor (t/r) coupling [2], which activates an actuator $\underline{a}$ according to the following relation:

$$t_i + r_j \mapsto a_k, \qquad (1)$$

where:

+ corresponds to the matching or binding operation between the transmitter and the receptor

$\mapsto$ corresponds to the actuator activation

i indicates the type of transmitters released by the pre-synaptic activation

j indicates the type of receptors involved on the post-synaptic matching process

k indicates the type of actuator activated by the t/r coupling.

The actuators exert some actions on both the pre and post-synaptic neurons, as well as over neighboring cells. For example, they can operate as controllers, which are activated by the t/r binding in order to release other post-synaptic receptors for future bindings with specific transmitters (see (9)).

The amount $q(a)$ of the activated actuator is calculated as

$$q(a) = f\big(q(t), q(r), \mu(t, r)\big), \qquad (2)$$

where:

$q(t) \rightarrow$ the amount of transmitter released by the pre-synaptic neuron

$q(r) \rightarrow$ the amount of available post-synaptic receptor

$\mu(t, r) \rightarrow$ the t/r matching compatibility defined in the closed interval $[0,1]$

Layer I: The purpose of Layer I is to determine the position of (x_{i+1}, y_{i+1}) relative to (x_i, y_i), deciding among one of eight possible relative positions encoded as shown in Fig. 2. Layer I is formed by two sensorial neurons N_x and N_y and one output neuron N_d, that perform the following computations:

• The input u_i ($u = x$ or y) sets the thresholds α_1 and α_2 of the neuron N_u to compute the output o_u depending on the value of the input u_{i+1} as:

$$o_u = \begin{cases} 0 & \text{if} & u_{i+1} < \alpha_1 \\ 0.5 & \text{if} & \alpha_1 \leq u_{i+1} \leq \alpha_2 \ , \\ 1 & \text{if} & u_{i+1} > \alpha_2 \end{cases} \qquad (3)$$

$$\text{where} \begin{cases} \alpha_1 = u_i - \varepsilon \\ \alpha_2 = u_i + \varepsilon \end{cases} \varepsilon \rightarrow 0.$$

• This computation is supported by the fact that the pre-synaptic axons make two different contacts with the post-synaptic neuron N_u ($u = x$ or y) such that the previous input u_i is still available at one site when the actual input u_{i+1} is presented at the second site of N_u.

• The neurons N_x, N_y release the transmitters t_x, t_y to bind respectively the receptors r_x, r_y at the post-synaptic neuron N_d. The amounts $q(t_x)$ and $q(t_y)$ released by these pre-synaptic neurons are:

$$q(t_x) = o_x; \qquad q(t_y) = o_y; \qquad (4)$$

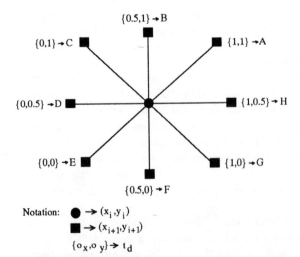

Fig. 2. The relative positions between (x_i, y_i) and (x_{i+1}, y_{i+1})

and the available amounts of r_x and r_y are assumed $q(r_x) = q(r_y) = 1$. Also, to allow up to eight different output values to be calculated at Layer I, we define:

$$\mu(t_x, r_x) = 0.5 ; \quad \mu(t_y, r_y) = 1; \quad (5)$$

Thus, assuming the function f in (2) as being a t-norm ($\times$), the activations promoted by N_x and N_y over N_d are:

$$\begin{cases} q(a_x) = q(t_x) \times q(r_x) \times \mu(t_x, r_x) = 0.5 o_x, \\ q(a_y) = q(t_y) \times q(r_y) \times \mu(t_y, r_y) = o_y, \end{cases} \quad (6)$$

and, from (6), the total activation v of neuron N_d is calculated as:

$$v = q(a_x) + q(a_y) = 0.5 o_x + o_y. \quad (7)$$

• The neuron N_d releases one of eight different types of transmitters depending on the actual value of v. Each of these transmitters encodes one of the directions (relative positions) defined in Fig. 2. Table 1 illustrates this encoding process that maps the pre-synaptic inputs o_x, o_y into the transmitter t_d released by the neuron N_d.

Layer II: This layer is composed of four associative neurons. Its purpose is to compute, at neuron N_{vd}, the variations of direction, and to store, at neurons N_{b_k} (k=1,2,3) the last three calculated variations. The computations at Layer II are summarized as follows:

• The transmitter t_d = A or B ...or H, released by the neuron N_d, binds the post-synaptic receptor $r_{vd} = \varnothing$ or A ...H located at the neuron N_{vd}, such that the t_d/r_{vd} coupling activates the actuator a_{vd} = Z or N or P or $\varnothing$ according to Table 2.

• The actuator a_{vd} performs the following actions:

◻ firstly, it activates N_{vd} to release the transmitter t_{vd} according to:

$$t_d + r_{vd} \mapsto a_{vd} \Rightarrow t_{vd} = \text{ Z or N or P or} \varnothing, \quad (8)$$

where:

Z → no change
N → clockwise change
P → counter-clockwise change
$\varnothing$ → no previous binding.

◻ secondly, it modifies the receptor r_{vd} according to:

$$t_d + r_{vd} \mapsto r_{vd} = t_d, \quad (9)$$

that is, it sets the receptor r_{vd} at time t_{i+1} equal to the transmitter t_d released at time t_i.

TABLE I
THE ENCODING PROCESS IN NEURON N_d: $\{o_x, o_y\} \rightarrow t_d$

o_x \ o_y	1	0.5	0
1	A	H	G
0.5	B	✕	F
0	C	D	E

TABLE II
THE MATCHING FUNCTION IN NEURON N_{vd}: $t_d + r_{vd} \mapsto a_{vd}$

r_{vd} \ t_d	A	B	C	D	E	F	G	H
A	Z	P	P	P	-	N	N	N
B	N	Z	P	P	P	-	N	N
C	N	N	Z	P	P	P	-	N
D	N	N	N	Z	P	P	P	-
E	-	N	N	N	Z	P	P	P
F	P	-	N	N	N	Z	P	P
G	P	P	-	N	N	N	Z	P
H	P	P	P	-	N	N	N	Z
$\varnothing$	$\varnothing$	$\varnothing$	$\varnothing$	$\varnothing$	$\varnothing$	$\varnothing$	$\varnothing$	$\varnothing$

• In this way, the neuron N_{vd} classifies the input points variation of direction into the type of released transmitter t_{vd}, and it stores information about the last detected direction into the receptor r_{vd}.

• The transmitter t_{vd} released by N_{vd} binds the receptor r_{b_1} of neuron N_{b_1} and it activates the actuator a_{b_1} to act upon the neuron N_{b_2}. The action of a_{b_1} is to set the transmitter released by neuron N_{b_2} at time t_{i+1} as the same transmitter released by N_{b_1} at time t_i. The actuator a_{b_2} released by neuron N_{b_2} acts in a similar way upon the neuron N_{b_3}. Thus, the transmitters released by N_{b_1}, N_{b_2} and N_{b_3} encode the sequence of the last three variations of direction.

Layer III: This layer is composed by three neurons N_{c1}, N_{c2} and N_{c3} deciding whether the input points sequence contains a representative point according to:

• The transmitters t_{b_k} (k=1,2,3) bind the correspondent receptors r_{c_j} of the neurons N_{c_j} (j=1,2,3) setting the output function according to:

$$o_{c_1} = \begin{cases} 1 & \text{if } t_{b_2} = t_{b_3} = \text{ N or P} \\ 0 & \text{otherwise} \end{cases}$$

$$o_{c_2} = \begin{cases} 1 & \text{if } t_{b_1} = t_{b_3} = \text{ Z and } t_{b_2} \neq \text{Z} \\ 0 & \text{otherwise} \end{cases} \quad (10)$$

$$o_{c_3} = \begin{cases} 1 & \text{if} \begin{cases} \left(t_{b_2} = \text{Z and } t_{b_1} = t_{b_3} \neq \text{Z} \right) \\ \left(t_{b_3} \neq \text{Z and } t_{b_1} = t_{b_2} = \text{Z} \right) \end{cases} \text{or} \\ 0 & \text{otherwise} \end{cases}$$

- If the sequence contains a representative point, it will be classified into three distinct patterns (Fig. 3a). Only one neuron N_{c_j} (j=1,2,3) may be activated at each processing time, according to (10), and

- N_{c_1} will classify Pattern I
- N_{c_2} will classify Pattern II
- N_{c_3} will classify Pattern III

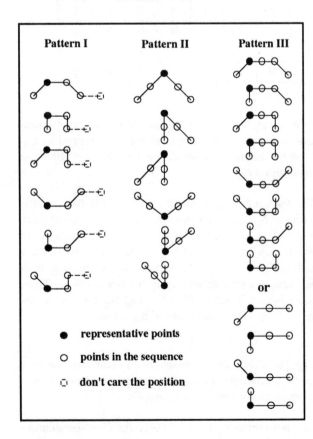

Fig. 3a. Three different types of patterns with representative points

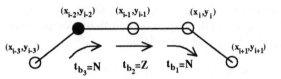

Fig. 3b. A pattern with a representative point

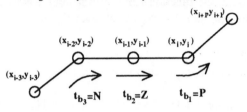

Fig. 3c. A pattern without a representative point

- Figs. 3b and 3c illustrate the sequence of transmitter released at neurons N_{b_j} (j=1,2,3) for two different input patterns. The values of t_{b_j} (j=1,2,3) in Fig. 3b set to one the output o_{c_3} of neuron N_{c_3}, classifying the input as Pattern III. The values of t_{b_j} (j=1,2,3) in Fig. 3c set to zero the outputs o_{c_j} (j=1,2,3), which means the absence of representative points in the input sequence.

Layer IV: This layer is composed of a set of five pairs of neurons storing the coordinates of the last five points in the input sequence, (x_j,y_j) (j=i-3, i-2, ...,i+1). The connections between Layers III and IV encode the decision process of selecting the representative point associated to the pattern classified at Layer III, such that:
- point (x_{i-2},y_{i-2}) is chosen in the case of patterns I and III
- point (x_{i-1},y_{i-1}) is chosen in the case of pattern II

The dynamic of the NSDC is described for the sequence of input points in Fig. 3b in what follows:

STEP 0 (Initialization)
- all variables are set to $\varnothing$

STEP 1
- NSDC inputs : $(x_{i-3},y_{i-3}),(x_{i-2},y_{i-2})$
- The neuron N_d releases the transmitter $t_d = \text{A}$.
- The coupling t_d/r_{vd} activates the actuator that acts:

    1. releasing the transmitter t_{vd} as :
$$\text{A} + \varnothing \rightarrow t_{vd} = \varnothing$$
    2. setting the receptor r_{vd} as :
$$\text{A} + \varnothing \rightarrow r_{vd} = t_d = \text{A}.$$

- $t_{b1} = t_{vd} = \varnothing$
  $t_{b2} = t_{b1} \text{ (step 0)} = \varnothing$
  $t_{b3} = t_{b2} \text{ (step 0)} = \varnothing$
- $o_{c1} = o_{c2} = o_{c3} = 0$
- $(x_r,y_r) = \varnothing$

1838

STEP 2
- NSDC inputs : $(x_{i-2}, y_{i-2}), (x_{i-1}, y_{i-1})$
- $t_d = H$.

- $H + A \mapsto \begin{cases} t_{vd} = N \\ r_{vd} = t_d = H \end{cases}$

- $t_{b1} = t_{vd} = N$
  $t_{b2} = t_{b1} \ (\text{step 1}) = \varnothing$
  $t_{b3} = t_{b2} \ (\text{step 1}) = \varnothing$
- $o_{c1} = o_{c2} = o_{c3} = 0$
- $(x_r, y_r) = \varnothing$

STEP 3
- NSDC inputs : $(x_{i-1}, y_{i-1}), (x_i, y_i)$
- $t_d = H$.

- $H + H \mapsto \begin{cases} t_{vd} = Z \\ r_{vd} = t_d = H \end{cases}$

- $t_{b1} = t_{vd} = Z$
  $t_{b2} = t_{b1} \ (\text{step 2}) = N$
  $t_{b3} = t_{b2} \ (\text{step 2}) = \varnothing$
- $o_{c1} = o_{c2} = o_{c3} = 0$
- $(x_r, y_r) = \varnothing$

STEP 4
- NSDC inputs : $(x_i, y_i), (x_{i+1}, y_{i+1})$
- $t_d = G$.

- $G + H \mapsto \begin{cases} t_{vd} = N \\ r_{vd} = t_d = G \end{cases}$

- $t_{b1} = t_{vd} = N$
  $t_{b2} = t_{b1} \ (\text{step 3}) = Z$
  $t_{b3} = t_{b2} \ (\text{step 3}) = N$
- $o_{c1} = o_{c2} = 0, \ o_{c3} = 1$.
- $(x_r, y_r) = (x_{i-2}, y_{i-2})$

III. The Nonlinear Fuzzy Interpolation

The nonlinear fuzzy interpolation (NLFI) [3] makes use of nonlinear fuzzy rules to interpolate general paths described by a set of sequential points and it is used here to restore the original data set from the compressed one.

Given the two-dimensional set of compressed data $\{(x_1, y_1), \dots (x_n, y_n)\}$, we want to interpolate the points of the intervals $[x_{i+1}, x_{i+2}]$ supported by the points (x_i, y_i), (x_{i+1}, y_{i+1}), (x_{i+2}, y_{i+2}) and (x_{i+3}, y_{i+3}) in order to recover the original data set. The three rules supporting the interpolation are:

$R^{(j)}$: If x is $A_{i+1}^{(j)}(x)$ then $y_{i+1}(x) = y_{i+1}^{(j)}(x)$ $j = 1, \dots, 3$; (11)

where:

$y_{i+1}^{(j)}(x) \rightarrow$ straight line passing through the points (x_{i+j-1}, y_{i+j-1}), (x_{i+j}, y_{i+j})

$A_{i+1}^{(j)}(x) \rightarrow$ fuzzy set with membership function $\mu_{A_{i+1}^{(j)}}(x)$

The nonlinear membership functions are defined as:

$$\mu_{A_{i+1}^{(1)}} = \begin{cases} \left[1 - \dfrac{x - x_i}{x_{i+1} - x_i} \right]^{k_1} & \text{if } x_i \neq x_{i+1} \\ 0 & \text{otherwise} \end{cases}$$

$$\mu_{A_{i+1}^{(2)}} = 1 \qquad\qquad (12)$$

$$\mu_{A_{i+1}^{(3)}} = \begin{cases} \left[\dfrac{x - x_i}{x_{i+1} - x_i} \right]^{k_2} & \text{if } x_i \neq x_{i+1} \\ 0 & \text{otherwise} \end{cases}$$

The exponents k_1 and k_2 are functions of the angles between the straight lines:

$$k_i = g(\alpha_i) \qquad i = 1, 2; \qquad (13)$$

where :

α_1 is the angle between $y_{i+1}^{(1)}$ and $y_{i+1}^{(2)}$
α_2 is the angle between $y_{i+1}^{(2)}$ and $y_{i+1}^{(3)}$

The y axis is translated to $y_{i+1}^{(2)}(x)$ and a factor $(-1)^n$ distinguishes function paths ($n \rightarrow$ odd values) from non-function paths ($n \rightarrow$ even values), in order to interpolate any kind of curve. The interpolated output is given by:

$$\hat{y}_{i+1}(x) = y_{i+1}^{(2)}(x) + \frac{\displaystyle\sum_{j=1}^{3} \mu_{A_{i+1}^{(j)}}(x) \times yrel_{i+1}^{(j)}(x) \times (-1)^n}{\displaystyle\sum_{j=1}^{3} \mu_{A_{i+1}^{(j)}}(x)}, \qquad (14)$$

where:

$$yrel_{i+1}^{(j)}(x) = y_{i+1}^{(j)}(x) - y_{i+1}^{(2)}(x) \qquad j = 1, 2, 3.$$

IV. SIMULATION RESULTS AND CONCLUSION

The simulation results (see Fig. 4) show the power of NSDC:

- Fig. 4a illustrates the original sequence of (x,y) coordinates, used as the input of the NSCD.
- Fig. 4b illustrates the compressed set of points produced by the NSCD as well as the interpolated curve generated from this compressed set.
- Fig. 4c shows that the nonlinear fuzzy interpolation is able to accurately reconstruct the original curve.

These results demonstrate the efficiency of the method proposed here and point to NSCD as a powerful system for data compression.

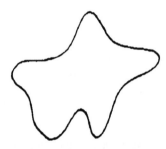

Fig. 4a. Original Curve

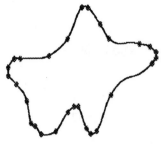

Fig. 4b. Interpolated Curve

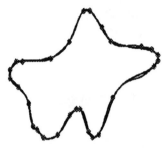

Fig. 4c. Superposition of Original and Interpolated Curves.

REFERENCES

[1] T. Kohonen, "Self-organization and associative memory," Springer-Verlag, 1989
[2] A. F. Rocha, "Neural nets: a theory for brains and machine," Lecture Notes in Artificial Intelligence, Springer-Verlag, 1992
[3] F. J. V. Zuben, M. Regattieri, and A. F. Rocha, "Neurofuzzy interpolation I - the theoretical background," Proceedings of the 2nd International Conference on Fuzzy Logic & Neural Networks, Iizuka, Japan, pp. 229-232, July 1992

Combination of Radial Basis Function Neural Networks with Optimized Learning Vector Quantization

Michael Vogt

University of Stuttgart

Institute for Parallel and Distributed High Performance Systems

Breitwiesenstr. 20–22, D–7000 Stuttgart 80, Fed. Rep. of Germany

Abstract—Radial basis function neural networks have received great interest during the last few years of neural network research. Using radial basis function networks, one important task is finding appropriate center vectors. A technique often used is simply selecting random center vectors out of the set of training patterns. Better network performance is achieved by using clustered vectors for initialization of the centers. One method which can be used to find such vectors is applying learning vector quantization. In this paper, randomly initialized networks are compared to networks whose centers are obtained by using vector quantization. It is shown that the error rate for small networks can be decreased by about 28 %. To achieve the same performance with a trained network as with a randomly initialized network, only half of the number of hidden neurons are needed. This fact may be important for time critical applications. Also, the time used for the training and initialization of a smaller network is comparable to the time used for the initialization of a larger network.

I. INTRODUCTION

Radial basis functions are a relatively new approach in simulating neural networks. They received a lot of interest in neural network research during the last few years ([2], [10]). Neural networks based on radial basis functions have been compared to backpropagation networks and to the method of k nearest neighbors in tasks of pattern recognition. They have been found to offer some interesting advantages ([8]).

Several approaches have been proposed to improve the generalization properties of radial basis function neural networks. Smoothing the network mapping, reducing the dimensionality, and clustering of the radial basis centers are some of the techniques used to achieve better network results.

In this paper I would like to describe a combination of optimized learning vector quantization (OLVQ) with radial basis function neural networks. Some interesting results concerning a sample application of handwritten digit recognition are presented.

This work was supported by the Ministry of Science and Art Baden–Württemberg on the contract number 7532.274–11/1.

II. RADIAL BASIS FUNCTIONS

A typical radial basis function neural network consists of three layers of neurons (input, hidden, output) which are components of a fully connected feedforward architecture. The special radial basis behavior is performed by the single layer of hidden neurons. The activation of a hidden neuron is determined in two steps: The first is computing the distance (usually by using the Euclidean norm) between the two vectors which are yielded by the activation of the input layer (x) and the link weights between the input layer and the current hidden neuron (m_j). Second, a function h which is usually bell–shaped (e.g. Gaussian) is applied, using the obtained distance to get the final activation of the hidden neuron. The activation of a neuron in the output layer (o_i) is determined as usual by computing the weighted sum of inputs. However, it is possible and often recommended to apply a sigmoidal activation function:

$$o_i = f_{sig}\left(\sum_{j=1}^{K} c_{j,i} \cdot h(\|x - m_j\|)\right) \quad (1)$$

Each of the K hidden neurons represents a point (center) in N–dimensional vector space, where N is the number of input neurons in the network. The position of the neuron in space is given by the N weights of the incoming links. One of the major advantages of radial basis function neural networks is the possibility of direct computation of optimal link weights between the hidden and the output layer. To perform this computation, the centers and a set of training patterns must be provided.

Using a bell–shaped function h, a hidden neuron becomes highly activated if the input vector is close to the represented center. The actual activation of the hidden neuron depends highly on its specific basis function h. Thinking of the Gaussian function, each hidden neuron may use a different standard deviation which performs stretching of the function along its single argument.

To demonstrate this effect, each hidden neuron can be seen as an N–dimensional hypersphere, the radius of which is given by the standard deviation. Input patterns yielding a point inside of the sphere will lead to a high activation of the corresponding neuron. Assuming a well–defined radial basis function neural network, the spheres which are represented by the hidden neurons cover the regions in vector space which correspond to the set of input patterns that are to be classified.

One of the difficulties concerning radial basis functions is choosing the appropriate center and the radius of each sphere. The radius can easily be set to a fraction of the distance between the current center and its nearest neighbor. The centers are usually determined by chosing a random subset of the training patterns.

Although the described procedure of setting centers and radii works satisfactorily for most problems, I would like to show the effect of a more intelligent choice of centers on the performance of the final network.

III. Learning Vector Quantization

Vector quantization is often used in pattern recognition tasks. Assuming a set of vectors placed into pattern space and labeled by class names, known as codebook vectors (cbvs), classification of an unknown vector x is done by locating the cbv m which is the nearest neighbor of x, and setting the class of x to the class to which m belongs.

Kohonen's learning vector quantization (LVQ, [4]) is one of the newer techniques of selecting proper cbvs. Pre–initialized cbvs are trained by moving in input space. For training of the vectors, the optimized-learning-rate LVQ (OLVQ) is often used ([3], [5]):

Let c be the index of the nearest vector m_c to x. Then learning is performed by:

$$m_c(t+1) = [1 - s(t)\alpha_c(t)]m_c(t) + s(t)\alpha_c(t)x(t) \quad (2)$$
$$m_i(t+1) = m_i(t) \quad \text{for} \quad i \neq c \quad (3)$$

The function $s(t)$ defines the direction of movement of m_c. If x is classified correctly by m_c, then m_c is moved in the direction of x. Otherwise, m_c is moved in the opposite direction:

$$s(t) = \begin{cases} +1 & : \quad \text{if } x \text{ is classified correctly by } m_c \\ -1 & : \quad \text{otherwise} \end{cases} \quad (4)$$

Each cbv m_i is trained by an individual learning rate α_i. The learning rate of the selected cbv m_c is determined by:

$$\alpha_c(t) = \frac{\alpha_c(t-1)}{1 + s(t)\alpha_c(t-1)} \quad (5)$$

The recursive definition causes α_c to decrease if m_c belongs to the same class as x. Otherwise, α_c increases.

Before training can be started, it is necessary to initialize all cbvs with properly defined values. After performing the training of the codebook several times, while using an adequate set of training samples x, the cbvs are distributed over all class domains in input space.

IV. Combining OLVQ and Radial Basis Function Neural Networks

Using trained cbvs as centers in radial basis function neural networks offers several advantages over using a simple random choice from the training data.

The main advantage is that the set of cbvs belonging to the same class will be distributed over the entire class domain in input space. For example, if the majority of the pre–initialized cbvs are located at the 'right hand side' of the class domain, some of them get pulled over by the 'left hand side' training patterns during training. In comparison, a randomly initialized set of centers in a radial basis network will never get repositioned unless a special training is performed. Training the centers of radial basis function networks by gradient descent is possible but since only very small learning rates can be used, the necessary number of training cycles increases ([12]).

Another advantage of using trained cbvs as centers is that the cbvs have learned something in addition to the specific features of their corresponding class. They have also learned which properties are misleading. Assume a cbv which represents the digit '5' in a task to recognize handwritten digits. This cbv has also learned not to recognize the digit '8', by learning negative coefficients (see fig. 1).

V. A Sample Application

The improvements which result from the initialization described above have been tested with a multitude of different

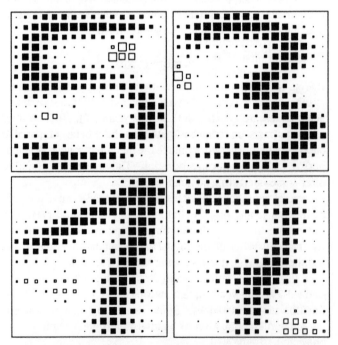

Fig. 1. Examples of trained codebook vectors. Negative coefficients (unfilled squares) are emphasized 30 times as compared to positive values (filled squares).

networks for the task of recognition of handwritten digits. The data consisted of 10,000 digits used for training and initialization, and another 10,000 digits used for testing. The digits had been taken from handwritten samples which were binarized, segmented, normalized in size and compressed to 16×16 images.

Based on the set of training digits, different numbers of cbvs (100, 200 and 400) were trained with different numbers of training cycles (10^3, 10^4, 10^5 and 10^6). The training was done using the program package 'LVQ_PAK' Version 2.0 ([5]) from Helsinki University of Technology.

Based on the trained cbvs, several radial basis function networks were created, using 100, 200 and 400 Gaussian hidden neurons respectively. The activation of the hidden neurons was performed using the Gaussian function

$$h(r) = e^{-\frac{r^2}{2\sigma^2}} \tag{6}$$

where r is the Euclidean distance between the input vector and the center of the current neuron. The standard deviation σ was set to $f \cdot r_{min}$ for different values of f, where r_{min} is the distance to the nearest neighbor of the corresponding cbv. During these experiments, the factor f of 1.2 was found empirically to be the best choice.

The link weights between the hidden layer and the 10 output neurons were determined by calculating the Moore–Penrose pseudo inverse matrix. This process, which is described in [10], assumes a linear activation of the hidden neurons. However, in classification tasks better results are achieved if sigmoidal activation functions are used. Therefore, the sigmoidal activation function was approximated by a linear activation function, whose slope had to be determined. The network was initialized to produce a net input of 4 at the output neurons when the desired output was 1 and a net input of -4 when the desired output was 0. Afterwards, the logistic activation function, instead of the linear function, was applied on each neuron in the output layer. This substitution scaled the network output to 0 resp. 1. The two values of 4 and -4 had empirically been determined as the best choice during preceding experiments ([12]).

All this work involving neural networks (creation, initialization, simulation, and testing) was done using the Stuttgart Neural Network Simulator (SNNS) Version 2.1 which includes a large radial basis function package ([14], [12]).

VI. RESULTS

All networks were tested using the 10,000 digit test set. The following classification rule was applied:

- A digit is classified right if the output neuron representing the digit's class is activated by o_r and all other output neurons are activated by less than $o_r - d$.

- A digit is classified wrong if there exists an output neuron activated by o_r, representing a class other than the digit's

class, while all other output neurons are activated by less than $o_r - d$.

- A digit is unclassified in all other cases.

Modifying the parameter d changes the recognition qualities of the network; the higher the selected value of d is, the lower the percentage of wrong classified digits and the higher the percentage of unclassified digits. Fig. 2 shows the achieved performance for two different sizes of the hidden layer (note the different scale used for the two diagrams).

Setting $d = 0.0$, i.e. allowing no unclassified digits, leads to Table I. The several rows of this table show the percentage of wrong classified digits using untrained radial basis function networks and using networks initialized by OLVQ with different counts of training cycles and different sizes.

The third column of the table shows the total percentage of misclassified digits. Although the error rate of pre–trained networks is smaller than the error rate of untrained networks of the same size, there are patterns which were classified correctly by the random network but misclassified by the network initialized with OLVQ trained cbvs. This fact is shown by the fourth column which gives the percentage of digits which were classified wrong by both networks, the current one and the network with the same size but without OLVQ initialization: The difference between an entry given for an untrained network in the third column and a value given in the fourth column for the same network size determines the improvement which is gained by pre–training the current network. On the other hand, the difference between an entry given for a trained network in the third column and the value given in the fourth column in the same row determines the rate of new misclassifications.

TABLE I

COMPARISON OF THE ERROR RATES OF RADIAL BASIS FUNCTION NETWORKS OF DIFFERENT SIZE WITH AND WITHOUT INITIALIZATION DONE BY OLVQ

network size	count of training cycles	% of digits classified wrong	% of intersected misclassifications	% total decrease in error rate
100 hidden neurons	0	6.82	—	—
	10^4	5.09	4.22	25.4
	10^5	4.89	3.99	28.3
	10^6	4.76	3.92	30.2
200 hidden neurons	0	4.63	—	—
	10^4	3.82	3.21	17.5
	10^5	3.54	2.92	23.5
	10^6	3.50	2.89	24.4
400 hidden neurons	0	3.28	—	—
	10^4	2.67	2.16	18.6
	10^5	2.54	2.10	22.6
	10^6	2.52	2.07	23.2

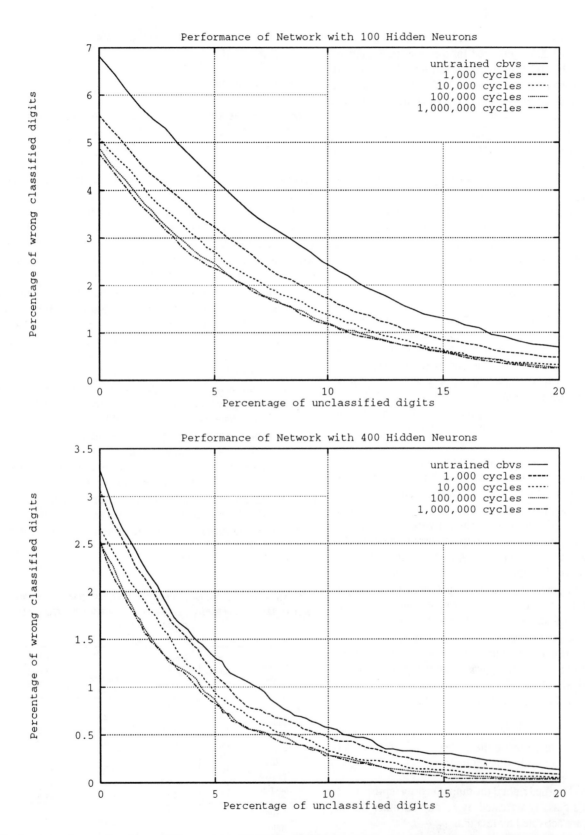

Fig. 2. Performance of networks with two different sizes of hidden layers (100 resp. 400 neurons). The different results were obtained by using untrained cbvs (random initialization) and cbvs which were trained 10^3, 10^4, 10^5, resp. 10^6 times.

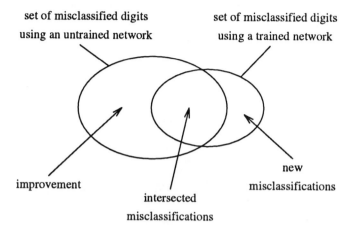

set of misclassified digits using an untrained network

set of misclassified digits using a trained network

improvement

intersected misclassifications

new misclassifications

Fig. 3. Illustration of the contents of Table I

TABLE II

COMPARISON OF TIMES USED FOR SELECTING AND TRAINING CBVS AND INITIALIZING THE NETWORK (MEASURED IN CPU MINUTES)

network size	count of training cycles	selection and train-ing of cbvs	creation and initial-ization of the net	total amount of time
100 hidden neurons	0	—	5.6	5.6
	10^4	5.6		11.2
	10^5	14.8		20.4
	10^6	106		111.6
200 hidden neurons	0	—	11.7	11.7
	10^4	7.0		18.7
	10^5	21.8		33.5
	10^6	170		181.7
400 hidden neurons	0	—	31.1	31.1
	10^4	9.8		40.9
	10^5	37.0		68.1
	10^6	310		341.6

Fig. 3 illustrates the connection between the different columns of Table I.

The total decrease in error rates achieved by using pre–trained networks instead of the randomly initialized ones is shown in the last column. These percentages can be seen as total increases in the network performance.

It can be seen that the extra performance offered by cbv training is greater when smaller networks are used. However, the performance of a larger network is much better. If larger networks are used, randomly chosen cbvs will fit better into the class domains, lowering the positive effect obtained by training.

The table also shows that the performance of a trained network with 100 hidden neurons (using 10^6 training cycles) is approximately equal to the performance of a randomly initialized radial basis function network with 200 hidden neurons. Also, a pre–trained 200 hidden neuron radial basis function network is comparable to an untrained 400 center radial basis function network. However, the small increase in network performance obtained by using a network initialized with 10^6 training cycles instead of 10^5 training cycles does not justify the enormous additional effort required for the training.

Training cbvs instead of selecting a random subset costs an additional amount of time during design of the network. Table II shows the amount of time used for selecting and training the cbvs and for creating and initializing the network. Each time was determined using an HP Apollo 9000/730 workstation and is measured in minutes of cpu time.

The time used for creating and initializing the networks includes the computation of the Moore–Penrose pseudo inverse matrix. This process has a time complexity in the order of n^3 where n is the number of hidden neurons. On the other hand, the process of selecting and training cbvs grows approximately linearly with the number of performed training cycles and less than linearly with the number of cbvs.

VII. CONCLUSIONS

In the example given, the performance of small radial basis function neural networks can be increased by about 28 % if the center vectors used are obtained by learning vector quantization. It is possible to achieve nearly the same performance of recognition using only half the number of hidden neurons if the centers of these hidden neurons are initialized by trained cbvs. It is obvious that a network half the size of a bigger network only needs half the time for classification of one pattern. Therefore, smaller networks may have a strong advantage in time critical applications. Although time is invested training the cbvs, it is used only during design of the network and not during application. However, for the given example it is not recommended to perform more than 10^5 training cycles because the improved performance does not compensate for the necessary additional effort.

Comparing a radial basis function network with 200 hidden neurons, whose centers were obtained by 10^5 cycles of OLVQ training, to an equivalent randomly initialized radial basis function network with 400 hidden neurons, about the same amount of time is used for the total design of the network (33.5 min. v. 31.1 min.) and about the same rate of error is achieved (3.54% v. 3.28%).

In applications other than the one demonstrated, it may be possible to obtain smaller and better performing networks, consuming less time on tasks both of network design and network usage, by applying OLVQ on a smaller network instead of randomly initializing a larger network, because the time complexity of these two processes (training cbvs and initializing the network) is different. Additional research has to be done to prove this assumption.

Further improvements of the initialization are possible: In

the current application, the standard deviation of each of the Gaussian functions has been set only with respect to the distance of the nearest neighbor. It is also possible to consider the class of the nearest neighbor ([9], [13]). If that class is different from the class of the current cbv, it would be advisable to use a smaller standard deviation which narrows the bell–shaped function. This method will sharpen the border of the class domains, which will lead to better results.

ACKNOWLEDGMENT

I would like to thank G. Mamier and H. Bayer for support with the simulations, A. Zell for reading the manuscript, and U. Kreßel for supplying training and test data.

REFERENCES

[1] Chris Bishop. Improving the generalization properties of radial basis function neural networks. In *Neural Computation, Vol. 3*, pages 579–588. MIT Press, 1991.

[2] D.S. Brommhead and D. Lowe. Multivariable functional interpolation and adaptive networks. In *Complex Systems, Vol. 2*, pages 321–355, 1988.

[3] Teuvo Kohonen. Improved versions of learning vector quantization. In *Proceedings of the International Joint Conference on Neural Networks, San Diego*, pages I 545–550, 1990.

[4] Teuvo Kohonen. The self-organizing map. In *Proceedings of the IEEE*, pages 78(9): 1464–1480, 1990.

[5] Teuvo Kohonen, Jari Kangas, Jorma Laaksonen, and Kari Torkkola. *LVQ_PAK, The Learning Vector Quantization Program Package, Version 2.0.* Helsinki University of Technology, 1992.

[6] U. Kreßel, J. Schürmann, and J. Franke. Neuronale Netze für die Musterklassifikation. Institut für Informationstechnik, Daimler Benz AG, Ulm, 1991.

[7] Jorma T. Laaksonen. A method for analyzing decision regions in learning vector quantization algorithms. In I. Aleksander and J. Taylor, editors, *Artificial Neural Networks, 2*, pages 1181–1184, 1992.

[8] Yuchun Lee. Handwritten digit recognition using k nearest–neighbor, radial–basis functions, and backpropagation neural networks. In *Neural Computation, Vol. 3*, pages 440–449. MIT Press, 1991.

[9] M.T. Musavi, W. Ahmed, K.H. Chan, K.B. Faris, and D.M. Hummels. On the training of radial basis function classifiers. In *Neural Networks, Vol. 5*, pages 595–603. Pergamon Press, 1992.

[10] Thomaso Poggio and Frederico Girosi. A theory of networks for approximation and learning. A.I. Memo No. 1140, MIT, 1989.

[11] Thomaso Poggio and Frederico Girosi. Extensions of a theory of networks for approximation and learning: dimensionality reduction and clustering. A.I. Memo No. 1167, MIT, 1990.

[12] Michael Vogt. Implementierung und Anwendung von 'Generalized Radial Basis Functions' in einem Simulator neuronaler Netze. IPVR, Universität Stuttgart, 1992. Diplomarbeit 875, in German.

[13] Michael Vogt. Improving the Performance of Radial Basis Function Neural Networks by Optimized Learning Vector Quantization. Unpublished, December 1992.

[14] A. Zell, N. Mache, R. Hübner, M. Schmalzl, T. Sommer, G. Mamier, and M. Vogt. SNNS User Manual, Version 2.1. Report No. 8/92, Universität Stuttgart, IPVR, 1992.

Comparative Fault Tolerance of Generalized Radial Basis Function and Multilayer Perceptron Networks

Bruce E. Segee
Department of Electrical and Computer Engineering
University of Maine
Orono, ME 04469
segee@watson.eece.maine.edu

Michael J. Carter
Intelligent Structures Group
Department of Electrical and Computer Engineering
University of New Hampshire
Durham, NH 03824
mj_carter@unhh.unh.edu

Abstract—A method for measuring fault tolerance was developed which provides the means to quantify the effect of large numbers of network faults without explosive computational complexity. The fault tolerance of two types of neural networks used for analog function approximation, the multilayer perceptron (MLP) and the generalized radial basis function (GRBF) network, has been assessed. When standard gradient descent learning was employed, the GRBF was considerably more fault tolerant than an MLP of the same size. Furthermore, when a fault tolerance enhancing training method was employed, the fault tolerance of the GRBF improved substantially while the fault tolerance of the MLP improved only marginally.

INTRODUCTION

Fault tolerance is frequently ascribed as an inherent property of artificial neural networks. The assertion of fault tolerance in artificial neural networks stems from the loose analogy between the architecture of such networks and the organization of biological neural networks. The implication is that if the number of network processing elements can be made large, then fault tolerance would be imbued in the network automatically by virtue of the gross similarity with biological neural networks. The folk theorem of implicit fault tolerance has been further reinforced by a number of papers in which anecdotal reports of fault tolerance properties appeared (see references cited in [3] and [1]), and by repeated incantation in journal and conference papers too numerous to cite here. However, several studies of artificial neural networks have shown that they are not inherently fault tolerant. [2,4,5,9,10,11,12,14]

Since fault tolerance is critical in many applications (e.g., flight control systems), it is important to understand the fault tolerance properties of artificial neural networks. In this paper we investigate the impact of weight faults in networks used for analog function approximation. This paper addresses three key issues. First, we propose a means of quantifying the fault tolerance of a neural network to the loss of an arbitrary number of weights. Next, using this

method we assess and compare the fault tolerance of two types of neural networks that have been trained using standard gradient descent methods: the multilayer perceptron (MLP), which is globally generalizing, and the generalized radial basis function (GRBF) network, which is locally generalizing [7]. Finally, we assess the improvement in fault tolerance for both types of networks that results from a fault tolerance enhancing training algorithm [13].

The networks tested were single-input single-output networks composed of one hundred processing elements arranged in a single hidden layer. Since the sigmoidal processing elements have weights associated with the inputs and outputs and the generalized radial basis function processing elements have weights only on their outputs, the multilayer perceptrons tested had two hundred weights while the generalized radial basis function networks had one hundred weights. These networks were trained to produce the sine of the input value in the range [-6,6]. The training set was composed of thirty evenly spaced samples. The networks were trained for 100,000 epochs.

MEASURING FAULT TOLERANCE

Essentially, the problem of measuring fault tolerance consists of two parts. The first is to formulate a reasonable error measure. The second is to formulate a suitable faulting method. Measuring fault tolerance then becomes an exercise in applying the faulting method and observing the effect on the measured error.

The selection of an appropriate error measure depends on the application at hand. For many tasks that involve learning a continuous function, the average squared error or the root mean squared (RMS) error is commonly used. The RMS error is defined as:

$$\text{RMS Error} = \left[\frac{1}{N} \sum_{i=1}^{N} (F(x_i) - y_i)^2 \right]^{\frac{1}{2}} \quad (1)$$

where $F(x)$ is the network approximation to the learned function and y is the corresponding true value of the learned function. The number of sampling points N and their locations are left unspecified for the moment.

One problem inherent in the RMS error measure is that it doesn't account for differences in scale of the function to be learned. Thus, one must be extremely careful in comparing networks trained to the same approximation error on functions with differences in scale.

It is important to somehow normalize the RMS approximation error with respect to the RMS value of the function to be learned. It is for this reason that the following error measure which is called AQ (standing for approximation quality) is proposed.

$$AQ = \frac{\text{Function RMS}}{\text{Function RMS} + \text{RMS error}} \qquad (2)$$

This dimensionless measure is always between zero and one, with the value one corresponding to no error, and the value zero corresponding to infinite error. Furthermore, for a value of 0.5, the function RMS and the RMS error are equal.

Once an appropriate error measure has been decided upon, the next step is to choose an appropriate faulting method. It is the authors' belief that to fully characterize network fault tolerance, one must consider worst case degradation in the face of multiple faults. Unfortunately, this is also the most difficult situation to evaluate. The number of ways that one can get N weight faults of a single type in a network having W weights is $_WC_N$, where:

$$_WC_N = \frac{W!}{N! \, (W-N)!} \qquad (3)$$

Unfortunately, this expression grows very rapidly. For instance, the curve below shows the combinatorial growth in the number of weight fault combinations for a network having fifty weights.

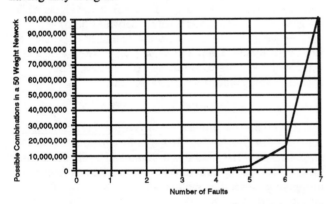

Figure 1: Graph showing the number of combinations of multiple weight faults (up to seven) for a network having fifty network weights.

As can be seen, evaluating even a modest number of weight fault combinations can rapidly lead to an exorbitant number of calculations. Of course, if one has a larger network, the growth is even faster! This leads to a dilemma. One can only characterize the worst case fault condition by evaluating all of the possible combinations; however, evaluating all of the combinations is simply not practical for typical network sizes. Some type of trade-off must be made to ease the computational burden.

A sequential worst case fault selection (worst case path) approach for evaluating multiple faults was employed which avoids combinatorial growth entirely. The assumptions made are that faults occur one at a time, and at each step the fault causing the largest incremental performance degradation is selected. For instance, one first evaluates all single weight faults to find the weight that causes the maximum performance degradation. This weight is then constrained to be one of the weights used in subsequent multiple fault evaluations.

This method has the advantage of eliminating the combinatorial growth in evaluating multiple faults. Additionally, it finds a worst case failure path assuming that faults occur one at a time. The disadvantage is that one cannot be sure that there are not multiple faults which cause larger degradation than the worst case path. For instance, there may exist three weights which when lost together cause a larger performance degradation than the loss of the first three weights in the worst case path. Nevertheless, the worst case path approach should give a reasonable approximation to worst case performance and is much less computationally expensive, being of order N^2.

COMPARING THE FAULT TOLERANCE OF THE MLP AND GRBF NETWORKS

The AQ metric with the worst case path fault selection method was used in evaluating the fault tolerance of the GRBF network and the MLP trained using ordinary gradient descent. The number of processing elements in the two networks was the same. The AQ values were plotted as a function of number of weights removed in the worst case path.

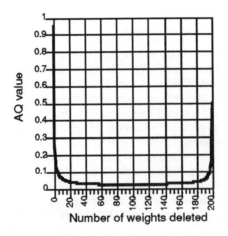

Figure 2: Approximation Quality (AQ) measure versus number of weights removed from the worst case path for the multilayer perceptron trained with ordinary backpropagation.

Figure 2 shows the results for the multilayer perceptron trained with ordinary backpropagation [8]. It is important to note two very striking features of this graph. The first is that even in a large network, the loss of the single most critical weight is sufficient to cause the RMS error to increase to a value much larger than the RMS value of the learned function. Thus, losing the single most critical weight is sufficient to render the network useless. The second feature to note is that as one follows the worst case fault path, the network error can increase by many times the RMS value of the learned function (for instance, an AQ value of 0.05 corresponds to the RMS error being about 20 times as large as the function RMS). Thus, with only the loss of a few weights the network becomes "actively bad", producing errors in excess of that which would result from having no network at all.

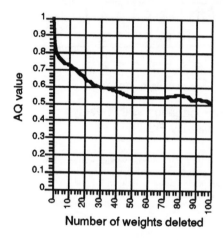

Figure 3: Approximation Quality (AQ) measure versus number of weights removed from the worst case path for the GRBF network.

A graph showing the worst case path performance for the generalized radial basis function network is shown in Figure 3. Note the qualitative change in character of the AQ curve relative to that found for the multilayer perceptron network. The radial basis function network is much more fault tolerant than the multilayer perceptron. As the worst case path is followed, the normalized approximation error measure slowly approaches a value of 0.5. The normalized error value never drops below 0.5, and thus the GRBF network always performs better than no network even in the face of an extreme number of faults.

It is interesting to note that after 100,000 training passes the MLP had an RMS approximation error of approximately 0.04 while the GRBF network had an RMS approximation error of approximately 0.01. Thus, the GRBF network outperforms the MLP not only in terms of fault tolerance but also in terms of fault free performance.

THE EFFECT OF FAULT TOLERANCE ENHANCING TRAINING METHODS

Given that we have established a baseline for fault tolerance performance for these two networks, it is natural to ask if the fault tolerance can be improved. Toward this end we investigated the effect of a training method that has been found to enhance fault tolerance. This method of improving fault tolerance was proposed by Séquin and Clay [14]. The method is very simple. During training, some number of randomly chosen nodes are disabled temporarily. These intermittent failures are generated throughout the training phase. The number of disabled nodes usually remains the same, but the particular choice of the affected nodes is changed periodically during the training interval. This method helps prevent highly critical units from forming, for if such a unit was disabled, the error would be large and the weights in the remainder of the network would be adjusted to compensate for the loss. This method has been found to improve the network fault tolerance at the expense of some degradation in fault-free approximation performance.

The graphs in Figure 4 show the effect on the normalized approximation error when weight faults in the worst case path are introduced into the multilayer perceptron after being trained by Séquin and Clay's technique. The number of randomly disabled nodes was varied between one and twenty.

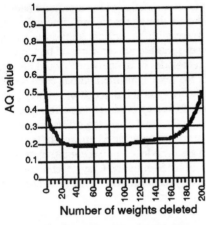

Backpropagation With One
Intermittently Failing Unit

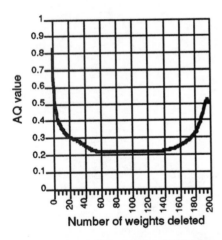

Backpropagation With Five
Intermittently Failing Units

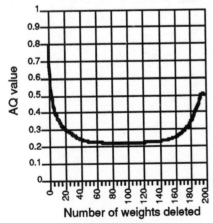

Backpropagation With Ten
Intermittently Failing Units

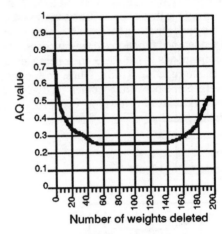

Backpropagation With Twenty
Intermittently Failing Units

Figure 4: Approximation Quality (AQ) measure versus number of weights removed from the worst case path for a multilayer perceptron trained by Séquin and Clay's intermittent node failure technique, (a) one intermittently failing node, (b) five intermittently failing nodes, (c) ten intermittently failing nodes, (d) twenty intermittently failing nodes.

Even when the number of intermittent failures was limited to one randomly chosen unit per training pass, the accuracy to which the multilayer perceptron could learn the function was significantly degraded . Nevertheless, the fault tolerance was improved. The network could tolerate the loss of several weights in the worst case path before the normalized approximation error value dropped below 0.5. Furthermore, the lowest value to which the normalized error dropped on the worst case path increased as more intermittent faults were introduced during training.

When the method of introducing intermittent faults during training was applied to the Gaussian radial basis function network, the results were more impressive. The general trend was again toward improved fault tolerance, albeit at the loss of fault-free performance. However, the relative effect on both fault tolerance and fault-free performance was much different than for the multilayer perceptron. The results for the Gaussian radial basis function network are shown in Figure 5.

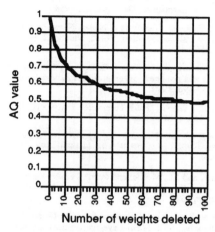

Generalized Radial Basis Function Network With One Intermittently Failing Unit

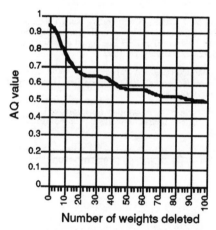

Generalized Radial Basis Function Network With Five Intermittently Failing Units

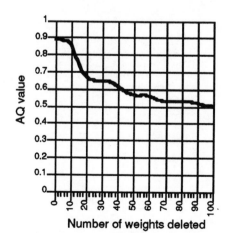

Generalized Radial Basis Function Network With Ten Intermittently Failing Units

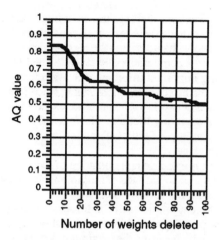

Generalized Radial Basis Function Network With Twenty Intermittently Failing Units

Figure 5: Approximation Quality(AQ) measure versus number of weights removed from the worst case path for a Gaussian radial basis function network trained with Séquin and Clay's intermittent node failure technique, (a) one intermittently failing node, (b) five intermittently failing nodes, (c) ten intermittently failing nodes, (d) twenty intermittently failing nodes.

Having a single intermittent failure during training had very little impact on the fault-free performance of the radial basis function network. Furthermore, the normalized approximation error dropped off somewhat more slowly than it did in the case of the multilayer perceptron as the worst case weight loss path was followed.

Increasing the number of intermittently failing units during training caused the fault-free performance to worsen, although this effect was much less than was observed with the multilayer perceptron. As more intermittent failures were introduced, something remarkable happened. The normalized approximation error curve became essentially flat for some number of weights (nearly 10% of the network weights). Thus, for the loss of a small number of weights, *the weight which causes the maximum degradation causes essentially no degradation from the nominal fault-free performance.*

SUMMARY

In determining the fault tolerance of neural networks in function approximation applications, it is necessary to first choose a faulting method and an error criterion. Then one can insert faults into the network and observe the effect on the error.

If one is interested in comparing the fault tolerance of different networks, or of the same network trained to perform different tasks, it is important that the error measure be normalized by the RMS value of the function to be learned. We proposed the measure given in Equation 2, which we call the approximation quality. This measure is always in the range (0,1] and is based on the relative sizes of the function RMS value and the network's RMS approximation error.

There are several important considerations when choosing a faulting method. Perhaps the most important is the tradeoff between exhaustively testing all possible faults (and thereby completely characterizing the network) and limiting the testing to a computationally feasible level (and thereby risk missing important information). It is clearly important to study the effect of multiple faults, since it is highly unlikely that a network will experience exactly one fault throughout its operating lifetime. However, the number of possible multiple fault combinations in a network grows explosively.

In order to get a reasonable representation of the network's fault tolerance in the face of multiple faults, while avoiding the combinatorial growth associated with evaluating all possible multiple fault conditions, we chose to use a worst case path approach. Thus, we first removed the network weight which caused the maximum degradation in performance, and then we removed the weight which caused the maximum degradation in the resulting network, and so forth. We believe that the worst case path approach is a good predictor of the true worst case performance.

A method for quantifying the fault tolerance of neural networks has been developed that is applicable to a wide range of network architectures and topologies. This method employs the normalized performance measure which we call AQ and a worst case path fault insertion scheme. Fault tolerant networks should have large AQ values for as many faults in the worst case path as possible, and then should slowly degrade toward an AQ of 0.5. We have applied this method to GRBF networks and MLP networks trained using standard gradient descent procedures, and to the same networks trained with a fault tolerance enhancing learning algorithm. For the GRBF networks, the AQ values slowly dropped toward 0.5 with increasing number of faults. For the MLP, on the other hand, the value of AQ resulting from the loss of the single most damaging fault was typically below 0.5, and the AQ values would drop substantially below 0.5 with increasing number of faults.

In both types of networks, the fault tolerance enhancing learning method tended to improve the network fault tolerance with respect to that observed with conventional gradient descent learning. In every case tested, the GRBF networks outperformed the MLP networks in terms of fault tolerance. This can be explained using frequency domain methods [12,13]. The Gaussian function provides a much better fit to the function to be learned and consequently the GRBF produces a solution that is both lower in error and more fault tolerant than the MLP approximation.

REFERENCES

[1]   G. Bolt, , J. Austin, and G. Morgan, " Fault Tolerance in Neural Networks", Technical Report, Computer Science Department, University of York, Heslington, York, YO1 5DD, U.K., 1990

[2]   D. Carrara, "Investigating and Improving the Fault Tolerance of the Multilayer Perceptron", Master's Thesis (In Preparation), University of New Hampshire, 1992

[3]   M.J. Carter, "The Illusion of Fault Tolerance in Neural Networks for Pattern Recognition and Signal Processing", *Proceedings*

Technical Session on Fault-Tolerant Integrated Systems, University of New Hampshire, Durham, NH, 1988

[4]   Y. Izui, and A. Pentland, "Analysis of Neural Networks with Redundancy", Neural Computation, Vol. 2, Number 2, pp. 226-238, Summer, 1990

[5]   C. Neti, M. Schneider, and E. Young, "Maximally fault tolerant neural networks and nonlinear programming", *Proceedings IJCNN*, pp II-483:496, 1990

[6]   D.S. Phatak, and I. Koren, "Fault Tolerance of Artificial Neural Nets", submitted for publication, 1990

[7]   T. Poggio, and F. Girosi, "Networks for Approximation and Learning", *Proceedings of the IEEE*, v78, pp1481:1497, September, 1990

[8]   D.E. Rumelhart, and J.L. McClelland (eds.), Parallel Distributed Processing, Explorations in the Microstructure of Cognition, MIT Press, Cambridge, 1986

[9]   B.E. Segee, and M.J. Carter "Fault Sensitivity and Nodal Relevance Relationships in Multi-Layer Perceptrons", UNH Intelligent Structures Group Report ECE.IS.90.02, March 9, 1990

[10]   B. E. Segee, and M. J. Carter, "Fault Tolerance of Pruned Multilayer Networks", *Proceedings IJCNN*, pp. II-447-452, Seattle, WA, 1991

[11]   B. E. Segee, and M. J. Carter, "Comparative Fault Tolerance of Parallel Distributed Processing Networks (Debunking the Myth of Inherent Fault Tolerance)", UNH Intelligent Structures Group Report ECE.IS.92.07, February 24, 1992

[12]   B. E. Segee, "Characterizing and Improving the Fault Tolerance of Artificial Neural Networks", PhD Dissertation, University of New Hampshire,1992

[13]   B. E. Segee, "Using spectral techniques for improved performance in artificial neural networks", Proceedings ICNN (in press), 1993

[14]   C. Séquin, and R. Clay, "Fault Tolerance in Artificial Neural Networks", *Proceedings IJCNN*, pp I-703:708, 1990

Radial basis functions and multilayer feedforward neural networks for optimal control of nonlinear stochastic systems

T. Parisini and R. Zoppoli

Department of Communications, Computer and System Sciences
DIST-University of Genoa, Via Opera Pia 11A, 16145 Genova, Italy

Abstract. This paper addresses the problem of designing a feedback feedforward controller to drive the state of a dynamic system so as to track any desired trajectory stochastically specified. In general, the dynamic system and the state observation channel are nonlinear, the cost function is non quadratic, and process and observation noises are non-Gaussian. As the classical Linear-Quadratic-Gaussian (LQG) assumptions are not verified, an approximate solution is sought by constraining control strategies to take on a fixed structure in which a certain number of parameters have to be optimized. Two nonlinear control structures are considered: Radial Basis Functions (RBF) and multilayer feedforward neural networks. The control structures are also shaped on the basis of what has been called the "LInear Structure Preserving Principle" (the LISP principle). The original functional problem is then reduced to a nonlinear programming one, which is solved by means of a gradient method. Simulation results related to non-LQG optimal control problems show the effectiveness of the proposed technique.

I. INTRODUCTION

In the paper, we address the problem of designing a controller that, in a fixed number N of temporal stages, drives a dynamic system (in general, nonlinear) so that its state vector may follow a specified trajectory $\{x_1^*, x_2^*, \ldots, x_N^*\}$, while minimizing a given cost function (in general, non-quadratic). The trajectories to be tracked are arbitrary, provided that they belong to a specified probability space. Random noises (in general, non-Gaussian) act on both the dynamic system and the state observation channel. The controller is allowed to have a perfect knowledge of the future points of the desired trajectory, and also to make noisy measurements on the present state vector. Then the control strategy is structured in a *feedback-feedforward* form.

As is well known, deriving the solution of the above problem in such a general formulation, for which the classical LQG assumptions are not verified, is one of the most difficult tasks involved in control theory. If all stochastic vectors are assumed to be mutually independent, dynamic programming can be applied, at least in principle (see, for instance, [1]). In reality, however, an analytical solution can be found only under LQG hypotheses (i.e., linear system and linear observation channel, quadratic cost, and Gaussian random variables).

For the general non-LQG case, several methods for approximate synthesis of optimal control strategies have been proposed in the literature. Among these, numerical techniques based on dynamic programming play a central role but are more or less penalized by the so-called "curse of dimensionality". The approximating technique, which constitutes the basic idea of our "neural" approach, consists in assigning the control strategies a given structure in which a certain number of parameters have to be determined in order to minimize the cost function. Two nonlinear control structures are considered: RBF networks and multilayer feedforward neural networks.

The method of approximating the control strategies by means of preassigned control structures so as to obtain a parametric (instead of functional) optimization problem was first considered in the '60s (see, for example, [2] for the general deterministic non-LQ case, and [3] and the survey reported in [4] for the LQ case). However, it does not seem that such a method met with great success, as the selected structures were characterized by too small a number of free parameters to attain satisfactory approximation properties. Moreover, such structures required rather complex computational procedures to determine the optimal values of the unknown parameters.

In general, multilayer feedforward neural networks are not affected by these drawbacks, and are well suited for the use of distributed optimization algorithms that keep the complexity of calculations substantially independent of the number of parameters to be tuned. Some successful results obtained by solving non-LQ optimal control problems are given in [5],[6],[7]. In the present paper, we consider the use of other neural structures, i.e., RBF neural networks (see [8] for a survey of this kind of networks). RBF networks are expected to perform very well in functional approximation problems like the one considered here, due to their direct derivation from the mathematical theory of regularization (see, for instance, [9]), which is a well-known tool for the solution of ill-posed problems like the problem of learning involved in neural networks.

The paper is organized as follows: In Section II, we state the N-stage optimal control problem. Then we substitute the fixed-structure parametrized strategies into the process cost, thus reducing the original functional optimization problem to a nonlinear programming one. Furthermore, we decompose the neural structure into three chains of nonlinear mappings, namely, the "controller chain", the "filter chain", and the "feedforward chain". This new structure, based on what we have called the "Linear-Structure Preserving principle" (the LISP principle), is motivated by the requirement for keeping time-invariant the structure of the nonlinear mappings. Such a requirement can be met by keeping time-invariant the dimensions of the input vectors (note that the number of points x_i^* to be tracked decreases in time, while the number of measurements made by the controller on the system state increases). Gradient techniques to solve the nonlinear programming problem are presented in Section III, where recursive equations to compute the gradient components are also provided. Such equations are suited for both RBF and multilayer feedforward networks. Simulation results are finally presented in Section IV.

II. STATEMENT OF THE N-STAGE OPTIMAL TRACKING PROBLEM

Let us consider the discrete-time stochastic dynamic system (in general, nonlinear)

$$x_{i+1} = f_i(x_i, u_i \, \xi_i), \quad i = 0, 1, \ldots, N-1 \qquad (1)$$

where $x_i \in \Re^n$ is the state vector, $u_i \in \Re^m$ is the control vector, and $\xi_i \in \Re^q$ is a random noise vector. The state vector is observed through the noisy measurement channel (in general, nonlinear)

$$y_i = g_i(x_i, \eta_i), \quad i = 0, 1, \ldots, N-1 \qquad (2)$$

where $y_i \in \Re^p$ is the observation vector, and $\eta_i \in \Re^r$ is a measurement random noise.

The cost function (in general, nonquadratic) is given by

$$J = \sum_{i=0}^{N-1} \left[h_i(x_i, u_i) + \rho_{i+1}(\|x_{i+1}^* - x_{i+1}\|) \right] \qquad (3)$$

where $\{x_1^*, x_2^*, \ldots, x_N^*\}$ is the state trajectory to be tracked, and $\| \cdot \|$ is the Euclidean norm on $\Re^n$. $\rho_i(z)$ are increasing functions for $z \geq 0$, with $\rho_i(0) = 0$. The probability density functions characterizing the random vectors x_0, $\xi \triangleq \operatorname{col}(\xi_0, \ldots, \xi_{N-1})$, $\eta \triangleq \operatorname{col}(\eta_0, \ldots, \eta_{N-1})$, and $X_1^* \triangleq \operatorname{col}(x_1^*, \ldots, x_N^*)$ are assumed to be known. The trajectory to be tracked is assumed to become perfectly (or deterministically) known at the initial stage

$i = 0$. All the functions f_i, g_i, h_i, ρ_i are assumed to be differentiable.

Let us define $I_i \triangleq \operatorname{col}(y_0, \ldots, y_i, u_0, \ldots, u_{i-1})$, $i = 0, 1, \ldots, N-1$, and $X_{i+1}^* \triangleq \operatorname{col}(x_{i+1}^*, \ldots, x_N^*)$. We assume the random vector X_1^* to be independent of all the other random vectors so that, at stage i, the controller can forget $x_1^*, \ldots, x_i^*$, since these vectors do not contain information on the present and future values of process and measurement noises. We can now state the following

Problem 1. *Find the optimal feedback feedforward control strategies* $\{u_i^\circ = \gamma_i^\circ(I_i, X_{i+1}^*), i = 0, 1, \ldots, N-1\}$ *that minimize the expected value of cost (3).*

□

As stated in the Introduction, deriving the solution of Problem 1 in its general formulation is a very difficult task. If all stochastic vectors are assumed to be mutually independent, dynamic programming can be applied at least in principle. This entails a recursive evaluation of the conditional densities $p(x_i|I_i)$ and $p(y_{i+1}|I_i, u_i)$ (see, for instance, [1]), which can be accomplished analytically in very few cases, typically, under the classical LQG assumptions.

For the general non-LQG case, several methods for an approximate synthesis of the optimal control strategies have been proposed in the literature. The approximating technique constituting the central idea of our "neural" approach consists 1) in assigning the control strategies a given structure in which a certain number of parameters have to be determined in order to minimize the cost function, 2) in choosing, as an assigned fixed structure, a RBF network or a multilayer feedforward neural network. Then, we constrain the control strategies to take on a fixed structure of the form

$$u_i = \gamma_i(I_i, X_{i+1}^*, w_i), \quad i = 0, 1, \ldots, N-1 \qquad (4)$$

where γ_i is the input/output mapping of the chosen approximating network, and w_i is the vector of the parameters to be determined. The control scheme gives rise to a chain of N neural networks, each followed by the dynamic system. This chain may remind one of the control scheme proposed in [10]. Our structure differs from that scheme in the presence of the feedforward action, in the fact that the dynamic system is stochastic, and in the fact that the state vector is observed through a noisy channel.

If we repeatedly substitute the mappings γ_i into the state and observation equations (1),(2) (thus eliminating the vectors x_i, u_i, y_i), the cost function takes on the form $J(w, x_0, X_1^*, \xi, \eta)$, where $w \triangleq \operatorname{col}(w_0, \ldots, w_{N-1})$. Then we have to solve the following

Problem 2. *Find the vector* w° *that minimizes the expected cost* $\underset{x_0, X_1^*, \xi, \eta}{\mathrm{E}} [J(w, x_0, X_1^*, \xi, \eta)]$.

□

It follows that the functional Problem 1 has been reduced to an unconstrained nonlinear programming problem.

It is necessary to note that the dimensions of the vectors I_i, X_{i+1}^* vary in time. This implies that the structures of the neural networks implementing the strategies γ_i are time-varying and hence not very suited for practical applications. To overcome this drawback, we introduce a suitable "LQG equivalent structure" for the original problem (this structure is described in [6]), and apply the following principle, which we have called the "Linear-Structure Preserving principle" (the LISP principle): "Once the LQG equivalent structure has been found and one of the corresponding LQG optimal control problems has been solved, maintain the same linear structure of the obtained solution. Then: 1) replace the linear state equation and the linear observation channel with the nonlinear ones appearing in the original non-LQG problem, and 2) replace the linear mappings (controller and filter gain matrices) with nonlinear ones (neural networks)".

According to the LISP principle, the filter and controller laws are given by

$$u_i = \gamma_1(x_i, v_i, w_i), \quad i = 0, 1, \ldots, N-1 \quad (5)$$

$$v_i = \gamma_2(v_{i+1}, x_{i+1}^*, \tilde{w}_i), \quad i = 0, 1, \ldots, N-2 \quad (6a)$$

$$v_{N-1} = \gamma_{2N}(x_N^*, \tilde{w}_N) \quad (6b)$$

$$\mu_i = \mu_i^p + \gamma_3(y_i - y_i^p, \bar{w}_i), \quad i = 0, 1, \ldots, N-1 \quad (7)$$

where $\mu_i^p \triangleq f_{i-1}(\mu_{i-1}, u_{i-1}, o)$, $y_i^p \triangleq g_i(\mu_i^p, o)$, μ_i are the state prediction, the measurement prediction, and the state estimate, respectively. $\mu_0^p = \alpha$ is the a priori state prediction. As desired, $\gamma_1, \gamma_2, \gamma_3$ are now neural networks with time-invariant structures (see Fig. 1), and $w_i, \tilde{w}_i, \bar{w}_i$ are the vectors of the parameters of the networks, as defined previously. It is worth noting that (7) implements an estimation mechanism that may be regarded as the neural version of the so-called "extended Kalman filter". By following the same procedure that led to Problem 2, repeated substitution of $\gamma_1, \gamma_2, \gamma_3$ into (3) yields the cost $J(w_T, x_0, X_1^*, \xi, \eta)$, where $w_T \triangleq \text{col}(w_i, \tilde{w}_i, \bar{w}_i, i = 0, 1, \ldots, N-1)$. By averaging $J(w_T, x_0, X_1^*, \xi, \eta)$, we reduce again the functional Problem 1 to the following nonlinear programming

Problem 2'. Find the vector w_T^o that minimizes the expected cost $\mathop{\mathrm{E}}_{x_0, X_1^*, \xi, \eta} [J(w_T, x_0, X_1^*, \xi, \eta)]$.

□

In the next section we present an algorithm to solve Problem 2'.

III. SOLUTION OF THE NONLINEAR PROGRAMMING PROBLEM BY THE GRADIENT METHOD

The unconstrained nonlinear programming Problem 2' can be solved by means of a gradient-type algorithm. However, due to the general statement of the problem, we are unable to express the average cost $E(J)$ in explicit form. This leads us to compute the "realization" $\nabla_{w_T} J[w_T(k), x_0(k), X_1^*(k), \xi(k), \eta(k)]$ instead of the gradient of the average cost. The sequence $\{[x_0(k), X_1^*(k), \xi(k), \eta(k)], k = 0, 1, \ldots\}$ is generated randomly according to the probability density functions of the random vectors, and the parameter weight vector w_T is optimized by means of the following probabilistic algorithm

$$w_T(k+1) = w_T(k) - \alpha(k)\nabla_{w_T} J[w_T(k), x_0(k), X_1^*(k), \xi(k), \eta(k)], \quad k = 0, 1, \ldots \quad (8)$$

Algorithm (8) is related to the concept of "stochastic approximation" (see, for instance, [11]). In the following, we give the recursive equations enabling one to compute the partial derivatives of cost J with respect to the components of w_T. We have

$$\frac{\partial J}{\partial w_i} = \frac{\partial J}{\partial u_i}\frac{\partial u_i}{\partial w_i}, \qquad \frac{\partial J}{\partial \tilde{w}_i} = \frac{\partial J}{\partial v_i}\frac{\partial v_i}{\partial \tilde{w}_i},$$
$$\frac{\partial J}{\partial \bar{w}_i} = \frac{\partial J}{\partial \mu_i}\frac{\partial \mu_i}{\partial \bar{w}_i} \quad (9)$$

As to the third equation in (9), note that, denoting by δ_i the output of the network γ_3 at stage i, we have written $\frac{\partial J}{\partial \delta_i} = \frac{\partial J}{\partial \mu_i}$.

Let us now compute the partial derivatives $\frac{\partial J}{\partial u_i}, \frac{\partial J}{\partial v_i}$, and $\frac{\partial J}{\partial \mu_i}$. Define $\lambda_i \triangleq \nabla_{x_i} J(w_T, x_0, X_1^*, \xi, \eta)$ and $\hat{\lambda}_i \triangleq \nabla_{\mu_i^p} J(w_T, x_0, X_1^*, \xi, \eta)$ for $i = 1, 2, \ldots, N$. Furthermore, denote by v_i^c the subvector corresponding to v_i in the input vector of γ_1, and by μ_i^c the subvector corresponding to μ_i in the same input vector (see Fig. 1). Likewise, denote by v_i^f the subvector corresponding to v_i in the input vector of γ_2. Finally, let $\tilde{h}_i(x_i, u_i, x_i^*) \triangleq h_i(x_i, u_i) + \rho_i(\|x_i^* - x_i\|)$, $i = 1, 2, \ldots, N-1$, and $\tilde{h}_0(x_0, u_0) \triangleq h_0(x_0, u_0)$. Then, we can write the following

Proposition. The partial derivatives $\frac{\partial J}{\partial u_i}, \frac{\partial J}{\partial v_i}, \frac{\partial J}{\partial \mu_i}$ can be computed by means of the following recursive relations:

$$\frac{\partial J}{\partial u_i} = \frac{\partial}{\partial u_i}\tilde{h}_i(x_i, u_i, x_i^*) + \lambda_{i+1}^T \frac{\partial}{\partial u_i} f_i(x_i, u_i, \xi_i)$$
$$+ \hat{\lambda}_{i+1}^T \frac{\partial}{\partial u_i} f_i(\mu_i, u_i, o), i = 0, 1, \ldots, N-1 \quad (10)$$

$$\frac{\partial J}{\partial \boldsymbol{v}_i} = \frac{\partial J}{\partial \boldsymbol{v}_i^f} + \frac{\partial J}{\partial \boldsymbol{v}_i^c}, \quad i = 1, 2, \ldots, N-1 \tag{11a}$$

$$\frac{\partial J}{\partial \boldsymbol{v}_0} = \frac{\partial J}{\partial \boldsymbol{v}_0^c} \tag{11b}$$

$$\frac{\partial J}{\partial \boldsymbol{\mu}_i} = \frac{\partial J}{\partial \boldsymbol{\mu}_i^c} + \hat{\boldsymbol{\lambda}}_{i+1}^T \frac{\partial}{\partial \boldsymbol{\mu}_i} \boldsymbol{f}_i(\boldsymbol{\mu}_i, \boldsymbol{u}_i, \boldsymbol{o}),$$
$$i = 0, 1, \ldots, N-1 \tag{12}$$

where the vectors $\boldsymbol{\lambda}_i^T$ and $\hat{\boldsymbol{\lambda}}_i^T$ can be computed as follows

$$\boldsymbol{\lambda}_i^T = \frac{\partial}{\partial \boldsymbol{x}_i} \tilde{h}_i(\boldsymbol{x}_i, \boldsymbol{u}_i, \boldsymbol{x}_i^*) + \boldsymbol{\lambda}_{i+1}^T \frac{\partial}{\partial \boldsymbol{x}_i} \boldsymbol{f}_i(\boldsymbol{x}_i, \boldsymbol{u}_i, \boldsymbol{\xi}_i)$$
$$+ \frac{\partial J}{\partial \boldsymbol{e}_i} \frac{\partial}{\partial \boldsymbol{x}_i} \boldsymbol{g}_i(\boldsymbol{x}_i, \boldsymbol{\eta}_i), \quad i = 1, \ldots, N-1 \tag{13a}$$

$$\boldsymbol{\lambda}_N^T = \frac{\partial}{\partial \boldsymbol{x}_N} \rho_N(\|\boldsymbol{x}_N^* - \boldsymbol{x}_N\|) \tag{13b}$$

and

$$\hat{\boldsymbol{\lambda}}_i^T = \frac{\partial J}{\partial \boldsymbol{\mu}_i^c} - \frac{\partial J}{\partial \boldsymbol{e}_i} \frac{\partial}{\partial \boldsymbol{\mu}_i^p} \boldsymbol{g}_i(\boldsymbol{\mu}_i^p, \boldsymbol{o})$$
$$+ \hat{\boldsymbol{\lambda}}_{i+1}^T \frac{\partial}{\partial} \boldsymbol{f}_i(\boldsymbol{\mu}_i, \boldsymbol{u}_i, \boldsymbol{o}), \quad i = 1, \ldots, N-1 \tag{14a}$$

$$\hat{\boldsymbol{\lambda}}_N^T = 0 \tag{14b}$$

□

As can be seen from the above proposition (which is demonstrated in [7]), we need to compute the partial derivatives $\frac{\partial J}{\partial \boldsymbol{v}_i^c} = \frac{\partial J}{\partial \boldsymbol{u}_i} \frac{\partial \boldsymbol{\gamma}_1}{\partial \boldsymbol{v}_i^c}$, $\frac{\partial J}{\partial \boldsymbol{\mu}_i^c} = \frac{\partial J}{\partial \boldsymbol{u}_i} \frac{\partial \boldsymbol{\gamma}_1}{\partial \boldsymbol{\mu}_i^c}$, $\frac{\partial J}{\partial \boldsymbol{v}_i^f} = \frac{\partial J}{\partial \boldsymbol{v}_{i-1}} \frac{\partial \boldsymbol{\gamma}_2}{\partial \boldsymbol{v}_i^f}$, $\frac{\partial J}{\partial \boldsymbol{e}_i} = \frac{\partial J}{\partial \boldsymbol{\mu}_i} \frac{\partial \boldsymbol{\gamma}_3}{\partial \boldsymbol{e}_i}$, and then the Jacobian matrices $\frac{\partial \boldsymbol{\gamma}_1}{\partial \boldsymbol{v}_i^c}, \frac{\partial \boldsymbol{\gamma}_1}{\partial \boldsymbol{\mu}_i^c}, \frac{\partial \boldsymbol{\gamma}_2}{\partial \boldsymbol{v}_i^f}, \frac{\partial \boldsymbol{\gamma}_3}{\partial \boldsymbol{e}_i}$. The computation of these Jacobians, as well as of $\frac{\partial \boldsymbol{u}_i}{\partial \boldsymbol{w}_i}, \frac{\partial \boldsymbol{v}_i}{\partial \tilde{\boldsymbol{w}}_i}, \frac{\partial \boldsymbol{\mu}_i}{\partial \bar{\boldsymbol{w}}_i}$ (see (9)), depends on the choice of the approximating networks. For the case of multilayer feedforward networks, in which the well-known backpropagation mechanism can be used, a detailed discussion is reported in [7]. In the following, we shall assume the strategies $\boldsymbol{\gamma}_1, \boldsymbol{\gamma}_2, \boldsymbol{\gamma}_3$ to be implemented by RBF networks. Let us describe these networks in some detail (for a more complete description, see, for instance, [8]). Without loss of generality, we refer to

the networks $\boldsymbol{\gamma}_1$. Every component j of the control vector $\boldsymbol{u}_i = \text{col}(u_{ij}, j = 1, \ldots, m)$, as given by (5), can be expressed as:

$$u_{ij} = \sum_{k=1}^{n_{ij}} c_k^{ij} G\left(\|\boldsymbol{z}_i - \boldsymbol{t}_k^{ij}\|_{A^{ij}}^2\right) \tag{15}$$

where $G(\cdot)$ is a radial activation function. Typical choices for G are: $G(b) = b^2 \log(b)$ (thin-plate-spline), $G(b) = \sqrt{b^2 + \sigma^2}$ (multiquadric), $G(b) = e^{-\frac{b^2}{\sigma^2}}$ Gaussian), and $G(b) = e^{-\frac{b}{\sigma}}$ exponential), where σ is a real constant. The choice of G is strictly related to the smoothness class of the function to be approximated, and therefore to the a-priori knowledge of the solution of the problem (see [8] for a deeper discussion about this issue). Moreover, $\boldsymbol{z}_i \triangleq \text{col}(\boldsymbol{x}_i, \boldsymbol{v}_i)$ represents the input vector to $\boldsymbol{\gamma}_1$ at stage i; the vectors $\boldsymbol{t}_k^{ij}$ are the so-called "centers" of the basis functions, and A^{ij} are symmetric positive definite weighting matrices. Then, the parameter vector appearing in (5) can be written as $\boldsymbol{w}_i \triangleq \text{col}(w_{ij}, j = 1, \ldots, m)$ and $\boldsymbol{w}_{ij} \triangleq \text{col}\left(c_1^{ij}, \ldots, c_{n_{ij}}^{ij}, \boldsymbol{t}_1^{ij}, \ldots, \boldsymbol{t}_{n_{ij}}^{ij}, a_{11}^{ij}, \ldots, a_{dd}^{ij}\right)$, where $a_{11}^{ij}, \ldots, a_{dd}^{ij}$ denote the elements of the matrix A^{ij}, and $d \triangleq 2n$ is the dimension of the vector $\boldsymbol{z}_i$. The input/output relationship (15) can be implemented by a three-layer network.

By using a little algebra, it is easy to see that the j-th rows of the Jacobian matrices $\frac{\partial \boldsymbol{\gamma}_1}{\partial \boldsymbol{\mu}_i^c}$ and $\frac{\partial \boldsymbol{\gamma}_1}{\partial \boldsymbol{v}_i^c}$ (denoted by $\frac{\partial \gamma_1^j}{\partial \boldsymbol{\mu}_i^c}$ and $\frac{\partial \gamma_1^j}{\partial \boldsymbol{v}_i^c}$) are respectively constituted, by the first n and the last n components of the vector

$$\frac{\partial \gamma_1^j}{\partial \boldsymbol{z}_i} = 2 \sum_{k=1}^{n_{ij}} c_k^{ij} G'\left(\|\boldsymbol{z}_i - \boldsymbol{t}_k^{ij}\|_{A^{ij}}^2\right) \left(\boldsymbol{z}_i - \boldsymbol{t}_k^{ij}\right)^T A^{ij} \tag{16}$$

Furthermore, $\frac{\partial u_{ij}}{\partial w_{ij}} = G\left(\|\boldsymbol{z}_i - \boldsymbol{t}_k^{ij}\|_{A^{ij}}^2\right)$, if w_{ij} is the component of the vector $\boldsymbol{w}_{ij}$ corresponding to the scalar parameter c_k^{ij}; $\frac{\partial u_{ij}}{\partial w_{ij}} = \left[-2 c_k^{ij} G'\left(\|\boldsymbol{z}_i - \boldsymbol{t}_k^{ij}\|_{A^{ij}}^2\right) A^{ij} \left(\boldsymbol{z}_i - \boldsymbol{t}_k^{ij}\right)\right]_h$, if w_{ij} is the element of the vector $\boldsymbol{w}_{ij}$ corresponding to the h-th component of the center $\boldsymbol{t}_k^{ij}$ (the notation $[\boldsymbol{a}]_h$ means h-th component of the vector $\boldsymbol{a}$); and $\frac{\partial u_{ij}}{\partial w_{ij}} = \left\{\sum_{k=1}^{n_{ij}} c_k^{ij} G'\left(\|\boldsymbol{z}_i - \boldsymbol{t}_k^{ij}\|_{A^{ij}}^2\right) \left(\boldsymbol{z}_i - \boldsymbol{t}_k^{ij}\right)\left(\boldsymbol{z}_i - \boldsymbol{t}_k^{ij}\right)^T\right\}_{hl}$, if w_{ij} is the component of $\boldsymbol{w}_{ij}$ corresponding to the element h, l of the matrix A^{ij} (the notation $\{B\}_{hl}$ means element h, l of the matrix

B). Obviously, analogous relations hold for $\dfrac{\partial v_{ij}}{\partial \tilde{w}_{ij}}$ and $\dfrac{\partial \mu_{ij}}{\partial \tilde{w}_{ij}}$.

It can be deduced that the learning algorithm consists of the following two "passes", which alternate up to convergence:

Forward pass . The vectors $x_0(k), X_1^*(k), \xi(k), \eta(k)$ are generated randomly according to their probability density functions. Then, the control sequence and the state trajectory are computed on the basis of these vectors and of $w(k)$, $\tilde{w}(k)$, and $\bar{w}(k)$.

Backward pass . All the variables involved in Eqs. (10) - (16) are computed, and the gradient $\nabla_{w_T} J[w_T(k), x_0(k), X_1^*(k), \xi(k), \eta(k)]$ is determined by using (9). Then, the new weight vector $w_T(k+1)$ is generated by means of (8).

In the next section, an example will be given to illustrate the effectiveness of the proposed method.

IV. SIMULATION RESULTS

To show the learning properties of the neural strategies, we consider the space robot presented in Fig. 2, which, for the sake of simplicity, is assumed to move in the plane of the coordinate system displayed in the figure.

The dynamics of the robot is described by the equations

$$F = (u_1 + \xi_1 + u_2 + \xi_2) e = m \frac{dv}{dt} \tag{17}$$

$$T = (u_1 + \xi_1 - u_2 - \xi_2) d = J \frac{d\omega}{dt} \tag{18}$$

where u_1 and u_2 are the control thrusts, ξ_1 and ξ_2 are zero-mean Gaussian noises, and F and T are the resulting force and torque, respectively. e is a vector of unit length, aligned with the axis of symmetry of the robot. The other symbols have clear meanings. The robot position is described by the Cartesian coordinates x, y and by the angle ϑ shown in the figure. Let $x_1 = x$, $x_2 = \dot{x}$, $x_3 = y$, $x_4 = \dot{y}$, $x_5 = \vartheta$, $x_6 = \dot{\vartheta}$, and $x \triangleq \text{col}(x_i, i = 1, \ldots, 6)$. Then, from (17) and (18), we derive the nonlinear differential dynamic system $\dot{x}_1 = x_2$, $\dot{x}_2 = \dfrac{1}{m}(u_1 + \xi_1 + u_2 + \xi_2)\cos x_5$, $\dot{x}_3 = x_4$, $\dot{x}_4 = \dfrac{1}{m}(u_1 + \xi_1 + u_2 + \xi_2)\sin x_5$, $\dot{x}_5 = x_6$, $\dot{x}_6 = \dfrac{d}{J}(u_1 + \xi_1 - u_2 - \xi_2)$, with the constraints $|u_1| \leq$ U, $|u_2| \leq U$, where U is the maximum thrust value allowed. The system state is observed through the linear measurement channel $y_i = x_i + \eta_i$, $i = 1, \ldots, 6$, where η_i are zero-mean Gaussian noises.

The space robot is requested to start from *any given* point of the segment AB shown in Fig. 3 (the parking edge of a space platform) and to reach *any given* point of the segment $A'B'$ (specified by the vector x_N^*). As the state robot starts from a given point of the platform edge, it is reasonable to assume the initial vector x_0 to be known. Then, $\mu_0 = x_0$, where x_0 is to be considered (before the process begins) as a random vector uniformly distributed on the segment AB. The manoeuvre has to be completed at a given time t_f, and $N = 20$ control stages are allowed. Two optimal trajectories are shown in Fig. 3.

Since the robot is requested not to track the N points of a desired trajectory but to move from x_0 to x_N^*, the related "point-to-point" optimal manoeuvring problem can be solved by means of a simpler scheme than that shown in Fig. 1. More specifically, it is not necessary to use neural networks γ_2, but it is sufficient to replace the inputs v_i to γ_1 with the vector x_N^*, without affecting the time-invariance property of the strategies γ_1.

The strategies γ_1 were implemented by means of RBF networks with 12 input variables and 150 Gaussian RBF units for each control component, whereas the mappings γ_3 were implemented by means of neural networks with 6 input variables and 150 Gaussian RBF units for each state-estimation component.

It should be noted that the state trajectories obtained after the learning phase practically coincide with the trajectories obtained by implementing the mappings γ_1 and γ_3 by means of feedforward multilayer neural networks (see [7]). However, computational requirements are heavier than for multilayer networks, due to the very large number of activation units needed to obtain the same performances (because of the *local* characteristics of the Radial Basis Functions), and to the more complex gradient formulas used (recall the simplicity of the backpropagation mechanism).

V. CONCLUSIONS

Non-LQG optimal control problems can be solved by constraining the control strategies to take on the form of a suitable configuration of RBF feedforward neural networks connected to one another. We have shown that such networks are very well suited to solving the control problem considered, because of their good approximating properties, which are mainly due to their mathematical derivation from regularization theory. A particularly interesting configuration, based on what has been called the "Linear-Structure Preserving principle" (the LISP principle), has been presented. Such a configuration has the desirable property of enabling us to implement the control strategies on neural networks characterized by a time-invariant structure.

As a final remark, we want to point out that the computational load involved by RBF networks seems to grow very fast with respect to the dimensionality of the control problem considered, due to the inherently local characteristics of their approximating capabilities. By contrast, multilayer feedforward networks do not exhibit this drawback.

REFERENCES

[1] M. Aoki, *Optimization of Stochastic Systems*. Academic Press, 1967.

[2] B. R. Eisenberg and A. P. Sage, "Closed-loop optimization of fixed configuration systems," *International Journal of Control*, Vol. 3, pp. 183-194, 1966.

[3] D.L. Kleinman and M. Athans, "The design of suboptimal linear time-varying systems," *IEEE Trans. Automatic Control*, Vol. AC-13, pp. 150-159, 1968.

[4] P. M. Mäkilä and H. T. Toivonen, "Computational methods for parametric LQ problems- A survey," *IEEE Trans. Automatic Control*, Vol. AC-32, pp. 658-671, 1987.

[5] T. Parisini and R. Zoppoli, "Neural networks for the solution of N-stage optimal control problems," in *Artificial Neural Networks*, T. Kohonen, K. Mäkisara, O. Simula, and J. Kangas, Eds., North-Holland, pp. 333-338, 1991.

[6] R. Zoppoli and T. Parisini, "Learning techniques and neural networks for the solution of *N*-stage nonlinear nonquadratic optimal control problems", in *Systems, Models and Feedback: Theory and Applications*, A. Isidori and T. J. Tarn, Eds., Birkhäuser, Boston, pp. 193-210, 1992.

[7] T. Parisini and R. Zoppoli, "Neural approximations for optimal control of nonlinear stochastic systems", *Proc. 31st Conf. on Decision and Control*, Tucson, Arizona, 1992.

[8] T. Poggio and F. Girosi "Networks for approximation and learning", *Proc. IEEE*, pp.1481-1487, 1990.

[9] A.N. Tikhonov and V.Y. Arsenin, *Solution of Ill-Posed Problems*, J. Wiley and Sons, New York, 1977.

[10] D. H. Nguyen and B. Widrow, "Neural networks for self-learning control systems," *IEEE Control System Magazine*, Vol. 10, pp. 18-23, 1990.

[11] B. T. Polyak and Ya. Z. Tsypkin, "Pseudogradient adaptation and training algorithms," *Automation and Remote Control*, Vol. 12, pp. 377-397, 1973.

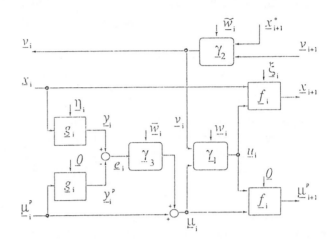

Figure 1: The three neural networks at stage i (note their time-invariant structures)

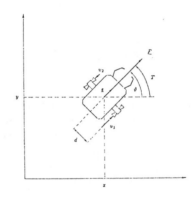

Figure 2: The space robot.

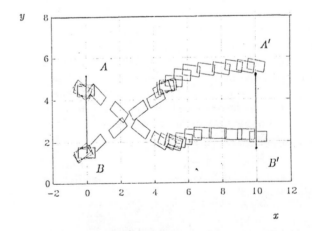

Figure 3: Two optimal trajectories.

Robust Construction of Radial Basis Function Networks for Classification

Shyh-Rong Lay,   Jenq-Neng Hwang

Information Processing Laboratory
Department of Electrical Engineering, FT-10
University of Washington
Seattle, WA 98195

ABSTRACT

In this paper, a neural network based on robust construction of locally tuned radial basis functions (RBFs) is proposed to design a pattern classifier. In this construction, a one-class one-network classification scheme is used to improve the data separation. A data sphering technique is applied to the raw training data for each class to decorrelate/normalize the data and to remove the potential outliers. The generalized Lloyd vector quantization clustering (also known as LBG) algorithm with centroid splitting is then applied on the sphered data to determine the centers and the diagonal covariance matrices of the Gaussian kernels. Better performance is achieved by our proposed method when compared with an existing improved RBF construction method on artificial data. Favorable simulation results are also achieved using the proposed technique when compared with other neural networks in classifying the Landsat-4 Thematic Mapper (TM) remote sensing data taken in July 1982 over an area in the vicinity of Washington, D.C..

I. INTRODUCTION

A radial basis function (RBF) network is a two-layer feedforward neural network [10] whose output nodes form a linear summation of the basis (usually Gaussian kernels) functions in the hidden layer. An RBF network can be regarded as an improved alternative of a probabilistic neural network (PNN) [13]. In a PNN, a symmetric RBF kernel is placed on each training data site so that the unknown density can be well interpolated and approximated. However, it is known that this design approach severely suffers from the "curse of dimensionality" and results in bad interpolation, not to mention its unreality on the implementation if the number of training data is huge. To overcome this problem, some kind of clustering algorithm must be applied to the training data to reduce the number of deployed kernels (hidden neurons) and, at the same time, improve the approximation ability of the network.

Sequential and batch versions of K-mean clustering have been commonly used in training the weights associated with the hidden layer weights [10, 1, 3]. The clustering algorithm can determine the center locations of the Gaussian kernels, it can also provide the insights about the covariance structures of kernels via simple data analysis techniques on the clustered data. Unfortunately, there is no guarantee that the resulting covariance structures can be simple enough (e.g., diagonal covariance structures) to be implemented based on an RBF-like network. To overcome this problem and to further improve the approximation capability of kernel methods, Mahalanobis Gaussian kernels of nondiagonal covariance matrix structures have been proposed [11]. These methods resulted in quite complicated learning procedures and quite sensitive control parameters.

To overcome the difficulties involved in constructing an RBF network, we propose to combine the statistical data sphering technique [4] with the centroid splitting generalized Lloyd clustering technique (also known as the LBG algorithm [5]). Our intention is to decorrelate and normalize the data so that simplified clustered covariance structures are obtained. Another additional benefit of this combined method is the capability of removing outlying noisy data to promotes the robustness of the center searching in the data clustering.

II. ROBUST CONSTRUCTION OF RBF NEURAL NETWORKS

In our construction of the RBF classifier, we adopt the *one-net-one-class* (ONOC) scheme, in which M RBF NNs are used in a M-class classification system [6]. In this scheme, each RBF NN (say m-th) is trained to represent m-th class of patterns. More specifically, in training the m-th RBF NN the training data of the m-th class is targeted to be output "1" and that of the rest classes is tar-

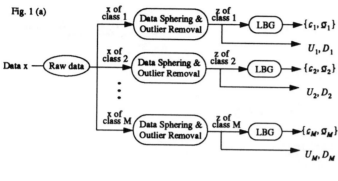

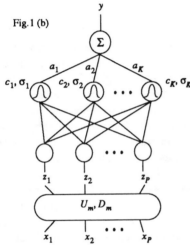

Figure 1: (a) The schematic construction diagram of the proposed robust RBF for an M-class classifier. (b) An RBF NN of K locally tuned units.

geted to be output "0".

Figure 1(a) shows the schematic diagram of the proposed robust RBF construction for an M-class classifier. Note that the data sphering (and outlier removing) procedure for each individual class can go several iterations.

A. Data Sphering for Structure Decorrelation

Let x be a random variable in R^p. The goal of data sphering is to transform x into a sphered data z so that $E[z] = 0$ and $E[zz^T] = I$, the identity matrix. In the application of classification, the sphering is performed on each individual class. Sphering operation starts with an eigen-decomposition of the data covariance matrix Σ

$$\Sigma = E[(x - E[x])(x - E[x])^T] = UDU^T \qquad (1)$$

where U is an orthonormal and D is a diagonal $p \times p$ matrix. Each column of U is an eigenvector of Σ and the

corresponding diagonal entry of D is its eigenvalue.

The data sphering procedure then transforms the original set of data $\{x\}$ into $\{z\}$

$$z = D^{-1/2}U^T(x - E[x]) \qquad (2)$$

All sphered data with larger norm (e.g., $\|z\| \geq \beta$), where β is a prespecified threshold, are treated as outlier and are excluded for clustering. This data sphering and outlier removing process can continue for several iterations on the original data $\{x\}$ until no outlying data can be removed. The sphered data $\{z\}$ are then clustered using the LBG algorithm [5].

B. LBG Algorithm for Data Clustering

The LBG algorithm has been successfully applied for searching the cluster centers of a data set, naming a codebook [5, 8]. To reduce the number of deployed kernels (hidden neurons) in an RBF NN, the LBG technique is very efficient in locating the representative clustering centers. With the splitting method [5, 8], this clustering technique is not so sensitive to the selection of initial codebook. More specifically, the LBG algorithm performs a distortion descent search to find a set of cluster centers which comprise a local minimum in the sense of the least mean squared (LMS) errors of the Euclidean space. The basic LBG algorithm is the following:

Step 0: Given: A set of training data and an initial codebook.

Step 1: Cluster the training data using the codebook of current iteration based on the Euclidean distance. If the average distortion is small enough, quit.

Step 2: Replace the old codebook by the centroids of clusters obtained in Step 1. Go to Step 1.

To obtain a good initial codebook, the splitting approach is applied. One first finds the optimum codebook of size one, i.e., the centroid of the entire training data set. This single codeword is then split to form the initial codewords of size two codebook and to ensure the distortion will decrease. The LBG algorithm is run to reach the local minimum. The technique is then applied repetitively to enlarge the codebook size. Class membership plays roles in the data clustering. The codebook of each class is obtained by running the LBG algorithm on that class of data.

C. The Construction of RBF Kernels

Given the set of training data $\{x\}$, an RBF NN of single output y (since the ONOC classification scheme is used) is generally constructed in the following form:

$$y(\mathbf{x}) = \sum_{i=1}^{K} a_i R_i(\mathbf{c}_i, \Sigma_i) \qquad (3)$$

$$R_i(\mathbf{c}_i, \Sigma_i) = \frac{1}{(\sqrt{2\pi})^p |\Sigma_i|^{1/2}} \, e^{-\frac{1}{2}(\mathbf{x}-\mathbf{c}_i)^T \Sigma_i^{-1}(\mathbf{x}-\mathbf{c}_i)} \qquad (4)$$

where $\mathbf{c}_i = (c_{i1}, c_{i2}, \cdots, c_{ip})^T$ denotes one of the center vectors (of the Gaussian kernels) which are obtained by employing the LBG clustering. Σ_i denotes the the data covariance matrix (of the i-th clustered data set) for the i-th Gaussian kernel, $\mathbf{a} = (a_1, a_2, \cdots, a_K)^T$ is the weight vector leading from hidden neurons to the output neuron and represent the heights of different kernels.

By applying the sphering operation on data $\mathbf{x}$, the covariance matrix for each data cluster of the sphered data $\mathbf{z}$ is expected to be a diagonal matrix, so that an RBF network of K locally tuned units, as shown in Figure 1(b), has a simplified overall response function:

$$y(\mathbf{z}) = \sum_{i=1}^{K} a_i R_i(\mathbf{c}_i, \sigma_i) \qquad (5)$$

$$R_i(\mathbf{c}_i, \sigma_i) = \frac{1}{(\sqrt{2\pi})^p \prod_{j=1}^{p} \sigma_{ij}} \, e^{-\frac{1}{2}\sum_{j=1}^{p} \frac{(z_j - c_{ij})^2}{\sigma_{ij}^2}} \qquad (6)$$

where $\sigma_i = [\sigma_{i1}, \sigma_{i2}, \cdots, \sigma_{iP}]^T$ is the width vector for each data cluster.

The kernel bandwidths $\{\sigma_{ij}\}$ of the Gaussian functions are simply designed to be proportional to (via a pre-specified global scaling constant η) the squared root of data variances in each dimension. Through the choice of the scaling constant η, one can appropriately adjust the smoothness of the reconstruction surface. Different selection of the scaling constant will lead to different solution set of kernel heights. In case of very small variance, a minimum bandwidth is used to avoid abrupt cutoffs along some dimensions, i.e., to ensure some degree of smoothness.

The determination of the height values of Gaussian functions $\mathbf{a}_m$ of the m-th class network is based on a simple least squares method, i.e., to minimize the square error

$$E_m = \sum_{n=1}^{N} (t_m^{(n)} - \mathbf{a}_m^T \mathbf{R}_m^{(n)})^2 \qquad (7)$$

where N is the total number of training data, $\mathbf{R}_m^{(n)} = (R_1, R_2, \ldots, R_K)^T$ denotes the hidden neuron output vector, and $t_m^{(n)}$ is the target value for the n-th data with respect to the m-th class, specifically $t_m^{(n)}$ is set to 1 if the n-th data belongs to the class m, 0 otherwise.

Since E_m is a quadratic function of $\mathbf{a}_m$, let

$$\mathbf{b} = (t_m^1, t_m^2, \ldots, t_m^N)^T$$

$$\mathbf{B} = \begin{pmatrix} (\mathbf{R}_m^{(1)})^T \\ (\mathbf{R}_m^2)^T \\ \vdots \\ (\mathbf{R}_m^{(N)})^T \end{pmatrix}$$

The least squares estimate $\hat{\mathbf{a}}_m$ of the height vector is obtained by solving

$$\hat{\mathbf{a}}_m = (\mathbf{B}^T \mathbf{B})^{-1} \mathbf{B}^T \mathbf{b}. \qquad (8)$$

Since each regressed RBF NN is supposed to generate the Bayesian probability for each class corresponding to the input vector, the network which produces the highest score (posterior probability) at the output will determine the Bayesian classification result.

III. COMPARATIVE SIMULATIONS OF ARTIFICIAL DATA

Two sets of binary classification data are used to evaluate the performance of our proposed robust RBF network construction technique and to compare with existing improved RBF construction method. To have a fair comparison with the method reported by Musavi et al [11], whose Gaussian kernels are built upon nondiagonal covariance matrices determined from a Gram-Schmidt orthogonalization process on some neighboring data, these two sets of training data are generated exactly the same manner as those reported in [11].

These two sets of data are 2-D and 8-D Gaussian random data $N(\mathbf{m}, \Sigma)$. For the 2-D case, the first class has zero mean vector $\mathbf{m} = (0, 0)^T$ with identity covariance matrix $\Sigma = \mathbf{I}$. The second class has mean vector $\mathbf{m} = (1, 2)^T$ and diagonal covariace matrix $\Sigma = diag(0.01, 4.0)$. Figure 2 shows the 400 training data which are randomly sampled from the distribution of this 2 Gaussian mixtures. After applying the data sphering operation on each class of the training data (roughly 200 each), the LBG algorithm is used to create 5 cluster centers for each class of sphered data $\{\mathbf{z}\}$ (see Figures 3(a) and (b)).

In comparison with the Musavi method, our total kernel number for both classes ($=10$) is much smaller than that of Musavi method ($=86$). Moreover, when evaluated on 20,000 randomly sampled testing data, our proposed robust RBF method achieves 7.1% error rate which outperforms the 9.26% error rate achieved by the Musavi method. The performance of our method is also very close to that of the theoretical optimal classifier (only for Gaussian data classification) which can achieve 6% error rate for this set of 2-D data. Experiments were also conducted

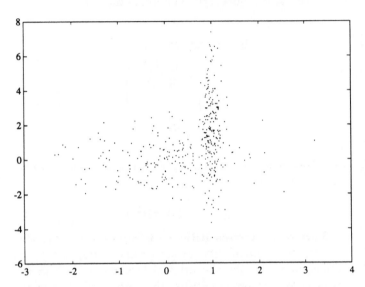

Figure 2: The 400 training data randomly sampled from the distribution of the 2 Gaussian mixtures.

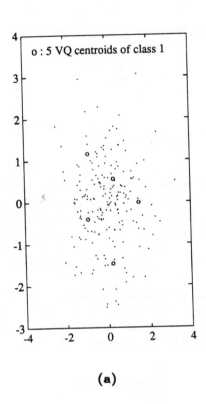

(a)

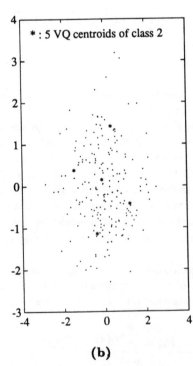

(b)

on smaller data size to see the effect of reduced training samples on the performance. The results is shown in Figure 4.

To further justify the superiority of the proposed robust RBF construction method, binary classification of 8-D Gaussian data were performed. The two classes of data have the same mean vector with covariace matrices $\Sigma = I$ and $\Sigma = 4I$. The number of cluster centers was tried between 2 to 9 for each class, and 8 was chosen for the final implementation. In comparison with the Musavi method, our total kernel number for both classes (=16) is again much smaller than that of Musavi method (=128). Moreover, performance evaluation on 20,000 randomly sampled testing data, our proposed robust RBF method achieves 11.1% error rate which outperforms the 12.0% error rate achieved by the Musavi method. The performance of our method is a little bit far away from that of the theoretical optimal classifier which can achieve 9% error data for this set of 8-D data. Experiments were also conducted on smaller data size to see the effect of reduced training samples on the performance. The results is shown in Figure 5.

IV. CLASSIFICATION OF REMOTELY SENSED DATA

In the coming decade, NASA's Mission to Planet Earth (MTPE) will address such pressing environmental issues as global warming, ozone depletion, deforestation and acid rain, with a fleet of advanced space platforms and extensive ground and air-borne observations. The expected data volume of MTPE is unprecedent – the Earth Observ-

Figure 3: (a) The 5 cluster centers created by LBG algorithm on the sphered data of class 1. (b) The 5 cluster centers created by LBG algorithm on the sphered data of class 2.

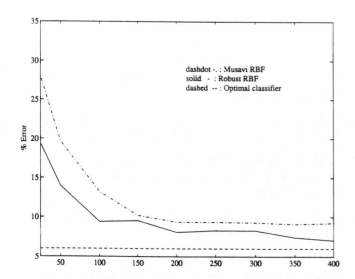

Figure 4: Classification performance comparison among our proposed method, the Musavi method and the optimal classifier for 2-D Gaussian mixture data.

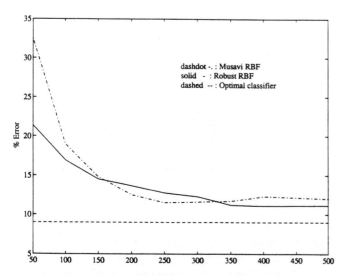

Figure 5: Classification performance comparison among our proposed method, the Musavi method and the optimal classifier for 8-D Gaussian mixture data.

ing System (EOS) alone will produce more than one terabyte of data a day. To timely process, analyze, archive and distribute the MTPE data not only presents a tremendous challenge to the data systems, but also demands innovative analytical methods and advanced computing and data communication technologies. In recent years, using neural networks for classifying remotely sensed data has shown promising results (e.g., [9, 2, 7]). As neural computing lends itself to massively parallel and distributed processing, information extraction based on neural networks could be a viable approach for analyzing the huge volume of MTPE data.

A. Protocols of Experiments

We applied the proposed technique to the Landsat-4 Thematic Mapper (TM) data taken in July 1982 over an area in the vicinity of Washington, D.C.. Only the first four TM bands were available, as the instruments for the three remaining IR bands had not stabilized. The area has 21,952 pixels, among which half of the pixels are used for training, and the other half for testing. The 17 information categories in the original ground truth were regrouped into six broader categories, as discussed in [7]. The six categories are (1) urban or built-up land (2754 pixels), (2) agricultural land (1670 pixels), (3) rangeland (3184 pixels), (4) forest land (13781 pixels), (5) water (28 pixels), and (6) bare soil/cleared land (535 pixels).

To verify the usefulness of the proposed robust RBF NN technique, two other commonly used neural network and statistical classification methods were experimented and compared.

Method 1: A multi-class-one-net (MCON) classification scheme based on a 2-layer (one hidden layer) perceptron, trained with the standard back-propagation learning algorithm in minimizing mean squared errors [12], was used. The input layer has four units, corresponding to the four TM bands. The hidden layer has 30 units, and the output layer has six units, corresponding to the six ground categories to be classified. Three learning rates, 0.1, 0.5, and 1.0, were tried for 500 iterations. Of three, the best testing performance in terms of accuracy percentage was achieved with the learning rate 0.5, and was tabulated in Table 1.

Method 2: An ONOC classification scheme based on 6 RBF networks without data sphering. There are 64 Gaussian kernels adopted for each RBF network. The best scaling constant η was chosen after several trials. Four different minimum variances, 0.2, 0.3, 0.4, and 0.5, were tried to ensure the interpolation smoothness. The best testing performance was tabulated in Table 1.

Method 3: Our proposed robust construction of RBF networks. It is an ONOC classification scheme based on 6 RBF networks with data sphering. There are also 64 Gaussian kernels adopted for each RBF network. The best scaling constant η was chosen after several trials. Four different minimum variances, 0.2, 0.3, 0.4, and 0.5, were tried to ensure the interpolation smoothness. The best testing performance was tabulated in Table 1.

B. Experiment result

As shown in Table 1, the best performance 78.43% is achieved by our proposed robust RBF networks.

Class	Method 1	Method 2	Method 3
1	66.67	77.78	73.64
2	30.30	45.75	39.76
3	32.66	38.00	51.13
4	95.72	90.86	91.58
5	0.00	7.14	28.57
6	53.73	41.42	50.00
overall	76.81	76.90	78.43

Table 1: Testing performance (in terms of classification accuracy %) for the classification of TM data.

V. Discussions

Note that, due to only 28 data (about 0.1% of the whole set of training/testing data) available for class 5, therefore very low accuracy is obtained for this class. It is interesting to point out that both RBF methods (with or without data sphering) performed slightly better than the MCON classification scheme based on multilayer perceptrons with back-propagation learning. It might be due to the fact that there are only four dimensional data used for classification, and the locally tuned RBF methods are believed to perform better than the projection based multilayer perceptrons in low dimensional applications without suffering from the "curse of dimensionality". It would be interesting to see the proposed method applied in a higher dimensional application (e.g., using more TM bands data). A final remark about the classifications of remotely sensed data is the feasibility of a postprocessing based on the local continuity assumption about the measured field to further improve the classification accuracy. More specifically, the classification results of a specific area can be treated as an image of few gray levels (e.g., 6 levels in this TM data), and those misclassified pixel (site) can be corrected by examining the classification results of its surrounding pixels (e.g., by Markov random field segmentation).

References

[1] P. Burrascano. Learning vector quantization for the probabilistic neural network. IEEE Trans. on Neural Networks, 2(4):458-461, July 1991.

[2] W. J. Campbell, S. E. Hill, R. F. Cromp. Automatic labeling and characterization of objects using artificial neural networks. Telematics and Information, Vol. 6, p.259, 1989.

[3] R. O. Duda, P. E. Hart. Pattern Classification and Scene Analysis. Wiley, New York, NY, 1973.

[4] J. H. Friedman. Exploratory projection pursuit. Journal of the American Statistic Association, Vol. 82, pp. 249-266, 1987.

[5] R.M. Gray. Vector Quantization. IEEE ASSP Mag., Vol 1, pp. 4-29, Apr. 1984.

[6] J.N. Hwang, H. Li. Interactive query learning for isolated speech recognition. IEEE Int'l Workshop on Neural Networks for Signal Processing, pp. 93-102, Denmark, September 1992.

[7] R. K. Kiang. Classifications of remotely sensed data using OCR-Inspired neural network techniques. Proceedings of 1992 International Geoscience and Remote Sensing Symposium, pp. 1081-1083, 1992.

[8] Y. Linde, A. Buzo, and R. M. Gray. An algorithm for vector quantizer design. IEEE Trans. on Communication, Vol 28, pp. 84-95, Jan. 1980.

[9] Z. K. Liu, J. Y. Xiao. Classification of remotely sensed image data using artificial neural networks. Int. Journal of Remote Sensing, Vol. 12, pp. 2433-2438, 1991.

[10] J. Moody and C.J. Darken Fast learning in networks of locally tuned processing units. Neural Computation, 1(3):281-294, 1989.

[11] M.T. Musavi, W. Ahmed, K. H. Chan, and K. B. Faris. On the training of radial basis function classifier. Neural Networks, 5:595-603, 1992.

[12] D. E. Rumelhart, G. E. Hinton, and R. J. Williams. Learning internal representation by error propagation. In D. E. Rumelhart and J. L. McClelland, editors, *Parallel Distributed Processing: Explorations in the Microstructure of Cognition: Volume 1: Foundations*, chapter 8. MIT Press, Cambridge, MA, 1986.

[13] D.F. Specht. Probabilistic neural networks. Neural Networks, Vol. 3, pp. 109-118, 1990.

Improved CNC Machining Using NARMA Neural Systems

Wei-Ren Chang and Benito Fernández
Mechanical Engineering Department
University of Texas at Austin

Abstract— The NARMA (Nonlinear ARMA) neural network is based on the Auto-Regressive Moving Average (ARMA) model widely used in time series analysis but can perform nonlinear analysis. Firstly, we show that NARMA networks are capable of learning linear and nonlinear system dynamics. Then the networks are used to improve Computer Numerical Control (CNC) machining precision. NARMA neural networks are used to learn the mapping between the actual workpiece dimensions and the commanded dimensions including the effect of the change of stiffness of the workpiece during cutting. After training, the network then predicts the necessary corrective CNC commands which can reduce machining inaccuracies significantly. Computer simulations were performed showing that the machining precision is greatly improved compared to uncorrective cutting.

I. INTRODUCTION

A. ARMA formulation

ARMA models are used for modeling unknown physical plants when it is difficult to obtain the analytical/exact models for the systems. Let's take a single-input single-output system as an example. The general ARMA(n,m) formulation for a system is

$$y(t) + \phi_1 y(t-T) + \ldots + \phi_n y(t-nT) \tag{1}$$

$$= \theta_0 u(t) + \theta_1 u(t-T) + \ldots + \theta_m u(t-mT), \tag{2}$$

where T is the sampling time. That is, $y(t)$ is a linear combination of previous values of input u and output y. The left-hand side of the equation is the Auto-Regressive (AR) part, the right-hand side is the Moving Average (MA) part. The use of ARMA models to describe various systems can be found in [1]. The order of delays (n, m) are unknown, but for most physical systems, the orders are usually lower than two[1]. The AR and MA parameters can be obtained by minimizing a cost function, which is usually the squared error between the ARMA system and actual output. Gradient descent and maximum likelihood method are two commonly used techniques for parameter estimation. The basic idea of ARMA is to use difference equations to approximate differential equations. For a typical linear finite dimensional time-invariant system, suppose the state equations are:

$$\dot{x} = Ax + Bu. \tag{3}$$

Then the discretized system is

$$x_{k+1} = e^{-AT} x_k + \int_{kT}^{(k+1)T} e^{-AT} Bu \, dt. \tag{4}$$

If the state equations are written in canonical form, then these equations can be combined into one ARMA model. So ARMA models can represent discretized version of general linear finite memory time-invariant systems. ARMA formulation is useful but *effective for linear systems only*. For nonlinear system, we need nonlinear ARMA models.

B. NARMA network

The Multi-Layered Perceptron (MLP) neural network is well known for its capability of function approximation[3]. The nonlinear mapping capability is accomplished by using sigmoidal functions in the hidden layers of an MLP. We can use an MLP to realize a NARMA implementation. The previous states are obtained using feedback and crosstalk links. Our design of a generic NARMA network is depicted in Fig. 1.

For NARMA networks to be useful, we use *dynamic learning*. That is, only current inputs are used as inputs to the network, and only the current outputs are used as desired outputs of the network. The history of previous states are handled using crosstalk and feedback links. In NARMA network simulation, the current neuron outputs are used for feedforward links; the old neuron outputs are used for cross-talk and feedback links, which produce the time-delay effects. NARMA network is being used as a system identification tool. Given the responses of the system for prescribed inputs, the NARMA network learns the unknown nonlinear dynamic relations between inputs and outputs.

1865

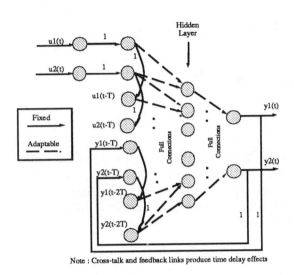

Figure 1: A 2-input, 2-output NARMA(1,2) neural network

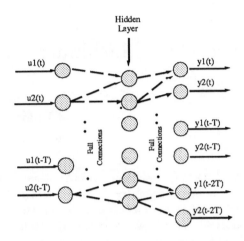

Figure 2: Equivalent static version of NARMA(1,2) network

Similar work using static learning was reported[8], but our work successfully showed that dynamic learning is also feasible (details are described below), though some caution need to be taken to insure the convergence. Static learning is similar to the term "series model" and dynamic learning is similar to the term "parallel model" in Narendra's paper[8]. The equivalent static version of NARMA network is shown in Fig. 2.

One important point of dynamic learning is that it uses *learned network outputs* as previous states rather than using stored desired system outputs. Learning is more difficult using dynamic learning, but once learned, the network is more effective in representing the real system. Static learning uses *desired/actual* outputs directly as its inputs, so it is easier to learn but it does not guarantee the effectiveness in approximating the real system once the learning is stopped. Let's take a simple ARMA model to illustrate this point. Suppose there is a system $y(t) = ay(t - T) + bu(t)$, and the exact value of a is 0.99, for simplicity, take $b = 1$. There are two possibilities for the initial estimation/guess of a, one is larger than 1, the other, less than 1. If one has $\hat{a}(0) = 1.5$, and uses static learning to estimate the $\hat{a}$, stopping the neural network training when $\hat{a}$ is 1.01, which means the error of $|a - \hat{a}|$ is 0.02. When the estimated $\hat{a}$ is used in the state equation $y(t) = 1.01y(t-T)+u(t)$ for simulation, the system blows up because the multiplication of 1.01 increases exponentially (the pole is outside the unit disk). If, instead, one has $\hat{a}(0) = 0.5$, and uses the static learning

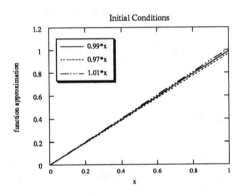

Figure 3: Static Learning for Different Initial Conditions

to update the $\hat{a}$, and stopped the neural network training when $\hat{a}$ is 0.97, which means the error $|a - \hat{a}|$ is *also* 0.02. When the estimated $\hat{a}$ is used in the state equation $y(t) = 0.97y(t - T) + u(t)$, the system is stable since the multiplication of 0.97 stays bounded (the pole is inside the unit disk). This is shown Fig. 3. This means that the stability of the system approximated the neural network using static learning depends on the initial guess/estimation of a. But if one uses dynamic learning, once it learns, it is guaranteed that the network approximation is in the stable region. One just has to choose proper learning rate, preferably selecting initial set of weights such that the system is stable, and the NARMA network will learn the system dynamics.

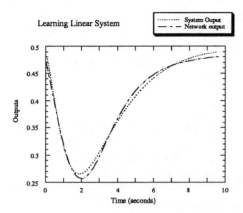

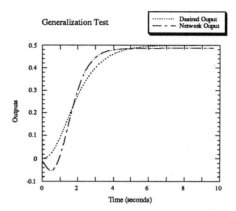

Figure 4: Learning linear system using NARMA network

Figure 5: Generalization test for NARMA network learning linear system

II. LINEAR SYSTEM IDENTIFICATION

We considered a typical second-order linear system $m\ddot{y} + b\dot{y} + ky = f(t)$. In computer simulation, an underdamped plant $\ddot{y} + 3\dot{y} + 2y = f(t)$ was used. For the training, the forcing function $f(t)$ was $1 - Exp(-t/2)$. The system response was calculated from 0 to 10 seconds. The response was then sampled every 0.1 second and used as training data for our NARMA neural network. A single-input, single-output NARMA(2,2) network with 10 hidden nodes was used as an approximate plant. We used dynamic learning employing Adaptive Back-Propagation (ABP)[4] learning algorithms with batch weight/bias updating[5]. ABP is a modified back-propagation learning method that is based on sliding-mode control theory. The cost function of a MLP-type neural network is reduced in the order of exponential function $e^{-\tau}$ if τ is the pseudo time–number of iterations of training.

The NARMA network learned the system response very well (see Fig. 4). After certain training, the weights and biases were then frozen, given a forcing function it has never seen before $(f(t) = Tanh(t))$ the network predicted the system response well (see Fig. 5). There is one thing we need to point out:the training time was rather long compared to static function approximation problems from our experiences. The reason is that there exist feedback from the learned network outputs. The learning was sensitive to the learning rates, a small increase in learning rates could cause oscillations in network learning. The exact effect of the learning rate to the convergence of dynamic learning and the optimal learning rate are yet to be investigated further.

III. NONLINEAR SYSTEM IDENTIFICATION

A typical second-order nonlinear mass-spring-damper system was used for study. The system is $m\ddot{y} + b\dot{y}|\dot{y}| + ky^3 = f(t)$, which has coulomb friction and high-order spring

effects. The values $m = 0.1, b = 1 = k$, were used for simulations. A single-input single-output NARMA(4,4) network with 20 hidden nodes was used to approximate this plant. Dynamic learning utilizing ABP with batch weight/bias updating was used in the neural network training. The forcing function used for training data was $f(t) = Sin(t) - Cos(3t) + 0.5e^{-t}$. The forcing functions for the test data set are $f(t) = Cos(1.5t) + Sin(4t) + e^{-2t} - 0.1$ and $f(t) = 1, for \ 0 \le t \le 5; -1, for \ 0 \le t \le 5$. The simulation results are shown in Fig. 6, Fig. 7, and Fig. 8. The graphs shows that the NARMA network learned the nonlinear plant very well and the capability of generalization is also satisfactory. This gave us confidence that NARMA networks can be used in learning more complex dynamic systems. We want to apply NARMA network to CNC turning process, which is a highly nonlinear system and very difficult to model.

IV. APPLICATION TO CNC MACHINING

A. General Problem Descriptions

We consider the CNC turning process as a typical manufacturing environment. When energy is transmitted from the machine to the part to perform the cutting, dynamic interaction occurs between the machine and the workpiece. As the tool cuts into the part, the part deflects. The larger the desired depth of cut is, the more the part deflects and hence the larger the error is. Currently, the common way to maintain accuracy is to minimize the interaction, that is, small depth of cut and feedrate are used. This results in small throughput. Also, as the material is removed during cutting, the stiffness (moment of inertia) changes with time and position. This further induces inaccuracies in the dimensions of the workpiece since the stiffness of the workpiece decreases as the tool cuts away more material. There is a need for a new tech-

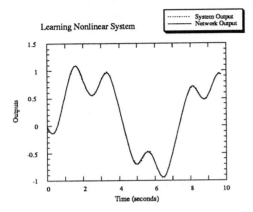

Figure 6: Learning nonlinear system using NARMA network

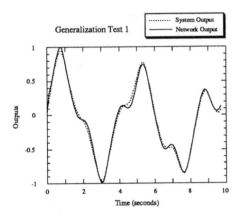

Figure 7: Generalization test for NARMA network learning nonlinear system (Part 1)

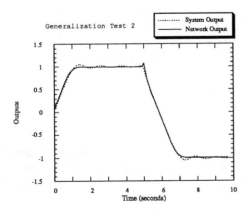

Figure 8: Generalization test for NARMA network learning nonlinear system (Part 2)

nology that provides geometric correction while maintaining high production rate[9]. This was was first proposed by Peklenik. Other researchers reported their adaptive geometric control schemes[6,10], but the techniques were complex. The authors reported a neural information processing approach for this need and have shown that it is simple and effective[2].

B. Geometric Correction

The feasibility of this new technology was proved, but only static effects were considered before[2]. In this paper, we further include dynamic effect using the NARMA neural network. The dynamic effect considered here is the change of the stiffness (moment of inertia) of the workpiece during cutting. We considered the workpiece axis as the "time axis". In the training stage, we consider the actual profile as the "forcing function", and the commanded profile as the "system response". In the generalization stage, *CNC code generation stage in this case*, the desired profile is used as "forcing function", the neural network outputs the corresponding "system response", which are the corrective CNC codes. More details of our approach of geometric correction can be found in [2].

C. Solving the True Depth of Cut

CNC turning is a typical orthogonal cutting. An analytical model of orthogonal cutting was derived by Merchant[7]. We combined Merchant's model[7] and simple beam theory[11] to generate a simple model of the lathe cutting. The goal of this paper is to demonstrate that it is suitable to use neural networks for geometric correction of metal cutting. We take the analytical models as if these are real metal cutting process. Computer simulations were performed, experimental validation is also being pursued by the authors.

The equations used in our computations are:

$$EI(x)y'''(x) = -V(x), and \qquad (5)$$

$$F_c = wt_1\mu cos(\beta - \alpha)/(sin(\phi)cos(\phi + \beta - \alpha)), \qquad (6)$$

where x is the position coordinate, $y(x)$ is the beam deflection at the position x, E is the Young's Modulus, $I(x)$ is the moment of inertia at x, $V(x)$ is the induced shear force at x, w is the cutting width (depth of cut in this case), t_1 is the feedrate (advance of the tool per revolution), μ is the coefficient of friction ($\mu = tan(\beta)$), ϕ is the shear angle in the cutting plane, τ is the shear stress on shear plane, α is the rake angle of the cutting tool, β is the friction angle at the cutting point, . The F_c used here is called the *cutting force* by Merchant, which is usually much larger than the *thrust force* F_t. F_t is neglected in our computations for the sake of simplification. Equation (5)

1868

is from Timoshenko's simple beam theory, and equation (6) is from Merchant's model.

A finite-element type of solution is obtained using symbolic mathematics computational tools. We look at the workpiece as a beam being clamped at one end while supported at the other end. The tool induces a moving force and the stiffness of the workpiece changes with respect to time (or the position of the tool). The *true* depth of cut (DOC) is the beam deflection subtracted form the *desired* DOC at that position. Since infinite number of solutions are needed to solve the exact *true* DOC at all positions, a discrete solution was used. That is, a beam is divided into n segments. It is assumed that every small segment of the beam has the same equilibrium force and the same moment of inertia. In this way, we obtained the deflection equation for each segment. And the *true* DOC within that segment was calculated according to that deflection equation.

Given a tool position, we solve the beam deflection equation , which is a static indeterminate problem. The cutting force is unknown since the *true* depth of cut and the *true* deflection at that position are unknown. The beam deflection is described by two equations–the one to the left of the cutting position, and the other to the right. One of the support reaction forces or moment is taken as redundant (assumed known first). Using the boundary conditions and by matching the deflections of the left side and the right side solutions at the cutting position, a closed form solution of the beam deflection, true DOC, as well as the equilibrium cutting force can be obtained.

After one segment is "cut", the stiffness moment of inertia) of the entire workpiece is updated and used to calculate the deflection in the next iteration. During each iteration, the equilibrium force, deflection, true DOC are calculated. This iterative computation emulates the CNC lathe cutting process. Two workpiece profiles were generated and taken as training data for NARMA network. Another one was used for generating corrective CNC codes for test purposes.

D. Simulation: Training & Test

The NARMA network used here is slightly different from the ones used for learning linear and nonlinear plants mentioned above. One more variable, the position, is also used as an input to the network. That is, the "time effect" is included in the NARMA network explicitly. To accomplish the computer simulations, we actually used the *actual* profile as the *desired* profile in the *training* stage. Then, in the *generalization/code generation* stage, given the *desired* profile, the NARMA network should generate the necessary *corrective commands* if it learns the system dynamics accurately.

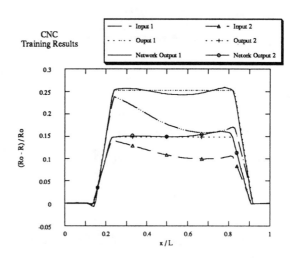

Figure 9: Learning CNC turning using NARMA network

The inputs of the network, the position and the actual profile, are made dimensionless for simplicity and consistency with our previous work. Two *actual* profiles used in training were obtained using the method described in the previous section. The results of learning is shown in in Fig. 9. A third profile was used for generalization test. The uncorrected actual profile was calculated first, the the desired profile was fed into the trained NARMA network, the corrective CNC codes was generated by the network. Then we used the corrective codes to do the "machining" simulation, the corrected profile was obtained. These curves are shown in Fig. 10. It shows that the NARMA network generalizes well, and it generates decent corrective CNC codes for the machine. The corrected profile is much better than the uncorrected profile. In Fig. 9 we see some overcuts according to the NARMA network output.

To avoid this in real cutting, a safety factor of 5% is included (i.e., 95% of the corrective depth of cuts are used) for the "machining" simulation. In Fig. 10, overcut is eliminated. If one uses a finish cut using the original CNC codes, a workpiece with minimal inaccuracy will be produced. In industry, tolerances are specified for every parts according to their use. Some parts allow positive and negative tolerances, but some may prefer positive or negative tolerances. For example, a shaft to be mounted into a support should prefer a negative tolerance. Therefore, the safety factor used here can be positive or negative depending upon the usage. But we don't want the overcut at the first time generally. Following finish cuts (if so desired) can bring the part to the specified dimensions more closely.

The authors also compared the corrective CNC codes

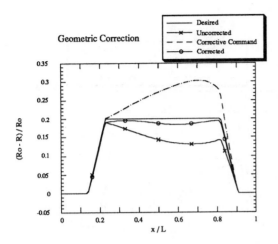

Figure 10: Generalization test for NARMA network learning CNC turning

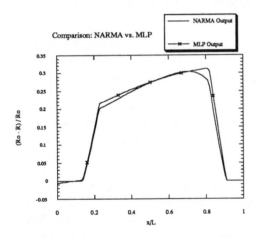

Figure 11: Comparison of NARMA and MLP network outputs

generated by the NARMA network and an MLP, which was used by the authors in the previous paper[2]. We found that the CNC codes generated by the static MLP were not as good as that generated by the dynamic NARMA network. The errors were larger, which can be seen in Fig. 11.

The computer simulations gave us assurance that if actual machining data were used to train the NARMA network, the network will be able to generate corrective CNC codes that drive the tool to cut the workpiece according to desired dimensions very accurately. Here we have shown one-pass compensation, if the work material is too hard for one-pass cutting, multiple-cutting compensation can also be obtained by using NARMA network scheme described above. The authors are working on this and will report the results in the near future.

V. Conclusions

We have shown the usefulness of NARMA network in the identification of general linear and nonlinear system dynamics. One very practical example, CNC turning, was used to demonstrate the effectiveness of the network. One-pass cutting was assumed in this paper, multiple-pass solution using similar techniques is already being developed by the authors. Further improvements to CNC turning is expected using this innovative technology. Experimental validation is currently being pursued.

References

[1] Box, G.E.P., and Jenkins, G.M., *Time Series Analysis:Forecasting and Control*, Holden-Day, San Francisco, 1976.

[2] Chang, W.-R., and B. Fernández, "Improving Precision in CNC Turning Process Using Artificial Neural Networks," *American Control Conference*, Chicago, June 1992.

[3] Cybenko, G., "Approximation by Superpositions of a Sigmoidal Function," *Math. Control Signals Sys.*, 303-314, 1989.

[4] Fernández, B., "Tools for ANN Learning" in *Intelligent Engineering System Through Artificial Neural Networks*, C.H. Dagli, S.R.T. Kumara, and Y.C. Shiu, Editors, ASME Press, N.Y. 1991.

[5] Hertz, J., Krogh, A., Palmer, R.G., *Introduction to the Theory of Neural Computation*, Addison-Wesley Co., Redwood City, CA, 1991.

[6] Liu, L., Sinha, N. K., and Elbestawi, M.A., "Adaptive Control of Geometric Tracking in Turning," *Computers in Industry*, Vol. 11., 147-159, 1988.

[7] Merchant, M.E., "Basic Mechanics of the Metal-Cutting Process," *Journal of Applied Mechanics*, ASME Transactions, A-168 to A-175, 1944.

[8] Narendra, K.S., and Parthasarathy, K., "Identification and Control of Dynamical Systems Using Neural Networks," *IEEE Trans. on Neural Networks*, Vol. 1, No. 1, 4-27, 1990.

[9] Peklenik, J.,"Geometrical Adaptive Control of Manufacturing Systems," *Annals of The CIRP*, Vol. 18, 265-272, 1970.

[10] Shiraishi, M. (1984), "Geometrical Adaptive Control in CNC Turning Operation," *ASME J. Eng. for Ind.*, Vol. 106, 75-80, 1984.

[11] Timoshenko, S.P., and Gere, J.M., *Mechanics of Materials*, Van Nostrand Reinhold Co., N.Y., 1972.

Neural and Cognitive Modeling of Analogical Reasoning

François Blanc, Sandrine Allemand, Michel Dufossé, Elie Sanchez
Neurinfo Lab. of Neurocomputing & Fuzzy Logic Systems
Institut Méditerranéen de Technologie, Technopôle de Château-Gombert
13451 Marseille Cedex 13, France

Abstract--This paper describes a connectionist model of analogical reasoning, *C A P S (Connectionist Analogical Problem Solver)*. It is focused on short-term information structuring. It started from some neuroscientific clues supplied by Neurophysiology of the prefrontal cortex. Here, the basic automaton is not a formal neuron but a model of the cortical column.

I. INTRODUCTION

The analysis of approximate reasoning appears in quite various domains such as Psychology, Artificial Intelligence, Logic, Probabilities and quite recently Connectionism. It plays an important part in Cognitive Sciences. Approximate reasoning is at the core of both commonsense and expert reasonings and it coexists with logical reasoning. Moreover those two types of reasonings complement each other. Approximate reasoning is widely involved in the problem solving process, in the learning of new knowledge and when using the context effects. Among these different types of reasoning, analogical reasoning appears as an essential element of cognition, discourse and thought as well.

Analogy involves three underlying principles of knowledge [1]. The first principle is the identification of objects features. The second one is the induction of relationships between these objects from their features. The third is the discovery of correlative features between several situations.

Analogical reasoning may be defined as a mapping from a field of known source to a field of unknown target. Several stages of processing can be defined when a simple analogy such as "A gives B, so C gives D" is solved [2]. The first stage is the encoding of the data. The subject codes the terms of the analogy and builds up an internal representation of the problem. During a second stage of inference, the subject compares the internal representation of the first two terms (A and B) and discovers relationships between these two terms. When term C is then presented, there is a mapping of the pattern C on pattern A in such a way that C is translated in the terms of A. During the last stage, the subject must apply to C a relationship which must be similar to the one linking A to B, to infer the missing pattern D. This modeling requires a series of operations which must done sequentially, but with overlapping.

Analogical reasoning has a great importance in Artificial Intelligence, because of its promise for the acquisition and effective use of knowledge. It can be involved in domains of automated deduction, problem solving and planning, natural language comprehension and machine learning (for a review, see [3]).

A logical frame defining the inference within analogical reasoning has been proposed as in [4]. It is based on the identification of the relationship structuring the fields united by analogy. Following Zadeh's theory of fuzzy sets and associated possibity distributions [5], some fuzzy logic study of analogical reasoning has been developed in order to narrow the gap between human reasoning and machine reasoning [6, 7, 8]. One of the targets of Artificial Intelligence is to get a general model of analogical reasoning to study its formal properties in order to provide an automaton with inferential capabilities derived from this type of reasoning.

However "most everyday reasoning probably involves assimilating the novel situation to other situations that are in some way similar - that is, reasoning by similarity. Now, it is possible to see a continuum of possible situations for reasoning by similarity involving at one pole what might be called *remembering* and at the other what might be called *analogical reasoning*. In between, we have such processes as *generalizing*, *being reminded*, and *reasoning by exemple*....Our ability to pattern-match is probably *the* essential component to most cognitive behavior" [9].

Within the framework of connectionist models, there are ideal mechanisms for accounting for these phenomena. To see this, it is useful to consider the following points. The notion of adaptive neuromimetic system provides the tools for modeling the learning in a way that can correspond to psychological knowledge and that can corroborate, at another level, neurobiological knowledge. The neuromimetic adaptive mechanisms constitute a way of integrating the statistic correlations that are the roots of associative processes determining the pattern matching. The neural networks convergence mechanisms to stable states can be read as modeling the reaching of decision from a correlation set.

Our focus throughout this study is on the issue of short-term information structuring. This issue is a major problem facing the application of connectionism to high-level cognitive processing. How are pieces of information put into temporary association with each other in a connectionist system [10] ? Unlike these authors technical approach, we started from some important neuroscientific clues to the elucidation of the mechanisms of higher brain functions, such as the clues supplied by the neurophysiology of the prefrontal cortex. Our purpose is to give a psychologically relevant and neurophysiologically plausible modeling of simple forms of analogical reasoning, by a connectionist network inspired by the functioning of the cerebral cortex.

II. METHODS

Unlike the pure mathematical approach, a neurobiologically plausible simulation of the cerebro-cortical functioning allows to propose a modeling coming from experimental results, which infers the relationship between the behavior and the activity of a population of cells. As it is the case for any neural network, we must give three basic characteristics of the neural network model, the activation rules of the elements, the plasticity rules of the connections between the elements, and the architecture.

Concerning the activation rules, the cerebral cortex cannot be simply considered as a set of formal neurons. As a matter of fact, it includes some twenty different cellular types carrying out each one complex processing, the modeling of which is more a matter for biophysics than for connectionism. The basic element of a connectionist modeling of the cerebral cortex cannot be the formal neuron as it is classically defined.

At a higher level of analysis, we can find out another basic element. This module of the cerebral cortex seen as a repetitive structure, is the cortical micro-column [11, 12]. It can also be shematised by an automaton. This automaton is linked to other micro-columns through the activities of the upper layers (supragranular) on one hand, and on the other hand they are connected to other nervous structures through the thalamic inputs received at intermediary (granular) layer and the outputs of the pyramidal cells of the lower layer (infragranular).

The way this automaton works can be considered as a three-valued logic corresponding to the notions of "true", "false" and "don't know" [13, 14]. These three levels are coded according to the level of activity of the cortical cells that are called E0 for a state of inactiveness, E1 for a state of intermediary activity, E2 for a state of strong activity. A decision table [13] gives the definitions of the levels of activity of the higher and lower layers of the automaton according to the values of these two types of input and its previous state. This model has been presented extensively elsewhere [13], and it has been tested on problems of pattern recognition [15]. In our model, only cortico-cortical connections (between higher layers of automata) are considered, because only prefrontal and fronto-temporal areas are concerned for us in the study of inferring, mapping and applying phases of visual analogical reasoning. Therefore we dont model pattern recognition processes studied elsewhere [15].

Concerning the plasticity rules, the long-term potentiation is the principal mode of plasticity of the cortical network. It is not basically different from the Hebb rule, stating that the synaptic efficiency changes according to a local covariation between pre-synaptic and post-synaptic signals. However this rule corresponds to a too low level of analysis to be used in the design of a connectionist model which must be kept at a more comprehensive global level. From the behavioral point of view, the mode of plasticity of the cerebral cortex is somewhat similar to the operating conditioning [13]. The functioning of a neural network using that mode of reinforcement has been also suggested by other authors [16].

From the architectural point of view, the cerebral cortex is composed of a set of areas, falling into three categories. There are the sensorial areas, the motor areas and the associative areas. The network is structured by topological relationships between automata dealing with similar information in nearby areas which work out similar operations. This topological notion of proximity does not only apply to a two-dimensional cortical area. The cortex is a multi-dimensional structure having privileged relationships. These privileged relationships between left and right hemispheres, between pre-central and post-central areas, between parietal and temporal lobes correspond to what physicists call symmetries (Fig.1, right).

The temporal organization of complex structures of behavior requires three subsidiary functions of prefrontal cortex: the anticipatory preparation of the organism for coming events, the memory of recent events and the suppression of interference [17]. These three fonctions are involved in all reasoning modes. Goldman-Rakic [18] have argued that prefrontal cortex is necessary for regulating behavior guided by representations or internalized models of reality, for building up expectations by internalizing our experiences. This is a fundamental ability that underlies our capacities to perform mental simulations, such as the ones involved within analogical visual tests. Among neurobiologically plausible models, the cortical model deals with this temporal organization of behavior [13]. The frontal mechanism can recognize structured sensory patterns in the outer world. From a set of sensory messages A, B, C, D, E, F frontal automata generate a structured information of the type $A*((B*((C*D)*E)*F))$, where the parentheses are internal levels of temporal organization, and operations (*) are sensory correlations in the associative areas.

III. CONNECTIONIST MODEL

We propose three stages for a neurophysiologically plausible modeling of analogical reasoning. The first stage aims at describing how the elements of a pattern and their spatial relationships can be distributed within cortical structures and stored in an associative memory. The second stage defines the relationship existing between two patterns, that is the inference which enables to describe the pattern B taking into account the pattern A. This function must be memorized on longer lapses of time. The third stage aims at applying this set of relationships to any new pattern C presented, in order to infer D.

The first stage (Fig. 1.1) of analysis of a pattern, or term of the analogy, is related to the elements it is composed of. The cortical model has been used for pattern recognition, from the architecture and the properties of visual maps. The architecture is Y-shaped, with a first stage of visual processing on retinotopic cerebral areas, then two branches, the parietal way dealing more with positions and the temporal way dealing chiefly with the shapes [15].

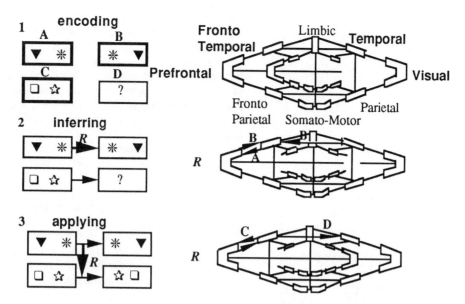

Fig. 1. Stages of analogical reasoning. Illustration of an analogical problem (left) together with a sheme of the corresponding cerebral areas involved (right): 1. Analysis of each term by activation of the temporal and parietal ways. 2. Relationship R between two terms A and B involves connectivity between pre- and post-central associative areas on the one hand, both the later and the prefrontal areas on the other hand. 3. The resulting term is found in precentral areas by applying to a new term the relationship R defined in 2.

The second stage (Fig. 1.2) aims at defining the relationships which can exist between two patterns A and B. The various modalities (features, relative positions, colors,...) of a pattern are stored in autoassociative memories in various areas of the associative cortex. For each postcentral area, parietal and temporal, involved in the first stage, we consider a symmetric precentral area. During learning of the relationship A R B, this precentral area is viewed both like input layer involving the pattern A and output layer involving the pattern B (Fig.2). The prefrontal cortex play the role of intermediary layer able to infer the relationship(s) between A and B. This relationship will be used on any new term C for inferring a term D such as "A gives B, so C gives D".

Following Guigon et al. [19] which propose a neural network model of frontal cortical circuits for learning conditional sequences, the processing units considered (Fig. 2) result from the adaptation of this model to take into account the psychological constraints detailed above. The output of the unit can be either continuous or discrete, according to the form of the f function (Fig. 3). We only consider three discrete levels of activity, namely E0, E1 and E2.

The activities of units are combined by a multilinear operation whith two terms. A linear one expresses the direct influence of each unit (coefficient L). A bilinear one expresses the non-linear interactions between units (coefficients Q). The supervised learning turns on a given set of terms (A1,B1), (A2, B2),...., (An, Bn). The units themselves can be seen as microfeatures. Certain collections of microfeatures might represent the physical characteristics of the terms of analogy, such as the color or size of an object being viewed, whether some particular object (circle, triangle...) is present, and so on. Other microfeatures more abstract relational aspects of a term, such as the relative

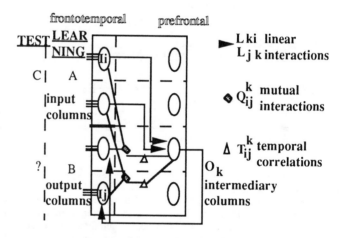

Fig. 2. Neural network model for learning and producing simple visual analogical reasoning. The index i correspond to the input columns, the index j to the output columns and the index k to the intermediary columns.

positions. The coefficients Q allow to correlate the features of terms A (activity pattern given in input layer) and the emergent features in output layer (activity pattern coding B determined by the internal representation, i.e. the activities of hidden prefrontal automata).

The calculation of coefficient Q (Fig. 3) is based on operant conditioning learning. To justify this, it is useful to conceptualize the internal representation as originating from manipulations of the environment so that it comes to represent something. Therefore the roots of concrete mental operation are in sensori-motricity [20, 21].

1873

ACTIVATION

$$O_k(t) = f \left(\sum_i \sum_j Q_{ij}^k I_i(t) I_j(t) + \sum_i L_{ki} I_i(t), \theta1, \theta2 \right) - \gamma O_k(t-1)$$

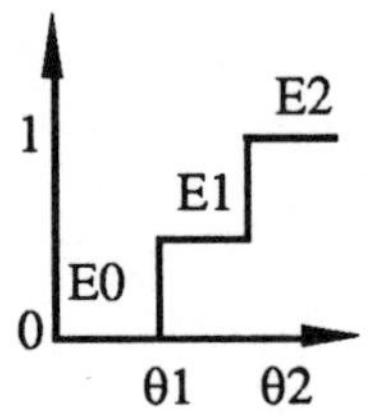

BISTABLE RULES

$O_k(t-1)$	CONDITIONS	$O_k(t)$	DURATION
OFF	$\dfrac{\sum_{ij} T_{ij}^k I_i}{/n^2} = E1 \text{ or } E2$ (1)	ON	$L_{23}^k = \alpha + \beta \sum_{ij} T_{ij}^k$
ON	$\dfrac{\sum_{ij} T_{ij}^k I_j}{/n^2} = E2$ (2)	OFF	$L_{12}^k = \mu + \lambda \sum_{ij} T_{ij}^k$

LEARNING

COEFF. Q : $Q_{ij}^k = \text{Prob} \, (\, I_j(t+1) = E2 \, / \, O_k(t) = E2$
et $I_i(t) = E2)$

COEFF. L : PERCEPTRON RULE /
CHOICE OF INTERNAL REPRESENTATIONS

COEFF. T : $T_{ij}^k = \text{Prob} \, (\, I_j(t+1) = E2 \, / \, I_i(t) = E2$
et $O_k(t) = E1)$

Fig. 3. Activation and learning rules of the model. The activation function is a function with two thresholds, $\theta1$ and $\theta2$, that allow to distinguish the activities E0, E1, E2. A decay term is included in the definition of activity Ok. At each presentation of terms (Ax, Bx) during learning, the calculation of coefficients Ljk between the intermediary prefrontal layer and output layer is made for automaton k under the condition (1) during I23 steps bound by the condition (2). A same type of rule apply to the calculation of coefficients Lki (the number of steps is then noted I12). The variables I23 and I12 are linear functions of the temporal coefficients Tij defined below.

The calculation of coefficient L (Fig. 3) is derived from Grossman et al. [22]: we consider two perceptrons, the first one between intermediary layer and the output layer, and the second one between the input layer and the intermediary layer. The psychology literature gives support to the notion of error correction in learning. Many tasks require the building up of an internal mesure of error, and it may be that this is in fact the commonest kind of learning [23]. Its biological plausibility is supported [24] and its implementation at the neural level is possible by the Hebb rule [25]. This is justifiably possible thanks to sustained activities of hidden prefrontal automata allowed during a certain duration determined by the coefficients T. These coefficients measure the sequence of activities in input then output layers.

Therefore the activation function is extended to a bistable activation function (Fig. 3) which is able to integrate non simultaneous inputs. Within each prefrontal cortex module, a sustained activity, which is the state ON of a bistable, can memorize sensory events, i.e. the terms A and B. This short-term-memory is similar to the "working memory" described in frontal cortical regions. The bistable activation rule performs a temporal AND operation upon pairs of non simultaneous inputs. This temporal AND is adjustable by learning through temporal coefficients T (Fig. 3). These coefficients are responsible for the selective short-term memorization of past events and for the selective expectation of future events.

The third stage (Fig. 1.3) involves the relationship inferred between A and B and applying this relationship to a pattern C, close to A. The third stage implicates a resonance process between the result of the presentation of C and the memory traces of R processed during learning phase. This stage will give then a new pattern D, the resulting term of the analogy.

In our approach, we might distinguish three types of learning. The first one is by correlations (coefficients Q). The second one is by error calculation (coefficient L).The third one is by attempts and errors. Therefore, the algorithm used allows to randomly change the internal representation, by permutations of hidden prefrontal automata states, until the overall error diminish in output of the firstly considered perceptron (between intermediary prefrontal layer and output layer).

IV. CONCLUDING REMARKS

During learning, it is observed a stabilization of coefficients Q and an increase of coefficients T. Closely related is the fact that the activities E1 (waiting) of hidden prefrontal automata (internal rapresentation) are more and more long sustained during learning.

One may note too the semantic abstraction capacity of the network: step by step, the configuration of coefficients L looks at the structural clues coded in input layer and neglects the superficial clues (for example in Fig. 1, only relative positions features are considered by the network after learning).

After learning this network can generalize to patterns C, not belonging to learning corpus (applying stage). We have to note that the three stages of inferring, mapping and applying, are closely bound in our model, because the learning phase consists in presenting to network the successive pairs (A1, B1), (A2, B2),...., (An, Bn). This fact corresponds to the observations of experimental Psychology: there is an overlapping of analogical reasoning phases.

The neuromimetic studies and simulations of reasoning, other than those belonging to connectionist experts systems domain [26, 27] are less explored. The explanation is may be the nature either too distributed, either too localist of representations manipulated by the networks. In the first case, one cannot have access to details of representations and inferences. In the second case one comes closer to methods more specific to Artificial Intelligence, such as frames [28].

A really connectionist approach of analogical reasoning, unrelated to AI, looks at some applications of Elman multilayers networks to analogies composed of four terms [29]. The inputs of the system are the termes A, B and C of the analogy "A gives B, so C gives D" and , during learning, the desired output is the term D. The terms of the analogy are strings of bits that can be considered like visual features. The type of learning used (backpropagation of error gradient) and the calculation times of this algorithm make this study far from neurobiological frame. From experimental basis closely related to our study, Dehaene and Changeux [30] elaborated a neuromimetic model of prefrontal functions involved in reasoning tasks. However the Wisconsin card sorting test studied is more a categorization problem resolved elsewhere [31] by a ART neuromimetic structure without nodes coding rules like in their approach.

Our connectionist modeling of analogical reasoning about simple problem involves various components allowing to apprehend human cortical functioning. It is difficult to think that the understanding of reasoning can be accomplished by a simple architecture with several formal neurons.

ACKNOWLEDGEMENT

This work was supported by the French Ministry of Research and Technology (grant "Sciences de la Cognition" 1991-C0954) and the program "Cognisud 1991" of the CNRS.

REFERENCES

[1] C. Spearman, *The nature of intelligence and the principles of cognition.* London: McMillan, 1923.

[2] R.J. Sternberg, *Intelligence, information processing, and analogical processing: the componential analysis of human habilities.* Hillsdale Lawrence Erlbaum, 1977.

[3] R.P. Hall, "Computational approaches to analogical reasoning: a comparative analysis," *Artif. Intell.*, vol. 39, pp.39-120,1989.

[4] L. Bourrelly and E. Chouraqui, "A formal approach to analogical reasoning," in *Approximate reasoning in expert system*, M.M. Gupta, A. Kandel, W. Bandler, J.B. Kiszka, Eds. Amsterdam: North Holland, 1985, pp. 87-104.

[5] L.A. Zadeh, "Fuzzy sets as a basis for a theory of possibility," *Fuzzy Sets & Systems*, vol. I (1), pp. 3-28, 1978.

[6] Léa Sombé, "Reasoning under incomplete information in artificial intelligence, a comparison of formalisms using a single example," *Int. Journal of Intelligent Systems*, vol. 5 (4), pp. 418-424, 1990.

[7] I. Arrazola, A. Plainfossé, H. Prade, C. Testemale, "Extrapolation of fuzzy values from incomplete data bases," *Information Systems*, vol. 14 (6), pp. 487-492, 1989.

[8] I.B. Turksen and Z. Zhong, "An approximate analogical reasoning schema based on similarity measures and interval-valued fuzzy sets," *Fuzzy Sets & Systems*, vol. 34, pp. 323-346, 1990.

[9] D.E. Rumelhart, "Toward a microstructural account of human reasoning," in *Similarity and analogical reasoning*, S. Vosniadou & A. Ortony, Eds. Cambridge University Press, 1987, pp. 298-312.

[10] J. Barden and K. Srinivas, "Encoding techniques for complex information structures in connectionist systems," *Connection Science*, vol. 3,pp. 269-315, 1991.

[11] V.B. Mountcastle, "An organizing principle for cerebral function: the unit module and the distributed system," in *The mindful brain*, F.O. Schmitt, Ed. MIT press, 1978, pp. 7-50.

[12] J. Szentagothai, "The module concept in cerebral cortex architecture," *Brain Res.*, vol. 95, pp. 475-496, 1975.

[13] Y. Burnod, *An adaptive neural network: the cerebral cortex.* Paris: Masson, 1988.

[14] G.L. Shaw and D.J. Silverman, "Simulations of the trion model and the search for the code of higher cortical processing," in *Computer simulation in brain science*, M.J. Cotterill, Ed. Cambridge University Press, 1988, pp. 189-209.

[15] F. Alexandre, F. Guyot, J.P. Haton, Y. Burnod, "The cortical column: a new processing unit for multilayered networks," *Neural Networks*, vol. 4, pp. 15-25, 1991.

[16] R.S. Sutton and A.G. Barto, "Toward a modern theory of adaptive networks: expectation and prediction," *Psychol. Rev.*, vol. 88, pp. 135-170, 1981.

[17] J.M. Fuster, *The Prefrontal Cortex.* New York: Raven press, 1980.

[18] P.S. Goldman-Rakic, "Topography of cognition: parallel distributed networks in primate association cortex," *Ann. Rev. Neurosci.*, vol. 11, pp. 137-56, 1988.

[19] E. Guigon, B. Dorizzi, Y. Burnod, W. Schultz, "A neural network model of prefrontal circuits predicting changes in neuronal activity during the step-by-step learning of a sensorimotor program," in press.

[20] J. Piaget, *La construction du réel chez l'enfant,* Neuchâtel: Delachaux et Niestlé, 1950.

[21] J. Piaget, *Six études de Psychologie,* Paris: Denoël, 1964.

[22] T. Grossman, R. Meir, E. Domany, "Learning by choice of internal representations," *Proc. of the 1988 Connectionist Models Summer School*, D. Touretzky, G. Hinton, T. Sejnowski, Eds. Morgan Kaufmann Pub., pp. 127-132, 1988.

[23] G. Mitchison, "Learning algorithms and networks of neurons," in *The computing neuron*, R. Durbin, C. Miall, G. Mitchison, Eds. Addison-Wesley, pp. 35-53, 1989.

[24] P.J.B. Hancock, L.S. Smith, W.A. Phillips, "A biologically supported error-correcting learning rule," *Neural Computation*, vol. 3, pp. 201-212, 1991.

[25] I. McLaren, "The computational unit as an assembly of neurons: an implementation of an error correcting learning algorithm," in *The computing neuron*, R. Durbin, C. Miall, G. Mitchison, Eds. Addison-Wesley, pp. 160-179, 1989.

[26] S.I. Gallant, "Connectionist expert systems," *Comm. ACM*, vol. 31 (2), 1988.

[27] E. Sanchez, "Fuzzy connectionist expert systems," *Proc. of Intern. Conf. on Fuzzy Logic & Neural Networks (Iizuka'90)*, vol. I, pp. 31-35, 1990.

[28] M. Derthick, "Introduction to mundane reasoning," *Proc. of 1988 Connectionist Models Summer School*, D. Touretzky, G. Hinton, T. Sejnowski, Eds. Morgan Kaufmann Pub., pp. 291-300, 1988.

[29] R.B. Allen, "Connectionist language users," *Connection Science*, vol. 2 (4), 1990.

[30] S. Dehaene, J.P. Changeux, "The Wisconsin card sorting test: theoretical analysis and modeling in a neuronal network," *Cerebral Cortex*, vol. 1, pp. 62-79, 1991.

[31] S.J. Leven, D.S. Levine, "Effects of reinforcement on knowledge retrieval and evaluation," *Proc. of the IEEE First Intern. Conf. on Neural Networks*, vol. II, pp. 269-279, 1987.

Failure Diagnosis System on Pneumatic Control Valves by Neural Network

Takeki Nogami

Shikoku Research Institute Inc.

2109-8, Yashimanishi-machi, Takamatsu-shi, Japan

Yoshihide Yokoi

The university of Tokushima

2-1, Minamijyosanjima-cho, Tokushima-shi, Japan

Masao Kasai, Katsunori Kawai and Katsuhisa Takaura

Mitsubishi Atomic Power Industries Inc.

4-1, Shibakouen 2-Chome Minato-ku, Tokyo, Japan

Abstract - A prototype failure diagnosis system has been developed using neural network technology for the actuators of pneumatic control valves. Because actual failure data was difficult to obtain, the data of 30 failure patterns were experimentally collected using more than 10 sensors. An FFT was carried out on the time series of the sensor signals. The data of the magnitude spectrum, phase difference and others are used as the characteristic parameters in our failure diagnosis. Appropriate failure diagnosis information was extracted from the data. Furthermore, similarities among the failure characteristics were established using fuzzy clustering and statistical analysis. The prototype that we developed consists of plural subnetworks and one main network. Each subnetwork is related to one specific sensor signal and deals with the magnitude spectra from the sensor signal. The main network makes the final decision according to the output from the sub-networks and other data. In our system, the number of network connections can be reduced by approximately 40% without degradation of the recognition capability in comparison with a conventional system where only one neural network is used.

I. INTRODUCTION

Generally, control valves are classified into 3 types by their actuator: pneumatic, electric, or oil hydraulic type. Our objective is to diagnose the actuators of pneumatic control valves which are frequently used in process control system of plants due to their easier isolation and quick response time properties. The failure of the actuator results in a shut down because of unstable control. There is a case of twin positioners at a control valve for keeping its reliability.[1] The diagnosis has been done intuitively and empirically by detecting the variability of the operational signal, open level, exhaust noise, pressure signal and so on by human experts. However the symptoms of failure and deterioration are subtle and it takes great skill to diagnose the problem. Therefore, research leading to a machine based diagnosis system seems worthwhile.

There are many ways for establishing such failure diagnosis systems. One way is the comparison of raw data with mathematical models of the pneumatic control valves. If the model was made, its diagnosability would be more reliable and universal. But the response characteristics of valves are non-liner and has also a time delay because of frictional force in the ground packing, mechanical slack etc. It is most difficult to diagnose the failure patterns when compared with the mathematical model simulating the normal or abnormal patterns.[2][3] A second approach is to employ an expert system based on empirical knowledge gleaned from the valves.[4] Unfortunately there are many valve components and at present it is not easy to summarize the knowledge of experts about the failure and wear of these individual parts. It is suggested that a neural network is suitable for solving problems involving pattern recognition and unalgorithmic diagnosis, because it is capable of being self-taught by teacher signals.[5][6]

For the purpose of establishing this new technology to diagnose actuator part failure, a prototype system has been developed using a neural network based on the premise that the pneumatic control valve is sinusoidally operated. The data of more than 10 sensors were experimentally collected for about 30 failure patterns. After extracting the useful characteristics with Fourier transformations and statistical analysis, similarities among the failure characteristics were revealed by using the fuzzy clustering. Furthermore, the usability of the plural sub-network was shown in comparison with using only one network.

II. EXPERIMENTAL EQUIPMENT

The experimental equipment is shown in Figure 1. It constitutes a valve, a diaphragm actuator and accessories (a booster relay, a positioner, an electric pneumatic transducer, pressure regulating valves etc).

When the valve receives an input signal to open wider, it operates as below: (1) Pressure increases in proportion to a input signal to an electric pneumatic transducer. (2) The balance beam moves up as the loading bellows in the positioner is pressurized. (3) The pilot valve stem top moves up and more air flows through the pilot valve, and the positioner output signal increases. (4) The positioner output signal is amplified by the booster to enhance the response, and pressure in the diaphragm increases. (5) The valve opens. At the same time, the drive lever moves up and the positioner cam rotates counterclockwise. (6) The spring beam moves

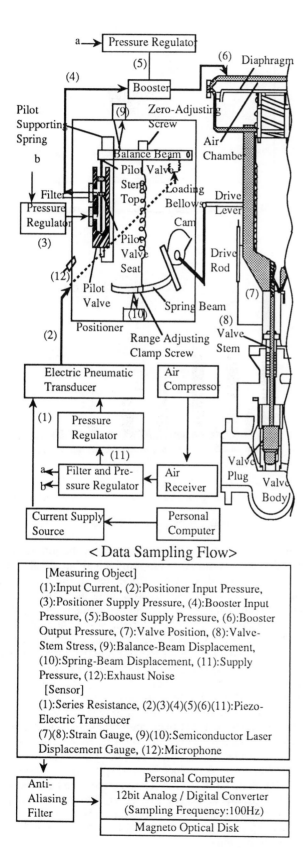

< Data Sampling Flow >

[Measuring Object]
(1):Input Current, (2):Positioner Input Pressure,
(3):Positioner Supply Pressure, (4):Booster Input
Pressure, (5):Booster Supply Pressure, (6):Booster
Output Pressure, (7):Valve Position, (8):Valve-
Stem Stress, (9):Balance-Beam Displacement,
(10):Spring-Beam Displacement, (11):Supply
Pressure, (12):Exhaust Noise
[Sensor]
(1):Series Resistance, (2)(3)(4)(5)(6)(11):Piezo-
Electric Transducer
(7)(8):Strain Gauge, (9)(10):Semiconductor Laser
Displacement Gauge, (12):Microphone

Anti-Aliasing Filter →

Personal Computer
12bit Analog / Digital Converter (Sampling Frequency:100Hz)
Magneto Optical Disk

Fig. 1. Experimental equipment

down and the balance beam is pulled down. (7) An upward force on the loading bellows reaches a balance with the force on the spring beam by feedback. Therefore the valve reaches an open position to match any input signal.

After the output signals go through the anti-aliasing filter, they are converted into digital signals and sent to a personal computer at 100 Hz sampling frequency.

III. DATA COLLECTION

To establish a diagnosis system based on a neural network, it is necessary to collect a lot of failure pattern data. However it is not practical to collect data from new sensors attached to pneumatic control valves in a running plant in view of the cost and time involved. Furthermore valve failure is rare and the process control system must be shut down in order to attach many sensors. Accordingly the data of about 30 failure patterns were experimentally obtained from more than 10 sensors that are attached to a pneumatic control valve in our laboratory.

Any past failures that occurred in a plant were studied together with mechanical engineers and human experts. The failure patterns were selected as shown in Table I with

TABLE I.
LIST OF FAILURE MODES

[Single Failure]
P-1(S):Pilot-Valve Seat Abrasion
P-2(S)(M):Pilot-Valve Stem-Top Abrasion
P-3:Pilot-Supporting Spring Curvature
P-4:Looseness of Screw Linking Drive-Rod to Driver-Lever
P-5:Filter Clog(Output Side)
P-6:Filter Clog(Supply Side)
P-7(M)(L):Cam Abrasion
P-8:Looseness of Cam Lock-Nut
P-9:Failure of Zero-Adjusting Screw
P-10:Looseness of Range-Adjusting Clamp-Screw
P-11(S)(M):Air Leakage of Input Line
P-12(S)(M):Air Leakage of Output Line
P-13:Air Leakage of Supply Line
B-1(S)(M)(L):Abnormal High Sensitivity
B-2:Leakage by Parts Failure(Input Side)
B-3:Leakage by Parts Failure(Supply Side)
B-4:Imbalance between input and output pressure
D-1(S)(M)(L):Air Leakage of Input Line
[Compound Failure]
P-1(S)+P-2(L)
P-5+P-6
B-2+B-3
[Note] Failure Grade (S:Small, M:Medium, L:Large)
Failed Accessory
(P:Positioner, B:Booster, D:Diaphragm)

1877

considerations given to the importance of the valve function and the occurrence frequency. The deterioration levels of a failure and compound failures were also considered. Moreover the sensor positions were determined on the basis of detectability and applicability in a plant.

The objective of our study is to diagnose the failure based on the sensor signals when the valve is sinusoidally operated. A valve with 50% open level (initial value) was operated by inputting a sine curve signal with 10% amplitude and 10 seconds frequency. And the sensor signals were obtained with sampling time of 100 Hz. The collection of failure data was done five times independently to derive the dispersion of the data and make both training data and non-training data for a neural network.

IV. SENSOR SIGNALS TRANFORMATION AND ITS CHARACTERRISTICS

The collected time series of sensor signals are shown in Figure 2.

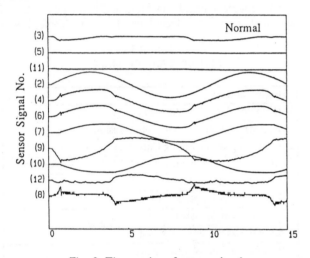

Fig. 2. Time series of sensor signal

Besides the wave pattern, these time series data include important information on wave phase, amplitude, initial value and so on. To analyze this information, an FFT was carried out because of the sinusoidal nature of the input signal curve and the cumulative probabilities were calculated.

The wave pattern frequency characteristics in the higher mode was about ten to fifteen times of the fundamental mode, hence the Fourier coefficients from the second to the sixteenth were used for diagnosis. The zero mode and first mode were not used, because the former is related to the initial value and the latter is related to the sinusoidal motion of a valve. Figure 3 shows the amplitude spectrum of a normal and a failure case. The characteristics of the failure case are seen in the higher modes. The number of modes is considered to be reasonable, because the coefficients above the fifteenth mode are relatively small. The phase differences between the input signal and each of the sensor signals were extracted. The mean and standard deviation were calculated. Supposing that the

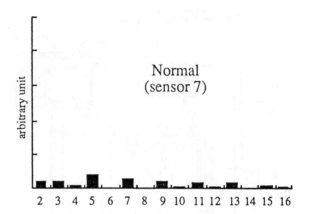

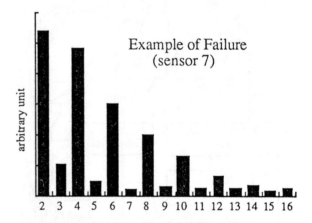

These spectra are obtained with Fourier transformation of time series data subtracted by ones averaged among 5 normal modes.

Fig. 3. Comparison of spectra

distribution is normal, the cumulative probabilities were inputted to a network. As to amplitudes and initial values the cumulative probabilities were calculated in the same way. Initial values were obtained by averaging the signals before inputting a sine curve. The characteristic of sensor signals is shown in Table II. The characteristic wave patterns, phase differences, amplitudes and initial values for each failure are easily seen. In the case of an actuator problem the valve stem stress signal (No.8) is important in diagnosing friction force and valve adhesion but the deviation of phase differences, amplitudes and initial values are large because of a residual stress in the valve stem. Therefore this signal is not useful because it was found that there are other signals to diagnose actuator problems instead of this sensor. There is also a case where the displacement sensor attached on a positioner was used to diagnose. A balance beam displacement sensor was tested experimentally to find it's sensitivity, and the balance beam was found to be useful. Also, the case of using a positioner displacement signal in diagnosis turned out to be quite useful as it is thought that a balance beam is highly sensitive to movement.

TABLE II.
CHARACTERISTIC OF SENSOR SIGNALS

Failure	Sensor Number — Wave Pattern / Phase Difference / Amplitude / Initial Value										
	2	3	4	5	6	7	8	9	10	11	12
P-1 (S)	●	●	△		○△	●●△△	●	●△	△	○ ●●	●
P-1 (S)					△	○ △		○ ○			
P-2 (M)			△		○	○ ○		○ ○			
P-3		○	△△		○△	○○△△ △		○△△●			
P-4											
P-5								△		△	
P-6								△		△	
P-7 (M)		△			△	△		△			
P-7 (L)		○			●	● ○		●		△	
P-8								○			
P-9		○				△ ●△					
P-10		●○				●					
P-11 (S)	●	●●●				△ △					
P-11 (M)	●	△●△			△	● ○○			○	△	
P-12 (S)		●○●	●△		●●	●● △●		●●●△○		○ ●●△	
P-12 (M)		●●○	●○		●●	●●○○●		●●●●○		○ ●●△	
P-13		○ ○								● ●●	
B-1 (S)			○○○		○	●△					
B-1 (M)			○●●	●	○△	●○		△●△			△
B-1 (L)		△●○●	●●●	●	●●	●●		● ○		△	△
B-2					△	△				△	
B-3			△		○	△				△ △	
B-4		○○	●		●△	●△ △●		●○ △		○ ○○△	
D-1 (S)		○△●	●○		●△	●△ △ ●		●○ ○△		○ ●○△	
D-1 (M)		●○●	●●●	●	●●	●● ○●		●●○○		○ ●●△	
D-1 (L)		●●	●●●	●	●●	●●△●		●●●●		○ ●●△	
P-1+P-2		○ ○	△		○△	○○ ○		○○ ●		○ ○●●	●
P-5+P-6											
B-2+B-3					●		△			△ △	

●:very characteristic　○:characteristic
△:a little characteristic　no mark:characterless

TABLE III.
RESULT OF FUZZY CLUSTERING

Failure	Classification (Failure Mode)																		
	Normal	P-1	P-2	P-3	P-4	P-5	P-6	P-7	P-8	P-9	P-10	P-11	P-12	P-13	B-1	B-2	B-3	B-4	D-1
Nor mal			0.1		1.0	1.0	1.0		0.5	0.4						0.2			
P-1 (S)		1.0																	
P-2 (S)	0.3		0.5		0.3	0.3	0.3		0.6	1.0						0.1			
P-2 (M)			1.0							0.1									
P-3				1.0															
P-4	1.0				1.0	1.0	1.0		0.5	0.3						0.2			
P-5	1.0		0.1		1.0	1.0	1.0		0.5	0.4						0.3			
P-6	1.0				1.0	1.0	1.0		0.4	0.3						0.2			
P-7 (M)	0.7		0.1		0.7	0.7	0.7		1.0	0.7						0.2			
P-7 (L)								1.0											
P-8	0.7		0.3		0.7	0.7	0.7		1.0	0.8	0.1					0.2			
P-9	0.3		0.2		0.3	0.3	0.3		0.5	1.0						0.1			
P-10	0.1				0.1	0.1	0.1		0.1	0.1	1.0								
P-11 (S)	0.6		0.1	0.2	0.6	0.6	0.6	0.1	0.4	0.3		0.8		0.1	1.0	0.3			
P-11 (M)												1.0							
P-12 (S)													1.0				0.2		
P-12 (M)													1.0						
P-13														1.0					
B-1 (S)	0.9	0.1	0.4	0.1	0.9	0.9	0.9	0.2	1.0	0.8	0.2	0.1			0.1	0.2	0.7	0.5	
B-1 (M)															1.0	0.1			
B-1 (L)															1.0				
B-2	0.9				0.9	1.0	1.0		0.4	0.3						1.0	0.1		
B-3	0.2				0.2	0.2	0.2		0.1	0.1						1.0	1.0		
B-4																		1.0	
D-1 (S)																	1.0		
D-1 (M)													0.1						1.0
D-1 (L)																			1.0
P-1+P-2	0.6	0.5	0.9	0.3	0.6	0.6	0.6	0.3	0.7	0.7	0.4	0.2		1.0	0.1	0.5	0.3	0.1	
P-5+P-6	1.0		0.1	0.2	1.0	1.0	1.0		0.6	0.4						0.3	0.1		
B-2+B-3	0.1				0.1	0.1	0.1		0.1	0.1						1.0	0.9		

Maximum grade of membership is normalized to 1.0

In a running plant human experts diagnose using the open level, pressure, exhaust noise and so on. If time series data were collected without touching valves in a plant, they wouldn't be badly affected by the sensors. Non-touching sensors (7), (9) and (10) seem useful to detect the displacement because the characteristics are seen. The deviation of signals is used to diagnose the health of valves now. It is thought that the failures for which the characteristics are seen on Table II are detectable using those sensors in a plant.

This table shows that P-4,5,6,8, B-2,3 failures are not characteristic. To analyze a similarity between the failures, a fuzzy clustering was carried out.[8][9] The result is shown in Table III. These failures are similar to a normal case (particularly P-4,5,6). It is said that filter clogs and loose failures are not distinctive. Also a similarity between P-2(S) and P-9 is caused by a drift of a balance beam. Therefore, exactly identifying these failures requires either the use of a high efficiency sensor or the detection of a change in the actuating pattern (amplitude or frequency of sine wave, step signal).

V. PROTOTYPE OF FAILURE DIAGNOSIS

One way to input the time series data for each sensor into a neural network is to sample the arbitrary wave patterns; but a network becomes very large because a lot of data is required to input the pattern of higher modes. (Perhaps about 100 samples for each sensor will be needed.) Therefore, in our system the Fourier coefficients, phase differences, amplitudes and initial values were inputted.

Two prototypes were developed using a backpropagation algorithm [7] to diagnose eighteen kinds of failures and a normal case. In the first prototype (called system 1), all information is directly inputted into one neural network as shown Figure 4, but the problem is that in this structure the number of network connections is large and the information of the Fourier coefficients is much larger than that of phase differences and so on. Therefore, the other system with plural sub-networks (called system 2) was also developed as shown Figure 5. The recognition capability was compared between both systems.

The merit of system 2 is that if a sub-network is changed, only the new sub-network and the main neural network need to be re-trained. In system 2, the sub-networks processing the time series data send the reduced data based on the Fourier coefficients of each sensor to the main network. Phase differences, amplitudes and initial values are directly inputted to the main network. There is a problem in how to decide on the number of sub-network output units and the teacher signals, as it is difficult to intuitively identify the number of sub-network output units needed for the classification of wave patterns. Also, even if the number of them were decided, it would be difficult to make the teacher signals that could classify the wave patterns. Thus a non-subjective method must be considered.

By using the principal component analysis, the components that have above 5% contribution factors are selected for distinguishing the wave pattern. Namely, the number of sub-network output units is set by the number of eigen vectors that has above 5% contribution factors. The teacher signals are set to the correlation values between the eigen vectors and the Fourier coefficients.

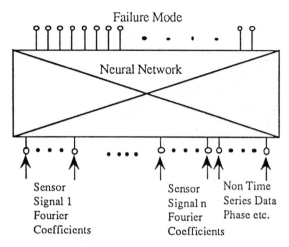

Fig. 4. Structure of System 1

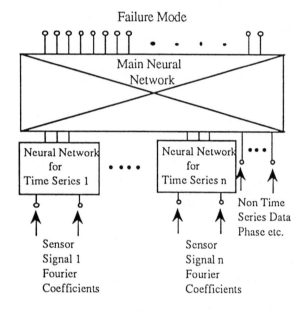

Fig. 5. Structure of System 2

TABLE IV.
RECOGNITION CAPABILITY NO.1

	System1					System2				
	Training			Non-training		Training			Non-training	
Failure	1	2	3	4	5	1	2	3	4	5
Normal	⊙	⊙	⊙	—	⊙	⊙	⊙	⊙	⊙	—
P-1(S)	⊙	⊙	⊙	⊙	⊙	⊙	⊙	⊙	⊙	⊙
P-2(M)	⊙	⊙	⊙	⊙	⊙	⊙	⊙	⊙	⊙	⊙
P-3	⊙	⊙	⊙	⊙	⊙	⊙	⊙	⊙	⊙	P-6
P-4	⊙	⊙	⊙	P-5	—	⊙	△	P-6	P-5	—
P-5	⊙	⊙	⊙	O	P-6	⊙	⊙	O	O	P-6
P-6	⊙	⊙	⊙	—	⊙	⊙	O	⊙	O	⊙
P-7(L)	⊙	⊙	⊙	⊙	⊙	⊙	⊙	⊙	⊙	⊙
P-8	⊙	⊙	⊙	⊙	—	⊙	⊙	⊙	⊙	Nor
P-9	⊙	⊙	⊙	⊙	—	⊙	⊙	⊙	⊙	P-2
P-10	⊙	⊙	—	—	—	⊙	⊙	⊙	P-9	P-2
P-11(M)	⊙	⊙	⊙	⊙	⊙	⊙	⊙	⊙	⊙	⊙
P-12(M)	⊙	⊙	⊙	⊙	⊙	⊙	⊙	⊙	⊙	⊙
P-13	⊙	⊙	⊙	⊙	⊙	⊙	⊙	⊙	⊙	⊙
B-1(L)	⊙	⊙	⊙	⊙	⊙	⊙	⊙	⊙	⊙	⊙
B-2	⊙	⊙	⊙	O	⊙	⊙	B-3	⊙	⊙	⊙
B-3	⊙	⊙	⊙	△	B-2	⊙	O	⊙	—	⊙
B-4	⊙	⊙	⊙	⊙	⊙	⊙	⊙	⊙	⊙	⊙
D-1(L)	⊙	⊙	⊙	⊙	⊙	⊙	⊙	⊙	⊙	⊙
P-1+P-2	⊙	⊙	⊙	⊙	⊙	⊙	⊙	⊙	⊙	⊙
P-5+P-6	⊙	⊙	⊙	⊙	△	⊙	⊙	⊙	△	△
B-2+B-3	⊙	⊙	⊙	⊙	⊙	⊙	⊙	△	—	⊙

⊙ : give correct answer
O : give more than one answer, but correct failure mode first
△ : give more than one answer, but correct failure mode after second
— : no answer
*-** : mistaken failure mode

TABLE V.
RECOGNITION CAPABILITY NO.2

	System1					System2				
	Non-training					Non-trainig				
Failure	1	2	3	4	5	1	2	3	4	5
P-2(S)	⊙	⊙	—	⊙	⊙	⊙	⊙	⊙	⊙	⊙
P-7(M)	⊙	—	—	⊙	—	P-10	—	—	P-8	—
P-11(S)	—	⊙	⊙	⊙	—	⊙	O	⊙	O	⊙
P-12(S)	—	—	—	—	—	⊙	—	⊙	—	⊙
B-1(S)	—	—	—	P-5	—	⊙	B-3	B-3	B-3	B-3
B-1(M)	⊙	—	—	—	—	⊙	⊙	⊙	⊙	⊙
D-1(S)	B-4	B-4	B-4	B-4	B-4	B-4	B-4	B-4	B-4	B-4
D-1(M)	⊙	⊙	—	—	—	⊙	⊙	⊙	⊙	O

VI. PERFORMANCE TEST

The five sets of data were collected for each failure. Three sets of them were used for training, the remainder were used for testing the detectability. Also some data was collected by changing the scale for the same failure. Tables IV and V show the recognition capability of both systems. In Table IV the recognition capability is tested using the same data as is used for training. In Table V it is tested using the small scale failure that is not used for training. In system 1 the recognition capability is near 100% using training data. In system 2 the recognition capability of some failures is inferior to system 1 because those failures P-4,5,6,B-2,3 are not characteristic and similar.

As to the non-training data, the recognition capability of both systems is identical. The recognition for normal, P-4,5,6,8,9,10, B-2,3 and compound P5+P6 is not well. However, those failures are difficult to to be distinguished as the result of a fuzzy clustering. This result doesn't limit the neural network capability, but shows the difficulty including those failures.

For the non-training data, Table V shows a good recognition capability in p-2(S),P-11(S),B-11(M) and D-1(M) in system 2. This result can be predicted from a fuzzy clustering, but both systems couldn't recognize other failures.

There are some ideas to resolve this problem. A high efficiency sensor will be used for catching the patterns of difficult failures. Also, it is necessary to develop a neural network system that can list up all predictable failures with teacher signal determined by a fuzzy-clustering.

The number of network connections in system 2 is approximately 60% of those in system 1. Considering the same recognition capability in systems, it is said that system 2 with sub-networks is better.

VII. CONCLUSIIONS

The prototype of a failure diagnosis system has been developed using neural network technology for the actuators of pneumatic control valves. Because actual failure data was difficult to obtain, the data of 30 failure patterns were experimentally collected using more than 10 sensors. The data of magnitude spectrum, phase difference and others are used as the characteristic parameters in our failure diagnosis system. The results are given below: (1) Some sensors are unsuitable to use because of deviation, especially a valve stem stress signal because of deviation in the cause of residual stress. (2) Signals from displacement gauges in a positioner are effective for diagnosis. (3) Some failures are not characteristic and difficult to find.

As this system needs to diagnose using many sensors, a network tends to become large. When the hardware configuration is changed, the training must be carried out again. Therefore a system that consists of plural sub-network and one main network was developed to minimize the size of networks and the re-training. Each sub-network is related to one specific sensor signal and deals with the magnitude spectra from the sensor signals. The main network makes the final decision according to the outputs from the sub-networks and other data. A teacher signal in each sub-network is determined by a principal component analysis. Moreover, a conventional network system that doesn't have sub-networks was developed.

Both can easily recognize failure for the raining data. However, it is not easy to recognize the non-training data of uncharacteristic failures. In comparing both systems the recognition capability is same, but the number of network connections can be reduced by approximately 40% in a new layered network system.

In our future works, a fuzzy clustering analysis will be used to obtain the teacher data for our prototype system. This improved system will list up the candidate failures for uncharacteristic failure cases. Furthermore, another diagnostic system will be developed for step-wise valve movement which is one of the standard movements used currently for failure diagnosis.

ACKNOWLEDGEMNTS

Special thanks to Mr.Onoshita, an engineer in ABB Gaderius Inc., for technically supporting our experiments and Mr.Hayashi, our staff of Shikoku Research Institute Inc., for failure data collection.

REFERENCES

[1] T.Mizumoto, et al., "Redundant System for Feedwater Control Valve's Pneumatic Subcontrol System in PWR Plant", Mitsubishi Atomic Energy Technical Review, Vol.30, 1983, pp14-15.

[2] T.Asakura, M.Danno, H.Ohtake, "Improvement of Dynamical Characteristics of Electropneumatic Valve Positioner", Transactions of the Japan Society of Mechanical Engineers, 56-524, C,1990-4, pp 50-55.

[3] Bau.D.Y, Prezillon.P.J, "Model-Based Diagnosis of Power Station Control Systems", IEEE Expert, Vol.7,No.1,1992, pp36-44.

[4] Y.Sato, "Development of Maintenance Assistant Expert System for PWR Feedwater System", Mitsubishi Atomic Energy Technical Review, 52, 1989, pp13-15.

[5] Sorsa.T, Koivo.H.N, Koivisto.H,"Neural Networks in Process Fault Diagnosis", IEEE Transactions Syst Man Cybern, Vol. 21,No.4, 1991, pp815-825.

[6] S.Yoshihara, et al., "Many Components Monitoring System by Using Neural Network", Proc. Fall Meeting of the Atomic Energy Society of Japan, 1991, pp401

[7] Rumelhart, D. E.,Hinton, G. E. and Williams, R. J., "Parallel Distributed Processing", MIT Press, Vol. 1, 1986, pp 318-362.

[8] J.C.Bezdek,"Pattern Structures: A Tutorial in Analysis of Fuzzy Information", Vol.1,CRC Press, 1987, pp81-107

[9] J.C.Bezdek,"A Convergence Theorem for the Fuzzy ISODATA Clustering Algorithms:, IEEE Transactions on Pattern Analysis and Machine Intelligence,Vol.PAMI-2, No.1,1980, pp1-8.

Implementation of a Multilayer Perceptron Network Using an Optically Addressed Photoconductive Array

Richard G. Stearns
Xerox Palo Alto Research Center
3333 Coyote Hill Road
Palo Alto, CA   94305

Abstract — A two-dimensional amorphous silicon photoconductor array and a liquid crystal display form the core components of a hardware system for implementation of a multilayer perceptron neural network. All connections between layers, as well as the nonlinear transfer characteristics associated with the hidden- and output-layer neurons, are implemented in analog circuitry so that the network, once trained, behaves as a standalone processor. The network is shown to train very successfully, using a standard backpropagation training algorithm, on the classification of handwritten digits. A computer simulation of the hardware network is also described, and excellent agreement is shown between the results of the hardware network and those of the computer simulation.

I. INTRODUCTION

In this paper, an optoelectronic system is described, which is configured to implement a three-layer perceptron network. The system is composed of two central components: a two-dimensional array of amorphous silicon photoconductors, and a liquid crystal display (LCD), used as a spatial light modulator to mask the sensor array. The two dimensional sensor array consists of a grid of horizontal and vertical conductive lines, with an amorphous silicon photoconductive element, of lateral geometry, resident at each node of the grid, as indicated schematically in Fig. 1. The sensor array essentially performs vector-matrix products, which are recognized as one of the central processing components of many neural networks. As indicated in Fig. 1, the array is generally operated by applying voltages V_i to the horizontal conductive lines, and measuring the currents I_j that flow through the vertical lines, which are maintained at virtual ground potential. Denoting the conductances of the sensor nodes G_{ij}, it follows that the current I_j are the vector-matrix product of the input voltages and the node conductances, i.e. $I_j = V_i^T G_{ij}$.

The conductances G_{ij} are optically programmed by modulation of the LCD placed directly over the sensor array. The artificial neural network is then constructed by appropriate transformation and routing of the electrical signals associated with the horizontal and vertical lines of the sensor array. Based on the combination of the LCD and sensor array, many neural network architectures may be explored. We have chosen to first consider a three-layer perceptron network, as it is one of the most thoroughly studied networks, and is known to be quite powerful in many applications. The network that will be described in this paper is fully trainable. Furthermore, all signal transformation and routing associated with the network is performed in hardware, so that the entire system may be operated as a standalone processor, once it is trained. Training of the network is demonstrated on classification of handwritten digits, with excellent results.

Before describing the current system, mention must be made of previous related work. Rietman et. al. originally proposed and demonstrated the use of a two-dimensional a-Si photoconductive array for artificial neural networks [1]. They implemented a Hopfield type network, using photographic film to modulate the light incident on the sensor array. Thus their network could not be trained. In addition, the recurrent feedback of the network was performed with intervention of a digital computer, so that the network did not perform in a standalone capacity. Finally, the

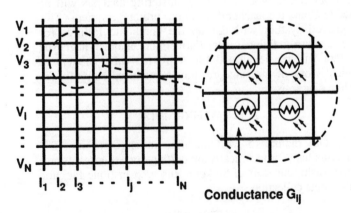

Fig. 1. Schematic of the two-dimensional photoconductive array.

photoconductors used were vertical in structure, and their current-voltage characteristics did not exhibit good symmetry. Later work by Rietman et al. and Frye et al. made use of photoconductors of lateral geometry [2,3]. In their later work, however, they abandoned the use of a two-dimensional sensor array, for a simpler one-dimensional array. This has significant consequences on the size of the network that can be reasonably implemented: their later network, a three-layer perceptron, consisted of only 50 interconnection weights in total. A projection CRT was used to optically address the sensor array.

Initial work on the sensor array / LCD architecture that is the subject of this paper has been described previously by Stearns [4]. In the earlier work, routing of signals between perceptron layers, and the nonlinear transformations associated with the individual neurons, were performed by a digital computer, so that the system was not a fully operational analog processor.

II. DESCRIPTION OF THE SYSTEM

The two-dimensional photoconductor array and the LCD are both fabricated at the Xerox Palo Alto Research Center. The photoconductor array has been previously described in detail, and will not be discussed in depth here [5]. Briefly, it consists of a grid of 128 horizontal by 128 vertical conductive lines. Associated with each node of the grid is an interdigitated lateral n^+- i -n^+ a-Si photoconductive element, which displays a linear, symmetric current-voltage characteristic. The pitch of the two-dimensional array is 272 µm, in both horizontal and vertical directions. The LCD is a twisted nematic device, and is driven using polysilicon TFT technology. It is composed of 512 x 512 pixels, on a square lattice of 68 µm pitch, so that a 4 x 4 pixel cell masks each photoconductive node on the sensor array.

The mapping of the neural network to the sensor array / LCD is shown in Fig. 2. In Fig. 2(a) a

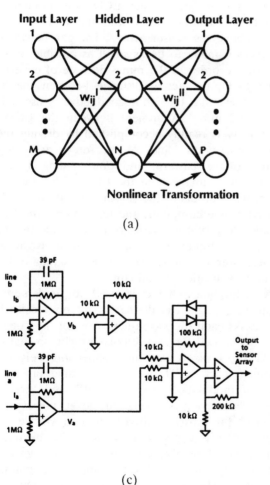

(a)

(c)

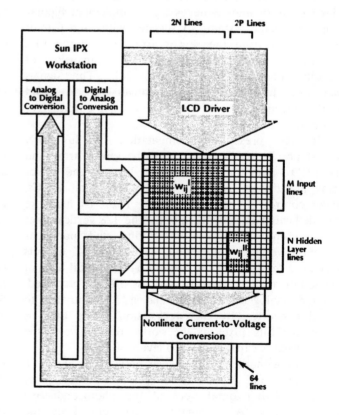

(b)

Fig. 2. The network architecture. (a) Schematic of the 3-layer perceptron. (b) The perceptron network implemented in hardware. (c) Circuit used to perform nonlinear amplification.

standard schematic diagram of a three-layer perceptron is shown. There are M input-layer, N hidden-layer, and P output-layer neurons, with interconnections weight fields w_{ij}^I between the input and hidden layers, and weights w_{ij}^{II} between the hidden and output layers. The hidden- and output-layer neurons perform a sigmoidal transformation on their summed inputs. In Fig. 2(b) is shown how this three-layer network is implemented in the present system. The central square block in the figure is meant to schematically indicate the sensor array, with its grid of vertical and horizontal lines, as seen through the LCD, which is placed above it. In general, horizontal lines of the sensor array have associated with them voltage levels which correspond to outputs of neurons. Vertical lines are maintained at virtual ground potential, and carry currents which correspond to the input of neurons (i.e. weighted sums of neurons outputs from a previous layer). The vertical lines are functionally grouped in pairs. In each pair, one line (e.g. line a) corresponds to positive weighting, the other (line b) to negative weighting, so that the neuron input associated with a vertical line pair is the differential current between the two lines. This pairing of lines is necessary to implement bipolar weighting in the system. Associated with each pair of vertical lines from the sensor array is a circuit that performs nonlinear current-to-voltage conversion of the differential current $I_a - I_b$ (Fig. 2c). The signals that result from the nonlinear conversion correspond to the output values of the hidden- and output-layer neurons.

In the present implementation, a Sun IPX workstation is interfaced to both the sensor array and the LCD. The top 64 horizontal lines of the sensor array are driven by 64 double-latched, 8-bit DACs, under control of the workstation. These 64 lines are thus dedicated to network input. The 128 vertical lines of the sensor array, after pairing and nonlinear current-to-voltage conversion, result in 64 outputs which are fed back to the bottom 64 horizontal lines of the sensor array. These 64 outputs are also acquired, through analog multiplexers and a 12-bit analog to digital converter, by the workstation. The LCD is driven at 8 bits/ pixel via the workstation, however the display itself is capable of ~ 16 levels of gray.

To implement the three layer network of Fig. 2(a), the M inputs are applied as voltages to a number M of the top 64 horizontal lines of the photoconductive sensor array. A rectangular area defined by the intersection of these M horizontal lines with 2N vertical lines corresponds to the interconnection matrix w_{ij}^I. The 2N vertical lines are processed through the nonlinear current-to-voltage conversion circuitry, and are routed back to N of the bottom 64 horizontal lines.

A second rectangular region, corresponding to the interconnection matrix w_{ij}^{II}, is defined by the intersection of these N horizontal lines with 2P vertical lines. The currents through the 2P vertical lines are likewise processed by the nonlinear current-to-voltage conversion circuitry, resulting in P output lines, which are acquired by the digital computer. During training and running of the hardware network, LCD pixels outside of the two rectangular regions defined above are maintained in a state of minimum optical transmission.

The nonlinear current-to-voltage conversion circuitry is shown schematically in Fig. 2(c) : one such circuit exists for each pair of vertical sensor lines. Following current-to-voltage conversion, nonlinearity is introduced through the placement of two back-to-back diodes in the feedback path of the amplifier which sums voltages V_a and $-V_b$. The circuit has a small signal gain of 2.1×10^8 V/A, and and output range of ~ ± 10V.

The sensor array and LCD are mounted on separate micrometer stages, and the LCD is aligned directly above the sensor array. The gap between the two arrays is made to be as small as possible, typically this is of the order of 0.5 mm. Because of coverplates on the LCD, the actual distance between the liquid crystal layer and the photoconductive sensors is at present ~2 mm. Alignment between the LCD and sensor array is readily accomplished by driving the 64 topmost horizontal lines of the sensor array with a specific voltage pattern, and downloading a specific complimentary image onto the LCD. The nonlinearly transformed outputs of the sensor vertical line pairs are acquired by the computer, and for example the LCD is translated to produce a series of maxima and minima at the sensor outputs. Good alignment is achieved routinely over the entire array, using a standard 35 mm projector for incident illumination.

A halftoning scheme is used to implement the optical weighting. Recall that a 4x4 pixel cell of the LCD masks each photoconductive sensor, and one pair of sensors is used for each bipolar weight, so that there are 32 LCD pixels per interconnection weight. In halftoning, each LCD pixel may assume one of five values of modulation (i.e. 'on', 'off', and three gray levels). For any given weighting level, however, only one pixel (at most) is driven in a gray-scale mode. Hence the halftoning scheme is essentially binary, with one pixel at a time allowed to be driven at a gray level. With this approach, 129 levels of bipolar weighting are achieved. The three gray levels are chosen to approximately correspond to equal increments in optical transmission through the LCD.

III. Experimental Results

As an initial exercise, the hardware network has been trained to classify bitmap images of handwritten digits. The network contains M = 49 input neurons, N = 36 hidden-layer neurons, and P = 10 output neurons, with one output neuron corresponding to each digit 0 through 9. This network is somewhat too small to successfully be trained to recognize digits of multiple authors [6]. Thus all training and testing data is derived from the handwriting of a single subject. Each digit bitmap is normalized to a 7 x 7 bounding box, with 16 levels of gray allowed for each bitmap pixel. In Fig. 3 are shown representative bitmap images of 30 digits: halftoning is used to simulate the gray-level information. The 49 pixels of each 7x7 bitmap image are input to the neural network as a simple raster of 49 contiguous elements.

The ideal network that the hardware system is to be mapped onto is one in which the neuron transfer function f(x) = tanh(x). A voltage of 10V along a horizontal line of the sensor array is associated with an ideal neuron output value of 1.0. The constraint on the length of this paper makes it infeasible to show detailed data concerning the characteristics of the hardware system, such as its weighting and nonlinear transformation properties. We note only that for a 10V signal applied to a single horizontal line, a single weight set at its maximum value is found experimentally to produce an output on average of

7.4V from the nonlinear circuit of Fig. 2(c). This implies that a single weight in the hardware network has a corresponding maximum value of ~tanh[-1](.74) = 0.95 in the ideal network. For simplicity, in training the network, the most positive and negative achievable weight values in the hardware implementation are mapped to the values + 1.0 and - 1.0, respectively, in the ideal network.[1] Weight updates that fall outside this range are simply set to the limits ± 1.0. Furthermore, due primarily to the sublinear response of the photoconductors with respect to illumination, the actual weighting in the hardware network is found to vary as :

$$ w_{ij}^{actual} = \frac{2\, w_{ij}^{intended}}{1 + \left| w_{ij}^{intended} \right|}, \qquad (1) $$

where $w_{ij}^{intended}$ denotes the weight as programmed (in the range ± 1.0) to the LCD, via the halftoning scheme described earlier. The transfer function of the hardware network is likewise not precisely the tanh(x) of the ideal network, but is better fit by the relation:

$$ f(x) = \frac{2.5\, x}{1 + 2.5\, |\, x\, |}. \qquad (2) $$

Training of the hardware network is performed using a standard backpropagation algorithm. The training set consists of 500 digits, with 50 sets of the digits 0 through 9. Network weights are initialized to random values in the range ± 0.05. The digits are selected randomly for presentation to the network while training, and weight updates occur after an epoch of ten digit presentations. Weight changes are calculated on the basis of the standard error term

$$ Error = \frac{1}{2} \sum_{k} (t_k - o_k)^2 \qquad (3) $$

[1]There is some arbitrariness in mapping the maximum weight of the hardware network to a value in the ideal network, since there is significant scatter in the weight values of the hardware network. Due to nonuniformities in the LCD as well as in the sensor array, weighting is found to vary by ~ ± 15% across the sensor array. It is largely for convenience that the maximum hardware weights are mapped to values of ± 1.0 in the ideal network.

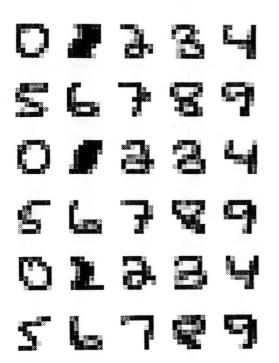

Fig. 3.   Bitmap images of 30 digits, of the type used to train and test the network.

where t_k is the desired value of output neuron k, and o_k is its actual value, for a given training example. The sum is over all output neurons. For iteration t' of the training procedure (one iteration here corresponds to one epoch), weights are therefore updated according to the rules:

$$\delta w_{jk}^{II} (t) = v \delta w_{jk}^{II} (t\text{-}1) \qquad (4a)$$

$$+ \frac{\eta}{10} \sum_{epoch} h_j (t_k - o_k) (1 - o_k^2),$$

$$\delta w_{ij}^{I} (t) = v \delta w_{ij}^{I} (t\text{-}1) \qquad (4b)$$

$$+ \frac{\eta}{10} \sum_{epoch} i_i (1 - h_j^2) \sum_k w_{jk}^{II} (t_k - o_k) (1 - o_k^2).$$

Here h_j denotes the output state of the jth hidden unit, and i_i denotes the value of the ith input unit. The learning coefficient is denoted by η, and the momentum coefficient by v. For all results described in this paper, $\eta = 0.4$ and $v = 0.2$. When the digit associated with a given output neuron is input to the network, that neuron is trained to yield an output of $t_k = 0.8$, otherwise the neuron is trained to yield an output of -0.8 (corresponding to $\pm 8V$ in the hardware network). At present (3) and (4) are calculated in the Sun workstation, based upon the hidden- and output-neuron values measured from the hardware system. Note from (4) that in training, a tanh(x) neuron transfer function has implicitly been assumed, when backpropagating the error through the network. Also the weights used in the error backpropagation are the intended weights. Thus the error is backpropagated as though the network were ideal. We have found that the network trains successfully under these assumptions. Indeed, incorporation of the network characteristics of (1) and (2) in backpropagation of the error has not been found to effect significantly the training performance of the network.

Results are shown in Fig. 4(a) of the network training error as a function of the epoch number of the training. The training error is the sum over each epoch of the error term of (3). Over 1500 epochs, the training error is seen to decrease from an initial value of 38 to a final value of ~0.03, a decrease of over

three orders of magnitude. This indicates very successful training.

To test the trained network, a second set of 300 digits, not used in training, is presented to it. In Fig. 4(b) is shown a scatter plot of the resulting classifications. Each point in the plot corresponds to the network classification of a digit. The position of the point along the x-axis denotes the value of the target output neuron for that given digit, that is, the

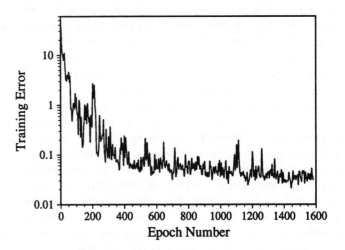

(a)

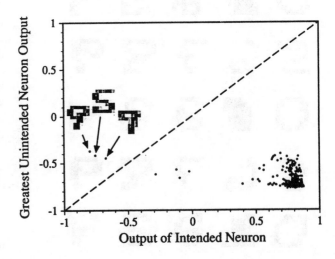

(b)

Fig. 4   (a) Training error of the hardware network in classifying handwritten digits.   (b) Testing of the network, after training for 1500 epochs, on a set of 300 digits.

1886

value of the neuron which should be activated by presentation of the digit. The position along the y-axis corresponds to the most positive value of all of the remaining 9 output neurons. Hence for perfect classification, each point should fall at the coordinate (0.8, -0.8). The space to the right of the dashed diagonal line in the plot of Fig. 4(b) corresponds to those points for which the target neuron had a greater output value than any other neuron. It is seen that three digits failed to meet this criterion: their bitmaps are indicated in the figure. The two 9's were classified mistakenly as the digit 8, while the 5 was classified as the digit 3. Importantly, the mistaken classification in all cases was very weak: the output neuron corresponding to the mistaken digit was well below zero. If one were to set the acceptance criterion for classification to be a positive neuron output that is a value of 0.5 greater than the next largest output, then from Fig. 4(b), it is apparent that seven digits would not be classified out of the 300 tested (with no misclassification). This corresponds to 97.7% correct classification.

For comparison, the same neural network has also been simulated in software. In the simulation, the forward propagation of the network is governed by the weight and transformation properties of (1) and (2). The backpropagation training is performed as described in (3) through (5), just as for the hardware system. Furthermore, weighting is quantized to 7 bits, as in the hardware network, and neuron output states are quantized to 12 bits. In Fig. 5 are shown simulation data equivalent to those of Fig. 4, obtained for the hardware network. It is important to note the excellent correspondence between the results of the hardware network and the computer simulation. This implies that the fundamental behavior of the hardware network can be well modeled through simulation. It should not however be inferred that the trained weights of the simulated network may simply be downloaded to the hardware network, with results equivalent to Fig. 4(b). This is not found to be the case: the similarity of the results of Figs. 4 and 5 indicates rather that the hardware network is able to adapt to its particular nonuniformities and nonidealities, to train to a level comparable to that of the simulated network. We have studied the dependence of the both hardware and the simulated network performance on weighting and neuron output quantization, as well as on random weighting defect level. The results are described in depth in another paper [7]. Briefly, it is found that the network performance degrades gracefully as weighting and neuron output quantization are made more crude, with noticeable performance degradation beginning for

weight quantization at ~6 bits, and neuron output quantization at ~8 bits. Network performance also degrades gracefully with increase in random weighting defects, with noticeable degradation beginning at defect levels of ~15%. In all cases, the behavior of the hardware and simulated networks to these nonidealities is very similar [7].

Finally, an ideal network, with a tanh(x) neuron

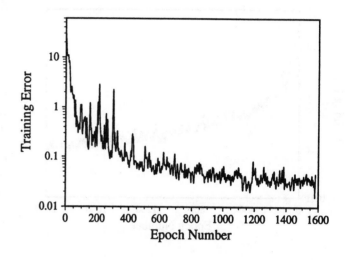

(a)

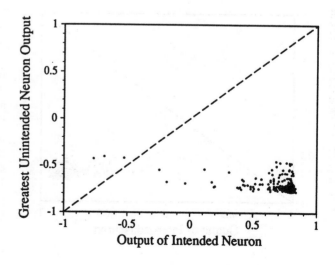

(b)

Fig. 5.   (a) Training error of a computer-simulated network in classifying handwritten digits.   (b) Testing of the simulated network, after training for 1500 epochs, on a set of 300 digits.

transfer function and ideal weighting, has been trained on the data. Training and testing results for the ideal network, comparable to those of Figs. 4 and 5, are shown in Fig. 6. Interestingly, the ideal network appears to train somewhat more slowly than the networks of Figs. 4 and 5. Comparison of Figs. 4(b) and 6(b) indicate that the hardware network trains to a level comparable to that of the ideal network.

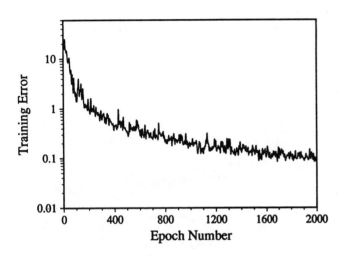

(a)

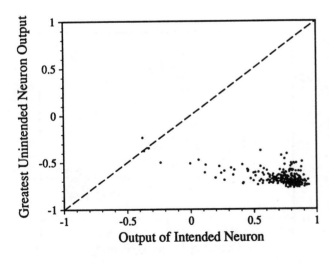

(b)

Fig. 6.   Training error of a computer-simulated network in classifying handwritten digits.   (b) Testing of the simulated network, after training for 2000 epochs, on a set of 300 digits.

4. DISCUSSION AND CONCLUSION

The present optoelectronic implementation of a three-layer perceptron has been shown to operate very successfully. The network has been trained to perform a task of some difficulty, the classification of handwritten digits, with good results. The hardware implementation is furthermore seen to agree well with computer simulation, indicating that the nonidealities and nonuniformities in the hardware system do not significantly limit its ability to train and run successfully.

Due to lack of space, data concerning the processing speed of the system has not been shown in this paper. Ultimately, the training speed is probably limited by the response of the LCD to updating of its projected image (i.e. updating of the weighting). For the present LCD, this response time is ~30 msec. Once trained, the network speed is dominated by the response time of the sensor array. The inherent response time of the photoconductive sensors has been found in earlier work to be ~3 µs [5]. In the present system, response times of hidden- and output-layer neurons are longer than this. The time for hidden-layer neurons to reach 90% of their output change following a change to the input layer is measured to be 50 µs, while the equivalent time for output-layer neurons is 75 µs [7]. The reason for this response time is that capacitance was purposely added to the network, in order to keep it from oscillating. Note that the bottom half of the sensor array is configured as a completely recurrent network (see Fig. 2b), and thus is prone to oscillation. In the present case this oscillation, typically at several hundred kHz, probably occurs due to capacitive coupling between horizontal and vertical lines on the sensor array. In a strictly feedforward network, the oscillation could probably be removed by simply severing the horizontal lines along a vertical plane that separates the two weight fields on the array. Then for example, by driving the lower 64 horizontal lines from the right side of the sensor array, the architecture would no longer be a recurrent one. It should be appreciated however that even with the ~100 µs time response, the present system should be able to classify ~10000 digits per second, with optimal feedthrough.

Because both the LCD and the sensor array are based on the same thin film technology, there is good opportunity to scale the architecture to implement much larger networks economically. It may even be possible to combine the sensor array and LCD on a single substrate, and to include a significant amount of circuitry in the thin film electronics. It may finally be noted that the present system may implement a large number of different network architectures. As mentioned above, the system is inherently capable of implementing recurrent networks, and may readily be configured to implement multilayer networks of more than three layers.

REFERENCES

[1] E. A. Rietman, R. C. Frye, C. C. Wong, and C. D. Kornfeld, "Amorphous Silicon Photoconductive Arrays for Artificial Neural Networks," *Appl. Opt.* vol 28(15), 3474 - 3478 (1989).

[2] E. A. Rietman, R. C. Frye, and C. C. Wong, "Signal Prediction by an Optically Controlled Neural Network," *Appl. Opt.* vol 30(8), 950 - 957 (1991).

[3] R. C. Frye, E. A. Rietman, and C. C. Wong, "Back-Propagation Learning and Nonidealities in Analog Neural Network Hardware," *IEEE Trans. Neural Networks* vol 2(1), 110 - 117 (1991).

[4] R. G. Stearns, "A Trainable Optically-Programmed Neural Network," Appl. Opt. vol **31(29), 6230-6239 (1992)**.

[5] R. G. Stearns and R. L. Weisfield, "Two-dimensional Amorphous-Silicon Photoconductor Array for Optical Imaging, " Appl. Opt. vol **31(32), 6874-6881 (1992)**.

[6] The network has too few hidden-layer, and probably too few input-layer neurons to successfully be trained to classify the handprinted digits of multiple authors. Some idea of the necessary network size for good performance on multi-author digits can be obtained by reading:

G. L. Martin and J. A. Pittman, "Recognizing Hand-Printed Letters and Digits Using Backpropagation Learning," Neural Comp. vol. 3, 258-267 (1991).

Y. LeCun, B. Boser, J. S. Denker, D. Henderson, R. E. Howard, W. Hubbard, and L. D. Jackel, "Backpropagation Applied to Handwritten Zip Code Recognition," Neural Comp. vol. 1, 542-555 (1989).

[7] R. G. Stearns, "An Optically-Programmed Neural Network Capable of Standalone Operation," submitted to Appl. Opt.

Problems of Massive Parallelism in Neural Network Simulation

Andreas Zell, Niels Mache, Michael Vogt, Markus Hüttel

University of Stuttgart,
Institute for Parallel and Distributed High Performance Systems (IPVR),
Breitwiesenstr. 20-22, D-7000 Stuttgart 80, Fed. Rep. Germany
E-mail: zell@informatik.uni-stuttgart.de

Abstract—We here present and compare different massively parallel implementations of multilayer feedforward neural networks on a MasPar MP-1216, a parallel SIMD computer with 16,384 processors. For multilayer feedforward networks we have obtained sustained rates of up to 348 M CPS and 129 M CUPS with backpropagation, a high mark for general purpose SIMD computers. This paper focuses on the problems of mapping neural networks to parallel hardware, on implementation problems in obtaining high propagation rates on a SIMD machine and on problems with the resulting learning algorithms.

Keywords: artificial neural networks, neural network simulators, massive parallelism

I. INTRODUCTION AND MOTIVATION

Our research group wants to understand the advantages and the trade-offs of the various artificial neural network paradigms and learning algorithms, their training efficiency and generalization capabilities and their suitability for massively parallel implementation. We have developed a neural network simulator, SNNS, which has proven well suited for research on learning algorithms, on issues of visualization, training and performance and on parallel implementation of neural networks. SNNS is also used in a number of other university research groups and with growing acceptance in industry as a neural network evaluation and prototyping tool. In this paper we are describing the experiences we gained in developing a massively parallel simulator kernel for SNNS running on our 16 K processor MasPar MP-1216.

II. STUTTGART NEURAL NETWORK SIMULATOR

SNNS (Stuttgart Neural Network Simulator) [1], [2], [3], is an efficient and portable neural network simulation environment for Unix workstations developed at the University of Stuttgart. It is a software tool to generate, train, test and visualize artificial neural networks. The whole network simulator has been developed in C on Unix workstations. The graphical user interface was implemented under X-Windows X11R5 (Athena widget set), for maximal portability.

SNNS now consists of a sequential and a parallel simulator kernel and a graphical user interface (Fig. 1). The simulator kernel operates on the internal representation of the neural networks and performs all operations of the learning and recall phase. It is coupled with the graphical user interface via an interface of function calls. The simulator kernel has already been ported to a number of architectures (Sun, HP, DEC, IBM, etc.).

A. Graphical User Interface of SNNS

The graphical user interface is used to create, visualize and modify the network topology interactively. All display elements are kept in separate windows and thus can be arbitrarily arranged. The user has a powerful set of operations (insertion, deletion, copying, moving) which may be applied to individual units or to selections of units and may affect links as well, like 'copy all selected units with their input links' or 'delete all links into the selected units'. Networks can be modified through the user interface during simulation. Units can be introduced, removed, or have their activation values changed. Connections among the units can be inserted, deleted, redirected, or have their strengths modified. Contrary to many other simulators most modifications can be done directly from the visual display of the network. Fig. 2 gives an overview of the graphical user interface of SNNS.

B. Connectionist Models supported by SNNS

From its design SNNS supports any network that can be specified as a directed graph with weighted links. The concept of sites which has been adapted from RCS [4] even allows multiple links between two units. Although most users of SNNS use simple multilayer feedforward networks with one or two hidden layers and standard sigmoid activation functions (logistic, sine or tanh), some recurrent networks have also been implemented. The following learning algorithms have been implemented: backpropagation [5], backpropagation with momentum, weight decay and flat spot elimination, batch backpropagation, quickprop [6], counterpropagation [7], backpercolation [8], cascade correlation [9], radial basis function networks (RBF) [10], ART1, ART2 and ARTMAP [11], Time-Delay Networks [12] and self organizing feature maps. Not all of them are available in the public distribution, however.

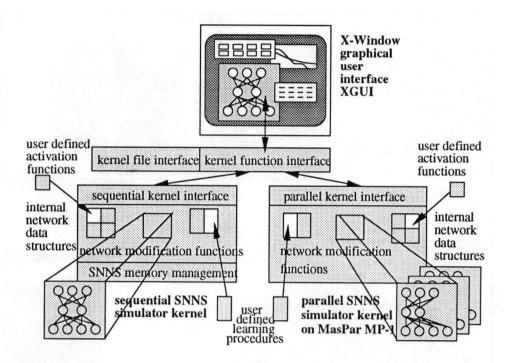

Fig. 1: Structure of SNNS consisting of sequential simulator kernel, parallel kernel and graphical user interface

C. Selected Applications of SNNS

SNNS is currently used in at least 300 installations worldwide, approx. one third of them each in Germany, other Europe and the U.S. Its main use so far is in university research but some commercial research projects use SNNS as a prototyping tool to find optimal learning procedures, network sizes and learning parameters for various neural network applications. Applications include rotation invariant pattern recognition, handwritten character recognition, stock price prediction, recognition and classification of exogenic and endogenic components of event correlated brain potentials, noise reduction in natural language communication in a telecom environment, prediction of secondary structure of proteins and texture analysis.

III. PARALLEL SNNS KERNELS ON THE MASPAR MP-1

Two parallel implementations for the SNNS kernel and one prototype implementation have been developed on our 16 K processor MasPar MP-1216 for multilayer feedforward networks. The goal of the parallelization was to enable the simulation of large neural networks, mainly for the tasks of image processing, feature extraction and pattern and object recognition. The parallel simulator is integrated with the sequential simulator as an alternative simulator kernel. From the X-Windows based graphical user interface it is possible to switch between both kernels at runtime, provided the user restricts itself to multilayer feedforward networks.

A. Architecture of the MP-1

The MasPar MP-1216 is a SIMD machine with up to 16,384 four-Bit processors. 32 processors are integrated on a single chip, 32 chips fit on a processor board. Our full scale model delivers a quoted peak performance of 30,000 MIPS (32 bit addition) and 1,500 resp. 600 MFLOPS (32 bit resp. 64 bit). There exist two separate communication architectures on the MasPar: one is a 3-stage global router which allows up to 1024 simultaneous connections between any two processors, the other is a torroidal two-dimensional 8 neighbour grid (X-net). Communication bandwidth is up to 1.5 GB/s peak global router and up to 24 GB/s peak X-net communication. From this data it can be seen that it is advisable to use the local grid as much as possible since the communication bandwidth is much larger than with the router. Also on our machine we experienced a number of router hardware failures which forced us to avoid it if possible. The MasPar can be programmed with parallel versions of C (AMPL) and Fortran. MPPE (MasPar parallel programming environment), an integrated graphical tool set based on X-Windows, facilitates program development and debugging.

Having investigated the trade-offs of different approaches to parallelization of neural networks, as given in [13], [14], [15] and [16] we decided on an implementation which combines unit parallelism with training vector parallelism. All implementations of our parallel simulator kernel were done in MPL, a parallel extension of C. Two of them have recently been converted to AMPL, the ANSI C extension of MPL.

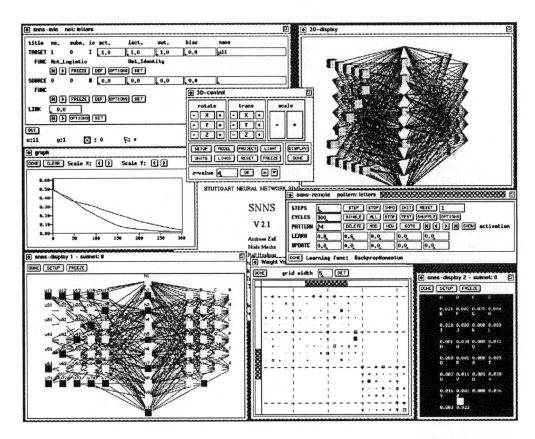

Fig. 2: Graphical user interface of SNNS with a toy letter recognition network: info panel (top left), 3D control panel (top center) and 3D-display (top right), error graph (center left), SNNS banner (center), remote control panel (center right), 2D-display (bottom left), Hinton diagram (bottom center), 2D-display (bottom right).

B. Implementation with Unit-Parallelism and Training Pattern Parallelism

The implementation of Mache [17] uses the following technique (Fig. 3): All hidden and output units of a vertical slice are mapped to a single processing element (PE) of the MasPar. The computation of unit activation is done in parallel for all units of a layer. Thus, a number of processors is needed which equals the largest number of processing elements in a layer, i.e. the width of the network determines the number of processors needed.

If the number of input units is greater than the number of units of the other layers, an additional PE is used to store the remaining components of the input pattern and to send them to its neighbor when they are needed. Each processor stores the weights of all of its input links. The processors are located in a logical ring communication structure which can easily be realized on the X-net grid (with possible copying at the fringes). During forward or backward propagation, the intermediate values for the net input or the accumulated error signal, resp., are shifted cyclically to the left. The weights are stored with a skew factor of 1 in each processor. This allows all units of a layer to perform the computation of the sum of all weighted

predecessor units outputs in a number of steps equal to the size of the preceding layer.

Since the width of a feedforward network is usually much smaller than the number of available processors on our MasPar, multiple copies of the network with different input patterns are updated in parallel. In this way weight changes have to be computed in each network individually without actually changing the weights. The sum of the weight changes is then computed and applied to all corresponding weights of the identical network copies. This results in a batech backpropagation algorithm with the batch size at least equal to the number of network copies in the machine or an integer multiple of it.

For an optimal 128-128-128 network which fits into the machine without an additional PE and which does not need copying at the end of a cycle this implementation we obtained 176 M CPS (connections per second) and 67 M CUPS (connection updates per second) for backpropagation training. The Nettalk network [18], a 203-120-26 network, can be trained with 41 M CUPS and operated with 98 M CPS. These times did not include the time for transfer of the input patterns from the frontend to the parallel machine.

One advantage of this approach is, that the numbers of proc-

1892

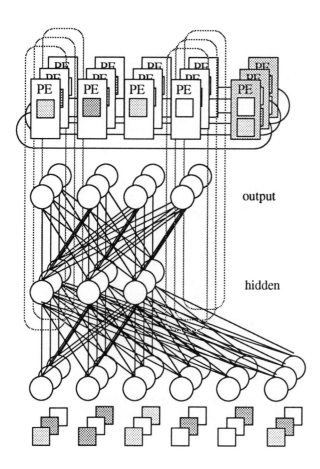

Fig. 3: First parallel SNNS kernel with a 6-3-4 feedforward network: all hidden and output neurons of a column and their input links are mapped onto a single processor. An additional PE holds the remaining input pattern parts. Multiple network copies with different input patterns are trained in parallel (training pattern parallelism).

essors used is not determined by the size of the input layer, which is usually much larger than any hidden or output layer. So a large number of networks can be trained in parallel. A disadvantage is the fact that the one additional PE has to store much more pattern elements than the others. In an SIMD machine with identical memory allocation on all PEs this memory becomes a limiting factor of how many patterns can be stored in parallel on the machine. Since pattern I/O was the limiting factor of our parallel implementation, a second implementation was performed.

C. Second Implementation with Unit-Parallelism and Training Pattern Parallelism

Our second implementation was done to alleviate the pattern I/O bandwidth problem of the first implementation. Its main objective was to store as many patterns as possible in the parallel PE memory, even if the number of PEs needed to store the network is larger. This implementation uses a number of PEs

which is equal to the size of the biggest layer, including input layer. If the input layer is the biggest layer, all PEs store a similar number of pattern components, otherwise some PEs may store no components. The mapping of neurons and training patterns to PEs of this implementation is diplayed in Fig. 4.

For an optimal 128-128-128 network we obtain sustained 348 M CPS in recall mode and 129 M CUPS for backpropagation training. The NETtalk network can be recalled with 47 M CPS and trained with 17.6 M CUPS. These times include the time for the transfer of the input patterns and the results. Since the I/O times dominated the learning and recall times in the previous implementation, the speed improvement of the latter version was even greater than the figures tell. It resulted from a new, better compiler and from extensive code optimizations. The fact that in this scheme less networks can be trained in parallel can be seen in the NetTalk benchmarks which yield lower performance results than the first implementation.

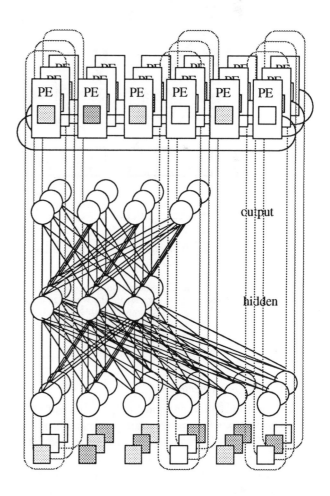

Fig. 4: Second parallel SNNS kernel with a 6-3-4 feedforward network: all neurons of a column and their input links are mapped onto a single processor. The number of processors needed is equal to the size of the biggest layer, usually the input layer. Multiple network copies with different input patterns are trained in parallel (training pattern parallelism).

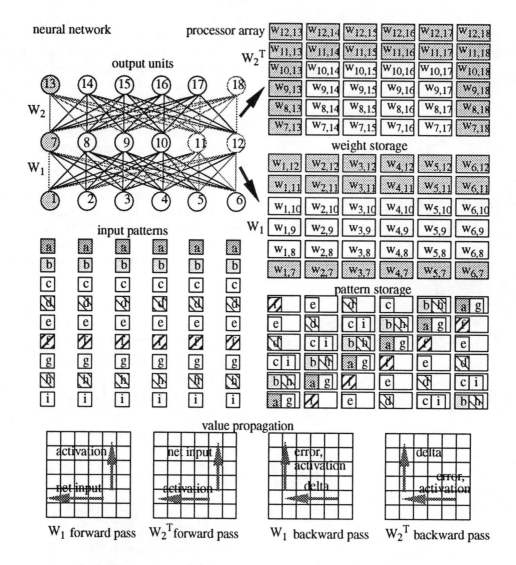

Fig. 5: Link-parallel prototype implementation with a 5-3-4 feedforward network: Each layer is filled up with dummy nodes to the size of the largest layer. There is a bias unit for each layer. The weight matrices are mapped to the processor array directly and in transposed form, in alternating order (W_1, W_2^T, W_3, W_4^T, ...). Dummy weights are set to 0 and prevented from updating with a mask (shown grey). Patterns are mapped to the processor array in diagonal order. The directions of propagation change in each layer according to the weight matrix.

D. Link-Parallel Implementation

The last implementation compared [19] is not a full SNNS kernel but was intended as a prototype implementation. It lacks the support of all SNNS kernel functions but can read SNNS network files. It is graphically displayed in Fig. 5.

First the network is extended with one bias unit for each layer and dummy units to make each layer of equal size n. All units of adjacent layers are connected. The weights to dummy units are initialized to zero and are prevented from being updated by masking them with zero in the last step of weight updates. In our terminology weights from source i to j are denoted by w_{ij}. If the weight matrices connecting adjacent layers are denoted W_1, ...W_m then the mapping of units to PEs of the MasPar follows the rule that if r is odd, the outgoing weights w_{ij} of unit i are mapped to columns of the PE array, with the source unit of lowest index giving the leftmost column, if r is even, the outgoing weights w_{ij} of unit i are mapped to rows of the PE array, with the source unit of lowest index giving the bottom row.

This parallel prototype implementation with link parallelism and training pattern parallelism [19] was measured at 136 M CUPS for a fully connected 127-127-127 network and 160 M CUPS for a 127-127 network on our MasPar MP-1216.

IV. PROBLEMS OF THE PARALLEL SIMULATOR KERNELS

All three parallel SNNS kernels on the MasPar yield impressive performance figures. However, these results have only been obtained after a lengthy period of optimization and several rewrites of the parallel kernel. Our biggest hurdle was the slow communication of the training patterns from the workstation to the parallel backend, which at first took minutes versus milliseconds for the actual training. A lot of effort was therefore spent to load training patterns in large blocks and to keep as many of them as possible in the distributed parallel PE memory.

Another problem concerns the batch backpropagation algorithm necessary for the training pattern parallel implementations: For applications with a large number of similar input patterns this learning algorithm is much slower than online backpropagation. We tested our simulator with handwritten character recognition problems. In this example the slower convergence of batch backpropagation offset most of the performance gain of the parallel architecture. However, some applications need batch backpropagation for convergence and others report better generalization results. Also, other batch learning algorithms like quickprop [3] may be used with better results.

V. CONCLUSIONS

We here have investigated different mappings of neural networks to a massively parallel SIMD computer. These different implementations have shown that it is possible, albeit not at all easy to obtain impressive performance figures for neural network simulation on current SIMD computers. However, these high marks are only obtained for simple network architectures with a network size that fits well into the parallel machine.

We have learned that propagation figures quoted for neural network algorithms are only meaningful if they take communication time from disk or workstation to the parallel machine into account. Overcoming slow pattern I/O took most of the time of the implementations and forced several fundamental changes in the algorithms. Our results can be extended to VLSI neural network hardware in the sense that the time go load training patterns into the parallel hardware must match the speed of forward or backward propagation.

Another lesson learned was that the speed advantage gained by a parallel implementation can be lost for certain applications because of the slower batch backpropagation algorithm. These results have been obtained with precise floating point computations. It would have been even more difficult with fixed point arithmetic or special VLSI hardware with limited precision.

REFERENCES

[1] A. Zell, Th. Korb, T. Sommer, R. Bayer: A Neural Network Simulation Environment, Proc. Applications of Neural Networks Conf., SPIE Vol. 1294, pp. 535-544

[2] A. Zell, N. Mache, T. Sommer. T. Korb: Recent Developments of the SNNS Neural Network Simulator, Applic. of Neural Networks Conf., Proc. SPIE´s 1991 Aerospace Sensing Intl. Symp., Vol. No. 1469, April 1991, Orlando, Florida, pp. 708-719

[3] A. Zell, N. Mache, R. Hübner, M. Schmalzl, T. Sommer, T. Korb: SNNS User Manual, Version 2.1, Universität Stuttgart, Fakultät Informatik, Report No. 8/92

[4] N. H. Goddard, K. .J. Lynne, T. Mintz, L. Bukys, The Rochester Connectionist Simulator: User Manual, Tech Report 233 (revised), Univ. of Rochester, NY, 1989

[5] D. E. Rumelhart, J. A. McClelland, the PDP Research Group: Parallel Distributed Processing, Vol. 1, 2, MIT Press, Cambridge MA, 1986

[6] S. E. Fahlman, : Faster Learning Variations on Backpropagation, in Touretzky et al: Proc. of the 1988 Connectionist Models Summer School, Morgan Kaufmann 1988

[7] R. Hecht-Nielsen: Neurocomputing, Addison-Wesley, 1990

[8] M. Jurik: Backpercolation, (unpublished) paper distributed by Jurik Research and Consulting, PO 2379, Aptos, CA 95001 USA

[9] S. E. Fahlman, C. Lebiere: The Cascade Correlation Learning Architecture, Report CMU-CS-90-100, School of Computer Science, CMU, Pittsburgh, PA 15213, August 1990

[10] T. Poggio, F. Girosi: A Theory of Networks for Approximation and Learning, A.I. Memo No. 1140, A.I. Lab., M.I.T., 1989

[11] G. A. Carpenter, S. Grossberg: The ART of Adaptive Pattern Recognition by a Self-Organizing Neural Network, IEEE Computer, March 1988, 77-88

[12] A. Waibel: Consonant Recognition by Modular Construction of Large Phonemic Time-Delay Neural Networks, in Touretzky (Ed.): NIPS 1, pp. 215-223, Morgan Kaufmann, 1989

[13] A. Singer: Implementations of Artificial Neural Networks on the Connection Machine, Thinking Machines Corp. Tech. Rep. RL 90-2, Jan. 1990 (also in Parallel Computing, summer 1990)

[14] K.A. Grajski, G. Chinn, C. Chen, C. Kuszmaul, S. Tomboulian: Neural Network Simulation on the MasPar MP-1 Massively Parallel Processor, INNC, Paris, France, 1990

[15] G. Chinn, K.A. Grajski, C. Chen, C. Kuszmaul, S. Tomboulian: Systolic Array Implementations of Neural Nets on the MasPar MP-1 Massively Parallel Processor, MasPar Corp. Int. Report

[16] X. Zhang, M. Mckenna, J.P. Mesirov, D. L. Waltz: An efficient implementation of the Back-propagation algorithm on the Connection Machine CM-2, Thinking Machines Corp. TR

[17] N. Mache: Entwicklung eines massiv parallelen Simulatorkerns für neuronale Netze auf der MasPar MP- 1216, Diplomarbeit Nr. 845, Univ. Stuttgart, Fakultät Informatik, Feb. 92 (in German)

[18] T. J. Sejnowski, C.R. Rosenberg: NETtalk: a parallel network that learns to read aloud, in: Anderson, Rosenfeld: Neurocomputing: Foundations, ch. 40, pp. 661-672, MIT Press, 1988

[19] M. Hüttel: Parallele Implementierungen mehrstufiger feedforward-Netze auf einem SIMD-Parallelrechner, Studienarbeit Nr. 1124, Univ. Stuttgart, Fakultät Informatik, Juli 92 (in German)

Neural Network Controller for Rearrangeable Switching Networks

Young-Keun Park* and Vladimir Cherkassky**
Department of Electrical Engineering,
University of Minnesota, Minneapolis, MN 55455
*email : park@ee.umn.edu, **email : cherkass@ee.umn.edu

Abstract—The rapid evolution in the field of communication networks requires high speed switching technologies. This involves a high degree of parallelism in switching control and routing performed at the hardware level. In this paper a neural network approach to controlling a three stage Clos network in real time is proposed. This controller provides optimal routing of communication traffic requests on a call-by-call basis by rearranging existing connections with a minimum length of rearrangement sequence so that a new blocked call request can be accommodated. The proposed neural network controller uses Paull's rearrangement algorithm, along with the special (least used) switch selection rule in order to minimize the length of rearrangement sequences. The functional behavior of our model is verified by simulations and it is shown that the convergence time required for finding an optimal solution is constant regardless of the switching network size. The performance is evaluated for random traffic with various traffic loads. Simulation results show that applying the least used switch selection rule increases the efficiency in switch rearrangements, reduces the network convergence time and also keeps the network from being trapped in local minima. The implementation aspects are also discussed to show the feasibility of the proposed approach.

Index terms — Constrained optimization, neural networks, rearrangeable switching networks.

I. INTRODUCTION : BACKGROUND AND MOTIVATION

Most communication systems contain a switching network as a basic functional unit. The controller for the switching network provides routing of communication traffic. Modern high performance communication channels support a port speed of more than 100 Mbits/sec. Hence, the switching speed must be fast enough in order to handle such a port speed without significant performance degradation. Switching functions of conventional packet switches are typically performed in software running on a general purpose computer. For large switching systems, implementation of routing algorithms on a sequential computer may not be effective since it requires a large amount of computation time. On the other hand, the neural network approach can offer a potential solution for fast switching due to its high degree of parallelism and rapid convergence. Advances in VLSI technology have made it possible to realize the neural networks on a single chip. In the rest of this section, we give a brief background on switching networks.

A connecting network is called a *rearrangeable switching network* if it can realize every connection between inputs and outputs and it can reconfigure existing connections to route a new call. There are two possible modes of operations : *synchronous* or *asynchronous*. In synchronous mode, all multiple input/output request pairs need to be routed simultaneously. On the other hand, in asynchronous mode, given a new call, the existing connection paths are reconfigured asynchronously on a call-by-call basis. For the rest of the paper, we only assume the asynchronous mode of operation. Such networks usually consist of several stages of crossbar switches.

In 1953, Clos[1] introduced three stage switching network(Fig.1). It consists of r input crossbar switches, m intermediate crossbar switches and r output crossbar switches. He showed that the total number of crosspoints required for three stages is minimized to $6N^{3/2} - 3N$, when $n = r = \sqrt{N}$ and $m = n$. A call request may be *blocked* when all available routes are occupied by other existing connections. However, since the switches are rearrangeable, it can perform all possible connections between inputs and outputs by rearranging its existing connections so that a connection path for a new input-output pair can always be established. Such a three stage rearrangeable network is called *non-blocking in the wide sense*.

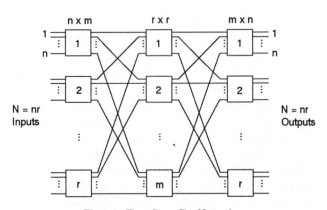

Figure 1. Three Stage Clos Network

1896

Now, the problem is to rearrange the existing connections in order to accommodate the new call request that is blocked and how to achieve it in an optimal fashion, i.e. with the minimum number of rearrangements of existing connections. In the following sections, we give detailed descriptions of known approaches and our approach to rearrangements in Clos networks.

II. CONVENTIONAL AND NEURAL NETWORK APPROACHES TO REARRANGEMENT

A. Rearrangement Algorithm

In 1962, M.C. Paull proposed a rearrangement algorithm for the three stage Clos network[2]. He showed that if $m = n = r$, then at most $n-1$ existing calls need be rearranged in order to unblock a blocked call request. In general, for $m = 2n - j$ ($j = 1..n$), no more than $j-1$ rearrangements are required. Fig.2 illustrates an example of this algorithm. For simplicity, in the rest of the paper we assume $m = n = r = 4$ in our examples. The rows correspond to the input switches (first stage) and the columns correspond to the output switches (third stage). Each entry may contain from zero to m symbols which correspond to the m intermediate switches (second stage). A symbol "A" in entry (i,j) implies that a call originating from input switch i is routed through center switch "A" to output switch j. In Fig.2(a), notice that there are two calls between the input switch 3 and the output switch 2. One is routed through center switch "A", the other is routed through center switch "D". A new call request $(2,2)$ is blocked. The corresponding connection paths of a Clos network are shown in Fig.3.

Since the input/output switches are composed of strictly non-blocking crossbars, we do not distinguish between the n external connections of a particular input/output switch. Since the connections on the input/output switches are uniquely specified by the connections on the intermediate switches, only the connections within the intermediate switches are considered. Call requests are therefore simply denoted as (i,j), where i is the input switch number and j is the output switch number.

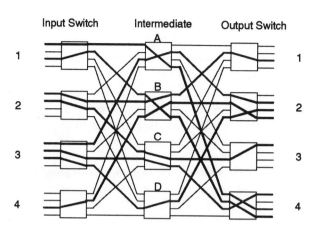

Figure 3. States of the switches

The following constraints must be considered:

1. There can be no more than m symbols in any row or column since the total number of intermediate switches is m.

2. No two symbols in any row (or column) may be the same.

3. Each entry (i,j) may contain up to m symbols depending on the number of calls.

When a call request arrives, determine whether it is *legal* or *illegal*. A call request (i,j) is called *illegal* if there are no available lines at the input switch i or at the output switch j. That is, if there are already m symbols in row i or m symbols in column j, it is not a legal call request. In this case, the call request is not accepted. If it is a legal call request, determine whether it is blocked or not. If there is any symbol Q that does not exist in row i and column j, it is not blocked. Then place a Q in entry (i,j) and no rearrangement is required. If it is blocked, we choose any symbol Q and place a Q in entry (i,j). Then there must be another row i' such that the entry (i',j) contains a Q also. Similarly, there may be another column j' such that the entry (i,j') has a Q. Then replace the Q in such entries with another symbol R. This procedure is successively continued until no two symbols appear in the same row or column. Paull proved that this algorithm could always find an unblocking rearrangement.

B. Conventional Approaches

Most of the conventional control algorithms are sequential and their computation complexities are $O(N\log_2 N)$ [8,9,10]. The processing time for the algorithms must be sufficiently short in order to handle high port speed. The performance of switching networks depends very much on the control overhead. Unfortunately, the conventional approaches are practical only for very small networks because the central control is the bottleneck of this approach. The

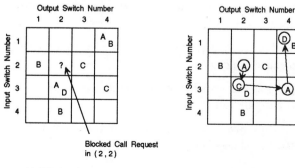

(a) A Blocked Call Request

(b) The algorithm chose "A" arbitrarily and three rearrangements occurred

Figure 2. An Example of Paull's Rearrangement Algorithm

switching capacity of current conventional packet switches ranges from 1 to 4 thousand packets per second, with average nodal delay of 20 ~ 50 msec[16]. Due to this control overhead, the maximum throughput is less than 50 percent[15]. The network throughput is defined as the ratio of the number of successfully handled requests to the offered load. Much research has been done to improve the network throughput by queueing call requests using input/output buffers (or internal buffers). However such queueing solutions are not cost-effective since they have too much hardware overhead for just 10 percent of throughput improvement.

C. Neural Network Approaches

One way to reduce the control overhead and to improve the throughput is to distribute the control function by using a high degree of parallelism and the hardware level routing control. We can realize this by using neural network approaches due to their analog parallel processing and the fast convergence.

Brown proposed a neural network model for the multistage rearrangeable switches[4]. He applied Paull's algorithm to the rearrangement problem using a time delay trick to produce the desired behavior of rearrangements. He used two different kinds of neurons (primary neurons and memory neurons). The memory neurons have larger time delays than the primary neurons. Each memory neuron is attached to each primary neuron and it is used to distinguish a primary neuron that has been on for a long time from a primary neuron that has recently turned on. This difference helps the rearrangement proceed sequentially without oscillating. However, the total number of neurons used was doubled ($2r^2m$, where r is the number of input/output crossbar switches and m is the number of intermediate crossbar switches) and he didn't provide any empirical performance evaluation results to verify his approach.

Funabiki and Takefuji recently proposed a parallel control algorithm for multistage interconnection networks of a base-2 structure[6]. They described a neural network model with N^2 (i.e. r^2m^2) neurons. They solved small-sized network (32×32) problems by simulations. Their model requires hundreds of iterations to find an optimal solution. They also proposed a parallel control algorithm for three stage Clos networks using r^2m neurons[7]. From their simulation results, it is shown that the network converges within 120 iterations with the average 97 percent of accuracy under medium traffic load conditions. We have implemented their model in software and duplicated their results for medium traffic loads. However, we found that for heavy traffic loads their model does not provide good performance. Therefore, we developed a better approach in the following section.

III. NEURAL NETWORK CONTROLLER

The physical consequence of rearrangements is to momentarily disturb network connections and the time duration of this disturbance may result in serious degradation of throughput in high speed communication networks. Therefore it is desirable to minimize this disturbance. During the rearrangement procedure of Paull's algorithm, the switches are chosen arbitrarily and such an approach has been implemented in a neural network controller[7]. In our model, we suggest to use Paull's algorithm with a better strategy for choosing switches. Notice that in Fig.2(b), if a "C" were chosen for entry (2 , 2), only one rearrangement would occur. Unfortunately, in real time, we cannot predict which choice would provide the shortest rearrangements. Jajszczyk and Rajski[5] showed that the intermediate switches selection rules affect the rearrangement process and the computation time required for rearrangements can be decreased by choosing the least used switches. Their theorem states that the number of calls in progress that need to be rerouted in order to connect an idle pair of terminals is not greater than minimum(a , b), where a, b are the number of existing connection paths passing through the switches A, B, respectively. Empirical simulations in the next section show that applying this rule to our neural network model not only saves the processing time for rearrangements but also keeps the network from being trapped in local minima.

We use the neural network topology originally proposed in [7] but with a different energy function. The network consists of r^2m neurons where r represents the number of input/output crossbar switches and m represents the number of intermediate crossbar switches. An example is shown in Fig.4. This figure corresponds to the state matrix shown in Fig.2(a) and the corresponding connection paths of a Clos network are shown in Fig.3. The shaded neurons represent their ON-states. The actual connections among the neurons are not shown in this figure. The states of neurons represent the connection states of the intermediate crossbar switches.

The following constraints must be satisfied :

1. In each entry (i , j), as many neurons as the number of calls may be ON.

2. Within each entry, always select the least used intermediate switch.

   (Select the switch with the minimum number of connection paths.)

3. In each row (or column), no two neurons with the same label may both be ON.

1898

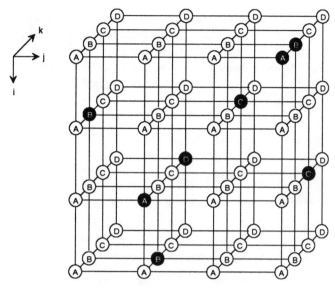

Figure 4. Neural Network Architecture ($m = n = r = 4$)

Notice that the least used intermediate switch is the switch "D" for the example in Fig.3. This neural network controller will offer fast solutions to the rearrangement problems provided that the network behavior and the appropriate set of connections and their weights between neurons are well defined.

Let U_{ijk} denote the total input of the ijk'th neuron where i, j, k represents i'th input switch, j'th output switch, k'th intermediate switch, respectively. Let V_{ijk} denote the output of the ijk'th neuron. The value of $V_{ijk} = 1$ means that the ijk'th neuron is ON and $V_{ijk} = 0$ means that the ijk'th neuron is OFF. For our model, we define V_{ijk} as suggested by Funabiki and Takefuji[6,7]:

$$V_{ijk}^{new} = \begin{cases} 0 & \text{if } U_{ijk} \le -\alpha \text{ ,} \\ 1 & \text{if } U_{ijk} \ge \alpha \text{ ,} \\ V_{ijk}^{old} & \text{if } -\alpha < U_{ijk} < \alpha \text{ ,} \\ & \text{where } \alpha > 0. \end{cases}$$

The constant α is determined empirically for the fastest convergence. Our simulation experiments (described in the next section) use the value $\alpha = 5$. With the three constraints described above, the following equation represents the total input change of a neuron.

$$\frac{dU_{ijk}}{dt} = (a - \frac{c}{r} \sum_{p=1}^{r} \sum_{q=1}^{r} V_{pqk}) f(t_{ij} - \sum_{l=1}^{m} V_{ijl})$$

$$- b(\sum_{p=1, p \ne i}^{r} V_{pjk} + \sum_{q=1, q \ne j}^{r} V_{iqk})$$

where a, b, c are positive constants, t_{ij} denotes the number of call requests in entry (i, j), r the number of crossbar switches in the input/output stage and m the number of center stage switches.

The function $f(x)$ is 1 if $x > 0$, 0 if $x = 0$, -1 if $x < 0$.

The first term in the above equation represents the first and the second constraints previously discussed. The second term represents the third constraint. The first term initiates the rearrangement procedure in such a way that the least used switch selection rule is applied whenever a new call request arrives.

The first term is zero, positive or negative depending on the difference between the number of call requests in entry (i, j) and the number of neurons turned on in entry (i, j). If a new call request arrives in entry (i, j), then the first term is positive and it forces the ijk'th neuron to be turned on. The second term is zero if there is no other neuron turned on in row i or column j with the same k. Otherwise it forces the ijk'th neuron to be turned off.

The factor $(a - \frac{c}{r} \sum_{p=1}^{r} \sum_{q=1}^{r} V_{pqk})$ is related to the least used switch selection rule (i.e. the second constraint) and the constants a and c must be defined in such a way that this factor is always positive, the denominator r (the number of input/output crossbar switches) normalizes the value of the total number of neurons turned on within the k'th intermediate switch. Whenever a new call request arrives, the total number of neurons turned on within the k'th intermediate switch affects on the amount of input change of ijk'th neuron. Since every neuron in entry (i, j) has different value of this factor, the neuron with the largest input (i.e. the least used one) wins the competition and this difference accelerates the convergence speed. This is also true when an existing call is released. In this case, the least used switch is released. The constant a must be larger than the constants b and c so that the rearrangements can proceed without oscillations. These constants are determined empirically. With these proper values of constants a, b and c, each neuron tries to converge to either ON or OFF state based on the three constraints discussed before.

IV. SOFTWARE SIMULATIONS

We used the random traffic model as most previous studies on switching networks. Both the heavy load and the medium load cases were considered, where the traffic load is defined as the number of existing connections when a new call comes in. In the case of *medium* traffic load, existing calls occupy roughly half of maximum allowable connections, and in the case of *heavy* traffic load, most of the switches are being used for the existing calls. For various sizes of networks, the average number of iterations (i.e. average number of updates per neuron, corresponding to network convergence time), the average length of rearrangement sequences, blocking rates (i.e. the probability that a new call is blocked) and the success rates(i.e. the ratio of the number of successful convergence to total number of call requests) are shown in Fig.5, Fig.6, Fig.7 and Fig.8, respectively. When the network did not converge within a specified iteration limit, it was counted as a failure. The rearrangement sequences are counted only when the blocked call is unblocked successfully by rearrangements. For our model, we used $a = 5$, $b = 1$, $c = 3$, $\alpha = 5$, Iteration limit = 200. We also simulated our model without applying the least used switch selection rule (i.e. the second constraint). For every size of network, sequences of rm number of new calls were used, where rm represents the maximum number of connections in m number of $r \times r$ center stage switches. Simulations show that our model with the least used switch selection rule converges at least two times faster than the model with the random selection of intermediate switches. By applying the least used switch selection rule, the average number of iterations and the average length of rearrangement sequences are halved and the better performance is achieved even with the smaller value of iteration limit.

The reason why the random selection method does not provide good success rates for heavy traffic load is that it doesn't solve the rearrangement problems well in blocking situations. Therefore, we can conclude that applying the least used switch selection rule not only increases the efficiency in switch rearrangements, but also reduces the network convergence time since it keeps the network from being trapped in local minima. It is also shown that the network convergence time and the average length of rearrangement sequences do not depend on the network size, rather they depend on the traffic loads. We can also notice that the blocking rate (this implies the frequency of rearrangements) depends on the traffic load. Under heavy traffic load, the blocking rate is slightly larger than that of the random selection method. However, it is less than that of the random selection method under light load.

V. IMPLEMENTATION ASPECTS AND FEASIBILITY STUDY

Recent studies have shown that the Hopfield Network can be implemented with analog VLSI circuit technology[14] and a general purpose neural network system has been developed which can simulate the Hopfield-type networks, back-propagation networks and many others by using neurochips[12]. Most of recent studies have used analog circuits in hardware implementations[13,14]. Unfortunately, with the current technologies it is difficult to implement large networks by using analog circuits since the high-precision resisters are required and the circuits are easily affected by electrical noise and the power consumption is very high. It is also shown that for large scale neural networks, digital circuits may be more suitable than analog circuits[11,12] since digital neurons can be easily integrated on a wafer by using CMOS technology and the neural functions can be mapped to digital circuits that are fully compatible with conventional computers.

Average Number of Iterations (Convergence Time)

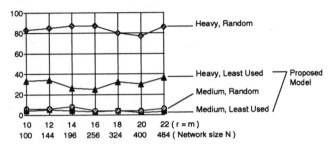

Figure 5. Average number of iterations

Average Rearrangement Sequences

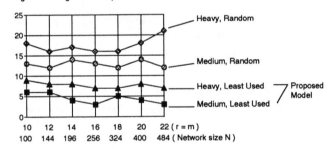

Figure 6. Average length of rearrangement sequences

Blocking Rates (%)

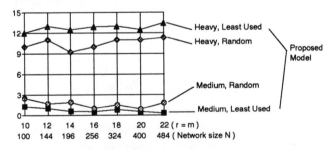

Figure 7. Blocking rates

Success Rates (%)

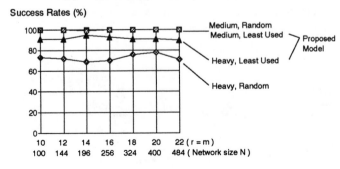

Figure 8. Success rates

Digital circuits also have some disadvantages : One digital neuron requires more transistors than one analog neuron, thus it requires much more chip area. Also in a digital implementation, the network convergence time is proportional to the number of neurons since they are using time sharing bus architecture in order to connect all neurons.

In our model for switch controller, all r^2m neurons are not fully interconnected but they are interconnected within each axis of the three dimensional grids (Fig.4). Therefore analog VLSI implementation would be more efficient than digital circuits provided that some technology-dependent limitations are overcome. This design may not be cost-effective with the current technology but the progress in modern analog VLSI technologies will enable the large VLSI implementation that was previously impossible. If this comes true, we can realize high speed switching networks without much throughput degradation that usually results from a low switching speed in conventional RAM controlled switching mechanism.

In a conventional RAM controlled switching mechanism, the processing time of the best algorithm is $7(N\log_2 N)$ cycle times (this includes the memory access time required to partition the memory and access times for the decomposition) for $N \times N$ switching networks[8]. For $N = 1000$ and the RAM with 50 nsec access time, and a 25 Mhz clock, on a 1-Mips machine, the processing time is about 60 msec. This means that the average nodal delay of the switching network is 60 msec which is too slow for a modern high speed channel with more than 100 Mbits/sec port speed. On the other hand, if the routing function is performed by the analog parallel processing, the average nodal delay lies in nano-second range. The performance of small size Hopfield type analog VLSI for a single crossbar control has already been evaluated[3]. The convergence time of such a network is 100 nsec. Hence, analog implementation of our neural network model can reduce the nodal delay to just 100 nsec, which is sufficient to support 100 Mbps port speeds.

Among design parameters, cost is another important factor. The hardware complexity of proposed model is $O(N\sqrt{N})$ (i.e. r^2m processing elements). Although the analog VLSI design is more costly than the digital single processor implementation, it does not suffer from time bottleneck ($O(N\log_2 N)$). Since the cost of integrated circuits is dropping exponentially and the transistor count on a chip is increasing by about 25 % per year, we expect to see cost-effective analog realizations of large neural networks in the near future.

VI. CONCLUSIONS

A lot of research has been done to compensate the mismatch between transmission speed and switching speed. As the transmission speed is getting faster and faster, new switching technologies are required to improve the performance in an efficient and cost-effective way. In this paper, a neural network approach to control a rearrangeable switching network is proposed. It is shown that the proposed neural network model converges in a constant time regardless of the switching network size. Success of the proposed model is due to incorporating conventional heuristic (least used switch selection rule) into the neural network controller. Based on our experience, we believe that successful neural network applications can be developed only by combining application-specific domain knowledge into neural network models. If the proposed model is implemented in analog VLSI, then apparently it would offer the maximum possible throughput with shorter nodal delays than other existing approaches.

REFERENCES

[1] C. Clos, "A study of non-blocking switching networks," Bell Syst. Tech. J., Vol. 32, pp. 406-424, March 1953.

[2] M. C. Paull, "Reswitching of connection networks," Bell Syst. Tech. J., Vol. 41, pp. 833-855, May 1962.

[3] A. Marrakchi and T. Troudet, "A neural net arbitrator for large crossbar packet-switches," IEEE Trans. on Circuits and Systems, Vol. 36, no. 7, pp. 1039-1041, July 1989.

[4] T. X. Brown, "Neural networks for switching," IEEE Communications Mag., pp. 72-81, Nov. 1989.

[5] A. Jajszczyk and J. Rajski, "The effect of choosing the switches for rearrangements in switching networks," IEEE Trans. on Communications, Vol. Com-28, NO. 10, pp. 1832-1834, Oct. 1980.

[6] N. Funabiki, Y. Takefuji, and K. C. Lee, "A neural network model for traffic controls in multistage interconnection networks," IJCNN 1991, Vol. II, pp. II A-898.

[7] N. Funabiki and Y. Takefuji, "A parallel algorithm for traffic control problems in three-stage connecting networks," Journal of Parallel and Distributed Computing, in press.

[8] D. C. Opferman and N. T. Tsao-Wu, "On a class of rearrangeable switching networks," Bell Syst. Tech. J., Vol. 50, pp. 1579-1618, May-June 1971.

[9] Nelson T. Tsao-wu, "On neiman's algorithm for the control of rearrangeable switching networks," IEEE Trans. on Communications, Vol. Com-22, NO. 6, pp. 737-742, June 1974.

[10] G. Colombo, C. Scarati and F. Settimo, "Asynchronous control algorithm for increasing the efficiency of three-stage connecting networks for multipoint services," IEEE Trans. on Communications, Vol. 38, NO. 6, pp. 898-905, June 1990.

[11] M. Yasunaga, N. Masuda, M. Yagyu, M. Asai, M.Yamada and A. Masaki, "Design, fabrication and evaluation of a 5-Inch wafer scale neural network LSI composed of 576 digital neurons," IJCNN 1990, Vol. II, pp. II-572 - II-535.

[12] Y. Hirai, K. Kamada, M. Yamada and M. Ooyama, "A digital neuro-chip with unlimited connectability for large scale neural networks," IJCNN 1989, Vol. II, pp. II-163 - II-169.

[13] J. Hopfield, "Neurons with graded response have collective computational properties like those of two-state neurons," Proc. Nat. Acad. Sci. USA, Vol.81, pp. 3088 - 3092, 1984.

[14] M. Sivilotti, M. Emerling and C. Mead, "VLSI architectures for implementation of neural networks," Conference on Neural Networks for Computing, AIP Conference Proceedings, pp. 408 - 413, 1896.

[15] H. Ahmadi and W. Denzel, "A survey of modern high-performance switching techniques," IEEE J. on Selected Areas in Communications, Vol.7, no.7, pp. 1091-1103, Sept. 1989.

[16] J. Huber and E. Mair, "A flexible architecture for small and large packet switching networks," in Proc. ISS'87, Phoenix, AZ, Mar. 1987, pp. B10.4.1-B10.4.6.

A Sound Localization System Based On Biological Analogy

Neal Bhadkamkar*   Boyd Fowler[†]

Electrical Engineering Department, Stanford University, Stanford, CA 94305

email: neal@milo.stanford.edu   fowler@isl.stanford.edu

Abstract—

We have designed, fabricated and tested a low-power analog VLSI system that implements a model of sound localization in the horizontal plane. The model uses the time difference between a sound arriving at each ear to determine the location of the sound source. The system consists of two chips fabricated through MOSIS in a standard 2μm, p-well, CMOS process. One chip contains circuitry to model left and right side cochleas, hair cells and auditory neurons, while the other chip contains circuitry to model the binaural cross-correlation activity of neurons in the superior olive of the brainstem. Measured test results are promising but reveal challenges that must be overcome in order to obtain reliable performance. This is necessary before subthreshold designs can be used in mass-produced products.

I. Introduction

Sound localization is a biologically important function for both predator and prey. It is a complex process involving the joint action of many stages of auditory processing. The location of a sound source in the horizontal plane, that is whether it is to the left or the right, results in a time difference between sounds arriving at each ear. This time difference is believed to be one of the main cues that the auditory system uses to localize sound sources [1]. For a human head this time difference can be as much as one millisecond, while for an elephant's head it is proportionately larger. The processing is believed to start in an evolutionarily old part of the brain called the brainstem. Specifically, a region of the brainstem called the superior olive contains cells that are preferentially responsive to sounds with specific interaural time differences; these cells receive inputs from both the left and right cochleas via their respective hair cells and auditory neurons and can discriminate differences of microseconds in the arrival time of sounds at the two ears [2].

We have designed a set of two CMOS chips that are meant to model the early processing done by the left and right cochlea, hair cells and auditory nerves, and the portion of the brainstem responsive to interaural time differences. Save for buffers for driving the signals off chip, the design is based almost entirely on circuits operating in the subthreshold region [3, 4]. Current flow in this region is governed by diffusion rather than by drift, and is exponentially related to the gate voltage of the transistor. Subthreshold current flows are so small that traditional CMOS designs consider the transistor to be off. The circuits used for the cochlea, hair cells and correlators are novel and differ from implementations by other researchers [5, 6, 7]. At a high level our approach to sound localization is similar to that in [8], but our implementation is radically different.

The remainder of this paper is organized as follows. Section II. provides an overview of the design of the system. Section III. provides more detail on the design of the cochlea-chip and correlator-chip, while Section IV. presents summary results for the two chips. Section V. presents a discussion of the results and the design challenges that arise from the use of subthreshold circuitry, and Section VI. presents our conclusions.

II. System Design

An overview of the two-chip system is shown in Figure 1. The **cochlea-chip**, receives its inputs through two microphones or function generators, representing the left and right ears. It contains two single input multiple output circuits to model the left and right cochleas. These circuits perform a frequency decomposition of the incoming sound, with high frequencies causing maximum excitation at the near end outputs, and low frequencies at the far end. The cochlea-chip also contains left and right circuitry meant to model the rectification and pulsing behavior of the inner hair cells and auditory nerve fibers associated with each cochlea. The output of the cochlea-chip is a set of 20 left signal lines and 20 right signal lines. The signals on these lines are pulses occurring as a function of the left and right

*Supported by NASA under Grant NAGW-419

[†] Supported by Texas Instruments

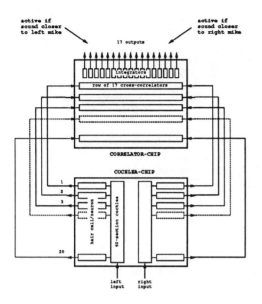

Figure 1: Overview of the two-chip sound localization system.

sounds entering the chip. These provide the input to the **correlator-chip**, which models that portion of the superior olive containing neurons sensitive to interaural time differences. It contains 20 rows of circuitry, each receiving a left and right input from the cochlea-chip. Each row has seventeen cross-correlation circuits that respond to the coincidence of pulses on the left and right input lines, but with different delays. The circuitry on the left side of the correlator-chip responds if the left inputs pulse before the right inputs, and vice-versa for the right side. The outputs of the cross-correlation circuits corresponding to a particular delay are summed and integrated across the twenty rows. These 17 integrated outputs form the output of the correlator-chip. The basic idea is that as a sound source moves from the left to the right, the excitation location of the outputs moves in the same fashion.

III. Analog Circuit Design

A. Cochlea-chip

The cochlea-chip contains two major subsystems, a 60-section cochlea and 60 hair-cell/auditory neuron circuits. Every third output of the system is brought to a pin, and a multiplexer allows the output of either the cochlea or the auditory neuron to be viewed. Each of these subsystems has a left and right version. A schematic of one cochlear section connected to one hair-cell and auditory neuron circuit is shown in Figure 2.

A.1. Cochlea circuit

The cochlea circuit is based on a cascade of 60 sections identical in every way save for their characteristic frequencies, which fall exponentially from the near to the far end of the cascade based on a linearly declining voltage along a polysilicon wire that runs the length of the cascade. Each section is meant to model the effect of a small section of the biological cochlea, which is assumed to contain active outer hair cells that enhance the motion of the basilar membrane. Details of the design can be found in [9], though for the current chip we have incorporated some of the techniques described in [10] to achieve larger output signal values.

The approach of cascading sections to model the cochlea was first used in analog VLSI implementations by Lyon and Mead [5], who used a cascade of second order sections. We use a more complex section in the cascade that we believe better approximates the behavior of the real cochlea. In particular, it allows the construction of cochleas of different granularities without imposing a delay penalty on fine grained implementations. Analysis of the other cascade designs reported in the literature [5, 6, 7] suggest that the number of sections in those designs must be limited in order to not incur an excessive delay. Also, since our design is structurally more similar to the biological cochlea, it mimics some of the latter's nonlinear behavior.

A.2. Hair-cell/auditory neuron circuit

The hair-cell circuit shown in Figure 2 rectifies and low pass filters the output of the cochlear section to which it is connected. The filter cutoff frequency is proportional to the bias current set by the *am_tau_bias* voltage and inversely proportional to the associated capacitor. The circuit pumps current into the auditory neuron circuit that follows it during the discharge time of the capacitor. At low frequencies this occurs for approximately half of every input cycle that it sees. At high frequencies, current is pumped in for a much smaller portion of the cycle. At these high frequencies, increases in the amplitude of an input sinusoid cause a sudden but temporary increase in the current pumped into the auditory neuron circuit. The circuit differs from the hysteretic-differentiator hair-cell circuit described in [11], which activates the circuitry that follows it at the peaks of its input waveform.

The auditory neuron circuit is similar in many respects to the self-resetting neuron circuit described in [4], but includes a refractory period control. In the quiescent state, the output voltage is high at V_{dd}. Sufficient time-integration of input current causes the state of the output to flip low to *Gnd*. The *PW_bias* voltage controls the duration of time for which the output stays low. Once the output flips high again, the *TR_bias* voltage controls the refractory period of the neuron, not permitting input cur-

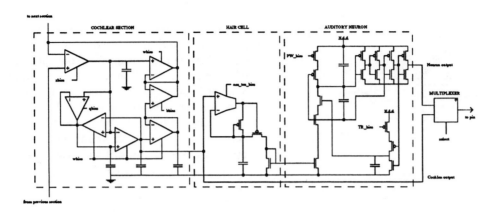

Figure 2: Cochlea-chip circuits. The triangular blocks in the cochlear section are simple transconductance amplifiers, while the snub-nosed triangular block in the hair-cell is a wide-range transconductance amplifier [4].

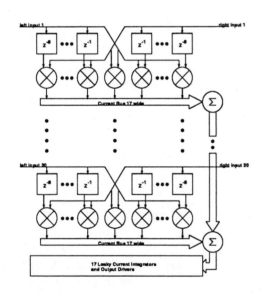

Figure 3: Correlator

rent to have any effect until a certain amount of time has passed.

B. Correlator-chip

The correlator-chip contains one subsystem, a 20 section cross correlation circuit. A block diagram of the correlator is shown in Figure 3.

B.1. Correlator circuit

The correlator is composed of twenty separate rows each with two digital input voltages and seventeen analog output currents. The set of output currents represent a

discrete-time cross-correlation of the input pulses. In other words, each row calculates the time difference between inputs. To perform this task two sets of delay elements are connected to a set of multipliers as shown in Figure 3 . Typically correlators are constructed with serial delay lines [12], but in an attempt to minimize error accumulation we have designed our correlator with parallel delay lines. Each of the seventeen analog output currents are summed over the set of twenty rows and integrated on leaky capacitors. A leaky capacitor is a capacitor with a shunt MOS transistor biased in subthreshold. The seventeen capacitor voltages constitute the outputs of the sound localization system.

As shown in Figure 4, the two building blocks in the correlator are the delay element and the multiplier. The delay circuit builds on the self-resetting neuron circuit described in [4] and has a controllable delay time and output pulse width. The time delay between input pulse and output pulse is determined by the equation

$$t_{delay} = \frac{V_{dd}C_2}{I_{delay}} \qquad (1)$$

where V_{dd} is the power supply voltage and I_{delay} is the current through $M4$ controlled by the *delay_bias* voltage. The output pulse width of the delay circuit is given by

$$t_{pw} = \frac{V_{dd}C_2}{I_{pw}} \qquad (2)$$

where I_{pw} is the current through $M6$ controlled by the *pw_bias* voltage. The multiplier is a NAND gate with a bias transistor at the base.

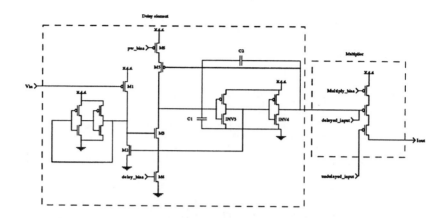

Figure 4: Correlation Delay Section

IV. Experimental Results

All of the testing was performed by an automated GPIB-based testing system controlled by an Apple Macintosh-IIsi with a National Instruments GPIB board. The software was initially developed at Apple Computer and then revised at Stanford in the analog-VLSI laboratory. The main control program ran under Matlab, which was also used for all the data analysis.

The results reported below are for the cochlea and correlator chips separately. Large variances in the correlator-chip, described in B., made the joint testing unfeasible. We are in the process of making extensive measurements on the cochlea-chip in order to simulate what the effect of a "perfect" correlator-chip would have been.

A. Cochlea

The top left, top right and lower left panels of Figure 5 show results from an earlier version of the cochlea in which all 60 taps were accessible for measurement. All three panels show results for the same settings of the bias voltages. The top left panel shows the transfer function at a particular tap (number 45 in this case), the top right panel shows how the peak frequency falls exponentially with tap number, and the lower left panel shows that the group delay flattens out at around 4 cycles of the peak frequency for these particular bias voltages. The lower right panel pertains to the current design, and uses different bias voltage settings. The upper and lower sinusoidal traces in the panel show the responses at the right and left cochlear tap when both cochleas are receiving a 30 mV sinusoidal input at the best frequency of the tap. The pulse like traces show the response of the auditory neurons connected to the cochlear taps, ensemble averaged over 64 cycles of input. The responses have been offset vertically to make the

data more readable. Ideally, both left and right responses should be identical, but variations in the chip cause them to be offset in phase.

B. Correlator

The correlator inputs were created by two HP3314A pulse generators, and the seventeen analog outputs were time multiplexed using two MC14051s and displayed on a HP54601A digital oscilloscope. Data from the oscilloscope was acquired and stored using the automated system described above.

The results of a typical correlator row and the sum of all correlator rows are show in Figure 6. The upper two plots show the correlator output results with a single row being excited, while the lower two show the results with all twenty rows being excited. Each of these plots represents the correlator outputs with pulses arriving at the right input before the left. The time delay between the inputs was varied between 2 ms and 0.2 ms. The individual row results show that for a typical row, the peak excitation location is correlated with the time delay; small time delays excite the center, near section 9, and large time delays excite the edge, near section 16. Unfortunately, the sum of row results do not show this desired correlation. This is because subthreshold parameter variation causes the delay time differences of various correlator rows to be large.

V. Discussion

The main problem with this design was the use of nominal analog circuit design methods, by which we mean using the nominal value of circuit and device parameters to complete a design. This works if CMOS devices are operated above threshold, where variations are small. However, devices operated below threshold have much greater varia-

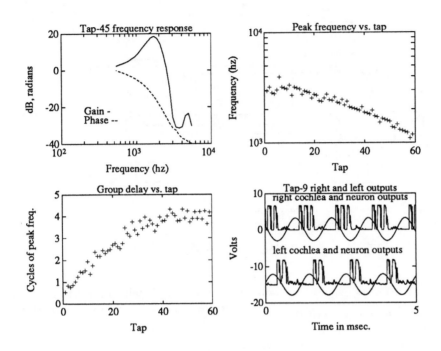

Figure 5: Performance of the cochlea-chip.

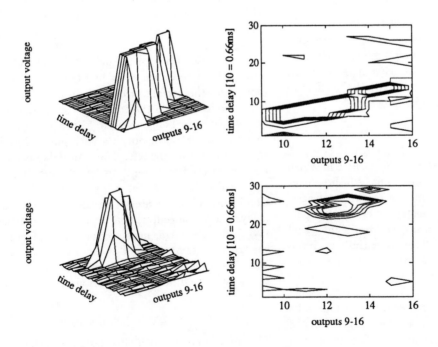

Figure 6: The correlator results were measured at 23.1^0 C with V_{dd}=5 V. The x, y and z axes of the mesh plots represent correlator outputs 9-16, output voltage and time delay between inputs, respectively. The x and y axes of the contour plots represent correlator outputs 9-16 and time delay between inputs respectively. Each contour plot is a top view of the mesh plot on its left.

tion [13, 14] that can make many nominally correct designs non-functional. We believe that in these circumstances a different design approach is called for that specifically takes into account the inherent variations in the transistor building blocks. We are working on approaches to this problem for the cochlea, hair cell, auditory neuron and correlator designs. Approaches that suggest themselves are automatic compensation for device variations, as well as statistical designs that use the law of large numbers to overcome the problem.

Another problem was the mixing of subthreshold and above threshold circuits without adequate isolation. High current circuits can cause small voltage drops in the V_{dd} line, and consequently cause substrate bias plugs to have different potentials at different points in the substrate. This causes potential gradients in the substrate, which change the subthreshold currents in native devices through the back-gate effect. Similarly, wells can have different potentials due to small voltage drops along the Gnd lines. This affects the current through well devices. Because of the exponential effect of substrate and well voltages on subthreshold current, the deviation from the expected current value can be quite high, leading to unwanted variations in the circuit behavior. This is a problem that has been observed in many of the chips designed in the Stanford analog-VLSI lab. We are working on general design approaches to overcome this problem. Some options we are evaluating include isolating low power from high power circuits, or obtaining the substrate and well biases from dedicated V_{dd} and Gnd nets respectively with no power drawn from them.

VI. CONCLUSIONS

Subthreshold analog VLSI allows systems with high computation rates to be constructed with very little power drain. Specifically, our construction of a sound localization system has demonstrated the cost, power and reduced complexity advantages of this technology. However, our system also reveals problems and suggests that traditional design methods must be modified if they are to result in reliable and mass-producible products.

VII. ACKNOWLEDGEMENT

We would like to thank Professors Michael Flynn and Michael Godfrey of the Electrical Engineering Department at Stanford University for their encouragement. We would also like to thank Apple Computer for providing support and equipment, Hewlett Packard for their test equipment, and MOSIS for their fabrication facilities.

REFERENCES

[1] J. Blauert. *Spatial Hearing – The Psychophysics of Human Sound Localization*. MIT Press, 1983.

[2] Richard F. Thompson. *The Brain*. W.H. Freeman and Company, 1985.

[3] E. A. Vittoz. Micropower techniques. In Y. Tsividis and P. Antognetti, editors, *Design of MOS VLSI Circuits for Telecommunications*, pages 104–144. Prentice Hall, 1985.

[4] Carver Mead. *Analog VLSI and Neural Systems*. Addison Wesley, 1989.

[5] Richard F. Lyon and Carver Mead. An analog electronic cochlea. *IEEE Transactions on Acoustics, Speech, and Signal Processing*, 36(7):1119–1134, July 1988.

[6] Richard F. Lyon. CCD correlators for auditory models. In *1991 Asilomar Conference on Signals, Systems, and Computers*, 1991.

[7] W. Liu, A. G. Andreou, and M. H. Goldstein, Jr. Voiced-speech representation by an analog silicon model of the auditory periphery. *IEEE Transactions on Neural Networks*, 3(3):477–487, May 1992.

[8] Noboru Sugie, Jie Huang, and Noboru Ohnishi. Localizing sound source by incorporating biological auditory mechanism. In *IEEE International Conference on Neural Networks*, pages II:243–250. IEEE, 1988.

[9] Neal Bhadkamkar. A variable resolution, nonlinear silicon cochlea. Technical Report CSL-TR-93-558, Stanford University, January 1993.

[10] Lloyd Watts, Douglas A. Kerns, Richard F. Lyon, and Carver A. Mead. Improved implementation of the silicon cochlea. *IEEE Journal of Solid-State Circuits*, 27(5):692–700, May 1992.

[11] John Lazarro and Carver Mead. Silicon modeling of pitch perception. *Proceedings of the National Academy of Science, USA*, 86:9597–9601, December 1989.

[12] J. Lazzaro. A Silicon Model of an Auditory Neural Representation of Spectral Shape. *IEEE Journal of Solid State Circuits*, 26(5):772–777, May 1991.

[13] Michael D. Godfrey. CMOS device modeling for subthreshold circuits. *IEEE Transactions on Circuits and Systems,II*, 39:532–539, August 1992.

[14] A. Pavasovic, A. G. Andreou, and C. R. Westgate. Characterization of CMOS process variations by measuring subthreshold current. In R. E. Green and C. O. Ruud, editors, *Nondestructive Characterization of Materials IV*. Plenum Press, 1991.

Using elastic nets for correspondence in range data[*]

Anupam Joshi
Computer Science Department
Purdue University
West Lafayette, IN 47907 USA [†]
Chia-Hoang Lee
Department of Computer and Information Sciences
National Chiao-Tung University
Hsinchu, Taiwan 30050 R.O.C

Abstract— The process of establishing correspondence between feature points is an integral part of dynamic image analysis. In this work, the authors present a robust new method to obtain correspondences between range data across image frames. The method is based on the concept of Elastic Nets. Elastic nets, which evolved out of research into mechanisms to establish ordered neural projections between structures of similar geometry, are used to cast correspondence as an optimisation problem. This formulation is then used to obtain approximations to the motion parameters under the assumption of rigidity. These parameters can be used to recover correspondence. Experimental results on synthesised data are also presented.

I. Introduction

Correspondence is defined by Ullman [25] as the process by which elements in different views are identified as representing the same object at different times, thereby maintaining the perceptual identity of objects in motion. It can be said *sans* hesitation that the problem of obtaining correspondence is a fundamental aspect of computational vision and underlies much work on motion. The various approaches to measurement of visual motion can be broadly categorised as either relying on optical flow techniques or on feature based techniques. It is with the latter that we concern ourselves in this work. Such methods operate by first establishing correspondence between feature points, or tokens obtained from the raw image data, and using these correspondences obtain the parameters that describe the motion in the image sequence. Establishing the correspondence is clearly a prerequisite to further processing in feature based schemes. Many efforts in the area of dynamic image analysis, however, assume that this underlying problem of correspondence has been resolved[21, 14, 24, 18, 1, 26, 8, 2].

While the objects in the real world are three dimensional, research in the area of correspondence has mostly dealt with their two dimensional images [22, 10, 20, 11]. For the special case of stereo correspondence, Neural Nets have also found use [19, 9, 27, 15, 17]. However, with the increasing availability of equipment to do range sensing, the problem of establishing correspondence between range data, the three dimensional representations of the object, is also becoming prominent. This issue has been addressed in some previous work. Huang and Chen [3] have proposed a scheme that uses preestablished correspondence between three points and the congruency of tetrahedrons to obtain the remaining correspondences. In [13] Huang and Lin propose a technique which works very effectively in a noise free case. They use centroids of the two token sets to obtain two new sets of tokens which are related by rotation only. These new point sets are used to get four candidates for the rotation matrix. Correspondence is obtained from these by chosing the correct **R**. Another technique, which can tolerate noise better is proposed in [12]. This however, involves obtaining a good initial estimate to the rotation axis, and

[*]This work was supported in part by the National Science Council of the R.O.C under grant NSC 81-0408-E-009-565

[†]This author would like to acknowledge the support of a research fellowship from the Purdue Research Foundation

uses Fourier transforms, making it computationally expensive. Magee and coauthors [16] have used subgraph matching when the objects in the scene are polyhedral or cylindrical to obtain correspondence in range data. In order to do an image to model match, Grimson and Lozano-Perez[7] use an involved tree pruning approach. Their approach requires knowing the surface normal at each measured point, and uses distance and angular constraints to do a matching.

In the present work, we propose a simple and elegant scheme to address this issue which uses an elastic net like approach. The proposed method is able to handle a substantial amount of noise in the data, and is computationally efficient. In the sections that follow, we briefly outline the concept of elastic nets, and then expound our method to obtain correspondences. We also include results of simulation with synthesised data.

II. ELASTIC NETS

Durbin and Willshaw, in a letter to *Nature* [5], proposed a novel scheme to solve combinatorial problems that involve geometrical structures and topographical mappings between them, such as TSP. Their basic concept involves using a deformable contour, which is changed in shape by forces to approximate the optimal valid tour. The forces that change its shape are a combination of forces that attract the contour points to cities and forces that try and keep the neighbouring points of the contour together. This is akin to stretching a rubber band to make it pass through all the cities to obtain the tour. Durbin and Willshaw show that deforming a contour in this manner is akin to minimising the energy of the system, which is formulated as

$$\mathcal{E} = -\alpha K \sum_i \ln \sum_j \phi(d_{ij}, K) + \beta \sum_j |y_{j+1} - y_j|^2 \tag{1}$$

where $d_{ij} = |x_i - y_j|$ and $\phi(d, K) = \exp(-d^2/2K^2)$

The x_i's represent the coordinates of the cities and y_j's represent the coordinate of the points on the contour . They show that if there are more points on the contour than there are cities(in their simulation, the ration is 2.5), then in the limit that $K \to 0$, a valid, close to optimal tour is produced. Since $\mathcal{E}$ is bounded from below, it

requires that as $K \to 0$,

$$\forall x_i \ \exists y_j \ \ \text{s.t.} \ \ |x_i - y_j| \to 0.$$

This ensures that the contour passes through all cities. Moreover, as the number of points on the rubber band is increased, the second term in the energy function is minimised by placing all points at equal distances from each other. If $\mathcal{D}$ be the total path length, such a configuration makes the value of the second term $\frac{\mathcal{D}^2}{\text{Number of points}}$, which is obviously minimised by reducing the path length.

To obtain the tour then , we merely need to do gradient descent on the energy surface defined by $\mathcal{E}$, which is achieved by updating the positions of the points on the rubber band, y_j, by $K \partial \mathcal{E}/\partial y_j$ at each iteration step. Computing this quantity, we obtain Δy_j, the change in value of y_j at a given iteration as

$$\Delta y_j = \alpha \sum w_{ij}(x_i - y_j) + \beta K(y_{j+1} - 2y_j + y_{j-1})$$

where

$$w_{ij} = \frac{\phi(d_{ij}, K)}{\sum_l \phi(d_{il}, K)}$$

Durbin and Willshaw noted that this approach produced better tours than the Hopfield net, and this method scaled better with the number of cities as well. Readers interested in a detailed theoretical analysis of this are refered to [4].

III. METHOD

We will now outline how the concept of elastic nets can be used to obtain correspondences. Let A_i' be a point token from the first set and B_i' be a token from the second set. We can represent the correspondence by a permutation σ such that the point $B_{\sigma(i)}'$ from the second frame corresponds to the token A_i' in the first frame. Let **R** and **T** be the rotation and translation, respectively, that define the motion from the first to the second frame. Assuming that the motion is rigid, we get

$$B_{\sigma(i)}' = \mathbf{R}A_i' + \mathbf{T} \tag{2}$$

As mentioned in section 1, Huang *et.al.* [3] showed that using the centroids, we can transform the point sets A' and B' into A and B such that

$$B_{\sigma(i)} = \mathbf{R}A_i \tag{3}$$

Moreover, since $\mathbf{R}$ is orthonormal,

$$\mathbf{Q}B_{\sigma(i)} \;=\; A_i \qquad (4)$$

where $\mathbf{Q} = \mathbf{R}^T$

Let us suppose that some oracle can give us the rotation matrix $\mathbf{Q}$. Then, correspondence can be trivially established by observing that if point i corresponds to point j, then $\mathbf{Q}B_j \equiv A_i$. If correspondences are unique, then this is a necessary and sufficient condition for establishing them. Suppose that instead of getting $\mathbf{Q}$, we get an approximation $\mathbf{Q}'$ to it. Correspondence can then be established by observing that $d_{ij} = min_k \, d_{kj}$ where d_{ij} is the distance between points $\mathbf{Q}'B_j$ and A_i

The use of elastic nets come in obtaining $\mathbf{Q}$. We take the energy function of elastic nets to be the following

$$\mathcal{E} = -\alpha K \sum_i ln \sum_j \phi(d_{ij}, K) \qquad (5)$$

where $\phi(d_{ij}, K) = e^{\frac{-d_{ij}^2}{2\kappa^2}}$.

The distance d_{ij} is used slightly differently here. In the original work of Durbin and Willshaw, each point on the contour could move independently of the others, and so distances between the current position of the contour and points representing the cities are computed directly. In our case however, the motion is assumed to be rigid. Hence, we do not individually move points from the first frame to the second. We merely look for the parameter of motion that would do it. Thus, we define d_{ij} to be $|QB_j - A_i|$. Observe that (5) is simply the first term of the energy function proposed in [5], with a suitably altered definition of the distance metric. The minimisation of this term ensures that

$$\lim K \to 0, \;\; \forall A_i \,, \exists B_j \;\; s.t. \;\; d_{ij} \to 0 \qquad (6)$$

In other words, for every point in the first frame, a corresponding point in the second frame exists. The second term of the energy function in [5] is used to minimise the path length of the TSP tour, and is of no consequence in this problem.

Now that we have formulated the energy of the system, we can essentially do a gradient descent to obtain its minimum. The parameter that changes here is the 3×3 rotation matrix, Q. The rotation of a body in 3 space is defined in terms

of it's axis of rotation and the angle by which it is rotated about this axis. If n_1, n_2 and n_3 be the direction cosines of the axis of rotation (which are determined by it's tilt and slant angles), then the following relation holds

$$n_1^2 + n_2^2 + n_3^2 = 1.$$

Thus there are only 3 free parameters, namely two of the direction cosines, and the angle of rotation. From the structure of the rotation matrix, it can be shown that it's nine elements are related nonlinearly to each other. In this work we chose to treat all nine entries as independent. We do this since our aim is merely to obtain correspondence, not an extremely accurate computation of the motion parameter. This reduces the amount of computation involved in obtaining the gradient, $\partial \mathcal{E}/\partial r_{ij}$.

Ideally, if we carried out sufficient iterations, the values of r_{ij}'s would converge. However, since our aim is only to establish correspondence, we can save on computation time. This is done by performing a few iterations, and then using the nearest neighbour criterion to select the corresponding points.

Note that in principle, we could have defined the distance metric to include the translation term, and then computed both the rotation and translation parameters. However, using Huang's approach leads to fewer computations while doing the gradient descent.

IV. RESULTS OF THE SIMULATION

In order to verify the proposed technique, and to examine if our simplifications hold well under experimental conditions, several simulations were performed. In line with [3], data were generated in as points in a cube, each of whose sides were two hundred units, with the origin as one of the corner points. The x, y and z coordinates of the points were chosen as independent random numbers. The data for the second set was obtained by applying a rotation and translation to the points of the first frame.

The algorithm outlined in the previous section was applied to a large number of data set, which covered a wide range of possible motion parameters, from small to large. As an initial approximation, the rotation matrix was set to be the identity matrix. It was observed that this gross initial approximation sufficed, in all but a few cases, to obtain correspondence. Also, it was observed that less than a hundred iterations were needed for a sufficiently close approximation to **R** be obtained, as would allow correspondence to be established. In Table 1, we present the actual rotation matrix as well as the approximation obtained by our method after a hundred iterations for two different instances, a and b. The motion parameters used to obtain the second frame from the first are as follows. For case 'a', the translation vector was $[100, 100, 100]^T$ and the tilt, slant and rotation angles were $20^o, 25^o$ and 50° respectively. For case 'b', the translation vector was $[200, 100, 50]^T$ and the angles were $25^o, 15^o$ and 40°. These examples had ten points in each frame, and all were correctly matched by our method. Similar results were obtained for larger number of points as well. As remarked earlier, in a few cases, the method would not compute the rotation matrix closely enough within a hundred iterations. This occurs when **R** is such that **I** does not serve as a good enough initial approximation. In such cases the method converged if the initial estimate was better chosen. In Table 2 we show the actual **R** which could not be approximated starting from **I** as well as the initial estimate which caused the method to operate correctly. Note that good initial estimates can be obtained by using Huang's method [13] amongst others.

In real world situations, the data are often noisy. Noises can be generated in the process of sensing, data acquisition and such. So the algorithm was next tested with noisy data to evaluate it's ability to operate in a real environment. The possible errors in data were modelled as zero mean gaussian noises(GN). Once again many simulations, with different motion parameters, as well as added GNs of different variances, were performed. The results demonstrate that the method was able to handle noises with variances of about 50 units with negligible degradation of performance. This variance corresponds to about 25% of the edge length of the cube in which data points were chosen to lie. However, higher values of variances saw a degradation of performance, and the method becomes unreliable after the variation of the added noise increases beyond 100 units. In Figure 1 we plot a graph between the variance of the noise added and the average(over 50 runs) of the number of

points correctly matched, which illustrates the above.

V. Conclusion

In this work, we have presented a technique that utilises concepts behind elastic nets to obtain correspondence in range data. The method uses approximations to the motion parameters to do this. Results of simulations carried out to establish the correctness of the technique have also been presented.

Huang *et. al.* in [13] also use the concept of obtaining motion parameters to obtain correspondence. However, their scheme is very sensitive to noise. In [12] the scheme proposed is not as sensitive to noise, but requires extensive computation to search for the axis of rotation before the rotation matrix can be computed. In [6] and [23], the idea of obtaining motion parameters by an optimisation approach is used. However, these methods are used to compute the motion parameters assuming that a matching is already known. Our scheme in contrast is tolerant of noise and does not require extensive computations.

References

[1] J.K. Aggarwal, *Motion and time varying imagery- an overview*, Proceedings of the IEEE Workshop on Motion: Representation and Analysis, 1986, pp. 1–6.

[2] W. Burger and B. Bhanu, *Estimating 3-d motion from perspective image sequences*, IEEE Transactions on Pattern Analysis and Machine Intelligence **12** (1990), no. 11.

[3] Homer.H. Chen and T.S. Huang, *Maximal matching of two 3 d point sets*, Proceedings International Conference on Pattern Recognition, 1986, pp. 1048–1050.

[4] R. Durbin, R. Szeliski, and A.L. Yuille, *An analysis of the elastic net approach to the travelling salesman problem*, Neural Computation **1** (1989), 348–358.

[5] R. Durbin and D Willshaw, *An analogue approach to the travelling salesman problem using an elastic net method*, Nature **326** (1987), 689–691.

$$\mathbf{R}_{act} = \begin{bmatrix} 0.699127 & -0.673766 & 0.239293 \\ 0.714755 & 0.650254 & -0.257423 \\ 0.017842 & 0.351012 & 0.936201 \end{bmatrix}$$

$$\mathbf{R}_{cmp} = \begin{bmatrix} 0.770529 & -0.505054 & 0.184246 \\ 0.693535 & 0.650696 & -0.254523 \\ 0.022059 & 0.334789 & 0.935294 \end{bmatrix}$$

case(a)

$$\mathbf{R}_{act} = \begin{bmatrix} 0.943012 & -0.328817 & 0.051074 \\ 0.331912 & 0.940415 & -0.073855 \\ -0.023746 & 0.086598 & 0.995960 \end{bmatrix}$$

$$\mathbf{R}_{cmp} = \begin{bmatrix} 0.967190 & -0.277282 & 0.033607 \\ 0.336185 & 0.910837 & -0.065618 \\ -0.015433 & 0.089932 & 0.992217 \end{bmatrix}$$

case(b)

Table 1:

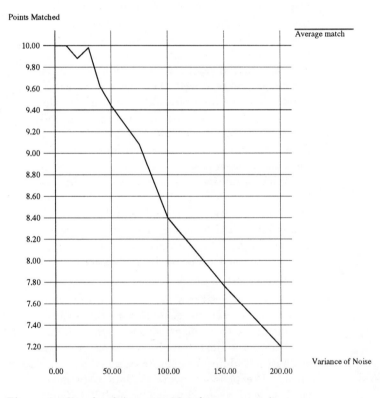

Figure 1: Graph of Average Match versus variance of noise added

$$\mathbf{R}_{act} = \begin{bmatrix} 0.543991 & -0.715635 & 0.438110 \\ 0.823867 & 0.356526 & -0.440604 \\ 0.159114 & 0.600629 & 0.783535 \end{bmatrix}$$

$$\mathbf{R}_{init-est} = \begin{bmatrix} 0.5 & -0.5 & 0.5 \\ 1.0 & 0.2 & -0.5 \\ 0.0 & 0.5 & 1.0 \end{bmatrix}$$

Table 2:

[6] O.D. Faugeras and M. Herbert, *A 3d recognition and positioning algorithm using geometrical matching between primitive surfaces*, IJCAI, 1983, pp. 996–1002.

[7] W.E.L. Grimson and T Lozano-Perez, *Model based recognition and localisation from sparse range or tactile data*, The International Robotics Research Journal **3** (1984), no. 3, 3–35.

[8] B.K.P. Horn, *Relative orientation*, International Journal of Computer Vision **4** (1990).

[9] A. Joshi and C.H. Lee, *Elastic nets and stereo correspondence*, Proceedings IJCNN '92, Beijing, 1992.

[10] Y.G. Leclerc and S.W. Zucker, *The local structure of image discontinuities in one dimension*, IEEE Transactions on Pattern Analysis and Machine Intelligence **9** (1987), 341–355.

[11] C.H. Lee and A. Joshi, *Correspondence problem in image sequence analysis*, Pattern Recognition (1992), in press.

[12] Z.C. Lin and T.S. Huang *et al*, *Motion estimation from 3d point sets with and without correspondence*, Proceedings Conference on Computer Vision and Pattern Recognition, 1986, pp. 194–201.

[13] Z.C. Lin, H. Lee, and T.S. Huang, *Finding 3 d point correspondences in motion estimation*, Proceedings International Conference on Pattern Recognition, 1986, pp. 303–305.

[14] H.C. Longuet-Higgens, *A computer algorithm for reconstructing a scene from two projections*, Nature **293** (1981).

[15] E. Maeda, *Generalised lyered neural networks for stereo disparity detection*, Proceedings International Joint Conference on Neural Networks, vol. 1, 1990, pp. 487–490.

[16] M.J. Magee, B.A. Boyter, C.H. Chien, and J.K. Aggarwal, *Experiments in intensity guided range sensing recognnition of three dimensional objects*, IEEE Transactions on Pattern Analysis and Machine Intelligence **7** (1985), 629–636.

[17] M.S. Moussavi and R.J. Schalkoff, *A neural network approach for stereo vision*, Proceedings of IEEE SouthEastCon90, 1990.

[18] H.H. Nagel, *Image sequences - ten(octal) years - from phenomenology towards a theoretical foundation*, Proceedings International Conference on Pattern Recognition, 1986, pp. 1174–1185.

[19] N.M. Nasrabadi and C.Y. Choo, *Hopfield network for stereo correspondence*, IEEE Transactions on Neural Networks **3** (1992), no. 1, 5–13.

[20] K. Rangarajan and M. Shah, *Estimating motion correspondence*, Proceedings Conference on Computer Vision and Pattern Recognition, 1991.

[21] J.W. Roach and J.K. Aggarwal, *Determining the movement of objects from a sequence of images*, IEEE Transactions on Pattern Analysis and Machine Intelligence **2** (1979).

[22] V. Salari and I.K. Sethi, *Feature point correspondence in presence of occlusion*, IEEE Transactions on Pattern Analysis and Machine Intelligence **12** (1990), 87–91.

[23] M.D. Shuster, *Approximate algorithms for fast optimal attitude computation*, AIAA Guidance and Control Specialists Conference, 1978, pp. 88–95.

[24] R.Y. Tsai and T.S Huang, *Uniqueness and estimation of three dimensional motion parameters of rigid objects with curved surfaces*, IEEE Transactions on Pattern Analysis and Machine Intelligence **6** (1984), no. 1.

[25] S Ullman, *The interpretation of visual motion*, MIT Press, Cambridge, MA, USA, 1979.

[26] G.S. Young and Rama Chellappa, *3-d motion estimation using a sequence of noisy images*, Proceedings Conference on Computer Vision and Pattern Recognition, 1988.

[27] Y-T. Zhou and R. Chellappa, *Neural network algorithms for motion stereo*, Proceedings International Joint Conference on Neural Networks, vol. 2, 1989, pp. 251–258.

Auditory Model Representation and Comparison for Speaker Recognition

John M. Colombi[†], Timothy R. Anderson[‡], Steven K. Rogers[†],
Dennis W. Ruck[†], Gregory T. Warhola[†]
[†]AFIT, Wright-Patterson AFB, OH, 45433
[‡]AL/CFBA, Wright-Patterson AFB, OH, 45433

Abstract—The **TIMIT** and **KING** databases are used to compare proven spectral processing techniques to an auditory neural representation for speaker identification. The feature sets compared were Linear Prediction Coding (LPC) cepstral coefficients and auditory nerve firing rates using the Payton model. Two clustering algorithms, one statistically based and the other a neural approach, were used to generate speaker-specific codebook vectors. These algorithms are the Linde-Buzo-Gray algorithm and a Kohonen self-organizing feature map. The resulting vector-quantized distortion-based classification indicates the auditory model performs statistically equal to the LPC cepstral representation in clean environments and outperforms the LPC cepstral in noisy environments and in test data recorded over multiple sessions (greater intra-speaker distortions).

I. INTRODUCTION

Speech recognition and speaker recognition research traditionally use proven Linear Prediction Coding (LPC) cepstral coefficients and various weighted and transitional derivatives of the voice production model [1, 2]. These have been shown to be better feature sets than other spectral representations. However, auditory models which incorporate spectral analysis, automatic gain control, neural adaptation and saturation effects have demonstrated superior results for speech recognition [3, 4, 5]. Recently, it was shown that auditory models can be used effectively for speaker identification [6, 7].

Success has been reported on Vector Quantization (VQ) techniques for speaker recognition [8]. More recent research demonstrates successful classification with Hidden Markov Models, gaussian mixture methods and artificial neural classifiers; these often compare their results to VQ approaches.

This paper presents results using a physiologically motivated model together with a neural post processor for speaker recognition. Using speech utterances from both the TIMIT and KING databases, this paper specifically examines the performance of the Payton auditory mean-rate firing responses compared to LPC cepstral representations using speaker-dependent codebooks and minimum mean-squared error for classification.

II. PAYTON AUDITORY MODEL

The Payton model is a composite collection of stages each chosen based on physiological data [9]. The model accepts 16 KHz sampled data and provides predicted neural firing responses for 20 points along the basilar membrane, corresponding to center frequencies of 440 Hz to 6600 Hz. See Figure 1. The model incorporates low frequency filtering characteristics of the middle ear based on the circuit analysis of Guinan and Peake [9].

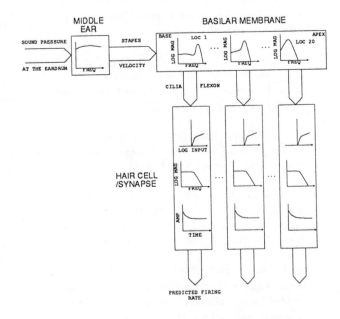

Figure 1: Payton Composite Model [9]

This model is unique in that displacement of the basilar membrane with respect to time and location is solved, using fluid dynamics and fixed plate equations. This section incorporates cochlea and cochlea partition physiological variables of fluid dynamics, tension, mass, size and shape of the membrane, using a method of solution by Sondhi and Allen [9]. A second filter is used to sharpen the basilar membrane responses to better approximate neural data. This modeling is theorized as effects due to inner and outer hair interactions with the tectorial membrane. The sharpening stage then feeds the non-linear transduction process of the inner hair cell/synapse. This stage provides half-wave rectification, amplitude compression, non-linear saturation, and time-varying adaptation. Due to shear caused by basilar membrane displacement, the potential of the inner hair cell changes, possibly, by the opening of ion channels. This potential change is phase selective for positive motion of the basilar membrane and subsequently triggers release of a neurotransmitter into the synapses of the auditory nerve. This phase selectivity is modeled by a half-wave rectification. To account for refractory properties of neural firing, amplitude compression and saturation effects of neural firing are provided by a static nonlinearity which introduces a "sloping saturation" for higher signal levels. Lastly, the cascade-reservoir model by Brachman [9] provides the correct temporal characteristics of adaptation, which is thought to be caused by depletion and replenishment rates of neurotransmitters or ions.

Other auditory models only approximate the auditory system response characteristics through a series of linear filterbanks [5, 10, 11]. However, as can be seen in Figure 2, nonlinear effects are evident at mid-to-high signal levels.

III. DATABASES

The narrowband portion of the KING Database contains 51 speakers collected in 10 sessions, speaking conversationally on several tasks for approximately one minute during each session. The speech is recorded over long distance telephone lines and sampled at 8 KHz. Typical evaluation on this database consists of training on the first 3 sessions, and testing on sessions 4 and 5.

The first 10 speakers of the KING database (sessions 1-5) were used in the comparison (all male). The data was framed using a 32 msec hamming window, stepped every 10.6 msecs. Tenth-order cepstral coefficients were derived from Tenth-order reflection coefficients calculated using the autocorrelation method. Each frame was tagged with a probability of voicing and a segment of 15 seconds was chosen per utterance which contained maximum voicing. These 15-second segments were used both for training (session 1 - 3) and testing (session 4 - 5). The calculated average signal-to-noise ratio (SNR), based on low voicing probability for noise power, was 14.75 dB over the first

five sessions.

In sharp contrast, the DARPA TIMIT Acoustic Phonetic Database contains over 630 speakers, speaking 10 sentences (3 - 4 sec) recorded in a single session. The speech is studio quality sampled at 16 KHz. Again 10 speakers were chosen (7 male, 3 female) from various dialects. Similar signal processing was performed on the TIMIT utterances, however, this database is phonetically labeled, and thus a probability of voicing was not performed. The sentences are divided into three types: dialect sensitive (sa), random text (si) and phonetically balanced (sx). The sa and sx sentences were used in training and testing, respectively. The calculated average SNR, using silence as noise power, was 36.95 dB.

IV. EXPERIMENTAL METHODS

The utterances were scaled appropriately to drive the auditory model to approximate conversational levels insuring not to saturate the neural responses. The Payton model references 0 dB with respect to a 1 KHz sinusoid, having adequate energy to drive firing of the 1 KHz Characteristic Frequency synapse to threshold, a firing level equal to 10% of its dynamic range. Scaling values of 4000 and 8000 were experimentally determined to provide adequate firing responses for the TIMIT and KING databases, respectively. These values correspond to model levels of approximately 52 dB for TIMIT and 43 dB for KING.

Typical values of codebook size tested in the literature range from 32 to 256 codewords. Computation time and storage often dictate codebook size for practical implementations; however, distortion improvements were insignificant above 64 codewords. Speaker-dependent codebooks were created, using the iterative Linde-Buzo-Gray (LBG) clustering algorithm with 64 codewords. Kohonen self-organizing feature maps were also used to create codebooks with 64 codewords (map size of 8 x 8). It was noted that Kohonen maps stabilized to a codebook configuration fairly quickly and improvements to overall SNR, using quantization error as noise, were small after 40 - 100 epochs. See Figure 3.

Classification was based on minimum average distortion defined over all speaker codebooks and N frames. For speaker s, the distortion, D_s, is

$$D_s = \frac{1}{N} \sum_{i=1}^{N} \min_{j \in k} \|x_i - m_{sj}\|^2$$

where the index over codewords is $k = 1, \ldots, 64$.

It was found that voiced speech carried more speaker-dependent information than all speech. This is shown in Figures 4 and 5 by relative distortions between speaker-dependent codebooks. Thus, all high ($\geq .9$) probability of voicing frames within the 15-second segments of KING were selected for quantization. TIMIT used all phonetically tagged vowels for quantization.

V. DISCUSSION

A. KING

Results indicate that an auditory model provides improved features for speaker classification in degraded environments using the KING database. The auditory model provides an increase of 20% identification over cepstral features, as shown in Table 1. The Kohonen self-organizing feature map does not perform as well as the LBG algorithm with either representation. Although the self-organizing feature map does show a larger delta between the representations (25%) than does the LBG algorithm (20%).

It should be pointed out that in this experiment the classifiers were trained and tested in the noise and that the noise and channel effects were different for each session.

Table 1: KING Database: Speaker classification error. Trained on sessions 1 - 3, tested on sessions 4 and 5.

Classifier	LPC Cepstral	Payton Model
Kohonen	55%	80%
LBG	65%	85%

B. TIMIT

In this experiment the classifiers were trained with clean speech and tested with clean and noisy speech with a given signal to noise ratio. LPC cepstral coefficients performed as expected for this small subset of speakers on this quality of speech. With additive white gaussian noise (AWGN) the codebooks could not generalize, as seen in Tables 2 and 3. The auditory model closely matches the results of cepstral with slight improvements in noise. Since both quantizers non-parametrically approximate the underlying probability density function of the speakers' training samples, any significant difference in recognition results should be attributed to the clustering characteristics of the feature set. The auditory model as shown in Figure 3 allows better vector quantization.

A comparison of the quantization SNR, shows comparable levels of quantizer designs (Table 4). Since LBG is a gradient-descent algorithm, it often finds local minima of the distortion objective function. Kohonen's neighborhood may help "pull" nodes out of these local minima, during the competition process.

Table 2: TIMIT Database: Speaker classification using LBG designed speaker codebooks.

Using LGB	Clean	AWGN (SNR = 10dB)
LPC Cepstrum	100%	10%
Payton Model	96%	10%

Table 3: TIMIT Database: Speaker classification using Kohonen designed speaker codebooks.

Using Kohonen	Clean	AWGN (SNR = 10dB)
LPC Cepstrum	100%	16%
Payton Model	80%	28%

Table 4: Quantization Signal-to-Noise Ratios (SNR in dB) for the different quantizers. Kohonen provides a slightly improved quantizer over LBG.

	male		female	
	TRAIN	TEST	TRAIN	TEST
LBG	12.52	8.70	9.90	8.27
Kohonen	12.60	8.93	9.15	9.15

VI. Summary

This initial examination of an auditory-model representation for speaker identification shows promise. Whereas distortion metrics and signal processing methods have been extensively developed for LPC and cepstral representations, these currently do not exist for neural data. Improvements in auditory modeling, often used for physiological understanding, should continue to be exploited for speech and speaker recognition.

Future work in this area will include the examination of temporal characteristics of the auditory-model firing patterns. It has been shown by Sachs and Young [12] that mean-rate firing patterns of synthetic vowels, presented to cats, saturate in noise and high stimulus levels. However, their proposed measure of synchrony (Average Localized Synchrony Rate) of interspike distributions provided a robust representation in these conditions. Similar results have been demonstrated by Ghitza's Ensemble Interval Histogram [10] and Seneff's Generalized Synchrony Detector [5].

Other classification schemes will also be investigated, such as Hidden Markov Models and recurrent neural networks. Each of these will be used to investigate the speaker-dependent temporal nature of speech for speaker recognition.

VII. Acknowledgement

The authors would like to thank Janet Slifka, Systems Research Laboratories, Inc., for development of several Entropic ESPS utilities used throughout this work, and for valuable discussions and editorial comments.

References

[1] Frank K. Soong and Aaron E. Rosenburg. On the use of instantaneous and transitional spectral information in speaker recognition. *IEEE Trans. ASSP*, 36(6):871–79, June 1988.

[2] Belle Tseng, Frank Soong, and Aaron Rosenburg. Continuous probabilistic acoustic map for speaker recognition. In *Proceedings of the 1992 International Conference on Acoustics, Speech and Signal Processing*, volume 2, pages 161–164, 1992.

[3] Timothy R. Anderson. A comparison of auditory models for speaker independent phoneme recognition. In *Proceedings of the 1993 International Conference on Acoustics, Speech and Signal Processing*, April 1993. In Press.

[4] Melvyn J. Hunt and Claude Lefebvre. Speaker dependent and independent speech recognition experiments with an auditory model. In *Proceedings of the 1988 International Conference on Acoustics, Speech, and Signal Processing*, pages 215–218, New York, 1988. IEEE Press.

[5] Stephanie Seneff. A joint synchrony/mean-rate model of auditory speech processing. *Journal of Phonetics*, 16:55 – 75, 1988.

[6] Hiroaki Hattori. Text-independent speaker recognition using neural networks. In *Proceedings of the 1992 International Conference on Acoustics, Speech and Signal Processing*, volume 2, pages 153–156, 1992.

[7] John M. Colombi, Timothy R. Anderson, Steven K. Rogers, et al. Auditory model representation for speaker recognition. In *Proceedings of the 1993 International Conference on Acoustics, Speech and Signal Processing*, April 1993. In Press.

[8] Soong, Rosenburg, Rabiner, and Juang. A vector quantization approach to speaker recognition. In *Proceedings of the 1985 International Conference on Acoustics, Speech and Signal Processing*, volume 1, pages 387–390, 1985.

[9] Karen L. Payton. Vowel processing by a model of the auditory periphery: A comparison to eighth-nerve responses. *J. Acoust. Soc. Amer.*, 83(1):145–162, 1988.

[10] Oded Ghitza. Auditory neural feedback as a basis for speech processing. In *Proceedings of the 1988 International Conference on Acoustics, Speech, and Signal Processing*, pages 91–94, New York, 1988. IEEE Press.

[11] Richard F. Lyon and Carver Mead. An analog electronic cochlea. *IEEE Trans. ASSP*, 36(7), 1988.

[12] Eric D. Young and Murray B. Sachs. Representation of steady-state vowels in the temporal aspects of the discharge patterns of populations of auditory nerve fibers. *J. Acoust. Soc. Amer.*, 66(5):1381–1403, November 1979.

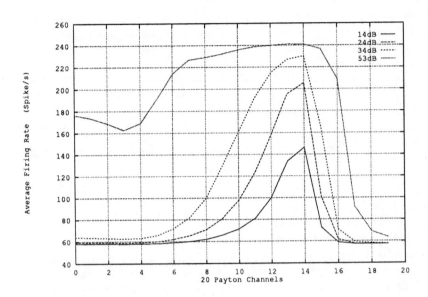

Figure 2: Model Neural Response. Channel 14 CF = 1133 Hz. Average response of the model to a 1 KHz sinusoid stimulus applied with varying energy levels. Note the non-linear response at mid-to-high stimulus levels.

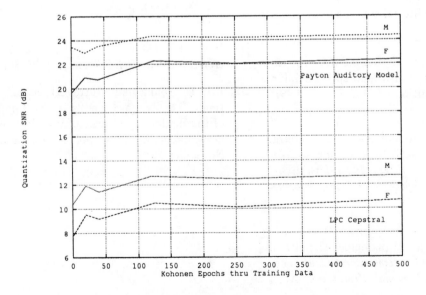

Figure 3: Kohonen learning for a TIMIT male(M) and female(F) speaker for varying iterations (epochs) for the two data sets examined. Quantizer "learns" in the first 100 epochs then stabilizes.

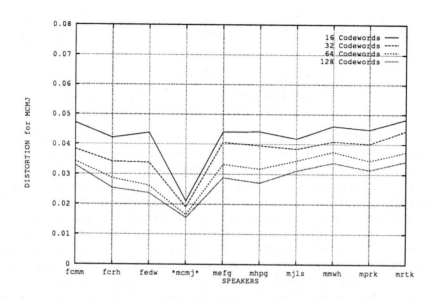

Figure 4: TIMIT speaker "mcmj" utterance showing distortions to all speaker dependent codebooks (LBG) using all speech. Note the low Figure of Merit for winning codebook.

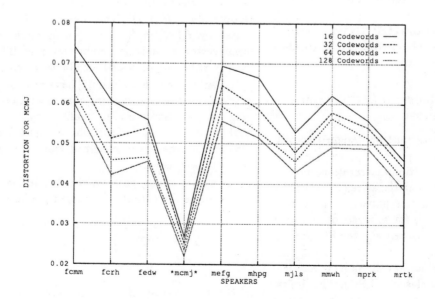

Figure 5: TIMIT speaker "mcmj" utterance showing distortions to all speaker dependent codebooks (LBG) using vowels. Note the higher Figure of Merit for winning codebook.

Prediction-Based Networks with ECG Application*

J.S. Taur and S.Y. Kung
Princeton University

Abstract— A new class of prediction-based independent training (PBIT) networks for temporal patterns classification is proposed. Our approach combines the universal NN approximator and TDNN. The input vectors of PBIT are consecutively created by the time-delayed segment of a pattern. The network is robust since all input segments contribute in equal share to the classification result. To demonstrate the feasibility of PBIT, extensive simulations on ECG classification have been conducted. They have all reported respectable training performance and relatively good generalization accuracy. IIR filters can be adopted as preprocessors to extract information out of the time sequence so that smaller networks will suffice. For a comparative study, we have included another independent training classifier - hidden Markov model(HMM) - for temporal patterns. We have also included in the study some mutually training (MT) models, e.g. the (static) decision-based neural network(DBNN)[4]. Hybrid IT and MT techniques are also proposed to further improve classification accuracy.

I. PREDICTION-BASED INDEPENDENT TRAINING MODEL

The temporal dynamic models must be designed according to the specific application needs. Typical temporal processings, such as differentiation, integration, prediction, smoothing, or harmonic analysis, all require specially tailored model structures. In this paper, we propose a prediction-based neural model, for analysis of transient behaviors, and analyze its performance in the ECG recognition applications.

The prediction-based classifier has the same theoretical basis as the linear predictive classifier(LPC). The limitation of the LPC is that the linear constraint often renders it ineffective to approximate a nonlinear model. Neural networks can be adopted to remedy this problem. Since it is nonlinear, it offers a much more effective means to model nonlinear behaviors. Also it adopts the independent training scheme, i.e. each subnet is trained by positive examples only. So it is named *prediction-based independent training* (PBIT) model. According to the OCON structure, one PBIT net is assigned to each class. Referring to Figure 1, the PBIT model combines a time-delay neural network and a (two-layer) back-propagation model, making it very similar to the NETtalk configuration.

A long sequence x with length $\bar{N}$ is input through a tapped-delay line, cf. Figure 1(a), from which a set of N-dimensional vectors ($N << \bar{N}$) are consecutively extracted:

$$\mathbf{x}_j = [x(j+1)\dots x(j+N)] \tag{1}$$

where $x(n)$ denotes the n-th sample value of the signal sequence x. These N-dimensional vectors serve as the inputs to the back-propagation network. Each vector is processed to yield a best prediction for its immediate future sample $x(j+N+1)$. The prediction function is represented by $f_a(\mathbf{x}_j) = f(\mathbf{x}_j, \mathbf{w})$ — a function of the current input vector $\mathbf{x}_j$ and the weight vector $\mathbf{w}$. The function is usually either sigmoid LBF or Gaussian RBF.

Cybenko[1] and Funahashi[2] have provided a useful approximation theorem showing that any input-output mapping can be approximately realized by a two-layer network with linear basis function. An RBF approximation theorem can be easily obtained from the classic Stone-Weierstrass theorem[5].

For each training pattern, the discriminant function ϕ is defined as the (negative) squared prediction error,

$$\phi = - \sum_{j=0}^{\bar{N}-N-1} (f_a(\mathbf{x}_j) - x(j+N+1))^2 \tag{2}$$

In the **retrieving phase** a pattern is input to *all* the PBIT subnets and is classified into the subnet which yields the largest discriminant function, (i.e., the smallest prediction error). In the **training phase**, the objective is to minimize the sum of the squared prediction errors of all the M training patterns in the same class,

*This research was supported in part by Air Force Office of Scientific Research under Grant AFOSR-89-0501A.

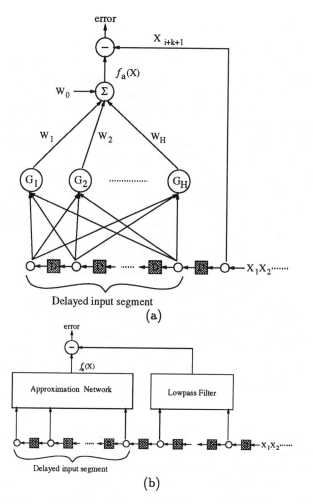

Figure 1: (a) A Gaussian RBF TDNN for prediction of a future sample. (b) Using output of a low-pass filter to replace the sample to be predicted.

$$E = \sum_{m=1}^{M} \sum_{j=1}^{\bar{N}-N} (f_a(x_j) - x(j + N + 1))^2 \qquad (3)$$

(This complies with the independent training principle.)In this formulation, the classifier is tolerant not only to shift but also to the length of the signal. The gradient-type updating rule can be adopted:

$$\triangle \mathbf{w} = -\eta \frac{\partial E}{\partial \mathbf{w}}$$

As shown in Figure 1(a), the tapped-delay line is followed by a multi-layer network. For the latter net, a Gaussian RBF classifier is favored. It offers a natural clustering capability, which is good for approximation/generalization in many applications. (The initial centroids of the hidden nodes can be estimated by the K-mean or VQ clustering algorithm, which usually yields a fast convergence

in the subsequent BP learning.) More importantly, the centroids of the Gaussian function can be trained to reflect the salient features in the signal. For example, some sample ECG waveforms are shown in Figure 2. It can be demonstrated that (cf. Figure 3) the centroids of the hidden nodes in the RBF networks actually capture the key segments in the original waveform. All but 2 of the 15 centroids represent the meaningful curves inherently embedded in the training ECG waveforms. When a test signal from the same class is presented, the trained centroids would be able to produce a close match and, therefore, a minimum prediction error.

We note that the window size for the PBIT model should be properly chosen so that it is robust with respect to time misalignments and uncertainty of the waveform length. Obviously, the window size must be adequate so that the information in each segment is sufficient to facilitate prediction. If the size is too large, it might hamper the network's ability to cope with temporal variations.

II. COMPARE STATIC AND TEMPORAL MODELS FOR ECG ANALYSIS

In this ECG classification experiment, there are 10 different classes. Each class has 10 sample waveforms, 5 used for training and the remaining, for testing. Some samples of the ECG pulses are shown in Figures 2(a) and (b). Both static and temporal networks are evaluated. Their generalization performance and tolerance to time misalignments are studied.

A. Static Models for ECG Analysis

In static models, the entire input waveform is treated as a long static input vector. For comparison, both decision and approximation based models are tried.

1. For the *approximation-based networks*, the teacher value is set to be 1 when the input sequence is in the class represented by the network; otherwise it is 0. Both the ACON (All-Class-in-One-Net) and OCON (One-Class-in-One-Net) models, with the conjugate-gradient algorithm, are adopted. The ACON model, using LBF, has 60 input neurons, 20 hidden neurons, and 10 output neurons. The OCON model has 10 subnets each using 4 (RBF) hidden neurons. Under the approximation-based formulation, the OCON and ACON models have very compatible performance, cf. Table 1.

2. For the *decision-based networks*[4], we adopt subcluster DBNNs with 10 subnets. Similar performances are reported for the DBNN(EBF), with 2 subclusters per subnet; and for the DBNN(RBF), with 4 subclusters per subnet. According to

	Model	Performance
Approximation-Based Static Models	LBF-ACON(20)	78%
	RBF-OCON(4)	80%
Decision-Based Static Models	DBNN(E_s)(2)	90%
	DBNN(R_s)(4)	90%

Table 1: Comparison of ECG classification by various static models. *All models reach 100% training accuracies.* For the DBNN(E_s)(2), a noise tolerance of 0.5 is adopted.

Algorithm	Noise Tolerance	Original	Shifted
DBNN(E_s)	0 (5 sweeps)	96%	93.6%
DBNN(E_s)	2.25	96%	96.8%
DBNN(R_h)	1.76	96%	97.2%
RBF-OCON	NA	96%	94%

Table 2: Networks are trained with right/left-shifted ECG data. In this simulation, the original set (50 patterns) and shifted data(250 patterns), respectively, are used to test the generalization capability of the network. The classification rates of the training set are 100% for all models. The number of subnodes is 4 for each subnet.

the ECG classification experiments summarized in Table 1, decision-based models outperform approximation-based models in convergence speed and training/generalization accuracy.

Tolerance to Temporal Misalignment Since the ECG segments are extracted from an original long waveform, it is likely that signal segments may be misaligned by an unknown time interval. It is critical that the neural model be made somewhat shift-tolerant. The static models are, unfortunately, not very tolerant. To enhance this, a special training procedure is adopted. All the (100) ECG waveforms are shifted forward or backward by one or two time steps. Samples of the shifted ECG waveforms are shown in Figure 2(c). Thus, the original data set is expanded by 5 fold. Half of the expanded set is randomly chosen as the training set. In the generalization experiments, both the original and shifted signals are used as test sets. The radial basis model DBNN(R_s) and the elliptic basis model DBNN(E_s) have very close generalization accuracies. For comparison, hidden-node DBNN(R_h) models are also experimented with. The results in Table 2 show that generalization performance is indeed improved by using shifted training data.

B. Temporal Models for ECG Analysis

In both training and retrieving phases, in order to smooth the noise in the signal, a small segment of signal is passed through a fixed-weight lowpass filter, and the output of the filter is used as teacher for the prediction network. The modified configuration is shown in Figure 1(b). In the ECG analysis, a 4-th order moving average low-pass filter appears to be adequate. To make the classifier tolerant to the DC level of the ECG segment, the values of the input segment and the output of the lowpass filter are both readjusted to have 0 DC-level. For both PBIT(LBF) and PBIT(RBF) networks, a window size of around 20 is found to be adequate. (In fact, the two networks have very similar accuracies.) All input segments contribute in equal share to the cost-criterion in Eq. 3, so the models are fairly robust. As expected, temporal models consistently outperform static models, cf. Table 3. In comparison with the HMM, the PBIT nets have either comparable or slightly better performance. However, more exhaustive experiments are needed before a more definitive conclusion can be reached. In a separate experiment, temporal models (based on sigmoid LBF net with a short window) were successfully applied to model nonlinear time-varying background noise in a ECG QRS detection application [3].

Tolerance to Temporal Misalignment It can be demonstrated by experiments, that the PBIT nets were inherently tolerant of temporal misalignment of waveforms. They were trained by the original unshifted patterns, and there is no need to use time-shifted patterns in the training set. (This is in contrast to the approach previously adopted for the static models.) Only the 50 original waveforms are used as the training set. By waveform time-shift, the original data set is expanded to a total of 500 patterns. Among them, 450 patterns were used as the test patterns. (Those used in the training set are excluded from the testing set.) The results of the experiment are summarized in Table 4. It appears that the PBIT nets have high generalization accuracy and were very shift-tolerant. Note that the linear predictive classifier (LPC) is somewhat intolerant to time-shift, although it has a very respectable generalization accuracy without time-shift. In comparison, PBIT(LBF) and PBIT(RBF) were more tolerant to shift. As predicted, the static DBNN(E_s) shows the least tolerance.

Hierarchical Training Strategy The design hierarchy is purposely divided into two stages. In the independent training rule, each model is trained by patterns from its own category. This is very appealing to temporal pattern recognition and offers cost-effective learning in the initial phase. If further training is needed, the mutual training

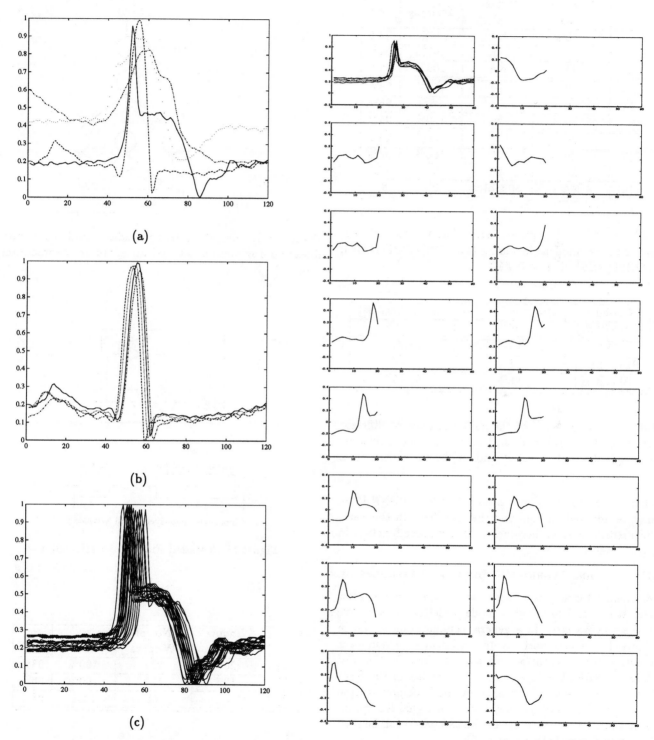

Figure 2: Samples of Electrocardiogram(ECG) signals: (a) original ECG waveforms from 4 different classes; (b) four ECG waveforms from the same class; and (c) time-shifted waveforms for the same class.

Figure 3: The centroids obtained for ECG Class No. 1. The training sequences are shown in the upper-left figure.

	Window Size	Hidden Units	Training	Test
(1)	30	NA	94%	94%
	40	NA	100%	94%
	45	NA	100%	76%
(2)	20	10	100%	98%
	20	15	98%	98%
	20	20	100%	94%
(3)	20	10	100%	94%
	20	15	100%	98%
	20	20	100%	96%
(4)	NA	30 states	0%	8%

Table 3: Training/generalization accuracies of several temporal models, including (1)LPC, (2)PBIT(LBF), (3)PBIT(RBF), and (4)HMM.

Classifier	Original Test Set	Shifted Test Set
DBNN(E_s)	90%	85.2%
LPC	94%	90%
PBIT(LBF)	98%	98%
PBIT(RBF)	98%	98.45%

Table 4: Comparison of the shift-tolerance of different static and temporal models. The models were trained by the original data but tested (mostly) by the shifted data.

scheme can always follow. Either DBNN or FDNN [4, 6] may be adopted to fine-tune the classifier. In this case, the prediction error becomes a discriminant function in those models.

III. ON-GOING WORK: IIR FILTER AS PREPROCESSOR

In general, it is not obvious how to select a proper window size. It is useful to design a model which is less sensitive to the window size. In a general configuration shown in Figure 4, the first part involves a linear or a nonlinear adaptive filter and the second part can be a feedforward (LBF or RBF) two-layer net. The weights in the feedforward network can be trained by the back-propagation algorithm. The back-propagation error signal for the interface neuron values (between the two parts) can be used for the training of the adaptive filter.

There are many ways to implement the adaptive filters. One example of the adaptive filter is the cascaded first-order IIR filter [7] in Figure 5. The parameter μ controls the memory depth of filter. The effective window size of the filter is N/μ, where N is the number of stages in

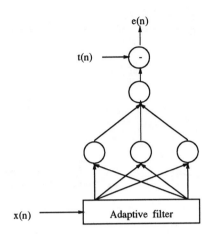

Figure 4: An overall system includes a multi-layer non-linear approximation net and an adaptive preprocessing filter.

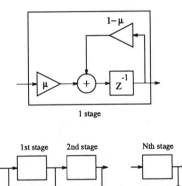

Figure 5: Cascaded First-Order IIR Filter.

	Window Size	No. of Weights	Training	Test
(1)	20	221	100%	98%
(2)	10	121	100%	96%
(3)	5	71	96%	98%

Table 5: Training/generalization accuracies of several temporal models, including (1)best PBIT(LBF), (2) PBIT(LBF) with a 10-stage filter and (3) PBIT(LBF) with a 5-stage filter.

the filter. The stability of the network requires only that $0 < \mu < 2$.

The simplest structure of the filter is the tapped delay line when $\mu = 1$. There are some disadvantages of it, for example, the performance might be sensitive to the window size of the tapped delay line. This is a genetic problem for every TDNN with a fixed window size.

By changing the value μ in the structure, we can adjust the window size to include enough information easily. For a smaller μ, the effective window size is larger but the resolution is coarser. The value μ can be trained by applying gradient-descent algorithm to the prediction error. Usually IIR filters can achieve the same performance with less parameters because of the redundant information in the time sequence. When the redundancy is high, a small number of stages and a small μ can be adopted. In this way, the training time and the number of parameters in the network can be greatly reduced.

From the previous experiments, we know that the best window size for the ECG classification application is around 20. We tried two different PBIT(LBF) configurations: a 10-stage filter with $\mu = 0.5$ and a 5-stage filter with $\mu = 0.25$. The results are listed in Table 5. The number of parameters in the network can be reduced from 221 to 71 while the performance remains about the same. Some other filter structures, e.g. lattice filter, are under investigation.

REFERENCES

[1] G. Cybenko. Approximation by superpositions of a sigmoidal function. *Mathematics of Control, Signals and Systems*, 2:303–314, 1989.

[2] K. Funahashi. On the approximate realization of continuous mappings by neural networks. *Neural Networks*, pages 183–192, 1989.

[3] Y. H. Hu, W. J. Tompkins, and Q. Xue. Artificial neural networks for ECG arryhthmia monitoring. In S. Y. Kung, F. Fallside, J. A. Sorensen, and C. A. Kamm, editors, *Neural Networks for Signal Processing, II*, pages 350–359. Proceedings of the 1992 IEEE Workshop, Helsingoer, Denmark, 1992.

[4] S. Y. Kung and J. S. Taur. Hierarchical Perceptron (hiper) networks for classifications. In S. Y. Kung, F. Fallside, J. A. Sorensen, and C. A. Kamm, editors, *Neural Networks for Signal Processing, II*. Proceedings of the 1992 IEEE Workshop, Helsingoer, Denmark, 1992.

[5] H. L. Royden. *Real Analysis*. Macmillan, New York, second edition, 1968.

[6] J. S. Taur and S. Y. Kung. Fuzzy-decision neural networks. Proceedings, IEEE International Conference on Acoustics, Speech, and Signal Processing, April 1993.

[7] B.D. Vries, J.C. Principe, and P.G.D. Oliveira. Adaline with adaptive recursive memory. In B. H. Juang, S. Y. Kung, and C. A. Kamm, editors, *Neural Networks for Signal Processing*, pages 101–110. Proceedings of the 1991 IEEE Workshop, Princeton, NJ, 1991.

Time-Optimal Terminal Control Using Neural Networks

Edward S. Plumer*

Stanford University

Durand 104, Department of Electrical Engineering, Stanford, CA, 94305-4055

e-mail: plumer@isl.stanford.edu

Abstract— Multilayer neural networks, trained by the back-propagation through time algorithm (BPTT), have been used successfully as state-feedback controllers for nonlinear terminal control problems. Current BPTT techniques, however, do not deal systematically with open final-time situations such as minimum-time problems. An extension of BPTT to open final-time problems called time-optimal backpropagation-through-time (TOBPTT) is presented. The derivation uses Lagrange multiplier methods for constrained optimization. The algorithm is tested on a Zermelo problem and the resulting trajectories compare favorably with classical optimal control results.

I. INTRODUCTION

The application of feedforward neural networks to the control of nonlinear dynamic systems has recently received much attention. These networks are capable of realizing adaptable, universal function approximators [1] and can thus be used as generic state feedback controllers and nonlinear compensators. The feasibility of training such neural controllers, moreover, has been demonstrated by numerous applications.

Controllers can be divided into two main classes: *regulators* and *terminal controllers*. A regulator maintains the state of the system indefinitely about some known reference despite external disturbances and internal uncertainties. Narendra and Parthasarathy, among others, have analyzed neural network regulator structures in detail [2]. Unlike a regulator, a terminal controller drives the plant to some final state at which point the control task is terminated. The truck-backer of Nguyen and Widrow [3] is one example of a terminal control process. These terminal controllers have received less theoretical attention in the neural network literature than regulators.

Such theoretical considerations should include an examination of an important class of terminal control problems: those in which the number of steps along the trajectory is unknown *a priori*. Such problems include rendezvous and docking as well as robotic manipulator placement. Often

in these situations, the trajectory-time is also included as part of the cost function. Such situations are classified as *open final-time* problems and have been dealt with for several decades using classical optimal control methods [4]. However, these optimal control methods typically find an open-loop control sequence valid only along a single trajectory. Feedforward neural networks trained by the backpropagation-through-time (BPTT) algorithm [5] can be used to overcome this limitation by implementing the required optimal state-feedback control over the entire desired range of state-space. Current BPTT techniques, however, have not provided a systematic way of incorporating the time elapsed along a trajectory — or number of steps along a trajectory — as part of the cost function. As a result, it has not been practical to solve problems such as minimum-time control using neural network techniques. This is mainly due to the fact that most derivations of BPTT stipulate a fixed number of steps, N. In regulator structures, this is not an issue since the trajectory length is effectively infinite and terminal transients are not considered. However, in terminal control problems appropriate choice of N for each possible trajectory is an important consideration.

This paper addresses the question of how to optimize the choice of trajectory length. In doing so, the terminal control problem is phrased as a constrained optimization problem and Lagrange multiplier techniques are used to derive first-order stationary conditions. This approach is typical of optimal control derivations and is similar to that taken by le Cun in describing backpropagation [6]. The result of this derivation is an extension of the standard BPTT algorithm. This extended algorithm, called time-optimal backpropagation-through-time (TOBPTT), is then tested on a Zermelo problem.

II. FORMULATION OF OPTIMAL CONTROL PROBLEM

We begin by formulating the optimization problem. First, we identify the controller structure and variables, the system constraints, and the cost function to be minimized. The neural network control structure used is shown in

---

*Supported by NASA Fellowship NGT-50642.

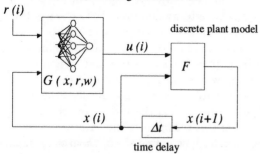

Controller, including neural network

r (i)

G (x, r, w)

discrete plant model

u (i)

F

x (i)

x (i+1)

Δt

time delay

Figure 1: *Feedback control loop with neural network controller.*

Fig. 1. This structure includes a next-state model of the dynamic plant, F, with fixed sampling interval Δt as well as a memoryless, nonlinear state-feedback controller, G. This controller includes a multilayer feedforward neural network with weight vector $\mathbf{w} \in \Re^w$. The state vector for the plant is $\mathbf{x}(i) \in \Re^n$ and control vector is $\mathbf{u}(i) \in \Re^m$. The state vector, as well as an exogenous reference input $\mathbf{r} \in \Re^r$, is assumed to be available to the controller at each iteration.

So that we can deal systematically with unknown trajectory lengths, we define a "time-to-go" function $N(\cdot) : \Re^n \to \mathcal{Z}^+$ which maps the initial state to the length of the associated trajectory. This is a multi-trajectory extension of the final-time parameter t_f used in optimal control. In order to formulate the optimization problem over many trajectories simultaneously, we assume that the initial state is a random vector $\mathbf{X}_0$ taking on values $\mathbf{x}_0$ from some bounded set X with some probability density function $p(\mathbf{x}_0)$. Given the system equations F and G, the specific choice of $N(\cdot)$ and $\mathbf{w}$, uniquely defines a state trajectory $[\mathbf{x}(0, \mathbf{x}_0), \ldots, \mathbf{x}(N(\mathbf{x}_0), \mathbf{x}_0)]$ and control sequence $[\mathbf{u}(0, \mathbf{x}_0), \ldots, \mathbf{u}(N(\mathbf{x}_0) - 1, \mathbf{x}_0)]$ for each initial state $\mathbf{x}_0 \in \mathsf{X}$. Based on these sequences, we define for each trajectory a cost function

$$\tilde{J}\big(\mathbf{x}(\cdot, \mathbf{x}_0), \mathbf{u}(\cdot, \mathbf{x}_0), N(\mathbf{x}_0)\big).$$

We now assume that the state and control sequences can be chosen independently of $\mathbf{w}$ and then attempt to find the $\mathbf{x}(\cdot, \cdot)$, $\mathbf{u}(\cdot, \cdot)$, $\mathbf{w}$, and $N(\cdot)$ which minimize the expected cost,

$$J = \int_{\mathsf{X}} \left\{ \tilde{J}\big(\mathbf{x}(\cdot, \mathbf{x}_0), \mathbf{u}(\cdot, \mathbf{x}_0), N(\mathbf{x}_0)\big) \right\} p(\mathbf{x}_0) \, d\mathbf{x}_0 \quad (1)$$

while also satisfying the system constraints,

$$\mathbf{x}(0, \mathbf{x}_0) = \mathbf{x}_0 \quad (2)$$

$$\mathbf{x}(i + 1, \mathbf{x}_0) = F(\mathbf{x}(i, \mathbf{x}_0), \mathbf{u}(i, \mathbf{x}_0)) \quad (3)$$

$$\mathbf{u}(i, \mathbf{x}_0) = G(\mathbf{x}(i, \mathbf{x}_0), \mathbf{w}, \mathbf{r}(i)) \quad (4)$$

for $i = 0, \ldots, N(\mathbf{x}_0) - 1$ and $\forall \mathbf{x}_0 \in \mathsf{X}$ [1]. Specifically, we use a Bolza formulation,

$$\tilde{J} = \phi[\mathbf{x}(N(\mathbf{x}_0), \mathbf{x}_0), N(\mathbf{x}_0)\,\Delta t]$$
$$+ \sum_{i=0}^{N(\mathbf{x}_0)-1} L[\mathbf{x}(i, \mathbf{x}_0), \mathbf{u}(i, \mathbf{x}_0)], \quad (5)$$

and again note that the trajectory length is an unknown function of the initial state which must be optimized. For notational convenience, we will drop the explicit dependence of $\mathbf{x}(\cdot, \cdot)$ and $\mathbf{u}(\cdot, \cdot)$ on $\mathbf{x}_0$.

We should also observe that, unlike typical open final-time optimal control problems, there are no added hard terminal constraints of the form $\psi(\mathbf{x}(N)) = 0$. Such terminal constraints are required for a minimum-time problem to be meaningful. However, if these constraints must be satisfied *exactly* for many trajectories, then the problem can become over-constrained due to the limited number of degrees of freedom in the controller network. Thus, it is more appropriate to use soft terminal constraints which need only be met *approximately*. For example, minimization of the cost function

$$Q_t N \Delta t + (\mathbf{x}_d - \mathbf{x}(N))^T Q_{\mathbf{x}} (\mathbf{x}_d - \mathbf{x}(N)) \quad (6)$$

will create a tradeoff between trajectory time minimization and maintenance of the desired terminal state $\mathbf{x}_d$. This terminal cost can also involve more complicated expressions if necessary.

III. DERIVATION OF FIRST-ORDER STATIONARY CONDITIONS

In this section we derive first-order stationary conditions for the TOBPTT algorithm. The main difficulty in deriving such extensions is the fact that the time-to-go function, $N(\cdot)$, is integer-valued and cannot be directly updated by gradient descent [2]. The time optimization techniques of open-loop optimal control, on the other hand, use a real-valued trajectory time which can be adapted by gradient methods to satisfy the required transversality condition.

To circumvent this difficulty, two alternatives have been proposed [3]. The first method is based on extending the idea of gradient descent adaption of the trajectory-time to

---

[1] This constrained formulation differs from typical BPTT derivations which keep track of the dynamic constraints implicitly during the application of chain-rule-like expansions.

[2] Note that methods based on optimizing Δt with fixed N are not appropriate in this context.

[3] These methods were first presented by the author in a NASA technical report [7]

the multi-trajectory case. In order to do this, the integer-valued time-to-go function, $N(\mathbf{x}_0)$, is replaced with a real-valued function, $t_f = T(\mathbf{x}_0) : \Re^n \to \Re$, implemented using a second neural network with weight $\mathbf{w}_\tau$. In order to simulate a trajectory with real-valued length, a final partial time step is computed by linearly interpolating between $\mathbf{x}(\lfloor t_f/\Delta t \rfloor)$ and $\mathbf{x}(\lceil t_f/\Delta t \rceil)$. The resulting stationary conditions include the transversality condition

$$0 = \int_{\mathsf{X}} \left\{ \left(\lambda_F(t_f)^T \left(\frac{F[\mathbf{x}(N), \mathbf{u}(N)] - \mathbf{x}(N)}{\Delta t} \right) \right. \right.$$
$$\left. \left. + \frac{\partial \phi}{\partial t_f} + \frac{L_N}{\Delta t} \right) \frac{\partial T}{\partial \mathbf{w}_\tau} \right\} p(\mathbf{x}_0) \, d\mathbf{x}_0 \qquad (7)$$

in addition to the backpropagation equations. This condition can be satisfied by adapting the secondary, time-to-go network. It is interesting to note that (7) is a first-order difference approximation to the transversality condition for open-loop optimal control. Further details of this method are given in [7].

Although this first method is theoretically interesting due to its close correspondence with classical optimal control, a simpler method can also be derived. This method effectively eliminates the time-variables from the optimization problem. It is this second technique that we focus on in this paper. We begin by reconsidering the general cost function (1):

$$J^o = \min_{\mathbf{x}, \mathbf{u}, \mathbf{w}, N(\cdot)} \int_{\mathsf{X}} \left\{ \tilde{J}(\cdot, \cdot, N(\mathbf{x}_0)) \right\} p(\mathbf{x}_0) \, d\mathbf{x}_0.$$

We can distribute the minimization over the function N across the expected value without affecting the result:

$$J^o = \min_{\mathbf{x}, \mathbf{u}, \mathbf{w}} \int_{\mathsf{X}} \left\{ \min_N \tilde{J}(\cdot, \cdot, N) \right\} p(\mathbf{x}_0) \, d\mathbf{x}_0$$

The minimizing value of the scalar N within the expected value will depend on the choice of $\mathbf{x}_0$ and $\mathbf{w}$ and is defined as

$$N^o = N^o(\mathbf{x}_0, \mathbf{w}) \equiv \arg \min_N \tilde{J}(\mathbf{x}(\cdot, \mathbf{x}_0), \mathbf{u}(\cdot, \mathbf{x}_0), N).$$

Note that this is not the desired function $N^o(\mathbf{x}_0)$ unless we have optimal $\mathbf{w}$. Assuming for the moment that N^o is known, we can substitute it back into the expression for J:

$$J^o = \min_{\mathbf{x}, \mathbf{u}, \mathbf{w}} \int_{\mathsf{X}} \left\{ \tilde{J}(\cdot, \cdot, N^o) \right\} p(\mathbf{x}_0) \, d\mathbf{x}_0. \qquad (8)$$

Thus, by appropriate substitution, the problem of optimizing over $\mathbf{x}(\cdot, \cdot)$, $\mathbf{u}(\cdot, \cdot)$, $\mathbf{w}$ and $N(\cdot)$ is reduced into a

problem of optimizing only over $\mathbf{x}(\cdot, \cdot)$, $\mathbf{u}(\cdot, \cdot)$, and $\mathbf{w}$. In doing this, the time-to-go function, $N^o(\mathbf{x}_0, \mathbf{w})$, is lost and is not available for use by the trained network. During training some method must be used to determine at which time-step to stop each forward run and compute the terminal error. However, during actual use, the evolution of the physical control system will typically provide a natural stopping point. Thus the loss of information about optimal $N(\cdot)$ in this technique is not a concern.

We now consider how to find the optimal $\mathbf{w}$ by again deriving a set of necessary first-order stationary conditions. As before, we seek the $\mathbf{x}(\cdot, \cdot)$, $\mathbf{u}(\cdot, \cdot)$, $\mathbf{w}$, and $N(\cdot)$ which minimize the Bolza cost function

$$J = \int_{\mathsf{X}} \left\{ \phi[\mathbf{x}(N(\mathbf{x}_0)), N(\mathbf{x}_0)\Delta t] \right.$$
$$\left. + \sum_{i=0}^{N(\mathbf{x}_0)-1} L[\mathbf{x}(i), \mathbf{u}(i)] \right\} p(\mathbf{x}_0) \, d\mathbf{x}_0 \qquad (9)$$

subject to the constraints given by (2-4). Substituting in the as of yet unknown, $N^o(\mathbf{x}_0, \mathbf{w})$, we can write

$$J = \int_{\mathsf{X}} \left\{ \phi[\mathbf{x}(N^o), N^o \Delta t] \right.$$
$$\left. + \sum_{i=0}^{N^o-1} L[\mathbf{x}(i), \mathbf{u}(i)] \right\} p(\mathbf{x}_0) \, d\mathbf{x}_0. \qquad (10)$$

We adjoin the system constraints to the cost function using two Lagrange multiplier sequences,

$$[\lambda_F(1, \mathbf{x}_0), \ldots, \lambda_F(N^o(\mathbf{x}_0, \mathbf{w}), \mathbf{x}_0)]$$
$$[\lambda_G(0, \mathbf{x}_0), \ldots, \lambda_G(N^o(\mathbf{x}_0, \mathbf{w}) - 1, \mathbf{x}_0)],$$

giving:

$$\bar{J} = \int_{\mathsf{X}} \left\{ \phi[\mathbf{x}(N^o), N^o \Delta t] + \sum_{i=0}^{N^o-1} \left\{ L[\mathbf{x}(i), \mathbf{u}(i)] \right. \right.$$
$$+ \lambda_F(i+1)^T \left(F_i - \mathbf{x}(i+1) \right)$$
$$\left. \left. + \lambda_G(i)^T \left(G_i - \mathbf{u}(i) \right) \right\} \right\} p(\mathbf{x}_0) \, d\mathbf{x}_0.$$

For notational convenience, we then substitute the Hamiltonian sequence,

$$H_i \equiv L[\mathbf{x}(i), \mathbf{u}(i)] + \lambda_F(i+1)^T F(\mathbf{x}(i), \mathbf{u}(i))$$
$$+ \lambda_G(i)^T G(\mathbf{x}(i), \mathbf{w}, \mathbf{r}(i)), \quad i = 0, \ldots, N^o - 1,$$

into $\bar{J}$ and rearrange the terms to produce

$$\bar{J} = \int_{\mathsf{X}} \left\{ \phi[\mathbf{x}(N^o), N^o \Delta t] - \lambda_F(N^o)^T \mathbf{x}(N^o) \right.$$

$$+ \sum_{i=1}^{N^o-1} \left(H_i - \lambda_F(i)^T \mathbf{x}(i) - \lambda_G(i)^T \mathbf{u}(i) \right)$$

$$+ H_0 - \lambda_G(0)^T \mathbf{u}(0) \Bigg\} p(\mathbf{x}_0)\, d\mathbf{x}_0.$$

We now consider changes in $\bar{J}$ due to changes in $\mathbf{w}$, $\mathbf{x}(1),\dots,\mathbf{x}(N^o)$, and $\mathbf{u}(0),\dots,\mathbf{u}(N^o-1)$. We do not need to consider variations in $\mathbf{r}(i)$ since it is independent of the optimization problem. We require that admissible $\delta\mathbf{w}$ are chosen small enough that $N^o(\mathbf{x}_0,\mathbf{w}) = N^o(\mathbf{x}_0,\mathbf{w}+\delta\mathbf{w})$ for all $\mathbf{x}_0$, thus treating N^o as a constant. Naturally, the trajectory lengths change during the adaption process. However, this is accomplished indirectly through updates to $\mathbf{w}$ which in turn affect the minimizing value of N on subsequent evaluations of the trajectory. This results in gradient descent over a continuous but only piecewise-differentiable surface. The resulting differential is:

$$d\bar{J} = \int_{\mathsf{X}} \Bigg\{ \frac{\partial H_0}{\partial \mathbf{x}(0)} d\mathbf{x}(0) + \sum_{i=0}^{N^o-1} \left(\frac{\partial H_i}{\partial \mathbf{w}} \right) d\mathbf{w}$$

$$+ \left(\frac{\partial \phi}{\partial \mathbf{x}(N^o)} - \lambda_F(N^o)^T \right) d\mathbf{x}(N^o)$$

$$+ \sum_{i=1}^{N^o-1} \left(\frac{\partial H_i}{\partial \mathbf{x}(i)} - \lambda_F(i)^T \right) d\mathbf{x}(i)$$

$$+ \sum_{i=0}^{N^o-1} \left(\frac{\partial H_i}{\partial \mathbf{u}(i)} - \lambda_G(i)^T \right) d\mathbf{u}(i) \Bigg\} p(\mathbf{x}_0)\, d\mathbf{x}_0.$$

Since $\mathbf{x}_0$ is given, we know that $d\mathbf{x}(0) = 0$. In order to have optimal $\mathbf{w}$, $\mathbf{x}(i)$ and $\mathbf{u}(i)$, we require that $d\bar{J} = 0$ for all choices of $d\mathbf{w}$, $d\mathbf{x}(1),\dots,d\mathbf{x}(N^o)$, and $d\mathbf{u}(0),\dots,d\mathbf{u}(N^o-1)$ along every trajectory. Thus, for $i = 1,\dots,N^o-1$ and $\forall \mathbf{x}_0 \in \mathsf{X}$, we require that the following conditions hold:

$$\lambda_F(N^o)^T = \frac{\partial \phi}{\partial \mathbf{x}(N^o)}, \tag{11}$$

$$\lambda_F(i)^T = \frac{\partial H_i}{\partial \mathbf{x}(i)}$$

$$= \frac{\partial L_i}{\partial \mathbf{x}(i)} + \lambda_F(i+1)^T \frac{\partial F_i}{\partial \mathbf{x}(i)}$$

$$\qquad + \lambda_G(i)^T \frac{\partial G_i}{\partial \mathbf{x}(i)}, \tag{12}$$

$$\lambda_G(i)^T = \frac{\partial H_i}{\partial u(i)}$$

$$= \frac{\partial L_i}{\partial \mathbf{u}(i)} + \lambda_F(i+1)^T \frac{\partial F_i}{\partial \mathbf{u}(i)}, \tag{13}$$

$$0 = \int_{\mathsf{X}} \left\{ \sum_{i=0}^{N^o-1} \frac{\partial H_i}{\partial \mathbf{w}} \right\} p(\mathbf{x}_0)\, d\mathbf{x}_0$$

$$= \int_{\mathsf{X}} \left\{ \sum_{i=0}^{N^o-1} \lambda_G(i)^T \frac{\partial G_i}{\partial \mathbf{w}} \right\} p(\mathbf{x}_0)\, d\mathbf{x}_0 \tag{14}$$

Equation (11) is the terminal value for the Lagrange multiplier. If the cost function is in the form of a quadratic terminal error such as (6), then this reduces to

$$\lambda_F(N^o)^T = 2\,(\mathbf{x}_d - \mathbf{x}(N))^T\, Q_{\mathbf{x}}. \tag{15}$$

Equations (12-13) sweep this terminal value back through the iterations of the feedback loop. The optimality condition (14) can be satisfied using stochastic gradient descent

$$(\mathbf{w})_{k+1} = (\mathbf{w})_k - \mu_w \sum_{i=0}^{N^o-1} \left(\lambda_g(i)^T \frac{\partial g_i}{\partial \mathbf{w}} \right)_k. \tag{16}$$

If the initial conditions for each run are drawn from the distribution of $\mathbf{X}_0$, (16) provides an unbiased estimate of the true gradient.

We see that (11-14) are identical to standard BPTT with the forward sweep terminated at time step N^o and the Lagrange multiplier acting as the backpropagated "error term". The extension beyond BPTT is the new expression

$$N^o = \arg\min_N \Bigg(\phi[\mathbf{x}(N), N\Delta t]$$

$$+ \sum_{i=0}^{N-1} L[\mathbf{x}(i), g(\mathbf{x}(i), \mathbf{w}, \mathbf{r}(i))] \Bigg) \tag{17}$$

which replaces the transversality condition (7). However, rather than being a stationary condition, (17) is an explicit expression for minimum value.

As with BPTT, the training procedure consists of a sequence of trial runs of the system with initial states drawn independently from the distribution of $\mathbf{X}_0$. Each run is followed by a computation of the terminal error, a backward sweep of that error, and a weight update based on the instantaneous gradient. The new algorithm differs from BPTT in that the index of the terminal step is chosen optimally based on (17). As the weight vector converges to a local minimum, $N^o(\mathbf{x}_0,\mathbf{w})$ converges to the appropriate minimizing value. Note that in implementing the algorithm, it is not necessary to maintain knowledge about $N(\cdot)$ for all $\mathbf{x}_0 \in \mathsf{X}$. Rather, it is only necessary to determine — and subsequently discard — N^o for one trajectory at a time. The only additional computation required to find N^o involves evaluating the cost function for each candidate stopping point of the forward pass.

IV. Experimental Results

As an example of minimum time control, consider the following discrete-time version of a Zermelo problem proposed by Bryson and Ho [4]. This problem is simple enough to allow the family of optimal trajectories to be visualized while still illustrating time-minimization. The physical system consists of a boat navigating in a river with a linear current profile as shown in Fig. 2. The boat location with respect to the goal is (x, y). The boat velocity with respect to the water, $V \angle \theta$, has constant magnitude, $V = 1$, in the direction the boat is pointing. The state vector is $\mathbf{x} = [x, y, \theta_r]$ where $\theta_r = \theta - \tan^{-1}(y/x) - \pi$ is the relative direction of the boat and the control vector is $\mathbf{u} = [\Delta \theta_r]$. The sampling interval is $\Delta t = 1$. In this problem, we assume a linear current profile $V_r(y) = -y/25$. The required controller must steer the boat to the goal at the center of the river in minimum time from many initial positions throughout the river. Given these definitions, the plant equations for this system are:

$$x(i+1) = x(i) + \cos\left(\theta_r(i) + \tan^{-1}\frac{y(i)}{x(i)} + \pi\right) - \frac{y(i)}{25}$$

$$y(i+1) = y(i) + \sin\left(\theta_r(i) + \tan^{-1}\frac{y(i)}{x(i)} + \pi\right)$$

$$\theta_r(i+1) = \theta_r(i) + u(i) \quad \text{normalized to } [-\pi, \pi]$$

We assume that the initial state for each run is chosen from a uniform distribution over the set $x \in [-50, 50]$, $y \in [-50, 50]$, $\theta_r \in [-\pi/4, \pi/4]$ and use a cost function consisting of a soft quadratic end-constraint and a time minimization term:

$$J = \int_X \left\{ N(\mathbf{x}_0)\Delta t + (x(N, \mathbf{x}_0) - 0)^2 \right.$$
$$\left. + (y(N, \mathbf{x}_0) - 0)^2 \right\} p(\mathbf{x}_0) \, d\mathbf{x}_0$$

In this example, the controller consists of a 2 layer sigmoidal network with 3 inputs, 10 hidden nodes, and 1 output. The network input is the scaled state vector $[x/50, y/50, \theta_r/\pi]$. The network output is the scaled control vector $[\Delta \theta_r/10]$. Before begining on-line training, it is desirable to apply some form of weight initialization which encodes any prior knowledge about the problem solution into the controller. In this case the controller weights were initially set to small random values. The controller was then trained, using teacher-forced learning, to emulate a coarse control law, thus providing a rough guess of the weights. This coarse controller simply pointed the boat towards the goal at all times which is the optimal control law in the absence of stream current. This weight initialization scheme was chosen as an alternative to the procedure used by Nguyen and Widrow in the truck backer

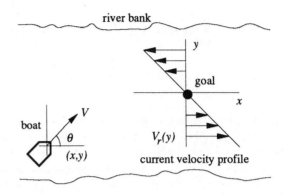

Figure 2: *Boat navigating in variable-current stream.*

which required a progressive expansion of the training set of initial states. Learning curves for the rough training with $\mu_w = 0.1$, $\mu_w = 0.01$ are shown in Fig. 3.

The roughly trained network was then optimized using the technique derived in the last section. The maximum possible trajectory length was assumed to be $N_{max} = 200$. Learning curves for the optimization process with $\mu_w = 0.001$, $\mu_w = 0.0005$, $\mu_w = 0.0001$ are shown in Fig. 4. Fig. 5 shows the test-set trajectories after $70,000$ training iterations with learning rate $\mu_w = 0.001$. The dotted lines in the figure show reference curves derived for each of the test trajectories separately using open-loop optimal control techniques. The network controller curves are very close to the reference curves with difference in average trajectory cost of 0.3.

V. Conclusions

This paper has presented an algorithm for training neural network state feedback controllers for open final-time problems. This algorithm, called time-optimal backpropagation-through-time, is similar to BPTT except that the forward runs are stopped and the terminal error is evaluated at the time-step which minimizes the total cost function, including any time-minimization term. When the algorithm was tested on a simple problem, the resulting state space trajectories corresponded closely to open-loop optimal control solutions computed for individual test trajectories.

It is important to note that even in situations which do not require final-time minimization it is still necessary to decide upon a stopping point for the forward run. This choice should not be made indiscriminately, as it will have a direct effect on the controller weights. In fact, without including the final time as part of the problem statement — either as a known quantity, or as an optimizable parameter — the idea of finding the optimal controller weights may not be well posed since the optimal set of weights, and the resulting cost may depend on the choice of N.

Because of this, some method, such as the one described here, should be used to stop the run at the appropriate time-step before computing the terminal error, even if the cost function does not explicitly involve trajectory-time.

There are a number of issues that have yet to be investigated. The analysis of first order stationary conditions needs to be extended to sufficient conditions for local minima, especially with regard to the effect of conjugate and focal points [4] on network training. Furthermore, the neural network control scheme presented here relies on full state information. In situations where the controller does not have this information, some form of state estimation must be used. This is an issue that needs to be addressed in the context of neural network terminal controllers.

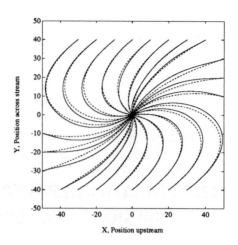

Figure 5: *(—) Test-set trajectories for trained neural network controller (- - -) Open-loop reference solutions.*

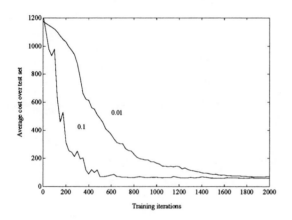

Figure 3: *Learning curve for neural controller during rough training,* $\mu_w = 0.01, 0.1$.

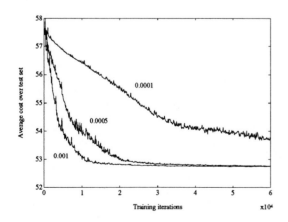

Figure 4: *Learning curve for neural controller during optimal training,* $\mu_w = 1 \times 10^{-3}, 5 \times 10^{-4}, 1 \times 10^{-4}$

REFERENCES

[1] G. Cybenko. Approximation by superpositions of a sigmoidal function. *Mathematics of Control, Signals, and Systems*, 2(4), 1989.

[2] K. S. Narendra and K. Parthasarathy. Identification and control of dynamic systems using neural networks. *IEEE Transactions on Neural Networks*, pages 4–27, March 1990.

[3] D. Nguyen and B. Widrow. The truck backer-upper: An example of self-learning in neural networks. In *Proceedings of the International Joint Conference on Neural Networks*, volume II, pages 357–363, Washington, DC, June 1989.

[4] A. E. Bryson, Jr. and Y. Ho. *Applied Optimal Control.* Blaisdell Publishing Co., New York, 1969.

[5] P. Werbos. Backpropagation through time: What it does and how to do it. *Proceedings of the IEEE*, 78:1550–1560, Oct. 1990.

[6] Y. le Cun. A theoretical framework for backpropagation. In *Proceedings of the 1988 Connectionist Models Summer School*, pages 21–28, San Mateo, CA, June 17-26 1988. Morgan Kauffman.

[7] E. S. Plumer. Two neural network algorithms for designing optimal terminal controllers with unknown final-time. Technical Report CR-177599, NASA Ames Research Center, Moffett Field, CA, July 1992.

THE FOLLOWING PAPERS ARE NOT IN THIER ASSIGNED SESSIONS BECAUSE THEY ARRIVED LATE

Classifying Fingerprint Images using Neural Network : Deriving the Classification State

Masayoshi KAMIJO
The Science University of Tokyo, Suwa College
Department of Management and System Science
5000-1,Toyohira,Chino,Nagano,391-02 Japan
Phone : +81-266-73-1201, Fax : +81-266-73-1230
E-mail:MASA@JPNSUT60(BITNET)

Abstract—In our study we have constructed a neural network for a classification of fingerprint images as an expert system which can classify the complicated fingerprint images. And we have proposed the so called *two-step learning method* as a learning process and the four-layered neural network which has one subnetwork for each category. The classification results for 500 unknown samples were 86.0 percent classification rate for the first candidate and 99.0 percent classification rate including the second candidate. Moreover, we carried out the principal component analysis with respect to the unit values of the second hidden layer and studied the fingerprint classification state represented by the internal state of the network. Consequently, we confirmed that the fingerprint patterns are roughly classified into each category in the second hidden layer and the effectiveness of the two-step learning process.

I. INTRODUCTION

The purpose of our study is to develop an automatic fingerprint classification system to create an efficient database for fingerprint matching. We thereby proposed a four-layered neural network which can extract feature from two-dimension data such as complicated fingerprint images. The neural network has one subnetwork for each category as the automatic classification system of the fingerprint images. To realize in one subnetwork the pattern information of one category, the networks are trained by supervised learning in the usual manner by the back propagation algorithm with a so called two-step training method.

Further, to demonstrate the reliability and effectiveness of our system, we carried out the principal component analysis with respect to the unit values of the second hidden layer and studied the pattern classification state represented by the internal state of the network. This was useful to improve the network structure and the training process.

The automatic processing of fingerprints can be roughly divided into fingerprint input equipment and fingerprint pattern recognition, and the latter is further divided into fingerprint classification and fingerprint matching. Among these, there is still room for improvement in fingerprint input equipment and fingerprint matching, but they have been made practical. On the other hand, it is still the case that fingerprint classification is a specially field and is generally performed by hand. As the number of fingerprints collected increases, problems in classification efficiency and reduction in reliability due to long run times still remain. For these reasons, the development of a fast, accurate automatic fingerprint classification system is desired, with the goal of creating an effective database for fingerprint comparison. However, It is difficult to establish an algorithm. Neural networks are ideally suited for the construction of an expert system for fingerprint classification which mimics the recognition capabilities of an expert handling the complicated fingerprint patterns, and recognize inaccurate and distorted patterns; they also make it possible to realize recognition capabilities with human-like adaptability.

II. CLASSIFICATION SYSTEM OF FINGERPRINT IMAGES

A. Fingerprint Images

Among fingerprint patterns, there are the following four types: Arch, Loop, Whorl, and Accidental. The Arch type can be divided into Normal Arch and Tented Arch types. The Loop type can be divided into Left Loop and Right Loop types.

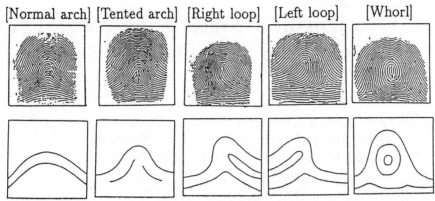

[Normal arch] [Tented arch] [Right loop] [Left loop] [Whorl]

Fig. I. Categories and characteristics of fingerprint images.

In this paper, we do not concern ourselves with accidental fingerprints and experiment only with the following five categories: Normal Arch, Tented Arch, Right Loop, Left Loop, and Whorl. Fig. I shows fingerprint images and their characteristic patterns.

Fingerprint classification can be divided into methods which key on feature points and methods that in turn key on ridge line orientations. In this paper, since features are easily extracted from complex print types, we use ridge line orientations as the features of a fingerprint pattern and employ this for classification. Since the fingerprint image data contains variations due to noise and variations in contrast, direction extraction is difficult. However, by combining projection and relaxation method and a so-called *ridge-tracing algorithm*, the feature ridge pattern is extracted from fingerprints which does not require additional preprocessing. Fig. II shows examples of the feature ridge patterns(16 × 16 pixels, 256 gray levels) which are actually used to classify the patterns. For detailed explanation, please refer to [2][3].

B. The Network Architecture

To effectively extract the feature of a two-dimensional fingerprint pattern, we propose a four-layered network which has one subnetwork for each category and has connections from each horizontal and vertical band in the input layer to the inputs of the first hidden layer (Fig. III). Each subnetwork is independent, and there are no connections within layers – only between them. Also, there are no weights on the connections from the third hidden layer to the output layer. The output layer is a layer used to display the outputs of the sub-

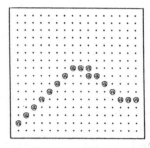

Fig. II. Characteristics fingerprint pattern (Normal arch). This pattern is a example of actual data.

networks. Many methods can be considered in order to form units in the hidden layers that classify spatial information in a fingerprint pattern. However, to reduce the number of links and the processing time, the forementioned extraction method using horizontal and vertical bands to effectively extract spatial information from the pattern can be thought to extract feature which are more local than every input unit being connected to every unit in the hidden layer. Further, if a network goes into saturation due to too much information being taught to one network, the learning state for each category falls into a local minimum and there is the possibility that the recognition rate will be reduced. However, with respect to this problem, given the interpretation that "an output which is biased toward some category will become the output state," if we consider applying this in reverse, we prepare one subnetwork corresponding to each category and have a structure that obtains an output using subnetwork cooperation. In this method, each subnetwork can be trained inde-

1933

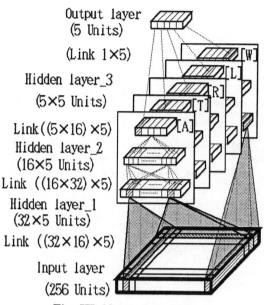

Output layer
(5 Units)

(Link 1×5)

Hidden layer_3
(5×5 Units)

Link((5×16)×5)
Hidden layer_2
(16×5 Units)
Link ((16×32)×5)
Hidden layer_1
(32×5 Units)

Link ((32×16)×5)

Input layer
(256 Units)

Fig. III. Network architecture

pendently; and since learning can proceed in categories other than one which suffers from shortened learning time and low recognition rate without being affected by it, we can expert an increase in learning accuracy.

C. Learning rule

Link weights and unit thresholds are adjusted using back error propagation learning rule, and the subnetwork are taught the characteristics of a category. Then, by using one subnetwork for each category, we expect to raise the recognition accuracy; to realize this, however, each subnetwork must respond correctly to every output to some extent and must perform compression between the input and the output while possessing the properties of parallelism, abstraction, and extensibility. To fulfill these conditions, all of the learning symbols must be presented to each subnetwork and each subnetwork trained as an expert in one category. To realize in one subnetwork the pattern information of one category, we use a two-step training method.

During learning, the training examples are presented in the order: Normal Arch, Tented Arch, Right Loop, Left Loop, and Whorl. The training patterns for each subnetwork consisted of setting to 1 just the output corresponding to the category of the pattern being input, and the outputs of the remaining units were set to zero. Ten patterns were given for each category, making a total of 50.

First, when each of the subnetworks is being trained, the most important patterns are identified and only those patterns are learned. Then learning is done by presenting all of the training patterns in the normal order. The termination condition for training is when the output error E_L at iteration L is less than ϵ_0 during the first step; and during the second step it is when the error becomes less than ϵ_1 and when the difference in the errors at steps L and $L-1$ becomes less than ϵ_2. The values $\epsilon_i (i = 0, 1, 2)$ determine convergence of the error to a stopping condition using the mean of the squared symbol. From the results of many experiments, appropriate values which did not fall into overtraining were determined to be $\epsilon_0 = 0.001, \epsilon_1 = 0.8, \epsilon_2 = 0.01$.

D. Classification Experiment

Using the internal state obtained through learning, we classified 100 fingerprints per category, for a total of 500 fingerprints. Since the neural network output is based on similarity with the learning data, classification is evaluated with the second candidate included in the classification result. The results of the classification experiment are given here. A recognition accuracy of 100 percent was obtained for the training samples; and as shown in Table I, the classification results for 500 unknown samples were 86.0 present for the first candidate and 99.0 present including the second candidate. Values in the table are numbers of discriminations; values in parentheses are classification rates with respect to 500.

III. EVALUATION OF THE INTERNAL STATE USING PRINCIPAL COMPONENT ANALYSIS

We found the effectiveness of the two-step learning process using the principal component analysis by deriving the fingerprint pattern classification state represented by the internal state of the networks. We performed the principal component analysis with respect to the unit values of the second hidden layer and studied the fingerprint classification state represented by the internal state of the network. This second layer contains 16 independent units and the values of these units are a partial transformation of the inputs.

A. Pattern classification state

As a result of applying principal component analysis to the values of the units of the second hidden layer in a case of classifying the training patterns by the network which is trained in the two-step

1934

Table I. Classification results for 500 unknown pattern data

	Normal arch	Tented arch	Right loop	Left loop	Whorl	Total (%)	
Number of First candidate patterns	88 (17.6)	52 (10.4)	97 (19.4)	98 (19.6)	95 (19.0)	430 (86.0)	495 (99.0)
Number of second candidate patterns	12 (2.4)	47 (9.4)	0 (0.0)	2 (0.4)	4 (0.8)	65 (13.0)	
Number of misclass-ified patterns	0 (0.0)	1 (0.2)	3 (0.6)	0 (0.0)	1 (0.2)	5 (1.0)	
Totals (%)	100 (20.0)	100 (20.0)	100 (20.0)	100 (20.0)	100 (20.0)	500 (100.0)	

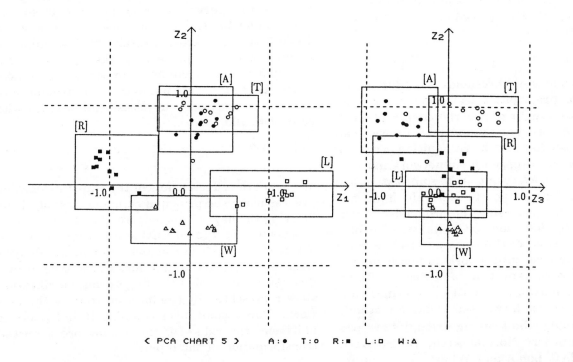

Fig. IV. Results of a principal component analysis of the unit values in the second hidden layer

learning process, Fig. IV shows a plot of the results with respect to these three principal components, i.e., with the first, second and third principal components as the axes. These principal components are shown as Z_1, Z_2, and Z_3 respectively. For each category, we let 40 percent of the distance between the maximum and minimum values represent the same category and enclosed that region with a rectangle. When an input pattern is summarized in the second hidden layer, we verified that it can be categorized to some extent. The similarity between Normal Arch [A] and Tented Arch [T] is strong in patterns up to here, and an overlap between those regions in Fig. IV is not a problem.

B. Effectiveness of the learning process

We considered two training processes : the so called two-step training process stated in the previous section and the so called one-step training process. The one-step training process means that the network is trained in the error back propagation learning rule using the fifty patterns of all categories in order, normal arch, tented arch, right loop. left loop and whorl. We compared the two classification state by the respective networks trained in the two different training process. The pattern classification state represented by the internal state of the network is evaluated by carrying out the principal component analysis with respect to the unit values of the second hidden layer. The link weight and threshold values were initialized by using normal random numbers because both the networks start to train from the same initial condition. In the previous section, the link weight and threshold values were initialized by using uniform random numbers.

Table II shows the classification results for the 50 training patterns by the networks initialized the normal random numbers with the mean value $Ave = 0$ and the variance $V = 0.001$. Values in parentheses are classification rates with respect to 50. We can see that the classification rate for the network trained in the one-step training process was 96.0 %; and since this is quite poor compared to the network trained in two-step training process.

Fig. V shows the pattern classification state when the training patterns are classified using the network trained by the one-step training process. Fig. VI shows the pattern classification state of the network by the two-step training process.

IV. Conclusion

Using the neural network proposed in this paper, we demonstrated that classification of two-dimensional fingerprint data is possible and we obtained classification rates of 86.0 percent for the first candidate and the high values of 99.0 percent by adding the second candidate. Since a classification rate of around 95 percent is reported previous work on fingerprint classification [4], our system can be said to be an exceptionally effective system for automatic fingerprint classification.

Further, in a comparison of the classification rate with other networks and from a principal component analysis in the second hidden layer, it is established that our network is effective at classifying fingerprint patterns.

The principal component analysis is useful to indicate the pattern classification state represented by the internal state of the network. The effectivity of the two step training method used here is confirmed by the principal component analysis.

Furthermore, we suggested that the principal component analysis is exceptionally useful to choose training data[1]. When high classification ratio is obtained, each category is separated well into the network. When low classification ratio is obtained each category is hardly separated.

References

[1] M. KAMIJO and H.MIENO et.al. Internal representation of neural networks addlied to classification of fingerprint images. *The Congress of The International Fuzzy System Association*, 73–76, 1991.

[2] M. Kamijo, K. Kojima, and H. Mieno. Classification of fingerprint images by the neural networks. *Trans. I.E.C.E., Japan*, J74-D-II(2):199–209, 1991.

[3] M. Kamijo, K. Kojima, and H. Mieno. Classification of fingerprint images using a neural network. *Systems and Computers in Japan*, **23(3)**, 1992.

[4] O.Nakamura, K. Gotoo, and S. Minami. Classification of fingerprint images using direction patterns. *Trans. I.E.C.E., Japan*, J65-D(10):1286–1293, 1982.

Table II. Classification results for the learning pattern $Ave = 0$, $V = 0.001$.

	Number of First Candidate Patterns	Number of Second Candidate Patterns	Number of misclass-ified Patterns
Two-step learning	50(100)	0 (0)	0 (0)
One-step learning	47(96)	3 (6)	0 (0)

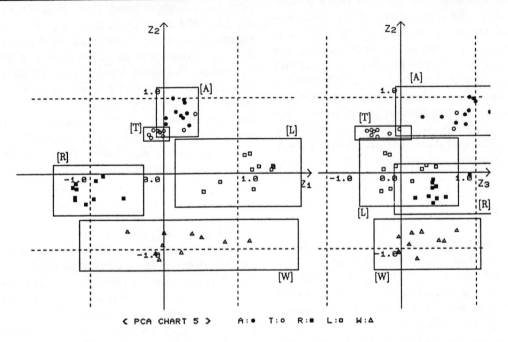

Fig. V. Results of a principal component analysis of the unit values in the second hidden layer for the network trained in the one-step training process.

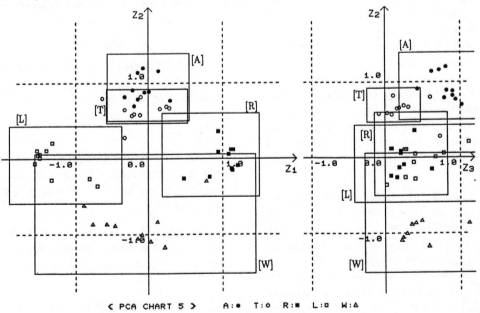

Fig. VI. Results of a principal component analysis of the unit values in the second hidden layer for the network trained in the two-step training process.

Perspective Reversal Caused by Chaotic Switching in PDP Schema Model

Kazuo Sakai

Meiji University, Izumi Campus, Division of Natural Science
213 Research Hall, 1-9-1 Eifuku, Suginami-ku, Tokyo 168, Japan

Tsuyoshi Katayama

Japan Automobile Research Institute, Inc.
Yatabe-cho, Tsukuba-gun, Ibaraki 305, Japan

Satoshi Wada

Meiji University, Surugadai Campus, School of Law
1-1 Kandasurugadai, Chiyoda-ku, Tokyo 101, Japan

Kotaro Oiwa

Oita University, Faculty of Education
700 Dan-no-haru, Oita, Oita 870-11, Japan

Abstract—A new dynamics of chaotic switching is proposed based upon a particular type of a network, i.e., PDP (Parallel Distributed Processing) schema model proposed by Rumelhart et al. By applying a mean-field approximation, a one-dimensional map is derived, by which a variety of dynamics in PDP schema model is well reproduced. This map has two bifurcation parameters and two attractors each of which becomes not only a stable fixed point but also chaotic attractor. And overlapping between these attractors can be taken place according to the bifurcation parameters.

Introducing a dynamics of the relative biases, successive chaotic switchings are realized. This new dynamics is applied to a well-known cognitive phenomena of perspective reversal for ambiguous patterns such as a Necker cube. The chaotic states of network activations are interpreted as wondering states to search a new percept.

New experimental results are also given, which are categorized into following three states, (1)one percept with confidence, (2)alternative percept, and (3)uncertain percept without confidence. The frequencies of persistent times in above three states are compared with simulations by the logistic maps. And it is shown that the chaotic theory could give new insights to a cognitive science.

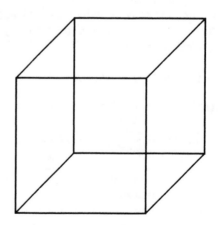

Figure 1: Necker cube.

I. Introduction

The study of ambiguous patterns such as a Necker cube[1] (Fig. 1) has intrigued psychologists for a long time. Peculiar is oscillatory behaviors between possible two percepts in a Necker cube. The best known hypothesis to explain these findings is that of saturation proposed by Köhler [2]. Upon this basis, a variety of theories has been published [3, 4, 5].

In this study we show a new experiment at a first time to clarify cognitive state without confidence whether it is

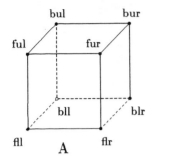 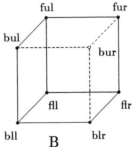

Figure 2: Two perspects of a Necker cube, and 16 hypotheses of the vertices which we assign to network units in a PDP schema model. Here 'ful' is meant by 'forward-upper-left', 'blr' by 'backward-lower-right', and so on.

one of two percepts. We interpret this uncertain state as chaotic wondering state to search a new percept. This is done by extracting chaotic dynamics from a PDP schema model[6, 7]

II. PDP SCHEMA MODEL

The PDP schema model[6, 7] is a simple constraint satisfaction model with two interpretations of a Necker cube (Fig. 1). We assume that 16 units represent hypotheses about the correct interpretations of the vertices (Fig. 2).

The update rule of a single unit is given by [6, 7]

$$a_i(t+1) = \{1 - |net_i(t)|\}\, a_i(t) + net_i(t)\, \theta(net_i(t)) \,, \quad (1)$$

where $net_i(t)$ indicates a net-input from other units, defined by

$$net_i(t) = \sum_j w_{ij}\, a_j(t) + bias_i \,. \quad (2)$$

Here w_{ij}'s denote inter-unit weights between i-th and j-th units, $bias_i$ a bias of i-th unit.

We now extend the original PDP schema model from $a_i(t) = [0,1]$ to $[-2,4]$ in order to allow chaotic responses. Secondly, the bias parameters are set equal within each schema, giving $\Delta B/2$ and $-\Delta B/2$ for A- and B-schema, respectively. These weights have been chosen so as to guarantee the balance condition (sum rule [8])

$$\sum_{j=\{A\}} w_{ij} + \sum_{j=\{B\}} w_{ij} = 0 \,, \quad (3)$$

between schemata for each i. Furthermore, the symmetricity is also assumed.

$$\sum_{j=\{A\},i\in\{A\}} w_{ij} = \sum_{l=\{B\},k\in\{B\}} w_{kl} \,. \quad (4)$$

These extensions of the schema model give us a variety of dynamics including chaotic responses[8, 9]. It should be noted that the unit itself has no origin to cause chaos, *i.e.*, which is not a chaotic unit.

III. MEAN-FIELD APPROXIMATION

We here introduce two schemata (A and B) representation[8, 9, 10], and take an average of surrounding units within the same schema.

$$\langle a(t)\rangle_A = \frac{\sum_{i=\{A\}} a_i(t)}{\sum_{i=\{A\}} 1} \,, \quad (5)$$

$$\langle a(t)\rangle_B = \frac{\sum_{i=\{B\}} a_i(t)}{\sum_{i=\{B\}} 1} \,. \quad (6)$$

Furthermore, assuming a bias in A-schema to be $+\Delta B/2$, and in B-schema $-\Delta B/2$, the net-inputs in (2) are replaced by

$$\langle net_i(t)\rangle_A = 3c\,\{\langle a(t)\rangle_A - \langle a(t)\rangle_B\} + \frac{\Delta B}{2} \,, \quad (7)$$

$$\langle net_i(t)\rangle_B = -3c\,\{\langle a(t)\rangle_A - \langle a(t)\rangle_B\} - \frac{\Delta B}{2} \,. \quad (8)$$

We have assumed no self-connections of units ($w_{ii} = 0$), and the sum-rules[8] (3) for inter-unit weights have been used. The parameter c denotes a weight parameter between units, which is defined by an average of weights within same schema, and (4) becomes $3c$.

IV. ONE-DIMENSIONAL LOGISTIC MAP

We now introduce a relative activation and a center-of-mass activation

$$\Delta a(t) = \langle a(t)\rangle_A - \langle a(t)\rangle_B \,, \quad (9)$$

$$\langle a(t)\rangle = \frac{\langle a(t)\rangle_A + \langle a(t)\rangle_B}{2} \,, \quad (10)$$

and scaled variables $X(t) = \{(A-1)/A\}\,\Delta a(t)$, $Y(t) = \langle a(t)\rangle$, and $Z = \Delta B/(2A)$. Here the definition $A \equiv 1 + 3c$ has been used.

We hereafter concentrate ourselves on the case of vanishing averaged bias, at which activation rules are decoupled with each other. In this simple case, we obtain the following map functions for $X(t+1) = F(X(t))$ and $Y(t+1) = G(Y(t))$,

$$F(X) = AX(1 - |X + Z|) + (A-1)\,Z \,, \quad (11)$$

$$G(Y) = Y - (Y - \frac{1}{2})\,A|X + Z| \,, \quad (12)$$

where we have introduced an period-1 fixed point $X_1^* = (A-1)/A$ in a one-dimensional logistic map $f(X) = AX(1-X)$.

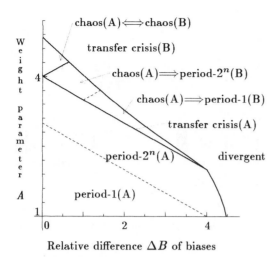

Figure 3: Phase diagram calculated by a one-dimensional logistic map (11). The initial value of $X(0)$ is set to be 0.001, at which A-schema is preferable for an initial transient. It is noted that a window escaping from A-schema to B is open above the line of 'transfer crisis(A)'. 'Period-2^n' denotes a period-doubling route to chaos.

From above equations, it is clarified that the dynamics of this system is essentially governed by one degree of freedom, $X(t)$, the average activation difference between schemata. The case of $\Delta B = 0$ and nonvanishing B is discussed in [10].

It is apparent that (11) is reduced to the well-known one-dimensional logistic map for vanishing Z and positive X, and is confirmed that the PDP schema model surely shows chaotic responses in a mean-field manner.

Fixed points of (11) is determined by $X^* = F(X^*)$ which gives three fixed points, $X^* = X_1^*, -X_1^*$ and $-Z$. It is noted that (11) is invariant under interchanges $X \to -X$ and $Z \to -Z$. This means that an interchange of A- and B-schemata holds good if Z is also interchanged into $-Z$. Therefore, we hereafter concentrate ourselves only on a case of $Z > 0$.

V. PHASE DIAGRAM AND TRANSFER CRISIS

The theoretical phase diagram based on (11) is plotted in Fig. 3, from which the relative difference ($\Delta B = 2AZ$) of biases between schemata is appeared to be a bifurcation parameter besides the weight parameter $A = 1 + 3c$. The numerical phase diagram based on (1) and (2) is also given in [9], in which qualitatively equivalent phase diagram is obtained as in Fig. 3.

Characteristics of the phase diagram Fig. 3 is the occurrence of transfer crises[9, 11]. This is a kind of 'local' boundary crisis[12]. In this case, the 'local' boundary is

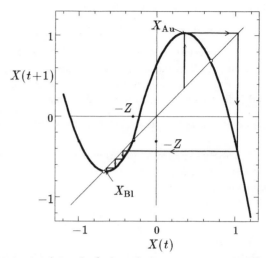

Figure 4: A typical situation to occur a transfer crisis. The weight parameter is set to be $A = 3.15(c = 0.7167)$ and the relative bias difference to be $\Delta B = 1.89(Z = 0.3)$ in (11). The uppermost point is mapped into larger value than $X = 1$. The chaotic orbit has a chance transferring to B-schema, through the narrow channel $[-1, F(X_{Au})]$. It is noted that, at this parameter set, the orbit falling in B-schema becomes stable at a period-1 fixed point near the lowermost point X_{Bl}.

the chaotic attractor of A-schema. The typical situation to take place the transfer crisis is shown in Fig. 4.

The transfer crisis is found and named by Yamaguchi and Sakai[11] in 1983 for a forced one-demensional logistic map by an alternating disturbance. This phenomenon has been found also in physical system of a Josephson junction[13, 14] by numerical calculations. Equation (11) is now the simplest map to occur the transfer crisis.

Peculiar is a hysteresis associated with the transfer crisis, which is seen in Fig. 3 along the line at constant weight parameter A. Starting from vanishing bias difference $\Delta B = 0$, the orbit is confined in A-schema. When the ΔB is increasing along the constant A line, the orbit becomes unstable and chaotic. Further increase takes an occurrence of the transfer crisis, and the orbit is falled into B-schema, when ΔB exceeds the critical line of 'transfer crisis(A)'. But, the reverse process never hold because of the hysteresis effect, even if ΔB is switched back to decrease.

The hysteresis is arose from breaking of the point symmetry in (11). This symmetry breaking is taken from the existence of the relative difference ΔB of biases between A- and B-schemata. At the next section, we make use this peculiar feature of a hysteresis, and the new interpretation is given for the oscillatory behaviors in cognitive phenomena observed such as in a Necker cube.

VI. Chaotic Switching

The interesting behavior can be obtained when we quasi-statically change ΔB along a line of constant weight parameter A in Fig. 3. To incorporate this slow change in ΔB, we add the following update rule for biases,

$$bias_i(t+1) = (1-\epsilon)\,bias_i(t) + \epsilon\,net_i(t)\,, \qquad (13)$$

where ϵ is a positive smallness parameter to detemine the velocity of changes. This can be rewritten in a mean-field approximation by

$$Z(t+1) = Z(t) + \epsilon X(t)\,, \qquad (14)$$

where $Z(t) = \Delta B(t)/(2A)$.

The cognitive meanings of (13) is as followings. When the particular hypothesis (say, i-th unit) is feasible ($net_i > 0$), enhanced is the tendency ($bias_i$) to believe that the hypothesis would hold good. This process is represented in (13).

The calculated profiles of time-series are shown in Fig. 5. The above profile is calculated with (1), (2) and (14). Furthermore, we have introduced a fluctuation η ($+\eta$ or $-\eta$) into $net_i(t)$, so as to avoid extra super-heating/cooling.

On the other hand, simulations of iterated logistic maps ((11) and (14)) are plotted in Fig. 6. Comparing these figures, it is appeared that qualitatively good agreements are obtained between simulations of network and of logistic map.

An alternation or switching phenomena seen in Figs. 5-6 is caused by a tranfer crisis[9, 11]. It is seen as an abrupt change of orbits from chaos confined in one attractor to a stable fixed point apart from the chaotic attractor. Equation (11) is the simplest logistic map showing transfer crisis between coexisting two attractors.

The dynamical behaviors in Figs. 5-6 might be interpreted in a cognitive sense as followings. Once a certain schema is confirmed, the confirmation becomes greater (corresponding to a growth of $|\Delta B|$ according to (13) or (14)). Further confirmation gives rise to a loss of confidence, and leads to a sudden discovery of another perspect.

VII. Perspective Reversal

The characteristic features in Figs. 5-6 are the existence of uncertain region in the time-series, $i.e.$, the chaotic wondering region. Since the published experiments of perspective reversal[15, 16] are not concerned to the existence of uncertain region, we have made experiments with a new method to extract the uncertain state of percepts.

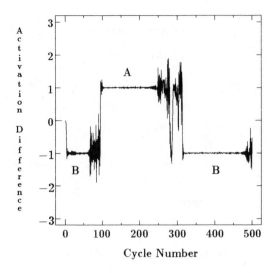

Figure 5: Time-series profile of an averaged activation difference $\Delta a(t)$ in an associative schema model with use of (1), (2) and (13). $\Delta a = 1$ and -1 denotes A- and B-schema, respectively. The adopted initial network parameters are $c = 0.6, \epsilon = 0.005, \eta = 0.02, \Delta B = 0$, where η denotes a strength of an external fluctuation added to (2). The weight parameters are chosen for intra-schema connections to be $w_{ij} = 0.714, 0.25, 0.107$, for nearest-neighbor, next neighbor, third neighbor, respectively. For inter-schema connections, w_{ij}'s can be uniquely chosen due to the sum rule (3).

The basic concept of our experiment is to take three kinds of times, $i.e.$, (1)times persisting A-schema, (2)B-shcema, (3)uncertain. The frequencies of these times are plotted in Figs. 7. The observers are 96 students aged 18 to 22 years, who did not know the aims of the experiments. The experimental run lasted at 10 min.

It is first shown that the distribution of the persistent time in uncertain state is quite different from those of A- and B-schema. The uncertain distribution is a monotonically decreasing function, although the others have a hump. This type of monotonically decreasing features is known to appear when chaotic burst[17, 18] is taken place. Thus this uncertain state could be expected to express in terms of the chaotic dynamics.

On the other hand, numerical results are plotted in Fig. 8, where the numerical calculation are performed up to 100,000 iterations with use of (11) and (14). The qualitative agreement is again obtained, if we neglect the lower duration below 20 cycles in Fig. 8. This neglection is rather meaningful, because such a shorter duration should not really recognized by a observer.

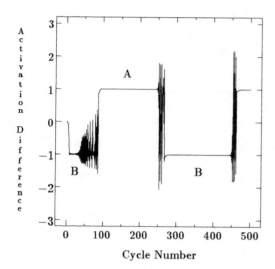

Figure 6: Time-series profile of an activation difference $\Delta a(t)$ in a mean-field theory with use of the map functions (11) and (14). $\Delta a = 1$ and -1 denotes A- and B-schema, respectively. The adopted initial parameters are $c = 0.6 (A = 2.8)$, $\epsilon = 0.01$, $\Delta B(t = 0) = Z = 0$, $X(t = 0) = -0.001$. Note that plotted are not $X(t)$ but $\Delta a(t) = X_1^* X(t)$ which is chosen because the period-1 fixed points are not affected by the bifurcation parameter A.

VIII. Conclusions and Discussions

We now point out some discrepancies in perspective reversals between experimental results and theoretical assumption of saturation commonly accepted thus far.

At first, it has been known by experiments[16] that there are two types of observers, *i.e.*, fast and slow observers, as shown in Fig. 7. We here point out that the slow observers become faster as experiments are repeated. And the observers with no experiences are almost all slow observers. This is supported in our experiments, since only 5 persons are fast in 96 observers who are made experiment at the first time.

This tendency seems to conflict with the saturation assumption in the following reasons.

1. The persistent times (durations) are of the order of one second or at most ten seconds. Is the saturation effects are so quick?

2. The persistent times become shorter and shorter as experiments are repeated. Does the observer familiar with the Necker cube become easy to saturate?

These questions are hard to say yes. And it is natural to regard that the strength of impressions being one percept plays an central roles to occur the perspective reversals. In our model, the strength of impressions could be taken

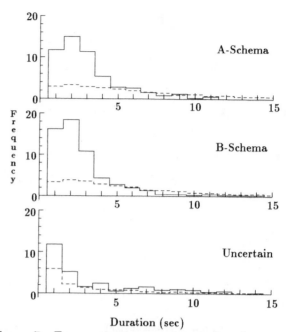

Figure 7: Frequencies in experiments by observers (96 students). The solid line denotes averaged frequencies of five fast observers with averaged durations of A- and B-schemata equal to or less than 3 sec. The broken line denotes averaged frequencies of ninety-one slow observers with averaged durations greater than 3 sec. The averaged persistent times for fast observers are 2.65, 2.36 and 5.00 sec in A-, B-schema and Uncertain states, respectively. Those for slow observers are 12.53, 8.79 and 2.99 sec.

as bias difference ΔB which cause a chaotic wondering and find a new attractor apart from the previous state.

In summary, we propose a new idea to interpret perspective reversals of ambiguous patters such as a Necker cube. Based on a PDP schema model, we derive a one-dimensional logistic map in a mean-field approximation, the obtained map shows a varieties of dynamics including chaos and transfer crises[9, 11] showing hysteresis.

It should be noted that the origin of chaos does not come from single unit itself but from averaged behaviors of units. In this sense, this type of chaos should be called as a *mean-field chaos*.

We have introduced a new experiment to take three categories of times for perspective reversal, *i.e.*, (1)one percept with confidence, (2)alternative percept, and (3)uncertain percept without confidence. A qualitatively good agreements are obtained between the experiments by observers and numerical results by the logistic maps. A new interpretation is given such that the uncertain times could be a chaotic wondering or searching state in a competitive-corporative network system.

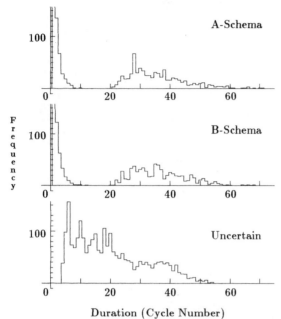

Duration (Cycle Number)

Figure 8: Frequencies in a mean-field approximation with use of the map functions (11) and (14). The iterations are performed up to 100,000 cycles, and the resulting time-series profiles such as in Fig. 6 are classified into three categorizes. The Δa is in A-schema if $\Delta a = 1 \pm 0.1$, and in B-schema if $\Delta a = -1 \pm 0.1$, otherwise, being classified into 'Uncertain'. And the persistent cycles being in the same state are counted as 'Duration'.

REFERENCES

[1] L. A. Necker, "Observations on some remarkable phenomena seen in Switzerland; and an optical phenomenon which occurs on viewing of a crystal or geometrical solid," *Philosophical Magazine*, vol. 3, pp. 329-337, 1832.

[2] W. Köhler, *Dynamics in Phsychology*, Liveright, New York, 1940.

[3] F. Attneave, "Multistability in perception," *Sci. Am.* vol. 225, pp. 62-71, 1971.

[4] A. H. Kawamoto and J. A. Anderson, "A neural network model of multistable perception," *Acta Psychologica*, vol. 59, pp. 35-65, 1985.

[5] H. Haken, *Synergetic Computers and Cognition*, Springer, Berlin, Chap. 13, 1991.

[6] D. E. Rumelhart, P. Smolensky, J. L. McClelland, and G. E. Hinton, *Parallel Distributed Processing*, The MIT Press, Camblidge, vols. 1 and 2, 1986.

[7] J. L. McClelland and D. E. Rumelhart, *Explorations in Parallel Distributed Processing*, The MIT Press, Cambridge, Chap. 3, 1988.

[8] K. Sakai, T. Katayama, K. Oiwa and S. Wada, "Theory of chaotic dynamics with transfer crises in a mean-field PDP schema model (Discovery of transfer crises and its cognitive meanings)," *The Bul. of Arts and Sci.* , Meiji Univ., vol. 249, pp. 105-150, 1992.

[9] K. Sakai, T. Katayama, K. Oiwa, S. Wada, "New mechanism to transfer schemata caused by transfer crises," *Proc. of The 2nd Int. Conf. on Fuzzy Logic and Neural Networks*, Iizuka, Japan, pp. 149-152, July 1992.

[10] K. Sakai, T. Katayama, K. Oiwa and S. Wada, "Theory of chaotic dynamics of PDP schema model in a mean-field approximation," *The Bul. of Arts and Sci.* , Meiji Univ., vol. 249, pp. 67-104, 1992 (in Japanese).

[11] Y. Yamaguchi and K. Sakai, "New type of ''crisis'' showing hysteresis," *Phys. Rev.* A, vol. 27, pp. 2755-2758, 1983.

[12] C. Grebogi, E. Ott and J. A. Yorke, "Chaotic attractors in crisis," *Phys. Rev. Lett.*, vol. 48, pp. 1507-1510, 1982.

[13] K. Sakai and Y. Yamaguchi, "Nonlinear dynamics of a Josephson oscillator with a $\cos\phi$ term driven by dc- and ac-current sources," *Phys. Rev.* B, vol. 30, pp. 1219-1230, 1984.

[14] M. Marek and I. Schreiber, *Chaotic Behaviour of Deterministic Dissipative Systems*, Cambridge University Press, Cambridge, p. 160, 1991.

[15] J. R. Price, "Perspective duration of a plane reversible figure," *Psychon. Sci.*, vol. 9(12), pp. 623-624, 1967.

[16] A. Borsellino, *et al.*, "Effects of visual angle on perspective reversal for ambiguous patterns," *Perception*, vol. 11, pp. 263-273, 1982.

[17] H. Fujisaka, H. Kamifukumoto and M. Inoue, "Intermittency associated with the breakdown of the chaos symmetry," *Prog. Theor. Phys.*, vol. 69, pp. 333-337, 1983.

[18] Y. Aizawa, "Global aspects of the dissipative dynamical systems. I," *Prog. Theor. Phys.*, vol. 68, pp. 64-84, 1982.

Kohonen Feature Maps as a Supervised Learning Machine

Hiroyuki ICHIKI Masafumi HAGIWARA Masao NAKAGAWA

Department of Electrical Engineering

Faculty of Science and Technology

Keio University

3-14-1 Hiyoshi, Kohoku-ku, Yokohama

223 Japan

Abstract— Kohonen Feature Maps as a Supervised Learning Machine are proposed and discussed. The proposed models adopt the supervised learning without modifying the basic learning algorithm. Therefore they behave as a supervised learning machine, which can learn input-
output functions in addition to the characteristics
of the conventional Kohonen feature maps. In the
pattern recognition problems, the proposed models can struct the recognition system simpler than
the conventional method that is to say structing
a pattern recognition machine using a supervised
learning machine after preprocessing by the Kohonen Feature Map. In addition, the proposed
models don't distinguish the input vectors from
the desired vectors because they regard them as
the same kind of vectors. That enables their bidirectional associations. And, we simulated several
examples in order to compare with the conventional supervised learning machines. The results
indicate the effectiveness of the proposed models.
For example, the property to noise, capacity storage and so on. We confirmed that the proposed
models had better characteristics than the conventional models (Back Propagation Network for a
pattern recognition and BAM for an associative
memory).

I. INTRODUCTION

Neural networks using supervised learning, for example,
back propagation network, have been applied to many
fields. They have shown excellent results in a field of a
pattern recognition. On the other hand, there is a Kohonen feature map, which produces a topological map in
unsupervised learning network.[1] But this model isn't fit
to use for pattern recognitions, which back propagation
networks are good at. Because a Kohonen feature map

can't learn desired input-output relation. It is ,however,
reported that the model hasa capability of the abstraction of features of input signals. So,it is much used for
preprocessing for pattern recognition etc.[3][4]

We integrate desired signals with Kohonen feature maps
without modifying the learning algorithm. We propose
Kohonen feature maps as supervised learning machine,
which can use like Back propagation networks, with characteristics of conventional maps. Relations between input
vectors and desired vectors may be reversed because proposed models regard two kind of vectors as the same kind
of vectors. So, this models can also use as a bidirectional
associative memory. Moreover, They need only one stage
for learning.

There are some researches to make supervised Kohonen
feature maps. However, a teaching signal in ref[3] is for
producing a topological map. So, it is different from our
target. In addition, the models are not for a supervised
learning machine. Models in ref[5] are equal to to our proposed models in respect of a supervised learning machine.
In ref[5] ,however, feature map algorithm is used between
the input layer and the feature map, and Hebbian algorithm is used between the feature map and the output
layer. That is to say they consist of three layers, need two
stages for learning.

In this paper, the algorithm and features of proposed
models are explained in section II. Comparisons between
the proposed models and the conventional models by computer simulations are shown in section III. As a realistic
experiment, the discrimination of sonar signals[9] is shown
in section IV. Discussion is described in section V.

II. STRUCTURE AND BEHAVIOR OF PROPOSED MODELS

A. Kohonen Feature Map

The Kohonen feature map[1] consists of an input layer and
a 2-dimensional neural sheet as an output layer. It has a
characteristic that similar inputs are mapped closer each

other. Eventually, it is the network for a topological mapping. The learning algorithm of conventional Kohonen feature map is represented as follows.

Input vector is

$$X = (X_1, X_2, X_3, \ldots, X_t) \tag{1}$$

t is dimension of input vectors. X is normalized to u in advance. Weights between an input layer and an output layer are

$$W_r = (W_{r1}, W_{r2}, W_{r3}, \ldots, W_{rt}) \tag{2}$$

where r is a position vector indicating a position of a unit on a map.

1. One of some input vectors are selected out of input vector space.

2. Input vector X is inputted into the network, outputs are calculated as follows.

$$y_r = X \cdot W_r \tag{3}$$

3. The largest y_r is decided.

$$y_{max} = \max[y_r] = \max[X \cdot W_r] \tag{4}$$

4. Weights learn as follows.

$$W_r^{(new)} = W_r^{(old)} + \varepsilon h_{rs}(X - W_r^{(old)}) \tag{5}$$

The extent of learning weights depend on h_{rs}. In the proposed models,

$$h_{rs} = \exp \frac{-\| r - s \|^2}{\sigma^2} \tag{6}$$

is used. σ is varying from σ_i to σ_f. $(\sigma_i > \sigma_f)$ Where the position vector indicating the unit having the maximum activity is s.

5. Learning weights are normalized to u.

$$\| W_r \| = u \tag{7}$$

Topological mapping is formed by repeating from 1. to 5.. The map has the following features:

1. The semantic relationships in the input data are reflected by their relative distances in the map.

2. Inputs appearing frequently are mapped by larger extent than inputs which doesn't appear frequently.

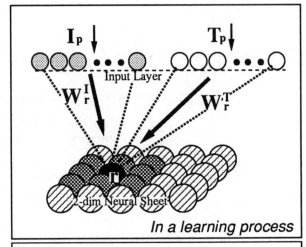

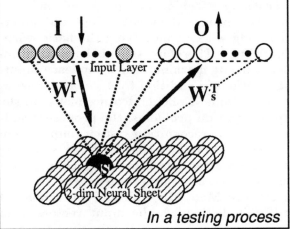

Figure 1: **Structure of a proposed model**

B. *Kohonen feature maps as a supervised learning machine*

Here we explain the proposed models. They regard the input vector consisting of different two components; an input part and an output part. As a result, the networks can be considered as a supervised learning machines. An input vector consists of an input part I_p and an output part T_p.

The learning vectors is represented as follows.

$$X_p = a \begin{bmatrix} I_p \\ o \end{bmatrix} + \begin{bmatrix} o \\ T_p \end{bmatrix} \tag{8}$$

where $a > 1$ in order that the input part can affect the formation of the map more than the output part does.

W_r is represented as follows.

$$W_r = \begin{bmatrix} W_r^I \\ W_r^T \end{bmatrix} \quad (9)$$

In testing process, a test vector is I. The algorithm for getting outputs is represented as follows.

1. When I is inputed into the network, the position vector s is defined by the unit having the maximum activity.

2. The unit having the maximum activity takes 1 as the output value, and the others take 0. Outputs O is actualized as follows.

$$O = (O_1, O_2, O_3, \ldots, O_k) \quad (10)$$

where,

$$O_m = \begin{cases} W_{s\ k}^T \cdot v, & \text{if Input vector is } I \\ W_{s\ k}^I \cdot w, & \text{if Input vector is } T \end{cases} \quad (11)$$

$$W_s^T = (W_{s\ 1}^T, W_{s\ 2}^T, W_{s\ 3}^T, \ldots, W_{s\ k}^T) \quad (12)$$

$$v = \frac{\sqrt{a^2 \|I\|^2 + \|T\|^2}}{u} \quad (13)$$

$$w = \frac{\sqrt{a^2 \|I\|^2 + \|T\|^2}}{ua} \quad (14)$$

v and w are constant, they need for the adjustment of the Euclidean norm of each vector.

A pair of I_p and T_p can be associated by this algorithm. Supervised learning is actualize without modifying Kohonen's learning algorithm. And the proposed models do not have to distinguish the input part from the output part: They regard them as the same kind of vectors.

III. COMPUTER SIMULATION

A. Basic property

In ordet to investigate the basic classification ability of proposed models, computer simulation was carried out using a 20-character recognition task. Characters used are shown in Figure2. Each learning vector consists of the 15-dimensional input vector and the 20-dimensional desired vector. The desired vector consists of one element of 1 and 19 elements of -1. In this simulation, we used the following parameters; $a = 5.0, \varepsilon = 0.6, \sigma_i = 4.0, \sigma_f = 0.5$. The size of the map is 5×5.

After 2000 epochs learning, we tested the network. We confirmed the perfect results: 20 kinds of the desired vector were inputted and the correct units had the maximum responses.

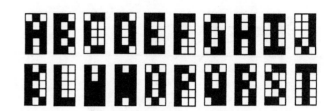

Figure 2: **Alphabet letters used in Simulation A**

B. Property to noise

Here we show the property of proposed models to noise. We compared the proposed models with three Back propagation type networks which differed in the number of hidden units. The task was recognition of 5 numerical letters which are shown in Figure3. Each learning vector consists of the 100-dimensional input vector and the 5-dimensional desired vector. The desired vector consists of one element of 1 and 4 elements of -1. In this simulation, we used the following parameters; $a = 5.0, \varepsilon = 0.6, \sigma_i = 4.0, \sigma_f = 0.5$. The size of the map is 5×5.

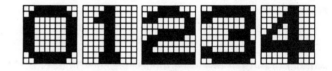

Figure 3: **Numerical letters used in Simulation B**

After 2000 learning, we have evaluated the recognition rate. The input vectors in the test vectors which were corrupted by randomly reversing each bit with several probabilities were inputted into the network. Figure4 shows the relation between the pixel reversed rate and the recognition rate.

We can easily see that the recognition rate of the proposed model is much higher than that of others.

C. Capacity

Here we show the performance of the proposed models when they were used as associative memories. Because the most important factor for an associative memory is its capacity. We used the same examples used in Ref.[7] to compare with the conventional models (BAM). While the dimensions of the input and output fields(n,p) are 100, and the number of training pairs (N) was changed from 1 to 50. The input vector and desired vector sets were generated randomly. In order to make the number of links in the proposed model equal to that in the BAM, the size of the map of the proposed models is 7×7. The

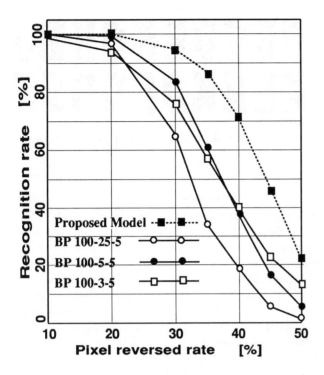

Figure 4: **Relation between pixel reversed rate and recognition rate**

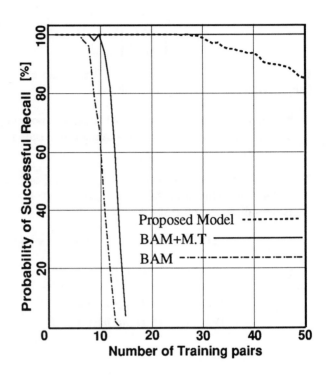

Figure 5: **Storage Capacity**

number of links of proposed models is 9800. That of BAM is 10000. Figure5 shows the result of comparison between the proposed models and the BAM. It can be easily seen that the capacity of the proposed model is much higher than the BAM.

IV. THE DISCRIMINATION OF SONAR SIGNALS

Gorman and Sejnowski had simulated the discrimination of sonar signals using a neural network[9]. The task is to train a network to discriminate between sonar signals bounced off a metal cylinder and those bounced off a roughly cylindrical rock. We treated with this problem in order to compare with the Back Propagation network and so on. We simulated using an "aspect-angle dependent" series in which the training and testing sets were carefully controlled to ensure that each set contained cases from each aspect angle in appropriate proportions. Each learning vector consists of the 60-dimensional input vector and the 2-dimensional desired vector. In this simulation, we used the following parameters; $a = 30.0, \varepsilon = 0.99, \sigma_i = 9.0, \sigma_f = 0.5$. The size of the map is 20×20. The total training time measured in epochs was between 20 and 60.

In the above condition, we simulated the discrimination of sonar signals 25 times. Table1 shows the results of the average of their recognition rates. In this results, that of

Back Propagation and LVQ were reported by Gorman and Sejnowski.

Table 1: Recognition rate of each model

Model	Recognition rate
Proposed Model	92.6%
Back Propagation	90.4%
LVQ	88.5%
Trained Human	91%

A Back Propagation network has the best result in the conventional models. The result of it is 90.4%. Gorman and Sejnowski had simulated them varying the number of the hidden units, they had found that the best score was acquired when the number of the hidden units is 12. That mean it is considerd that the result is the capability of a Back Propagation network.

As against that, the result of our proposed model is beyond those of the conventional models. Practically, the number of rinks of the proposed model are much more than that of a Back Propagation network. However, even if a back propagation network has a lot of rinks, it is considered that the recognition rate never go up. Therefore, it is considered that the proposed model is superior in the property of generalization to conventional models.

V. Discussion

The proposed models behave as a supervised learning machine which can learn functions like a back propagation type network by adopting desired vectors. The proposed models have a excellent characteristic relative to inputs with noise as compared with back propagation networks. And, relations between input vectors and desired vectors may be reversed because proposed models regard them as the same kind of vectors. So, our models can use as the bidirectional associative memories. As the result of comparisons between BAM and the proposed model by a computer simulation, we confirmed that our model could associate much more patterns exactly than the BAM.

The parameter a in Eq.8 influences on the relative importance between input vectors and desired vectors. For a pattern recognition, the map should have continuity to the input data because the learning data itself is hardly inputted in the testing process. When we want input vectors to be much more important than desired vectors in forming the feature map, and the elements of each vector consist of 1 or -1, permissible value of a is calculated as follows.

Let us assume an arbitrary input part vector to be I_p, the nearest input part vector to be I_q, and the second nearest input part vector to be I_r. Then, the following equation should be satisfied.

$$I_p \cdot I_q > I_p \cdot I_r \tag{15}$$

The vectors learned practically is, however, learning vectors X. Eventually, the following equation is required.

$$X_p \cdot X_q > X_p \cdot X_r \tag{16}$$

$$X_p = (aI_p^1, aI_p^2, \ldots, aI_p^j, T_p^1, T_p^2, \ldots, T_p^k) \tag{17}$$

$$X_q = (-aI_p^1, aI_p^2, \ldots, aI_p^j, -T_p^1, -T_p^2, \ldots, -T_p^k) \tag{18}$$

$$X_r = (-aI_p^1, -aI_p^2, \ldots, aI_p^j, T_p^1, T_p^2, \ldots, T_p^k) \tag{19}$$

When j is dimension of I_p and k is that of T_p, this equation becomes

$$\frac{ja^2 - 2a^2 - k}{ja^2 + k} > \frac{ja^2 - 4a^2 + k}{ja^2 + k} \tag{20}$$

This equation becomes

$$a > \sqrt{k} \quad (k : dimension \ of \ T_p) \tag{21}$$

VI. Conclusion

Kohonen feature maps as a supervised learning machine have been proposed and simulated. We have confirmed the effectiveness of the proposed models in respect of the recognition capability, the robustness to noise and the capacity. According to our simulations, the proposed models are superior to the back propagation type networks in respect of recognition ability. In addition, as for being an associative memory, the proposed model has higher capacity than BAM. The proposed models don't distinguish the input vectors from the desired vectors because they regard them as the same kind of vectors, which enables their bidirecional associations.

References

[1] T.Kohonen, Self-organized formation of topographically correct feature maps, Biol. Cybern., 43, 59-69, 1982

[2] H.Ritter T.Kohonen, Self-Organizing Semantic Maps, Biol. Cybern. 61, pp.241-254, 1989

[3] J.Urata T.Koizumi S.Taniguchi, Phoneme Recognition Using Self-organizing Feature Maps and HMMs, IEICE Tech. Report,NLC90-26 pp.61, 1990

[4] M.Tateishi T.Kinoshita, Handwritten Character Recognition Model using Kohonen's Feature Map and Multi Layer Perceptron Networks, IEICE Tech. Report, NC91-84 pp.13, 1991

[5] T.Hirano M.Sase Y.Kosugi, The Characteristics of Bidirectional Feature Map which Expanded from Counter Propagation, IEICE Tech. Report, NC91-43 pp.99, 1991

[6] B.Kosko. Bidirectional associative memories, Appl. Opt., vol. 18, no. 1, pp. 49-60, Jan./Feb. 1988.

[7] Yeou-Fang Wang , Jose B.Cruz JR. , James H.Mulligan JR. , Two Coding Strategies for Bidirectional Associative Memory, IEEE Trans. on Neural Networks, Vol.1,No.1,March 1990

[8] M.Hagiwara, Novel back propagation algorithm for reduction of hidden units and acceleration of convergence using artificial selection, International Joint Conference on Neural Networks, II, pp. 625-630 (1990-06)

[9] Gorman, R. P., and Sejnowski, T. J. (1988). "Analysis of Hidden Units in a Layered Network Trained to Classify Sonar Targets" in Neural Networks, Vol. 1, pp. 75-89.

Classification with Missing and Uncertain Inputs

Subutai Ahmad
Siemens Research, ZFE ST SN61,
Otto-Hahn Ring 6, 8000 Munich 83, Germany.
ahmad@icsi.berkeley.edu

Volker Tresp
Siemens Research, ZFE ST SN41,
Otto-Hahn Ring 6, 8000 Munich 83, Germany.
tresp@inf21.zfe.siemens.de

Abstract--In many classification tasks the ability to deal with missing or uncertain inputs is crucial. In this paper we discuss some Bayesian techniques for extracting class probabilities given only partial or noisy inputs. The optimal solution involves integrating over the missing dimensions weighted by the local probability densities. We then show how to obtain closed-form approximations to the Bayesian solution using gaussian basis function networks. Simulation results on the complex task of 3D hand gesture recognition validate the theory. Using the Bayesian technique significant information can be extracted even in the presence of a large amount of noise. The results also show that a classifier that works well with perfect inputs is not necessarily very good at dealing with missing or noisy inputs.

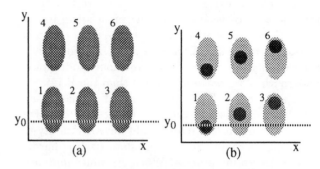

Fig. 1. The images show two possible situations for a 6-class classification problem. (Dark shading denotes high-probability regions.) If the value of feature x is unknown, the correct solution depends both on the classification boundaries along the missing dimension and on the distribution of exemplars.

I. INTRODUCTION

The ability of classifiers to deal with missing inputs or features is vital in many real-world situations. To date this issue has not been dealt with in neural networks in a systematic way. Instead the usual practice is to substitute a single value for the missing feature (e.g. *0*, the mean value of the feature, or a pre-computed value) and use the network's output on that feature vector. With noisy values the usual practice is to just use the measured noisy features directly. The point of this paper is to show that this approach is not optimal. By applying standard statistical techniques to neural networks, we can in fact do much better.

A simple example serves to illustrate why one needs to be careful in dealing with this problem. Consider the situation depicted in Fig. 1(a). It shows a *2-d* feature space with *6* possible classes. Assume a network has already been trained to correctly classify these regions. During classification of a novel exemplar, only feature *y* has been measured, as y_0; the value of feature *x* is unknown. For each class C_i, we would like to compute $p(C_i=1|y=y_0)$. One possibility would be to simply substitute zero (or perhaps the mean value of x) in place of the missing value. This would result in the classifier assigning a probability near 1 to class 1 (or 2 if the mean is used). Since nothing is known about x, the classifier should assign classes 1-3 a uniform probability *1/3* and classes 4-6 a probability of 0. Note that substituting any *single* value will always produce the wrong result. For example, if the mean value of x is substituted,

the classifier would assign a probability near 1 for class 2. To obtain the correct posterior, it is necessary to integrate the network output over all values of x. But there is one other fact to consider: the probable values of x may be highly constrained by the known feature y. With a distribution as in Fig. 1(b) the classifier should assign class 1 the highest probability. Thus it is necessary to *integrate over the values of x along the line $y=y_0$ weighted by the joint distribution p(x,y)*. When features are uncertain (i.e. $y=y_0$ and $x=x_0 + noise$) the solution is similar except that the integration should also be weighted according to the noise model.

Correct solutions incorporating the above intuitions would be important. In real-world applications features often highly constrain each other so classifiers must be able to deal with unusual distributions. We will consider one such example in our simulations in Section IV.

II. MISSING AND UNCERTAIN INPUTS

We first show how the intituitive arguments for missing inputs can be formalized using Bayes rule. Let $\grave{x}$ represent a complete feature vector. We assume the classifier outputs reasonable estimates of $p(C_i|\grave{x})$. In a given instance, $\grave{x}$ can be split up into $\grave{x}_c$, the vector of known (certain) features, and $\grave{x}_u$, the unknown features. When features are missing the task is to estimate $p(C_i|\grave{x}_c)$. Computing marginal probabilities:

$$p(C_i|\overset{\rightharpoonup}{x}_c) = \frac{\int p(C_i, \overset{\rightharpoonup}{x}_c, \overset{\rightharpoonup}{x}_u)\, d\overset{\rightharpoonup}{x}_u}{p(\overset{\rightharpoonup}{x}_c)}$$

$$= \frac{\int p(C_i|\overset{\rightharpoonup}{x}_c, \overset{\rightharpoonup}{x}_u)\, p(\overset{\rightharpoonup}{x}_c, \overset{\rightharpoonup}{x}_u)\, d\overset{\rightharpoonup}{x}_u}{p(\overset{\rightharpoonup}{x}_c)} \qquad (1)$$

Note that $p(C_i|\overset{\rightharpoonup}{x}_c, \overset{\rightharpoonup}{x}_u)$ is approximated by the network output and that in order to use (1) effectively we need estimates of the joint probabilities of the inputs.

A. Uncertain Inputs

In many situations feature values are noisy. The standard approach has been to simply use the noisy value, but as with the missing inputs case, using any single value is suboptimal. In particular, if some information about the noise is available, it is possible to obtain a better estimate. The missing feature scenario can be extended to deal with noisy inputs. (Missing features are simply noisy features in the limiting case of complete noise.) Let $\overset{\rightharpoonup}{x}_c$ be the vector of features measured with complete certainty, $\overset{\rightharpoonup}{x}_u$ the vector of measured, uncertain features, and $\overset{\rightharpoonup}{x}_{tu}$ the true values of the features in $\overset{\rightharpoonup}{x}_u$. $p(\overset{\rightharpoonup}{x}_u|\overset{\rightharpoonup}{x}_{tu})$ denotes our knowledge of the noise (i.e. the probability of measuring the (uncertain) value $\overset{\rightharpoonup}{x}_u$ given that the true value is $\overset{\rightharpoonup}{x}_{tu}$). We assume that this is independent of $\overset{\rightharpoonup}{x}_c$ and C_i, i.e. that $P(\overset{\rightharpoonup}{x}_u|\overset{\rightharpoonup}{x}_{tu}, \overset{\rightharpoonup}{x}_c, C_i) = P(\overset{\rightharpoonup}{x}_u|\overset{\rightharpoonup}{x}_{tu})$. (Of course the value of $\overset{\rightharpoonup}{x}_{tu}$ is dependent on $\overset{\rightharpoonup}{x}_c$ and C_i.)

We want to compute $p(C_i|\overset{\rightharpoonup}{x}_c, \overset{\rightharpoonup}{x}_u)$. This can be expressed as:

$$p(C_i|\overset{\rightharpoonup}{x}_c, \overset{\rightharpoonup}{x}_u) = \frac{\int p(\overset{\rightharpoonup}{x}_c, \overset{\rightharpoonup}{x}_u, \overset{\rightharpoonup}{x}_{tu}|C_i)\, p(C_i)\, d\overset{\rightharpoonup}{x}_{tu}}{p(\overset{\rightharpoonup}{x}_c, \overset{\rightharpoonup}{x}_u)}$$

$$= \frac{\int p(\overset{\rightharpoonup}{x}_c, \overset{\rightharpoonup}{x}_u, \overset{\rightharpoonup}{x}_{tu}, C_i)\, d\overset{\rightharpoonup}{x}_{tu}}{p(\overset{\rightharpoonup}{x}_c, \overset{\rightharpoonup}{x}_u)} \qquad (2)$$

According to our assumption:

$$p(\overset{\rightharpoonup}{x}_c, \overset{\rightharpoonup}{x}_u, \overset{\rightharpoonup}{x}_{tu}, C_i) = p(\overset{\rightharpoonup}{x}_u|\overset{\rightharpoonup}{x}_c, \overset{\rightharpoonup}{x}_{tu}, C_i)\, p(\overset{\rightharpoonup}{x}_c, \overset{\rightharpoonup}{x}_{tu}, C_i)$$

$$= p(\overset{\rightharpoonup}{x}_u|\overset{\rightharpoonup}{x}_{tu})\, p(C_i|\overset{\rightharpoonup}{x}_c, \overset{\rightharpoonup}{x}_{tu})\, p(\overset{\rightharpoonup}{x}_c, \overset{\rightharpoonup}{x}_{tu})$$

and:

$$p(\overset{\rightharpoonup}{x}_c, \overset{\rightharpoonup}{x}_u) = \int p(\overset{\rightharpoonup}{x}_u|\overset{\rightharpoonup}{x}_c, \overset{\rightharpoonup}{x}_{tu})\, p(\overset{\rightharpoonup}{x}_c, \overset{\rightharpoonup}{x}_{tu})\, d\overset{\rightharpoonup}{x}_{tu}$$

$$= \int p(\overset{\rightharpoonup}{x}_u|\overset{\rightharpoonup}{x}_{tu})\, p(\overset{\rightharpoonup}{x}_c, \overset{\rightharpoonup}{x}_{tu})\, d\overset{\rightharpoonup}{x}_{tu}$$

Substituting back into (2) we get:

$$p(C_i|\overset{\rightharpoonup}{x}_c, \overset{\rightharpoonup}{x}_u) = \qquad (3)$$

$$\frac{\int p(C_i|\overset{\rightharpoonup}{x}_c, \overset{\rightharpoonup}{x}_{tu})\, p(\overset{\rightharpoonup}{x}_c, \overset{\rightharpoonup}{x}_{tu})\, p(\overset{\rightharpoonup}{x}_u|\overset{\rightharpoonup}{x}_{tu})\, d\overset{\rightharpoonup}{x}_{tu}}{\int p(\overset{\rightharpoonup}{x}_c, \overset{\rightharpoonup}{x}_{tu})\, p(\overset{\rightharpoonup}{x}_u|\overset{\rightharpoonup}{x}_{tu})\, d\overset{\rightharpoonup}{x}_{tu}}$$

As before, $p(C_i|\overset{\rightharpoonup}{x}_c, \overset{\rightharpoonup}{x}_{tu})$ is given by the classifier. (3) is almost the same as (1) except that the integral now has to be weighted by the noise model. As with the missing feature case using any single value (such as the measured values) is suboptimal. Note that in the case of complete uncertainty about the features (i.e. the noise is uniform), the equations reduce to the missing feature case.

III. TWO COMMON CLASSIFIERS

The above discussion shows how to optimally deal with missing and uncertain inputs in a statistical sense. We now show how these equations can be approximated using two common neural network classifiers.

A. Gaussian Basis Function Networks

Let us consider networks with Gaussian basis functions (GBF nets) with diagonal covariance matrices [4]. Such networks have proven to be useful in a number of real-world applications [7]. Each hidden unit is characterized by a mean vector $\overset{\rightharpoonup}{\mu}_j$ and by $\overset{\rightharpoonup}{\sigma}_j$, a vector representing the diagonal of the covariance matrix. The network output is:

$$y_i(\overset{\rightharpoonup}{x}) = \frac{\sum_j w_{ij} b_j(\overset{\rightharpoonup}{x})}{\sum_j b_j(\overset{\rightharpoonup}{x})} \qquad (4)$$

with $b_j(\overset{\rightharpoonup}{x}) = \pi_j n(\overset{\rightharpoonup}{x}; \overset{\rightharpoonup}{\mu}_j, \overset{\rightharpoonup}{\sigma}_j^2)$

$$= \frac{\pi_j}{(2\pi)^{\frac{d}{2}} \prod_k^d \overset{\rightharpoonup}{\sigma}_{kj}} exp\left[-\sum_i^d \frac{(x_i - \mu_{ji})^2}{2\overset{\rightharpoonup}{\sigma}_{ji}^2} \right]$$

w_{ji} is the weight from the j'th basis unit to the i'th output unit, π_j is the probability of choosing unit j, and d is the dimensionality of $\overset{\rightharpoonup}{x}$. Under certain training regimes such as Gaussian mixture modeling, EM or "soft clustering" [1-2, 4] or an approximation as in [3] the hidden units adapt to represent local probability densities. For our purposes, a major advantage of this architecture is that the densities required in (3) are directly approximated. In particular $y_i(\overset{\rightharpoonup}{x}) \approx p(C_i|\overset{\rightharpoonup}{x})$ and $p(\overset{\rightharpoonup}{x}) \approx \sum_j b_j(\overset{\rightharpoonup}{x})$. In this section we show how this can be exploited to obtain closed form solutions to (1) and (3). Substituting into (3):

$$p(C_i|\overset{\rightharpoonup}{x}_c, \overset{\rightharpoonup}{x}_u) =$$

$$\frac{\int y_i(\vec{x}_c, \vec{x}_{lu})\left(\sum_j b_j(\vec{x}_c, \vec{x}_{lu})\right) p(\vec{x}_u|\vec{x}_{lu}) d\vec{x}_{lu}}{\int \left(\sum_j b_j(\vec{x}_c, \vec{x}_{lu})\right) p(\vec{x}_u|\vec{x}_{lu}) d\vec{x}_{lu}}$$

$$= \frac{\int \left(\sum_j w_{ij} b_j(\vec{x}_c, \vec{x}_{lu})\right) p(\vec{x}_u|\vec{x}_{lu}) d\vec{x}_{lu}}{\int \left(\sum_j b_j(\vec{x}_c, \vec{x}_{lu})\right) p(\vec{x}_u|\vec{x}_{lu}) d\vec{x}_{lu}} \tag{5}$$

As noted before, (1) is simply (3) with $p(\vec{x}_u|\vec{x}_{lu})$ uniform. The indefinite integral along each dimension of a multivariate normal density is one so (5) can now be computed directly. So for the case of missing features we get:

$$p(C_i|\vec{x}_c) \approx \frac{\sum_j w_{ji} b_j(\vec{x}_c)}{\sum_j b_j(\vec{x}_c)} \tag{6}$$

(Here $b_j(\vec{x}_c)$ denotes the same function as in (4) except that it is only evaluated over $\vec{x}_c$.) Equation (6) is appealing since it gives us a closed form solution. Intuitively the solution is nothing more than projecting the Gaussians onto the dimensions which are available and evaluating the resulting network.

B. GBF Networks with Uncertain Features

With noisy features the situation is a little more complicated and the solution depends on the form of the noise. If the noise is known to be uniform in some region $[\vec{a}, \vec{b}]$ then (5) becomes:

$$P(C_i|\vec{x}_c, \vec{x}_u) = \frac{\int_{\vec{a}}^{\vec{b}} \left(\sum_j w_{ij} b_j(\vec{x}_c, \vec{x}_{lu})\right) d\vec{x}_{lu}}{\int_{\vec{a}}^{\vec{b}} \left(\sum_j b_j(\vec{x}_c, \vec{x}_{lu})\right) d\vec{x}_{lu}}$$

$$= \frac{\sum_j w_{ij} b_j(\vec{x}_c) \int_{\vec{a}}^{\vec{b}} b_j(\vec{x}_{lu}) d\vec{x}_{lu}}{\sum_j b_j(\vec{x}_c) \int_{\vec{a}}^{\vec{b}} b_j(\vec{x}_{lu}) d\vec{x}_{lu}} \tag{7}$$

$$\int_{\vec{a}}^{\vec{b}} b_j(\vec{x}_{lu}) d\vec{x}_{lu} = \prod_{i \in U} \int_{a_i}^{b_i} n(x_i; \mu_{ij}, \sigma_{ij}^2) dx_i$$

$$= \prod_{i \in U} [N(b_i; \mu_{ij}, \sigma_{ij}^2) - N(a_i; \mu_{ij}, \sigma_{ij}^2)] \tag{8}$$

Here $\vec{\mu}_{ij}$ and $\vec{\sigma}_{ij}^2$ select the i'th component of the j'th mean and variance vectors. U ranges over the noisy feature indices. Good closed form approximations to the normal distri-

bution function $N(x; \mu, \sigma^2)$ are available [5].

In the case of Gaussian noise we can also write down a closed form solution. In this case we have to integrate a product of two Gaussians. If the variance of the noise is σ_u^2 we end up with:

$$p(C_i|\vec{x}_c, \vec{x}_u) = \frac{\sum_j w_{ij} b'_j(\vec{x}_c, \vec{x}_u)}{\sum_j b'_j(\vec{x}_c, \vec{x}_u)}$$

where $b'_j(\vec{x}_c, \vec{x}_u) = n(\vec{x}_u; \vec{\mu}_{ju}, \vec{\sigma}_u^2 + \vec{\sigma}_{ju}^2) b_j(\vec{x}_c)$

C. Backpropagation Networks

As the number of samples tends to infinity, the outputs of a network trained with back-propagation using the LMS error function converges to the optimal Bayes a posteriori estimates of the class memberhips [6]. Let $B_i(\vec{x})$ be the output of the i'th output unit when presented with input $\vec{x}$. Then, assuming the network has been trained on a large enough training set, $B_i(\vec{x}) \approx p(C_i|\vec{x})$. Unfortunately, unlike basis function networks, access to the input distribution is not available with backpropagation. However (3) can still be exploited to provide some information. If we assume that the input distribution is uniform, the right hand side of (3) can be simplfied to:

$$p(C_i|\vec{x}_c) \approx \frac{\int p(C_i|\vec{x}_c, \vec{x}_{lu}) p(\vec{x}_u|\vec{x}_{lu}) d\vec{x}_{lu}}{\int p(\vec{x}_u|\vec{x}_{lu}) d\vec{x}_{lu}} \tag{9}$$

If the noise is uniform in an interval $[\vec{a}, \vec{b}]$, then this reduces to (ignoring normalizing constants):

$$p(C_i|\vec{x}_c) \approx \int_a^b p(C_i|\vec{x}_c, \vec{x}_{lu}) d\vec{x}_{lu} \tag{10}$$

This equation is appealing since only an estimate of $p(C_i|\vec{x})$ is required. (The intergral may be approximated using standard Monte Carlo techniques [5].) Strictly these are only valid in restricted situations but even a degraded estimate using (9) or (10) should be better than random guessing. With missing features the integral in (10) should be computed over the entire range of each missing features.

IV. AN EXAMPLE TASK: 3D HAND GESTURE RECOGNITION

A simple realistic example serves to illustrate the utility of the above techniques. We consider the task of recognizing a set of hand gestures from single 2D images independent of 3D orientation (Fig. 2). As input, each classifier is given the 2D polar coordinates of the five fingertip positions relative to the 2D center of mass of the hand (so the input space is 10-dimensional). Each classifier is trained on a training set of 4368 examples (624 poses for each gesture) and tested on a similar independent test set.

The task forms a good benchmark for testing performance with missing and uncertain inputs. The classification task itself is non-trivial. The classifier must learn to deal with hands (which are complex non-rigid objects) and with perspective transformation. In fact it is impossible to obtain a perfect score since in certain poses some of the gestures are indistinguishable (e.g. when the hand is pointing directly at the screen). Moreover, the task is characteristic of real vision problems. The position of each finger is highly (but not completely) constrained by the others resulting in a very non-uniform input distribution. Finally it is often easy to see what the classifier should output if features are uncertain. For example suppose the real gesture is "five" but for some reason the features from the thumb are not reliably computed. In this case the gestures "four" and "five" should both get a positive probability whereas the rest should get zero. (No other class in the training set contains a gesture with the other four fingers extended.) In many such cases only a single class should get the highest score, e.g. if the features for the little finger are uncertain the correct class is still "five".

The theory predicts that classifiers with knowledge about the probability distribution would perform best with missing or uncertain features. To test this we tried out three different classifiers on this task: standard sigmoidal networks trained with backpropagation (BP), and two types of gaussian networks as described in (4). In the first (Gauss-RBF), the gaussians were radial and the centers were determined using k-means clustering as in [3]. σ^2 was set to

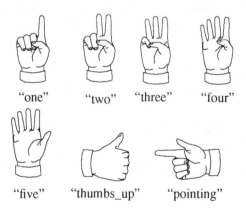

Fig. 2. Examples of the 7 gestures used to train the classifier. A 3D computer model of the hand is used to generate images of the hand in various poses. For each training example, we choose a 3D orientation, compute the 3D positions of the fingertips and project them onto 2D. For this task we assume that the correspondence between image and model features are known, and that during training all feature values are always available.

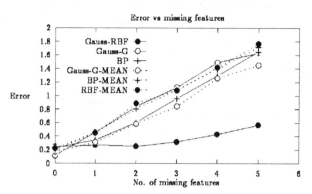

Fig. 3. The error of various classifiers when dealing with missing features. Each data point denotes an average over 1000 random samples from an independent test set. For each sample, random features were considered missing. The graph plots the average number of classes that were ranked above the correct class.

twice the average distance of each point to its nearest gaussian (all gaussians had the same width). After clustering, π_j was set to:

$$\pi_j = \sum_k \left[\frac{n(\dot{x}_k; \dot{\mu}_j; \dot{\sigma}_j^2)}{\sum_i n(\dot{x}_k; \dot{\mu}_i; \dot{\sigma}_i^2)} \right]$$

The output weights were then determined using LMS gradient descent. In the second (Gauss-G), each gaussian had a unique diagonal covariance matrix. The centers and variances were determined using gradient descent on all the parameters [7]. With this type of training, even though gaussian hidden units are used, there is no guarantee that the distribution information will be preserved. Both BP and Gauss-G were very good at learning the task. The best BP network (60 hidden units) managed to score 95.3% and 93.3% on the training and test sets, respectively. Gauss-G with 28 hidden units scored 94% and 92%. Gauss-RBF scored 97.7% and 91.4% but required 2000 units to achieve it. (Larger numbers of hidden units led to overtraining.)

A. Performance with Missing Inputs

We tested the performance of each network in the presence of missing features. For backpropagation we used a numerical approximation to (10). For both gaussian basis function networks we used (6). To test the networks we randomly picked samples from the test set and deleted random features. We calculated an error score as the average number of classes that were ranked above the correct class. Fig. 4 displays the results. For comparison we also tested each classifier by substituting the mean value of each missing feature and using the normal update equation.

It is clear from the figure that the performance of Gauss-RBF was consistently better than the others. BP and Gauss-G performed relatively poorly. This agrees well with the theory which predicts good performance when the input distribution is taken into account. Perhaps most astonishing (and encouraging) is the result that even with 50% of the features missing, Gauss-RBF chooses the correct class about half the time. Further inspection shows that, in fact, Gauss-RBF ranks the correct class among the top two scores almost 90% of the time. This clearly shows that if the distribution is taken into account, and the missing features are integrated out, then a significant amount of information can be extracted.

B. Performance with Noisy Inputs

We also tested the performance of each network in the presence of noisy features. We randomly picked samples from the test set and added uniform noise to random features. The noise interval was calculated as $[x_i - 2\sigma_i, x_i + 2\sigma_i]$ where x_i is the feature value and σ_i is the standard deviation of that feature over the training set. (For all features, $2\sigma_i$ corresponded to about 1/3 of the entire range of feature values so the noise interval was quite large.) The error measure was the same as the missing feature case. For BP we used to (10) evaluated over the noise interval. For both gaussian basis function networks we used (8) evaluated over the noise interval. Fig. 4 displays the results. For comparison we also tested each classifier by substituting the noisy value of each noisy feature and using the normal update equation.

As with missing features, the performance of Gauss-RBF was much better than the others with a large number of noisy features. BP and Gauss-G both performed poorly when the number of noisy features was large. The error y substituting the measured noisy value was consistently the worst indicating that, in the presence of some noise, the integration step might be crucial. As would be expected, overall performance was better than with missing features (note the change in scale from Fig. 4). Again, the performance of Gauss-RBF under a large amount of noise is quite encouraging.

V. DISCUSSION

In our opinion the performance of Gauss-RBF clearly shows the advantages of estimating the input distribution and computing the integrals. The results are not due to the use of gaussian hidden units over sigmoidal units since both BP and Gauss-G performed poorly. However on complete input vectors Gauss-RBF was not the best. To get the best of both worlds, one could possible use an alternate "hybrid" technique: e.g. numerically integrate (9) and use Gauss-RBF to estimate the probabilities combined with either BP or Gauss-G for classification.

One way to improve the performance of BP and Gauss-

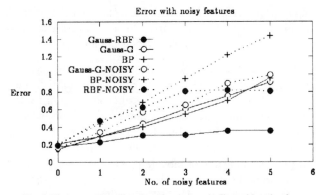

Fig. 4. The error of various classifiers when dealing with noisy features. Each data point denotes an average over 1000 random samples from an independent test set. For each sample, random features were considered missing. The graph plots the average number of classes that were ranked above the correct class.

G might be to use a training set that contained missing features. Given the unusual distributions that can arise in real-world applications, in order to guarantee accuracy such a training set should include every possible combination of missing features. In addition, for each such combination, enough patterns must be included to accurately estimate the posterior density. In general this type of training is impractical since the number of combinations is exponential in the number of features. Note that if input distribution is available (as in Gauss-RBF), then such a training scenario is unnecessary.

There are a number of tradeoffs which must be considered in deciding which classifier to use. Although Gauss-RBF performed well in this task, these types of networks encounter problems if the input dimensionality is high. Even with 10 inputs the network required a large number of hidden units for good performance. (Although this would decrease if a diagonal covariance matrix was used, it is unclear whether the total number of parameters would decrease.) Due to this problem, in higher dimensions BP or Gauss-G might be the tool of choice despite the lack of distribution information.

Note that we have assumed in the discussion that enough training data is available to estimate the required densities. In some applications this can be a problem as little training data is available. In such cases some sort of prior information needs to be incorporated. We have not addressed this issue here but see [8] for one approach to this problem.

ACKNOWLEDGMENT

We thank D. Goryn, C. Maggioni, S. Omohundro, A. Stolcke, and R. Schuster for helpful discussions, and also B. Wirtz for providing the computer hand model. V.T. is supported in part by a grant from the Bundesministerium für Forschung und Technologie.

REFERENCES

[1] A.P. Dempster, N.M. Laird, and D.B. Rubin. Maximum-likelihood from incomplete data via the EM algorithm. *J. Royal Statistical Soc. Ser. B*, **39**:1-38, 1977.

[2] R. O. Duda and P. E. Hart. *Pattern Classification and Scene Analysis*. New York: John Wiley & Sons., 1973.

[3] J. Moody and C. Darken. Learning with localized receptive fields. In: D. Touretzky, G. Hinton, T. Sejnowski, (eds.), *Proceedings of the 1988 Connectionist Models Summer School*, San Mateo, CA: Morgan Kaufmann, 1988.

[4] S. Nowlan. Maximum Likelihood Competitive Learning. In: *Advances in Neural Information Processing Systems 4*, pages 574-582, 1990.

[5] W.H. Press, B.P. Flannery, S.A. Teukolsky, and W.T. Vetterling. *Numerical Recipes: The Art of Scientific Computing*, Cambridge, UK: Cambridge University Press, 1986.

[6] M. D. Richard and R.P. Lippmann. Neural Network Classifiers Estimate Bayesian *a posteriori* Probabilities, *Neural Computation*, **3**:461-483, 1991.

[7] M. Röscheisen, R. Hofman, and V. Tresp. Neural Control for Rolling Mills: Incorporating Domain Theories to Overcome Data Deficiency. In: *Advances in Neural Information Processing Systems 4*, pages 659-666, 1992.

[8] V. Tresp, J. Hollatz, and S. Ahmad. Network Structuring and Training Using Rule-based Knowledge. In: S. J. Hanson, J.D. Cowan, and C. L. Giles (eds.), *Advances in Neural Information Processing Systems 5*. San Mateo, CA: Morgan Kaufmann, 1993.

Adaptive Retina-Like Preprocessing for Imaging Detector Arrays

D. A. Scribner, K. A. Sarkady, M. R. Kruer, J. T. Caulfield,
J. D. Hunt, M. Colbert, and M. Descour

Naval Research Laboratory, Code 5652

Washington, DC 20375

Abstract—This paper discusses retina-like processing techniques to perform nonuniformity correction of infrared focal plane arrays (IRFPA). The objective of the work is to design and test electronic structures based on early vision processes in the vertebra retina. Two adaptive techniques have been successfully developed. Both are stable and convergent and have been used to process existing infrared images in non-realtime on the NRL Connection machine as well as implemented on a realtime image array processor interfaced to an IRFPA in the laboratory. Conceptual designs for an analog chip have been prepared and partially simulated.

I. INTRODUCTION

Advanced imaging sensors will use staring detector arrays which are now becoming available in large formats and in different spectral bands (e.g. ultraviolet, visible, and infrared). In some cases detector arrays are being fabricated with greater than 10^6 detectors per chip. Although detector array technology has been developing rapidly, there are still many fundamental problems with respect to generating high quality images, particularly in non-silicon-based detector arrays.

One example of an imaging problem with infrared detector arrays [1] (IRFPA) is that no two detector channels respond exactly alike. Even though all the detector channels may be very low in noise, their outputs may all be uniquely nonlinear or have nonuniform responses. Similar non-idealities also occur in the photoreceptors of biological retinas, and yet in spite of these problems, biological retinas are still able to provide superior imaging capabilities through the use of neural processing. In fact, the retina is an excellent neural system to study not only imaging arrays but also for the purpose of solving the general problem of self-calibration of unit cells within an analog network.

Over the past several years, we have been studying retina-like processes and applying them in the area of IRFPA nonuniformity correction (NUC). It is interesting to note that in the general literature on the retina there does not seem to be any explicit discussion of how this process is performed in the retina. With regard to human retinas, measurements of the center-to-center spacing of individual photoreceptors yields a variation of $\pm 10\%$ [2]. This variation alone implies a corresponding difference in area and would result in a very noisy image if left uncorrected. We believe the retina is able to perform this type of correction and deal with response nonuniformity and several other types of non-idealities in a very elegant and efficient manner.

Biological systems process images in a completely different manner than digital image processing systems. Although retinal processes are only partially understood, the neural structure and some of the underlying principles are known. Of particular relevancy to our work has been the lateral spread of information and associated processing across the outer plexiform layer of the retina. Another important retinal feature is the temporal processing performed in the bipolar cells.

Our objective has been to design and simulate retina-like electronic structures derived from existing studies of early vision processes in vertebrate retinas. This will ultimately lead to micro-electronic *neural* chips that could be used to accomplish important functions such as gain-control, dynamic range compression, and photoreceptor nonuniformity correction.

NRL has been involved in three basic areas: 1) conceptualizing and mathematically modeling specific electronic neural networks for IRFPA processing and analyzing stability and nonlinear behavior, and making performance predictions; 2) testing these networks on a massively parallel computer (e.g., the Connection Machine) and on a realtime image array processor to study the resulting image transforms and special processing features; 3) refining these *neural algorithms* and conceptual designs for implementation as electronic networks using either high speed digital boards or analog VLSI technology.

II. Structures, Processing Techniques, and Analysis

Work at NRL on performance measurements and calibration of IRFPA's has been in progress for a number of years and recently has been expanded to include adaptive nonuniformity correction (NUC) techniques [3]. Our preliminary efforts have focused on two adaptive NUC structures which have been devised and tested as digital software algorithms. They generally incorporate aspects of the temporal response of bipolar cells and the spatial responses of horizonal cells in the retina. Theoretical analysis and experimental testing have shown these methods to be stable and convergent.

The first NUC technique (shown schematically in Fig. 1 and discussed in reference 3) operates basically as an array of temporal highpass filters (THPF), one for each detector in a staring IRFPA. This is accomplished by using a temporal lowpass filter and differencing this result with the input signal. This is roughly equivalent to taking a running average of the output signal of each detector and differencing it with the input signal. In our work we used an *infinite impulse response* digital filter, which is computationally much more efficient than performing a running average. Because image sequences are highly correlated on a local scale, the process essentially computes an offset correction coefficient for each detector. Bipolar cells in the retina are believed to perform lowpass temporal filtering and difference their outputs with the photoreceptor output in a similar manner [4].

The second NUC technique, which is derived using an adaptive least mean squares (LMS) approach, is shown schematically in Fig. 2a and discussed in reference 3. It is structured as a recurrent neural network with a hidden layer that is similar to the structure of the photoreceptors and horizonal cells in the retina. Local neighborhood sums are compared to photoreceptor outputs to compute nonuniformities and this information is fedback to the photoreceptor layer. A least mean square error function is used in conjunction with the method of steepest descent to derive an iterative algorithm that slowly optimizes gain and offset coefficients over a nominal time period of 10 to 100 frames. An important aspect of the LMS algorithm is that it uses neighborhood processing to compute the gain and offset correction coefficients. Thus some of the information computed can be used to perform dynamic range compression of the output image [5]. This is important because input images from IR sensors with 12 to 14 bits of dynamic range can be represented with fewer bits making analog processing more feasible and allowing for eventual on-chip neural based processing.

The effects of image motion on the focal plane are important to both the THPF and LMS techniques studied.

Although motion is needed, it need not be large and can be easily achieved by slow random dither or by slow panning motions. Again, this is very similar to the case of biological retinas where drift and saccadic motion of the eye are always at work [6]. For example, in human vision, involuntary drift motion is at a rate of approximately 20 photoreceptors per second.

Before discussing these two techniques in more detail, it is important to understand how IRFPA's have been calibrated and operated in the past. A simple calibration mode, two-point nonuniformity correction technique assumes that each pixel can be corrected using the expression

$$y_{ij} = G_{ij} \cdot x_{ij}(\phi_{ij}) + O_{ij} \qquad (1)$$

where $x_{ij}(\phi_{ij})$ is the uncorrected output voltage of each detector ij in a two dimensional focal plane array. $\phi_{ij}(t)$ is the time-dependent discrete image which is the irradiant photon flux on the detectors and G_{ij} and O_{ij} are the NUC gain and offset correction coefficients respectively determined by laboratory measurements and computations [7]. By storing these coefficients in the memory of a dedicated processor board, a fixed correction can be performed on a frame-by-frame basis. This approach can significantly improve performance. However in applications that demand very high sensitivity, any non-linearities or instabilities can greatly degrade performance. In these cases, adaptive NUC techniques can generally solve the problem. A brief discussion is given below of some theoretical and practical considerations associated with each adaptive technique.

THPF technique: The full implementation of the THPF shown in Fig. 1, would require an array of parallel filters - one THPF for each detector. Stability is not an issue as the THPF technique is in fact a linear filter. The filter inherently attenuates low temporal frequencies from the output of each detector on an individual basis and conversely passes high temporal frequencies. This can be shown very clearly using a z-transform analysis. If there is no image motion whatsoever, then the individual detectors have a constant output which implies all the signal energy is at zero frequency. In this case, the image begins to fade. If motion is restored, then edges and point sources create high temporal frequencies which are passed by the filter. For moderate image motion when viewing natural IR scenes, it is well known that most *clutter* has a power spectral density that is heavily weighted toward the low frequencies.

One limitation of the THPF technique is that it basically corrects only offset coefficients and not gain coefficients. Using this technique on an array of detectors that have both nonuniform offsets and gains would have limited effectiveness. However if the gains are relatively stable (albeit nonuniform) then pre-determined gain coefficients can be calculated and stored in memory as shown in Fig. 1 and as used in our implementation. The THPF technique has performed extremely well on many IR image sequences. Furthermore, its simplicity makes it very practical for realtime signal processing applications and possible on-chip implementations.

LMS technique: The network shown in Fig. 2 uses a hidden layer to sum local neighborhood outputs which are fedback to the two-point NUC *neurons* located at each input. The feedback allows comparisons between neighboring pixels as new frames of data are input, making it a spatio-temporal process. In this configuration, and assuming that the scene is always moving with respect to the detectors, the local spatial neighborhood average f_{ij} can be used to estimate the desired output of pixel ij. For example, using the four nearest neighbor pixels

$$f_{ij} = (x_{i,j+1} + x_{i-1,j} + x_{i,j-1} + x_{i+1,j})/4.$$

To simplify the notation, we drop all the following subscripts for ij. Thus Eq.(1) can be rewritten in terms of the approximate desired output of pixel ij as

$$f \approx Gx + O$$

and the resulting error function F for all incorrect values of G and O can be written as

$$F(G,O) = (Gx + O - f)^2. \qquad (2)$$

Using this simple error function the correct values for G and O can be found by applying the *method of steepest descent* [8] to sequential inputs of each x_{ij} to obtain recursive estimates of G and O. The gradient of $F(G,O)$ essentially gives the direction of the path of steepest descent and has components in the G- and O-*directions* of

$$F_G = \frac{\partial F}{\partial G} = 2x(Gx + O - f)$$

$$F_O = \frac{\partial F}{\partial O} = 2(Gx + O - f).$$

The descending path, using a frame-by-frame iteration and substituting Eq.(1), can be written as two discrete expressions:

$$G_{n+1} = G_n - 2\alpha x(y - f)$$

$$O_{n+1} = O_n - 2\alpha(y - f). \qquad (3)$$

The term α controls the step size (which must be chosen to be small enough to ensure stability) and n is the frame number.

A number of important issues must be considered when implementing Eqs.(3) in terms of stability and convergence. Although a full discussion of these problems is beyond the scope of this paper, we have used Lyapunov functions and eigenvalue analysis to study these issues. Some modifications to the algorithms given in Eqs.(3) are to normalize the inputs ($0 \leq x \leq 2$) and globally normalize the gains to a mean of unity after each frame.

III. IMAGE PROCESSING RESULTS

Both correction techniques have been applied to real image sequences digitally recorded from a number of IRFPA's including a HgCdTe, InSb, and a ferroelectric uncooled array. The processing was performed on the NRL Connection Machine (a large parallel computer with 16K processors). In all cases quantitative results were obtained by computing local spatial noise values of image segments for both standard 2-point corrected images and those processed with adaptive NUC techniques. Generally, these results were very favorable, however, storage of very large image sequences became impractical and limited our ability to obtain long term processing results with real infrared image data.

For the real-time testing, a laboratory experiment was configured as shown schematically in Fig. 3. The primary technique tested was the LMS neural network (discussed above) that performs both gain and offset compensation. This technique was applied to the output of a HgCdTe 200 x 200 MWIR IRFPA array. A motor drive was used to create a slow motion of the image across the focal plane in both the horizonal (azimuthal) and vertical (elevation) directions. The motor drive controller was programmed using a pc. The motion of the mirror attached to the motor drive was typically only a few degrees in either direction in a slowly repeating pattern with speeds on the order of 10 pixels per second. Although it would be desirable to make direct comparisons between *two-point calibration mode* NUC and adaptive NUC techniques, the data processing was limited to a one-point correction (offset only) by the software in the image processor.

The purpose of the testing was to adaptively perform nonuniformity correction using image sequences in real-time under varying background conditions. Because the LMS neural network requires time to adjust coefficients, the step size α must be small enough such that there is no smearing of the image. On the other hand, α must be large enough such that the updating of the gain and offset coefficients occur at an expeditious rate so that the image is promptly updated. Another parameter that can be changed in the execution of the image processor is the number of interconnects between the nearest neighbors in the LMS neural network. For the purposes of testing, a full range of conditions were viewed on the RS-170 output monitor and trial-and-error adjustments were made. For test results shown in this paper, a value of $\alpha = 0.01$ was used and a nearest neighbor interconnect of 21 x 21 pixels.

Qualitative results from viewing barchart images revealed that the LMS neural network was capable of successfully processing very stressing images while remaining stable. Quantitative noise measurements showed that the neural network provided up to an order of magnitude better sensitivity than a simple one-point correction at extreme flux levels. As an example of the results obtained, pairs of images are shown in Figures 3 and 4. In each figure the image on the left is the one-point NUC result and the image on the right is the neural network result. It is clear from the one-point NUC images that there is a noticeable contrast inversion due to the correction (notice there is no contrast inversion of the barchart image). The inversion is caused by differences in the gains of the individual pixels. Observe that the round blotches tend to be white at low well capacity and black at high well capacity. This implies that these areas are of somewhat lower in gain. A small number of isolated pixels appear that have higher gains than average which results in black pixels at low well capacity and white pixels at high well capacities. Another more subtle effect is that a soft shading pattern appears across the image. Part of this effect can be seen as a dark area across the left side of the image at low well capacity and as a light area at high well capacity. This is believed to be a result of inhomogeneities in the IRFPA materials. Thus it is clear from the one-point NUC images that there is a significant variation in individual pixel gains which is a stressing condition for adaptive NUC techniques.

An area of concern is the ability of the LMS neural net to handle bad pixels. Experiments have shown that using very small interconnect neighborhoods tends to result in light or dark halos around bad pixels. The bad pixels (e.g., those with very low gains) can be corrected to a degree by finding an offset value equal to the mean background level. The halos can be effectively eliminated by increasing the neighborhood size.

IV. IMPLEMENTATION ISSUES

Some consideration has been given to implementing these techniques on highspeed digital boards as well as designing and fabricating analog VLSI circuits. The algorithms discussed above are easily implemented as digital software. The implementation as an analog chip is much more complex for several reasons. First, any non-idealities in the analog devices might create spatial noise which is the very thing we are trying to eliminate. Second, any spatial processing that requires global operations (such as normalizing the gains after each frame) would be impractical. With respect to the first point, we have carried out some simulations that indicate that our techniques can be made

self correcting. With regard to the second, for the LMS neural net, we have found that the use of a sigmoid activation function in the gain feedback loop alleviates the need for any global normalization.

The retina uses the basic characteristics of the photoreceptors and neurons as computational primitives [9]. Similarly, our implementation in VLSI has the important design goal to use as computational primitives, the basic device physics of the VLSI components. This will lead to massively parallel processing chips, that are very simple in their unit structures, very low in power, and fault tolerant. With this goal in mind we are using the following approach. The analog processing will be performed directly on the detector output - no charge storage. The generation of control currents for the gain and offset NUC coefficients can be accomplished with voltage controlled current sources. Gain and offset coefficients will be stored on capacitors. The most critical step is to design a controllable analog multiplier, which will be accomplished using a translinear multiplier concept [10].

V. SUMMARY

In summary, adaptive nonuniformity correction techniques offer improved performance compared to calibration mode techniques. Our experiments demonstrate that both the temporal highpass filter and the LMS neural network techniques can provide better sensitivity and increased dynamic range. Traditional *calibration* mode approaches to nonuniformity correction can be quite limiting when used in real sensors. Adaptive nonuniformity correction is expected to be very important in future IRFPA sensors because of the improved performance they offer. Our experiments demonstrate that the neural network can provide increased sensitivity. The techniques are stable, robust, and conceptually simple to implement as digital software. Future directions include: digital applications for scanning and staring sensors; experimental on-chip neuromorphic electronic design and fabrication; and improved algorithms with increased speed and performance.

REFERENCES

[1] D. A. Scribner, M. R. Kruer, and J. M. Killiany, "Infrared focal plane array technology," *Proc. IEEE,* vol. 79 pp. 66-85, Jan.1991.

[2] J. Hirsch and C. A. Curcio, "The spatial resolution capacity of human foveal retina," *Vision Research,* vol.29, p. 1095, 1989.

[3] D. A. Scribner, K. A. Sarkady, M. R. Kruer, and J. T. Caulfield, "Adaptive nonuniformity correction for staring IR focal plane arrays using neural networks", *SPIE* vol. 1541, 1991.

[4] J. C. Curlander and V. Z. Marmarelis, "Processing of visual information in the distal neurons of the vertebra retina", *IEEE SMC-13*, PP.934-943, 1983.

[5] C. Mead and M. A. Mahowald, "A silicon model of early visual processing", *Neural Networks*, vol. 1, pp. 91-97, 1988.

[6] U. Tulunay-Keeseym "The role of eye movements in maintenance of vision" in *Eye Movements and Psychological Processes*, R. A. Monty and J. W. Senders (Eds.), (Wiley, New York, 1976).

[7] A. F. Milton, F. R. Barone, and M. R. Kruer, "Influence of nonuniformity correction on infrared focal plane arrays," Opt. Eng., vol. 24, pp. 855-862, 1985.

[8] B. Widrow and S. D. Sterns, *Adaptive Signal Processing*, (Prentice Hall, New Jersey, 1985).

[9] C. Mead, "Neuromorphic electronic systems," *Proc. IEEE,* vol. 78, p. 1629, 1990.

[10] A. Andreau et. al., "Current-mode subthreshold MOS circuits for analog VLSI neural systems", *IEEE Trans. Neural Networks,* vol. 2, pp. 205-213, Mar. 1991.

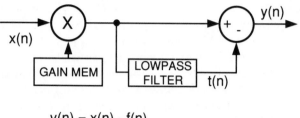

$$y(n) = x(n) - f(n)$$

$$f(n) = \frac{1}{M} \cdot x(n) + (1-\frac{1}{M})f(n-1)$$

WHERE M IS NO. OF FRAMES

FIGURE 1. TEMPORAL HIGHPASS FILTER FOR ADAPTIVE NONUNIFORMITY CORRECTION (ONE FILTER PER PIXEL).

(a) NEURAL NETWORK INTERCONNECTS

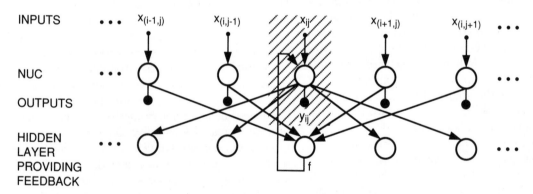

(b) PROCESSING WITHIN NEURON ij (HIGHLIGHTED ABOVE)

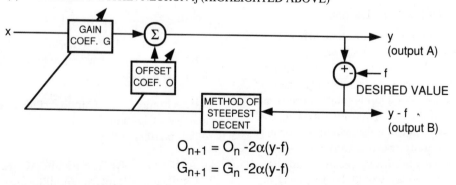

$$O_{n+1} = O_n - 2\alpha(y-f)$$
$$G_{n+1} = G_n - 2\alpha(y-f)$$

FIGURE 2. NEURAL NET FOR ADAPTIVE NONUNIFORMITY CORRECTION.

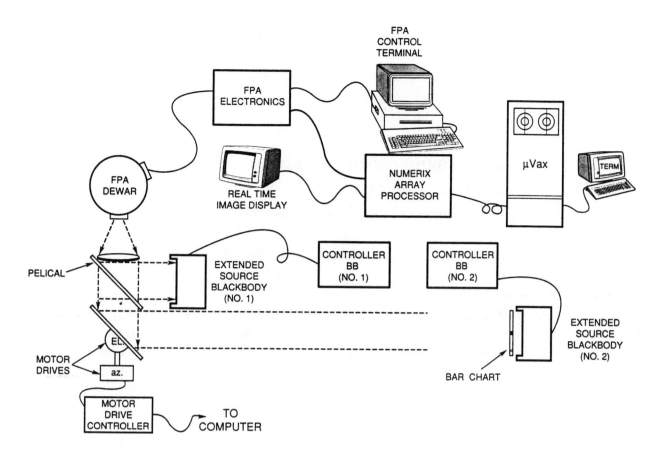

FIGURE 3. ADAPTIVE NUC REALTIME TEST SETUP AND DATA ACQUISITION SYSTEM

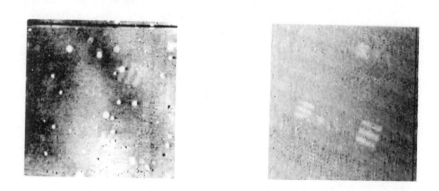

FIGURE 4. STANDARD ONE-POINT CALIBRATION VS. LMS NEURAL NETWORK AT 12% FLUX CAPACITY.

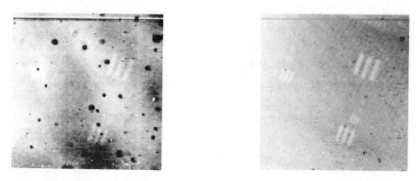

FIGURE 5. STANDARD ONE-POINT CALIBRATION VS. LMS NEURAL NETWORK AT 90% FLUX CAPACITY.

Autonomous Trajectory Generation of a Biped Locomotive Robot Using Neuro Oscillator

Yasuo Kurematsu, Takuji Maeda and Shinzo Kitamura
Department of Computer and Systems Engineering,
Faculty of Engineering, Kobe University

Abstract— The trajectory of a biped locomotive robot is generated using a neuro oscillator. This oscillator consists of four neuron cells which are mutually coupled with inhibitory connections. This model shows a stationary periodic oscillation for an appropriate set of parameters. Stability analysis of the neuro oscillator can be done by the linearization method. A stationary periodic oscillation appears in the unstable region for equilibrium states and this periodic oscillation generates a trajectory for stationary walking by assigning the state variables of neuron cells to joint angles of robot. The simulation studies assured the relevancy of the proposed method.

I. INTRODUCTION

Robots in future will be expected to work in the extreme environment, for example on the sea bottom or on the rough terrain, where a human cannot work. Biped locomotive robots will provide an efficient moving mechanism in such conditions. But there are difficulties in this mechanism, and many reserchers have attempted to develop prototypes of walking mechanism.[1, 2, 3, 4] Also the research on autonomous trajectory generation are important in order to develop intelligent and human-like robots, because a simple procedure cannot cope with the change of gait modes or with the disturbances caused by floor conditions. Some attempts in this direction have already been discussed.[5]

From a physiological viewpoint, some studies simulating the motion of animals by a neuron model have been reported.[6, 7]; further, dynamic biped locomotion by utilizing a stable limit cycle[8], the modeling of a neural pattern generator with coupled nonlinear oscillators [9], a biped locomotive motion using van der Pol oscillators[10], and the stable and flexible locomotion by global entrainment between the rhythmic activities of neural oscilltors and the rhythmic movements of a musculo-skeletal system.[11]

Under the background mentioned above, we have studied a neuro oscillator model consisting of four neuron cells, which generates the trajectory of a biped locomotive robot. Stability of the neuro oscillator was analyzed by the linearization around the equilibria. The walking modes were also examined in relation to the parameters in the model.

II. MODEL OF NEURO OSCILLATOR

A neuro oscillator consists of inhibitory connected neuron cells as in Figure 1 is considered. The ith neuron cell satisfies the following equations, which have been discussed in detail by Matsuoka.[12]

$$T_r\frac{dx_i}{dt} + x_i = -\sum_{j=0}^{n-1} a_{ij}y_j + s_i - bf_i$$

$$y_i = m_i x_i$$

$$m_i = \begin{cases} 1 & x_i \geq 0 \\ 0 & x_i < 0 \end{cases}$$

$$T_a\frac{df_i}{dt} + f_i = y_i$$

$$i = 0, 1, 2, \cdots, n-1 \tag{1}$$

where

x_i : internal state variable of the ith neuron

y_i : output variable of the ith neuron

f_i : variable that represents the degree of fatigue of the ith neuron

b : coefficient of the degree of fatigue

s_i : constant input to the ith neuron cell

a_{ij} : a weight of inhibitory synaptic connection from jth neuron to ith neuron

T_r, T_a : time constant

n : the number of neurons

When an appropriate set of parameters b, T_r, T_a, and a_{ij} is given to eqs.(1), they yield a periodic solution. The stability of this neuro oscillator is discussed in the section 5.

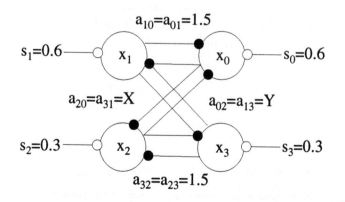

Figure 1: Structure of four neuron cells model

III. APPLICATION TO THE TRAJECTORY GENERATION OF A BIPED LOCOMOTIVE ROBOT

The trajectory generation system is shown in Figure 2.

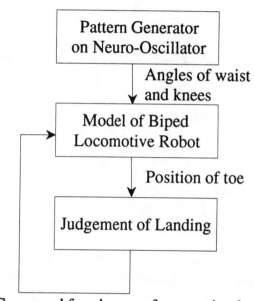

Figure 2: Trajectory generation system

The state variables of the neuro oscillator correspond to the absolute angles of robot's joints as in Figure 3. In this study, only the single leg supporting phase is assumed. Therefore, a supporting leg should be switched, when it lands at the floor, by another swinging leg. The stationary walking here was defined by the conditions;

- A knee does not bend reversely.

- The robot moves forward.

IV. SIMULATION RESULTS

A stick diagram of stationary walking yielded by the neuro oscillator with the parameters in Table 1 is shown in Figure 4. Lower four charts in Figure 4 are the waveforms corresponding to the time courses of the variables x_0 to x_3. Such

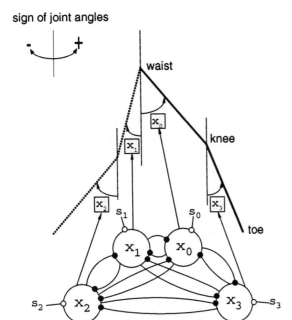

sign of joint angles

Figure 3: Correspondence between the neuro oscillator and the link model of a biped locomotive robot

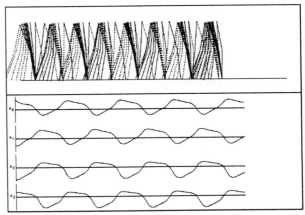

Figure 4: Simulation result for stationary walking

trajectories are robust in the sense that the generated limit-cycle in the phase-plane is asymptotically stable. An example is shown in Figure 5 where an impulsive disturbance was added to the waist joint angle at the point *, and the recovery process to the stationary walking can be observed there.

As for the parameter b in eqs.(1), the period of the solution becomes shorter, as a result, the step width becomes larger for tuning b to be small, and vice versa. However, it happened that the normal walking pattern could not be obtained, even if the eqs.(1) yield a periodic solution. For example, a strange walking patterns is shown in Figure 6 , for which $(X, Y) = (2.0, 1.3)$ is assigned in the unstable zone which will be discussed in the next section.

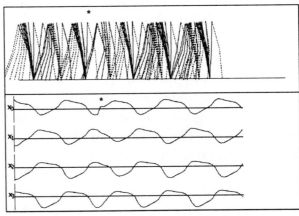

Figure 5: Simulation result for impulsive disturbance

Table 1: Parameters in the simulation studies

i	s_i	a_{0i}	a_{1i}	a_{2i}	a_{3i}	T_r	T_a	b
0	0.6	0.0	1.5	1.0	0.0			
1	0.6	1.5	0.0	0.0	1.0	1.0	12.0	2.5
2	0.3	0.2	0.0	0.0	1.5			
3	0.3	0.0	0.2	1.5	0.0			

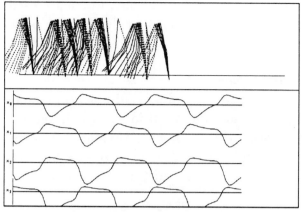

Figure 6: Simulation result for strange walking patterns

$$\mathbf{A_{21}} = \begin{pmatrix} m_0 & 0 & 0 & 0 \\ 0 & m_1 & 0 & 0 \\ 0 & 0 & m_2 & 0 \\ 0 & 0 & 0 & m_3 \end{pmatrix}$$

$$\boldsymbol{B} = \begin{pmatrix} \frac{1}{T_r} & 0 & 0 & 0 \\ 0 & \frac{1}{T_r} & 0 & 0 \\ 0 & 0 & \frac{1}{T_r} & 0 \\ 0 & 0 & 0 & \frac{1}{T_r} \\ 0 & 0 & 0 & 0 \\ 0 & 0 & 0 & 0 \\ 0 & 0 & 0 & 0 \\ 0 & 0 & 0 & 0 \end{pmatrix} \qquad (6)$$

V. STABILITY ANALYSIS

The neuro oscillator in the section 1 could generate the trajectories for the walking robot as shown in the previous section. However, the selection of parameters in eqs.(1) by simulation studies has been ineffective. Since the boundedness of the solution of eqs.(1) was already proved by Matsuoka [13], the analysis of the existence of equilibrium states and their stability is important in this study. Let

$$\boldsymbol{u} \equiv \begin{pmatrix} x_0 & x_1 & x_2 & x_3 & f_0 & f_1 & f_2 & f_3 \end{pmatrix}^t \quad (2)$$

$$\boldsymbol{s} \equiv \begin{pmatrix} s_0 & s_1 & s_2 & s_3 \end{pmatrix}^t \qquad (3)$$

then we obtain a representation as

$$\dot{\boldsymbol{u}} = \boldsymbol{A}\boldsymbol{u} + \boldsymbol{B}\boldsymbol{s} \qquad (4)$$

where $\boldsymbol{A}$ is an 8×8 matrix and $\boldsymbol{B}$ is an 8×4 matrix in the following.

$$\mathbf{A} = \begin{pmatrix} -\frac{1}{T_r}\mathbf{A_{11}} & -\frac{b}{T_r}\mathbf{I}_4 \\ \frac{1}{T_a}\mathbf{A_{21}} & -\frac{1}{T_a}\mathbf{I}_4 \end{pmatrix} \qquad (5)$$

$$\mathbf{A_{11}} = \begin{pmatrix} 1 & a_{01}m_1 & a_{02}m_2 & a_{03}m_3 \\ a_{10}m_0 & 1 & a_{12}m_2 & \dot{a}_{13}m_3 \\ a_{20}m_0 & a_{21}m_1 & 1 & a_{23}m_3 \\ a_{30}m_0 & a_{31}m_1 & a_{32}m_2 & 1 \end{pmatrix}$$

The equilibrium states of eq.(4) are obtained by the condition $\dot{\boldsymbol{u}} \equiv 0$. Then, the linearized equations can be obtained around an equilibrium and their stability can be examined by the *Hurwitz* criterion. In the following, we take two parameters $a_{20} \equiv a_{31} \equiv X$ and $a_{02} \equiv a_{13} \equiv Y$ (other parameters are shown in Figure 1 and Table 1).

Under the given conditions, it could be clarified that three equilibria exist in the quadrants of $(m_0, m_1, m_2, m_3) = (1,1,1,1), (1,1,0,0)$ and $(1,1,0,1)$. The stability chart is shown in Figure 7. In the unstable zone, oscillations appear. However, note that, as stated previously, all the oscillations in this zone cannot accommodate to the stationary walking patterns for the biped locomotive robot. Also, note that chaotic oscillations may appear. This situation is difficult for theoretical analysis, and we used simulation studies. As a result, a zone corresponding to the mode of stationary walking is depicted by two black circles in Figure 7.

VI. CONCLUSION

A trajectory for the biped locomotive robot has been generated using a mutually coupled neuro oscillator with four cells. Its relevancy was studied by stability analysis and simulation. The existence of equilibria and their stability were found by theoretical analysis, while the stationary walking zone in the parameter plane could be obtained by the computer simulation. With the parameters in this walking zone, the neuro oscillator can generate various modes for the biped locomotion.

Achnowledgement

The research was financially supported by the grant-in-aid for scientific research on priority areas, "Autonomous Distributed Systems (Nos.03234109 and 04218109)", by the Ministry of Education, Science and Culture of Japan.

REFERENCES

[1] H.Miura(*ed.*): Status of the Research on the Mechanism and Control of Biped Locomotive Robots; Report for the Grant-in-Aids for the Scientific Research by the Ministry of Education, Science and Culture of Japan. (1987) (in Japanese)

[2] Y.Kurematsu, S.Kitamura and Y.Kondo: Trajectory Planning and Control of a Biped Locomotive Robot-Simulation and Experiment-; Robotics and Manufacturing, Recent Trends in Research, Education, and Applications, M.Jamshidi (*ed.*), pp.65-72, ASME Press. (1988)

[3] A.Takanishi, M.Ishida, Y.Yamazaki and I.Kato: The Realization of Dynamic Walking by the Biped Walking Robot WL-10RD, Journal of the Robotics Society of Japan, Vol.2, No.4, pp.67-78 (1985) (in Japanese)

[4] E.Igarashi and T.Nogai: Study on the Lower Level Adaptive Walking in Sagittal Plane by a Biped Locomotion Robot, Journal of the Robotics Society of Japan, Vol.7, No.6, pp.12-22, (1989) (in Japanese)

[5] S.Kitamura, Y.Kurematsu and M.Iwata: Motion Generation of a Biped Locomotive Robot Using an Inverted Pendulum Model and Neural Networks, Proc. 29th IEEE Conference on Decision and Control, pp.3308-3313 (1990)

[6] H.Yuasa, Y.Ito and M.Ito: Autonomous Distributed Systems which Generate Various Patterns Using Bifurcation, Trans.

Region for existence of an equilibrium state in the quadrant of (1111), (1101) and (1100).

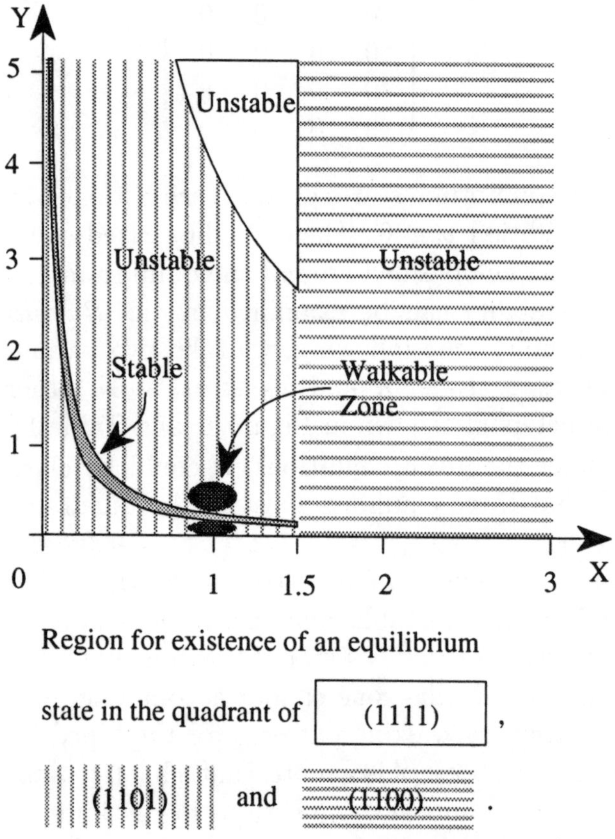

Figure 7: Stability chart for equilibria of eqs.(1) and the walking zone in the region $[0,3] \times [0,5]$

of the SICE, Vol.27, No.11, pp.1307-1314 (1991) (in Japanese)

[7] S.Kumagai et al: Coupling Between Respiratory and Stepping Ryhthms during Controlled Locomotion in Decerebrate Cats, MBE88-165, Institute of Electronics, Information and Communication Engineers, pp.57-62 (1988) (in Japanese)

[8] R.Katoh and M.Mori: Control Method of Biped Locomotion Giving Asymptotic Stability of Trajectory, Automatica., Vol.20, No.4, pp.405-414 (1984)

[9] J.S.Bay and H.Hemami: Modeling of a Neural Pattern Generator with Coupled Nonlinear Oscillators, IEEE Transactions on Biomedical Engineering, Vol. BME-34, No.4 pp.297-306 (1987)

[10] M.Frik: A nonlinear pattern generator for legged locomotion systems, The 4th Japanese-German Seminar on Nonlinear Problems in Dynamical System - Theory and Applications -, K.Hirai and E.Shimemura(eds.) ,pp.12-20 (1989)

[11] G.Taga, Y.Yamaguchi and H.Shimizu: Self-organized control of bipedal locomotion by neural oscillators in unpredictable environment, Biol. Cybern. 65, pp.147-159 (1991)

[12] K.Matsuoka: Mechanisms of Frequency and Pattern Control in the Neural Rhythm Generators, Biol. Cybern. 56, pp.345-353 (1987)

[13] K.Matsuoka: The Dynamic Model of Binocular Rivalry, Biol. Cybern. 49, pp.201-208 (1984)

Fuzzy Min-Max Neural Networks for Function Approximation

Patrick K. Simpson
Gary Jahns
ORINCON Corporation
9363 Towne Centre Drive
San Diego, CA 92121

Abstract - The fuzzy min-max function approximation neural network is introduced and results of its performance on a sample problem are presented. The function approximation network is realized by modifying the previously developed fuzzy min-max clustering network to include an ouput layer that sums and thresholds the hidden layer membership functions. Approximation of a test function to a small tolerance and robustness when trained on sparse data is demonstrated.

I. INTRODUCTION

Fuzzy min-max neural networks represent a synergism of fuzzy sets and neural networks in a unified framework. The use of fuzzy sets as classes (Zadeh, 1965) and as clusters (Ruspini, 1969) has been well known for over twenty years. Fuzzy min-max neural networks create fuzzy set classes and clusters in a similar fashion with a membership function based on a hyperbox core. Fuzzy min-max neural network classification (Simpson, 1992a) creates classes from the union of fuzzy sets. Fuzzy min-max neural network clustering (Simpson, 1990a & 1992b) creates clusters from individual fuzzy sets. This paper presents the next evolution of fuzzy min-max neural networks where fuzzy sets are used as the basis set for function approximation. Recently it has been shown that fuzzy sets can be used for universal approximation where fuzzy rules and Gaussian membership functions act as the basis functions (Wang, 1992). This paper will present a fuzzy neural network that is capable of approximating functions by first finding a basis set of fuzzy sets and then finding the linear combination of these clusters that provides the necessary functional mapping. Each fuzzy set in the basis set is treated as an individual cluster that is found using the fuzzy min-max neural network cluster learning. The use of a linear combination of clusters to perform function approximation is not new. Radial basis functions (Poggio & Girosi, 1990) are an important example of this technique.

This paper is organized as follows. In section two is a review of fuzzy sets and the hyperbox membership functions used by fuzzy min-max neural networks. Section three reviews fuzzy min-max neural network clustering. Section four builds on section three by forming linear combinations of fuzzy hyperbox clusters to form function approximation. Examples of the function approximation capabilities and advantages of this approach are also presented. Section five provides a list of the references cited throughout this paper.

II. FUZZY SETS AND FUZZY MIN-MAX CLUSTERS

A. Fuzzy Set Definition

A fuzzy set α is defined as an ordered pair

$$\alpha = \{x, m_\alpha(x)\} \ \forall \ x \in X \tag{1}$$

where X is the entire space of objects, x is an object from X, and $0 \le m_\alpha(x) \le 1$ is a membership function that describes that degree to which x belongs to the set α.

B. Fuzzy Sets as Clusters

Fuzzy sets bring a new dimension to traditional clustering systems by allowing a pattern to belong to multiple clusters to different degrees. Each fuzzy set is a separate cluster. In the fuzzy min-max clustering neural network, a fuzzy set is defined as a membership function that uses a hyperbox core. If the patterns being clustered have only one dimension, the hyperbox membership function collapses to the common trapezoid membership function.

To make the computations simpler, the pattern space is rescaled to the unit hypercube. As such, hyperboxes lie within the unit hypercube. A hyperbox is completely defined by a min-point and a max-point. The hyperbox membership function for the j'th hyperbox, b_j, is defined as

$$
\begin{aligned}
b_j &= f(A_h, V_j, W_j) \\
&= \frac{1}{n}\sum_{i=1}^{n}\left[1 - g(v_{ji} - a_{hi}, \gamma) \right. \\
&\qquad \left. - g(a_{hi} - w_{ji}, \gamma)\right]
\end{aligned} \tag{2}
$$

where g is the common ramp transfer function defined as

$$
g(x, \gamma) = \begin{cases} 1 & \text{if} \quad x\gamma > 1 \\ x & \text{if} \quad 0 \le x\gamma \le 1 \\ 0 & \text{if} \quad x < 0 \end{cases} \tag{3}
$$

and where the remaining parameters are defined as follows:

$A_h \in [0,1]^n$ h'th input pattern $A_h = (a_{h1}, a_{h2}, ..., a_{hn})$,

h index for the patterns. The number of patterns is not specified here. It is not necessary for the algorithm to have this information because it is an on-line learning clusterer,

n number of dimensions for the input patterns and the input layer,

p number of fuzzy set hyperboxes (i.e. number of clusters),

γ *the slope of the membership function*. A value of $\gamma = 1.0$ will guarantee that the membership function will cover the entire space. Values greater than *1* will sharpen the sides of the trapezoidal membership function,

$V_j \in [0,1]^n$ min vector for the j'th hyperbox fuzzy set, $V_j = (v_{j1}, v_{j2}, ..., v_{jn})$, $j = 1, 2, ..., p$, and

$W_j \in [0,1]^n$ max vector for the j'th hyperbox fuzzy set $W_j = (w_{j1}, w_{j2}, ..., w_{jn})$, $j = 1, 2, ..., p$.

III. FUZZY MIN-MAX NEURAL NETWORK CLUSTERING

The fuzzy min-max neural network clusterer adds new hyperbox fuzzy sets as they are needed. The maximum size of a hyperbox is bound above by the parameter θ. This value represents the upper bound of the average length of the side of a hyperbox. The learning algorithm will only briefly be described here. For details, please refer to Simpson (1992b). Clustering differs from classification in that there are no labels associated with input patterns and the objective is to find the natural structure of the data. In the following sections it will be assumed that we are clustering a set of patterns $A = \{A_1, A_2, ..., A_m\}$.

A. Learning

Fuzzy min-max clustering neural network learning proceeds in three steps: (1) find a hyperbox that will allow expansion (or add a new hyperbox if one can not be found), (2) expand the hyperbox, and (3) eliminate overlap with other hyperboxes. Each of these steps is outlined below.

1. *Expansion Test*. Given the input pattern A_h, find a hyperbox that can be expanded to include this hyperbox. The hyperbox expansion test is defined as

$$\theta \le \frac{1}{n} \sum_{i=1}^{n} \left[\max(a_{hi}, w_{ji}) - \min(a_{hi}, v_{ji}) \right]$$

(4)

If a hyperbox can not be found that satisfies (4), then a new hyperbox, b_J, is created that has its min and max points defined as follows

$$V_J = (1, 1, ..., 1)$$ (5)

$$W_J = (0, 0, ..., 0)$$ (6)

which will ensure that the expansion steps taken below will result in the input pattern, A_h, becoming the initial min point and max point (initially all hyperboxes have zero volume).

2. *Expansion*. Assume that the hyperbox that will be expanded to include the input pattern, A_h, is b_j. The expansion of the min point is performed using

$$v_{ji}^{new} = \min(v_{ji}^{old}, a_{hi})$$ (7)

and the expansion of the max point is performed using

$$w_{ji}^{new} = \max(w_{ji}^{old}, a_{hi})$$ (8)

3. *Overlap Test*. The fuzzy min-max clustering neural network does not allow any point to have full membership (a membership value of 1) in more than one hyperbox. To eliminate the overlap between hyperboxes, the expanded hyperbox is compared with each of the existing hyperboxes. If overlap is found, it is eliminated along each dimension. Although the operations that perform the overlap elimination are not difficult to implement, their exposition is beyond the scope of this paper. Please refer to Simpson (1992b) for details of the hyperbox overlap elimination procedure.

B. Neural Network Implementation

The implemention of a fuzzy set hyperbox and its membership function fits very naturally into a neural network framework. As **Figure 1** shows, the input pattern, A_h, is represented as n input nodes, the min and max points, V_j and W_j, are represented as dual connections, and the membership function, $f(A_h, V_j, W_j)$, becomes the j'th cluster's output value, b_j. This network represents a fuzzy set.

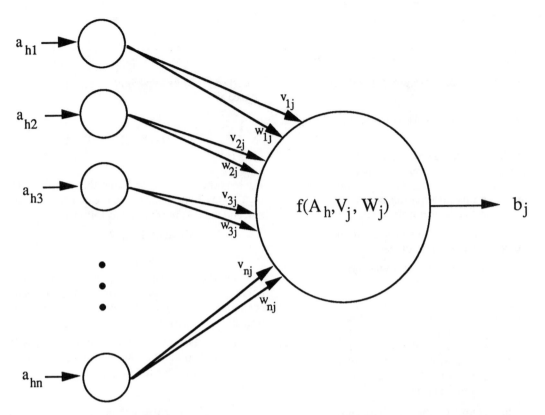

Fig. 1. Neural network implementation of fuzzy set hyperbox cluster.

IV. FUZZY MIN-MAX NEURAL NETWORK FUNCTION APPROXIMATION

Function approximation is mathematically described as $/ F(A_h) - G(A_h) / < \varepsilon \ \forall A_h$ where $F(A_h)$ is the true (and often unknown) function, $G(A_h)$ is the approximation of the true function (computed here by the fuzzy min-max function approximation neural network), and $\varepsilon > 0$. The ability of neural networks to perform function approximation for a broad class of functions is clearly one of their greater strengths. Recently, the use of fuzzy sets to perform function approximation has also been introduced (Wang, 1992). In the following sections, the learning algorithm for the fuzzy min-max function approximation neural network will be described. Throughout this section, it is assumed that the input patterns are $A_h \in [0,1]^n$, the output patterns are $F(A_h) = D_h \in \mathfrak{R}^q$, and the data set is the collection of pattern pairs $D = \{(A_h, D_h): h = 1, 2, ..., m\}$.

A. Fuzzy Clusters as Basis Functions

The radial basis function network has been shown to be very good for function approximation (Poggio & Girosi, 1990). Radial basis functions are typically constructed in three steps: (1) represent the data as a set of clusters, (2) assign a radial basis function to the centroid of each cluster -- typically this will be a gaussian function, and (3) approximate the function from a linear combination of the basis functions. The approach taken here will be similar. Hyperbox fuzzy sets will be formed using the algorithm described in section 3 and linear combinations of these fuzzy sets will be used to approximate a function.

To perform function approximation requires an alteration to the trapezoidal membership function given by (2). The flat region between the min and max of the membership function does not provide a continuous graded response that a triangular membership function would, so the membership function described by (2) is replaced with the membership function

$$b_j = f(A_h, V_j, W_j) = \frac{1}{n} \sum_{i=1}^{n} \left[1 - g \left(\left| z_{ji} - a_{hi} \right|, \gamma \right) \right] \quad (9)$$

where z_{ji} is defined as

$$z_{ji} = \frac{w_{ji} + v_{ji}}{2} \quad (10)$$

for all hyperboxes $j = 1, 2, ..., p$ and all dimensions $i = 1, 2, ..., n$. The vectors $Z_j = (z_{j1}, z_{j2}, ..., z_{jn})$ represent the mid-points of the hyperboxes that are defined by the min point and the max point. Note that the min and max points are preserved and the mid-point is computed from these values.

B. Fuzzy Min-Max Function Approximation Neural Network Topology

The fuzzy min-max function approximation neural network has three layers: (1) the input layer F_A, (2) the fuzzy hyperbox cluster layer F_B, and (3) the output layer F_C. **Figure 2** shows a fuzzy min-max function approximation neural network with four F_A nodes, five F_B nodes (including the bias node), and three F_C nodes. Each of the hidden nodes is a fuzzy hyperbox node like that shown in **Figure 1**. The connections between the F_A and F_B nodes are the min-max dual connections described in the previous section. The connections between the F_B and F_C nodes are real-valued connections $U = u_{jk}, j = 1, 2, ..., p$ and $k = 1, 2, ..., q$, where u_{jk} represents the single connection from b_j to c_k. In addition to the F_B and F_C connections, each F_C node has a bias input, denoted as u_{0k}, which can be treated like an F_B node that is held constant at 1.

C. Fuzzy Min-Max Function Approximation Learning

Fuzzy min-max function approximation learning occurs in two steps. First, the input data is clustered into a set of hyperbox fuzzy set clusters using the algorithm described in section III. When the clustering process is completed, the first two layers

and their associated connections are held fixed for the second phase of the learning process.

Each F_B node produces an output value, b_j, using (9) defined above. The F_C nodes, c_k, produce output values using the equation

$$c_k = \sum_{j=1}^{p} b_j u_{jk} + u_{0k} \qquad (11)$$

for all $k = 1, 2, ..., q$. The F_B to F_C connections are adjusted using the LMS (Least Mean Square) algorithm as follows:

1. A_h is presented to F_A.

2. Each F_B node computes its membership value using (9).

3. The value of the F_B nodes are propagated through the U connections and the computed output values, c_k, are produced using (11).

4. The computed output values are compared with the desired output values. The difference is used to adjust the U connections using the equation

$$u_{jk}^{new} = u_{jk}^{old} + \alpha(d_{hk} - c_k)b_j \qquad (12)$$

5. Steps 1-4 are repeated until the sum of the errors has reached the desired level.

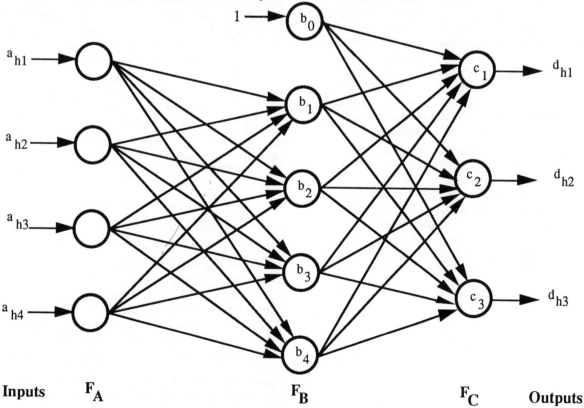

Inputs　　F_A　　　　　　　　F_B　　　　　　F_C　　**Outputs**

Fig. 2. Topology of the Fuzzy Min-Max Function Approximation Neural Network.

D. Results

For the sake of illustration, a one-dimensional nonlinear function was arbitrarily chosen to demonstrate the function approximation capabilities of the fuzzy min-max neural network. The following sigmoid function was approiximated

$$f(x) = \frac{2x}{1+x^2} \qquad (13)$$

A set of 300 exemplars was generated randomly with an equiprobable distribution over the interval [-1,+1], producing an input of x and an output f(x). **Figure 3** shows a scatterplot of the data produced for this function.

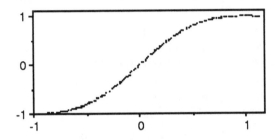

Fig. 3. Scatterplot of the data used for function approximation.

The fuzzy min-max function approximation neural network used to encode this function had one input (x) and one output. The input values where rescaled to the range [0,1], but the outputs remained untouched. Two experiments were conducted. First, using all 300 data points, determine if the fuzzy min-max function approximation neural network can approximate the sigmoid function. Second, reduce the data set to determine how the function approximation capability suffers when sparse data is used

The first experiment clustered the input data into 12 hyperbox fuzzy sets using a hyperbox size of 0.10. The LMS algorithm iterated 10,000 times at a learning rate of 0.10 and was stopped with an average error of 0.00465 and a maximum error of 0.0376 for any given exemplar. A scatterplot of the resulting function is shown in **Figure 4** with the original function lying underneath each scatterplot to illustrate where the function approximation was in error.

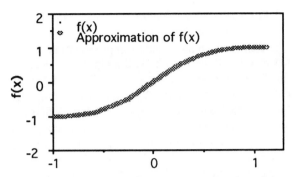

Fig. 4. Scatterplot of the function approximation of the sigmoid using 300 exemplars.

The second experiment tested the function approximation ability of the network with sparse data. If the function approximation is being performed using fuzzy sets as basis functions, the degradation in performance should be gradual. The first part of this experiment reduced the number of exemplars by an order of magnitude, using only 30 for training and all 300 for testing. The 30 exemplars were clustered into 10 hyperbox fuzzy sets using a hyperbox size of 0.10. The LMS algorithm iterated 10,000 times at a learning rate of 0.10 and was stopped with an average error of 0.0030 and a maximum error of 0.0136 for any given exemplar. A scatterplot of the resulting function is shown in **Figure 5** with the original function lying underneath each scatterplot to illustrate where the function approximation was in error. As the scatterplot shows, the function approximation did not suffer at all, and in fact performed better.

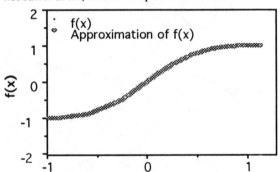

Fig. 5. Scatterplot of the function approximation of the sigmoid using 30 exemplars.

The second portion of this experiment utilized only 10 randomly selected exemplars. The 10 exemplars were clustered into 6 hyperbox fuzzy sets using a hyperbox size of 0.10. The LMS algorithm iterated 10,000 times with a learning rate of 0.10 and was stopped with an average error of 0.00298 and a maximum error of 0.0103 for any given examplar. A scatterplot of the resulting function is shown in **Figure 6** with the original function lying underneath the scatterplot to illustrate where the function approximation was in error. As the scatterplot shows, the function approximation did degrade significantly. What was interesting was how the function approximation degraded. It is visibly noticable that a piecewise linear approximation of the function resulted from the sparse data.

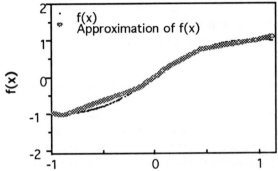

Fig. 6. Scatterplot of the function approximation of the sigmoid using 10 exemplars.

V. CONCLUSIONS AND FUTURE WORK

The fuzzy min-max function approximation neural network has been introduced and an example of its function approximation capability has been briefly examined. The fuzzy min-max function approximation network is similar in many ways to radial basis function networks in that a basis set of functions is first defined and then a linear combination of these functions is then found. In addition to properties listed for the clustering portion of the function approximation process described in section 3.3, the use of the LMS algorithm makes this technique relatively fast to train.

There are several areas where this work will continue. First, a proof that this function approximation approach is valid for a large range of functions will be explored. Second, the application of this function approximation technique to other function approximation problems needs to be explored, including forecasting and control. Finally, a methodology for the extraction of fuzzy rules from a trained fuzzy min-max network will be investigated.

REFERENCES

Bezdek, J. (1981). *Pattern Recognition with Fuzzy Objective Function Algorithms*, Plenum Press, New York.

Bezdek, J. (1987). Some non-standard clustering algorithms, *NATO ASI Series, vol. G14: Developments in Numerical Ecology*, P; Legendre & L. Legendre, Eds., Springer-Verlag, Berlin.

Ignizio Burke, L. (1991). Clustering characteriaion of adaptive resonance, *Neural Networks*, **4**, pp. 485-492.

Kohonen, T. (1990). *Self-Organization and Associative Memory: Third Edition*, Springer-Verlag, Berlin.

Poggio, T. & Girosi, F. (1990). Networks for approximation and learning, *Proceedings of the IEEE*, **78**, pp. 1481-1497.

Ruspini, E. (1969). A new approach to clustering, *Information and Control*, **15**, pp. 22-32.

Simpson, P. (1990a). Fuzzy adaptive resonance theory, *SIUC Neuroengineering Workshop*, Sept. 6-7, Carbondale, IL. Also, General Dynamics Electronics Division, Technical Report, GDE-ISG-PKS-11.

Simpson, P. (1990b). *Artificial Neural Systems: Foundations, Paradigms, Applications, and Implementations*, Pergamon Press: Elmsford, NY.

Simpson, P. (1991). Fuzzy min-max classification with neural networks, *Heuristics*, **4**, No. 1, pp. pp. 1-9.

Simpson, P. (1992a). Fuzzy min-max neural networks: 1. classification, *IEEE Trans. on Neural Networks*, **3**, PP. 776-786.

Simpson, P. (1992b). Fuzzy min-max neural networks: 2. clustering, *IEEE Trans. on Fuzzy Systems*, in review.

Simpson, P.& Perlow, D (1992c). Feature analysis with the fuzzy min-max clustering neural network, in preparation.

Wang, L & Mendel, J. (1992). Universal approximation with fuzzy sets, *Proceedings of the First IEEE International Conference on Fuzzy Systems*, San Diego, CA, March 8-12.

Zadeh, L. (1965). Fuzzy sets, *Information and Control*, **8**, pp. 338-353.

Networks that approximate vector–valued mappings

Ferdinando A. Mussa-Ivaldi and Francesca Gandolfo
MIT – Department of Brain and Cognitive Sciences. Cambridge, MA 02139.

Abstract— We propose a network architecture capable of approximating an arbitrary pattern of vectors by a linear superposition of non–linear vector fields. Our approach is based on a direct extension of the method of basis functions to the representation of vector–valued mappings. In the proposed network architecture vector approximation is represented as a form of auto–association: the output field must reproduce as closely as possible the set of input vectors. We show that with a simple and relatively small set of connection weights it is possible to represent a broad spectrum of vector patterns and to generate a functionally meaningful decomposition of these patterns into zero–curl and zero–divergence components.

I. INTRODUCTION

This paper deals with the problem of reconstructing continuous vector-valued mappings by the linear superposition of local vector fields. The issue of approximating and representing vector–valued mappings emerges in a number of important computational problems. Some of these problems are related to the analysis of optical flows– the fields of velocity vectors associated with the motion of an observer. For example, how is it possible to separate rotational and translational components and to determine the "center of expansion" of an optical flow? Problems of field combination also arise in control theory. For instance, one may express a control law as a field of generalized forces over the state space of a manipulator. One issue is then how to achieve an arbitrarily specified control law from the superposition of independent controllers, each one tuning a local non-linear field. Still other issues of vector field representation arise in areas of research that are not related to brain science or cybernetics, such as weather forecasting. In this case, for example one faces the problem of reconstructing a wind flow field from a number of sparse samples [9].

A field-approximation problem that is shared among these different areas of investigation can be stated as follows. Given a set of vectors at a set of points find a vector–valued map that approximates these vectors at the sampling points while at the same time providing a smooth estimate of the underlying field at non-sampled locations. This problem is formally identical to the ordinary approximation of a scalar map. One may be tempted to treat each component of the approximating map as an independent scalar entity, to be represented as a combination of scalar basis functions. However, a disadvantage of this "component–based" approach is that the values assumed by a vector component are contingent upon the arbitrary choice of a coordinate system. In contrast, most if not all the interesting properties of a vector field do not depend on such a choice. For example, a vector field may contain a point attractor or it may be characterized by a circulating pattern. These interesting properties involve *relations* among components, such as the relation defining the curl and the divergence of a field. One way to capture the invariant properties expressed by these relations is to use vector fields instead of scalar functions as computational primitives.

Following this point of view, Mussa-Ivaldi [5] has recently suggested a method for extending to vector fields the paradigm of function approximation by the superposition of scalar basis functions. Essentially, this method consists in deriving from a known set of scalar basis functions, a corresponding set of vector fields that have been named *basis fields*. A set of vectors can be approximated by the linear superposition:

$$F(x) = \sum_{i=1}^{K} c_i \phi^i(x) \tag{1}$$

where $\phi^i(x)$ are K distinct basis fields[1] and $c_i \in \Re$ are weighting coefficients.

---

[1] We adopt the convention of using superscript indices to label different multidimensional *objects* (points, vectors and matrices). In contrast, we will indicate the *components* of a multidimensional objects (e.g. the coordinate of a vector or the elements of a matrix) by subscript indices.

The above expression is formally identical to the representation of a scalar mapping as a sum of basis functions. We propose a neural network architecture for vector-field approximation that is based upon the linear combination of basis fields (1). This general idea, of course, is not new. The reconstruction of scalar map by combining basis functions is already a well-established theoretical framework for a wide class of multilayer networks [2, 6, 1]. However, we would like to stress a point of departure of our approach from the current design of basis-function networks. Basis-function networks are usually intended to store a *finite* number of scalar maps. Each map is provided by a set of connection weights that correspond to the coefficients c_i of Equation (1) (in its scalar version). These connection weights are learned from a set of examples of the map that has to be stored. In contrast, our network architecture, that we call "field combination network" (FCN), is capable of storing a continuous repertoire of maps[2]. In other words, the purpose of FCNs is not to approximate this or that vector field from this or that set of examples. A FCN is set up to learn the task of approximating *any* set of vectors presented at a given set of sampling points. We will show that this goal is achieved by considering the combination coefficients, c_i, in (1) not as connection weights but as *signals*. These signals modulate via a set of "product units" [3] the outputs of the units implementing the basis fields.

We represent the problem of field reconstruction as an auto-association problem: the primary task of a FCN is to match an input pattern of sampled vectors with an output field that at the sampling points is "as close as possible" to the input vectors. We show that this task can be achieved by a network that (a) projects the input vectors into a coordinate system defined by the basis fields and then (b) linearly combines these projections with a set of appropriate weights. The output of this network are the desired signals that modulate the basis fields. Thus, we can conclude non only that the vectorial combination of basis fields is a powerful method for reconstructing a variety of non-linear vector mappings but also that the task of finding the appropriate combination parameters can be solved once and for all by a simple auto-associative network.

---

[2]Of course this is strictly true for an ideal analog computer. With a finite-state machine the number of stored fields is bound to be finite as well. However, here we are implying that in a FCN a relatively small set of connection weights can store a very large number of fields.

II. VECTOR–FIELD APPROXIMATION

We are concerned with the representation of N-dimensional vector fields defined over some domain $\mathcal{E}$ of $\Re^N$. These vector fields are collections of N real-valued maps with the important assumption that such a collection belongs to a vector space—that is that the operations of addition and scalar multiplication are defined.

The goal of vector field approximation can be stated as follows. Let us choose M distinct points in $\mathcal{E}$: $x^1, x^2, \ldots, x^M$. We will call these points *sampling locations*. Now, suppose that we are presented with one N-dimensional vector at each sampling location. So, we have M such vectors $v^1, v^2, \ldots, v^M$ that we may call the "data". These data are samples of some unknown field, $\hat{F}(x)$. Then, we consider a known family of vector-fields, $F(x \mid c_1, c_2, \ldots, c_K)$, parameterized by K real numbers, c_i. The goal of vector-field approximation is equivalent to the goal of scalar approximation [8], namely: find a set of values for c_i that minimize the distance between $\hat{F}(x)$ and $F(x \mid c_1, \ldots, c_K)$.

In the case of a scalar map, the approximating function may be represented and parameterized as a weighted sum of non-linear basis functions, $g_i(x)$:

$$f(x) = \sum_{i=1}^{K} c_i g_i(x).$$

This approach is particularly significant since it has been shown that the form of the basis functions can be directly related to the presumed properties of the unknown map [6, 7]. Mussa-Ivaldi [5] has proposed to extend the same approach to vector-field approximation, by representing the approximating field as a weighted sum of *basis fields*, $\phi^i(x)$ (Eq. 1).

Basis fields can be directly derived from scalar basis functions by taking advantage of a well-known theorem of potential theory [4]. This theorem states that any continuous vector field, $F(x)$, can be expressed as the sum of two fields,

$$F(x) = C(x) + S(x). \qquad (2)$$

The first field, $C(x)$, is *irrotational* and the second field, $S(x)$, is *solenoidal*. We remind that an irrotational field is defined as a field having zero curl and a solenoidal field is a field with zero divergence, that is: $curl(C) = \nabla \wedge C(x) = 0$ and $div(S) = \nabla \cdot S(x) = 0$. The symbols $\wedge$ and ∇ indicate, respectively, the external product and the differential operator $\sum_{i=1}^{N} \partial/\partial x_i$. In the above expressions, we have implicitly assumed that the metric of the input domain, $\mathcal{E}$, is Euclidean. For simplicity we will maintain this assumption throughout the paper. However, the main results can be applied with some precautions (in the expression of the differential operators) to the more general Riemannian metric.

We now proceed with a brief account of the derivation of basis fields from basis functions. In this derivation we will assume that one set of scalar basis functions, for example Gaussians, multiquadrics or splines, has been chosen. We indicate these functions as $g_i(x)$. Following the field–decomposition theorem, we will derive from these scalar basis functions a set of irrotational basis fields (IBF) and a set of solenoidal basis fields (SBF).

Irrotational basis fields. Let us start from the assumption that the approximating field, $F(x)$, has only an irrotational component. An equivalent way to state that the field $C(x)$ in (2) is irrotational is to postulate the existence of a *scalar* potential function, $U(x)$, such that $C(x)$ is the gradient of this function:

$$C(x) = \nabla U(x). \tag{3}$$

Then, it is possible to represent the approximating potential as a weighted sum of scalar basis functions:

$$U(x) = \sum_{i=1}^{K} c_i g_i(x). \tag{4}$$

The above expression cannot be used for finding an approximation because the data supplied in our problem are not scalar values for $U(x)$. However, one may take advantage of the fact that the gradient is a linear operator and combine Eqs. (3) and (4) to express the irrotational approximating field as

$$C(x) = \sum_{i=1}^{K} c_i \varphi^i(x) \tag{5}$$

with $\varphi^i(x) = \nabla g_i(x)$.

Unlike equation (4), equation (5) can be directly used for vector–field approximation by relating the vector data to the values of $C(x)$ at the sampling points. The fields $\varphi^i(x)$ are irrotational basis fields derived as gradients of scalar basis functions. A particular class of IBFs is derived by taking the gradient of radial basis functions (RBFs). A generic RBF has the form $g_i(x) = h(\| x - t^i \|)$, where the parameter t^i is a center of symmetry. The corresponding gradient field is $\phi^i(x) = ((x - t^i)/\| x - t^i \|) (\partial h/\partial \| x - t^i \|)$. For any point, x, the vector $\phi^i(x)$ is directed toward the center, t^i. Thus, the basis fields obtained

by taking the gradients of RBFs have central symmetry.

Note that the point at which $g_i(x)$ reaches a maximum is also the point at which the corresponding basis field vanishes, thus exerting the least influence. This observation suggests that a good strategy for placing the centers of the basis fields in vector approximation needs not to be that of placing the centers at the data points, as is often the rule of thumb with scalar basis functions.

Solenoidal basis fields. Now, let us consider the solenoidal field $S(x)$ in (2). It is easy to prove that *in the Euclidean metric, a solenoidal field is obtained from an irrotational field when the latter is multiplied by an antisymmetric matrix.* This statement provides us with a very simple way to generate solenoidal basis fields from basis functions. First, take the gradient of a basis function to obtain an irrotational field. Then, multiply this irrotational field by some antisymmetric matrix, A. The resulting field

$$\psi^i(x) = A \nabla g_i(x) \tag{6}$$

is solenoidal, that is $\nabla \cdot \psi^i(x) = 0$. Note that in 2D, there is essentially one antisymmetric matrix– that corresponds to a 90 degree rotation operator. In contrast, in higher dimensional spaces it is possible to generate a larger number of linearly independent antisymmetric matrices. Thus, we can say that in general from a set of K scalar basis functions it is possible to generate K_S ($\geq K$) solenoidal basis fields as in (6).

Complete field representation Putting together the sets of IBFs and SBFs we obtain a general representation for a continuous field as:

$$F(x) = \sum_{i=1}^{K} c_i \varphi^i(x) + \sum_{i=1}^{K_S} d_i \psi^i(x) \tag{7}$$

The task of field approximation is to determine the coefficients c_i and d_i given a set of data presented at a set of sampling points. Note that, once this problem is solved, the basis field representation provides a powerful framework for extracting important features from the pattern of data. For example: (1) The solenoidal and the irrotational component can be immediately separated; (2) The divergence and the curl of the total field can be readily estimated from the known divergence and curl of the IBF and SBF, respectively; (3) The irrotational component of the field can be integrated from the known set of scalar basis functions $g_i(x)$ that have been used to generate the IBFs. Note in fact that the coefficients c_i in (4) and (7) are the same. Then, once the irrotational component is estimated also the corresponding potential is also obtained as a byproduct.

To simplify our notation, in the remaining sections we will use expression (1) instead of (7) with the implicit assumption that the basis field $\phi^i(x)$ can be either conservative or solenoidal.

III. Basis fields as a coordinate system

A direct way for using Eq. (1) in a field approximation problem consists in equating the field combination to the data, and then solving algebraically for the unknown combination parameters, c_i. With M vectorial data we have M vector equations

$$\sum_{k=1}^{K} c_k \phi^k(x^j) = v^j \qquad (8)$$

for $j = 1, \ldots, M$. Each one of these vector equations can be explicitly decomposed in N (dimension of the vector space) real-valued components. Thus, we end up with $N \times M$ "scalar" equations in K unknowns. A discussion of this rather straightforward algebraic method can be found in Mussa–Ivaldi (1992).

In this paper we take a different path. We would like to start by pointing out what we consider to be an unsatisfactory aspect of the above mentioned approach, namely the coordinate representation of the input pattern. The numerical components of the scalar equations derived from (8) have to be specified in some arbitrary coordinate system. In contrast to the use of such an arbitrary coordinate system, we would like to represent the pattern of input data– i.e. the vectors v^i– *in the coordinate system that is inherently specified by the basis fields*. To this end, for each basis field, $\phi^i(x)$, we define the projection of the data–set $v^1, v^2, \ldots, v^M$ on $\phi^i(x)$ as:

$$\Lambda_i = \sum_{j=1}^{M} < \phi^i(x^j)|v^j > \qquad (9)$$

where operator $< u|v >$ is the inner product between two N-dimensional vectors u and v. This operation is a form of "vector–filtering" of the sampled data, carried out by taking the inner product of the field $\phi^i(x)$ with each input vector. If the data were sampled continuously, the summation could be replaced by an integration.

Given the definition (9), it is easy to show that the least–squares solution to (8) is

$$c_k = \sum_{i=1}^{K} [\Phi]_{k,i}^{-1} \Lambda_i \qquad (10)$$

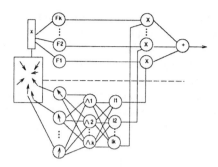

Figure 1: Field Combination Network.

where the matrix $[\Phi]^{-1}$ is the inverse of the $K \times K$ matrix

$$[\Phi]_{l,m} = \sum_{j=1}^{M} < \phi^l(x^j)|\phi^m(x^j) > . \qquad (11)$$

If the number of basis fields is equal to the number of data components (that is if $K = MN$) then Eq. (10) yields the exact solution of (8). Equation (10) is the vectorial counterpart to the solution for the combination coefficients in scalar basis function networks.

IV. Field Combination Networks.

Equations (1) and (10) provide a simple paradigm for representing and reconstructing vector fields. This paradigm can be directly translated into a network architecture that we call "field combination networks" (FCN) (Figure 1).

The input space of a field combination network is a spatial domain, $\mathcal{E}$ with M fixed sampling points. An input vector, v^i, is presented at each sampling point. The purpose of the the network is to reconstruct the vector field over the entire spatial domain, $\mathcal{E}$. The network is divided into two subnetworks: a basis–field network and a modulator network.

1. The basis–field network (Figure 1, upper part) takes as input a representation of a point in $\mathcal{E}$. This input is delivered to a set of units (labelled F_i in Fig. 1), each one implementing the input/output map of a basis field, $\phi^i(x)$. These basis–fields units are not network units in a conventional sense: they do not generate a scalar signal but a collection of N such signals, one for each vector–field component. The outputs of the basis–fields units are multiplied (via product units) by a set of coefficients that are continuously generated by the modulator network.

2. The job of the modulator network (Figure 1,

lower part) is to generate the combination coefficients corresponding to a set of vectors presented at the sampling points. The input vectors are "projected" by a set of K units (labelled Λ_i) implementing the filtering operation (9). Then the outputs of these projection units are combined by another set of K units (Labelled L_i)implementing the linear transformation.

$$c_i = \sum_{j=1}^{K} w_{i,j}\Lambda_j. \qquad (12)$$

The coefficients $w_{i,j}$ correspond to a set of connection weights that effectively implement the inverse of the basis–field correlation matrix Φ (11). We will discuss a simple learning rule for these coefficients.

In essence, the purpose of FCNs is to acquire the ability to combine vectorial modules (the basis-field units) in order to generate arbitrary continuous fields that are specified by a discrete set of samples. Thus, vector–field approximation is expressed as an auto–association task: the output of the network must try to match the input vectors at the sampling points. Naturally, the network does more than that as it "completes" the input pattern outside (or within) the sampling points.

We would like to add a remark concerning information storage. In a "standard" basis–function network (e.g. see Bishop, 1989) with K basis functions, $K \times M$ weights are required to store M different mappings. Each mapping is stored by K connection weights. In a field combination network with K basis fields, there are $K \times K$ connection weights (in the modulator subnetwork). The number of distinct mappings that are stored by these weights depends upon the resolution of each "parameter line", c_i. for example, if all the parameter lines have the same resolution of L bits, then the field combination network can generate 2^{KL} distinct output fields.

A learning rule. As we have mentioned above, the connection weights, $w_{i,j}$, (Eq. (12)) yielding the least–squares solution for the system (8) are obtained from the inverse of the basis–field correlation matrix Φ. On way to calculate them through an iterative procedure is to use the following learning rule:

$$\Delta w_{l,m} = \eta \left((\sum_i \Phi_{i,l}^2) w_{l,m} - \Phi_{m,l} \right) \qquad (13)$$

where η is a learning–rate parameter. This learning

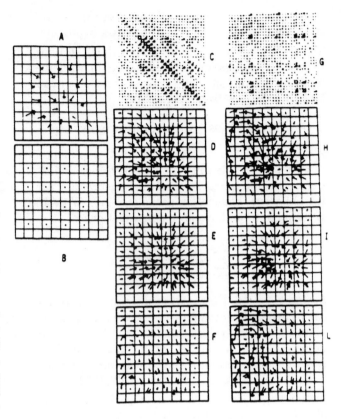

Figure 2: Simulation results.

rule is derived by minimizing the cost function

$$J = \frac{1}{2} \parallel \Phi W - I \parallel^2$$

where the norm of a matrix A is defined as $\parallel A \parallel^2 = \sum_{i,j} A_{i,j}^2$. This learning procedure is a simplified form of gradient descent and is computationally advantageous with respect to matrix inversion when the number of basis–fields is large and when a coarse approximation of the pseudoinverse may be acceptable.

V. EXAMPLE

The following example illustrates the performance of our network and of the learning algorithm (13). The input space is shown in Figure 2 as a square planar domain covered by a regular grid. We consider a set of 20 sampling points. A pattern of vectors presented at these sampling points is shown in Figure 2A. The basis–field subnetwork is composed of 32 units implementing an equal number of basis fields. The locations of the basis–field centers are indicated in Figure 2B. Each center location is shared by an irrotational and by a solenoidal basis field. These irrotational and solenoidal fields were derived as described in Section 2 from a set of bivariate Gaussians with variance $\sigma = 1.67$ (in grid–step units). Therefore, there was a significant degree of overlap between contiguous basis fields. Figure 2C shows the Hinton's diagram of the connection weights corresponding to $W = \Phi^{-1}$ (Moore–Penrose solution). Each weight is represented by a square with area proportional to the weight size in absolute value. Empty and filled squares represent, respectively, positive and negative weights. Figure 2D shows the approximating field for the set of examples shown in Figure 2A, corresponding to this least squares solution. Figure 2E and F show, respectively, the irrotational and the conservative component of the approximating field. Note that these components correspond to a pattern converging at a single point and a pattern circulating around a different location. The learning algorithm (13) can be used to derive an acceptable, although not optimal, approximation field after a relatively small number of iteration. This number of iterations depends on the dimension of the weight space– that is on the square of the number of basis fields. The weight matrix obtained after 3002 iterations of the learning rule is shown in Figure 2G. Learning started from an initial random state of the connections. After 3002 iterations, some of the features of the least–squares matrix have begun to develop, although the overall patterns of Figure 2c and g are still fairly different. Figures 2H, I and L show the total approximating field, its irrotational and solenoidal components obtained at this early stage of learning. This approximation is visibly less accurate (and smooth) than the least–square approximation. However one can see that the most relevant qualitative features of the least–square approximation have already emerged.

VI. SUMMARY AND CONCLUSIONS

Vector–field approximation can be formulated as an auto–association problem: given a set of (input) vectors at a number of sampling locations, the task is to find a mapping whose output reproduces "at best" (for example, in the sense of least squares) the input vectors at the same sampling locations. We investigated a network architecture, the "field combination network" that is capable of performing this auto–association task. Field combination networks are based on the idea of representing a vector–valued mapping as a combination of local basis fields [5]. Basis fields are the vectorial equivalent of basis functions: their linear combination defines

a vector space of continuous fields. Starting from a set of scalar basis functions one may derive two classes of basis fields: (a) irrotational basis fields and (b) solenoidal basis fields. These two classes provide a rich vocabulary for expressing a broad repertoire of continuous vector–valued mappings. In a field reconstruction network, the task of learning this whole repertoire is accomplished by inverting a square matrix expressing the mutual correlation of the network's basis fields.

ACKNOWLEDGMENT

Francesca Gandolfo was supported by a fellowship of the International Superior School for Advanced Studies (SISSA) of Trieste (Italy). This research was supported by NIH grants NS09343 and AR26710 and by ONR grant N00014/88/K/0372.

REFERENCES

[1] C. Bishop. Improving the generalization properties of radial basis function neural networks. *Neural Computation*, 3:579 – 588, 1991.

[2] D. S. Broomhead and D. Lowe. Multi–variable functional interpolation and adaptive networks. *Complex Systems*, 2:321 – 355, 1988.

[3] R. Durbin and D. E. Rumelhart. Produc units: A computationally powerful and biologically plausible extension to backpropagation networks. *Neural Computation*, 1:133 – 142, 1989.

[4] O. D. Kellogg. *Foundations of Potential Theory*. Dover, New York, NY, 1953.

[5] F. A. Mussa-Ivaldi. From basis functions to basis fields: Using vector primitives to capture vector patterns. *Biological Cybernetics*, 1992. (In Press).

[6] T. Poggio and F. Girosi. Networks for approximation and learning. *Proc. of the IEEE*, 78:1481 – 1497, 1990.

[7] T. Poggio and F. Girosi. A theory of networks for learning. *Science*, 247:978 – 982, 1990.

[8] J. R. Rice. *The Approximation of Functions*. Addison-Wesley, Reading, MA, 1964.

[9] G. Wahba. Vector splines on the sphere, with application to the estimation of vorticity and divergence from discrete noisy data. In W. Schempp and K. Zeller, editors, *Multivariate Approximation Theory*, pages 407 – 429. Birkhauser Verlag, 1982.

Neural Plant Inverse Control Approach to Color Error Reduction for Scanner and Printer

Gao-Wei Chang, and Po-Rong Chang*

Opto-Electronics and System Laboratory, Industrial Technology Research Institute
Chutung, 31015, Hsinchu, Taiwan, R.O.C.
and
* Dept. of Communication Engineering, National Chiao-Tung University
Hsinchu, Taiwan, R.O.C.

Abstract— The process of eliminating the color errors from the gamut mismatch, resolution conversion, quantization and nonlinearity between scanner and printer is usually recognized as an essential issue of color reproduction. This paper presents a new formulation based on the inverse plant control for the color error reduction process. In our formulation, the printer input and scanner output correspond to the input and output of a system plant respectively. Obviously, if the printer input equals the scanner output, then there are no color errors involved in the entire system. In other words, the plant becomes an identity system. To achieve this goal, a plant inverse should be identified and added to the original system. Since the system of a combination of both scanner and printer is highly nonlinear, a multilayer back-propagation neural networks, which have the capability to learn arbitrary nonlinearity, are applied to identify the plant inverse. Finally, a number of test samples are conducted to verify the effectiveness of the proposed method.

I. Introduction

With rapid progress of electronic color scanner and printing technology, considerable excitement has been caused by the generation of documents containing color material for individual users. The color content in the document can range from colored texts to full-color pictorial images for graphic-arts applications. This widening use of color has given rise to consideration of how color can be faithfully represented in the output of various printers such as thermal transfer, ink jet, laser printers,..., etc. In other words, color digital image printing system attempt to reproduce on output accurately those color present in the original image. The color spaces associated with the scanner and printer devices are tied directly to the physics of these devices, and as a result vary from device to device. Consequently, the color coordinates obtained on input have little meaning in terms of the color coordinates at the output of a printing system. Thus, some procedure is required for the accurate mapping of input colors, scanned from the original, into colors available at the system output. Iteratively scanning, printing, and adjusting an input/output color map might eventually allow one to to achieve the desire accuracy of color reproduction. Unfortunately, due to the large number of possible inputs colors, this technique is impractical. A subset of the input colors could be used and polynomial regression techniques[1][2]employed to solve the system of equations provided by this input set and the resulting color data. As a result, for a given input color, an appropriate output color could be selected which would produce approximately the same color as that presents in the original. This direct conversion between input and output is acceptable provided no intermediate processing is required. However, it may be desirable to carry out image processing steps in quantization, resolution conversion, and the correction for a mismatch between the color gamuts of the scanner and printer. Since these undesired factors are highly nonlinear and truly degrade the quality of color reproduction, several nonlinear compensation technique[1][2][3][4] have been proposed to overcome the artifacts. Nevertheless, the costs of computation and storage are extremely high.

Kang and Anderson[5] introduced an alternative technique based on the concept of feedforward neural network[6] to calibrate the scanner and printer individually. Unfortunately, their approach cannot eliminate the color errors from color gamut mismatch and resolution conversion between scanner and printer. To tackle this difficulty, this paper presents a new color-correction method which can eliminate the undesired mismatch, conversion and individual color errors simultaneously. This basic concept of our method is based on neural inverse plant control[7]. As discussed in the next two sections, the input and output to the system plant are the printer input and scanner output respectively. If the total color error from both scanner and printer becomes zero, then the response values at both input and output to the plant should be identical. Otherwise, a control process is then proposed to eliminate the total color error and force the plant become an identity system. This controller is usually recognized as a plant inverse of the system. Srinivasan, Barto and Ydstie [6] use the multilayer feedforward neural network to identify the nonlinear plant inverse. More details about the neural inverse plant controller will be discussed below.

II. Neural Inverse Plant Control Techniques

A back-propagation feedforward neural network[6] can be used to solve highly nonlinear self-tuning control problems. Traditional self-tuning adaptive control techniques can only deal with linear systems or some special nonlinear systems. The emerging back-propagation neural networks have the capability to learn arbitrary nonlinearity and show great potential for adaptive control applications. This section shows how the neural network can learn of its own accord to control a nonlinear dynamic system. To design an effective control law, the plant should be adequately modeled within the assumed class of models. This modeling process is called the system identification. In contrast to the conventional system-identification procedure, Figure 1.a shows how a multilayer back-propagation network can be used to identify the inverse of a system plant. Here the input to the network is the output of the plant, and the target output of the network is the plant input. If the network can be trained to match these targets, it will implement a mapping that is a plant inverse. Once one has such an inverse, it can be used for control purposes as shown in Figure 1.b. The desired plant output is provided as input to the plant. If the network is a plant inverse, then the plant input causes the desired plant output.

A back-propagation neural network shown in Figure 2 is a layered network consisting of an input layer, an output layer, and at least one layer of nonlinear processing elements. The nonlinear processing elements, which sum incoming signal and generate output signals according to some predefined function, are called neurons. In this paper, the function used by nonlinear neurons is called the sigmoidal hyperbolic tangent function G, which is similar to a smoothed step function

$$G(x) = \tanh(x) \qquad (1)$$

The neurons are connected by terms with variable weights. The output of one neuron multiplied by a weight becomes the input of an adjacent neuron of the next layer.

In 1986, Rumelhart et at. [6] proposed a generalized delta rule known as back-propagation for training layered neural networks. For control engineers, it is appropriate to consider back-propagation neural networks as a tool to solve function approximation problems rather than pattern recognition problems. Consider a layered neural network $\mathbf{F}(\mathbf{x}, \mathbf{w})$ with $\mathbf{x}$ as a vecter representing inputs and $\mathbf{w}$ as a vector representing variable weights. It is desired to train $\mathbf{F}(\mathbf{x}, \mathbf{w})$ to approximate a function $\mathbf{f} : A \subset R^n \to R^m$, from compact subset A of n-dimensional Euclidean space to a bounded subset $\mathbf{f}(A)$ of m-dimensional Euclidean space. In iteration k, let $\mathbf{x}_k$ which belongs to A be selected randomly as the input of the neural network, let $\mathbf{F}(\mathbf{x}_k, \mathbf{w}_k)$ be the output of the neural network, and let $\mathbf{f}(\mathbf{x}_k)$ which also belongs to $\mathbf{f}(A)$ be the desired output. This task is to adjust all the variable weights of the neural network such the error E_k can be reduced, where E_k is defined as

$$E_k = \frac{1}{2} \parallel \mathbf{F}(\mathbf{x}_k, \mathbf{w}(k)) - \mathbf{f}(\mathbf{x}_k) \parallel^2 \qquad (2)$$

Let $w^i(k)$ be any element in $\mathbf{w}(k)$. The effect of adjusting $w^i(k)$ to the error E_k is determined directly by the partial derivative $\partial E_k / \partial w^i(k)$. How to evaluate the partial derivative is really the contribution of the back-propagation algorithm. Details can be found in [6].

III. Neural Color-Correction for Scanner-Printer

Since the location and existence of colors in a color space associated with a particular device are tied directly to the physics of that device, it is desired to provide an absolute color coordinate system whose values are device independent. In the context of colorimeter matching, the intent of color scanner-printer correction is to characterize the device-dependent responses to device-independent representations such as CIELAB. CIELAB coordinate system is also a uniform color space which is the suitable quantitive measure to the color difference. An illustration of the type of color reproduction system considered in this paper is provided in Figure 3. The RGB coordinates produced by a scanner for each pixel in an image are converted to their corresponding CIELAB coordinates. Due to the mismatching and nonlinearity of both scanner and printer, a correction processor based on the neural network is provided to eliminate those undesired factors and ensure the quality of color reproduction. After the neural processor, the corrected CIELAB coordinates would be converted into the RGB coordinates which reproduces the image on the printer. To design this effective color correction processor, the system architecture shown in Figure 3 should be changed. Figure 4 shows how the neural inverse plant control can be applied to the color correction. The plant input (L_p, a_p, b_p) to the printer and the plant output (L_s, a_s, b_s) of the scanner correspond to the output and input of a back-propagation neural network respectively. One may generate a number of test samples $\mathbf{x}_k = (L_p, a_p, b_p)$ belonging to CIELAB space randomly to train the neural plant inverse. If the network becomes a plant inverse, the color error for the system is totally eliminated. The image shown in Figure 6 is the resulting image on the HP Paint-Jet printer output with resolution 180 dpi by passing the original image of Figure 5 through the uncorrected system. The color of the face skin seems not very nature and is quite different from the original one. Compared to this unpleased result, the image in Figure 6 shows how the color of the face skin is corrected by our method and is close to the original picture.

IV. Conclusion

In this paper, we have developed a cost-effective color correction algorithm based on neural inverse plant control which can eliminate the total color error due to the mismatch and the nonlinearity of both scanner and printer. The combination of both scanner and printer is recognized as a control plant in our formulation. The strategy of the inverse plant control is to add a plant inverse in front of the target plant output.Therefore, the resulting system becomes an identity plant. In other words, the color errors are totally eliminated. Experiment shows that the colors of several test samples are corrected effectively.

Acknowledgments

We would like to thank Dr. Wang, Han-Chung who is a director of Opto-Electronics and Syst. Lab. and Mr. Shik-Liang Chang for enormous measurements and useful comments. Many thanks go to Mr. K. L. Huang for his technical support. One of the authors wants to express his gratitude to Ms. Mary Chon for her great consideration.

References

[1] Benno Petschchik, " Color Hard Copy - a self-tuning color correction algorithm based on a colorimetric model", *Printing Technologies for Images, Gray Scale, and Color, Proc. SPIE* Vol. 1458, pp. 108-114, 1991.

[2] Gary K. Starkweather, "A Color-Correction Scheme for Color Electronic Printers," *COLOR research and application*, Supplement Vol. 11, pp. 67-72, 1986.

[3] R. Takeuchi, M. Tsumura, M. Tadauchi, and H. Shio, "Color image scanner with an RGB linear image sensor," *J. Imaging Technol.* vol. 14,pp. 68-72, 1988.

[4] S. Suzuki, T. Kusunoki, and M. Mori, "Color characteristic design for color scanners", *Appl. Opt.* Vol. 29, pp. 5187-5192 ,1990.

[5] Henry R. Kang and Peter G. Anderson, "Neural Network Application to the Color Scanner and Printer Calibrations," *Journal of Electronic Imaging,* Vol. 1(2), pp. 125–135, 1992.

[6] D. E. Remelhart, G. E. Hinton and R. J. Williams "Learning Internal Representations by Error Propagation," in *Parallel Distributed Processing Explorations in the Microstructure of Cognition,* Vol. 1: Foundation, D. E. Rumelhart and J. L. McClelland, Eds., MIT Press, Cambridge, 1986 Parallel Distributed Processing

[7] V. Srinivasan, A. G. Barto, and B. Z. Ydstie, Pattern Recognition and Feedback via Parallel Distributed Processing. *Annual Meeting of the American Institute of Chemical Engineers,* Washington. D. C. November 1988.

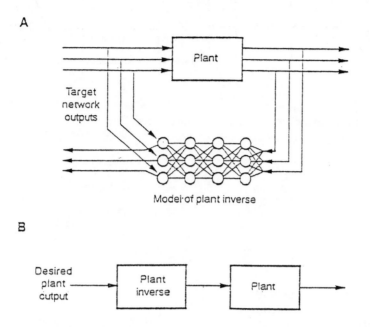

Figure 1: Using a back-propagation network for identifying a system inverse.

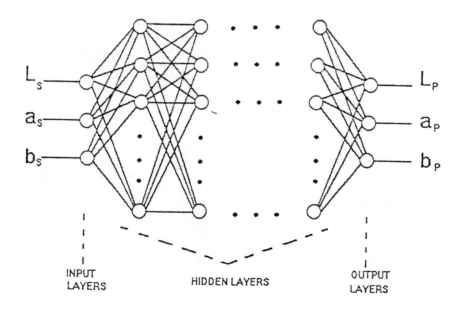

Figure 2: Architecture of multi-layered neural network.

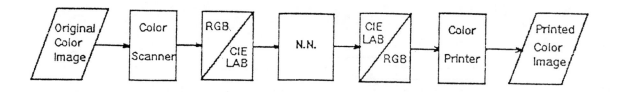

Figure 3: The system architecture for neural color correction scheme

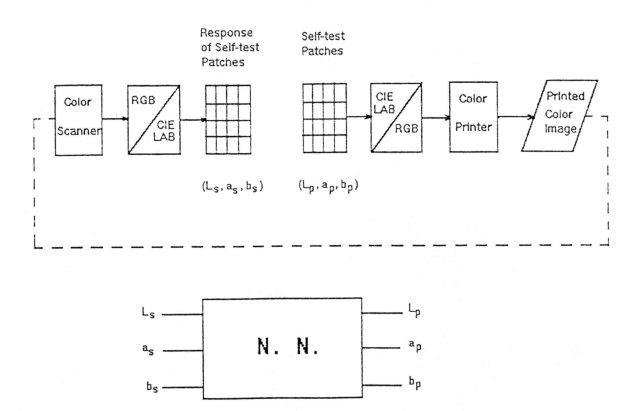

Figure 4: The plant system architecture for scanner-printer

Conference Author Index

A

Abd-El-Barr, M. H. 1295
Abdul-Aziz, M. 1252
Adler, D. 1104
Adomaitis, R. A. 382
Ahmad, S. 1949
Ahn, S. K. 347
Ahned, H. M. 15
Akhyar, S. 552
Allemand, S. 1871
Alnuweiri, H. 580
Alpaydin, E. 9
Amari, S.-i. 1385
Anantharaman, K. S. 690
Andersen, R. A. 1321
Anderson, T. R. 1914
Andreae, J. H. 335
Anton, J.-L. 732
Aourid, M. 1092
Arai, K. 70
Arata, L. 1277
Arnold, J. 923
Attikiouzel, Y. 1622
Augusteijn, M. F. 392
Avellana, N. 1242
Azema-Barac, M. 1419

B

Badal, D. Z. 1283
Bakker, R. R. N. 919
Baldi, P. 1172
Baldwin, J. L. 1776
Baozong, Y. 1570
Barhen, J. 836
Beaufays, F. 1
Benediktsson, J. A. 27
Bengio, Y. 1183
Bhadkamkar, N. 1902
Bhandarkar, S. M. 1270
Bhide, S. 1096
Bi, N. 1823
Bileillo, M. 1
Bisio, G. M. 755
Blackmore, J. 450
Blanc, F. 1871
Bock, W. J. 1713
Bodenhausen, U. 1627
Bonissone, P. P. 610
Botros, N. M. 1252, 1770
Boubez, T. I. 1544
Braun, H. 586
Bregler, C. 667
Brunner, B. 150
Budinich, M. 371
Burdick, J. W. 836
Burel, G. 727
Burkhardt, H. 678
Burnod, Y. 732

C

Caelli, T. M. 851, 1474
Cai, Y. J. 1667
Çakmakci, A. M. 564
Card, H. C. 110, 711
Carrabina, J. 1242
Carter, M. J. 1847
Catros, J.-Y. 727
Caulfield, J. T. 1955
Caviglia, D. D. 755
Cawley, G. 1414
Cetin, B. C. 836
Chakraborty, G. 466
Chandrasekaran, V. 851, 1474
Chang, C.-H. 989
Chang, G.-W. 1979
Chang, P.-R. 1979
Chang, R.-I. 103
Chang, W. 661
Chang, W.-R. 1865
Chelappa, R. 132
Chella, A. 605
Chen, C.-J. 462
Chen, D. 1196
Chen, E. T.-Y. 1702
Chen, F.-C. 983
Chen, H. H. 1196
Chen, H. J. 923
Chen, H.-W. 479
Chen, T. 215, 1034
Cheng, W. 749
Cherkassky, V. 1896
Cheung, J. Y. 462, 989
Cheung, K. F. 489
Chiang, C.-C. 1177
Chinrungrueng, C. 626
Chiu, C.-T. 783
Chiu, D. K. Y. 956
Choi, C.-H. 428
Choi, J. Y. 428
Chu, S. R. 1289
Chung, P.-C. 1366
Chung, Y.-N. 1366
Cohen, M. E. 527
Colbert, M. 1955
Colombi, J. M. 1914
Coronado, J. L. 944
Corwin, E. M. 1129
Cottrell, G. W. 39
Creaney, M. J. 1644
Crestani, F. 244

D

Dabija, V. G. 281
Dahanayake, B. W. 831
Dalkilic, M. E. 275
da Mota Tenorio, M. F. 1402
Dandapani, R. 1724
Daoudi, M. 1633
Das, C. R. 1684
Decaestecker, C. 822-O

deF

deFigueiredo, R. J. P. 869
Deiri, M. Z. 1770
del Pilar Gomex-Gil, M. 1618
Dempsey, J. 1492
Denbigh, P. N. 187
Descour, M. 1955
Dhawan, A. P. 203, 1115, 1277
Dickerson, J. A. 1162
Dickson, J. A. 711
Digney, B. 144
Dillon, T. S. 794, 972
Di Martino, M. 936
Dimitriadis, Y. A. 944
Dimopoulos, N. J. 568
Dingle, A. A. 335
Dolenko, B. K. 110
Dow, R. J. F. 1754
Downs, T. 1812
Drake, R. M. 434
Dufossé, M. 1871
Duin, R. P. W. 598, 919
Durg, A. 1719
Durham, J. T. 506

E

Edelman, J. A. 70
Edwards, R. T. 1247
Ekong, D. U. 1295
Eliashberg, V. 1333
Elmasry, M. I. 1338
El-Sherief, H. 825
English, T. M. 1618
Errington, P. A. 1236
Ersoy, O. K. 27
Etemad, K. 132

F

Fagg, A. H. 772
Fakhr, W. 1338
Fanelli, S. 936
Feldkamp, L. A. 1189
Feng, J. 678, 1516
Feng, X. 1780
Fernández, B. 232, 1865
Fiser, J. 772
Fogel, D. B. 875, 1829
Fong, K. F. 529, 592
Fowler, B. 1902
Francelin, R. A. 1433
Franklin, J. A. 737
Franquelo, L. G. 1498
Frasconi, P. 1183, 1818
Fritsch, T. 93, 822-D
Frye, R. C. 1265
Fu, H.-C. 1177
Fu, L. 215, 413
Fukuda, T. 209
Furst, M. 199